P9-APV-957

AMERICAN INSTITUTE OF PHYSICS HANDBOOK

McGRAW-HILL HANDBOOKS

Abbott and Smith · National Electrical Code Handbook, 8th ed.
American Institute of Physics
    American Institute of Physics Handbook
American Society of Mechanical Engineers
    ASME Handbook: Engineering Tables
    ASME Handbook: Metals Engineering—Design
    ASME Handbook: Metals Properties
American Society of Tool Engineers · Die Design Handbook
American Society of Tool Engineers · Tool Engineers Handbook
Beeman · Industrial Power Systems Handbook
Berry, Bollay, and Beers · Handbook of Meteorology
Brady · Materials Handbook, 8th ed.
Compressed Air and Gas Institute · Compressed Air Handbook, 2d ed.
Crocker · Piping Handbook, 4th ed.
Croft · American Electricians' Handbook, 7th ed.
Davis · Handbook of Applied Hydraulics, 2d ed.
Fink · Television Engineering Handbook
Henney · Radio Engineering Handbook, 4th ed.
Hunter · Handbook of Semiconductor Electronics
Johnson and Auth · Fuels and Combustion Handbook
Juran · Quality-control Handbook
Ketchum · Structural Engineers' Handbook, 3d ed.
King · Handbook of Hydraulics, 4th ed.
Knowlton · Standard Handbook for Electrical Engineers, 8th ed.
Kurtz · The Lineman's Handbook, 3d ed.
Labberton and Marks · Marine Engineers' Handbook
Laughner and Hargan · Handbook of Fastening and Joining of Metal Parts
Le Grand · The New American Machinist's Handbook
Liddell · Handbook of Nonferrous Metallurgy, 2 vols. 2d ed.
Magill, Holden, and Ackley · Air Pollution Handbook
Manas · National Plumbing Code Handbook
Marks · Mechanical Engineers' Handbook, 5th ed.
Markus and Zeluff · Handbook of Industrial Control Circuits
Markus and Zeluff · Handbook of Industrial Electronic Control Circuits
Maynard · Industrial Engineering Handbook
Morrow · Maintenance Engineering Handbook
O'Rourke · General Engineering Handbook, 2d ed.
Pacific Coast Gas Association · Gas Engineers' Handbook
Perry · Chemical Business Handbook
Perry · Chemical Engineers' Handbook, 3d ed.
Staniar · Plant Engineering Handbook
Terman · Radio Engineers' Handbook
Urquhart · Civil Engineering Handbook, 3d ed.

American Institute of Physics Handbook

Section Editors

Albert A. Bennett, Ph.D.
Professor of Mathematics
Brown University

Bruce H. Billings, Ph.D.
Vice President
Baird-Atomic, Inc.

D. F. Bleil, Ph.D.
Chief, Physics Research Department
U.S. Naval Ordnance Laboratory, White Oak, Md.

G. H. Dieke, Ph.D.
Chairman, Department of Physics
The Johns Hopkins University

Floyd A. Firestone, Ph.D.
Editor, The Journal of the Acoustical Society of America

F. N. D. Kurie, Ph.D.
Technical Director
U.S. Navy Electronics Laboratory

R. Bruce Lindsay, Ph.D.
Dean of the Graduate School
Brown University

Mark W. Zemansky, Ph.D.
Professor of Physics
The City College of New York

Coordinating Editor

Dwight E. Gray, Ph.D.
Program Director for Government Research Information
National Science Foundation

McGraw-Hill Book Company, Inc.
New York *Toronto* *London*
1957

AMERICAN INSTITUTE OF PHYSICS HANDBOOK

Library of Congress catalog card number: 56-7553

II

THE MAPLE PRESS COMPANY, YORK, PA.

Contributors

F. Ajzenberg-Selove, Ph.D., *Haverford College*
W. P. Allis, D.Sc., *Massachusetts Institute of Technology*
D. J. Angelakos, Ph.D., *University of California*
Stephen J. Angello, Ph.D., *Westinghouse Electric Corporation*
Frank Asaro, Ph.D., *University of California*
Fred D. Ayres, Ph.D., *Reed College*
S. S. Ballard, Ph.D., *Scripps Institution of Oceanography*
Albert A. Bennett, Ph.D., *Brown University*
Leo L. Beranek, Sc.D., *Bolt Beranek and Newman, Inc.*
Bruce H. Billings, Ph.D., *Baird-Atomic, Inc.*
D. F. Bleil, Ph.D., *U.S. Naval Ordnance Laboratory, White Oak, Md.*
R. M. Bozorth, Ph.D., *Bell Telephone Laboratories, Inc.*
L. M. Branscomb, Ph.D., *The National Bureau of Standards*
P. W. Bridgman, Ph.D., Sc.D., *Harvard University*
W. Brouwer, M.S., *Baird-Atomic, Inc.*
S. C. Brown, Ph.D., *Massachusetts Institute of Technology*
R. M. Burley, A.B., *Baird-Atomic, Inc.*
Robert O'B. Carpenter, Ph.D., *Baird-Atomic, Inc.*
J. M. Cork, Ph.D., *University of Michigan*
R. J. Corruccini, Ph.D., *NBS-AEC Cryogenic Engineering Laboratory*
H. M. Crosswhite, Ph.D., *The Johns Hopkins University*
Evan A. Davis, *Westinghouse Electric Corporation*
Thomas J. Derby, B.A.E., *Pratt and Whitney Aircraft Corporation*
G. H. Dieke, Ph.D., *The Johns Hopkins University*
T. B. Douglas, Ph.D., *The National Bureau of Standards*
D. Edelson, Ph.D., *Bell Telephone Laboratories, Inc.*
Phillip Eisenberg, B.S., C.E., *Office of Naval Research*
R. D. Fay, S.B., *Massachusetts Institute of Technology*
K. A. Fegley, Ph.D., *University of Pennsylvania*
Floyd A. Firestone, Ph.D., *The Journal of the Acoustical Society of America*
W. E. Forsythe, Ph.D., *The Smithsonian Institution*
Eli H. Freedman, Ph.D., *University of Buffalo*
R. J. Friauf, Ph.D., *University of Kansas*
Abraham S. Friedman, Ph.D., *U.S. Atomic Energy Commission*
M. M. Fulk, *NBS-AEC Cryogenic Engineering Laboratory*
Dudley D. Fuller, M.S., *Columbia University*
G. T. Furukawa, Ph.D., *The National Bureau of Standards*
Edward F. Greene, Ph.D., *Brown University*
B. Gutenberg, Ph.D., *California Institute of Technology*
Cyril M. Harris, Ph.D., *Columbia University*
F. K. Harris, Ph.D., *The National Bureau of Standards*
J. A. Harvey, Ph.D., *Oak Ridge National Laboratory*
George Hass, Ph.D., *Engineer Research and Development Laboratories, Ft. Belvoir*
W. A. Heiskanen, Ph.D., *The Ohio State University and the Finnish Geodetic Institute*
G. Herzberg, Dr.Ing., F.R.S., *National Research Council of Canada*

L. Herzberg, Ph.D., *National Research Council of Canada*
Peter Hidnert, Ph.D., *The National Bureau of Standards*
Joseph Hilsenrath, B.S., *The National Bureau of Standards*
Ralph P. Hudson, Ph.D., *The National Bureau of Standards*
D. J. Hughes, Ph.D., *Brookhaven National Laboratory*
Frederick V. Hunt, Ph.D., *Harvard University*
H. S. Isbin, Sc.D., *University of Minnesota*
Walter John, Ph.D., *University of Illinois*
J. Kestin, Ph.D., *Brown University*
David G. Knapp, B.S., *U.S. Coast and Geodetic Survey*
E. H. Krause, Ph.D., *Aeronutronic Systems, Inc.*
H. S. Krider, *The National Bureau of Standards*
Franz N. D. Kurie, Ph.D., *U.S. Navy Electronics Laboratory*
T. Lauritsen, Ph.D., *California Institute of Technology*
L. Leventhal, M. S., *Tracerlab, Inc.*
Robert Lindsay, Ph.D., *Trinity College*
R. Bruce Lindsay, Ph.D., *Brown University*
R. J. List, M. S., *U.S. Weather Bureau*
L. G. Longsworth, Ph.D., *Rockefeller Institute for Medical Research*
D. L. MacAdam, Ph.D., *Eastman Kodak Corporation*
K. A. McCarthy, M.S., *Tufts University*
W. McMahon, B.S., *Bell Telephone Laboratories, Inc.*
W. P. Mason, Ph.D., *Bell Telephone Laboratories, Inc.*
Frank Massa, M.S., *Massa Laboratories, Inc.*
W. J. Merz, Ph.D., *RCA Laboratories*
David Mintzer, Ph.D., *Yale University*
R. B. Montgomery, Sc.D., *Chesapeake Bay Institute, The Johns Hopkins University*
Karl Z. Morgan, Ph.D., *Oak Ridge National Laboratory*
S. O. Morgan, Ph. D., *Bell Telephone Laboratories, Inc.*
R. W. Morse, Ph.D., *Brown University*
Edwin B. Newman, Ph.D., *Harvard University*
Wesley L. Nyborg, Ph.D., *Brown University*
Harry F. Olson, Ph.D., *RCA Laboratories*
D. H. Perkel, A.B., *Aerojet-General Nucleonics*
I. Perlman, Ph.D., *University of California*
Wladimir Philippoff, *Franklin Institute*
B. B. Phillips, M.S., *U.S. Weather Bureau*
Robert L. Powell, M.A., *NBS-AEC Cyrogenic Engineering Laroratory*
M. M. Reynolds, M.S., *Linde Air Products Co.*
R. C. Roberts, Ph.D., *U.S. Naval Ordnance Laboratory, White Oak, Md.*
Arthur F. Scott, Ph.D., *Reed College*
Maurice M. Shapiro, Ph.D., *U.S. Naval Research Laboratory*
W. A. Shurcliff, Ph.D., *Polaroid Corporation*
S. Silver, Ph.D., *University of California*
L. Slack, Ph.D., *George Washington University*
Thor L. Smith, Ph.D., *Jet Propulsion Laboratory, California Institute of Technology*
W. R. Smythe, Ph.D., *California Institute of Technology*
R. L. Sproull, Ph.D., *Cornell University*
D. E. Stone, A.B., *Naval Research Laboratory*
Paul Tamarkin, Ph.D., *RAND Corporation*
H. M. Trent, Ph.D., *Naval Research Laboratory*
George L. Trigg, Ph.D., *Oregon State College*
R. G. Van Nostrand, Ph.D., *Magnolia Petroleum Company*
D. D. Wagman, M. A., *The National Bureau of Standards*
C. B. West, Ph.D., *Polaroid Corporation*
C. N. Weygandt, Ph.D., *University of Pennsylvania*
J. R. Whinnery, Ph.D., *University of California*
David White, Ph.D., *The Ohio State University*
R. E. Wilson, *Hughes Research and Development Laboratories*
E. A. Wood, Ph.D., *Bell Telephone Laboratories, Inc.*
Robert W. Young, Ph.D., *U.S. Navy Electronics Laboratory*
T. F. Young, Ph.D., *University of Chicago*
L. R. Zumwalt, Ph.D., *General Dynamics Corporation*

Preface

The American Institute of Physics Handbook has been prepared as an important working tool for those employing physical methods in research, application, and teaching. It should prove especially valuable in this period of scientific development, particularly since the impact of wartime research, when the science of physics has expanded into many specialized fields. The many new discoveries and advances have been taken into consideration by the board of editors so as to select and compile the most generally useful data.

This volume represents the first handbook specifically on physics to be published in America. It is also the first such volume to be sponsored by the American Institute of Physics, the organization which acts as the central service agency of the five member societies in physics. Prior to this time, the profession of physics has had to depend on handbooks prepared primarily for other disciplines.

The book has been over four years in the making under the guidance of Dwight E. Gray, coordinating editor. Its publication would not have been possible without his patient direction and the active cooperation of many of the leading physicists in the nation as well as the help and assistance of hundreds of other scientists. The American Institute of Physics owes much to their unselfish spirit.

This handbook will be of primary usefulness to the young scientific investigator and will also have value as a reference work to the senior physicist. It should be of assistance to the individual engaged in applied physics and engineering. The volume has been divided into the logical areas of physics.

We are pleased to add this handbook to the many publications sponsored by the Institute and to invite the suggestions and criticism of physicists so that future editions may be more complete and useful.

THE AMERICAN INSTITUTE OF PHYSICS

Contents

Contributors . . . . *v*

Preface . . . . *vii*

Section

MATHEMATICAL AIDS TO COMPUTATION 1
Editor, *Dr. Albert A. Bennett,* Brown University

MECHANICS 2
Editor, *Dr. R. Bruce Lindsay,* Brown University

Fundamental concepts of mechanics. Units and conversion factors. Density of solids. Centers of mass and moments of inertia. Coefficients of friction. Crystallographic data. Elastic constants, hardness, strength, and elastic limits of solids. Mechanical properties of gels and thixotropic substances. Viscosity of solids. Astronomical data. Geodetic data. Seismological and related data. Oceanographic data. Meteorological data. Density and compressibility of liquids. Viscosity of liquids. Tensile strength and surface tension of liquids. Fluid-flow properties of porous media and viscosity of suspension. Cavitation in flowing liquids. Diffusion in liquids. Liquid jets. Density of gases at standard temperature and pressure. Viscosity of gases. Diffusion of gases. Compressible flow of gases. Laminar and turbulent flow of gases. Shock waves.

ACOUSTICS 3
Editor, *Dr. Floyd A. Firestone,* The Journal of the Acoustical Society of America

Acoustical definitions. Letter symbols and conversion factors for acoustical quantities. Propagation of sound in fluids. Acoustic properties of gases. Acoustic properties of liquids. Acoustic properties of solids. Properties of transducer materials. Frequencies of simple vibrators. Radiation of sound. Architectural acoustics. Speech and hearing. Classical electrodynamical analogies. The mobility and classical impedance analogies. Selected references on acoustics.

HEAT 4
Editor, *Dr. Mark W. Zemansky*, The City College of New York

Temperature scales, thermocouples, and resistance thermometers. Very low temperature data. Properties of paramagnetic salts. Critical constants. High-pressure effects. Heat capacities. Thermal expansion. Thermal conductivity. Thermodynamic properties of gases. Pressure-volume-temperature relationships of fluids. Virial coefficients. Temperature, pressure, heat, and entropy change of transition, fusion, and vaporization.

ELECTRICITY AND MAGNETISM 5
Editor, *Dr. D. F. Bleil*, U.S. Naval Ordnance Laboratory, White Oak, Md.

Definitions, units, nomenclature, symbols, conversion tables. Formulas. Electrical standards. Properties of dielectrics. Properties of semiconductors. Properties of nonmetallic conductors. Properties of metallic conductors. Magnetic properties of materials. Electrical power practices. Electrochemical information. Electrical and magnetic properties of the earth and stars.

OPTICS 6
Editor, *Dr. Bruce H. Billings*, Baird-Atomic, Inc.

Fundamental definitions, standards, and photometric units. Index of refraction. Absorption and transmission. Reflection. Glass, polarizing and interference filters. Colorimetry. Radiometry. Wavelengths for spectrographic calibrations. Magneto- and electro-optics. Specific rotation. Optical constants of metals. Fluorescence and phosphorence. Radiation detection. Velocity of light. Radio astronomy.

ATOMIC AND MOLECULAR PHYSICS 7
Editor, *Dr. G. H. Dieke*, The Johns Hopkins University

Atomic constants. The periodic system. The electronic structure of atoms. Structure of atomic spectra. Energy-level diagrams of atoms. Persistent lines of the elements. Important atomic spectra. Data on characteristic X-ray spectra. Constants and energy levels of diatomic molecules. Constants of polyatomic molecules. Wave mechanics. Zeeman effect. Motions of electrons and ions in gases.

NUCLEAR PHYSICS 8
Editor, *Dr. F. N. D. Kurie*, U.S. Navy Electronics Laboratory

Introduction and general constants. Systematics of stable nuclei. Passage of particles through matter. Decay-energy systematics of the heavy elements. Energy levels of the light nuclei. Gamma rays. Artificial radioisotopes and isomers. Neutrons. Particle accelerators. Fission-product chains and yields. Nuclear reactors. Mesons and hyperons. Health physics.

Index

Section 1

MATHEMATICAL AIDS TO COMPUTATION

ALBERT A. BENNETT

Brown University

and

THOMAS J. DERBY

Pratt and Whitney Aircraft Corporation

To the physicist who is equipped by training and temperament to use them, many mathematical aids of a variety of kinds are available for dealing with mathematical relationships among physical quantities. Such aids include mechanical computing devices, numerical tables of functional values, collections of formulas, syllabi of computational techniques and artifices, and the like. None of these is the outcome of physical theory or of laboratory experimentation but frequently physicists find them very useful.

Among mechanical computing devices are slide rules and desk computers. In widespread use, beside the pocket-size "7-inch" slide rule and the portable "10-inch" rule, are the larger "20-inch" (or more properly "50-cm") slide rules and plane circular slide rules of various diameters. Rules of comparable quality and value are manufactured by several well-known companies. Various larger devices, suggested by the conventional Mannheim style slide rule, have cylindrical, and even squirrel-cage scales, but these are seldom favored by practical experts. Among desk computers, the most widely used in America (in alphabetic order) are the Friden, the Marchant, and the Monroe; each ranges from simple hand-powered devices to electric-driven machines with numerous semiautomatic features. Such computing devices have practically displaced common logarithms for simple multiplication and division. High-speed electronic digital computers, where they are available, also are rendering superfluous many mathematical artifices and tables of special functions.

Numerical tables of the simpler mathematical functions are widely owned. These vary as to tabular interval and numbers of significant digits. Mathematical handbooks often contain much material which, while of service to the number theorist or actuary, may seldom be relevant to work in the physical laboratory. Statistical tables and techniques of sampling are gradually finding increasing use in the calculus of observations for the physical laboratory technologist no less than for the sociologist and practical geneticist. A single mathematical handbook may be adequate for most routine laboratory situations and may occupy all the immediate desk space that the physicist is willing to devote to such aids. Often such a handbook has been acquired in connection with an undergraduate course in mathematics. To save computing labor many computers prefer (particularly for inverse interpolation) to use tables which give values to more significant figures than are to be retained.

Most American standard mathematical handbooks of tables contain at least the following:

Squares, cubes, square roots, cube roots, reciprocals
Common logarithms
Natural trigonometric functions in degrees and minutes
Common logarithms of the trigonometric functions
Natural logarithms
Exponential and hyperbolic functions
Values of the probability integral

Among the compilations of tables most widely used in this country are the following, most of which are revised and republished from time to time:

Allen, Edward S.: "Six-place Tables," 7th ed., McGraw-Hill Book Company, Inc., New York, 1947, 232 pages:

Squares, cubes, square roots, cube roots, reciprocals, common logarithms; natural trigonometric functions; logarithms of the trigonometric functions; natural logarithms; exponential and hyperbolic functions, probability integral; gamma function; integrals; miscellaneous constants; formulas and conversion tables.

Burington, Richard S.: "Handbook of Mathematical Tables and Formulas," 3d ed., Handbook Publishers Inc., Sandusky, 1949, 269 pages:

Squares, cubes, square roots, cube roots, reciprocals; common logarithms (4- and 5-place, 7-place of 1,000–1,200); natural trigonometric functions (4- and 5-place); logarithms of trigonometric functions (4- and 5-place); natural logarithms (5-place); exponential and hyperbolic functions; probability integral; derivatives; elliptic integrals; gamma function; integrals; logarithms of prime numbers (10-place); miscellaneous constants, formulas, and conversion tables.

Carmichael, Robert D., and Edwin R. Smith: "Mathematical Tables and Formulas," Ginn & Company, Boston, 1931, 269 pages:

Squares, cubes, square roots, cube roots, reciprocals, common logarithms (4- and 5-place); natural trigonometric functions (4- and 5-place); logarithms of trigonometric functions (4- and 5-place); natural logarithms (5-place); exponential and hyperbolic functions; integrals; logarithms of prime numbers (10-place); miscellaneous constants, formulas, conversion tables, and reference curves.

Comrie, Leslie J.: "Barlow's Tables of Squares, Cubes, Square Roots, Cube Roots, and Reciprocals of All Integer Numbers up to 10,000," 3d ed., E. & F. N. Spon, Ltd., London, 1935, 208 pages:

Squares, cubes, square roots, cube roots, reciprocals; miscellaneous constants; powers (4th–20th).

Comrie, Leslie J.: "Chambers' Shorter Six-figure Mathematical Tables," W. and R. Chambers, Ltd., Edinburgh and London, 1950, 387 pages:

Squares, cubes, square roots, cube roots, reciprocals, common logarithms; natural trigonometric functions; logarithms of trigonometric functions (5-place); natural logarithms; exponential and hyperbolic functions; derivatives; integrals; inverse functions; miscellaneous constants, formulas, and conversion tables.

Dwight, Herbert B.: "Mathematical Tables," McGraw-Hill Book Company, Inc., New York, 1941, 231 pages:

Common logarithms (4-place); natural trigonometric functions (5-place); logarithms of trigonometric functions (5-place); natural logarithms (4-place); exponential and hyperbolic functions; probability integral; Bernoulli's and Euler's numbers; Bessel functions; elliptic integrals; gamma function; Riemann zeta function; zonal harmonics.

Dwight, Herbert B.: "Tables of Integrals and Other Mathematical Data," rev. ed., The Macmillan Company, New York, 1947, 250 pages:

Common logarithms (4-place); natural trigonometric functions (4-place); natural logarithms (4-place); exponential and hyperbolic functions; probability integral; Bessel functions; derivatives; elliptic integrals; gamma function; integrals; miscellaneous constants, formulas, and conversion tables.

Hedrick, Earle R.: "Logarithmic and Trigonometric Tables" (bound with tables from "The Calculus" by Ellery W. Davis and William C. Brenke), The Macmillan Company, New York, 1938, 142 + 50 pages:

Squares, cubes, square roots, cube roots, reciprocals; common logarithms (4- and 5-place); natural trigonometric functions (4- and 5-place); logarithms of trigonometric functions (5-place); natural logarithms (5-place); exponential and hyperbolic functions; haversines; logarithms of prime numbers (10-place); miscellaneous constants and conversion tables.

Hodgman, Charles D.: "Mathematical Tables" (based on his "Handbook of Chemistry and Physics"), 10th ed., Chemical Rubber Publishing Co., Cleveland, 1954, 406 pages:

Squares, cubes, square roots, cube roots, reciprocals; common logarithms (4-, 5-, and 7-place); natural trigonometric functions (5-place); logarithms of trigonometric functions (5-place); natural logarithms (5-place); exponential and hyperbolic functions; probability integral; derivatives; elliptic integrals; gamma function; haversines; integrals, interest tables; miscellaneous constants, formulas and conversion tables; mathematical symbols and abbreviations.

Hodgman, Charles D.: "Standard Mathematical Tables" (based on his "Handbook of Chemistry and Physics") 10th ed., Chemical Rubber Publishing Co., Cleveland, 1955, 433 pages. Similar to preceding item in content but of larger page size.

Hudson, Ralph G., and Joseph Lipka: "A Manual of Mathematics, John Wiley & Sons, Inc., New York, Chapman & Hall, Ltd., London, 1940, 135 pages:

Squares, cubes, square roots, cube roots, reciprocals; common logarithms (4-place); natural trigonometric functions (4-place); logarithms of trigonometric functions (4-place); natural logarithms (4-place); exponential and hyperbolic functions; derivatives; integrals; miscellaneous constants, formulas, and conversion tables.

Huntington, Edward V.: "Handbook of Mathematics" (from "Mechanical Engineers' Handbook," by Lionel S. Marks), 3d ed., McGraw-Hill Book Company, Inc., New York, 1943, 193 pages:

Squares, cubes, square roots, cube roots, reciprocals; common logarithms (4-place); natural trigonometric functions (4-place); logarithms of trigonometric functions (4-place); natural logarithms (4-place); exponential and hyperbolic functions; derivatives; integrals; miscellaneous constants, formulas, and conversion tables.

Jahnke, Eugene, and Fritz Emde: "Tables of Functions with Formulae and Curves," 4th ed., (German and English), Dover Publication., Inc., New York, 1945, 382 pages:

Bessel functions, circular and hyperbolic functions of a complex variable; cubic equations; elliptic integrals; exponential functions; factorial functions; Legendre functions; miscellaneous conversion tables; Planck's radiation function; powers (2nd to 15th); probability integral and related functions; reciprocals and square roots of complex numbers; Riemann zeta function; sine, cosine, and logarithmic integral; theta functions; transcendental equations; vector addition.

Larsen, Harold D.: "Rinehart Mathematical Tables, Formulas and Curves," Rinehart & Company, Inc., New York, 1953, 280 pages:

Squares, cubes, square roots, cube roots, reciprocals, common logarithms (4- and 5-place); natural trigonometric functions (5-place); logarithms of trigonometric functions (5-place); natural logarithms (4-place); exponential and hyperbolic functions; probability integral; Bessel functions; derivatives; elliptic integrals; integrals; miscellaneous constants, formulas, conversion tables, and reference curves.

Peirce, Benjamin O.: "A Short Table of Integrals," 4th rev. ed., Ginn & Company, Boston, 1956, 189 pages:

Squares; common logarithms (4-place); natural trigonometric functions (3- and 4-place); logarithms of trigonometric functions (4-place); natural logarithms (5-place); exponential and hyperbolic functions; probability integral; derivatives; elliptic integrals; integrals; miscellaneous constants, formulas, and conversion tables.

Potin, Louis F.: "Formulas and Numerical Tables Pertaining to Circular, Hyperbolic, and Elliptic Functions" (Formules et tables numeriques relatives aux functions circulaires, hyperboliques, elliptiques), G. Doin, Gauthier-Villars & Cie, Paris, 1925, 802 pages.

Natural trigonometric functions (4- and 5-place); Bernoulli's and Euler's numbers; elliptic integrals; hyperbolic functions; integrals; miscellaneous formulas and conversion tables.

Rosenbach, Joseph B., Edwin A. Whitman, and David Moscovitz: "Mathematical Tables," Ginn & Company, Boston, 1943, 212 pages:

Squares, cubes, square roots, cube roots, reciprocals, common logarithms (4- and 5-place); natural trigonometric functions (4- and 5-place); logarithms of trigonometric functions (4- and 5-place); natural logarithms (5-place); exponential and hyperbolic functions; probability integral; Bernoulli's numbers; Bessel functions; elliptic integrals; gamma functions; haversines; logarithms of prime numbers (20-place); miscellaneous constants and conversion tables.

Silberstein, Ludwik: "Synopsis of Applicable Mathematics with Tables," G. Bell & Sons, Ltd., London, 1923, 250 pages:

Reciprocals; common logarithms (4-, 5-, and 6-place); natural trigonometric functions (4-place); logarithms of trigonometric functions (5-place); hyperbolic functions; probability integral; Bessel functions; derivatives; elliptic integrals; gamma functions; integrals; miscellaneous formulas and conversion tables; zonal harmonics.

Many of these or analogous tables are incorporated as appendixes in standard college texts on trigonometry or general mathematics and appear in such handbooks as:

Eshbach, Ovid W.: "Handbook of Engineering Fundamentals," 2d ed., John Wiley & Sons, Inc., New York, 1952, lv.

Hodgman, Charles D.: "Handbook of Chemistry and Physics," 37th ed. (1955–1956), Chemical Rubber Publishing Co., Cleveland, 1955, 3156 pages.

Of a special kind, the following volume may be mentioned:

Kober, H.: "Dictionary of Conformal Representations," Dover Publications, Inc., New York, 1952, 208 pages.

In view of the hundreds of published special-purpose mathematical tables, no short selected list is likely to be of great service in an emergency. During the depression of the 1930's, several large volume mathematical tables for higher functions were prepared under A. N. Lowan and associates as New York W.P.A. projects; additional tables prepared under his direction have been issued by the Bureau of Standards in Washington. Using high-speed digital computers, the Computation Laboratory of Harvard University has prepared and is issuing a series of tables of higher mathematical functions. These and the impressive series of tables being published for the British Association by the Cambridge University Press (since 1931) should be available in every science library.

Some tables for statistics are found in:

Burington, Richard S., and Donald C. May: "Handbook of Probability and Statistics with Tables," Handbook Publishers, Inc., Sandusky, 1953, 332 pages.

Hald, Anders: "Statistical Tables and Formulas," John Wiley & Sons, Inc., New York; Chapman & Hall, Ltd., London, 1952, 97 pages.

Kelley, Truman L.: "The Kelley Statistical Tables," Harvard University Press, Cambridge, 1948, 223 pages.

Waugh, Albert E.: "Statistical Tables and Problems," 3d ed., McGraw-Hill Book Company, Inc., New York, 1952, 242 pages.

For ready reference to modern mathematical tables (but previous to 1945), one should consult the extensive and definitive work:

Fletcher, Alan, Jeffrey C. P. Miller, and Louis Rosenhead: "An Index of Mathematical Tables," Scientific Computing Service, Ltd., London, 1946, 450 pages. This valuable index states for each table the range, tabular interval, number of significant figures in the values, whether or not tables of proportional parts are given, what order or orders of differences are shown, and so forth.

Information on new publications and critiques in the field appears in the periodical:

"Mathematical Tables and Other Aids to Computation," Washington, National Research Council, (quarterly).

Section 2

MECHANICS

R. BRUCE LINDSAY, Editor

Brown University

CONTENTS

2a. Fundamental Concepts of Mechanics. Units and Conversion Factors ... 2-2
2b. Density of Solids ... 2-17
2c. Centers of Mass and Moments of Inertia ... 2-36
2d. Coefficients of Friction ... 2-39
2e. Crystallographic Data ... 2-44
2f. Elastic Constants, Hardness, Strength, and Elastic Limits of Solids ... 2-55
2g. Mechanical Properties of Gels and Thixotropic Substances ... 2-81
2h. Viscosity of Solids ... 2-84
2i. Astronomical Data ... 2-90
2j. Geodetic Data ... 2-92
2k. Seismological and Related Data ... 2-101
2l. Oceanographic Data ... 2-115
2m. Meteorological Data ... 2-124
2n. Density and Compressibility of Liquids ... 2-136
2o. Viscosity of Liquids ... 2-165
2p. Tensile Strength and Surface Tension of Liquids ... 2-169
2q. Fluid-flow Properties of Porous Media and Viscosity of Suspensions ... 2-179
2r. Cavitation in Flowing Liquids ... 2-182
2s. Diffusion in Liquids ... 2-189
2t. Liquid Jets ... 2-195
2u. Density of Gases at Standard Temperature and Pressure ... 2-197
2v. Viscosity of Gases ... 2-201
2w. Diffusion of Gases ... 2-211
2x. Compressible Flow of Gases ... 2-214
2y. Laminar and Turbulent Flow of Gases ... 2-220
2z. Shock Waves ... 2-231

2a. Fundamental Concepts of Mechanics. Units and Conversion Factors

DAVID MINTZER,[1] PAUL TAMARKIN,[2] AND R. BRUCE LINDSAY

Department of Physics
Brown University

2a-1. Newtonian Concepts of Mechanics. The science of mechanics deals with the motion of material bodies, which ideally can be considered as made up of point particles. In order to describe the motion of a particle three concepts are needed: *a frame of reference, distance* and *time interval.* These concepts are left undefined as intuitive concepts with sufficiently universal meanings. Distance and time intervals are measured in terms of standards which have a wide range of acceptance, such as the *standard meter* and the *sidereal day.* (The important systems of units are tabulated in Secs. 2a-8 and 2a-9.) The frame of reference consists of a *reference point* and a *coordinate system* (whose origin may be at the reference point); a *reference* event is necessary as well as a frame of reference.

The position of a particle may be specified with respect to the reference point by considering a rectangular coordinate system whose origin is at the reference point. The position of any particle is then given in terms of the distances along the coordinate axes from the origin to the projection on these axes of the point representing the position of the particle.

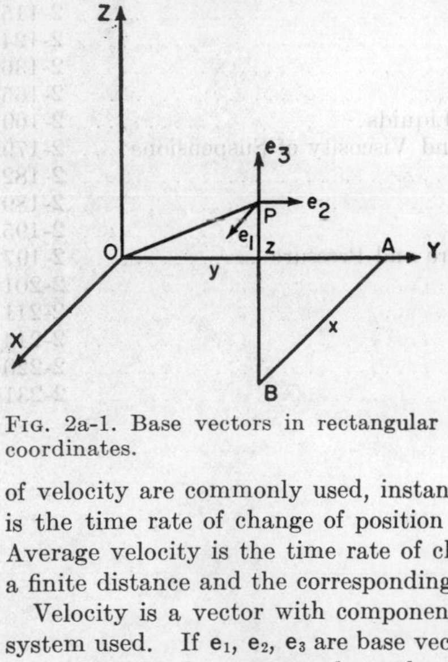

FIG. 2a-1. Base vectors in rectangular coordinates.

The location of an event in time, or the time of an event, similarly is expressed in terms of the time interval with respect to the reference event. The terms "time interval" and "time" are usually used interchangeably.

The above concepts are usually referred to as Newtonian; they suffice for classical mechanics.

2a-2. Kinematics—The Space-Time Relationships in the Motions of Point Particles. *Velocity.* Velocity is the rate of change of position with respect to time. Two types of velocity are commonly used, instantaneous and average. Instantaneous velocity is the time rate of change of position calculated pointwise, thus being a derivative. Average velocity is the time rate of change of position calculated as the quotient of a finite distance and the corresponding finite time interval.

Velocity is a vector with components which depend in general on the coordinate system used. If $\mathbf{e}_1$, $\mathbf{e}_2$, $\mathbf{e}_3$ are base vectors of the coordinate system under consideration, then, for three commonly used systems:

[1] Now at Yale University.
[2] Now at RAND Corporation, Santa Monica, California.

(1) Rectangular coordinates (cf. Fig. 2a-1):

$$\mathbf{v} = \mathbf{e}_1 v_x + \mathbf{e}_2 v_y + \mathbf{e}_3 v_z = \mathbf{e}_1 \frac{dx}{dt} + \mathbf{e}_2 \frac{dy}{dt} + \mathbf{e}_3 \frac{dz}{dt} \qquad \text{(2a-1)}$$

(2) Cylindrical coordinates (cf. Fig. 2a-2):

$$\mathbf{v} = \mathbf{e}_1 v_r + \mathbf{e}_2 v_\theta + \mathbf{e}_3 v_z = \mathbf{e}_1 \frac{dr}{dt} + \mathbf{e}_2 r \frac{d\theta}{dt} + \mathbf{e}_3 \frac{dz}{dt} \qquad \text{(2a-2)}$$

(3) Spherical coordinates (cf. Fig. 2a-3):

$$\mathbf{v} = \mathbf{e}_1 v_r + \mathbf{e}_2 v_\theta + \mathbf{e}_3 v_\phi = \mathbf{e}_1 \frac{dr}{dt} + \mathbf{e}_2 r \frac{d\theta}{dt} + \mathbf{e}_3 r \sin\theta \frac{d\phi}{dt} \qquad \text{(2a-3)}$$

Acceleration. Acceleration is the rate of change of velocity with respect to time. Instantaneous and average acceleration may be defined analogously to instantaneous and average velocities; however, instantaneous acceleration, or the time derivative of velocity (or equivalently the second time derivative of position) is the more commonly used quantity. Acceleration is a vector with components which depend in general on the coordinate system used. If $\mathbf{e}_1$, $\mathbf{e}_2$, $\mathbf{e}_3$ are the unit base vectors of the coordinate system under consideration, then for the commonly used systems:

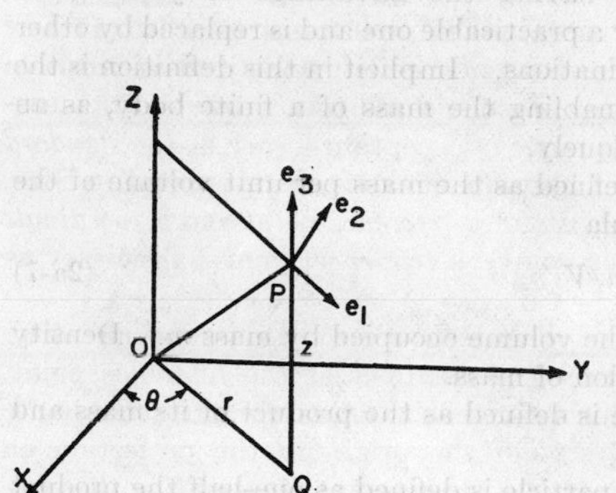

FIG. 2a-2. Base vectors in cylindrical coordinates.

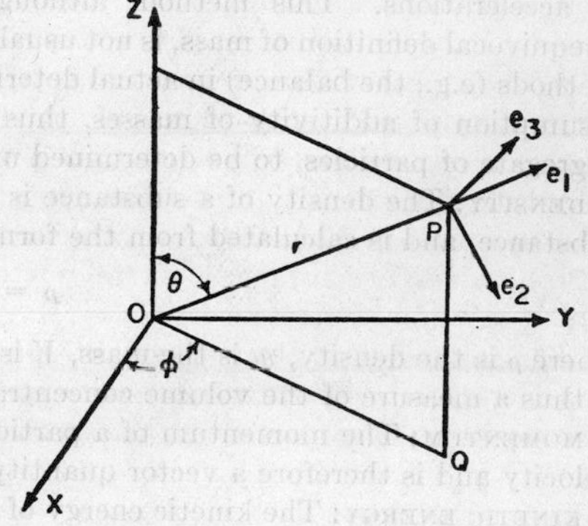

FIG. 2a-3. Base vectors in spherical coordinates.

(1) Rectangular coordinates:

$$\mathbf{a} = \mathbf{e}_1 a_x + \mathbf{e}_2 a_y + \mathbf{e}_3 a_z = \mathbf{e}_1 \frac{d^2x}{dt^2} + \mathbf{e}_2 \frac{d^2y}{dt^2} + \mathbf{e}_3 \frac{d^2z}{dt^2} \qquad \text{(2a-4)}$$

(2) Cylindrical coordinates:

$$\mathbf{a} = \mathbf{e}_1 a_r + \mathbf{e}_2 a_\theta + \mathbf{e}_3 a_z = \mathbf{e}_1 \left[\frac{d^2r}{dt^2} - r\left(\frac{d\theta}{dt}\right)^2 \right] + \mathbf{e}_2 \left[r\frac{d^2\theta}{dt^2} + 2\frac{dr}{dt}\frac{d\theta}{dt} \right] + \mathbf{e}_3 \frac{d^2z}{dt^2} \qquad \text{(2a-5)}$$

(3) Spherical coordinates:

$$\begin{aligned} \mathbf{a} = \mathbf{e}_1 a_r + \mathbf{e}_2 a_\theta + \mathbf{e}_3 a_\phi = {} & \mathbf{e}_1 \left[\frac{d^2r}{dt^2} - r\left(\frac{d\theta}{dt}\right)^2 - r \sin^2\theta \left(\frac{d\phi}{dt}\right)^2 \right] \\ & + \mathbf{e}_2 \left[r\frac{d^2\theta}{dt^2} + 2\frac{dr}{dt}\frac{d\theta}{dt} - r\sin\theta\cos\theta\left(\frac{d\phi}{dt}\right)^2 \right] \\ & + \mathbf{e}_3 \left[r\sin\theta\frac{d^2\phi}{dt^2} + 2r\cos\theta\frac{d\theta}{dt}\frac{d\phi}{dt} + 2\sin\theta\frac{dr}{dt}\frac{d\phi}{dt} \right] \end{aligned} \qquad \text{(2a-6)}$$

2a-3. Newtonian Dynamics of Particles—Relationship of the Motion of Particles to the Forces Acting upon Them. *Inertial Frames of Reference.* Not all frames of reference are equally useful in describing the motion of a body; of all possible frames there is a set, called "inertial frames of reference," in which particularly simple laws describe the motion of a particle. An intuitive definition of an inertial frame of reference regards such a frame as being one which is "embedded in space" with respect to an observer; more exactly, an inertial frame of reference is one in which an isolated body moves with constant velocity. It may be easily seen from Newton's second law of motion (below) that any inertial frame is transformed to any other by uniform motion in a straight line.

Definitions of Useful Concepts. MASS: The Newtonian mass of a particle may be defined by considering the acceleration associated with the mutual interaction of this particle with a second, a test particle, when the two form an isolated system. The mass of the first particle is defined as a constant times the ratio of the magnitude of the accelerations of the second and first particles, respectively. The constant depends only on the choice of the second particle, and by mutual consent the constant may arbitrarily be set equal to unity. The second particle then represents the standard unit of mass, and the mass of the first is thus determined by the above-mentioned ratio of accelerations. This method, although having the advantage of yielding an unequivocal definition of mass, is not usually a practicable one and is replaced by other methods (e.g., the balance) in actual determinations. Implicit in this definition is the assumption of additivity of masses, thus enabling the mass of a finite body, as an aggregate of particles, to be determined uniquely.

DENSITY: The density of a substance is defined as the mass per unit volume of the substance, and is calculated from the formula

$$\rho = m/V \tag{2a-7}$$

where ρ is the density, m is the mass, V is the volume occupied by mass m. Density is thus a measure of the volume concentration of mass.

MOMENTUM: The momentum of a particle is defined as the product of its mass and velocity and is therefore a vector quantity.

KINETIC ENERGY: The kinetic energy of a particle is defined as one-half the product of its mass and the square of its velocity, and is a scalar.

FORCE: The force acting upon a particle is assumed as the cause of the acceleration of the particle. It may be defined as that vector function which, in magnitude and direction, equals the time rate of change of momentum of the particle. Thus

$$\mathbf{F} = \frac{d}{dt}(m\mathbf{v}) \tag{2a-8}$$

where $\mathbf{F}$ represents the force, and m and $\mathbf{v}$ are the particle mass and velocity, respectively.

This force depends in general not only on the particle in question but also on the nature of other particles in, and properties of, the system of which the original particle is a part, the mutual separations and velocities of the particles and possibly of the time. Although force has been defined so far only for a particle, the definition may be extended to finite distributions of matter by considering infinitesimal portions as particles and integrating.

Newton's Laws. The dynamics of particles situated in an inertial frame of reference is governed by Newton's three laws of motion. The extension of these laws to a noninertial frame is, in principle, immediately forthcoming by considerations of the accelerations of the noninertial frame with respect to an inertial one; thus Newton's laws govern the dynamics of particles when Newtonian concepts are valid. Newton's laws are as follows:

1. A particle, not under the action of a force, will maintain its velocity unchanged in magnitude and direction.

2. A force acting on a particle causes a change of momentum of the particle, the rate of change of momentum being vectorially equal to the force.

3. If one particle exerts a force on a second, then the second exerts a force, equal in magnitude but opposite in direction, on the first.

Statics. The branch of dynamics which deals with particles undergoing no acceleration is termed "statics." We see from Newton's second law that, in this case,

$$\mathbf{F} = 0 \tag{2a-9}$$

where **F** refers to the vectorial sum of all the forces acting on the particle.

Noninertial Dynamics. At times it is convenient to consider the dynamics of a particle in a noninertial frame, e.g., motion relative to rotating or other moving axes. There will then be an apparent force acting on the particle which is the difference between the Newtonian force (that acting in the inertial system) and the inertial force $m\mathbf{a}_0$, where $\mathbf{a}_0$ is the acceleration of the noninertial system with respect to the inertial frame. Symbolically, $\mathbf{F}_d = \mathbf{F} - m\mathbf{a}_0$, where $\mathbf{F}_d$ is the apparent force, and **F** is the Newtonian force. We can set $\mathbf{F}_d = m\mathbf{a}_d$ where $\mathbf{a}_d$ is the acceleration of the particle with respect to the noninertial frame.

D'ALEMBERT'S PRINCIPLE: Often it is advantageous to choose a noninertial system such that $\mathbf{F}_d = 0$; the dynamical problem in the noninertial system then reduces to a statical one. That such a noninertial system can be chosen is one statement of D'Alembert's principle.

INERTIAL FORCES—CENTRIFUGAL AND CORIOLIS FORCES: The difference between the Newtonian force and the apparent noninertial force can be termed the "inertial force." Centrifugal and Coriolis forces are two commonly occurring examples of such inertial forces. The centrifugal force is given by

$$\mathbf{f}_c = \boldsymbol{\omega} \times (\boldsymbol{\omega} \times \mathbf{r}) \tag{2a-10}$$

where $\boldsymbol{\omega}$ is the instantaneous angular velocity of the moving axes about the axis of rotation and **r** is the position vector of the particle with respect to the moving axes. The Coriolis force is given by

$$\mathbf{f}_c = 2\boldsymbol{\omega} \times \mathbf{v} \tag{2a-11}$$

where $\boldsymbol{\omega}$ has the same meaning as above and **v** is the apparent velocity of the particle with respect to the moving axes.

Conservation of Momentum. IMPULSE-MOMENTUM THEOREM: The impulse of a force acting between times t_0 and t_1 is defined by

$$\mathcal{I} = \int_{t_0}^{t_1} \mathbf{F}\, dt \tag{2a-12}$$

From Newton's second law, the impulse of the total force acting on a particle during some time interval is equal to the change in the momentum of the particle during the time interval, i.e.,

$$\mathcal{I} = m\mathbf{v}_1 - m\mathbf{v}_0 \tag{2a-13}$$

CONSERVATION OF MOMENTUM: When the total force acting upon a particle is zero, the momentum of the particle is a constant; this follows directly from the impulse-momentum theorem.

Conservation of Energy. WORK-ENERGY THEOREM: The work done on a particle by a force acting during the displacement of a particle from position P_0 to position P_1 is defined as

$$W = \int_{P_0}^{P_1} \mathbf{F} \cdot d\mathbf{s} \tag{2a-14}$$

where $d\mathbf{s}$ is an infinitesimal displacement along the path of the particle. From Newton's second law the work done by the total force acting on a particle during some displacement of the particle is equal to the change in kinetic energy of the particle:

$$W = \tfrac{1}{2}mv_1^2 - \tfrac{1}{2}mv_0^2 \tag{2a-15}$$

POTENTIAL ENERGY: If the work done by a force acting on a particle does not depend upon the path of the particle, but only on the initial and end points of its motion, we call the force a "conservative force." The condition for a force to be conservative is that its curl shall vanish, i.e.,

$$\nabla \times \mathbf{F} = 0 \tag{2a-16}$$

If the force is conservative, we may define a potential-energy function of position V such that

$$\mathbf{F} = -\nabla V \tag{2a-17}$$

CONSERVATION OF ENERGY: If the total force acting upon a particle is conservative, the sum of the kinetic and potential energies is a constant; this follows from the work-energy theorem and the definition of the potential energy:

$$\tfrac{1}{2}mv^2 + V(x,y,z) = U \tag{2a-18}$$

where U, the total mechanical energy, is a constant.

2a-4. Dynamics of Systems of Particles. In examining the dynamics of a system of point masses, consider N point particles, each of mass m_i, where $i = 1, 2, \ldots, N$. The total force acting on m_i due to m_j is $\mathbf{F}_{ij}$; in addition, a total external force $\mathbf{F}_i$ acts on m_i. At any time t, m_i has a position $\mathbf{r}_i$, a velocity $\dot{\mathbf{r}}_i$, and an acceleration $\ddot{\mathbf{r}}_i$, all relative to some inertial frame. (The dots denote differentiation with respect to time.)

Definition of Useful Concepts. CENTER OF MASS: The position of the center of mass of the above system is given by

$$\mathbf{R} = \frac{\sum_{i=1}^{N} m_i \mathbf{r}_i}{\sum_{i=1}^{N} m_i} \tag{2a-19}$$

MOMENT OF MOMENTUM: The moment of momentum of the ith particle in the above system is defined as

$$\mathbf{L}_i = \mathbf{r}_i \times m_i \dot{\mathbf{r}}_i \tag{2a-20}$$

The total moment of momentum of the system is

$$\mathbf{L} = \sum_{i=1}^{N} \mathbf{L}_i = \sum_{i=1}^{N} m_i(\mathbf{r}_i \times \dot{\mathbf{r}}_i) \tag{2a-21}$$

If the collection of particles is a rigid body, the moment of momentum is called the "angular momentum" (cf. Sec. 2a-5).

TORQUE (MOMENT OF FORCE): The torque due to a force $\mathbf{F}_i$ acting on the ith particle in the above system is defined as

$$\mathbf{T}_i = \mathbf{r}_i \times \mathbf{F}_i \tag{2a-22}$$

The total torque acting on the system is $\mathbf{T} = \sum_{i=1}^{N} \mathbf{T}_i$. (The force $\mathbf{F}_i$ includes forces externally applied to the particle, as well as internal forces of interaction among the particles of the system.)

Application of Newton's Laws. We may apply Newton's second law to each particle of the system, and obtain

$$m_i \ddot{\mathbf{r}}_i = \mathbf{F}_i{}^i + \mathbf{F}_i{}^e \tag{2a-23}$$

where $\mathbf{F}_i{}^i = \Sigma_{j \neq 1} \mathbf{F}_{ij}$ is the total internal force acting on m_i (due to all other particles), and $\mathbf{F}_i{}^e$ is the external force on the ith particle.

If we sum over all particles of the system, we obtain, by use of Newton's third law,

$$\sum_{i=1}^{N} \mathbf{F}_i{}^i = 0 \tag{2a-24}$$

MOTION OF THE CENTER OF MASS: The analogue of Newton's second law for the entire system is therefore

$$M\ddot{\mathbf{R}} = \sum_{i=1}^{N} \mathbf{F}_i{}^e \tag{2a-25}$$

where $M = \sum_{i=1}^{N} m_i$ is the total mass of the system, $\ddot{\mathbf{R}}$ is the acceleration of the center of mass of the system, and $\Sigma_i \mathbf{F}_i{}^e$ is the total external force.

MOMENT OF MOMENTUM AND TORQUE: By forming the cross product of both sides of Eq. (2a-23) with $\mathbf{r}_i$ and summing over all particles we can show that

$$\frac{d}{dt} \sum [\mathbf{r}_i \times (m_i \dot{\mathbf{r}}_i)] = \sum \mathbf{T}_i{}^e = \mathbf{T}^e \tag{2a-26}$$

provided that the internal force $\mathbf{F}_{ij}$ acts along the straight line connecting the particles i and j in each case.

In particular, if $\mathbf{r}_{ic}$ is the position of the ith particle with respect to the center of mass, so that

$$\mathbf{r}_{ic} = \mathbf{r}_i - \mathbf{R}$$

it follows from Eq. (2a-26) that

$$\frac{d}{dt} \sum_{i=1}^{N} \mathbf{r}_{ic} \times (m_i \dot{\mathbf{r}}_{ic}) = \sum_{i=1}^{N} \mathbf{r}_{ic} \times \mathbf{F}^e \tag{2a-27}$$

That is, the time rate of change of the moment of momentum is equal to the total external torque when both are taken with respect to the center of mass. The above equation is also true if the center of mass is replaced by any point moving with the velocity of the center of mass, which may, of course, also be at rest.

Conservation of Momentum. It follows from Eqs. (2a-25) and (2a-26) that

1. If the total external force is zero, the linear momentum of the center of mass is constant.

2. If the total external torque about a fixed point, or one moving with velocity of the center of mass, is zero, the moment of momentum about that point is constant.

Conservation of Energy. WORK-ENERGY THEOREM: The total work done by the external and internal forces acting on the system is equal to the change in the total kinetic energy of the system (the sum of the kinetic energy of each article)

$$\tfrac{1}{2} \sum_{i=1}^{N} m_i(v_i''^2 - v_i'^2) = \sum_{1=1}^{N} \int_{r_i'}^{r_i''} (\mathbf{F}_i{}^e + \mathbf{F}_i{}^i) \cdot d\mathbf{r}_i \tag{2a-28}$$

where $\mathbf{v}_i'$, $\mathbf{v}_i''$ are the velocities of the ith particle at position $\mathbf{r}_i'$ and $\mathbf{r}_i''$, respectively, and $\mathbf{F}_i{}^i = \Sigma_{j\neq 1}\, \mathbf{F}_{ij}$ is the total internal force acting on the ith particle.

CONSERVATION OF ENERGY: If the internal and external forces are conservative, so that they can be derived from potentials,

$$\mathbf{F}_i{}^i = -\nabla V_i{}^i \qquad \text{and} \qquad \mathbf{F}_i{}^e = -\nabla V_i{}^e \tag{2a-29}$$

then the sum of the kinetic and potential energies of all the particles is a constant

$$\sum_{i=1}^{N} (\tfrac{1}{2} m_i v_i{}^2 + V_i{}^i + V_i{}^e) = U \tag{2a-30}$$

where U is the total energy of the system.

2a-5. Dynamics of Rigid Bodies. *Definitions of Kinematical Concepts.* A rigid body is an aggregate of particles the distance between any two of which remains constant. The position of a rigid body in any frame of reference is completely determined by fixing the position of three noncollinear points. This means that the number of degrees of freedom of the rigid body is six. There are two principal types of motion of a rigid body: (1) *translation,* in which all particles move with the same velocity and acceleration in parallel paths, and (2) *rotation,* in which some point or line of points (axis) remains fixed in space. Every motion of a rigid body can be considered as a combination of translations and rotations.

The instantaneous angular velocity $\boldsymbol{\omega}$ is the primary quantity descriptive of the kinematics of a rigid body. This is a vector lying along the instantaneous axis of rotation and having the magnitude such that its cross product with the position vector $\mathbf{r}_P$ of any point P of the rigid body relative to an origin on the axis yields the velocity of the point P. Symbolically

$$\mathbf{v}_P = \dot{\mathbf{r}}_P = \boldsymbol{\omega} \times \mathbf{r}_P \tag{2a-31}$$

The angular velocity can always be resolved into rectangular components ω_x, ω_y, ω_z, i.e.,

$$\boldsymbol{\omega} = \mathbf{i}\omega_x + \mathbf{j}\omega_y + \mathbf{k}\omega_z \tag{2a-32}$$

Angular acceleration is the time rate of change of angular velocity, i.e. (to use the dot notation),

$$\boldsymbol{\alpha} = \dot{\boldsymbol{\omega}} \tag{2a-33}$$

Dynamical Concepts and Equations of Motion. The total moment of momentum $\mathbf{L}$ of the rigid body with respect to some fixed origin of coordinates either inside or outside the body [cf. Eq. (2a-20)] is called the angular momentum of the rigid body about the origin. By expansion of the summand in Eq. (2a-21) after employing Eq. (2a-31) there results

$$\begin{aligned} \mathbf{L} &= \mathbf{i}(\omega_x I_{xx} - \omega_y I_{xy} - \omega_z I_{xz}) \\ &\quad + \mathbf{j}(-\omega_x I_{yx} + \omega_y I_{yy} - \omega_z I_{yz}) \\ &\quad + \mathbf{k}(-\omega_x I_{yx} - \omega_y I_{zy} + \omega_z I_{zz}) \end{aligned} \tag{2a-34}$$

where I_{xx}, I_{yy}, I_{zz} are called the "moments of inertia" of the rigid body about the x, y, z axes, respectively, and I_{xy}, I_{yz}, I_{xz}, etc., are called "products of inertia." We have

$$\begin{aligned} I_{xx} &= \Sigma m_i(y_i{}^2 + z_i{}^2) \qquad \text{etc.} \\ I_{xy} &= \Sigma m_i x_i y_i \qquad \text{etc.} \end{aligned} \tag{2a-35}$$

By proper choice of axes (called "principal" axes) the products of inertia can be made to vanish. If we write

$$I_{xx} = MR^2 \tag{2a-36}$$

where

$$R^2 = \frac{\Sigma m_i(y_i^2 + z_i^2)}{M} \tag{2a-37}$$

and M is the total mass of the rigid body, R is termed the "radius of gyration" about the x axis.

The fundamental equation of motion (Newton's second law) of the rigid body about a *fixed* origin is

$$\dot{\mathbf{L}} = \mathbf{T} \tag{2a-38}$$

where **T** is the total torque about the instantaneous axis through the fixed origin. If the fixed origin is chosen as the center of mass, the total motion is obtained by superposing the translational motion of the center of mass on the rotational motion about the center of mass.

Static Equilibrium. A rigid body is in translational equilibrium if its center of mass moves with constant velocity in an inertial frame. It is in rotational equilibrium about any point if the resultant torque about the point vanishes. This means $\dot{\mathbf{L}} = 0$ and corresponds to conservation of angular momentum. The behavior of a rigid body under these conditions is the subject matter of rigid statics.

Moving Axes. Euler's Equation. For axes fixed in space, $\boldsymbol{\omega}$ and the moments and products of inertia in general change with time as the rigid body moves. Simplification often results by using axes *fixed in the body,* since then I_{xx}, I_{xy}, etc., remain constant. Then, for motion about a fixed point the axes rotate, and we have

$$\dot{\mathbf{L}} = \mathbf{i}\dot{L}_x + \mathbf{j}\dot{L}_y + \mathbf{k}\dot{L}_z + \boldsymbol{\omega} \times \mathbf{L} \tag{2a-39}$$

where L_x, L_y, L_z are the components of angular momentum about the moving axes and $\boldsymbol{\omega}$ is the instantaneous angular velocity of the body about the instantaneous axis of rotation. If we choose principal axes the equation of motion (2a-38) becomes

$$\begin{aligned}\mathbf{T} = \mathbf{i}[I_{xx}\dot{\omega}_x + (I_{zz} - I_{yy})\omega_y\omega_z] \\ + \mathbf{j}[I_{yy}\dot{\omega}_y + (I_{xx} - I_{zz})\omega_z\omega_x] \\ + \mathbf{k}[I_{zz}\dot{\omega}_z + (I_{yy} - I_{xx})\omega_x\omega_y]\end{aligned} \tag{2a-40}$$

This is *Euler's equation.* The three component equations to which it reduces are usually called Euler's equations.

Kinetic Energy. Work-Energy Theorem. If a rigid body has one point fixed in space and the angular momentum about this point is **L**, while the angular velocity about an instantaneous axis through the point is $\boldsymbol{\omega}$, the kinetic energy of rotational motion is

$$K = \tfrac{1}{2}\boldsymbol{\omega} \cdot \mathbf{L} \tag{2a-41}$$

The work done by the resultant torque **T** about the fixed point in time dt is

$$dW = \mathbf{T} \cdot \boldsymbol{\omega}\, dt \tag{2a-42}$$

measured with respect to axes fixed in the body. Since

$$\boldsymbol{\omega} \cdot d\mathbf{L} = dK \tag{2a-43}$$

it follows that the work done by the resultant torque in any time interval is equal to the change in kinetic energy of rotation during this same interval.

Total Energy. The total kinetic energy of a rigid body is the sum of the kinetic energy of translation of the center of mass (assuming all the mass to be concentrated there) and the kinetic energy of rotation about the center of mass. The total potential energy is the sum of the potential energy of the center of mass (with all the mass concentrated there) due to the external forces acting on the body and the potential energy of all the particles of the body due to the internal forces of cohesion that hold the body together. If the body remains really rigid throughout its motion, the last-named potential energy remains constant. With this understanding, the law of conservation of energy of a rigid body is phrased as precisely as that in the case of a particle.

2a-6. Dynamics of Deformable Media. *General Concepts of Strain and Stress.* Whenever an extended medium moves in such a way that the distance between any two particles constituting the medium changes, the medium is said to be *deformed.* Deformations are of two general types: (1) dilatational or extensional, in which a change in the density of the medium takes place (change in the size, if the medium is finite) and (2) shear, in which a change in the shape alone takes place. The corresponding *fractional* deformations (nondimensional quantities) are termed *strains.* Thus the *dilatational strain* is the negative of the change in density divided by the mean density. The *extensional strain* (in the case of a rod, string, or other linear medium) is the change in length divided by the mean length. The *shear strain* is the difference in displacement of two parallel planes in the medium divided by the perpendicular distance between them.

When a medium is deformed by the application of external forces, the dynamics of the deformation is best described in terms of internal *stresses* which are assumed to change with the deformation. A stress is a force per unit area with which the part of the medium on one side of an imaginary surface acts on the part on the other side. If the force is normal to the surface, the stress is dilatational; if the force is parallel to the surface, the stress is a shear. The stresses associated with deformations are strictly *excess* stresses (i.e., the change in stress produced by the application of the external force). The adjective is normally omitted.

Elastic Media. Hooke's Law. If when the deforming forces are removed a medium reverts to its original condition, it is said to be *elastic.* In such media the ratio of stress to strain is approximately a constant for a certain range of stress variation. This is Hooke's law. For all solid media the imposition of a sufficiently large deforming force leads to a breakdown of this linear relation; i.e., they possess an elastic limit (cf. Sec. 2f). Indeed even larger deforming forces may cause the solid to flow (strain dependent on time) and it becomes *plastic.* Even elastic substances do not always return *immediately* to their original condition after the removal of the deforming force (elastic lag or relaxation). Fluids can experience change of state under sufficiently high stresses.

For an elastic medium for which Hooke's law holds it is possible to define elastic moduli, i.e., ratios of stress to strain. Thus,

$$\frac{\text{Compressional stress}}{\text{Volume strain}} = k = \text{bulk modulus or modulus of volume elasticity}$$

$$\frac{\text{Tensile stress}}{\text{Linear strain}} = Y = \text{Young's modulus}$$

$$\frac{\text{Shearing stress}}{\text{Shear strain}} = \mu = \text{shear modulus or rigidity}$$

The deformation of a homogeneous isotropic elastic medium can be completely described in terms of these three moduli. A fourth, Poisson's ratio σ, is usually added. This is the reciprocal of the ratio of linear extensional strain in a wire or rod to the concomitant lateral contractional strain. The following relations hold among the moduli:

$$Y = 3k(1 - 2\sigma) = 2\mu(1 + \sigma)$$

$$Y = \frac{9k\mu}{\mu + 3k} \tag{2a-44}$$

Evidently for such media

$$-1 < \sigma < \tfrac{1}{2} \tag{2a-45}$$

General Stress and Strain Expressions for an Arbitrary Medium. If the displacement from its equilibrium position of any particle of a deformable medium is denoted by the vector

$$\mathbf{\Delta} = \mathbf{i}\xi + \mathbf{j}\eta + \mathbf{k}\zeta \tag{2a-46}$$

where the displacement components ξ, η, ζ are in general functions of both space and time, the effective *strain* is denoted by the covariant tensor of the second order written in matrix form as follows:

$$\mathbf{D} = \begin{Vmatrix} \partial\xi/\partial x, \ \frac{1}{2}(\partial\eta/\partial x + \partial\xi/\partial y), \ \frac{1}{2}(\partial\zeta/\partial x + \partial\xi/\partial z) \\ \frac{1}{2}(\partial\eta/\partial x + \partial\xi/\partial y), \ \partial\eta/\partial y, \ \frac{1}{2}(\partial\eta/\partial z + \partial\zeta/\partial y) \\ \frac{1}{2}(\partial\zeta/\partial x + \partial\xi/\partial z), \ \frac{1}{2}(\partial\zeta/\partial y + \partial\eta/\partial z), \ \partial\zeta/\partial z \end{Vmatrix} \tag{2a-47}$$

This is often written in the abbreviated symbolic form

$$D = \begin{Vmatrix} e_{xx}, \ \frac{1}{2}e_{xy}, \ \frac{1}{2}e_{xz} \\ \frac{1}{2}e_{xy}, \ e_{yy}, \ \frac{1}{2}e_{yz} \\ \frac{1}{2}e_{xz}, \ \frac{1}{2}e_{yz}, \ e_{zz} \end{Vmatrix} \tag{2a-48}$$

The diagonal elements in this matrix are dilatational strain components, whereas the nondiagonal elements are shear strain components.

The total stress in a deformable medium is most adequately expressed in terms of the stress tensor S which is represented by the following matrix:

$$\mathbf{S} = \begin{Vmatrix} X_x, \ X_y, \ X_z \\ Y_x, \ Y_y, \ Y_z \\ Z_x, \ Z_y, \ Z_z \end{Vmatrix} \tag{2a-49}$$

Here X_x = tensile stress in x direction on surface normal to x axis
X_y = shear stress in y direction on surface normal to x axis
X_z = shear stress in z direction on surface normal to x axis
etc.

It should be noted that the stress tensor is symmetrical, i.e., $X_y = Y_x$, etc. The same is true of the strain tensor ($e_{zx} = e_{xz}$, etc.).

Hooke's Law in Tensor Form for a Homogeneous, Isotropic Elastic Medium. For this case Hooke's law takes the form

$$\mathbf{S} = 2\mu\mathbf{D} + \lambda\mathbf{D}' \tag{2a-50}$$

where μ is still the shear modulus, and $\lambda = k - 2\mu/3$. $\mathbf{D}'$ is the diagonal tensor.

$$\mathbf{D}' = \begin{Vmatrix} \Theta & 0 & 0 \\ 0 & \Theta & 0 \\ 0 & 0 & \Theta \end{Vmatrix} \tag{2a-51}$$

with

$$\Theta = e_{xx} + e_{yy} + e_{zz} \tag{2a-52}$$

Hooke's Law for an Arbitrary Crystalline Medium. If the medium is a crystal with different properties in different directions, Hooke's law takes the form of the following linear equations expressing the strain components in terms of the stress components.

$$\begin{aligned} e_{xx} &= S_{11}X_x + S_{12}Y_y + S_{13}Z_z + S_{14}Y_z + S_{15}Z_x + S_{16}X_y \\ e_{yy} &= S_{21}X_x + S_{22}Y_y + S_{23}Z_z + S_{24}Y_z + S_{25}Z_x + S_{26}X_y \\ e_{zz} &= S_{31}X_x + S_{32}Y_y + S_{33}Z_z + S_{34}Y_z + S_{35}Z_x + S_{36}X_y \\ e_{zx} &= S_{41}X_x + S_{42}Y_y + S_{43}Z_z + S_{44}Y_z + S_{45}Z_x + S_{46}X_y \\ e_{zy} &= S_{51}X_x + S_{52}Y_y + S_{53}Z_z + S_{54}Y_z + S_{55}Z_x + S_{56}X_y \\ e_{xy} &= S_{61}X_x + S_{62}Y_y + S_{63}Z_z + S_{64}Y_z + S_{65}Z_x + S_{66}X_y \end{aligned} \tag{2a-53}$$

The 36 coefficients $S_{11}, S_{12}, \ldots, S_{ij}, \ldots, S_{66}$ are called the "elastic constants." If the above linear equations are solved for the stress components in terms of the strain components, the corresponding coefficients C_{ij} are called "elastic coefficients." It can be shown that, for any i_{ij}, $C_{ij} = C_{ji}$ and $S_{ij} = S_{ji}$.

For a cubic crystal the elastic coefficient matrix reduces to

$$\mathbf{C} = \begin{Vmatrix} C_{11} & C_{12} & C_{12} & 0 & 0 & 0 \\ C_{12} & C_{11} & C_{12} & 0 & 0 & 0 \\ C_{12} & C_{12} & C_{11} & 0 & 0 & 0 \\ 0 & 0 & 0 & C_{44} & 0 & 0 \\ 0 & 0 & 0 & 0 & C_{44} & 0 \\ 0 & 0 & 0 & 0 & 0 & C_{44} \end{Vmatrix} \tag{2a-54}$$

Moreover for a cubic crystal $C_{44} = 1/S_{44}$. The bulk modulus in this case is given by

$$k = \frac{C_{11} + 2C_{12}}{3} \tag{2a-55}$$

Equation of Motion of a Deformed Homogeneous Isotropic Elastic Medium. The equation of motion of such a medium of density ρ, in which the displacement from equilibrium is the vector $\mathbf{\Delta}$, takes the form

$$\rho\ddot{\mathbf{\Delta}} = \left(k + \frac{4\mu}{3}\right)\nabla\nabla\cdot\mathbf{\Delta} - \mu\nabla\times\nabla\mathbf{\Delta} \tag{2a-56}$$

If $\nabla \times \mathbf{\Delta} = 0$ this is the equation of *irrotational* waves traveling with velocity

$$v_i = \sqrt{\frac{k + 4\mu/3}{\rho}} \tag{2a-57}$$

If $\nabla \cdot \mathbf{\Delta} = 0$, this is the equation of solenoidal waves traveling with velocity

$$V_s = \sqrt{\frac{\mu}{\rho}} \tag{2a-58}$$

2a-7. Fluid Dynamics. *General Concepts. Fluids in Equilibrium.* A perfect fluid is a deformable medium in which deforming forces give rise only to dilatations and never to shears. This is an ideal concept and is realized only approximately for actual fluids. Gases manifest the property more nearly than liquids, though both are normally considered to be fluids. Liquids can present under many circumstances the phenomenon of a free surface.

The dilatational stress in the case of a fluid is termed the *pressure,* which is the force per unit area directed *against* any surface imagined to exist in the fluid. A perfect fluid in equilibrium under the influence of an external force F acting on unit mass is subject to the relation

$$\rho\mathbf{F} = \nabla p \tag{2a-59}$$

where p is the pressure (here treated for simplicity as a scalar since it acts *normally* to every surface when the fluid is in equilibrium) and ρ the density, all quantities being considered as functions of space alone. The solution of this equation for given $\mathbf{F}$ gives p as a function of position in space and yields Pascal's law of the transmissibility of pressure in a fluid in equilibrium. From this also follows at once the principle of Archimedes that any fluid in equilibrium exerts on a body immersed in it a buoyant force equal in magnitude to the weight of the fluid displaced by the body and directed upward through the center of gravity.

Flow Concepts. Equations of Continuity. In the Eulerian system to which this review is confined the flow velocity of a fluid is the vector **v** whose magnitude at any point and at any time is the volume flow per unit time per unit area placed normal to the direction of flow, the latter being the direction of **v**. This quantity is a function of both space and time. In any continuous indestructible fluid of density ρ containing no sources or sinks **v** obeys the so-called equation of continuity

$$\nabla \cdot (\rho \mathbf{v}) = -\dot{\rho} \tag{2a-60}$$

where it is to be noted that ρ also is a function of space and time. For a homogeneous incompressible fluid this equation reduces to

$$\nabla \cdot \mathbf{v} = 0 \tag{2a-61}$$

i.e., **v** is a solenoidal vector. If further **v** is irrotational, so that $\nabla \times \mathbf{v} = 0$, it follows that

$$\mathbf{v} = \nabla \phi \tag{2a-62}$$

where ϕ is a scalar potential, called the "velocity potential" and the equation of continuity reduces to Laplace's equation

$$\nabla^2 \phi = 0 \tag{2a-63}$$

Equation of Motion. Bernoulli's Principle. The vector equation of motion of a compressible fluid of density subject to an external force F is

$$\dot{\mathbf{v}} + \mathbf{v} \cdot \nabla \mathbf{v} = \mathbf{F} - \frac{\nabla p}{\rho} \tag{2a-64}$$

where p is the pressure.

For irrotational flow in a conservative force field ($\mathbf{F} = -\nabla V$) it follows from the equation of motion that

$$\tfrac{1}{2}\rho v^2 + \rho V + p = \text{const} \tag{2a-65}$$

which is the principle of Bernoulli. It can also be shown that, even if the flow is not irrotational, as long as it is *steady* and in streamlines, so that **v** does not depend on the time, the above equation of Bernoulli will still hold as one proceeds along any given streamline, though the constant will in general be different for different streamlines.

Viscous Fluids. In contrast to a perfect fluid in which no shearing strains can exist, a viscous fluid is one in which the part of the medium flowing in one layer exerts a tangential or shearing stress on that flowing in the same direction in an adjacent layer. In the simplest type of viscous flow the tangential force is proportional to the velocity gradient normal to the layer and the coefficient of proportionality is called the viscosity η. Specifically

$$\eta = \frac{\text{shearing stress}}{\text{velocity gradient normal to flow}} \tag{2a-66}$$

The analogy between this relation and that defining the shear modulus for an elastic medium is obvious, the difference being that here the denominator is the rate of *change* of shear strain instead of the strain itself. The suggestion is immediate that the discussion of viscous flow can develop along the lines of the analysis of the behavior of deformable media in general (cf. Sec. 2a-6). This is indeed the case; it makes pressure appear as a tensor (analogous to the stress tensor). See also Secs. 2o, 2v, 2y.

A solid moving through a viscous fluid encounters increased resistance because of the viscosity. The simplest case is that in which a sphere of radius a moves through a fluid of viscosity η with *constant* velocity **v**. The resisting force is then given by Stokes' law

$$F = 6\pi\eta a v \tag{2a-67}$$

Surface Tension in Liquids. This is the force per unit length γ in the surface separating a liquid from the material surrounding it. Details concerning this as well as numerical values will be found in Sec. 2p.

Surface Waves in Liquids. When the free surface of a liquid is deformed, the forces acting on the deformed elements are primarily surface tension and gravity. The velocity of the resulting surface wave, if it is harmonic and has wavelength λ, is

$$V = \sqrt{\left(\frac{g\lambda}{2\pi} + \frac{2\pi\gamma}{\rho\lambda}\right)\tanh\frac{2\pi l}{\lambda}} \tag{2a-68}$$

where g is the acceleration of gravity, ρ the density, γ the surface tension, and l the depth of the liquid. For a relatively shallow liquid, for which $l \ll \lambda$, and the surface tension not very large, we have

$$V \doteq \sqrt{gl} \tag{2a-69}$$

If the liquid is relatively deep, or $l \gg \lambda$,

$$V \doteq \sqrt{\frac{g\lambda}{2\pi} + \frac{2\pi\gamma}{k\lambda}} \tag{2a-70}$$

For long waves

$$V \doteq \sqrt{\frac{g\lambda}{2\pi}}$$

while for ripples (small λ), surface tension predominates and

$$V \doteq \sqrt{\frac{2\pi\gamma}{k\lambda}}$$

Compressional Waves in Fluids. The combination of the equation of motion (2a-64), the equation of continuity (2a-60), and the equation of state of the fluid, i.e., the relation connecting change in density with change in pressure, leads to the wave equation for compressional waves traveling with velocity

$$V = \sqrt{\frac{dp}{d\rho}} \tag{2a-71}$$

The values of V for gases and liquids will be found in Sec. 3.

2a-8. Fundamental Units

Circular Mil. Area of circle whose diameter is 0.001 in.

Day. Period taken for one revolution of earth about its axis.

Degree. Angle subtended at the center by a circular arc which is $\frac{1}{360}$ of the circumference.

Hour. $\frac{1}{24}$ part of day.

Light-year. Distance traveled by light in 1 year at rate of approximately 186×10^3 miles/sec.

Minute. $\frac{1}{60}$ part of hour.

Radian. Angle subtended at the center by a circular arc which is equal in length to radius of circle.

Second. $\frac{1}{60}$ part of minute.

Steradian. Solid angle subtended at the center by $1/4\pi$ of the surface area of a sphere of unit radius.

Year (Sidereal). Time taken by sun (as seen from earth) in leaving and returning to meridian of a given star.

Year (Tropical, Mean Solar). Time taken by sun (as seen from earth) in leaving and returning to the same equinox.

2a-9. Derived Units

Atmosphere. Pressure exerted by air at sea level under standard conditions.

British Thermal Unit (Mean). Energy required to raise temperature of 1 lb mass of water 1°F (averaged from 32 to 212°F).

Calorie (Mean). Energy required to raise 1 g mass of water 1°C (averaged from 0 to 100°C).

Centimeters of Hg at 0°C. Pressure exerted by column of Hg of stated height at 0°C.

Dyne. Force necessary to give 1 g mass acceleration of 1 cm/sec^2.

Erg. Work done by force of 1 dyne applied over distance of 1 cm.

Feet of Water at 4°C. Pressure exerted by column of water of stated height at 4°C.

Kilowatthour. Work done in 1 hr at power level or rate of 10^3 watts.

Newton. Force necessary to give 1 kg mass acceleration of 1 m/sec^2.

Poundal. Force necessary to give 1 lb mass acceleration of 1 ft/sec^2.

Watt. Rate of doing work, or power expended, in the amount of 10^7 ergs/sec.

TABLE 2a-1. UNITS AND CONVERSION FACTORS, LENGTH

	Angstrom	Centimeter	Fathom	Foot	Inch (U.S.)	Kilometer	Light-year
Angstrom	1	10^{-8}	......	3.281×10^{-10}	3.937×10^{-9}	10^{-13}	
Centimeter	10^8	1	......	3.281×10^{-2}	0.3937	10^{-5}	
Fathom			1	6	72		
Foot		30.48	0.1667	1	12		
Inch (U.S.)	2.540×10^8	2.540	......	8.333×10^{-2}	1		
Kilometer		10^5	......	3.281×10^3		1	1.057×10^{-13}
Light-year			......			9.46×10^{12}	1
Meter	10^{10}	10^2	0.5468	3.281	39.37	10^{-3}	
Micron	10^4	10^{-4}	......		3.937×10^{-5}		
Mil		2.540×10^{-3}	......		10^{-3}		
Mile (statute)			......	5.280×10^3	6.336×10^4	1.609	1.69×10^{-13}
Millimeter		10^{-1}	......		3.937×10^{-2}		
Millimicron	10	10^{-7}					
Yard (U.S.)		91.44	......	3	36		

	Meter	Micron	Mil	Mile (statute)	Millimeter	Millimicron	Yard (U.S.)
Angstrom	10^{-10}	10^{-4}	3.937×10^{-6}		10^{-7}	10^{-1}	1.094×10^{-10}
Centimeter	10^{-2}	10^4	3.937×10^2		10	10^7	1.094×10^{-2}
Fathom	1.829	....				...	2
Foot	0.3048	....		1.894×10^{-4}		...	0.3333
Inch (U.S.)		....	10^3	1.578×10^{-5}	25.40	...	2.778×10^{-2}
Kilometer	10^3	....		0.6214		...	1.094×10^3
Light-year		....		5.9×10^{12}			
Meter	1	....		6.214×10^{-4}		10^9	1.094
Micron	10^{-6}	1	3.937×10^{-2}		10^{-3}	10^3	
Mil		25.40	1		2.450×10^2		
Mile (statute)	1.609×10^3	....		1		...	1.760×10^3
Millimeter	10^{-3}	10^3	39.37		1		
Millimicron	10^{-9}	10^{-3}				1	
Yard (U.S.)	0.9144	....		5.682×10^{-4}		...	1

Table 2a-2. Units and Conversion Factors, Area

	Circular mil	Square centimeter	Square foot (U.S.)	Square inch (U.S.)	Square kilometer	Square meter	Square mile	Square millimeter	Square yard
Circular mil	1	5.067×10^{-6}		7.854×10^{-7}				5.067×10^{-4}	
Square centimeter	1.974×10^{5}	1	1.076×10^{-3}	0.1550		10^{-4}		10^{2}	1.196×10^{-4}
Square foot (U.S.)		9.290×10^{2}	1	1.44×10^{2}		9.290×10^{-2}	3.587×10^{-8}		0.1111
Square inch (U.S.)	1.273×10^{6}	6.452	6.944×10^{-3}	1		6.452×10^{-4}		6.452×10^{2}	7.716×10^{-4}
Square kilometer			1.076×10^{7}		1	10^{6}	0.3861		1.196×10^{6}
Square meter		10^{4}	10.76	1.550×10^{3}	10^{-6}	1	3.861×10^{-7}	10^{6}	1.196
Square mile			2.788×10^{7}		2.590	2.590×10^{6}	1		3.098×10^{6}
Square millimeter	1.974×10^{3}	10^{-2}		1.550×10^{-3}		10^{-6}		1	
Square yard		8.361×10^{3}	9	1.296×10^{3}		0.8361	3.228×10^{-7}		1

Table 2a-3. Units and Conversion Factors, Volume

	Cubic centimeter	Cubic foot	Cubic inch	Cubic meter	Cubic yard	Fluid ounce (U.S.)	Gallon (U.S.)	Liter*	Pint, dry (U.S.)	Pint, liquid (U.S.)	Quart, dry (U.S.)	Quart, liquid (U.S.)
Cubic centimeter	1	3.531×10^{-5}	6.102×10^{-2}	10^{-6}	1.308×10^{-6}	3.381×10^{-2}	2.642×10^{-4}	9.9997×10^{-4}	1.816×10^{-3}	2.113×10^{-3}	9.081×10^{-4}	1.057×10^{-3}
Cubic foot	2.832×10^{4}	1	1.728×10^{3}	2.832×10^{-2}	3.704×10^{-2}		7.481	28.32		59.84	25.71	29.92
Cubic inch	16.39	5.787×10^{-4}	1	1.639×10^{-5}	2.143×10^{-5}	0.5541	4.329×10^{-3}	1.639×10^{-2}	2.976×10^{-2}		1.488×10^{-2}	1.732×10^{-2}
Cubic meter	10^{6}	35.31	6.102×10^{4}	1	1.308		2.642×10^{2}	9.9997×10^{2}		2.113×10^{3}		1.057×10^{3}
Cubic yard	7.646×10^{5}	27	4.666×10^{4}	0.7646	1		2.020×10^{2}	7.645×10^{2}		1.616×10^{3}		8.079×10^{2}
Fluid ounce (U.S.)	29.57		1.805			1	7.813×10^{-3}	2.957×10^{-2}		6.250×10^{-2}		3.125×10^{-2}
Gallon (U.S.)	3.785×10^{3}	0.1337	2.310×10^{2}	3.785×10^{-3}	4.951×10^{-3}	1.280×10^{2}	1	3.785		8		4
Liter*	1.000×10^{3}	3.532×10^{-2}	61.03	1.000×10^{-3}	1.308×10^{-3}	33.81	0.2642	1	1.816	2.113	0.9081	1.057
Pint, dry (U.S.)	5.506×10^{2}		33.60					0.5506	1		0.5000	
Pint, liquid (U.S.)	4.732×10^{2}	1.671×10^{-2}	28.88		6.188×10^{-4}	16	0.1250	0.4732		1		0.5000
Quart, dry (U.S.)	1.101×10^{3}	3.889×10^{-2}	67.20					1.101	2		1	
Quart, liquid (U.S.)	9.464×10^{2}	3.342×10^{-2}	57.75			32	0.2500	0.9463		2		1

* 1 milliliter = 1.000027 cubic centimeters.

2b. Density of Solids

H. M. TRENT AND D. E. STONE

Naval Research Laboratory

R. BRUCE LINDSAY

Brown University

For the definition of density ρ consult Sec. 2a-2. The cgs unit of density is the gram per cubic centimeter and this is used throughout the tables in this subsection.

Densities of the elements in solid form are given in Table 2b-1. All data are taken from "Smithsonian Physical Tables" (9th revised edition, 1954) unless otherwise stated. The values marked * are calculated densities from X-ray crystallographic data at room temperature and are taken from International Critical Tables (1926). All others are measured values for polycrystalline condition, save when otherwise stated. Standard room temperature is understood, unless otherwise stated.

TABLE 2b-1. DENSITY OF THE ELEMENTS IN SOLID FORM

Element	Physical state	Density, g/cm³	Temp., °C
Aluminum	Commercial hard-drawn solid	2.70	20
Aluminum	Single crystal	2.692*	
Antimony	Vacuo-distilled solid	6.62	20
Antimony	Single crystal	6.73*	
Argon	Solid	1.65	−233
Argon	Single crystal	1.645*	−253
Arsenic	Crystallized solid	5.73	14
Arsenic	Single crystal	5.75*	
Barium	Solid	3.5	20
Beryllium	Solid	1.85	20
Beryllium	Single crystal	1.83*	
Bismuth	Vacuo-distilled solid	9.78	20
Bismuth	Single crystal	9.86*	
Boron	Crystallized solid	2.535	
Bromine	Solid	4.2	−273
Cadmium	Vacuo-distilled solid	8.65	20
Cadmium	Single crystal	8.56*	
Calcium	Solid	1.55	20
Calcium	Single crystal	1.54*	
Carbon	Diamond	3.52	20

TABLE 2b-1. DENSITY OF THE ELEMENTS IN SOLID FORM (*Continued*)

Element	Physical state	Density, g/cm³	Temp., °C
Carbon	Graphite	2.25	20
Cerium	Solid	6.90	20
Cerium	Cubic crystal	6.90*	
Cerium	Hexagonal crystal	6.73*	
Cesium	Solid	1.873	20
Chlorine	Solid	2.2	−273
Chromium	Solid	7.14	20
Chromium	Crystal	7.22*	
Cobalt	Solid	8.71	21
Cobalt	Cubic crystal	8.67*	
Columbium	Solid	8.4	20
Copper	Vacuo-distilled solid	8.933	20
Copper	Single crystal	8.95*	
Erbium	Solid	4.77	
Fluorine	Solid	1.5	−273
Gallium	Solid	5.93	23
Germanium	Solid	5.46	
Germanium	Single crystal	5.38*	
Gold	Vacuo-distilled solid	18.88	20
Gold	Cast	19.3	20
Gold	Single crystal	19.4*	
Hafnium	Solid	13.3	20
Hafnium	Single crystal	11.3*	
Helium	Solid	0.19	−273
Hydrogen	Solid	0.763	−260
Indium	Solid	7.28	
Indium	Single crystal	7.43*	
Iodine	Solid	4.94	20
Iridium	Solid	22.42	17
Iridium	Single crystal	22.8*	
Iron	Pure solid	7.86	
Iron	Single crystal Fe-α	7.92*	
Krypton	Solid	3.4	−273
Lanthanum	Solid	6.15	
Lead	Vacuo-distilled	11.342	20
Lead	Single crystal	11.48*	
Lithium	Solid	0.534	20
Lithium	Single crystal	0.534*	
Magnesium	Solid	1.74	20
Magnesium	Single crystal	1.71*	
Manganese	Solid	7.3	
Manganese	Single crystal Mn-α	7.21*	
Mercury	Solid	14.193	−38.8
Molybdenum	Solid	9.01	
Molybdenum	Single crystal	10.20*	
Neodymium	Solid	7.00	

TABLE 2b-1. DENSITY OF THE ELEMENTS IN SOLID FORM (*Continued*)

Element	Physical state	Density, g/cm³	Temp., °C
Neon	Solid	1.204	−245
Nickel	Solid	8.8	
Nickel	Single crystal	9.04*	
Nitrogen	Solid	1.14	−273
Osmium	Solid	22.5	
Osmium	Single crystal	22.8*	
Oxygen	Solid	1.568	−273
Palladium	Solid	12.16	
Palladium	Single crystal	12.25*	
Phosphorus	Solid, white	1.83	
Phosphorus	Solid, red	2.20	
Phosphorus	Solid, black	2.69	
Platinum	Solid	21.37	
Platinum	Single crystal	21.5*	
Potassium	Solid	0.87	20
Praseodymium	Solid	6.48	20
Radium	Solid	5(?)	
Rhenium	Solid	20.53	
Rhodium	Solid	12.44	
Rubidium	Solid	1.53	20
Ruthenium	Solid	12.1	19
Samarium	Solid	7.7–7.8	
Scandium	Solid	3.02(?)	
Selenium	Solid	4.82	
Selenium	Single crystal	4.86*	
Silicon	Solid crystal	2.42	20
Silicon	Single crystal	2.32*	
Silver	Vacuo-distilled	10.492	20
Silver	Single crystal	10.49*	
Sodium	Solid	0.9712	20
Sodium	Single crystal	0.954*	
Strontium	Solid	2.60	
Sulfur	Solid, rhombic	2.07	
Sulfur	Solid, monoclinic	1.96	
Sulfur	Single crystal	2.02*	
Tantalum	Solid	16.6	
Tantalum	Single crystal	17.1*	
Tellurium	Solid, crystal	6.25	
Tellurium	Single crystal	6.26*	
Thallium	Solid	11.86	
Thallium	Single crystal	11.7*	
Thorium	Solid	11.00	17
Thorium	Single crystal	12.0*	
Tin	Solid, white tetragonal	7.29	20
Tin	Solid, white rhombic	6.55	
Tin	Solid, gray	5.75	20

TABLE 2b-1. DENSITY OF THE ELEMENTS IN SOLID FORM (*Continued*)

Element	Physical state	Density, g/cm³	Temp., °C
Tin	White single crystal	7.30*	
Titanium	Solid	4.5	18
Titanium	Single crystal	4.58*	
Tungsten	Solid	19.3	
Tungsten	Single crystal	19.3*	
Uranium	Solid	18.7	13
Vanadium	Solid	5.87	15
Vanadium	Single crystal	5.98*	
Yttrium	Solid	3.8	
Zinc	Solid, vacuo-distilled	6.92	20
Zinc	Solid	4.32	−273
Zinc	Single crystal	7.04*	
Zirconium	Solid	6.44	
Zirconium	Single crystal	6.47*	

TABLE 2b-2. DENSITY OF COMMON SOLIDS AT 20°C*

Substance	Density, g/cm³	Substance	Density, g/cm³
Agate	2.5–2.7	Gypsum	2.31–2.33
Amber	1.06–1.11	Hematite	4.9–5.3
Anthracite	1.4–1.8	Hornblende	3.0
Aragonite	2.93	Ice	0.917
Asbestos	2.0–2.8	Ivory	1.83–1.92
Basalt	2.4–3.1	Lava, basaltic	2.8–3.0
Beeswax	0.96–0.97	Lava, trachytic	2.0–2.7
Beryl	2.69–2.7	Leather, dry	0.86
Bone	1.7–2.0	Leather, greased	1.02
Brick	1.4–2.2	Lime, mortar	1.65–1.78
Butter	0.86–0.87	Lime, slaked	1.3–1.4
Calcite	2.71	Limestone	2.68–2.76
Camphor	0.99	Magnetite	4.9–5.2
Cauotchoric	0.92–0.99	Malachite	3.7–4.1
Celluloid	1.4	Marble	2.6–2.84
Cement (set)	2.7–3.0	Mica	2.6–3.2
Chalk	1.9–2.8	Olivine	3.27–3.37
Charcoal, oak	0.57	Opal	2.2
Charcoal, pine	0.28–0.44	Paper	0.7–1.15
Cinnabar	8.12	Paraffin	0.87–0.91
Clay	1.8–2.6	Pitch	1.07
Coal, soft	1.2–1.5	Porcelain	2.3–2.5
Coke	1.0–1.7	Pyrite	4.95–5.1
Cork	0.22–0.26	Quartz	2.65
Cork linoleum	0.55	Resin	1.07
Corundum	3.9–4.0	Rock salt	2.18
Dolomite	2.84	Rubber, hard	1.19
Ebonite	1.15	Rubber, soft	1.1
Emery	4.0	Rutile	4.2
Feldspar	2.55–2.75	Sandstone	2.19–2.36
Flint	2.63	Slate	2.6–3.3
Fluorite	3.18	Soapstone	2.6–2.8
Garnet	3.15–4.3	Starch	1.53
Gelatin	1.27	Sugar	1.61
Glass, common	2.4–2.8	Talc	2.7–2.8
Glass, flint	2.9–5.9	Tallow	0.91–0.97
Glue	1.27	Tar	1.02
Granite	2.64–2.76	Topaz	3.5–3.6
Graphite	2.30–2.72	Tourmaline	3.0–3.2
Gum arabic	1.3–1.4	Wax, sealing	1.8

* The density varies with the state and previous treatment of the solids. The figures quoted may be considered reasonable limits (taken largely from "Smithsonian Physical Tables," 9th ed.).

TABLE 2b-3. DENSITY OF STEELS*
(At room temperature)

Type of steel	ρ, g/cm³	Composition % C	% Si	% Mn	% C-	% Ni	Condition
Carbon steel..........	7.871	0.06	0.01	0.38	....		Annealed at 1700°F
Carbon steel..........	7.859	0.23	0.11	0.635	....		Annealed at 1700°F
Carbon steel..........	7.844	0.435	0.20	0.69	....		Annealed at 1580°F
Carbon steel..........	7.830	1.22	0.16	0.35	....		Annealed at 1470°F
Low-Cr steel..........	7.84	0.31	....	0.74	1.00		Oil-quenched at 1650°F, tempered at 1350°F
Low-Cr steel..........	7.84	0.315	....	0.69	1.09		Annealed at 1580°F
Low-Cr steel..........	7.83	0.35	....	0.24	1.56		Annealed by 1580°F
Low-Cr steel..........	7.80	1.73	....	0.30	1.65		Annealed at 1580°F
Low-Cr steel..........	7.82	0.80	....	0.28	1.67		Annealed at 1580°F
Low-Cr steel..........	7.82	0.62	....	0.22	1.67		Annealed at 1580°F
Low-Cr steel..........	7.81	0.98	....	0.28	1.68		Annealed at 1580°F
Low-Cr steel..........	7.84	0.20	....	0.14	1.85		Oil-quenched at 1650°F, tempered at 1380°F
Low-Cr steel..........	7.82	0.22	....	0.10	2.80		Oil-quenched at 1650°F, tempered at 1380°F
Low-Cr steel..........	7.81	0.21	....	0.19	3.88		Oil-quenched at 1650°F, tempered at 1380°F
Low-Cr steel..........	7.79	0.30	....	0.08	5.54		Oil-quenched at 1650°F, tempered at 1380°F
Low-Cr steel..........	7.845	0.35	....	0.59	0.88 + 0.20 Mo		Annealed at 1580°F, tempered at 1185°F
Low-alloy Ni-Cr steel...	7.85	0.33	....	0.53	0.80	3.38	Annealed at 1580°F, tempered at 1185°F
Low-alloy Ni-Cr steel...	7.85	0.325	....	0.55	0.71	3.41	Annealed at 1580°F, tempered at 1185°F
Low-alloy Ni-Cr steel...	7.92	1.28	....	0.24	1.80	3.46	Brine quenched at 2190°F
Low-alloy Ni-Cr steel...	7.82	1.28	....	0.24	1.80	3.46	Annealed at 1435°F
Low-alloy Ni-Cr steel...	7.855	0.325	....	0.55	0.17	3.47	Annealed at 1580°F
Low-alloy Ni-Cr steel...	7.835	0.51	....	0.22	1.72	3.52	Annealed at 1435°F
Low-alloy Ni-Cr steel...	7.86	0.34	....	0.55	0.78	3.53 + 0.39 Mo	Annealed at 1580°F, tempered at 1185°F

	ρ, g/cm³	% C	% Cr	% Ni	% Mo	% Zr	% Ti	% Cu	% Mn	Condition
Wrought stainless and heat-resisting steels...	7.93	0.10	18	9						
Wrought stainless and heat-resisting steels...	7.93	....	18	9	0.5					
Wrought stainless and heat-resisting steels...	7.98	....	23	13						
Wrought stainless and heat-resisting steels...	7.98	....	25	20.5						
Wrought stainless and heat-resisting steels...	7.98	....	17	12	2.25					
Wrought stainless and heat-resisting steels...	8.02	....	18	10.5						
Wrought stainless and heat-resisting steels...	7.75	....	12.5							
Wrought stainless and heat-resisting steels...	7.73	....	13	......	0.5					

* "Metals Handbook," 48th ed., American Society for Metals.

TABLE 2b-3. DENSITY OF STEELS (*Continued*)

Type of steel	ρ, g/cm³	Composition								Condition
		% C	% Cr	% Ni	% Mo	% Zr	% Ti	% Cu	% Mn	
Wrought stainless and heat-resisting steels...	7.70	....	13							
Wrought stainless and heat-resisting steels...	7.70	....	16							
Wrought stainless and heat-resisting steels...	7.68	....	17	......	0.6					
Wrought stainless and heat-resisting steels...	7.60	....	25							
Wrought stainless and heat-resisting steels...	7.77	....	17.88	......	....	..	..	...	8.26	
Wrought stainless and heat-resisting steels...	7.76	....	17.55	......	....	..	..	...	10.48	
Wrought stainless and heat-resisting steels...	7.91	....	18.40	4.07	....	..	..	0.78	5.33	
Wrought stainless and heat-resisting steels...	7.90	....	18.50	4.06	....	..	..	...	6.79	
Wrought stainless and heat-resisting steels...	7.78	....	18.04	2.06	....	..	..	...	7.90	
Wrought stainless and heat-resisting steels...	7.77	....	17.70	......	....	..	..	0.68	9.40	

	ρ, g/cm³	% W	% Cr	% V	% Mo	% Co	% C	Condition
Tool steel	8.67	18	4	1				
Tool steel	8.67	18	4	2				
Tool steel	7.925	1.64	3.68	1.00	8.24	....	0.80	Quenched at 2200°F
Tool steel	7.93	5.20	4.60	4.00	4.11	....	1.32	Hardened
Tool steel	7.76	.....	4.39	4.10	7.75	....	1.20	Hardened
Tool steel	8.89	20	4	2	....	12	...	Annealed
Tool steel	8.68	18	4	1	....	5	...	Annealed
Tool steel	8.16	6	......	2	5	....	...	Annealed
Tool steel	7.88	1.5	......	1	8			
		% Ni	% Al	% Co	% Cu			
Permanent-magnet alloys	6.892	20	12	5	....	....	...	Alnico
Permanent-magnet alloys	7.086	17	10	12.5	6	....	...	Cast Alnico
Permanent-magnet alloys	6.892	25	12					
Permanent-magnet alloys	7.003	28	12	5				
Permanent-magnet alloys	7.307	14	8	24	3			
Permanent-magnet alloys	7.197	18	6	35				8% Ti
		% Ni	% C	% Mn				
Miscellaneous ferrous alloys	8.16	28.37	......	....	....	....	...	Quenched at 1740°F
Miscellaneous ferrous alloys	8.00	36	......	....	....	....	...	Invar
Miscellaneous ferrous alloys	8.3	45	......	....	....	....	...	Radio metal
Miscellaneous ferrous alloys	8.25	50	......	....	....	....	...	Hipernik
Miscellaneous ferrous alloys	7.87	....	1.2	13	....	....	...	Austenitic manganese steel. Air-cooled at 1920°F

TABLE 2b-4. DENSITY OF ALUMINUM ALLOYS*
(At 20°C)

Material	ρ, g/cm³	% Al	% Mn	% Co	% Pb	% Bi	% Mg	% Si	% Ni	% Cr	% Zn
Wrought alloys:											
Pure aluminum..	2.6989	99.996									
(Commercially pure Al) 2S...	2.71	99.0+									
3S..............	2.73	98.8	1.2								
11S.............	2.82	93.5	....	5.5	0.5	0.5					
R-317..........	2.81	93.8	0.6	4.0	0.5	0.5	0.6				
14S.............	2.80	93.6	0.8	4.4	...	...	0.4	0.8			
R-30I (clad).....	2.78	93.3	0.8	4.5	...	...	0.4	1.0			
17S.............	2.79	95.0	0.5	4.0	...	...	0.5				
18S.............	2.80	93.5	....	4.0	...	...	0.5	....	.0		
24S.............	2.77	93.4	0.6	4.5	...	...	1.5				
25S.............	2.79	93.9	0.8	4.5	...	...	...	0.8			
32S.............	2.69	84.7	....	0.9	...	...	1.0	12.5	0.9		
A51S............	2.69	98.15	....	....	...	...	0.6	1.0		0.25	
52S.............	2.68	97.25	....	....	...	...	2.5	...	...	0.25	
53S.............	2.69	97.75	....	....	...	...	1.3	0.7	...	0.25	
56S.............	2.64	94.6	0.1	....	...	...	5.2	...	...	0.10	
61S.............	2.70	97.9	....	0.25	...	...	1.0	0.6	...	0.25	
75S.............	2.80	90.0	0.20	1.5	...	...	2.5	...	...	0.30	5.5
R-303..........	2.82	89.9	....	1.2	...	...	2.5	....	...	....	6.4

Material	ρ, g/cm³	% Al	% Mn	% Mg	% Cu	% Zn	% Cr	% Si	% Ni	% Bi	% Sn	% Ti
Casting alloys:												
13 alloy......	2.66	88	...	....	...	...	...	12				
43 alloy......	2.69	95	...	....	...	...	...	5				
85 alloy......	2.78	91	...	...	4	...	...	5				
108 alloy.....	2.79	93	...	...	4	...	...	3				
Allcast........	2.76	92	...	...	3	...	...	5				
A108 alloy....	2.79	90	...	....	4.5	...	...	5.5				
113 alloy.....	2.91	89.3	...	....	7	1.7	...	2				
C113 alloy....	2.91	89.5	...	...	7	...	...	3.5				
122 alloy.....	2.95	89.8	...	0.2	10							
A132 alloy....	2.68	83.5	...	1.2	0.8	...	...	12	2.5			
Red X-13.....	2.7	85.1	0.7	0.7	1.5	...	...	12				
142 alloy.....	2.81	92.5	...	1.5	4	...	...	....	2			
195 alloy.....	2.81	95.5	...	....	4.5							
B195 alloy....	2.78	93.0	...	...	4.5	...	...	2.5				
214 alloy.....	2.65	96.2	...	3.8								
A214 alloy....	2.65	94.4	...	3.8	...	1.8						
218 alloy.....	2.53	92.0	...	8								
220 alloy.....	2.58	90.0	...	10								
319 alloy.....	2.77	90.5	...	....	3.5			6				
355 alloy.....	2.70	93.2	...	0.5	1.3	...	...	5				
356 alloy.....	2.68	92.7	...	0.3	....	...	...	7				
Red X-8......	2.73	89.9	0.3	0.3	1.5	...	...	8				
360 alloy.....	2.68	90.0	...	0.5	....	...	...	9.5				
380 alloy.....	2.76	88.0	...	...	3.5	...	...	8.5				
750 alloy.....	2.89	91.5	...	...	1.0	...	...	...	1.0	...	6.5	
40E alloy.....	2.81	93.2	...	0.6	...	5.5	0.5	...	...	...	...	0.2

* "Metals Handbook," 48th ed., American Society for Metals.

TABLE 2b-5. DENSITY OF COBALT ALLOYS*

Material	ρ, g/cm³	% Co	% W	% Ni	% Cr	% Mo	% Cb	% Fe
Pure cobalt...........	8.9	100						
61 alloy (cast).........	8.54	70.0	5.0	2.0	23.0			
Vitallium.............	8.30	65.0	...	2.0	27.0	6.0		
X-40 alloy............	8.61	60.0	7.0	10.0	23.0			
422-19 alloy...........	8.31	55.0	...	16.0	23.0	6.0		
S-816 alloy...........	8.59	50.0	4.0	20.0	19.0	...	4.0	3.0
6059.................	8.21	39.0	...	32.0	23.0	6.0		

* "Metals Handbook," 48th ed., American Society for Metals.

TABLE 2b-6. DENSITY OF COPPER ALLOYS*

Material	ρ, g/cm³	% Cu	% O	% P	% Zn	% Pb	% Sn	% Fe	% Mn	% Al	% Ni	% Si	% Be
Wrought alloys:													
Pure copper	8.96	100											
Electrolytic tough-pitch copper	8.89–8.94	99.92	0.04										
Deoxidized copper	8.94	99.94	....	0.02									
Gilding metal	8.86	95.0	....	....	5.0								
Commercial bronze	8.80	90.0	....	....	10.0								
Red brass	8.75	85.0	....	....	15.0								
Low brass	8.67	80.0	....	....	20.0								
Cartridge brass	8.53	70.0	....	....	30.0								
Yellow brass	8.47	65.0	....	....	35.0								
Muntz metal	8.39	60.0	....	....	40.0								
Leaded commercial bronze	8.83	89.0	....	....	9.25	1.75							
Low-leaded brass	8.47	64.5	....	....	35.0	0.5							
Low-leaded brass (tube)	8.50	67.0	....	....	32.5	0.5							
Medium-leaded brass	8.47	64.5	....	....	34.5	1.0							
High-leaded brass	8.47	62.5	....	....	35.75	1.75							
Extra-high-leaded brass	8.50	62.5	....	....	35.0	2.5							
Free-cutting brass	8.50	61.5	....	....	35.5	3.0							
Leaded muntz metal	8.41	60.0	....	....	39.5	0.5							
Free-cutting muntz metal	8.41	60.5	....	....	38.4	1.1							
Forging brass	8.44	60.0	....	....	38.0	2.0							
Architectural bronze	8.47	57.0	....	....	40.0	3.0							
Admiralty metal	8.53	71.0	....	....	28.0	......	1.00						
Naval brass	8.41	60.0	....	....	39.25	......	0.75						
Leaded naval brass	8.44	60.0	....	....	37.5	1.75	0.75						
Manganese bronze	8.53	58.5	....	....	39.0	......	1.00	1.4	0.1				

Aluminum brass	8.33												
Aluminum brass	8.33	76.0	....	....	22.0	....	....	....	....	2			
Phosphor bronze	8.86	95.0	....	....	....	....	5.0						
Phosphor bronze 8% grade C	8.80	92.0	....	....	....	....	8.0						
Phosphor bronze 10% grade D	8.78	90.0	....	....	....	....	10.0						
Phosphor bronze 1.25% grade E	8.89	98.75	....	....	....	....	1.25						
Cupronickel, 30%	8.94	70.0	....	....	....	....	....	....	....	....	30.0		
Nickel silver, 18% alloy A	8.73	65.0	....	....	17.0	....	....	....	....	....	18.0		
Ni-Ag, 18%, alloy B	8.70	55.0	....	....	27.0	....	....	....	....	....	18.0		
Silicon bronze, type A	8.53	97.0	....	....	....	....	....	....	....	....	....	3.0	
Silicon bronze, type B	8.75	98.5	....	....	....	....	....	....	....	....	....	1.5	
5% aluminum bronze	8.17	95.0	....	....	....	....	....	....	....	5.0			
8% aluminum bronze	?	92.0	....	....	....	....	....	....	....	8.0			
10% aluminum bronze	7.58	90.0	....	....	....	....	....	....	....	10.0			
Aluminum bronze	7.58	82.5	....	....	....	....	....	2.50	...	10.0	5.0		
Constantan	8.9	55.0	....	....	....	....	....	....	....	....	45.0		
Beryllium copper	8.23 ± 0.02	97.65	....	....	....	....	....	....	....	....	0.35	...	2.0
Casting alloys (room temp.):													
Leaded tin bronze	8.7	88.0	....	....	4.5	1.5	6.0						
Leaded tin bearing bronze	8.80	87.0	....	....	4.0	1.0	8.0						
High-leaded tin bronze	8.87	85.0	....	....	1.0	9.0	5.0						
High-leaded tin bronze	8.93	83.0	....	....	3.0	7.0	7.0						
High-leaded tin bronze	8.80	80.0	....	....	....	10.0	10.0						
High-leaded tin bronze	9.25	78.0	....	....	....	15.0	7.0						
High-leaded tin bronze	9.30	70.0	....	....	....	25.0	5.0						
85-5-5-5	8.80	85.0	....	....	5.0	5.0	5.0						
Leaded red brass	8.6	83.0	....	....	7.0	6.0	4.0						
Leaded semired brass	8.70	81.0	....	....	9.0	7.0	3.0						
Leaded semired brass	8.6	76.0	....	....	15.0	6.0	3.0						
Leaded yellow brass	8.50	71.0	....	....	25.0	3.0	1.0						
Leaded yellow brass	8.4	66.0	....	....	30.0	3.0	1.0						

* "Metals Handbook," 48th ed., American Society for Metals.

TABLE 2b-6. DENSITY OF COPPER ALLOYS* (*Continued*)

Material	ρ, g/cm³	% Cu	% O	% P	% Zn	% Pb	% Sn	% Fe	% Mn	% Al	% Ni	% Si	% Be
Leaded yellow brass	8.40	60.0	....	....	38.0	1.0	1.0						
High-strength yellow brass	7.9	62.0	....	....	26.0	....	....	3.0	3.5	5.5			
High-strength yellow brass	8.2	58.0	....	....	39.25	....	....	1.25	0.25	1.25			
Leaded manganese brass	8.2	59.0	....	....	37.0	....	0.75	1.25	0.50	0.75			
Nickel silver	8.8–8.9	66.0	....	....	2.0	1.5	5.0	....	....	....	25.0		
Nickel silver	8.85	64.0	....	....	8.0	4.0	4.0	....	....	....	20.0		
Nickel silver	8.95	57.0	....	....	20.0	9.0	2.0	....	....	....	12.0		
Leaded nickel brass	8.95	60.0	....	....	16.0	5.0	3.0	....	....	....	16.0		
Aluminum bronze	?	89.0	....	....	....	....	....	1.0	....	10.0			
Aluminum bronze	7.4	87.5	....	....	....	....	....	3.5	....	9.0			
Aluminum bronze	7.5	86.0	....	....	....	....	....	4.0	....	10.0			
Aluminum bronze	?	79.0	....	....	....	....	....	5.0	....	11.0	5.0		

* "Metals Handbook," 48th ed., American Society for Metals.

TABLE 2b-7. DENSITY OF LEAD ALLOYS*

Material	ρ, g/cm³	% Pb	% Ca	% Sb	% Sn	% As	% Co
Pure lead	11.34	99.73					
Chemically pure lead	11.34						
Cable-sheath alloy	11.34	99.8	0.028				
1% antimonial lead	11.27	99.0	.....	1.0			
Hard lead	11.04	96.0	.....	4.0			
Hard lead	10.88	94.0	.....	6.0			
8% antimonial lead	10.74	92.0	.....	8.0			
Grid metal	10.66	91.0	.....	9.0			
ASTM-12 bearing metal	10.67	90.0	.....	10.0			
ASTM-11 bearing metal	10.28	85.0	.....	15.0			
Lead-base babbitt	10.24	85.0	.....	10.0	5.0		
G lead-base babbitt	10.1	83.0	.....	12.75	0.75	3.0	
S lead-base babbitt	10.1	83.0	.....	15.0	1.0	1.0	
ASTM-10 bearing metal	10.07	83.0	.....	15.0	2.0		
Lead-base babbitt	10.04	80.0	.....	15.0	5.0		
Lead-base babbitt	9.73	75.0	.....	15.0	10.0		
ASTM-6 bearing metal	9.33	63.5	.....	15.0	20.0	...	1.5
Tin-lead solder	11.0	95.0	.....	.....	5.0		
Tin-lead solder	10.2	80.0	.....	.....	20.0		
50-50 half and half	8.89	50.0	.....	.....	50.0		

* "Metals Handbook," 48th ed., American Society for Metals.

TABLE 2b-8. DENSITY OF MAGNESIUM ALLOYS*

Material	ρ, g/cm³	% Mg	% Al	% Mn	% Zn	% Sn	Remarks
Magnesium	1.74	99.8					
A10 alloy	1.81	89.9	10.0	0.1	...	...	Wrought, sand cast, and permanent-mold cast
AZ91 alloy	1.81	....	9.0	0.2	0.7	...	Die cast
AZ92 alloy	1.82	....	9.0	0.1	2.0	...	Sand cast and permanent-mold cast
A8 alloy	1.80	....	8.0	0.2	...	...	Sand cast
AZ61X alloy	1.80	....	6.0	0.2	1.0	...	Wrought
AM244 alloy	1.76	....	4.0	0.2	...	...	Sand cast
AM11 alloy	1.70	....	1.25	1	...	...	Die cast
AZ80X alloy	1.80	....	8.5	0.15	0.5	...	Wrought
AZ63 alloy	1.84	....	6.0	0.2	3.0	...	Sand cast
AZ51X alloy	1.79	....	5.0	0.25	1.0	...	Wrought
AZ31X alloy	1.78	....	3.0	0.3	1.0	...	Wrought
M1	1.76	....	....	1.5	...	...	Wrought
TA54	1.84	....	3.0	0.5	...	5.0	Wrought
Mg-Al alloy	1.75	98.0	2.0				
Mg-Al alloy	1.77	96.0	4.0				
Mg-Al alloy	1.78	94.0	6.0				
Mg-Al alloy	1.80	92.0	8.0				
Mg-Al alloy	1.81	90.0	10.0				
Mg-Al alloy	1.82	88.0	12.0				

* "Metals Handbook," 48th ed., American Society for Metals.

TABLE 2b-9. DENSITY OF NICKEL ALLOYS*

Material	ρ, g/cm³	% Ni	% Co	% Si	% Mn	% C	% Al	% Cu	% Fe	% Mo	% Cr	% W
Nickel	8.902	99.95										
A nickel	8.885	99.4										
Cast nickel	8.34	97.0	..	1.5	0.5	0.5						
D nickel	8.78	95.2	..	...	4.5							
Z nickel	8.75	94	..	...	...	....	4.5					
Monel	8.84	67	..	...	1.0	0.15	...	30	1.4			
Cast monel	8.63	63	..	1.6	...	0.2	...	32				
K monel	8.47	66	..	...	...	....	3	29				
S monel	8.36	63	..	4	...	....	...	30	2			
Hastelloy A	8.80	60	..	...	...	....	...	..	20	20		
Hastelloy B	9.24	65	..	...	...	....	...	..	5	30		
Hastelloy C	8.94	58	..	...	...	....	...	..	5	17	15	5
Hastelloy D	7.8	85	..	8–11	...	....	...	3				
Illium G	8.58	58	..	...	...	0.2	...	6	6	6	22	
Inconel	8.51	80	..	...	...	....	...	..	6	..	14	
Cast Inconel	8.3	77.5	..	2	...	....	...	..	6	..	13.5	
Chromel A	8.4	80	..	...	...	....	...	..	....	..	20	
Nichrome	8.25	60	..	...	...	....	...	..	24		16	
Chromax	7.95	35	..	...	...	....	...	..	50	..	15	
Constantin (wrought)	8.9	45	..	...	...	....	...	55				
Ni-Fe alloys	8.8	90	..	...	...	....	...	..	10			
Ni-Fe alloys	8.6	80	..	...	...	....	...	..	20			
Ni-Fe alloys	8.5	70	..	...	...	....	...	..	30			
Ni-Fe alloys	8.35	60	..	...	...	....	...	..	40			
Permalloy	8.6	78	..	...	...	....	...	..	22			
Numetal	8.6	76	..	...	...	....	...	6	16		2	

* "Metals Handbook," 48th ed., American Society for Metals.

TABLE 2b-10. DENSITY OF ZINC ALLOYS*

Material	ρ, g/cm³	% Zn	% Al	% Cu	% Mg	% Pb	% Cd
Zinc	7.133	100					
Zamak (2)	6.7	92	4	3	0.03		
Zamak (3)	6.6	95	4	..	0.04		
Zamak (5)	6.7	94	4	1	0.04		
SAE 63, T-11 (cast)	6.9	86	4	10			
Commercial rolled zinc	7.14	99	..	..	....	0.08	
Commercial rolled zinc	7.14	99	..	..	...	0.06	0.06
Commercial rolled zinc	7.14	99	..	..	....	0.3	0.3
Zilloy 40 (rolled)	7.18	98	..	1	....	0.08	
Zilloy 15 (rolled)	7.18	98	..	1	0.01	0.1	

* "Metals Handbook," 48th ed., American Society for Metals.

TABLE 2b-11. DENSITY OF WOODS (OVEN-DRY)*

Common name	Botanical name	[illegible]
Applewood or wild apple	*Pyrus malus*	[illegible]
Ash, black	*Fraxinus nigra*	[illegible]
Ash, blue	*Fraxinus quadrangulata*	0[illegible]
Ash, green	*Fraxinus pennsylvanica lanceolata*	0.[illegible]
Ash, white	*Fraxinus americana*	0.638
Aspen	*Populus tremuloides*	0.401
Aspen, large-toothed	*Populus grandidentata*	0.412
Balsa, tropical American	*Ochroma*	0.12–0.20†
Basswood	*Tilia glabra* or *Tilia americanus*	0.398
Beech	*Fagus grandifolia* or *Fagus americana*	0.655
Beech, blue	*Carpinus caroliniana*	0.717
Birch, gray	*Betula populifolia*	0.552
Birch, paper	*Betula papyrifera*	0.600
Birch, sweet	*Betula lenta*	0.714
Birch, yellow	*Betula lutea*	0.668
Buckeye, yellow	*Aesculus octandra*	0.383
Butternut	*Juglans cinera*	0.404
Cedar, eastern red	*Juniperus virginiana*	0.492
Cedar, northern white	*Thuja occidentalis*	0.315
Cedar, southern white	*Chamaecyparis thyoides*	0.352
Cedar, tropical American	*Cedrela odorata*	0.37–0.70†
Cedar, western red	*Thuja plicata*	0.344
Cherry, black	*Prunus serotine*	0.534
Cherry, wild red	*Prunus pennsylvanica*	0.425
Chestnut	*Castanea dentata*	0.454
Corkwood	*Leitneria floridana*	0.207
Cottonwood, eastern	*Populus deltoides*	0.433
Cypress, southern	*Taxodium distichum*	0.482
Dogwood (flowering)	*Cornus florida*	0.796
Douglas fir (coast type)	*Pseudotsuga taxifolia*	0.512
Douglas fir (mountain type)	*Pseudotsuga taxifolia*	0.446
Ebony, Andaman marblewood (India)	*Diospyros Kurzii*	0.978†
Ebony, Ebene marbre (Mauritius, East Africa)	*Diospyros melanida*	0.768†
Elm, American	*Ulmus americana*	0.554
Elm, rock	*Ulmus racemosa* or *Ulmus thomasi*	0.658
Elm, slippery	*Ulmus fulva* or *Ulmus pubescens*	0.568
Eucalyptus, Karri (west Australia)	*Eucalyptus diversicolor*	0.829†
Eucalyptus, mahogany (New South Wales)	*Eucalyptus hemilampra*	1.058†
Eucalyptus, west Australian mahogany	*Eucalyptus marginata*	0.787†
Fir, balsam	*Abies balsamea*	0.414
Fir, silver	*Abies amabilis*	0.415
Greenheart (British Guiana)	*Nectandra rodioci*	1.06–1.23†

See page 2–33 for footnotes.

TABLE 2b-11. DENSITY OF WOODS (OVEN-DRY)* (*Continued*)

Common name	Botanical name	ρ, g/cm³
Gum, black	*Nyssa sylvatica*	0.552
Gum, blue	*Eucalyptus globulus*	0.796
Gum, red	*Liquidambar styraciflua*	0.530
Gum, tupelo	*Nussa aquatica*	0.524
Hemlock, eastern	*Tsuga canadensis*	0.431
Hemlock, mountain	*Tsuga martensiana*	0.480
Hemlock, western	*Tsuga heterophylla*	0.432
Hickory, bigleaf shagbark	*Hicoria laciniosa*	0.809
Hickory, mockernut	*Hicoria alba*	0.820
Hickory, pignut	*Hicoria glabra*	0.820
Hickory, shagbark	*Hicoria ovata*	0.836
Hornbeam	*Ostryra virginiana*	0.762
Ironwood, black	*Rhamnidium ferreum*	1.077
Jacaranda, Brazilian rosewood	*Dalbergia nigra*	0.85†
Larch, western	*Larix occidentalis*	0.587
Locust, black or yellow	*Robinia pseudacacia*	0.708
Locust, honey	*Gleditsia triacanthos*	0.666
Magnolia, cucumber	*Magnolia acuminata*	0.516
Mahogany (West Africa)	*Khaya ivorensis*	0.668†
Mahogany (East India)	*Swietenia macrophylla*	0.54†
Mahogany (East India)	*Swietenia mahogani*	0.54†
Maple, black	*Acer nigrum*	0.620
Maple, red	*Acer rubrum*	0.546
Maple, silver	*Acer saccharinum*	0.506
Maple, sugar	*Acer saccharum*	0.676
Oak, black	*Quercus velutina*	0.669
Oak, bur	*Quercus macrocarpa*	0.671
Oak, canyon live	*Quercus chrysolepsis*	0.838
Oak, chestnut	*Quercus montana*	0.674
Oak, laurel	*Quercus laurifolia*	0.703
Oak, live	*Quercus virginiana*	0.977
Oak, pin	*Quercus palustris*	0.677
Oak, post	*Quercus stellata* or *Quercus minor*	0.738
Oak, red	*Quercus borealis*	0.657
Oak, scarlet	*Quercus coccinea*	0.709
Oak, swamp chestnut	*Quercus prinus*	0.756
Oak, swamp white	*Quercus bicolor* or *Quercus platanoides*	0.792
Oak, white	*Quercus alba*	0.710
Persimmon	*Diospyros virginiana*	0.776
Pine, eastern white	*Pinus strobus*	0.373
Pine, jack	*Pinus banksiana* or *Pinus divaricata*	0.461
Pine, loblolly	*Pinus taeda*	0.593
Pine, longleaf	*Pinus palustris*	0.638
Pine, pitch	*Pinus rigida*	0.542
Pine, red	*Pinus resinosa*	0.507

See page 2–23 for footnotes.

TABLE 2b-11. DENSITY OF WOODS (OVEN-DRY)* (*Continued*)

Common name	Botanical name	ρ, g/cm³
Pine, shortleaf	*Pinus echinata*	0.584
Poplar, balsam	*Populus balsamifera* or *Populus candicans*	0.331
Poplar, yellow	*Liriodendron tulipifera*	0.427
Redwood	*Sequoia sempervivens*	0.436
Sassafras	*Sassafras variafolium*	0.473
Satinwood (Ceylon)	*Chloroxylon swietenia*	1.031†
Sourwood	*Oxydendrum arboreum*	0.593
Spruce, black	*Picea mariana*	0.428
Spruce, red	*Picea rubra* or *Picea rubens*	0.413
Spruce, white	*Picea glauca*	0.431
Sycamore	*Platanus occidentalis*	0.539
Tamarack	*Larix laricina* or *Larix americana*	0.558
Teak (India)	*Tectona grandis*	0.582†
Walnut, black	*Juglans nigra*	0.562
Willow, black	*Salix nigra*	0.408

* "Handbook of Chemistry and Physics," 30th ed.
† Air-dry.

TABLE 2b-12. DENSITY OF PLASTICS*

Resin group and subgroup	Trade names	ρ, g/cm³	
		Lower limit	Upper limit
Acrylate and methacrylate	Lucite, Crystalite, Plexiglas	1.16	1.20
Casein	Ameroid	1.34	1.35
Cellulose acetate (sheet)	Bakelite, Lumarith, Plastecele, Protectoid	1.27	1.60
Cellulose acetate (molded)	Fibestos, Hercules, Nixonite, Tenite	1.27	1.60
Cellulose acetobutyrate	Tenite II	1.14	1.23
Cellulose nitrate	Celluloid, Nitron, Nixonoid, Pyralin	1.35	1.60
Ethyl cellulose	Ditzler, Ethocel, Ethofoil, Lumarith, Nixon, Hercules	1.05	1.25
Phenol-formaldehyde compounds:			
Wood-flour-filled (molded)	Bakelite, Durez, Durite, Micarta, Catalin, Haveg, Indur, Makalot, Resinox, Textolite, Formica	1.25	1.52
Mineral-filled (molded)	Bakelite, Durez, Durite, Micarta, Catalin, Haveg, Indur, Makalot, Resinox, Textolite, Formica	1.59	2.09
Macerated-fabric-filled (molded)	Bakelite, Durez, Durite, Micarta, Catalin, Haveg, Indur, Makalot, Resinox, Textolite, Formica	1.36	1.47
Paper-base (laminated)	Bakelite, Durez, Durite, Micarta, Catalin, Haveg, Indur, Makalot, Resinox, Textolite, Formica	1.30	1.40
Fabric base (laminated)	Bakelite, Durez, Durite, Micarta, Catalin, Haveg, Indur, Makalot, Resinox, Textolite, Formica	1.30	1.40
Cast (unfilled)	Bakelite, Catalin, Gemstone, Marblette, Opalon, Prystal	1.20	1.10
Phenolic furfural (filled)	Durite	1.3	2.0
Polyvinyl acetals (unfilled)	Alvar, Formvar, Saflex, Butacite, Vinylite X, etc.	1.05	1.23
Polyvinyl acetate	Gelva, Vinylite A, etc.	1.19	(?)
Copolyvinyl chloride acetate	Vinylite V, etc.	1.34	1.37
Polyvinyl chloride (and copolymer) plasticized	Koroseal, Vinylite	1.2	1.7
Polystyrene	Bakelite, Loalin, Lustron, Styron	1.054	1.070

* "Handbook of Chemistry and Physics," 30th ed., p. 1282.

TABLE 2b-12. DENSITY OF PLASTICS (*Continued*)

Resin group and subgroup	Trade names	ρ, g/cm³	
		Lower limit	Upper limit
Modified isomerized rubber	Plioform, Pliolite	1.06	(?)
Chlorinated rubber	Torneseit, Parlon	1.64	(?)
Urea formaldehyde	Bakelite, Beetle, Plascon	1.45	1.55
Melamine formaldehyde filled	Catalin, Melmac, Plaskon	1.49	1.86
Vinylidene chloride	Saran, Velon	1.68	1.75

TABLE 2b-13. DENSITY OF RUBBERS*

Rubber; raw polymer	Trade Name	At 25°C
Natural rubber	Hevea	0.92
Butadienestyrene copolymer		0.94
Butadieneacrylonitrile copolymer		1.00
Polychloroprene (neoprene)		1.25
Isobutylenediolefin copolymer (butyl)		0.91
Alkylene polysulfide		1.35

* "Handbook of Chemistry and Physics," 30th ed., p. 1282.

2c. Centers of Mass and Moments of Inertia

R. B. LINDSAY
Brown University

TABLE 2c-1. CENTERS OF MASS*

Body	Center of Mass
1. Uniform circular wire of radius R, subtending angle 2θ at center	On axis of symmetry distant $(R \sin \theta)/\theta$ from center
2. Uniform triangular sheet	At intersection of the medians
3. Uniform rectangular sheet	At intersection of the diagonals
4. Uniform quadrilateral sheet	From each vertex lay off segments equal to $\frac{1}{3}$ the length of the corresponding sides meeting at this vertex. Draw extended lines through the ends of the segments associated with each vertex, respectively. These intersect to form a parallelogram. The intersection of the diagonals of this parallelogram is the center of mass of the quadrilateral
5. Uniform circular sector sheet of radius R subtending angle 2θ at center of circular arc	On axis of symmetry distant $(2R \sin \theta)/3\theta$ from center
6. Uniform circular segment sheet of radius R, subtending angle 2θ at center of circular arc and length of chord equal to $l = 2R \sin \theta$	On axis of symmetry distant $l^3/12A$ from center, where A = area of segment $= \dfrac{R^2(2\theta - \sin 2\theta)}{2}$
7. Uniform semielliptical sheet, major and minor axes of equivalent ellipse equal to $2a$ and $2b$, respectively	On axis of symmetry distant $4a/3\pi$ from center of equivalent ellipse if the semiellipse is bounded by minor axis. The distance is $4b/3\pi$ if the semiellipse is bounded by the major axis
8. Uniform quarter-elliptical sheet, major and minor axes of equivalent ellipse equal to $2a$ and $2b$, respectively	At point $4b/3\pi$ above major axis and $4a/3\pi$ above minor axis
9. Uniform parabolic sheet segment. Chord $= 2l$ perpendicular to axis of symmetry distant h from vertex	On axis of symmetry distant $3h/5$ from vertex
10. Right rectangular pyramid (rectangular base with sides a and b and with height h)	On axis of symmetry distant $h/4$ from vertex
11. Pyramid (general)	On line joining apex with center of symmetry of base at distance three-quarters of its length from apex

* For definition see Sec. 2a-4. All bodies cited are homogeneous rigid bodies.

TABLE 2c-1. CENTERS OF MASS (*Continued*)

Body	Center of Mass
12. Frustum of pyramid with area of larger base S and smaller base s, and altitude h	On line joining apex of corresponding pyramid with center of symmetry of larger base and distant $\frac{h(S + 2\sqrt{Ss} + 3s)}{4(S + \sqrt{Ss} + s)}$ from the larger base
13. Right circular cone (height h)	On axis of symmetry distant $h/4$ from base
14. Frustum of right circular cone (altitude h, radii of larger and smaller bases R and r, respectively)	On axis of symmetry distant $\frac{h[(R + r)^2 + 2r^2]}{4[(R + r)^2 - Rr]}$ from the base
15. Cone (general)	On line joining apex with center of base at distance three-quarters of its length from apex
16. Frustum of cone with altitude h and radii of larger and smaller bases R and r, respectively	On line joining apex of corresponding cone with center of larger base and distant $\frac{h[(R + r)^2 + 2r^2]}{4[(R + r)^2 - Rr]}$ from the larger base
17. Spherical sector of radius R, with plane vertex angle equal to 2θ	On axis of symmetry distant $\frac{3R}{8}(1 + \cos\theta)$ from the vertex
18. Hemisphere of radius R	On axis of symmetry distant $3R/8$ from center of corresponding sphere
19. Spherical segment of radius R and maximum height from base equal to h	On axis of symmetry distant $\frac{h(4R - h)}{4(3R - h)}$ above the base of the segment
20. Octant of ellipsoid with semiaxes a, b, c, respectively, and center of corresponding ellipsoid at origin of system of rectangular coordinates	Point with coordinates $\bar{x} = \frac{3a}{8}$ $\bar{y} = \frac{3b}{8}$ $\bar{z} = \frac{3c}{8}$
21. Paraboloid of revolution with altitude h and radius of circular base equal to R	On axis of symmetry distant $h/3$ from the base
22. Uniform hemispherical shell of radius R (excluding base)	On axis of symmetry distant $R/2$ from center of corresponding sphere
23. Conical shell (excluding base)	On line joining the apex with the center of symmetry of the base at distance two-thirds its length from the apex

TABLE 2c-2. MOMENTS OF INERTIA*

Body	Axis	Moment of inertia
Uniform rectangular sheet of sides a and b	Through the center parallel to b	$m\frac{a^2}{12}$
Uniform rectangular sheet of sides a and b	Through the center perpendicular to the sheet	$m\frac{a^2+b^2}{12}$
Uniform circular sheet of radius r	Normal to the plate through the center	$m\frac{r^2}{2}$
Uniform circular sheet of radius r	Along any diameter	$m\frac{r^2}{4}$
Uniform circular ring sheet. Radii r_1 and r_2	Through center normal to plane of ring	$m\frac{r_1^2+r_2^2}{2}$
Uniform circular ring sheet. Radii r_1 and r_2	A diameter	$m\frac{r_1^2+r_2^2}{4}$
Uniform thin spherical shell, mean radius r	A diameter	$m\frac{2r^2}{3}$
Uniform cylindrical shell, radius r, length l	Longitudinal axis	mr^2
Right circular cylinder of radius r, length l	Longitudinal axis	$m\frac{r^2}{2}$
Right circular cone, altitude h, radius of base r	Axis of the figure	$m\frac{3}{10}r^2$
Spheroid of revolution, equatorial radius r	Polar axis	$m\frac{2r^2}{5}$
Ellipsoid, axes $2a$, $2b$, $2c$....	Axis $2a$	$m\frac{(b^2+c^2)}{5}$
Uniform thin rod..........	Normal to the length, at one end	$m\frac{l^2}{3}$
Uniform thin rod..........	Normal to the length, at the center	$m\frac{l^2}{12}$
Rectangular prism, dimensions $2a$, $2b$, $2c$	Axis $2a$	$m\frac{(b^2+c^2)}{3}$
Sphere, radius r.......	A diameter	$m\frac{2}{5}r^2$
Rectangular parallelepiped, edges a, b, and c	Through center perpendicular to face ab (parallel to edge c)	$m\frac{a^2+b^2}{12}$
Right circular cylinder of radius r, length l	Through center perpendicular to the axis of the figure	$m\left(\frac{r^2}{4}+\frac{l^2}{12}\right)$
Spherical shell, external radius r_1, internal radius r_2	A diameter	$m\frac{2}{5}\frac{(r_1^5-r_2^5)}{(r_1^3-r_2^3)}$
Hollow circular cylinder, length l, external radius r_1, internal radius r_2	Longitudinal axis	$m\frac{(r_1^2+r_2^2)}{2}$
Hollow circular cylinder, length l, radii r_1 and r_2	Transverse diameter	$m\left(\frac{r_1^2+r_2^2}{4}+\frac{l^2}{12}\right)$

* For definitions see Sec. 2a-5; m = mass of body. All bodies are homogeneous.

TABLE 2c-2. MOMENTS OF INERTIA (*Continued*)

Body	Axis	Moment of inertia
Hollow circular cylinder, length l, very thin, mean radius r	Transverse diameter	$m\left(\frac{r^2}{2}+\frac{l^2}{12}\right)$
Right elliptical cylinder, length $2a$, transverse axes $2b$, $2c$	Longitudinal axis $2a$ through center of mass	$m\frac{(b^2+c^2)}{4}$
Right elliptical cylinder, length $2a$, transverse axes $2b$, $2c$	Transverse axis $2b$ through center of mass	$m\left(\frac{c^2}{4}+\frac{a^2}{3}\right)$
Frustum of right circular cone with radii of larger and smaller bases, equal to R and r, respectively	Axis of symmetry	$\frac{3m(R^5-r^5)}{10(R^3-r^3)}$
Right circular cone, radius of base r, altitude h	Perpendicular to axis of symmetry, through center of mass	$\frac{3m}{20}\left(r^2+\frac{h^2}{4}\right)$
Hemisphere of radius r	Axis of symmetry	$\frac{2mr^2}{5}$
Spherical sector of radius r, with plane angle at vertex $= 2\theta$	Axis of symmetry through vertex	$\frac{mr^2(1-\cos\theta)(2+\cos\theta)}{5}$
Spherical segment of radius r and maximum height h	Axis of symmetry perpendicular to base	$m\left(r^2-\frac{3rh}{4}+\frac{3h^2}{20}\right)\frac{2h}{(3r-h)}$
Torus or anchor ring mean radius R, radius of circular cross section r	Axis of symmetry perpendicular to plane of ring	$\frac{m(4R^2+3r^2)}{4}$
Torus mean radius R, radius of circular cross section r	Axis of symmetry in plane of ring	$\frac{m(4R^2+5r^2)}{8}$

2d. Coefficients of Friction

DUDLEY D. FULLER

Columbia University

2d-1. Static and Sliding Friction. All surfaces encountered in experience are more or less rough in the sense that as bodies move on them they exert forces parallel to the surface and in such direction as to resist motion. Such forces are termed "frictional." Frictional force is proportional to the normal thrust between body and surface; however, the coefficient of proportionality, known as the coefficient of friction, can for the same body and surface vary a great deal depending on the nature of the contact and the motion. It is customary to define

$$f_s = \frac{\text{magnitude of maximum frictional force}}{\text{magnitude of normal thrust}} \tag{2d-1}$$

as the *coefficient of static friction* if motion is just on the point of starting. On the other hand, f_K, called the coefficient of *kinetic or sliding friction*, is the value of the ratio in Eq. (2d-1), when motion has once been established. In general $f_K < f_s$ for the same body and surface or the same two surfaces.

The friction between surfaces is dependent upon many variables. These include the nature of the materials themselves, surface finish and surface condition, atmospheric dust, humidity, oxide and other surface films, velocity of sliding, temperature, vibration, and extent of contamination.

In many instances the degree of contamination is perhaps the most important single variable. For example, Table 2d-1 lists values for the static coefficient of friction f_s for steel on steel under various test conditions.

TABLE 2d-1. COEFFICIENTS OF STATIC FRICTION FOR STEEL ON STEEL

Test condition	f_s	Ref.*
Degassed at elevated temp. in high vacuum	Weld on contact	20
Grease-free in vacuum	0.78	1
Grease-free in air	0.39	8
Clean and coated with oleic acid	0.11	1
Clean and coated with solution of stearic acid	0.013	21

* References follow Table 2d-4.

The most effective lubricants for nonfluid lubrication are generally those which react chemically with the solid surface and form an adhering film that is attached to the surface with a chemical bond. This action depends upon the nature of the lubricant and upon the reactivity of the solid surface. Table 2d-2 indicates that a fatty acid such as those found in animal, vegetable, and marine oils reduces the coefficient

TABLE 2d-2. COEFFICIENTS OF STATIC FRICTION AT ROOM TEMPERATURE

Surfaces	Clean	Paraffin oil	Paraffin oil + 1% lauric acid	Degree of reactivity of solid
Nickel	0.7	0.3	0.28	Low
Chromium	0.4	0.3	0.3	Low
Platinum	1.2	0.28	0.25	Low
Silver	1.4	0.8	0.7	Low
Glass	0.9	. . .	0.4	Low
Copper	1.4	0.3	0.08	High
Cadmium	0.5	0.45	0.05	High
Zinc	0.6	0.2	0.04	High
Magnesium	0.6	0.5	0.08	High
Iron	1.0	0.3	0.2	Mild
Aluminum	1.4	0.7	0.3	Mild

of friction markedly only if it can react effectively with the solid surface. Paraffin oil is almost completely nonreactive. The data are taken from ref. 22.

It is generally recognized that coefficients of friction reduce on dry surfaces as sliding velocity increases. Dokos (ref. 4) has measured this for steel on steel. It is difficult to screen out the effect of temperature, however, which also increases with sliding velocity so that frequently, under these conditions, both variables are present. Table 2d-3 gives values which are the average of four tests at high contact pressures.

TABLE 2d-3. COEFFICIENTS OF FRICTION, STEEL ON STEEL, UNLUBRICATED

Velocity, in./sec.	0.0001	0.001	0.01	0.1	1	10	100
Coefficient of friction f_K	0.53	0.48	0.39	0.31	0.23	0.19	0.18

Table 2d-4 presents typical values of the coefficients of static and sliding friction for various materials under a variety of conditions.

TABLE 2d-4. COEFFICIENTS OF STATIC AND SLIDING FRICTION*

Materials	Static friction		Sliding friction	
	Dry	Greasy	Dry	Greasy
Hard steel on hard steel	0.78(1)	0.11(1,a)	0.42(2)	0.029(5,h)
		0.23(1,b)	....	0.081(5,c)
		0.15(1,c)	....	0.080(5,i)
		0.11(1,d)	....	0.058(5,j)
		0.0075(18,p)	....	0.084(5,d)
		0.0052(18,h)		0.105(5,k)
				0.096(5,l)
				0.108(5,m)
				0.12(5,a)
Mild steel on mild steel	0.74(19)	....	0.57(3)	0.09(3,a)
				0.19(3,u)
Hard steel on graphite	0.21(1)	0.09(1,a)		
Hard steel on babbitt (ASTM 1)	0.70(11)	0.23(1,b)	0.33(6)	0.16(1,b)
		0.15(1,c)	....	0.06(1,c)
		0.08(1,d)	....	0.11(1,d)
		0.085(1,e)		
Hard steel on babbitt (ASTM 8)	0.42(11)	0.17(1,b)	0.35(11)	0.14(1,b)
		0.11(1,c)	....	0.065(1,c)
		0.09(1,d)	....	0.07(1,d)
		0.08(1,e)	....	0.08(11,h)
Hard steel on babbitt (ASTM 10)	....	0.25(1,b)	....	0.13(1,b)
		0.12(1,c)	....	0.06(1,c)
		0.10(1,d)	....	0.055(1,d)
Mild steel on cadmium silver	....	....	....	0.097(2,f)
Mild steel on phosphor bronze	....	....	0.34(3)	0.173(2,f)
Mild steel on copper lead	....	....	....	0.145(2,f)
Mild steel on cast iron	....	0.183(15,c)	0.23(6)	0.133(2,f)
Mild steel on lead	0.95(11)	0.5(1,f)	0.95(11)	0.3(11,f)
Nickel on mild steel	....	....	0.64(3)	0.178(3,x)
Aluminum on mild steel	0.61(8)	....	0.47(3)	
Magnesium on mild steel	....	....	0.42(3)	
Magnesium on magnesium	0.6(22)	0.08(22,y)		

* Numbers in parentheses indicate references to data sources; letters identify lubricant in following list.

TABLE 2d-4. COEFFICIENTS OF STATIC AND SLIDING FRICTION (*Continued*)

Materials	Static friction		Sliding friction	
	Dry	Greasy	Dry	Greasy
Cadmium on mild steel	....	....	0.46(3)	
Copper on mild steel	0.53(8)	....	0.36(3)	0.18(17,a)
Nickel on nickel	1.10(16)	0.28(22,y)	0.53(3)	0.12(3,w)
Brass on mild steel	0.51(8)	0.11(22,c)	0.44(6)	
Brass on cast iron	....	....	0.30(6)	
Zinc on cast iron	0.85(16)	....	0.21(7)	
Magnesium on cast iron	....	....	0.25(7)	
Copper on cast iron	1.05(16)	....	0.29(7)	
Tin on cast iron	....	....	0.32(7)	
Lead on cast iron	....	....	0.43(7)	
Aluminum on aluminum	1.05(16)	0.30(22,y)	1.4(3)	
Glass on glass	0.94(8)	0.35(22,y) 0.1(22,q)	0.4(3)	0.09(3,a)
Carbon on glass	....	....	0.18(3)	
Garnet on mild steel	....	....	0.39(3)	
Glass on nickel	0.78(8)	....	0.56(3)	
Copper on glass	0.68(8)	....	0.53(3)	
Cast iron on cast iron	1.10(16)	0.2(22,y)	0.15(9)	0.070(9,d)
Bronze on cast iron	....	....	0.22(9)	0.077(9,n)
Oak on oak (parallel to grain)	0.62(9)	....	0.48(9)	0.164(9,r) 0.067(9,s)
Oak on oak (perpendicular)	0.54(9)	....	0.32(9)	0.072(9,s)
Leather on oak (parallel)	0.61(9)	....	0.52(9)	
Cast iron on oak	....	....	0.49(9)	0.075(9,n)
Leather on cast iron	....	....	0.56(9)	0.36(9,t)
Teflon on Teflon	0.04(22)	....	0.04(22,f)	
Teflon on steel	0.04(22)	....	0.04(22,f)	
Fluted rubber bearing on steel	....	....	....	0.05(13,t)
Laminated plastic on steel	....	....	0.35(12)	0.05(12,t)
Tungsten carbide on tungsten carbide	0.2(22)	0.12(22,a)		
Tungsten carbide on steel	0.5(22)	0.08(22,a)		

Lubricant References for Table 2d-4

a. Oleic acid
b. Atlantic spindle oil (light mineral)
c. Castor oil
d. Lard oil
e. Atlantic spindle oil plus 2 per cent oleic acid
f. Medium mineral oil
g. Medium mineral oil plus $\frac{1}{2}$ per cent oleic acid
h. Stearic acid
i. Grease (zinc oxide base)
j. Graphite
k. Turbine oil plus 1 per cent graphite
l. Turbine oil plus 1 per cent stearic aid
m. Turbine oil (medium mineral)
n. Olive oil
p. Palmitic acid
q. Ricinoleic acid
r. Dry soap
s. Lard
t. Water
u. Rape oil
v. 3-in-1 oil
w. Octyl alcohol
x. Triolein
y. 1 per cent lauric acid in paraffin oil

References for Table 2d-4

1. Campbell, W. E.: Studies in Boundary Lubrication, *Trans. ASME* **61** (7), 633–641 (1939).
2. Clark, G. L., B. H. Lincoln, and R. R. Sterrett: Fundamental Physical and Chemical Forces in Lubrication, *Proc. API* **16,** 68–80 (1935).
3. Beare, W. G., and F. P. Bowden: Physical Properties of Surfaces. 1, Kinetic Friction, *Trans. Roy. Soc.* (*London*), ser. A, **234,** 329–354 (June 6, 1935).
4. Dokos, S. J.: Sliding Friction under Extreme Pressures—1, *J. Appl. Mech.* **13,** A-148–156 (1946).
5. Boyd, J., and B. P. Robertson: The Friction Properties of Various Lubricants at High Pressures, *Trans. ASME* **67** (1), 51–56 (January, 1945).
6. Sachs, G.: Versuche über die Reibung fester Korper (Experiments about the Friction of Solid Bodies), *Z. angew. Math. Mech.* **4,** 1–32 (February, 1924).
7. Honda, K., and R. Yamada: Some Experiments on the Abrasion of Metals, *J. Inst. Metals* **33** (1), 49–69 (1925).
8. Tomlinson, G. A.: A Molecular Theory of Friction, *Phil. Mag.*, ser. 7, **7** (46), 905–939 (suppl., June, 1929).
9. Morin, A.: Nouvelles experiences sur le frottement (New Experiments on Friction), *Acad. roy. Sciences, Paris* (*a*) **57,** 128 (1832); (*b*) **59,** 104 (1834); (*c*) **60,** 143 (1835); (*d*) **63,** 99 (1838).
10. Claypoole, W.: Static Friction, *Trans. ASME* **65,** 317–324 (May, 1943).
11. Tabor, D.: The Frictional Properties of Some White-metal Bearing Alloys: The Role of the Matrix and Hard Particles, *J. Appl. Phys.* **16** (6), 325–337 (June, 1945).
12. Eyssen, G. R.: Properties and Performance of Bearing Materials Bonded with Synthetic Resin, General Discussion on Lubrication and Lubricants, *Inst. Mech. Engrs., J.* **1,** 84–92 (1937).
13. Brazier, S. A., and W. Holland-Bowyer: Rubber as a Material for Bearings, General Discussion on Lubrication and Lubricants, *Inst. Mech. Engrs., J.* **1,** 30–37 (1937); *India-Rubber J.* **94** (22), 636–638 (Nov. 27, 1937).
14. Burwell, J. T.: The Role of Surface Chemistry and Profile in Boundary Lubrication, *J. SAE* **50** (10), 450–457 (1942).
15. Stanton, T. E.: "Friction," Longmans, Green & Co., Ltd., London, 1923.
16. Ernst, H., and M. E. Merchant: Surface Friction of Clean Metals—A Basic Factor in Metal Cutting Process, *Proc. Conf. Friction and Surface Finish* (MIT) June, 1940, pp. 76–101.
17. Gongwer, C. A.: *Proc. Conf. Friction and Surface Finish* (MIT.) June, 1940, pp. 239–244.
18. Hardy, W., and I. Bircumshaw: Boundary Lubrication—Plane Surfaces and the Limitations of Amontons' Law, *Proc. Roy. Soc.* (*London*), ser. A, **108** (A 745), 1–27 (May, 1925).
19. Hardy, W. R., and J. K. Hardy: Note on Static Friction and on the Lubricating Properties of Certain Chemical Substances, *Phil. Mag.*, ser. 6, **38** (233), 32–48 (1919).
20. Bowden, F. P., and J. E. Young: Friction of Clean Metals and Influence of Adsorbed Films, *Proc. Roy. Soc.* (*London*), ser. A, **208** (A 1094), 311–325 (September, 1951).
21. Hardy, W. B., and I. Doubleday: Boundary Lubrication—The Latent Period and Mixtures of Two Lubricants, *Proc. Roy. Soc.* (*London*), ser. A, **104** (A 724), 25–38 (August, 1923).
22. Bowden, F. P., and D. Tabor: "The Friction and Lubrication of Solids," Oxford University Press, New York, 1950.

2d-2. Rolling Friction. Rolling is frequently substituted for sliding friction. The resistance to motion is substantially smaller than for sliding under nonfluid film conditions. The frictional resistance to rolling under the action of load W may be designated as P in Fig. 2d-1. The coefficient of rolling friction is then defined as

$$f_R = \frac{P}{W} \tag{2d-2}$$

The frictional resistance P to the rolling of a cylinder under load is applied at the center of the roller and is inversely proportional to the radius r of the roller and proportional to a factor k, a function of the material and its surface condition. Thus

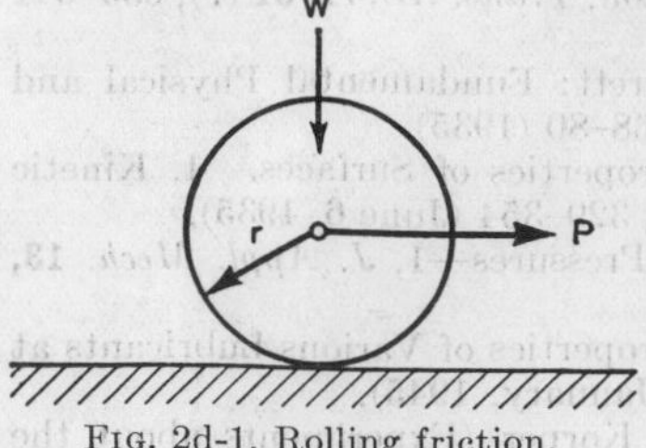

FIG. 2d-1. Rolling friction.

$$P = \frac{k}{r} W \tag{2d-3}$$

If r is in inches, values of k may be taken as follows: hardwood on hardwood, 0.02; iron on iron, steel on steel, 0.002; hard polished steel on hard polished steel, 0.0002 to 0.0004. Noonan and Strange suggest, for steel rollers on steel plates: surfaces well finished and clean, 0.005 to 0.001; surfaces well oiled, 0.001 to 0.002; surfaces covered with silt, 0.003 to 0.005; surfaces rusty, 0.005 to 0.01.

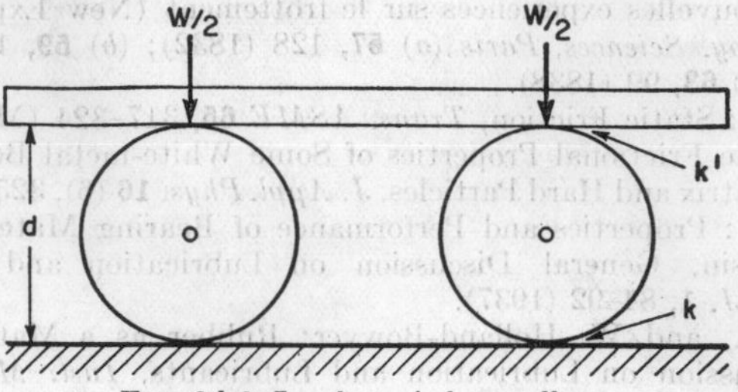

FIG. 2d-2. Load carried on rollers.

If the load is carried on rollers as in Fig. 2d-2, and k and k' are the respective factors for lower and upper surfaces, the force P is

$$P = \frac{(k + k')W}{d} \tag{2d-4}$$

2e. Crystallographic Data

W. P. MASON AND E. A. WOOD

Bell Telephone Laboratories, Inc.

This section presents data relating to the crystals of the elements and certain important compounds. For details about crystal structure the references at the end of the subsection may be consulted.

The lattice constants tabulated in Tables 2e-2 and 2e-3 are referred to crystallographic axes a, b, and c, making axial angles α, β, γ with each other as shown in Fig. 2e-1.

The relationships which obtain among these quantities in the various crystal systems are listed in Table 2e-1.

TABLE 2e-1. LATTICE-CONSTANT RELATIONSHIPS FOR VARIOUS CRYSTAL SYSTEMS

Crystal System	*Lattice-constant Relationships*	
Cubic (= isometric)	$a = b = c$	$\alpha = \beta = \gamma = 90°$
Tetragonal	$a = b \neq c$	$\alpha = \beta = \gamma = 90°$
Orthorhombic	$a \neq b \neq c$	$\alpha = \beta = \gamma = 90°$
Trigonal, if rhombohedral (see following text)	$a = b = c$	$\alpha = \beta = \gamma \neq 90°$
Hexagonal (see Fig. 2e-2)	$a = b \neq c$	$\alpha = \beta = 90°$ $\gamma = 120°$
Monoclinic	$a \neq b \neq c$	$\alpha = \gamma = 90°$ $\beta > 90°$
Triclinic	$a \neq b \neq c$	$\alpha \neq \beta \neq \gamma$

Only those lattice constants whose values are not specified by the relationships in Table 2e-1 are actually listed in Tables 2e-2 and 2e-3. For example, in the tetragonal system, it is only necessary to give values for a and c.

The following are the Hermann-Mauguin point-group symbols for the 32 classes of symmetry, grouped into seven crystal systems, included here for comparison with the space-group symbols of Tables 2e-2 and 2e-3. (The alternative Schönflies symbol, enclosed in parentheses, follows the Hermann-Mauguin symbol to which it is equivalent.)

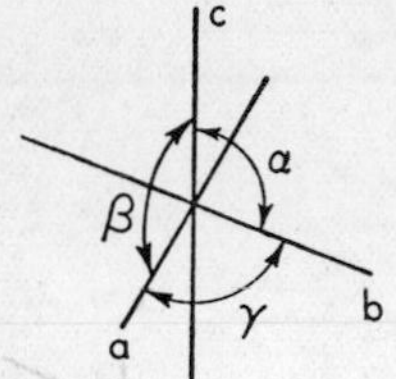

FIG. 2e-1. Crystallographic axes.

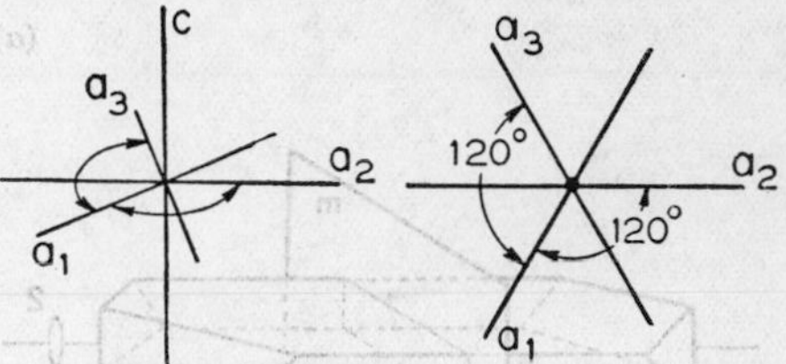

FIG. 2e-2. Crystallographic axes for the hexagonal system.

Triclinic: $1(C_1)$, $\bar{1}(C_i)$
Monoclinic: $2(C_2)$, $m(C_s)$, $2/m(C_{2h})$
Orthorhombic: $mm(C_{2v})$, $222(D_2)$, $mmm(D_{2h})$
Trigonal: $3(C_3)$, $\bar{3}(C_{3i})$, $3m(C_{3v})$, $\bar{3}m(D_{3d})$, $32(D_3)$
Hexagonal: $6(C_6)$, $\bar{6}(C_{3h})$, $6/m(C_{6h})$, $6mm(C_{6v})$, $\bar{6}2m(D_{3h})$, $62(D_6)$, $6/mmm(D_{6h})$
Tetragonal: $4(C_4)$, $\bar{4}(S_4)$, $4/m(C_{4h})$, $\bar{4}2m(D_{2d})$, $4mm(C_{4v})$, $42(D_4)$, $4/mmm(D_{4h})$
Cubic: $23(T)$, $m3(T_h)$, $\bar{4}3m(T_d)$, $43(O)$, $m3m(O_h)$

These symbols describe the symmetry operations which relate equivalent directions in the crystal. All the bulk physical properties of the crystal have this symmetry. The numbers (1, 2, 3, etc.) refer to axes of symmetry (2-fold, 3-fold, etc.); a number with a bar indicates an inversion axis. For example, $\bar{4}$ indicates the symmetry operation of a quarter turn combined with an inversion through a center of symmetry. Symmetry planes are indicated by m, placed beside the axial number when the plane is parallel to the axis, beneath it when the plane is normal to the axis, except in the cubic system where the 3-fold axes are always in the $\langle 111 \rangle$ directions[1] and the symmetry planes parallel to the $\{100\}$ planes and, where m is the third symbol, the $\{110\}$ planes.

Figure 2e-3a, b, c, d illustrates the operations of some of these symmetry elements.

[1] For the Miller indices notation for crystal planes or faces, see any of the books listed in the references. A simple summary is given in ref. 6. See also ref. 9, p. 24.

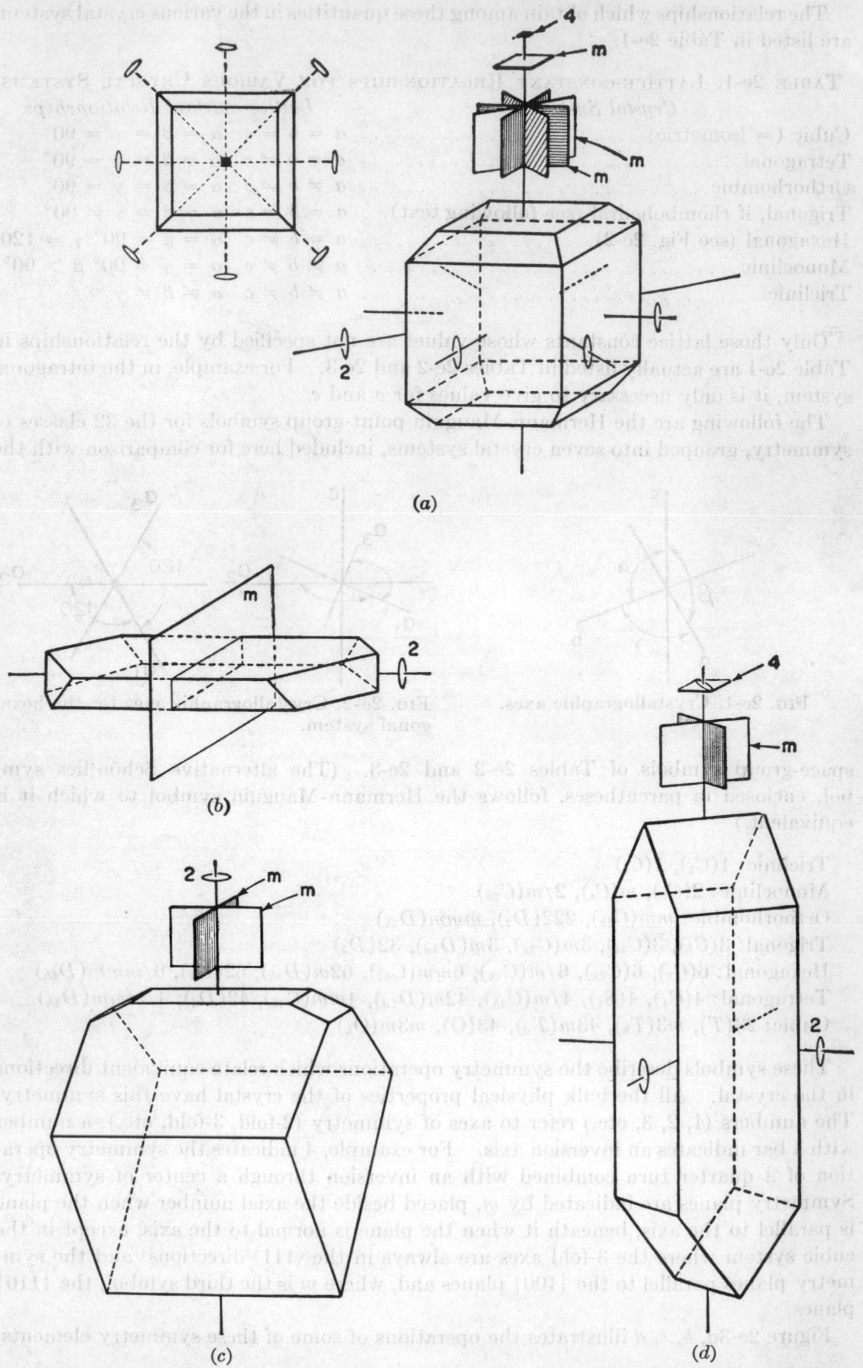

Fig. 2e-3. Operations of symmetry elements. (*a*) tetragonal, $4/mm$; (*b*) monoclinic, $2/m$; (*c*) orthorhombic, mm; (*d*) tetragonal, $42m$.

In the space-group symbols some of the plane and axis point-group symbols are replaced by symbols for glide planes (*a*, *b*, *c*, *d*, *n*) and screw axes (e.g. 2_1) which relate the atom positions in the crystal structure and are preceded by a capital letter indicating whether the lattice is rhombohedral (*R*), primitive (*P*), body-centered (*I*), side-centered (*A*, *B*, or *C*), or centered on all faces (*F*). Thus *Fm*3*m*, for example, indicates a face-centered cubic structure.

In the column of crystal systems, all crystals with a unique 3-fold axis of symmetry are listed as trigonal. For some of these, the smallest unit cell is rhombohedral. Alternatively one may say their structures may be referred to a rhombohedral lattice. For these the Hermann-Mauguin space-group symbol begins with *R*. For other trigonal structures the smallest unit cell is the same shape as that of the hexagonal crystals. For these the space-group symbol begins with *P*.

(Caution: Orthorhombic is sometimes abbreviated to rhombic in the literature. Care must be taken not to confuse this with rhombohedral.)

The reader is referred to X-ray crystallographic texts (e.g. refs. 6 to 9) for the interpretation of the glide-plane and screw-axis symbols. For the symmetry of the bulk physical properties of the crystal he can replace the former by *m* and omit the subscript of the latter.

The value *Z* in the fourth column of Tables 2e-2 and 2e-3 is the number of formula units (e.g., atoms in the case of most elements) per unit cell.

The symbols in the last column of the tables refer to structure types described in the *Strukturbericht* (refs. 3 and 4): *A*1, cubic-close-packed (= face-centered cubic, f.c.c.); *A*2, body-centered cubic (b.c.c.); *A*3, hexagonal close-packed (h.c.p.); *A*4, diamond structure. For types other than these common ones, the reader is referred to the *Strukturbericht*. In some cases, where the structure is commonly known by the name of some substance exhibiting it, this is indicated; e.g., for Bi, structure type *A*7 (As) and for $NiFe_2O_4$, structure type *H*11 (spinel).

The conventional choice of the coordinate axes ("crystallographic axes") *x* or *a*, *y* or *b*, *z* or *c* is usually dictated by symmetry. Where this is not so, the dimensions of the unit cell determined from X-ray diffraction work govern the choice of axes (see ref. 2, p. 6).

The following list may be useful in determining axial directions in crystals for which the symmetry elements are determinable. Many crystal drawings should be used to supplement this list. For these the reader is referred to the texts, e.g., "A Textbook of Mineralogy" by E. S. Dana and W. E. Ford (4th ed., John Wiley & Sons, Inc., New York, 1932). This list should be used in conjunction with the list of lattice-constant relationships (Table 2e-1) for the various systems.

Cubic. The *a* axis makes equal angles (54°44′) with the four 3-fold symmetry axes. In most cases the *a* axis will be a 4-fold symmetry axis. *b* and *c* are indistinguishable from *a*.

Rhombohedral. The 3-fold symmetry axis makes equal angles with the three symmetrically equivalent (indistinguishable) crystallographic axes.

Tetragonal. The unique (4-fold) axis is taken as *c*.

Hexagonal. The unique (6-fold) axis is taken as *c*.

Orthorhombic. The crystallographic axes are parallel to the three 2-fold axes where present; normal to the three symmetry planes where present.

Monoclinic. The 2-fold symmetry axis, if present, is taken as the *b* axis. Otherwise the normal to the symmetry plane is taken as *b*.

Triclinic. Choice of crystallographic axes is not indicated by symmetry.

Tables 2e-2 and 2e-3 list the various quantities which characterize the crystal lattices of the elements and certain compounds, respectively. All values in these tables came from ref. 1, except as indicated.

TABLE 2e-2. CRYSTALLOGRAPHIC DATA FOR THE ELEMENTS

Formula (temp., °C, for the lattice constants given)	Crystal system	Space group	Z	Lattice constants, A,* $a, b, c; \alpha, \beta, \gamma$	Structure type
A (−235°)......	Cub.	$Fm3m$	4	5.43	*A*1 (f.c.c.)
Ag (18°).......	Cub.	$Fm3m$	4	4.086 ± 0.0006	*A*1 (f.c.c.)
Al (25°)........	Cub.	$Fm3m$	4	4.0495 to 4.0507	*A*1 (f.c.c.)
As............	Trig.	$R\bar{3}m$	6	3.77, 10.57*	*A*7
			2	(a_{rh} 4.142, α 54°7′)	
Au (18°).......	Cub.	$Fm3m$	4	4.0781 ± 0.0003	*A*1 (f.c.c.)
B.............	Tet.	$P\bar{4}n2$	50	8.74, 5.07	
Ba.............	Cub.	$Im3m$	2	5.025 ± 0.003	*A*2 (b.c.c.)
Be (18°).......	Hex.	$P6_3/mmc$	2	2.2808, 3.5735*	*A*3 (h.c.p.)
(630°) (stable 5–700°).....	Hex.	....	*ca.* 60	7.1, 10.8*	
Bi.............	Trig.	$R\bar{3}m$	6	4.53726 ± 0.0002	*A*7 (As)
				11.8381 ± 0.0008*	
			2	(a_{rh} 4.7364 ± 0.0003	
				α 57°14′13″ ± 23″)	
Br_2 (−150°)....	Orth.	$Bmab$	4	6.67, 8.72, 4.48*	*A*14 (I_2)
C (diamond)....	Cub.	$Fd3m$	8	3.56696 ± 0.00005	*A*4 (diamond)
C (graphite) (15°)	Hex.	$P6_3/mmc$	4	2.4612 ± 0.0001, 6.7079 ± 0.0007*	*A*9
C (graphite)....	Trig.	$R\bar{3}m$	6	2.461, 10.064*	
			2	(a_{rh} 3.642, α 39.49°)	
Ca (α) (electrolytic)......	Cub.	$Fm3m$	4	5.57	*A*1 (f.c.c.)
Ca (β) (450°) (stable above 450°)......	Hex.	$P6_3/mmc$	2	3.98, 6.52*	*A*3 (h.c.p.)
Cb (see Nb)					
Cd.............	Hex.	$P6_3/mmc$	2	2.9736 ± 0.0005, 5.6058 ± 0.0005*	*A*3 (h.c.p.)
Ce.............	Cub.	$Fm3m$	4	5.150 ± 0.002	*A*1 (f.c.c.)
Ce.............	Hex.	$P6_3/mmc$	2	3.65, 5.96*	*A*3 (h.c.p.)
Ce at 15,000 atmos.........	Cub.	$Fm3m$	4	4.84 ± 0.03	*A*1 (f.c.c.)
Cl_2 (−185°)....	Tet.	$P4_2/ncm$	8	8.56, 6.12*	*A*18
Co (20°)........	Hex.	$P6_3/mmc$	2	2.5074, 4.0699	*A*3 (h.c.p.)
Co (20°)........	Cub.	$Fm3m$	4	3.5442	*A*1 (f.c.c.)
Cp.............	Hex.	$P6_3/mmc$	2	3.509, 3.559*	*A*3 (h.c.p.)
Cr.............	Cub.	$Im3m$	2	2.8845 ± 0.001	*A*2 (b.c.c.)
Cs (−100°).....	Cub.	$Im3m$	2	6.08	*A*2 (b.c.c.)
Cu (20°).......	Cub.	$Fm3m$	4	3.6147 ± 0.0020	*A*1 (f.c.c.)
Dy.............	Hex.	$P6_3/mmc$	2	3.578, 5.648*	*A*3 (h.c.p.)
Er.............	Hex.	$P6_3/mmc$	2	3.532 ± 0.002, 5.589 ± 0.005*	*A*3 (h.c.p.)
Eu.............	Cub.	$Im3m$	2	4.573	*A*2 (b.c.c.)

* Starred values probably are not in angstroms (A) but in kX (1 kX = 1.00202 A), since they come from a reference published prior to 1949. See *Acta Cryst.* **1**, 46 (1948). Cubic-lattice constants have all been converted to Angstrom units.

TABLE 2e-2. CRYSTALLOGRAPHIC DATA FOR THE ELEMENTS (*Continued*)

Formula (temp., °C, for the lattice constants given)	Crystal system	Space group	Z	Lattice constants, A,* $a, b, c; \alpha, \beta, \gamma$	Structure type
Fe (α) (20°) (stable to 910°)..	Cub.	*Im3m*	2	2.86645	*A*2 (b.c.c.)
Fe (γ) (stable 910–1400°)...	Cub.	*Fm3m*	4	3.64	*A*1 (f.c.c.)
Fe (δ) (stable above 1400°)..	Cub.	*Im3m*	2	2.94	*A*2 (b.c.c.)
Ga............	Orth.	*Abam* (alt. *Cmca*)	8	4.5167 ± 0.0001, 7.6448 ± 0.0002, 4.5107 ± 0.0001	*A*11
Gd............	Hex.	$P6_3/mmc$	2	3.622, 5.748*	*A*3 (h.c.p.)
Ge (25°)........	Cub.	*Fd3m*	8	5.6575†	*A*4 (diamond)
H_2 (4.2°K, and 1.65°K)......	Hex.	$P6_3/mmc$	2	3.75, 6.12*	*A*3 (h.c.p.)
He (1.45°K, *ca.* 37 atm)......	Hex.	$P6_3/mmc$	2	3.57, 5.83*	*A*3 (h.c.p.)
Hf............	Hex.	$P6_3/mmc$	2	3.1952, 5.0569	*A*3 (h.c.p.)
Hg (−46°).....	Trig.	$R\bar{3}m$	1	2.999; 70°32′*	*A*10
Ho............	Hex.	$P6_3/mmc$	2	3.557 ± 0.003, 5.620 ± 0.005*	*A*3 (h.c.p.)
I_2............	Orth.	*Bmab*	4	7.250, 9.772, 4.774	*A*14
In............	Tet.	*I*4/*mmm*	2	3.241, 4.936 ± 0.002*	*A*6
Ir............	Cub.	*Fm3m*	4	3.8389 ± 0.0005	*A*1 (f.c.c.)
K (20°)........	Cub.	*Im3m*	2	5.344 ± 0.005	*A*2 (b.c.c.)
Kr (−252.5°)...	Cub.	*Fm3m*	4	5.60 (est. 98% pure)	*A*1 (f.c.c.)
(−184°).....	Cub.	....	..	5.706 ± 0.017	
La............	Hex.	$P6_3/mmc$	2	3.754 ± 0.010, 6.063 ± 0.030*	*A*3 (h.c.p.)
La (β).........	Cub.	*Fm3m*	4	5.307 ± 0.002 (99.6% pure)	*A*1 (f.c.c.)
Li............	Cub.	*Im3m*	2	3.5087 ± 0.0002	*A*2 (b.c.c.)
Li (−196°).....	Cub.	*Im3m*	2	3.50	*A*2 (b.c.c.)
Li (−196°).....	Cub.	*Fm3m*	4	4.41 (induced by plastic deformation)	*A*1 (f.c.c.)
Mg (25°).......	Hex.	$P6_3/mmc$	2	3.20280 ± 0.00003, 5.19983 ± 0.00005* (99.995% pure)	*A*3 (h.c.p.)
Mn (α).........	Cub.	$I\bar{4}3m$	58	8.894	*A*12
Mn (β).........	Tet.	$P4_13$	20	6.30	*A*13
Mn (γ).........	Tet.	*F* tet.	4	3.774, 3.533	
Mo............	Cub.	*Im3m*	2	3.150 ± 0.005	*A*2 (b.c.c.)
N (α) (at liquid H_2) (stable below 35.4°K)...	Cub.	$P2_13$	8	5.667	*B*21 (?)

* Starred values probably are not in Angstroms (A) but in kX (1 kX = 1.00202 A), since they come from a reference published prior to 1949. See *Acta Cryst.* **1,** 46 (1948). Cubic-lattice constants have all been converted to Angstrom units.

TABLE 2e-2. CRYSTALLOGRAPHIC DATA FOR THE ELEMENTS (*Continued*)

Formula (temp., °C, for the lattice constants given)	Crystal system	Space group	Z	Lattice constants, A,* $a, b, c; \alpha, \beta, \gamma$	Structure type
N_2 (β) (45°K) (stable above 35.4°K)	Hex.	$P6_3/mmc$	2	4.039, 6.670*	$A3$ (h.c.p.)
Na	Cub.	$Im3m$	2	4.2906 ± 0.0005	$A2$ (b.c.c.)
Na (−195°)	Cub.	$Fm3m$	4	5.339 (induced by plastic deformation at −253°)	$A1$ (f.c.c.)
Nb (20°)	Cub.	$Im3m$	2	3.3008 ± 0.0003 (H_2 free)	$A2$ (b.c.c.)
Nd	Hex.	$P6_3/mmc$	2	3.650 ± 0.003, 5.890 ± 0.005*	$A3$ (h.c.p.)
Ne (at liquid He)	Cub.	$Fm3m$	4	4.53	$A1$ (f.c.c.)
Ni (25°)	Cub.	$Fm3m$	4	3.52394 (99.99% pure)	$A1$ (f.c.c.)
O_2 (α) (stable below 23.5°K)				Existing data are in conflict	
O_2 (β) (stable 23.5–43.4°K)					
O_2 (γ) (50°K)	Cub.	$Pa3$ (?)		6.84	
Os (18°)	Hex.	$P6_3/mmc$	2	2.7304 ± 0.0005, 4.3097 ± 0.0005	$A3$ (h.c.p.)
P (white) (−35°)	Cub.	cub.	4	7.18 not cubic at liquid-air temp	
P (black)	Orth.	$Abam$	8	4.38, 10.50, 3.31	$A17$
P (red)	Mon.?			7.34 (pseudo-cubic)	
Pb (18°)	Cub.	$Fm3m$	4	4.9496 ± 0.0003 (99.9% pure)	$A1$ (f.c.c.)
Pd (18°)	Cub.	$Fm3m$	4	3.8902 ± 0.0003	$A1$ (f.c.c.)
Po	Mon.?		12	14.10, 4.29 ± 0.04, 7.42 ± 0.07; *ca.* 92°	$A19$?
Pr (α) (18°)	Hex.	$P6_3/mmc$	2	3.657, 5.924* (99.4% pure)	$A3$ (h.c.p.)
Pr	Cub.	$Fm3m$	4	5.151	$A1$ (f.c.c.)
Pt (18°)	Cub.	$Fm3m$	4	3.9237 ± 0.0003	$A1$ (f.c.c.)
(208°)	Cub.	$Fm3m$		3.9310	$A1$ (f.c.c.)
(600°)	Cub.	$Fm2m$		3.9460	$A1$ (f.c.c.)
Rb (19°)	Cub.	$Im3m$	2	5.709	$A2$ (b.c.c.)
Re	Hex.	$P6_3/mmc$	2	2.7553 ± 0.0004, 4.4493 ± 0.0003*	$A3$ (h.c.p.)
Rh	Cub.	$Fm3m$	4	3.8044 ± 0.0001	$A1$ (f.c.c.)
Ru (20°)	Hex.	$P6_3/mmc$	2	2.69844, 4.27305*	$A3$ (h.c.p.)
S (103°)	Mon.	$P2_1/c$	48	10.90, 10.96, 11.02; 96°44′	
S	Orth	$Fddd$	128	12.92, 24.55, 10.48	$A16$
S (unstable)	Trig.	$R\bar{3}$ (?)	18	10.9, 4.26 kX	

See page 2–52 for footnotes.

TABLE 2e-2. CRYSTALLOGRAPHIC DATA FOR THE ELEMENTS (*Continued*)

Formula (temp., °C, for the lattice constants given)	Crystal system	Space group	Z	Lattice constants, A,* $a, b, c; \alpha, \beta, \gamma$	Structure type
Sb	Trig.	$R\bar{3}m$	6	4.2995 ± 0.0002, 11.2516 ± 0.0004*	*A*7
			2	(a_{rh} 4.49762 ± 0.00018; α 57°6′27″ ± 19″)*	
Sc	Hex.	$P6_3/mmc$	2	3.302 ± 0.003, 5.245 ± 0.006*	*A*3 (h.c.p.)
Sc	Cub.	$Fm3m$	4	4.541 ± 0.005	*A*1 (f.c.c.)
Se (18°)	Trig.	$P3_121$ or $P3_221$	3	4.35448 ± 0.00004, 4.94962 ± 0.00002*	*A*8
Se (α or I)	Mon.		32	9.05, 9.07, 11.61, ± 0.02; 90°46′ ± 5′	
Se (β or II)	Mon.	$P2_1/a$	32	12.85, 8.07, 9.31 ± 0.02; 93°8′ ± 5′‡	
Si (25°)	Cub.	$Fd3m$	8	5.43059 ± 0.00005§	*A*4 (diamond)
Sn (α, gray)	Cub.	$Fd3m$	8	6.47	*A*4 (diamond)
Sn (β, white) (25°)	Tet.	$I4/amd$	4	5.81970 ± 0.00002 3.17488 ± 0.00005*	*A*5
Sr	Cub.	$Fm3m$	4	6.06	*A*1 (f.c.c.)
Ta (20°)	Cub.	$Im3m$	2	3.3026 ± 0.0003	*A*2 (b.c.c.)
Tb	Hex.	$P6_3/mmc$	2	3.585, 5.662*	*A*3 (h.c.p.)
Tc	Hex.	$P6_3/mmc$	2	2.735 ± 0.001, 4.388 ± 0.001*	*A*3 (h.c.p.)
Te (18°)	Trig.	$P3_121$ or $P3_221$	3	4.44669 ± 0.00012, 5.91494 ± 0.00002*	*A*8 (Se)
Th	Cub.	$Fm3m$	4	5.084 ± 0.002 and 5.091 ± 0.002 on two different samples	*A*1 (f.c.c.)
Ti (α)	Hex.	$P6_3/mmc$	2	2.953, 4.729*	*A*3 (h.c.p.)
Ti (β, 900°) (stable above 882 ± 20°)	Cub.	$Im3m$	2	3.33	*A*2 (b.c.c.)
Tl (18°)	Hex.	$P6_3/mmc$	2	3.4496 ± 0.0002, 5.5137 ± 0.0004* (99.995% pure)	*A*3 (h.c.p.)
Tl (262°) (stable above 230° ?)	Cub.	$Im3m$	2	3.874 ± 0.001 (99.995% pure)	*A*2 (b.c.c.)
Tm	Hex.	$P6_3/mmc$	2	3.523, 5.564*	*A*3 (h.c.p.)
U	Orth.	$Amam$	4	4.945, 5.865, 2.852*	*A*20
U (β) (stable 660–760°)	Tet.	$P4nm$ or $P\bar{4}n2$	30	10.52, 5.57	
U (γ) (stable, 760° to mp) (room temperature)	Cub.	$Im3m$	2	3.474 ± 0.005	*A*2 (b.c.c.)
(800°)	Cub.	$Im3m$	2	3.49	*A*2 (b.c.c.)

* Starred values probably are not in angstroms (A) but in kX (1 kX = 1.00202 A), since they come from a reference published prior to 1949. See *Acta Cryst.* **1,** 46 (1948). Cubic-lattice constants have all been converted to Angstrom units.

TABLE 2e-2. CRYSTALLOGRAPHIC DATA FOR THE ELEMENTS (*Continued*)

Formula (temp., °C, for the lattice constants given)	Crystal system	Space group	*Z*	Lattice constants, A,* *a*, *b*, *c*; *α*, *β*, *γ*	Structure type
V (25°)	Cub.	*Im3m*	2	3.0399 ± 0.0003	*A*2 (b.c.c.)
W (*α*) (25°)	Cub.	*Im3m*	2	3.16475 ± 0.00012	*A*2 (b.c.c.)
W (*β*) (transforms irreversibly to *α* above 700°)	Cub.	*Pm3n*	8	5.048 ± 0.003	*A*15
Xe (88°K)	Cub.	*Fm3m*	4	6.25 ± 0.025	*A*1 (f.c.c.)
Y	Hex.	$P6_3/mmc$	2	3.663 ± 0.008, 5.814 ± 0.012* (99.5% pure)	*A*3 (h.c.p.)
Yb	Cub.	*Fm3m*	4	5.479	*A*1 (f.c.c.)
Zn	Hex.	$P6_3/mmc$	2	2.6590 ± 0.0005, 4.9351 ± 0.0009 (99.99% pure)	*A*3 (h.c.p.)
Zr	Hex.	$P6_3/mmc$	2	3.229, 5.141*	*A*3 (h.c.p.)
Zr (*β*) (840°)	Cub.	*Im3m*	2	3.62	*A*2 (b.c.c.)

* Starred values probably are not in Angstroms (A) but in kX (1 kX = 1.00202 A), since they come from a reference published prior to 1949. See *Acta Cryst.* **1,** 46 (1948). Cubic-lattice constants have all been converted to Angstrom units.

† Greiner and Breidt, *J. Metals* **7,** 187 (1955).

‡ Burbank, R. D., *Acta Cryst.* **4,** 140 (1951).

¶ Burbank, R. D., *Acta Cryst.* **5,** 236 (1952).

§ Lipson and Rogers, *Phil. Mag.* **35,** 544 (1944).

TABLE 2e-3. CRYSTALLOGRAPHIC DATA FOR SELECTED COMPOUNDS

Formula (temp., °C, for the lattice constants given)	Crystal system	Space group	Z	Lattice constants, A* a, b, c; α, β, γ	Structure type
Al_2O_3 (α) (corundum)	Trig.	$R\bar{3}c$	6	4.76 kX, 13.01 kX	*D*51
			2	(a_{rh} 5.13 kX ± 0.02; α 55°16′ ± 5′)	
Al_2O_3 (β)	Hex.	*P*6/*mmc*	12	5.56 kX, 22.55 kX	*D*56
$BaTiO_3$ (barium titanate)	Tet.	*P*4/*mmm*	1	3.9860, 4.0259*	Distortion of *G*5
$BaTiO_3$ (200°)	Cub.	*Pm*3*m*	1	4.012 kX	*G*5 ("perovskite type")†
$CaCO_3$ (calcite)	Trig.	$R\bar{3}c$	6	4.983, 17.02*	*G*1
			2	(a_{rh} 6.361; α 46°7′)*	
				d cleavage = 3.02904 kX for first order	
$CaCO_3$ (aragonite)	Orth.	*Pnam*	4	5.72, 7.94, 4.94*	*G*2
CaF_2 (fluorite)	Cub.	*Fm*3*m*	4	5.462 ± 0.003	*C*1
CdI_2	Trig.	$P\bar{3}m1$		4.24, 6.835*	*C*6
$CoFe_2O_4$ (cobalt ferrite)	Cub.	*Fd*3*m*	8	8.37; also reported: 8.38 and 8.412	*H*11 (spinel)‡
COOK·$(CHOH)_2$·COONa·$4H_2O$ (rochelle salt)	Orth.	$P2_12_12$	4	11.91 ± 0.04, 14.32 ± 0.05, 6.20 ± 0.02	
CsCl	Cub.	*Pm*3*m*	1	4.121 ± 0.003	*B*2
Fe_3O_4 (26°) (iron ferrite or magnetite)	Cub.	*Fd*3*m*	8	8.380 ± 0.002	*H*11 (spinel)‡
KH_2PO_4 (20°) (potassium dihydrogen phosphate)	Tet.	$I\bar{4}2d$	4	7.437, 6.945 ± 0.002;* also reported: 7.43, 6.97*	*H*22
$MgAl_2O_4$ (spinel)	Cub.	*Fd*3*m*	8	8.116 ± 0.004 (containing Fe, Cr, Mn)	*H*11
$MgFe_2O_4$ (magnesium ferrite)	Cub.	*Fd*3*m*	8	8.359 ± 0.005; also reported: 8.37 ± 0.3% and 8.38 ± 0.01	*H*11 (spinel)‡
$MnFe_2O_4$ (manganese ferrite)	Cub.	*Fd*3*m*	8	8.419 ± 0.003; also reported: 8.589 ± 0.006	*H*11 (spinel)‡
NaCl (18°)	Cub.	*Fm*3*m*	4	5.63874 ± 0.00002	*B*1
NiAs	Hex.	$P6_3/mmc$	2	3.610, 5.028*	*B*8
$NiFe_2O_4$ (nickel ferrite)	Cub.	*Fd*3*m*	8	8.357 ± 0.005; also reported: 8.43	*H*11 (spinel)‡
$NH_4H_2PO_4$ (ammonium dihydrogen phosphate)	Tet.	$I\bar{4}2d$	4	7.51, 7.53;* also reported: 7.48, 7.56, and 7.479, 7.516 ± 0.005*	*H*22

See page 2–54 for footnotes.

TABLE 2e-3. CRYSTALLOGRAPHIC DATA FOR SELECTED COMPOUNDS (*Continued*)

Formula (temp., °C, for the lattice constants given)	Crystal system	Space group	Z	Lattice constants, A* $a, b, c; \alpha, \beta, \gamma$	Structure type
SiO_2 (low quartz, stable up to 573° ± 1°)	Trig.	$P3_221$ or $P3_121$	3	4.910 ± 0.01, 5.394 ± 0.01	*C*8-like
SiO_2 (high quartz, stable 573–870°)	Hex.	$P6_222$ or $P6_422$	3	5.01, 5.47	*C*8
SiO_2 (upper high tridymite; stable 870–1470°)	Hex.	$P6_3/mmc$	4	5.03, 8.22 (determined outside its stability range?)	*C*10
SiO_2 (high cristobalite, stable 1470–1710°, mp)	Cub.	$P2_13$ (also as $Fd3m$)	8	7.1473 (at 1300°C)	*C*9
ZnS ("blende" or sphalerite)	Cub.	$F\bar{4}3m$	4	5.423 ± 0.006 (containing 0.16 wt. % Fe)	*B*3
ZnS (wurtzite) . . .	Hex.	$P6mc$	2	3.811, 6.234*	*B*4

* Starred values probably are not in Angstroms (A) but in kX (1 kX = 1.00202 A), since they come from a reference published prior to 1949. See *Acta Cryst.* **1**, 46 (1948). Cubic-lattice constants have been converted to Angstrom units.

† Now known not to be the structure of perovskite.

‡ "Spinel" in this table includes "inverse spinel."

Illustrative References

References 1 to 5 give crystallographic data. References 6 to 10 are texts dealing with crystal structure.

1. Donnay, J. D. H., and Werner Nowacki: "Crystal Data," Geological Society of America Memoir 60, Geological Society of America, New York, 1954.
2. Palache, C., H. Berman, and C. Frondel: "The System of Mineralogy," 7th ed., John Wiley & Sons, Inc., New York; Chapman & Hall, Ltd., London, vol. 1, 1944; vol. II, 1951.
3. *Structure Reports,* the continuation of the *Strukturbericht,* published for the International Union of Crystallography by N. V. A. Oosthoek's Uitgevers MIJ, Utrecht, Netherlands.
4. *Strukturbericht,* a digest of crystal-structure literature from 1913 through 1939, published in conjunction with the *Zeitschrift für Kristallographie.*
5. Wyckoff, R. W. G.: *Crystal Structures,* Interscience Publishers, Inc., New York and London, vol. I, 1948; vol. II, 1951; vol. III, 1953.
6. Barrett, C. S.: "Structure of Metals," 2d ed., McGraw-Hill Book Company, Inc., New York, 1952.
7. Bragg, W. L.: "The Crystalline State," George Bell & Sons, Ltd., London; The Macmillan Company, New York, 1939.
8. Buerger, M. J.: "X-ray Crystallography," John Wiley & Sons, Inc., New York; Chapman & Hall, Ltd., London, 1942.
9. Bunn, C. W.: "Chemical Crystallography," Oxford University Press, New York, 1946.
10. Mason, W. P.: "Piezoelectric Crystals and Their Application to Ultrasonics," D. Van Nostrand Company, Inc., New York, 1950.

2f. Elastic Constants, Hardness, Strength, and Elastic Limits of Solids

H. M. TRENT AND D. E. STONE

Naval Research Laboratory

2f-1. Introduction. For the fundamental ideas connected with elasticity and the definition of the elastic constant, see Sec. 2a-6. The notation used in this section is presented below. For other definitions see Sec. 2f-3.

Symbols

E	Young's modulus	S.S.	shear strength
G	rigidity modulus	El.	elongation
σ	Poisson's ratio	R.A.	reduction in area
ρ	density	Bhn	Brinell hardness number
S_{ij}	elastic constant (cf. Sec. 2a-6)	R	Rockwell hardness number (often used with subscripts)
C_{ij}	elastic coefficient (cf. Sec. 2a-6)		
T.S.	tensile strength	VDH, Vhn	Vickers hardness number
Y.S.	yield strength	D	diffusion coefficient
Y.P.	yield point		

2f-2. Elastic Constants and Coefficients of Crystals. Tables 2f-1 to 5 present tabulated values of the elastic constants S_{ij} and elastic coefficients C_{ij} for cubic, tetragonal, trigonal, hexagonal, and rhombic crystals (cf. Sec. 2e for X-ray crystallographic data).

For other values, see also Tables 2h-2 and 3h-3.

2f-3. Elastic Constants, Hardness, Strength, and Elastic Limits of Polycrystalline Solids. Tables 2f-6 through 2f-15 contain data on the Young's modulus, modulus of rigidity, hardness, etc., of various solids, metals, and alloys. The elastic constants, tensile strength, yield strength, shear strength, and all other quantities having the dimensions of stress are expressed in dynes per square centimeter. The definitions of these and other tabulated quantities are given in the following list.

Definitions (*Continued on pages 2-69, 2-78, 2-80*)

1. *Tensile Strength.*[1] "The maximum tensile stress which a material is capable of developing."

Note: In practice, it is considered to be the maximum stress developed by a specimen representing the material in a tension test carried to rupture, under definite prescribed conditions. Tensile strength is calculated from the maximum load P carried during a tension test and the original cross-sectional area of the specimen A_0 from the formula

$$\text{Tensile strength} = \frac{P}{A_0}$$

2. *Yield Strength.*[1] "The stress at which a material exhibits a specified permanent set."

[1] Standard Definitions of Terms Relating to Methods of Testing, ASTM E6-36.

TABLE 2f-1. ELASTIC CONSTANTS AND COEFFICIENTS OF CUBIC CRYSTALS
(S_{ij} in units of 10^{-13} cm²/dyne; C_{ij} in units of 10^{11} dynes/cm²)

Material	Test temp.	S_{11} (1)	S_{12} (2)	S_{44} (3)	C_{11} (4)	C_{12} (5)	C_{44} (6)	Ref.* cols. 1–3	Ref.* cols. 4–6
Silver (Ag)	Room	23.2	−9.93	22.9	12.0	8.97	4.36	23	54
75 Ag, 25 Au	Room	20.7	−8.91	20.5				58	
50 Ag, 50 Au	Room	19.7	−8.52	19.7				58	
Alum					2.56	1.07	0.86	..	51
Aluminum (Al)	Room	15.9	−5.80	35.16	10.56	6.39	2.853	10	37
Al, 5 Cu	Room	15	−6.9	37				56	
Ammonium alum					2.50	1.06	0.80	..	66
Gold (Au)	Room	23.3	−10.65	23.8	18.7	15.7	4.36	13	54
75 Au, 25 Ag	Room	20.5	−9.09	20.6				58	
Barium nitrate	Room				6.02	1.86	1.21	..	67
Copper (Cu)	Room	14.91	−6.25	13.28	17.10	12.39	7.56	13	37
Cu_3Au	20°C	13.44	−5.65	15.08				29	
Cu_3Au	100°C	13.80	−6.10	15.45				29	
Cu_3Au	300°C	15.12	−6.46	15.93				29	
CuZn					12.91	10.97	8.24	..	37
72 Cu, 28 Zn	Room	19.4	−8.4	13.9				57	
$Cu_{53}Zn_{47}$ (β-brass)	24°	38.8	−15.2	5.78	5.40	3.55	17.3	46	62
$Cu_{53}Zn_{47}$ (β-brass)	195°C	36.1	−14.2	5.80				46	
$Cu_{53}Zn_{47}$ (β brass)	389°C	41.5	−15.3	6.24				46	
$Cu_{53}Zn_{47}$ (α brass)	Room				15.22	11.62	7.19	..	62
Cu, 4 Si	Room				16.2	12.0	7.55	..	64
Cr. Alum	Room				2.37	0.93	0.77	..	66
CaF_2 (fluorspar)	Room	6.92	−1.49	29.6	16.4	4.48	3.38	26	53
Diamond	Room				95.0	39.0	43.0	..	42
FeS_2 (pyrite)	Room	2.89	+0.44	9.48	36.1	−4.74	10.55	26	53
Garnet 21.8% FeO	Room				19.7	9.0	5.7	..	65
Garnet 22.7% FeO	Room				19.2	9.9	5.9	..	65
Garnet 23.0% FeO	Room				22.2	10.4	7.0	..	65
Garnet 23.6% FeO	Room				21.0	10.3	6.7	..	65
Garnet 26.2% FeO	Room				22.6	12.6	6.2	..	65
Garnet 28.7% FeO	Room				27.3	15.7	6.8	..	65
Garnet 33.5% FeO	Room				32.7	12.4	8.9	..	65
Fe	Room	7.72	−2.85	9.02	23.7	14.1	11.6	59	62
Germanium	25°C	9.685	−2.70	14.94	12.98	4.88	6.73	38	49
KBr	Room	31.7	−4.7	161	3.33	0.58	0.62	3	52
KCl	−193°C	21.36	−2.3	150.7				6	
KCl	−3°C	25.23	−3.3	157.3				6	
KCl	Room	27.4	−1.38	156	4.095	0.705	0.630	26	37
KI	Room	39.2	−5.4	238				3	
Potassium alum	Room				2.56	1.07	0.86	..	66
K	Room	833	−370	380	0.459	0.372	0.263	39	62
LiF	Room	10.6	−2.9	15.9	9.9	4.3	5.4	24	63
MgO	−193°C	3.839	−0.855	6.380				6	
MgO	−103°C	3.888	−0.878	6.399				6	
MgO	−3°C	3.991	−0.922	6.447				6	
MgO	97°C	4.109	−0.972	6.502				6	
MgO	197°C	4.243	−1.027	6.564				6	
MgO	287°C	4.383	−1.085	6.626				6	
Na	−193°C	482.6	−208.7	168.5				22	
Na	−63°C	535.4	−232.1	203.7				22	
Na	Room				0.945	0.779	0.618	..	62
NaBr	Room	40.0	−11.5	75.4				3	
NaCl	−3°C	22.08	−4.49	78.26				6	
NaCl	Room	24.3	−5.27	78.8	4.911	1.225	1.284	26	37
NaCl	97°C	24.40	−5.43	80.36				6	
NaCl	197°C	27.33	−6.62	82.85				6	
$NaClO_3$	Room	24.60	+12.5	83.7				26	
$NaClO_3$	26°C				4.89	1.39	1.173	..	44
NH_4Br	Room				2.96	0.59	0.53	..	66
NH_4Cl	Room				3.90	0.72	0.68	..	66
Nickel (Ni)	Room				24.4	15.8	10.2	..	68
Lead (Pb)	Room	93	−42.6	69.4	4.76	4.03	1.44	13	62
Si	25°C				16.740	6.523	7.957	..	47
W (tungsten)	Room	2.573	−0.729	6.604	50.2	19.9	15.1	2	62
Zinc blende	Room	20.0	−8.0	24.3	10.79	7.22	4.12	61	121
Galena	Room				8.69	4.01	4.42	..	116
Chromium oxide	Room				32.25	14.37	11.67	..	117
Iron purite	Room				36.7	−4.64	10.52	..	118
Fluorspar	Room				16.44	5.02	3.47	..	119
Magnelite					27.25	10.6	9.71	..	118
Sodium chlorate					5.09	1.55	1.18	..	120
Rock salt					4.97	1.27	1.27	..	119

* References are on p. 2–58.

TABLE 2f-2. ELASTIC CONSTANTS AND COEFFICIENTS FOR TETRAGONAL CRYSTALS
(S_{ij} in units of 10^{-13} cm²/dyne; C_{ij} in units of 10^{11} dynes/cm²)

Material	Test temp.	S_{11} (1)	S_{33} (2)	S_{44} (3)	S_{66} (4)	S_{12} (5)	S_{13} (6)	C_{11} (7)	C_{66} (8)	C_{12} (9)	Ref.* cols. 1–6	Ref.* cols. 7–9
Tin (Sn)	Room	18.5	11.8	57.0	135	−9.9	−2.5	....	....	....	73	
KD_2PO_4	26°C	....	....	....	....	....	....	7.04	0.607	0.46	..	72
RbH_2PO_4	26°C	....	....	....	....	....	....	6.7	0.4	0.2	..	72

* References are on p. 2–58.

TABLE 2f-3. ELASTIC CONSTANTS AND COEFFICIENTS FOR TRIGONAL CRYSTALS
(C_{ij} in units of 10^{11} dynes/cm²; S_{ij} in units of 10^{-13} cm²/dyne)

Material	Test temp.	C_{11}	C_{33}	C_{44}	C_{12}	C_{13}	C_{14}	Ref.*
Calespar	Room	13.74	8.01	3.42	4.40	4.50	−2.03	74
Corundum	Room	46.5	56.3	23.3	12.4	11.7	10.1	75
Quartz	Room	86.94	106.80	57.62	6.96	15.60	17.43	75
Sodium nitrate	Room	8.67	3.74	2.13	1.63	1.60	0.82	74
		S_{11}	S_{33}	S_{44}	S_{12}	S_{13}	S_{14}	
α quartz	Room	12.98	9.90	20.05	−1.66	−1.52	−4.31	26
Bismuth (B_1)	Room	2.69	28.7	104.8	−14	−6.2	+16.0	73
Calespar	Room	11.3	17.5	40.3	−3.7	−4.3	+9.1	70
Fe_2O_3	Room	4.42	4.44	11.93	−1.02	−0.23	+0.80	26
Hematite	Room	4.41	4.43	11.9	−1.02	−0.23	+0.79	70
Hg	−190°	15.4	4.5	15.1	−11.9	−2.1	−10.0	15
Quartz	Room	13.0	9.9	20.0	−1.66	−1.52	−4.30	70
Sb	Room	17.7	33.8	41.0	−3.8	−8.5	−8.0	73
Tellurium	Room	48.7	23.4	58.1	−6.9	−13.8		2
Tourmaline	Room	3.99	6.24	15.14	−1.03	−0.16	+0.58	26

* References are on p. 2–58.

TABLE 2f-4. ELASTIC CONSTANTS AND COEFFICIENTS FOR HEXAGONAL CRYSTALS
(C_{ij} in units of 10^{11} dynes/cm²; S_{ij} in units of 10^{-13} cm²/dyne)

Material	Test temp.	C_{11} (1)	C_{33} (2)	C_{44} (3)	C_{12} (4)	C_{13} (5)	S_{11} (6)	S_{33} (7)	S_{44} (8)	S_{12} (9)	S_{13} (10)	Ref.* cols. 1–5	Ref.* cols. 6–10
Beryl (sea green)	Room	29.71	26.50	7.54	10.26	7.39	4.42	4.70	15.3	−1.37	−0.86	67	70
β quartz	600°C	11.84	10.70	3.585	1.90	3.20	9.257	10.85	27.89	−0.802	−2.52	45	45
Phosphorite	Room	16.67	13.96	6.63	....	6.55	....	....	....	....	....	122	
Cadmium (Cd)	Room	....	....	....	....	....	12.3	35.5	54.0	−1.5	−9.3	...	14
Magnesium (Mg)	Room	....	....	....	....	....	22.1	19.7	60.3	−7.7	−4.9	...	11
Zinc (Zn)	25°C	....	....	....	....	....	8.38	28.4	26.1	0.5	−7.31	...	69

* References are on p. 2–58.

TABLE 2f-5. ELASTIC CONSTANTS AND COEFFICIENTS FOR RHOMBIC CRYSTALS
(At room temperature; C_{ij} in units of 10^{11} dynes/cm^2;
S_{ij} in units of 10^{-13} cm^2/dyne)

Material	C_{11}	C_{22}	C_{33}	C_{44}	C_{55}	C_{66}	C_{12}	C_{13}	C_{23}	Ref.*
Sodium tartrate	4.61	5.47	6.65	1.24	0.31	0.98	2.86	3.20	3.52	76
Rochelle salt	4.06	5.20	6.40	1.22	0.30	0.95	2.56	3.46	3.20	76
$MgSO_4 \cdot 7H_2O$	6.98	5.29	8.22	1.07	2.33	2.22	3.90	2.82	2.83	76
$ZnSO_4 \cdot 7H_2O$	4.00	3.22	5.45	0.50	1.70	1.81	1.32	1.08	1.19	76
S (orthorhombic)	2.40	2.05	4.83	0.43	0.87	0.76	1.33	1.71	1.59	77
	S_{11}	S_{22}	S_{33}	S_{44}	S_{55}	S_{66}	S_{12}	S_{13}	S_{23}	
Sodium tartrate	37.1	31.6	26.4	80.6	323	100	−12.0	−11.5	−10.9	76
Rochelle salt	50.2	30.4	31.7	82.0	333	106	−11.6	−21.4	−8.95	76
$MgSO_4 \cdot 7H_2O$	24.5	34.1	15.0	93.5	42.9	45.0	−16.6	−2.68	−6.05	76
$ZnSO_4 \cdot 7H_2O$	29.5	37.7	20.4	200.0	58.8	55.5	−10.8	−3.49	−6.10	76
S (orthorhombic)	89.9	106.0	38.4	232	115	132	45.2	13.6	18.8	77
Aragonite	6.97	13.2	12.2	24.3	39.0	23.5	−2.37	0.43	−3.04	26
Barite	16.45	18.94	10.63	83.9	34.9	36.0	−2.51	−1.92	−8.97	26
Ammonium rochelle salt	55.7	38.5	37.3	87.4	359.9	118.4	−5.0	−34.3	−8.7	20
Topaz	4.43	3.53	3.84	9.24	7.54	7.64	−0.66	−0.86	−1.37	26

* References are below.

References for Tables 2f-1 through 2f-5

1. Birch and Bancroft: unpublished.
2. Bridgman: *Proc. Am. Acad. Arts Sci.* **60,** 305 (1925).
3. Bridgman: *Proc. Am. Acad. Arts Sci.* **64,** 19 (1929).
4. Bridgman: *Proc. Am. Acad. Arts Sci.* **67,** 29 (1932).
5. Bridgman: *Phys. Rev.* **47,** 393 (1935).
6. Durard: *Phys. Rev.* **50,** 449 (1936); Rose, *Phys. Rev.* **49,** 50 (1936).
7. Giebe and Blechschmidt: *Ann. Physik* **18,** 417, 457 (1933).
8. Giebe and Scheibe: *Ann. Physik* **9,** 39 (1931).
9. Goens: *Ann. Physik* **16,** 793 (1933).
10. Goens: *Ann. Physik* **17,** 233 (1933).
11. Goens and Schmid: *Physik Z.* **37,** 385 (1936).
12. Goens and Schmid: *Naturwiss.* **19,** 521 (1931).
13. Goens and Weerts: *Physik Z.* **37,** 321 (1936).
14. Gruneisen and Goens: *Z. Physik* **26,** 235 (1924).
15. Gruneisen and Sckell: *Ann. Physik* **19,** 387 (1934).
16. Hanson: *Phys. Rev.* **45,** 324 (1934).
17. Kimura: *Sci. Repts. Tôhoku Imp. Univ.* **22,** 533 (1933).
18. Kimura and Ohno: *Sci. Repts. Tôhoku Imp. Univ.* **23,** 359 (1934).
19. Mandell: *Proc. Roy. Soc. (London)* **116,** 623 (1927).
20. Mandell: *Proc. Roy. Soc. (London)* **121,** 122 (1928).
21. Perrier and Mandrot: *Compt. rend.* **175,** 622, 1006 (1922); also Freedericks and Michailov: *Z. Physik* **76,** 328 (1932); de Mandrot, *Helv. Phys. Acta* **5,** 362 (1932).
22. Quimby and Siegel: *Phys. Rev.* **52,** 665 (1937); **54,** 293 (1938).
23. Rohl, *Ann. Phys.* **16,** 887 (1933).
24. Schaeter and Beramann: *Sitzber. preuss. Akad. Wiss. Physik-math. Ke.* **222** (1935).
25. Tyndall: *Phys. Rev.* **47,** 398 (1935).
26. Voigt: "Lehrbuch der Kristallphysik," Teubner Verlagsgesellschaft, Berlin, 1928.
27. Wright: *Proc. Roy. Soc. (London)* **126,** 613 (1929).
28. Mason: *Phys. Rev.* **55,** 775 (1939).
29. Siegel: *Phys. Rev.* **57,** 537 (1940).
30. Rinehart, *Phys. Rev.* **58,** 365 (1940).

31. Mason: *Bell System Tech. J.* **19,** 74 (1940).
32. Beckmann, H. F.: *Tech. U. El AK* **44,** 145 (1934).
33. Schmid and Boas: "Kristallplastizität," p. 202, Springer-Verlag OHG, Berlin, 1935.
34. Atanasoff and Kammer: *Phys. Rev.* **59,** 97 (1941).
35. Lawson: *Phys. Rev.* **59,** 608 (1941).
36. Atansoff and Hart: *Phys. Rev.* **59,** 85 (1941).
37. Lazarus, D.: *Phys. Rev.* **75,** 545 (1949).
38. Fine, Morris E.: *J. Appl. Phys.* **24,** 338 (1953).
39. Seitz, Frederick: *J. Appl. Phys.* **12,** 100 (1941).
40. Neighbours, J. R., F. W. Bratten, and C. S. Smith: *J. Appl. Phys.* **23,** 389 (1952).
41. Artman, R. A., and D. O. Thompson: *J. Appl. Phys.* **23,** 470 (1952).
42. Bhagavantam, S., and J. Bhimasenachar: *Proc. Indian Acad. Sci.* **1945** (Department of Physics, Andhra University).
43. Wert, G. A., and E. P. T. Tyrdall: *J. Appl. Phys.* **20,** 587 (1948).
44. Jona, Franco: *Helv. Phys. Acta* **24,** VII (1950).
45. Kammer, E. W., and J. V. Atansoff: *Phys. Rev.* **62,** 395, 1942.
46. Good, Walter A.: *Phys. Rev.* **60,** 605, 1941.
47. McSkimin, H. J., W. L. Bond, E. Buehler, and G. K. Teal: *Phys. Rev.* **83,** 1080 (1952).
48. Lazarus, David: *Phys. Rev.* **74,** 1726 (1948).
49. Bond, W. L., W. P. Mason, H. J. McSkimin, K. M. Oleson, and G. K. Teal: *Phys. Rev.* **78,** 176, 1950.
50. Rao, B. Ramachandra: *Current Sci.* (*India*) **14.**
51. Rao, Sundara: *Nature* **162,** 818.
52. Bridgman, P. W.: *Proc. Am. Acad. Arts Sci.* **64,** 19 (1929).
53. Voigt, W.: *Wiedemanns Ann.* **35,** 642 (1888).
54. Rohl, H.: *Ann. Phys.* **16** (5), 887 (1933).
55. Wright, S. J.: *Proc. Roy. Soc.* (*London*) **126,** 613 (1930).
56. Karnop, R., and G. Sachs: *Z. Physik* **53,** 605 (1929).
57. Masima, M., and G. Sachs: *Z. Physik* **50,** 161 (1928).
58. Rohl, H.: *Ann. Physik* **16,** 887 (1933).
59. Kimura, R.: *Proc. Phys.-Math. Soc. Japan* **21,** 686, 786 (1939); **22,** 45, 219 (1940).
60. Voigt, W.: *Nachr. Ges. Wiss. Göttingen,* 85 (1918).
61. Bhagavantam and Suryanavayana: *Proc. Indian Acad. Sci.* **20,** 304 (1944).
62. Jones, H.: *Physica* **15,** 13 (1949).
63. Hoerni, J., and W. Wooster: *Acta Cryst.* **5,** 386 (1952).
64. Smith, G. S., and J. W. Burns: *J. Appl. Phys.* **24,** 15 (1952).
65. Rao, B. Ramachandra: *Proc. Indian Acad. Sci.* **22A,** 194 (1945).
66. Rao, Sundara: *Current Sci.* (*India*) **17,** 50 (1948).
67. Rao, Sundara, and T. S. Balakrishnan: *Proc. Indian Acad. Sci.* **28A,** 475 (1948).
68. Yamomolo, M.: *Phys. Rev.* **77,** 566 (1950).
69. Wert, C., and E. Tyndall: *J. Appl. Phys.* **20,** 587, 1948.
70. Voigt, W.: "Lehrbuch der Kristallphysik," 1910.
71. Kammer, E.
72. Jona, F.: *Helv. Phys. Acta* **23** (24VII, 1950).
73. Bridgman, P. W.: *Proc. Natl. Acad. Sci. U.S.* **10,** 411 (1924).
74. Bhimasenacher, J.: *Proc. Indian Acad. Sci.* **22,** 199 (1945).
75. Bhimasenachar, J.: *Current Sci.* (*India*) **18.**
76. Rao, Sundara: *Proc. Indian Acad. Sci.* **28,** 185 (1948).
77. Rao, Sundara: *Proc. Indian Acad. Sci.* **31,** 365 (1950).
78. Adams and Coker: *Carnegie Inst. Wash. Publ.* 46 (1906).
79. Birch: *J. Appl. Phys.* **8,** 129 (1937).
80. Birch and Bancroft: *J. Geol.* **46,** 59, 113 (1938).
81. Birch and Bancroft: *J. Geol.* **48,** 752 (1940).
82. Birch and Bancroft: *Am. J. Sci.* **2,** 237 (1939).
83. Birch and Bancroft: *Bull. Seism. Soc. Am.* **28,** 243 (1938).
84. Boyle and Sproule: *Can. J. Research* **5,** 601 (1931).
85. Breyer: *Z. Geophys.* **6,** 98 (1930).

86. Bridgman: *Proc. Am. Acad. Arts Sci.* **63**, 401 (1929); **64**, 39 (1929).
87. Drane: *Proc. Roy. Soc.* (*London*), ser. A, **122**, 274 (1929).
88. Drude and Voigt: *Wiedemanns Ann.* **42**, 537 (1891).
89. Ewing, Crary, and Thorne: *Physics* **5**, 165 (1934).
90. Hermann, Stocke, and Udluft: *Beitr. angew. Geophys.* **6**, 206 (1937).
91. Horton: *Trans. Roy. Soc.* (*London*), ser. A, **204**, 407 (1905); Iida: *Bull. Earthquake Research Inst.* **13**, 665 (1935).
92. Ide: *Proc. Natl. Acad. Sci. U.S.* **22**, 81, 482 (1936).
93. Ide: *J. Geol.* **45**, 689 (1937).
94. Koch: *Ann. Physik* **45**, 237 (1914).
95. Koch and Dannecker: *Ann. Physik* **47**, 197 (1915).
96. Koch and Dieterle: *Ann. Physik* **68**, 441 (1922).
97. Kusakabe: *Earthquake Invest. Comm. Tokyo* **14**, 1 (1903); **17**, 1 (1904); **22**, 38 (1906).
98. Nagaoka: *Phil. Mag.* **50**, 53 (1900).
99. Perman and Urry: *Proc. Phys. Soc.* (*London*) **40**, 186 (1928).
100. Pierce: *Proc. Inst. Radio Engrs.* **17**, 42 (1929).
101. Richards: *Proc. Phys. Soc.* (*London*) **45**, 70 (1933).
102. Zisman; *Proc. Natl. Acad. Sci. U.S.* **19**, 653 (1933).
103. Weatherby, Born, and Harding: *Bull. Am. Assoc. Petroleum Geol.* **19**, 9 (1935).
104. Andrews: *Proc. Phys. Soc.* (*London*) **37**, 169 (1925).
105. Bancroft and Jacobs: *Rev. Sci. Instr.* **9**, 279 (1938).
106. Vose: unpublished.
107. Abram, *J. Iron Steel Inst.* (*London*) **129**, 325 (1934).
108. Regula: *Z. Geophys.* **16**, 40 (1940).
109. Obert, *U.S. Bur. Mines, Rept. Invest.* 3444 (1939).
110. Lawson: *Phys. Rev.* **57**, 417 (1940).
111. Birch and Bancroft: *J. Chem. Phys.* **8**, 641 (1940).
112. Birch and Bancroft: unpublished.
113. Kimura: *Proc. Phys.-Math. Soc. Japan* **21**, 786 (1939).
114. McKeown, J., and E. D. Ward: *Brit. Non-ferrous Metals Research Assoc., Research Rept.*, Assoc. Series 473 (1938).
115. Rogers, B. A., I. C. Schoonover, and L. Jordan: *Natl. Bur. Standards* (*U.S.*) *Circ.* C412 (1936).
116. Bhagavantam, S., and J. Bhimasenachar: *Proc. Indian Acad. Sci.* **20** (1944).
117. Doraiswami, M. S.: *Proc. Indian Acad. Sci.* **25A** (1947).
118. Doraiswami, M. S.: *Proc. Indian Acad. Sci.* **25A** (1947).
119. Bhagavantam, S.: *Proc. 33rd Indian Sci. Congr.*, pt. II, sec. III, Physics, 1946.
120. Bhagavantam, S., and D. Suryanavayana: *Phys. Rev.* **2**, 71 (1947).
121. Bhagavantam, S., and D. Suryanavayana: *Proc. Indian Acad. Sci.* **20A** (1944).
122. Bhimasenashar, J.: *Proc. Indian Acad. Sci.* **22** (1945).

Abbreviations in Tables 2f-6 *through* 2f-15

Abbreviation	*Definition*
H.R	Hot rolled
C.R	Cold rolled
W.Q	Water quenched
O.Q	Oil quenched
A.Q	Air quenched
A.C	Air cooled
F.C	Furnace cooled
h-t	Heat-treated
wr	Wrought
ann	Annealed
art. aged	Artificially aged
nat. aged	Naturally aged
spec	Specimen
G.S	Grain size

TABLE 2f-6. ELASTIC AND STRENGTH CONSTANTS FOR VARIOUS SOLIDS

Material	Condition	E	G	Tensile strength	Yield strength at 0.2% offset	Elongation	Bhn	Ref.*
Iridium	Ann.	52×10^{11}	......	......	......	......	Vhn 170	1
Osmium	Ann.	56×10^{11}	......	......	......	......	Vhn 400	1
Rhodium	Ann.	......	......	50×10^{8}	......	......	......	1
Ruthenium	As cast	41×10^{11}	......	......	......	......	Vhn 390	1
Antimony	......	7.78×10^{11}	......	1.1×10^{8}	......	......	30–58	1
Beryllium	Vacuum cast	29×10^{11}	......	$12\text{–}15 \times 10^{8}$	......	......	......	1
Cadmium	Chill cast 1-in. section	5.5×10^{11}†	......	7.1×10^{8}	......	50	21–23	1
Calcium	Cast slab	$2\text{–}3 \times 10^{11}$	......	5.5×10^{8}	3.8×10^{8}	53–60	17	1
Chromium	As cast	......	......	......	......	......	110–170	1
Cobalt	Cast	21×10^{11}	......	23.7×10^{8}	......	......	125	1
Columbium	Sheet, ann. 0.01-in. section	......	......	34×10^{8}	......	30	......	1
Columbium	Sheet, worked 0.01-in. section	......	......	69×10^{8}	......	1	......	1
Lithium	......	......	......	......	......	......	Softer than pure lead	1
Manganese	Quenched	......	......	50×10^{8}	24×10^{8}	40	R_C35	1
Molybdenum	Pressed + sintered (sheet)	34×10^{11}	......	69×10^{8}	......	......	156	1
Silicon	Chill cast 3.55 × 0.97 × 0.97 in.	11.26×10^{11}	......	......	......	......	......	1
Sodium	......	......	......	......	......	......	0.07‡	1
Tantalum	Ann. 0.010-in. sheet	......	......	34×10^{8}	......	40	R_E60	1
Tantalum	Worked 0.010-in. sheet	......	......	76×10^{8}	......	1	R_E95	1
Titanium	Ann.	11.6×10^{11}	......	54×10^{8}	43×10^{8}	25.2	R_G76	1
Titanium	Hard, 60% reduction	......	......	76.82×10^{8}	......	1.5	R_G72	1
Tungsten	......	34×10^{11}	13.5×10^{11}	......	......	......	......	1
Zirconium	Hard drawn	9.99×10^{11}	......	84×10^{8}	48×10^{8}	18¶	$R_B87.4$	1

* References are on p. 2-78.
† Sand cast.
‡ 3.2-kg load, 10-mm ball.
¶ Per cent in 4 in.

TABLE 2f-7. ELASTIC AND STRENGTH CONSTANTS FOR SILVER, GOLD, PLATINUM, PALLADIUM ALLOYS

Material	Condition	E	σ	Tensile strength	Yield strength at 0.2% offset	Elongation	Reduction in area	Bhn	Ref.*
Ag	Strained 5%, heated 5 hr at 350°C	$7.1–7.8 \times 10^{11}$	....	....	....	.....	....	....	1
Ag	Ann.		0.37	....	....	.....	....	....	1
Ag + 80 Mo			....	55×10^8	....	.....	....	190	1
Ag + 40 Mo			....	41×10^8	....	.....	....	160	1
Ag + 20 Mo			....	24×10^8	....	.....	....	40	1
Ag + 20 W			....	34×10^8	....	.....	....	40	1
Ag + 40 W			....	41×10^8	....	.....	....	150	1
Ag + 80 W			....	55×10^8	....	.....	....	240	1
Ag + 40 Ni	Ann.		....	26×10	....	.....	....	Vhn 70	1
Ag + 20 Ni	Ann.		....	21×10^8	....	.....	....	Vhn 45	1
Ag + 1 graphite			....	....	....	.....	....	$R_{15T}68$	1
Ag + 5 graphite			....	....	....	.....	....	$R_{15T}55$	1
Ag + 10 graphite			....	....	....	.....	....	$R_{15T}40$	1
Ag + 5 Cd			....	16×10^8	....	.....	....	R_F30	1
Ag + 10 Cd			....	19×10^8	....	.....	....	R_F44	1
Ag + 20 Cd			....	20×10^8	....	.....	....	R_F55	1
33 Ag, 52 Hg, 12.5 Sn, 2 Cu, 0.5 Zn		1.0×10^{11}	....	$2.8–5.9 \times 10^8$	....	.....	....	....	1
Au 99.99%	Cast	7.44×10^{11}	0.42	12.4×10^8	....	30	....	33	1
Au 99.99%	Wrought, ann.	8.00×10^{11}	0.42	13.1×10^8	Nil	45	....	25	1
58.3 Au, 4.9 Ag, 31.6 Cu, 5.2 Ni	Air cooled	....	....	56.9×10^8	33.1×10^8 at 0.1% offset	41.0	36.0	R_B87	1

TABLE 2f-7. ELASTIC AND STRENGTH CONSTANTS FOR SILVER, GOLD, PLATINUM, PALLADIUM ALLOYS (*Continued*)

Material	Condition	E	σ	Tensile strength	Yield strength at 0.2% offset	Elongation	Reduction in area	Bhn	Ref.*
41.6 Au, 4.6 Ag, 43.4 Cu, 5.0 Ni, 5.4 Zn	Air cooled	....	....	46.8×10^8	26.7×10^8 at 0.1% offset	41.5	36.0	R_B68	1
69 Au, 25 Ag, 6 Pt........	Ann.	....	....	37.6×10^8	....	.....	....	Vhn 112	1
Pt 99.99%............	Ann.	14.7×10^{11}	0.39	12–13 $\times 10^8$	....	25–40	....	Vhn 38–40	1
Pt + 5 Ir............	Ann.	....	....	27×10^8	....	.....	....	90	1
Pt + 10 Ir............	Ann.	....	....	38×10^8	....	.....	....	130	1
Pt + 25 Ir............	Ann.	....	....	86×10^8	....	.....	....	240	1
Pt + 3.5 Rh............	Ann.	....	....	17×10^8	....	.....	....	60	1
Pt + 5.0 Rh............	Ann.	....	....	21×10^8	....	.....	....	70	1
Pt + 10.0 Rh............	Ann.	....	....	31×10^8	....	35	....	90	1
Pt + 20.0 Rh............	Ann.	....	....	48×10^8	....	40	....	120	1
Pt + 5 Ru............	Ann.	....	....	41×10^8	....	.....	....	130	1
Pt + 10 Ru............	Ann.	....	....	59×10^8	....	.....	....	190	1
Pt + 1 Ni............	Ann.	....	....	21×10^8	....	.....	....	Vhn 60–65	1
Pt + 2 Ni............	Ann.	....	....	28×10^8	....	.....	....	Vhn 80–90	1
Pt + 5 Ni............	Ann.	....	....	45×10^8	....	.....	....	Vhn 130–140	1
84 Pt, 10 Pd, 6 Ru........	Ann.	....	....	55×10^8	....	18–25	....	Vhn 150–170	1
96 Pt, 4 W............	Ann.	....	....	48–52 $\times 10^8$	....	25	....	Vhn 140–150	1
Pd (pure)............	Ann. and rolled	12.1×10^{11}	....	$\geq 15 \times 10^8$	....	24	....	Vhn 37–39	1
60 Pd, 40 Ag............	Ann.	....	....	35×10^8	....	47	....	Vhn 100	1
60 Pd, 40 Cu............	Ann.	....	....	52×10^8					
95 Pd, 4 Ru, 1 Rh........	Ann.	....	....	38–41 $\times 10^8$	....	25	....	Vhn 100–110	1

* References are on p. 2–78.

TABLE 2f-8. ELASTIC AND STRENGTH CONSTANTS FOR ALUMINUM ALLOYS

Alloys	Condition	E	G	σ	Tensile strength	Yield strength	Elongation	Bhn	Shear strength	Ref.*
Cast alloys:										
Al, 12 Si	Die cast	7.10×10^{11}	2.65×10^{11}	0.33	25.5×10^8	12.4×10^8	1.8†			1
Al, 5 Si	Die cast	7.10×10^{11}	2.65×10^{11}	0.33	20.7×10^8	9.65×10^8	7.0†			1
Al, 5 Si	Sand cast	7.10×10^{11}	2.65×10^{11}	0.33	13.1×10^8	6.20×10^8	6.0‡	40¶	9.65×10^8	1
Al, 5 Si, 4 Cu	Die cast	7.10×10^{11}	2.65×10^{11}	0.33	27.6×10^8	15.2×10^8	3.5†			1
Al, 4 Cu, 3 Si	Sand cast	7.10×10^{11}	2.65×10^{11}	0.33	14.5×10^8	9.65×10^8	2.5‡	55¶	13.8×10^8	1
Al, 5 Si, 3 Cu	Sand cast	7.10×10^{11}	2.65×10^{11}	0.33	18.6×10^8	9.65×10^8	2.5‡	R_E65		1
Al, 5 Si, 3 Cu	Sand cast, h-t, aged	7.10×10^{11}	2.65×10^{11}	0.33	24.1×10^8	13.8×10^8	4.0‡	R_E80		1
Al, 5 Si, 3 Cu	Perm. mold cast, h-t, aged	7.10×10^{11}	2.65×10^{11}	0.33	28.9×10^8	15.2×10^8	5.0‡	R_E85		1
Al, 5.5 Si, 4.5 Cu	Perm. mold cast, h-t, aged	7.10×10^{11}	2.65×10^{11}	0.33	19.3×10^8	11.0×10^8	2.0‡	70¶	17.2×10^8	1
Al, 7 Cu, 2 Si, 1.7 Zn	Sand cast	7.10×10^{11}	2.65×10^{11}	0.33	16.5×10^8	10.3×10^8	1.5‡	70¶	13.8×10^8	1
Al, 7 Cu, 3.5 Si	Perm. mold cast	7.10×10^{11}	2.65×10^{11}	0.33	20.7×10^8	16.5×10^8	1.0‡	80¶	15.2×10^8	1
Al, 10 Cu, 0.2 Mg	Sand cast (ann.)	7.10×10^{11}	2.65×10^{11}	0.33	18.6×10^8	13.8×10^8	1.0‡	80¶	14.5×10^8	1
Al, 10 Cu, 0.2 Mg	H-t, artificially aged	7.10×10^{11}	2.65×10^{11}	0.33	27.6×10^8	20.7×10^8	0.5‡	115¶	20.0×10^8	1
Al, 12 Si, 2.5 Ni, 1.2 Mg, 0.8 Cu	Perm. mold cast, art. aged	7.10×10^{11}	2.65×10^{11}	0.33	24.8×10^8	19.3×10^8	0.5‡	105¶	16.5×10^8	1
Al, 12 Si, 1.5 Cu, 0.7 Mn, 0.7 Mg	Perm. mold cast (stress relieved)	7.10×10^{11}	2.65×10^{11}	0.33	24.8×10^8		0.5‡	100¶		1
Al, 4 Cu, 2 Ni, 1.5 Mg	Ann. (sand cast)	7.10×10^{11}	2.65×10^{11}	0.33	18.6×10^8	12.4×10^8	1.0‡	70¶	14.5×10^8	1
Al, 4.5 Cu	H-t, nat. aged	7.10×10^{11}	2.65×10^{11}	0.33	22.0×10^8	11.0×10^8	8.5‡	60¶	16.5×10^8	1
Al, 4.5 Cu, 2.5 Si	H-t, nat. aged	7.10×10^{11}	2.65×10^{11}	0.33	27.6×10^8	15.2×10^8	10.0‡	75¶	20.7×10^8	1
Al, 3.8 Mg	Perm. mold cast	7.10×10^{11}	2.65×10^{11}	0.33	18.6×10^8	11.0×10^8	7.0‡	60¶	15.2×10^8	1
Al, 8 Mg	Die cast	7.10×10^{11}	2.65×10^{11}	0.33	28.9×10^8	15.8×10^8	7.0†			1
Al, 10 Mg	Sand cast, h-t, nat. aged	7.10×10^{11}	2.65×10^{11}	0.33	31.7×10^8	17.2×10^8	14.0‡	75¶	22.7×10^8	1
Al, 6 Si, 3.5 Cu	H-t, art. aged	7.10×10^{11}	2.65×10^{11}	0.33	24.8×10^8	16.5×10^8	2.0‡	80¶		1
Al, 6 Si, 3.5 Cu	As cast	7.10×10^{11}	2.65×10^{11}	0.33	18.6×10^8	12.4×10^8	2.0‡	70¶	16.5×10^8	1
Al, 5 Si, 1.3 Cu, 0.5 Mg	H-t, art. aged (sand cast)	7.10×10^{11}	2.65×10^{11}	0.33	24.1×10^8	17.2×10^8	2.5‡	80¶	20.8×10^8	1
Al, 5 Si, 1.3 Cu, 0.5 Mg	H-t, art. aged (perm. mold cast)	7.10×10^{11}	2.65×10^{11}	0.33	29.6×10^8	18.6×10^8	4.0‡	90¶	20.8×10^8	1
Al, 7 Si, 0.3 Mg	H-t, art. aged (sand cast)	7.10×10^{11}	2.65×10^{11}	0.33	22.7×10^8	16.5×10^8	4.0‡	70¶	18.6×10^8	1
Al, 7 Si, 0.3 Mg	H-t, art. aged (perm. mold cast)	7.10×10^{11}	2.65×10^{11}	0.33	27.6×10^8	18.6×10^8	5.0‡	90¶		1
Al, 8 Si, 1.5 Cu, 0.3 Mg, 0.3 Mn	Sand cast (stress relieved)	7.10×10^{11}	2.65×10^{11}	0.33	20.7×10^8	14.5×10^8	1.5‡	R_E76		1
Al, 8 Si, 1.5 Cu, 0.3 Mg, 0.3 Mn	Perm. mold (stress relieved)	7.10×10^{11}	2.65×10^{11}	0.33	24.8×10^8		1.0‡	R_E88		1
Al, 9.5 Si, 0.5 Mg	Die cast	7.10×10^{11}	2.65×10^{11}	0.33	28.9×10^8	15.8×10^8	1.8†			1
Al, 8.5 Si, 3.5 Cu	Die cast	7.10×10^{11}	2.65×10^{11}	0.33	31.0×10^8	17.2×10^8	2.0†			1
Al, 6.5 Sn, 1 Cu, 1 Ni	(Perm. mold cast) art. aged	7.10×10^{11}	2.65×10^{11}	0.33	15.2×10^8	6.89×10^8	12.0‡	45¶	9.65×10^8	1
Al, 5.5 Zn, 0.6 Mg, 0.5 Cr, 0.2 Ti	Sand cast	7.10×10^{11}	2.65×10^{11}	0.33	24.1×10^8	17.2×10^8	5.0‡	80¶	19.2×10^8	1

Wrought alloys:										
Aluminum 99.996 Al	Ann.	6.89×10^{11}	2.65×10^{11}	0.33	4.74×10^{8}	1.22×10^{8}	48.8§	17¶		1
Aluminum 99.996 Al	Cold rolled 75%	6.89×10^{11}	2.65×10^{11}	0.33	11.2×10^{8}	10.6×10^{8}	5.5§	27¶		1
Aluminum 99.0+ Al	Ann.	6.89×10^{11}	2.65×10^{11}	0.33	8.96×10^{8}	3.45×10^{8}	35§	23¶	6.55×10^{8}	1
Aluminum 99.0+ Al	Hard H‖	6.89×10^{11}	2.65×10^{11}	0.33	16.6×10^{8}	14.5×10^{8}	5§	44¶	8.96×10^{8}	1
Al, 1.2 Mn	Ann.	6.89×10^{11}	2.65×10^{11}	0.33	11.0×10^{8}	4.14×10^{8}	30§	28¶	7.58×10^{8}	1
Al, 1.2 Mn	Hard H‖	6.89×10^{11}	2.65×10^{11}	0.33	20.0×10^{8}	17.2×10^{8}	4§	55¶	11.0×10^{8}	1
Al, 5.5 Cu, 0.5 Pb, 0.5 Bi	H-t, then cold-worked	7.10×10^{11}	2.65×10^{11}	0.33	36.5×10^{8}	32.4×10^{8}	15‡	95¶	20.7×10^{8}	1
Al, 5.5 Cu, 0.5 Pb, 0.5 Bi	H-t, then cold-worked, then art. aged	7.10×10^{11}	2.65×10^{11}	0.33	39.3×10^{8}	30.3×10^{8}	14‡	100¶	22.8×10^{8}	1
Al, 4 Cu, 0.6 Mn, 0.6 Mg, 0.5 Pb, 0.5 Bi	Quenched (h-t)	7.10×10^{11}	2.65×10^{11}	0.33	42.1×10^{8}	24.1×10^{8}	22§	100¶		1
Al, 4.4 Cu, 0.8 Si, 0.8 Mn, 0.4 Mg	Ann.	7.31×10^{11}	2.65×10^{11}	0.33	18.6×10^{8}	9.65×10^{8}	18‡	45¶	12.4×10^{8}	1
Al, 4.4 Cu, 0.8 Si, 0.8 Mn, 0.4 Mg	H-t, art. aged	7.31×10^{11}	2.65×10^{11}	0.33	48.3×10^{8}	41.4×10^{8}	13‡	135¶	29.0×10^{8}	1
Al, 4 Cu, 0.5 Mg, 0.5 Mn	Ann.	7.17×10^{11}	2.65×10^{11}	0.33	17.9×10^{8}	6.89×10^{8}	22§	45¶	12.4×10^{8}	1
Al, 4 Cu, 0.5 Mg, 0.5 Mn	H-t, nat. aged	7.17×10^{11}	2.65×10^{11}	0.33	42.7×10^{8}	27.6×10^{8}		105¶	26.2×10^{8}	1
Al, 4 Cu, 2 Ni, 0.5 Mg	Forged, h-t, aged	7.10×10^{11}	2.65×10^{11}	0.33	43.4×10^{8}	32.4×10^{8}	17‡	115¶		2
Al, 4 Cu, 2 Ni, 1.5 Mg	Sand cast	7.10×10^{11}	2.65×10^{11}	0.33	19.3×10^{8}	16.6×10^{8}	1‡	80¶	16.6×10^{8}	2
Al, 4.5 Cu, 1.5 Mg, 0.6 Mn	Ann.	7.31×10^{11}	2.65×10^{11}	0.33	18.6×10^{8}	7.58×10^{8}	19§	42¶	12.4×10^{8}	1
Al, 4.5 Cu, 1.5 Mg, 0.6 Mn	H-t, nat. aged	7.31×10^{11}	2.65×10^{11}	0.33	46.9×10^{8}	31.7×10^{8}	11§	120¶	28.3×10^{8}	1
Al, 4.5 Cu, 0.8 Mn, 0.8 Si	H-t, art. aged	7.17×10^{11}	2.65×10^{11}	0.33	39.3×10^{8}	24.1×10^{8}	18‡	110¶	24.1×10^{8}	1
Al, 12.5 Si, 1.0 Mg, 0.9 Cu, 0.9 Ni	H-t, art. aged	7.10×10^{11}	2.65×10^{11}	0.33	38.6×10^{8}	31.7×10^{8}	8‡	125¶	26.2×10^{8}	1
Al, 1.0 Si, 0.6 Mg, 0.25 Cr	H-t, art. aged	7.03×10^{11}	2.65×10^{11}	0.33	32.4×10^{8}	27.6×10^{8}	20‡	100¶	22.1×10^{8}	1
Al, 2.5 Mg, 0.25 Cr	Ann.	7.03×10^{11}	2.65×10^{11}	0.33	20.0×10^{8}	9.65×10^{8}	25§	45¶	12.4×10^{8}	1
Al, 2.5 Mg, 0.25 Cr	Strain hardened (H)	7.03×10^{11}	2.65×10^{11}	0.33	28.3×10^{8}	24.8×10^{8}	7§	85¶	16.6×10^{8}	1
Al, 1.3 Mg, 0.7 Si, 0.25 Cr	Ann.	6.89×10^{11}	2.65×10^{11}	0.33	11.0×10^{8}	4.83×10^{8}	35‡	26¶	7.58×10^{8}	1
Al, 1.3 Mg, 0.7 Si, 0.25 Cr	H-t, nat. aged	6.89×10^{11}	2.65×10^{11}	0.33	22.8×10^{8}	13.8×10^{8}	30‡	65¶	13.8×10^{8}	1
Al, 5.2 Mg, 0.1 Mn, 0.1 Cr	Ann.	7.10×10^{11}	2.65×10^{11}	0.33	29.0×10^{8}	13.8×10^{8}	35‡			1
Al, 5.2 Mg, 0.1 Mn, 0.1 Cr	Hard H‖	7.10×10^{11}	2.65×10^{11}	0.33	40.0×10^{8}	33.1×10^{8}	7‡			1
Al, 1.0 Mg, 0.6 Si, 0.25 Cu, 0.25 Cr	Ann.	6.89×10^{11}	2.65×10^{11}	0.33	12.4×10^{8}	5.52×10^{8}	22§	30¶	8.62×10^{8}	1
Al, 1.0 Mg, 0.6 Si, 0.25 Cu, 0.25 Cr	H-t, nat. aged	6.89×10^{11}	2.65×10^{11}	0.33	24.1×10^{8}	14.5×10^{8}	22§	65¶	16.5×10^{8}	1
Al, 5.5 Zn, 2.5 Mg, 1.5 Cu, 0.3 Cr, 0.2 Mn	Ann.	7.17×10^{11}	2.65×10^{11}	0.33	22.8×10^{8}	10.3×10^{8}	17§			1
Al, 5.5 Zn, 2.5 Mg, 1.5 Cu, 0.3 Cr, 0.2 Mn	H-t, art. aged	7.17×10^{11}	2.65×10^{11}	0.33	56.5×10^{8}	49.6×10^{8}	11§	150¶		1
Al, 6.4 Zn, 2.5 Mg, 1.2 Cu	Ann. (0.064 sheet)	7.17×10^{11}	2.69×10^{11}	0.33	20.7×10^{8}	10.3×10^{8}	18	R_E57–R_E62		1

* References are on p. 2–78.
† ¼-in. round specimen.
‡ ½-in. round specimen.
¶ 10-mm ball, 500-kg load.
§ 1/16-in. sheet specimen.
‖ H-strain hardened to a prescribed hardness.

Table 2f-9. Elastic and Strength Constants for Copper Alloys

Alloy	Condition	E	G	σ	Tensile strength	Yield strength	Elongation	Reduction in area	Bhn	Shear strength	Ref.*
99.997 Cu, 0.0016 S	½-in. rod, cold drawn	12.77×10^{11}	4.68×10^{11}	0.364	35.1×10^8	34.0×10^8†	14	88	R_B37	....	2
99.996 Cu, 0.002 S, 0.002 Fe	Ann., ¾-in. rod	11.2×10^{11}	....	....	21.3×10^8	3.44×10^8†	60	92	....	....	2
99.950 Cu, 0.043 O_2, 0.002 Fe, 0.002 S	Ann., ¾-in. rod	10.9×10^{11}	....	....	21.7×10^8	3.79×10^8†	53	71	....	....	2
99.92 Cu, 0.04 O_2	H.R. (0.040-in. flat)	11.7×10^{11}	....	0.33 ± 0.01	23.4×10^8	6.89×10^8†	45	....	R_F45	15.8×10^8	1
99.94 Cu, 0.02 P	0.040 in. flat spec. (G.S. 0.050 mm)	11.7×10^{11}	....	....	22.0×10^8	6.89×10^8†	45	....	R_F40	15.2×10^8	1
95 Cu, 5 Zn	Rolled strip 0.040 in. (G.S. 0.050 mm)	11.7×10^{11}	....	....	23.4×10^8	6.89×10^8†	45	....	R_F46	....	1
95 Cu, 5 Zn	Rolled strip 0.040 in. (spring)	11.7×10^{11}	....	....	44.1×10^8	40.0×10^8†	4	....	R_B73	27.6×10^8	1
90 Cu, 10 Zn	Flat, 0.040 in. (spring)	11.7×10^{11}	....	....	49.6×10^8	42.7×10^8†	3	....	R_B78	28.9×10^8	1
90 Cu, 10 Zn	Flat, 0.040 in. as H.R.	11.7×10^{11}	....	....	26.9×10^8	9.65×10^8†	44	....	R_F60	21.4×10^8	1
85 Cu, 15 Zn	Flat, 0.040 in. (G.S. 0.050 mm)	11.7×10^{11}	....	....	27.6×10^8	8.27×10^8†	47	....	R_F59	21.4×10^8	1
85 Cu, 15 Zn	Flat, 0.040 in. (spring temper)	11.7×10^{11}	....	....	57.9×10^8	43.4×10^8†	3	....	R_B86	31.7×10^8	1
80 Cu, 20 Zn	Flat, 0.040 in. (G.S. 0.050 mm)	11.7×10^{11}	....	....	30.3×10^8	9.65×10^8†	50	....	R_F61	22.0×10^8	1
80 Cu, 20 Zn	Flat, 0.040 in. (spring temper)	11.0×10^{11}	....	....	62.7×10^8	44.8×10^8†	3	....	R_B91	33.1×10^8	1
70 Cu, 30 Zn	Flat, 0.040 in. (G.S. 0.070 mm)	11.0×10^{11}	....	....	31.7×10^8	9.65×10^8†	65	....	R_F58	22.0×10^8	1
70 Cu, 30 Zn	Flat, 0.040 in. (spring temper)	11.0×10^{11}	....	....	64.8×10^8	44.8×10^8†	3	....	R_B91	33.1×10^8	1
70 Cu, 30 Zn	Flat, 0.040 in. (extra spring temper)	11.0×10^{11}	....	....	68.2×10^8	44.8×10^8†	3	....	R_B93	....	1
65 Cu, 35 Zn	Flat, 0.040 in., ann.	10.3×10^{11}	....	....	33.8×10^8	11.7×10^8†	57	....	R_F68	23.4×10^8	1
65 Cu, 35 Zn	Flat, 0.040 in. (spring temper)	10.3×10^{11}	....	....	62.7×10^8	42.7×10^8†	3	....	R_B90	32.4×10^8	1
60 Cu, 40 Zn	Flat, 0.040 in., ann.	10.3×10^{11}	....	....	37.2×10^8	14.4×10^8†	45	....	R_F80	27.6×10^8	1
89 Cu, 9.25 Zn, 1.75 Pb	Rod, ann.	11.7×10^{11}	....	....	25.5×10^8	8.27×10^8†	45	70	R_F55	16.5×10^8	1
64.5 Cu, 35 Zn, 0.5 Pb	Flat specimen, ann.	10.3×10^{11}	....	....	33.8×10^8	11.7×10^8†	57	....	R_F68	23.4×10^8	1
67 Cu, 32.5 Zn, 0.5 Pb	Tubular specimen, ann.	10.3×10^{11}	....	....	32.4×10^8	10.3×10^8†	60	....	R_F64	....	1
64.5 Cu, 34.5 Zn, 1.0 Pb	Rolled, flat spec., ann.	10.3×10^{11}	....	....	33.8×10^8	11.7×10^8†	54	....	R_F68	23.4×10^8	1
62.5 Cu, 35.75 Zn, 1.75 Pb	Rolled, flat spec., ann.	10.3×10^{11}	....	....	33.8×10^8	11.7×10^8†	52	....	R_F68	23.4×10^8	1
62.5 Cu, 35 Zn, 2.5 Pb	Rolled, flat spec., ann.	9.65×10^{11}	....	....	33.8×10^8	11.7×10^8†	50	....	R_F68	21.4×10^8	1
61.5 Cu, 35.5 Zn, 3 Pb	Rod, ann.	9.65×10^{11}	....	....	33.8×10^8	12.4×10^8†	53	....	R_F68	20.7×10^8	1
60 Cu, 39.5 Zn, 0.5 Pb	H.R. 1-in. plate	10.3×10^{11}	....	....	37.2×10^8	13.8×10^8	45	....	R_F80	27.6×10^8	1
60.5 Cu, 38.4 Zn, 1.1 Pb	Light ann. 1.5-in. OD tubing	10.3×10^{11}	....	....	37.2×10^8	13.8×10^8	40	....	R_F80	....	1
60 Cu, 38 Zn, 2 Pb	Extruded 1-in. rod	10.3×10^{11}	....	....	35.8×10^8	13.8×10^8	45	....	R_F78	....	1
57 Cu, 40 Zn, 3 Pb	Extruded 1-in. section	9.65×10^{11}	....	....	41.3×10^8	13.8×10^8	30	....	R_B65	....	1
71 Cu, 28 Zn, 1 Sn	As H.R. (1-in. plate)	10.3×10^{11}	....	....	33.1×10^8	12.4×10^8†	65	....	R_F70	....	1
60 Cu, 39.25 Zn, 0.75 Sn	As H.R. (1-in. plate)	10.3×10^{11}	....	....	37.9×10^8	17.2×10^8†	50	....	R_B55	27.6×10^8	1

60 Cu, 37.5 Zn, 1.75 Pb, 0.75 Sn	1-in. rod, soft ann.	10.3×10^{11}	...	...	39.3×10^{8}	20.7×10^{8}†	40	...	R_B55	24.8×10^{8}	1
58.5 Cu, 39 Zn, 1.4 Fe, 1 Sn, 0.1 Mn	1-in. rod, soft ann.	10.3×10^{11}	...	...	44.8×10^{8}	20.7×10^{8}†	33	...	R_B65	28.9×10^{8}	1
95 Cu, 5 Sn	Ann., flat spec.	11.0×10^{11}	...	...	32.4×10^{8}	13.1×10^{8}	64	...	R_B26	...	1
92 Cu, 8 Sn	Ann., flat plate (0.040 in.)	11.0×10^{11}	...	...	37.9×10^{8}	...	70	...	R_F75	...	1
92 Cu, 8 Sn	Spring temper plate (0.040 in.)	11.0×10^{11}	...	...	77.2×10^{8}	...	3	...	R_B93	...	1
90 Cu, 10 Sn	Ann. flat plate (0.040 in.)	11.0×10^{11}	...	...	45.5×10^{8}	...	68	...	R_B55	...	1
90 Cu, 10 Sn	Spring, flat plate (0.040 in.)	11.0×10^{11}	...	...	84.1×10^{8}	...	4	...	R_B101	...	1
98.75 Cu, 1.25 Sn	Ann., flat plate (0.040 in.)	11.7×10^{11}	...	...	27.6×10^{8}	9.65×10^{8}	48	...	R_F60	...	1
98.75 Cu, 1.25 Sn	Spring, flat plate (0.040 in.)	11.7×10^{11}	...	...	51.7×10^{8}	...	4	...	R_B79	...	1
70 Cu, 30 Ni	H.R. 1-in. plate.	15.2×10^{11}	...	...	37.9×10^{8}	13.8×10^{8}	45	...	R_B35	...	1
65 Cu, 18 Ni, 17 Zn	Ann., flat plate (0.040 in.)	12.4×10^{11}	...	...	40.0×10^{8}	17.2×10^{8}	40	...	R_B40	...	1
55 Cu, 27 Zn, 18 Ni	Ann., flat plate (0.040 in.)	12.4×10^{11}	...	...	41.3×10^{8}	18.6×10^{8}	40	...	R_B55	...	1
55 Cu, 27 Zn, 18 Ni	Spring, flat plate (0.040 in.)	12.4×10^{11}	...	...	79.2×10^{8}	64.1×10^{8}	2.5	...	R_B99	...	1
Cu, 3 Si	Flat plate (0.040 in.) (G.S. 0.070 mm)	...	...	...	38.6×10^{8}	14.5×10^{8}†	63	...	R_B40	28.9×10^{8}	1
Cu, 3 Si	Flat plate (0.040 in.) spring	...	...	...	75.8×10^{8}	42.7×10^{8}†	4	...	R_B97	43.4×10^{8}	1
Cu, 1.5 Si	1-in. rod (G.S. 0.035 mm)	10.3×10^{11}	...	...	27.6×10^{8}	10.3×10^{8}†	50	...	R_F55	...	1
94.88 Cu, 5.02 Al, 0.04 Fe, 0.06 Zn	0.041-in. sheet, ann. at 500°C	...	...	...	41.5×10^{8}	17.6×10^{8}†	65.8	...	$R_B48.5$	...	1
94.88 Cu, 5.02 Al, 0.04 Fe, 0.06 Zn	0.041-in. sheet, C.R., 44% reduction	...	...	...	68.9×10^{8}	44.0×10^{8}†	8.0	...	$R_B93.5$	...	1
91.74 Cu, 8.10 Al, 0.04 Fe, 0.02 Ni, 0.10 Zn	0.020-in. sheet, ann. at 400°C	...	...	...	53.9×10^{8}	29.1×10^{8}†	41.8	...	...	...	1
91.74 Cu, 8.10 Al, 0.04 Fe, 0.02 Ni, 0.10 Zn	0.020-in. sheet, C.R., 37% reduction	...	...	...	62.7×10^{8}	45.3×10^{8}†	12.8	...	...	...	1
92.65 Cu, 7.35 Al	H.R.	...	...	...	43.4×10^{8}	...	73	...	134‡	...	1
92 Cu, 7 Al, 1 Ni	C.R., ann.	...	...	...	85.4×10^{8}	...	4.5	...	...	...	1
89.25 Cu, 9.25 Al, 0.6 Fe, 0.5 Ni	Ann., rod	...	...	...	55.1×10^{8}	27.6×10^{8}†	22	...	...	...	1
87.45 Cu, 5.62 Al, 6.93 Ni	H.R.	...	...	...	75.7×10^{8}	71.2×10^{8}	20	...	241‡	...	1
85.75 Cu, 10.75 Al, 3.50 Fe	Sand cast	...	...	...	62.0×10^{8}	25.5×10^{8}†	14	...	175§	...	1
81.3 Cu, 10.7 Al, 4.0 Fe, 4.0 Ni	Forged, ann. at 845°C	11.2×10^{11}	...	...	65.1×10^{8}	41.4×10^{8}	28.0	...	R_B90	...	1
Cu, 2 Be, 0.25 Co (or 0.35 Ni)	Solution treated, quenched	11.7×10^{11}	...	...	49.6×10^{8}	17.2×10^{8}¶	50	...	R_B60	...	1
88 Cu, 6 Sn, 1.5 Pb, 4.5 Zn	Sand cast 0.505-in. section	8.96×10^{11}	...	...	26.2×10^{8}	11.0×10^{8}†	35	35	66‡	...	1
87 Cu, 8 Sn, 1 Pb, 4 Zn	Sand cast 0.505-in. section	9.65×10^{11}	...	...	24.8×10^{8}	12.4×10^{8}†	30	...	68‡	...	1
85 Cu, 5 Sn, 9 Pb, 1 Zn	Sand cast 0.505-in. section	...	...	...	20.7×10^{8}	10.3×10^{8}†	15	16	60‡	...	1
83 Cu, 7 Sn, 7 Pb, 3 Zn	Sand cast 0.505-in. section	9.99×10^{11}	...	...	23.4×10^{8}	11.7×10^{8}†	20	18	60‡	...	1
80 Cu, 10 Sn, 10 Pb	Sand cast 0.505-in. section	7.58×10^{11}	...	...	22.0×10^{8}	11.7×10^{8}†	12	10.0	65‡	...	1
78 Cu, 7 Sn, 15 Pb	Sand cast	7.23×10^{11}	...	...	20.7×10^{8}	11.0×10^{8}†	15	15	55‡	...	1
70 Cu, 5 Sn, 25 Pb	Sand cast	6.89×10^{11}	...	...	14.5×10^{8}	...	10	8	48‡	...	1
85 Cu, 5 Sn, 5 Pb, 5 Zn	Sand cast	9.30×10^{11}	...	...	23.4×10^{8}	11.7×10^{8}†	25	25	60‡	...	1
83 Cu, 4 Sn, 6 Pb, 7 Zn	Sand cast	...	...	...	22.0×10^{8}	10.3×10^{8}†	24	20	55‡	...	1
81 Cu, 3 Sn, 7 Pb, 9 Zn	Sand cast	8.96×10^{11}	...	...	22.0×10^{8}	10.3×10^{8}†	22	20	55‡	...	1

See page 2–68 for footnotes.

TABLE 2f-9. ELASTIC AND STRENGTH CONSTANTS FOR COPPER ALLOYS (*Continued*)

Alloy	Condition	E	G	σ	Tensile strength	Yield strength	Elongation	Reduction in area	Bhn	Shear strength	Ref.*
76 Cu, 3 Sn, 6 Pb, 15 Zn	Sand cast	8.27×10^{11}	....	....	22.0×10^8	10.3×10^8†	30	30	55‡	....	1
71 Cu, 1 Sn, 3 Pb, 25 Zn	Sand cast 0.505-in. section	8.96×10^{11}	....	....	24.1×10^8	8.27×10^8†	35	30	48‡	....	1
66 Cu, 1 Sn, 3 Pb, 30 Zn	Sand cast 0.505-in. section	8.96×10^{11}	....	....	23.4×10^8	8.96×10^8†	35	30	50‡	....	1
60 Cu, 1 Sn, 1 Pb, 38 Zn	Sand cast	9.65×10^{11}	....	....	27.6×10^8	9.65×10^8†	25	25	65‡	....	1
62 Cu, 26 Zn, 3 Fe, 5.5 Al, 3.5 Mn	Sand cast	10.7×10^{11}	....	....	79.2×10^8	48.2×10^8†	15	15	210§	....	1
58 Cu, 39.25 Zn, 1.25 Fe, 1.25 Al, 0.25 Mn	Sand cast	10.3×10^{11}	....	....	48.2×10^8	19.3×10^8†	30	30	125‡	....	1
59 Cu, 0.75 Sn, 0.75 Pb, 37 Zn, 1.25 Fe, 0.75 Al, 0.5 Mn	Sand cast	10.3×10^{11}	....	....	44.8×10^8	20.7×10^8†	18	20	85‡	....	1
66 Cu, 5 Sn, 1.5 Pb, 2 Zn, 25 Ni	Sand cast	....	....	....	34.4×10^8	16.5×10^8†	15	15	130‡	....	1
64 Cu, 4 Sn, 4 Pb, 8 Zn, 20 Ni	Sand cast	....	....	....	27.6×10^8	17.2×10^8†	15	14	105‡	....	1
57 Cu, 2 Sn, 9 Pb, 20 Zn, 12 Ni	Sand cast	....	....	....	23.4×10^8	10.3×10^8†	20	20	60‡	....	1
60 Cu, 3 Sn, 5 Pb, 16 Zn, 16 Ni	Sand cast	....	....	....	26.2×10^8	11.7×10^8†	25	25	75‡	....	1
89 Cu, 1 Fe, 10 Al	Sand cast, cooled in sand	....	....	....	46.2×10^8	22.0×10^8†	15	15	140§	....	1
87.5 Cu, 3.5 Fe, 9 Al	Sand cast	11.7×10^{11}	....	....	51.7×10^8	18.6×10^8†	35	32	120§	....	1
86 Cu, 4 Fe, 10 Al	Sand cast, cooled in sand	12.4×10^{11}	....	....	51.7×10^8	24.1×10^8†	18	15	155§	....	1
79 Cu, 5 Fe, 11 Al, 5 Ni	Sand cast	11.7×10^{11}	....	....	65.5×10^8	31.0×10^8†	7	7	195§	....	1

* References are on p. 2–78.
† At 0.5% extension.
‡ 10-mm ball, 500-kg load.
¶ At 0.01% offset.
§ 10-mm ball, 3,000-kg load.

The yield strength is conventionally determined in either of two ways. In the first method, a specimen of the material is repeatedly loaded and unloaded with the load being increased at each cycle, the process being continued until a specified permanent set is obtained after one of the unloadings. The stress which produces this specified permanent set is called the yield strength.

In the second method, known as the offset method, a load-elongation curve is determined experimentally, the elongation being measured in units of extension per unit length of the undeformed specimen. A straight line is then drawn having a slope equal to the initial slope of the load-elongation curve and an intercept on the elongation axis equal to the specified offset, which is usually given in units of per cent elongation. The yield strength is taken to be that load defined by the interaction of the added straight line with the load-elongation curve.

Further discussion of yield strength can be found in ASTM E6-36.

3. *Yield Point.*[1] The stress at which a marked increase in deformation takes place without increase in the load.

4. *Shear Strength.*[2] "The stress, usually expressed in pounds per square inch, required to produce fracture when impressed perpendicularly upon the cross-section of a material."

5. *Elongation.*[3] "In tensile testing the elongation of a specimen is the increase in gage length, after rupture, referred to the original gage length. It is reported as percentage elongation."

6. *Reduction in Area.*[3] "In tensile testing the reduction in area of a specimen is the ratio of the difference between the original cross-sectional area of the specimen and the cross-sectional area after rupture, to the original cross-sectional area. It is reported as the percentage reduction of area."

7. *Rockwell Hardness Number.*[2] "A hardness value indicated on a direct-reading dial when a designated load is imposed on a metallic material in the Rockwell hardness testing machine using a steel ball or a diamond penetrator. The value must be qualified by reference to the load and penetrator used. Several scales are in common use: Rockwell A hardness is determined with a minor load of 10 kg and a major load of 60 kg using the diamond cone (brale); Rockwell B hardness is determined with a minor load of 10 kg and a major load of 100 kg using a $\frac{1}{16}$-in. steel ball; Rockwell C hardness is determined with a minor load of 10 kg and a major load of 150 kg using the diamond cone"; Rockwell D hardness is determined with a minor load of 10 kg and a major load of 100 kg using a diamond cone indenter; Rockwell E hardness is determined with a minor load of 10 kg and a major load of 100 kg using a $\frac{1}{8}$-in. steel ball indenter; Rockwell F hardness is determined with a minor load of 10 kg and a major load of 60 kg using a $\frac{1}{16}$-in. steel ball; Rockwell G hardness is determined with a minor load of 10 kg and a major load of 150 kg, using a $\frac{1}{16}$-in. steel ball indenter.

A second set of Rockwell hardness numbers are the Rockwell superficial hardness numbers. One of these is the Rockwell 15T hardness which is determined with a minor load of 3 kg and a major load of 15 kg, using a $\frac{1}{16}$-in. steel ball.

Note: The methods of determining the hardness values can be found in Standard Methods of Test for Rockwell Hardness and Rockwell Superficial Hardness of Metallic Materials, ASTM E18-42.

8. *Brinell Hardness Number.*[4] "A hard spherical indenter of diameter D mm is pressed into the metal surface under a load W kg and the mean chordal diameter of the*

[1] "Metals Handbook," 1948 ed., American Society for Metals.
[2] J. G. Henderson, "Metallurgical Dictionary."
[3] *Natl. Bur. Standards (U.S.) Circ.* C447.
[4] D. Tabor, "The Hardness of Metals."
* Continued on p. **2**-78.

TABLE 2f-10. ELASTIC AND STRENGTH CONSTANTS FOR IRON AND STEEL ALLOYS

% C	Alloy	Condition	E	G	σ	Tensile strength	Yield strength	Elongation	Reduction in area	Bhn	Shear strength	Ref.*
	Iron:											
	2.50 C, 0.79 Si, 0.09 S, 0.04 P	Cast	13.8×10^{11}	....	.....	32.8×10^{8}	....	....	....	266	30.7×10^{8}	2
	3.52 C, 2.55 Si, 1.01 Mn, 0.215 P, 0.086 S	⅞-in. cast, ann. bar	12.1×10^{11}	5.10×10^{11}	.....	23.5×10^{8}	....	....	....	163	30.2×10^{8}	2
	3.52 C, 2.55 Si, 1.01 Mn, 0.215 P, 0.086 S	2-in. bar	8.27×10^{11}	43.4×10^{11}	.....	15.5×10^{8}	....	....	....	164	25.1×10^{8}	2
	1.15–2.30 C, 0.85–1.20 Si, 0.40 Mn, 0.020 P, 0.012 S	Malleable, cast, ann.	17.2×10^{11}	8.61×10^{11}	0.17	39.3×10^{8}	25.8×10^{8}†	22	....	111–145	33.1×10^{8}	2
	2.25–2.70 C, 0.80–1.10 Si	....	17.2×10^{11}	8.61×10^{11}	0.17	34.4×10^{8}	22.4×10^{8}†	14	....	....	33.1×10^{8}	2
	Steel:											
0.03	0.12 Mn, 0.005 Si, 0.45 Cu, 0.07 Mo	H.R. at 540°C	....	....	.....	34.3×10^{8}	24.0×10^{8}†	35.8	65	....	....	12
0.02	0.5 Cu	As normalized	....	....	.....	34×10^{8}	27×10^{8}‡	46	78	....	....	1
0.02	1.0 Cu	As normalized	....	....	.....	39×10^{8}	31×10^{8}‡	41	73	....	....	1
0.02	1.5 Cu	As normalized	....	....	.....	48×10^{8}	43×10^{8}‡	36	70	....	....	1
0.02	2.0 Cu	As normalized	....	....	.....	55×10^{8}	50×10^{8}‡	31	67	....	....	1
0.02	2.5 Cu	As normalized	....	....	.....	56×10^{8}	52×10^{8}‡	27	66	....	....	1
0.02	3.0 Cu	As normalized	....	....	.....	56×10^{8}	52×10^{8}‡	26	65	....	....	1
0.05	0.39 Si, 0.25 Mn, 0.014 P, 0.049 S	As rolled	....	....	.....	40.0×10^{8}	27.9×10^{8}‡	29.5¶	72	117	....	1
0.07	1.17 Si, 0.32 Mn, 0.013 P, 0.034 S	As rolled	....	....	.....	46.5×10^{8}	32.7×10^{8}‡	29.5¶	71.5	130	....	1
0.05	1.73 Si, 0.35 Mn, 0.014 P, 0.030 S	As rolled	....	....	.....	50.0×10^{8}	37.6×10^{8}‡	29.5¶	64	140	....	1
0.06	2.39 Si, 0.16 Mn, 0.010 P, 0.016 S	As rolled	....	....	.....	52.7×10^{8}	36.9×10^{8}‡	24.5¶	53.5	181	....	1
0.054	0.42 Mn, 0.025 Si, 0.031 Al, 0.265 Ti	H.R., 5% strained, aged	....	....	.....	48.9×10^{8}	46.9×10^{8}‡	11.9§	67.0	....	....	13
0.025	0.30 Mn, 0.010 P, 0.023 S, 0.09 Ni, 0.09 Cu, 0.26 V	Annealed	....	....	.....	29.2×10^{8}	15.8×10^{8}‡	28.1	....	....	....	1
0.08	1.01 Cr, 0.41 Cu, 0.80 Si, 27 Mn, 0.145 P, 0.020 S	H.R. ¾-in. bar	20.7×10^{11}	8.20×10^{11}	.....	54.0×10^{8}	41.3×10^{8}‖	40	72	156	....	2
0.07	18.95 Cr, 7.69 Ni	C.R. ⅜-in. bar	17.2×10^{11}	....	.....	98.5×10^{8}	....	21††	....	302	....	2
0.03	13.47 Cr, 0.27 V, 0.04 P, 0.01 S	H.R. 3⅜-in. bar	18.2×10^{11}	8.54×10^{11}	.....	56.8×10^{8}	....	16§	26	175	47.2×10^{8}	2
0.08	1.07 Cu, 0.54 Ni, 0.43 Mn, 0.16 Si, 0.104 P, 0.022 S	H.R. ¾-in. bar	20.5×10^{11}	7.92×10^{11}	.....	48.8×10^{8}	38.7×10^{8}**	38	69	145	....	2
0.08	1.46 Si, 0.102 Mn	W.Q. from 1830°F	20.9×10^{11}	....	.....	63.7×10^{8}	47.1×10^{8}**	16	....	....	....	2
0.10	0.45 Mn, 3.71 Ni, 0.10 S	A.C. from 1550°F	....	....	.....	60.4×10^{8}	34.4×10^{8}†	37	72	138	....	4
0.10	0.5 Cr, 0.3 Mo, 2.5 Ni	O.Q. from 820°C (carburized)	....	....	.....	93.1×10^{8}	78.4×10^{8}†	13‡‡	....	....	....	5
0.10	0.6 Cr, 0.3 Mo, 3.3 Ni	O.Q. from 820°C (carburized)	....	....	.....	122×10^{8}	108×10^{8}†	10‡‡	....	....	....	5
0.10	0.07 Si, 0.69 Mn, 0.092 P, 0.027 S, 0.16 Al, 1.09 Cu, 0.15 Mo, 0.63 Ni	H.R. 4 hr at 540°C	....	....	.....	52.8×10^{8}	39.2×10^{8}†	45.8	....	....	....	6
0.11	0.6 Mn, 1.4 Cr, 0.17 Mo, 1.0 Ni	W.Q. from 900°C (carburized)	....	....	.....	85.8×10^{8}	60.8×10^{8}†	12.8¶¶	....	....	....	5
0.12	0.84 Mn, 0.12 S, 0.099 P, 0.01 Si	1⅛-in. diam C.R. bar	20.9×10^{11}	....	.....	57.4×10^{8}	52.4×10^{8}	18	52	Vhn 205	....	2
0.15	0.75 Mn, 0.30 Si, 1.75 Ni, 0.25 Mo	Cast	....	....	.....	68.9×10^{8}	44.8×10^{8}†	20.0	35.0	200	....	7
0.15	0.75 Mn, 0.30 Si, 3.50 Ni	Cast	....	....	.....	68.9×10^{8}	44.8×10^{8}†	20.0	35.0	200	....	7
0.16	0.4 Mn, 1.2 Cr, 0.25 Mo, 4.1 Ni	O.Q. from 780 to 180°	....	....	.....	135×10^{8}	120×10^{8}†	15.8	50.0	....	....	8
0.15	13.50 Cr, 0.11 Si	O.Q. from 1740°F, T at 1110°F	21.6×10^{11}	....	.....	90.9×10^{8}	75.8×10^{8}	21	63	85	....	2
0.17	0.5 Mn, 0.25 Mo, 1.8 Ni	P.(O.Q.)(carburized)	....	....	.....	83.8×10^{8}	66.8×10^{8}†	21.2	52.1	....	....	9
0.18	0.55 Mn, 0.25 Si	....	....	....	.....	45×10^{8}	25×10^{8}†	32.0	53.0	130	....	7
0.18	2.50 Cr, 0.55 Mn, 0.40 Si, 0.40 Mo, 0.20 V	Cast	....	....	.....	96.5×10^{8}	82.7×10^{8}†	15.0	50.0	....	....	7
0.18	0.92 Mn, 0.115 P, 0.12 S, 0.02 Si	C.R.	20.5×10^{11}	....	.....	67.6×10^{8}	45.5×10^{8}	15	46	....	....	2
0.20	16.17 Cr, 1.06 Mn, 0.30 Si	O.Q. from 1740°F, T at 840°F	22.6×10^{11}	....	.....	130×10^{8}	61.2×10^{8}	10	....	357	....	2

0.19	1.35 Mn, 0.10 S	W.Q. from 1550°F	...	...	...	89.6×10^8†	60.8×10^8	16	44	251	...	4
0.20	0.45 Cr, 1.19 Mn, 0.67 Si, 0.033 P, 0.019 S	Rolled	20.9×10^{11}	82.0×10^{11}	0.276	59.0×10^8	37.4×10^8	30	...	156	58.0×10^8	2
0.25	0.45 Mn, 0.40 S, 0.03 Si, 0.012 P	Rolled, ¾-in. plate	20.4×10^{11}	...	0.306	43.5×10^8	22.3×10^8	40	70	122	...	2
0.25	to 0.35	...	20.3×10^{11}	78.5×10^{11}	0.297	...	...	...	...	...	...	2
0.15	to 0.25; 0.3–0.6 Mn, 0.045 P, 0.05 S	H.R.	20.53×10^{11}	78.06×10^{11}	0.313	...	...	...	...	...	...	10
0.15	to 0.25; 0.3–0.6 Mn, 0.045 P, 0.05 S	C.R.	20.12×10^{11}	78.20×10^{11}	0.286	...	...	...	...	...	...	10
0.27	0.72 Mn, 0.21 Si, 0.024 S, 0.014 P	Wr., ann. at 1450°F, F.C.	18.9×10^{11}	81.3×10^{11}	0.316	46.4×10^8	25.8×10^8	46	64	153	52.3×10^8	2
0.27	0.72 Mn, 0.21 Si, 0.024 S, 0.014 P	Wr. W.Q. from 1600°F, T at 1100°F	20.4×10^{11}	82.7×10^{11}	0.310	62.8×10^8	37.9×10^8	42	70	191	...	2
0.19	0.85 Mn, 0.05 (max) S, 0.045 (max) P	H.R. (trans. prop.)	...	...	...	42.6×10^8	22.5×10^8	36.0	53.7	...	...	1
0.19	0.85 Mn, 0.05 (max) S, 0.045 (max) P	H.R. (long. prop.)	...	...	...	44.1×10^8	25.0×10^8	43.5§§	66.5	...	...	1
0.10	0.75 Mn, 0.20 S, 0.10 P	H.R. (trans. prop.)	...	...	...	43.1×10^8	24.7×10^8	22.6§§	24.5	...	...	1
0.10	0.75 Mn, 0.20 S, 0.10 P	H.R. (long. prop.)	...	...	...	46.1×10^8	27.5×10^8	37.5§§	60.5	...	...	1
0.30	0.70 Mn, 3.5 Ni	Ann.	...	...	...	54.7×10^8	39.3×10^8	31.5	57.2	...	...	1
0.34	0.88 Mn, 0.35 Si, 0.035 S, 0.019 P	Rolled ¾-in. plate	20.5×10^{11}	...	0.291	59.5×10^8	24.1×10^8‖‖	33	58	168	...	2
0.38	0.65 Mn, 0.22 Si	Wr., ann. at 1450°F; F.C.	19.8×10^{11}	8.06×10^{11}	0.287	52.2×10^8	28.6×10^8‖‖	44	56	146	55.0×10^8	2
0.91	0.38 Mn, 0.16 Si, 0.036 P	O.Q. from 1575°F, T at 940°F	20.8×10^{11}	7.44×10^{11}	...	155×10^8	99.2×10^8‖‖	7	...	444	...	2
1.04	0.36 Mn, 0.16 Si, 0.018 S, 0.015 P	⅓ hr at 1550°F, O.Q. from 120°F, T ½ hr at 800°F	20.5×10^{11}	7.44×10^{11}	...	163×10^8	99.2×10^8‖‖	5	...	...	...	2
0.37	0.50 Cr, 1.14 Mn, 0.84 Si, 0.033 S, 0.021 P	H.R. ¾-in. bar	21×10^{11}	...	...	86.1×10^8	55.6×10^8‖	23	58	255	...	2
0.60	0.56 Cr, 0.62 Mn, 0.26 Si	O.Q. from 1470°F, T at 750°F	21.1×10^{11}	8.27×10^{11}	...	164×10^8	...	2.5§	2.0	469	...	2
0.45	1.14 Cr, 0.69 Mn, 0.12 Si	N at 1525°F	21×10^{11}	...	...	83.4×10^8	61.7×10^8	12§	50	250	...	2
0.33	0.78 Cr, 0.24 Mo, 0.54 Mn, 0.21 Si, 0.025 P, 0.029 S	W., F.C. from 1450°F	19.7×10^{11}	8.27×10^{11}	0.288	52.8×10^8	29.3×10^8	48	66	170	60.2×10^8	2
0.33	0.78 Cr, 0.24 Mo, 0.54 Mn, 0.21 Si, 0.025 P, 0.029 S	Wr., O.Q. from 1600°F, T at 1100°F	19.8×10^{11}	8.13×10^{11}	0.272	86.8×10^8	62.4×10^8	28	60	229	78.5×10^8	2
0.34	0.46 Mn, 21.39 Cr, 10.95 Ni, 3.16 W, 1.39 Si	A.C. from 1740°F	20.1×10^{11}	...	...	88.2×10^8	30.9×10^8***	25	35	269	...	2
0.37	1.18 Cr, 0.16 V, 0.71 Mn, 0.33 Si, 0.037 S, 0.024 P	Wr., F.C. from 1450°F	20.3×10^{11}	8.13×10^{11}	0.289	61.1×10^8	33.9×10^8	42	62	179	61.7×10^8	2
0.31	1.66 Mn, 0.25 Si, 0.024 S, 0.015 P	Wr. F.C. from 1450°F	19.2×10^{11}	8.27×10^{11}	0.295	58.5×10^8	29.8×10^8	42	54	169	58.1×10^8	2
0.43	3.47 Ni, 0.64 Mn, 0.20 Si, 0.023 S, 0.015 P	Wr. F.C. from 1450°F	21×10^{11}	8.34×10^{11}	0.308	65.0×10^8	36.5×10^8	33	45	187	60×10^8	2
0.40	1.65 Ni, 0.99 Cr, 0.51 Mn, 0.20 Si, 0.028 S, 0.019 P	Wr., F.C. from 1450°F	19.8×10^{11}	7.78×10^{11}	0.299	61.9×10^8	30.2×10^8	40	54	170	62.4×10^8	2
0.32	1.92 Ni, 0.86 Cr, 0.30 Mo, 0.60 Mn, 0.16 Si, 0.019 S, 0.014 P	Wr., F.C. from 1450°F	19.8×10^{11}	7.92×10^{11}	0.288	66.2×10^8	34.2×10^8	37	58	202	66.0×10^8	2
0.32	2.42 Ni, 0.49 Cr, 0.38 Mo, 0.88 Mn, 0.23 Si, 0.13 Cu, 0.04 S, 0.03 P	Cast ann. at 1575°F, 6-in. bar, T at 1200°F	20.2×10^{11}	7.92×10^{11}	...	81.3×10^8	67.5×10^8	10†††	16	260	72.3×10^8	2
1.27	12.69 Mn, 0.12 Si	W.Q. from 1830°F	...	...	...	102×10^8	53.2×10^8	44	49	...	...	1
0.78	0.10 Mn	Ann. at 1472°F	...	...	...	68.2×10^8	65.4×10^8	12	35	...	...	1

* References are on p. 2–78.
† At yield point.
‡ At 0.2% offset.
¶ % in 70 mm.
§ % in 8 in.
‖ At 0.005% permanent set.
** At 0.05% permanent set.
†† % in 1.5 in.
‡‡ % in 3.94 in.
¶¶ % in 1.97 in.
§§ % in 0.75 in.
‖‖ At 0.001% permanent set.
*** At 0.1% offset.
††† % in $4/\sqrt{\text{area}}$.

TABLE 2f-11. ELASTIC AND STRENGTH CONSTANTS FOR LEAD AND LEAD ALLOYS

Alloy	Condition	E	σ	Tensile strength	Yield strength at 0.5% offset	Elongation, % in 2 in.	Reduction in area	Bhn	Shear strength	Ref.*
99.90 Pb	Rolled, aged			1.77×10^8	0.95×10^8	22		R_B75		1
99.73 Pb	Sand cast	1.38×10^{11}		$1.1–1.3 \times 10^8$	0.55×10^8	30	100	3.2–4.5	1.2×10^8	1
99.73 Pb	Chill cast		0.40–0.45	1.4×10^8		47	100	4.2		1
0.023–0.033 Ca, 0.02–0.1 Cu, 0.002–0.02 Ag	Extruded			2.1×10^8		40				1
1 Sb	Extruded and aged	1.38×10^{11}		2.1×10^8		50		7		1
4 Sb	Rolled, 95% reduction			2.77×10^8		48.3		8.1		1
6 Sb	Chill cast			4.71×10^8		24		13.0		1
6 Sb	Extruded			2.27×10^8		65		10.7		1
6 Sb	Cold rolled, 95% reduction			2.82×10^8		47				1
8 Sb	Rolled, 95% reduction			3.20×10^8		31.3		9.5†		1
9 Sb	Chill cast			5.2×10^8		17		15.4		1
4.5–5.5 Sn				2.3×10^8	1.0×10^8	50	80	8		1
20 Sn				4.0×10^8	2.51×10^8	16	50	11.3		1
50 Sn				4.2×10^8	3.3×10^8	60	70	14.5	4.04×10^8	1
4.50–5.50 Sn, 9.25–10.75 Sb	Chill cast	2.89×10^{11}		6.9×10^8		5		19		1
4.50 + 5.50 Sn, 14–16 Sb	Chill cast	2.89×10^{11}		6.9×10^8		5		20		1
9.3–10.7 Sn, 14–16 Sb	Cast	2.89×10^{11}		7.2×10^8		4		22		1
0.75–1.25 Sn, 0.8–1.4 As, 14.5–17.5 Sb	Chill cast	2.89×10^{11}		7.1×10^8		2		20		1
0.6–1.0 Sn, 1.5–3.0 As, 12.0–13.5 Sb	Chill cast	2.89×10^{11}		6.8×10^8		1.5		22		1

* References are on p. 2-78.
† 1/16-in. ball, 9.85-kg load for 30 sec.

TABLE 2f-12. ELASTIC AND STRENGTH CONSTANTS FOR MAGNESIUM ALLOYS

Alloy	Condition	E	G	σ	Tensile strength	Yield strength at 0.2% offset	Elongation, % in 2 in.	Bhn	Shear strength	Ref.*
99.9+ Mg		4.48×10^{11}	1.67×10^{11}	0.35						
8.3–9.7 Al, 0.10 Mn, 1.7–2.3 Zn, ≤0.3 Si, ≤0.05 Cu, ≤0.01 Ni, 0.3 other	Sand and permanent cast molds, as fabricated	4.48×10^{11}	1.67×10^{11}	0.35	16.5×10^8	9.65×10^8	2	65	13.1×10^8	14
8.3–9.7 Al, 0.10 Mn, 1.7–2.3 Zn, ≤0.3 Si, ≤0.05 Cu, ≤0.01 Ni, 0.3 other	Sand and permanent cast molds, cast and stabilized	4.48×10^{11}	1.67×10^{11}	0.35	16.5×10^8	9.65×10^8	2	..	13.1×10^8	14
8.3–9.7 Al, 0.10 Mn, 1.7–2.3 Zn, ≤0.3 Si, ≤0.05 Cu, ≤0.01 Ni, 0.3 other	Sand and permanent cast, solution h-t	4.48×10^{11}	1.67×10^{11}	0.35	27.6×10^8	9.65×10^8	10	63	13.8×10^8	14
5.3–6.7 Al, ≥0.15 Mn, 2.5–3.5 Zn, ≤0.3 Si, ≤0.05 Cu, ≤0.01 Ni, 0.3 other	Sand and permanent cast molds, as fabricated	4.48×10^{11}	1.67×10^{11}	0.35	20.0×10^8	9.65×10^8	6	50	12.4×10^8	14
5.3–6.7 Al, ≥0.15 Mn, 2.5–3.5 Zn, ≤0.3 Si, ≤0.05 Cu, ≤0.01 Ni, 0.3 other	Sand and permanent cast molds, cast and stabilized	4.48×10^{11}	1.67×10^{11}	0.35	20.0×10^8	9.65×10^8	5	..	13.1×10^8	14
5.3–6.7 Al, ≥0.15 Mn, 2.5–3.5 Zn, ≤0.3 Si, ≤0.05 Cu, ≤0.01 Ni, 0.3 other	Sand and permanent cast molds, solution h-t	4.48×10^{11}	1.67×10^{11}	0.35	27.6×10^8	9.65×10^8	12	55	13.1×10^8	14
8.3–9.7 Al, ≥0.13 Mn, 0.4–1.0 Zn, ≤0.5 Si, ≤0.10 Cu, ≤0.01 Ni, 0.3 other	Sand and permanent cast molds, as fabricated	4.48×10^{11}	1.67×10^{11}	0.35	16.5×10^8	9.65×10^8	2	52	....	14
8.3–9.7 Al, ≥0.13 Mn, 0.4–1.0 Zn, ≤0.5 Si, ≤0.10 Cu, ≤0.01 Ni, 0.3 other	Sand and permanent cast molds, solution h-t	4.48×10^{11}	1.67×10^{11}	0.35	27.6×10^8	9.65×10^8	11	53	....	14
8.3–9.7 Al, ≥0.13 Mn, 0.4–1.0 Zn, ≤0.5 Si, ≤0.10 Cu, ≤0.01 Ni, 0.3 other	Sand and permanent cast, solution h-t, aged	4.48×10^{11}	1.67×10^{11}	0.35	27.6×10^8	13.1×10^8	4	66	....	14
8.3–9.7 Al, ≥0.13 Mn, 0.4–1.0 Zn, ≤0.5 Si, 0.10 Cu, ≤0.01 Ni, 0.3 other	Die cast, as fabricated	4.48×10^{11}	1.67×10^{11}	0.35	22.7×10^8	15.2×10^8	3	60	13.8×10^8	14
8.3–9.7 Al, ≥0.10 Mn, 0.4–1.0 Zn, ≤0.5 Si, ≤0.3 Cu, ≤0.01 Ni, 0.3 other	Die cast, as fabricated	4.48×10^{11}	1.67×10^{11}	0.35	22.7×10^8	15.2×10^8	3	60	13.8×10^8	14
2.5–3.5 Al, ≥0.20 Mn, 0.6–1.4 Zn, 0.08–0.30 Ca, ≤0.3 Si, ≤0.05 Cu, ≤0.005 Fe, ≤0.005 Ni, 0.3 other	Sheet, ann.	4.48×10^{11}	1.67×10^{11}	0.35	25.5×10^8	15.2×10^8	21	56	14.5×10^8	14
2.5–3.5 Al, ≥0.20 Mn, 0.6–1.4 Zn, 0.08–0.30 Ca, ≤0.3 Si, ≤0.05 Cu, ≤0.005 Fe, ≤0.005 Ni, 0.3 other	Sheet, hard rolled	4.48×10^{11}	1.67×10^{11}	0.35	28.9×10^8	22.0×10^8	16	73	15.8×10^8	14

TABLE 2f-12. ELASTIC AND STRENGTH CONSTANTS FOR MAGNESIUM ALLOYS (*Continued*)

Alloy	Condition	E	G	σ	Tensile strength	Yield strength at 0.2% offset	Elongation, % in 2 in.	Bhn	Shear strength	Ref.*
2.5–3.5 Al, ≥0.20 Mn, 0.6–1.4 Zn, 0.08–0.30 Ca, ≤0.3 Si, ≤0.05 Cu, ≤0.005 Fe, ≤0.005 Ni, 0.3 other	Sheet, as fabricated	4.48×10^{11}	1.67×10^{11}	0.35	25.5×10^8	15.2×10^8	21	..	14.5×10^8	14
≥1.20 Mn, 0.08–0.14 Ca, ≤0.3 Si, ≤0.05 Cu, ≤0.01 Ni, 0.3 other	Sheet, ann.	4.48×10^{11}	1.67×10^{11}	0.35	22.7×10^8	12.4×10^8	16	48	12.4×10^8	14
≥1.20 Mn, 0.08–0.14 Ca, ≤0.3 Si, ≤0.05 Cu, ≤0.01 Ni, 0.3 other	Sheet, hard rolled	4.48×10^{11}	1.67×10^{11}	0.35	25.5×10^8	19.3×10^8	7	56	11.7×10^8	14
≤1.20 Mn, 0.08–0.14 Ca, ≤0.3 Si, ≤0.05 Cu, ≤0.01 Ni, ≤0.3 other	Sheet, as fabricated	4.48×10^{11}	1.67×10^{11}	0.35	22.7×10^8	....	..	..	....	14
5.8–7.2 Al, 0.15 Mn, 0.4–1.5 Zn, ≤0.3 Si, ≤0.05 Cu, ≤0.005 Ni, ≤0.005 Fe, +0.3 other	Extruded bars, rods, or shapes, as fabricated	4.48×10^{11}	1.67×10^{11}	0.35	30.3×10^8	20.7×10^8	14	60	13.1×10^8	14
7.8–9.2 Al, ≥0.15 Mn, 0.2–0.8 Zn, ≤0.3 Si, ≤0.05 Cu, ≤0.005 Ni, ≤0.005 Fe, 0.3 other	Extruded bars, rods, or shapes, as fabricated	4.48×10^{11}	1.67×10^{11}	0.35	33.1×10^8	22.0×10^8	12	60	15.2×10^8	14
7.8–9.2 Al, ≥0.15 Mn, 0.2–0.8 Zn, ≤0.3 Si, ≤0.05 Cu, ≤0.005 Ni, ≤0.005 Fe, 0.3 other	Extruded bars, rods, or shapes, aged	4.48×10^{11}	1.67×10^{11}	0.35	35.8×10^8	24.8×10^8	5	82	16.5×10^8	14
≥0.06 Mn, 4.3–6.2 Zn, ≥0.45 Zr, 0.3 other	Extruded bars, rods, or shapes, as fabricated	4.48×10^{11}	1.67×10^{11}	0.35	33.8×10^8	26.2×10^8	12	75	16.5×10^8	14
≥0.06 Mn, 4.3–6.2 Zn, ≥0.45 Zr, 0.3 other	Extruded bars, rods, or shapes, aged	4.48×10^{11}	1.67×10^{11}	0.35	35.1×10^8	28.9×10^8	10	82	17.2×10^8	14

* References are on p. 2-78.

TABLE 2f-13. ELASTIC AND STRENGTH CONSTANTS FOR NICKEL AND NICKEL ALLOYS

Alloy	Condition	*E*	*G*	Tensile strength	Yield strength at 0.2% offset	Elongation	Reduction in area	Bhn	Shear strength	Ref.*
63–70 Ni, ≤2.5 Fe, ≤2.0 Mn, remainder Cu	Wr., ann.	....	....	51.7 × 10⁸	24.1 × 10⁸	40	.....	125	34–44 × 10⁸	15
63–70 Ni, ≤2.5 Fe, ≤2.0 Mn, remainder Cu	Wr., H.R.	17.9 × 10¹¹	....	62.0 × 10⁸	34.4 × 10⁸	35	.....	150	34–44 × 10⁸	15
63–70 Ni, ≤2.5 Fe, ≤2.0 Mn, remainder Cu	Wr., cold drawn	....	....	68.9 × 10⁸	55.1 × 10⁸	25	.....	190	34–44 × 10⁸	15
63–70 Ni, ≤2.5 Fe, ≤2.0 Mn, remainder Cu	Wr., C.R. (hard temper)	....	....	75.8 × 10⁸	68.9 × 10⁸	5	.....	240	34–44 × 10⁸	15
63–70 Ni, 2.0–4.0 Al, 0.25–1.0 Ti, remainder Cu	H.R.	18 × 10¹¹	0.32	68.9 × 10⁸	31.0 × 10⁸	40	.....	160	....	15
63–70 Ni, 2.0–4.0 Al, 0.25–1.0 Ti, remainder Cu	H.R., age hardened	18 × 10¹¹	....	103 × 10⁸	75.8 × 10⁸	25	.....	280	....	15
63–70 Ni, 2.0–4.0 Al, 0.25–1.0 Ti, remainder Cu	Cold drawn	18 × 10¹¹	....	79.2 × 10⁸	58.6 × 10⁸	25	.....	210	....	15
63–70 Ni, 2.0–4.0 Al, 0.25–1.0 Ti, remainder Cu	Cold drawn, age hardened	18 × 10¹¹	....	107 × 10⁸	79.2 × 10⁸	20	.....	290	....	15
≥99.0 Ni, ≤0.15 C, ≤0.35 Mn, ≤0.40 Fe	Wr., ann.	21 × 10¹¹	0.31	48.2 × 10⁸	13.8 × 10⁸	40	.....	100	36 × 10⁸	15
≥99.0 Ni, ≤0.15 C, ≤0.35 Mn, ≤0.40 Fe	Wr., H.R.	....	....	51.7 × 10⁸	17.2 × 10⁸	40	.....	110	....	15
≥99.0 Ni, ≤0.15 C, ≤0.35 Mn, ≤0.40 Fe	Wr., cold drawn	....	....	65.4 × 10⁸	48.2 × 10⁸	25	.....	170	....	15
≥99.0 Ni, ≤0.15 C, ≤0.35 Mn, ≤0.40 Fe	Wr., cold rolled (hard temper)	....	....	72.3 × 10⁸	65.4 × 10⁸	5	.....	210	....	15
≥99.0 Ni, ≤0.02 C	Ann.	21 × 10¹¹	0.31	41.3 × 10⁸	10.3 × 10⁸	50	.....	90	....	15
≥93.0 Ni, 4.00–4.75 Al, 0.25–1.0 Ti, ≤0.30 C	H.R.	21 × 10¹¹	0.31	72.3 × 10⁸	34.4 × 10⁸	35	.....	180	....	15
≥93.0 Ni, 4.00–4.75 Al, 0.25–1.0 Ti, ≤0.30 C	H.R., age hardened	....	....	117 × 10⁸	89.6 × 10⁸	15	.....	320	....	15
≥93.0 Ni, 4.00–4.75 Al, 0.25–1.0 Ti, ≤0.30 C	Cold drawn	....	....	82.7 × 10⁸	62.0 × 10⁸	25	.....	220	....	15
≥93.0 Ni, 4.00–4.75 Al, 0.25–1.0 Ti, ≤0.30 C	Cold drawn, age hardened	....	....	121 × 10⁸	93.0 × 10⁸	15	.....	340	....	15

* References are on page 2–78.

TABLE 2f-13. ELASTIC AND STRENGTH CONSTANTS FOR NICKEL AND NICKEL ALLOYS (*Continued*)

Alloy	Condition	E	G	Tensile strength	Yield strength at 0.2% offset	Elongation	Reduction in area	Bhn	Shear strength	Ref.*
≥72.0 Ni, 14.0–17.0 Cr, 6.0–10.0 Fe, ≤0.15 C	Wr., ann.	....	....	58.6×10^{8}	24.1×10^{8}	45	.....	150	....	15
≥72.0 Ni, 14.0–17.0 Cr, 6.0–10.0 Fe, ≤0.15 C	Wr., H.R.	....	....	68.9×10^{8}	41.3×10^{8}	35	.....	180	....	15
≥72.0 Ni, 14.0–17.0 Cr, 6.0–10.0 Fe, ≤0.15 C	Wr., cold drawn	....	....	79.2×10^{8}	62.0×10^{8}	20	.....	200	....	15
≥72.0 Ni, 14.0–17.0 Cr, 6.0–10.0 Fe, ≤0.15 C	Wr., C.R. (hard temper)	....	....	93.0×10^{8}	75.8×10^{8}	5	.....	260	....	15
≤70.0 Ni, 14.0–16.0 Cr, 5.0–9.0 Fe, 2.25–2.75 Ti, 0.4–1.0 Al, 0.7–1.2 Cb (+Ta)	Ann.	21×10^{11}	....	79.2×10^{8}	34.4×10^{8}	50	.....	200	....	15
≥70.0 Ni, 14.0–16.0 Cr, 5.0–9.0 Fe, 2.25–2.75 Ti, 0.4–1.0 Al, 0.7–1.2 Cb (+Ta)	H.R., age hardened	21×10^{11}	....	124×10^{8}	82.7×10^{8}	25	.....	360	....	15
63 Ni, 30 Cu, 4 Si, 2 Fe +	Sand cast	14.5×10^{11}	....	$76–100 \times 10^{8}$	$55–79 \times 10^{8}$	1–4	.....	275–350	....	1
57 Ni, 20 Mo, 20 Fe +	Ann.	18.6×10^{11}	....	$76–83 \times 10^{8}$	$32.4–36 \times 10^{8}$	40–48	40–54	200–215	....	1
62 Ni, 30 Mo, 5 Fe +	Rolled, ann.	21.19×10^{11}	....	$90–96 \times 10^{8}$	$41–45 \times 10^{8}$	40–45	40–45	210–235	....	1
58 Ni, 17 Mo, 15 Cr, 5 W, 5 Fe +	Ann. plate	19.6×10^{11}	....	$79–88 \times 10^{8}$	$38–45 \times 10^{8}$	25–50	.....	160–210	....	1
85 Ni, 10 Si, 3 Cu +	Sand cast	19.88×10^{11}	....	$25–27.9 \times 10^{8}$	....	.....	.....	....	....	1
80 Ni, 14 Cr, 6 Fe +	Ann.	21×10^{11}	....	....	19.3×10^{8}	.....	.....	....	41.9×10^{8}	1
58 Ni, 22 Cr, 6 Cu, 6 Mo, 6 Fe	Sand cast	18.38×10^{11}	....	$41–50 \times 10^{8}$	....	4–9.5	8–11	160–210	....	1
80 Ni, 20 Cr +	Ann.	21×10^{11}	....	65.4×10^{8}	....	25–35	55	RB85–90	....	1

* References are on p. 2–78.

TABLE 2f-14. ELASTIC AND STRENGTH CONSTANTS FOR TIN AND TIN ALLOYS

Alloy	Condition	E	σ	Tensile strength	Yield strength at 0.2% offset	Elongation	Bhn	Shear strength	Ref.*
Pure tin	Cast	$4.1–4.5 \times 10^{11}$	....	2.14×10^8	....	55	5.3	2.00×10^8	1
Pure tin	Chill cast	....	....	1.45×10^8	....	69	....	....	1
Pure tin	0.1-in. sheet, ann.	....	....	1.65×10^8	....	96	....	....	1
99.8 Sn†	Cast	4.13×10^{11}	....	1.45×10^8	....	54†	....	....	1
99.8 Sn†	Ann., 0.040-in. sheet	4.13×10^{11}	0.33	1.52×10^8	....	45	Vhn 7.2	0.896×10^8	1
95 Sn, 5 Sb	Cast	....	....	4.06×10^8	....	38†	....	4.13×10^8	1
95 Sn, 5 Ag	0.040-in. sheet, aged at room temp.	....	....	3.17×10^8	2.48×10^8	49	....	....	1
70 Sn, 30 Pb	Cast	....	....	4.68×10^8	....	...	12	....	1
63 Sn, 37 Pb	Cast	....	....	5.17×10^8	....	32†	14	4.27×10^8	1
91 Sn, 4.5 Sb, 4.5 Cu	Chill cast	5.03×10^{11}	....	6.41×10^8	4.34×10^8‡	...	17	....	1
83.4 Sn, 8.3 Sb, 8.3 Cu	Chill cast	....	....	....	5.51×10^8‡	...	27	....	1

* References are on p. **2**–78.
† % in 4 in.
‡ At 0.3% offset.

TABLE 2f-15. ELASTIC AND STRENGTH CONSTANTS FOR ZINC AND ZINC ALLOYS

Alloy	Condition	Tensile strength	Elongation, % in 2 in.	Bhn	Shear strength	Ref.*
3.5–4.3 Al, 0.03–0.08 Mg......	Die cast, ¼-in. section	28×10^8	10	82	21×10^8	1
3.5–4.3 Al, 0.75–1.25 Cu, 0.03–0.08 Mg	Die cast, ¼-in. section	33×10^8	7	91	26×10^8	1
3.5–4.5 Al, 2.5–3.5 Cu, 0.02–0.10 Mg	Die cast, ¼-in. section	35.9×10^8	8	100	32×10^8	1
4.5–5.0 Al, 0.2–0.3 Cu	Chill cast, ½-in. section	19×10^8	.....	...	....	1
5.25–5.75 Al.................	Chill cast, ½-in. section	17×10^8	1	...	....	1
≤0.10 Pb....................	H.R. strip	$13.4\text{–}16 \times 10^8$	50–65	38	....	1
0.05–0.10 Pb, 0.05–0.08 Cd......	H.R. strip	$14\text{–}17 \times 10^8$	30–52	43	....	1
0.25–0.50 Pb, 0.25–0.45 Cd......	H.R. strip	$16\text{–}20 \times 10^8$	32–50	47	....	1
0.85–1.25 Cu................	H.R. strip	$16\text{–}22 \times 10^8$	15–20	52	....	1
0.85–1.25 Cu, 0.006–0.016 Mg...	H.R. strip	$19\text{–}25 \times 10^8$	10–20	61	....	1

* References are below.

References for Tables 2f-6 through 2f-15

1. "Metals Handbook," 1948 ed., American Society for Metals.
2. *Natl. Bur. Standards (U.S.) Circ.* C447, 1943.
3. Bain, E. C.: "Functions of the Alloying Elements in Steel," American Society for Metals, 1939.
4. Hoyt, S. L.: "Metals and Alloys Data Book," Reinhold Publishing Corporation, New York, 1943.
5. "Selection of Special Steels, Data Sheet," D.T.A. 72, Société de commentry, Paris, France, 1946.
6. Halley, J. W.: Pat. 2402135, 1946.
7. "Nickel Alloy Steel," 2d ed., The International Nickel Co., Inc., New York, 1949.
8. "Fox Alloy Steels," Samuel Fox and Co. Ltd., Sheffield, England, 1942.
9. "Case Hardening of Nickel Alloy Steels," International Nickel Co., New York, 1941.
10. Everett, F. L., and J. Miklowitz: *J. Appl. Phys.* **15** (1944).
11. Climax Molybdenum Company Laboratory Records.
12. "Sheet Iron, a Primer," Republic Steel Corp., 1934.
13. Comstock, G. F.: *J. Am. Ceram. Soc.* **29** (1946).
14. "Magnesium Alloys and Products," Dow Chemical Co., 1950.
15. "Nickel," The International Nickel Co., Inc., rev. 1951.

resultant indentation measured (d mm). The Brinell hardness number (Bhn) is defined as

$$\text{Bhn} = \frac{W}{\text{curved area of indentation}} = \frac{2W}{\pi D(D - \sqrt{D^2 - d^2})}$$

and is expressed in kg/mm^2."

9. *Vickers Hardness Number.*[1] "A pyramidal diamond indenter is pressed into the surface of a metal under a load of W kg and the mean diagonal of the resultant indenta-

[1] D. Tabor, "The Hardness of Metals."

TABLE 2f-16. DIFFUSION COEFFICIENTS FOR METALS

Metal	Test temp.	$D\left(\frac{cm^2}{sec}\right)$	Ref.
Ag into Ag	Room	0.895	1
Ag into Ag	460°C	8.0×10^{-14}	11
Ag into Ag	600°C	5.9×10^{-12}	11
Ag into Ag	666°C	2.45×10^{-11}	2
Ag into Ag	794°C	3.64×10^{-10}	2
Ag into Ag	936°C	4.61×10^{-9}	2
Al into Cu	Room	1.75×10^{-2}	1
Au into Au	Room	0.160	3
Au into Cu	Room	0.1 ± 0.06	4
Be into Cu	Room	2.32×10^{-4}	1
Bi into Pb	Room	0.018	3
Cd into Cu	Room	1.97×10^{-9}	3
Cd into Ag	Room	7.3×10^{-5}	3
Cd into Pb	Room	1.8×10^{-3}	3
Cl^- into NaCl single crystals	650°C	7.25×10^{-11}	5
Cl^- into NaCl single crystals	681°C	2.84×10^{-10}	5
Cl^- into NaCl single crystals	703°C	6.76×10^{-10}	5
Cl^- into NaCl single crystals	735°C	1.67×10^{-9}	5
Cl^- into NaCl single crystals	762°C	2.52×10^{-9}	5
Cu into Cu	Room	0.1–47	1
Cu into Cu	700°C	4.06×10^{-12}	7
Cu into Cu	900°C	3.58×10^{-10}	7
Cu into Cu	1000°C	1.95×10^{-9}	7
Cu into CuO	800°C	0.19×10^{-8}	6
Cu into CuO	900°C	0.77×10^{-8}	6
Cu into CuO	1000°C	3.2×10^{-8}	6
Cu into Ag	Room	5.95×10^{-5}	1
In into In	49.95°C	$7\text{–}8.5 \times 10^{-13}$	9
In into In	87.25°C	$1.4\text{–}1.5 \times 10^{-11}$	9
In into In	155.50°C	1.14×10^{-9}	9
In into In	155.81°C	1.70×10^{-7}	9
In into In	156.60°C	6.52×10^{-6}	9
In into In	157.30°C	1.23×10^{-5}	9
In into Ag	Room	4.85×10^{-5}	1
Liq. Hg into liq. Hg	2.5°C	1.52×10^{-5}	8
Liq. Hg into liq. Hg	16.4°C	1.68×10^{-5}	8
Lig. Hg into liq. Hg	23.0°C	1.79×10^{-5}	8
Liq. Hg into liq. Hg	31.9°C	1.88×10^{-5}	8
Liq. Hg into liq. Hg	41.5°C	1.98×10^{-5}	8
Liq. Hg into liq. Hg	66.1°C	2.24×10^{-5}	8
Liq. Hg into liq. Hg	91.2°C	2.57×10^{-5}	8
Mn into Cu	Room	0.72×10^{-5}	1
Ni into Cu	Room	6.5×10^{-5}	1
Ni into Pb	Room	0.66	1
Pd into Cu	Room	0.16×10^{-5}	1

TABLE 2f-16. DIFFUSION COEFFICIENTS FOR METALS (*Continued*)

Metal	Test temp.	$D\left(\frac{cm^2}{sec}\right)$	Ref.
Pt into Cu	Room	1.02×10^{-4}	1
Pb into Pb	Room	6.6	1
Sb into Ag	Room	5.31×10^{-5}	1
Si into ferrite	1435 ± 5°C	1.1×10^{-7}	10
Si into Cu	Room	3.7×10^{-2}	1
Sn into Ag	Room	7.82×10^{-5}	1
Sn into Cu	Room	1.13	1
Sn into Pb	Room	3.96	1
Ti into In	49.27°C	1.4×10^{-12}	9
Ti into In	74.19°C	9.2×10^{-12}	9
Ti into In	101.55°C	$4.6\text{–}4.8 \times 10^{-11}$	9
Ti into In	139.16°C	$2.8\text{–}3.2 \times 10^{-10}$	9
Ti into In	155.60°C	2.17×10^{-9}	9
Ti into In	155.91°C	1.87×10^{-7}	9
Ti into In	157.80°C	2.27×10^{-5}	9
Ti into Pb	Room	0.025	1

N. B. The values quoted from ref. 1 are for D_0 in the equation $D = D_0e^{-H/RT}$. Cf. ref. 1 for values of H.

References

1. Nowick, A. S.: *J. Appl. Phys.* **22,** 1182 (1951).
2. Slifkin, L., D. Lazarus, and T. Tomizuka: *J. Appl. Phys.* **23,** 1032 (1952).
3. Smithells, C. J.: "Metals Reference Book."
4. Martin, A. B.: and F. Asaro: *Phys. Rev.* **80,** 123A (1950).
5. Chemla, Marius: *Compt. rend.* **234,** 2601 (1952).
6. Moore, W. J., and Bernard Selikson: *J. Chem. Phys.* **19,** 1539 (1951).
7. Cohen, G., and G. C. Kuczynski: *J. Appl. Phys.* **21,** 1339L (1950).
8. Hoffman, R. E.: *J. Chem. Phys.* **20,** 1567 (1951).
9. Eckert, R. E., and H. G. Drickamer: *J. Chem. Phys.* **20,** 13 (1951).
10. Bradshaw, F. J., G. Hoyle, and K. Speight: *Nature* **171,** 488 (1953).
11. Kuczynski, G. C.: *J. Appl. Phys.* **21,** 632 (1950).

tion measured (d mm). The Vickers hardness number (Vhn), or Vickers diamond hardness (Vdh), is defined as

$$\text{Vdh (or Vhn)} = \frac{W}{\text{pyramidal area of indentation}}$$

The indenter has an angle of 136° between opposite faces and 146° between opposite edges. From simple geometry, this means that the pyramidal area of the indentation is greater than the projected area of the indentation by the ratio 1:0.9272. Hence

$$\text{Vdh} = \frac{0.9272W}{\text{projected area of indentation}} = 1.8544W/d^2$$

The value is expressed in kg/mm²."

10. *Diffusion Coefficient.* If the concentration (mass of solid per unit volume of solution) at one surface of a layer of liquid is d_1, and at the other surface d_2, the thickness of the layer is h, the area under consideration is A, and the mass of a given substance which diffuses through the cross section A in time t is m, then the diffusion coefficient is defined as

$$D = \frac{mh}{A(d_2 - d_1)t}$$

2g. Mechanical Properties of Gels and Thixotropic Substances

THOR L. SMITH

Jet Propulsion Laboratory
California Institute of Technology

2g-1. Introduction. A gel[1] may be defined as a colloidal disperse system which (1) contains a dispersed component and a dispersion medium, both of which extend continuously throughout the system and (2) has time-independent or equilibrium elastic properties, e.g., it will support a static shear stress without undergoing permanent deformation. Gels are similar to solids in that they have a shear modulus of rigidity, but they are similar to liquids in most of their other physical properties.

The dispersed component of a gel must be a three-dimensional network held together by bonds or junction points whose lifetimes are essentially infinite. The junction points may be formed by primary valence bonds, long-range attractive forces, or secondary valence bonds that cause association between segments of polymer chains or formation of submicroscopic crystalline regions.

Certain systems, such as moderately concentrated polymer solutions, are similar to gels but differ in an important respect: they undergo flow when a shear stress, no matter how small, is applied, since they contain a network formed by molecular entanglements and the junction points are transient. They exhibit time-dependent elastic properties, as shown by stress-relaxation experiments or dynamic experiments with periodic stress,[2] but they do not have equilibrium elastic properties as do true gels.

A class of materials that includes dry gelatin, agar, and lightly cross-linked rubber is called xerogels. Xerogels when in contact with suitable solvents swell to form gels.

A thixotropic substance is a gel which can undergo an isothermal gel-sol-gel transformation. The gel is transformed into a sol by mechanical agitation, and the sol reverts to a gel when the agitation is discontinued. The gel-sol transformation occurs if the gel is subjected to a shear stress greater than some critical amount, called the yield value.

2g-2. Gels. The equilibrium rigidity modulus of gels that have a dispersed component composed of randomly kinked long molecular chains which are cross-linked by primary valence bonds (or occasionally secondary valence bonds) is given approximately by the statistical theory of rubber elasticity.[3] The theory equates the total elastic force of a deformed gel to the decrease in configurational entropy of the network chains. The theory can be applied to gels formed in several different ways: (1) by swelling a lightly cross-linked polymer such as rubber; (2) by introducing sufficient

[1] P. H. Hermans, Gels, in "Colloid Science," vol. II, H. R. Kruyt, ed., Elsevier Press, Inc., New York, 1949.

[2] J. D. Ferry, Physical Properties of High Polymers, in "Annual Review of Physical Chemistry," vol. 4, Annual Reviews, Inc., Stanford, Calif.

[3] P. J. Flory, "Principles of Polymer Chemistry," Cornell University Press, Ithaca, N.Y., 1953.

cross links between polymer molecules in solution to form a three-dimensional network; or (3) by adding or removing some of the solvent in the gels formed under (2).

The modulus of rigidity G for any gel of the three classes is given by the equation

$$G = \frac{\rho}{M_c} RTv_2^{\frac{1}{3}}(v_2^0)^{\frac{2}{3}} \tag{2g-1}$$

where ρ is the density of the dry polymeric material, M_c the number average molecular weight of polymer segments between cross links, R the gas constant, and T the absolute temperature. The quantity v_2^0 is the volume fraction of polymer in the state when cross links were formed; and v_2 is the volume fraction of polymer in the gel of rigidity G. Thus, for gels of class (1), v_2^0 equals unity; for gel of class (2), v_2^0 equals v_2; for gels of class (3), v_2^0 equals the volume fraction of the polymer in the solution when the cross links were formed, and v_2 is the volume fraction of the polymer in the gel formed by addition or removal of solvent.

The ratio ρ/M_c can be calculated from the measured rigidity of the gel in a given state using Eq. (2g-1) or from equilibrium swelling measurements.[1]

The rigidities of a variety of gels are listed in Table 2g-1. These rigidities were obtained from the original literature and are given here without critical evaluation. Whenever Young's modulus E was reported in the literature, it has been converted into the shear modulus by using the relation $E = 2G(1 + \nu)$ with ν, Poisson's ratio, set equal to 0.5.

The rigidity of most gels depends on their age, method of preparation, temperature, and the concentration of the dispersed component. Hence ranges of rigidity moduli are given in Table 2g-1. Because of the time dependence of the rigidity of many gels, the moduli listed may not be equilibrium values. Also, some of the gels may show appreciable permanent deformation; therefore they may not conform strictly to the definition of a gel given previously.

2g-3. Thixotropic Substances. Numerous colloidal systems are thixotropic. Examples are paints, printing inks, iron oxide sols, solutions of sodium carboxymethylcellulose and agar, suspensions of glass spheres, kaolin, bentonite, carbon black, and kieselguhr. In fact, it appears that many gelling systems may become thixotropic under certain conditions of concentration, temperature, or ionic strength.[2]

The complete characterization of the mechanical properties of thixotropic substances[3] should include the rigidity of the gel at various stages of its formation, and the flow curves (shear rate vs. shear stress curve) of the sol for all stages of breakdown. The latter is difficult to obtain since the degree of breakdown is changed by shear. However, several methods that give considerable information have been used to investigate a wide variety of thixotropic gels.

Pryce-Jones[4] uses a concentric-cylinder apparatus whose inner cylinder is attached to a torsion wire. Data are obtained on the rate of change of viscous properties of the sol and elastic properties of the gel. Green and Weltman[5] subject thixotropic systems to increasing shear rates, followed immediately by decreasing shear rates. A loop is obtained in the flow curves, from which a coefficient of thixotropic breakdown is calculated. They also calculate a coefficient of thixotropic breakdown with time from the decrease in viscosity (measured at a given rate) with time. Goodeve and Whitfield[6]

[1] Flory, *op. cit.*

[2] Hermans, *op. cit.*

[3] Turner Alfrey, Jr., "Mechanical Behavior of High Polymers," Interscience Publishers, Inc., New York, 1948.

[4] Pryce-Jones, *Kolloid-Z.* (in English) **129**, 96 (1952).

[5] H. Green, "Industrial Rheology and Rheological Structures," John Wiley & Sons, Inc., New York, 1949.

[6] Goodeve and Whitfield, *Trans. Faraday Soc.* **34**, 511 (1938); Goodeve, *Trans. Faraday Soc.* **35**, 342 (1939).

have introduced a coefficient of thixotropy Θ, defined by the equation

$$\eta - \eta_0 = \frac{\Theta}{D} \qquad (2g\text{-}2)$$

where η is an apparent viscosity, η_0 the limiting viscosity at high shear rates, and D the rate of shear. However, the equation is applicable only to comparatively simple systems.

TABLE 2g-1. SHEAR MODULUS OF GELS

Gel	Conc., %	Temp., °C	Age of gel	Modulus G, dynes/cm²	Ref.
Inorganic gels:					
Agar	5	.....	2–24 hr	9×10^5	1
Agar	0.05–0.4	15	....	4×10^0–5.2×10^5	2
Cupric ferrocyanide	0.24–0.37	.....	....	0.86–2.7	3
Cadmium sulfide	0.3–0.77	.....	....	0.9–3.7	3
Silicic acid	5	.....	6.5–133 hr	2.2×10^5–8.5×10^5	1
Silicic acid	3.8–6.1	.....	28–52 hr	0.61×10^5–4.8×10^5	4
Ferric oxide	0.47–0.53	.....	0–5 hr	5×10^2–4.5×10^5	5
Metal-organic gels:					
Ammonium oleate	0.57	.....	0–20 hr	0.43–2.9	6
Mercury sulfosalicylate	1.5	14	0–16 days	1–19	6
Lithium-based grease	....	.....	....	0.53×10^6	7
Sodium-based grease	....	.....	....	2.3×10^6	7
Organic gels:					
Benzopurpurin	0.3, 1.0	.....	0–23 hr	0.75, 11.1	6
Cellulose acetate–benzyl alcohol	5–25	5–20	....	10^5–10^7	8
Cotton yellow	0.5, 0.75	15	0–68 hr	2.3–23.6	6
Fibrin	0.15–2.4	.....	....	10^3–10^5	9
Fibrin film	30	.....	....	2×10^6	9, 10
Collagen	1–16	21–65	....	1×10^5–4×10^5	11
Gelatin	1–20	10	....	1×10^3–5×10^5	12
Gelatin	2–5.9	0–25	....	Modulus as function of molecular weight	13
Polyvinyl chloride–organic solvents	2.3–100	.....	....	2.3×10^3–1.2×10^{10}	14–19
Polyacrylonitrile-dimethylformamide	20	Modulus as function of time and temperature			20
Rubber-organic solvents	33–100	Modulus of various gels of rubber			21
Cornstarch	3–10	70–120	....	0–400	22
Tapioca	5–10	70–90	....	0–450	22

References for Table 2g-1

1. Hatschek, E.: *J. Phys. Chem.* **36,** 2994 (1932).
2. Michaud: *Ann. phys.* **19,** 63 (1923).
3. McDowell and Usher: *Proc. Roy. Soc.* (*London*), ser. A, **131,** 409, 564 (1931).
4. Prasad: *Kolloid-Z.* **33,** 279 (1923).
5. Amiot: *Compt. rend.* **224,** 388 (1947).
6. Hatschek and Jane: *Kolloid-Z.* **39,** 300 (1926).
7. Hutton and Matthews: Viscoelastic Behavior of Lubricating Greases, in "Proceedings of the Second International Rheological Congress," Harrison, ed., Academic Press, Inc., New York, 1954.
8. Poole, H. J.: *Trans. Faraday Soc.* **22,** 82 (1926).
9. Ferry, J. D., and P. R. Morrison: *J. Am. Chem. Soc.* **69,** 388, 400 (1947).
10. Ferry, Singer, Morrison, Porsche, and Kutz: *J. Am. Chem. Soc.* **69,** 409 (1947). Also see Ferry, Protein Gels, in "Advances in Protein Chemistry," vol. IV, Anson and Edsall, eds., Academic Press, Inc., New York, 1948.
11. Wiederhorn and Reardon: *J. Polymer Sci.* **9,** 315 (1952).

12. Saunders and Ward: An Absolute Method for the Rigidity Modulus of Gelatine Gels, in "Proceedings of the Second International Rheological Congress," Harrison, ed., Academic Press, Inc., New York, 1954.
13. Ferry and Eldridge: *J. Phys. & Colloid Chem.* **53**, 184 (1949); Miller, Ferry, Schremp, and Eldridge: *J. Phys. & Colloid Chem.* **55**, 1387 (1951).
14. Walter, A. T.: *J. Polymer Sci.* **13**, 207 (1954).
15. Fitzgerald and Ferry: *J. Colloid Sci.* **8**, 1 (1953); Ferry and Fitzgerald: *J. Colloid. Sci.* **8**, 224 (1953).
16. Davies, Miller, and Busse: *J. Am. Chem. Soc.* **63**, 361 (1941).
17. Aiken, Alfrey, Janssen, and Mark: *J. Polymer Sci.* **2**, 178 (1947).
18. Dyson: *J. Polymer Sci* **7**, 147 (1951).
19. Nielsen, Buchdahl, and Levreault: *J. Appl. Phys.* **21**, 607 (1950).
20. Bisschops, J.: *J. Polymer Sci.* **12**, 583 (1954).
21. Gee, G.: *Trans. Faraday Soc.* **42**, 585 (1946).
22. Brimhall and Hixon: *Ind. Eng. Chem., Anal. Ed.* **11**, 358 (1939).

2h. Viscosity of Solids

EVAN A. DAVIS

Westinghouse Electric Corporation

2h-1. Anelasticity. A perfectly elastic solid is truly an ideal material. Actual materials contain structural imperfections which prohibit them from behaving in a perfectly elastic manner. Even when the stresses are low enough to ensure that no perceptible permanent deformation takes place the total strain is made up of a purely elastic part that is directly proportional to the load and a time-dependent but fully recoverable part that will vary with the rate of loading and the duration of the load. The behavior associated with the time-dependent part of the strain has been called "anelasticity" by Zener,[1] who has endeavored to explain this behavior in terms of the atomic arrangement and the microstructure of the material.

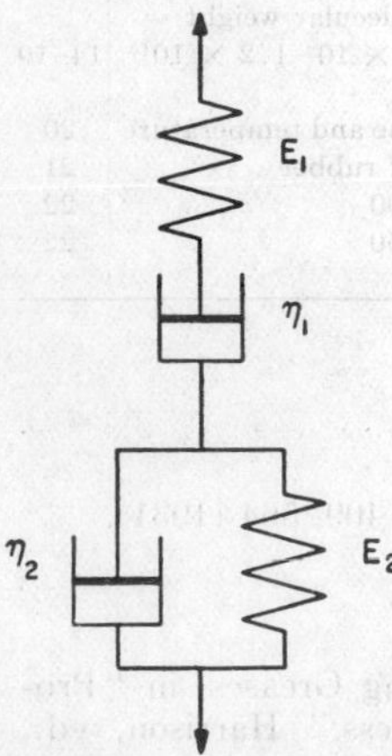

FIG. 2h-1. Mechanical model for demonstrating anelastic and creep behavior of solids.

Anelastic behavior is observed in many ways, depending upon the manner in which the material is loaded. Its effect may be referred to as elastic hysteresis, internal friction, elastic aftereffect, specific damping capacity, or dynamic and static moduli of elasticity. The fact that the term anelasticity has been limited to the region of no permanent deformation does not exclude the existence of such behavior at higher stresses. When a material deforms permanently, however, the anelastic effects are overshadowed by and engulfed in the plastic behavior.

In the realm of small deformations a metal or a plastic can be represented qualita-

[1] C. Zener, "Elasticity and Anelasticity of Metals," University of Chicago Press, Chicago, 1948.

tively by the mechanical model of springs and dashpots shown in Fig. 2h-1. For the anelastic behavior at low stresses the viscosity η_1 of the upper dashpot can be considered as infinite. The spring with the elastic modulus E_1 contributes the purely elastic strain. The time-dependent part of the strain comes from the parallel arrangement of spring E_2 and dashpot η_2. This model will exhibit, though not in a quantitative manner, the various anelastic effects of solids.

If the unit is elongated at a slow rate, dashpot η_2 will have little effect in resisting the deformation of spring E_2. The static or isothermal modulus of elasticity will be that of springs E_1 and E_2 connected in series. If the unit is elongated rapidly dashpot η_2 will tend to act as a rigid mechanism. The dynamic or adiabatic modulus of elasticity will be that of spring E_1 acting alone.

If the unit is put through a constant-rate loading and unloading cycle a hysteresis loop will be traced out in the stress-strain diagram. The area of the loop will be proportional to the amount of energy dissipated in dashpot η_2.

If the unit is loaded slowly and then unloaded rapidly the strain will not immediately return to zero. What appears to be a permanent strain or elastic aftereffect will be observed. The strain will return to zero when the stress trapped in the spring E_2 by dashpot η_2 has been relaxed.

If a mass is attached to the lower end of the unit and the entire mechanism is allowed to vibrate freely the amplitude of vibration will decrease with each cycle. The decrease in amplitude of vibration is due to the dissipation of energy in dashpot η_2. If the springs are linear and elastic and the dashpot behaves in a perfectly viscous manner the ratio of the decrease in amplitude for any given cycle to the amplitude at the beginning of the cycle will be a constant. This constant is called the logarithmic decrement δ, and it is probably the most-used measure of the anelastic behavior of materials.

The logarithmic decrement of actual materials is relatively high for dielectric materials and low for metals. Since this quantity depends upon imperfections in the atomic structure it will vary with such factors as heat-treatment, grain size, or the amount of cold working, and it will be impossible to assign a value to a specific material such as steel. The values listed by Kimball[1] and shown in Table 2h-1 and those listed by Gemant[2] and shown in Table 2h-2 are to be considered as representative values which give the order of magnitude of the decrement or internal friction.

The factors which affect the logarithmic decrement are discussed in detail by Zener and by Gemant. The decrement is influenced by such factors as frequency, temperature, amplitude, elastic modulus, grain size, annealing temperature, and aging time.

In general there is not much change in decrement with frequency. Gemant and Jackson[3] found slight increases in the decrement of ebonite and glass over rather narrow frequency ranges (Fig. 2h-2). Gemant shows a slight increase in the decrement for paraffin wax and a slight decrease in the decrement for steel (Fig. 2h-3). An exception to this rule was found by Rinehart,[4] who reported an appreciable increase in the decrement of Lucite at room temperature (Fig. 2h-4).

Certain materials show steep peaks in the log decrement vs. log frequency curve. These peaks are associated with frequencies that correspond to the reciprocal of some characteristic time for the material. Such a curve, taken from Gemant and based on the work of Zener and Bennewitz and Rötger,[5] is shown in Fig. 2h-5. In this case the peak in the internal-friction curve is due to the diffusion of heat from parts heated by compression to parts cooled by tensile stresses.

[1] A. L. Kimball, "Vibration Prevention in Engineering," John Wiley & Sons, Inc., New York, 1932.

[2] A. Gemant, "Frictional Phenomena," Chemical Publishing Company, Inc., New York, 1950.

[3] A. Gemant and W. Jackson, *Phil. Mag.* **23**, 960 (1937).

[4] J. S. Rinehart, *J. Appl. Phys.* **12**, 811 (1941).

[5] K. Bennewitz and H. Rötger, *Z. tech. Phys.* **19**, 521 (1938).

The logarithmic decrement usually increases with increasing temperature. The viscous behavior changes more rapidly than the elastic properties with temperature, with the result that at higher temperatures more energy is dissipated in the dashpot.

The decrement does not vary greatly with amplitude when the amplitudes are small. The decrement increases at higher amplitudes. This is evidence that the viscosity of materials is not of a pure viscous nature. The rate of strain increases more rapidly at the higher stresses than the linear viscous law would predict.

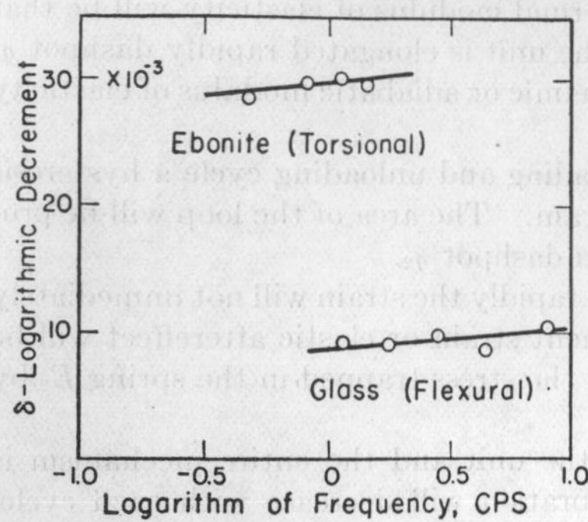

Fig. 2h-2. Logarithmic decrement vs. logarithm of frequency for ebonite and glass. (*Gemant and Jackson.*)

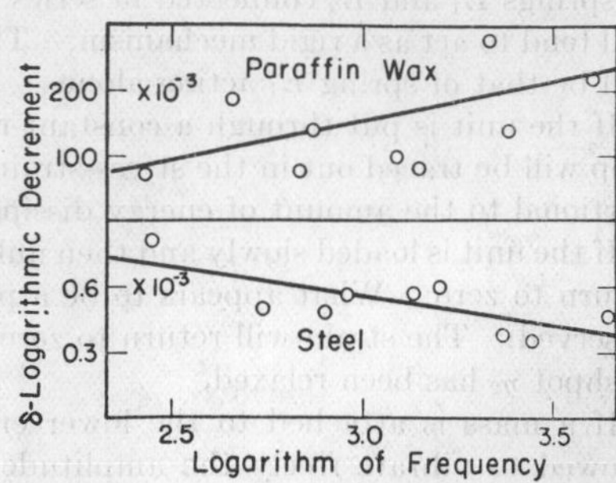

Fig. 2h-3. Logarithmic decrement vs. frequency at room temperature for steel and paraffin wax. (*Gemant.*)

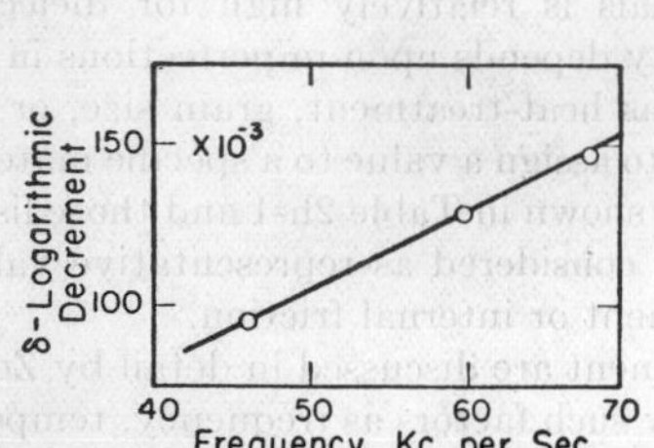

Fig. 2h-4. Logarithmic decrement vs. frequency for Lucite at 26°C. (*Rinehart.*)

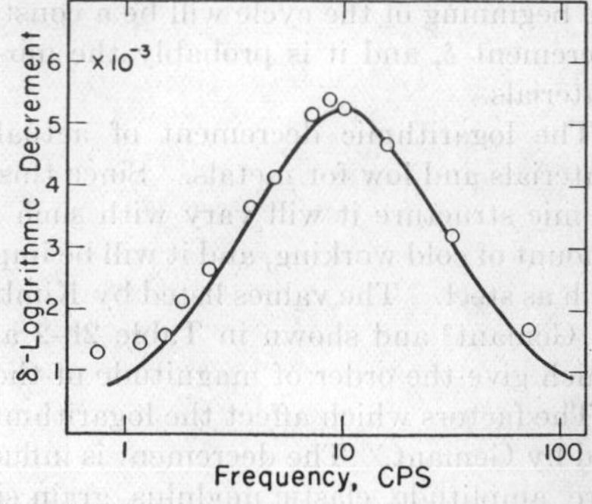

Fig. 2h-5. Logarithmic decrement vs. frequency for German silver. (*Measured points after Bennemitz and Rötger; theoretical curve after Zener.*)

Materials with high elastic moduli have lower decrements than those with low moduli. There is some evidence to show that the product of the elastic modulus and the decrement is nearly a constant value.

2h-2. Creep. When a material is subjected to the proper combination of high stress and temperature it will deform permanently. A representative behavior will be produced by the model shown in Fig. 2h-1 if the viscosity of both dashpots η_1 and η_2 is finite. The continuing deformation of a material under a constant load is called "creep." If the model is loaded with a given load at $t = 0$ there will be an instantaneous elastic deflection ϵ' of spring E_1, dashpot η_1 will deform at some constant rate u''_0, and dashpot η_2 will deform at a decreasing rate.[1] The rate of strain in dashpot η_2

[1] A prime (′) on a strain or strain rate indicates elastic deformation; a double prime (″) indicates plastic or permanent strain. The total strain or strain rate, is the sum of the elastic and the plastic parts, i.e.,

$$\epsilon = \epsilon' + \epsilon'' \quad \text{or} \quad u = u' + u''$$

TABLE 2h-1. LOGARITHMIC DECREMENTS FOR VARIOUS MATERIALS*

Material	*Logarithmic Decrement* δ
Phosphor bronze, cold rolled	0.37×10^{-3}
Monel, cold rolled	1.43
Nickel steel, $3\frac{1}{2}\%$ swaged	2.3
Nickel, cold rolled	3.2
Phosphor bronze, annealed	3.2
Aluminum, cold rolled	3.4
Brass, cold rolled	4.8
Mild steel, cold rolled	4.9
Copper, cold rolled	5.0
Glass	6.4
Molybdenum, swaged	6.9
Swedish iron, annealed	7.9
Tungsten, swaged	16.5
Zinc, swaged	20
Maple wood	22
Celluloid	45
Tin, swaged	129
Rubber, 90% pure	260

* A. L. Kimball, "Vibration Prevention in Engineering," John Wiley & Sons, Inc., New York, 1932.

TABLE 2h-2. LOGARITHMIC DECREMENT OF VARIOUS MATERIALS*

Material	*Logarithmic Decrement* δ
Steel	0.6×10^{-3}
Quartz	2.6
Copper	3.2
Lead glass	4.2
Wood	27
Polystyrene	48
Ebonite	85
Paraffin wax	150

* A. Gemant, "Frictional Phenomena," Chemical Publishing Company, Inc., New York, 1950.

decreases because the load is gradually transferred to spring E_2 as the deformation takes place, and this part of the deformation stops at a strain ϵ_0'' when the spring E_2 carries the complete load. The creep curve for the model and for materials which are not stressed high enough to cause fracture will have the form shown in Fig. 2h-6 (the elastic strain ϵ' is not shown). The plastic strain starts at a rapid rate but approaches the asymptotic value given by

$$\epsilon'' = \epsilon_0'' + u_0''t \qquad (2h\text{-}1)$$

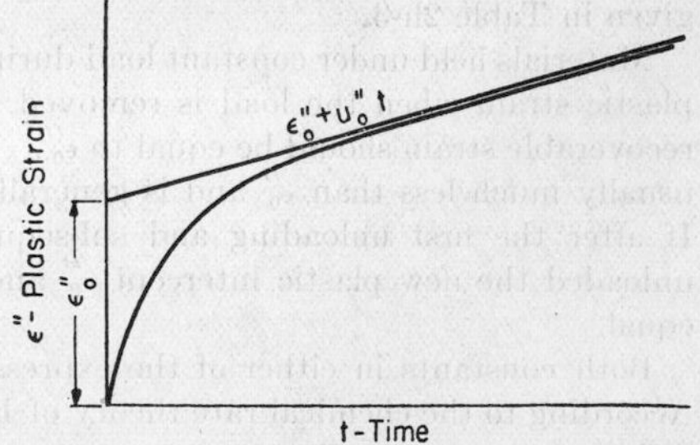

FIG. 2h-6. Typical creep curve.

The shape of the initial part of the creep curve or the manner in which the curve approaches the asymptote has been studied by Andrade[1] and by McVetty.[2]

[1] E. N. da C. Andrade, *Proc. Roy. Soc.* (*London*), ser. *A*, **84**, 1 (1911); **90,** 329 (1914).
[2] P. G. McVetty, *Mech. Eng.* **56,** 149 (March, 1934).

Andrade found that the increase of strain during the first part of the test was proportional to the cube root of the time.

$$\epsilon'' = \beta t^{1/3} \tag{2h-2}$$

McVetty used an exponential relationship to describe the initial deformation.

$$\epsilon'' = \epsilon_0''(1 - e^{-\alpha t}) + u_0'' t \tag{2h-3}$$

When creep tests are made to obtain design data for equipment having long service life, and most of the early creep tests were made under these conditions, the major part of the strain is accounted for by the $u_0''t$ term in Eq. (2h-1). The important relationship to be established, then, is that between the minimum creep rate u_0'' and the stress σ, and this is the only information reported by many investigations.

If shorter service times are considered the initial part of the creep curve becomes more important, and it becomes desirable to know the relationship between the plastic intercept ϵ_0'' and the stress σ. McVetty shows a plot of this relationship for the lower stress range where a power function or hyperbolic sine relationship would be suitable.

$$\epsilon_0'' = A\sigma^n \qquad \text{or} \qquad \epsilon_0'' = B \sinh \frac{\sigma}{\sigma_0} \tag{2h-4}$$

Such relationships indicate that, if the model of Fig. 2h-1 is to represent actual materials, spring E_2 must be nonlinear. At higher stresses these relationships do not hold. As the stress is increased a maximum value is reached above which the value of ϵ_0'' decreases with increasing stress.

In the range of strain rates that can be tolerated in reasonable testing times the minimum creep rate u_0'' vs. stress σ curve can be approximated by a straight line on either a double-log or a semilog plot.

$$u_0'' = D\sigma^m \qquad \text{or} \qquad u_0'' = u_1'' \sinh \frac{\sigma}{\sigma_0} \tag{2h-5}$$

The hyperbolic sine relationship has been shown by Kauzmann[1] to have some theoretical foundation in terms of the "chemical rate theory." The power-function relationship has the advantage of being more workable from a mathematical point of view, but it suffers somewhat from the illogical conclusion that the viscosity of dashpot η_1 should approach infinity as the stress approaches zero. Creep properties, like anelastic properties, vary with many factors, and compilation of creep data means very little unless heat-treatment, grain size, and amount of cold working are also specified. A few representative values of the stress required for a creep rate of 10^{-6} per hour taken from the 1943 compilation of the National Bureau of Standards,[2] are given in Table 2h-3.

Materials held under constant load during long-time creep tests recover part of their plastic strain when the load is removed. According to the model of Fig. 2h-1 the recoverable strain should be equal to ϵ_0''. In actual practice, however, the recovery is usually much less than ϵ_0'' and is generally less than the elastic strain of unloading. If after the first unloading and subsequent recovery the specimen is loaded and unloaded the new plastic intercept ϵ_0'' and the recoverable strain are approximately equal.

Both constants in either of the expressions of Eq. (2h-5) vary with temperature. According to the chemical rate theory of Kauzmann and the various theories based on diffusion phenomena the constants D or u_1 should decrease with increasing temperature according to an exponential expression

$$u_1'' = C_1 e^{-(C_2/T)} \tag{2h-6}$$

[1] W. Kauzmann, *Trans. AIME* **143**, 57–83 (1941).

[2] Mechanical Properties of Metals and Alloys, *Natl. Bur. Standards (U.S.) Circ.* C447, 1943.

TABLE 2h-3. CREEP RATES FOR VARIOUS MATERIALS*

Material and composition	Condition	Temp °C	Temp °F	Stress for 0.001 strain in 1,000 hr, psi
Aluminum copper alloy, Cu 4.25, Mn 0.63, Mg 0.44, Fe 0.52, Si 0.25	$\frac{5}{8}$ diam rod, wrought, aged	150	302	22,000
		250	482	5,700
		350	662	1,500
Aluminum silicon alloy, Si 13.18, Ni 3.08, Cu 2.96, Mg 1.04, Fe 0.53	Wrought	205	400	8,800
		315	600	950
Electrocopper	Fully annealed	205	400	6,700
Deoxidized copper	$\frac{3}{4}$ diam rod, cold drawn, annealed	205	400	20,500
Copper nickel alloy, Ni 20.0, Zn 5.08, Mn 0.69	$\frac{3}{4}$ diam rod, cold drawn, annealed at 1200°F	315	600	27,800
Copper tin alloy, Sn 5.99, Zn 5.10, Pb 2.33, Ni 0.23, Fe 0.06	Cast	260	500	10,000
		315	600	3,000
Copper zinc alloy, Cu 96.43, Pb 0.05, Fe 0.01, Zn remainder	$\frac{1}{8}$ diam wire, drawn, fine-grained	149	300	50,000
		205	400	3,500
		260	500	700
Carbon steel, C 0.15, Mn 0.46, Si 0.28 (basic open hearth)	1 in. diam bar, wrought, annealed at 1500°F, grain size 5–6 ASTM	427	800	17,200
		538	1000	3,300
		648	1200	540
Carbon steel, C 0.15, Mn 0.50, Si 0.23 (basic electric furnace)	1 in. diam bar, wrought, annealed at 1550°F, grain size 4–5 ASTM	427	800	26,800
		482	900	16,900
		538	1000	5,750
		593	1100	1,800
		648	1200	620
Chromium steel, C 0.10, Cr 5.09, Mo 0.55, Mn 0.45, Si 0.18	1 in. diam bar, wrought, annealed at 1550°F, grain size 4–5 ASTM	482	900	15,200
		538	1000	10,100
		593	1100	5,850
		648	1200	2,800
Molybdenum steel, C 0.22, Mo 1.06, Mn 0.50, Si 0.13 (induction furnace)	Bar $1\frac{1}{4}$ sq. cast, annealed at 1650°F, grain size 7	427	800	28,000
		482	900	20,800
		538	1000	11,200
Nickel steel, C 0.36, Ni 1.19, Mn 0.58, Cr 0.51, Mo 0.51, Si 0.22 (induction furnace)	1 in. diam bar, hot rolled, normalized at 1600°F, tempered 3 hr at 1250°F	454	850	40,000
		538	1000	12,300
		593	1100	3,600
		648	1200	1,600
Lead	Grade 2	43	110	320
Magnesium alloy, Al 3, Zn 1	Sand cast, $\frac{1}{2}$ diam rods	150	302	4,900†
Nickel alloy, Cu 28.46, Fe 1.24, Mn 0.94, C 0.18, Si 0.10	Wrought	427	800	30,000
		482	900	23,000
		538	1000	3,700
		593	1100	1,300
		648	1200	450

* Mechanical Properties of Metals and Alloys, *Natl. Bur. Standards (U.S.) Circ.* C447, 1943.
† Stress for 0.005 strain in 1,000 hr.

TABLE 2h-3. CREEP RATES FOR VARIOUS MATERIALS (*Continued*)

Material and composition	Condition	Temp °C	Temp °F	Stress for 0.001 strain in 1,000 hr, psi
Zinc alloy, Cd 0.3, Pb 0.3	Rolled, soft, tested parallel to rolling direction	20	68	10,100
		40	104	8,000
		60	140	6,300
Zinc alloy, Cd 0.3, Pb 0.3	Rolled, soft, tested perpendicular to rolling direction	20	68	15,400
		40	104	12,100
		60	140	8,000

This has been checked experimentally over reasonably wide temperature ranges. The constant σ_0, in the lower stress range, usually decreases slightly with increasing temperature. If the constant m changes with temperature caution must be observed in extrapolating toward regions where the curves for two different temperatures would cross.

2i. Astronomical Data

R. BRUCE LINDSAY

Brown University

TABLE 2i-1. PLANETARY ORBITS*

Planet	Mean distance to sun, million km	Sidereal period, mean days	Inclination to the ecliptic	Eccentricity
Mercury	57.9	87.97	7°00′14″	0.2056
Venus	108.1	224.70	3°23′39″	0.0068
Earth	149.5	365.26	....	0.0167
Mars	227.8	686.98	1°50′60″	0.0934
Jupiter	777.8	4,332.58	1°18′20″	0.0484
Saturn	1,426.1	10,759.20	2°29′25″	0.0557
Uranus	2,867.70	30,685.16	0°46′23″	0.0472
Neptune	4,493.63	60,189.56	1°46′27″	0.0086
Pluto	5,907.90	90,737.07	17°08′38″	0.2486

* Taken from the "American Ephemeris and Nautical Almanac" for the year 1955, Government Printing Office, Washington, D.C., 1952.

Table 2i-2. Physical Data for the Planets and the Moon*

Planet	Mass (Earth = 1)	Mean diam (Earth = 1)	Mean density, g/cm³	Surface gravity (Earth = 1)	Velocity of escape, km/sec	Rotation period, days
Mercury.....	0.054	0.38	5.46	0.38	4.3	88.0
Venus........	0.814	0.97	4.96	0.87	10.4	15–30(?)
Earth........	1.000	1.00	5.52	1.00	11.3	1.00
Mars........	0.107	0.52	4.12	0.39	5.1	1.03
Jupiter.......	318.35	10.97	1.33	2.65	61.0	0.41
Saturn.......	95.3	9.03	0.71	1.17	36.7	0.43
Uranus.......	14.58	3.72	1.56	1.05	22.4	0.45
Neptune.....	17.26	3.38	2.47	1.23	25.6	0.66
Pluto........	<0.1	0.45	<5.5(?)	<0.5(?)	<5.3(?)	(?)
Moon........	0.012	0.27	3.33	0.16	2.4	27.3

* Taken from "Smithsonian Physical Tables," 9th ed., 1954.

Table 2i-3. Miscellaneous Astronomical Constants*

Mean solar day........................	86,400 sec = 1.0027379 sidereal day
Sidereal day..............................	86,164.09054 mean solar sec = 23 hr 56 min 40.09054 sec mean solar time
Mass of the earth.......................	5.975×10^{27} g
Mass of the sun..........................	1.987×10^{33} g
Mass of the moon........................	7.343×10^{25} g
Moon's mean distance from the earth....	384,400 km
Moon's sidereal period..................	27.322 days
Earth's orbital velocity.................	18.5 miles/sec
Gravitation constant G.................	$(6.670 \pm 0.005) \times 10^{-8}$ dyne cm² gram⁻²
Acceleration of gravity g..............	978.0495 cm sec⁻² (sea level at equator)
Precession of the equinoxes.............	$50.2564 + 0.000222(t - 1900)$ in seconds of arc per year (t = year in question)
Sun's diameter..........................	864,408 miles
Solar parallax............................	8.80 seconds of arc
Sun's mean density......................	1.41 g/cm³
Sun's radius..............................	6.965×10^{10} cm
Obliquity of the ecliptic.................	$23°27'8.26'' - 0.4684(t - 1900)''$

* Taken from "Smithsonian Physical Tables," 9th ed., 1954.

2j. Geodetic Data

W. A. HEISKANEN

The Ohio State University and the Finnish Geodetic Institute

2j-1. List of Symbols

a equatorial radius of the earth
b polar radius of the earth
α flattening of the meridian
e eccentricity of meridian ellipse
R earth's radius
M meridian radius of curvature
L east-west radius of curvature
l length of arc along the geoid's surface
v angle subtended by arc at center of earth
θ deflection of the vertical
ξ meridian component of deflection of the vertical
η east-west component of deflection of the vertical
N distance between geoid and ellipsoid or undulation of geoid
ϕ' astronomical latitude
λ' astronomical longitude
A' astronomical azimuth
ϕ geodetic latitude
λ geodetic longitude
A geodetic azimuth
Δg gravity anomaly $= g_o - \gamma$
γ theoretically computed acceleration of gravity
g_o observed acceleration of gravity reduced to geoid level
k gravitational constant

2j-2. Principal Problems of Geodesy. The principal task of geodesy is to determine the size and shape of the earth or, as we often say, the dimensions of the earth, and to measure and compute control points for the mapping and charting work. When we have only a small area to survey, as, for instance, a city, we can use a *plane* as representative of the earth. When larger areas are concerned, we must consider the curvature of the earth, i.e., we have to carry out the computations along the sphere. In case a whole country has to be mapped, we must use instead of a sphere an ellipsoid of revolution, or *reference ellipsoid.* Lastly, if we have to connect different countries and different continents with one another, we must know how big the differences are between the used reference ellipsoid and the equipotential surface of the earth, or *geoid.*

Much has been written also about the triaxial earth ellipsoid, but this, if in fact it exists, has only scientific significance; it has no value for practical purposes.

Until the last few decades we have used the reference ellipsoid of revolution. It is known, of course, if we can determine two of its parameters, for instance, equator radius a, and flattening α, of the meridian. The flattening α is $\alpha = (a - b)/a$ where b is the polar radius of the earth. From the two quantities a and α we can compute the eccentricity e of the meridian ellipse as well as the important radii of the curvature at different latitudes and in different directions on the ellipsoid.

In order to be able to determine the dimensions of the earth, we have to solve two problems. First is the *geodetic problem*, i.e., to measure in some direction the length of arc l of a great circle along the earth's surface. Earlier these arcs were in general measured at or close to the meridian direction. Now it does not make any difference in which direction the arcs are measured, because we can determine the geographic longitude with nearly as high accuracy as the latitude. The measurement of the

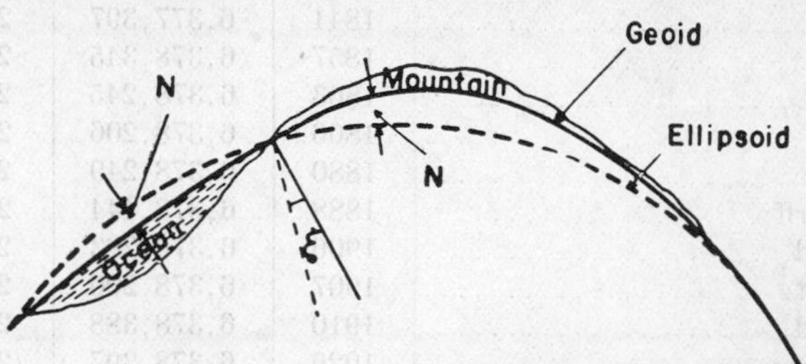

FIG. 2j-1. Mass surplus of the mountains and the mass deficiencies of the oceans bring about the undulations N of the geoid and the deflections of the vertical ξ.

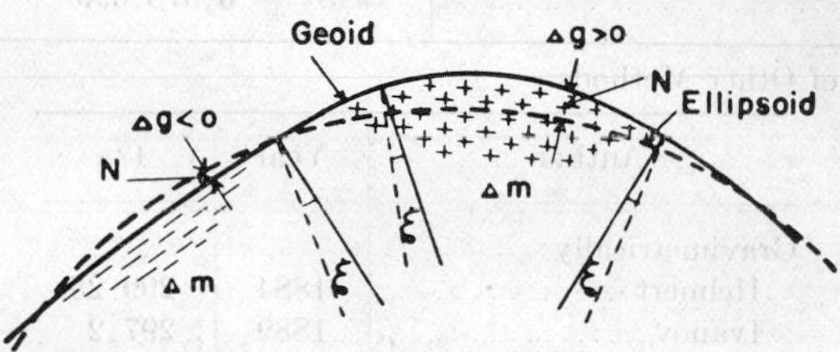

FIG. 2j-2. The mass anomalies Δm (surpluses or deficiencies) bring about the gravity anomalies Δg, the undulations N, and the deflections of the vertical ξ. Δg can be observed, N and ξ computed using Δg.

central angle v corresponding to the arc is the *astronomic problem*. By the aid of l and v, the earth's radius R will be obtained from the formula

$$R = \frac{l}{v} \tag{2j-1}$$

where v is given in radians.

If the measured arc is sufficiently long, or if we have different arcs, we can compute not only the radius a of the equator, but the flattening α as well. The arcs l have been measured by the aid of *triangulation* since 1615, when the Dutch scientist Willebrord Snellius used it for the first time. The corresponding central angle v can be observed by different types of astronomical measuring instruments. We can anticipate that, by the aid of the *arc-measuring method,* we shall obtain rather accurate values for the constants a and α. The list of the dimensions of the reference ellipsoid computed by different authors and by the aid of different material (Table 2j-1) shows that the different α values agree quite well but that the a values may differ as much as some hundreds of meters. This discrepancy is brought about by the fact that the geoid, to which we refer our geodetic measurements, is not the same as the reference ellipsoid. Quite on the contrary, it has "humps" and "hollows" as compared with the reference ellipsoid. Figures 2j-1, 2, 3 show why this is so. Figure 2j-1 shows that the *visible*

TABLE 2j-1. DIMENSIONS OF THE EARTH ELLIPSOID
(a = equator radius; α = flattening of the meridian)

From Arc Measurings

Author	Year	a	$1/\alpha$
Bouguer, Maupertuis	1738	6,397,300m	216.8
Delambre	1800	6,375,653	334.0
Walbeck	1819	6,376,896	302.8
Everest	1830	6,377,276	300.8
Airy	1830	6,376,542	299.3
Bessel	1841	6,377,397	299.15
Clarke	1857	6,378,345	294.26
Pratt	1863	6,378,245	295.3
Clarke	1866	6,378,206	295.0
Clarke	1880	6,378,249	293.5
Bonsdorff	1888	6,378,444	298.6
Hayford	1906	6,378,283	297.8
Helmert	1907	6,378,200	298.3
Hayford	1910	6,378,388	297.0
Heiskanen	1926	6,378,397	(297.0)
Krassowski	1938	6,378,245	298.3
Jeffreys	1948	6,378,099	297.1

$1/\alpha$ by the Aid of Other Methods

Author	Year	$1/\alpha$
Gravimetrically:		
Helmert	1884	299.25
Ivanov	1889	297.2
Helmert	1901	298.2
Bowie	1917	297.4
Berroth	1916	297.4
Helmert	1915	296.7
Heiskanen	1924	297.4
Heiskanen	1928	297.0
Heiskanen	1938	298.2
Niskanen	1945	297.8
Astronomically:		
de Sitter		296.96
de Sitter		296.75
Bullard	1948	297.34
Jeffreys	1948	297.10
Spencer-Jones	1941	296.78

topography, mountains, and oceans bring about irregularities to the geoid. According to Fig. 2j-2, similar irregularities will also be caused by the *invisible* mass anomalies. They (Figs. 2j-1 and 2j-2) show also that the normal of the ellipsoid and the normal of the geoid or plumb line will in general not have the same direction. The angle between these normals is the important *deflection of the vertical* θ. It cannot be observed itself, but only its meridian component ξ and east-west component η. We have, of course, the equation $\theta^2 = \xi^2 + \eta^2$.

Figure 2j-3 shows that, if the measured arc is in the area where the geoid is above the ellipsoid, we get too small dimensions R_2 for the earth's ellipsoid. In case the geoid is under the ellipsoid, we generally get too large dimensions R_1, while the correct radius is R_0.

2j-3. Different Geodetic Systems. The geodesist is, in a way, in an embarrassing situation. He has to reduce his triangulation, gravity measurements, and elevation determinations to sea level, i.e., to the geoid. But he must make his geodetic computations of the coordinates along the regular reference ellipsoid. In order to eliminate this "dualism" he ought to know the deviations between these two surfaces, i.e., the distance N and the tilting θ between them.

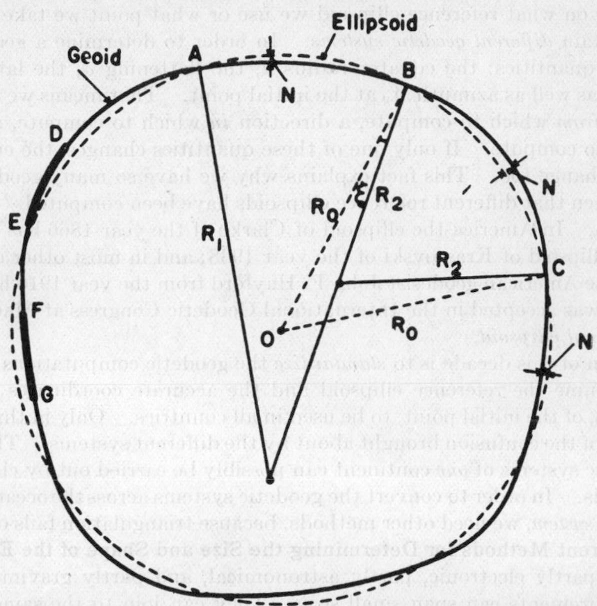

FIG. 2j-3. Because of the undulations N of the geoid we get the wrong dimensions for the earth's ellipsoid. Arc AB, which is below the ellipsoid, gives too large a reduction R_1; arc BC, where the geoid is above the ellipsoid, gives too small a reduction R_2; the correct value is R_0. Even if we "smooth" the effect of the undulation N by the aid of isostatic reductions, we cannot quite eliminate this source of error. Likewise, the arc ED gives too small a reduction and the arc FG too large a reduction.

The general procedure for solving this problem has been the following: We carry out the triangulation, and make astronomical observations, i.e., the astronomical latitude ϕ_0', longitude λ_0', and azimuth A_0', at one triangulation point. Starting from this *initial point of the geodetic datum* we compute along the reference ellipsoid the coordinates ϕ and λ and azimuth A of the successive triangulation points. These geodetic coordinates are referred to the used *ellipsoid* and they will be used as control points for practical mapping work. If the astronomical coordinates ϕ' and λ' and the astronomical azimuth A', which refer to the *geoid*, have been observed, not only at the initial point but at other triangulation points as well, we get the deflections of the vertical components at all such triangulation points. The following equations give the meridian component ξ and the east-west component η:

$$\xi = \phi' - \phi$$

$$\eta = (\lambda' - \lambda) \cos \phi \qquad \text{(2j-2)}$$

or

$$\eta = (A' - A) \cot \phi$$

As we see, we get η from the longitude differences $(\lambda' - \lambda)$ as well as from the azimuth differences $(A' - A)$. Between them there exists the Laplace equation

$$A' - A = (\lambda' - \lambda) \sin \phi \tag{2j-3}$$

These quantities ξ and η can be computed at all astronomical points of the measured arc. Assuming that they can be used as observation errors, we correct the quantities a and α, so that the square sums $\Sigma\xi^2$ or $\Sigma\eta^2$ or the sum $\Sigma(\xi^2 + \eta^2)$ will be minimum. We use $\Sigma\xi^2 = \min$ if the arc is measured mostly on the meridian direction, $\Sigma\eta^2 = \min$ if it goes in an east-west direction, and $\Sigma(\xi^2 + \eta^2) = \min$ if the arc is oblique.

Depending on what reference ellipsoid we use or what point we take as the initial point, we obtain *different geodetic systems.* In order to determine a geodetic system we need *five* quantities: the equator radius a, the flattening α, the latitude ϕ_0 and longitude λ_0, as well as azimuth A_0 at the initial point. That means we must have an initial point *from* which to compute, a direction *in* which to compute, and a surface *along* which to compute. If only one of these quantities changes, the entire geodetic system will change too. This fact explains why we have so many geodetic systems.

We have seen that different reference ellipsoids have been computed. We must use some of them. In America the ellipsoid of Clarke of the year 1866 has been used; in Russia, the ellipsoid of Krassovski of the year 1938; and in most other countries, the ellipsoid of the American geodesist John F. Hayford from the year 1910 has been used. The last one was accepted in the International Geodetic Congress at Madrid, 1924, as the *international ellipsoid.*

The mission of this decade is to *standardize* the geodetic computations of the world, i.e., to determine the reference ellipsoid and the accurate coordinates and azimuth ϕ_0, λ_0, and A_0, of the initial point, to be used in all countries. Only in this way can we rid ourselves of the confusion brought about by the different systems. The conversion of the geodetic systems of *one* continent can possibly be carried out by classic triangulation methods. In order to convert the geodetic systems across the oceans to the same *world geodetic system,* we need other methods, because triangulation fails on the oceans.

2j-4. Different Methods for Determining the Size and Shape of the Earth. These methods are partly electronic, partly astronomical, and partly gravimetrical. The Shoran measurements can span small seas. They can join to the same system, for example, different islands and the coastal areas around the Gulf of Mexico and the Caribbean Sea. They can also be used successfully in the Arctic areas. However, at least so far, they have failed in measurements across oceans.

In order to get distances across oceans, we must use either the *gravimetrical method* or *celestial triangulation.* In all three celestial techniques, the solar-eclipse method, the occultation method, and the moon-camera method, i.e., photographing the moon with the neighboring stars on the same photographic plate, we use the moon as one triangulation point.

In the solar-eclipse method the *total eclipse* of the sun brought about by the moon is used. We know that the moon's shadow travels along the zone of totality approximately from west to east. When we know the exact distance of the moon (and the sun), we can compute the exact speed of this shadow in different parts of the zone of totality. If, in addition, we determine by the aid of modern sound-film techniques the time points when the totality of the eclipse either begins or ends at one western and one eastern station, we can get the exact time which the shadow of the moon requires to travel from the western observation point to the eastern one. By the aid of this travel time and the speed of the shadow it is possible to compute distances between the observation points, quite regardless of whether the points are on the same or different continents.

If the moon's topography were well known, this method would give an accuracy of about 30 m for the distances between the continents.

The *star-occultation method* is similar. We have to observe at only two different points as accurately as possible the times when a star disappears behind the moon's limb or reappears from behind the limb. As the distance to the moon M is not infinite, this phenomena will be seen in different parts of the world at different times. When we make such observations from two different observation points A and B, we get celestial triangle ABM. As the distance of the moon is known, the distance AB along the earth's surface can be obtained. The more accurately the time of the occultation can be obtained, the more stars that are used, and the better we know the moon's distance at the observation moment, the more accurate are the results.

A technique based on the direct *photographing of the moon* has been developed at the Naval Observatory by Markowitz. In this method the moon and the neighboring stars are photographed on the same plate. It was not used earlier because the stars require time to make images on photographic plates. During the exposure time the moon had changed its position so much that its image was hazy. Markowitz has developed a device by the aid of which the relative movement of the moon in respect to the stars can be stopped for the exposure time. In this way, the pictures of the stars are quite clear. We have only to measure the distances of the different distinguishing points of the moon's limb from the neighboring stars. Thus we get the exact position from the moon as observed from different points of the earth's surface. Needless to say, this promising method can be used on any clear moonlight night and on any continent.

Arc measurements give us several arcs on many continents. By the aid of celestial methods we can have such geodetic yardsticks also across the oceans. If we still knew accurately the central angle v which corresponds to these different measured arcs, we would be able to get the dimensions of the earth with high accuracy.

In order to get the central angle, we must measure astronomically ϕ' and λ' and correct them because of the deflection of vertical components ξ and η, at least at the end points of the different arcs. The quantities ξ and η can now be determined by the aid of the *gravity anomalies*.

The gravity anomalies Δg, the deflections of the vertical ξ, η, and the undulations N of the geoid are brought about by the same cause, by the disturbing masses Δm of the earth's topography and the earth's interior. The gravity anomalies can be measured, and the deflections of the vertical as well as the undulations of the geoid can be computed.

Thus, we get at the end points A and B of the arc, the deflections of the vertical ξ and η astronomic-geodetically as well as ξ_g, η_g gravimetrically (the index g refers to the gravimetric method). The quantities ξ and η depend on the used dimensions of the reference ellipsoid: ξ_g, η_g are independent from it. If the residuals $(\xi - \xi_g)$ at the points A and B and likewise the residuals $\eta - \eta_g$ are approximately equal, the used reference ellipsoid is good. If systematic differences exist, we have to correct the dimensions of the used ellipsoid so that the systematic differences disappear. In this way, every measured arc gives a correction to the used a and α values of the reference ellipsoid. By the least-square method, the most probable corrections to the earth's ellipsoid can then be computed.

The flattening value α itself can be obtained directly from gravity anomalies and also by astronomical methods. The precession of the earth is brought about by the flattening of the earth, or, more accurately, by the differences between the polar and equatorial moments of inertia C and A. When we know the precession constant accurately and make logical assumptions about the mass distribution of the earth, we obtain accurate values for α.

Also, the irregularity of the moon's revolution around the earth renders the flattening of the meridian. In our list, the α values obtained by different methods are given.

2j-5. The Constants of the International Ellipsoid and of the International Gravity Formula. If the earth were homogeneous, the equilibrium figure of the rotating earth would be an exact ellipsoid of revolution. Because the mass density of the earth increases toward the earth's center, the figure of the earth will not be an ellipsoid, but another body, a *spheroid,* which differs from the ellipsoid very little. Depending on what hypothesis concerning the inner constitution of the earth is accepted, we get different spheroids. They are closely related to the *gravity formula,* which gives the *normal* acceleration of gravity γ at any part of the earth's surface.

The gravity formula, if we neglect the longitude term, is of the form

$$\gamma = \gamma_E(1 + \beta \sin^2 \phi + \epsilon \sin^2 2\phi) \tag{2j-4}$$

where γ_E is the equator value of gravity, β the important coefficient of the $\sin^2 \phi$ term, and ϵ depends on the internal constitution of the earth.

Between the quantities β and α, we have the following relation:

$$\alpha + \beta = \frac{5m}{2} - \alpha\left(\alpha + \frac{m}{2}\right) + \frac{2\delta}{7} \tag{2j-5}$$

where m is the ratio between the centrifugal force and gravity at the equator. From these coefficients, α, β, and m are small quantities of first order; δ is of second order.

Equation (2j-5) gives the famous Clairaut's formula, which often is shown in the approximate form

$$\alpha = \frac{5m}{2} - \beta \tag{2j-5a}$$

The small quantity of second order, δ, determines the *type* of the spheroid and is

$$\delta = \frac{7\alpha^2 - 4\alpha\beta - 4\epsilon}{3} \tag{2j-6}$$

If we put $\delta = 0$, we get a spheroid, often called the normal spheroid, which is geometrically a surface of the fourteenth degree.

Helmert introduced the terms with δ, which he computed from the hypotheses of Wiechert and Darwin concerning the internal structure of the earth. He got the values $\delta = 0.0000125$ and $\epsilon = -0.000007$ and a spheroid which differs from the ellipsoid of revolution of the same axis most at latitude 45°, by only $3m$.

Also the ellipsoid is one of the spheroids, i.e., where

$$\delta = \frac{7\alpha^2}{2} - \frac{5\alpha m}{2} \tag{2j-7}$$

Then the two coefficients of the gravity formula are

$$\beta = \frac{5m}{2} - \alpha - \frac{17\alpha m}{14}$$
$$\epsilon = \frac{\alpha(5m - \alpha)}{8} \tag{2j-8}$$

The coefficient β can be either determined by the aid of the gravity anomalies or computed from Eq. (2j-8), if the flattening α has already been accepted. If we use the α value of the international ellipsoid $\alpha = 1/297.0$, we obtain $\beta = 0.0052884$ and $\epsilon = -0.0000059$. In such a way we get the international gravity formula.

$$\gamma = 978.0490(1 + 0.0052884 \sin^2 \phi - 0.0000059 \sin^2 2\phi) \tag{2j-9}$$

The unit is cm/sec² or 1 gal (from Galileo). If we use the unit 1 milligal = 0.001 gal, we have to push the decimal sign three figures to the right.

The equator value $\gamma_E = 978.0490$ gal was computed by Heiskanen in 1928.

The parameters a and α of the international earth ellipsoid and the parameters γ_E, β, and ϵ determine the geometry of the earth ellipsoid and the normal gravity along it. These parameters are

$$\begin{aligned} a &= 6{,}378{,}388.0 \text{ m} \\ \alpha &= 1/297.0 \\ \gamma_E &= 978.0490 \text{ cm/sec}^2 \\ \beta &= 0.0052884 \\ \epsilon &= -0.0000059 \end{aligned} \tag{2j-10}$$

The international earth's ellipsoid and the international gravity formula are in agreement. If it seems necessary to change, for instance, the coefficient β of the gravity formula, then we have to change also the flattening value α of the meridian. Therefore, it is best to use the international ellipsoid and the international gravity formulas until we know exactly how much we have to change β. The change of the equator gravity value γ_E will do no harm for the reference ellipsoid.

The gravity anomaly is $\Delta g = g_0 - \gamma$, where g_0 is the observed gravity value reduced to sea level. The "gravity" does not mean the gravity force, but the acceleration brought about by it.

The gravity anomalies are, in large parts of Europe and the eastern Atlantic, systematically positive; in America and still more clearly in India and northwest of it, they are systematically negative. Gravity formulas are therefore computed also *with* a longitude term, which would correspond to the triaxial ellipsoid. On the largest gravity material bases, the gravity formula with longitude term is

$$\gamma = 987.0524[1 + 0.0052970 \sin^2 \phi - 0.0000059 \sin^2 2\phi + 0.0000276 \cos^2 \phi \cos 2(\lambda + 25°)] \tag{2j-11}$$

ϕ and λ are, of course, the latitude and longitude of the point at which the normal gravity is needed. According to this formula, computed by Heiskanen in 1938, the longitude of the long equator axis, at which longitude the gravity is largest (at the same latitude) is 25° west of Greenwich.

2j-6. Isostatic Equilibrium. The mountains are, in general, no absolute mass surplus and the oceans no absolute mass deficiency in the earth's crust but are compensated by invisible masses of smaller density under the mountains and by masses of higher density under the oceans. Thus at a certain depth the mass unit is subjected to the same pressure regardless of whether it is under a mountain, level land, or the ocean. This is the meaning of isostatic equilibrium.

On the assumption that isostatic equilibrium results from the fact that the mountains rise from the under layer so that the crustal density is smaller the higher the mountains (the Pratt-Hayford hypothesis), the hydrostatic equilibrium prevails (i.e., the depth of compensation is) according to Helmert, at the depth of 122 km; according to Hayford at 113 km, and according to Bowie at 96 km.

If one assumes that the mountains have sunk deeper in the under layer the higher they are, so that they will have "roots" and the oceans corresponding "antiroots" (the Airy-Heiskanen hypothesis), the thickness T of the earth's crust is greater under the mountains and smaller under the oceans than under level terrain. The "normal" thickness T corresponding to the zero elevation of the topography, as obtained from isostatic analysis of the gravity anomalies, is (Heiskanen, 1952) in Norway 32 km, in Fergana basin 38 km, in the Carpathian mountains 30 km, in the central Alps 20 km, in north Italy 29 km, in South Africa 30–35 km, and in France 30 km.

2j-7. Gravimetrical Undulations of the Geoid and Deflections of the Vertical. To compute the undulations N of the geoid and the deflection of the vertical components ξ and η, not only along the measured arcs but in any part of the continents or the oceans, we must know the gravity field of the earth, i.e., the gravity anomalies

Δg reduced to sea level, in the vicinity of the computation point well and all over the world in broad lines. With this information, the undulations N can be obtained with the aid of the famous Stokes formula, derived in 1849, as well as the deflection of the vertical components using the Vening Meinesz formulas, derived in 1928.

The Stokes formula can be written as a finite sum:

$$N = \frac{1}{4\pi}\frac{R}{g}\sum \Delta g_q \int_q S(\psi)dq \qquad \text{(2j-12)}$$

where R is the mean radius and g the mean gravity of the earth, q a fixed square element on the unit sphere, e.g., $1° \times 1°$, Δg_q the corresponding mean gravity anomaly, ψ the angular distance of g from the computation point, and $S(\psi)$ the Stokes function

$$S(\psi) = \csc(\psi/2) + 1 - 6\sin(\psi/2) - 5\cos\psi - 3\cos\psi \ln[\sin(\psi/2) + \sin^2(\psi/2)] \qquad \text{(2j-13)}$$

The formula (2j-12) can be written

$$N = \Sigma c_q \Delta g_q \qquad \text{(2j-14)}$$

$$c_q = \frac{1}{4\pi}\frac{R}{g}\int_q S(\psi)dq$$

Δg_q can be taken from the gravity-anomaly map; the corresponding coefficient c_q can be computed. The summation $\Sigma c_q \Delta g_q$ all over the globe will give the distance N.

The formula for computing the deflections of the vertical component ξ is as follows (Vening Meinesz):

$$\xi'' = \frac{\sin A_2 - \sin A_1}{2\pi}\sum \Delta g_\psi \int_\psi^{\psi+d\psi} Q(\psi)d\psi \qquad \text{(2j-15)}$$

$$Q(\psi) = \frac{\rho''}{2g}\cdot\cos^2\frac{\psi}{2}\left[\csc\frac{\psi}{2} + \frac{3}{1+\sin(\psi/2)} + 12\sin\frac{\psi}{2} - 32\sin^2\frac{\psi}{2} - 12\sin^2\frac{\psi}{2}\ln\left(\sin\frac{\psi}{2} + \sin^2\frac{\psi}{2}\right)\right] \qquad \text{(2j-16)}$$

This formula gives the effect of a compartment between the azimuths A_2 and A_1 as well as between the circle rings with the angular distances ψ and $\psi + d\psi$. Δg_q is the mean gravity anomaly of this compartment. The formula for η will be similar; instead of $(\sin A_2 - \sin A_1)$ it will be $(\cos A_1 - \cos A_2)$.

2j-8. Some Quantities Which Concern the International Ellipsoid

Equator radius a = 6,378,388 m

Polar radius b = 6,356,911 m

Polar radius of curvature $c = a^2/b$ = 6,399,937 m

Mean radius $(2a + b)/3$ = 6,371,229 m

Radius of sphere of same volume = 6,371,221 m

Length of meridian quadrant = 10,002,288 m

Length of equatorial quadrant = 10,019,148 m

Volume of the ellipsoid = $1{,}083{,}319.78 \times 10^6$ km³

Flattening $\alpha = 1/297.0 = 0.00336700$

$$\text{Eccentricity } e = \frac{\sqrt{a^2 - b^2}}{a} = \alpha(2 - \alpha) = 0.08199189;\ e^2 = 0.00672267$$

$$\text{Second eccentricity } e' = \frac{\sqrt{a^2 - b^2}}{b} = 0.08226889;\ e'^2 = 0.00676817$$

$$\text{Function } W = \sqrt{1 - e^2\sin^2\phi}$$

$$\text{Function } V = \sqrt{1 + e'^2\cos^2\phi}$$

$$\text{Meridian radius of curvature } M = a(1 - e^2)/W^3 = c/V^3$$

$$\text{East-west radius of curvature } L = a/W = c/V$$

$$\text{Mean radius of curvature } r = \sqrt{ML} = a\sqrt{1 - e^2}/W^2 = c/V^2$$

General radius of curvature R_A in the aximuth A will be obtained from Euler's formula:

$$\frac{1}{R_A} = \frac{\cos^2 \alpha}{M} + \frac{\sin^2 \alpha}{L}$$

International gravity formula $\gamma = 978.0490[1 + 0.0052884 \sin^2 \phi - 0.0000059 \sin^2 2\phi]$

Normal gravity at equator $\gamma_0 = 978.0490$ cm/sec²

Normal gravity at latitude 45° $\gamma_{45} = 980.6294$ cm/sec²

Normal gravity at pole $\gamma_{90} = 983.2213$ cm/sec²

$$(C - A)/A = 0.003273 = \tfrac{1}{305}$$

where C and A are the moments of inertia about the polar and equatorial axes.

Mean solar day $d = 86{,}400$ sec

Sidereal day $S = 86{,}164.09$ sec

Angular velocity of the earth's rotation $\omega = 2\pi/S = 7.29211585 \times 10^{-5}$ radian/sec.

Gravitational constant $k = 6.673 \times 10^{-8}$ cm² dynes/g²

Mean density of the earth $\rho_m = 5.517$ g/cm³

Mass of the earth $M = 5.975 \times 10^{27}$ g

2k. Seismological and Related Data

B. GUTENBERG

California Institute of Technology

2k-1. List of Symbols

- V velocity of longitudinal wave P
- v velocity of transverse wave S
- P symbol denoting longitudinal wave
- S symbol denoting transverse wave
- k bulk modulus or volume elasticity
- μ rigidity or shear modulus
- ρ density
- σ Poisson's ratio
- A ratio V/v
- t temperature in degrees centigrade, time
- p pressure in bars
- h depth in the earth
- T period of seismic disturbance
- G symbol denoting surface shear waves
- R_a symbol denoting Rayleigh waves
- Δ epicentral distance in degrees

SH	symbol denoting horizontal component of S wave
SV	symbol denoting vertical component of S wave
i	actual angle of incidence at a discontinuity
$\bar{i}$	apparent angle of incidence at a discontinuity
u	ratio of horizontal ground displacement to incident amplitude

2k-2. Fundamental Equations for Elastic Constants and Wave Velocities. In purely elastic, isotropic, homogeneous media the velocity V of longitudinal waves P, v of transverse waves S, the bulk modulus k, the rigidity μ, the density ρ and Poisson's ratio σ are connected by the following equations:

$$V^2 = \frac{k + \frac{4}{3}\mu}{\rho} \qquad v^2 = \frac{\mu}{\rho} \tag{2k-1}$$

$$\sigma = \frac{\frac{1}{2}A^2 - 1}{A^2 - 1} \qquad A = \frac{V}{v} \tag{2k-2}$$

$$k = \rho(V^2 - \tfrac{4}{3}v^2) \qquad \mu = v^2\rho \tag{2k-3}$$

TABLE 2k-1. CORRESPONDING VALUES OF POISSON'S RATIO σ AND V/v

σ	0.00	0.10	0.20	0.22	0.24	0.25	0.26	0.28	0.30	0.40	0.50
V/v	1.414	1.500	1.633	1.670	1.710	1.732	1.756	1.809	1.871	2.449	∞

2k-3. Elastic Constants and Wave Velocities in Rocks (Laboratory Experiments). In rocks the elastic constants and the wave velocities usually increase with increasing pressure p (Tables 2k-2 and 2k-3) and decrease with increasing temperature t and with porosity. Phase changes affect all elastic quantities. At normal pressure, values of Young's modulus have been found[1] to be as shown in Table 2k-4. Wavelengths are usually great enough in geophysics to permit assumption of isotropy.

TABLE 2k-2. ELASTIC CONSTANTS AND WAVE VELOCITIES IN ROCKS AT ROOM TEMPERATURE*

	μ, 10^{11} dynes/cm²		k, 10^{11} dynes/cm²		σ	V, km/sec	v, km/sec
	1 atm	4,000 atm	1 atm	4,000 atm			
Dunite	$4\frac{3}{4}$–6	$6\frac{1}{2}$–7	?	12 ±	0.25–0.30	$7\frac{1}{2}$–$8\frac{1}{2}$	$4\frac{1}{4}$–$4\frac{3}{4}$
Gabbro	3–4	4–5	6 ±	$8\frac{3}{4}$ ±	0.2–0.3	5–7	$3\frac{1}{2}$–4
Granite	$1\frac{1}{2}$–$2\frac{1}{2}$	$3\frac{1}{4}$–$3\frac{1}{2}$	$2\frac{3}{4}$–$3\frac{1}{2}$	$5\frac{1}{4}$ ±	0.20–0.26	5–$6\frac{1}{4}$	2–$3\frac{1}{2}$
Obsidian glass	$2\frac{3}{4}$–3	?	$3\frac{1}{4}$ ±	$3\frac{3}{4}$–4	0.1–0.2?	5 ±	$3\frac{1}{2}$ ±
Ice	$\frac{1}{4}$–$\frac{1}{2}$	?	$\frac{3}{4}$–1	?	0.3–0.4	$3\frac{1}{4}$–$3\frac{3}{4}$	$1\frac{1}{2}$–2

* F. Birch, ed., Handbook of Physical Constants, *Geol. Soc. Amer., Spec. Paper* 36 (1942); L. H. Adams, Elastic Properties of Materials of the Earth's Crust, in "Internal Constitution of the Earth," 2d ed., pp. 50–80, 1951.

2k-4. Periods and Amplitudes of Seismic Waves. Most seismographs have their maximum magnification for waves with periods T between 0.1 sec (short-period instruments, mainly for nearby shocks) and 15 sec (for teleseisms, especially transverse and surface waves); most instruments for recording of artificial explosions in com-

[1] F. Birch, ed., Handbook of Physical Constants, *Geol. Soc. Amer., Spec. Paper* 36, 70 (1942).

TABLE 2k-3. LONGITUDINAL VELOCITIES, KM/SEC, AT PRESSURES p AND TEMPERATURES t CORRESPONDING TO THE DEPTH h IN THE EARTH AFTER LABORATORY MEASUREMENT*

p, bars	t, °C	h, km	Dunite	Solenhofen limestone	Barrifield granite	Quincy granite	Cheshire quartzite
90	25	0.33	8.60	6.00	5.85	5.88	6.00
750	100	2.8 ±	8.77	5.93	6.28	6.17	6.04
1,620	200	6.1 ±	8.78	5.84	6.35	6.23	5.83
2,540	300	9.4 ±	8.70	5.82	....	....	5.59

* D. S. Hughes, and J. H. Cross, Elastic Wave Velocities at High Pressures and Temperatures, *Geophysics* **16**, 577 (1951).

TABLE 2k-4. YOUNG'S MODULUS FOR QUARTZ AT NORMAL PRESSURE (Units 10^{11} dynes/cm^2)

	α quartz		β quartz
	0°C	570°C	600°C
⊥ optic axis.	10.3	5.9	9.5
∥ optic axis.	7.9	3.0	10.7

mercial work record mainly waves with $0.001 < T < 0.1$ sec. In longitudinal body waves of earthquakes, usually $T = 0.1$ to 0.5 sec near the epicenter, but shorter periods exist. With distance increasing beyond 5,000 ± km T increases to several seconds. In transverse body waves the prevailing periods T are frequently about twice those of the longitudinal; the two waves then have roughly the same length. In surface waves of nearby shocks T is usually a fraction of a second, but longer waves ($T > 10$ sec) are recorded. T increases with distance; beyond about 4,000 km, surface waves usually do not contain well-recorded waves with $T < 12$ sec. In major shocks the fastest surface waves have periods $T \geq 1$ min; after traveling a few times around the earth (each time in about $2\frac{1}{2}$ hr) they frequently start with periods of many minutes.

Periods of natural microseisms (continued motion from meteorological sources and ocean waves) range from a fraction of a second to a minute or more. The largest amplitudes of the most frequent types of microseisms ($4 \leq T \leq 10$ sec) are a few microns at inland stations on rock and between 10 and 100 μ at stations near oceans during heavy storms (hurricanes).

In great distant earthquakes, waves through the earth's interior may exhibit ground amplitudes of over 10 μ with $T \sim 5$ sec, and surface waves may have ground amplitudes of 10 mm with $T \sim 20$ sec. Much greater amplitudes occur near the source. In motion from not too close artificial explosions longitudinal waves usually carry the largest amplitudes, and even waves through the earth's core have been identified on their records.[1]

2k-5. Travel Times of Earthquake Waves. Examples of travel times are given in Table 2k-5. Surface waves traveling a few times around the earth have travel times of several hours. No dispersion has been established for body waves. However, the prevailing increase of their velocity with depth results in an increase in wave velocity

[1] B. Gutenberg, Travel Times of Longitudinal Waves from Surface Foci, *Proc. Natl. Acad. Sci. U.S.* **39**, 849 (1953).

of surface waves as their wavelength (depth of energy penetration) increases. The corresponding group velocity has a minimum[1] for periods of several seconds, depending on the crustal structure.

TABLE 2k-5. TRAVEL TIMES* (MIN:SEC) OF DIRECT LONGITUDINAL WAVES P AND TRANSVERSE WAVES S THROUGH THE EARTH STARTING AT DEPTH h, AND OF SURFACE SHEAR WAVES G AND RAYLEIGH WAVES R_a WITH PERIODS OF ABOUT 1 MIN (INDEPENDENT OF FOCAL DEPTH)

(Δ = epicentral distance, deg; P waves arriving at $\Delta > 100$ deg enter the earth's core.)

Δ	h = 25 km		G, min	R_a, min	h = 300 km		h = 700 km	
	P	S			P	S	P	S
0	0:04	0:07	....	....	0:39	1:08	1:20	2:24
2	0:32	0:55	....	....	0:46	1:24	1:24	2:30
4	0:59	1:56	....	....	1:07	1:51	1:32	2:48
10	2:28	.....	4.1	4.5	2:17	4:03	2:20	4:12
20	4:34	8:16	8.3	9.0	4:15	7:39	3:55	7:02
40	7:36	13:42	16.5	17.9	7:11	12:52	6:44	12:01
70	11:12	20:20	28.9	31.4	10:44	19:21	10:11	18:20
100	13:46	25:14	41.3	44.8	13:15	24:23	12:37	23:14
120	18:54	28:00	49.5	53.8	18:19	27:09	17:38	26:01
150	19:46	.....	61.9	67.2	19:11	.....	18:31	
180	20:10	.....	74.2	80.6	19:35	.....	18:54	

* B. Gutenberg, Travel Times of Longitudinal Waves from Surface Foci, *Proc. Natl. Acad. Sci. U.S.* **39,** 849 (1953); H. Jeffreys and K. E. Bullen, "Seismological Tables," British Association for the Advancement of Science, 1940; B. Gutenberg, and C. F. Richter, On Seismic Waves, *Gerlands Beitr. Geophys.* **43,** 56–133 (1934); **54,** 94–136 (1939).

2k-6. Reflection and Refraction of Waves. If a body wave P or S arrives at a discontinuity, one P and one S wave are reflected and one of each type is refracted if the velocity ratio V_r/V_i of the reflected or refracted (r) and incident (i) wave permits.[2]

$$\sin i_r = \frac{V_r}{V_i} \sin i_i \tag{2k-4}$$

where i = angle of incidence. Examples are given in Table 2k-6. Amplitudes of transverse waves (vibrations perpendicular to the ray) are frequently resolved into two components, SH in the horizontal plane, and SV (with a vertical component) perpendicular to SH. If an SH wave is incident, the reflected wave and the refracted wave (if it exists) are always of the SH type.

If a wave arrives at the earth's surface (actual angle of incidence i) a wave of the same type is reflected (angle i), and one of the other type may be reflected [Eq. (2k-4)] (see Table 2k-7). As a consequence of these three waves, the apparent angle of incidence $\bar{\imath}$ calculated from records of horizontal H and vertical V instruments ($\tan \bar{\imath} = H/V$) differs from i. In case of incident transverse waves the particles move in ellipses,[3] if $(V \sin i)/v > 1$. If an SH wave is incident, the reflected wave has the same amplitude as the incident wave, the ground displacement is twice the incident

[1] M. Ewing and F. Press, Crustal Structure and Surface-wave Dispersion, *Bull. Seis. Soc. Amer.* **40,** 271–280 (1950); **42,** 315–325 (1952); **43,** 137–144 (1953).

[2] J. B. Macelwane, "Introduction to Theoretical Seismology," pt. 1, pp. 156–178, 1936; B. Gutenberg, Energy Ratio of Reflected and Refracted Seismic Waves, *Bull. Seis. Soc. Amer.* **34,** 85–102 (1944).

[3] B. Gutenberg, *SV* and *SH*, *Trans. Am. Geophys. Union* **33,** 573–584 (1952).

TABLE 2k-6. SQUARE ROOT OF ENERGY REFLECTED OR TRANSMITTED AT A DISCONTINUITY WITH DENSITY RATIO (UPPER LAYER TO LOWER) 1.103, CORRESPONDING VELOCITY RATIO 1.286 FOR P AND FOR S, POISSON'S RATIO 0.25 IN BOTH LAYERS

(Incident energy taken as unity. Based on Slichter-Gabriel.* 1– indicates values between 0.95 and 1.0. i = angle of incidence. P = longitudinal, SV = component of transverse wave in plane of ray)

$i°$	Refracted waves								Reflected waves							
	P from				*SV* from				*P* from				*SV* from			
	Above		Below		Above		Below		Above		Below		Above		Below	
	P	*SV*	*P*	*SV*	*P*	*SV*	*P*	*SV*	*P*	*SV*	*P*	*SV*	*P*	*SV*	*P*	*SV*
0	1–	0.0	1–	0.0	0.0	0.2	0.0	1–	0.2	0.0	0.2	0.0	1.0	0.0	0.0	0.2
15	1–	0.1	1–	0.1	0.1	0.1	0.1	1–	0.2	0.1	0.2	0.1	1–	0.1	0.1	0.1
30	1–	0.1	1–	0.1	. . .	0.2	0.2	1–	0.1	0.1	0.1	0.1	0.9	0.2	0.1	0.0
45	0.5	0.2	0.9	0.1	. . .	0.4	0.3	1–	0.2	0.0	0.1	0.1	0.9	0.3	. . .	0.2
60	. . .	0.3	0.9	0.2	. . .	. . .	. . .	1–	0.9	0.1	0.2	0.1	. . .	. . .	. . .	0.3
75	. . .	0.4	0.8	0.3	. . .	. . .	. . .	0.8	0.9	0.1	0.4	0.1	. . .	. . .	. . .	0.5
90	. . .	0.0	0.0	0.0	. . .	. . .	. . .	0.0	1.0	0.0	1.0	0.0	. . .	. . .	. . .	1.0

* B. Gutenberg, *Bull. Seis. Soc. Amer.* **34,** 85 (1944).

TABLE 2k-7. SQUARE ROOTS OF RATIO OF REFLECTED TO INCIDENT ENERGY a AT EARTH'S SURFACE AS FUNCTION OF ANGLE OF INCIDENCE i AND RATIO OF HORIZONTAL u AND VERTICAL w GROUND DISPLACEMENTS TO INCIDENT AMPLITUDE FOR CONTINUOUS SINUSOIDAL WAVES IF POISSON'S RATIO IS 0.25

(Elliptic motion of ground is indicated by *, and corresponding values for $\bar{\imath}$ are calculated on the assumption that the vertical and horizontal component reach their maximum simultaneously.† SV = component of transverse wave in plane of ray)

i	Longitudinal wave *P* incident					*SV* incident				
	a of *P*	a of *SV*	u	w	$\bar{\imath}$, deg	a of *P*	a of *SV*	u	w	$\bar{\imath}$, deg
0°	1.0	0.0	0.0	2.0	0	0.0	1.0	2.0	0.0	0
20	0.8	0.6	0.8	1.9	23	0.9	0.4	1.8	0.8	23
30	0.6	0.8	1.2	1.7	34	1.0	0.0	1.7	1.0	30
35.3	0.5	0.9	1.3	1.5	39	0.0	1.0	4.9	0.0	±0
40	0.4	0.9	1.4	1.4	44	. . .	1.0	0.7*	1.6*	−64*
45	0.3	0.9	1.5	1.3	48	. . .	1.0	0.0	1.4	±90
60	0.0	1.0	1.7	1.0	60	. . .	1.0	0.5*	1.1*	66*
80	0.1	1.0	1.3	0.5	69	. . .	1.0	0.3*	0.5*	59*
90	1.0	0.0	0.0	0.0	71	. . .	1.0	0.0*	0.0*	60*

† B. Gutenberg, *SV* and *SH*, *Trans. Am. Geophys. Union* **33,** 573–584 (1952).

amplitude, and $\bar{\imath} = i$. For energy ratios of waves reflected and refracted at the boundary of the earth's core, see Table 2k-8. An *SH* wave incident upon the core is totally reflected.

TABLE 2k-8. SQUARE ROOTS OF ENERGY RATIOS FOR WAVES REFRACTED (REFR.) AND REFLECTED (REFL.) AT THE BOUNDARY OF THE EARTH'S CORE*

[Assumed at the core boundary: densities 5.4 (mantle), 10.1 (core); longitudinal velocities 13.7 and 8.0 km/sec, respectively; transverse velocity in the mantle 7.25 km/sec, 0 in core. i = angle of incidence of the arriving wave]

P incident in mantle				*P* incident in core				*SV* incident in mantle			
i	Refr. *P*	Refl. *P*	Refl. *S*	i	Refr. *P*	Refr. *S*	Refl. *P*	i	Refr. *P*	Refl. *P*	Refl. *S*
0	0.999	0.04	0.00	0	0.999	0.00	0.04	0	0.00	0.00	1.00
20	0.96	0.12	0.24	20	0.90	0.44	0.08	20	0.50	0.39	0.78
40	0.87	0.29	0.39	33½	0.79	0.62	0.00	30	0.61	0.47	0.64
60	0.79	0.42	0.44	35	0.83	0.55	0.10	31	0.58	0.49	0.65
80	0.84	0.20	0.51	35.7	0.00	0.00	1.00	32.0	0.00	0.00	1.00
83.8	0.85	0.00	0.52	37	.....	0.85	0.53	33	0.84	....	0.54
85	0.85	0.10	0.52	50	.....	0.92	0.40	40	0.92	....	0.40
89	0.60	0.71	0.36	80	.....	0.62	0.78	64	0.55	....	0.84
90	0.00	1.00	0.00	90	.....	0.00	1.00	65.0	....	....	1.00

* After S. Dana, The Partition of Energy among Seismic Waves Reflected and Refracted at the Earth's Core, *Bull. Seis. Soc. Amer.* **34,** 189–197 (1944).

2k-7. Wave Types and Their Symbols. The main discontinuities of the earth (Fig. 2k-1) are its surface, the "Mohorovičić discontinuity" (depth 10 ± km in the deeper parts of the major oceans, 30 ± km under the lower parts of continents, perhaps

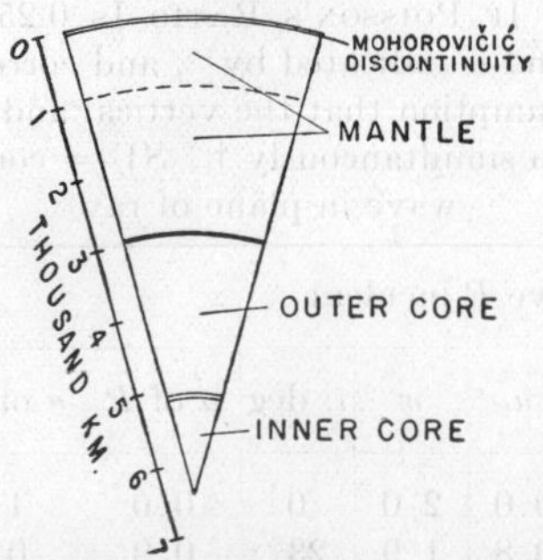

FIG. 2k-1. Main discontinuities of the earth.

up to 60 km under high mountain ranges) and the boundary of the earth's core at a depth of 2,900 ± 20 km (radius r = 3,470 km). There is doubt whether the boundary of the "inner core" (r = 1,300 ± km) is a discontinuity or whether the transition extends over a zone with a depth range of 100 to 200 km.

By international agreement longitudinal waves in the mantle are indicated by *P* (starting downward at the source) or *p* (starting upward), transverse waves by *S* or *s*, longitudinal waves through the outer core by *K*, through the inner core by *I*, and (hypothetical) transverse waves through the inner core by *J*. $P' \equiv PKP$, $P'' \equiv PKIKP$. For a source below the surface, there is one reflection at the surface near the epicenter, another about halfway between source and station. The symbols for these waves are, respectively, pP and PP, sP and SP, pS and PS, sS and SS. Similarly, for twice-reflected waves pPP, PPP, etc., are used. Time differences $pP - P$, $sP - P$, $sS - S$, etc., give a good indication for the focal depth (Table 2k-9).[1] Among waves through the core reflected at the surface of the earth are $pPKP$, $sPKP$, $P'P' \equiv PKPPKP$, $P'P'P'$ (with a travel time of about 1 hr).

Waves in the mantle with a reflection at the core surface permit accurate determination of the radius of the core. They are indicated by c, e.g., PcP, PcS, ScS; $pPcP$, $ScSScS$, etc., are in addition, reflected at the surface. All these waves have periods of 1 to 4 sec. Waves reflected inside the core are indicated by $PKKP$, $SKKS$, etc. Their periods, too, are small ($PKKP$ waves with wavelengths $L < 10$ km have been observed) indicating a sharp boundary of the core. Waves refracted through the core (in addition to PKP) are PKS, SKP, SKS, etc. All observed travel times agree within a few seconds with those following from the velocities for P, K, and S (see Table 2k-11).

TABLE 2k-9. FOCAL DEPTH, KM, OF EARTHQUAKES FOR GIVEN TIME DIFFERENCES $pP - P$, $sP - P$, AND $sS - S$ FOR EPICENTRAL DISTANCES Δ OF 30, 80, AND 145 DEG

(* indicates that pP, sP, or sS, respectively, does not exist under given conditions)

Time diff., min:sec	$\Delta = 30$ deg			$\Delta = 80$ deg			$\Delta = 145$ deg	
	$pP - P$	$sP - P$	$sS - S$	$pP - P$	$sP - P$	$sS - S$	$pP' - P'$	$sP' - P'$
0:20	100	60	50	75	55	40	70	55
0:40	205	120	100	160	105	85	150	105
1:00	310	195	165	250	165	140	235	160
1:30	*	295	270	395	255	220	375	250
2:00	*	415	425	565	350	300	525	345
2:30	*	535	*	755	460	390	690	440
3:00	*	*	*	?	575	485	?	540

2k-8. Equations Used in Calculating Travel Times and Velocities. If i = angle of incidence (between ray and vertical), r = radius vector measured from center of earth, V = velocity, and if quantities at the surface of the earth are indicated by the index o, the ray equation is

$$\frac{r \sin i}{V} = \frac{r_0 \sin i_0}{V_0} = \text{const} \tag{2k-5}$$

The radius R of curvature of the ray is given by

$$R = \frac{V}{(dV/dr) \sin i} \tag{2k-6}$$

If $dV/dr = V/r$, and $i = 90$ deg, $R = r$. If V decreases with depth at a greater rate, no ray can have its deepest point in the respective layer, and the travel-time curve is interrupted. The angle of incidence i_o at the surface at a given epicentral distance Δ is found from

$$\sin i_0 = \frac{V_0}{\overline{V}_0} \tag{2k-7}$$

where $\overline{V} = d\Delta/dt$.

[1] B. Gutenberg and C. F. Richter, Materials for the Study of Deep-focus Earthquakes, *Bull. Seis. Soc. Amer.* **26**, 341–390 (1936); see also H. Jeffreys and K. E. Bullen, "Seismological Tables," p. 24, British Association for the Advancement of Science, 1940.

The angular distance θ of a ray section (or the whole ray) and the corresponding travel time t are given by

$$\Theta = \int_{r_1}^{r_2} \frac{\tan i}{r}\, dr \qquad t = \int_{r_1}^{r_2} \frac{dr}{V \cos i} \tag{2k-8}$$

The radius r_S to the deepest point of a ray arriving at the distance Δ in degrees and the corresponding velocity V_S are found from

$$\log r_S = \log r_o - 0.0024127 \int_0^\Delta q\, d\Delta \tag{2k-9}$$

where $\cosh q = \overline{V}_\Delta / \overline{V}(\Delta)$.

$$V_S = \overline{V} \frac{r_S}{r_0} \tag{2k-10}$$

$\overline{V}_\Delta = \overline{V}$ at the distance Δ, $\overline{V}(\Delta)$ is variable as a function of Δ. Equation (2k-9) cannot be used if V decreases suddenly with depth between r_o and r_S or if it decreases gradually at a rate in excess of that given by $dV/dr = V/r$.[1]

2k-9. Wave Velocity, Elastic Constants, and Pressure in the Earth. Equations (2k-9) and (2k-10) or other methods are used to calculate V and v as a function of r. Poisson's ratio follows from Eq. (2k-2). If the density ρ is known as a function of depth, Eqs. (2k-3) give the bulk modulus k and the rigidity μ. The pressure p and gravity g are given by

$$g = \frac{4\pi K}{r^2} \int_0^r \rho r^2\, dr = \frac{3g_0}{\rho_m r_0 r^2} \int_0^r \rho r^2\, dr \qquad p = \int_r^{r_0} g\, dr \tag{2k-11}$$

K = gravitational constant (6.673×10^{-8} cgs), ρ_m = mean density of the earth (5.517 g/cm³), r_o = radius of the earth (6,371 km) and g_o = gravity at the surface (981 gal).

In sediments (thickness usually < 2 km, but up to 20 km in some basins) the longitudinal velocity V ranges from 1 ± km/sec for sand to 7 ± in well-cemented rocks. In the continents frequently "granitic rocks," $V = 6 \pm$ km/sec, are below the sediments. At a depth of 15 ± km V and v seem to have minima[2] (compare Table 2k-3). In the next deeper layer in the continents V is usually $6\frac{1}{2}$ to 7 km/sec which is, e.g., characteristic of gabbro and olivine-gabbro (selected data in Table 2k-10; details differ appreciably). In some regions indications of velocities of 7 to $7\frac{1}{2}$ km/sec have been found immediately above the Mohorovičić discontinuity. The values found for the velocity v of transverse waves corresponding to $V = 6 \pm$ km/sec scatter between about 3.0 and 3.5 ± km/sec; a few data corresponding to $V = 6\frac{1}{2}$ km/sec are near 3.7 km/sec; below the Mohorovičić discontinuity, see Table 2k-10.

Below 60 ± km no regional differences in V have been established (Table 2k-11).

2k-10. Intensity, Magnitude, and Energy of Earthquakes, and Related Quantities. The "intensity" of an earthquake refers to the effects of shaking at a given point. In the United States the modified Mercalli scale[3] (I to XII) is used; a few greatly condensed examples follow.

II. Felt by few persons at rest.

IV. Felt outdoors by few; some sleepers awakened; dishes, windows disturbed.

V. Some dishes, windows broken; unstable objects overturned; pendulum clocks may stop.

VI. Felt by all; some fallen plaster or damaged chimneys.*

[1] For other limitations, see L. B. Slichter, The Theory of the Interpretation of Seismic Travel Time Curves in Horizontal Structures, *Physics* **3**, 273 (1932); H. Witte, Beiträge zur Berechnung der Geschwindigkeit der Raumwellen im Erdinnern, *Nachr. Ges. Wiss. Göttingen, Math.-physik Kl.*, 1932, p. 199.

[2] B. Gutenberg, Low Velocity Layers in the Earth's Mantle, *Bull. Geol. Soc. Amer.* **65**, 337–347 (1954); Channel Waves in the Earth's Crust, *Geophysics* **20**, 283–294 (1955).

[3] H. O. Wood and F. Neumann, Modified Mercalli Intensity Scale of 1931, *Bull. Seis. Soc. Amer.* **21**, 277–283 (1931).

* Continued on p. **2**–110.

TABLE 2k-10. VELOCITY V, KM/SEC, OF LONGITUDINAL WAVES AT SELECTED DEPTH INTERVALS h, KM, OBSERVED IN VARIOUS REGIONS, 1950–1953*

(SE = source of energy, AE = artificial explosions, EQ = earthquake, RB = rock burst. M_0 is the depth of the Mohorovičić discontinuity below sea level; V_M, v_M are reported longitudinal and transverse velocities, respectively, just below M_0. Corresponding values of Poisson's ratio are 0.23 to 0.27)

Region	SE	h	V	h	V	M_0	V_M	v_M
N. Germany......	AE	2–10	5.9	10–?	6.7	?	?	?
N.W. Germany...	AE	6–15±	5.5±	15–28	6.4±	28±	8.18	4.58
Black Forest......	AE	1–21	6.0	21–31	6.55	31	8.2	4.82
Southern Alps....	EQ	0–35	5.7±	35–45±	6.6±	45±	8.1	?
Northern Italy....	EQ	?	5.2–5.5	?	6.4–7.0	40±	7.8–8.0	4.4–4.8
South Africa......	RB	4–36(?)	6.1	?	6.8?	36	8.27	4.83
New York........	AE	0–34	6.3			34	8.2	4.68
Eastern U.S......	AE	0–5	6.0	5–15	6.5±	45±	8.1	?
Wisconsin.........	AE	$\frac{1}{2}$–3	$4\frac{1}{2}$	3–42±	6.0–6.9	42±	8.17	?
So. California....	AE	1±	5.8	4–12	6.1–6.7	32±	8.2	?
So. California.....	EQ	?	?	?	?	32–40±	8.17	4.60
Sierra Nevada....	EQ					50±	8.17	?
Canadian Shield..	RB	0–35(?)	6.23	?	7.0?	$36\frac{1}{2}$	8.18	4.85
Japan............	AE	$1\frac{1}{2}$–27	6.1±	27–32	7.4	32±	8.2?	?
W. Atlantic Basic.	AE	(Water)		5–10±	6.7	10±	8.1	?
Pacific Basin.....	AE	(Water)		5–11±	6.8±	11±	8.2	?

* B. Gutenberg, Wave Velocities in the Earth's Crust, *Geol. Soc. Amer. Spec. Paper* **62**, 19–34 (1955).

TABLE 2k-11. WAVE VELOCITIES V (LONGITUDINAL) AND v (TRANSVERSE), KM/SEC

[Poisson's ratio σ, Eq. (2), density ρ, g/cm³ (Bullen*), bulk modulus k and rigidity μ, both in 10^{12} dynes/cm², Eq. (3), gravitational acceleration g, cm/sec², and pressure p, million atm (Bullen*) in the earth as function of depth, km]

Depth	V	v	σ	ρ	k	μ	g	p
Mantle:								
50	8.2	4.45	0.26	3.3	1.3	0.65	985	0.014
100	8.0	4.4	0.27	3.4	1.3	0.65	987	0.03
150	7.9	4.35	0.27	3.4	1.3	0.64	989	0.05
200	8.0	4.4	0.28	3.5	1.3	0.68	990	0.06
250	8.2	4.5	0.28	3.5	1.4	0.71	991	0.08
300	8.3	4.6	0.29	3.6	1.6	0.8	992	0.10
500	9.6	5.3	0.28	3.9	2	1.1	997	0.17
1,000	11.5	6.4	0.28	4.7	$3\frac{1}{2}$	1.9	991	0.39
1,500	12.2	6.7	0.28	5.1	$4\frac{1}{2}$	2.3	979	0.6
2,000	12.8	6.9	0.29	$5\frac{1}{4}$	5	2.6	972	1
2,900	13.7	7.3	0.30	$5\frac{3}{4}$	$6\frac{1}{2}$	3.1	1,000	$1\frac{1}{2}$
Outer core:								
2,900	8.0	No S waves	0.5	$9\frac{1}{2}$±	6±	$\mu = 0$	1,000	$1\frac{1}{2}$
4,000	9.4	known	0.5	11±	10±	assumed	910±	$2\frac{1}{4}$
5,000	10.0		0.5	12±	12±		630±	$3\frac{1}{4}$±
Inner core:								
5,400	11.1	?	?	15?	18?	?	560±	$3\frac{1}{2}$±
6,370	11.2	?	?	15?	18?	?	0	$3\frac{3}{4}$±

* K. E. Bullen, "An Introduction to the Theory of Seismology," 2d ed., pp. 212–223, Cambridge, 1953.

Table 2k-12. Values of $F(\Delta)$ and $f(\Delta,h)$ in Eq. (2k-12) for Vertical Components Z of P and PP, Horizontal Component SH of S, and Horizontal Component of Maximum (Max)
(h = focal depth; Δ = epicentral distance, deg*)

Δ	h = 25 km				h = 300 km			h = 600 km		
	PZ	PPZ	SH	Max	PZ	PPZ	SH	PZ	PPZ	SH
20	6.3	...	5.9	4.0	5.0	...	6.0	6.1	...	6.0
30	6.5	6.7	6.1	4.3	6.6	5.9	6.3	6.2	6.0	6.1
50	6.8	6.7	6.6	4.6	6.5	6.4	6.4	6.4	6.3	6.3
80	6.8	7.1	6.9	5.0	6.3	7.0	6.6	6.5	6.9	6.7
100	7.3	7.0	7.2	5.1	7.2	6.7	6.8	7.2	7.0	6.8
160	...	6.8	...	5.4	...	6.6	...	...	6.7	

* B. Gutenberg, Amplitudes of Surface Waves and Magnitudes of Shallow Earthquakes, *Bull. Seis. Soc. Amer.* **35**, 3–12 (1945); Magnitude Determination for Deep-focus Earthquakes, *Bull. Seis. Soc. Amer.* **35**, 117–130 (1945).

VII. Considerable damage in poorly built structures.
IX. Buildings shifted off foundations; ground cracked.
XI. Few structures remain standing; rails bent.

The observed intensity depends on the depth of focus, the ground, the type of building, the density of population, etc. The intensity is useful for engineers but not for studies of seismicity, for which the earthquake magnitude M is used. Magnitude M originally was defined[1] for Southern California as the common logarithm of the maximum trace amplitude expressed in microns with which a seismograph with $T = 0.8$ sec, magnification 2,800, damping 65:1 would record the shock at a distance of 100 km. Tables[1] permit the determination of M. In addition, for $\Delta > 15°$, M is now found (1) from ground amplitudes b (in microns) of surface waves with periods of 20 sec in shallow earthquakes; (2) from amplitudes a of P, PP, and S waves in shocks (focal depth h) recorded at the epicentral distance $\Delta°$:

$$(1)\ M_S = \log b + F(\Delta) \qquad (2)\ M_B = \log a - \log T + f(\Delta,h) \qquad (2k\text{-}12)$$

For $F(\Delta)$ and $f(\Delta,h)$, see Table 2k-12; small station corrections are to be added. The amplitudes b of surface waves of length L decrease with increasing focal depth h corresponding to a factor $e^{-qh/L}$, where q (about 2) depends on crustal structure.

The energy E corresponding to the amplitude M depends on duration of the shock, periods of the motion, depth of focus, etc. To a first approximation,

$$\log E = m + nM \qquad (2k\text{-}13)$$

$m = 12$, $n = 1.8$ have been used,[2] but the resulting E was too great, and $m = 5.8$, $n = 2.4$ are preferable in connection with M_B.[3]

2k-11. Seismicity of the Earth. Earthquakes are divided into shallow shocks ($h \leq 60$ km), intermediate ($60 < h \leq 300$), and deep ($h > 300$, maximum $720 \pm$ km). Most shocks occur in narrow belts (Table 2k-14).[2] Deep and intermediate shocks are limited to the circumpacific belt and the trans-Asiatic (Alpide) belt.*

[1] C. F. Richter, An Instrumental Earthquake Magnitude Scale, *Bull. Seis. Soc. Amer.* **25**, 1–32 (1935).
[2] B. Gutenberg and C. F. Richter, "Seismicity of the Earth," 2d ed., Princeton University Press, Princeton, N.J., 1954.
[3] B. Gutenberg and C. F. Richter, Magnitude and Energy of Earthquakes, *Nature* **176**, 795 (1955).
* Continued after Table 2k-17, p. 2-112.

TABLE 2k-13. INTENSITY I AT THE EPICENTER, CORRESPONDING MAXIMUM ACCELERATION α, CM/SEC^2, MEAN RADIUS r_p OF AREA OF PERCEPTIBILITY, KM, LOG E OF ENERGY, ERGS, FOR A GIVEN MAGNITUDE M, IN AVERAGE SHOCKS IN SOUTHERN CALIFORNIA ($h = 16 \pm$ KM)

[Values for I, α, r are based on empirical equations, those for log E on Eq. (2k-13) with $m = 11$, $n = 1.6$]*

M	2.2	3	4	5	6	7	8	$8\frac{1}{2}$
I	1.5	2.8	4.5	6.2	7.8	9.5	11.2	12.0
α	1	3	10	36	130	460	1,670	3,160
r_p	0	25	55	110	200	390	740	1,000
log E	14.5	15.8	17.4	19.0	20.6	22.2	23.8	24.6

* B. Gutenberg and C. F. Richter, Earthquake Magnitude, Intensity, Energy, and Acceleration, *Bull. Seis. Soc. Amer.* **32,** 163–191 (1942). Recent values (1955) for log E using M_B and $m = 5.8$, $n = 2.4$ in Eq. (2k-13) agree within the limits of error with those in Table 2k-13. M, M_S, and M_B agree with each other only near $M = 6$ to 7. For details see *Nature* **176,** 795 (1955).

TABLE 2k-14. NUMBER OF SHALLOW, INTERMEDIATE, AND DEEP-FOCUS EARTHQUAKES, % OF ALL EARTHQUAKES IN THE GIVEN DEPTH RANGE, AND CORRESPONDING ENERGY RELEASE (a) IN THE MAJOR UNITS OF THE EARTH AND (b) IN SELECTED AREAS

Region	Number, %			Energy, %		
	Shallow	Inter-med.	Deep	Shallow	Inter-med.	Deep
(a) Circumpacific belt	82	91	100	75	89	100
Trans-Asiatic belt	10	9	0	23	11	0.3
Atlantic and Indian Ocean	5	0	0	1	0	0
All others	3	0	0	1	0	0
Total	100	100	100	100	100	100
(b) Pacific region, Alaska to U.S.	2	0	0	2	0	0
North and Central America, West Coast	12	10	0	12	8	0
South America, western part	10	19	6	15	9	19
Kermadec-Tonga Is.	3	3	41	4	5	25
New Hebrides and Solomon Is.	12	20	4	7	18	3
Marianas Is.	2	6	6	1	8	3
Japan-Kamchatka	15	16	35	19	22	44
Philippine Is.	5	3	4	6	2	3
Celebes-Sunda Is.	8	11	4	6	15	3
Hindu Kush	0	5	0	0	6	0
Asia Minor to Italy	2	2	0	1	4	0
Total	71	95	100	73	97	100

TABLE 2k-15. (a) MAGNITUDE M OF GREATEST KNOWN SHOCK (1905–1952) IN DEPTH INTERVALS d, CENTERING AT h; (b) PERCENTAGE OF SHOCKS FOR THE WHOLE EARTH; (c) CORRESPONDING FREQUENCY FOR SELECTED PARTS OF THE CIRCUMPACIFIC BELT

d, km	60	60	100	100	100	100	100	50	50
h, km	30	90	175	275	375	475	575	650	700
(a) Largest observed M	8.6	8.1	8.2	7.8	8.0	7.5	7.8	7.6	6.9
(b) Number of shocks, %	72	12	7	2	2	2	2	1	$\frac{1}{3}$
(c) Mexico, Central America, %	73	20	6	1	0	0	0	0	0
Andes, %	36	30	20	5	0	0	4	4	0
New Zealand–Samoa, %	30	10	10	6	7	6	25	5	$\frac{1}{2}$
New Hebrides–New Guinea, %	43	30	20	4	3	1	0	0	0
Japan–Manchuria, %	36	16	11	6	15	9	6	$\frac{1}{4}$	0
Sunda Arc, %	30	26	20	1	4	1	10	2	5

TABLE 2k-16. AVERAGE ANNUAL ENERGY RELEASE IN ALL EARTHQUAKES WITH $M \leq M^*$

(Units 10^{23} ergs. Ratios of figures are good approximations; absolute values may be incorrect by factor 100)

M^*	6	7	8
Shallow shocks	0.2	1	5
Intermediate shocks	?	0.2	0.6
Deep shocks	?	0.05	0.1

TABLE 2k-17. MAXIMUM, MINIMUM, AND AVERAGE ANNUAL ENERGY RELEASE IN EARTHQUAKES 1904–1952*

(Units 10^{23} ergs. Accuracy as in Table 2k-16)

	Max	Year	Min	Year	Avg
Shallow shocks	340	1906	9	1954	70
Intermediate shocks	100	1911	1	1933	16
Deep shocks	75	1906	0.2	Several	3
All shocks	430	1906	12	1930	90

* B. Gutenberg, Energy of Earthquakes, *Science* **122,** 876 (1955).

For the magnitude of the largest observed shock and the relative frequency of earthquakes in various depth intervals, see Table 2k-15, which also shows examples of regional differences.

2k-12. Energy E of Earthquakes. Most calculations of E depend on Eq. (2k-13). Estimated errors in log E are ± 1, but relative values of E are fairly accurate. The shocks of magnitudes over 7 account for most of the total energy release (Table 2k-16). For annual extreme and average energy release, 1904 to 1952, see Table 2k-17. The annual energy release by heat flow from the earth's interior through the surface is about $70{,}000 \times 10^{23}$ ergs.

2k-13. Aftershocks and Earthquake Sequences. Investigations by Benioff[1] show that elastic strain-rebound increments in series of earthquake aftershocks follow two types of functions:

$$(1)\ S_1 = A + B \log t \qquad (2)\ S_2 = C - De^{-\sqrt{t}} \tag{2k-14}$$

where t is time from a selected zero point and A, B, C, D are constants of the process. (1) was given previously by Griggs for compressional recoverable creep strain, (2) by Michelson for shearing creep recovery. For series of earthquakes in certain areas and for all earthquakes in certain depth ranges Benioff[2] has found strain-rebound characteristics of forms similar to Eq. (2k-14). Yearly strain rebound in all deep shocks shows a decrease between at least 1905 and 1950 following Eq. (1), whereas most great shallow shocks have occurred in five active periods. The units of the Pacific belt have different patterns of activity.[3]

2k-14. Nonelastic Properties of the Earth's Interior. The strain produced in the earth by a tangential stress S in nonelastic processes is frequently expressed to a first (frequently poor) approximation by

$$\gamma = \frac{S}{\mu} - \lambda_r \frac{d\gamma}{dt} + \frac{1}{\eta} \int S\, dt \tag{2k-15}$$

where $\eta = \mu\tau$, $\nu = \mu\lambda_r$, μ = rigidity, η = coefficient of viscosity, τ = time of relaxation in viscous flow, ν = "coefficient of internal friction" or "coefficient of retarded elastic motion," and λ_r = time of retardation, i.e., the time in which the strain is reduced to $1/e$ in elastic processes, if the stress is removed. $\gamma = S/\mu$ is Hooke's law; the following two terms express, respectively, delaying action (of importance only in high-speed processes) and viscous flow (in processes of long duration).

The distance Δ^* to which seismic body waves (velocity V, period T) have to travel before their amplitude a is reduced to $1/e$ of its value is given approximately by[4]

$$\lambda_r = \frac{2V}{p^2\Delta^*} \tag{2k-16}$$

where $p = 2\pi/T$. Observations give $\Delta^* = 8{,}000 \pm$ km. With p about unity, $\lambda_r \sim 10^{-2}$ to 10^{-3} sec and $\nu \sim 10^9$ to 10^{10} poises. If the whole absorption is a consequence of internal friction, the waves in traveling from the source (period T_o) to the distance Δ (period T_Δ) are getting longer and flatter and[5] approximately

$$T_\Delta{}^2 = T_o{}^2 + \frac{5\nu\Delta}{\rho V^3} \tag{2k-17}$$

where ρ = density. Application of Eq. (2k-17) to observed increase in T indicates that λ_r and ν depend on the wavelength L. ν increases from about 10^7 to 10^9 poises as L increases from 0.1 to 100 km, and λ_r decreases from 10^{-4} to 5×10^{-3} sec.[6] The order of magnitude is in good agreement with the result from Eq. (2k-16) and with laboratory measurements in which a dimensionless quantity Q is used to indicate internal friction:

$$\frac{1}{Q} = \frac{dE}{2\pi E} = \frac{\delta}{\pi} \tag{2k-18}$$

[1] H. Benioff, Earthquakes and Rock Creep, *Bull. Seis. Soc. Amer.* **41**, 31–62 (1951).
[2] H. Benioff, Global Strain Accumulation and Release as Revealed by Great Earthquakes, *Bull. Geol. Soc. Amer.* **62**, 331–338 (1951).
[3] H. Benioff, Orogenesis and Deep Crustal Structure—Additional Evidence from Seismology, *Bull. Geol. Soc. Amer.* **65**, 385–400 (1954).
[4] H. Jeffreys, "The Earth," 3d ed., p. 242, Cambridge Univ. Press, New York, 1952.
[5] B. Gutenberg, "Handbuch der Geophysik," vol. 4, p. 22, Borntraeger, Berlin, 1932.
[6] B. Gutenberg, "Internal Constitution of the Earth," 2d ed., p. 385, Dover Publications, New York, 1951.

where dE = loss of energy per cycle in a vibrating body, E = total energy, and δ = logarithmic decrement of free vibrations. $1/Q$ has been found from longitudinal and transverse vibrations of bars to be of the order of 10^{-2} to 10^{-3} for rock samples. For elastic waves of periods T traveling through the earth, the time of retardation is approximately given by

$$\lambda_r = \frac{1}{pQ} \tag{2k-19}$$

where $p = 2\pi/T$. For seismic waves with periods of a few seconds, λ_r in seconds about equals $1/Q$.

The most reliable values for the viscosity η in the outer part of the earth's mantle (10^{22} to 10^{23} poises[1]) result from the observed time of relaxation λ (8,000 ± years) in Fennoscandia which is rising to restore the equilibrium disturbed by the melting of the Pleistocene ice masses (maximum thickness about $2\frac{1}{2}$ km). η may decrease below 10^{20} poises at a depth of 700 ± km, if the discontinuance of earthquakes below this depth is due to decrease in viscosity. Jeffreys[2] estimates that inside the core η is not over 10^8 and is probably nearer 10^5 poises. For numerical values of ν, η, τ in the earth, see Table 2k-18.

Since 10 km high mountains do not show a noticeable change by flow, it has been concluded that their strength (resistance to flow) is 10^9 ± dynes/cm². This may hold[3] to a depth of 25 ± km, but it may decrease below 10^7 dynes/cm² at 80 ± km, since gravity observations indicate that, except for recently disturbed narrow crustal belts, there is approximately hydrostatic equilibrium at this depth, "isostasy."

Table 2k-18. Order of Magnitude of Nonelastic Constants (*a*) in Some Materials at the Surface of the Earth, and (*b*) at Selected Depths in the Interior of the Earth

(Str. = strength resisting viscous flow, in poises; η = coefficient of viscosity, in poises; τ = corresponding time of relaxation; ν = coefficient of retarded elastic response for elastic waves with periods of 0.1 to 20 ± sec, in poises; λ_r = corresponding time of retardation, sec)

	Log str.	log η	log τ		log ν	log λ_r
			Sec	Years		
(*a*) Material:						
Solenhofen limestone..	$9\frac{1}{2}$ ±	22 ±	$10\frac{1}{2}$ ±	3 ±	9 ±	$-2\frac{1}{2}$ ±
Gabbro...........	?	?	?	?	$9\frac{1}{4}$ ±	$-2\frac{1}{2}$ ±
Glacier ice..........	?	13 to 14	3 ±	−4 ±	?	?
Flowing lava..........	?	≤5 ±	?	?	?	?
Flowing mud..........	?	≤4 ±	?	?	?	?
(*b*) Depth:						
10 km (continent).....	9 ±	22 to 23	11	4 ±	9 ±	−2 to −3
100..............	7?	22 ±	10	2 ±	9 ±	−2 to −3?
700..............	<7?	20 ± ?	8?	1?	9 to 10?	−3 ± ?
700–2,900........	<7?	<20?	≤7?	≤0?	10?	−3?
>2,900...........	≪7?	5??	?	?	?	?

[1] B. Gutenberg, "Internal Constitution of the Earth", 2d ed., p. 385, Dover Publications, New York, 1951.

[2] *Op. cit.*, pp. 244, 247.

[3] Jeffreys, *op. cit.*, p. 192.

2l. Oceanographic Data[1]

R. B. MONTGOMERY

Chesapeake Bay Institute
The Johns Hopkins University

2l-1. Depth, Pressure, Temperature. The surface of the earth's crust occurs at two prevailing levels, as shown by Table 2l-1. The higher of these levels is the *continental platform,* which, embracing sea level, includes the continental shelf and most land. The other, lying about 5 km lower, is the *oceanic platform.* The three less prevalent levels are mountains above the continental platform, continental slopes

Table 2l-1. Areas of Earth's Crust Classed According to Height or Depth from Sea Level. After Meinardus*

Proportion in interval		Proportion above	
	[Highest land†	8.85 km (314 mb‡)]	
Land above 5 km	0.1%	5 km (540 mb)	0.1%
Land 4–5 km	0.4%	4 km (616 mb)	0.5%
Land 3–4 km	1.1%	3 km (701 mb)	1.6%
Land 2–3 km	2.2%	2 km (795 mb)	3.8%
Land 1–2 km	4.5%	1 km (899 mb)	8.3%
Land 0–1 km	20.8%	0 km (1,013 mb)	29.1%
Ocean 0–1 km	8.5%	1 km (1,010 decibars¶)	37.6%
Ocean 1–2 km	2.9%	2 km (2,024 decibars)	40.5%
Ocean 2–3 km	4.7%	3 km (3,045 decibars)	45.2%
Ocean 3–4 km	14.1%	4 km (4,069 decibars)	59.3%
Ocean 4–5 km	23.9%	5 km (5,098 decibars)	83.2%
Ocean 5–6 km	16.0%	6 km (6,132 decibars)	99.2%
Ocean 6–7 km	0.7%	7 km (7,169 decibars)	99.9%
Ocean below 7 km	0.1%		
	[Greatest depth§	10.86 km (11,216 decibars)]	

* Wilhelm Meinardus, Die bathygraphische Kurve des Tiefseebodens und die hypsographische Kurve der Erdkruste (Tabelle 6), *Ann. Hydrogr. mar. Meteor.* **70,** 225–244 (1942).

† Mt. Everest.

‡ Pressure according to NACA standard atmosphere. See, e.g., Smithsonian Meteorological Tables, 6th ed., *Smithsonian Misc. Collections* **114** (1951).

¶ Sea pressure in water at 0°C, salinity 35 per mille, gravity at sea level being 9.8 m/sec^2. From Vilhelm Bjerknes, Hydrographic Tables, *Carnegie Inst. Wash. Publ.* **88,** 1A–36A (1910).

§ Marianas Trench, adjacent to Mariana Islands, Pacific Ocean. Soundings from H.M. Survey Ship *Challenger* in 1951. T. F. Gaskell, J. C. Swallow, and G. S. Ritchie, Further Notes on the Greatest Oceanic Sounding and the Topography of the Marianas Trench, *Deep-sea Research* **1,** 60–63 (1953).

[1] For a more extensive compilation, see *Ozeanographie,* Landolt-Börnstein Zahlenwerte und Funktionen, 6 Auflage, **3,** 426–541 (1952).

between the two platforms, and trenches below the oceanic platform. The mean level of the crust's surface is 2.43 km below sea level.

The ocean floor is more rugged than the dry land, at least in large-scale features.[1] Submarine ridges and numerous seamounts as well as islands rise from the prevailing depth, while trenches extend below. The continental slopes are high and steep and are cut by deep submarine canyons.

Pressures in a standard atmosphere and ocean are included in parentheses in Table 2l-1. For the ocean, the quantity tabulated is sea pressure; the total pressure is sea pressure plus atmospheric pressure (10 decibars). The units are defined by

$$10^6 \text{ dyne/cm}^2 = \text{bar} = 10 \text{ decibars} = 10^3 \text{ millibars}$$

The upper limit of temperature in the open ocean is rather definite at about 32°C, although more than half the ocean surface is warmer than 20°C. The lower limit for liquid sea water is the melting point −2°C. The temperature of sea ice ranges from 0°C down to something like −50°C.

The warm tropical water forms a relatively thin surface layer, which in the open ocean is underlain by cold water from high latitudes. Nearly everywhere in the open ocean the temperature at depths greater than 1 km is below 10°C and at depths greater than 2 km is below 4°C.

2l-2. Properties of Sea Water. *Composition.* Sea water, not including the suspended particles (inorganic matter, living organisms, and organic detritus), is a solution of a large number of constituents, which may be divided into four groups: water, major solids, minor solids (and liquids), and gases. The major solids are those which have appreciable influence on density. The minor solids compose only some 0.025 per cent of the total solids in typical sea water.

The major solids are composed of salts that are almost completely ionized, the proportions by mass being as follows:[2]

Na^+	30.61%	Cl^-	55.04%	H_3BO_3	0.07%
Mg^{++}	3.69	$SO_4^=$	7.68		
Ca^{++}	1.16	HCO_3^-	0.41		
K^+	1.10	Br^-	0.19		
Sr^{++}	0.04				

These proportions have been found to be highly constant throughout the ocean except where the water is nearly fresh (the salt in river water is very different from sea salt). Hence, the measurement of the concentration of any of the major solids in sea water permits the calculation of the concentration of total solids.

The constituent commonly measured (by chemical titration) is the sum of the halide ions (Cl^-, Br^-, I^-). The quantity *chlorinity* is approximately the ratio, by mass, of halides to total sample of sea water, but for the precise technical definition the reader is referred elsewhere.[3] Similarly, *salinity* is approximately the ratio of total solids to total sample of sea water, but the definition[4] used in practice is the one given by the empirical formula

$$\text{Salinity} = 0.00003 + 1.805 \times \text{chlorinity} \tag{2l-1}$$

[1] P. H. Kuenen, "Marine Geology," John Wiley & Sons, Inc., New York, 1950; J. T. Wilson, The Development and Structure of the Crust, "The Earth as a Planet," J. P. Kuiper, The University of Chicago Press, pp. 138–214, 1954.

[2] H. U. Sverdrup, M. W. Johnson, and R. H. Fleming, "The Oceans, Their Physics, Chemistry, and General Biology," Table 33, Prentice-Hall, Inc., New York, 1942.

[3] E.g., Sverdrup et al., *op. cit.*, p. 52.

[4] Bjørn Helland-Hansen, J. P. Jacobsen, and T. G. Thompson, Chemical Methods and Units, *Publ. sci. Ass. Océanogr. phys.* **9**, 28 (1948).

Both chlorinity and salinity are customarily expressed in per mille, meaning 10^{-3}.

The salinity of most water in the open ocean lies between 33 and 37 per mille, and 35 per mille is often chosen as standard.

Because the major solids are uniform in composition, the density and some other physical properties of sea water depend on only three variables: temperature, salinity, and pressure. Some of these properties at a pressure of 1 atm are shown in Fig. 2l-1.

Density and Melting Point. Density at 1 atm is shown in Fig. 2l-1*a*.[1] The effect of pressure on the density of sea water of salinity 35 per mille at temperature 0°C is as follows:

Sea pressure, decibars	0	2,000	4,000	6,000	8,000	10,000
Density, g/ml	1.02813	1.03748	1.04640	1.05495	1.06315	1.07104

Water that is more saline or warmer is less compressible.

The temperature of maximum density, shown for 1 atm on the graph, decreases as pressure increases. For pure water at 1 atm the decrease is 2.22°C per thousand decibars.[2]

The melting point decreases with increasing salinity or pressure. The melting point depression at 1 atm equals 56.90°C times the salinity according to Miyake[3] and is shown as the dotted line on the graphs. The decrease with pressure for pure water at 1 atm is 0.742°C per thousand decibars.[4]

Many tables and other aids have been prepared for the routine calculation of density and specific volume of sea water. A selection follows.

References on Calculation of Density and Specific Volume of Sea Water

Density at a Pressure of 1 Atm

Knudsen, Martin: "Hydrographical Tables," Copenhagen, 63 pp., 1901. (Range −2 to 33°C, salinity 2 to 41 per mille.) Part of Knudsen's can be replaced with the following more detailed tables: Matthews, D. J.: "Tables for the Determination of the Density of Seawater under Normal Pressure, σ_t," Andr. Fred. Høst & Fils, Copenhagen, 56 pp., 1932.

Kalle, Kurt, und Hermann Thorade: Tabellen und Tafeln für die Dichte des Seewassers (σ_t), *Arch. deut. Seewarte Marineobs.* **60** (2), 49 pp. (1940). (Range −2 to 30°C, salinity 0 to 41.5 per mille.)

Ennis, C. C.: Note on computation of density of sea water and on corrections for deep-sea reversing thermometers, *Carnegie Inst. Wash. Publ.* **545A,** 23–45 (1944). (Range −2 to 30°C, salinity 34 to 36 per mille.)

LaFond, E. C.: Processing Oceanographic Data (Table X), U.S. Navy Hydrographic Office, H. O. Pub. 614, 1951. (Range −2 to 30°C, salinity 30 to 38 per mille.)

U.S. Navy Hydrographic Office: "Tables for Sea Water Density," H.O. Pub. 615, 265 pp., 1952 (range −2 to 30°C, salinity 0 to 40 per mille.) Recomputed from same empirical formulas as preceding tables but expressed to one more decimal place (10^{-6} g/ml) and tabulated for each 0.01°C of temperature argument.

Bein, Willy: Physikalische und chemische Konstanten des Meerwassers (pp. 102–103), *Veröffentl. Inst. Meeresk. Univ. Berlin,* neue Folge, A, **28,** 36–190 (1935). The arguments are temperature (0, 1, . . . , 40°C) and the ratio of density at 17.5°C to density of pure water at 17.5°C (1.000, 1.002, . . . , 1.032). This table is based on Bein's own measurements, the most recent. Argument converted to salinity by

[1] Martin Knudsen, "Hydrographical Tables," Copenhagen, 1901; N. E. Dorsey, "Properties of Ordinary Water Substance," Reinhold Publishing Corporation, New York, 1940.

[2] Dorsey, *op. cit.*, p. 275.

[3] Yasuo Miyake, Chemical Studies of the Western Pacific Ocean, III, Freezing Point, Osmotic Pressure, Boiling Point and Vapour Pressure of Sea Water, *Bull. Chem. Soc. Japan* **14,** 58–62 (1939).

[4] Dorsey, *op. cit.*, Table 267.

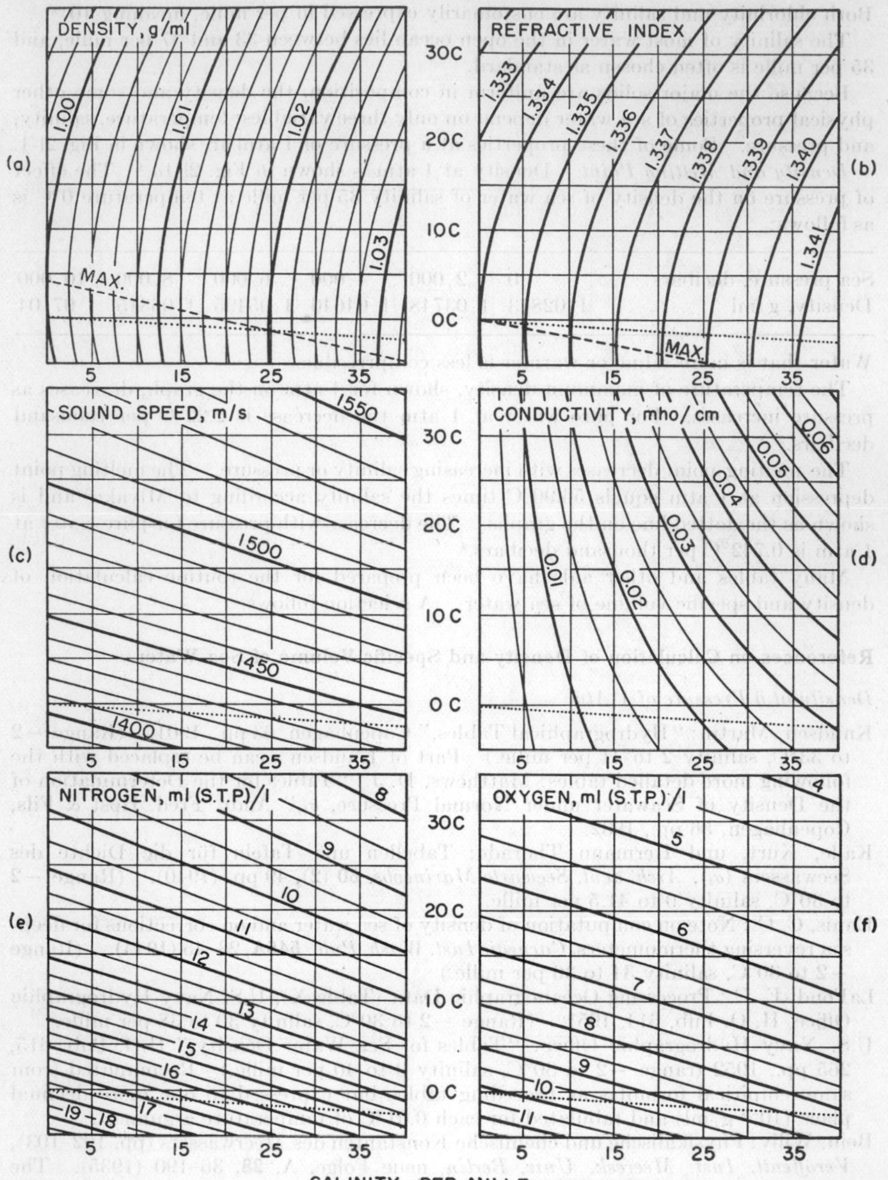

FIG. 2l-1. Temperature-salinity diagrams for sea water at 1 atm pressure: (*a*) density, (*b*) refractive index for sodium light (0.5893 micron) relative to air, (*c*) sound speed, (*d*) conductivity, (*e*) concentration of nitrogen in equilibrium with 1 atm (1013.25 mb) of air saturated with aqueous vapor, (*f*) concentration of oxygen under same equilibrium conditions. Freezing point is shown by dotted line; values below it pertain to undercooled water.

G. Dietrich, Landolt-Börnstein Zahlenwerte und Funktionen, *Ozeanographie* 6 Auflage, **3**, 428 (1952). (Temperature 0, 1, . . . , 32°C, salinity 0, 5, . . . , 40 per mille.)

Specific Volume at a Pressure of 1 *Atm*

LaFond, above, Table V. (Range −2° to 30°C, salinity 21 to 38 per mille)

Density at Greater Pressures

Ekman, V. W.: Tables for Sea Water under Pressure, *Publ. Circ. Cons. int. Explor. Mer* **49,** 48 pp., 1910. [The arguments are density at 1 atm and 0°C, pressure (0 to 10,000 decibars), and temperature.]

Specific Volume at Greater Pressures

Bjerknes, Vilhelm: Hydrographic Tables, *Carnegie Inst. Wash. Publ.* **88,** 1A–36A (1910). (Range −2 to 30°C, salinity 0 to 40 per mille, 0 to 10,000 decibars.)

Subow, N. N., S. W. Brujewicz, and W. W. Shoulejkin: "Oceanographical Tables," Moscow, 208 pp., 1931.

Matthews, D. J.: "Tables for Calculating the Specific Volume of Seawater under Pressure," Andr. Fred. Høst & Fils, Copenhagen, 67 pp., 1938. [The arguments are density at 1 atm, pressure (0 to 12,000 decibars), and temperature.]

Sverdrup, H. U., M. W. Johnson, and R. H. Fleming: "The Oceans," Appendix, Prentice-Hall, Inc., New York, 1942. [The arguments are density at 1 atm, pressure (0 to 10,000 decibars), temperature, and salinity.]

LaFond, above, Tables IV–VII. (Range −2 to 30°C, salinity 21 to 38 per mille, 0 to 10,000 decibars.)

Refractive Index. For given wavelength, temperature, and pressure the relation between refractive index and salinity is very nearly linear. The graph of refractive index for sodium light in Fig. 2l-1*b* is based on the formulas of Utterback et al.[1] The formulas have been adjusted slightly to agree at zero chlorinity with the measurements of Tilton and Taylor.[2] Measurements by Bein[3] give values higher than those of Utterback et al. by as much as 0.00012. The effect of pressure is roughly such that, if n is refractive index and ρ is density, $(n - 1)/\rho$ is constant for given temperature, salinity, and wavelength.[4]

Sound Speed. The graph of sound speed in Fig. 2l-1*c* at 1 atm represents Del Grosso's[5] formula based on his new laboratory measurements. Since there were no measurements at salinities between 0 and 19 per mille, this area on the graph is uncertain. Only pure water has been studied at temperatures below 0°C.[6]

For greater pressures, Matthews[7] and Kuwahara[8] have computed the sound speed c

[1] C. L. Utterback, T. G. Thompson, and B. D. Thomas, Refractivity-chlorinity-temperature Relationships of Ocean Waters, *J. Cons. Int. Explor. Mer* **9**, 35–38 (1934). (Table for 0, 5, . . . , 25°C, chlorinity 1, 2, . . . , 22 per mille.)

[2] L. W. Tilton and J. K. Taylor, Refractive Index and Dispersion of Distilled Water for Visible Radiation, at Temperatures 0 to 60°C, *J. Research Natl. Bur. Standards* **20,** 419–477 (1938).

[3] Willy Bein, Physikalische und chemische Konstanten des Meerwassers, *Veröffentl. Inst. Meeresk. Univ. Berlin,* neue Folge, A, **28,** 162 (1935).

[4] Dorsey, *op. cit.*, Table 144.

[5] V. A. Del Grosso, The Velocity of Sound in Sea Water at Zero Depth. *Naval Research Lab. Rept.* 4002, 39 pp., 1952. (Tables for range 0 to 40°C, salinity 0 and 19 to 41 per mille.)

[6] R. T. Lagemann, L. W. Gilley, and E. G. McLeroy, The Ultrasonic Velocity, Density, and Compressibility of Supercooled H_2O and D_2O, *J. Chem. Phys.* **21**, 819–821 (1953).

[7] D. J. Matthews, "Tables of the Velocity of Sound in Pure Water and Sea Water for Use in Echo-sounding and Sound-ranging," 2d ed., H.D. 282, Hydrographic Department, Admiralty, London, 52 pp., 1939. (Range −2 to 30°C, salinity 0 to 41 per mille, depth 0 to 10,900 m.)

[8] Susumu Kuwahara, The Velocity of Sound in Sea Water and Calculation of the Velocity for Use in Sonic Sounding, *Japan. J. Astron. Geophys.* **16**, 1–17 (1938). (Tables for range −2 to 30°C, salinity 30 to 40 per mille, pressure 0 to 10,000 decibars.) Kuwahara's tables are reproduced and extended in salinity down to 21 per mille by E. C. LaFond, "Processing Oceanographic Data," Table XIV, U.S. Navy Hydrographic Office, H.O. Pub. 614, 1951.

from $c^2 = (dp/d\rho)_s$, which is the adiabatic change of pressure with density and can be expressed in terms of known properties (isothermal compressibility, thermal expansion, specific heat, temperature, and specific volume). Some values for 0°C and salinity 35 per mille are as follows:[1]

Sea pressure, decibars.....	0	2,000	4,000	6,000	8,000	10,000
Sound speed, m/sec.......	1,448.6	1,484.4	1,519.7	1,554.2	1,587.7	1,620.0

Electrical Conductivity. The graph shown in Fig. 2l-1*d* is based on measurements by Thomas.[2] Somewhat different results were obtained by Bein.[3] Measurements have been confined in temperature to the range 0 to 25°C and in pressure to 1 atm.

Dissolved Nitrogen and Oxygen. The two principal atmospheric gases are differently distributed in the ocean. Because nitrogen is highly inert, its concentration is determined entirely by contact with the atmosphere. Oxygen is both released and consumed by biological processes, so that its concentration is much more variable. Right at the sea surface, there is equilibrium between the two phases; the nitrogen and oxygen in the liquid phase depend on their partial pressures in the gaseous phase, while the partial pressure of aqueous vapor depends on the salinity of the liquid phase (see below).

Figures 2l-1*e* and *f* show the concentrations of nitrogen and oxygen in equilibrium with saturated air at a pressure of 1 atm. For a given temperature, solubility decreases linearly with increasing salinity. The nitrogen graph has been calculated from Fox's[4] table for pure water and from Rakestraw and Emmel's[5] data for sea water. The oxygen graph is based on Fox's[6] table. For temperatures below 0°C and for part of the high-temperature areas, the graphs depend on extrapolation.

The equilibrium concentration of dissolved nitrogen or oxygen is proportional to its partial pressure in the gaseous phase (Henry's law) up to several atmospheres. As the partial pressure increases to 1,000 atm, however, the concentration attains only about half the value given by simple proportionality.[7] Sea water has not been studied at pressures greater than 1 atm.

Vapor Pressure. The vapor-pressure lowering of an aqueous solution is related to the melting-point depression. At the melting point of the solution the vapor pressure is the same as the vapor pressure of ice.

Let e be the vapor pressure of sea water of given salinity and temperature, and let e_0

[1] Kuwahara's values increased by 3.1 m/sec to gain agreement with Del Grosso's.

[2] B. D. Thomas with T. G. Thompson and C. L. Utterback, The Electrical Conductivity of Sea Water, *J. Cons. int. Explor. Mer* **9**, 28–35 (1934). (Table for 0, 5, . . . , 25°C, chlorinity 1, 2, . . . , 22 per mille.)

[3] Bein, *op. cit.*, p. 174.

[4] C. J. J. Fox, On the Coefficients of Absorption of Nitrogen and Oxygen in Distilled Water and Sea-water, and of Atmospheric Carbonic Acid in Sea-water, *Trans. Faraday Soc.* **5**, 68–87 (1909). (Table 1 gives nitrogen dissolved in pure water from 1 atm of pure nitrogen for 0, 1, . . . , 50°C.)

[5] N. W. Rakestraw and V. M. Emmel, The Solubility of Nitrogen and Argon in Sea Water, *J. Phys. Chem.* **42**, 1211–1215 (1938). (Table 2 gives nitrogen dissolved in sea water from 1 atm of saturated air for 0, 1, . . . , 28°C, chlorinity 15, 16, . . . , 21 per mille.) A personal communication from Dr. Rakestraw states that all values pertain to air saturated with aqueous vapor. Data in Table 1 used in present work.

[6] C. J. J. Fox, On the Coefficients of Absorption of the Atmospheric Gases in Distilled Water and Sea Water, pt. I, Nitrogen and Oxygen, *Publ. Circ. Cons. int. Explor. Mer* **41**, 23 pp (1907). (Table 11 gives oxygen dissolved in sea water from 1 atm of dry air at −2, −1, . . . , 30°C, chlorinity 0, 1, . . . , 20 per mille.) Table reproduced by K. Kalle, Landolt-Börnstein Zahlenwerte und Funktionen, 6 Auflage, **3**, 478 (1952).

[7] Dorsey, *op. cit.*, Table 233.

be the vapor pressure of pure water at the same temperature. Then

$$\frac{e_0 - e}{e_0} = 0.537 \times \text{salinity} \tag{2l-2}$$

so the vapor pressure for salinity 35 per mille is 98.12 per cent of that for pure water. This formula by Witting[1] is satisfactory for the range of conditions occurring at the natural ocean surface, but for greater salinity or higher temperature the results of recent measurements should be consulted.[2]

Latent Heats and Specific Heat. The latent heats of fusion and vaporization are practically the same for sea water as for pure water.

The specific heat at constant pressure depends on salinity as follows at 17.5°C and 1 atm:[3]

Salinity, per mille.	0	5	10	15	20	25	30	35	40
c_p, cal g^{-1} °C^{-1}...	1.000	0.982	0.968	0.958	0.951	0.945	0.939	0.932	0.926

The changes with temperature and pressure have not been measured. The effect of pressure can be computed by use of the thermodynamic formula

$$\left(\frac{dc_p}{dp}\right)_T = -T\left(\frac{d^2v}{dT^2}\right)_p \tag{2l-3}$$

where v is specific volume and T is absolute temperature. The following values of the decrease in specific heat at 0°C and salinity 35 per mille are from Ekman's[4] table:

Sea pressure, decibars..........	0	2,000	4,000	6,000	8,000	10,000
$(c_p)_{0\ \text{decibars}} - c_p$, cal g^{-1} °C^{-1}..	0	0.0159	0.0291	0.0401	0.0492	0.0566

Adiabatic Temperature Change. This quantity is computed from the thermodynamic formula

$$\left(\frac{dT}{dp}\right)_s = \frac{T}{c_p}\left(\frac{dv}{dT}\right)_p \tag{2l-4}$$

The following values for 0°C and salinity 35 per mille are converted from Ekman's paper:

Sea pressure, decibars.........	0	2,000	4,000	6,000	8,000	10,000
$(dT/dp)_s$, °C/1,000 decibars....	0.035	0.072	0.104	0.133	0.159	0.181

Transport Phenomena. The values for a pressure of 1 atm are assembled in Table 2l-2. Measurements with sea water are restricted to viscosity; the other properties tabulated under sea water are from measurements with sodium chloride solutions. The diffusivities of nitrogen and oxygen are especially uncertain and may be incorrect by as much as 15 per cent.

[1] Rolf Witting, Untersuchungen zur Kenntnis der Wasserbewegungen und der Wasserumsetzung in den Finland umgebenden Meeren, I, *Finnländische Hydrographisch-biologische Untersuchungen* **2,** 173 (1908).

[2] A. B. Arons and C. F. Kientzler, Vapor Pressure of Sea-salt Solutions, *Trans. Am. Geophys. Union* **35,** 722–728 (1954).

[3] Otto Krümmel, "Handbuch der Ozeanographie," vol. 1, p. 279, Stuttgart, 1907.

[4] V. W. Ekman, Der adiabatische Temperaturgradient im Meere, *Ann. Hydrogr. mar. Meteor.* **42,** 340–344 (1914).

Dynamic and kinematic viscosities and thermal conductivity change linearly with salinity. In contrast, both thermal diffusivity (associated with specific heat) and diffusivity of sodium chloride go through minima at salinities less than 35 per mille.

TABLE 2l-2. TRANSPORT PHENOMENA IN WATER AT A PRESSURE OF 1 ATM

Name, symbol, units	Pure water		Sea water, salinity 35 per mille	
	0°C	20°C	0°C	20°C
Dynamic viscosity, η, g cm^{-1} sec^{-1} = poise	0.01787[a]	0.01002[b]	0.01877[a]	0.01075[a]
Thermal conductivity, k, watt cm^{-1} °C^{-1}	0.00566[c]	0.00599[c]	0.00563[c]	0.00596[c]
Kinematic viscosity, $\nu = \eta/\rho$, cm^2 sec^{-1}	0.01787	0.01004	0.01826	0.01049
Thermal diffusivity,[d] $\kappa = k/c_p\rho$, cm^2 sec^{-1}	0.00134	0.00143	0.00139	0.00149
Diffusivity, D, cm^2 sec^{-1}:				
NaCl	0.0000074[e]	0.0000141[f]	0.0000068[e]	0.0000129[f]
N_2	0.0000106[g]	0.0000169[g]		
O_2		0.000021[h]		
Prandtl number, $N_P = \nu/\kappa$	13.3	7.0	13.1	7.0

[a] Yasuo Miyake and Masami Koizumi, The Measurement of the Viscosity Coefficient of Sea Water, *J. Marine Research* **7**, 63–66 (1948). Values taken from their Table I and reduced by 0.00007 poise to agree with Swindells et al. (Table III presents smoothed values for 0, 1, . . . , 30°C, chlorinity 0, 1, . . . , 20 per mille.)

[b] J. F. Swindells, J. R. Coe, Jr., and T. B. Godfrey, Absolute Viscosity of Water at 20°C, *J. Research Natl. Bur. Standards* **48**, 1–31 (1952).

[c] L. Riedel, Die Wärmeleitfähigkeit von wässrigen Lösungen starker Elektrolyte, *Chem.-Ing.-Technik* **23**, 59–64 (1951).

[d] Thermal diffusivity is also called thermometric conductivity.

[e] Values for 0°C calculated from those at 20°C by use of temperature coefficient of L. W. Öholm, Über die Hydrodiffusion der Elektrolyte, *Z. physik. Chem.* **50**, 309–349 (1904).

[f] A. R. Gordon, The Diffusion Constant of an Electrolyte, and Its Relation to Concentration, *J. Chem. Phys.* **5**, 522–526 (1937). Gordon used measurements by B. W. Clack, On the Study of Diffusion in Liquids by an Optical Method, *Proc. Phys. Soc.* (*London*) **36**, 313–335 (1924). R. H. Stokes, The Diffusion Coefficients of Eight Uni-univalent Electrolytes in Aqueous Solution at 25°, *J. Am. Chem. Soc.* **72**, 2243–2247 (1950).

[g] Gustav Tammann und Vitus Jessen, Über die Diffusionskoeffizienten von Gasen in Wasser und ihre Temperaturabhängigkeit, *Z. anorg. Chem.* **179**, 125–144 (1929).

[h] Tor Carlson, The Diffusion of Oxygen in Water, *J. Am. Chem. Soc.* **33**, 1027–1032 (1911); I. M. Kolthoff and C. S. Miller, The Reduction of Oxygen at the Dropping Mercury Electrode, *J. Am. Chem. Soc.* **63**, 1013–1017 (1941); H. A. Laitinen and I. M. Kolthoff, Voltammetry with Stationary Microelectrodes of Platinum Wire, *J. Phys. Chem.* **45**, 1061–1079 (1941).

For pure water, pressure increasing to 10,000 decibars has a nonlinear effect on the dynamic viscosity, which decreases at 0°C by 8 per cent and increases at 30°C by 5 per cent.[1] The thermal conductivity at 30°C increases linearly with pressure and becomes 6 per cent greater at 10,000 decibars.[2]

2l-3. Gravity Waves. *Wave Speed.* Most of the ocean is stabilized by a downward increase of density, so that *internal waves* as well as *surface waves* are common. Only surface waves are discussed here.

Let L be wavelength, T be period, and c be wave speed. Then $L = Tc$. Let h be the depth of water (undisturbed surface to bottom) and g be gravity.

For a uniform train of long-crested sinusoidal waves of small amplitude in an ideal liquid of uniform depth, in general[3]

$$c^2 = \frac{gL}{2\pi} \tanh 2\pi \frac{h}{L} \tag{2l-5}$$

For $h/L \gg 1$, *deep-water waves*, the general formula reduces to $c^2 = gL/2\pi$, and the

[1] Dorsey, *op. cit.*, Table 86.

[2] *Ibid.*, Table 131.

[3] See, e.g., C. A. Coulson, "Waves," 6th ed., Oliver & Boyd, Ltd., Edinburgh, 1952.

group speed equals half the wave speed. For $h/L \ll 1$, *shallow-water waves*, $c^2 = gh$, and group speed equals wave speed (there is no dispersion, and any wave form of small amplitude is propagated unchanged at this speed). Within 5 per cent, sufficient accuracy for many problems, the deep-water formula holds if $h/L \sim h/L_0 > \frac{1}{3}$ and the shallow-water formula holds if $h/L < \frac{1}{11}$ or $h/L_0 < \frac{1}{22}$; L_0 is defined below.

TABLE 2l-3. SELECTED TIDAL CONSTITUENTS

Symbol	Name	Argument	Period	Speed, degrees per hour	Relative coefficient of equilibrium tide
Sa	Solar annual	h	1.0 year	0.0411	0.012
Ssa	Solar semiannual	$2h$	0.5 year	0.0821	0.073
Mm	Lunar monthly	$s - p$	27.55 day	0.5444	0.083
Mf	Lunar fortnightly	$2s$	13.66 day	1.0980	0.156
K_1	Lunisolar declinational diurnal	$T + h - 90°$	23.93 hr	15.0411	0.531
O_1	Lunar declinational diurnal	$T + h - 2s + 90°$	25.82 hr	13.9430	0.377
P_1	Solar declinational diurnal	$T - h + 90°$	24.07 hr	14.9589	0.176
Q_1	Lunar diurnal	$T + h - 3s + p + 90°$	26.87 hr	13.3987	0.072
M_2	Principal lunar semidiurnal	$2T + 2h - 2s$	12.42 hr	28.9841	0.908
S_2	Principal solar semidiurnal	$2T$	12.00 hr	30.0000	0.423
N_2	Larger lunar elliptic semidiurnal	$2T + 2h - 3s + p$	12.66 hr	28.4397	0.174
K_2	Lunisolar declinational semidiurnal	$2T + 2h$	11.97 hr	30.0821	0.115

Change in depth along wave rays changes the speed and length of sufficiently long waves. Near shore, therefore, waves often experience refraction and accompanying convergence and divergence. Such phenomena are conveniently treated by relating the speed and length of waves of any given period to the speed and length for the same period in deep water, c_0 and L_0. As $T = L/c = L_0/c_0$ and $c_0^2 = gL_0/2\pi$, (2l-5) may be written

$$\frac{c}{c_0} = \frac{L}{L_0} = \tanh 2\pi \frac{h}{L_0}\frac{L_0}{L} \qquad \text{(2l-6)}$$

Functions of h/L_0 have been presented in an extensive table,[1] from which the following values are extracted:

h/L_0	0	0.001	0.01	0.02	0.05	0.1	0.2	0.3	0.4	0.5	1
$c/c_0 = L/L_0$	0	0.0792	0.2480	0.3470	0.5310	0.7093	0.8884	0.9611	0.9877	0.9964	1.0000

[1] U.S. Department of the Army, Corps of Engineers, *Bulletin of the Beach Erosion Board*, Special Issue 2, Appendix D, 1953.

These elementary results are not suitable for direct application to the irregular aperiodic waves in areas of generation by wind.

Tidal Constituents.[1] The gravitational fluctuations that produce tides can be resolved into harmonic constituents. Some are listed in Table 2l-3, their periods being determined by the constant rates of change of four angles:

T = hour angle of mean sun (increasing by 15°/hr)
h = mean celestial longitude of sun (increasing by 0.0411°/hr)
s = mean celestial longitude of moon (increasing by 0.5490°/hr)
p = mean celestial longitude of lunar perigee (increasing by 0.0046°/hr)

2m. Meteorological Data[2]

R. J. LIST

United States Weather Bureau

2m-1. List of Symbols

c_p	specific heat of dry air at constant pressure
c_v	specific heat of dry air at constant volume
d	coefficient of molecular diffusion
D	coefficient of eddy diffusion
f	Coriolis parameter
g	acceleration of gravity
n	distance; spacing
p	pressure
r	radius of curvature
R	gas constant for dry air
T	temperature
T_v	virtual temperature
T_{mv}	mean virtual temperature
v	speed
V_g	geostrophic wind speed
V	gradient wind speed
Z, z	height
γ	lapse rate of temperature
ζ	mean molecular speed; mixing velocity

[1] Paul Schureman, Manual of Harmonic Analysis and Prediction of Tides, U.S. Coast and Geodetic Survey, Special Publication 98, rev. ed., 1940; A. T. Doodson and H. D. Warburg, "Admiralty Manual of Tides," H. M. Stationery Office, London, 1941.

[2] All material not otherwise credited is abstracted from R. J. List, ed., "Smithsonian Meteorological Tables," 6th ed., Smithsonian Institution, Washington, D.C., 1951. This publication should be consulted for more complete explanations and additional references. For an encyclopedic summary of the current status of knowledge in the principal fields of meteorology and atmospheric physics, including extensive references, see T. F. Malone, ed., "Compendium of Meteorology," American Meteorological Society, Boston, 1951.

λ	free path; mixing length
ρ	density of air
ϕ	latitude
Φ	geopotential
ω	angular velocity of the earth

2m-2. Physical Constants

Pressure at mean sea level, 1 atmosphere

$$= 1{,}013.250 \text{ millibars (mb)} = 1.013250 \times 10^6 \text{ dynes cm}^{-2}$$

$$= 760 \text{ cm Hg (at standard gravity of 980.665 cm}^2\text{ sec}^{-2}\text{ and temperature of 0°C)}$$

Mass of the atmosphere $= 5.14 \times 10^{21}$ g

Apparent molecular weight of dry air $M = 28.966$

Gas constant for 1 g of dry air, $R = 2.8704 \times 10^6$ erg gm^{-1} °K^{-1}

$= 6.8557 \times 10^{-2}$ ITcal[1] gm^{-1} °K^{-1}

Specific heat of dry air at constant pressure $c_p = \dfrac{7R}{2} = 0.240$ ITcal gm^{-1} °K^{-1}

Specific heat of dry air at constant volume $c_v = \dfrac{5R}{2} = 0.171$ ITcal g^{-1} °K^{-1}

2m-3. Composition of the Atmosphere

TABLE 2m-1. COMPOSITION OF DRY AIR UP TO ABOUT 25 KM ALTITUDE*

Constituent gas	Formula	Mole fraction, %	Molecular wt.
Nitrogen	N_2	78.09	28.016
Oxygen	O_2	20.95	32.000
Argon	Ar	0.93	39.944
Carbon dioxide†	CO_2	0.03	44.010
Neon	Ne	1.8×10^{-3}	20.183
Helium	He	5.24×10^{-4}	4.003
Krypton	Kr	1.0×10^{-4}	83.7
Hydrogen	H_2	5.0×10^{-5}	2.0160
Xenon	Xe	8.0×10^{-6}	131.3
Ozone‡	O_3	1.0×10^{-6}	48.000
Radon¶	Rn	6.0×10^{-18}	222

* See E. Glueckauf, "Compendium of Meteorology," T. F. Malone, ed., pp. 3–10, American Meteorological Society, Boston, 1951.

† Variable; see T. M. Carpenter, *J. Am. Chem. Soc.* **59**, 358 (1937); J. B. S. Haldane, *Nature* **1037**, 575 (1936); G. S. Callendar, *Quart. J. Roy. Meteorol. Soc.* **66**, 395 (1947).

‡ Variable, increasing with height.

¶ Variable, decreasing with height.

2m-4. Geopotential. The geopotential Φ of a point at a height z above mean sea level is the work which must be done against gravity in raising a unit mass from sea level to height z.

$$\Phi = \int_0^z g\, dz \tag{2m-1}$$

where g is the local acceleration of gravity at height z. For most meteorological work geopotential is measured in terms of the *geopotential meter* (gpm). By definition, 1 gpm $= 9.8 \times 10^4$ cm^2 sec^{-2}. For almost all practical purposes, 1 gpm = 1 geometric

[1] ITcal refers to the "International Steam Tables" calorie, which is equivalent to $\frac{1}{860} \times 10^{-3}$ mean international kilowatthours.

meter. Table 2m-2 shows the relationship between geopotential and geometric height as a function of latitude.

TABLE 2m-2. RELATION OF GEOPOTENTIAL TO GEOMETRIC HEIGHT

Latitude	Geopotential meters (gpm)										
	10,000	20,000	30,000	40,000	50,000	100,000	200,000	300,000	400,000	500,000	600,000
	m	m	m	m	m	m	m	m	m	m	m
0°	10,036	20,104	30,204	40,336	50,500	101,811	206,948	315,577	427,874	544,029	664,243
30°	10,023	20,077	30,163	40,282	50,432	101,672	206,656	315,115	427,225	543,174	663,161
45°	10,009	20,050	30,123	40,228	50,365	101,534	206,363	314,653	426,576	542,318	662,080
60°	9,996	20,024	30,083	40,174	50,297	101,395	206,071	314,191	425,927	541,465	661,000
90°	9,983	19,997	30,043	40,120	50,229	101,256	205,779	313,730	425,280	540,613	659,923

2m-5. Hypsometry. The differential form of the hydrostatic equation, the equation expressing the relationship of pressure p, density ρ, and height z, in the atmosphere, is

$$dp = -\rho g \, dz \tag{2m-2}$$

Introducing the definition of geopotential, the hydrostatic equation becomes

$$dp = -\rho \, d\Phi \tag{2m-3}$$

Substituting the equation of state for dry air, introducing the concept of virtual temperature (see below), and integrating, Eq. (2m-3) becomes

$$\Delta\Phi = RT_{mv} \log_e \frac{p_1}{p_2} \tag{2m-4}$$

where $\Delta\Phi$ is the geopotential difference between levels having pressures p_1 and p_2, T_{mv} is the mean[1] virtual temperature of the layer of air between p_1 and p_2, and R is the gas constant for dry air. For temperatures in °K and geopotential in gpm (i.e., geometric meters for most practical purposes) Eq. (2m-4) becomes

$$\Delta\Phi = 67.442 T_{mv} \log_{10} \frac{p_1}{p_2} \tag{2m-5}$$

2m-6. Virtual Temperature. The concept of virtual temperature is introduced to take into account the decreased density of moist air when compared with dry air of the same temperature. By definition, T_v is the temperature which dry air must have at a given barometric pressure in order to have the same density as the moist air at the same pressure but at temperature T and with a specified moisture content, provided the dry and moist air behave in accordance with the perfect-gas equation of state. (The deviation of moist air from perfect-gas behavior can be neglected in most practical problems.[2]) Table 2m-3 gives the virtual-temperature increment for saturated air ΔT_v, where $T_v = T + \Delta T_v$. For unsaturated moist air with relative humidity U(per cent), $T_v = T + (U/100)\,\Delta T_v$, to a close approximation.

2m-7. Lapse Rates. The lapse rate γ in the atmosphere is defined as the rate of decrease of temperature with increasing height (or geopotential), $\gamma = -dT/dz$. γ is ordinarily expressed in °C per 100 m (or 100 gpm).

[1] The logarithmic mean virtual temperature is required. This quantity can be approximated graphically on most standard aerological diagrams.

[2] See List, *op. cit.*, p. 295.

Dry-adiabatic Lapse Rate. Dry air, or moist air in which the water vapor enters into no change of state, which ascends (or descends) adiabatically in the atmosphere will decrease (or increase) in temperature at the rate of 0.98°C per 100 m. The dry-adiabatic lapse rate is therefore 0.98°C/100 m.

TABLE 2m-3. VIRTUAL-TEMPERATURE INCREMENT OF SATURATED AIR, °C

Temp., °C	Pressure, mb								
	1000	900	800	700	600	500	400	300	200
−40	0.02	0.02	0.02	0.02	0.03	0.03	0.04	0.06	0.08
−20	0.12	0.13	0.15	0.17	0.20	0.24	0.30	0.40	0.60
0	0.64	0.70	0.79	0.91	1.06	1.27	1.59	2.12	3.19
10	1.32	1.47	1.66	1.90	2.21	2.66	3.33	4.46	6.73
20	2.62	2.92	3.29	3.76	4.40	5.29	6.64	8.92	13.57
30	4.97	5.53	6.23	7.14	8.36	10.08	12.70		
40	9.03	10.06	11.36	13.05	15.33	18.57			
50	15.90	17.76	20.11	23.18					
60	27.32	30.62							

TABLE 2m-4. PSEUDOADIABATIC LAPSE RATE FOR THE WATER STAGE, °C/100 M

Temp., °C	Pressure, mb									
	1000	900	800	700	600	500	400	300	200	100
−50	0.966	0.965	0.963	0.961	0.959	0.955	0.951	0.943	0.928	0.886
−40	0.950	0.947	0.944	0.939	0.934	0.925	0.913	0.896	0.863	0.775
−30	0.917	0.910	0.903	0.893	0.882	0.866	0.842	0.807	0.746	0.615
−20	0.855	0.844	0.830	0.814	0.794	0.767	0.730	0.677	0.596	0.454
−10	0.763	0.745	0.725	0.701	0.672	0.637	0.592	0.532	0.452	0.335
0	0.645	0.624	0.601	0.573	0.542	0.505	0.462	0.409	0.345	0.262
10	0.527	0.506	0.483	0.457	0.429	0.398	0.362	0.323	0.276	
20	0.426	0.408	0.389	0.368	0.346	0.322	0.296			
30	0.352	0.338	0.323	0.307	0.291	0.273				
40	0.301	0.290	0.279	0.267						
50	0.267	0.259								

Pseudoadiabatic Lapse Rate. Saturated air ascending adiabatically in the atmosphere, so that all condensation of water vapor is into liquid water which falls out immediately and all latent heat of condensation is realized in warming the air, decreases in temperature at the pseudoadiabatic (or moist-adiabatic) lapse rate for the water stage. Table 2m-4 gives the pseudoadiabatic lapse rate for the water stage as a function of temperature and pressure.

2m-8. Standard Atmosphere, Lower Atmosphere. A revised standard atmosphere for levels up to 20 km was approved by the Council of the International Civil Aviation Organization (ICAO) in November, 1952, and has been adopted by the National Advisory Committee on Aeronautics (NACA) to supersede the earlier NACA standard atmosphere. The values of pressure, temperature, and density are in fairly good agreement with the average annual values observed at 40°N in North America.

Basic Assumptions. The temperature at altitude[1] 0 (mean sea level) is 288.16°K (15°C). The lapse rate of temperature in the troposphere is 0.65°C per 100 m. The temperature at the tropopause is 216.66°K, which makes the altitude of the tropopause 11 km. The temperature above 11 km is constant, 216.66°K. It is assumed that the

TABLE 2m-5. STANDARD ATMOSPHERE, LOWER ATMOSPHERE*

Altitude, m	Temp., °K	Pressure, mb	Density, kg m^{-3}	Viscosity, poises	Speed of sound, m sec^{-1}
−5,000	320.660	1776.88	1.9305	1.9497 × 10^{-4}	359.114
−4,000	314.160	1595.55	1.7694	1.9191	355.455
−3,000	307.660	1429.51	1.6187	1.8881	351.759
−2,000	301.160	1277.74	1.4781	1.8568	348.023
−1,000	294.660	1139.29	1.3470	1.8252	344.247
0	288.160	1013.25	1.2250	1.7932	340.429
1,000	281.660	898.74	1.1117	1.7609	336.567
2,000	275.160	794.95	1.0065	1.7283	332.661
3,000	268.660	701.08	0.90913	1.6953	328.709
4,000	262.160	616.40	0.81914	1.6620	324.708
5,000	255.660	540.20	0.73612	1.6282	320.657
6,000	249.160	471.81	0.65970	1.5941	316.555
7,000	242.660	410.61	0.58950	1.5596	312.398
8,000	236.160	356.00	0.52517	1.5247	308.186
9,000	229.660	307.42	0.46635	1.4893	303.915
10,000	223.160	264.36	0.41271	1.4536	299.583
11,000	216.660	226.32	0.36392	1.4174	295.188
12,000	216.660	193.30	0.31083	1.4174	295.188
13,000	216.660	165.10	0.26548	1.4174	295.188
14,000	216.660	141.02	0.22675	1.4174	295.188
15,000	216.660	120.45	0.19367	1.4174	295.188
16,000	216.660	102.87	0.16542	1.4174	295.188
17,000	216.660	87.867	0.14129	1.4174	295.188
18,000	216.660	75.048	0.12068	1.4174	295.188
19,000	216.660	64.100	0.10307	1.4174	295.188
20,000	216.660	54.749	0.088035	1.4174	295.188

* Manual of the ICAO Standard Atmosphere, *NACA Tech. Note*, Washington, D.C., May, 1954.

air is dry, obeys the perfect gas law, and is in hydrostatic equilibrium. (The other necessary physical constants used are given in Sec. 2m-2.)

2m-9. Properties of the Upper Atmosphere. The average temperature in January and July in the Northern Hemisphere in the lowest 20 km of the atmosphere as a function of latitude and height is given by the thin lines in Fig. 2m-1.[2] The heavy lines

[1] The unit of altitude used in the standard atmosphere is actually a unit of geopotential, the *standard geopotential meter* = 0.980665 × 10^5 cm^2 sec^{-2} (see Sec. 2m-4). For engineering purposes these may be taken as meters.

[2] H. Wexler, *Tellus* **2** (4), 262–273 (November, 1950).

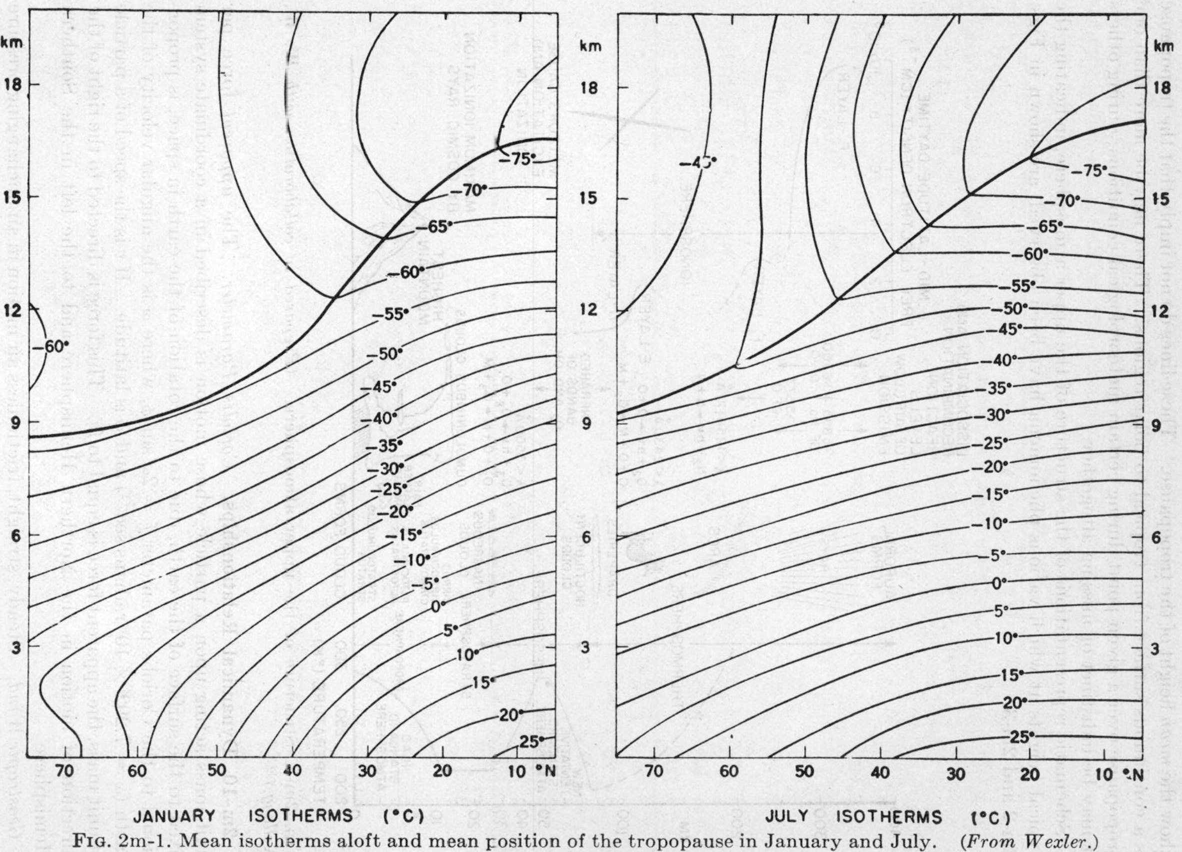

FIG. 2m-1. Mean isotherms aloft and mean position of the tropopause in January and July. (*From Wexler.*)

show the *mean* height of the tropopause. These lines do not imply that the tropopause is a continuous surface from tropical to polar regions. There may be more than one tropopause over a given point during certain meteorological conditions; during others it may be indistinct or missing altogether.

Schematic representations of the structure of the upper atmosphere, indicating the typical heights at which various phenomena have been observed, are shown in Figs. 2m-2 and 2m-3.

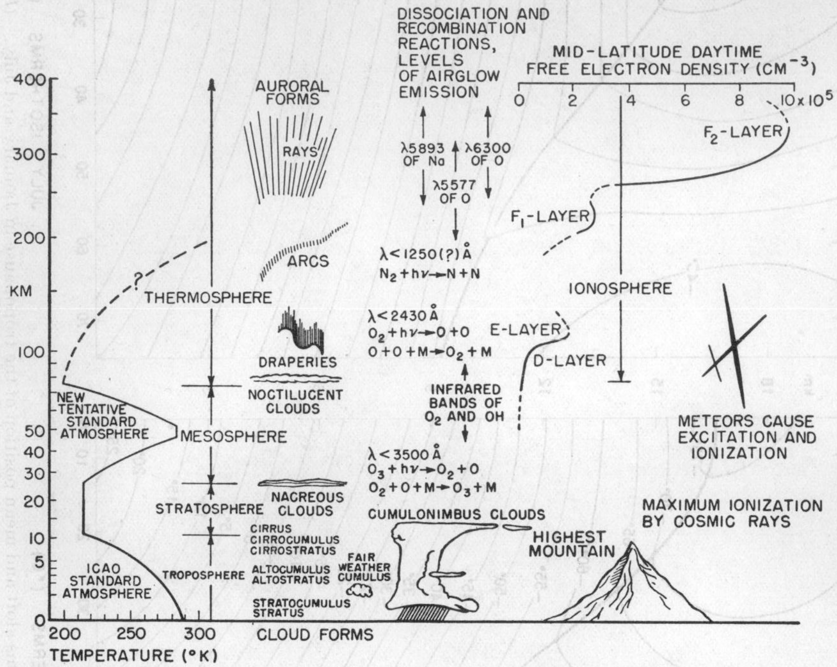

FIG. 2m-2. Structure of the upper atmosphere. (*Prepared in collaboration with W. W. Kellogg.*)

2m-10. Dynamical Relationships. *Coriolis Parameter.* The *apparent* force per unit mass acting upon a particle whose motion is described in a coordinate system fixed to the surface of the earth, due to the rotation of the earth in space, is proportional to the Coriolis parameter $f = 2\omega \sin \phi$, where ω is the angular velocity of the earth ($\omega = 7.292 \times 10^5$ radians sec^{-1}) and ϕ is latitude. If v is the speed of a particle of unit mass, the apparent force is equal to fv. This force is directed to the right of the direction of motion in the Northern Hemisphere and to the left in the Southern Hemisphere.

Geostropic Wind. Steady, straight, frictionless air motion in an unchanging pressure field, with gravity as the only external force acting, such that the horizontal pressure-gradient force is balanced by the apparent force due to the earth's rotation (the Coriolis force), is called the geostrophic wind. The geostrophic wind blows perpendicular to the direction of the pressure gradient with low pressure to the left in the Northern Hemisphere, to the right in the Southern Hemisphere.

On a surface of constant pressure, the equation for the speed of the geostropic wind V_g is given by

$$V_g = \frac{1}{f} \frac{\partial \Phi}{\partial n} \tag{2m-6}$$

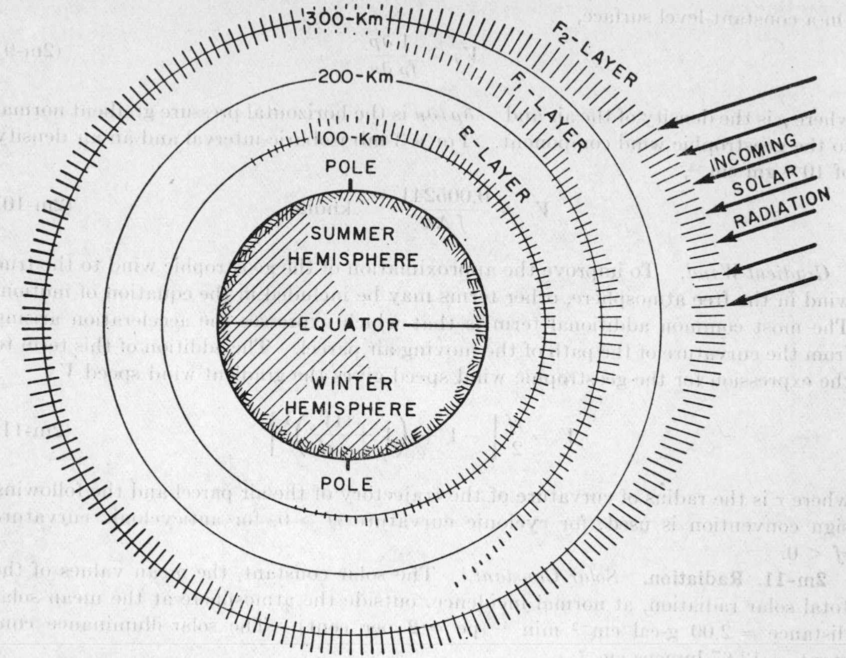

FIG. 2m-3. Diurnal and seasonal variation in the structure of the ionosphere. (*Prepared by W. W. Kellogg.*)

TABLE 2m-6. VALUE OF THE CORIOLIS PARAMETER f

Latitude	f, $\sec^{-1}$	Latitude	f, $\sec^{-1}$
0°	0	50°	1.1172×10^{-4}
10°	0.2533×10^{-4}	60°	1.2630×10^{-4}
20°	0.4988×10^{-4}	70°	1.3705×10^{-4}
30°	0.7292×10^{-4}	80°	1.4363×10^{-4}
40°	0.9375×10^{-4}	90°	1.4584×10^{-4}
45°	1.0313×10^{-4}		

where $-\partial\Phi/\partial n$ is the gradient of geopotential on the constant-pressure surface normal to the direction of the geostrophic wind. For contours drawn at intervals of 100 gpm on a constant-pressure map, Eq. (2m-6) reduces to

$$V_g = \frac{0.01712}{f\,\Delta n} \quad \text{knots} \tag{2m-7}$$

where Δn is the spacing between successive contours measured normal to the direction of the geostrophic wind component in units of degrees of latitude. For contours drawn at intervals of 200 geopotential feet

$$V_g = \frac{0.01044}{f\,\Delta n} \quad \text{knots} \tag{2m-8}$$

On a constant-level surface,

$$V_g = \frac{1}{f\rho} \frac{\partial p}{\partial n} \tag{2m-9}$$

where ρ is the density of the air and $-\partial p/\partial n$ is the horizontal pressure gradient normal to the geostrophic wind component. For a 3-mb isobaric interval and an air density of 10^{-3} gm cm^{-3},

$$V_g = \frac{0.005241}{f\,\Delta n} \quad \text{knots} \tag{2m-10}$$

Gradient Wind. To improve the approximation of the geostrophic wind to the true wind in the free atmosphere, other terms may be included in the equation of motion. The most common additional term is that which expresses the acceleration arising from the curvature of the path of the moving air parcel. The addition of this term to the expression for the geostrophic wind speed gives the gradient wind speed V.

$$V = \frac{rf}{2}\left[-1 + \left(1 + \frac{4V_g}{rf}\right)^{\frac{1}{2}}\right] \tag{2m-11}$$

where r is the radius of curvature of the trajectory of the air parcel and the following sign convention is used: for cyclonic curvature $rf > 0$, for anticyclonic curvature $rf < 0$.

2m-11. Radiation. *Solar Constant.*[1] The solar constant, the mean values of the total solar radiation, at normal incidence, outside the atmosphere at the mean solar distance = 2.00 g-cal cm^{-2} min^{-1} (pe = 2 per cent). The solar-illuminance constant = 13.67 lumens cm^{-2}.

Insolation. Figure 2m-4 shows the average daily solar radiation received on a square centimeter of horizontal surface at the ground during January and July on cloudless days[2] (solid lines) and on days with average cloudiness[3] (dotted lines). The units are gram-calories per square centimeter per day.

Albedo. Table 2m-7 gives a range of albedo measurements[4] observed for various types of surfaces.

TABLE 2m-7. ALBEDO MEASUREMENTS

	%
Forest	3–10
Fields, grass, etc	3–37
Bare ground	3–30
Snow, fresh	80–90
Snow, old	45–70
Whole earth, visible spectrum	39
Whole earth, total spectrum	35
Clouds*	5–85
Water (reflectivity values are given in the following table)†	

Elevation of sun	90°	70°	50°	40°	30°	20°	10°	5°	0°
Reflectivity, %	2.0	2.1	2.5	3.4	6.0	13.4	34.8	58.4	100.0

* For clouds in the absence of absorption, the albedo is a function of the drop-size distribution, liquid-water content, and cloud thickness. See S. Fritz, *J. Meteorol.* **11** (4), 291–300 (1954).

† The reflectivity of a water surface for solar radiation is a function of the sun's elevation angle. The values given have been computed for a plane surface; however, the observed reflection from disturbed surfaces shows only small deviation from these values.

[1] F. S. Johnson, *J. Meteorol.* **11** (6), (December, 1954).
[2] S. Fritz, *Heating and Ventilating* **46** (1), (January, 1949).
[3] S. Fritz and T. H. MacDonald, *Heating and Ventilating* **46** (7), (July, 1949).
[4] For a more complete list, including sources, see R. J. List, *op. cit.*, pp. 442–444.

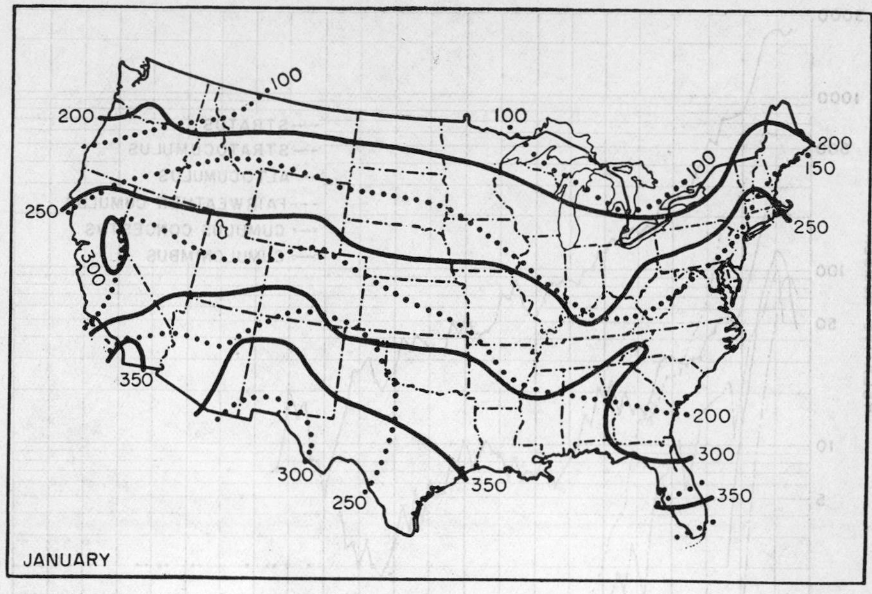

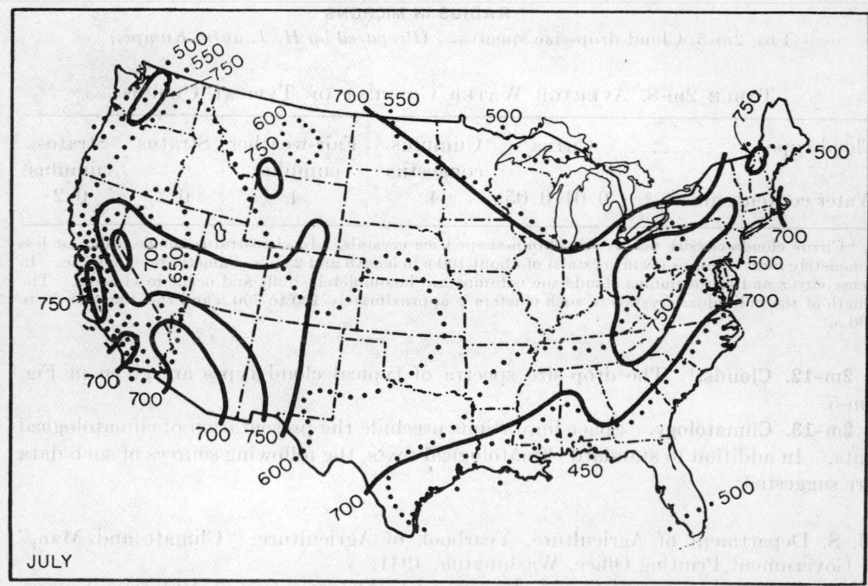

FIG. 2m-4. Average daily solar insolation (gcal cm^{-2} day^{-1}) at the ground on cloudless days (solid lines) and on days of average cloudiness (dotted lines). (*After Fritz.*)

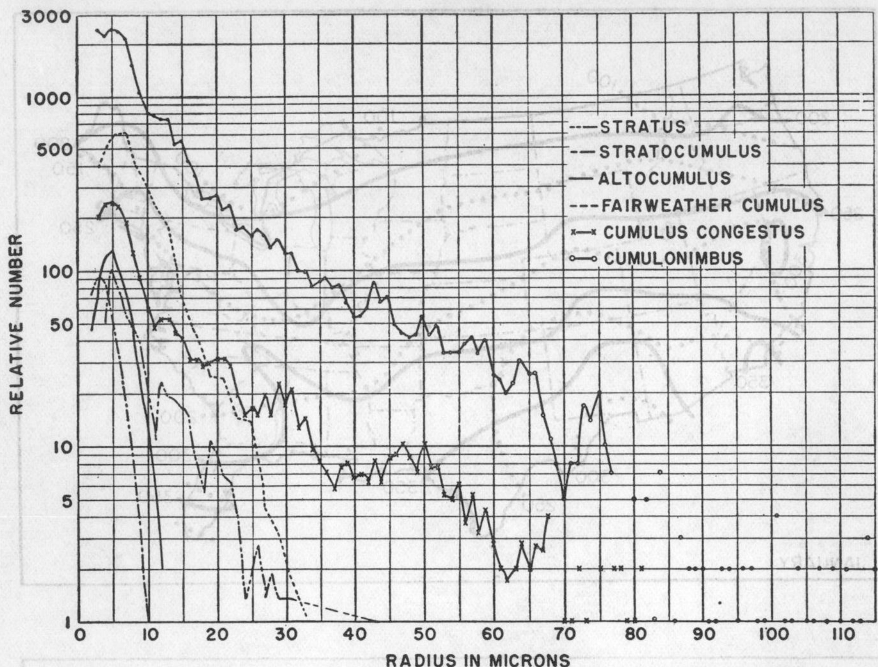

FIG. 2m-5. Cloud drop-size spectra. (*Prepared by H. J. aufm Kampe.*)

TABLE 2m-8. AVERAGE WATER CONTENT OF TYPICAL CLOUDS

Cloud type..............	Cirrus*	Cumulus congestus	Fair-weather cumulus	Stratus	Strato-cumulus
Water content, gm m^{-3}...	0.01–0.05	4	1	0.3	0.2

* Cirrus clouds consist mainly of column-shaped ice crystals. In cirrostratus, single, more or less completely built columns (twin crystals) of about 100 μ in length and 25 μ in diameter predominate. In dense cirrus and cirrocumulus clouds the columns are incompletely built and occur in clusters. The length of the individual crystals in such clusters is approximately 100 to 300 μ and the diameter 30 to 100 μ.

2m-12. Clouds.[1] The drop-size spectra of typical cloud types are given in Fig. 2m-5.

2m-13. Climatology. Space limitations preclude the presentation of climatological data. In addition to standard climatological texts, the following sources of such data are suggested:

U. S. Department of Agriculture, Yearbook of Agriculture: "Climate and Man," Government Printing Office, Washington, 1941.

Glenn A. Greathouse, and Carl J. Wessel, ed.: "Deterioration of Materials, Causes, and Preventative Techniques," Chap. I, Climate and Deterioration, Reinhold Publishing Corporation, New York, 1954.

U.S. Weather Bureau: Climatological Data, National Summary (issued monthly, with an annual summary).

[1] Data furnished by Dr. H. J. aufm Kampe, Signal Corps Engineering Laboratories, Ft. Monmouth, N.J.

Note: Also available from the U.S. Weather Bureau are more detailed climatological summaries for individual states and local climatological data for individual cities, as well as many unpublished data.

2m-14. Atmospheric Diffusion.[1] In most meteorological problems, the effects of molecular diffusion are far outweighed by the turbulent eddies present in the atmosphere. One approach to this problem is to treat the phenomenon in a manner analogous to that of molecular diffusion. The coefficient of diffusion in such applications is a function of the size of the turbulent eddies and is therefore dependent on the time and space scale being considered. Figure 2m-6[2] gives the magnitude of the

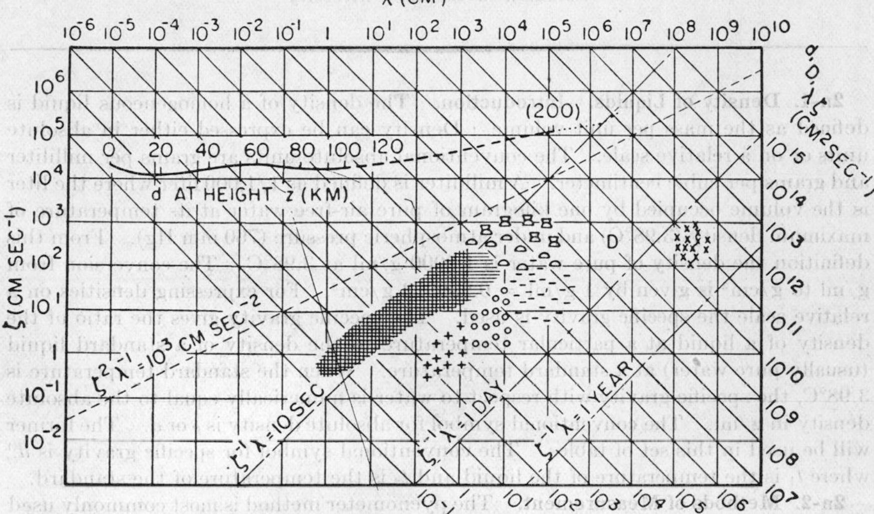

D AT HEIGHT z IS DENOTED BY CHARACTERISTIC AREAS ON THE DIFFUSION DIAGRAM:

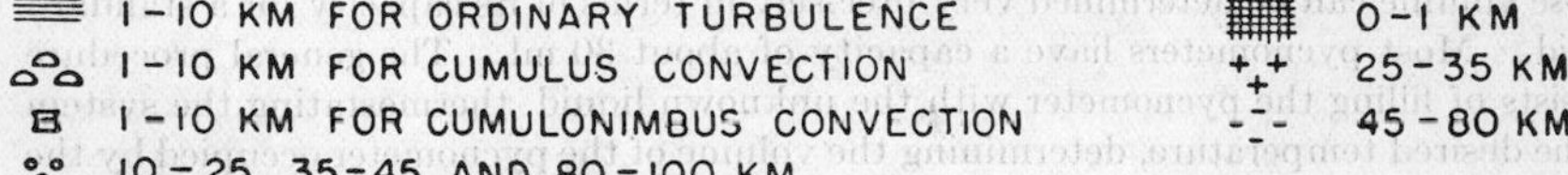

Fig. 2m-6. Diffusion diagram. (*From Lettau.*)

coefficient of eddy diffusion D as a function of the characteristics of the eddies, as well as the variation of the coefficient of molecular diffusion d with height. In Fig. 2m-6, each point of the λ, ζ plane determines a diffusion coefficient ($cm^2\ sec^{-1}$). In molecular diffusion, $\lambda \approx$ free path and $\zeta \approx$ mean molecular speed; $d = \lambda\zeta$ is fixed by the density and temperature of the atmosphere; consequently, the height variation of d is marked by a curve. In eddy diffusion, $\lambda \approx$ mixing length and $\zeta \approx$ mixing velocity; owing to the variability of these elements, $D = \lambda\zeta$ and its variation with height are denoted by characteristic areas when the possible variability of D is narrowed by the consideration of limiting values of eddy accelerations (ζ^2/λ) and time terms (λ/ζ).

For another approach to the problem of turbulent diffusion, especially in dealing with the diffusion of contaminants in the lower atmosphere, see Sutton.[3]

[1] For the definition of diffusion coefficient cf. pp. 2-189 and 2-211.

[2] H. Lettau, "Compendium of Meteorology," T. F. Malone, ed., pp. 320–333, American Meteorological Society, Boston, 1951.

[3] O. G. Sutton, "Micrometeorology," McGraw-Hill Book Company, Inc., New York, 1953.

2n. Density and Compressibility of Liquids

ROBERT LINDSAY[1]

Southern Methodist University

2n-1. Density of Liquids. Introduction. The density of a homogeneous liquid is defined as the mass per unit volume. Density can be expressed either in absolute units or on a relative scale. The conventional absolute units are grams per milliliter and grams per cubic centimeter. A milliliter is defined as 1/1,000 liter where the liter is the volume occupied by one kilogram of pure air-free water at its temperature of maximum density (3.98°C) and under atmospheric pressure (760 mm Hg). From this definition the density of pure water is 1.0000 g/ml at 3.98°C. The conversion from g/ml to g/cm^3 is given by 1 g/ml = 0.999973 g/cm^3. For expressing densities on a relative scale the specific gravity is used. The specific gravity gives the ratio of the density of a liquid at a particular temperature to the density of a standard liquid (usually pure water) at a standard temperature. When the standard temperature is 3.98°C, the specific gravity with respect to water is numerically equal to the absolute density in g/ml. The conventional symbol for absolute density is ρ or d. The former will be used in this set of tables. The conventional symbol for specific gravity is $d_{t_2}^{t_1}$ where t_1 is the temperature of the liquid and t_2 is the temperature of the standard.

2n-2. Methods of Measurement. The pycnometer method is most commonly used when precise density measurements on a particular liquid are desired at fixed temperatures.[2] A pycnometer is a vessel made of glass with a low coefficient of expansion whose volume can be determined very precisely in terms of its capacity for a standard liquid. Most pycnometers have a capacity of about 30 ml. The general procedure consists of filling the pycnometer with the unknown liquid, thermostating the system at the desired temperature, determining the volume of the pycnometer occupied by the liquid, and then weighing the pycnometer. For determining densities of the same sample over a range of temperatures, the dilatometer method is sometimes used. In one variation of this method a secondary standard liquid such as mercury is placed in contact with the liquid sample. As the temperature is raised the secondary liquid is displaced out of the dilatometer. The weight of the displaced secondary liquid is a measure of the change in volume of the unknown liquid. Another variation of this method involves the observation of the change in level of the unknown liquid in a narrow calibrated capillary attached to the main flask. The measurements of densities of liquefied gases at or near their boiling points are more complicated, since a closed system may have to be used and significant corrections must be made for the density of the vapor in equilibrium with the liquid.[3]

[1] Now at Trinity College.

[2] A. Weissberger and W. N. Rae, "Physical Methods of Organic Chemistry," 2d ed., vol. I, pt. 1, pp. 253ff., Interscience Publishers, Inc., New York, 1949; V. Reilly and W. N. Rae, "Physico-Chemical Methods," 3d ed., vol. I, pp. 61ff., D. Van Nostrand Company, Inc., New York, 1949.

[3] W. H. Keeson, "Helium," pp. 206ff., Elsevier Press, Inc., New York, 1942; E. R. Grilly, E. F. Hammel, and S. G. Sydoriak, *Phys. Rev.* **75,** 1103 (1949); E. R. Grilly, *J. Am. Chem. Soc.* **73,** 5307 (1951).

2n-3. Reliability. The reliability of the density measurements tabulated is variable. This compilation does not pretend to evaluate for extreme accuracy. Such factors as uncertainty in the temperature scale, possible impurities of the samples, and in some cases even changes in atomic weights must be taken into consideration when applying a critical analysis. The data are given as reported in the original literature or in other standard works and are to be interpreted in the spirit of being representative values. Reference to the original literature is recommended in cases of doubt. Among the organic liquids there are some very recent and complete investigations to examine. Among many of the inorganic liquids data are both old and scarce.

2n-4. Standard Reference Works with Density Data

"International Critical Tables," McGraw-Hill Book Company, Inc., New York, 1928.

Landolt-Börnstein: "Physikalisch-Chemische Tabellen," 5th ed. and supplements, Springer-Verlag OHG, Berlin, 1923–1935 (Edwards Bros. Inc., Ann Arbor, Mich., 1943).

Timmermans, J.: "Physico-chemical Constants of Pure Organic Compounds," Elsevier Press, Inc., New York, 1950.

Mellor, J. F.: "Comprehensive Treatise of Inorganic and Theoretical Chemistry," Longmans, Green & Co., Inc., New York, 1921–1929.

Simons, J. H., ed.: "Fluorine Chemistry," Academic Press, Inc., New York, 1950.

2n-5. Density of Water. A rather complete analysis of all the investigations of the physical properties of water is given by N. Ernest Dorsey.[1] He points out that the data from which the density tables are made up do not take into consideration the isotope effect. Because of this there may be uncertainties of the order of 8 parts in 10^7 introduced when the densities of samples from various sources are considered. Fractional distillation of D_2 has revealed differences of the order of 20 parts in 10^6 in deuterium content in different samples. There is also some reason to believe that the polymerization is a factor in the variability of the physical properties of water. Values of the density of water as a function of temperature are presented in Table 2n-1. Similar data for other liquids follow in Tables 2n-2 through 2n-11.

[1] N. Ernest Dorsey, "Properties of Ordinary Water Substance," Reinhold Publishing Corporation, New York, 1948.

TABLE 2n-1. DENSITY OF PURE AIR-FREE H_2O AT ATMOSPHERIC PRESSURE
(ρ = g/ml; t = °C)

Range 0–40°C*

t	ρ	t	ρ	t	ρ
0	0.9998676	5	0.9999919	10	0.9997281
1	0.9999265	6	0.9999683	11	0.9996336
2	0.9999678	7	0.9999297	12	0.9995261
3	0.9999922	8	0.9998765	13	0.9994059
4	1.0000	9	0.9998092	14	0.9992732

t	0.0	0.1	0.2	0.3	0.4	0.5	0.6	0.7	0.8	0.9
15	0.9991286	1134	0982	0828	0674	0518	0360	0202	0043	9882
16	0.9989721	9558	9394	9229	9062	8895	8726	8557	8386	8214
17	0.9988041	7867	7691	7515	7337	7158	6979	6798	6616	6433
18	0.9986248	6063	5877	5689	5501	5311	5120	4928	4735	4541
19	0.9984346	4150	3953	3754	3555	3355	3153	2950	2747	2542
20	0.9982336	2130	1922	1713	1503	1292	1080	0867	0653	0438
21	0.9980221	0004	9786	9567	9346	9125	8903	8679	8455	8230
22	0.9978003	7776	7547	7318	7088	6856	6624	6390	6156	5921
23	0.9975684	5447	5208	4969	4729	4487	4245	4002	3758	3512
24	0.9973266	3019	2771	2522	2272	2021	1769	1516	1262	1007
25	0.9970751	0494	0237	9978	9718	9458	9196	8934	8671	8406

t	ρ	t	ρ	t	ρ
26	0.9968141	31	0.9953722	36	0.9937159
27	0.9965437	32	0.9950575	37	0.9933604
28	0.9962642	33	0.9947344	38	0.9929970
29	0.9959757	34	0.9954030	39	0.9926260
30	0.9956783	35	0.9950635	40	0.9922473

Range 40–100°C†

t	ρ	t	ρ	t	ρ
40	0.99224	65	0.98059	90	0.96534
45	0.99024	70	0.97781	95	0.96192
50	0.98807	75	0.97489	100	0.95838
55	0.98573	80	0.97183		
60	0.98324	85	0.96865		

Range 100–370°C‡

t	ρ	t	ρ	t	ρ
100	0.95841	190	0.87639	280	0.75063
110	0.95099	200	0.86492	290	0.73237
120	0.94317	210	0.85290	300	0.71266
130	0.93494	220	0.84031	310	0.69118
140	0.92629	230	0.82712	320	0.66747
150	0.91721	240	0.81330	330	0.64095
160	0.90771	250	0.79881	340	0.61071
170	0.89776	260	0.78368	350	0.57497
180	0.88733	270	0.76769	360	0.52872

See page 2–139 for footnotes.

TABLE 2n-1. DENSITY OF PURE AIR-FREE H_2O AT ATMOSPHERIC PRESSURE (*Continued*)

Range 0 to −13°C¶

t	ρ	t	ρ	t	ρ
0	0.999868	−5	0.999176	−10	0.997935
−1	0.999773	−6	0.998950	−11	0.997636
−2	0.999673	−7	0.998720	−12	0.997292
−3	0.999553	−8	0.998501	−13	0.997292
−4	0.999380	−9	0.998249		

* L. W. Tilton and J. K. Taylor, *J. Research Natl. Bur. Standards* **18,** 205 (1937).
† V. Stott and P. H. Bigg, "International Critical Tables," vol. 3, p. 24, McGraw-Hill Book Company, Inc., New York, 1928.
‡ F. G. Keyes and L. B. Smith, *Mech. Eng.* **53,** 132 (1931).
¶ J. F. Mohler, *Phys. Rev.* **35,** 236 (1912).

TABLE 2n-2. DENSITY OF D_2O (100% D_2O WITH NORMAL OXYGEN ISOTOPE COMPOSITION)

(ρ = g/ml; t = °C)

Range 3.8–20°C*

t	ρ
3.8	1.10533
5	1.10549
10	1.10588
15	1.10577
20	1.10527

Range 20–100°C†

t	ρ	t	ρ	t	ρ
20	1.10530	50	1.09562	80	1.07815
25	1.10437	55	1.09316	85	1.07467
30	1.10315	60	1.09051	90	1.07104
35	1.10167	65	1.08766	95	1.06729
40	1.09989	70	1.08466	100	1.06339
45	1.09786	75	1.08148		

Range 90–250°C‡

t	ρ	t	ρ	t	ρ
90	1.0708	150	1.0167	210	0.943
100	1.0630	160	1.0058	220	0.928
110	1.0547	170	0.9950	230	0.913
120	1.0459	180	0.9826	240	0.897
130	1.0366	190	0.970	250	0.881
140	1.0268	200	0.957		

* T. L.-Chang and J. Y. Chien, *J. Am. Chem. Soc.* **63,** 1709 (1941).
† R. Schrader and K. Wirtz, *Z. Naturforsch.* **6a,** 220 (1951).
‡ J. R. Heiks, M. K. Barnett, L. V. Jones, and E. Orban, *J. Phys. Chem.* **58,** 488 (1954).

The maximum density of D_2O has been determined to be 1.10596 g/ml at 11.23°C. K. Stokland, E. Ronaess, and L. Tronstad, *Trans. Faraday Soc.* **35,** 312 (1938). This is based on a value for d_{25}^{25} of 1.10764. L. Tronstad and Brun, *Trans. Faraday Soc.* **34,** 766 (1938). See H. L. Johnston, *J. Am. Chem. Soc.* **61,** 878 (1939), for a discussion of these values.

The density of H_2O and D_2O at 370°C are approximately the same. E. H. Riesenfeld and T. L.-Chang, *Z. physik. Chem.* **B30,** 61 (1935); **B28,** 408 (1935).

TABLE 2n-3. DENSITY OF MERCURY (Hg)
(ρ = g/ml; t = °C)
Range −38.87 to 100°C*

t	ρ	t	ρ
−38.87	13.691_9	24	13.536_4
−30	13.669_8	25	13.534_0
−20	13.645_0	30	13.521_8
−10	13.620_2	35	13.509_6
0	13.595_5	40	13.497_3
5	13.583_2	45	13.485_1
10	13.570_9	50	13.472_9
15	13.558_6	55	13.460_8
16	13.556_2	60	13.448_6
17	13.553_7	65	13.436_5
18	13.551_3	70	13.424_3
19	13.548_8	75	13.412_2
20	13.546_3	80	13.400_1
21	13.543_9	85	13.388_0
22	13.541_3	90	13.375_9
23	13.538_9	95	13.363_9
		100	13.351_8

Range 100–360°C†

t	ρ	t	ρ	t	ρ
100	13.3518	200	13.113	300	12.875
120	13.304	220	13.065	320	12.827
140	13.256	240	13.018	340	12.779
160	13.208	260	12.970	357.1	12.737
180	13.160	280	12.922		

* Stott and Bigg, "International Critical Tables," vol. 2, p. 457, McGraw-Hill Book Company, Inc., New York, 1928; Sears, *Proc. Phys. Soc.* (*London*) **26,** 95 (1913).

† G. W. C. Kaye and T. H. Laby, "Tables of Physical and Chemical Constants," 10th Ed., Longmans, Green & Co., Inc., New York, 1948; Chappuis, "Traveaux et memoires du bureau international des poids et mesures," vol. 16, 1917.

TABLE 2n-4. DENSITY OF METHYL ALCOHOL (CH_3OH)
(ρ = g/ml; t = °C)

Density at Fixed Points

t	ρ
0	0.809985*
5	0.80535*
25	0.78654*
25	0.78655†
30	0.78181*

TABLE 2n-4. DENSITY OF METHYL ALCOHOL (CH_3OH) (*Continued*)

Density as a Function of Temperature

Range 0–60°C‡

t	ρ
0	0.80999
5	0.80536
10	0.80070
15	0.79602
20	0.79132
25	0.78660
30	0.78186
35	0.77710
40	0.77232
45	0.76753
50	0.76270
60	0.75300

These data fit a formula

$$\rho = 0.80999 - 0.0009253t - 0.00000041t^2 \tag{2n-1}$$

Range −94.5 to 15°C¶

$$\rho = 0.81015 - 0.0010041t - 0.000001802t^2 - 0.00000001657t^3 \tag{2n-2}$$

* A. Rakowski and A. B. Frost, *Trans. Inst. Pure Chem. Reagents U.S.S.R.* **9** (334), 95 (1930).

† R. E. Gibson, *J. Am. Chem. Soc.* **57**, 1551 (1935).

‡ Brunel and Van Bibber, "International Critical Tables," vol. 3, p. 27, McGraw-Hill Book Company, Inc., New York, 1928.

¶ J. Timmermans, *Sci. Proc. Roy. Dublin Soc.* **13**, 310 (1912).

TABLE 2n-5. DENSITY OF ETHYL ALCOHOL (C_2H_5OH)
(ρ = g/ml; t = °C)

Density at Fixed Points

t	ρ
0	0.806306*
25	0.785063*
25	0.78506†
50	0.763137*

Density as a Function of Temperature

Range 0–40°C‡

t	ρ
10	0.79784
15	0.79360
20	0.78934
25	0.78506
30	0.78075
35	0.77641
40	0.77203

These data fit a formula

$$\rho = 0.78506 - 0.0008591(t - 25) - 0.00000056(t - 25)^2 - 0.000000005(t - 25)^3 \quad \text{(2n-3)}$$

Range 40–78°C¶

t	ρ
45	0.76773
50	0.76329
60	0.75423
70	0.74491
78	0.73720

These data fit a formula

$$\rho = 0.80625 - 0.0008461t + 0.000000160t^2 - 0.0000000085t^3 \quad \text{(2n-4)}$$

Range below 0°C§

t	ρ
−59	0.856
−78	0.872

* Kretschmer, Nowakowska, and Wieba, *J. Am. Chem. Soc.* **70,** 1785 (1948).

† N. S. Osborne, E. C. McKelvey, and H. W. Bearce, *Natl. Bur. Standards (U.S.) Bull.* **9,** 327 (1913).

‡ N. S. Osborne, E. C. McKelvey, and H. W. Bearce, *Natl. Bur. Standards (U.S.) Bull.* **9,** 327 (1913).

¶ Brunel and Van Bibber, "International Critical Tables," vol. 3, p. 27, McGraw-Hill Book Company, Inc., New York, 1928.

§ Beilstein, "Organische Chemie," vol. 1, p. 148, 1928.

TABLE 2n-6. DENSITIES OF SELECTED INORGANIC LIQUIDS
(Range 0–50°C; ρ = g/ml; t = °C; pressure atmospheric)

Substance	Formula	t	ρ	Year	Ref.
Arsenic trichloride	$AsCl_3$	20	2.161	1880	1
Arsenic trifluoride	AsF_3	20	2.590	1880	1
Bromine pentafluoride	BrF_5	25	2.4604	1954	2
Bromine trifluoride	BrF_3	25	2.8030	1954	2
Carbon disulfide	CS_2	0	1.29272	1923	3
		20	1.2632	1926	4
Carbonyl chloride	$COCl_2$	0	1.4187	1946	5
Chlorine trifluoride	ClF_3	0	1.891	1950	6
Chromium oxychloride	CrO_2Cl_2	20	1.923	1880	1
Hydrazine	NH_2NH_2	0	0.9816	1950	7
Hydrogen fluoride	HF	0	1.0015	1933	8
Hydrogen peroxide	H_2O_2	19.90	1.4419	1920	9
Hydrogen disulfide	H_2S_2	25	1.3270	1930	10
Iodine pentafluoride	IF_5	0	3.29	1933	16
Iron penta-carbonyl	$Fe(CO)_5$	18	1.4644	1891	11
Nickel carbonyl	$Ni(CO)_4$	20	1.310	1891	1
Nitric acid (100%)	HNO_3	20	1.502	1919	1
Nitrogen dioxide	NO_2	20	1.348	1919	1
Dinitrogen oxide	N_2O_3	0	1.450	1888	1
Phosphorus tribromide	PBr_3	20	2.877	1845	1
Phosphorus trichloride	PCl_3	20	1.575	1880	1
Phosphorus oxychloride	$POCl_3$	20	1.675	1880	1
Selenium tetrafluoride	SeF_4	20	2.77	1928	12
Silicon tetrachloride	$SiCl_4$	20	1.483	1880	1
Stannic chloride	$SnCl_4$	20	2.231	1880	1
Sulfur chloride	S_2Cl_2	20	1.678	1880	1
Sulfuric acid (100%)	H_2SO_4	20	1.834	1923	1
Sulfur trioxide	SO_3	20.46	1.9207	1941	13
Sulfuryl chloride	SO_2Cl_2	20	1.673	1897	1
Sulfuryl chlorofluoride	SO_2FCl	0	1.623	1936	14
Thiocarbonyl tetrabromide	$CSBr_4$	20	3.0240	1929	15
Thiocarbonyl tetrachloride	$CSCl_4$	20	1.6996	1929	15
Thionyl chloride	$SOCl_2$	20	1.638	1880	1
Vanadium oxytrichloride	$VOCl_3$	20	1.828	1910	1

References for Table 2n-6

1. Baxter, G. P.: "International Critical Tables," vol. 3, p. 22, McGraw-Hill Book Company, Inc., New York, 1928.
2. Stein, L., R. C. Vogel, and W. H. Ludewig: *J. Am. Chem. Soc.* **76**, 4287 (1954).
3. Timmermans, J.: *Bull. soc. chim. Belges* **32**, 299 (1923).
4. Mathews, J. H.: *J. Am. Chem. Soc.* **48,** 562 (1926).
5. Davies, C. N.: *J. Chem. Phys.* **14,** 48 (1946).
6. Simons, J. H., ed.: "Fluorine Chemistry," Academic Press, Inc., New York, 1950 (private communication to editor from C. F. Swinehart and F. J. Burton, Jr.).
7. Hough, E. W., D. M. Mason, and B. H. Sage: *J. Am. Chem. Soc.* **72,** 5774 (1950).
8. Simons, J. H., and J. W. Bouknight: *J. Am. Chem. Soc.* **54,** 129 (1932); *J. Am. Chem. Soc.* **55,** 1458 (1933).
9. Maass, O., and W. H. Hatcher: *J. Am. Chem. Soc.* **42,** 2548 (1920).
10. Butler, K. H., and O. Maass: *J. Am. Chem. Soc.* **52,** 2184 (1930).
11. Mond and Langer: *J. Chem. Soc.* (*London*) **59,** 1090 (1891).
12. Prideaux, E. B. R., and C. B. Cox: *J. Chem. Soc.* (*London*) **133,** 1603 (1928).

13. Westrink, R.: Acad. Proefschrift Univ. Amsterdam, N. V. Drukkerij en Uitgeversgaak de Mercuur, Hilversum, 1941.
14. Booth, H. S., and C. V. Herrmann: *J. Am. Chem. Soc.* **58,** 63 (1936).
15. Briscoe, H. T., J. B. Peel, and P. L. Robinson: *J. Chem. Soc. (London)* **1929,** 1048.
16. Ruff, O., and A. Braida: *Z. anorg. u. allgem. Chem.* **206,** 63 (1932); **214,** 91 (1933).

TABLE 2n-7. LIQUID DENSITIES OF ELEMENTARY AND INORGANIC SUBSTANCES WHICH ARE NORMALLY GASEOUS UNDER STANDARD CONDITIONS
(Range below 0°C; ρ = g/ml; t = °C; pressure atmospheric*)

Substance	Formula	t	ρ	Year	Ref.
Air	20.9% Oxygen	−194	0.92	....	1
	53.6% Oxygen	−194	1.015	....	1
	72.15% Oxygen	−194	1.068	....	1
	94.4% Oxygen	−194	1.133	....	1
Ammonia	NH_4	−40	0.6900	1923	24
Argon	A	−189.38 (T.P.)	1.4195	1940	2
		−183.15	1.3740	1912	14
Boron trifluoride	BF_3	−101.0 (N.B.P.)	1.595	1932	3
Diborane	B_2H_6	−108.2	0.4542	1941	4
Carbon dioxide	CO_2	−56.6 (T.P.)	1.179	1928	5
Carbon monoxide	CO	−195.08 (orthobaric)	0.80640	1936	6
Chlorine	Cl_2	−33.7 (N.B.P.)	1.568	1909	7
		−40	1.574	1926	8
Fluorine	F_2	−195.94	1.562_2	1954	9
Hydrogen bromide	HBr	−68.7	2.157	1906	10
Hydrogen chloride	HCl	−85.8	1.1937	1906	10
Hydrogen iodide	HI	−35.7 (N.B.P.)	2.799	1906	10
Hydrogen selenide	H_2Se	−42	2.12	1902	13
		−27 (orthobaric)	1.961	1932	12
Hydrogen sulfide	H_2S	−60.1 (N.B.P.)	0.964	1906	10
		−63	0.9539	1932	11
Hydrogen telluride	H_2Te	−17.7	2.701	1932	12
Krypton	Kr	−157.21 (T.P.)	2.4525	1940	2
Neon	Ne	−245.9 (N.B.P.)	1.204	1915	14
Nitric oxide	NO	−150.2 (N.B.P.)	1.269	1910	16
		−153.6	1.227	1932	17
Nitrogen	N_2	−195.84 (N.B.P.)	0.808_4	1915	14
		−198.3	0.8297	1902	15
Nitrous oxide	N_2O	−89.4 (N.B.P.)	1.2257	1904	18
Dinitrogen oxide	N_2O_3	−8	1.464	1888	19
Oxygen	O_2	−182.97 (N.B.P.)	1.144_7	1911	14
		−182.5	1.1181	1904	20
		−195.0	1.1953	1930	21
Ozone	O_3	−112.4 (N.B.P.)	1.63	1924	14
Radon	Rn	−62 (N.B.P.)	4.40	1912	14
Silicane	SiH_4	−185	0.68	1916	22
Disilicane	Si_2H_6	−25	0.69	1916	22
Sulfur dioxide	SO_2	−10	1.4601	1899	22
Uranium hexafluoride	UF_6	−209.11 (T.P.)	3.630	1949	23
Xenon	Xe	−111.80 (T.P.)	3.0506	1932	2
		−106.9 (N.B.P.)	3.063	1912	14

N.B.P. = normal boiling point; T.P. = triple point.
See Table 2n-8 for liquid hydrogen and liquid helium.
* Unless specified as orthobaric (i.e., corresponding to thermodynamic equilibrium of coexistent liquid and vapor phases) or T.P.

References for Table 2n-7

1. Landolt-Börnstein: "Physikalisch-Chemische Tabellen," 5th ed., Springer-Verlag OHG, Berlin, 1923 (Edwards Bros., Inc., Ann Arbor, Mich., 1943).
2. Clusius, K., and K. Wiegand: *Z. physik. Chem.* **B46**, 1 (1940).
3. Ruff, O., A. Braida, O. Breitschneider, W. Menzel, and H. Plaut: *Z. anorg. u. allgem. Chem.* **206**, 59 (1932).
4. Laubengayer, A. W., R. P. Ferguson, and A. W. Newkirk: *J. Am. Chem. Soc.* **63**, 559 (1941).
5. Keyes, F. G.: "International Critical Tables," vol. 3, p. 235, McGraw-Hill Book Company, Inc., New York, 1928.
6. Timmermans, J.: "Physico-Chemical Constants of Pure Organic Compounds," p. 366, Elsevier Press, Inc., New York, 1950; Mathias, E., and C. A. Crommelin: Comm. Inst. Intern. Froid. (le comm. 12th rap.) 1936.
7. Johnson, F. M. G., and D. McIntosh: *J. Am. Chem. Soc.* **31**, 1138 (1909).
8. Van Aubel: *Bull. acad. Belges* **12** (5), 374 (1926).
9. White, D., J. H. Hu, and H. L. Johnston: *J. Am. Chem. Soc.* **76**, 2584 (1954).
10. McIntosh, S., B. D. Steele, and E. H. Archibald: *Z. physik Chem.* **55**, 129 (1906).
11. Klemenc, A., and O. Bankowski: *Z. anorg. u. allgem. Chem.* **208**, 348 (1932); *Z. Elektrochem.* **38**, 592 (1932).
12. Robinson, P. L., and W. E. Scott: *J. Chem. Soc. (London)* **1932**, 972.
13. Fonzes-Diacon, H.: *Compt. rend.* **134**, 171 (1902).
14. Porter, A. W.: "International Critical Tables," vol. 3, p. 20, McGraw-Hill Book Company, Inc., New York, 1928.
15. Inglis and Coates: *J. Chem. Soc. (London)* **89**, 886 (1902).
16. Adwentowski: *Chem. Zentr.* **1910I**, 1107.
17. Cheesman, G. H.: *J. Chem. Soc. (London)* **1932**, 889.
18. Grunmach: *Berlin Sitzber.* **1904**, 1198; *Ann. Physik* **15**, 401 (1904).
19. Geuther: *Liebigs Ann. Chem.* **1888**, 245.
20. Dewar: *Proc. Roy. Soc. (London)* **73**, 251 (1904).
21. Biltz, Fischer, and Wunnenberg: *Z. anorg. u. allgem. Chem.* **193**, 358 (1930).
22. Baxter, G. P.: "International Critical Tables," vol. 3, p. 22, McGraw-Hill Book Company, Inc., New York, 1928.
23. Hoge, J., and M. T. Wechsler: *J. Chem. Phys.* **17**, 617 (1949).
24. Timmermans, J.: *Bull. Soc. Belges* **32**, 299 (1923).

TABLE 2n-8. DENSITIES OF CRYOGENIC LIQUIDS

Helium (isotope 4)[a]

N.B.P. = 4.216°K

T = 4.20°K; pressure = 1 atm; ρ = 0.1251 g/ml

T_λ = 2.186°K; pressure = 38.3 mm Hg; ρ = 0.1462 g/ml

T_λ = 2.178°K; pressure = 1 atm.; ρ = 0.1473 g/ml

Helium (isotope 3)[b]

T = 3.20°K (N.B.P.); $\rho = 0.057_0$ g/ml

Normal hydrogen (isotope 1)[c]

T = 20.39°K (N.B.P.); ρ = 0.07098 g/ml

Parahydrogen (isotope 1)[d]

T = 20.27°K (N.B.P.); ρ = 0.07076 g/ml

Hydrogen deuteride (HD)[e]

T = 16.604°K (T.P.); pressure = 92.8 mm Hg; ρ = 0.1234 g/ml

Deuterium (isotope 2)[f]

T = 18.72°K (T.P.); pressure = 128.5 mm Hg; ρ = 0.1739 g/ml

Tritium (isotope 3)[g]

T = 25.04°K (N.B.P.); ρ = 0.2571 g/ml

N.B.P. = normal boiling point; T.P. = triple point.

For a discussion of the provisional temperature scale in the liquid-hydrogen region see ref. *e* and H. J. Hoge and F. G. Brickwedde, *J. Research Natl. Bur. Standards* **22,** 351 (1939).

[a] W. H. Keesom, "Helium," pp. 240, 207, 226, Elsevier Press, Inc., New York, 1940. The temperature scale in the liquid-helium range must be considered when evaluating the reported results of density measurements. A discussion of the problems involved and the most recent conventions adopted is given in C. F. Squire, "Low Temperature Physics," p. 25, McGraw-Hill Book Company, Inc., 1953.

[b] E. R. Grilly, E. F. Hammel, S. G. Sydoriak, *Phys. Rev.* **75,** 1103 (1949). Interpolated value by private communication.

[c] R. B. Scott and F. G. Brickwedde, *J. Research Natl. Bur. Standards* **19,** 237 (1937).

[d] R. B. Scott and F. G. Brickwedde, *J. Research Natl. Bur. Standards* **19,** 237 (1937).

[e] H. W. Woolley, R. B. Scott, and F. G. Brickwedde, *J. Research Natl. Bur. Standards* **41,** 379 (1948).

[f] K. Clusius and E. Bartholome, *Z. phys. Chem.* **B30,** 1237 (1935).

[g] E. R. Grilly, *J. Am. Chem. Soc.* **73,** 5307 (1951). Interpolated value by private communication.

TABLE 2n-9. DENSITIES OF SELECTED ORGANIC LIQUIDS
(Range 0 to 25°C; ρ = g/ml; t = °C; pressure atmospheric)

Substance	Formula	t	ρ	Year	Ref.
Acetic acid	$CH_3 \cdot CO_2H$	20	1.04926	1930	1
Acetone	$CH_3 \cdot CO \cdot CH_3$	20	0.79053	1930	2
Alcohol, amyl	$C_5H_{11}OH$	15	0.81837	1932	3
Alcohol, *n*-butyl	C_4H_9OH	25	0.80567	1943	4
Alcohol, ethyl*					
Alcohol, methyl†					
Alcohol, *n*-propyl	C_3H_7OH	20	0.8035	1949	5
Alcohol, isopropyl	$(CH_3)_2 \cdot CHOH$	25	0.78087	1935	6
Aniline	$C_6H_5NH_2$	20	1.02173	1949	7
Benzene	C_6H_6	20	0.87903	1946	8
Bromobenzene	C_6H_5Br	20	1.49519	1930	9
Bromoform	$CHBr_3$	20	2.8905	1935	10
Carbon disulfide	CS_2	20	1.2632	1926	11
Carbon tetrachloride	CCl_4	20	1.5940	1938	12
Chloroform	$CHCl_3$	20	1.48913	1930	9
Chlorobenzene	C_6H_5Cl	20	1.10617	1930	9
Cyclohexane	C_6H_{12}	20	0.77853	1946	8
Cyclopentane	C_5H_{10}	20	0.74538	1946	8
Diethyl ether	$(C_2H_5)_2O$	15	0.71925	1928	13
Ethyl acetate	$CH_3 \cdot CO_2C_2H_5$	25	0.89468	1937	14
Ethyl formate	$H \cdot CO_2C_2H_5$	15	0.92892	1932	15
Formic acid	$H \cdot CO_2H$	15	1.22647	1930	1
Glycerol (glycerin)	$CH_2OH \cdot CHOH \cdot CH_2OH$	20	1.2613	1937	16
Glycol, ethylene	$(CH_2OH)_2$	15	1.11710	1935	17
n-Heptane	$n\text{-}C_7H_{16}$	20	0.68367	1946	8
Heptene-1	$CH_2{=}CH{-}(CH_2)_4{-}CH_3$	20	0.6972	1946	19
n-Hexane	$n\text{-}C_6H_{14}$	20	0.6595	1946	18
Hexene-1	$CH_2{=}CH{-}(CH_2)_3{-}CH_3$	20	0.6736	1946	19
Hydrogen cyanide	HCN	20	0.6876	1932	20
Iodobenzene	C_6H_5I	30	1.81548	1932	21
Isoprene	$CH_2{=}C(CH_3){-}CH{=}CH_3$	20	0.6805	1936	22
Methyl formate	$H \cdot CO_2CH_3$	20	0.97421	1930	1
Methyl iodide	CH_3I	15	2.29300	1934	23
Nicotine	$C_5H_4N \cdot C_4H_7N(CH_3)$	20	1.0093	1925	24
Nitrobenzene	$C_6H_5NO_2$	25	1.1983	1944	25
Nitroglycerin	$NH_2NO_3 \cdot CHNO_3 \cdot CH_2NO_3$	15	1.5964	1930	26
n-Nonane	$n\text{-}C_9H_{20}$	20	0.7174	1946	18
n-Octane	$n\text{-}C_8H_{18}$	20	0.70252	1946	8
n-Pentane	$n\text{-}C_5H_{12}$	20	0.62619	1947	27
Isopentane	$\text{iso-}C_5H_{12}$	20	0.61963	1947	27
Pentene-1	$CH_2{=}CH{-}CH_2{-}CH_2{-}CH_3$	20	0.6406	1946	19
n-Propylbenzene	$C_6H_5\text{-}n\text{-}C_3H_7$	20	0.8618	1946	28
Toluene	$C_6H_5{-}CH_3$	20	0.86683	1946	8

General reference: J. Timmermans, "Physico-Chemical Constants of Pure Organic Compounds," Elsevier Press, Inc., New York, 1950.

* See Table 2n-5.

† See Table 2n-4.

References for Table 2n-9

1. Bureau d'Etalons (International Bureau of Physico-Chemical Standards), Brussels, 1930.
2. Zmaczynski, M. A.: *J. Chim. phys.* **27**, 503 (1930).
3. Bureau d'Etalons, 1932.
4. Brunjes, A. S., and M. J. P. Bogart: *Ind. Eng. Chem.* **35**, 256 (1943).
5. Hatem, S.: *Compt. rend.* **1949**, 601.
6. Olsen, A. L., and E. R. Washburn: *J. Am. Chem. Soc.* **57**, 303 (1935).
7. Dreisbach, R. R., and R. A. Martin: *Ind. Eng. Chem.* **41**, 2875 (1949).
8. Forziati, A. F., A. R. Glasgow, Jr., C. B. Willingham, and F. D. Rossini: *J. Research Natl. Bur. Standards* **36**, 129 (1946).
9. Zmaczynski, M. A.: *J. chim. phys.* **27**, 503 (1930).
10. Desreux, V.: *Bull. soc. chim. Belges* **44**, 249 (1935).
11. Bureau d'Etalons, 1928.
12. Michielewicz, C.: *Roczniki Chem.* **18**, 718 (1938).
13. Bureau d'Etalons, 1928.
14. Wojciechowski, M., and E. Smith: *Roczniki Chem.* **17**, 118 (1937).
15. Bureau d'Etalons, 1932.
16. Albright, P. S.: *J. Am. Chem. Soc.* **59**, 2098 (1937).
17. Bureau d'Etalons, 1937.
18. Vogel, A. I.: *J. Chem. Soc.* (*London*) **1946**, 133.
19. Wibaut, J. P., and H. Geldof: *Rec. trav. chim.* **65**, 125 (1946).
20. Lowry, T. M., and S. T. Henderson: *Proc. Roy. Soc.* (*London*), ser. A, **136**, 474 (1932).
21. Bureau d'Etalons, 1932.
22. Bekkadahl, N., L. A. Wood, and M. Wocjiechowski: *J. Research. Natl. Bur. Standards* **17**, 883 (1936).
23. Bureau d'Etalons, 1934.
24. Lowry, T. M., and B. K. Singh: *Compt. rend.* **181**, 909 (1925).
25. Coates, G. E., and J. E. Coates: *J. Chem. Soc.* (*London*) **1944**, 77.
26. Peterson, J. M.: *J. Am. Chem. Soc.* **52**, 3669 (1930).
27. Howard, F. L., T. W. Mears, A. Fookson, P. Pomerantz, and D. B. Brooks: *J. Research Natl. Bur. Standards* **38**, 365 (1947).
28. Gibbons, L. C., J. F. Thomson, T. W. Reynolds, J. I. Wright, H. H. Chanau, J. M. Lamberti, H. F. Hipsher, and J. V. Karabinas: *J. Am. Chem. Soc.* **68**, 1130 (1946).

TABLE 2n-10. DENSITIES OF SELECTED FLUOROCARBON AND CHLORO-FLUORO LIQUIDS
(Range all temperatures; ρ = g/ml; t = °C)

Substance	Index	t	ρ	Year	Ref.
n-Butforane	C_4F_{10}	20.8	1.47 (orthobaric)	1939	1
Cyclopentforane	C_5F_{10}	20	1.648	1947	2
Ethforane	C_2F_6	−78.2	1.61	1933	3
Ethforene	C_2F_4	−76.3	1.519	1933	3
Fluoroform	CF_3H	−84.4	1.465	1936	4
Freon-11	CCl_3F	15	1.4995	1940	5
Freon-12	CCl_2F_2	20	1.326 (orthobaric)	1942	6
Freon-13	$CClF_3$	−130	1.726	1931	7
Freon-21	$CHCl_2F$	15	1.3906 (orthobaric)	1940	5
Freon-22	$CHClF_2$	20	1.2130	1940	5
Freon-112	$C_2Cl_4F_2$	25	1.6447	1934	8
Hexforanes (mixture)	C_6F_{14}	20	1.697	1947	2
Methforane	CF_4	−130	1.62	1933	3
Octforanes (mixture)	C_8F_{18}	20	1.802	1947	2
n-Pentforane	C_5F_{12}	20	1.634	1947	2
Propforane	C_3F_8	0.2	1.45 (orthobaric)	1939	1
Benzo trifluoride	$C_6H_5CF_3$	30	1.1762	1953	9
p-Fluorotoluene	$CH_3C_6H_4F$	30	0.9869	1953	9
p-Fluorobromobenzene	BrC_6H_4F	30	1.5859	1953	9

General reference: J. H. Simons, ed., "Fluorine Chemistry," vol. I, Academic Press, Inc., New York, 1950.

Pressure is atmospheric unless indicated as orthobaric conditions.

References for Table 2n-10

1. Simons, J. H., and L. P. Block: *J. Am. Chem. Soc.* **61,** 2962 (1939); **59,** 1407 (1937).
2. Simons, J. H., ed., "Fluorine Chemistry," vol. I, p. 412, Academic Press, Inc., New York, 1950.
3. Ruff, O. and O. Breitschneider: *Z. anorg. u. allgem. Chem.* **210,** 173 (1933).
4. Ruff, O., O. Breitschneider, W. Luchsinger, and G. Millschitzky: *Ber.* **69,** 299 (1936).
5. Simons, J. H., ed.: "Fluorine Chemistry," vol. I, Academic Press, Inc., New York, 1950; Benning, A. F., and R. C. McHarness: *Ind. Eng. Chem.* **31,** 912 (1939); **32,** 814 (1940).
6. Benning, A. F., and W. H. Markwood, Jr.: "Thermodynamic Properties of Freon 12," Kinetic Chemicals, Inc., Wilmington, Del., 1942.
7. Ruff, O., and R. Keim: *Z. anorg. u. allgem. Chem.* **201,** 255 (1931).
8. Locke, E. G., W. R. Brode, and A. L. Henne: *J. Am. Chem. Soc.* **56,** 1726 (1934).
9. Rutledge, G. P., and W. T. Smith, Jr.: *J. Am. Chem. Soc.* **75,** 5762 (1953).

TABLE 2n-11. SPECIFIC GRAVITIES OF SELECTED VEGETABLE AND ANIMAL OILS*
(Range 15–25°C; t = °C; $d_{t_2}^{t_1}$ = ratio of density of oil at temperature t_1 to density of water at temperature t_2.)

Substance	t_1 / t_2	$d_{t_2}^{t_1}$
Castor oil	15 / 15	0.960–0.967
Cod-liver oil	15 / 15	0.922–0.931
Coconut oil	15 / 15	0.926
Cottonseed oil	25 / 25	0.917–0.918
Lard oil	15 / 15	0.913–0.915
Linseed oil	15 / 15	0.930–0.938
Neat's-foot oil	15 / 15	0.913–0.918
Olive	20 / 4	0.91268
Shark	15 / 15	0.918
Sperm	15 / 15	0.878
Tallow	15 / 15	0.914–0.919
Tung	15 / 15	0.94

* C. A. Mitchell, "International Critical Tables," vol. 3, p. 201, McGraw-Hill Book Company, Inc., New York, 1928.

2n-6. Volume of Liquids as a Function of Pressure and Temperature. Introduction. When pressure is applied to a confined liquid, the volume of the liquid decreases. In the following tables the volumes of several representative liquids are listed at a number of pressures and temperatures. These data were all determined by experimental measurement. The range of pressures is from 1 to 50,000 atm (or to the freezing point). The range of temperatures is from 0 to 200°C (in a few cases there are points outside this range). In addition a compilation of many other liquids for which high-pressure data are available is given with references.

In the tables the volume as a function of pressure and temperature is expressed in one of three ways:

1. Specific volume at a pressure and temperature. Units, ml/g.
2. Relative volume v/v_0, where v is the volume at the particular pressure and temperature and v_0 is the volume in the reference state (usually 0°C and 760 mm).
3. The change in volume of a given mass of liquid from a reference pressure of 5,000 kg/cm^2 along each experimental isotherm. All the data in the very-high-pressure range (5,000 to 50,000 kg/cm^2) are expressed in this way.

Several thermodynamically important parameters can be derived from these data. The isothermal instantaneous compressibility is defined by

$$\kappa_{\text{iso}} = -\frac{1}{v}\left(\frac{\partial v}{\partial p}\right)_T \tag{2n-5}$$

A good approximation of this quantity can be obtained from the shape of the isotherms. The coefficient of instantaneous cubical expansion is defined by

$$\beta = \frac{1}{v}\left(\frac{\partial v}{\partial T}\right)_p \tag{2n-6}$$

This quantity can also be derived from the experimental data. The second derivative of the volume with respect to the temperature $\partial^2 v/\partial T^2$ is an especially important parameter in the theory of liquids. Other quantities which can be derived from the data are the work of compression and the pressure coefficient. The work of compression is given by

$$W = -\int p\left(\frac{\partial v}{\partial p}\right)_T dp \tag{2n-7}$$

The pressure coefficient is the ratio of the thermal expansion to the isothermal compressibility:

$$\frac{(\partial v/\partial T)_p}{(\partial v/\partial p)_T} \tag{2n-8}$$

2n-7. Experimental Methods for Studying Compressibility of Liquids. A thorough description of the techniques employed in the experimental determination of the volume of liquids as a function of pressure and temperature is given by P. W. Bridgman in his text.[1] Even more extensive details are given in his original publications. The sylphon method, which was used in the pressure range 1 to 12,000 atm, is described in *Proc. Am. Acad. Arts Sci.* **66**, 185 (1931). The differential method, which was used in the pressure range 5,000 to 50,000 atm, is described in *Proc. Am. Acad. Arts Sci.* **74,** 21 (1940); and **74,** 399 (1942).

[1] P. W. Bridgman, "The Physics of High Pressure," George Bell & Sons, Ltd., London, 1952; *Rev. Modern Phys.* **18,** 1 (1946).

2n-8. General Features of the Behavior of Liquids under Pressure[1]

1. Mercury is the least compressible of all the liquids (in range −30 to 200°C). In the nonmetallic group glycerin is the least compressible liquid.
2. At pressures above 10,000 atm, the relative volume change for all liquids is about the same.
3. The melting curve appears to exist up to the highest pressures experimentally obtainable with no indication of either a critical point or a maximum. However, at very high pressures, the viscosity of some liquids becomes so large that internal changes take place infinitely slowly and a subcooling phenomenon appears.
4. The difference in volume between the solid and the liquid phase tends to decrease with increasing pressure but does not tend to become zero at any finite pressure.
5. Differences in specific volumes among isomers (i.e., compounds having the same chemical formula but different structural formulas) tend to disappear at around 12,000 atm.
6. The sign of $(\partial^2 v/\partial T^2)_p$ changes from plus to minus with increasing temperature at constant pressure at pressures above about 3,000 to 4,000 atm.
7. The quantity $(\partial p/\partial T)_v$ is not a function of volume alone.

TABLE 2n-12. VOLUME OF PURE AIR-FREE H_2O AS A FUNCTION OF PRESSURE AND TEMPERATURE

Temp. range −20 to 100°C;* pressure range 1–12,000 kg/cm²; specific volume in ml/g

p, kg/cm²	−20°C	−15°C	−10°C	−5°C	0°C	20°C	40°C	60°C	80°C	100°C
1	......	......	......	......	1.0001	1.0018	1.0079	1.0171	1.0284	1.0435
500	......	......	......	......	0.9770	0.9819	0.9880	0.9959	1.0063	1.0183
1,000	......	......	......	0.9566	0.9576	0.9632	0.9706	0.9786	0.9883	0.9993
1,500	......	0.9370	0.9380	0.9394	0.9409	0.9476	0.9550	0.9632	0.9724	0.9826
2,000	0.9203	0.9214	0.9228	0.9246	0.9261	0.9328	0.9408	0.9492	0.9582	0.9679
2,500	0.9061	0.9080	0.9097	0.9116	0.9132	0.9199	0.9282	0.9365	4.9453	0.9545
3,000	......	0.8959	0.8977	0.9000	0.9015	0.9084	0.9167	0.9020	9.9334	0.9424
3,500	......	0.8851	0.8871	0.8892	0.8909	0.8984	0.9062	0.7912	0.9225	0.9312
4,000	......	......	0.8771	0.8794	0.8812	0.8888	0.8966	0.9044	0.9126	0.9208
5,000	......	......	0.8596	0.8622	0.8639	0.8709	0.8796	0.8874	0.8949	0.9028
6,000	......	......	......	......	0.8489	0.8565	0.8645	0.8721	0.8794	0.8871
7,000	......	......	......	......	......	......	0.8515	0.8586	0.8659	0.8731
8,000	......	......	......	......	......	......	0.8396	0.8564	0.8534	0.8604
9,000	......	......	......	......	......	......	0.8287	0.8354	0.8422	0.8490
10,000	......	......	......	......	......	......	0.8186	0.8252	0.8318	0.8385
11,000	......	......	......	......	......	......	0.8090	0.8157	0.8222	0.8385
12,000	......	......	......	......	......	......	0.8006	0.8070	0.8134	0.8199

TABLE 2n-12. VOLUME OF PURE AIR-FREE H_2O AS A FUNCTION OF PRESSURE AND TEMPERATURE (*Continued*)

Temp. range 25–175°C;† pressure range 5,000–36,560 kg/cm²; Δv in cm²/1.000 g from 5,000 kg/cm²

p, kg/cm²	25°C	75°C	125°C	175°C
5,000	0.000	0.000	0.000	0.000
9,800	0.057			
10,000		0.063	0.066	0.070
15,000	Ice VI	0.105	0.112	0.120
20,000		0.136	0.146	0.157
21,430		0.144		
25,000			0.173	0.185
28,140		Ice VII	0.186	
30,000				0.207
35,000			Ice VII	0.226
36,560				0.231
				Ice VII

Temp. range 0–360°C;‡ pressure range 1–350 atm; specific volume in ml/g

p, atm	0°C	20°C	40°C	60°C	80°C	100°C	120°C	140°C
1	1.0002	1.0020	1.0079	1.0170	1.0289	1.0434		
25	0.9991	1.0009	1.0068	1.0159	1.0277	1.0421	1.0590	1.0785
50	0.9980	0.9998	1.0057	1.0147	1.0265	1.0408	1.0576	1.0769
75	0.9968	0.9987	1.0046	1.0136	1.0253	1.0396	1.0562	1.0754
100	0.9957	0.9976	1.0034	1.0124	1.0241	1.0383	1.0548	1.0738
125	0.9946	0.9965	1.0024	1.0113	1.0230	1.0370	1.0535	1.0723
150	0.9935	0.9955	1.0013	1.0102	1.0218	1.0358	1.0521	1.0708
175	0.9935	0.9944	1.0002	1.0091	1.0207	1.0346	1.0508	1.0694
200	0.9914	0.9934	0.9992	1.0080	1.0195	1.0334	1.0495	1.0679
250	0.9893	0.9913	0.9971	1.0059	1.0173	1.0310	1.0469	1.0650
300	0.9873	0.9893	0.9950	1.0038	1.0151	1.0286	1.0444	1.0622
350	0.9853	0.9873	0.9930	1.0017	1.0129	1.0264	1.0419	1.0595

p, atm	160°C	180°C	200°C	220°C	240°C	260°C	280°C	300°C	320°C
1									
25	1.1007	1.1262	1.1155	1.1897					
50	1.0989	1.1241	1.1530	1.1866	1.2264	1.2747	1.3285		
75	1.0972	1.1221	1.1506	1.1836	1.2225	1.2694	1.3213		
100	1.0954	1.1200	1.1482	1.1806	1.2187	1.2644	1.3146	1.3965	
125	1.0937	1.1181	1.1458	1.1778	1.2150	1.2596	1.3082	1.3860	1.4882
150	1.0920	1.1161	1.1435	1.1749	1.2115	1.2549	1.3020	1.3764	1.4712
175	1.0904	1.1142	1.1412	1.1722	1.2080	1.2505	1.2962	1.3675	1.4563
200	1.0887	1.1123	1.1390	1.1694	1.2047	1.2461	1.2962	1.3591	1.4428
250	1.0855	1.1086	1.1346	1.1642	1.1982	1.2379	1.2854	1.3438	1.4192
300	1.0824	1.1050	1.1304	1.1592	1.1921	1.2302	1.2754	1.3303	1.3992
350	1.0793	1.1015	1.1263	1.1544	1.1862	1.2230	1.2662	1.3181	1.3816

TABLE 2n-12. VOLUME OF PURE AIR-FREE H_2O AS A FUNCTION OF PRESSURE AND TEMPERATURE (*Continued*)

Temp. range 0–360°C;‡ pressure range 1–350 atm; specific volume in ml/g

p, atm	340°C	360°C
1		
150	1.6287	
175	1.5943	
200	1.5671	1.8140
250	1.5243	1.6905
300	1.4908	1.6232
350	1.4631	1.5758

* N. F. Dorsey, "Properties of Ordinary Water Substance," Reinhold Publishing Corporation, New York, 1948. Based on data of P. W. Bridgman, *J. Chem. Phys.* **3**, 597 (1936). See Dorsey for a further discussion of the factors involved in the interpretation of these data.

† P. W. Bridgman, *Proc. Am. Acad. Arts. Sci.* **74**, 419 (1942). These data were taken directly from the original publication.

‡ L. B. Smith and F. G. Keyes, *Proc. Am. Acad. Arts Sci.* **69**, 285 (1934). See Dorsey for a comment on these data.

TABLE 2n-13. VOLUME OF 99.9% D_2O AS A FUNCTION OF PRESSURE AND TEMPERATURE*

Temp. range −20 to 100°C; pressure range 1–12,000 kg/cm²; specific volume in ml/g

p, kg/cm²	−20°C	−15°C	−10°C	−5°C	0°C	20°C	40°C	60°C	80°C	100°C
1	......	......	......	......	0.9048	0.9049	0.9087	0.9169	0.9272	
500	......	......	......	......	0.8833	0.8857	0.8905	0.8979	0.9074	0.9187
1,000	......	......	......	0.8642	0.8652	0.8690	0.8744	0.8820	0.8912	0.9011
1,500	......	......	0.8475	0.8485	0.8495	0.8543	0.8605	0.8680	0.8769	0.8864
2,000	......	0.8318	0.8331	0.8344	0.8359	0.8415	0.8479	0.8553	0.8639	0.8731
2,500	0.8178	0.8193	0.8208	0.8222	0.8239	0.8298	0.8365	0.8440	0.8521	0.8613
3,000	0.8066	0.8082	0.8099	0.8116	0.8132	0.8194	0.8260	0.8335	0.8413	0.8502
3,500	......	0.7982	0.8001	0.8019	0.8036	0.8096	0.8165	0.8240	0.8317	0.8400
4,000	......	0.7892	0.7910	0.7928	0.7946	0.8009	0.8078	0.8153	0.8227	0.8305
5,000	......	......	......	0.7772	0.7789	0.7854	0.7924	0.7996	0.8064	0.8143
6,000	......	......	......	......	0.7665	0.7722	0.7787	0.7860	0.7926	0.8000
7,000	......	......	......	......	......	0.7597	0.7668	0.7736	0.7801	0.7870
8,000	......	......	......	......	......	0.7490	0.7559	0.7625	0.7690	0.7755
9,000	......	......	......	......	......	0.7391	0.7461	0.7526	0.7588	0.7653
10,000	......	......	......	......	......	......	0.7373	0.7432	0.7493	0.7558
11,000	......	......	......	......	......	......	0.7293	0.7348	0.7407	0.7470
12,000	......	......	......	......	......	......	0.7216	0.7271	0.7328	0.7393

* P. W. Bridgman, *J. Chem. Phys.* **3**, 597 (1936). These values were calculated from the original data assuming a molecular weight of 20.028 (chemical scale) for D_2O.

TABLE 2n-14. VOLUME OF MERCURY AS A FUNCTION OF PRESSURE AND TEMPERATURE

Temp. range −30 to 20°C;* pressure range 1–12,000 atm; specific volume in ml/g

p, atm	−30°C	−20°C	−10°C	0°C	10°C	20°C
1	0.073155	0.073288	0.073421	0.073554	0.073687	0.073820
1,000	0.072888	0.073016	0.073143	0.073270	0.073397	0.073524
2,000	0.072626	0.072748	0.072871	0.072993	0.073115	0.073237
3,000		0.072487	0.072605	0.072724	0.072842	0.072961
4,000		0.072233	0.072348	0.072463	0.072579	0.072696
5,000			0.072101	0.072213	0.072372	0.072440
6,000			0.071863	0.071973	0.072085	0.072196
7,000				0.071744	0.071853	0.071962
8,000					0.071632	0.071740
9,000					0.071422	0.071528
10,000					0.071223	0.071328
11,000						0.071140
12,000						0.070962

Temp. range 30–300°C;† pressure range 1–350 atm

p, atm	30°C	100°C	150°C	200°C	250°C	300°C
1–50	3.873×10^{-6}	4.259×10^{-6}	4.518×10^{-6}	4.879×10^{-6}	5.551×10^{-6}	6.970×10^{-6}
1–100	3.859	4.231	4.480	4.835	5.461	6.413
1–150	3.850	4.208	4.447	4.798	5.375	6.004
1–200	3.843	4.188	4.417	4.762	5.292	5.757
1–250	3.834	4.165	4.384	4.724	5.206	5.608
1–300	3.823	4.140	4.348	4.683	5.117	5.520
1–350	3.809	4.112	4.311	4.641	5.026	5.422

* P. W. Bridgman, *Proc. Am. Acad. Arts Sci.* **47,** 345 (1911). These values were calculated from the original data assuming the density of mercury at 0°C and 760 mm to be 13.5955 g/ml.

† L. B. Smith and F. G. Keyes, *Proc. Am. Acad. Arts Sci.* **69,** 313 (1934). The mean compressibility coefficient $(1/v)(\Delta v/\Delta p)$. These data were obtained from the study of the dilation of a nickel container under pressure from compressed mercury.

TABLE 2n-15. VOLUME OF METHYL ALCOHOL (CH_3OH) AS A FUNCTION OF PRESSURE AND TEMPERATURE

The Relative Volumes in Terms of the Volume at 0°C and 760 mm*

Temp. range 20–80°C; pressure range 1–12,000 atm; v/v_0; v = volume at (p,t); v_0 = volume at 0°C and 760 mm

p, atm	20°C	40°C	60°C	80°C
1	1.0238	1.0483	1.0737	1.1005
500	0.9811	0.9987	1.0182	1.0400
1,000	0.9494	0.9651	0.9808	0.9993
1,500	0.9256	0.9393	0.9526	0.9672
2,000	0.9064	0.9189	0.9306	0.9429
2,500	0.8906	0.9019	0.9124	0.9231
3,000	0.8763	0.8870	0.8966	0.9065
3,500	0.8636	0.8733	0.8824	0.8915
4,000	0.8523	0.8613	0.8700	0.8782
4,500	0.8420	0.8505	0.8587	0.8663
5,000	0.8325	0.8407	0.8487	0.8559
6,000	0.8163	0.8240	0.8314	0.8381
7,000	0.8023	0.8099	0.8163	0.8231
8,000	0.7907	0.7973	0.8039	0.8102
9,000	0.7797	0.7859	0.7920	0.7981
10,000	0.7696	0.7756	0.7816	0.7875
11,000	0.7605	0.7664	0.7728	0.7785
12,000	0.7527	0.7587	0.7652	0.7709

The Change in Volume in cm³ per 0.792 g from a Reference Pressure of 5,000 kg/cm² along Each Isotherm†

Temp. range 25–175°C; pressure range 5,000–50,000 kg/cm²; Δv in cm³/0.792 g

p, kg/cm²	25°C	75°C	125°C	175°C
5,000	0.000	0.000	0.000	0.000
10,000	0.062	0.066	0.073	0.082
15,000	0.099	0.106	0.117	0.128
20,000	0.125	0.135	0.139	0.161
25,000	0.145	0.157	0.174	0.187
30,000	0.161‡	0.173	0.194	0.208
35,000	0.173	0.187	0.210	0.226
40,000	0.183	0.198	0.223	0.240
45,000	0.191	0.208	0.234	0.253
50,000	0.199	0.218		

* P. W. Bridgman, "International Critical Tables," vol. 3, p. 41, McGraw-Hill Book Company, Inc., New York, 1928.

† P. W. Bridgman, *Proc. Am. Acad. Arts Sci.* **74,** 403 (1942).

‡ Displays subcooling at higher pressures.

TABLE 2n-16. VOLUME OF ETHYL ALCOHOL (C_2H_5OH) AS A FUNCTION OF PRESSURE AND TEMPERATURE

The Relative Volumes in Terms of the Volume at 0°C and 760 mm*

Temp. range 20–80°C; pressure range 1–12,000 atm; v/v_0; v = volume at (p,t); v_0 = volume at 0°C and 760 mm

p, atm	20°C	40°C	60°C	80°C
1	1.0212	1.0438	1.0679	1.0934
500	0.9782	0.9943	1.0121	1.0319
1,000	0.9479	0.9608	0.9760	0.9922
1,500	0.9247	0.9358	0.9482	0.9615
2,000	0.9059	0.9159	0.9266	0.9280
2,500	0.8899	0.8991	0.9088	0.9187
3,000	0.8760	0.8848	0.8935	0.9025
3,500	0.8634	0.8718	0.8800	0.8884
4,000	0.8517	0.8599	0.8678	0.8756
4,500	0.8410	0.8491	0.8567	0.8640
5,000	0.8314	0.8394	0.8467	0.8536
6,000	0.8149	0.8225	0.8291	0.8354
7,000	0.8009	0.8080	0.8139	0.8196
8,000	0.7888	0.7953	0.8005	0.8060
9,000	0.7776	0.7836	0.7884	0.7940
10,000	0.7671	0.7726	0.7776	0.7830
11,000	0.7574	0.7626	0.7682	0.7734
12,000	0.7485	0.7535	0.7600	0.7648

The Change in Volume in cm³ per 0.789 g from a Reference Pressure of 5,000 kg/cm² along Each Isotherm†

Temp. range 25–175°C; pressure range 5,000 kg/cm² to 45,000 kg/cm²; Δv in cm³ per 0.789 g

p, kg/cm²	25°C	75°C	125°C	175°C
5,000	0.000	0.000	0.000	0.000
10,000	0.063	0.069	0.071	0.076
15,000	0.100	0.109	0.113	0.119
20,000	0.128‡	0.137	0.144	0.151
25,000		0.159	0.168	0.175
28,700		0.174‡		
30,000			0.187	0.195
35,000			0.203	0.211
40,000			0.217	0.225
45,000			0.230	0.238

* P. W. Bridgman, "International Critical Tables," vol. 3, p. 41, McGraw-Hill Book Company, Inc., New York, 1928.

† P. W. Bridgman, *Proc. Am. Acad. Arts. Sci.* **74**, 399 (1942).

‡ Solid below this.

TABLE 2n-17. VOLUME OF ACETONE ($CH_3 \cdot CO \cdot CH_3$) AS A FUNCTION OF PRESSURE AND TEMPERATURE*

The Relative Volumes in Terms of the Volume at 0°C and 760 mm

Temp. range 20–80°C; pressure range 1–12,000 atm; v/v_0; v = volume at (p,t); v_0 = volume at 0°C and 760 mm

p, atm	20°C	40°C	60°C	80°C
1	1.0279	1.0585	1.0925	
500	0.9819	1.0032	1.0282	
1,000	0.9526	0.9706	0.9894	1.0082
1,500	0.9286	0.9441	0.9594	0.9736
2,000	0.9076	0.9217	0.9347	0.9467
2,500	0.8900	0.9028	0.9141	0.9253
3,000	0.8748	0.8868	0.8968	0.9073
3,500	0.8619	0.8729	0.8821	0.8920
4,000	0.8504	0.8607	0.8694	0.8786
4,500	0.8402	0.8498	0.8583	0.8666
5,000	0.8309	0.8398	0.8482	0.8558
6,000	0.8143	0.8225	0.8306	0.8370
7,000	0.7997	0.8072	0.8148	0.8209
8,000	0.7866	0.7935	0.8003	0.8066
9,000	......	0.7815	0.7876	0.7939
10,000	......	0.7707	0.7764	0.7821
11,000	Freezes	0.7607	0.7665	0.7715
12,000	......	0.7515	0.7577	0.7617

* P. W. Bridgman, "International Critical Tables," vol. 3, p. 42, McGraw-Hill Book Company, Inc. New York, 1928.

TABLE 2n-18. VOLUME OF BENZENE (C_6H_6) AS A FUNCTION OF PRESSURE AND TEMPERATURE*

Pressure range 1–3,500 kg/cm²; v/v_0; v = volume at (p,t); v_0 = volume at 0°C and 760 mm

p, kg/cm²	50°C	95°C
0	1.0630	1.1295
500	1.0160	
1,000	0.9841	1.0201
1,500	0.9591	0.9916
2,000		0.9684
2,500		0.9494
3,000		0.9325
3,500		0.9177

* P. W. Bridgman, *Proc. Am. Acad. Arts. Sci.* **66,** 210 (1931). Phase diagram of benzene given in P. W. Bridgman, *Phys. Rev.* **3,** 171 (1914).

TABLE 2n-19. VOLUME OF CARBON BISULFIDE (CS_2) AS A FUNCTION OF PRESSURE AND TEMPERATURE

The Relative Volumes in Terms of the Volume at 0°C and 760 mm*

Temp. range 20–80°C; pressure range 1–12,000 atm; v/v_0; v = volume at (p,t); v_0 = volume at 0°C and 760 mm

p, atm	20°C	40°C	60°C	80°C
1	1.0235	1.0490	1.0774	1.1092
500	0.9854	1.0051	1.0243	1.0458
1,000	0.9567	0.9734	0.9887	1.0061
1,500	0.9338	0.9483	0.9615	0.9762
2,000	0.9151	0.9277	0.9397	0.9592
2,500	0.8994	0.9105	0.9215	0.9327
3,000	0.8852	0.8953	0.9055	0.9154
3,500	0.8730	0.8820	0.8916	0.9003
4,000	0.8620	0.8702	0.8790	0.8870
4,500	0.8521	0.8596	0.8679	0.8754
5,000	0.8429	0.8501	0.8578	0.8649
6,000	0.8265	0.8337	0.8405	0.8468
7,000	0.8119	0.8196	0.8258	0.8316
8,000	0.7990	0.8070	0.8130	0.8188
9,000	0.7875	0.7954	0.8014	0.8071
10,000	0.7774	0.7844	0.7906	0.7962
11,000	0.7686	0.7741	0.7802	0.7857
12,000	0.7609	0.7646	0.7706	0.7758

The Change in Volume in cm³ per 1.261 g from a Reference Pressure of 5,000 kg/cm² along Each Isotherm†

Temp. range 25–175°C; pressure range 5,000–30,000 kg/cm²; Δv in cm³ per 1.261 g

p, kg/cm²	25°C	75°C	125°C	175°C
5,000	0.000	0.000	0.000	0.000
10,000	0.063	0.068	0.073	0.078
12,600	0.086‡			
15,000		0.110	0.118	0.126
18,300		0.131‡		
20,000			0.148	0.159
24,400			0.170‡	
25,000				0.184
30,000				0.204
30,700				0.206‡

* P. W. Bridgman, "International Critical Tables," vol. 3, p. 41, McGraw-Hill Book Company, Inc., New York, 1928.

† P. W. Bridgman, *Proc. Am. Acad. Arts. Sci.* **74,** 415 (1941).

‡ Solid below this.

TABLE 2n-20. VOLUME OF CARBON TETRACHLORIDE (CCl_4) AS A FUNCTION OF PRESSURE AND TEMPERATURE*

The Relative Volumes in Terms of the Volume at 50°C and 760 mm Pressure

Pressure range 1–3,500 kg/cm²; v/v_0; v = volume at (p,t); v_0 = volume at 50°C and 760 mm

p, kg/cm²	50°C	95°C
0	1.000	
500	0.9519	0.9928
1,000	0.9192	0.9540
1,500	0.8962	0.9362
2,000	......	0.9049
2,500	......	0.8872
3,000	......	0.8762
3,500	......	0.8603

* P. W. Bridgman, *Proc. Am. Acad. Arts Sci.* **66,** 212 (1931).

TABLE 2n-21. VOLUME OF CHLOROFORM ($CHCl_3$) AS A FUNCTION OF PRESSURE AND TEMPERATURE*

The Change in Volume in cm³ per 1.489 g from a Reference Pressure of 5,000 kg/cm² along Each Isotherm

Temp. range 25–175°C; pressure range 5,000–18,400 kg/cm²; Δv in cm³ per 1,489 g from a reference pressure of 5,000 kg/cm²

p, kg/cm²	25°C	75°C	125°C	175°C
5,000	0.000	0.000	0.000	0.000
6,200	0.016†			
10,000	......	0.067†	0.073	0.079
14,000	......	......	0.109†	
15,000	......	......	......	0.124
18,400	......	......	......	0.148†

* P. W. Bridgman, *Proc. Am. Acad. Arts Sci.* **74,** 413 (1941).
† Solid below this.

TABLE 2n-22. VOLUME OF ETHER ($(C_2H_5)_2O$) AS A FUNCTION OF PRESSURE AND TEMPERATURE*

The Relative Volumes in Terms of the Volume at 0°C and 760 mm

Temp. range 20–80°C, pressure range 1–12,000 atm; v/v_0; v = volume at (p,t); v_0 = volume at 0°C and 760 mm

p, atm	20°C	40°C	60°C	80°C
1	1.0315	1.0669		
500	0.9668	0.9884	1.0123	1.0369
1,000	0.9337	0.9498	0.9683	0.9874
1,500	0.9070	0.9195	0.9336	0.9484
2,000	0.8850	0.8952	0.9069	0.9189
2,500	0.8663	0.8756	0.8860	0.8962
3,000	0.8503	0.8594	0.8688	0.8776
4,000	0.8246	0.8329	0.8407	0.8481
5,000	0.8044	0.8121	0.8189	0.8252
6,000	0.7883	0.7953	0.8017	0.8070
7,000	0.7743	0.7806	0.7865	0.7917
8,000	0.7613	0.7670	0.7725	0.7779
9,000	0.7492	0.7545	0.7597	0.7652
10,000	0.7380	0.7431	0.7482	0.7535
11,000	0.7275	0.7325	0.7377	0.7427
12,000	0.7178	0.7225	0.8280	0.7326

* P. W. Bridgman, "International Critical Tables," vol. 3, p. 41, McGraw-Hill Book Company, Inc., New York, 1928. Additional data on ether are reported in the same temperature and pressure range by Bridgman, *Proc. Am. Acad. Arts Sci.* **66**, 218 (1931). These data were obtained by a method different from that above.

TABLE 2n-23. VOLUME OF GLYCERIN ($CH_2OHCHOHCH_2OH$) AS A FUNCTION OF PRESSURE AND TEMPERATURE*

The Relative Volumes in Terms of the Volume at 0°C and 760 mm

Temp. range 0–95°C; pressure range 1–12,000 kg/cm²; v/v_0; v = volume at (p,t); v_0 = volume at 0°C and 760 mm

p, kg/cm²	0°C	50°C	95°C
1	1.000	1.0266	
500	0.9900	1.0136	
1,000	0.9806	1.0025	1.0240
1,500	0.9721	0.9930	1.0125
2,000	0.9641	0.9843	1.0024
3,000	0.9501	0.9688	0.9853
4,000	0.9373	0.9548	0.9700
5,000	0.9264	0.9423	0.9565
6,000	0.9157	0.9310	0.9447
7,000	0.9057	0.9211	0.9342
8,000	0.8958	0.9121	0.9244
9,000	0.8867	0.9036	0.9152
10,000	0.8783	0.8955	0.9070
11,000	0.8712	0.8879	0.8994
12,000	0.8648	0.8800	0.8925

* P. W. Bridgman, *Proc. Am. Acad. Arts Sci.* **67**, 10 (1932).

TABLE 2n-24. ISOTHERMAL COMPRESSIBILITY OF SULFURIC AND NITRIC ACIDS*

Mean compressibility coefficient $\beta = \frac{10^6}{v_1}\left(\frac{v_1 - v_2}{p_2 - p_1}\right)$

Substance	t, °C	p_1, p_2, atm	β
Sulfuric acid	12.6	1, 161	~33
Nitric acid	0	1, 32	~35

* L. Decombe and J. Decombe, "International Critical Tables," vol. 3, p. 35, McGraw-Hill Book Company, Inc., New York, 1928.

TABLE 2n-25. ISOTHERMAL COMPRESSIBILITY OF LIQUEFIED GASES*

Pressure range 1–14,500 atm; mean compressibility coefficient $\beta = \frac{10^6}{v_1}\left(\frac{v_1 - v_2}{p_2 - p_1}\right)$

Substance	t, °C	p_1, p_2, atm	β
Bromine	20	100, 200	~57
Carbon dioxide	0	95 1	430†
Chlorine	20	100, 200	108‡
Helium	−271.6	1, 14,500	>38
Hydrogen	−260	1, 14,500	>31
Nitrogen	−205	1, 14,500	>15

* L. Decombe and J. Decombe, "International Critical Tables," vol. 3, p. 35, McGraw-Hill Book Company, Inc., New York, 1928.

† Instantaneous compressibility coefficient $\beta = -\frac{10^6}{v_1}\left(\frac{\partial v}{\partial P}\right)_T$.

‡ Estimated value.

2n-9. References to Compressibility Data for Other Substances

Reference: P. W. Bridgman, *Proc. Am. Acad. Arts Sci.* **67**, 6 (1932)
Pressure range: 0 to 12,000 kg/cm²
Substances:

Ethylene glycol	Methyl oleate
Trimethylene glycol	Tri-caproin
Propylene glycol	*n*-Butyl phthalate
Diethylene glycol	Eugenol
Tri-*o*-cresyl phosphate	Isooctane (2,2,4 tri-methyl pentane)
Tri-acetin	Isoprene
Ethyl dibenzyl malonate	

Reference: P. W. Bridgman, *Proc. Am. Acad. Arts Sci.* **66,** 198 (1931)
Pressure range: 0 to 12,000 kg/cm²
Substances:

Normal pentane	Chlorobenzene
Isopentane	Bromobenzene
2-Methyl pentane	Bromoform
3-Methyl pentane	Isopropyl alcohol
2-2-Dimethyl butane	Normal-butyl alcohol
2-3-Dimethyl butane	Normal-hexyl alcohol
Normal Heptane	
Normal Octane	
Normal Decane	

Reference: P. W. Bridgman, *Proc. Am. Acad. Arts Sci.* **68**, 1 (1933)
Pressure range: 0 to 12,000 kg/cm²
Substances:

Triethanolamine	Normal-amyl bromide
Normal-propyl chloride	Normal-amyl iodide
Normal-propyl bromide	Octanol-3
Normal-propyl iodide	2-methyl heptanol-3
Normal-butyl chloride	2-methyl heptanol-5
Normal-butyl bromide	2-methyl heptanol-1
Normal-butyl iodide	3-methyl heptanol-4
Normal-amyl chloride	

Reference: P. W. Bridgman, *Proc. Am. Acad. Arts Sci.* **74**, 403 (1942)
Pressure range: 5,000 kg/cm² to 50,000 kg/cm²
Substances:

Normal-propyl alcohol	Chloroform
Isopropyl alcohol	Chlorobenzene
Normal-butyl alcohol	Methylene chloride
Normal-amyl alcohol	Ethylene bromide
Ethyl bromide	Cyclohexane
Normal-propyl bromide	Methyl cyclohexane
Normal-butyl bromide	*p*-Xylene
Ethyl acetate	Benzene
Normal-amyl ether	

Reference: P. W. Bridgman, "International Critical Tables," vol. 3, p. 40, McGraw-Hill Book Company, Inc., New York, 1928.
Pressure range: 1 to 12,000 atm
Substances:

Phosphorous trichloride
Ethyl iodide
Ethyl chloride
Isobutyl alcohol

Reference: R. S. Jessup, *Natl. Bur. Standards (U.S.) Research Paper* 244, 1930.
Pressure range: 1 to 50 kg/cm²
Temperature range, 0° to 300°C
Substances: 14 petroleum oils

Reference: F. R. Russell and H. C. Hottel, *Ind. Eng. Chem.* **30**, 372 (1938)
Pressure range: 1 to 400 kg/cm². Max. temperature: 425°C
Substance: Liquid naphthalene

2n-10. Adiabatic and Isothermal Compressibilities of Liquids. The adiabatic compressibilities β_{ad} of a great many organic liquids at room temperature are available from measurements of the velocity of sound.[1]

$$c = \sqrt{\frac{1}{\beta_{ad}\rho}} \tag{2n-9}$$

The isothermal compressibility β_{iso} can be obtained from the adiabatic compressibility by the thermodynamic relation

$$\beta_{iso} = \beta_{ad} + \frac{T\alpha^2}{\rho c_p} \tag{2n-10}$$

in which α = thermal coefficient of volume expansion, T = Kelvin temperature, and c_p = specific heat at constant pressure.

[1] G. L. Bergmann, "Der Ultraschall," 6th ed., pp. 375ff., Stuttgart, 1954.

TABLE 2n-26. ADIABATIC AND ISOTHERMAL COMPRESSIBILITIES OF CERTAIN ORGANIC LIQUIDS

All values in cm²/dyne at 20°C unless otherwise stated; data were obtained in fashion described in text

Liquid	$\beta_{ad} \times 10^{12}$	$\beta_{iso} \times 10^{12}$	Remarks
Acetic acid	75	91	*
Acetone	90.6	125.6	†
Aniline	36	45	*
Benzene	65.8	95.4	†
Carbon bisulfide	59.8	92.7	†
Carbon tetrachloride	72.8	105.8	†
Chlorobenzene	55	74	*
Chloroform	67.8	100.7	†
Cyclohexane	83	110	25°*
Ether	140.6	186.8	†
Ethyl acetate	82	113	*
Ethyl alcohol	94.1	111.3	†
Ethylene chloride	55	80	*
Heptane	111.4	143.9	†
Methyl alcohol	101.9	123.4	†
Nitrobenzene	40	49	*
Toluene	66.4	90.6	†

* Data from "International Critical Tables," McGraw-Hill Book Company, Inc., New York, 1928.
† Data from Tables annuelles de constantes et donnees numeriques, vol. IX. (Gauthier-Villars & Cie, Paris, and McGraw-Hill Book Company, Inc., New York, 1929.)

TABLE 2n-27. ISOTHERMAL COMPRESSIBILITIES OF AQUEOUS SOLUTIONS

All values in cm²/dyne at 20°C unless otherwise stated

Solution	Concentration, % of solute	$\beta_{iso} \times 10^{12}$	Remarks
Ammonium nitrate	11.50	42.21	
	28.00	36.90	
Calcium chloride	4.095	41.4	
	20.22	31.2	30°C
Hydrochloric acid	7.15	43.42	
	21.92	40.58	
Potassium chloride	2.51	42.9	
	22.19	32.8	30°C
Potassium nitrate	6.25	43.25	
	21.8	35.90	
Pure water	......	45.80	
Sodium sulfate	2.55	43.60	
	11.90	35.70	

All values are taken from Tables annuelles de constantes et donnees numeriques, vol. IX, 1929.

2o. Viscosity of Liquids

WLADIMIR PHILIPPOFF

Franklin Institute

The viscosity η of a liquid is defined as the ratio between the shearing stress in dynes/cm^2 and the rate of shear in sec^{-1} according to Newton's law. The unit is dynes · sec/cm^2 = 1 poise, and 0.01 poise = 1 centipoise (cp). One often uses the kinematic viscosity $\nu = \eta/\rho$ in stokes or 0.01 stokes = 1 cs, where ρ is the density in grams/cc. A practical unit is the Reyn; 1 Reyn in psi · sec = 69,000 poises. Sometimes the reciprocal unit, the fluidity $\phi = 1/\eta$ in Rhes is used.

Viscosity is measured with a large variety of viscometers. Often the shearing stress is given by the hydrostatic head of the liquid itself; in this case the instruments measure ν. Such an instrument is the technical Saybolt viscometer that measures the viscosity in seconds Saybolt Universal (SSU) or seconds Saybolt Furol (SSF). The relation between these units and cgs units is given in tables.[1] For the calibration of viscometers the calculation of the viscosity from the dimensions is difficult. The best standard is water, which has been rechecked recently.[2] In the calibration of capillary viscometers, the values have to be corrected for the kinetic energy of the emerging liquid. Faster flow causes turbulence. In a standardization of viscometers for higher viscosities, a calibration with higher-viscosity liquids such as the National Bureau of Standards (NBS) oils as secondary standards, listed in the tables below, can be used.

Viscosity increases exponentially with hydrostatic pressure. Most complete tables are given in an ASME report (1953) for oils and P. W. Bridgman[3] for organic liquids. Also, viscosity depends strongly on temperature; generally, the higher the viscosity, the higher is the temperature dependence. Values for oils can usually be plotted as a straight line in the Refutas chart (ASTM chart) according to the empirical Walther equation log-log $(\nu + 0.8) = m \log T$, where ν is in centistokes and T is the absolute temperature in °K.

The viscosity of the usual oils is constant from the smallest rate of shear up to at least 10^5 sec^{-1}. Solutions of high polymers or greases have viscosities that are strongly dependent on the applied shearing stress or rate of shear. The former can be considered to be non-Newtonian liquids, which means that their viscosity changes from a high value at low rates of shear to a low value at high rates of shear. Greases have yield values below which no flow exists.

The viscosity of solutions of polymers depends very strongly on the concentration of the solute, reaching enormous values for high concentrations. Empirical formulas are used to describe this in a wide range of variables. In describing the viscosity of a solution, the relative viscosity η_{rel} is used. It is defined as viscosity of solution/viscosity of solvent. Solutes are characterized by their "intrinsic viscosity,"

[1] *J. Inst. Petroleum Technol.* **22,** 21 (1936).

[2] By J. F. Swindells, J. R. Coe, Jr., and T. B. Godfrey, *J. Research Natl. Bur. Standards* **48,** 1 (1952).

[3] *Proc. Am. Acad. Arts Sci.* **61,** 57 (1926).

TABLE 2o-1. VISCOSITY OF COMMON LIQUIDS

	−40°C	−30°C	−20°C	−10°C	0°C	10°C	20°C	30°C	40°C	50°C	60°C	80°C	100°C	120°C	140°C	160°C	180°C
Acetic acid[a]							1.22	1.04	0.90	0.79	0.70	0.56	0.46				
Acetone[a]	0.66	0.57	0.50	0.442	0.395	0.356	0.322	0.293	0.268	0.246							
Aniline[a]					10.2	6.5	4.40	3.12	2.30	1.80	1.50	1.10	0.80	0.59			
Benzene[a]					0.91	0.76	0.65	0.56	0.492	0.436	0.390	0.316	0.261	0.219	0.185	0.156	0.132
Bromobenzene[a]					1.52	1.31	1.13	1.00	0.89	0.79	0.72	0.60	0.52				
Butyl acetate[a]					1.004	0.851	0.732	0.637	0.563		0.448	0.366	0.304				
Butyl alcohol[a]	22.4	14.6	10.3	7.4	5.19	3.87	2.95	2.28	1.78	1.41	1.14	0.76	0.54				
Carbon disulfide[a]				0.495	0.433	0.396	0.366	0.341	0.319								
Carbon tetrachloride[a]				1.68	1.35	1.13	0.97	0.84	0.74	0.65	0.59	0.472	0.387	0.323	0.276	0.234	0.201
Castor oil[b]			87,600	22,520	6,406	2,383	961	456.5	224.2	120.5	72.0	33.1	16.9				
Chlorobenzene[a]					1.06	0.91	0.80	0.71	0.64	0.57	0.52	0.435	0.370	0.320	0.275	0.240	0.210
Chloroform[a]					0.70	0.63	0.57	0.51	0.466	0.426	0.390						
m-Cresol[a]					95	44	21	10	6.2	4.4	3.2	2.1	1.6				
Cyclohexane[a]							0.97	0.82	0.71	0.61	0.54						
Cyclohexanol[a]							68.0	36.1	20.3	12.1	7.8	3.5					
Cyclohexanone[f]						2.51	2.19	1.83	1.52	1.28	1.09	0.85					
Decalin[a]							2.40			1.58							
Decane[d]		2.15	1.852	1.556	1.291	1.081	0.920	0.796	0.697	0.615	0.546	0.441	0.364	0.304	0.257	0.219	
Dioxane[a]							1.26	1.06	0.917	0.778	0.685	0.539					
Dodecane[d]				2.87	2.268	1.816	1.488	1.248	1.066	0.9215	0.8046	0.6320	0.5110	0.422	0.352	0.297	0.253
Ethyl acetate[a]					0.578	0.507	0.449	0.400	0.360	0.326	0.297	0.248	0.210	0.178	0.152	0.129	0.109
Ethyl alcohol[a]	4.79	3.65	2.38	2.23	1.78	1.46	1.19	1.00	0.825	0.701	0.591	0.435	0.326	0.248	0.190		
Ethyl ether[a]	0.47	0.41	0.364	0.328	0.296	0.268	0.243	0.220	0.199		0.166	0.140	0.118				
Ethylene glycol[c]							19.9		9.13		4.95	3.02	1.99				
Formic acid[a]						2.25	1.78	1.46	1.22	1.03	0.89	0.68	0.54				
Glycerin[a c]			1.34×10^5	31,600	12,100	3,950	1,499	624									
Heptane[a d]	0.865	0.770	0.682	0.600	0.517	0.458	0.409	0.367	0.332	0.301	0.275	0.231					
Hexane[a d]	0.611	0.545	0.486	0.432	0.397	0.355	0.320	0.290	0.264	0.241	0.221						
Isopropyl alcohol[a]	23.2	14.9	10.1	6.8	4.60	3.26	2.39	1.76	1.33		0.80	0.52					
Methyl acetate[a]							0.381	0.344	0.312	0.284	0.258	0.217	0.182	0.154	0.130		
Methyl alcohol[a]	1.75	1.39	1.16	0.970	0.817	0.68	0.584		0.450	0.396	0.351						
i-Pentane[a]					0.272	0.246	0.233	0.202									
n-Pentane[d]	0.432	0.385	0.345	0.309	0.2766	0.2496	0.2259	0.2052	0.187								
Propyl acetate[a]					0.77	0.67	0.58	0.51	0.46	0.41	0.368	0.304	0.250				
Pyridine[a]					1.33	1.12	0.95	0.83	0.73		0.58	0.482					
Tetralin[a]							2.02			1.3							
Toluene[a]					0.768	0.667	0.586	0.522	0.466	0.420	0.381	0.319	0.271	0.231	0.199	0.150	
Trichlorethylene[a]				0.79	0.71	0.64	0.58	0.53	0.48	0.45	0.41						
m-Xylene[c]					0.806	0.700	0.620	0.545	0.497	0.443	0.403	0.339	0.289	0.250			
o-Xylene[c]					1.105	0.953	0.810	0.710	0.627	0.56	0.50	0.411	0.346	0.294	0.254		
p-Xylene[c]						0.750	0.648	0.573	0.513	0.456	0.414	0.345	0.292	0.251			
Water[e]					1.7834	1.3022	1.0019	0.7995	0.6513	0.5481	0.4687	0.3545	0.2813				

[a] J. D'Ans and E. Lax, "Taschenbuch, Für Chemiker und Physiker," Springer-Verlag OHG, Berlin, 1943 (mean values from original sources).
[b] Marcel Bourdiol, Contribution à l'étude de la viscosité et de la congélation der huiles.
[c] "Handbook of Chemistry and Physics," 34th ed., Chemical Rubber Publishing Company.
[d] Selected Values of Properties of Hydrocarbons, *Natl. Bur. Standards (U.S.) Circ.* C461.
[e] J. F. Swindells, J. R. Coe, and T. B. Godfrey, *J. Research Natl. Bur. Standards* **48**, 1–31 (1952).
[f] W. Herz and W. Block, *Z. physik. Chem.* **110**, 23 (1924).

$[\eta] = [(\eta_{rel} - 1)/c]_{c \to 0}$ where c is the concentration in g/100-ml solution. This quantity is connected with the molecular weight or degree of polymerization of the polymer.

The quoted values for the viscosity of organic compounds depend on their chemical purity. They must be regarded as reference values only, as in many cases the exact chemical purity is not stated.

Table 2o-1 contains values of the viscosity in centipoises of a series of well-known liquids as function of temperature in the range from −40 to 180°C. Superscripts refer to the accompanying bibliography.

TABLE 2o-2. SECONDARY STANDARDS OF VISCOSITY. APPROXIMATE VISCOSITIES OF NBS OILS FOR CALIBRATING VISCOMETERS

Oil	Absolute, poises			Kinematic, stokes		
	20°C	25°C	37.78°C (100°F)	20°C	25°C	37.78°C (100°F)
D	0.020	0.018	0.014	0.026	0.023	0.019
H	0.074	0.063	0.044	0.091	0.078	0.055
I	0.12	0.10	0.066	0.14	0.12	0.081
J	0.21	0.17	0.11	0.25	0.21	0.13
K	0.41	0.32	0.18	0.48	0.38	0.22
L	1.0	0.74	0.37	1.1	0.84	0.43
M	3.0	2.1	1.0	3.4	2.4	1.1
N	14	9.6	4.0	16	11	4.6
OB	330	210	62*	380	240	70*
P	480†	200*	95‡	540†	230*	110‡

These oils are not intended for use as permanent standards. They are not suitable for stockroom items and should be ordered only for immediate use in 1-lb samples. The exact viscosities are listed by the NBS for each sample. The National Bureau of Standards should be consulted about these oils.

* 40°C.
† 30°C.
‡ 50°C.

TABLE 2o-3. SECONDARY STANDARDS OF VISCOSITY. APPROXIMATE VISCOSITIES OF NBS OILS FOR CALIBRATING SAYBOLT VISCOMETERS

Oil	Temp., °F	Viscosity	ν, cs
SB	100	300 SSU	65
SC	130	300 SSU	65
SF	122	170 SSF	360

These oils are not intended for use as permanent standards. They are not suitable for stockroom items and should be ordered only for immediate use in 1-lb samples. The exact viscosities are listed by the NBS for each sample. The National Bureau of Standards should be consulted about these oils.

TABLE 2o-4. VISCOSITIES OF INDUSTRIAL OILS AND LUBRICANTS

Grade	100°F		210°F	
	SUS	cs	SUS	cs
Typical automotive crankcase lubricants (Mid-Continent crude):*				
SAE 10	165	35.4	44	5.44
SAE 20	340	73.5	54	8.48
SAE 30	550	119	64	11.3
SAE 40	850	184	77	14.8
SAE 50	1,200	260	94	19.0
Typical turbine oil characteristics (steam turbines):†				
Light	150	32.1	43	5.12
Medium	300	64.9	51	7.60
Heavy	400	86.6	58	9.65
Synthetic crankcase oil (polyalkylene glycol derivative—Prestone motor oil)‡				
NO 200	175	37.6	48	6.68
NO 300	300	64.9	62	10.8
Silicone synthetic fluids:¶				
DC-200-350	1,617	350	651.2	140
DC-200-20	77.2	15	49.0	7
Light mineral hydraulic oil§	125	26.4	42	4.82

* "Physical Properties of Lubricants," American Society of Lubricating Engineers, 1951.
† Forbes, Pope, and Everett, "Lubrication of Industrial and Marine Machinery," p. 211, John Wiley & Sons, Inc., New York, 1954.
‡ Wilson, Synthetic Engine Lubs Found Economical, *SAE J.*, October, 1947, p. 25.
¶ Dow Corning Catalog.
§ "Physical Properties of Materials," American Society of Lubricating Engineers, 1951.

TABLE 2o-5. AIRCRAFT-ENGINE LUBRICATING-OIL SPECIFICATIONS (RECIPROCATING) GOVERNMENT SPECIFICATIONS MIL-0-6082*

Grade	Temp., °F	Viscosity, SUS	Viscosity, cs
65 (1065)	210	62–68	10.8–12.4
80 (1080)	210	76–84	14.5–16.6
100 (1100)	210	93–103	18.8–21.2
120 (1120)	210	115–125	23.9–26.2
Aircraft Gas-turbine Lubricating Oils—Typical Tests†			
AN-0-9 grade (1010)	−40	12,936	
AN-0-9 grade (1010)	100	59.4	10.2
AN-0-9 grade (1010)	210	34.5	2.46
AN-0-8 grade (1065)	100	530	115
AN-0-8 grade (1065)	210	67	12.2

* Forbes, Pope, and Everett, "Lubrication of Industrial and Marine Machinery," p. 134, John Wiley & Sons, Inc., New York, 1954.
† *Lubrication* **34,** 48 (April, 1948).

TABLE 2o-6. VISCOSITY OF PLASTICIZERS AND OTHER ORGANIC LIQUIDS AT ROOM TEMPERATURE

	Temp., °C	Viscosity, cp
Dioctyl phthalate*	20	81.4
Dibutyl phthalate†	25	15.8
Diethyl phthalate‡	25	10.0
Dimethyl phthalate‡	20	17.1
Octyl alcohol*	25	7.07
Tricresyl phosphate‡	20	106
Dioctyl adipate‡	20	12.9
Dioctyl sebacate‡	20	17.9

* Carbide and Carbon Chemical Co.
† Commercial Solvents Corp.
‡ D. N. Buttrey, "Plasticizers."

TABLE 2o-7. VISCOSITY OF MERCURY IN CENTIPOISES*

−20°C	−10°C	0°C	10°C	20°C	30°C	40°C	50°C	60°C	80°C	100°C
1.855	1.764	1.685	1.615	1.554	1.499	1.450	1.407	1.367	1.298	1.240

* "Handbook of Chemistry and Physics," 37th ed., Chemical Rubber Publishing Company, Cleveland, 1955.

2p. Tensile Strength and Surface Tension of Liquids

ARTHUR F. SCOTT

Reed College

FRED D. AYRES

Reed College

WESLEY L. NYBORG

Brown University

2p-1. Tensile Strength. *Historical and General.* The maximum negative pressure (tensile strength) that a liquid can withstand has been the object of numerous investigations. Experimental values are quite discordant among themselves and are generally much lower than the theoretical estimates. The tensile strength of a liquid, measured in a device known as a tonometer, is taken as that stress (negative pressure) under which the liquid ruptures. A point of concern has been the possibility that rupture occurs at the wall of the container rather than in the body of the liquid and that therefore the observed negative pressure is a measure of adhesive force rather than of the assumed cohesive force.

TABLE 2p-1. TENSILE STRENGTH OF LIQUIDS BY VARIOUS METHODS

Liquid and method	Max negative pressure, atm	Ref.	Liquid and method	Max negative pressure, atm	Ref.
Water:			Ether:		
A-1*	50–150	1	A-2	72	1
A-1†	157	2	B-1	2.2	1
A-1‡	17–56	3	Mineral oil:		
A-1	68	4	A-1	119	2
A-2	34	1	A-1¶	24	2
A-3	17	1	A-4	7.8	7
B-1	1.5	4	B-1	2.9	1
B-2	0.2–0.5	1	Acetic acid, C-3	288	8
B-3	4	1, 8	Benzene, C-3	150	8
C-1	4.8	1	Aniline, C-3	300	8
C-1	6.0	5	Carbon tetrachloride, C-3	276	8
C-2	5.6	5	Chloroform, C-3	317	8
C-3	277	6	Mercury, C-3	425	9
Alcohol:					
A-2	40	1			
A-3	17	1			
B-1	2.4	1			
C-1	7.9	1			

* Values reported prior to 1941.
† Tubes boiled for 8 hr to expel air.
‡ Tubes filled by vacuum technique to eliminate air.
¶ Tube sealed by liquid frozen in capillary side arm.

References for Table 2p-1

1. Vincent, R. S.: *Proc. Phys. Soc.* **53,** 141 (1941).
2. Vincent, R. S., and G. H. Simmonds, *Proc. Phys. Soc.* **55,** 376 (1943).
3. Scott, A. F., D. P. Shoemaker, K. N. Tanner, and J. G. Wendel, *J. Chem. Phys.* **16,** 495 (1948).
4. Scott, A. F., and G. M. Pound, *J. Chem. Phys.* **9,** 726 (1941).
5. Temperly, H. N. V., and L. G. Chambers, *Proc. Phys. Soc.* **58,** 420 (1946).
6. Briggs, Lyman J.: *J. Appl. Phys.* **21,** 721 (1950).
7. Vincent, R. S.: *Proc. Phys. Soc.* **55,** 41 (1943).
8. Briggs, Lyman J.: *J. Chem. Phys.* **19,** 970 (1951).
9. Briggs, Lyman J.: *J. Appl. Phys.* **24,** 488 (1953).

Methods of Measuring Tensile Strength. Brief descriptions of these methods are given below, arranged according to the means used to produce the stress in the liquid. Each method is given a code designation for identification in Table 2p-1.

A. STRESS PRODUCED BY COOLING AND THUS CONTRACTING THE LIQUID: In Berthelot's method (A-1) the liquid, sealed in a thick-walled capillary tube, is first warmed until it just fills the tube and is then cooled until the liquid "breaks." The maximum negative pressure is calculated from the known mechanical properties of the liquid, assuming its extensibility to be the same as its compressibility. In Meyer's method

(A-2) a spiral glass capillary is part of the tonometer and indicates the pressure exerted by the liquid, which completely fills the vessel. Meyer calibrated his spiral manometers under both positive and reduced pressure. Worthington, in a single experiment (A-3), measured the tension by means of a mercury-in-glass dilatometer, the bulb of which was enclosed within the tonometer. The calibration curve of the dilatometer, obtained previously by applying positive pressure, was extrapolated into the negative region. Vincent used a viscosity tonometer (A-4) in which the liquid completely filled a glass bulb and a fine capillary tube attached to it. By controlled cooling of the bulb, a gradually increasing tension is exerted on the liquid, measured at any time by the rate of flow through the capillary. The maximum tension can be calculated from the observed rates of flow before and after the liquid ruptures.

B. STRESS PRODUCED BY EXPANDING THE VOLUME OF TONOMETER: Vincent has described a new method (B-1) which employs a metal bellows completely filled with the liquid. Extension of the bellows exerts a pull on the contained liquid. An early method (B-2) involved the use of a long (2-m) tube closed at one end with a semipermeable membrane. After being filled with air-free water the tube is inverted and the open end is placed in a mercury trough. Evaporation of the water through the membrane causes the mercury to rise in the tube. The tension is estimated from the length of the column in excess of normal barometric height. Hulett (1903), in connection with an experiment of this type, observed a marked decrease in rate of evaporation as the mercury column rose and called attention to the analogy between negative pressure and osmotic pressure. This relationship forms the basis of a method for measuring the osmotic pressure of a solution. Budgett (B-3) measured the force required to pull apart flat steel surfaces wetted by a thin film of the liquid.

C. STRESS PRODUCED BY CENTRIFUGAL FORCE: Several experiments have been reported in which tension is developed by rotation of the tube containing the liquid. Reynolds (C-1) used U tubes sealed at both ends, with one arm longer than the other. One arm is filled completely with liquid; the other arm is only partially filled with liquid under its own vapor pressure. The tube is rotated about an axis positioned somewhat above the open part of the U. Temperly used a similar method (C-2), except that the short arm was open to the atmosphere. Recently Briggs (C-3) employed a Z-shaped capillary tube, open at both ends, rotating in the Z plane about an axis passing through the center of the Z and perpendicular to the plane. The liquid menisci are located in the bent-back short arms of the Z. The speed of rotation is increased gradually until the liquid in the capillary "breaks."

A fairly complete summary of the experimental measurements of the tensile strength of pure liquids is tabulated below. Information and references pertaining to work prior to 1941 are to be found in ref. 1, a paper which also gives an account of method B-1. This tabulation does not include the results of those experiments in which materials such as wood or steel were introduced into a glass tonometer in an effort to ascertain the adhesive forces between the liquid and these materials; nor does it include the results of measurements with aqueous solutions.

The tensile strength of liquids has been considered in connection with the rise of sap in trees[1] and bubble formation in supersaturated liquids.[2] Recently, tonometerlike devices have been described[3] for the purpose of detecting cosmic particles. In one such "bubble chamber," provided with a movable piston inserted through an O ring, the liquid is stressed by retracting the piston. This particular chamber is filled with isopentane and operates at a negative pressure of approximately 6 atm.[4] The fact

[1] Robert E. Hungate, *Plant Physiol.* **9,** 783 (1934).
[2] E. C. Marboe, *Chem. Eng. News* **27,** 2198 (1949).
[3] D. A. Glaser, *Phys. Rev.* **87,** 665 (1952).
[4] Jere Lord, University of Washington, private communication.

that cosmic particles can act to produce bubbles in liquids under tension and so break the stress casts serious doubts on the significance of all measurements of tensile strength. For it is conceivable that the limit to the observed maximum tension attainable in any particular tonometer is not simply the cohesive or adhesive forces, but the chance release of the tension resulting from the passage of a cosmic particle.

2p-2. Surface Tensions and Surface Energy of Liquids.[3] *Definitions.* Owing to molecular attraction two fluids in contact adjust themselves so that the area of their

TABLE 2p-2. SURFACE TENSION OF WATER AGAINST AIR*

Temp., °C	Surface tension, dynes/cm	Temp., °C	Surface tension, dynes/cm	Temp., °C	Surface tension, dynes/cm
−8	77.0	15	73.49	40	69.56
−5	76.4	18	73.05	50	67.91
0	75.6	20	72.75	60	66.18
5	74.9	25	71.97	70	64.4
10	74.22	30	71.18	80	62.6
				100	58.9

* General reference: "Handbook of Chemistry and Physics," 37th ed., Chemical Rubber Publishing Company, Cleveland, 1955.

TABLE 2p-3. SURFACE TENSION OF VARIOUS LIQUIDS

Name	Formula	In contact with	Temp., °C	Surface tension, dynes/cm	Ref.*
Acetic acid	$C_2H_4O_2$	Vapor	10	28.8	AC(22,23,25);
Acetic acid	C_2H_4O	Vapor	50	24.8	GC(1); JS(14); tPRS(1); ZC(1,6)
Acetone	C_3H_6O	Air or vapor	0	26.21	AC(20,24,25); AdC(1); BF(1);
Acetone	C_3H_6O	Air or vapor	40	21.16	JP(5); JS(4,14); ZC(6)
Ammonia	NH_3	Vapor	11.1	23.4	JP(7)
Ammonia	NH_3	Vapor	34.1	18.1	JP(7)
Argon	A	Vapor	−188	13.2	JS(15)
Benzene	C_6H_6	Air	10	30.22	AC(3,5,31,32,34);
Benzene	C_6H_4	Air	30	27.56	BF(2); JP(5); JS(4,9,10,11,14); PRS(2); tRIA(1); tPRS(1); ZC(4,5)
Benzophenone	$C_{13}H_{10}O$	Air or vapor	20	45.1	AC(27); AS(1); ZC(5)
Bromine	Br_2	Air or vapor	20	41.5	AC(17); AdP(3); GC(1)
n-Butyric acid	$C_4H_8O_2$	Air	20	26.8	AC(27); GC(1); JS(4)

[3] General references: Neil K. Adam, "The Physics and Chemistry of Surfaces," Chap. IX, Oxford University Press, New York, 1941; H. S. Taylor and S. Glasstone, "A Treatise on Physical Chemistry," D. Van Nostrand Company, Inc., New York, 1952.

TABLE 2p-3. SURFACE TENSION OF VARIOUS LIQUIDS (*Continued*)

Name	Formula	In contact with	Temp., °C	Surface tension, dynes/cm	Ref.*
Carbon bisulfide	CS_2	Vapor	20	32.33	AC(17,28); GC(1); BF(2); JS(14); PRS(2), ZC(6)
Carbon dioxide	CO_2	Vapor	20	1.16	VK(1,2)
Carbon dioxide	CO_2	Vapor	−25	9.13	VK(1,2)
Carbon monoxide	CO	Vapor	−193	9.8	JS(15)
Carbon tetrachloride	CCl_4	Vapor	20	26.95	AC(3,5,6,28,31);
Carbon tetrachloride	CCl_4	Vapor	200	6.53	PRS(1,2); ZC(5)
Chlorine	Cl_2	Vapor	20	18.4	AC(11); JP(3)
Chlorine	Cl_2	Vapor	−60	31.2	AC(11); JP(3)
Chlorobenzene	C_6H_5Cl	Vapor	20	33.56	AC(6,20,28); JP(5); JS(11); PRS(2); tRIA(1); tPRS(1); ZC(5)
Chloroform	$CHCl_3$	Air	20	27.14	AC(6,28,31); AdC(1); PRS(2); tRIA(1); ZC(6)
Cyclohexane	C_6H_{12}	Air	20	25.5	PRS(1); ZA(1)
Ethyl acetate	$C_4H_8O_2$	Air	0	26.5	AC(26,33);
Ethyl acetate	$C_4H_8O_2$	Air	50	20.2	AdC(1); AS(2); JP(5); tPRS(1); ZC(6)
Ethyl alcohol	C_2H_6O	Air	0	24.05	AC(22,23,25,32);
Ethyl alcohol	C_2H_6O	Vapor	30	21.89	BF(2); JP(5); tRIA(1); tPRS(1)
Ethyl ether	$C_4H_{10}O$	Vapor	20	17.01	AC(4,15,28,31);
Ethyl ether	$C_4H_{10}O$	Vapor	50	13.47	AdC(1); tPRS(1)
Glycerol	$C_3H_8O_3$	Air	20	63.4	JR(1); MB(1);
Glycerol	$C_3H_8O_3$	Air	150	51.9	ZA(1); ZC(3)
Helium	He	Vapor	−269	0.12	cUL(2); PRA(2)
Helium	He	Vapor	−271.5	0.353	cUL(2); PRA(2)
n-Hexane	C_6H_{14}	Air	20	18.43	AC(5,6,16); AdC(1); AS(1)
Hydrogen	H_2	Vapor	−255	2.31	cUL(1); PRA(1)
Hydrogen peroxide	H_2O_2	Vapor	18.2	76.1	AC(13)
Methyl alcohol	CH_4O	Air	0	24.49	AC(22,23,25,32);
Methyl alcohol	CH_4O	Vapor	50	20.14	tPRS(1)
Neon	Ne	Vapor	−248	5.50	cUL(3); PRA(3)
Nitric acid (98.8%)	HNO_3	Air	11.6	42.7	JS(2)
Nitrogen	N_2	Vapor	−183	6.6	JS(15)
Nitrogen	N_2	Vapor	−203	10.53	JS(15)
Nitrogen tetra oxide	N_2O_4	Vapor	19.8	27.5	JS(4)
n-Octane	C_8H_{18}	Vapor	20	21.80	AC(4,5,34); JS(4)
n-Octyl alcohol	$C_8H_{18}O$	Air	20	27.53	AC(4,5)
Oxygen	O_2	Vapor	−183	13.2	JS(15)

TABLE 2p-3. SURFACE TENSION OF VARIOUS LIQUIDS (*Continued*)

Name	Formula	In contact with	Temp., °C	Surface tension, dynes/cm	Ref.*
Oxygen	O_2	Vapor	−203	18.3	JS(15)
Phenol	C_6H_6O	Air or vapor	20	40.9	AC(18,19,25); JS(2,6,13); JP(4)
Phosphorus trichloride	PCl_3	Vapor	20	29.1	AC(17); GC(1); JP(2); JS(4)
n-Propylamine	C_3H_9N	Air	20	22.4	GC(1); JS(3)
Sulfuric acid (98.5%)	H_2SO_4	Air or vapor	20	55.1	AC(17a); AdP(7); JS(2)
Toluene	C_7H_8	Vapor	10	27.7	AC(4,17,20,31)
Toluene	C_7H_8	Vapor	30	27.4	JP(5); PRS(2); ZC(5,6)

* General reference: "Handbook of Chemistry and Physics," 37th ed., Chemical Rubber Publishing Company, Cleveland, 1955. A reference key is on pp. 2-176 and 2-178.

TABLE 2p-4. SURFACE TENSION OF METALS

Substance		Gas	Temp., °C	Surface tension, dynes/cm	Ref.*
Name	Symbol				
Aluminum	Al	Air	700	840	CR(1)
Antimony	Sb	H_2	750	368	ZA(4)
Antimony	Sb	H_2	640	350	PM(1)
Bismuth	Bi	H_2	300	388	PM(1)
Bismuth	Bi	H_2	583	354	ZA(4)
Bismuth	Bi	CO	700–800	346	AdP(2)
Cadmium	Cd	H_2	320	630	AC(10)
Copper	Cu	H_2	1131	1,103	ZA(4)
Gallium	Ga	CO_2	30	358	AC(30)
Gold	Au	H_2	1070	580–1,000	AdP(1); AdP(2); JI(1)
Lead	Pb	H_2	350	453	PM(1)
Lead	Pb	H_2	750	423	ZA(4)
Mercury	Hg	Vacuum	0	480.3	AC(7)
Mercury	Hg	Air	15	487	AC(9); AdP(5); AdP(6); CR(2)
Mercury	Hg	H_2	19	470	PM(1)
Mercury	Hg	Vacuum	60	467.1	AC(7)
Platinum	Pt	Air	2000	1,819	AdP(2)
Potassium	K	CO_2	62	411	AdP(3)
Silver	Ag	Air	970	800	AdP(2); AdP(4); JI(1)
Sodium	Na	CO_2	90	294	AdP(3)
Sodium	Na	Vacuum	100	206.4	PR(1)
Sodium	Na	Vacuum	250	199.5	PR(1)
Tin	Sn	H_2	253	526	PM(1)
Tin	Sn	H_2	878	508	ZA(4)
Zinc	Zn	H_2	477	753	AC(10)
Zinc	Zn	Air	590	708	JI(1)

* General reference: "Handbook of Chemistry and Physics," 37th ed., Chemical Rubber Publishing Company, Cleveland, 1955. A reference key is on pp. 2-176 and 2-178.

interface is a minimum consistent with other requirements. The work required to extend the surface by unit area is called the "free surface energy." In solving problems it is convenient to replace the concept of free surface energy by that of a hypothetical tension, acting parallel to the surface. Named the surface tension and its value denoted by γ, this is defined as the normal tensile force per unit of length across any line traced on the surface. The free surface energy and the surface tension have the same dimensions (MT^{-2}) and are numerically equal; the units of γ may be given as either dynes/cm or as ergs/cm².

TABLE 2p-5. SURFACE TENSIONS OF AQUEOUS SOLUTIONS AGAINST AIR—ORGANIC*

Substance	°C		γ = surface tension for concentrations indicated							
Acetic acid.........	30	%	1.000	2.475	5.001	10.01	30.09	49.96	69.91	100.00
		γ	68.0	64.4	60.1	54.6	43.6	38.4	34.3	26.6
Acetone...........	25	%	5.00	10.0	20.00	25.00	50.00	75.0	95.0	100.00
		γ	55.5	48.9	41.1	38.3	30.4	26.8	24.2	23.0
Ethyl alcohol......	30	%	0.979	2.143	4.994	10.39	25.00	50.00	75.06	100.00
		γ	66.1	61.6	54.2	45.9	34.1	27.5	24.7	21.5
Sucrose............	25	%	10.0	20.0	30.0	40.0	55.0			
		γ	72.5	73.0	73.4	74.1	75.7			

* General reference: "Handbook of Chemistry and Physics," 37th ed., Chemical Rubber Publishing Company, Cleveland, 1955.

Formulas Involving Surface Tension. When the interfacial surface between two fluids is curved the pressure p_1 on the concave side exceeds that, p_2, on the convex side by the amount

$$(p_1 - p_2) = \gamma(R_1^{-1} + R_2^{-1}) \tag{2p-1}$$

where R_1, R_2 are the principal radii of curvature. The pressure p due to surface tension within a liquid drop or gas bubble of radius R surrounded by liquid is

$$p = \frac{2\gamma}{R} \tag{2p-2}$$

The velocity v of sinusoidal ripples on the surface of a liquid of great depth is given by[1]

$$v^2 = \frac{g\lambda}{2\pi} + \frac{2\pi\gamma}{\rho\lambda} \tag{2p-3}$$

where λ is the wavelength of the ripples, g is the acceleration due to gravity, and ρ is the density of the liquid (cf. Sec. 2a).

Methods of Measuring the Surface Tension of a Liquid Relative to a Gas Phase. 1. Capillary-height method. If a vertical capillary tube whose bore radius r is sufficiently small rests with its lower end below a liquid surface the liquid in it will rise to a height h

[1] Rayleigh, *Phil. Mag.* **30,** 386 (1890).

given approximately by

$$h = \frac{2\gamma \cos \theta}{gr(\rho - \rho_v)} \tag{2p-4}$$

where ρ_v is the density of the gas above the liquid, and θ is the contact angle of the meniscus with the tube wall (θ is often zero). If the tube is not sufficiently small, corrections must be applied to the above formula.[1]

2. Maximum-bubble-pressure method. If a bubble is blown at the lower end of a tube of small bore dipping into a liquid the pressure in the bubble reaches a maximum value given by

$$p = \frac{2\gamma}{r} \tag{2p-5}$$

where r, as before, is the bore radius. If r is not sufficiently small, corrections must be applied to the above formula.[1]

3. Drop-weight method. The weight ω of a drop falling from the tip of a vertical tube is given by

$$W = \frac{r\gamma}{F} \tag{2p-6}$$

where F is an empirical function[1] of (V/r^3), V being the drop volume. When (V/r^3) is 5,000, F is 0.172; as (V/r^3) decreases to 1.55, F increases steadily to 0.26; further decrease of (V/r^3) causes F to oscillate slightly around 0.25.

Reference Key to Surface-tension Data

AC. *Journal of the American Chemical Society.* (1) Baker and Gilbert, **62,** 2479–2480 1940. (2) H. Brown, **56,** 2564–2568 (1938). (3) Harkins and Brown, **41,** 449 (1919). (4) Harkins, Brown, and Davies, **39,** 354 1917. (5) Harkins and Cheng, **43,** 35 (1921). (6) Harkins, Clark, and Roberts, **42,** 700 (1920). (7) Harkins and Ewing, **42,** 2539 (1920). (8) Harkins and Feldman, **44,** 2665 (1922). (9) Harkins and Grafton, **42,** 2534 (1920). (10) Hogness, **43,** 1621 (1921). (11) Johnson and McIntosh, **31,** 1139 (1909). (12) Maass and Boomer, **44,** 1709 (1922). (13) Maass and Hatcher, **42,** 2548 (1920). (14) Maass and McIntosh, **31,** 1139 (1909). (15) Maass and Wright, **43,** 1098 (1921). (16) Morgan and Chazel, **35,** 1821 (1913). (17) Morgan and Daghlian, **33,** 672 (1911). (17a) Morgan and Davis, **38,** 555 (1916). (18) Morgan and Egloff, **38,** 844 (1916). (19) Morgan and Evans, **39,** 2151 (1917). (20) Morgan and Griggs, **39,** 2261 (1917). (21) Morgan and Kramer, **35,** 1834 (1913). (22) Morgan and McAfee, **33,** 1275 (1911). (23) Morgan and Neidle, **35,** 1856 (1913). (24) Morgan and Owen, **33,** 1713 (1911). (25) Morgan and Scarlett, **39,** 2275 (1917). (26) Morgan and Schwartz, **33,** 1041 (1911). (27) Morgan and Stone, **35,** 1505 (1913). (28) Morgan and Thomssen, **33,** 657 (1911). (29) Morgan and Woodward, **35,** 1249 (1913). (30) Richards and Boyer, **43,** 274 (1921). (31) Richards and Carver, **43,** 827 (1921). (32) Richards and Coombs, **37,** 1656 (1915). (33) Richards and Matthews, **30,** 8 (1908). (34) Richards, Speyers, and Carver, **46,** 1196 (1924).

AD. *Atti della reale accademia nazionale dei Lincei.* (1) Magini, **1911,** 184, 10.

AdC. *Annalen der Chemie, Justus Liebigs.* (1) Schiff, **223,** (47) 84.

AdP. *Annalen der Physik.* (1) Heydweiller, **62,** 694 (1897). (2) Quincke, **134,** 356 (1868). (3) Quincke, **135,** 621 (1868). (4) Gradenwitz, **67,** 467 (1899). (5) Meyer, **66,** 523 (1898). (6) Stöckle, **66,** 499 (1898). (7) Röntgen and Schneider, **29,** 165 (1886).*

[1] Adam, *op. cit.* Chap. IX.

*Continued on p. 2-178.

TABLE 2p-6. SURFACE TENSION OF AQUEOUS SOLUTIONS AGAINST AIR—INORGANIC*

(f = gram formula weights per 1,000 g of solvent)

For these aqueous solutions the values of $\Delta\gamma$ are given. $\Delta\gamma$ is the difference between the surface tension of the solution and that of the solvent at the same temperature. Positive values of $\Delta\gamma$ mean that the surface tension of the solution is greater than that of the solvent; negative values the reverse. For convenience in computing the surface tension, the current accepted value for the surface tension of water at the stated temperature is given in the second column.

Formula	°C (γH_2O)		$\Delta\gamma$ for concentrations indicated							
$CaCl_2$	25	f	0.1	0.5	1.0	2.0	3.0	5.0	11.2	
	(71.97)	$\Delta\gamma$	0.35	1.5	3.2	6.9	11.0	18.4	35	
HCl	20	f	....	0.5	1.0	2.0	4.0	6.0	9.0	17.7
	(72.75)	$\Delta\gamma$	....	−0.2	−0.3	−0.5	−0.9	−1.3	−2.2	−7
NH_4OH	18	f	....	0.5	1.0	1.5	3.0	6.0	15.0	34.0
	(73.05)	$\Delta\gamma$	....	−1.4	−2.4	−3.1	−5.2	−7.8	−12.0	−16.0
HNO_3	20	f	....	0.7	1.5	2.8	....	....	8.5	
	(72.75)	$\Delta\gamma$	....	−0.6	−1.1	−1.8	....	....	−4	
KCl	20	f	0.1	0.5	1.0	2.0	3.0	4.0	4.4	
	(72.75)	$\Delta\gamma$	0.16	0.70	1.4	2.8	4.2	5.5	6.0	
KOH	18	f	....	0.5	1.0	2.0	3.8			
	(73.05)	$\Delta\gamma$	....	0.9	1.8	3.5	6.7			
$MgCl_2$	20	f	0.1	0.5	1.0	2.0	3.0	3.65		
	(72.75)	$\Delta\gamma$	0.32	1.52	3.0	6.4	10.2	13.0		
$MgSO_4$	20	f	0.1	0.5	1.0	2.0	2.7			
	(72.75)	$\Delta\gamma$	0.26	1.03	2.1	4.6	6.5			
NaBr	20	f	....	0.5	1.0	1.5	2.9			
	(72.75)	$\Delta\gamma$	....	0.7	1.3	2.0	3.8			
NaCl	20	f	0.1	0.5	1.0	2.0	3.0	5.0	6.0	
	(72.75)	$\Delta\gamma$	0.17	0.82	1.64	3.3	4.9	8.2	9.8	
Na_2CO_3	20	f	0.25	0.5	1.0	1.5				
	(72.75)	$\Delta\gamma$	0.7	1.3	2.7	4.0				
$NaNO_3$	20	f	0.1	0.5	1.0	2.0	3.0	5.0	7.0	12.2
	(72.75)	$\Delta\gamma$	0.12	0.60	1.2	2.4	3.5	5.6	7.5	11.3
NaOH	18	f	....	0.7	1.5	....	....	5.0	11.0	14.0
	(73.05)	$\Delta\gamma$	....	1.3	2.8	....	....	10.0	23	28
Na_2SO_4	20	f	0.2	0.5	1.0					
	(72.75)	$\Delta\gamma$	0.5	1.4	2.7					

* General reference: "Handbook of Chemistry and Physics," 37th ed., Chemical Rubber Publishing Company, Cleveland, 1955.

AS. *Archives des sciences physiques et naturelles.* (1) Dutoit and Friederich, **9,** 105 (1900). (2) Guye and Baud, **11,** 449 (1901). (3) Herzen, **14,** 232 (1902).

BD. *Berichte der deutschen chemischen Gesellschaft.* (1) Lorenz and Kauffler, **41,** 3727 (1908). (2) Schenck and Ellenberger, **37,** 3443 (1904).

BF. *Bulletin de la société chimique de France.* (1) Dutoit and Friederich, **19,** 321 (1898). (2) Santis Ann. Univ. Grenoble, **27,** 593 (1904).

CR. *Comptes rendus.* (1) A. Portevin and P. Bastien, **202,** 1072–1074 (1936). (2) Popesco, **172,** 1474 (1921).

cUL. *Communications from the Physical Laboratory at the University of Leiden.* (1) No. 142. (2) No. 179a. (3) No. 182b.

GC. *Gazzetta chimica italiana.* (1) Schiff, **14,** 368 (1884). (2) A. Giacolone and D. DiMaggio, **3,** 198–206 (1939).

JI. *Journal of the Institute of Metals.* (1) Smith, **12,** 168 (1914).

JP. *Journal de chimie physique.* (1) Dutoit and Fath, **1,** 358 (1903). (2) Dutoit and Mojoiu, **7,** 169 (1909). (3) Marchand, **11,** 573 (1913). (4) Bolle and Guye, **3,** 38 (1905). (5) Renard and Guye, **5,** 81 (1907). (6) Berthoud, **21,** 143 (1924). (7) Berthoud, **16,** 429 (1918). (8) Homfray and Guye, **1,** 505 (1903). (9) Przyluska, **7,** 511 (1909).

JR. *Journal of the Russian Physical Chemical Society.* (1) Elisseev and Kurbatov, **41,** 1426 (1909).

JS. *Journal of the Chemical Society (London).* (1) Kellas, **113,** 903 (1918). (2) Aston and Ramsay, **65,** 167 (1894). (3) Turner and Merry, **97,** 2069 (1910). (4) Ramsay and Shields, **63,** 1089 (1893). (5) Sugden, Reed, and Wilkins, **127,** 1525 (1925). (6) Hewitt and Winmill, **91,** 441 (1907). (7) Smith, 105, 1703 (1914). (8) Atkins, **99,** 10 (1911). (9) Sugden, **119,** 1483 (1921). (10) Sugden, **121,** 858 (1922). (11) Sugden, **125,** 32 (1924). (12) Sugden, **125,** 1167 (1924). (13) Worley, **105,** 260 (1914). (14) Worley **105,** 273 (1914). (15) Baly and Donnan, **81,** 907 (1902).

JSG. *Jahresberichte Schles. Ges. Vaterl. Kultur.* (1) Wilborn, **1912,** 56.

MB. *Metron. Beit.* (1) Weinstein, no. 6, 89.

MfC. *Monatschefte für Chemie und verwandte Teile anderer Wissenscheften.* (1) Kremann and Meingast, **35,** 1323 (1914).

PM. *The London, Edinburgh & Dublin Philosophical Magazine and Journal of Science.* (1) Bircumshaw, **2,** 341 (1926); **3,** 1286 (1927). (2) R. C. Brown, **13,** 578–584 (1932). (3) A. E. Bate, **28,** 252–255 (1939).

PR. *The Physical Review.* (1) Poindexter, **27,** 820 (1926).

PRA. *Proceedings of the Royal Academy of Sciences of Amsterdam.* (1) Kamerlingh, Onnes, and Kuypers, **17,** 528 (1914). (2) Van Urk, Keesom, and Onnes, **28,** 958, (1925). (3) Van Urk, Keesom, and Nijhoff, **29,** 914 (1926). (4) Jaeger and Kahn, **18,** 75 (1915).

PRS. *Proceedings of the Royal Society (London).* (1) Hardy, **88,** 303 (1913). (2) Ramsay and Aston, **56,** 162, 182 (1894).

tPRS. *Philosophical Transactions of the Royal Society of London, Series A.* (1) Ramsay and Shields, **184,** 647 (1893).

tRIA. *Royal Irish Academy Transactions.* (1) Ramsay and Aston, **32A,** 93 (1902).

VK. *Verslag koninklijke Akademie van Wetenschappen te Amsterdam.* (1) Verschaffelt, no. 18, 74 (1895). (2) Verschaffelt, no. 28, 94 (1896).

WN. *Wissenschaftliche Natuurk, Tydschr.* (1) Verschaffelt, **2,** 231 (1925).

ZA. *Zeitschrift für anorganische und allegeime Chemie.* (1) Jaeger, **101,** 1 (1917). (2) Motylewski, **38,** 410 (1904). (3) Lorenz, Liebmann, and Hochberg, **94,** 301 (1916). (4) Sauerwald and Drath, **154,** 79 (1926).

ZC. *Zeitschrift für physikalische Chemie.* (1) Bennett and Mitchell, **84,** 475 (1913). (2) Walden and Swinne, **82,** 271 (1913). (3) Drucker, **52,** 641 (1905). (4) Walden, **75,** 555 (1910). (5) Walden and Swinne, **79,** 700 (1912). (6) Whatmough, **39,** 129 (1902).

ZE. *Zeitschrift für Elektrochemie und angewandte physikalische Chemie.* (1) Bredig and Tiechmann, **31,** 449 (1925).

ZK. *Kolloid-Zeitschrift.* (1) N. Jermolanko, **48,** 14–146 (1929).

2q. Fluid-flow Properties of Porous Media and Viscosity of Suspensions

R. W. MORSE
Brown University

2q-1. List of Symbols

P	percentage porosity
k	permeability
v	volume of fluid crossing unit area per unit time
η	shear viscosity
k'	k/η
R	Reynolds number
r	flow resistance
p	fluid pressure
η_a	shear viscosity of suspensoid
η_0	shear viscosity of suspending fluid
c	concentration of particles
f	ratio of semimajor to semiminor axis of ellipsoid

2q-2. Percentage Porosity. P is a measure of the fluid capacity of a porous medium. It is defined as the percentage volume of voids per unit total volume. In dealing with the flow properties of a porous medium one is concerned with the percentage porosity actually available during flow, i.e., the relative amount of interconnected pore space. Therefore, the available porosity (quoted in Table 2q-1) may be somewhat less than the total porosity calculated from the density of the medium.

2q-3. Permeability. k is a measure of the ease with which a fluid flows through a porous medium under the influence of a pressure gradient. It is defined from the empirical relation known as Darcy's law in the following way: If v is the volume of fluid crossing unit area per unit time under the pressure gradient dp/dx, for small values of v (to be specified below), one finds empirically that

$$k' \frac{dp}{dx} = v \tag{2q-1}$$

where k' is a constant dependent on both the fluid and the medium. It is found, further, that the constant k' can be written as $k' = k/\eta$, where η is the coefficient of shear viscosity of the fluid, and k is by definition the *permeability*. Defined in this way, k is practically independent of the properties of the fluid and depends only upon the character of the porous structure.

If a Reynolds number is defined as $R = av\rho/\eta$ (where ρ is the fluid density and a is a length characteristic of the porous structure, such as the average pore size), it is found empirically that Darcy's law as given above holds for R less than about 5.

Many attempts have been made to calculate permeabilities in terms of more fundamental properties of the medium, but in general this has not met with success, and k is usually looked upon as a parameter which can be known only by direct measurement. One exception to this is Kozeny's equation which gives a good approximation to the permeability of powders having a negligible number of "blind" pores. In particular, it agrees well with experiment for a given medium in which the porosity is changed by alteration of packing. The equation is

$$k = \frac{1}{5}\left[\frac{P^3}{(1-P)^2S^2}\right] \tag{2q-2}$$

where P is the fractional porosity (percentage porosity/100) and S is the total surface area of the particles contained in a unit volume of the medium.

TABLE 2q-1. TYPICAL FLOW PARAMETERS OF SOME POROUS MATERIALS*

Material	% porosity	Permeability, darcys
Graded sand:		
30–40 mesh	40	345
40–50 mesh	40	66
50–60 mesh	40	44
60–70 mesh	40	31
70–80 mesh	40	26
80–100 mesh	40	11
100–120 mesh	40	10
120–140 mesh	40	9
Fine heterogeneous sands	30–35	1–10
Silts	35–45	5–180
Fine powders	35–70	0.01–0.1
Sandstones	10–20	0.01–1.0
Acoustic absorbing materials	90–95	35–180
Hair felt	95	900

* The permeability of a given type of porous substance varies widely depending upon such factors as the degree of cementation and the nature of the interconnections between pores, and so the values quoted above represent only typical values that have been reported in the literature cited in the references at the end of this section.

In geophysical work the most common unit of permeability is the *darcy;* this is the unit that results when length is measured in centimeters, time in seconds, viscosity in centipoises, and pressure in atmospheres. Consequently a porous structure will have a permeability of 1 darcy if, for a fluid of 1 centipoise viscosity, the volume flow is 1 cc/cm² area under a pressure gradient of 1 atm/cm.

In acoustical transmission in which air is the fluid medium and where the flow properties of a material determine its acoustic impedance, the constant usually specified is the flow resistance $r = \eta/k$, where η is the viscosity of air (1.8×10^{-2} cp at room temperature).

Permeability measured in darcys can be converted to a self-consistent cgs system of units by the relation

$$1 \text{ darcy} = 9.8697 \times 10^{-9} \text{ poise (cm/sec)/(dynes/cm}^2)$$

2q-4. Viscosity of Suspensions. The suspension of small numbers of solid particles in a liquid affects the apparent viscosity of the mixture in a predictable way for that class of suspensions known as *lyophobic* sols, or "suspensoids." These are systems in which the principal forces between particles are of a mechanical nature (i.e., viscous). In suspensoids the particles are microscopic in size and precipitation is easy and is irreversible in the sense that a purely chemical change will not make the coagulum go back into suspension. In *lyophilic* sols (gels), on the other hand, coagulation is reversible and a submicroscopic structure usually exists. Here small changes in the state of the system can lead to large alterations of gross physical properties. Only the class known as *lyophobic* sols, or suspensoids, will be discussed here (cf. Sec. 2g for gels).

For *spherical* particles, and for small concentrations of particles, it has been found possible to express the apparent-shear-viscosity coefficient η_a of a suspensoid in terms of the shear-viscosity coefficient of the fluid η_0 and the volume concentration of particles c by the expression first derived by Einstein:

$$\eta_a = \eta_0(1 + \tfrac{5}{2}c) \tag{2q-3}$$

This result is independent of particle-size distribution. Einstein's equation gives fair agreement with measurements for concentrations up to about 1 per cent.

Various other expressions have been proposed for higher concentrations. One that fits measurements quite well up to about 30 per cent concentration, again for spherical particles, is

$$\eta_a = \eta_0(1 - c)^{\frac{5}{2}} \tag{2q-4}$$

To some extent the viscosity of suspensoids having particles of nonspherical shape can be approximated. In general one has for small concentrations

$$\eta_a = \eta_0(1 + \phi c) \tag{2q-5}$$

where ϕ depends upon the shape of the individual particles but not upon their size distribution. For ellipsoids where f is the ratio of semimajor to semiminor axes, Eisenschitz gives, for the case where f is large compared with unity and where the particles are large enough so that Brownian motion is negligible,

$$\phi = \frac{1.15}{\pi} \frac{f}{\log 2f} \tag{2q-6}$$

Again for long particles, but when Brownian motion of the particles is large, one has

$$\phi = \frac{f^2}{15(\log 2f - 1.5)} \tag{2q-7}$$

References

Muskat, M.: "The Flow of Homogeneous Fluids through Porous Media," McGraw-Hill Book Company, Inc., New York, 1937.

Rose, H. E.: "The Measurement of Particle Size," Constable & Co., Ltd., London, 1953.

Traxler and Baum: *Physics* **7**, 9 (1936).

Morse and Bolt: *Revs. Modern Phys.* **16**, 69 (1944).

Andrade, E. N. da C.: "Viscosity and Plasticity," W. Heffer & Sons, Ltd., Cambridge, England, 1947.

Burgers, J. M.: 2nd Report on Viscosity and Plasticity, *Koninkl. Ned. Akad. Verband.* (Eersti Sectie), D1, **16**, 113 (1938).

The Physics of Particle Size Analysis, suppl. 3, *Brit. J. Appl. Phys.* **5** (1954).

2r. Cavitation in Flowing Liquids

PHILLIP EISENBERG

Office of Naval Research

2r-1. Introduction—Status of Available Data. Although the possibility of occurrence of cavitation in hydrodynamic systems was recognized as long ago as 1754 by Euler,[1] significant researches on the physical phenomena have been developed only during the first half of the present century. This has resulted from the growing importance of the effects of cavitation (both useful and detrimental) in such diverse fields as underwater propulsion and hydraulic machinery (loss of efficiency, damage to materials, noise), underwater signaling (background noise, absorption of acoustical power), hydroballistics (increased drag and instability of missiles), medicine (divers' bends, bullet wounds), and chemical processing (acceleration of reactions and mixing processes, industrial cleaning). Because of the complexities of the phenomena—hydrodynamical and physicochemical—in cavitated regions, research activity continues to emphasize understanding and description of events. Consequently, this section is restricted to brief descriptions of the various factors involved in the cavitation process and to the presentation of data which, while consistent within themselves, are intended primarily to illustrate the text. In all cases, reference should be made to the original source for guidance in judging the limits of accuracy and applicability of these data.

The discussion given here is concerned particularly with phenomena associated with flowing liquids and excludes cavitation produced by heat addition (boiling) and acoustical pressure waves as well as problems of pure liquids (e.g., ultimate tensile strength). Rather complete discussions of cavitation in flowing liquids (and about forms moving through stationary liquids) have been given by Ackeret[2] and Eisenberg,[3] and extensive bibliographies will be found in the papers of these authors and in a compilation by Raven et al.[4]

2r-2. Definitions and Nomenclature

$\sigma = \dfrac{P - p_v}{\frac{1}{2}\rho U^2}$ cavitation number

P ambient pressure

[1] Leonhard, Euler, Théorie plus complète des machines, qui sont mises en mouvement par la réaction de l'éau, *Historie de l'Academie Royale des Sciences et Belles Lettres*, Classe de Philosophie Experimentale, Mem. 10, pp. 227–295, 1754 (Berlin, 1756).

[2] J. Ackeret, Kavitation (Hohlraumbildung), *Handbuch der Experimentalphysik* **IV** (1), 461–486 (Leipzig, 1932).

[3] Phillip Eisenberg, Kavitation, *Forschungshefte für Schiffstechnik* **3,** 111–124, 1953; **4,** 155–168 (1953); **5,** 201–212 (1954); On the Mechanism and Prevention of Cavitation, *David Taylor Model Basin, U.S. Navy Dept. Rept.* 712, July, 1950; A Brief Survey of Progress on the Mechanics of Cavitation, *David Taylor Model Basin, U.S. Navy Dept. Rept.* 842, June, 1953.

[4] F. A. Raven, A. M. Feiler, and Anna Jesperson, An Annotated Bibliography of Cavitation, *David Taylor Model Basin, U.S. Navy Dept. Rept.* R-81, December, 1947.

p_v	vapor pressure or actual pressure within a cavity
ρ	mass density of liquid
U	stream velocity
σ_i or K	cavitation number for inception of cavitation ("critical" cavitation number)
$Re = \dfrac{Ud}{\nu}$	Reynolds number
ν	kinematic viscosity
d	diameter of a body of revolution
d_m	maximum diameter of steady-state cavity
l	length of a steady-state cavity
R	radius of a transient cavity
h	altitude of a cone
$C_D = \dfrac{D}{\frac{1}{2}\rho U^2 A}$	drag coefficient
D	drag
A	area of body in plane normal to stream or cross-sectional area of circular cylinder
$C_D(\sigma)$	drag coefficient at cavitation number σ
α	total absolute air content
α_s	total saturation air content

2r-3. Inception of Cavitation. It is now generally agreed that cavitation originates with the growth of undissolved vapor or gas nuclei existing in the liquid or trapped on microscopic foreign particles. It is well known that the rupture forces of very clean and carefully degassed liquids are of the order of those predicted by kinetic theoretical formulations. Experimental evidence has also been obtained that water saturated with air, but denucleated by application of very high pressures, exhibits large tensile strength (of the order of several hundred atmospheres).[1] Thus the presence of nuclei is evidently necessary for the inception of cavitation at pressures of the order of vapor pressure. In supersaturated liquids, it is easy to account for the presence and stability of such nuclei, but in saturated and undersaturated liquids, the situation is not clear, and the presence of nuclei is usually accounted for on the basis that they are stabilized on suspended particles.[2] As a consequence, depending upon the size and number of these nuclei, cavitation may be expected to begin above as well as below the vapor pressure. The effect of total air content was shown in experiments of Crump[3] using a venturi nozzle having a diffuser of 5° included angle. Figure 2r-1 shows that in the undersaturated liquid it was possible to obtain tensions as the air content was reduced. Results in a nozzle with an abrupt expansion, however, show opposite trends in the pressures required for inception,[4] although here too tensions were obtained. Comparable results for sea water[5] are shown in Fig. 2r-2; since the

[1] Newton E. Harvey, W. D. McElroy, and A. H. Whiteley, On Cavity Formation in Water, *J. Appl. Phys.* **18,** 162–172 (February, 1947).

[2] Eisenberg, *loc. cit.*; P. S. Epstein and M. S. Plesset, On the Stability of Gas Bubbles in Liquid-Gas Solutions, *J. Chem. Phys.* **18,** (11), 1505–1509 (November, 1950).

[3] S. F. Crump, Determination of Critical Pressures for the Inception of Cavitation in Fresh and Sea Water as Influenced by Air Content of the Water, *David Taylor Model Basin, U.S. Navy Dept. Rept.* 575, October, 1949.

[4] S. F. Crump, Critical Pressures for the Inception of Cavitation in a Large-scale Numachi Nozzle as Influenced by the Air Content of the Water, *David Taylor Model Basin, U.S. Navy Dept. Rept.* 770, July, 1951.

[5] S. F. Crump, Determination of Critical Pressures for the Inception of Cavitation in Fresh and Sea Water as Influenced by Air Content of the Water, *David Taylor Model Basin, U.S. Navy Dept. Rept.* 575, October, 1949.

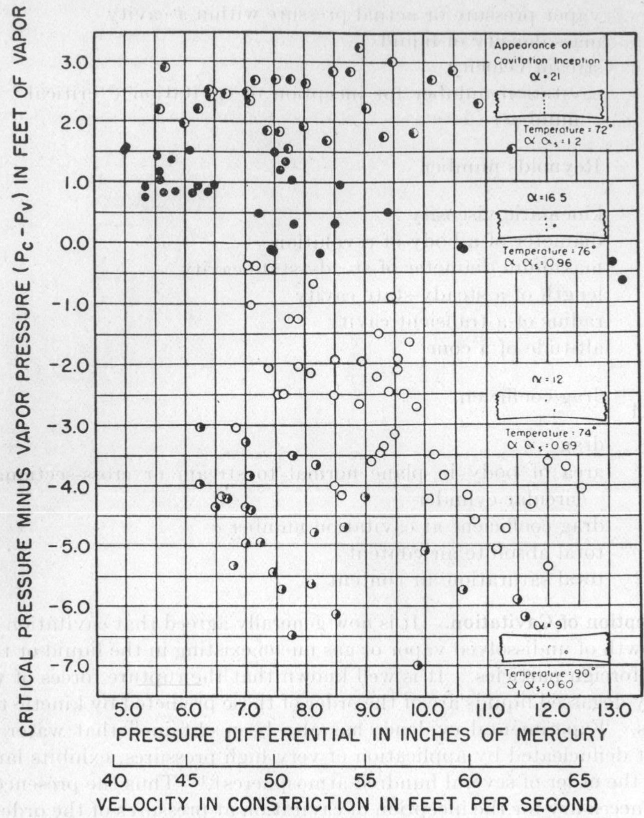

FIG. 2r-1. Cavitation inception in fresh water of varying air content. (*After Crump.*)

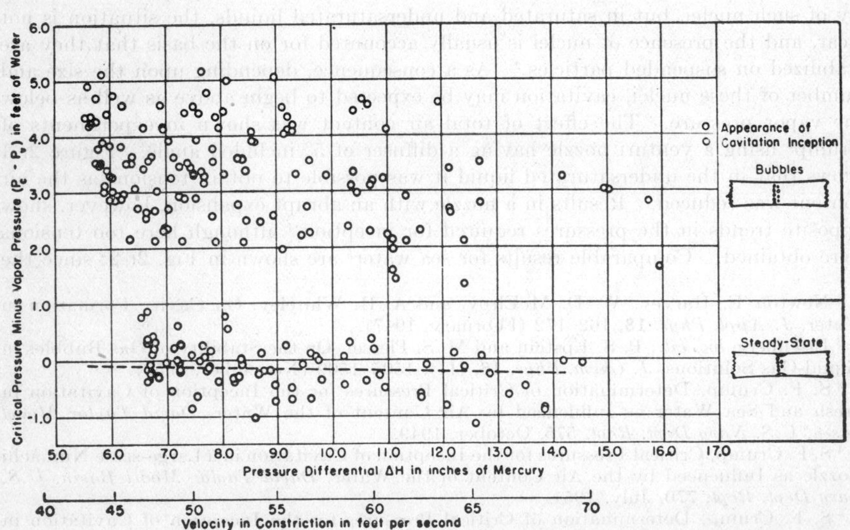

FIG. 2r-2. Critical pressure for inception of cavitation in sea water. (*After Crump.*)

water is supersaturated, thus presumably containing a large number of undissolved nuclei, bursts of cavitation are observed at pressures well above vapor pressure.

Properties of the liquid such as viscosity and surface tension influence the growth of nuclei and, consequently, the inception pressures. In this connection, the presence of surface-active materials (detergents, etc.) affect inception pressures through alteration of surface tension.

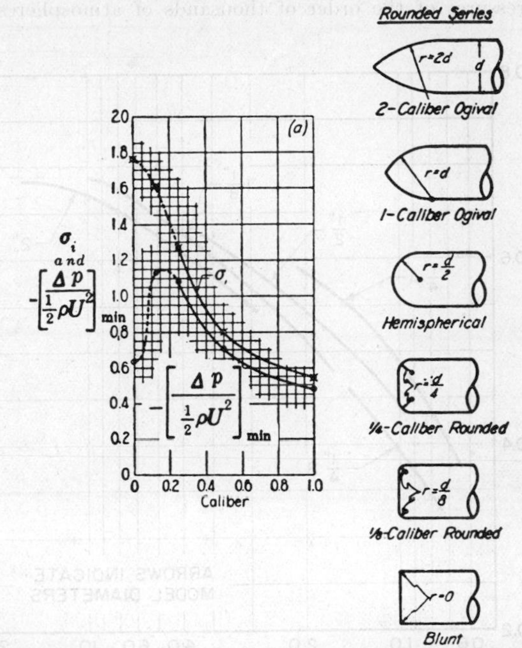

FIG. 2r-3. Critical cavitation number for first change in minimum pressure coefficient of bodies of revolution and minimum pressure coefficient vs. caliber of rounding. (*After Rouse and McNown.*)

Environmental factors which must be considered when attempting to predict inception include not only the average pressure and pressure-gradient conditions determined by the flow boundaries (such as bounding walls or a moving body) but also the magnitude and duration of pressure fluctuations in turbulent regions and boundary-layer effects including flow in zones of separation. An example of the effects of the boundary layer and, in particular, local separation is shown in Fig. 2r-3 from the work of Rouse and McNown.[1] In this figure are compared the minimum pressure coefficients with the cavitation numbers at which the pressure distribution first showed a change. This change is attributed to microscale cavitation in locally separated flows and served to define the critical cavitation number. Effect of model size on inception has been studied by Kermeen[2] and others.[3] While the mechanisms are still only incompletely understood, trends are fairly well established and are con-

[1] Hunter Rouse and John S. McNown, Cavitation and Pressure Distribution; Head Forms at Zero Angle of Yaw, *State Univ. Iowa Studies Eng. Bull.* 32, 1948.

[2] R. W. Kermeen, Some Observations of Cavitation on Hemispherical Head Models, *Calif. Inst. Technol. Hydrodynamics Lab. Rept.* E-35.1, June, 1952.

[3] Blaine R. Parkin, Scale Effects in Cavitating Flow, *Calif. Inst. Technol. Hydrodynamics Lab. Rept.* 21–8, July 31, 1952.

sistent with the concept of nuclei and the role of the boundary layer.[1] An example of Kermeen's results is shown in Fig. 2r-4 wherein the average values of a large number of data are plotted for models of various diameters.

2r-4. Transient (Bubble) Cavities. These are small individual bubbles which grow, sometimes oscillate, and eventually collapse and disappear. Of particular interest here are the pressures produced in the vicinity of such cavities when they collapse. From studies of damage and acoustic radiation produced by such cavities, it is known that pressures of the order of thousands of atmospheres are developed.

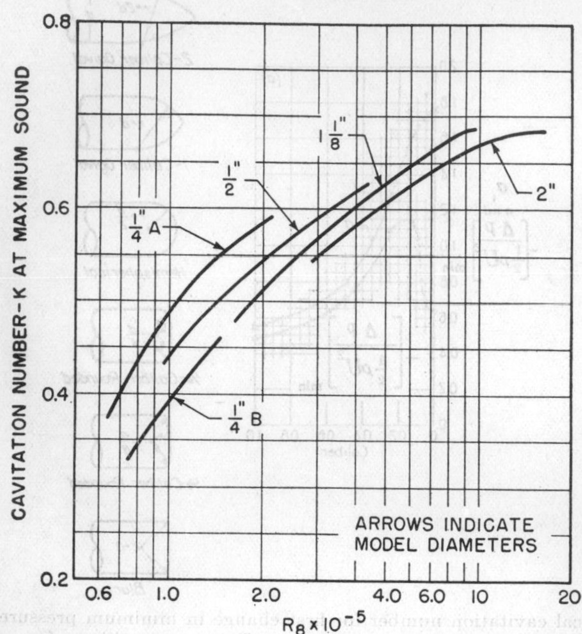

FIG. 2r-4. Cavitation number K for incipient cavitation (as defined by value at which noise disappears) as a function of Reynolds number for bodies with hemispherical heads and cylindrical middle bodies. (The ¼-in. A model was more accurately constructed than the ¼-in. B model.) (*After Kermeen.*)

However, since the maximum pressure rise is confined to durations of the order of a microsecond, definitive measurements have not yet been achieved. The motion of such cavities depends not only upon the ambient pressure conditions but also upon the amount of permanent gas in the bubble and the condensation rates of the vapor as well as the properties of the liquid—compressibility, viscosity, surface tension. Except for surface tension, all these factors tend to decrease the rate of collapse; in addition, distortion from spherical shape caused by pressure gradients or bubble-wall instability tends to result in reduced collapse rates and thus reduced pressures.

Plesset,[2] employing Rayleigh's[3] theoretical formulation for collapse of a spherical cavity in incompressible inviscid fluid but including effect of surface tension and

[1] Eisenberg, *loc. cit.*; Parkin, *loc. cit.*

[2] M. S. Plesset, The Dynamics of Cavitation Bubbles, *J. Appl. Mech.* **16**, 277–282 (September, 1949).

[3] Lord Rayleigh, On the Pressure Developed in a Liquid during the Collapse of a Spherical Cavity, *Phil. Mag.* **34**, 94–98 (1917).

comparing with the experimental results of Knapp and Hollander,[1] has shown that, in the region from maximum radius down to about one-quarter the maximum radius, the motion can be predicted with fair accuracy as long as the bubble is approximately spherical. This idealized theory, which predicts that the bubble-wall velocity is of the order of $R^{-\frac{3}{2}}$ as $R \to 0$ (and that the maximum pressure is infinite) is, of course, inadequate for the final stages of collapse where the effects mentioned above become important. For example, a further approximation carried out by Gilmore[2] shows that the effect of compressibility of the liquid is to reduce the wall velocity to the order of $R^{-\frac{1}{2}}$.

2r-5. Steady-state Cavities. Such cavities (also referred to as "fixed" and "sheet") are large stationary cavities observed behind blunt obstacles and on hydrofoil profiles with relatively sharp leading edges. While such cavities are, especially at low cavitation numbers, usually filled only with vapor phase and other gas, they are often observed to contain a mixture of individual bubbles and liquid phase. The surface usually oscillates, and often parts or the entire cavity are observed to grow and collapse; the average envelope, however, behaves essentially as the boundary of a time-independent flow.[3]

Reliable measurements of cavity shape have been made up to now only for axisymmetric cavities. Data for the principal dimensions of cavities formed behind truncated forms with the apex upstream (disks, cones, hemispheres, semiellipsoids, ogives) have been reported by Reichardt[4] and Eisenberg and Pond.[5] Such measurements for cavities about bodies of revolution composed of cylindrical middle bodies and various head shapes have been reported by Rouse and McNown.[6] Reichardt's data are particularly of interest, since they extend to the lowest cavitation numbers yet attained (as low as 0.013).

For the truncated forms for which the leading edge of the cavity is essentially fixed at the trailing edge of the form (cones, disks), measurements of the principal dimensions can be represented within the experimental error by formulas given by Reichardt.[7] The ratio of maximum cavity diameter to diameter of disk or base of cone is

$$\frac{d_m}{d} = \sqrt{C_D(0)\,\frac{1+\sigma}{\sigma f}} \tag{2r-1}$$

where

$$f = 1 - 0.132\sigma^{\frac{1}{7}} \tag{2r-2}$$

and values of $C_D(0)$ are given in Table 2r-1. The ratio of maximum cavity diameter to cavity length is

$$\frac{d_m}{1} = \frac{(0.066 + 1.70\sigma)}{\sigma + 0.008} \tag{2r-3}$$

2r-6. Drag in Cavitating Flow. Available data indicate that, for the truncated bodies discussed above, the drag coefficient is a linear function of the cavitation num-

[1] R. T. Knapp, and A. Hollander, Laboratory Investigations of the Mechanism of Cavitation, *Trans. Am. Soc. Mech. Engrs.* **70**, (5), 419–435 (July, 1948).

[2] Forrest R. Gilmore, The Growth or Collapse of a Spherical Bubble in a Viscous Compressible Liquid, *Calif. Inst. Technol. Hydrodynamics Lab. Rept.* 26-4, Apr. 1, 1952.

[3] Eisenberg, *loc. cit.*

[4] H. Reichardt, The Laws of Cavitation Bubbles at Axially Symmetrical Bodies in a Flow, *Ministry Aircraft Prod., Rept. Translations* 766, Aug. 15, 1946 (distributed in the United States by the Office of Naval Research, Washington, D.C.)

[5] Eisenberg, *loc. cit.;* Phillip Eisenberg and Hartley L. Pond, Water Tunnel Investigations of Steady State Cavities, *David Taylor Model Basin, U.S. Navy Dept. Rept.* 668, October, 1948.

[6] *Loc. cit.*

[7] *Loc. cit.*

ber. Available data may be represented by[1]

$$C_D(\sigma) = C_D(0)(1 + \beta\sigma) \tag{2r-4}$$

where the value of β is given in Table 2r-1. This formula can also be used to represent available data for a circular cylinder with its axis normal to the flow. The value of $C_D(0)$ for the disk is the average of the extrapolated values of Reichardt[2] and Eisenberg and Pond.[3] The results for the cones are from Reichardt; the results for the hemisphere, semiellipsoid, and ogive are from Eisenberg and Pond. In each of these cases, the values of $C_D(0)$ are extrapolated from the experimental data from

TABLE 2r-1. VALUES OF β IN EQ. 2r-4

Model	$C_D(0)$	Range of σ	β	Reynolds No.
Disk, $h/d = 0$	0.80	0.038–0.56	1.0	$2.6\text{–}7.9 \times 10^5$*
Cones:				
$h/d = \frac{1}{4}$	0.63	0.033–0.125	1.0	
$h/d = \frac{1}{2}$	0.5	0.032–0.118	1.0	
$h/d = 1$	0.32	0.026–0.069	1.0	
$h/d = 2$	0.15	0.013–0.086	1.0	
Hemisphere	0.241	0.168–0.38	2.024	$3\text{–}8.3 \times 10^5$
2:1 semiellipsoid and 2 caliber ogive	0.114	0.133–0.394	3.65	$\approx 3\text{–}9 \times 10^5$
Circular cylinder	≈ 0.55	....	0.81	2.72×10^5
			0.68	1.75×10^5
			0.73	$2\text{–}6 \times 10^5$

* Phillip Eisenberg and Hartley L. Pond, Water Tunnel Investigations of Steady State Cavities, *David Taylor Model Basin, U.S. Navy Dept. Rept.* 668, October, 1948.

which the values of β were also obtained. The value of $C_D(0)$ for the circular cylinder is from a computation of Brodetsky.[4] The value of $\beta = 0.73$ for the circular cylinder is given by Birkhoff[5] based on experiments of Martyrer. The other values of β for the circular cylinder are based on Kanstantinov's[6] experiments, which show differences depending on Reynolds number (based on cylinder diameter). It should be noted that Kanstantinov's results are for constant Reynolds number, whereas in Martyrer's tests the Reynolds number varied as the cavitation number was varied. There may be a question, however, as to the accuracy of Kanstantinov's results, since the forces were found by integrating pressure distributions rather than by direct measurement.

2r-7. Nonstationary Cavities and Other Topics. A third type of flow which may be defined as part of a general classification of cavitating flows is the "nonstationary" (or "unsteady") cavity. This is a cavity resembling steady-state cavities but varying in time as in the air-water entry of an air-dropped missile or as in the motion of an initially submerged but accelerating body. Although all three are free-boundary

[1] Eisenberg, *loc. cit.*

[2] *Loc. cit.*

[3] *Loc. cit.*

[4] S. Brodetsky, Discontinuous Fluid Motion Past Circular and Elliptic Cylinders, *Proc. Roy. Soc. (London)*, ser. A, **102**, (A718), 542–553 (February, 1923).

[5] Garrett Birkhoff, "Hydrodynamics," chap. 2, Princeton University Press, Princeton, N.J., 1950.

[6] W. A. Kanstantinov, Influence of the Reynolds Number on the Separation (Cavitation) Flow, *David Taylor Model Basin, U.S. Navy Dept. Translation* 233, November, 1950.

flows, in the transient cavity, the pressure at the boundary varies with time; in the steady-state cavity, the boundaries are free streamlines; and, in the third, the boundaries are such that the material lines are not necessarily free streamlines. The nomenclature used here was chosen to provide a consistent representation for both the physical phenomena and the corresponding mathematical descriptions. Further discussions of nonstationary cavities and references will be found in Eisenberg[1] and Birkhoff.[1]

For problems of lift in cavitating flows and of damage produced by cavitation, reference may be made to Eisenberg[2] and Raven, Feiler, and Jesperson[3] and the bibliographies therein.

2s. Diffusion in Liquids

L. G. LONGSWORTH

Rockefeller Institute for Medical Research

The diffusion coefficient in liquid solutions is defined as the coefficient D in Fick's diffusion equation

$$\frac{\partial c}{\partial t} = D \frac{\partial^2 c}{\partial x^2} \tag{2s-1}$$

in which c is the concentration of the solution and D is a function of the concentration. This coefficient is sometimes called the differential value of the diffusion. In the tables of this section it is always these values which are tabulated. The units of D throughout are $cm^2\ sec^{-1}$ multiplied by 10^5. The methods employed and the average deviations of the reported data from smooth interpolation curves are indicated by the following abbreviation scheme:

C. conductance (±0.2%)
D. diaphragm cell (±0.2%)
G. Gouy interference (±0.1%)
L. Layer analysis (±0.2%)
R. Rayleigh interference (±0.1%)

[1] *Loc. cit.*
[2] *Loc. cit.*
[3] *Loc. cit.*

Table 2s-1. Diffusion Coefficients of Dilute Aqueous Solutions of Electrolytes at 25°C
(Concentration, moles/liter)

Electrolyte	0.000	0.0006	0.001	0.002	0.003	0.005	0.007	0.010	Ref.	Method
LiCl	1.366	1.349	1.345	1.337	1.331	1.323	1.318	1.312	10	C
NaCl	1.612	......	1.586	1.576	1.570	1.561	1.554	1.545	10	C
KCl	1.994	......	1.964	1.952	1.944	1.933	1.924	1.915	10	C
RbCl	2.057	......	2.024	2.012	2.003	1.991	1.983	1.972	10	C
CsCl	2.046	......	2.013	2.001	1.992	1.978	1.969	1.958	10	C
KNO_3	1.931	......	1.899	1.887	1.879	1.866	1.856	1.844	10	C
$AgNO_3$	1.767	......	......	......	1.720	1.708	1.699	.....	10	C
$MgCl_2$	1.251	......	1.189	1.172	1.161	.....	.....	.....	9	C
$CaCl_2$	1.335	......	1.249	1.224	1.206	1.180	.....	.....	1	C
$SrCl_2$	1.336	......	1.269	1.249	1.236	1.219	1.210	.....	8	C
$BaCl_2$	1.387	1.332	1.320	1.299	1.285	1.264	.....	.....	9	C
Li_2SO_4	1.041	1.000	.990	0.975	0.965	0.950	.....	.....	2	C
Na_2SO_4	1.230	......	1.175	1.159	1.145	1.124	.....	.....	2	C
Cs_2SO_4	1.569	......	1.487	1.460	1.442	1.418	.....	.....	7	C
$MgSO_4$	0.849	0.784	0.767	0.741	0.726	0.708	0.700	.....	6	C
$ZnSO_4$	0.849	......	0.741	0.734	0.723	0.706	.....	.....	3	C
$LaCl_3$	1.294	......	1.173	1.144	1.125	1.102	1.087	.....	4	C
$K_4Fe(CN)_6$	1.473	......	......	......	1.211	1.183	.....	.....	5	C

References

1. Harned, H. S., and A. L. Levy: *J. Am. Chem. Soc.* **71**, 2781 (1949).
2. Harned, H. S., and C. A. Blake, Jr.: *J. Am. Chem. Soc.* **73**, 2448 (1951).
3. Harned, H. S., and R. M. Hudson: *J. Am. Chem. Soc.* **73**, 3781 (1951).
4. Harned, H. S., and C. A. Blake, Jr.: *J. Am. Chem. Soc.* **73**, 4255 (1951).
5. Harned, H. S., and R. M. Hudson: *J. Am. Chem. Soc.* **73**, 5083 (1951).
6. Harned, H. S., and R. M. Hudson: *J. Am. Chem. Soc.* **73**, 5880 (1951).
7. Harned, H. S., and C. A. Blake, Jr.: *J. Am. Chem. Soc.* **73**, 5882 (1951).
8. Harned, H. S., and F. M. Polestra: *J. Am. Chem. Soc.* **75**, 4168 (1953).
9. Harned, H. S., and F. M. Polestra: *J. Am. Chem. Soc.* **76**, 2064 (1954).
10. Harned, H. S.: *Proc. Natl. Acad. Sci. U.S.* **40**, 551 (1954).

TABLE 2s-2. DIFFUSION COEFFICIENTS OF CONCENTRATED AQUEOUS SOLUTIONS OF ELECTROLYTES AT 25°C
(Concentration, moles/liter)

Electrolyte	0.00	0.05	0.1	0.2	0.3	0.5	0.7	1.0	1.5	2.0	2.5	3.0	3.5	4.0	5.0	6.0	8.0	Ref.	Method
HCl	3.337	3.073	3.050	3.064	3.093	3.184	3.286	3.436	3.743	4.046	4.337	4.658	4.920	5.17	.....	.....	.....	4	D
LiCl	1.366	1.280	1.269	1.267	1.269	1.278	1.288	1.302	1.331	1.363	1.397	1.430	1.464	.....	.....	.....	.....	4	D
NaCl	1.612	1.506	1.484	1.478	1.477	1.474	1.475	1.483	1.495	1.514	1.529	1.544	1.559	1.584	.....	.....	.....	4	D
KCl	1.994	1.863	1.848	1.835	1.826	1.835	1.846	1.876	1.951	2.011	2.064	2.110	2.152	.....	.....	.....	.....	4	D
KCl	.....	1.864	1.847	1.839	1.839	1.850	1.865	1.892	1.943	1.999	2.057	2.112	2.160	2.204	.....	.....	.....	2	G
NH_4Cl	.....	.....	1.838	1.836	1.841	1.861	1.883	1.921	1.986	2.051	2.113	2.164	2.203	2.235	2.264	.....	.....	3	G
HBr	3.402	3.156	3.146	3.190	3.249	3.388	3.552	3.869	.....	.....	.....	.....	.....	.....	.....	.....	.....	4	D
LiBr	1.377	1.300	1.279	1.285	1.296	1.328	1.360	1.404	1.473	1.542	1.597	1.650	1.693	.....	.....	.....	.....	4	D
NaBr	1.627	1.533	1.517	1.507	1.515	1.542	1.569	1.596	1.629	1.668	1.702	.....	.....	.....	.....	.....	.....	4	D
KBr	2.017	1.892	1.874	1.870	1.872	1.885	1.917	1.975	2.062	2.132	2.199	2.280	2.354	2.434	.....	.....	.....	4	D
NaI	1.616	1.527	1.520	1.532	1.547	1.580	1.612	1.662	1.751	1.846	1.925	1.992	.....	.....	.....	.....	.....	1	D
KI	2.000	1.891	1.865	1.859	1.884	1.955	2.001	2.065	2.166	2.254	2.347	2.440	2.533	.....	.....	.....	.....	1	D
$LiNO_3$	1.337	.....	1.240	1.243	.....	1.260	.....	1.293	1.317	1.332	1.336	1.332	.....	1.292	1.238	1.157	.....	5	G
NH_4NO_3	1.928	.....	1.769	1.749	.....	1.724	.....	1.690	1.661	1.633	1.605	1.578	.....	1.524	1.472	1.421	1.320	5	G
$(NH_4)_2SO_4$	1.527	0.802	0.825	0.867	.....	0.938	.....	1.011	1.047	1.069	1.088	1.106	.....	.....	.....	.....	.....	5	G
$CaCl_2$	1.335	.....	1.110	1.111	1.118	1.140	1.166	1.203	1.263	1.307	1.306	1.265	1.195	.....	.....	.....	.....	3	G

References

1. Dunlop, P. J., and R. H. Stokes: *J. Am. Chem. Soc.* **73,** 5456 (1951).
2. Gosting, L. J.: *J. Am. Chem. Soc.* **72,** 4418 (1950).
3. Hall, J. R., B. F. Wishaw, and R. H. Stokes: *J. Am. Chem. Soc.* **75,** 1556 (1953).
4. Stokes, R. H.: *J. Am. Chem. Soc.* **72,** 2243 (1950).
5. Wishaw, B. F., and R. H. Stokes: *J. Am. Chem. Soc.* **76,** 2065 (1954).

TABLE 2s-3. DIFFUSION COEFFICIENTS OF AQUEOUS SOLUTIONS OF NONELECTROLYTES AT 25°C
(Gouy interference method)

Concentration, p g/100 ml	Nonelectrolyte					
	Urea	Glycolamide	Glycine	n-Butyl alcohol	α-Alanine	Sucrose
0.00	1.3817	1.1423	1.0635	0.9720	0.9145	0.5233
0.25	......	....	1.0571	0.9610	0.9105	
0.50	......	1.1359	1.0507	0.9500	0.9065	0.5194
0.75	1.3720	1.1328	1.0443	0.9390	0.9026	0.5175
1.00	1.3688	1.1296	1.0379	0.9282	0.8987	0.5155
2	1.3561	1.1171	1.0122	0.8854	0.8834	0.5078
3	1.3437	1.1047	0.9866	0.8436	0.8686	0.5001
5	1.3197	1.0804	0.9353	0.7629	0.8405	0.4846
10	1.2642	1.0222	......	......	0.7787	
15	1.2151	0.9676	......	......	0.7292	
20	1.1725	0.9167				
25	1.1363	0.8694				
30	......	0.8257				
Ref.	3	1	5	6	4	2

The data from which this table was prepared may be represented analytically as follows:

Urea: $D \times 10^5 \pm 0.05\% = 1.3817 - 0.01304p + 0.0001288p^2$ for $p \leq 25$
Glycolamide: $D \times 10^5 \pm 0.08\% = 1.1423 - 0.01274p + 0.0000729p^2$ for $p \leq 30$
Glycine: $D \times 10^5 \pm 0.08\% = 1.0635 - 0.02563p$ for $p \leq 5$
n-Butyl alcohol: $D \times 10^5 \pm 0.03\% = 0.9720 - 0.04430p + 0.000496p^2$ for $p \leq 5$
α-Alanine: $D \times 10^5 \pm 0.09\% = 0.9145 - 0.01603p + 0.0002449p^2$ for $p \leq 15$
Sucrose: $D \times 10^5 \pm 0.04\% = 0.5233 - 0.007745p$ for $p \leq 5$

References

1. Dunlop, P. J., and L. J. Gosting: *J. Am. Chem. Soc.* **75,** 5073 (1953).
2. Gosting, L. J., and M. S. Morris: *J. Am. Chem. Soc.* **71,** 1998 (1949).
3. Gosting, L. J., and D. F. Akeley: *J. Am. Chem. Soc.* **74,** 2058 (1952).
4. Gutter, F. J., and G. Kegeles: *J. Am. Chem. Soc.* **75,** 3893 (1953).
5. Lyons, M. S., and J. V. Thomas: *J. Am. Chem. Soc.* **72,** 4506 (1950).
6. Lyons, P. A., and C. L. Sandquist: *J. Am. Chem. Soc.* **75,** 3896 (1953).

TABLE 2s-4. DIFFUSION OF ORGANIC COMPOUNDS IN DILUTE AQUEOUS SOLUTION AT 25°C*

Compound	Wt. %	$D \times 10^5$
Methyl alcohol	0.00	1.58_7†
Ethyl alcohol	0.00	1.24_8†
Propyl alcohol	0.59	1.02_2†
Isopropyl alcohol	0.59	1.02_0†
Butyl alcohol	0.49	0.95_2†
Isobutyl alcohol	0.49	0.93_3†
Sec. isobutyl alcohol	0.49	0.92_2†
Tert. isobutyl alcohol	0.47	0.87_9†
Glycine	0.30	1.0554
Glycolamide	0.30	1.1385‡
α-Alanine	0.32	0.9097
β-Alanine	0.31	0.9327
Sarcosine	0.32	0.9674
Serine	0.31	0.8802
α-Aminobutyric acid	0.31	0.8288
β-Aminobutyric acid	0.32	0.8367
γ-Aminobutyric acid	0.32	0.8259
α-Amino isobutyric acid	0.32	0.8130
Threonine	0.32	0.7984
Valine	0.31	0.7725
Norvaline	0.32	0.7682
Leucine	0.32	0.7255
Norleucine	0.32	0.7249
Asparagine	0.29	0.8300
Glycylglycine	0.29	0.7909
Glutamine	0.34	0.7623
Glycylalanine	0.30	0.7221
Alanylglycine	0.30	0.7207
Glycylleucine	0.29	0.6231
Leucylglycine	0.31	0.6129

Compound	Wt. %	$D \times 10^5$
Glycylglycylglycine	0.29	0.6652
Leucylglycylglycine	0.30	0.5507
o-Aminobenzoic acid	0.24	0.840
m-Aminobenzoic acid	0.24	0.774
p-Aminobenzoic acid	0.23	0.842
Proline	0.32	0.8789
Hydroxyproline	0.32	0.8255
Histidine	0.28	0.7328
Phenylalanine	0.25	0.7047
Tryptophane	0.23	0.6592
d(−)Ribose	0.41	0.7769
l(+)Arabinose	0.39	0.7599
d(−)Lyxose	0.40	0.7591
d(+)Xylose	0.40	0.7462
d(−)Levulose	0.39	0.6944
d(+)Mannose	0.39	0.6875
l(−)Sorbose	0.39	0.6791
d(+)Dextrose	0.39	0.6728
d(+)Galactose	0.38	0.6655
d(+)Sucrose	0.39	0.5209
d(+)Lactose·H_2O	0.40	0.5076
d(+)Cellobiose	0.38	0.5039
d(+)Melibiose·$2H_2O$	0.41	0.5022
d(+)Maltose·H_2O	0.40	0.4929
d(+)Melezitose·$2H_2O$	0.40	0.4478
d(+)Raffinose·$5H_2O$	0.45	0.4339
Cycloheptaamylose	0.39	0.3224
Bovine plasma albumin	0.25	0.0670

Isomers are in groups. Rayleigh interference method except glycolamide.

* L. G. Longsworth, *J. Am. Chem. Soc.* **75**, 5705 (1953) and previously unpublished work except for glycolamide.

† *D* strongly concentration-dependent.

‡ P. J. Dunlop and L. J. Gosting, *J. Am. Chem. Soc.* **75**, 5073 (1953).

TABLE 2s-5. DIFFUSION COEFFICIENTS IN AQUEOUS SOLUTION AT DIFFERENT TEMPERATURES

Solute	Wt. %	5°C	15°C	25°C	35°C	45°C	55°C	Ref.	Method
H^+	0.00	6.208	7.737	9.313	10.919	12.538	14.150	2	*
Li^+	0.00	0.5654	0.7769	1.0286	1.3197	1.6483	2.0142	2	
Na^+	0.00	0.7524	1.0218	1.3349	1.6928	2.0959	2.5439	2	
K^+	0.00	1.1604	1.5335	1.9565	2.4265	2.9403	3.4943	2	
Cl^+	0.00	1.1796	1.5801	2.0324	2.5368	3.0935	3.7031	2	
Br^+	0.00	1.2233	1.6259	2.0808	2.5869	3.1426	3.7465	2	
I^-	0.00	1.2066	1.6007	2.0457	2.5409	3.0850	3.6762	2	
Ca^{++}	0.00	......	0.6043	0.7919	1.0078	1.2528	......	1	
$H^1H^2O^{16}$	0.00	1.294	1.743	2.261	......	......	......	3	R
Urea	0.38	0.790	1.063	1.377	1.731	......	......	3	R
Glycine	0.30	0.593	0.806	1.054	1.337	......	......	3	R
Alanine	0.32	0.500	0.688	0.909	1.164	......	......	3	R
Dextrose	0.38	0.3640	0.5038	0.6713	0.867	......	......	3	R
Cycloheptaamylose	0.38	0.1738	0.2418	0.3225	0.4160	......	......	3	R
Bovine plasma albumin	0.25	0.0356	0.0493	0.0657	......	......	......	3	R

* D for ions computed from ionic conductances λ, with the aid of the relation $D = RT\lambda/ZF^2$, where $R = 8.3144$ joules/deg, T = deg Kelvin $= 273.13 + t$, Z = valence, and $F = 96{,}500$ coulombs/equivalent.

$$D_{\text{salt}} = \frac{(Z_+ + Z_-)D_+D_-}{Z_+D_+ + Z_-D_-}$$

Since the Stokes radius $r_s = kT/6\pi\eta D$ varies but little with temperature, a plot of r_s vs. t affords precise interpolation. Here $k = 1.3712 \times 10^{-6}$ erg/degree, and η is the viscosity of the solvent in poises.

References

1. Benson, G. C., and A. R. Gordon: *J. Chem. Phys.* **13,** 470 (1945).
2. Harned, H. S., and B. B. Owen: "Physical Chemistry of Electrolytic Solutions," 2d ed., p. 590, Reinhold Publishing Corporation, New York, 1950.
3. Longsworth, L. G.: *J. Phys. Chem.* **58,** 770 (1954).

TABLE 2s-6. DIFFUSION COEFFICIENTS IN NONAQUEOUS SOLUTIONS

Solvent	Solute	Concn., moles/liter	t, °C	$D \times 10^5$	Ref.	Method
Hexane	Iodine	0.00	25	4.05	4	D
Heptane	Iodine	0.00	25	3.42	4	D
Carbon tetrachloride	Iodine	0.00	25	1.50	4	D
Carbon tetrachloride	Carbon tetrabromide	0.00	25	1.07_4	2	R
Dioxane	Iodine	0.00	25	1.07	4	D
Benzene	Iodine	0.00	25	2.13	4	D
Benzene	Diphenyl	0.00	25	1.558	3	G
Benzene	Diphenyl	0.00	35	1.847	3	G
Toluene	Iodine	0.00	25	2.13	4	D
m-Xylene	Iodine	0.00	25	1.89	4	D
Mesitylene	Iodine	0.00	25	1.49	4	D
Tetrachlorethane (sym.)	Tetrabromethane (sym.)	0.03	0.44	0.351	1	L
Tetrachlorethane (sym.)	Tetrabromethane (sym.)	0.03	7.70	0.419	1	L
Tetrachlorethane (sym.)	Tetrabromethane (sym.)	0.03	15.00	0.496_5	1	L
Tetrachlorethane (sym.)	Tetrabromethane (sym.)	0.03	25.00	0.611	1	L
Tetrachlorethane (sym.)	Tetrabromethane (sym.)	0.03	35.61	0.741	1	L
Tetrachlorethane (sym.)	Tetrabromethane (sym.)	0.03	51.10	0.954	1	L

References

1. Cohen, E., and H. R. Bruin: *Z. physik. Chem.* **103**, 404 (1923).
2. Longsworth, L. G.: previously unpublished data.
3. Sandquist, C. L., and P. A. Lyons: *J. Am. Chem. Soc.* **76**, 4641 (1954).
4. Stokes, R. H., P. J. Dunlop, and J. R. Hall: *Trans. Faraday Soc.* **49**, 886 (1953).

2t. Liquid Jets

W. L. NYBORG

Brown University

2t-1. Circular Jet. We first deal with the laminar flow due to a circular jet of viscous fluid issuing from a point orifice into a space filled with the same fluid.

Symbols

- J momentum crossing a plane normal to the axis of the jet per second
- u, v x, y components, respectively, of fluid velocity in the jet
- x distance parallel to the axis of the jet
- y distance perpendicular to the axis of the jet
- ρ fluid density
- ν kinematic viscosity of the fluid

The flow-velocity components in the jet are given by the following formulas due to Schlichting[1]

$$u = \frac{3}{8\pi}\frac{K}{\nu x}\frac{1}{(1+\epsilon^2/4)^2}$$
$$v = \frac{1}{4}\sqrt{\frac{3K}{\pi}}\frac{1}{x}\frac{\epsilon(1-\epsilon^2/4)}{(1+\epsilon^2/4)^2} \qquad (2t\text{-}1)$$

where

$$\epsilon = \frac{1}{4}\sqrt{\frac{3K}{\pi}}\frac{1}{\nu}\frac{y}{x}$$
$$K = \frac{J}{\rho} \qquad (2t\text{-}2)$$

The formulas (2t-1) have been checked experimentally by Andrade and Tsien,[2] who found good agreement between the theory and experimental results for a jet of finite

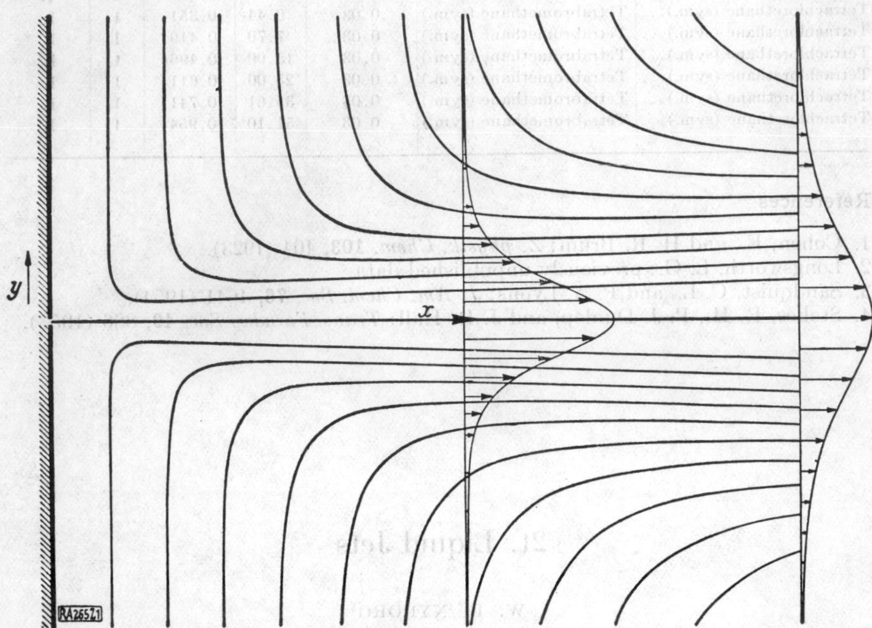

FIG. 2t-1. Streamlines for a circular jet from a point orifice.

radius a at a distance of 8 jet diameters or more from the orifice, provided the x in (2t-1) is given by

$$x = x_o + 0.16u_o\frac{a^2}{\nu} \qquad (2t\text{-}3)$$

where x_0 is the actual distance to the real orifice, and x may be interpreted as the distance to an effective point orifice upstream from the real one.

Figure 2t-1 shows a family of streamlines for a circular jet from a point orifice plotted from Eq. (2t-1). (For reasons of clarity the figure is expanded in the y direction.) Typical velocity profiles (plots of u vs. y) are also given for two distances x from the orifice.

[1] L. Schlichting, *Z. angew. Math. Mech.* **13,** 260 (1933).
[2] E. N. da C. Andrade and L. C. Tsien, *Proc. Phys. Soc.* (*London*) **49,** 381 (1937).

2t-2. Plane Jet. Laminar flow due to a *plane* jet of viscous fluid issuing from a line orifice into a space filled with the same fluid is described by the following formulas

$$u = 0.4543 \left(\frac{K^2}{\nu x}\right)^{\frac{1}{3}} \operatorname{sech}^2 \epsilon$$

$$v = 0.5503 \left(\frac{K\nu}{x^2}\right)^{\frac{1}{3}} (2\epsilon \operatorname{sech}^2 \epsilon - \tanh \epsilon) \tag{2t-4}$$

where

$$\epsilon = 0.2751 \left(\frac{K}{\nu^2}\right)^{\frac{1}{3}} yx^{-\frac{2}{3}}$$

$$K = \frac{J}{\rho}$$

Here x is distance from the line source, measured parallel to the plane of symmetry of the jet and y is measured normal to this plane; all other symbols have meanings analogous to those used in Eq. (2t-1). This theoretical result due to Bickley[1] has been checked experimentally by Andrade[2] and found to be valid for jets from slits of finite width w, provided that x in Bickley's formula is given by

$$x = x_o + \frac{0.65Kw}{v\nu} \tag{2t-5}$$

2u. Density of Gases at Standard Temperature and Pressure

ROBERT LINDSAY

Trinity College

2u-1. Introduction. The normal density of a gas is defined as the mass per unit volume under standard conditions. Standard conditions are defined to be a temperature of 0°C and a pressure of 760 mm of mercury (at 0°C and sea level in a latitude of 45°). The conventional absolute units are grams per liter, grams per cubic centimeter, and grams per milliliter. In this compilation the unit g/liter will be used and will be symbolized by d.

2u-2. Methods of Measurement. Several methods have been utilized to measure densities of gases. In the so-called direct method a mass determination is made of the amount of gas occupying a known volume in a glass flask. This method and various refinements on it were used by the early workers in the field such as Ramsay, Leduc, Rayleigh, and Morley (ref. 1). The buoyancy-type balance is a more recent development (ref. 2). In this method a balance assembly is enclosed within a gas-tight chamber. The pressure of the gas in the chamber is adjusted until the system is in equilibrium. Dry purified air is then admitted to the chamber after the gas has been flushed out and a new equilibrium point obtained. The specific gravity of the gas with respect to the air can then be determined. For extreme accuracy a correc-

[1] W. G. Bickley, *Phil. Mag.* **23,** 727 (1937).
[2] E. N. da C. Andrade, *Proc. Phys. Soc.* (*London*) **51,** 784 (1939).

tion for the compressibility factor (deviation from ideal behavior) for both the air and the unknown gas must be made. Descriptions of these and other methods for determining the densities of gases are included in refs. 1 and 2.

2u-3. Reliability. The reliability of the density measurements tabulated is variable. The following compilation has not been evaluated for extreme accuracy. In some instances the values recorded are taken from the tables of Landolt and Börnstein (ref. 3), who have recalculated original data. These recalculations were undertaken in cases where better values for certain contributing factors such as the density of water, the acceleration of gravity, and coefficients of expansion of mercury and glass became known subsequent to the date of original data. In such cases the original experimental reference is given as well as a notation indicating the compilation from which it was taken. For a good general critique of the philosophy to be employed in examining groups of experimental data, reference is made to Timmermans (ref. 4). Unless otherwise noted it is felt that the values can be considered accurate in the next to last place.

References

1. Reilly, J., and W. N. Rae: "Physico-Chemical Methods," vol. II, p. 52, D. Van Nostrand Company, Inc., New York, 1939.
2. Bauer, N.: "Encyclopedia of Chemical Technology," vol. 4, p. 890, Interscience Publishers, Inc., New York, 1949.
3. Landolt-Börnstein, "Physikalisch-Chemische Tabellen," 5th ed. and suppl., Springer-Verlag OHG, Berlin, 1927.
4. Timmermans, J.: "Physico-Chemical Constants of Pure Organic Compounds," Elsevier Press, Inc., New York, 1950.
5. "International Critical Tables," McGraw-Hill Book Company, Inc., New York, 1928.
6. Mellor, J. F.: "Comprehensive Treatise of Inorganic and Theoretical Chemistry," Longmans, Green & Co., Inc., New York, 1921.
7. Simons, J. H., ed.: "Fluorine Chemistry," Academic Press, Inc., New York, 1950.

Standard reference works which have data on the density of gases are refs. 3 to 7.

TABLE 2u-1. DENSITY OF ELEMENTARY GASES UNDER STANDARD CONDITIONS
(t = 0°C; pressure = 760 mm of mercury)

Gas	Formula	d, g/liter	Year	Ref.
Air	Dry CO_2-free atmospheric air	1.29284	1927	1
Argon	A	1.78364	1928	2
Chlorine	Cl_2	3.214	1913	3
Deuterium	D_2	0.1796	1948	4
Fluorine	F_2	1.696	1904	5
Helium	He	0.17846_7	1940	6
Hydrogen	H_2	0.08988_8	1948	7
Krypton	Kr	3.743	1934	8
Neon	Ne	0.89990	1928	2
Nitrogen	N_2	1.25036	1926	9
Oxygen	O_2	1.42896	1926	9
Radon	Ra	9.96	1910	10
Xenon	Xe	5.896	1934	11

References for Table 2u-1

1. Landolt-Börnstein: "Physikalisch-Chemische Tabellen," 5th ed., 1st suppl., p. 160, Springer-Verlag OHG, Berlin, 1927 (based on a value at sea level at Barcelona, Spain, determined by C. O. E. Moles and M. Paya).
2. Baxter, G. P., and H. W. Starkweather: *Proc. Natl. Acad. Sci.* **14,** 57 (1928).

3. Jaquerod, A., and M. Tourpaian: *J. chim. phys.* **11,** (2) 269 (1913).
4. Calculated value from formula given in H. W. Woolley, R. B. Scott, and F. G. Brickwedde, *J. Research Natl. Bur. Standards* **41,** 379 (1948).
5. Moissan, H.: *Compt. rend.* **138,** 728 (1904).
6. Baxter, G. P., and H. W. Starkweather: *Proc. Natl. Acad. Sci. U.S.* **12,** 20 (1926); recalculated by W. H. Keesom, "Helium," p. 27, Elsevier Press, Inc., New York, 1940.
7. Woolley, H. W., R. B. Scott, and F. G. Brickwedde: ref. 4 (value used in their correlation).
8. Heuse, W., and J. Otto: *Phys. Z.* **35,** 57 (1934).
9. Baxter, G. P., and H. W. Starkweather: *Proc. Natl. Acad. Sci. U.S.* **12,** 703 (1926).
10. Ramsay, W., and R. W. Gray: *Compt. rend.* **151,** 126 (1910); recalculated by editors of Landolt-Börnstein, 5th ed., 1st suppl., p. 162, Springer-Verlag OHG, Berlin, 1927.
11. Heuse, W., and J. Otto: *Phys. Z.* **35,** 628 (1934).

TABLE 2u-2. DENSITY OF SELECTED INORGANIC GASES UNDER STANDARD CONDITIONS

(t = 0°C; pressure = 760 mm of mercury)

Gas	Formula	d, g/liter	Year	Ref.
Ammonia	NH_3	0.77126	1933	1
Antimony hydride (stibine)	SbH_3	5.30 (15°C, 754 mm)	1904	2
Arsenic trihydride (arsine)	AsH_3	3.48	1826	3
Boron trifluoride	BF_3	3.065	1933	4
Carbon dioxide	CO_2	1.9769	1938	5
Carbon monoxide	CO	1.25004	1932	6
Carbon tetrafluoride	CF_4	3.94	1932	7
Carbonyl sulfide	COS	2.721	1901	8
Chlorine fluoride	ClF	2.425	1928	9
Disilicane	Si_2H_6	2.85	1916	10
Freon-12	CF_2Cl_2	5.083	1932	29
Germanium tetrafluoride	GeF_4	6.650	1932	11
Hydrogen chloride	HCl	1.6392	1909	12
Hydrogen bromide	HBr	3.6443	1925	13
Hydrogen iodide	HI	5.7888	1927	14
Hydrogen selenide	H_2Se	3.6643	1924	16
Hydrogen sulfide	H_2S	1.5392	1932	15
Hydrogen telluride	H_2Te	5.76	1900	17
Nitric oxide	NO	1.3402	1914	18
Nitrous oxide	N_2O	1.9804	1931	19
Nitrosyl chloride	NOCl	2.9919	1912	20
Oxygen difluoride	OF_2	2.421	1932	27
Phosphorus hydride (phosphine)	PH_3	1.5307	1930	21
Phosphorus oxyfluoride	POF_3	4.8	1886	22
Phosphorus pentafluoride	PF_5	5.80	1906	23
Phosphorus trifluoride	PF_3	3.922	1922	24
Selenium hexafluoride	SeF_6	8.687	1932	7
Silicon hydride	SiH_4	1.44	1916	10
Silicon tetrafluoride	SiF_4	4.684	1917	25
Sulfur dioxide	SO_2	2.9262	1914	26
Sulfur hexafluoride	SF_6	6.602	1930	28
Tellurium hexafluoride	TeF_6	10.915	1932	7

References for Table 2u-2

1. Dietrichson, G., L. J. Bircher, and J. J. O'Brien: *J. Am. Chem. Soc.* **55**, 1 (1933).
2. Stock, A., and O. Guttman: *Ber. deut. chem. Ges.* **37**, 885 (1904).
3. Dumas: *Ann. chim. et phys.* **33**, 337 (1826).
4. Fischer, W., and W. Wiedemann: *Z. anorg. u. allgem. Chem.* **213**, 106 (1933).
5. Moles, C. O. E., and A. Escribano; *Compt. rend.* **207**, 66 (1938).
6. Moles, C. O. E., and M. T. Salazar: *Anales soc. españ. fís. quím.* **30**, 182 (1932).
7. Klemm, W., and P. Henkel: *Z. anorg. u. allgem. Chem.* **207**, 75 (1932).
8. Hempel, W., *Z. angew. Chem.* **14**, 866 (1901).
9. Ruff, O., E. Ascher, and F. Laass; *Z. anorg. u. allgem. Chem.* **176**, 258 (1928).
10. Stock, A., and C. Somieski: *Ber. deut. chem. Ges.* **49**, 111 (1916).
11. Biltz, W., L. LeBoucher, and W. Fischer: *Z. anorg. u. allgem. Chem.* **207**, 67 (1932).
12. Gray, R. W., and F. P. Burt: *J. Chem. Soc.* **95**, 1633 (1909) (recalculated by C. O. E. Moles; see Landolt-Börnstein, 5th ed., 1st suppl., p. 161).
13. Moles, C. O. E.: *Z. physik. Chem.* **115**, 61 (1925).
14. Landolt-Börnstein, "Physikalisch-Chemische Tabelen," 5th ed., 1st suppl., p. 162, Springer-Verlag OHG, Berlin, 1927 (based on a value reported to editors by C. O. E. Moles and R. Miravelles).
15. Klemenc, A., and O. Bankowski: *Z. anorg. u. allgem. Chem.* **208**, 348 (1932).
16. Bruylants, P., F. Lafortune, and L. Verbruggen: *Bull. soc. chim. Belges* **33**, 587 (1927).
17. Ernyei, E.: *Z. anorg. Chem.* **25**, 317 (1900) (recalculated by editors of Landolt-Börnstein, 5th ed., 3d suppl., p. 248).
18. Scheuer, O.: *Wien. Ber.* **123** (2a), 1 (1914).
19. Batuecas, T.: *Z. physik. Chem.* (Bodenstein volume) **78**, (1931).
20. Wourtzel, E.: *Compt. rend.* **34**, 155 (1912).
21. Ritchie, M.: *Proc. Roy. Soc.* (*London*), ser. A, **128**, 551 (1930).
22. Moissan, H.: *Compt. rend.* **102**, 1245 (1886).
23. Moissan, H.: *Compt. rend.* **138**, 789 (1906) (recalculated by editors of Landolt-Börnstein, 5th ed., 1st suppl., p. 162).
24. Ebel, F., and E. Bretscher: *Helv. Chim. Acta* **12**, 450 (1929).
25. Germann, A. F. O., and H. S. Booth: *J. Phys. Chem.* **21**, 81 (1917).
26. Scheuer, O.: *Wien Ber.* **123** (2a), 1 (1914) [recalculated by C. O. E. Moles, *Rec. trav. chim.* **48**, 864 (1929)].
27. Ruff, O., W. Menzel, and W. Neumann: *Z. anorg. u. allgem. Chem.* **208**, 294 (1932).
28. Schumb, W. C., and E. L. Gamble: *J. Am. Chem. Soc.* **52**, 4302 (1930).
29. Booth, H. S., and K. S. Wilson: *Ind. Eng. Chem., Anal. Ed.* **4**, 427 (1932).

Table 2u-3. Density of Selected Organic Gases under Standard Conditions
(t = 0°C; pressure = 760 mm of mercury)

Gas	Formula	d, g/liter	Year	Ref.
Acetylene	C_2H_2	1.17910	1920	1
n-Butane	*n*-C_4H_{10}	2.5185 (710 mm)	1930	2
iso-Butane	iso-C_4H_{10}	2.673	1909	3
Ethane	C_2H_6	1.3562	1909	4
Ethylene	C_2H_4	1.26036	1938	5
Methane	CH_4	0.7168	1909	4
Methyl amine	CH_3NH_2	1.396	1910	6
Methyl bromide	CH_3Br	3.9739 (25°C)	1938	7
Methyl chloride	CH_3Cl	2.3075	1926	8
Methyl fluoride	CH_3F	1.5451	1920	9
Propane	C_3H_8	2.02000	1920	10
Propene	$CH_2{=}CH{-}CH_3$	1.9149	1934	11

References for Table 2u-3

1. Stahrfoss, R.: *J. Chim. phys.* **16,** 175 (1918).
2. Beckers, M.: *Bull. soc. chim. Belges* **39,** 470 (1930).
3. Ouedinoff: *Bull. soc. chim. France* **23,** 266 (1909).
4. Baume, G., and F. L. Perrot: *J. chim. phys.* **7,** 369 (1909); *Compt. rend.* **148,** 39 (1909).
5. Moles, C. O. E., M. T. Toral, and A. Escribano: *Compt. rend.* **207,** 1044 (1938).
6. Muller, J. A.: *Ann. chim. et phys.* **20,** 116 (1910).
7. Egan, C. J., and J. D. Kemp: *J. Am. Chem. Soc.* **60,** 2097 (1938).
8. Batuecas, T.: *Anales soc. españ. fís. quím.* **24,** 528 (1926).
9. Moles, C. O. E., and T. Batuecas: *J. chim. phys.* **18,** 353 (1920).
10. Timmermans, J.: *J. chim. phys.* **18,** 133 (1920).
11. Batuecas, T.: *J. chim. phys.* **31,** 165 (1934).

2v. Viscosity of Gases

J. KESTIN

Brown University

2v-1. Definitions. The *viscosity* of a fluid is defined in relation to a *macroscopic* system which is assumed to possess the properties of a *continuum.* To obtain an *elementary definition* of viscosity (Fig. 2v-1) consider two infinite flat plates, a at rest and b moving at a constant velocity u, the space between them being filled with the fluid under consideration. In the resulting *shear flow* the velocity distribution is linear with a constant transverse gradient du/dy. It is assumed (*Newton's law of fluid friction*) that the shearing stress τ_0 at either wall is proportional to the velocity gradient

$$\tau_0 = \mu \frac{du}{dy} \qquad \text{(2v-1)}$$

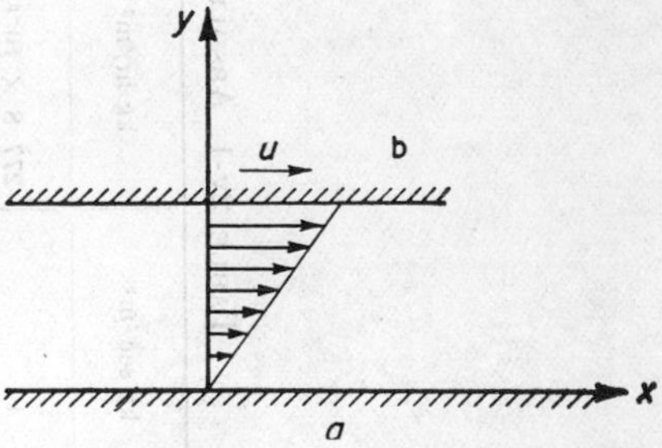

FIG. 2v-1. Illustration of Newton's law of fluid friction.

The coefficient of proportionality μ is known as the viscosity, or more precisely, as the *dynamic* or *absolute viscosity* of the fluid. The various units of viscosity and their conversion factors are given in Table 2v-1.

The ratio

$$\nu = \frac{\mu}{\rho} \qquad \text{(2v-2)}$$

is known as the *kinematic viscosity;* the respective units and conversion factors are given in Table 2v-2.

TABLE 2v-1. ABSOLUTE VISCOSITY μ; UNITS AND CONVERSION FACTORS

	kg sec/m²	kg hr/m²	g*/cm sec (poise)	kg*/m hr	lb sec/ft²	lb hr/ft²	lb*/ft sec
kg sec/m²	1	277.8×10^{-6}	98.1	3.5316×10^{4}	0.2048	56.89×10^{-6}	6.5919
kg hr/m²	3,600	1	0.3316×10^{6}	127.1×10^{6}	737.28	0.2048	2.373×10^{4}
g*/cm sec (poise)	0.01019	2.833×10^{-6}	1	360	2.088×10^{-3}	0.58×10^{-6}	0.06721
kg*/m hr	2.831×10^{-5}	7.8655×10^{-9}	2.788×10^{-3}	1	5.798×10^{-6}	1.6107×10^{-9}	0.1866×10^{-3}
lb sec/ft²	4.882	1.356×10^{-3}	478.96	0.1724×10^{6}	1	277.7×10^{-6}	32.185
lb hr/ft²	1.7578×10^{4}	4.882	1.7244×10^{6}	620.8×10^{6}	3,600	1	11.587×10^{4}
lb*/ft sec	0.1517	42.139×10^{-6}	14.882	5.358×10^{3}	0.03107	8.631×10^{-6}	1

From British Standard Code B.S. 1042: 1943 amended March, 1946.
* Asterisks denote mass units. For more extensive tables see Hawkins, Solberg, and Sibbitt, *Power Plant Eng.* **45,** 62 (November, 1941).

TABLE 2v-2. KINEMATIC VISCOSITY ν; UNITS AND CONVERSION FACTORS

	m²/sec	m²/hr	cm²/sec (stokes)	ft²/sec	ft²/hr
m²/sec............	1	3,600	1×10^4	10.7639	3.875×10^4
m²/hr............	277.8×10^{-6}	1	2.778	299.9×10^{-4}	10.7639
cm²/sec (stokes).....	1×10^{-4}	0.36	1	10.7639×10^{-4}	3.875
ft²/sec............	0.092903	334.45	929.03	1	3,600
ft²/hr............	25.806×10^{-6}	0.092903	0.25806	277.8×10^{-6}	1

From British Standard Code B.S. 1042: 1943 amended March, 1946.

In a general field of flow, u_1, u_2, u_3 of a homogeneous Newtonian incompressible fluid the *shearing stresses* are proportional to the respective *rates of change of strain* (Stokes' law). The symmetric *stress tensor* t_{ij} is assumed to be a linear function of the *rate of strain tensor* e_{ij}. Taking into account that in a fluid at rest the stress is an isotropic tensor, we put

$$t_{ij} = -p\delta_{ij} + \lambda\delta_{ij}e_{kk} + 2\mu e_{ij}$$

where δ_{ij} is the Kronecker symbol ($\delta = 1$ for $i = j$ and $\delta = 0$ for $i \neq j$) and p is arbitrary. Since $t_{ij} = 0$ for $e_{ij} = 0$, we have $t_{ii} = -3p$ and $3\lambda + 2\mu = 0$. Consequently

$$t_{ij} = -p\delta_{ij} - \tfrac{2}{3}\mu\delta_{ij}e_{kk} + 2\mu e_{ij} \qquad \text{(2v-3)}$$

where now p denotes the hydrostatic pressure. The scalar μ is defined as *the absolute viscosity of the fluid.*

The viscosity is assumed to be a function of the thermodynamic state of the fluid and independent of the velocity field. For a homogeneous fluid μ is a function of *two properties.* It is customary to use either of the following two alternative representations:

$$\mu = \mu(p,T) \qquad \text{or} \qquad \mu = \mu(\rho,T)$$

where T is the absolute temperature, p is the pressure, and ρ is the density of the fluid.

Numerical values of viscosity cannot be calculated with the aid of the equations of thermodynamics. They must be measured directly, the measurement being usually very difficult, particularly at higher pressures and temperatures. In principle, values of viscosity can be calculated by the methods of the kinetic theory of gases and statistical and quantum mechanics.

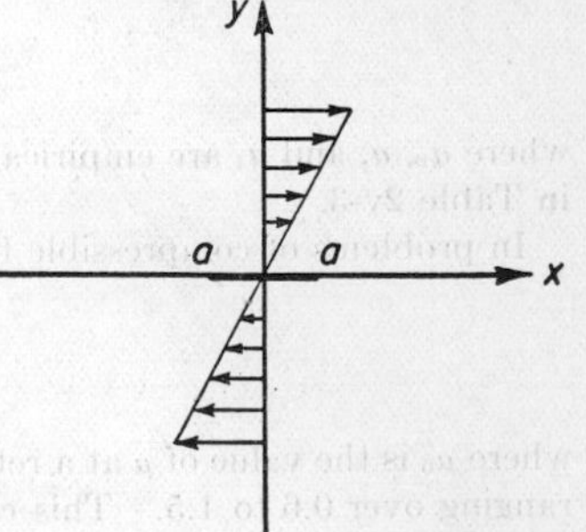

FIG. 2v-2. Kinetic interpretation of viscosity.

In relation to a *microscopically* defined system the viscosity of a gas is assumed to be due to a transfer of momentum effected by molecules, their velocity being composed of the molecular (random) velocity and the macroscopic (ordered) velocity. In shear flow (Fig. 2v-2) the shearing stress acting on a small element of area *aa* is equal to the integral of the change in momentum effected by the particles moving across, both from above and from below it, the integral extending over all particles crossing.

2v-2. Variation of Viscosity with Temperature and Pressure. The calculation of the viscosity of gases has so far met with only limited success, extensive experimental determinations still forming the basis for practical applications. The calculation of the viscosity of gases must make use of a *molecular model* for the gas, increasing refinements being possible.

On the simplest assumption of infinitely small, perfectly elastic molecules with zero fields of force (Maxwell) it is found that the absolute viscosity of a gas is independent of pressure and that it increases in proportion to $T^{\frac{1}{2}}$:

$$\mu = K_1 T^{\frac{1}{2}} \qquad \left(\frac{\partial \mu}{\partial p}\right)_T = 0$$
$$\nu = K_2 T^{\frac{3}{2}} \qquad p = \text{const} \tag{2v-4}$$

where K_1 and K_2 are empirical constants.

On the assumption of hard elastic spheres with a weak attraction force (Sutherland), it is found that

$$\mu = \frac{KT^{\frac{1}{2}}}{C + \tau} \qquad \tau = \frac{1}{T} \tag{2v-5}$$

where K and C are empirical constants. Sutherland's equation (2v-5), as well as experimental results, show the increase with temperature to be *faster* than that in Maxwell's equation (2v-4).

This behavior can be understood if it is realized that in gases the effects of molecular motion dominate over those due to intermolecular forces. In liquids cohesion forces are more important, and since the molecular bonds in a liquid are loosened as the temperature is increased, the absolute viscosity of a *liquid* decreases with temperature; that for a *gas* increases with temperature.

Sutherland's equation (2v-5) is inadequate for the correlation of experimental data over large temperature intervals. A more suitable semiempirical equation was given by Keyes:

$$\mu = \frac{a_0 T^{\frac{1}{2}}}{1 + a\tau \times 10^{-a_1\tau}} \tag{2v-6}$$

where a_0, a, and a_1 are empirical constants. These have been listed for several gases in Table 2v-3.

In problems of compressible fluid flow it is customary to use the empirical relation

$$\frac{\mu}{\mu_0} = \left(\frac{T}{T_0}\right)^{\omega} \tag{2v-7}$$

where μ_0 is the value of μ at a reference temperature T_0 and ω is an empirical constant ranging over 0.6 to 1.5. This correlation is less precise than that in Keyes' equation (2v-6).

All preceding formulas relate to gases at low pressures (say, atmospheric). Experimental results (which are still very scarce) show that the viscosity of gases at constant temperature *increases* with pressure, the increase being of the order of 20 to 40 per cent per 1,000 atm. For moderate pressure ranges it is possible to use a linear interpolation formula

$$\frac{\mu}{\mu_a} = 1 + kp \tag{2v-8}$$

where μ_a is the viscosity at temperature T, but at atmospheric pressure, k is an empirical constant, and p is the excess of pressure over atmospheric.

In recent times attempts have been made to calculate the viscosity of gases with the aid of the methods of statistical mechanics and to obtain a unified theory with that for virial coefficients (see Sec. 4i). The calculations are made on the basis of assumed semiempirical force potentials. For nonpolar gases the most widely used potentials have been the Lennard-Jones six-twelve potential, the nine-six potentia and the exp-six potential; that used for polar gases is the Stockmeyer potential· These methods have not yet met with complete success.

TABLE 2v-3. CONSTANTS IN KEYES' EQUATION (2v-6) FOR SEVERAL GASES*

Gas	Symbol	$a_0 \times 10^5$	a	a_1	Temp. range, °K
Air		1.488	122.1	5	79–1845
Ammonia	NH_3	1.715	667.1	20	194–680
Argon†	A				
Carbon dioxide	CO_2	1.554	246.0	3	198–1686
Carbon monoxide	CO	1.495	143.2	6	80–550
Helium†	He				
Hydrogen†	H_2				
Methane	CH_4	1.103	232.5	12.5	78–373
Nitric oxide‡	NO	1.587	127.6	0	118–300
Nitrous oxide	N_2O	1.531	239.4	2	185–550
Nitrogen	N_2	1.418	116.4	5	81–1695
Oxygen	O_2	1.739	142.0	5	72–550
Steam (water vapor)‡	H_2O	1.501	446.8	0	373–873

* F. G. Keyes, The Heat Conductivity, Viscosity, Specific Heat and Prandtl Number for Thirteen Gases, Project SQUID, *MIT Tech. Rept.* 37, 1952.

† The viscosity of helium, argon, and hydrogen cannot be represented by Keyes' formula over the whole range of temperature with a single set of constants. The respective correlations follow:

1. Argon, range 55–273°K: $$10^5\mu = \frac{2.173T^{\frac{1}{2}}}{1 + 218.4\tau \times 10^{-14\tau}}$$

(deviation 2.2% at 55°K; otherwise about 0.6%; max deviation for data by Johnston and Grilly, 0.36%)

Range 180–1873°K: $$10^5\mu = \frac{1.910T^{\frac{1}{2}}}{1 + 136.6\tau}$$

(largest deviation from data by Kopsch 1.5%, 140–294°K)

2. Helium, range 1.64–20°K: $$10^5\mu = \frac{0.848T^{\frac{1}{2}}}{1 + 1.593\tau}$$

Range 20–140°K: $$10^5\mu = 1.722 + 0.6268 \log T$$

Range 104–373°K: $$10^5\mu = \frac{1.805T^{\frac{1}{2}}}{1 + 253\tau \times 10^{-50\tau}}$$

3. Hydrogen, range 14–90°K: $$10^5\mu = \frac{0.507T^{\frac{1}{2}}}{1 + 21.8\tau}$$

Range 90–550°K: $$10^5\mu = \frac{0.623T^{\frac{1}{2}}}{1 + 70.8\tau \times 10^{-17.3\tau}}$$

‡ Sutherland's formula gives sufficiently good correlation.

2v-3. Mixtures of Gases. The viscosity of a gaseous mixture cannot be deduced from the knowledge of its composition and of the viscosities of its components by macroscopic methods, and methods of statistical mechanics must be used. In any case it should be noted that the viscosity of a mixture is not equal to the weighted mean of the viscosity of its components, it being possible for the viscosity of a mixture to be higher than that of its components. For example, a mixture of argon ($\mu_A = 222 \times 10^{-6}$ poise) and helium ($\mu_{He} = 195 \times 10^{-6}$ poise) containing 40 per cent He and 60 per cent A has a viscosity of $\mu = 230$ poises.

On the simplest assumptions the viscosity of a mixture is a measure of the sum of the momenta contributed by each molecular species on crossing an elementary surface aa (Fig. 2v-2). From this it is found that

$$\mu = \sum_i \frac{\mu_i}{1 + \sum_{j \neq i} \xi_{ij}(n_j/n_i)} \qquad \xi_{ij} = \frac{S_{ij}(1 + M_i/M_j)^{\frac{1}{2}}}{\sqrt{2}} \tag{2v-9}$$

where n_i denotes the volumetric (molar) concentrations, M_i the molecular weights, S_i is the equivalent cross section for collisions within a species, and S_{ij} is that between species.

In the case of *binary mixtures* this leads to

$$\mu = \frac{\mu_1}{1 + \xi_{12}(n_2/n_1)} + \frac{\mu_2}{1 + \xi_{21}(n_1/n_2)} \tag{2v-10}$$

where the *two* factors ξ_{12} and ξ_{21} can be interpreted as empirical constants. They are independent of composition and characteristic of the pair of gases.

A more complete analysis due to Chapman leads to a formula with *four* adjustable constants μ_{12}, a_1, a_2, b:

$$\mu = \frac{a_1 n_1^2 \mu_1 + n_1 n_2 \mu_{12} + a_2 n_2^2 \mu_2}{a_1 n_1^2 + b n_1 n_2 + a_2 n_2^2} \tag{2v-11}$$

With the meager experimental data available at present a definite choice between the two formulas is not possible. For practical purposes the following simple quadratic formula containing *one* empirical constant may be used:

$$\mu = \mu_1 \left(\frac{n_1}{n}\right)^2 + \frac{\mu_{12} n_1 n_2}{n^2} + \mu_2 \left(\frac{n_2}{n}\right)^2 \tag{2v-12}$$

$$n = n_1 + n_2$$

2v-4. Tables of Viscosity. The variation of the viscosity of several gases at low pressure with temperature has been correlated by Keyes (1952) and the results are given in Table 2v-3. Table 2v-4 contains the best available data on the absolute viscosity μ of gases at 20°C *and atmospheric pressure* together with temperature increment $(\Delta\mu)_T$ and the pressure increment $(\Delta\mu)_p$ at that point. Table 2v-5 lists the same values for the kinematic viscosity ν with the values of density ρ from Sec. 2u. The values have been carefully selected in each case, either mean values or preferred values having been chosen depending on the merits of the available experimental material. The estimated uncertainties are also based on a critical assessment of available data and are, to a certain extent, arbitrary. Experimental results for both high pressures and temperatures are, for all intents and purposes, nonexistent.

The dynamic and kinematic viscosity of steam is given in Tables 2v-6 and 2v-7. At present large discrepancies between measured values at higher pressures and temperatures still exist, discrepancies reaching values of just over 60 per cent. The values quoted in the tables are those measured by Timroth et al., and interpolated by Vukalovitch (1951). The values for steam in Table 2v-6 are well represented by the formula

$$\mu = \xi \mu_a \tag{2v-13}$$

where μ_a is the viscosity at temperature T and zero pressure. This in turn can be calculated with reference to the ice-point viscosity μ_0 with the aid of Sutherland's

TABLE 2v-4. ABSOLUTE VISCOSITY μ OF GASES IN POISES ($\equiv$ GR/CM SEC $\equiv$ DYNE SEC/CM^2)
(At 20°C and 1 atm)

Gas	Symbol	$\mu \times 10^7$ poises	Estimated uncertainty $\pm\Delta\mu \times 10^7$ poises	Temp. increment $(\Delta\mu)_T \times 10^7$ poises/°C	Pressure increment $(\Delta\mu)_P \times 10^7$ poise/atm	Source
Acetylene	C_2H_2	935 (at 0°C)	..	....	....	"International Critical Tables"
Air	....	1,813	1	4.78	2.4	Wtd. mean of 15 values
Ammonia	NH_3	974	30	4.25	....	Wtd. mean of 2 values
Argon	A	2,225	15	6.37	3.0	Wtd. mean of 11 values
Isobutane	C_4H_{10}	748	..	2.37	....	Ishida, *Phys. Rev.* **21**, 550 (1923)
n-Butane	C_4H_{10}	848	..	3.00	....	Kuenen and Visser, *Amsterdam Acad. Sci.* **22**, 336 (1913)
Carbon dioxide	CO_2	1,463	15	4.50	3.6	Wtd. mean of 11 values
Carbon monoxide	CO	1,753	1	4.74	....	Wtd. mean of 4 values
Chlorine	Cl_2	1,330	..	4.51	....	Rankine, *Proc. Roy. Soc.* (*London*), ser. A, **86**, 162 (1912)
Ethane	C_2H_6	910	8	2.77	....	Wtd. mean of 2 values
Ethylene	C_2H_4	1,000	..	8.20	....	van Cleave and Mass, *Can. J. Research* **13B**, 140 (1935)
Helium	He	1,953	5	4.64	0.22	Wtd. mean of 12 values
Hydrogen	H_2	882	1	2.00	0.14	Wtd. mean of 9 values
Krypton	Kr	2,474	..	7.35	....	Rankine, *Proc. Roy. Soc.* (*London*), ser. A, **83**, 516 (1910)
Methane	CH_4	1,090	13	3.30	....	Wtd. mean of 5 values
Methyl chloride	CH_3Cl	1,070	..	4.25	....	Breitenbach, *Ann. Phys.* **5**, 166 (1901)
Neon	Ne	3,112	30	6.97	....	Wtd. mean of 5 values
Nitric oxide	NO	1,898	1	5.38	....	Wtd. mean of 3 values
Nitrogen	N_2	1,750	4	4.55	2.28	Wtd. mean of 8 values
Nitrous oxide	N_2O	1,456	..	4.75	....	Johnston and McCloskey, *J. Phys. Chem.* **44**, 1038 (1940)
Oxygen	O_2	2,031	4	5.87	....	Wtd. mean of 6 values
Xenon	Xe	2,246	..	7.25	....	Rankine, *Proc. Roy. Soc.* (*London*), ser. A, **84**, 181 (1911)

TABLE 2v-5. KINEMATIC VISCOSITY ν OF GASES IN STOKES (cm^2/sec)*
(At 20°C and 1 atm)

Gas	Symbol	$\nu \times 10^3$ stokes	Estimated uncertainty $\pm\Delta\nu \times 10^3$ stokes	Temp increment $(\Delta\nu)_T \times 10^3$ stokes/°C	Pressure† increment $(\Delta\nu)_P \times 10^3$ stokes/atm
Acetylene	C_2H_2	79.71(0°C)			
Air	......	150.46	0.08	0.909	−150.26
Ammonia	NH_3	135.58	4.00	1.044	
Argon	A	133.96	0.91	0.843	−133.69
Isobutane	C_4H_{10}	30.03	.....	0.198	
n-Butane	C_4H_{10}	33.50	.....	0.232	
Carbon dioxide	CO_2	79.42	0.81	0.516	−79.23
Carbon monoxide	CO	150.60	0.086	0.924	
Chlorine	Cl_2	44.40	.....	0.302	
Ethane	C_2H_6	71.99	0.63	0.464	
Ethylene	C_2H_4	85.18	.....	0.989	
Helium	He	1,176.50	3.0	7.035	−1,174.25
Hydrogen	H_2	1,053.70	1.2	6.037	−1,052.97
Krypton	Kr	71.77	.....	0.457	
Methane	CH_4	163.17	1.95	1.056	
Methyl chloride	CH_3Cl	49.77	.....	0.367	
Neon	Ne	370.90	3.57	2.113	
Nitric oxide	NO	151.96	0.08	0.942	
Nitrogen	N_2	149.96	0.35	0.904	−149.76
Oxygen	O_2	179.73	0.35	1.124	
Nitrous oxide	N_2O	79.00	.....	0.528	
Xenon	Xe	41.19	.....	0.273	

* The values of kinematic viscosity ν in this table have been obtained by dividing the values of absolute viscosity μ from Table 2v-4 by the values of density ρ from the tables in Sec. 2u.

† Since the rate of change of ν with P is large near 1 atm, these corrections are valid for small pressure increments only.

formula

$$\mu_a = \mu_0 \frac{1 + (C/273)}{1 + (C/T)} \sqrt{\frac{T}{273}} \tag{2v-14}$$

$$\mu_0 = 8.17 \times 10^{-15} \text{ poise} \qquad \text{and} \qquad C = 961°\text{K}$$

The pressure factor ξ in Eq. (2v-13) can be taken for superheated steam:

$$\xi = \frac{1}{(1 - b/v)^2} \tag{2v-15}$$

$$b = 2.1(t - 120) \times 10^{-6}$$

For saturated steam:

$$\xi = \frac{1}{0.955 - 0.00142/v} \tag{2v-16}$$

where v is the specific volume in dm^3/g, and t is in degrees centigrade.

The alternative values due to Sibbitt et al. can be represented by Keyes' empirical formula

$$\mu = \mu_a + (0.0151 - 5.9 \times 10^{-5}p)p \times 10^{-4} \tag{2v-17}$$

where μ, μ_a is in poises and p in atmospheres. The value of μ_a at low pressure may be taken from Keyes' equation (2v-6) with

$$a_0 = 1.851 \times 10^{-5}$$
$$a = 680.1$$
$$a_1 = 0$$

which differs somewhat from that given in Table 2v-3.

TABLE 2v-6. VISCOSITY OF WATER AND SUPERHEATED WATER VAPOR (TIMROTH-VUKALOVITCH, 1951*)
($10^5 \times \mu$ poise; pressure p, kg/cm²)

t, °C	p = 1 μ	p = 20 μ	p = 40 μ	p = 60 μ	p = 80 μ	p = 100 μ	p = 150 μ	p = 200 μ	p = 250 μ	p = 300 μ	t, °C
100	12.08	282.5	283.5	284.5	285.5	287.4	290.4	294.3	298.2	304.1	100
110	12.48	254.1	255.0	256.0	257.0	259.0	261.9	264.9	269.8	272.7	110
120	12.87	230.5	231.5	232.5	233.5	235.4	238.4	241.3	246.2	248.2	120
130	13.27	211.9	212.9	213.9	214.8	216.8	219.7	222.7	226.6	229.6	130
140	13.66	197.2	198.2	199.1	201.1	202.1	204.0	207.0	210.9	213.9	140
150	14.06	184.4	185.4	186.4	188.4	190.3	191.3	194.2	197.2	200.1	150
160	14.46	172.7	173.6	174.6	176.6	177.6	179.5	181.5	184.1	187.4	160
170	14.86	162.8	163.8	163.8	165.8	166.8	168.7	169.7	172.6	175.6	170
180	15.25	154.0	155.0	155.0	156.0	157.0	158.9	159.9	161.9	164.8	180
190	15.65	146.2	146.2	147.2	148.1	148.1	150.0	151.1	153.0	155.0	190
200	16.05	138.3	138.3	139.3	140.3	140.3	142.2	143.2	145.2	146.2	200
210	16.45	131.4	131.5	132.4	133.4	134.4	135.4	136.4	137.3	139.3	210
220	16.84	16.90	125.6	126.5	126.5	127.5	128.5	129.5	130.5	132.4	220
230	17.24	17.31	119.6	120.7	120.7	121.6	122.6	123.6	124.6	126.5	230
240	17.63	17.71	114.8	115.8	115.8	116.7	117.7	118.7	119.7	120.7	240
250	18.03	18.11	18.21	110.9	110.9	111.8	112.8	113.8	114.8	115.8	250
260	18.43	18.51	18.62	105.9	106.9	106.9	107.9	108.9	109.9	110.9	260
270	18.82	18.91	19.02	102.0	102.0	103.0	104.0	105.0	105.9	106.9	270
280	19.22	19.31	19.43	19.58	98.1	99.1	100.1	101.0	102.0	103.0	280
290	19.61	19.71	19.84	19.98	95.2	95.2	96.1	98.1	99.1	100.1	290
300	20.00	20.11	20.24	20.39	20.59	92.2	93.2	94.2	95.2	97.1	300
310	20.40	20.51	20.65	20.80	21.00	22.00	90.3	91.2	92.2	94.2	310
320	20.79	20.91	21.05	21.21	21.40	21.65	86.3	88.3	89.3	91.2	320
330	21.18	21.31	21.45	21.62	21.81	22.06	82.4	84.4	85.3	88.3	330
340	21.57	21.71	21.85	22.02	22.22	22.46	77.5	79.5	81.4	84.4	340
350	21.96	22.10	22.25	22.43	22.63	22.86	23.77	73.6	76.5	80.4	350
360	22.35	22.50	22.66	22.84	23.04	23.28	24.12	67.7	72.5	75.5	360
370	22.74	22.89	23.06	23.25	23.45	23.69	24.49	27.86	65.7	70.6	370
380	23.13	23.29	23.46	23.65	23.86	24.10	24.88	27.27	53.0	64.7	380
390	23.52	23.68	23.86	24.06	24.27	24.51	25.27	26.50	33.3	55.9	390
400	23.90	24.07	24.26	24.46	24.68	24.93	25.68	26.80	31.4	45.1	400
410	24.29	24.46	24.66	24.87	25.09	25.34	26.09	27.15	30.4	38.3	410
420	24.68	24.86	25.06	25.27	25.50	25.75	26.50	27.53	29.10	36.30	420
430	25.06	25.24	25.45	25.67	25.91	26.16	26.92	27.91	29.36	34.34	430
440	25.45	25.63	25.85	26.07	26.32	26.58	27.33	28.32	29.67	33.35	440
450	25.83	26.02	26.24	26.47	26.72	26.99	27.75	28.72	30.00	33.35	450
460	26.21	26.41	26.64	26.87	27.13	27.40	28.17	29.13	30.37	33.35	460
470	26.59	26.80	27.03	27.28	27.53	27.81	28.50	29.55	30.76	32.38	470
480	26.97	27.19	27.42	27.67	27.94	28.22	29.01	29.97	31.16	32.70	480
490	27.35	27.57	27.81	28.07	28.34	28.63	29.43	30.39	31.57	33.06	490
500	27.73	27.96	28.20	28.47	28.75	29.04	29.85	30.82	31.99	33.43	500
510	28.11	28.34	28.59	28.86	29.15	29.44	30.27	31.24	32.42	33.84	510
520	28.48	28.72	28.98	29.26	29.55	29.85	30.69	31.66	32.84	34.25	520
530	28.86	29.11	29.37	29.65	29.96	30.26	31.12	32.09	33.27	34.68	530
540	29.24	29.49	29.76	30.05	30.36	30.67	31.54	32.52	33.71	35.10	540
550	29.61	29.87	30.15	30.45	30.77	31.08	31.96	32.96	34.15	35.53	550
560	29.98	30.25	30.54	30.84	31.17	31.50	32.39	33.40	34.59	35.96	560
570	30.35	30.63	30.93	31.24	31.58	31.91	32.82	33.85	35.03	36.40	570
580	30.73	31.01	31.32	31.64	31.98	32.32	33.25	34.29	35.48	36.84	580
590	31.10	31.39	31.71	32.03	32.38	32.73	33.68	34.73	35.93	37.28	590
600	31.47	31.77	32.09	32.42	32.78	33.14	34.10	35.17	36.37	37.72	600
610	31.84	32.14	32.47	32.81	33.17	33.54	34.52	35.60	36.81	38.17	610
620	32.20	32.51	32.85	33.20	33.56	33.94	34.93	36.03	37.25	38.61	620
630	32.57	32.89	33.23	33.59	33.95	34.34	35.35	36.46	37.69	39.06	630
640	32.94	33.26	33.61	33.97	34.35	34.73	35.76	36.89	38.13	39.50	640
650	33.31	33.63	33.99	34.36	34.74	35.13	36.17	37.32	38.57	39.95	650
660	33.67	34.00	34.37	34.74	35.13	35.53	36.58	37.74	39.00	40.40	660
670	34.03	34.37	34.74	35.12	35.52	35.92	36.99	38.17	39.44	40.85	670
680	34.39	34.74	35.11	35.50	35.90	36.31	37.40	38.59	39.88	41.30	680
690	34.75	35.11	35.49	35.88	36.29	36.71	37.81	39.01	40.32	41.75	690
700	35.11	35.47	35.86	36.26	36.67	37.10	38.22	39.43	40.75	42.20	700

* Measured by Timroth, interpolated by Vukalovitch, "Thermodynamic Properties of Water and Water Vapor," Moscow, 1951, translation by General Electric Company, Schenectady, 1954.

TABLE 2v-7. KINEMATIC VISCOSITY OF WATER AND SUPERHEATED WATER VAPOR (TIMROTH-VUKALOVITCH, 1951*)
($10^2 \times \nu$ cm²/sec; pressure p kg/cm²)

t, °C \ p	1	20	40	60	80	100	150	200	250	300
100	20.90	0.295	0.296	0.297	0.298	0.299	0.301	0.304	0.308	0.313
110	22.23	0.267	0.268	0.269	0.269	0.271	0.273	0.276	0.280	0.283
120	23.55	0.244	0.245	0.246	0.247	0.248	0.251	0.254	0.258	0.260
130	24.92	0.226	0.227	0.228	0.229	0.230	0.233	0.236	0.240	0.242
140	26.31	0.213	0.214	0.215	0.216	0.217	0.219	0.221	0.225	0.227
150	27.77	0.201	0.202	0.204	0.205	0.206	0.207	0.208	0.212	0.215
160	29.25	0.190	0.191	0.192	0.194	0.195	0.196	0.198	0.200	0.202
170	30.77	0.182	0.182	0.182	0.184	0.185	0.186	0.187	0.189	0.191
180	32.31	0.174	0.174	0.174	0.175	0.176	0.177	0.178	0.180	0.181
190	33.90	0.167	0.167	0.167	0.168	0.168	0.169	0.171	0.172	0.172
200	35.53	0.160	0.160	0.161	0.161	0.162	0.163	0.163	0.165	0.165
210	37.21	0.154	0.154	0.155	0.156	0.156	0.157	0.157	0.158	0.159
220	38.90	1.763	0.149	0.150	0.150	0.151	0.151	0.152	0.152	0.154
230	40.63	1.864	0.145	0.145	0.145	0.146	0.147	0.147	0.147	0.149
240	42.40	1.962	0.141	0.141	0.141	0.142	0.143	0.143	0.143	0.144
250	44.21	2.061	0.928	0.138	0.138	0.139	0.139	0.139	0.139	0.140
260	46.07	2.162	0.987	0.135	0.136	0.136	0.136	0.136	0.136	0.136
270	47.93	2.263	1.045	0.133	0.133	0.133	0.133	0.133	0.133	0.133
280	49.88	2.365	1.103	0.667	0.131	0.131	0.131	0.131	0.131	0.131
290	51.81	2.470	1.161	0.712	0.129	0.129	0.129	0.130	0.13	0.13
300	53.80	2.576	1.219	0.757	0.515	0.128	0.128	0.128	0.13	0.13
310	55.83	2.683	1.277	0.800	0.553	0.410	0.128	0.128	0.13	0.13
320	57.88	2.789	1.334	0.843	0.590	0.430	0.127	0.127	0.13	0.13
330	59.98	2.898	1.392	0.886	0.626	0.464	0.127	0.127	0.13	0.13
340	62.12	3.009	1.450	0.928	0.661	0.496	0.127	0.126	0.12	0.13
350	64.28	3.120	1.509	0.970	0.696	0.527	0.285	0.123	0.12	0.12
360	66.49	3.235	1.570	1.012	0.731	0.558	0.315	0.125	0.12	0.12
370	68.72	3.353	1.630	1.055	0.765	0.588	0.342	0.208	0.123	0.12
380	70.96	3.472	1.692	1.098	0.799	0.617	0.367	0.237	0.135	0.12
390	73.26	3.590	1.754	1.141	0.833	0.646	0.391	0.254	0.171	0.126
400	75.60	3.712	1.817	1.185	0.867	0.676	0.414	0.277	0.200	0.136
410	77.97	3.833	1.881	1.230	0.902	0.705	0.437	0.298	0.218	0.164
420	80.38	3.958	1.945	1.274	0.937	0.734	0.459	0.318	0.229	0.188
430	82.80	4.081	2.010	1.319	0.972	0.763	0.482	0.337	0.248	0.202
440	85.31	4.208	2.076	1.364	1.007	0.793	0.504	0.356	0.266	0.217
450	87.80	4.337	2.142	1.410	1.043	0.822	0.526	0.375	0.284	0.232
460	90.32	4.469	2.209	1.456	1.079	0.852	0.548	0.394	0.301	0.247
470	92.88	4.602	2.277	1.504	1.115	0.882	0.570	0.412	0.317	0.253
480	95.47	4.734	2.346	1.551	1.152	0.912	0.592	0.430	0.333	0.268
490	98.10	4.866	2.416	1.599	1.189	0.942	0.614	0.448	0.348	0.283
500	100.8	5.005	2.486	1.647	1.226	0.973	0.635	0.466	0.364	0.297
510	103.5	5.144	2.557	1.695	1.264	1.004	0.658	0.484	0.380	0.311
520	106.2	5.284	2.630	1.744	1.302	1.035	0.680	0.502	0.395	0.324
530	109.0	5.426	2.703	1.794	1.340	1.067	0.702	0.520	0.411	0.338
540	111.8	5.568	2.777	1.844	1.378	1.098	0.725	0.538	0.426	0.353
550	114.6	5.714	2.851	1.895	1.417	1.131	0.748	0.557	0.442	0.367
560	117.5	5.862	2.927	1.947	1.457	1.163	0.771	0.575	0.458	0.381
570	120.4	6.012	3.003	2.000	1.498	1.196	0.795	0.594	0.474	0.395
580	123.3	6.164	3.080	2.053	1.539	1.230	0.819	0.613	0.490	0.409
590	126.2	6.316	3.158	2.106	1.580	1.264	0.843	0.632	0.506	0.423
600	129.2	6.468	3.236	2.159	1.621	1.298	0.867	0.652	0.523	0.438
610	132.3	6.621	3.315	2.213	1.662	1.331	0.891	0.671	0.539	0.452
620	135.3	6.776	3.394	2.267	1.703	1.365	0.915	0.690	0.556	0.466
630	138.4	6.933	3.474	2.322	1.745	1.399	0.939	0.709	0.572	0.480
640	141.5	7.091	3.555	2.377	1.788	1.434	0.964	0.728	0.588	0.495
650	144.6	7.251	3.637	2.433	1.830	1.469	0.988	0.748	0.604	0.509
660	147.8	7.412	3.720	2.489	1.873	1.504	1.013	0.768	0.621	0.524
670	151.0	7.575	3.803	2.546	1.917	1.540	1.038	0.788	0.638	0.538
680	154.2	7.740	3.887	2.603	1.961	1.576	1.063	0.808	0.655	0.553
690	157.4	7.906	3.972	2.660	2.005	1.612	1.088	0.828	0.672	0.568
700	160.7	8.073	4.057	2.718	2.049	1.648	1.114	0.848	0.689	0.583

* Measured by Timroth, interpolated by Vukalovitch, "Thermodynamic Properties of Water and Water Vapor," Moscow, 1951, translation by General Electric Company, Schenectady, 1954.

2w. Diffusion of Gases

R. C. ROBERTS

Naval Ordnance Laboratory

In the simple diffusion of one gas into another, the concentration of either component obeys the equation

$$\frac{\partial C}{\partial t} = \frac{\partial}{\partial x}\left(D\frac{\partial C}{\partial x}\right) + \frac{\partial}{\partial y}\left(D\frac{\partial C}{\partial y}\right) + \frac{\partial}{\partial z}\left(D\frac{\partial C}{\partial z}\right) \tag{2w-1}$$

where C = concentration of gas
t = time
x, y, z = position coordinates
D = diffusion coefficient

Although the diffusion coefficient is, in general, a function of temperature, pressure, and concentration, it can often be considered as constant provided the variations of temperature, pressure, etc., are small. The usual cgs units for the diffusion coefficient are cm²/sec.

The elementary kinetic theory of gases shows that, for a two-component mixture,

$$D_{12} = \frac{1}{3}\,\frac{n_1\lambda_2\bar{C}_2 + n_2\lambda_1\bar{C}_1}{n_1 + n_2} \tag{2w-2}$$

where $n_{1,2}$ = molecular density
$\lambda_{1,2}$ = mean free path
$\bar{C}_{1,2}$ = average velocity

The more exact theories show a quite complicated behavior for D. For example, in a model consisting of rigid elastic spheres

$$D_{12} = \frac{3}{8(n_1 + n_2)\sigma_r^2}\left[\frac{kT(m_1 + m_2)}{2\pi m_1 m_2}\right]^{\frac{1}{2}} \tag{2w-3}$$

where $m_{1,2}$ = mass of molecule
$n_{1,2}$ = number of molecules per cu cm
T = absolute temperature
σ_r = effective molecular collision diameter
k = Boltzmann's constant

For most gases a convenient reduction formula may be given to reduce the diffusion coefficient to standard temperature T and pressure p. It is

$$D = D_0\left(\frac{T}{T_0}\right)^n \frac{p_0}{p} \tag{2w-4}$$

where n varies between 1.75 and 2. This is reasonably valid over a range of normal temperature and pressure.

The following tables contain data on the diffusion coefficients for a number of gases and vapors. In Table 2w-1 values of n are given (if known) so that Eq. (2w-4) may be used to convert the coefficients to other than standard temperature and pressure.*

* Continued on p. 2–214.

TABLE 2w-1. DIFFUSION COEFFICIENTS D_0 AT STANDARD TEMPERATURE AND PRESSURE
(p = 760 mm Hg; T = 273°K)

Gas pair	D_0, cm²/sec	n
H_2O-CO_2	0.1384	2
H_2O-air	0.219	1.75
H_2O-H_2	0.747	1.75
Ethyl alcohol-CO_2	0.0686	2
Ethyl alcohol-air	0.099	2
Ethyl alcohol-H_2	0.377	2
Ethyl ether-CO_2	0.0541	2
Ethyl ether-air	0.0786	2
Ethyl ether-H_2	0.299	2
Benzene-O_2	0.0797	1.75
Benzene-H_2	0.318	1.75
CCl_4-O_2	0.0636	
CCl_4-H_2	0.293	
Acetone-H_2	0.361	
Mercury-N_2	0.1190	2
Iodine-N_2	0.070	2
Iodine-air	0.0692	2
He-A	0.641	.75
H_2-D_2	1.20	
H_2-O_2	0.697	1.75
H_2-N_2	0.674	1.75
H_2-CO	0.651	1.75
H_2-CO_2	0.550	1.75
H_2-CH_4	0.625	1.75
H_2-SO_2	0.480	1.75
H_2-N_2O	0.535	1.75
H_2-C_2H_4	0.625	1.75
H_2-A	0.77 (20°C)	
O_2-N_2	0.181	1.75
O_2-CO	0.185	1.75
O_2-CO_2	0.139	2
CO-N_2	0.192	
CO-CO_2	0.137	1.75
CO-C_2H_4	0.116	1.75
CO_2-N_2	0.144	
CO_2-CH_4	0.153	1.75
CO_2-N_2O	0.096	
H_2-air	0.611	1.75
O_2-air	0.178	1.75
CO_2-air	0.138	2
CH_4-air	0.196	
A-N_2	0.20 (20°C)	
A-O_2	0.20 (20°C)	
A-CO_2	0.14 (20°C)	

TABLE 2w-2. DEPENDENCE OF DIFFUSION COEFFICIENTS ON CONCENTRATION

Pair of gases	n_1/n_2	D_{12}
First gas H_2; second gas CO_2	3	0.594
	1	0.605
	$\frac{1}{3}$	0.633
First gas He; second gas A	2.65	0.678
	2.26	0.693
	1.66	0.696
	1	0.706
	0.477	0.712
	0.311	0.731

TABLE 2w-3. DEPENDENCE OF DIFFUSION COEFFICIENT ON PRESSURE

Gas pair	D, cm²/sec	t, °C	p, mm Hg	$\frac{Dp}{760}$
CO_2-air	0.1653	17.6	751	0.163
CO_2-air	0.3376	15.2	364	0.162
CO_2-air	0.4139	15.7	309	0.164
CO_2-H_2	0.6142	12.8	757	0.612
CO_2-H_2	0.9184	15.4	510	0.616
H_2-O_2	0.8012	11.4	748	0.790
H_2-O_2	1.1718	15.8	512	0.791

TABLE 2w-4. COEFFICIENTS OF SELF-DIFFUSION*

Gas	Temp, °K	D, cm²/sec, experimental
Hydrogen (para-hydrogen into ortho-hydrogen)	273	1.285 ± 0.0025
	85	0.172 ± 0.008
	20.4	0.00816 ± 0.0002
Deuterium into hydrogen	288	1.24
Neon	293	0.473 ± 0.002
Argon	326.7	0.212 ± 0.002
	295.2	0.180 ± 0.001
	273.2	0.158 ± 0.002
	194.7	0.0833 ± 0.0009
	90.2	0.028 ± 0.0010
Krypton	294.0	0.09 ± 0.004
Xenon	292.1	0.0443 ± 0.002
Nitrogen	293	0.200 ± 0.008
Methane (p = 60 mm Hg)	292	26.32 ± 0.73
Hydrogen chloride	295.0	0.1246
Hydrogen bromide	295.3	0.0792
Uranium hexafluoride (p = 10 mm Hg)	303	$D \times \rho = (234 \pm 9) \times 10^{-6}$ g/cm × sec

* p = 760 mm Hg except where noted.

Tables 2w-2 and 2w-3 give certain data on the variation of D with pressure and concentration. Table 2w-4 gives some of the latest data on self-diffusion.

Chapman and Cowling[1] should be consulted for the advanced theory. A good bibliography may be found in Jost.[2]

References

1. Chapman, S., and T. G. Cowling: "The Mathematical Theory of Non-uniform Gases," Cambridge University Press, London, 1939.
2. Jost, W.: "Diffusion in Solids, Liquids, Gases," Academic Press, Inc., New York, 1952.
3. Jeans, J. H.: "An Introduction to the Kinetic Theory of Gases," Cambridge University Press, New York, 1940.
4. Kennard, E. H.: "Kinetic Theory of Gases," McGraw-Hill Book Company, Inc., New York, 1938.
5. Loeb, L. B.: "Kinetic Theory of Gases," McGraw-Hill Book Company, Inc., New York, 1934.
6. "International Critical Tables," vol. 5, pp. 62–63, McGraw-Hill Book Company, Inc., New York, 1928.
7. Hirshfelder, J. O., R. B. Bird, and E. L. Spotz: *Chem. Revs.* **44,** 205 (1949).

2x. Compressible Flow of Gases

R. C. ROBERTS

Naval Ordnance Laboratory

2x-1. Basic Equations in Rectangular Coordinates. The basic equations of motion for a compressible inviscid gas may be written as follows.

Momentum Equation. By applying Newton's laws of motion the Euler momentum equation may be derived in the form

$$\begin{aligned}\frac{\partial u}{\partial t} + u\frac{\partial u}{\partial x} + v\frac{\partial u}{\partial y} + w\frac{\partial u}{\partial z} &= \frac{-1}{\rho}\frac{\partial p}{\partial x} + X\\ \frac{\partial v}{\partial t} + w\frac{\partial v}{\partial x} + v\frac{\partial v}{\partial y} + w\frac{\partial v}{\partial z} &= \frac{-1}{\rho}\frac{\partial p}{\partial y} + Y\\ \frac{\partial w}{\partial t} + u\frac{\partial w}{\partial x} + v\frac{\partial w}{\partial y} + w\frac{\partial w}{\partial z} &= \frac{-1}{\rho}\frac{\partial p}{\partial z} + Z\end{aligned} \qquad (2x\text{-}1)$$

where x, y, z = rectangular coordinates
t = time
u, v, w = velocity components in the direction of the x, y, and z axes, respectively
p = pressure
ρ = density
X, Y, Z = rectangular components of external body force

[1] S. Chapman and T. G. Cowling, "The Mathematical Theory of Non-uniform Gases," Cambridge University Press, London, 1939.

[2] W. Jost, "Diffusion in Solids, Liquids, Gases," Academic Press, Inc., New York, 1952.

Continuity Equation. The assumption that the gas is a continuous medium is expressed by the equation

$$\frac{\partial \rho}{\partial t} + \frac{\partial}{\partial x}(\rho u) + \frac{\partial}{\partial y}(\rho v) + \frac{\partial}{\partial z}(\rho w) = 0 \qquad \text{(2x-2)}$$

Equation of State. For a perfect gas the relation between the pressure p, density ρ, and temperature T is

$$p = \rho RT \qquad \text{(2x-3)}$$

In the case of isentropic flow the pressure depends only on the density, as follows:

$$p = K\rho^\gamma \qquad \text{(2x-4)}$$

where K is a constant and $\gamma = C_p/C_v$ is the ratio of the specific heat at constant pressure to the specific heat at constant volume.

Energy Equation. In the case of isentropic flow, the equation of state together with the momentum and continuity equations are sufficient to determine completely the flow. An important type of nonisentropic flow is characterized by the fact that the entropy S of each fluid particle remains constant but may vary from particle to particle. This is expressed by the equation

$$\frac{\partial S}{\partial t} + u\frac{\partial S}{\partial x} + v\frac{\partial S}{\partial y} + w\frac{\partial S}{\partial z} = 0$$

or

$$\frac{\partial}{\partial t}\left(\frac{p}{\rho^\gamma}\right) + u\frac{\partial}{\partial x}\left(\frac{p}{\rho^\gamma}\right) + v\frac{\partial}{\partial y}\left(\frac{p}{\rho^\gamma}\right) + w\frac{\partial}{\partial z}\left(\frac{p}{\rho^\gamma}\right) = 0 \qquad \text{(2x-5)}$$

2x-2. Dynamic Similarity and Definition of Basic Flow Parameters. In the testing of scale models, it is necessary to maintain a proper scaling of certain dynamic parameters in addition to the geometric scaling. For compressible inviscid flow there is only a single dynamic dimensionless parameter, the Mach number.

Definition of Mach Number. The local Mach number is defined as the ratio of the local flow velocity q to the local sound velocity a, i.e.,

$$M = \frac{q}{a} \qquad \text{(2x-6)}$$

Thus in a nonuniform flow the Mach number will vary from point to point. It should be noted that when $M < 1$, the flow velocity is less than the velocity of sound and there is subsonic flow. In the case $M > 1$ there is supersonic flow. If there is a region of flow in which the Mach number is close to one, $M \simeq 1$, then the flow is said to be transsonic.

Dynamic Similarity. If the flows around two geometrically similar bodies are considered, it might be expected that the resulting flow pattern, e.g., the configuration of the streamlines, would also be similar. This last condition is satisfied for a compressible inviscid flow provided the Mach numbers of the two flows are equal. It then follows that all other dimensional coefficients such as drag coefficient and pressure coefficient are also equal.

In determining the Mach number in a flow it is necessary to know not only the flow velocity but the sound velocity as well. For a perfect gas the sound velocity is proportional to the square root of the temperature, i.e.,

$$a = \sqrt{\gamma RT}$$

Table 2x-1 is based on this relationship.

2x-3. Basic Idea of One-dimensional Flow. In many cases, as in a pipe of slowly varying cross section, it is possible to make the assumption of constant flow properties across any cross section perpendicular to the pipe axis. Although strictly speaking there are no one-dimensional flows, because of viscous effects on the boundaries, it is still possible to get much valuable information of a practical nature from the assumptions.

TABLE 2x-1. VARIATION OF VELOCITY OF SOUND WITH TEMPERATURE

T, °K	a, fps	a, m/sec
150	805	246
160	832	254
170	857	261
180	882	269
190	907	276
200	930	283
210	953	290
220	975	297
230	997	304
240	1,019	311
250	1,040	317
260	1,060	323
270	1,081	329
280	1,100	335
290	1,120	341
300	1,139	347
310	1,158	353
320	1,176	359
330	1,195	364
340	1,213	370
350	1,230	375

Basic Equations. Making the assumption of isentropic flow the equations of motion are

$$\frac{\partial u}{\partial t} + u\frac{\partial u}{\partial x} = -\frac{1}{\rho}\frac{\partial p}{\partial x} \qquad \text{(momentum)} \tag{2x-7}$$

$$\frac{\partial \rho}{\partial t} + \frac{1}{A}\frac{\partial}{\partial x}(\rho u A) = 0 \qquad \text{(continuity)} \tag{2x-8}$$

where A = cross-sectional area. For unsteady one-dimensional flow in general and in particular for an excellent treatment of flow in pipes of constant area see ref. 3. The above equations also cover the case of cylindrical and spherically symmetric flow, i.e.,

$$\frac{1}{A}\frac{\partial A}{\partial x} = \frac{1}{x} \qquad \text{(for cylindrical flow)}$$

$$\frac{1}{A}\frac{\partial A}{\partial x} = \frac{2}{x} \qquad \text{(for spherically symmetric flow)}$$

In the important case of steady flow the equation can be integrated to give

$$\frac{\gamma}{\gamma - 1}\frac{p}{\rho} + \frac{1}{2}u^2 = \text{const} \tag{2x-9}$$

$$\rho u A = m = \text{const} \tag{2x-10}$$

where m = mass flow. By taking logarithmic derivatives and remembering the definition of the Mach number M, the continuity equation may be written

$$\frac{du}{u}(1 - M^2) + \frac{dA}{A} = 0 \tag{2x-11}$$

Thus, if $du \neq 0$ and $M = 1$, we see that $dA = 0$. In other words, the Mach number becomes equal to unity only in a section of the pipe where the area is a minimum. This fact is of prime importance in the design of supersonic wind tunnels.

The dependence of the various flow variables on the Mach number for steady one-dimensional isentropic flow is given in Table 2x-2.

Velocity Potential and Stream Function. In many important flow problems it is convenient to introduce the velocity potential and stream functions. The velocity potential exists whenever there is a state of irrotational flow, i.e., the velocity components satisfy the equations

$$\frac{\partial w}{\partial y} - \frac{\partial v}{\partial z} = 0 \qquad \frac{\partial w}{\partial x} - \frac{\partial u}{\partial z} = 0 \qquad \frac{\partial v}{\partial x} - \frac{\partial u}{\partial y} = 0 \tag{2x-12}$$

Then the velocity components u, v, w can be expressed as the components of the quotient of the velocity potential ϕ. Thus

$$u = \frac{\partial \phi}{\partial x} \qquad v = \frac{\partial \phi}{\partial y} \qquad w = \frac{\partial \phi}{\partial z} \tag{2x-13}$$

The equation of motion may be reduced to the single equation for ϕ,

$$\phi_{xx}\left(1 - \frac{\phi_x{}^2}{a^2}\right) + \phi_{yy}\left(1 - \frac{\phi_y{}^2}{a^2}\right) + \phi_{zz}\left(1 - \frac{\phi_z{}^2}{a^2}\right) - 2\phi_{yz}\frac{\phi_y\phi_x}{a^2} - 2\phi_{zx}\frac{\phi_z\phi_x}{a^2} - 2\phi_{xy}\frac{\phi_y\phi_y}{a^2} = 0 \tag{2x-14}$$

where
$$a^2 = \frac{\gamma - 1}{2}(q_{\max}{}^2 - \phi_x{}^2 - \phi_y{}^2 - \phi_z{}^2)$$

and $q_{\max}$ is the velocity with which the gas flows into a vacuum.

For two-dimensional steady flow or for three-dimensional axially symmetric steady flow a stream function ψ may be introduced. In two-dimensional flow

$$u = \frac{1}{\rho}\psi_y \qquad v = -\frac{1}{\rho}\psi_x \tag{2x-15}$$

If cylindrical coordinates (x,r,θ) are used and the flow is independent of 0, then the function ψ may be defined by

$$u = \frac{1}{\rho r}\psi_r \qquad v = -\frac{1}{\rho r}\psi_x \tag{2x-16}$$

Note that u and v are now the velocity components in the x and r directions and $r = \sqrt{y^2 + z^2}$.

2x-4. Two-dimensional and Axially Symmetric Flow. Many important types of flow belong to the class of two-dimensional or axially symmetric flows. These include flows past wedges, cones, bodies of revolution, etc. The important distinctions to be made are those between subsonic and supersonic flow. Purely subsonic flow is qualitatively quite similar to incompressible flow, while supersonic flow exhibits many startlingly different properties. Among these are the appearance of shock waves (see Sec. 2z) and the existence of wave fronts. A general discussion of the above topics may be found in ref. 3.

TABLE 2x-2. DEPENDENCE OF FLOW VARIABLES ON MACH NUMBER FOR ONE-DIMENSIONAL ISENTROPIC FLOW*

M	p/p_0	u/a_0	A/A^*	$\rho u^2/2p_0$	$\rho u/\rho_0 a_0$	ρ/ρ_0	T/T_0	a/a_0
0.0	1.00000	0.00000	∞	0.00000	0.00000	1.00000	1.00000	1.00000
0.1	0.99303	0.09990	5.822	0.00695	0.09940	0.99502	0.99800	0.99900
0.2	0.97250	0.19920	2.9635	0.02723	0.19528	0.98028	0.99206	0.99602
0.3	0.93947	0.29734	2.0351	0.05919	0.28437	0.95638	0.98232	0.99112
0.4	0.89561	0.39375	1.5901	0.10031	0.36393	0.92427	0.96899	0.98437
0.5	0.84302	0.48795	1.3398	0.14753	0.43192	0.88517	0.95238	0.97590
0.6	0.78400	0.57950	1.1882	0.19757	0.48704	0.84045	0.93284	0.96583
0.7	0.72093	0.66803	1.0944	0.24728	0.52880	0.79161	0.91075	0.95433
0.8	0.65602	0.75324	1.0382	0.29390	0.55739	0.73999	0.88652	0.94155
0.9	0.59126	0.83491	1.0089	0.33524	0.57362	0.68704	0.86059	0.92768
1.0	0.52828	0.91287	1.00000	0.36980	0.57870	0.63394	0.83333	0.91287
1.1	0.46835	0.98703	1.0079	0.39670	0.57415	0.58170	0.80515	0.89730
1.2	0.41238	1.0574	1.0304	0.41568	0.56161	0.53114	0.77640	0.88113
1.3	0.36091	1.1239	1.0663	0.42696	0.54272	0.48290	0.74738	0.86451
1.4	0.31424	1.1866	1.1149	0.43114	0.51905	0.43742	0.71839	0.84758
1.5	0.27240	1.2457	1.1762	0.42903	0.49203	0.39484	0.68966	0.83045
1.6	0.23527	1.3012	1.2502	0.42161	0.46288	0.35573	0.66138	0.81325
1.7	0.20259	1.3533	1.3376	0.40985	0.43264	0.31969	0.63371	0.79606
1.8	0.17404	1.4023	1.4390	0.39476	0.40216	0.28684	0.60680	0.77904
1.9	0.14924	1.4479	1.5553	0.37713	0.37210	0.25699	0.58072	0.76205
2.0	0.12780	1.4907	1.6875	0.35785	0.34294	0.23005	0.55556	0.74535
2.1	0.10935	1.5308	1.8369	0.33757	0.31504	0.20580	0.53135	0.72894
2.2	0.09352	1.5682	2.0050	0.31685	0.28863	0.18405	0.50813	0.71283
2.3	0.07997	1.6033	2.1931	0.29614	0.26387	0.16458	0.48591	0.69707
2.4	0.06840	1.6360	2.4031	0.27579	0.24082	0.14719	0.46468	0.68168
2.5	0.05853	1.6667	2.6367	0.25606	0.21948	0.13169	0.44444	0.66667
2.6	0.05012	1.6953	2.8960	0.23715	0.19983	0.11788	0.42517	0.65205
2.7	0.04295	1.7222	3.1830	0.21917	0.18181	0.10557	0.40683	0.63784
2.8	0.03685	1.7473	3.5001	0.20222	0.16534	0.09463	0.38941	0.62403
2.9	0.03165	1.7708	3.8498	0.18633	0.15032	0.08489	0.37286	0.61062
3.0	0.02722	1.7928	4.2346	0.17151	0.13666	0.07623	0.35714	0.59761
3.1	0.02345	1.8135	4.6573	0.15774	0.12426	0.06852	0.34223	0.58501
3.2	0.02023	1.8329	5.1210	0.14499	0.11301	0.06165	0.32808	0.57279
3.3	0.01748	1.8511	5.6287	0.13322	0.10281	0.05554	0.31466	0.56094
3.4	0.01512	1.8682	6.184	0.12239	0.09359	0.05009	0.30193	0.54948
3.5	0.01311	1.8843	6.790	0.11243	0.08523	0.04523	0.28986	0.53838
3.6	0.01138	1.8995	7.450	0.10328	0.07768	0.04089	0.27840	0.52763
3.7	0.00990	1.9137	8.169	0.09490	0.07084	0.03702	0.26752	0.51723
3.8	0.00863	1.9272	8.951	0.08722	0.06466	0.03355	0.25720	0.50715
3.9	0.00753	1.9398	9.799	0.08019	0.05906	0.03044	0.24740	0.49740
4.0	0.00659	1.9518	10.72	0.07379	0.05399	0.02766	0.23810	0.48795
4.1	0.00577	1.9631	11.71	0.06788	0.04940	0.02516	0.22925	0.47880
4.2	0.00506	1.9738	12.79	0.06250	0.04524	0.02292	0.22084	0.46994
4.3	0.00445	1.9839	13.95	0.05759	0.04147	0.02090	0.21286	0.46136
4.4	0.00392	1.9934	15.21	0.05309	0.03805	0.01909	0.20525	0.45305
4.5	0.00346	2.0025	16.56	0.04898	0.03494	0.01745	0.19802	0.44499
4.6	0.00305	2.0111	18.02	0.04521	0.03212	0.01597	0.19113	0.43719
4.7	0.00270	2.0192	19.58	0.04177	0.02955	0.01464	0.18457	0.42962
4.8	0.00239	2.0269	21.26	0.03862	0.02722	0.01343	0.17832	0.42228
4.9	0.00213	2.0343	23.07	0.03572	0.02509	0.01233	0.17235	0.41516
5.0	0.00189	2.0412	25.00	0.03308	0.02315	0.01134	0.16667	0.40825

* A more complete table may be found in refs. 4 and 5.

Equations of Linearized Theory. For very slender two- and three-dimensional bodies it may be assumed that the flow disturbances are very small. This leads to a linearization of the nonlinear equation for the velocity potential to

$$(1 - M_\infty{}^2)\frac{\partial^2\phi}{\partial x^2} + \frac{\partial^2\phi}{\partial y^2} + \frac{\partial^2\phi}{\partial z^2} = 0 \qquad \text{(2x-17)}$$

In the above equation M_∞ is the free-stream Mach number and ϕ is the so-called disturbance potential, i.e.,

$$u = U + \phi_x \qquad v = \phi_y \qquad w = \phi_z \qquad \text{(2x-18)}$$

where U is the free-stream velocity. For further details, consult refs. 1 and 2.

Prandtl-Glauert Rule. For subsonic linearized flow there exists a useful correspondence between compressible and incompressible flow. In two dimensions this is given by the velocity relations

$$u_{\text{compr}} = \frac{1}{\sqrt{1 - M_\infty{}^2}}\, u_{\text{incompr}} \qquad \text{(2x-19)}$$

$$\phi(x,y)_{\text{compr}} = \frac{1}{\sqrt{1 - M_\infty{}^2}}\, \phi(x_1,y_1)_{\text{incompr}} \qquad \text{(2x-20)}$$

where $x_1 = x$

$y_1 = \sqrt{1 - M_\infty{}^2}\,y$

Thus, if an incompressible flow about a given body is known in the (x_1,y_1) plane, then the corresponding flow about the same body in the (x,y) plane is given by the above relations; see ref. 1. A similar relation exists for axially symmetric flow. Here

$$\phi(x,r)_{\text{compr}} = \frac{1}{\beta^2}\,\phi(x,\beta r)_{\text{incompr}} \qquad \beta = \sqrt{1 - M_\infty{}^2}$$

However, in this case the comparison is not between the same bodies but one of the r coordinates must be scaled by the factor β; see ref. 1.

Hypersonic Similarity Rule. In very high-speed two-dimensional linearized supersonic flow it is possible to show that the lift and drag coefficients depend solely on the Mach number and the hypersonic similarity parameter $K = M\delta/b$, where M is the free-stream Mach number, δ is the maximum thickness of the body, and b is the body length, i.e., $\tau = \delta/b$ is the thickness ratio. Thus

$$C_D = \frac{1}{M^3}\,f(K) \qquad \text{(2x-21)}$$

$$C_L = \frac{1}{M^2}\,g(K) \qquad \text{(2x-22)}$$

In three dimensions,

$$C_D = \frac{1}{M^2}\,h(K) \qquad \text{(2x-23)}$$

Transonic Similarity Rule. For two-dimensional transonic flows there exists a similarity parameter $H = (1 - M)/(\tau\Gamma)^{\frac{2}{3}}$, where $\tau = \delta/b$ and $\Gamma = \frac{1}{2}(\gamma + 1)$. The lift and drag coefficients can be shown to depend only on the thickness ratio and the transonic similarity parameter H. Thus

$$C_D = \frac{\tau^{\frac{5}{3}}}{\Gamma^{\frac{1}{3}}}\,f(H) \qquad \text{(2x-24)}$$

$$C_L = \frac{\tau^{\frac{2}{3}}}{\Gamma^{\frac{1}{3}}}\,g(H) \qquad \text{(2x-25)}$$

In three dimensions,

$$C_D = \tau^2 h \left(\frac{1 - M}{\tau^2 \Gamma}\right) \tag{2x-26}$$

References

1. Liepmann, H. W., and A. E. Puckett: "Introduction to Aerodynamics of a Compressible Fluid," John Wiley & Sons, Inc., New York, 1947.
2. Ferri, A.: "Elements of Aerodynamics of Supersonic Flows," The Macmillan Company, New York, 1949.
3. Courant, R., and K. O. Friedrichs: "Supersonic Flow and Shock Waves," Interscience Publishers, Inc., New York, 1948.
4. Emmons, H. W.: "Gas Dynamics Tables for Air," Dover Publications, New York, 1947.
5. Aeronautical Research Council: "Compressible Airflow Tables," Oxford University Press, New York, 1952.
6. Sears, W. R.: A Second Note on Compressible Flow about Bodies of Revolution, *Quart. Appl. Math.* **5**, 1 (April, 1947).
7. Von Kármán, T.: The Similarity Law of Transonic Flow, *J. Math. Phys.* **26**, 2 (July, 1947).
8. Tsien, H. S.: Similarity Laws of Hypersonic Flows, *J. Math. Phys.* **25**, 3 (October, 1946).

2y. Laminar and Turbulent Flow of Gases

R. C. ROBERTS

Naval Ordnance Laboratory

2y-1. Equations of Motion. The study of the motion of any real gas or fluid must of necessity take into consideration the effects of viscosity. The transfer of momentum due to viscosity and the transformation of kinetic energy into heat must be considered in formulating the equations of motion. The following equations govern the motion of a viscous, compressible, heat-conducting gas. The viscosity and heat conductivity are assumed to be functions of the temperature only.

Momentum Equations. In rectangular coordinates, the momentum equations may be written as

$$\rho\left(\frac{\partial u}{\partial t} + u\frac{\partial u}{\partial x} + v\frac{\partial u}{\partial y} + w\frac{\partial u}{\partial z}\right) = \rho X + \frac{\partial}{\partial x}\left[\frac{4}{3}\mu\frac{\partial u}{\partial x} - \frac{2}{3}\mu\left(\frac{\partial v}{\partial y} + \frac{\partial w}{\partial z}\right)\right] + \frac{\partial}{\partial y}\left[\mu\left(\frac{\partial u}{\partial y} + \frac{\partial v}{\partial x}\right)\right] + \frac{\partial}{\partial z}\left[\mu\left(\frac{\partial w}{\partial x} + \frac{\partial u}{\partial z}\right)\right] - \frac{\partial p}{\partial x}$$

$$\rho\left(\frac{\partial v}{\partial t} + u\frac{\partial v}{\partial x} + v\frac{\partial v}{\partial y} + w\frac{\partial v}{\partial z}\right) = \rho Y + \frac{\partial}{\partial x}\left[\mu\left(\frac{\partial v}{\partial x} + \frac{\partial u}{\partial y}\right)\right] + \frac{\partial}{\partial y}\left[\frac{4}{3}\mu\frac{\partial v}{\partial y} - \frac{2}{3}\mu\left(\frac{\partial u}{\partial x} + \frac{\partial w}{\partial z}\right)\right] + \frac{\partial}{\partial z}\left[\mu\left(\frac{\partial v}{\partial z} + \frac{\partial w}{\partial y}\right)\right] - \frac{\partial p}{\partial y}$$

$$\rho\left(\frac{\partial w}{\partial t} + u\frac{\partial w}{\partial x} + v\frac{\partial w}{\partial y} + w\frac{\partial w}{\partial z}\right) = \rho Z + \frac{\partial}{\partial x}\left[\mu\left(\frac{\partial w}{\partial x} + \frac{\partial u}{\partial z}\right)\right] + \frac{\partial}{\partial y}\left[\mu\left(\frac{\partial w}{\partial y} + \frac{\partial v}{\partial z}\right)\right] + \frac{\partial}{\partial z}\left[\frac{4}{3}\mu\frac{\partial w}{\partial z} - \frac{2}{3}\mu\left(\frac{\partial u}{\partial x} + \frac{\partial v}{\partial y}\right)\right] - \frac{\partial p}{\partial z} \tag{2y-1}$$

where μ is the coefficient of viscosity and the other terms are as defined in Sec. 2x.

Continuity Equation. The equation of continuity is

$$\frac{\partial \rho}{\partial t} + \frac{\partial}{\partial x}(\rho u) + \frac{\partial}{\partial y}(\rho v) + \frac{\partial}{\partial z}(\rho w) = 0 \tag{2y-2}$$

Energy Equation. By using the first law of thermodynamics and by considering that heat conduction may take place in the gas, the following energy equation may be written

$$\begin{aligned}\rho\left[\frac{\partial E}{\partial t} + u\frac{\partial E}{\partial x} + v\frac{\partial E}{\partial y} + w\frac{\partial E}{\partial z}\right] + p\left(\frac{\partial u}{\partial x} + \frac{\partial v}{\partial y} + \frac{\partial w}{\partial z}\right) \\ = \frac{\partial Q}{\partial t} + \frac{\partial}{\partial x}\left(k\frac{\partial T}{\partial x}\right) + \frac{\partial}{\partial y}\left(k\frac{\partial T}{\partial y}\right) + \frac{\partial}{\partial z}\left(k\frac{\partial T}{\partial z}\right) + 2\mu\left[\left(\frac{\partial u}{\partial x}\right)^2 + \left(\frac{\partial v}{\partial y}\right)^2 + \left(\frac{\partial w}{\partial z}\right)^2\right] \\ - \frac{2}{3}\mu\left(\frac{\partial u}{\partial x} + \frac{\partial v}{\partial y} + \frac{\partial w}{\partial z}\right)^2 + \mu\left(\frac{\partial u}{\partial y} + \frac{\partial v}{\partial x}\right)^2 + \mu\left(\frac{\partial u}{\partial z} + \frac{\partial w}{\partial x}\right)^2 + \mu\left(\frac{\partial v}{\partial z} + \frac{\partial w}{\partial y}\right)^2\end{aligned} \tag{2y-3}$$

where k = heat-conductivity coefficient
E = internal energy per unit mass
$\frac{\partial Q}{\partial t}$ = external heat production rate per unit volume

Equation of State. For a perfect gas the equation of state is

$$p = \rho RT \tag{2y-4}$$

Stream Function. For a steady flow in two dimensions or for axially symmetric flow a stream function may be defined as in Sec. 2x. It has great utility in boundary-layer work (see ref. 3).

2y-2. Definitions of Basic Parameters. The basic dimensionless parameters of a viscous, compressible, heat-conducting gas are usually considered to be the Mach number, the Reynolds number, the Prandtl number, and the Grashof number (see ref. 2). The Mach number has been defined in Sec. 2x. The other three parameters may be defined as follows:

Reynolds Number. In a flow with reference velocity u and reference length L, the Reynolds number R is defined as

$$R = \frac{uL}{\nu} \tag{2y-5}$$

where $\nu = \mu/\rho$ is the kinematic viscosity. Two viscous flows may not be dynamically similar unless their respective Reynolds numbers are the same.

Prandtl Number. The Prandtl number is defined as

$$P_r = \frac{\mu C_p}{k} \tag{2y-6}$$

where C_p is the specific heat at constant pressure and k is the heat conductivity. The Prandtl number depends only on the material properties of the gas.

The Prandtl number is primarily a function of the temperature only. For small temperature changes it is often assumed to be constant (see ref. 2). The variation of P_r with temperature is shown in Tables 2y-1 and 2y-2 for air and for molecular hydrogen H_2.

Grashof Number. The Grashof number may be defined as

$$G_r = \frac{L^3 g(T_1 - T_0)}{\nu^2 T_0} \tag{2y-7}$$

where g is the acceleration of gravity and T_1 and T_2 are two reference temperatures. The Grashof number often appears when there is a transfer of heat through a boundary into or out of the gas.

2y-3. Exact Solutions. Because of the extreme complexity of the equations of motion, few exact solutions have been found. Nearly all of these are limited to the incompressible steady flow case. Since gases may often be assumed incompressible, these solutions may have practical importance.

Pipe Flow. The exact incompressible solution for two-dimensional or axially symmetric steady flow through a pipe of constant cross section is characterized by a

TABLE 2y-1. PRANDTL NUMBER P_r FOR AIR

T, °K	P_r	T, °K	P_r
100	0.770	560	0.680
120	0.766	580	0.680
140	0.761	600	0.680
160	0.754	620	0.681
180	0.746	640	0.682
200	0.739	660	0.682
220	0.732	680	0.683
240	0.725	700	0.684
260	0.719	720	0.685
280	0.713	740	0.686
300	0.708	760	0.687
320	0.703	780	0.688
340	0.699	800	0.689
360	0.695	820	0.690
380	0.691	840	0.692
400	0.689	860	0.693
420	0.686	880	0.695
440	0.684	900	0.696
460	0.683	920	0.697
480	0.681	940	0.698
500	0.680	960	0.700
520	0.680	980	0.701
540	0.680	1000	0.702

parabolic velocity distribution. In the two-dimensional case the complete solution is given by

$$u = -\frac{1}{2\mu} z(h - z) \frac{\partial p}{\partial x}$$
$$v = w = 0 \qquad \text{(2y-8)}$$
$$\frac{\partial p}{\partial x} = \text{const} \qquad \frac{\partial p}{\partial y} = \frac{\partial p}{\partial z} = 0$$

where the boundaries are at $z = 0$ and $z = h$. In the case of flow through a circular pipe, the theoretical solution has been shown to coincide almost exactly with experiment for laminar flow.

Other Exact Solutions. There are a number of other exact solutions for the incompressible case such as steady flow between concentric cylinders and flow through tubes of noncircular cross section. These may be found by consulting refs. 1 and 3. Hamel (ref. 5) has found a number of nontrivial exact solutions.

2y-4. Boundary Layer. When the Reynolds number of the flow is large, most of the viscous effects take place in the immediate vicinity of the boundaries. The outer flow may then be considered determined by the inviscid flow equations while in the boundary layer certain simplifications of the equation of motion may be made. For the case of two-dimensional flow past flat or slowly curving surfaces the pressure may be assumed to be completely determined by the outer flow.

TABLE 2y-2. PRANDTL NUMBER FOR MOLECULAR HYDROGEN H_2*

T, °K	P_r	T, °K	P_r
60	0.713	440	0.684
80	0.711	460	0.681
100	0.712	480	0.678
120	0.715	500	0.675
140	0.718	520	0.671
160	0.719	540	0.669
180	0.720	560	0.667
200	0.719	580	0.665
220	0.717	600	0.664
240	0.715	620	0.663
260	0.712	640	0.663
280	0.709	660	0.662
300	0.706	680	0.661
320	0.703	700	0.661
340	0.699	720	0.661
360	0.696	740	0.660
380	0.693	760	0.660
400	0.690	780	0.660
420	0.687	800	0.660

* The values in Tables 2y-1 and 2y-2 are taken from the National Bureau of Standards, "NACA Tables of Thermal Properties of Gases" (cf. ref. 6).

Basic Equations. For two-dimensional steady flow as outlined above, the momentum, continuity, and energy equations are, respectively,

$$
\begin{gathered}
\rho\left(u\frac{\partial u}{\partial x}+v\frac{\partial u}{\partial y}\right)=\frac{\partial}{\partial y}\left(\mu\frac{\partial u}{\partial y}\right)-\frac{\partial p}{\partial x}\\
0=\frac{\partial p}{\partial y}\\
\frac{\partial}{\partial x}(\rho u)+\frac{\partial}{\partial y}(\rho v)=0\\
\rho\left(u\frac{\partial E}{\partial x}+v\frac{\partial E}{\partial y}\right)+p\left[u\frac{\partial}{\partial x}\left(\frac{1}{\rho}\right)+v\frac{\partial}{\partial y}\left(\frac{1}{\rho}\right)\right]=\frac{\partial}{\partial y}\left(k\frac{\partial T}{\partial y}\right)+\mu\left(\frac{\partial u}{\partial y}\right)^2
\end{gathered}
\tag{2y-9}
$$

For a perfect gas the equation of state is $p = \rho RT$. In the above equations x may be considered as the distance along the boundary while y is the distance perpendicular to the boundary. The velocity components u and v are interpreted in like manner. The equations then hold also for a slowly curving boundary.

Blasius Flow. For incompressible steady flow past a flat plate with no pressure gradient, the equations of motion are

$$u \frac{\partial u}{\partial x} + v \frac{\partial u}{\partial y} = \nu \frac{\partial^2 u}{\partial y^2}$$
$$\frac{\partial u}{\partial x} + \frac{\partial v}{\partial y} = 0 \qquad \text{(2y-10)}$$

with the boundary conditions $u = v = 0$ at $y = 0$ and $u = u_1 =$ const at $y = \infty$ and at $x = 0$. u_1 is the free-stream velocity. Blasius solved this problem by means of the change of variable

$$\eta = \frac{1}{2}\left(\frac{u_1}{\nu x}\right)^{\frac{1}{2}} y \qquad u = \frac{1}{2} u_1 f' \qquad v = \frac{1}{2}\left(\frac{u_1 \nu}{x}\right)^{\frac{1}{2}} (\eta f' - f) \qquad \text{(2y-11)}$$

This reduces the problem to the ordinary differential equation and boundary conditions

$$\frac{d^3 f}{d\eta^3} + f \frac{d^2 f}{d\eta^2} = 0$$
$$f = f' = 0 \text{ at } \eta = 0 \qquad \text{and} \qquad f' = 2 \text{ at } \eta = \infty \qquad \text{(2y-12)}$$

2y-5. Turbulent Motion. For small values of the Reynolds number most flows are characterized by a certain uniformity of velocity distribution and smoothness of the streamline pattern. This condition is called laminar flow. As the Reynolds number is increased the flow will remain laminar until some critical value of R is reached. At this time the small-scale motions of the flow are seen to be chaotic or random in nature and consequently difficult to follow or predict. This is called turbulent flow.

Because of the random nature of turbulent flow one usually considers or measures only average values of the flow variables. The assumption is usually made that the flow variables may be expressed as the sum of an average value plus a randomly fluctuating term, the latter term having zero as its average. In the following discussion the turbulent-flow quantities given are the average values of the flow variables.

2y-6. Data on Turbulent Flow through Pipes. The following data show the behavior of the skin friction for incompressible turbulent flow through smooth and rough pipes. These data come from Nikuradse (see refs. 7 and 8).

Smooth Pipes. The skin-friction coefficient C_f is a function of the Reynolds number R, for smooth pipes,

$$C_f = \frac{\tau_w}{\frac{1}{2}\rho\, u^2}$$
$$R_1 = \frac{r u_1}{\nu}$$

where τ_w = wall shear stress per unit area
ρ = density
ν = kinematic viscosity
u_1 = velocity in center of pipe
r = pipe radius

The behavior of C_f with R_1 is shown in Fig. 2y-1. An empirical curve which fits the data is also shown.

Rough Pipes. For rough pipes with average projection of the roughness k, the skin-friction data are shown in Fig. 2y-2. The friction factor λ is plotted against

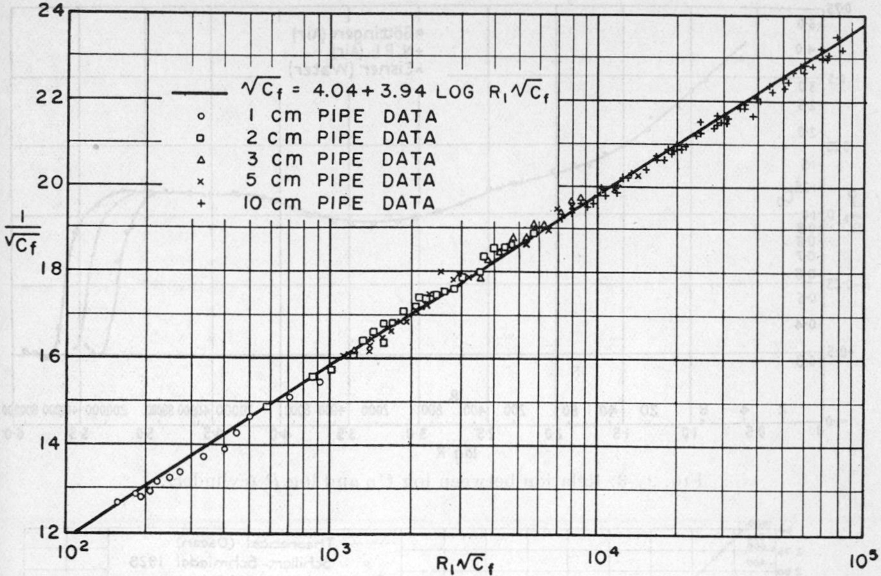

FIG. 2y-1. Universal wall-friction functional relation.

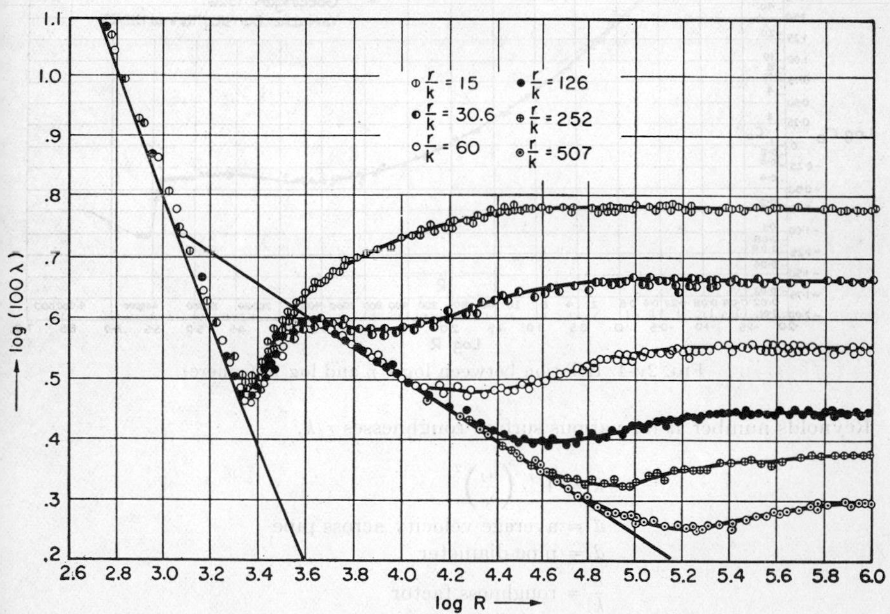

FIG. 2y-2. Relation between log (100λ) and log R (rough pipe).

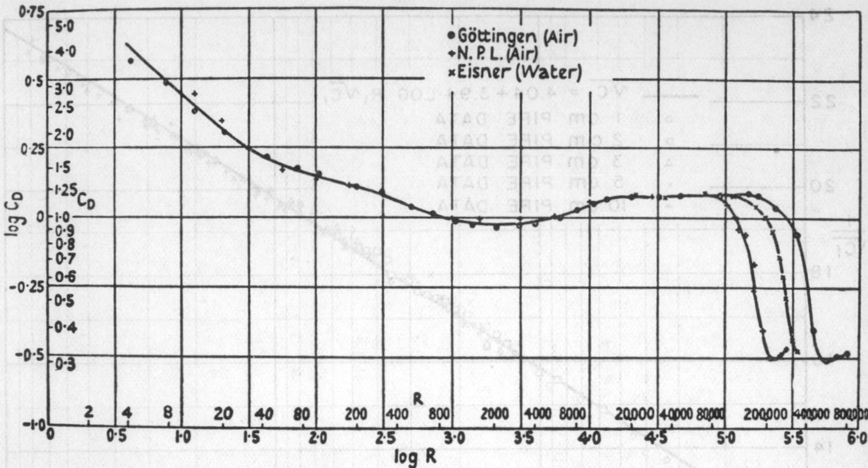

FIG. 2y-3. Relation between log C_D and log R (cylinder).

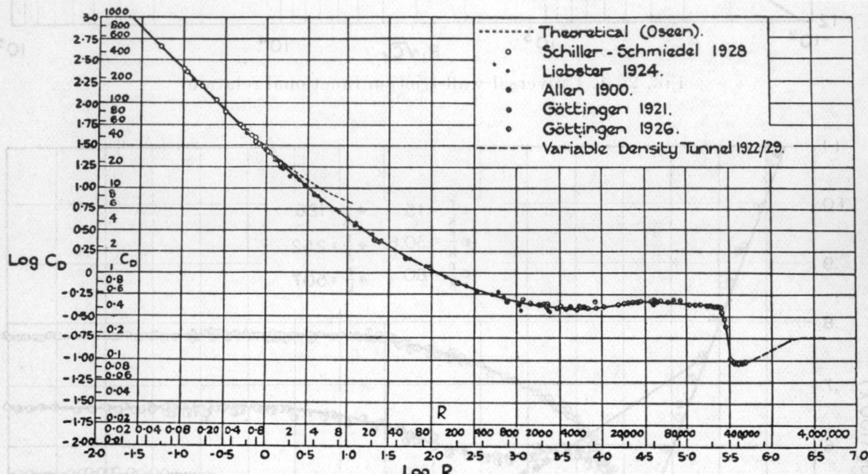

FIG. 2y-4. Relation between log C_D and log R (sphere).

Reynolds number R for various surface roughnesses r/k,

$$\lambda = 4C_f \left(\frac{u_1}{u}\right)^2$$

$\bar{u}$ = average velocity across pipe

d = pipe diameter

$\frac{r}{k}$ = roughness factor

r = pipe radius

2y-7. Drag Data for Spheres and Cylinders. For incompressible viscous steady flow the drag coefficient is a function of the Reynolds number only. The graphs of Figs. 2y-3 and 2y-4 give curves of the experimental data for C_D, the drag coefficient, for a cylinder in cross flow and for a sphere, respectively.

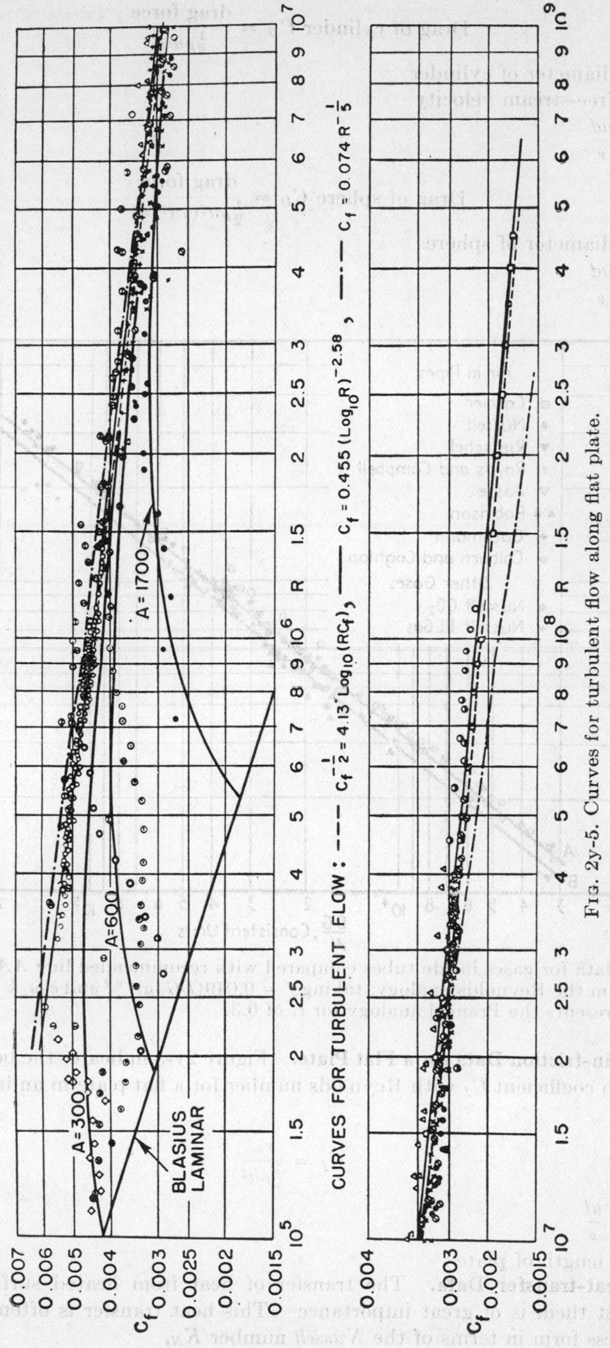

FIG. 2y-5. Curves for turbulent flow along flat plate.

$$\text{Drag of cylinder } C_D = \frac{\text{drag force}}{\frac{1}{2}\rho u^2 d}$$

where d = diameter of cylinder
u = free-stream velocity
$R = \frac{ud}{\nu}$

$$\text{Drag of sphere } C_D = \frac{\text{drag force}}{\frac{1}{2}\rho u^2(\pi d^2/4)}$$

where d = diameter of sphere
$R = \frac{ud}{\nu}$

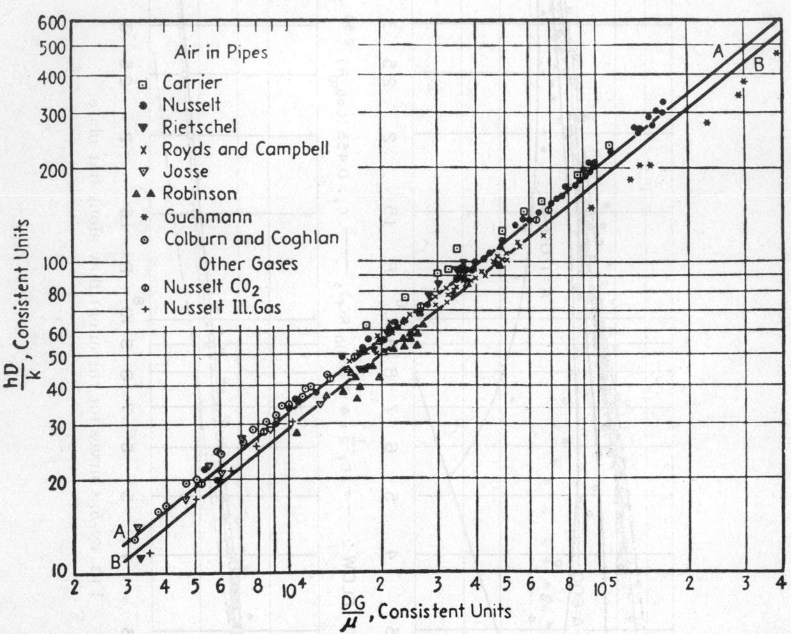

FIG. 2y-6. Data for gases inside tubes compared with recommended line AA. Line BB is obtained from the Reynolds analogy, taking $f = 0.049(DG/\mu)^{-0.2}$ and $c_p\mu/k = 0.74$. Line BB also represents the Prandtl analogy for r_v of 0.3.

2y-8. Skin-friction Data for a Flat Plate. Figure 2y-5 indicates the behavior of the skin-friction coefficient C_f with Reynolds number for a flat plate in an incompressible fluid.

$$C_f = \frac{\tau_w}{\frac{1}{2}\rho u^2}$$

where $R = \frac{ul}{\nu}$
l = length of plate

2y-9. Heat-transfer Data. The transfer of heat from heated surfaces to gases moving past them is of great importance. This heat transfer is often expressed in dimensionless form in terms of the *Nusselt* number K_N,

$$K_N = \frac{hD}{k}$$

where h = coefficient of heat transfer
D = length
k = thermal conductivity

For incompressible flow K_N is a fraction of the Reynolds number only. The behavior K_N with R for pipe flow and for a flat plate is given below.

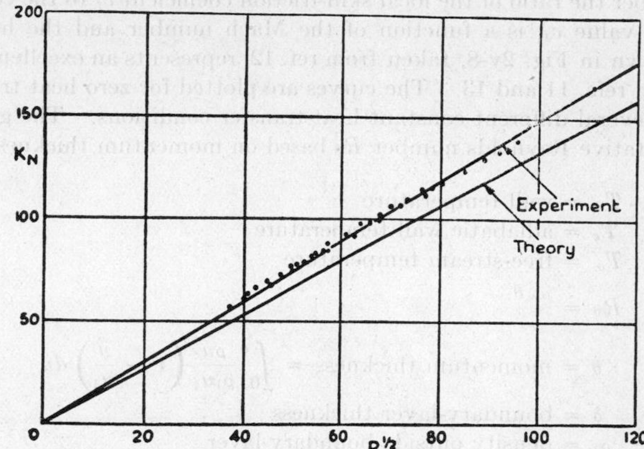

FIG. 2y-7. Comparison between theory and experiment for heat transfer from plate.

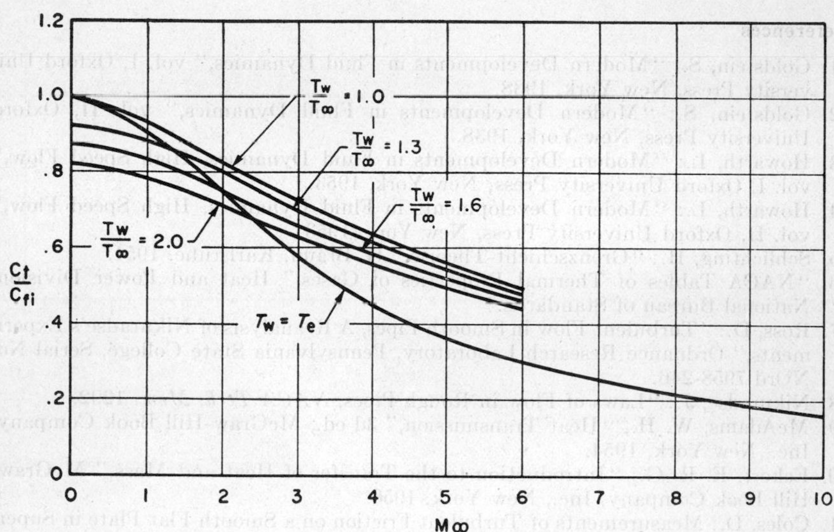

FIG. 2y-8. Variation of skin-friction ratio with Mach number for several constant values of wall-temperature ratio and $Re_\theta = 13{,}500$.

Pipe Flow. The variation of K_N with R for a circular pipe is given in Fig. 2y-6, where D is the pipe diameter.

$$R = \frac{DG}{\mu}$$

where $G = \frac{w}{s}$

w = mass rate of flow
s = cross-sectional area of pipe

Flat Plate. For a flat plate the variation of K_N with R for small R is shown in Fig. 2y-7, where D is the length of the flat plate. For higher values of R recourse must be made to empirical formulas converting the pipe-flow into equivalent flat-plate data; see page 117 of ref. 10.

2y-10. Effect of Compressibility and Heat Transfer on Skin Friction. For a fixed Reynolds number the ratio of the local skin-friction coefficient c_f to the corresponding incompressible value c_{f_i} is a function of the Mach number and the heat transfer. The graph shown in Fig. 2y-8, taken from ref. 12, represents an excellent theoretical fit to data from refs. 11 and 13. The curves are plotted for zero heat transfer where $T_e = T_w$ and several different constant heat-transfer conditions. The graph is for a single representative Reynolds number R_θ based on momentum thickness.

T_w = wall temperature
T_e = adiabatic wall temperature
T_∞ = free-stream temperature

$$R_\theta = \frac{u_\infty \theta}{\nu}$$

$$\theta = \text{momentum thickness} = \int_0^\delta \frac{\rho u}{\rho_1 u_1}\left(1 - \frac{u}{u_1}\right) dy$$

δ = boundary-layer thickness
ρ_1 = density outside boundary layer
u_1 = velocity outside boundary layer

References

1. Goldstein, S.: "Modern Developments in Fluid Dynamics," vol. I, Oxford University Press, New York, 1938.
2. Goldstein, S.: "Modern Developments in Fluid Dynamics," vol. II, Oxford University Press, New York, 1938.
3. Howarth, L.: "Modern Developments in Fluid Dynamics, High Speed Flow," vol. I, Oxford University Press, New York, 1953.
4. Howarth, L.: "Modern Developments in Fluid Dynamics, High Speed Flow," vol. II, Oxford University Press, New York, 1953.
5. Schlichting, H.: "Grenzschicht-Theorie," G. Braun, Karlsruhe, 1951.
6. "NACA Tables of Thermal Properties of Gases," Heat and Power Division, National Bureau of Standards.
7. Ross, D.: "Turbulent Flow in Smooth Pipes, A Reanalysis of Nikuradse's Experiments," Ordnance Research Laboratory, Pennsylvania State College, Serial No. NOrd 7958-246.
8. Nikuradse, J.: "Laws of Flow in Rough Pipes, *NACA Tech. Mem.* 1292.
9. McAdams, W. H., "Heat Transmission," 3d ed., McGraw-Hill Book Company, Inc., New York, 1954.
10. Eckert, E. R. G.: "Introduction to the Transfer of Heat and Mass," McGraw-Hill Book Company, Inc., New York, 1950.
11. Coles, D.: Measurements of Turbulent Friction on a Smooth Flat Plate in Supersonic Flow, *J. Aeronaut. Sci.* **21,** 7 (July, 1954).
12. Persh, Jerome: A Theoretical Investigation of Turbulent Boundary Layer Flow with Heat Transfer at Supersonic and Hypersonic Speeds, *NavOrd Rept.* 3854, U.S. Naval Ordnance Laboratory.
13. Lobb, R. K., E. M. Winkler, and J. Persh: Experimental Investigation of Turbulent Boundary Layers in Hypersonic Flow, *J. Aeronaut. Sci.* **22,** 1 (January, 1955). See also *NavOrd Rept.* 3880, U.S. Naval Ordnance Laboratory, by the same authors.

2z. Shock Waves

ELI H. FREEDMAN

University of Buffalo

EDWARD F. GREENE

Brown University

2z-1. List of Symbols

u	flow velocity, measured in a coordinate system moving with the shock front
p	pressure
ρ	density
γ	ratio of heat capacities $= C_P/C_V$
H	enthalpy
E	internal energy
T	absolute temperature
S	entropy
R^*	gas constant per gram
c	local sound velocity
M_1	Mach number of incident shock $= u_1/c_1$
n	empirical constant in the Tait equation for liquids
$B(S)$	constant in the Tait equation for water
$\mathbf{n}$	unit vector normal to surface
$\mathbf{u}$	velocity vector
M_R	Mach number of reflected shock $= u_{2R}/c_2$

Subscripts 1, 2, and 3 on any quantity (e.g., u_1, p_2, ρ_3) mean that the quantity is measured in front of an incident shock, behind the incident shock, or behind a reflected shock, respectively.

Primed and double-primed quantities (e.g., p', u'') are measured, respectively, on the two sides of a boundary between two media.

Subscript R on any quantity means that that quantity is measured in a coordinate system moving with a reflected shock.

2z-2. Introduction. Sound waves of infinitesimal amplitude in fluids always propagate without change of form (neglecting the effects of viscosity, thermal conductivity, and relaxation). For waves of finite amplitude this is no longer true; the denser regions move faster than the less dense and hence the denser regions are always catching up with less dense ones in front of them; but since the velocity increases with density the effect becomes more and more pronounced, the front of the wave becoming steeper and steeper until the density, temperature, and pressure changes across it are virtually discontinuous—a shock wave is formed. Mathematically, a shock wave is an actual discontinuity propagating with a velocity greater than the local sound velocity. Physically, although a shock transition is extremely abrupt (of the order of 10 mean free paths for a typical shock in a gas), it nevertheless is continuous, because of the action of dissipative forces. In what follows, attention will be focused exclusively on the regions behind or in front of the shock front. The relations that will be given are of general validity (except as noted) and are in any case independent of the actual course of events within the front itself.

It might be imagined that there could be a flow in which a shock moves from a dense region to a rarefied one. However, it can be shown from the energy-conservation law that steady-state flows of this type cannot exist in any fluid having an adiabat that is concave upward, the almost universally prevailing situation.

Another type of discontinuity occurring in gas flows is called a "contact discontinuity." It differs from a shock in that there is no mass flow across it, as there is in the case of a shock. Contact discontinuities cannot occur in steady-state flows and will not be further considered.

2z-3. Steady-state One-dimensional Flow. *General Relations.* Consider a shock propagating steadily in a fluid. Relative to a coordinate system moving with the shock, the equations of steady compressible flow are

$$u\frac{\partial \rho}{\partial x} + \rho\frac{\partial u}{\partial x} = 0 \tag{2z-1a}$$

$$u\frac{\partial u}{\partial x} + \frac{1}{\rho}\frac{\partial p}{\partial x} = 0 \tag{2z-1b}$$

Equation (2z-1*a*) leads to

$$\rho_2 u_2 = \rho_1 u_1 \tag{2z-2}$$

From Eqs. (2z-1) and (2z-2) we have

$$\rho_2 u_2^2 + p_2 = \rho_1 u_1^2 + p_1 \tag{2z-3}$$

Also, from (2z-1*b*),

$$\frac{1}{2}u^2 + \int \frac{dp}{\rho} = \text{const} \tag{2z-4a}$$

From the energy-conservation equation, it can be shown that

$$\tfrac{1}{2}u_2^2 + H_2 = \tfrac{1}{2}u_1^2 + H_1 \tag{2z-4b}$$

These equations lead at once to the *Rankine-Hugoniot relations:*

$$E_2 - E_1 = \Delta E = \frac{1}{2}(p_2 + p_1)\left(\frac{1}{\rho_1} - \frac{1}{\rho_2}\right) \tag{2z-5a}$$

$$H_2 - H_1 = \Delta H = \frac{1}{2}(p_2 - p_1)\left(\frac{1}{\rho_1} + \frac{1}{\rho_2}\right) \tag{2z-5b}$$

and

$$u_1 = \frac{1}{\rho_1}\left[\frac{p_2 - p_1}{1/\rho_1 - 1/\rho_2}\right]^{\frac{1}{2}} \tag{2z-5c}$$

Equations (2z-5*a*), (2z-5*b*), and (2z-5*c*) are based solely upon hydrodynamics and thermodynamics and are valid for all fluids. Further progress can now be made only when they are supplemented by an equation of state for the fluid.

Special Cases. THE IDEAL GAS:

$$p = \rho R^* T$$

From Eqs. (2z-5*a*), (2z-5*b*), and (2z-5*c*) and the equation of state it can be shown that

$$\frac{p_2}{p_1} = \frac{\rho_2(\gamma + 1) - \rho_1(\gamma - 1)}{\rho_1(\gamma + 1) - \rho_2(\gamma - 1)} \tag{2z-6a}$$

$$\frac{\rho_2}{\rho_1} = \frac{p_2(\gamma + 1) + p_1(\gamma - 1)}{p_1(\gamma + 1) + p_2(\gamma - 1)} \tag{2z-6b}$$

and

$$\frac{T_2}{T_1} = \frac{p_2\rho_1}{p_1\rho_2} \tag{2z-6c}$$

In terms of the Mach number of the incident shock M_1,

$$\frac{p_2}{p_1} = \frac{2M_1^2\gamma - \gamma + 1}{\gamma + 1} \qquad (2z\text{-}7a)$$

and

$$\frac{\rho_2}{\rho_1} = \frac{M_1^2(\gamma + 1)}{M_1^2(\gamma - 1) + 2} \qquad (2z\text{-}7b)$$

LIQUIDS: An often-used equation of state for liquids, especially water, is the Tait equation. A convenient form of it is

$$p = B(S)\left[\left(\frac{\rho(T,p)}{\rho(T,0)}\right)^n - 1\right] \qquad (2z\text{-}8a)$$

Approximately

$$B = \frac{\rho_1 c_1^2}{n} \qquad (2z\text{-}8b)$$

It is a good approximation in liquids to assume that the initial and final states are connected by an adiabatic compression. With this assumption,

$$u_1 = c_1\left[1 + \frac{n+1}{4c}\sigma\right] \qquad (2z\text{-}9a)$$

where

$$\sigma = \frac{2c_1}{n-1}\left[\left(\frac{\rho_2}{\rho_1}\right)^{(n-1)/2} - 1\right] \qquad (2z\text{-}9b)$$

Systems Subject to Chemical Reaction. The Rankine-Hugoniot relation, Eq. (2z-5a), is plotted in the $(p, 1/\rho)$ plane in Fig. 2z-1 with an adiabat for comparison. This relation is of course valid when the system reacts chemically, if the chemical energy is included in ΔE. In this case the point (p_1,ρ_1) does not lie on the Rankine-Hugoniot curve, but either above or below it, depending on whether the chemical reaction is endothermic or exothermic. An especially interesting case, detonation, occurs when there is enough chemical energy alone to sustain the shock wave. Since the wave velocity is measured by the slope of the line through (p_1,ρ_1) which intersects the Rankine-Hugoniot curve [see Eqs. (2z-5)], there is usually an infinite number of possible velocities. However, in a steady-state detonation the lowest possible velocity, which corresponds to a line through (p_1,ρ_1) just tangent to the Rankine-Hugoniot curve, is the one that occurs. This is the *Chapman-Jouguet condition:*

$$u_{1\,\text{detonation}} = \frac{1}{\rho_1}\left(\frac{p_2 - p_1}{1/\rho_1 - 1/\rho_2}\right)^{\frac{1}{2}}_{\min} \qquad (2z\text{-}10)$$

which provides the extra relation needed so that the detonation velocity may be calculated from Eqs. (2z-5).

When mechanical as well as chemical energy is available, the velocity increases from the Chapman-Jouguet value as (p_2,ρ_2) moves upward along the Rankine-Hugoniot curve. There is no common physical process corresponding to the value of (p_2,ρ_2) below the Chapman-Jouguet value. The other branch of the Rankine-Hugoniot curve for which $p_2 < p_1$ and $\rho_2 < \rho_1$ corresponds to a deflagration and is a subsonic process.

2z-4. Reflection and Refraction at a Rigid Wall. At a rigid boundary, in addition to the previous Eqs. (2z-5) there must be added the condition

$$\mathbf{u} \cdot \mathbf{n} = 0 \qquad (2z\text{-}11)$$

Normal Incidence. The use of (2z-11) along with (2z-5) for a perfect gas leads to

$$\frac{p_3}{p_2} = \frac{(3\gamma - 1)(p_2/p_1) - \gamma + 1}{(\gamma - 1)(p_2/p_1) + \gamma + 1} \qquad (2z\text{-}12a)$$

and $$-u_{3R} = c_1 \frac{2(p_2/p_1)(\gamma - 1) + 2}{\{2\gamma[(\gamma + 1)(p_2/p_1) + \gamma - 1]\}^{\frac{1}{2}}} \qquad (2z\text{-}12b)$$

which is the velocity of the reflected shock relative to the reflecting surface.

Oblique Incidence. In this case a second condition may be imposed: the incident and reflected waves should intersect at the surface. This condition cannot always be satisfied; when it is one speaks of *regular reflection.* Regular reflection always occurs at a sufficiently small angle of incidence (i.e., the angle between the normal to the surface and the normal to the shock front). The two boundary conditions then completely determine the direction and strength of the reflected shock.

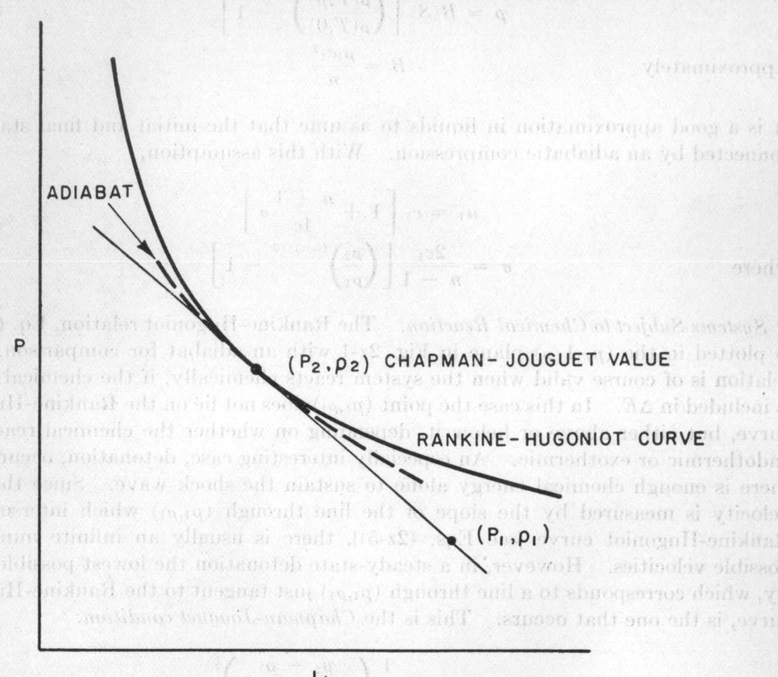

FIG. 2z-1. Plot of Rankine-Hugoniot relation.

There exists a critical angle of incidence above which regular reflection cannot occur. The point of intersection of the incident and reflected shocks rises above the surface and is joined to it by a third shock, called the Mach stem. This case is called "Mach reflection." Experimentally it is found that Mach reflection sets in at angles smaller than those predicted by theory.

2z-5. Reflection and Refraction at a Nonrigid Wall. There are now two boundary conditions that must be satisfied

$$\mathbf{u}' \cdot \mathbf{n}' = \mathbf{u}'' \cdot \mathbf{n}'' \qquad (2z\text{-}13a)$$

and $$p' = p'' \qquad (2z\text{-}13b)$$

Normal Incidence. In order to satisfy both (2z-13*a*) and (2z-13*b*) it is necessary that there be a transmitted and a reflected wave. The transmitted wave is always a shock, but the reflected wave may be either a shock or a rarefaction wave, depending on the properties of the two media, and, in some cases, on the strength of the incident shock.

Oblique Incidence. There can occur either regular reflection or Mach reflection, of which the first case has been well investigated. It is shown that there is always a transmitted wave (i.e., total reflection of a shock wave cannot occur). If the second medium has a high acoustic impedance, the observed phenomena are similar to those found at a rigid surface; if the second medium has a low acoustic impedance, the observed phenomena are similar to those found at a free surface.

Free Surface (for Liquids Only). The condition (2z-13*b*) here becomes $p' = 0$. For a sufficiently small angle of incidence there is always a reflected rarefaction wave intersecting the incident shock at the surface. At some critical angle of incidence, determined by the strength of the incident shock as well as the properties of the liquid, this picture no longer applies. The phenomena in this case have not yet been intensively investigated.

Table 2z-1 lists some important properties of shock waves in ideal monatomic and diatomic gases. The following values have been used for γ, the ratio of heat capacities: For the monatomic gas, $\gamma = \frac{5}{3}$; for the diatomic gas, $\gamma = \frac{7}{5}$. For both gases,

TABLE 2z-1. SOME PROPERTIES OF SHOCKS IN IDEAL GASES

M_1	Monatomic				Diatomic			
	p_2/p_1	ρ_2/ρ_1	T_2/T_1	M_R	p_2/p_1	ρ_2/ρ_1	T_2/T_1	M_R
1	1.000	1.000	1.000	1.000	1.000	1.000	1.000	1.000
1.5	2.562	1.714	1.495	1.397	2.458	1.862	1.320	1.426
2	4.750	2.286	2.078	1.648	4.500	2.667	1.688	1.732
2.5	7.562	2.703	2.798	1.808	7.125	3.333	2.138	1.949
3	11.00	3.000	3.667	1.915	10.33	3.857	2.679	2.104
4	19.75	3.368	5.863	2.041	18.50	4.571	4.047	2.297
5	31.00	3.571	8.680	2.104	29.00	5.000	5.800	2.408
6	44.75	3.692	12.12	2.142				
8	79.75	3.821	20.87	2.182				
10	124.8	3.884	32.12	2.201				
15	281.0	3.947	71.19	2.220				
20	499.8	3.970	125.9	2.227				

the possibility of electronic excitation has been neglected. In addition, for the diatomic gas, the possibilities of dissociation and the activation of the vibrational heat capacity have been neglected. Since the latter assumption becomes increasingly unrealistic at high temperatures, this part of the table has not been extended beyond $M_1 = 5$.

References

General

Courant, R., and K. O. Friedrichs: "Supersonic Flow and Shock Waves," Interscience Publishers, Inc., New York, 1948. Comprehensive, thorough treatment of entire subject, emphasizing mathematical aspects; 198 references.

Penney, W. G., and H. H. M. Pike: *Repts. Progr. in Phys.* **13,** 46–82 (1950). Over-all survey of problems and results, emphasizing physical aspects; 40 references.

Special

Cole, R. H.: "Underwater Explosions," Princeton University Press, Princeton, N.J., 1946. Thorough treatment of propagation of shocks in water.

Lewis, Bernard, and Guenther von Elbe: "Combustion, Flames and Explosions of Gases," Academic Press, Inc., New York, 1951; chap. XI treats detonation waves in gases.

Taub, A. H.: *Phys. Rev.* **72,** 51–60 (1947). Reflection and refraction of plane shocks.

Bleakney, W., and A. H. Taub: *Revs. Modern Phys.* **21,** 584–605 (1949).

Fletcher, C. H., A. H. Taub, and W. Bleakney: *Revs. Modern Phys.* **23,** 271–286 (1951). Mach reflection considered theoretically and experimentally.

Polachek, H., and R. J. Seeger: *Phys. Rev.* **84,** 922–929 (1951). Refraction at a gaseous interface.

See also pp. 3-37 to 3-39 of this book, "Waves of Finite Amplitude," Sec. 3c-6.

Section 3

ACOUSTICS

FLOYD A. FIRESTONE, Editor

The Journal of the Acoustical Society of America

CONTENTS

3a.	Acoustical Definitions	3-2
3b.	Letter Symbols and Conversion Factors for Acoustical Quantities	3-18
3c.	Propagation of Sound in Fluids	3-25
3d.	Acoustic Properties of Gases	3-56
3e.	Acoustic Properties of Liquids	3-67
3f.	Acoustic Properties of Solids	3-74
3g.	Properties of Transducer Materials	3-89
3h.	Frequencies of Simple Vibrators. Musical Scales	3-100
3i.	Radiation of Sound	3-108
3j.	Architectural Acoustics	3-113
3k.	Speech and Hearing	3-123
3l.	Classical Electro-dynamical Analogies	3-134
3m.	The Mobility and Classical Impedance Analogies	3-140
3n.	Selected References on Acoustics	3-178

3a. Acoustical Definitions[1]

LEO L. BERANEK

Bolt Beranek and Newman, Inc.

3a-1. General

Acceleration. The acceleration of a point is the time rate of change of the velocity of the point.

Acoustic, acoustical. The qualifying adjectives acoustic and acoustical mean containing, producing, arising from, actuated by, related to, or associated with sound. *Acoustic* is used when the term being qualified designates something that has the properties, dimensions, or physical characteristics associated with sound waves; *acoustical* is used when the term being qualified does *not* designate explicitly something which has such properties, dimensions, or physical characteristics.

EXAMPLES: Acoustic singularities manifested through acoustic impedance irregularities make possible acoustical flaw-detection methods based on acoustic flaw detection. Positive acoustical advantages can accrue from good acoustical utilization of such acoustic signals, which represent an acoustical manifestation of electricity transmitted acoustically by an acoustic medium. From the acoustical point of view, acoustic loading is an excellent method of effecting the acoustical termination of an acoustical system with an acoustic termination.

Acoustics. Acoustics is the science of sound including its production, transmission, and effects.

Anechoic Space or Chamber. An anechoic space or chamber is a bounded space in which reflected waves are sufficiently weak as to be negligible in the region of interest; more literally, echo-free space.

Antinodes (Loops). Antinodes are the points, lines, or surfaces in a standing-wave system where some characteristic of the wave field has maximum amplitude.

Note: The appropriate modifier should be used with the word "antinode" to signify the type that is intended (pressure antinode, velocity antinode, etc.).

Audio Frequency. An audio frequency is any frequency corresponding to a normally audible sound wave.

Note 1: Audio frequencies range roughly from 15 to 20,000 cycles per second.
Note 2: The word "audio" may be used as a modifier to indicate a device or system intended to operate at audio frequencies, e.g., "audio amplifier."

Band Power Level. The band power level of a sound for a specified frequency band is the acoustic power level for the acoustic power contained within the band. The width of the band and the reference power must be specified. The unit is the decibel.

Band Pressure Level. The band pressure level of a sound for a specified frequency band is the effective sound pressure level for the sound energy contained within the band. The width of the band and the reference pressure must be specified. The unit is the decibel.

[1] From American Standard Z24.1-1951, American Standards Association.

Beats. Beats are periodic variations that result from the superposition of waves having different frequencies.

Compressional Wave. A compressional wave is a wave in an elastic medium which causes an element of the medium to change its volume without undergoing rotation.

Note 1: Mathematically, a compressional wave is one whose velocity field has zero curl.
Note 2: A compressional plane wave is a longitudinal wave.

Continuous Spectrum. A continuous spectrum is the spectrum of a wave the components of which are continuously distributed over a frequency region.

Decibel. The decibel is a dimensionless unit for expressing the ratio of two values of power, the number of decibels being 10 times the logarithm to the base 10 of the power ratio.

Note: With P_1 and P_2 designating two amounts of power and n the number of decibels corresponding to their ratio,

$$n = 10 \log_{10} \frac{P_1}{P_2}$$

When the conditions are such that scalar ratios of currents or of voltages (or analogous quantities in other fields such as pressures, or particle velocities in sound) are the square roots of the corresponding power ratios, the number of decibels by which the corresponding powers differ is expressed by the following formulas:

$$n = 20 \log_{10} \frac{I_1}{I_2}$$

$$n = 20 \log_{10} \frac{V_1}{V_2}$$

where I_1/I_2 and V_1/V_2 are the given current and voltage ratios, respectively.

By extension, these relations between numbers of decibels and scalar ratios of currents or voltages are sometimes applied where these ratios are not the square roots of the corresponding power ratios; to avoid confusion, such usage should be accompanied by a specific statement of this application.

Doppler Effect. The Doppler effect is the phenomenon evidenced by the change in the observed frequency of a wave in a transmission system caused by a time rate of change in the effective length of the path of travel between the source and the point of observation.

Echo. An echo is a wave which has been reflected or otherwise returned with sufficient magnitude and delay to be perceived in some manner as a wave distinct from that directly transmitted.

Effective Particle Velocity. The effective particle velocity at a point is the root mean square of the instantaneous particle velocity (see Effective Sound Pressure for details). The unit is the meter per second (in the cgs system the unit is the centimeter per second).

Effective Sound Pressure (Root-mean-square Sound Pressure). The effective sound pressure at a point is the root-mean-square value of the instantaneous sound pressures, over a time interval at the point under consideration. In the case of periodic sound pressures, the interval must be an integral number of periods or an interval which is long compared with a period. In the case of nonperiodic sound pressures, the interval should be long enough to make the value obtained essentially independent of small changes in the length of the interval.

Note: The term "effective sound pressure" is frequently shortened to "sound pressure."

Electric Power Level, or *Sound Intensity Level.* The electric power level, or the acoustic intensity level, is a quantity expressing the ratio of two electric powers or of two sound intensities in logarithmic form. The unit is the decibel. Definitions are

$$\text{Electric power level} = 10 \log_{10} \frac{W_1}{W_2} \quad \text{db}$$

$$\text{Acoustic intensity level} = 10 \log_{10} \frac{I_1}{I_2} \quad \text{db}$$

where W_1 and W_2 are two electric powers and I_1 and I_2 are two sound intensities. Extending this thought further, we see that

$$\text{Electric power level} = 10 \log_{10} \frac{E_1^2}{R_1} \frac{R_2}{E_2^2}$$

$$= 20 \log_{10} \frac{E_1}{E_2} + 10 \log_{10} \frac{R_2}{R_1} \quad \text{db}$$

where E_1 is the voltage across the resistance R_1 in which a power W_1 is being dissipated and E_2 is the voltage across the resistance R_2 in which a power W_2 is being dissipated. Similarly,

$$\text{Acoustic intensity level} = 20 \log_{10} \frac{p_1}{p_2} + 10 \log_{10} \frac{R_{s2}}{R_{s1}} \quad \text{db}$$

where p_1 is the pressure at a point where the specific acoustic resistance (i.e., the real part of the specific acoustic impedance) is R_{s1} and p_2 is the pressure at a point where the specific acoustic resistance is R_{s2}. We note that $10 \log_{10} (W_1/W_2) = 20 \log_{10} (E_1/E_2)$ only if $R_1 = R_2$ and that $10 \log_{10} (I_1/I_2) = 20 \log_{10} (p_1/p_2)$ only if $R_{s2} = R_{s1}$.

Levels involving voltage and pressure alone are sometimes spoken of with no regard to the equalities of the electric resistances or specific acoustic resistances. This practice leads to serious confusion. It is emphasized that the manner in which the terms are used always should be clearly stated by the user in order to avoid confusion.

Flutter Echo. A flutter echo is a rapid succession of reflected pulses resulting from a single initial pulse.

Free Field. A free field is a field (wave or potential) in a homogeneous isotropic medium free from boundaries. In practice it is a field in which the effects of the boundaries are negligible over the region of interest.

Note: The actual pressure impinging on an object (e.g., electroacoustic transducer) placed in an otherwise free sound field will differ from the pressure which would exist at that point with the object removed, unless the acoustic impedance of the object matches the acoustic impedance of the medium.

Infrasonic Frequency (Subsonic Frequency). An infrasonic frequency is a frequency lying below the audio-frequency range.

Note: The word "infrasonic" may be used as a modifier to indicate a device or system intended to operate at infrasonic frequencies.

Instantaneous Particle Velocity (Particle Velocity). The instantaneous particle velocity at a point is the velocity, due to the sound wave only, of a given infinitesimal part of the medium at a given instant. It is measured over and above any motion of the medium as a whole. The unit is the meter per second (in the cgs system the unit is the centimeter per second).

Instantaneous Sound Pressure. The instantaneous sound pressure at a point is the total instantaneous pressure at that point minus the static pressure at that point. The commonly used unit is the microbar.

Intensity Level. The intensity level of a sound, in decibels, is 10 times the logarithm to the base 10 of the ratio of the intensity of this sound to a reference intensity. That is,

$$L_I = 10 \log_{10} \frac{I}{I_{\text{ref}}}$$

In the United States the reference intensity is often taken to be 10^{-16} watt/cm^2(10^{-12} watt/m^2). This reference at standard atmospheric conditions in a plane or spherical progressive wave was originally selected as corresponding approximately to the reference pressure (0.0002 microbar).

Line Spectrum. A line spectrum is the spectrum of a wave the components of which are confined to a number of discrete frequencies.

Longitudinal Wave. A longitudinal wave is a wave in which the direction of displacement at each point of the medium is normal to the wave front.

Microbar (μb). A microbar is a unit of pressure commonly used in acoustics. One microbar is equal to 0.1 newton per square meter or 1 dyne per square centimeter.

Neper. The neper is a unit used to express the scalar ratio of two currents or two voltages, the number of nepers being the natural logarithm of such a ratio.

Note 1: With I_1 and I_2 designating the scalar value of two currents, and n the number of nepers denoting their scalar ratio, then

$$n = \log_e \frac{I_1}{I_2}$$

When the conditions are such that the power ratio is the square of the corresponding current or voltage ratio, the number of nepers by which the corresponding voltages or currents differ may be expressed by the following formula:

$$n = \frac{1}{2} \log_e \frac{P_1}{P_2}$$

where P_1/P_2 is the given power ratio.

By extension, this relation between number of nepers and power ratio is sometimes applied where this ratio is not the square of the corresponding current or voltage ratio; to avoid confusion, such usage should be accompanied by a specific statement of this application.

Note 2: One neper is equal to 8.686 db.

Note 3: The neper is used in mechanics and acoustics by extending the above definition to include all scalar ratios of like quantities which are analogous to current or voltage.

Nodes. Nodes are the points, lines, or surfaces in a standing-wave system where some characteristic of the wave field has essentially zero amplitude.

Note: The appropriate modifier should be used with the word "node" to signify the type that is intended (pressure node, velocity node, etc.).

Noise. Noise is any undesired sound. By extension, noise is any unwanted disturbance within a useful frequency band, such as undesired electric waves in any transmission channel or device.

Plane Wave. A plane wave is a wave in which the wave fronts are everywhere parallel planes normal to the direction of propagation.

Power Spectrum Level. The power spectrum level of a sound at a specified frequency is the power level for the acoustic power contained in a band one cycle per second wide, centered at this specified frequency. The reference power must be specified. The unit is the decibel (see also the discussion under Pressure Spectrum Level).

Pressure Spectrum Level. The pressure spectrum level of a sound at specified frequency is the effective sound pressure level for the sound energy contained within a band one cycle per second wide, centered at this specified frequency. The reference pressure must be explicitly stated. The unit is the decibel.

Note: The concept of pressure spectrum level ordinarily has significance only for sound having a continuous distribution of energy within the frequency range under consideration. The level of a uniform band of noise with a continuous spectrum exceeds the spectrum level by

$$C_n = 10 \log_{10} (f_b - f_a) \qquad \text{db}$$

where f_b and f_a are the upper and lower frequencies of the band, respectively. The level of a uniform noise with a continuous spectrum in a band of width $f_b - f_a$ cps is therefore related to the spectrum level by the formula

$$L_n = C_n + S_n$$

where L_n = sound pressure level in decibels of the noise in the band of width $f_b - f_a$; for C_n see above, S_n = spectrum level of the noise, and n = designation number for the band being considered.

Rate of Decay. The rate of decay is the time rate at which the sound pressure level (or velocity level, or sound-energy density level) is decreasing at a given point and at a given time. The practical unit is the decibel per second.

Reverberation. Reverberation is the persistence of sound at a given point after direct reception from the source has stopped.

Note: This may be due (1) (as in the case of rooms) to repeated reflections from a small number of boundaries or to the free decay of the normal modes of vibration that were excited by the sound source, (2) (as in the case of underwater sound in the ocean) to scattering from a large number of inhomogeneities in the medium or reflection from bounding surfaces.

Shear Wave (Rotational Wave). A shear wave is a wave in an elastic medium which causes an element of the medium to change its shape without a change of volume.

Note 1: Mathematically, a shear wave is one whose velocity field has zero divergence.
Note 2: A shear plane wave in an isotropic medium is a transverse wave.

Sound-Energy Density. The sound-energy density is the sound energy in a given infinitesimal part of the gas divided by the volume of that part of the gas. The unit is the watt-second per cubic meter. (In the cgs system the unit is the erg per cubic centimeter). In many acoustic environments such as in a plane wave the sound-energy density at a point is

$$D = \frac{p^2}{\rho_0 c^2} = \frac{p^2}{\gamma P_0}$$

where γ is the ratio of specific heats for a gas and is equal to 1.4 for air and other diatomic gases. The quantity γ is dimensionless. P_0 is the barometric pressure.

Sound Field. A sound field is a region containing sound waves.

Sound Intensity (I). The sound intensity measured in a specified direction at a point is the average rate at which sound energy is transmitted through a unit area perpendicular to the specified direction at the point considered. The unit is the watt per square meter. (In the cgs system the unit is the erg per second per square centimeter.) In a plane or spherical free-progressive sound wave the intensity in the direction of propagation is

$$I = \frac{p^2}{\rho_0 c} \quad \text{watts/m}^2 \text{ or erg-sec}^{-1}\text{/cm}^2$$

Note: In the acoustical literature the intensity has often been expressed in the units of watts per square centimeter, which is equal to 10^{-7} times the number of ergs per second per square centimeter.

Sound Intensity Level. See Electric Power Level.

Sound Level. The sound level at a point in a sound field is the reading in decibels of a sound-level meter constructed and operated in accordance with the latest edition of American Standard Sound Level Meters for the Measurement of Noise and Other Sounds.[1]

The meter reading (in decibels) corresponds to a value of the sound pressure

[1] American Standard Sound Level Meters for the Measurement of Noise and Other Sounds, Z24.3-1944, American Standards Association, Inc., New York. This standard is in process of revision.

integrated over the audible frequency range with a specified frequency weighting and integration time.

Sound Power Level. The acoustic power level of a sound source in decibels is 10 times the logarithm to the base 10 of the ratio of the acoustic power radiated by the source to a reference acoustic power. That is,

$$L_W = 10 \log_{10} \frac{W}{W_{\text{ref}}} \quad \text{db}$$

Often, W_{ref} is 10^{-13} watt. This means that a source radiating 1 acoustic watt has a power level of 130 db.

Sound Pressure Level. The pressure level of a sound, in decibels, is 20 times the logarithm to the base 10 of the ratio of the measured effective sound pressure of this sound to a reference effective sound pressure. That is,

$$L_p = 20 \log_{10} \frac{p}{p_{\text{ref}}} \quad \text{db}$$

In the United States p_{ref} is either (1) $p_{\text{ref}} = 0.0002$ microbar (2×10^{-5} newton/m^2) or (2) $p_{\text{ref}} = 1$ microbar (0.1 newton/m^2). Reference pressure (1) has been in general use for measurements dealing with hearing and for sound-level and noise measurements in air and liquids. Reference pressure (2) has gained widespread use for calibration of transducers and some types of sound-level measurements in liquids. The two reference levels are almost exactly 74 db apart. The reference pressure must always be stated explicitly.

Spectrum. The spectrum of a wave is the distribution in frequency of the magnitudes (and sometimes phases) of the components of the wave. Spectrum also is used to signify a continuous range of frequencies, usually wide in extent, within which waves have some specified common characteristic, e.g., audio-frequency spectrum, radio-frequency spectrum, etc.

Spherical Wave. A spherical wave is a wave in which the wave fronts are concentric spheres.

Standing Waves. Standing waves are periodic waves having a fixed distribution in space which is the result of interference of progressive waves of the same frequency and kind. Such waves are characterized by the existence of nodes or partial nodes and antinodes that are fixed in space.

Static Pressure (P_0). The static pressure at a point in the medium is the pressure that would exist at that point with no sound waves present. At normal barometric pressure, P_0 equals approximately 10^5 newtons/m^2 (10^6 dynes/cm^2). This corresponds to a barometer reading of 0.751 m (29.6 in.) Hg(mercury) when the temperature of the mercury is 0°C. Standard atmospheric pressure is usually taken to be 0.760 m Hg at 0°C.

Stationary Waves. Stationary waves are standing waves in which the energy flux is zero at all points.

Note: Stationary waves can only be approximated in practice.

Strength of a Simple Sound Source. The strength of a simple sound source is the rms magnitude of the total air flow at the surface of a simple source in cubic meters per second (or cubic centimeters per second), where a simple source is taken to be a spherical source whose radius is small compared with one-sixth wavelength.

Ultrasonic Frequency (Supersonic Frequency). An ultrasonic frequency is a frequency lying above the audio-frequency range. The term is commonly applied to elastic waves propagated in gases, liquids, or solids.

Note: The word "ultrasonic" may be used as a modifier to indicate a device or system intended to operate at ultrasonic frequencies.

Velocity. The velocity of a point is the time rate of change of a position vector of that point with respect to an inertial frame.

Note: In most cases the approximation is made that axes fixed to the earth constitute an inertial frame.

Volume Velocity. The volume velocity, due to a sound wave only, is the rate of flow of the medium perpendicularly through a specified area S. That is, $U = uS$, where u is the particle velocity and U is the volume velocity. The unit is the cubic meter per second. (In the cgs system the unit is the cubic centimeter per second.)

Wave. A wave is a disturbance which is propagated in a medium in such a manner that at any point in the medium the displacement is a function of the time, while at any instant the displacement at the point is a function of the position of the point.

Any physical quantity which has the same relationship to some independent variable (usually time) that a propagated disturbance has, at a particular instant, with respect to space, may be called a wave.

Note: In this definition, displacement is used as a general term, indicating not only mechanical displacement, but also electric displacement, etc.

Wavefront. (1) The wavefront of a progressive wave in space is a continuous surface which is a locus of points having the same phase at a given instant. (2) The wavefront of a progressive surface wave is a continuous line which is a locus of points having the same phase at a given instant.

Wave Interference. Wave interference is the phenomenon which results when waves of the same or nearly the same frequency are superposed and is characterized by a spatial or temporal distribution of amplitude of some specified characteristic differing from that of the individual superposed waves.

3a-2. Sound Transmission and Propagation

Acoustic Attenuation Constant (Attenuation Constant). The acoustic attenuation constant is the real part of the acoustic propagation constant. The commonly used unit is the neper per section or per unit distance.

Note: In the case of a symmetrical structure, the imaginary parts of both the transfer constant and the acoustic propagation constant are identical, and hence either one may be called simply the attenuation constant.

Acoustic Compliance. The acoustic compliance of an enclosed volume of gas is equal to the magnitude of the ratio of the volume displacement of a piston forming one side of the volume to the pressure causing the displacement (units cm^5/dyne or m^5/newton).

Acoustic Impedance (American Standard Acoustic Impedance). The acoustic impedance at a given surface is defined as the complex ratio[1] of effective sound pressure averaged over the surface to effective volume velocity through it. The surface may be either a hypothetical surface in an acoustic medium or the moving surface of a mechanical device. The unit is newton-sec/m^5, or the mks acoustic ohm.[2] (In the cgs system the unit is dyne-sec/cm^5, or acoustic ohm.)

$$Z_A = \frac{p}{U} \quad \text{newton-sec/m}^5 \text{ (mks acoustic ohms)}$$

Acoustic Mass (Inertance). The acoustic mass is the quantity which, when multiplied by 2π times the frequency, gives the acoustic reactance associated with the kinetic energy of the medium (units gm/cm^4 or kg/m^4).

[1] "Complex ratio" has the same meaning as the complex ratio of voltage and current in electric-circuit theory.

[2] This notation is taken from Table 12.1 of American Standard Z24.1-1951.

Acoustic Ohm. The acoustic ohm is the magnitude of an acoustic resistance, reactance, or impedance for which a sound pressure of one microbar produces a volume velocity of one cubic centimeter per second (dyne-sec/cm^5). When expressed in newton-sec/m^5, it is called the mks acoustic ohm.

Acoustic Phase Constant. The acoustic phase constant is the imaginary part of the acoustic propagation constant. The commonly used unit is the radian per section or per unit distance.

Note: In the case of a symmetrical structure, the imaginary parts of both the transfer constant and the acoustic propagation constant are identical, and have been called the "wavelength constant."

Acoustic Propagation Constant. The acoustic propagation constant of a uniform system or of a section of a system of recurrent structures is the natural logarithm of the complex ratio of the steady-state particle velocities, volume velocities, or pressures at two points separated by unit distance in the uniform system (assumed to be of infinite length), or at two successive corresponding points in the system of recurrent structures (assumed to be of infinite length). The ratio is determined by dividing the value at the point nearer the transmitting end by the corresponding value at the more remote point.

Acoustic Resistance. Acoustic resistance is the real component of the acoustic impedance. The cgs unit is the acoustic ohm. The mks unit is the specific acoustic ohm.

Acoustic, Specific Acoustic, and Mechanical Reactance. The acoustic reactance, the specific acoustic reactance, and the mechanical reactance are, respectively, the imaginary parts of the acoustic impedance, the specific acoustic impedance, and the mechanical impedance. The units are the same, respectively, as for the real, i.e., the resistive parts.

Characteristic Impedance. The characteristic impedance is the ratio of the effective sound pressure at a given point to the effective particle velocity at that point in a free, plane, progressive sound wave. It is equal to the product of the density of the medium times the speed of sound in the medium. It is analogous to the characteristic impedance of an infinitely long, dissipationless transmission line. The unit is the mks rayl, or newton-sec/m^3. (In the cgs system, the unit is the rayl, or dyne-sec/cm^3.)

Insertion Loss. The insertion loss resulting from the insertion of a transducer in a transmission system is the ratio of the power delivered to that part of the system which will follow the transducer, before insertion of the transducer, to the power delivered to that same part of the system after insertion of the transducer.

Note 1: If the input power, the output power, or both consist of more than one component, the particular components used must be specified.
Note 2: This ratio is usually expressed in decibels.

Mechanical Compliance. The mechanical compliance of a springlike device is equal to the magnitude of the ratio of the displacement of the device to the force that produced the displacement (units cm/dyne or m/newton).

Mechanical Impedance. The mechanical impedance is the complex ratio of the effective force acting on a specified area of an acoustic medium or mechanical device to the resulting effective linear velocity through or of that area, respectively. The unit is the newton-sec/m, or the mks mechanical ohm. (In the cgs system the unit is the dyne-sec/cm, or the mechanical ohm.) That is, $Z_M = f/u$ newton-sec/m (mks mechanical ohms).

Mechanical Ohm. The mechanical ohm is the magnitude of a mechanical resistance, reactance, or impedance for which a force of one dyne produces a linear velocity of one centimeter per second (dyne-sec/cm). When expressed in newton-sec/m, it is called the mks mechanical ohm.

Mechanical Resistance. Mechanical resistance is the real part of the mechanical impedance. The cgs unit is the mechanical ohm. The mks unit is the mks mechanical ohm.

Natural Frequency. A natural frequency of a body or system is a frequency of free oscillation.

Normal Mode of Vibration. A normal mode of vibration is a characteristic distribution of vibration amplitudes among the parts of the system, each part of which is vibrating freely at the same frequency. Complex free vibrations are combinations of these simple vibration forms.

Rayl.[1] The rayl is the magnitude of a specific acoustic resistance, reactance, or impedance for which a sound pressure of one microbar produces a linear velocity of one centimeter per second (dyne-sec/cm³). When expressed in newton-sec/m³ it is called the mks rayl.

Resonance Frequency. A resonance frequency is a frequency at which resonance exists. The commonly used unit is the cycle per second.

Note: In cases where there is a possibility of confusion, it is necessary to specify the type of resonance frequency, e.g., displacement resonance frequency or velocity resonance frequency.

Specific Acoustic Compliance. The specific acoustic compliance of a springlike device or an enclosed volume of gas is equal to the magnitude of the ratio of the displacement of the device or of a piston forming one side of the volume to the pressure that produced the displacement (units cm³/dyne or m³/newton).

Specific Acoustic Impedance. The specific acoustic impedance is the complex ratio of the effective sound pressure at a point of an acoustic medium or mechanical device to the effective particle velocity at that point. The unit is newton-sec/m³, or the mks rayl. (In the cgs system the unit is dyne-sec/cm³, or the rayl.) That is, $Z_s = p/u$ newton-sec/m³ (mks rayls).

Specific Acoustic Mass. The specific acoustic mass is the quantity which when multiplied by 2π times the frequency gives the specific acoustic reactance associated with the kinetic energy of the medium (units gm/cm² or kg/m²).

Transmission Loss. In communication, transmission loss (frequently abbreviated "loss") is a general term used to denote a decrease in power in transmission from one point to another. Transmission loss is usually expressed in decibels.

3a-3. Transmission Systems and Components

Acoustical Reciprocity Theorem. In an acoustic system comprising a fluid medium having bounding surfaces S_1, S_2, S_3, . . . , and subject to no impressed body forces, if two distributions of normal velocities v'_n and v''_n of the bounding surfaces produce pressure fields p' and p'', respectively, throughout the region, then the surface integral of $(p''v'_n - p'v''_n)$ over all the bounding surfaces S_1, S_2, S_3, . . . , vanishes.

Note: If the region contains only one simple source, the theorem reduces to the form ascribed to Helmholtz, viz., in a region as described, a simple source at A produces the same sound pressure at another point B as would have been produced at A had the source been located at B.

Directivity Factor. (1) The directivity factor on a particular axis of a sound source is the ratio of the sound intensity at a point in the far field on the designated axis to the sound intensity that would be produced at that same point by a spherical source radiating the same total acoustic power. The frequency or the frequency band must be stated. (2) The directivity factor on a particular axis of a sound receptor (transducer, ear trumpet, etc.) is the ratio of the energy per second produced in the receptor

[1] Named in honor of Lord Rayleigh.

in response to a plane sound wave arriving along the designated axis to the energy per second that would be produced if plane sound waves having the same mean-square sound pressure were arriving simultaneously from all directions with random phase. The frequency or frequency band must be specified.

Directivity Index (Directional Gain). The directivity index of a transducer is an expression of the directivity factor in decibels, viz., 10 times the logarithm to the base 10 of the directivity factor.

Effective Acoustic Center. The effective acoustic center of an acoustic generator is the point from which the spherically divergent sound waves, observable at remote points, appear to diverge.

Effective Bandwidth. The effective bandwidth may be expressed mathematically as follows:

$$\text{Effective bandwidth} = \int_0^\infty G\,df$$

where f is the frequency in cycles per second and G is the ratio of the power transmission at the frequency f, to the transmission at the frequency of maximum transmission.

Electroacoustical Reciprocity Theorem. For an electroacoustic transducer satisfying the reciprocity principle, the quotient of the magnitude of the ratio of the open-circuit voltage at the output terminals (or the short-circuit output current) of the transducer, when used as a sound receiver, to the free-field sound pressure referred to an arbitrarily selected reference point on or near the transducer, divided by the magnitude of the ratio of the sound pressure apparent at a distance d from the reference point to the current flowing at the transducer input terminals (or the voltage applied at the input terminals), when used as a sound emitter, is a constant, called the "reciprocity constant," independent of the type or constructional details of the transducer.

Note: The reciprocity constant is given by

$$\left|\frac{M_0}{S_0}\right| = \left|\frac{M_s}{S_s}\right| = \frac{2d}{\rho f} \times 10^{-7}$$

where M_0 = free-field voltage response as a sound receiver, in open-circuit volts per microbar, referred to the arbitrary reference point on or near the transducer

M_s = free-field current response in short-circuit amperes per microbar, referred to the arbitrary reference point on or near the transducer

S_0 = sound pressure produced at a distance d cm from the arbitrary reference point in microbars per ampere of input current

S_s = sound pressure produced at a distance d cm from the arbitrary reference point in microbars per volt applied at the input terminals

f = frequency in cycles per second

ρ = density of the medium in grams per cubic centimeter

d = distance in centimeters from the arbitrary reference point on or near the transducer to the point at which the sound pressure established by the transducer when emitting is evaluated

Principal Axis. The principal axis of a transducer used for sound emission or reception is a reference direction for angular coordinates used in describing the directional characteristics of the transducer. It is usually an axis of structural symmetry, or the direction of maximum response; but if these do not coincide, the reference direction must be described explicitly.

Relative Response. The relative response is the ratio, usually expressed in decibels, of the response under some particular conditions to the response under reference conditions, which should be stated explicitly.

Response. The response of a device or system is a quantitative expression of the output as a function of the input under conditions which must be explicitly stated. The response characteristic, often presented graphically, gives the response as a function of some independent variable such as frequency or direction.

3a-4. Ultrasonics

Supersonics. Supersonics is the general subject covering phenomena associated with speed higher than the speed of sound (as in case of aircraft and projectiles traveling faster than sound).

Note: This term has been used in acoustics synonymously with "ultrasonics." Such usage is now deprecated.

Ultrasonics. Ultrasonics is the general subject of sound in the frequency range above about 15 kilocycles per second.

Ultrasonic Detector. An ultrasonic detector is a device for the detection and measurement of ultrasonic waves.

Note: Such devices may be mechanical, electrical, thermal, or optical in nature.

Ultrasonic Generator. An ultrasonic generator is a device for the production of sound waves of ultrasonic frequency.

3a-5. Hearing and Speech

Articulation (Per Cent Articulation) and *Intelligibility* (Per Cent Intelligibility). Per cent articulation or per cent intelligibility of a communication system is the percentage of the speech units spoken by a talker or talkers that is understood correctly by a listener or listeners.

The word "articulation" is customarily used when the contextual relations among the units of the speech material are thought to play an unimportant role; the word "intelligibility" is customarily used when the context is thought to play an important role in determining the listener's perception.

Note 1: It is important to specify the type of speech material and the units into which it is analyzed for the purpose of computing the percentage. The units may be fundamental speech sounds, syllables, words, sentences, etc.

Note 2: The per cent articulation or per cent intelligibility is a property of the entire communication system: talker, transmission equipment or medium, and listener. Even when attention is focused upon one component of the system (e.g., a talker, a radio receiver), the other components of the system should be specified.

Audiogram (Threshold Audiogram). An audiogram is a graph showing hearing loss, per cent hearing loss, or per cent hearing as a function of frequency.

Aural Harmonic. An aural harmonic is a harmonic generated in the auditory mechanism.

Average Speech Power. The average speech power for any given time interval is the average value of the instantaneous speech power over that interval.

Difference Limen (Differential Threshold) (Just-noticeable Difference). A difference limen is the increment in a stimulus which is just noticed in a specified fraction of the trials. The relative difference limen is the ratio of the difference limen to the absolute magnitude of the stimulus to which it is related.

Discrete Word (or *Discrete Sentence*) *Intelligibility.* Discrete word intelligibility is the per cent intelligibility obtained when the speech units considered are words (or sentences).

Electrophonic Effect. Electrophonic effect is the sensation of hearing produced when an alternating current of suitable frequency and magnitude from an external source is passed through an animal.

Hearing Loss (Deafness). The hearing loss of an ear at a specified frequency is the ratio, expressed in decibels, of the threshold of audibility for that ear to the normal threshold.[1]

[1] See also American Standard Specification for Audiometers for General Diagnostic Purposes, Z24.5-1951, or the latest revision thereof approved by the ASA.

Hearing Loss for Speech. Hearing loss for speech is the difference in decibels between the speech levels at which the average normal ear and the defective ear, respectively, reach the same intelligibility, often arbitrarily set at 50 per cent.

Instantaneous Speech Power. The instantaneous speech power is the rate at which sound energy is being radiated by a speech source at any given instant.

Loudness. Loudness is the intensive attribute of an auditory sensation, in terms of which sounds may be ordered on a scale extending from soft to loud.

Note: Loudness depends primarily upon the sound pressure of the stimulus, but it also depends upon the frequency and waveform of the stimulus.

Loudness Contours. Loudness contours are curves which show the related values of sound pressure level and frequency required to produce a given loudness sensation for the typical listener.

Loudness Level. The loudness level, in phons, of a sound is numerically equal to the sound pressure level in decibels, relative to 0.0002 μb, of a simple tone of frequency 1,000 cps which is judged by the listeners to be equivalent in loudness.

Masking. Masking is the amount by which the threshold of audibility of a sound is raised by the presence of another (masking) sound. The unit customarily used is the decibel.

Masking Audiogram. A masking audiogram is a graphical presentation of the masking due to a stated noise. This is plotted, in decibels, as a function of the frequency of the masked tone.

Mel. The mel is a unit of pitch. By definition, a simple tone of frequency, 1,000 cps, 40 db above a listener's threshold, produces a pitch of 1,000 mels. The pitch of any sound that is judged by the listener to be n times that of a 1-mel tone is n mels.

Peak Speech Power. The peak speech power is the maximum value of the instantaneous speech power within the time interval considered.

Per Cent Hearing. The per cent hearing at any given frequency is 100 minus the per cent hearing loss at that frequency.

Per Cent Hearing Loss (Per Cent Deafness). The per cent hearing loss at a given frequency is 100 times the ratio of the hearing loss in decibels to the number of decibels between the normal threshold levels of audibility and feeling.

Note 1: A weighted mean of the per cent hearing losses at specified frequencies is often used as a single measure of the loss of hearing.

Note 2: The American Medical Association has defined percentage loss of hearing for medicolegal use.[1]

Phon. The phon is the unit of loudness level. (See definition for Loudness Level.)

Pitch. Pitch is that attribute of auditory sensation in terms of which sounds may be ordered on a scale extending from low to high, such as a musical scale.

Note 1: Pitch depends primarily upon the frequency of the sound stimulus, but it also depends upon the sound pressure and waveform of the stimulus.

Note 2: The pitch of a sound may be described by the frequency of that simple tone, having a specified sound pressure or loudness level, which seems to the average normal ear to produce the same pitch.

Sone. The sone is a unit of loudness. By definition, a simple tone of frequency 1,000 cps, 40 db above a listener's threshold, produces a loudness of 1 sone. The loudness of any sound that is judged by the listener to be n times that of the 1-sone tone is n sones.

Syllable (or *Sound,* or *Vowel,* or *Consonant*) *Articulation.*[2] Syllable (or sound or

[1] See *J. Am. Med. Assoc.* **133**, 396, 397 (Feb. 8, 1947).

[2] See notes above under Articulation and Intelligibility.

vowel or consonant) articulation is the per cent articulation obtained when the speech units considered are syllables (or fundamental sounds, or vowels, or consonants).

Threshold of Audibility (Threshold of Detectability). The threshold of audibility for a specified signal is the minimum effective sound pressure of the signal that is capable of evoking an auditory sensation in a specified fraction of the trials. The characteristics of the signal, the manner in which it is presented to the listener, and the point at which the sound pressure is measured must be specified. The threshold is usually expressed in decibels relative to 0.0002 μb.

Threshold of Feeling (or Discomfort, Tickle, or Pain). The threshold of feeling (or discomfort, tickle, or pain) for a specified signal is the minimum effective sound pressure of that signal which, in a specified fraction of the trials, will stimulate the ear to a point such that there is the sensation of feeling (or discomfort, tickle, or pain). This threshold is customarily expressed in decibels relative to 0.0002 μb.

3a-6. Music

Cent. A cent is the interval between two sounds whose basic frequency ratio is the twelve-hundredth root of 2.

Note: The interval, in cents, between any two frequencies is 1,200 times the logarithm to the base 2 of the frequency ratio. Thus, 1,200 cents = 12 equally tempered semitones = 1 octave.

Complex Tone. (1) A complex tone is a sound wave produced by the combination of simple sinusoidal components of different frequencies. (2) A complex tone is a sound sensation characterized by more than one pitch.

Equally Tempered Scale. An equally tempered scale is a series of notes selected from a division of the octave (usually into 12 equal intervals, see Table 3a-1).

TABLE 3a-1. EQUALLY TEMPERED INTERVALS

Name of interval	Frequency ratio	Cents
Unison	1:1	0
Minor second or semitone	1.059463:1	100
Major second or whole tone	1.122462:1	200
Minor third	1.189207:1	300
Major third	1.259921:1	400
Perfect fourth	1.334840:1	500
Augmented fourth; diminished fifth	1.414214:1	600
Perfect fifth	1.498307:1	700
Minor sixth	1.587401:1	800
Major sixth	1.681793:1	900
Minor seventh	1.781797:1	1,000
Major seventh	1.887749:1	1,100
Octave	2:1	1,200

Fundamental Tone. (1) The funamental tone is the component in a periodic wave corresponding to the fundamental frequency. (2) The fundamental tone is the component tone of lowest pitch in a complex tone.

Harmonic. A harmonic is a partial whose frequency is an integral multiple of the fundamental frequency.

Note: The above definition is in musical terms (for the definition in physical terms, see Sound).

Harmonic Series of Sounds. A harmonic series of sounds is one in which each basic frequency in the series is an integral multiple of a fundamental frequency.

Interval. The interval between two sounds is their spacing in pitch or frequency, whichever is indicated by the context. The frequency interval is expressed by the ratio of the frequencies or by a logarithm of this ratio.

Octave. An octave is the interval between two sounds having a basic frequency ratio of 2. By extension, the octave is the interval between any two frequencies having the ratio 2:1.

Note: The interval, in octaves, between any two frequencies is the logarithm to the base 2 (or 3.322 times the logarithm to the base 10) of the frequency ratio.

Overtone. (1) An overtone is a physical component of a complex sound having a frequency higher than that of the basic frequency (see Partial below). (2) An overtone is a component of a complex tone having a pitch higher than that of the fundamental pitch.

Note: The term "overtone" has frequently been used in place of "harmonic," the nth harmonic being called the (n-1)st overtone. There is, however, ambiguity sometimes in the numbering of components of a complex sound when the word overtone is employed. Moreover, the word "tone" has many different meanings, so that it is preferable to employ terms which do not involve "tone" wherever possible.

Partial. A partial is a physical component of a sound sensation which may be distinguished as a simple tone that cannot be further analyzed by the ear and which contributes to the character of the complex sound.

Note 1: The frequency of a partial may be either higher or lower than the basic frequency and may or may not be an integral multiple or submultiple of the basic frequency (for definition of basic frequency see Basic Frequency). If the frequency is not a multiple or submultiple, the partial is inharmonic.

Note 2: When a system is maintained in steady forced vibration at a basic frequency equal to one of the frequencies of the normal modes of vibration of the system, the partials in the resulting complex tone are not necessarily identical in frequency with those of the other normal modes of vibration.

Scale. A musical scale is a series of notes (symbols, sensations, or stimuli) arranged from low to high by a specified scheme of intervals, suitable for musical purposes.

Semitone (Half Step). A semitone is the interval between two sounds whose basic frequency ratio is approximately equal to the twelfth root of 2.

Note: The interval, in equally tempered semitones, between any two frequencies, is 12 times the logarithm to the base 2 (or 39.86 times the logarithm to the base 10) of the frequency ratio.

Simple Tone (Pure Tone). (1) A simple tone is a sound wave, the instantaneous sound pressure of which is a simple sinusoidal function of the time. (2) A simple tone is a sound sensation characterized by its singleness of pitch.

Standard Pitch. The standard pitch is based on the tone A of 440 cps (see Table 3a-2).

Note 1: With this standard the frequency of middle C is 261.626 cps (see Table 3a-2).

Note 2: Musical instruments are to be capable of complying with this standard when played where the ambient temperature is 22°C (72°F).

Tone. (1) A tone is a sound wave capable of exciting an auditory sensation having pitch. (2) A tone is a sound sensation having pitch.

Whole Tone (Whole Step). A whole tone is the interval between two sounds whose basic frequency ratio is approximately equal to the sixth root of 2.

TABLE 3a-2. FREQUENCIES OF THE TONES OF THE USUAL EQUALLY TEMPERED SCALE, ARRANGED BY CORRESPONDING PIANO-KEY NUMBERS, AND BASED ON THE A OF 440 CPS

Note name	Key No.	Frequency, cps	Key No.	Frequency, cps	Key No.	Frequency, cps	Key No.	Frequency, cps	Key No.	Frequency, cps	Key No.	Frequency, cps	Key No.	Frequency, cps	Key No.	Frequency, cps
A	1	27.500	13	55.000	25	110.000	37	220.000	49	440.000	61	880.000	73	1,760.000	85	3,520.000
A#, B♭	2	29.135	14	58.270	26	116.541	38	233.082	50	466.164	62	932.328	74	1,864.655	86	3,729.310
B	3	30.868	15	61.735	27	123.471	39	246.942	51	493.883	63	987.767	75	1,975.533	87	3,951.066
C	4	32.703	16	65.406	28	130.813	40	261.626	52	523.251	64	1,046.502	76	2,093.005	88	4,186.009
C#, D♭	5	34.648	17	69.296	29	138.591	41	277.183	53	554.365	65	1,108.731	77	2,217.461		
D	6	36.708	18	73.416	30	146.832	42	293.665	54	587.330	66	1,174.659	78	2,349.318		
D#, E♭	7	38.891	19	77.782	31	155.563	43	311.127	55	622.254	67	1,244.508	79	2,489.016		
E	8	41.203	20	82.407	32	164.814	44	329.628	56	659.255	68	1,318.510	80	2,637.021		
F	9	43.654	21	87.307	33	174.614	45	349.228	57	698.456	69	1,396.913	81	2,793.826		
F#, G♭	10	46.249	22	92.499	34	184.997	46	369.994	58	739.989	70	1,479.978	82	2,959.955		
G	11	48.999	23	97.999	35	195.998	47	391.995	59	783.991	71	1,567.982	83	3,135.964		
G#, A♭	12	51.913	24	103.826	36	207.652	48	415.305	60	830.609	72	1,661.219	84	3,322.438		

3a-7. Architectural Acoustics

Anechoic Chamber. An anechoic chamber is a bounded space in which reflected waves are sufficiently weak as to be negligible in the region of interest; more literally, echo-free space.

Attenuation Constant. See Acoustic Attenuation Constant in Sec. 3a-2.

Dead Room. A dead room is a room that subjectively sounds nonreverberant. It is commonly a room having an unusually large amount of sound absorption.

Decay Constant. The decay constant is the exponential power by which sound decays after the source is stopped (units $\sec^{-1}$).

Note: If p_0 is the effective sound pressure at $t = 0$, $p(t)$ is the effective sound pressure at time t, and the two are related by

$$p(t) = p_0 e^{-kt}$$

then k is the decay constant.

Direct Sound Wave. A direct sound wave in an enclosure is a wave emitted from a source prior to the time it has undergone its first reflection from a boundary of the enclosure.

Note: Frequently, a sound wave is said to be direct if it contains reflections that have occurred from surfaces within about 0.05 sec after the sound was first emitted.

Live Room. A live room is a room that subjectively sounds reverberant. It is commonly a room having an unusually small amount of sound absorption.

Mean Free Path. The mean free path for sound waves in an enclosure is the average distance sound travels between successive reflections in the enclosure.

Noise Reduction. In architectural acoustics, noise reduction generally is the difference between the effective sound pressure levels (in decibels) between the noise fields on opposite sides of a noise-reducing panel, with all sources of sound being on one side of the panel.

Reverberant Sound. Reverberant sound is that part of the sound in an enclosure that has undergone one or more reflections from the boundaries of the enclosure.

Reverberation Chamber. A reverberation chamber is an enclosure in which all the surfaces have been made as sound-reflective as possible. Reverberation chambers are used for certain acoustical measurements.

Room Constant. The room constant is given by the formula

$$R = \frac{S\bar{\alpha}}{1 - \bar{\alpha}}$$

where $\bar{\alpha}$ is the average sound-absorption coefficient and S is the total area of the boundaries of the room.

Sabin (Square Foot Unit of Absorption). A sabin is a measure of the sound absorption of a surface. It is the equivalent of 1 square foot of a perfectly absorptive surface.

Sound (Energy) *Absorption Coefficient.* (1) At a particular angle of wave incident, the sound-absorption coefficient is the ratio of the sound energy absorbed by the surface to the energy in the plane wave incident upon it. (2) For random wave incidence, the sound-absorption coefficient is the ratio of the sound energy absorbed by the surface to the energy incident upon it from a sound field in which sound waves are striking the surface equally from all angles of incidence. (3) The average sound-absorption coefficient for a room is the weighted average of the random-incidence absorption coefficients computed from the formula

$$\bar{\alpha} = \frac{S_1\alpha_1 + S_2\alpha_2 + S_3\alpha_3 + \cdots + S_n\alpha_n}{S_1 + S_2 + S_3 + \cdots + S_n}$$

where S_1, S_2, S_3, . . . are areas of particular surfaces in the room; α_1, α_2, α_3, . . . are the random-incidence absorption coefficients associated, respectively, with those areas; and $\bar{\alpha}$ is the average sound-absorption coefficient for the room.

Transmission Loss. In architectural acoustics, transmission loss for a wall or panel is 10 times the logarithm to the base 10 of the ratio of the sound energy incident upon the wall or panel to the sound energy transmitted through it. The transmission loss is generally measured under conditions of randomly incident sound waves. The unit is the decibel.

3b. Letter Symbols and Conversion Factors for Acoustical Quantities

LEO L. BERANEK

Bolt Beranek and Newman, Inc.

T	absolute temperature, degrees Kelvin
a	absorption, energy, acoustic, total in a room
α	absorption coefficient, energy
$\bar{\alpha}$	absorption coefficient, energy, average
Y_A	acoustic admittance
C_A	acoustic compliance
G_A	acoustic conductance
x_A	acoustic excitability
y_A	acoustic immobility
Z_A	acoustic impedance (complex)
M_A	acoustic mass (inertance)
z_A	acoustic mobility
W_A, P_A	acoustic power
X_A	acoustic reactance
R_A	acoustic resistance
r_A	acoustic responsiveness
B_A	acoustic susceptance
b_A	acoustic unexcitability
g_A	acoustic unresponsiveness
Y_A	admittance, acoustic
Y_E, Y	admittance, electric
Y_M	admittance, mechanical
Y_R	admittance, rotational
Y_S	admittance, specific acoustic
A, Φ	amplitude of velocity potential
Ω	angle, solid
ϕ	angular displacement
ω	angular velocity ($2\pi f$)

f_A	antiresonant frequency
S	area (diaphragm, tube, room, or radiator)
P_0, p_0	atmospheric pressure
α	attenuation constant
$\bar{\alpha}$	average absorption coefficient, energy
C_E	capacitance, electrical
$\rho_0 c$	characteristic impedance
Q, q	charge, electric
α	coefficient of absorption
C_A	compliance, acoustic
C_S	compliance, specific acoustic
C_M	compliance, mechanical
C_R	compliance, rotational
$\xi, \eta, \zeta; \xi_x, \xi_y, \xi_z$	components of the particle displacement in the x, y, z directions
$u, v, w; u_x, u_y, u_z$	components of the particle velocity in x, y, z directions
s	condensation
G_A	conductance, acoustic
G_E, G	conductance, electric
G_M	conductance, mechanical
G_R	conductance, rotational
G_S	conductance, specific acoustic
κ	conductivity, thermal
I, i	current, electric
U	current, volume (volume per second) (volume velocity)
λ, k, δ	decay constant
D, E	density, energy
ρ	density of the medium (instantaneous)
ρ_0	density of the medium (static)
ϵ	dielectric coefficient
Δ	dilatation
D_i, DI	directivity index
R_θ	directivity ratio
ϕ	displacement, angular
ξ_x, x	displacement, linear
ξ	displacement, particle
X	displacement, volume
r	distance from source
s, x_1	distance, linear
μ	elasticity, shear
Y_E, Y	electric admittance
C_E, C	electric capacitance
Q, q	electric charge
G_E, G	electric conductance
I, i	electric current
Z_E, Z	electric impedance (complex)
P_E, W_E, P, W	electric power
X_E, X	electric reactance
R_E, R	electric resistance
ρ	electric resistivity
B_E, B	electric susceptance

E, e	electromotive force, voltage
E	energy
D, E	energy density
T, E_K	energy, kinetic
V, E_p	energy potential
x_A	excitability, acoustic
x_M	excitability, mechanical
x_R	excitability, rotational
x_S	excitability, specific acoustic
H	field strength, magnetic
m	flare coefficient in a horn
B	flux density, magnetic
Φ	flux, magnetic
f_M, F	force
f	frequency
y_A	immobility, acoustic
y_M	immobility, mechanical
y_R	immobility, rotational
y_S	immobility, specific acoustic
Z_A	impedance, acoustic (complex)
$\rho_0 c$	impedance, characteristic
Z_E, Z	impedance, electric (complex)
Z_M	impedance, mechanical (complex)
Z_R	impedance, rotational (complex)
Z_S	impedance, specific acoustic (complex)
n	index of refraction
L	inductance
M_A	inertance, acoustic mass
I	inertia, moment of
I	intensity
L_I, IL	intensity level, decibels
ν	kinematic viscosity
T, E_K	kinetic energy (inductive energy)
σ	leakage coefficient, magnetic
l	length of a vibrating string, pipe, or rod
L	level in decibels, general
x, ξ	linear displacement
s, x_1	linear distance
L, N	loudness, sones
L_N, LL	loudness level, decibels or phons
H	magnetic field strength
Φ	magnetic flux
B	magnetic flux density
σ	magnetic leakage coefficient
$\mathfrak{F}$	magnetomotive force
K, Δ	magnetostriction constant
m, M_M	mass
M_A	mass, acoustic
M_S	mass, specific acoustic

Y_M	mechanical admittance
C_M	mechanical compliance
G_M	mechanical conductance
x_M	mechanical excitability
y_M	mechanical immobility
Z_M	mechanical impedance (complex)
z_M	mechanical mobility
W_M, P_M	mechanical power
X_M	mechanical reactance
R_M	mechanical resistance
r_M	mechanical responsiveness
B_M	mechanical susceptance
b_M	mechanical unexcitability
g_M	mechanical unresponsiveness
z_A	mobility, acoustic
z_M	mobility, mechanical
z_R	mobility, rotational
z_S	mobility, specific acoustic
Y, E	modulus of elasticity
I	moment of inertia
L_{NR}, NR	noise reduction, decibels
N	number of turns
ξ	particle displacement
$\xi, \eta, \zeta; \xi_x, \xi_y, \xi_z$	particle-displacement components in the x, y, z directions
u_a	particle velocity (average)
$u, v, w; u_x, u_y, u_z$	particle-velocity components in the x, y, z directions
u_i	particle velocity (instantaneous)
u_m	particle velocity (maximum)[1]
u_p	particle velocity (peak)[1]
u	particle velocity (rms)
P	perimeter
T	period $T = 1/f$
θ, ϕ, ψ	phase angle
β	phase constant
f_{ij}, g_{ij}, d_{ij}	piezoelectric constants
σ	Poisson's ratio
Y, P	porosity (of an acoustical material)
V, E_p	potential energy (capacitive energy)
ϕ	potential, velocity
A, Φ	potential, velocity, amplitude
W, P	power
W_A, P_A	power, acoustic
W_E, P_E, P, E	power, electric
W_M, P_M	power, mechanical
W_R, P_R	power, rotational
P_0, p_0	pressure, atmospheric
p_a	pressure, sound (average)
p	pressure, sound (rms)
p_i	pressure, sound (instantaneous)

[1] For definitions of "peak" and "maximum" see American Standard Acoustical Terminology (ASA Z24.1-1951).

p_m	pressure, sound (maximum)[1]
p_p	pressure, sound (peak)[1]
γ, Γ	propagation constant
a	radius of a diaphragm, tube, or radiator
Q	ratio of mass (or inductive) reactance to resistance
γ	ratio of specific heats
X_A	reactance, acoustic
X_E, X	reactance, electric
X_M	reactance, mechanical
X_R	reactance, rotational
X_S	reactance, specific acoustic
n	refraction, index of
τ	relaxation time
$\mathcal{R}$	reluctance
R_A	resistance, acoustic
R_E, R	resistance, electric
R_M	resistance, mechanical
R_R	resistance, rotational
R_S	resistance, specific acoustic
ρ	resistivity, electrical
r_A	responsiveness, acoustic
r_M	responsiveness, mechanical
r_R	responsiveness, rotational
r_S	responsiveness, specific acoustic
T, t_{60}	reverberation time
R	room constant $\bar{a}S/(1 - \bar{a})$
Y_R	rotational admittance
C_R	rotational compliance
G_R	rotational conductance
x_R	rotational excitability
y_R	rotational immobility
Z_R	rotational impedance (complex)
z_R	rotational mobility
W_R, P_R	rotational power
X_R	rotational reactance
R_R	rotational resistance
r_R	rotational responsiveness
B_R	rotational susceptance
b_R	rotational unexcitability
g_R	rotational unresponsiveness
L_S, SL	sensation level, decibels
μ	shear elasticity
A, U_0	simple source strength
Ω	solid angle
L_W, PWL	sound power level, decibels
p_a	sound pressure (average)
p_i	sound pressure (instantaneous)
p_M	sound pressure (maximum)[1]
p_p	sound pressure (peak)[1]

[1] For definitions of "peak" and "maximum" see American Standard Acoustical Terminology (ASA Z24.1-1951).

p	sound pressure (rms)
L_P, SPL	sound pressure level, decibels
A, U_0	source, simple, strength of
r	source, distance from
Y_S	specific acoustic admittance
C_S	specific acoustic compliance
G_S	specific acoustic conductance
x_S	specific acoustic excitability
y_S	specific acoustic immobility
M_S	specific acoustic mass
z_S	specific acoustic mobility
X_S	specific acoustic reactance
R_S	specific acoustic resistance
r_S	specific acoustic responsiveness
B_S	specific acoustic susceptance
b_S	specific acoustic unexcitability
g_S	specific acoustic unresponsiveness
γ	specific heats, ratio of
c	speed of sound
s, S	stiffness
A, U_0	strength of a simple source
B_A	susceptance, acoustic
B_E, B	susceptance, electric
B_M	susceptance, mechanical
B_R	susceptance, rotational
B_S	susceptance, specific acoustic
G_x	system-rating constant
T	temperature, absolute, degrees Kelvin
F	tension (force) in a membrane or string
κ	thermal conductivity
t	thickness
t	time
τ	time, relaxation
T, t_{60}	time, reverberation
f_R, T	torque
a	total acoustical (energy) absorption in a room
τ	transmission coefficient, energy, barriers
L_T, TL	transmission loss of building structures, decibels
N	turns, number of
b_A	unexcitability, acoustic
b_M	unexcitability, mechanical
b_R	unexcitability, rotational
b_S	unexcitability, specific acoustic
g_A	unresponsiveness, acoustic
g_M	unresponsiveness, mechanical
g_R	unresponsiveness, rotational
g_S	unresponsiveness, specific acoustic
u	velocity
ω	velocity, angular ($2\pi f$)
c	velocity of sound
u_a	velocity, particle (average)

u_i	velocity, particle (instantaneous)
u_m	velocity, particle (maximum)[1]
u_p	velocity, particle (peak)[1]
u	velocity, particle (rms)
ϕ	velocity potential
A, Φ	velocity potential amplitude
U	velocity, volume
η	viscosity, dissipative or frictional
ν	viscosity, kinematic
E, e	voltage, electromotive force
V	volume
U	volume current; volume velocity
X	volume displacement
U	volume velocity; volume current
λ	wavelength
k	wave number, $\frac{\omega}{c} = \frac{2\pi f}{c} = \frac{2\pi}{\lambda}$
w	width
Y, E	Young's modulus

Table 3b-1. Conversion Factors for Acoustical Quantities

Multiply the number of	By	To obtain the number of	Conversely multiply by
Acoustic ohms	10^5	Mks acoustic ohms	10^{-5}
Atmospheres	406.80	Inches of water at 4°C	2.458×10^{-3}
Centimeters	10^{-2}	Meters	10^2
Cubic centimeters	10^{-6}	Cubic meters	10^6
Dynes	10^{-5}	Newtons	10^5
Dynes/cm²	10^{-1}	Newtons per square meter	10
Ergs	10^{-7}	Joules	10^7
Ergs per second	10^{-7}	Watts	10^7
Ergs per second/cm²	10^{-3}	Watts per square meter	10^3
Gauss	10^{-4}	Webers per square meter	10^4
Kilograms	10^3	Grams	10^{-3}
Mechanical ohms	10^{-3}	Mks mechanical ohms	10^3
Meters	10^2	Centimeters	10^{-2}
Microbars	10^{-1}	Newtons per square meter	10
Newtons	10^5	Dynes	10^{-5}
Newtons per square meter	10	Dynes per square centimeter	10^{-1}
Pounds per square foot	0.4882	Grams per square centimeter	2.0481
Rayls	10	Mks rayls	10^{-1}
Watts per square meter	10^{-4}	Watts per square centimeter	10^4
Webers per square centimeter	10^4	Gauss	10^{-4}

[1] For definitions of "peak" and "maximum" see American Standard Acoustical Terminology (ASA Z24.1-1951).

3c. Propagation of Sound in Fluids

FREDERICK V. HUNT
Harvard University

3c-1. Glossary of Symbols[1]

$a, a_1; a_i$	material coordinate (31); surface element (12)
A; $\mathbf{A}_1$	surface (12), attenuation per wavelength (76), Avogadro's number (95); first order vector potential
B	coefficient relating $\nabla\rho$ and ∇p (58)
$c, c_0; c^0, c^\infty$	speed of sound, reference speed (25); low- and high-frequency limit speeds (84)
c'	speed of thermal wave (78*b*)
C_p, C_v	specific heats at constant pressure, constant volume (14)
d_{ij}	rate of deformation tensor (9)
D	material differential operator (2)
E, F, G, H	algebraic abbreviations (74)
$E, E_k, E_I; E_{\text{diss}}$	energy densities per unit mass (60), (12); degraded component of internal energy (66)
f, $\mathbf{f}_v$, $f(\ )$, $f(h)$	frequency, sum of viscosity terms (62), "function of" (45), special tabulated function (75)
Δf_c	critical bandwidth (98)
F_i, $\mathbf{F}$	vector body force per unit mass (6)
$g(h)$	tabulated function (75)
h	material mass coordinate (37), argument of tabulated function (75), Planck's constant (89)
i, j, k	coordinate indexes (1)
$\mathbf{I}$	average sound-energy-flux density = sound intensity (64)
j	designation of imaginary axis, $[e^{+j\omega t}]$ (69)
$\mathbf{J}$	sound-energy flux vector (54)
k, k_0	phase constant $= \omega/c = 2\pi/\lambda$, Boltzmann's constant (89), $k_0 = \omega/c_0 = 2\pi/\lambda_0$ (47)
$K; K_s, K_0, K_T$	elastic modulus $= -V(DP/DV)$ (25), material constant $= c^0/c^\infty$ (84); isentropic modulus, reference modulus, isothermal modulus
L	mean free path (86), a sum of linear dimensions (90)
M	peak particle-velocity Mach number $= \omega\xi_0/c_0$ (49), molecular weight (95)
n_v	total number of molecules per unit volume (95)
N	number of modes of vibration (90)
$0(\ )$	additive terms of indicated order of magnitude (76)

[1] Numbers indicate equation number in or near which quantity is defined.

$p;\ p_1,\ p_2$	incremental, or sound, pressure; first- and second-order sound pressures (25)
$P,\ P_0;\ P_m,\ P_{\text{th}}$	total pressure (7), equilibrium or reference pressure (25); mean pressure (7), thermodynamic pressure (14)
$P_1,\ P_2;\ \mathcal{P}$	rms fundamental and second-harmonic pressure (49*a*); Prandtl number (72)
$\mathbf{q},\ q_i;\ \mathfrak{q}$	heat flux vector (12); Stokes radiation coefficient (21*b*)
$q;\ q^E,\ q^L$	exemplar of state or condition variable (39); superscript indicates function of spatial (*E*) variables, or material (*L*) variables (32*b*)
$\mathbf{R},\ R;\ R_1,\ R_2$	vorticity $= \frac{1}{2}\nabla \times \mathbf{u}$ (11*d*), real part of complex impedance; first- and second-order components of vorticity (57)
$s,\ s_1$	specific entropy per unit mass (14), first-order condensation $= \rho_1/\rho_0$ (59)
$S;\ S';\ S_{\text{irr}}$	Stokes number $= \omega\eta/\rho_0 c_0^2$ (72), total interior surface (90); frequency number for radiation $= \omega/\mathfrak{q}$ (72); entropy generated irreversibly (15*a*)
$t;\ t_{ij}$	time (2); stress tensor (6)
T	absolute temperature (12)
$\mathbf{u},\ u_1;\ u_1,\ u_2,\ u_3$	particle velocity (1); velocity components
$\mathbf{u}_1,\ \mathbf{u}_2$	first- and second-order components of particle velocity (25)
$v;\ \bar{v}$	specific volume $= \rho^{-1}$ (1); mean molecular velocity (86)
$\mathcal{V}$	viscosity number $= 2 + \eta'/\eta$ (10)
$V;\ V_{ij}$	volume (1); residual stress tensor (7)
$x_1,\ x_2,\ x_3$	cartesian coordinates (1)
$X;\ X'$	frequency number $= \omega\eta\mathcal{V}/\rho_0 c_0^2$ (72), specific acoustic reactance (69); frequency number for relaxation (84)
Y	thermoviscous number $= \kappa/\eta\mathcal{V}C_p$ (72)
$z,\ Z$	specific acoustic impedance ratio (87), and impedance (69)
$\alpha;\ \alpha_K,\ \alpha_C$	attenuation constant (69); "Kirchhoff" and "classical" attenuation (79*a,b*)
$\beta;\ \beta_{\text{noise}}$	coefficient of thermal expansion $= \rho(\partial v/\partial T)_P$ (22); spectrum level $= 10 \log_{10} d(p^2/p_0^2)/df$ (98)
γ	ratio of specific heats $= C_p/C_v$ (14)
$\delta;\ \delta_{ij};\ \Delta$	finite increment (32); Kronecker delta (7); dilatation rate $= \nabla \cdot \mathbf{u}$ (4)
ϵ	specific internal energy per unit mass (13)
$\eta,\ \eta',\ \eta_B$	coefficient of shear viscosity (10), "second" or dilatational viscosity (10), bulk viscosity (10)
$\theta_1,\ \theta_2$	first- and second-order variational components of temperature (25)
κ	thermal conductivity (21*a*)
$\lambda;\ \lambda_0$	wavelength $= c/f$ (47); $\lambda_0 = c_0/f$
$\nu,\ \nu',\ \nu_B$	kinematic viscosity coefficients (10) $= \eta/\rho$, etc.
$\xi;\ \xi_t$	displacement of particle from equilibrium (31); partial derivative with respect to subscript variable (41*b*)
$\rho,\ \rho_0;\ \rho_1,\ \rho_2$	densities: total, equilibrium; first- and second-order variational components
$\tau_r,\ \tau_v,\ \tau_k$	relaxation times (83, 85)
$\varphi_2;\ \phi_\eta,\ \phi_k$	scalar velocity potential (55); viscous and thermal dissipation functions (16, 18)
χ	complex propagation constant $= \alpha + jk$ (69)
ψ	functional relation (71)
$\omega;\ \omega_r,\ \omega_v,\ \omega_k$	angular frequency $= 2\pi f$; relaxation angular frequencies (84)
$\nabla,\ \nabla\cdot,\ \nabla\times$	gradient, divergence, and curl operators
$\langle\ \rangle$	time average

3c-2. The Motion of Viscous Fluids. The motions of a fluid medium that comprise sound waves are governed by equations that include (1) a continuity equation expressing the conservation of mass, (2) a force equation expressing the conservation of momentum, (3) a heat-exchange equation expressing the conservation of energy, and (4) one or more defining equations expressing the constitutive relations that characterize the medium and its response to thermal or mechanical stress. These equations will first be presented in their complete exact form in order to provide a rigorous point of departure for the approximations that must ultimately be made in formulating the linearized, or small-signal, acoustic equations.

The transformation properties of these equations can be indicated by writing them in either vectorial or tensorial form, and both forms will be exhibited in order to facilitate contacts with the rich literature dealing with the motion of fluids.[1]

Cartesian spatial coordinates will be designated x_1, x_2, x_3, and the vector velocity of a material particle will be identified as $\mathbf{u}$ with components u_1, u_2, u_3. These will also be written as x_i and u_i, where it is implied that the subscript i, j, or k takes on successively the values 1, 2, 3. The term "material particle" denotes a finite mass element of the medium small enough for the values assumed by the state variables at every interior point of the particle not to differ significantly from the values they have at the interior reference point whose coordinates "locate" the particle.

Equation of Continuity. The conservation of mass requires that $\rho V = \rho_0 V_0$, where ρ_0 and V_0 are initial and ρ and V are subsequent values assumed by the density and volume of a particular material element of the medium. It follows that

$$\rho DV + V D\rho = 0 \qquad \frac{DV}{V} = -\frac{D\rho}{\rho} \tag{3c-1}$$

If $\rho_0 V_0$ is set equal to 1, V_0 becomes the *specific volume*, $v \equiv 1/\rho$; whence the relation between the total logarithmic time derivatives of v and ρ is

$$\frac{1}{v}\frac{Dv}{Dt} = -\frac{1}{\rho}\frac{D\rho}{Dt} = \frac{D \log v}{Dt} = -\frac{D \log \rho}{Dt} \tag{3c-2}$$

where $D(\ )/Dt$ denotes the "material" derivative, i.e., one that follows the motion of a material "particle" of the medium relative to a fixed spatial coordinate system, and is defined by

$$\frac{D(\ )}{Dt} \equiv \frac{\partial(\ )}{\partial t} + \mathbf{u} \cdot \mathbf{grad}\,(\ ) \equiv \frac{\partial(\ )}{\partial t} + u_i \frac{\partial(\ )}{\partial x_i} \tag{3c-3}$$

Analysis of the rate of deformation of a volume element yields the kinematical relation

$$\frac{1}{v}\frac{Dv}{Dt} = \operatorname{div} \mathbf{u} \equiv \Delta = \frac{\partial u_i}{\partial x_i} \tag{3c-4}$$

where Δ is the *dilatation rate.* Note that in the last terms of (3c-3) and (3c-4) summation is implied over all the allowable values of the subscript index. Equations (3c-2), (3c-3), and (3c-4) can be combined to yield the following equivalent forms of Euler's *continuity equation:*

[1] A definitive restatement of the classical-continuum point of view, with critical comments on more than 800 bibliographical references, has been given by C. Truesdell, The Mechanical Foundations of Elasticity and Fluid Dynamics, *J. Rational Mechanics and Analysis* **1,** 125–300 (January and April, 1952), and Corrections and Additions . . . , *J. Rational Mechanics and Analysis* **2,** 593–616 (July, 1953). See also Lamb, "Hydrodynamics," 6th ed., Dover Publications, New York, 1945; Rayleigh, "Theory of Sound," 2d ed. rev., Dover Publications, New York, 1945; and L. Howarth, ed., "Modern Developments in Fluid Dynamics, vol. I, chap. III, Oxford University Press, New York, 1953.

$$\frac{D\rho}{Dt} + \rho \frac{\partial u_i}{\partial x_i} = \frac{\partial \rho}{\partial t} + u_i \frac{\partial \rho}{\partial x_i} + \rho \frac{\partial u_i}{\partial x_i} = \frac{D\rho}{Dt} + \rho \operatorname{div} \mathbf{u} = 0$$

$$= \frac{1}{\rho}\frac{D\rho}{Dt} + \Delta = \frac{\partial \rho}{\partial t} + \mathbf{u} \cdot \mathbf{grad}\, \rho + \rho \operatorname{div} \mathbf{u}$$

$$= \frac{\partial \rho}{\partial t} + \mathbf{u} \cdot \nabla \rho + \rho \nabla \cdot \mathbf{u} = \frac{\partial \rho}{\partial t} + \nabla \cdot (\rho \mathbf{u}) \qquad \text{(3c-5)}$$

In the last line of (3c-5), the Gibbs-Hamilton notation has been used for the differential vector operators, $\nabla \equiv$ **grad**; $\nabla \cdot \equiv$ **div**; $\nabla \times \equiv$ **curl**.

Force Equation. The linear-momentum principle can be stated in terms of Cauchy's first law of motion,

$$\rho \frac{Du_i}{Dt} = \rho F_i + \frac{\partial t_{ij}}{\partial x_j} \qquad \text{(3c-6)}$$

where the vector F_i is an extraneous body force per unit mass, and where t_{ij} is a second-rank *stress tensor* that represents the net mechanical action of contiguous material on a volume element of the medium due to the actual forces of material continuity. For an isotropic medium in which the stress is a linear function of the rate of deformation, as here assumed, the stress tensor can be resolved arbitrarily as the sum of a scalar, or hydrostatic, pressure function P and a residual stress tensor V_{ij} defined by

$$t_{ij} = -P\delta_{ij} + V_{ij} \qquad t_{ij} = t_{ji} \qquad \text{(3c-7)}$$

where δ_{ij} is the Kronecker delta which equals unity if $i = j$, but is zero otherwise. Unless V_{ii} vanishes, P is *not* identical with the mean pressure, $P_m = -\frac{1}{3}t_{ii}$. The resolution given by (3c-7) is both unique and useful, however, if P is made equal to the thermodynamic pressure P_{th} defined below. Then the residual stress tensor is given, to a first approximation, by the linear terms of an expansion in powers of the viscosity coefficients;

$$V_{ij} = \eta' d_{kk}\delta_{ij} + 2\eta d_{ij} \qquad V_{ij} = V_{ji} \qquad \text{(3c-8)}$$

in which d_{ij} is the *rate of deformation* tensor defined by

$$d_{ij} = \frac{1}{2}\left(\frac{\partial u_i}{\partial x_j} + \frac{\partial u_j}{\partial x_i}\right) \qquad \text{(3c-9)}$$

and where η is the "first," or conventional shear, viscosity coefficient. In accordance with current proposals for standardization, η' replaces λ, the symbol used by Stokes, Rayleigh, Lamb, et al., to designate the "second," or dilatational, viscosity coefficient. The term "bulk" viscosity is reserved for $(\lambda + \frac{2}{3}\mu) \rightarrow (\eta' + \frac{2}{3}\eta)$, the linear combination of coefficients that vanishes when the *Stokes relation* holds. Thus, $\eta \equiv$ first, or shear, viscosity; $\eta' \equiv$ second, or dilatational, viscosity; $\eta_B \equiv \eta' + \frac{2}{3}\eta =$ bulk viscosity; $\nu \equiv \eta/\rho$; $\nu' \equiv \eta'/\rho$; $\nu_B \equiv \eta_B/\rho$ (kinematic viscosities);

$$(\lambda + 2\mu) \rightarrow \eta' + 2\eta = \eta_B + \frac{4}{3}\eta = \eta\left(\frac{4}{3} + \frac{\eta_B}{\eta}\right) = \eta\mathcal{V} \qquad \text{(3c-10)}$$

$$\mathcal{V} \equiv \frac{4}{3} + \frac{\eta_B}{\eta} = 2 + \frac{\eta'}{\eta} \equiv \text{viscosity number}$$

Putting (3c-7), (3c-8), (3c-9) into (3c-6) yields the vector *force equation* in the following equivalent forms:

$$\rho \frac{\partial u_i}{\partial t} + \rho u_j \frac{\partial u_i}{\partial x_j} = \rho F_i - \frac{\partial P}{\partial x_i} + \frac{\partial}{\partial x_j}(\eta' d_{kk}\delta_{ij} + 2\eta d_{ij})$$

$$= \rho F_i - \frac{\partial P}{\partial x_i} + \eta' \frac{\partial^2 u_k}{\partial x_i \partial x_k} + \eta \frac{\partial}{\partial x_j}\left(\frac{\partial u_i}{\partial x_j} + \frac{\partial u_j}{\partial x_i}\right)$$

$$+ \frac{\partial u_k}{\partial x_k}\frac{\partial \eta'}{\partial x_i} + \frac{\partial u_i}{\partial x_j}\frac{\partial \eta}{\partial x_j} + \frac{\partial u_j}{\partial x_i}\frac{\partial \eta}{\partial x_j} \qquad \text{(3c-11a)}$$

$$\rho \frac{D\mathbf{u}}{Dt} = \rho\mathbf{F} - \mathbf{grad}\, P + (\eta' + \eta)\, \mathbf{grad}\, (\mathrm{div}\, \mathbf{u}) + \eta\nabla^2(\mathbf{u})$$
$$+ (\mathrm{div}\, \mathbf{u})\, \mathbf{grad}\, \eta' + 2\, (\mathbf{grad}\, \eta \cdot \mathbf{grad})\, \mathbf{u} + \mathbf{grad}\, \eta \times \mathbf{curl}\, \mathbf{u} \qquad (3c\text{-}11b)$$

$$\rho \frac{\partial \mathbf{u}}{\partial t} = \rho\mathbf{F} - \rho(\mathbf{u} \cdot \nabla)\mathbf{u} - \nabla P + (\eta' + 2\eta)\nabla(\nabla \cdot \mathbf{u}) - \eta\nabla \times (\nabla \times \mathbf{u})$$
$$+ (\nabla \cdot \mathbf{u})\nabla\eta' + 2(\nabla\eta \cdot \nabla)\mathbf{u} + \nabla\eta \times (\nabla \times \mathbf{u}) \qquad (3c\text{-}11c)$$

The vorticity, defined by $\mathbf{R} = \frac{1}{2}\, \mathbf{curl}\, \mathbf{u} = \frac{1}{2}(\nabla \times \mathbf{u})$, and the dilatation rate, $\Delta \equiv \nabla \cdot \mathbf{u}$, can be introduced as useful abbreviations. A somewhat more symmetrical expression in terms of the mass transport velocity $\rho\mathbf{u}$ is obtained if the last form of the continuity equation (3c-5) is multiplied by $\mathbf{u}$ and added to (3c-11c), giving

$$\frac{\partial(\rho\mathbf{u})}{\partial t} + \mathbf{u}(\nabla \cdot \rho\mathbf{u}) + (\rho\mathbf{u} \cdot \nabla)\mathbf{u} = \rho\mathbf{F} - \nabla P + \eta\mathcal{V}\nabla\Delta - 2\eta\nabla \times \mathbf{R} + \Delta\nabla\eta'$$
$$+ 2(\nabla\eta \cdot \nabla)\mathbf{u} + 2\nabla\eta \times \mathbf{R} \qquad (3c\text{-}11d)$$

These equations reduce to the so-called *Navier-Stokes equations* when it is assumed that η and η' are constant ($\nabla\eta = \nabla\eta' = 0$) and that the Stokes relation holds ($\eta_B = 0$, $\mathcal{V} = \frac{4}{3}$); and still further simplification follows if the motion is assumed irrotational so that $\mathbf{R} = 0$. If the viscosity coefficients are to be regarded as functions of one or more of the state variables, however, the gradients of the η's must be retained so that the implicit functional dependence can be introduced by writing, for example, $\nabla\eta = (\partial\eta/\partial T)\nabla T + \cdots$.

Energy Relations and Equations of State. The conservation of energy requires that the following power equation be satisfied:

$$\frac{D(E_k + E_I)}{Dt} = \int_V \rho F_i u_i\, dV + \int_A t_{ij} u_j\, da_i - \int_A q_i\, da_i \qquad (3c\text{-}12)$$

where E_k is the kinetic energy associated with the material velocity, E_I is the total internal energy, V is a volume bounded by the surface A, da_i is the projection of a surface element of A on the plane normal to the $+x_i$ axis, F_i is the extraneous body force (per unit mass), and q_i is the total heat flux vector (mechanical units). After the surface integrals are converted to volume integrals by using the divergence theorem, and with the help of (3c-6), this equation reduces to the Fourier–Kirchhoff–C. Neumann[1] energy equation,

$$\rho \frac{D\epsilon}{Dt} = t_{ij} d_{ij} - \frac{\partial q_i}{\partial x_i} \qquad (3c\text{-}13)$$

where ϵ is the local value of the specific internal energy (per unit mass) defined through $E_I = \int_V \rho\epsilon\, dV$. It is now postulated that the state of the fluid is completely specified by ϵ and two other local state variables, which can be taken as the specific entropy s (per unit mass) and the specific volume $v = \rho^{-1}$, in terms of which the thermodynamic pressure and temperature, and the specific heats can be defined by

$$\epsilon = \epsilon(s,v) \qquad P_{\mathrm{th}} \equiv -\left(\frac{\partial\epsilon}{\partial v}\right)_s \qquad T \equiv \left(\frac{\partial\epsilon}{\partial s}\right)_v$$
$$C_p \equiv T\left(\frac{\partial s}{\partial T}\right)_p \qquad C_v \equiv T\left(\frac{\partial s}{\partial T}\right)_v \qquad \gamma \equiv \frac{C_p}{C_v} \qquad (3c\text{-}14)$$

The second law of thermodynamics can be introduced in the form of an equality, which replaces the classical Clausius-Duhem inequality, through the expedient of accounting explicitly for the creation of entropy S_{irr} (per unit volume) by irreversible

[1] See footnote, p. 3–27.

dissipative processes;[1] thus

$$\frac{D}{Dt}\int_V \rho s\, dV = -\int_A \frac{q_i}{T}\, da_i + \int_V \frac{DS_{\text{irr}}}{Dt} dV \tag{3c-15a}$$

This relation states that the increase of entropy in a material element is accounted for by the influx of heat and by the irreversible production of entropy within the element. The left-hand side of (3c-15a) can also be written, with the help of the continuity relation, as $\int_V \rho(Ds/Dt)\, dV$. Then, after converting the surface integral to a volume integral, the second law can be given in differential form as

$$\begin{aligned} \rho \frac{Ds}{Dt} &= -\frac{\partial}{\partial x_i}\frac{q_i}{T} + \frac{DS_{\text{irr}}}{Dt} \\ &= -\frac{1}{T}\frac{\partial q_i}{\partial x_i} + \frac{q_i}{T^2}\frac{\partial T}{\partial x_i} + \frac{DS_{\text{irr}}}{Dt} \end{aligned} \tag{3c-15b}$$

A thermal-dissipation function ϕ_k can be defined by

$$\phi_\kappa = -\frac{q_i}{T}\frac{\partial T}{\partial x_i} \tag{3c-16}$$

whereupon multiplying (3c-15b) by T yields the second-law equality in the form

$$\rho T \frac{Ds}{Dt} = -\frac{\partial q_i}{\partial x_i} - \phi_\kappa + T\frac{DS_{\text{irr}}}{Dt} \tag{3c-15c}$$

Taking the material derivative of the basic equation of state (3c-14$_1$) (where the subscript added to an equation number indicates the serial number of the equality sign to which reference is made when several relations are grouped under one marginal identification number), introducing the definitions for P_{th} and T, multiplying by ρ, and using (3c-4), gives

$$\rho T \frac{Ds}{Dt} = \rho \frac{D\epsilon}{Dt} + P_{\text{th}}\Delta \tag{3c-17}$$

The energy equation (3c-13) can be recast, using (3c-7) and (3c-9), in the form

$$\rho \frac{D\epsilon}{Dt} + P\Delta + \frac{\partial q_i}{\partial x_i} = V_{ij}d_{ij} = \phi_\eta \tag{3c-18}$$

in which $V_{ij}d_{ij}$, the dissipative component of the stress power $t_{ij}d_{ij}$, is defined as the viscous dissipation function ϕ_η. The usefulness of specifying the arbitrary scalar in (3c-7) as the thermodynamic pressure, so that $P = P_{\text{th}}$, becomes apparent when $\rho\, D\epsilon/Dt$ is eliminated between (3c-18) and (3c-17), giving

$$\begin{aligned} \rho T \frac{Ds}{Dt} &= (P_{\text{th}} - P)\Delta + \phi_\eta - \frac{\partial q_i}{\partial x_i} \\ &= \phi_\eta - \frac{\partial q_i}{\partial x_i} \end{aligned} \tag{3c-19}$$

The viscous dissipation function (dissipated energy per unit volume) is thus seen to account for either an efflux of heat or an increase of entropy. Subtracting (3c-19) from (3c-15c) then allows the rate of irreversible production of entropy to be evaluated directly in terms of the two dissipation functions,

$$T\frac{DS_{\text{irr}}}{Dt} = \phi_\eta + \phi_\kappa \tag{3c-20}$$

The total heat-flux vector q_i, whose divergence is the energy transferred *away* from the volume element, must account for energy transport by either conduction or radi-

[1] Tolman and Fine, *Revs. Modern Phys.* **20,** 51–77 (1948).

ation. The part due to conduction is given by the Fourier relation, which serves also to define the heat conductivity κ;

$$(q_i)_{\text{cond}} = -\kappa \frac{\partial T}{\partial x_i}$$

$$\frac{\partial (q_i)_{\text{cond}}}{\partial x_i} = -\frac{\partial(\kappa \partial T/\partial x_i)}{\partial x_i} = -\kappa \frac{\partial^2 T}{\partial x_i^2} - \frac{\partial T}{\partial x_i}\frac{\partial \kappa}{\partial x_i} \qquad \text{(3d-21}a\text{)}$$

The last term, containing the gradient of κ, must be retained if implicit dependence of κ on the state variables is to be represented. On the other hand, if κ is assumed to be constant, (3c-21a) reduces to the more familiar form

$$\nabla \cdot \mathbf{q}_{\text{cond}} = -\kappa \nabla^2 T$$

The component of heat flux due to radiation can be approximated, for small temperature differences, by Newton's law of cooling,

$$\frac{\partial (q_i)_{\text{rad}}}{\partial x_i} = \rho C_v \mathfrak{q}(T - T_0) = \nabla \cdot \mathbf{q}_{\text{rad}} \qquad \text{(3c-21}b\text{)}$$

where $(T - T_0)$ is the local temperature excess and $\mathfrak{q}$ is a radiation coefficient introduced by Stokes.[1] The foregoing thermal relations can be combined with the equations of continuity and momentum more readily if the term $T(Ds/Dt)$ appearing in (3c-19) is expressed in terms of the variables $\mathbf{u}$, v, and T. The defining equations (3c-14) establish that $P = P(v,s)$ and $T = T(v,s)$; from which it follows that one may also write $s = s(T,v)$ or $s = s(T,P)$. Using both of the latter leads, after some manipulation,[2] to the identity

$$\rho T \frac{Ds}{Dt} = \rho C_v \left[(\gamma - 1)\frac{\Delta}{\beta} + \frac{DT}{Dt} \right] \qquad \text{(3c-22)}$$

in which β is the coefficient of thermal expansion, $\beta \equiv \rho(\partial v/\partial T)_P$. After (3c-22) and (3c-21) are combined with (3c-19), the energy equation can be written in the alternate forms

$$\frac{\rho C_v DT}{Dt} + \rho C_v \frac{\gamma - 1}{\beta}\frac{\partial u_i}{\partial x_i} + \frac{\partial q_i}{\partial x_i} - \phi_\eta = 0$$

$$\rho C_v \left(\frac{\partial T}{\partial t} + \mathbf{u} \cdot \nabla T \right) + \frac{\rho(C_p - C_v)}{\beta}\Delta - \nabla \cdot (\kappa \nabla T) + \rho C_v \mathfrak{q}(T - T_0) - \phi_\eta = 0 \qquad \text{(3c-23)}$$

$$\frac{\partial T}{\partial t} + \mathbf{u} \cdot \nabla T + \frac{(\gamma - 1)}{\beta}\Delta - \frac{\kappa}{\rho C_v}\nabla^2 T - \frac{\nabla T \cdot \nabla \kappa}{\rho C_v} + \mathfrak{q}(T - T_0) - \frac{\phi_\eta}{\rho C_v}$$

The viscous dissipation function ϕ_η can be evaluated, with the aid of (3c-8) and (3c-9) in the explicit form

$$\begin{aligned}\phi_\eta &= V_{ij}d_{ji} = \eta' d_{kk}d_{ii} + 2\eta d_{ij}d_{ji} \\ &= \eta_B \Delta^2 + \frac{4}{3}\eta \left[\left(\frac{\partial u_1}{\partial x_1}\right)^2 + \left(\frac{\partial u_2}{\partial x_2}\right)^2 + \left(\frac{\partial u_3}{\partial x_3}\right)^2 - \frac{\partial u_1}{\partial x_1}\frac{\partial u_2}{\partial x_2} - \frac{\partial u_2}{\partial x_2}\frac{\partial u_3}{\partial x_3} - \frac{\partial u_3}{\partial x_3}\frac{\partial u_1}{\partial x_1} \right] \\ &\quad + \eta \left[\left(\frac{\partial u_1}{\partial x_2} + \frac{\partial u_2}{\partial x_1} \right)^2 + \left(\frac{\partial u_2}{\partial x_3} + \frac{\partial u_3}{\partial x_2} \right)^2 + \left(\frac{\partial u_3}{\partial x_1} + \frac{\partial u_1}{\partial x_3} \right)^2 \right] \end{aligned} \qquad \text{(3c-24}a\text{)}$$

The thermal dissipation function ϕ_κ due to heat conduction can be evaluated, with the aid of (3c-16) and (3c-21a), in the form

$$\phi_\kappa = -\frac{q_i}{T}\frac{\partial T}{\partial x_i} = +\frac{\kappa}{T}\left(\frac{\partial T}{\partial x_i}\right)^2 = \frac{\kappa}{T}(\nabla T)^2 \qquad \text{(3c-24}b\text{)}$$

It does not appear explicitly in (3c-23), but it is there implicitly as a consequence of the heat-transfer processes described by (3c-23).

[1] *Phil. Mag.* (4) **1**, 305–317 (1851).

[2] See, for example, Zemansky, "Heat and Thermodynamics," 3d ed., pp. 246–255, McGraw-Hill Book Company, Inc., New York, 1951.

Summary of Assumptions. The fluid considered is assumed to be continuous except at boundaries or interfaces, locally homogeneous and isotropic when at rest, viscous, thermally conducting, and chemically inert, and its local thermodynamic condition is assumed to be completely determined by specifying three "state" variables, any two of which determine the third uniquely through an equation of state. No structural or thermal "relaxation" mechanism has been presumed up to this point in the analysis, except to the extent that ordinary heat conduction and viscous losses may be described in such terms. Local thermodynamic reversibility has been assumed in using conventional thermodynamic identities based on the second law, but the irreversible production of entropy by dissipative processes has been accounted for explicitly. It is also assumed that the stress tensor is a linear function of the rate of deformation, and that the tractions due to viscosity can be represented by the linear terms of an expansion in powers of the viscosity coefficients. The viscosity and heat-exchange parameters of the fluid η, η', κ, and $\mathfrak{q}$, may depend in any continuous way on the state variables and hence may be implicit functions of time and the spatial coordinates. Within the scope thus defined the equations given are exact.

The functional dependence on time and the spatial coordinates of the condition and motion variables P, T, ρ, and $\mathbf{u}$ can be evaluated, in a formal sense at least, by solving the set of four simultaneous equations connecting these variables [Eqs. (3c-5), (3c-11), (3c-23), and (3c-15) or one of its alternates]. No general solution of these complete equations has been given, however, and one or another of the least important terms are usually omitted in order to render the equations tractable for dealing with specific problems.

3c-3. The Small-signal Acoustic Equations. The physical theory of sound waves deals with systematic motions of a material medium relative to an equilibrium state and thus comprises the variational aspects of elasticity and fluid dynamics. Such perturbations of state can be described by incremental, or acoustic, variables and approximate equations governing them can be obtained by arbitrarily "linearizing" the general equations of motion. These results, as well as higher-order approximations, can be derived in an orderly way by invoking a modified perturbation analysis.[1] This consists of replacing the dependent variables appearing in (3c-5), (3c-11), and (3c-23) by the sum of their equilibrium or zero-order values and their first- and second-order variational components, and then forming the separate equations that must be satisfied by the variables of each order. Two of the composite state variables, for example ρ and T, can be defined arbitrarily, whereupon the third, P, is determined by the functional equation of state. These definitions, some self-evident manipulations, and the subscript notation identifying the orders can be exhibited as follows:

$$\rho \equiv \rho_0 + \rho_1 + \rho_2 \qquad T \equiv T_0 + \theta_1 + \theta_2$$

$$\nabla\rho = \nabla\rho_1 + \nabla\rho_2 \qquad \nabla T = \nabla\theta_1 + \nabla\theta_2$$

$$P(\rho,T) \equiv P_0(\rho_0,T_0) + p_1 + p_2$$

$$p_1 + p_2 = \left[\left(\frac{\partial P}{\partial \rho}\right)_T\right]_0 (\rho - \rho_0) + \left[\left(\frac{\partial P}{\partial T}\right)_\rho\right]_0 (T - T_0) + \cdots \tag{3c-25}$$

$$K = K_T \equiv \rho\left(\frac{\partial P}{\partial \rho}\right)_T \qquad \beta \equiv -\frac{1}{\rho}\left(\frac{\partial \rho}{\partial T}\right)_P \qquad c_0{}^2 \equiv \left[\left(\frac{\partial P}{\partial \rho}\right)_s\right]_0 \equiv \frac{(K_s)_0}{\rho_0}$$

$$\gamma = \frac{K_s}{K_T} = \frac{C_p}{C_v}$$

$$p_1 = \frac{c_0{}^2}{\gamma}(\rho_1 + \beta_0\rho_0\theta_1) \qquad p_2 = \frac{c_0{}^2}{\gamma}(\rho_2 + \beta_0\rho_0\theta_2)$$

$$\mathbf{u} \equiv 0 + \mathbf{u}_1 + \mathbf{u}_2 \qquad \nabla\cdot\mathbf{u} \equiv \Delta \equiv \Delta_1 + \Delta_2 = \nabla\cdot\mathbf{u}_1 + \nabla\cdot\mathbf{u}_2$$

$$\rho\mathbf{u} = [\rho_0\mathbf{u}_1]_1 + [\rho_1\mathbf{u}_1 + \rho_0\mathbf{u}_2]_2 + \cdots$$

$$\nabla\cdot(\rho\mathbf{u}) = [\rho_0\nabla\cdot\mathbf{u}_1]_1 + [\rho_1\nabla\cdot\mathbf{u}_1 + \mathbf{u}_1\cdot\nabla\rho_1 + \rho_0\nabla\cdot\mathbf{u}_2]_2 + \cdots$$

[1] Eckart, *Phys. Rev.* **73**, 68–76 (1948).

Terms containing $\nabla\rho_0$ have been omitted in writing out $\nabla \cdot (\rho\mathbf{u})$, on the assumption that ρ_0, T_0, and P_0 are constant and $\mathbf{u}_0 = 0$. The reference state need not be so restricted to one of static equilibrium provided its time and space rates of change are presumed small in comparison with the corresponding change rates of the acoustic variables. The extraneous body force **F** will also be omitted hereafter; it would become important in cases involving electromagnetic interaction, but it usually derives from a gravitation potential and affects primarily the equilibrium configuration.[1] Little generality is sacrificed by omitting **F** and assuming a static reference, moreover, since the basic equations characterize directly the equilibrium condition and since the "cross-modulation" effects brought in by nonlinearity are dealt with adequately through second- or higher-order approximations.

Notice that the foregoing represents a mathematical-approximation procedure that is concerned only with the *precision* achieved in interpreting the content of the basic equations. The *accuracy* with which the basic equations themselves delineate the behavior of a real fluid is an entirely different question that must be considered independently on its own merits. It follows that, while good judgment may restrain the effort, there is no impropriety involved in pursuing higher-order solutions of the acoustic equations, even though the equations themselves may embody first-order approximations to reality such as that represented by assuming linear dependence on the viscosity coefficients and the deformation rate.

When the appropriate relations from (3c-25) are substituted in (3c-5), (3c-11), and (3c-23), the *first-order acoustic equations* can be separated out in the form

$$\frac{\partial \rho_1}{\partial t} + \rho_0(\nabla \cdot \mathbf{u}_1) = 0 \tag{3c-26a}$$

$$\rho_0 \frac{\partial \mathbf{u}_1}{\partial t} + \frac{c_0^2}{\gamma}\left(1 + \beta_0\rho_0 \frac{\nabla\theta_1}{\nabla\rho_1}\right)\nabla\rho_1 - (\eta_0\mathcal{V})\nabla(\nabla \cdot \mathbf{u}_1) + \eta_0\nabla \times (\nabla \times \mathbf{u}_1) = 0 \tag{3c-26b}$$

$$\rho_0 C_v \frac{\partial \theta_1}{\partial t} + \frac{\rho_0 C_v(\gamma - 1)}{\beta_0}(\nabla \cdot \mathbf{u}_1) - \kappa_0\nabla^2\theta_1 + \rho_0 C_v \mathfrak{q}\theta_1 = 0 \tag{3c-26c}$$

Inasmuch as the first-order effects of both shear and dilatational viscosity and of heat conduction and radiation have been included, these equations comprehend a *viscothermal theory* of small-signal sound waves. The sound absorption and velocity dispersion predicted by this theory are discussed below. Note especially that taking heat exchange into account explicitly by including (3c-26c) has precluded the conventional adiabatic assumption and denied the simplifying assumption that $P = P(\rho)$.

Adiabatic behavior would be assured, on the other hand, if it were assumed at the outset that $\kappa = \mathfrak{q} = 0$, but the behavior would *not* at the same time be strictly isentropic so long as irreversible viscous losses are still present and accounted for. The difference between adiabatic and isentropic behavior in this case is of second order, however, as indicated by the fact that the second-order dissipation functions ϕ do not appear in the first-order energy equation (3c-26c), which is thereby reduced to yielding just the isentropic relation between dilatation and excess temperature. It is allowable, therefore, in this first-order approximation, to replace the quotient $(\nabla\theta_1/\nabla\rho_1)$ appearing in (3c-26b) with the isentropic derivative $(\partial T/\partial\rho)_s = (\gamma - 1)/\rho\beta$, whereupon the first-order equation of motion for an *adiabatic viscous* fluid can be written as

$$\rho_0 \frac{\partial \mathbf{u}_1}{\partial t} + c_0^2\nabla\rho_1 - \eta_0\mathcal{V}\nabla(\nabla \cdot \mathbf{u}_1) + 2\eta_0(\nabla \times \mathbf{R}_1) = 0 \tag{3c-27}$$

If the effects of viscosity, as well as of heat exchange, are to be neglected, the divergence of what is left of (3c-27) can be subtracted from the time derivative of (3c-26a)

[1] But, for a case in which **F** and $\nabla\rho_0$ cannot be neglected, see Haskell, *J. Appl. Phys.* **22**, 157–168 (February, 1951).

to yield the typical *small-signal scalar wave equation* of classical acoustics,

$$\frac{\partial^2 \rho_1}{\partial t^2} = \left(\frac{\partial P}{\partial \rho}\right)_s \nabla^2 \rho_1 \tag{3c-28a}$$

and, with the help of the first-order isentropic relation $p_1 = c_0^2(\rho_1)_s$, this wave equation becomes, in terms of the sound pressure,

$$\frac{\partial^2 p_1}{\partial t^2} = c_0^2 \nabla^2 p_1 \tag{3c-28b}$$

3c-4. The Second-order Acoustic Equations. The same substitution of composite variables that delivered (3c-26*a*), (3c-26*b*), and (3c-26*c*) will also yield directly the second-order equations of acoustics, which can now be marshaled as follows:

$$\frac{\partial \rho_2}{\partial t} + \rho_0(\nabla \cdot \mathbf{u}_2) + \nabla \cdot (\rho_1 \mathbf{u}_1) = 0 \tag{3c-29a}$$

$$\rho_0 \frac{\partial \mathbf{u}_2}{\partial t} + \frac{\partial(\rho_1 \mathbf{u}_1)}{\partial t} + \rho_0 \mathbf{u}_1(\nabla \cdot \mathbf{u}_1) + (\mathbf{u}_1 \cdot \nabla)\mathbf{u}_1 + \frac{c_0^2}{\gamma}\left(1 + \beta_0 \rho_0 \frac{\nabla \theta_2}{\nabla \rho_2}\right)\nabla \rho_2 - \eta_0 \mathfrak{V} \nabla(\nabla \cdot \mathbf{u}_2) + 2\eta_0(\nabla \times \mathbf{R}_2) - (\nabla \eta_1')(\nabla \cdot \mathbf{u}_1) - 2(\nabla \eta_1 \cdot \nabla)\mathbf{u}_1 - 2(\nabla \eta_1) \times \mathbf{R}_1 = 0 \tag{3c-29b}$$

$$\frac{\partial \theta_2}{\partial t} + \mathbf{u}_1 \cdot (\nabla \theta_1) + \frac{\gamma - 1}{\beta_0}(\nabla \cdot \mathbf{u}_2) - \frac{\kappa_0}{\rho_0 C_v}\nabla^2 \theta_2 + \frac{\kappa_0}{\rho_0^2 C_v}\rho_1 \nabla^2 \theta_1 - \frac{\nabla \theta_1 \cdot \nabla \kappa_1}{\rho_0 C_v} + q\theta_2 - \frac{\phi_\eta}{\rho_0 C_v} = 0 \tag{3c-29c}$$

The subscripts appended to κ and the η's imply that each may be expressed in the generic form

$$\eta(T, \rho, \cdot \cdot \cdot) = \eta_0(T_0, \rho_0, \cdot \cdot \cdot) + \eta_1 \qquad \eta_1 = \frac{\partial \eta}{\partial T}\theta_1 + \frac{\partial \eta}{\partial \rho}\rho_1 + \cdot \cdot \cdot \tag{3c-30}$$

No general solution of these complete second-order equations has been given, but they provide a useful point of departure for making approximations and for investigating some second-order phenomena that cannot be predicted by the first-order equations alone.

3c-5. Spatial and Material Coordinates. Equations (3c-26) and (3c-29) are couched in terms of the local values assumed by the dependent variables ρ, P, T, and $\mathbf{u}$ at *places* identified by their coordinates x_i in a fixed *spatial* reference frame, commonly called *Eulerian* coordinates (in spite of their first use by d'Alembert). As an alternate method of representation, the behavior of the medium can be described in terms of the sequence of values assumed by the dependent condition and state variables pertaining to identified *material* particles of the medium no matter how these particles may move with respect to the spatial coordinate system. The independent variables in this case are the identification coordinates a_i, rather than the position coordinates; the latter then become dependent variables that describe, as time progresses, the travel history of each particle of the medium. Such a representation in terms of *material* coordinates is commonly called *Lagrangian* (in spite of its first introduction and use by Euler).

The Wave Equation in Material Coordinates. The use of material coordinates can be demonstrated by deriving the exact equations governing one-dimensional (plane-wave) propagation in a *nonviscous adiabatic* fluid. Consider a cylindrical segment of the medium of unit cross section with its axis along $+x$, the direction of propagation, and let x and $x + \delta x$ define the boundaries of a thin laminar "particle" whose undisturbed equilibrium position is given by a and $a + \delta a$. The difference $x - a = \xi$ defines the displacement of the a particle from its equilibrium position and provides a convenient incremental, or acoustic, dependent variable in terms of which to describe the position, velocity, and acceleration of the particle; thus

$$x(a,t) = a + \xi(a,t) \qquad \frac{\partial x}{\partial t} = u^L(a,t) = \frac{\partial \xi}{\partial t} \qquad \frac{\partial u^L}{\partial t} = \frac{\partial^2 \xi}{\partial t^2} \tag{3c-31}$$

Continuity requires that the mass of the particle remain constant during any displacement, which means that

$$\rho_0 \delta a = \rho^L \delta x = \rho^L \left(\delta a + \frac{\partial \xi}{\partial a} \delta a \right) \qquad \frac{\rho_0}{\rho^L} = \frac{\partial x}{\partial a} = 1 + \frac{\partial \xi}{\partial a} \tag{3c-32a}$$

or, for three-dimensional disturbances and in general,

$$\frac{\rho_0}{\rho^L} = \frac{\partial(x_1,x_2,x_3)}{\partial(a_1,a_2,a_3)} \tag{3c-32b}$$

in which the symbolic derivative stands for the Jacobian functional determinant. The superscript L is used here and below as a reminder that the dependent variable so tagged adheres to, or "follows" in the Lagrangian sense, a specific particle, and that it is a function of the independent identification coordinates. When not so tagged, or with superscript E added for emphasis, the state variables ρ, P, T, and the condition variable u are each assumed to be functions of time and the spatial coordinate x.

The net force per unit mass acting on the particle at time t is $-(\rho^L)^{-1}\partial P^L/\partial x$, where ρ^L and P^L are the density and pressure at x, the "now" position of the moving particle. However, inasmuch as x is not an independent variable in this case, the pressure gradient must be rewritten as $(\partial P^L/\partial a)(\partial a/\partial x)$, from which the second factor can be eliminated by recourse to (3c-32*a*). The momentum equation then becomes just

$$\frac{\rho_0 \partial^2 \xi}{\partial t^2} = \frac{-\partial P^L}{\partial a} \tag{3c-33}$$

The adiabatic assumption makes available the simplified equation of state, $P = P(\rho)$, and this relation, in turn, allows the material gradient, $\partial P^L/\partial a$, to be written as

$$\frac{\partial P^L}{\partial a} = -\left(\frac{\partial P^L}{\partial \rho^L}\right)_s \frac{\partial \rho^L}{\partial a} = -c^2 \frac{\partial \rho^L}{\partial a} \tag{3c-34}$$

from which the last factor can be eliminated by using (3c-32*a*) again. This leads at once to the exact wave equation[1]

$$\frac{\partial^2 \xi}{\partial t^2} = \left(\frac{c\rho^L}{\rho_0}\right)^2 \frac{\partial^2 \xi}{\partial a^2} = c^2 \left(1 + \frac{\partial \xi}{\partial a}\right)^{-2} \frac{\partial^2 \xi}{\partial a^2} \tag{3c-35}$$

The pressure-density relation for a perfect adiabatic gas is $P = P_0(\rho/\rho_0)^\gamma$, from which it can be deduced that

$$c^2 = \left(\frac{\partial P}{\partial \rho}\right)_s = \frac{\gamma P_0}{\rho_0}\left(\frac{\rho}{\rho_0}\right)^{\gamma-1} = c_0^2\left(\frac{\rho}{\rho_0}\right)^{\gamma-1} \tag{3c-36}$$

No generalization of comparable simplicity is available for liquids.[2] When (3c-36) is introduced in (3c-35), the exact "Lagrangian" wave equation for an adiabatic perfect gas becomes

$$\frac{\partial^2 \xi}{\partial t^2} = c_0^2 \left(\frac{\rho^L}{\rho_0}\right)^{\gamma+1} \frac{\partial^2 \xi}{\partial a^2} = c_0^2 \left(1 + \frac{\partial \xi}{\partial a}\right)^{-(\gamma+1)} \frac{\partial^2 \xi}{\partial a^2} \tag{3c-37}$$

In the Lagrangian formulation illustrated above, the choice of a, the initial-position coordinate, as the independent variable is useful but any other coordinate that

[1] Rayleigh, "Theory of Sound" vol. II, §249; Lamb, "Hydrodynamics" §§13–15, 279–284.
[2] But see Courant and Friedrichs, "Supersonic Flow and Shock Waves," p. 8, Interscience Publishers, Inc., New York, 1948.

identifies the particles would serve the same purpose. For example, the particle located momentarily at x can be uniquely identified by the material coordinate $h \equiv \int_0^x \rho\, dx$, where h represents the mass of fluid contained between the origin and the particle. Inasmuch as this included mass will not change as the particle moves, the use of h as an independent "mass" variable automatically satisfies the requirements of continuity, with some attendant simplification in the analysis of transient disturbances. In the undisturbed condition, $\rho = \rho_0$ and $x = a$, whence the relation $a = h/\rho_0$ allows the independent variables to be interchanged by direct substitution in (3c-37).

Material and Spatial Coordinate Transforms. It is useful to have available a systematic procedure for converting a functional expression for one of the state variables from the form involving material coordinates to the corresponding form in spatial coordinates, or the inverse. One should avoid, however, the trap of referring to the state variables themselves as Lagrangian or Eulerian *quantities;* density and pressure, for example, are scalar point functions that can have only one value at a given place and time. On the other hand, it is of prime importance to distinguish carefully (and to specify!) the independent variables when computing the derivatives of these quantities.

The E and L functions are tied together by the displacement variable ξ, which provides a single-valued connection between the a particle and its instantaneous position coordinate x and which may therefore be regarded as a function of either of its terminal coordinates a or x. This can be indicated [cf. (3c-31)] by writing $x(a,t) = a + \xi(a,t)$, or the inverse relation $a(x,t) = x - \xi(x,t)$; from which follow the alternate expressions

$$a = x - \xi(a,t) \qquad x = a + \xi(x,t) \tag{3c-38}$$

The desired coordinate transforms can then be established by means of Taylor series expansions, the two forms following according to whether the expansion is centered on the instantaneous particle position or spatial coordinate x, or on the particle's equilibrium position or material coordinate a. Thus, if q is used to represent any one of the variables ρ, P, T, or u, one of the expansions can be based on the obvious identity

$$\begin{aligned} q^L(a,t) &= q^E(x,t)_{x=a+\xi(x,t)} \\ &= q^E(x,t)_{x=a} + \left[\xi(x,t)\frac{\partial q^E(x,t)}{\partial x}\right]_{x=a} + \frac{1}{2}\left[\xi^2(x,t)\frac{\partial^2 q^E(x,t)}{\partial x^2}\right]_{x=a} + \cdots \end{aligned} \tag{3c-39}$$

Note that all terms on the right of (3c-39) are functions of the spatial coordinates and that each is to be evaluated at the equilibrium position coordinate a. This transform yields, therefore, the instantaneous value in material coordinates of the variable represented by q, in terms of the local value of q modified by correction terms (comprising the succeeding terms of the series) based on the spatial rate of change of q and the instantaneous displacement.

The inverse transform is derived in a similar way from the identity

$$\begin{aligned} q^E(x,t) &= [q^L(a,t)]_{a=x-\xi(a,t)} \\ q^E(x,t) &= [q^L(a,t)]_{a=x} - \left[\xi(a,t)\frac{\partial q^L(a,t)}{\partial a}\right]_{a=x} + \frac{1}{2}\left[\xi^2(a,t)\frac{\partial^2 q^L(a,t)}{\partial a^2}\right]_{a=x} - \cdots \end{aligned} \tag{3c-40}$$

In symmetrical contrast with (3c-39), all terms on the right in (3c-40) are functions of the material coordinates and are to be evaluated for $a = x$. This transform, therefore, yields the instantaneous local value of the variable q at the place x, in terms of the instantaneous value of q for the now-displaced particle whose equilibrium position or material coordinate is $a = x$, modified by the succeeding terms of the series in accordance with the material-coordinate rate of change of q and the instantaneous displacement.

The transforms (3c-39) and (3c-40) indicate that the differences between q^L and q^E are of second order, which explains why the troublesome distinction between spatial and material coordinates does not intrude when only first-order effects are being considered. It also follows that the first two terms of these transforms are sufficient to deliver all terms of q^L or q^E through the second order. The use of these transforms can be illustrated by writing them out explicitly for u and ρ, including all second-order terms;

$$u^L \equiv \xi_t \qquad u^E = u^L - \xi u_a{}^L = \xi_t - \xi\xi_{ta} \tag{3c-41a}$$

$$\rho^L = \rho_0(1 + \xi_a)^{-1} = \rho_0(1 - \xi_a + \xi_a{}^2 - \cdot \cdot \cdot)$$

$$\rho^E = \rho_0(1 - \xi_a + \xi_a{}^2 + \xi\xi_{aa}) = \rho_0[1 - \xi_a + (\xi\xi_a)_a] \tag{3c-41b}$$

in which the subscripts indicate partial differentiation with respect to a or t. The product of (3c-41a) and (3c-41b) gives at once the relation between the material and spatial coordinate expressions for the mass transport ρu; thus, through second order,

$$\rho^E u^E = \rho^L u^L - \xi(\rho^L u^L)_a + \xi^2(\rho_a{}^L u_a{}^L) = \rho_0[\xi_t - (\xi\xi_t)_a] = \rho_0[\xi - \xi\xi_a]_t \tag{3c-42}$$

It is then straightforward to show that, if the particle velocity ξ_t is simple harmonic, the time average of the local mass transport $\rho^E u^E$ will vanish through the second order, even though the average value of u^E is not zero. Note, however, that the displacement velocity ξ_t is measured from an equilibrium position that is here assumed to be static; the average mass transport may indeed take on nonvanishing values if the wave motion as a whole leads to gross streaming (see Sec. 3c-7).

3c-6. Waves of Finite Amplitude. A distinguished tradition adheres to the study of the propagation of unrestricted compressional waves. That the particle velocity is forwarded more rapidly in the condensed portion of the wave was known early (Poisson, 1808; Earnshaw, 1858; Riemann, 1859); and that this should lead eventually to the formation of a discontinuity or shock wave was recognized by Stokes (1848), interpreted by Rayleigh,[1] discussed more recently by Fubini,[2] and has been reviewed still more recently with heightened interest by modern students of blast-wave transmission.[3]

By virtue of the adiabatic assumption underlying $P = P(\rho)$, the speed of sound is also a function of density alone and may be approximated by the leading terms of its expansion about the equilibrium density:

$$c^2 = c_0{}^2 \left[1 - 2\xi_a \frac{\rho_0}{c_0} \left(\frac{Dc}{D\rho} \right)_0 + \cdot \cdot \cdot \right] \tag{3c-43}$$

When (3c-43) is introduced in the exact wave equation in material coordinates, (3c-35), the latter can be recast in the following form, using the subscript convention for partial differentiation and retaining only, but all, terms through second order:

$$\xi_{tt} - c_0{}^2\xi_{aa} = -c_0{}^2 \left[1 + \frac{\rho_0}{c_0} \left(\frac{Dc}{D\rho} \right)_0 \right] (\xi_a{}^2)_a \tag{3c-44}$$

If it is then assumed that an arbitrary plane displacement $\xi(0,t) = f(t)$ is impressed at the origin, it can be verified by direct substitution that a solution of (3c-44) is

$$\xi(a,t) = f\left(t - \frac{a}{c_0}\right) + \frac{a}{2c_0{}^2} \left[1 + \frac{\rho_0}{c_0} \left(\frac{Dc}{D\rho} \right)_0 \right] \left[f'\left(t - \frac{a}{c_0}\right) \right]^2 \tag{3c-45}$$

The density variations associated with these displacements are to be found by entering (3c-45) in (3c-32), and the variational pressure can then be evaluated in terms of the adiabatic compressibility of the medium.

Relatively more attention has been devoted to the analysis of solutions of (3c-37) for the case of an adiabatic perfect gas. For an arbitrary initial displacement, as

[1] "Theory of Sound," vol. II, §§249–253.
[2] *Alta Frequenza* **4**, 530–581 (1935).
[3] See also Sec. 2z of this book, "Shock Waves," pp. 2-231 to 2-236.

above, the solution of the corresponding wave equation (3c-37), again including all terms through second order, is

$$\xi(a,t) = f\left(t - \frac{a}{c_0}\right) + \frac{a}{2c_0^2}\,\frac{\gamma + 1}{2}\left[f'\left(t - \frac{a}{c_0}\right)\right]^2 \tag{3c-46}$$

Technological interest in this problem centers on the generation of spurious harmonics, which can be studied by assuming the initial displacement to be simple harmonic, viz., $f(t) = \xi_0\,(1 - \cos \omega t)$ at the origin. The solution then takes the explicit form

$$\xi(a,t) = \xi_0\,[1 - \cos\,(\omega t - k_0 a)] + \frac{\gamma + 1}{8}\,k_0^2 \xi_0^2 a[1 - \cos 2(\omega t - k_0 a)] \tag{3c-47}$$

in which k_0 is written for the phase constant, $k_0 = \omega/c_0 = 2\pi/\lambda_0$.

The most striking feature of the solutions (3c-45) and (3c-47) is the appearance of the material coordinate a in the coefficient of the second-harmonic term. As a consequence, the condensation wave front becomes progressively steeper as the wave propagates, the energy supplied at fundamental frequency being gradually diverted toward the higher harmonic components. The compensating diminution of the fundamental-frequency component would be exhibited explicitly if third-order terms had been retained in (3c-46) and (3c-47) inasmuch as all odd-order terms include a "contribution" to the fundamental. When such higher terms are retained it is predicted that propagation will always culminate in the formation of a shock wave at a distance from the source given approximately by $a \doteq 2\xi_0/(\gamma + 1)M^2$, where M is the peak value of the particle-velocity Mach number.[1] On the other hand, when dissipative mechanisms are taken into account, the fact that attenuation increases with frequency for either liquids or gases leads to the result that, except for very large initial disturbances, a stable value of wave-front steepness will be reached at which the rate of energy conversion to higher frequencies by nonlinearity is just compensated by the increase of absorption at higher frequencies. If attention is centered on the fundamental component, however, such diversion of energy to higher frequencies appears as an attenuation and accounts for the relatively more rapid absorption sometimes observed near a sound source.[2]

The variational or acoustic pressure, in material coordinates, can be expressed generally as a function of the displacement gradients by using the adiabatic pressure-density relation $P^L = P_0(\rho^L/\rho_0)^\gamma$ in conjunction with the continuity relation (3c-32); thus,

$$P^L - P_0 = p^L = \gamma P_0[-\xi_a + \tfrac{1}{2}(\gamma + 1)\xi_a^2] = \langle p^L \rangle + p_1{}^L + p_2{}^L \tag{3c-48}$$

in which the last member identifies the steady-state alteration of the average pressure and the fundamental and second-harmonic components of sound pressure. When the harmonic solution (3c-47) is introduced in (3c-48), the two alternating components of pressure for $a^2 \gg (\lambda/4\pi)^2$ can be shown, after some algebraic manipulation, to be

$$p_1{}^L = +\gamma P_0 M \sin\,(\omega t - k_0 a) = +\sqrt{2}\,P_1 \sin\,(\omega t - k_0 a) \tag{3c-49a}$$

$$p_2{}^L = \gamma P_0 M^2 k_0 a \tfrac{1}{4}(\gamma + 1) \sin 2(\omega t - k_0 a) = \sqrt{2}\,P_2 \sin 2(\omega t - k_0 a) \tag{3c-49b}$$

in which P_1 and P_2 are the rms values of the fundamental and second-harmonic sound pressures, and $M = k_0\xi_0 = \omega\xi_0/c_0$ is again the peak value of the particle-velocity Mach number at the origin. The relative magnitude of P_2 increases linearly with distance from the origin and is directly proportional to the peak Mach number, as may be deduced from (3c-49a) and (3c-49b); thus

$$\frac{P_2}{P_1} = \frac{1}{4}\,(\gamma + 1)Mk_0 a \qquad P_2 = \frac{P_1{}^2 k_0 a(\gamma + 1)}{2\sqrt{2}\,\gamma P_0} \tag{3c-50}$$

[1] Fubini, *Alta Frequenza* **4**, 530–581 (1935).

[2] Fox and Wallace, *J. Acoust. Soc. Am.* **26**, 994–1006 (1954).

Various experimental studies of second-harmonic generation have given results in reasonably good agreement with the predictions of (3c-50).[1]

The sound-induced alteration of mean total pressure, or "average" acoustic pressure, is given by the time-independent terms yielded by the substitution of (3c-47) in (3c-48), viz.,

$$\langle p^L \rangle = + \frac{\gamma P_0 M^2(\gamma + 1)}{8} \tag{3c-51}$$

Note that this pressure increment is given as a function of the material coordinates, which means that it pertains to a *moving* element of the fluid. The *local* value of the pressure change can be found by means of the transform (3c-40), which gives, through second-order terms, the following replacement for (3c-48);

$$p^E = p^L - \xi \frac{\partial p^L}{\partial a} = \gamma P_0 \left[-\xi_a + \frac{1}{2}(\gamma + 1)\xi_a{}^2 + \xi\xi_{aa} \right] \tag{3c-52}$$

When (3c-47) is introduced in (3c-52), the time-independent terms give the local change in mean pressure as

$$\langle p^E \rangle = + \frac{\gamma P_0 M^2(\gamma - 3)}{8} \tag{3c-53}$$

and since γ is usually less than 2, it follows that the local value of mean pressure will be *reduced* by the presence of the sound wave, in striking contrast to the *increase* of mean pressure that would be observed when following the motion of a particle of the medium. Negative pressure increments as large as 10 newtons m^{-2} (100 dynes cm^{-2}) have been reported experimentally, in reasonably good agreement with (3c-53).

The mean value of the material particle velocity, $u^L \equiv \xi_t$, vanishes, as may be seen by differentiating (3c-47). The local particle velocity that would be observed at a fixed spatial position does not similarly vanish, however, and may be shown, by using the transform (3c-40) again, to be

$$u^E = \xi_t - \xi\xi_{ta} \qquad \langle u^E \rangle = -\frac{1}{2} c_0 M^2 = -\frac{\rho_0 c_0 \omega^2 \xi_0{}^2}{2\rho_0 c_0{}^2} = -(\rho_0 c_0{}^2)^{-1}\langle J \rangle \tag{3c-54}$$

where $\langle J \rangle$ is the average sound energy flux, or sound intensity.[2]

3c-7. Vorticity and Streaming. As suggested above, and with scant respect for the traditional symmetry of simple-harmonic motion, sound waves are found experimentally to exert net time-independent forces on the surfaces on which they impinge, and there is often aroused in the medium a pattern of steady-state flow that includes the formation of streams and eddies. The exact wave equation considered in the preceding section has been solved only for one-parameter waves (i.e., plane or spherical), and these solutions do not embrace some of the gross rotational flow patterns that are observed to occur. It is necessary, therefore, to revert for the study of these phenomena to the perturbation procedures introduced by the first- and second-order equations (3c-26) and (3c-29).

It is plausible that vortices and eddies should arise, if there is any net transport at all, inasmuch as material continuity would require that any net flow in the direction of sound propagation must be made good in the steady state by recirculation toward the source. Streaming effects can be studied most usefully, therefore, in terms of the generation and diffusion of circulation, or vorticity. More specifically, the time average of the second-order velocity $\mathbf{u}_2$ will be a first-order measure of the streaming

[1] Thuras, Jenkins, and O'Neil, *J. Acoust. Soc. Am.* **6**, 173–180 (1935); Fay, *J. Acoust. Soc. Am.* **3**, 222–241 (October, 1931); O. N. Geertsen, unpublished (ONR) Tech. Report no. III, May, 1951, U.C.L.A.

[2] Westervelt, *J. Acoust. Soc. Am.* **22**, 319–327 (1950).

velocity. The vector function describing $\mathbf{u}_2$ can always be resolved into solenoidal and lamellar components defined by

$$\mathbf{u}_2 \equiv -\nabla\varphi_2 + \nabla \times \mathbf{A}_2 \qquad \nabla^2\varphi_2 \equiv -\nabla \cdot \mathbf{u}_2 \qquad \nabla^2\mathbf{A}_2 = -(\nabla \times \mathbf{u}_2) \tag{3c-55}$$

The irrotational component that represents the compressible, or acoustic, part of the fluid motion is derived from the scalar potential φ_2. The vector potential $\mathbf{A}_2$ is associated with the rotational component comprising the incompressible circulatory flow that is of primary interest in streaming phenomena.

The failure of the first-order equations to predict streaming can be demonstrated by writing directly the curl of the first-order force equation (3c-26*b*). The gradient terms are eliminated by this operation, since $\nabla \times \nabla(\quad) \equiv 0$, leaving just

$$\frac{\partial \mathbf{R}_1}{\partial t} - \nu_0\nabla^2\mathbf{R}_1 = 0 \tag{3c-56}$$

Thus the first-order vorticity, $\mathbf{R}_1 \equiv \frac{1}{2}(\nabla \times \mathbf{u}_1)$, if it has any value other than zero, obeys a typical homogeneous diffusion equation. On the other hand, it would appear to follow that, if $\mathbf{R}_1$ were ever zero everywhere, its time derivative would also vanish everywhere and $\mathbf{R}_1$ would be constrained always thereafter to remain zero. This is *not* a valid proof of the famous Lagrange-Cauchy proposition on the permanence of the irrotational state, but the absence of any source terms on the right-hand side of (3c-56) does indicate correctly[1] that first-order vorticity cannot be generated in the interior of a fluid even when viscosity and heat conduction are taken into account. Instead, first-order vorticity, if it exists at all, must diffuse inward from the boundaries under control of (3c-56).

A notably different result is obtained when the second-order equations are dealt with in the same way. It is useful, before taking the curl of (3c-29*b*), to eliminate the second and third terms of this equation by subtracting from it the product of (ρ_1/ρ_0) and (3c-26*b*), and the product of $\mathbf{u}_1$ and (3c-26*a*). In effect this raises the first-order equations to second order and then combines the information in both sets. The augmented second-order force equation can then be arranged in the form

$$\begin{aligned}\rho_0\frac{\partial \mathbf{u}_2}{\partial t} &+ 2\eta_0(\nabla \times \mathbf{R}_2) + \nu_0\mathcal{V}\rho_1\nabla(\nabla\cdot\mathbf{u}_1) - 2\nu_0\rho_1(\nabla\times\mathbf{R}_1) - 2\rho_0(\mathbf{u}_1\times\mathbf{R}_1)\\ &-2[(\nabla\eta_1\cdot\nabla)\mathbf{u}_1 + \nabla\eta_1\times(\nabla\times\mathbf{u}_1)] + 2(\nabla\eta_1\times\mathbf{R}_1) + \rho_0\nabla\left(\frac{1}{2}\mathbf{u}_1\cdot\mathbf{u}_1\right) + B_2\nabla\rho_2\\ &- B_1\nabla\left(\frac{1}{2}\rho_1^2\right) - \eta_0\mathcal{V}\nabla(\nabla\cdot\mathbf{u}_2) - \nabla\eta_1'(\nabla\cdot\mathbf{u}_1) = 0\end{aligned} \tag{3c-57}$$

The following abbreviations have been used for the coefficients of $\nabla\rho_1$ in (3c-26*b*) and of $\nabla\rho_2$ in (3c-29*b*):

$$B_1 \equiv \frac{c_0^2}{\gamma}\left[1 + \beta_0\rho_0\left(\frac{D\theta_1}{D\rho_1}\right)_0\right] \qquad B_2 \equiv \frac{c_0^2}{\gamma}\left[1 + \beta_0\rho_0\left(\frac{D\theta_2}{D\rho_2}\right)_0\right] \tag{3c-58}$$

in which the quotients $(\nabla\theta_1/\nabla\rho_1)$ and $(\nabla\theta_2/\nabla\rho_2)$ have been replaced by the corresponding material derivatives $D\theta/D\rho$, which must be evaluated, of course, for the particular conditions of heat exchange satisfying the energy equations (3c-26*c*) and (3c-29*c*). This evaluation can be evaded temporarily (at the cost of neglecting ∇B_1 and ∇B_2) by observing that each of the last five terms of (3c-57) contains a gradient. These disappear on taking the curl of (3c-57), whereupon the vorticity equation emerges as

$$\begin{aligned}\frac{\partial \mathbf{R}_2}{\partial t} - \nu_0\nabla^2\mathbf{R}_2 &= \frac{1}{2}\nu_0\mathcal{V}\left(\nabla s_1 \times \nabla\frac{\partial s_1}{\partial t}\right) + \rho_0^{-1}\nabla\times(\mathbf{u}_1\cdot\nabla)\nabla\eta_1 + \nu_0 s_1\nabla^2\mathbf{R}_1\\ &- \nu_0\nabla s_1\times(\nabla\times\mathbf{R}_1) - \nabla\times(\mathbf{u}_1\times\mathbf{R}_1) + \rho_0^{-1}\nabla\times(\nabla\eta_1\times\mathbf{R}_1)\end{aligned} \tag{3c-59}$$

[1] St. Venant, *Compt. rend.* **68**, 221–237 (1869).

in which s_1 has been introduced as an abbreviation for the first-order condensation, $s_1 = \rho_1/\rho_0$. This inhomogeneous diffusion equation puts in evidence various second-order sources of vorticity: four vanish if the first-order motion is irrotational ($\mathbf{R}_1 = 0$), and two drop out when the shear viscosity is constant ($\nabla\eta_1 = 0$). It is notable that the dilatational viscosity η' does not appear in any of these source terms except through the ratio η'/η that forms part of the dimensionless viscosity number $\mathcal{V} \equiv 2 + (\eta'/\eta)$.

Except for the third source term, which (3c-56) shows to be one order smaller than the change rate of $\mathbf{R}_1$, *all* the vorticity sources would vanish—and the streaming would "stall"—if the wave front were strictly plane with $\mathbf{u}_1$, s_1, and η functions of only one space coordinate. Wave fronts cannot remain strictly plane at grazing incidence, however,[1] and rapid changes in the direction and magnitude of $\mathbf{u}_1$ will occur near reflecting surfaces, in the neighborhood of sound-scattering obstacles, and in thin viscous boundary layers. As a consequence, the "surface" source terms containing $\mathbf{R}_1$ become relatively more important in these cases.[2] In other circumstances, when the sound field is spatially restricted by source directionality, the first source term in (3c-59) dominates and leads to a steady-state streaming velocity proportional to the *ratio* of the dilatational and shear viscosity coefficients—and hence to a unique independent method of measuring this moot ratio.[3] Both the force that drives the fluid circulation and the viscous drag that opposes it are proportional to the kinematic viscosity, which does not therefore control the final value of streaming velocity but only the time constant of the motion, i.e., the time required to establish the steady state.[4]

Evaluating the second-order vorticity source terms in any specific case requires that the first-order velocity field be known, and this calls in the usual way for solutions that satisfy the experimental boundary conditions and the wave equation. Unusual requirements of exactness are imposed on such solutions, moreover, by the fact that even the second-order acoustic equations yield only a first approximation to the mean particle velocity.

The analysis of vorticity can be recast, by skillful abbreviation and judicious regrouping of the elements of (3c-57), in such a way as to yield a general law of rotational motion, according to which the average rate of increase of the moment of momentum of a fluid element responds to the difference between the sound-induced torque and a viscous torque arising from the induced flow.[5] A close relation has also been shown to exist in some cases between the streaming potential and the attenuation of sound by the medium without regard for whether the attenuation is caused by viscosity, heat conduction, or by some relaxation process; in effect the average momentum of the stream "conserves" the momentum diverted from the sound wave by absorption.[6] This principle has so far been established rigorously only for the adiabatic assumption under which $P = P(\rho)$, and under restrictive assumptions on the variability of η and $\mathcal{V}$, but its prospective importance would appear to justify efforts to extend the generalization.

3c-8. Acoustical Energetics and Radiation Pressure. If the kinetic energy density that appeared briefly in (3c-12) is restored to (3c-18), the change rate of the specific

[1] Morse, "Vibration and Sound," 2d ed., pp. 368–371, McGraw-Hill Book Company, Inc., New York, 1948.

[2] Medwin and Rudnick, *J. Acoust. Soc. Am.* **25**, 538–540 (1953).

[3] Liebermann, *Phys. Rev.* **75,** 1415–1422 (1949); Medwin, *J. Acoust. Soc. Am.* **26,** 332–341 (1954).

[4] Eckart, *Phys. Rev.* **73,** 68–76 (1948).

[5] Nyborg, *J. Acoust. Soc. Am.* **25,** 938–944 (1953); Westervelt, *J. Acoust. Soc. Am.* **25,** 60–67 and *errata*, 799 (1953).

[6] Nyborg, *J. Acoust. Soc. Am.* **25,** 68–75 (1953); Doak, *Proc. Roy. Soc.* (*London*), ser. A, **226,** 7–16 (1954); Piercy and Lamb, *Proc. Roy. Soc.* (*London*), ser. A, **226,** 43–50 (1954).

total energy density (per unit mass), E/ρ, can be formulated in terms of

$$\rho \frac{D(E/\rho)}{Dt} = \rho \frac{D(\frac{1}{2}\mathbf{u}\cdot\mathbf{u})}{Dt} + \rho \frac{D\epsilon}{Dt} = \rho \frac{D(\frac{1}{2}\mathbf{u}\cdot\mathbf{u})}{Dt} - \rho P \frac{Dv}{Dt} - \nabla\cdot\mathbf{q} + \phi_\eta \qquad (3c\text{-}60)$$

Material derivatives are used here so that the energy balance reckoned for a particular volume element will continue to hold as the derivatives "follow" the motion of the material particles. The mechanical work term on the right in (3c-60) can be resolved into two components by writing $P = P_0 + p$, where the excess, or sound, pressure p now represents the sum of the variational components of all orders

$$(p = p_1 + p_2 + \cdots)$$

Thus

$$\rho \frac{D(E/\rho)}{Dt} = \rho \frac{D(\frac{1}{2}\mathbf{u}\cdot\mathbf{u})}{Dt} - \rho p \frac{Dv}{Dt} + \rho P_0 \frac{Dv}{Dt} - \nabla\cdot\mathbf{q} + \phi_\eta \qquad (3c\text{-}61)$$

A second equation involving the first two terms on the right of (3c-61) can be formed by multiplying the continuity equation (3c-5) by p and adding it to the scalar product of the vector $\mathbf{u}$ and the vector force equation (3c-11*b*); thus

$$\rho\mathbf{u}\cdot\frac{D\mathbf{u}}{Dt} + \mathbf{u}\cdot\nabla p + p\left(\frac{1}{\rho}\frac{D\rho}{Dt} + \nabla\cdot\mathbf{u}\right) = \mathbf{u}\cdot\mathbf{f}_v(\eta,\eta',\mathbf{u}) = \rho\mathbf{u}\cdot\frac{D\mathbf{u}}{Dt} - p\rho\frac{Dv}{Dt} + \mathbf{u}\cdot\nabla p + p\nabla\cdot\mathbf{u} \qquad (3c\text{-}62)$$

where $\mathbf{f}_v$ stands for the sum of the five viscosity terms that appear on the right-hand side of (3c-11*b*). Combining this result with (3c-61) gives

$$\rho \frac{D(\frac{1}{2}\mathbf{u}\cdot\mathbf{u})}{Dt} - \rho p \frac{Dv}{Dt} + \nabla\cdot(p\mathbf{u}) = +\mathbf{u}\cdot\mathbf{f}_v$$
$$\rho \frac{D(E/\rho)}{Dt} + \nabla\cdot(p\mathbf{u}) = -\rho P_0 \frac{Dv}{Dt} - \nabla\cdot\mathbf{q} + \phi_\eta + \mathbf{u}\cdot\mathbf{f}_v \qquad (3c\text{-}63)$$

The significance of this result can be made more apparent by using the continuity equation again, this time in the form $(E/\rho)[\partial\rho/\partial t + \nabla\cdot(\rho\mathbf{u})] = 0$. Adding this "zero" to the left-hand side of (3c-63), after first using (3c-3) to express the material derivative in terms of fixed spatial coordinates, allows the continuity of acoustic energy to be expressed by

$$\rho \frac{D(E/\rho)}{Dt} + \nabla\cdot(p\mathbf{u}) = \rho \frac{\partial(E/\rho)}{\partial t} + \rho\mathbf{u}\cdot\nabla\frac{E}{\rho} + \nabla\cdot(p\mathbf{u}) + \left[\frac{E}{\rho}\frac{\partial\rho}{\partial t} + \frac{E}{\rho}\nabla(\rho\mathbf{u})\right]$$
$$\frac{\partial E}{\partial t} = -\nabla\cdot(p\mathbf{u} + E\mathbf{u}) - P_0\Delta - \nabla\cdot\mathbf{q} + \mathbf{u}\cdot\mathbf{f}_v + \phi_\eta \qquad (3c\text{-}64)$$

The acoustic energy-flux vector can be identified as $p\mathbf{u} = \mathbf{J}$, inasmuch as this term represents the instantaneous rate at which one portion of the medium does mechanical work on a contiguous portion in the process of forwarding the sound energy. The time average of the sound-energy flux through unit area normal to $\mathbf{u}$ is defined as the *sound intensity*, $\langle\mathbf{J}\rangle \equiv \mathbf{I}$. Ordinarily it is only the time average of each term of (3c-64) that is of interest, but the equation itself holds at every instant and asserts that growth of the total energy density of a volume element is accounted for by the influx of acoustic and thermal energy across the boundaries of the element, by the energy dissipated in viscous losses, and by the work done by the equilibrium pressure on the volume element during condensation. The latter component is represented by $(-P_0\Delta)$ and by a corresponding linear term contained implicitly in E [cf. (3c-19)]. It is omitted in most textbook descriptions of acoustic energy density, the neglect being justified if at all on the grounds that the stored energy varies linearly with the dilatation and hence will have a vanishing net value when averaged over an integral number of periods or wavelengths, or over the entire region occupied by the sound field. Care must be taken to ensure that it does indeed vanish rigorously on the average inasmuch as the peak values of this component of energy storage are larger than the acoustic energy in the ratio P_0/p.

Acoustic Radiation Pressure. The appearance of the product $E\mathbf{u}$ as an additive term in the first right-hand member of (3c-64) is notable and represents the net energy density carried across the boundary of a volume element by convection, the net flow being measured by the divergence of the particle velocity.[1] No approximations have been made in deducing (3c-64), which holds, therefore, within the scope of validity of the basic assumptions.

It is significant to remark the fact that E is directly additive to p when the divergence term is written as $\nabla \cdot (p + E)\mathbf{u}$, thereby identifying the additive term as a *radiation pressure* whose magnitude at every instant is just equal to the total energy density, $E = \frac{1}{2}\rho\mathbf{u} \cdot \mathbf{u} + \rho\epsilon$. This interpretation can be fortified by revising (3c-64) by expanding $\nabla \cdot (E\mathbf{u}) = E(\nabla \cdot \mathbf{u}) + \mathbf{u} \cdot \nabla E$. The last term can be used to restore the material time derivative of E and the other can be merged with the linear term in P_0, yielding a revised power equation in the form

$$\frac{DE}{Dt} = -\nabla \cdot (p\mathbf{u}) - (P_0 + E)\Delta - \nabla \cdot \mathbf{q} + \phi_\eta + \mathbf{u} \cdot \mathbf{f}_v \qquad \text{(3c-65)}$$

The role of E as an additive, or radiation pressure is thus retained in (3c-65) where its time-independent part is now exhibited appropriately as a slight change in the equilibrium pressure.

When seeking to evaluate the net mechanical force due to radiation pressure on a material obstacle or screen exposed to a sound field, care must be taken to specify the boundary conditions and to account for *all* the reaction forces involved, including the steady-state interaction of the obstacle with the medium as well as the dynamic interaction of the obstacle with the sound field itself. Thus, for example, if a long tube is "filled" with a progressive plane wave, the walls of the tube, which interact only with the medium, would experience only the mean increment of the equilibrium pressure [cf. (3c-53)], and this would disappear if the walls were permeable to the medium, but not to the sound wave (e.g., with capillary holes). On the other hand, if a sound-absorbing screen were freely suspended athwart the wavefronts, it would experience just the pressure E shown by (3c-64) to be additive to p; but if the screen were to form an impermeable termination of the tube it would experience both components of pressure, including changes due to the enhancement of $\langle E \rangle$ by the reflected wave.[2]

3c-9. Sound Absorption and Dispersion. The basic manifestation of the absorption or attenuation of sound is the conversion of organized systematic motions of the particles of the medium into the uncoordinated random motions of thermal agitation.

[1] Schock, *Acustica* **3**, 181–184 (1953).

[2] The literature on radiation pressure is extensive, and much of it is confusing. The fundamentals are soundly discussed by L. Brillouin, "Les Tenseurs en mécanique et en élasticité," Dover Publications, New York, 1946. The influence of oblique incidence and of the reflection coefficient of the obstacle is discussed in detail by F. E. Borgnis, On the Forces upon Plane Obstacles Produced by Acoustic Radiation, *J. Madras Inst. Technology* **1** (2), pp. 171–210 (November, 1953); (3), pp. 1–33 (September, 1954); also a condensed version in *Revs. Modern Phys.* **25**, 653–664 (1953). A suggestive review, with a critical bibliography, has been given recently by E. J. Post, *J. Acoust. Soc. Am.* **25**, 55–60 (1953).

Various agencies of conversion can be identified as viscosity, heat conduction, or as some other mechanism that gives rise to a delay in the establishment of thermodynamic equilibrium; but all are mechanisms of interaction that lead to the same result, viz. that the energy of mass motion imparted intermittently to the medium by the sound source becomes increasingly disordered and "unavailable." Describing this in terms of the irreversible production of entropy leads to the definition of dissipation functions and paves the way for formulating an acoustic energy balance.

Equation of Continuity for Acoustic Energy. This may take the form of a statement that the mean net influx of sound energy across the boundaries of a volume element situated in a sound field must just balance the average time rate at which this energy is degraded, or made unavailable, throughout the volume element by irreversible increase of entropy; thus, by extension of (3c-20),

$$-\int_A J_i\,da_i = \int_V \frac{DE_{\text{diss}}}{Dt}\,dV = \int_V T\,\frac{DS_{\text{irr}}}{Dt}\,dV = \int_V (\phi_\kappa + \phi_\eta)\,dV \qquad \text{(3c-66)}$$

where the sound energy flux vector is $J_i = pu_i$, and E_{diss} is the degraded component of internal energy associated with the irreversible entropy S_{irr}.

The differential form of (3c-66) can be obtained in the usual way by using the divergence theorem to convert the surface integral to a volume integral. Then, after introducing the explicit forms of the dissipation functions, (3c-24a) and (3c-24b), the acoustic energy continuity relation becomes

$$-\nabla\cdot\mathbf{J} = -\frac{\partial(pu_i)}{\partial x_i} = \phi_\kappa + \phi_\eta = \frac{\kappa}{T}\left(\frac{\partial T}{\partial x_i}\right)^2 + \eta'\,\frac{\partial u_k}{\partial x_k}\frac{\partial u_i}{\partial x_i} + \frac{1}{2}\,\eta\left[\left(\frac{\partial u_i}{\partial x_j}\right)^2 + \left(\frac{\partial u_j}{\partial x_i}\right)^2 + 2\,\frac{\partial u_i}{\partial x_j}\frac{\partial u_j}{\partial x_i}\right] \qquad \text{(3c-67a)}$$

where it is understood that only the time-independent parts of each side of (3c-67a) are to be retained. The algebraic complexity of dealing with (3c-67a) is considerably abated by considering only plane waves, for which case the running subscripts each reduce to unity and can be dropped. The plane-wave form of the acoustic-energy relation then becomes, after introducing P as an implicit variable in ∇T,

$$-\frac{\partial(pu)}{\partial x} = \frac{\kappa}{T}\left(\frac{DT}{DP}\right)^2\left(\frac{\partial p}{\partial x}\right)^2 + \eta\mathcal{V}\left(\frac{\partial u}{\partial x}\right)^2 \qquad \text{(3c-67b)}$$

in which $\eta\mathcal{V}$ has been written for $\eta' + 2\eta$ [cf. (3c-10)]. The thermal dissipation term can then be maneuvered into more suggestive form by further manipulation involving the equation of state $T = T(P,\rho)$ and various thermodynamic identities including the useful relation that holds for all fluids, $T\beta^2c^2 = C_p(\gamma - 1)$. This leads, still without approximation, and with the time average explicitly indicated, to

$$\left\langle -\frac{\partial(pu)}{\partial x}\right\rangle = \left\langle \eta\mathcal{V}\left(\frac{\partial u}{\partial x}\right)^2\right\rangle + \left\langle \frac{\kappa}{\rho C_p}\,\frac{[(\rho c^2/K_T) - 1]^2}{(\gamma - 1)\rho c^2}\left(\frac{\partial p}{\partial x}\right)^2\right\rangle \qquad \text{(3c-68)}$$

It can now be observed that p, u, and their derivatives must be known throughout the sound field in order to evaluate the sound energy flux and the dissipation functions that make up (3c-67a) or its reduced form (3c-68). On the other hand, if these field variables are known explicitly, the effects of dissipation will already be in evidence without recourse to (3c-68). Such a continuity equation for *acoustic* energy is therefore redundant, as might have been expected inasmuch as the conservation of energy has already been incorporated in the basic equations (3c-5), (3c-15), and (3c-23). Nevertheless, (3c-68) retains some logical utility as an auxiliary relation, even though it no longer needs to be relied on for the pursuit of absorption measures, at least for plane waves.

Exact Solution of the First-order Equations. An exact solution of the complete first-order equations (3c-26*a*), (3c-26*b*), (3c-26*c*) for the plane-wave case, and a definitive discussion of its implications, have been given recently by Truesdell.[1] The specific problem considered is that of forced plane damped waves in a viscous, conducting fluid medium. It is assumed that each of the first-order incremental state and field variables can be described by the real parts of

$$u_1 = u_{10} e^{j\omega t} e^{-(\alpha + jk)x} \tag{3c-69}$$

and of similar equations for ρ_1, p_1, θ_1. It is assumed that $(u_1)_{x=0} = u_{10}e^{j\omega t}$ is the simple-harmonic velocity imparted to the medium by the vibrating surface of a source located at $x = 0$, but the other amplitude coefficients may be complex in order to embody the phase angles by which these variables lead or lag u_1. The exponent expressing time dependence is written $+j\omega t$, as required in order to preserve both the conventional form $R + jX$ for complex impedances *and* the positive sign for inductive or mass reactance. The attenuation constant α and the phase constant $k \equiv \omega/c$, or $k_0 \equiv \omega/c_0$, are the real and imaginary parts of the complex propagation constant $\chi \equiv \alpha + jk$; and $c_0 \equiv (\partial P/\partial \rho)_s^{\frac{1}{2}}$ is the *reference* value of sound speed.

When the assumed solutions (3c-69) are systematically introduced in (3c-26*a*), (3c-26*b*), and (3c-26*c*), three algebraic equations in ρ_1, u_1, θ_1 are obtained, as follows:

$$\begin{aligned} \rho_0(\alpha + jk)u_1 \quad & -j\omega\rho_1 && = 0 \\ [j\omega\rho_0 - \eta\mathcal{V}(\alpha + jk)^2]u_1 \quad & -(\alpha + jk)\left[\frac{c_0^2}{\gamma}(\rho_1 + \beta_0\rho_0\theta_1)\right] && = 0 \\ -\frac{\gamma - 1}{\beta_0}(\alpha + jk)u_1 \quad & + \left[j\omega - \frac{\kappa}{\rho_0 C_v}(\alpha + jk)^2 + \mathfrak{q}\right]\theta_1 && = 0 \end{aligned} \tag{3c-70}$$

If these equations are indeed to admit solutions of the assumed form (3c-69), the determinant of the coefficients of u_1, ρ_1, and θ_1 must vanish. The characteristic or *secular equation* formed in this way (Kirchhoff, for perfect gases, 1868; extended to any fluid with arbitrary equation of state by P. Langevin[2]) turns out to be a biquadratic in the dimensionless complex propagation variable $(\alpha + jk)/k_0$. Writing this out in full, however, will be facilitated by first considering the question of how best to specify the properties of the medium.

Dimensional Analysis and Absorption Measure. Examination of (3c-70) reveals that, in addition to $(\alpha + jk)/k_0$ and the three independent variables, there are 10 parameters that pertain to the behavior of the medium at the angular frequency ω. One of these could be eliminated, in principle at least, by using the relation $T\beta^2c^2 = (\gamma - 1)C_p$, leaving 9 that are independent: C_p, C_v, η, η', κ, ρ_0, c_0, $\mathfrak{q}$, and ω. Then, since each of these can be expressed in terms of 4 basic dimensional units (e.g., mass, length, time, and temperature), it follows from the pi theorem of dimensional analysis[3] that just 5 independent dimensionless ratios can be formed out of combinations of these 9 parameters. This leads to a functional expression of the absorption measure in the symbolic form

$$\frac{\alpha + jk}{k_0} = \psi\left(\frac{C_p}{C_v}, \frac{\eta'}{\eta}, \frac{\eta C_p}{\kappa}, \frac{\omega\eta}{\rho_0 c_0^2}, \frac{\mathfrak{q}}{\omega}\right) \tag{3c-71}$$

The first two ratios have already been incorporated in γ and the viscosity number $\mathcal{V} = 2 + \eta'/\eta$; the third is the Prandtl number $\mathcal{P} \equiv \eta C_p/\kappa$, and the fourth and fifth can be identified as Stokes numbers $S \equiv \omega\eta/\rho_0 c_0^2$ and $S' \equiv \omega/\mathfrak{q}$. The present purpose

[1] C. A. Truesdell, Precise Theory of the Absorption and Dispersion of Forced Plane Infinitesimal Waves According to the Navier-Stokes Equations, *J. Rational Mechanics and Analysis* **2**, 643–741 (October, 1953).

[2] Reported by Biquard, *Ann. phys.* (11) **6**, 195–304 (1936).

[3] E. Buckingham, *Phys. Rev.* **4**, 345 (1914); *Phil. Mag.* (6) **42**, 696 (1921).

is served somewhat better by substituting for the third and fourth ratios their products with the dimensionless viscosity number, thus defining a frequency number X and thermoviscous number Y through

$$X \equiv \mathcal{V}S = \frac{\omega\eta\mathcal{V}}{\rho_0 c_0^2} \qquad Y \equiv (\mathcal{P}\mathcal{V})^{-1} = \frac{\kappa}{\eta\mathcal{V}C_p} \qquad XY = \frac{\omega\kappa}{\rho_0 c_0^2} \tag{3c-72}$$

The frequency parameter X also provides a natural criterion for designating frequencies as "low," "medium," or "high" according to whether X is much less than, comparable with, or much greater than unity. It may also be noted that, for nearly perfect gases, $\rho_0 c_0^2 \doteq \gamma P_0$, from which it follows that $X_{\text{gas}} \doteq (\omega/P_0)(\eta\mathcal{V}/\gamma)$. Hence variation of pressure may be used to extend in effect the accessible range of frequency in measurements on gases, and the ratio ω/P_0 is a proper parameter in terms of which to report such results.

Solutions of the Characteristic Equation. If the dimensionless ratios discussed above are now introduced in the expanded determinant of the coefficients of (3c-70), the resulting Kirchhoff-Langevin secular equation can be written as

$$\left(1 - \frac{j}{S'}\right) + \left(\frac{\alpha + jk}{k_0}\right)^2 \left[1 + jX(1 + \gamma Y) + \frac{\gamma X - j}{\gamma S'}\right] + \left(\frac{\alpha + jk}{k_0}\right)^4 XY(j - \gamma X) = 0 \tag{3c-73}$$

The standard "quadratic formula" can be used at once to solve (3c-73) for the reciprocal square of the propagation constant;

$$\begin{aligned} -2\left(1 - \frac{j}{S'}\right)\left(\frac{k_0}{\alpha + jk}\right)^2 = 1 + \frac{X}{S'} + j\left[X(1 + \gamma Y) - \frac{1}{\gamma S'}\right] \\ \pm \left[\left(1 + \frac{X}{S'}\right)^2 - \left[X(1 - \gamma Y) - \frac{1}{\gamma S'}\right]^2 \right. \\ \left. + 2j\left\{X[1 - (2 - \gamma)Y] + X^2\frac{1 - \gamma Y}{S'} - \frac{[1 + (X/S')]}{\gamma S'}\right\}\right]^{\frac{1}{2}} \end{aligned} \tag{3c-74a}$$

Skillful abbreviation might allow this complete solution to be carried somewhat further but no algebraic magic can lighten very much the burden of depicting the behavior of α and k as a function of *four* independent parameters—and it might have been five but for the welcome fact that $\mathcal{V}$ does not appear except as embodied in X and Y. Moreover, each parameter that does appear in (3c-74a) occurs in one or more product combinations, and hence it can *not* be assumed in general that the effects of viscosity and heat exchange will be linearly additive. The common practice of assessing these one at a time and then superimposing the results must therefore be considered unreliable unless justified explicitly and quantitatively. Nevertheless, something must give, and it is customary to abandon first the radiant-heat exchange, at least temporarily, by letting S' become infinite in (3c-74a). With this simplification, and with some new abbreviations, (3c-74a) becomes

$$\begin{aligned} -2\left(\frac{k_0}{\alpha + jk}\right)^2 &= 1 + jX(1 + \gamma Y) \pm \{1 - X^2(1 - \gamma Y)^2 + j2X[1 - (2 - \gamma)Y]\}^{\frac{1}{2}} \\ &\equiv G + jH = 1 + jX(1 + \gamma Y) \pm (E + jF)^{\frac{1}{2}} \\ E &\equiv 1 - X^2(1 - \gamma Y)^2 \qquad F \equiv 2X[1 - (2 - \gamma)Y] \end{aligned} \tag{3c-74b}$$

This equation has two pairs of noncoincident complex roots, but only the one of each pair that has a nonnegative real part corresponding to real attenuation is to be retained. These two physical solutions comprise the two branches of a complex square root; one branch pertains to typical compressional sound waves identified as type I, the other to so-called thermal waves identified as type II. It is an unwarranted oversimplification, however, to describe these simply as "pressure" waves and "thermal" waves inasmuch as *all* the state and condition variables—pressure, density, velocity, temperature, heat flux, etc.—are simultaneously entrained and propagated by *each* wave-type, and waves of *both* types are always excited simultaneously by any source. On the other hand, the absorption and dispersion measures for waves of type I and type II will, in general, be quite different and will vary differently with the frequency parameter X and with the thermoviscous parameters γ and Y that characterize the fluid. For example, type II waves are so rapidly attenuated in ordinary fluids at accessible frequencies that they cannot be observed, whereas in strongly conducting liquids such as mercury (and perhaps in liquid helium II) the absorption for type II waves becomes less than for type I waves when the frequency is high enough for X to exceed $\frac{1}{3}$.

It should be noticed, parenthetically, that if the basic first-order equations (3c-70) had not been restricted to plane waves, the last term of (3c-26*b*) would not have dropped out. Instead, there would have turned up eventually in (3c-70) a pair of terms in the first-order vector velocity potential $\mathbf{A}_1$ [see (3c-55)] on the basis of which it would have been predicted that still another type of allowed wave motion can exist in viscous fluids—a transverse *viscous wave* that is propagated by virtue of the transverse shear reactions due to viscosity.[1]

Viscothermal Absorption and Dispersion Measures. The problem of branch determination arising in the solution of (3c-64*b*) has been discussed thoroughly by Truesdell.[2] One view of it can be expressed by writing the formal solution in the explicit form

$$\frac{\alpha}{k} \equiv \frac{A}{2\pi} = \frac{H}{+(G^2+H^2)^{\frac{1}{2}}+G} \qquad \left(\frac{c}{c_0}\right)^2 = \frac{2(G^2+H^2)}{+(G^2+H^2)^{\frac{1}{2}}+G}$$
$$2G = 1 \pm f(h)(+E^{\frac{1}{2}}) \qquad 2H = X(1+\gamma Y) \pm (\operatorname{sgn} F)g(h)(+E^{\frac{1}{2}}) \tag{3c-75a}$$

(upper signs yield type I waves, lower signs type II waves)

$$h \equiv \frac{F}{E} \qquad f(h) \equiv +\sqrt{2}\,[+(1+h^2)^{\frac{1}{2}}+1] = +\cosh\tfrac{1}{2}(\sinh^{-1}h)$$
$$g(h) \equiv +\sqrt{2}\,[+(1+h^2)^{\frac{1}{2}}-1] = +\sinh\tfrac{1}{2}(\sinh^{-1}h) \tag{3c-75b}$$

where the plus signs associated with roots denoted by fractional exponents indicate that the principal or positive root is to be used. The solution (3c-75*a*) can now be attacked frontally, either by means of power-series expansions for large or small values of X, or by resorting to brute-force numerical computation for intermediate frequencies. The several square-root operations on complex quantities required by the latter procedure are often facilitated by using the f and g functions defined by (3c-75*b*), for which the principal values have been tabulated.[3]

The clue to a basis for classifying fluids according to their viscothermal behavior is afforded by noting that the algebraic sign of F appears in (3c-75*a*) in such a way as to interchange the wave types when F changes sign, and that this occurs when $(2-\gamma)Y$ passes through unity. On this basis, one may categorize fluids as *strong* conductors if Y is greater than $(2-\gamma)^{-1}$. The contrary alternative can be further subdivided usefully[2] into *weak* conductors for which Y is less than γ^{-1}, and *moderate* conductors for which Y has intermediate values. Most liquids (including the liquefied noble gases) qualify as weak conductors, most gases as moderate conductors. On the other hand, the fact that mercury, the molten metals, and liquid helium II rank as strong

[1] Rayleigh, "Theory of Sound," vol. II, §§347; Mason, *Trans. ASME* **69**, 359–367 (1947); Epstein and Carhart, *J. Acoust. Soc. Am.* **25**, 553–565, [557] (1953).

[2] C. A. Truesdell, Precise Theory of the Absorption and Dispersion of Forced Plane Infinitesimal Waves According to the Navier-Stokes Equations, *J. Rational Mechanics and Analysis* **2**, 643–741 (October, 1953).

[3] G. W. Pierce, *Proc. Am. Acad. Arts Sci.* **57**, 175–191 (1922).

conductors emphasizes the value of including a wide range of parameter values in any general survey of thermoviscous behavior.

For weak or moderate conductors, the absorption and dispersion measures for type I waves at moderately low frequencies can be expressed with any desired precision by means of power-series expansions in the frequency number X:

$$\left(\frac{c}{c_0}\right)^2 = 1 + \frac{1}{4}X^2[3 + 10(\gamma - 1)Y - (\gamma - 1)(7 - 3\gamma)Y^2] + 0(X^4)$$

$$\frac{\alpha}{k_0} \equiv \frac{A_0}{2\pi} = \frac{1}{2}X\left\{1 + (\gamma - 1)Y - \frac{1}{8}X^2[5 + 35(\gamma - 1)Y + (\gamma - 1)(35\gamma - 63)Y^2 + (\gamma - 1)(5\gamma^2 - 30\gamma + 33)Y^3]\right\} + O(X^5) \quad \text{(3c-76)}$$

$$\frac{\alpha}{k} \equiv \frac{A}{2\pi} = \frac{1}{2}X\left\{1 + (\gamma - 1)Y - \frac{1}{4}X^2[1 + 11(\gamma - 1)Y - (\gamma - 1)(23 - 11\gamma)Y^2 + (\gamma - 1)(\gamma^2 - 10\gamma + 13)Y^3]\right\} + O(X^5)$$

Note that $\alpha/k \equiv \alpha\lambda/2\pi \equiv A/2\pi$, where A is the amplitude attenuation per wavelength, and that α/k_0 is similarly related to the attenuation per reference wavelength λ_0. The series (3c-76) can be used with confidence for almost any values of γ and Y so long as the frequency is low enough to keep $X < 0.1$, and for a somewhat wider range of X when certain restrictions on γ and Y are satisfied.[1]

On the other hand, for frequencies high enough to make $X^{-2} \ll 1$, the absorption and dispersion are given, within $O(X^{-2})$, by

$$\frac{(c/c_0)^2}{2X} = \frac{\alpha}{k} \equiv \frac{A}{2\pi} = \frac{A_0{}^2X}{2\pi^2} = \left(\frac{\alpha}{k_0}\right)^2 2X = 1 - \frac{1 - Y}{(1 - \gamma Y)X} \quad \text{(3c-77)}$$

It can be inferred at once from (3c-77) that, for sufficiently high frequencies, dispersion is always anomalous (i.e., speed *increases* with frequency) regardless of γ and Y; that $\alpha/k = A/2\pi$ approaches the limit 1, and that α/k_0 and A_0 recede to zero as the actual wavelength decreases with respect to the reference wavelength λ_0. It also follows, from comparison of this result with (3c-76$_3$), that as frequency increases, $\alpha = A/\lambda = A_0/\lambda_0$ *will always have at least one maximum that is characteristic of viscothermal resonance.* The frequency at which this resonance occurs lies in the range $X = 1$ to 1.7, but the peak is relatively broad and flat and often cannot be located experimentally with high precision.

It can also be deduced from (3c-77) that the asymptotic speed of sound at very high frequencies will always be determined by viscosity alone, without regard for the form of the equation of state; thus,

$$(c^2)_{X\to\infty} = \frac{2\omega\eta\mathcal{V}}{\rho} \quad \text{(3c-78a)}$$

Under the same limiting conditions, the asymptotic speed of type II, or "thermal," waves is similarly determined by thermal conductivity alone, according to

$$(c'^2)_{X\to\infty} = \frac{2\omega\kappa}{\rho_0 C_p} \quad \text{(3c-78b)}$$

The steady increase of c' with $\omega^{\frac{1}{2}}$ predicted by (3c-78*b*) has sometimes been cited as a basis for denying that second sound in helium II, which displays small dispersion and low attenuation,[2] can be a type II thermal wave of the sort predicted by viscothermal

[1] Truesdell, *J. Rational Mechanics and Analysis* **2**, 643–741 (October, 1953).

[2] Peshkof, *J. Phys.* (*U.S.S.R.*) **8**, 381 (1944); **10**, 389–398 (1946); Lane, Fairbank, and Fairbank. *Phys. Rev.* **71**, 600–605 (1947).

theory. This conclusion is probably correct but the argument is faulty inasmuch as the vanishing viscosity of the superfluid would make it more appropriate to use as a type criterion the behavior predicted for the limiting condition $X \to 0$. Thus, if the Kirchhoff-Langevin secular equation (3c-73) is reduced by letting $X \to 0$ while XY is held fixed, and if XY is then allowed to increase indefinitely as required by the superconductivity of helium II, what is left of (3c-73) *does* have a pair of roots for which the attenuation vanishes and the speed is nondispersive, viz., $\alpha = A_0 = 0$, and $c = c_0/\gamma^{\frac{1}{2}}$. This result looks, at first sight, like just an isothermal velocity for type I waves, as might be expected to prevail if uniform temperature were enforced by infinite conductivity. On the other hand, the wave types would be expected to interchange, according to (3c-75*a*), as Y becomes very large; and one has also to deal with the standing conclusion that any viscosity however small will eventually take over control of dispersion when X departs sufficiently from zero. These remarks are intended to emphasize primarily the fact that the problem of branch determination, or type identification, under such extreme circumstances needs probably to be attacked by considering the relative *rates* at which the various limiting conditions are approached. Other considerations need also to be taken into account, of course, in dealing with the two-fluid-mixture theory of liquid helium; but it seems clear that further inquiry is warranted concerning the relevance of classical viscothermal concepts now that a more exact theory of these effects is available.

The Kirchhoff approximation for weak or moderate conductors at low frequencies can be obtained directly from (3c-76) by neglecting terms in X^2 or higher. The dispersion is thereby predicted to be negligible, so that $c \doteq c_0$; and the "Kirchhoff" attenuation α_K is given by

$$\begin{aligned}\alpha_K &= \frac{1}{2}\,k_0[X + (\gamma - 1)XY] = \frac{1}{2}\,k_0 S\left(\mathcal{V} + \frac{\gamma - 1}{\mathcal{P}}\right)\\ &= \frac{\omega^2}{2\rho_0 c_0{}^3}\left[\eta\mathcal{V} + \frac{(\gamma - 1)\kappa}{C_p}\right]\end{aligned} \tag{3c-79a}$$

If the Stokes relation is then presumed, by setting $\mathcal{V} = \frac{4}{3}$ (which neither Kirchhoff nor Stokes himself did in this connection), (3c-79*a*) becomes

$$\alpha_C = \frac{1}{2}\,k_0 S\left(\frac{4}{3} + \frac{\gamma - 1}{\mathcal{P}}\right) = \frac{\omega^2}{2\rho_0 c_0{}^3}\left[\frac{4}{3}\,\eta + \frac{(\gamma - 1)\kappa}{C_p}\right] \tag{3c-79b}$$

The absorption predicted by (3c-79*b*) is commonly, but not very appropriately, referred to as "classical"; but such an emasculated theoretical prediction neither accounts adequately for the attenuation observed experimentally, except in the case of a few monatomic gases, nor does it do justice to the essential content of the classical theory of viscous conducting fluids.

Even when terms through X^2 are included, no change occurs in the odd function α/k_0, but dispersion is then predicted according to (3c-76$_1$) which accounts for the second-order effects of both compressional and shear viscosity, heat conduction, and their interaction. This dispersion is anomalous for weak or moderate conductors (small Y) but becomes normal if the speed-reducing influence of thermal conductivity becomes large enough to make $(7 - 3\gamma)Y > 10$. On the other hand, if heat exchange were to be ignored altogether, the first two terms of (3c-76$_1$) would give, for the dispersion due to viscosity alone,

$$\begin{aligned}\left(\frac{c}{c_0}\right)^2 &\doteq 1 + \frac{3}{4}X^2 = 1 + \frac{3}{4}\left(\frac{\omega\eta\mathcal{V}}{\rho_0 c_0{}^2}\right)^2\\ c &\doteq c_0\left[1 + \frac{3}{8}\left(\frac{\omega\eta\mathcal{V}}{\rho_0 c_0{}^2}\right)^2\right]\end{aligned} \tag{3c-80}$$

Absorption and Dispersion Due to Heat Radiation. The effects of heat exchange by radiation, which were abandoned above in order to make (3c-74) more manageable, can now be assessed by reverting to (3c-73). The nonlinear interaction between radiation and viscosity will be neglected, for the sake of expediency, even though (3c-74) suggests that it may be as large as second order. The primary effects of viscosity and heat conduction can be eliminated from (3c-73) by letting both X and XY go to zero while holding the frequency variable $S' = \omega/\mathfrak{q}$ finite. This reduces the characteristic secular equation to the simple quadratic form

$$\gamma(S' - j) + \left(\frac{\alpha + jk}{k_0}\right)^2 (\gamma S' - j) = 0 \tag{3c-81}$$

which can be solved directly to yield the following exact expressions for the attenuation and dispersion due to radiation alone:

$$\begin{aligned} \frac{A}{2\pi}\left(\frac{c_0}{c}\right)^2 &= \frac{\alpha}{k}\left(\frac{c_0}{c}\right)^2 = \gamma S' \frac{\gamma - 1}{2[1 + (\gamma S')^2]} \\ \left(\frac{A_0}{2\pi}\right)^2 &= \left(\frac{\alpha}{k_0}\right)^2 = \frac{1}{2}\gamma \frac{(1 + S')^{\frac{1}{2}}(1 + \gamma^2 S'^2)^{\frac{1}{2}} - (1 + \gamma S'^2)}{1 + (\gamma S')^2} \\ \left(\frac{c}{c_0}\right)^2 &= \frac{2}{\gamma_\alpha(1 + \gamma S'^2) + (1 + S'^2)^{\frac{1}{2}}(1 + \gamma^2 S'^2)^{\frac{1}{2}}} \frac{1 + (\gamma S')^2}{} \end{aligned} \tag{3c-82}$$

These equations indicate that both attenuation and dispersion become vanishingly small for either very large or very small values of S', and that a maximum of attenuation occurs in mid-range, near the single point of inflection of the dispersion curve. This absorption peak is characterized by

$$\begin{aligned} \left(\frac{\alpha}{k}\right)_{\max} &= \frac{\gamma^{\frac{1}{4}} - 1}{\gamma^{\frac{1}{2}} + 1} \qquad S'_{\max A} = \gamma^{-\frac{1}{2}} \qquad \tau_{\text{rad}} = \frac{2\pi\gamma^{\frac{1}{2}}}{\mathfrak{q}} \\ \left(\frac{\alpha}{k_0}\right)_{\max} &= \frac{A_0}{2\pi} = \frac{\gamma - 1}{[8(\gamma + 1)]^{\frac{1}{2}}} \qquad S'_{\max A_0} = \gamma^{-1}\frac{(3\gamma + 1)^{\frac{1}{2}}}{(\gamma + 3)^{\frac{1}{2}}} \end{aligned} \tag{3c-83}$$

There is a curious dearth of quantitative information concerning the radiation coefficient $\mathfrak{q}$, and little is added to this by noticing the low attenuation and negligible dispersion observed for a wide range of audible sounds in air since these might correspond to values of S' either far above or far below the resonance peak described by (3c-83). The choice $S' \gg 1$ is unambiguously dictated, however, by the fact that the observed speed of sound is very close to the isentropic value c_0, whereas (3c-82$_5$) indicates that the isothermal speed $c_0/\gamma^{\frac{1}{2}}$ would prevail if $\mathfrak{q}$ were large enough to make S' small for all audio frequencies. Truesdell[1] has pointed out that these conclusions leave still in effect a prediction that at some lower subaudible frequency a peak of attenuation should appear with a magnitude $A_0 = 0.185\pi$ ($\approx$5 db per reference wavelength). This absorption peak has not been observed yet, at least deliberately, although its possible bearing on the acoustical character of thunder might be worth investigating.

Relaxation Processes and Sound Absorption. The foregoing analysis of heat exchange by radiation puts in evidence the first example of what would now be called a typical relaxation process. The characteristic feature of such a process, in so far as the gross hydrodynamical response of the medium is concerned, is the existence of two relations among the state variables, one of which prevails asymptotically for slow variations, the other for rapid changes. Such bivalent behavior is typical of fluid mixtures containing two interacting components, such as a partly dissociated gas[2] or an ionic solution.[3] In these cases the relative concentrations of the two components either follow faithfully, in quasi-static equilibrium, the dictates of slowly changing external variables, or else, at the other asymptotic limit, they do not change at all

[1] C. A. Truesdell, *J. Rational Mechanics and Analysis* **2**, 643–741 [666] (October, 1953).
[2] Einstein, *Sitzber. deut. Akad. Wiss. Berlin Math.-Phys. Kl.* **1920**, 380–385.
[3] Liebermann, *Phys. Rev.* **76**, 1520–1524 (1949).

when the finite reaction rate is such that the external variables can complete cyclic changes too rapidly for the concentrations to "follow." A different but comparable kind of mixture is exemplified by an ensemble of atoms or molecules capable of being excited to different energy levels, of which the most common example is a diatomic gas in which the rotational degrees of freedom may or may not share the cyclic work of compression depending on whether an appropriately normalized frequency variable is "low" or "high."

The *physical* problem of characterizing the rate-dependent properties of mixtures can be studied without regard for its acoustical consequences, and various approaches to this problem have turned on the assignment of two or more different internal or "partial" temperatures, different compressibilities, specific heats, etc. All the physical theories of pure relaxation appear to converge, however, in predicting the same *acoustical* behavior; viz., at low frequencies an asymptotic speed of sound c^0, a transition region of anomalous dispersion ($dc/d\omega > 0$) within which a maximum of attenuation occurs, and at high frequencies an asymptotic sound speed c^∞ which can be related to c^0 by writing $K \equiv c^0/c^\infty \leq 1$, where K is a material constant of the two-component medium. It follows then that, when the constant K and a dimensionless frequency variable X' can be properly identified and interpreted in terms of the *physical* mechanism involved, the *acoustical* behavior for any pure relaxation process will be described exactly by the following expressions derived from (3c-82) and (3c-83) by substitution:

$$\left(\frac{c}{c^0}\right)^2 = \frac{2(1 + X'^2)}{1 + K^2X'^2 + [(1 + K^4X'^2)(1 + X'^2)]^{\frac{1}{2}}} \doteq \frac{1 + X'^2}{1 + K^2X'^2}$$

$$\frac{\alpha}{k}\left(\frac{c^0}{c}\right)^2 = \frac{1}{2}\,\frac{(1 - K^2)X'}{1 + X'^2} \tag{3c-84}$$

$$\left(\frac{\alpha}{k}\right)_{\max} = \frac{1 - K}{1 + K} \qquad \left(\frac{\alpha}{k_0}\right)_{\max} = \frac{1 - K^2}{[8(1 + K^2)]^{\frac{1}{2}}}$$

$$X'_{\max A} = K^{-1} = \frac{c^\infty}{c^0} \qquad X'_{\max A_0} = \left(\frac{3 + K^2}{1 + 3K^2}\right)^{\frac{1}{2}}$$

These equations revert exactly to (3c-82) and (3c-83) when the substitutions $K^2 = \gamma^{-1}$, and $X' = \gamma S'$, are made, and when a factor γ^{-1} is introduced to convert the low-frequency reference speed c^0 to the usual isentropic reference c_0.

The "resonance" frequency characterizing a relaxation process is usually defined as the angular frequency at which the maximum attenuation per wavelength, $A = \alpha\lambda$, occurs; thus, $\omega_r \equiv 2\pi/\tau_r = (\omega/X')X'_{\max A}$, where τ_r is the related "relaxation period." It has been pointed out that *any* mechanism of sound absorption can be interpreted as a relaxation phenomenon by suitably defining its relaxation time. For example, viscosity and heat-conduction "relaxation times" and their associated "resonance frequencies" can be defined by writing

$$\tau_v = \frac{2\pi}{\omega_v} = \frac{X}{\omega}\,\frac{4}{3\mathfrak{V}} = \frac{\frac{4}{3}\eta}{\rho_0 c_0^2} \qquad \tau_\kappa = \frac{2\pi}{\omega_\kappa} = \frac{XY}{\omega} = \frac{\kappa}{\rho_0 c_0^2 C_p} \tag{3c-85}$$

Note that ω_v is specified in such a way that it reduces to ω/X when $\mathfrak{V}$ has the Stokes-relation value $\frac{4}{3}$. When these relaxation frequencies are introduced in (3c-79) and (3c-80), the second-order dispersion and the Kirchhoff linear approximation for attenuation become

$$c \doteq c_0\left[1 + \frac{3}{8}(2\pi)^2\left(\frac{3\mathfrak{V}}{4}\right)^2\frac{\omega^2}{\omega_v^2}\right]$$

$$\alpha_K = \pi k_0\left[\frac{3\mathfrak{V}}{4}\,\frac{\omega}{\omega_v} + (\gamma - 1)\,\frac{\omega}{\omega_\kappa}\right] \tag{3c-86}$$

When the fluid medium consists of an ideal monatomic gas, the physical significance of the relaxation times τ_v and τ_κ can readily be interpreted as the time required for subsidence of a momentary departure from the equilibrium distribution of energy among the translational degrees of freedom. In the classical kinetic theory of gases, this recovery time is shown to be approximately $L/\bar{v}$, the mean free path divided by the mean molecular velocity.[1] The conformity of the definitions (3c-85) with this concept can then be verified by recalling the kinetic-theory evaluations of viscosity $[\eta \doteq \frac{1}{2}\rho\bar{v}L]$, thermal conductivity $[(\kappa/C_p) \doteq (5/4\gamma)\rho\bar{v}L]$, and the speed of sound $[c \doteq 0.74\bar{v}]$. These considerations show, incidentally, that for such a gas the attenuation per reference wavelength is contributed almost equally by viscosity and heat conduction, and is proportional to the ratio of mean free path to wavelength.

The precise physical significance of τ_v and τ_κ is less obvious for polyatomic gases and liquids; but if this is glossed over, the frequency ratios $\frac{3}{2}\pi\mathcal{V}\omega/\omega_v$, $\frac{4}{3}\omega_v/\omega_\kappa\mathcal{V}$, and $2\pi\omega/\omega_\kappa$ can be substituted directly for X, Y, and XY in any of the viscothermal relations deduced above. Merely introducing these "relaxation" frequencies, however, does not invest heat conduction or viscosity with any new or different relaxation-like properties, and the exact viscothermal theory, in whatever symbols expressed, continues to predict that sound speed will increase indefinitely with frequency, that A_0 will display a typical broad maximum for some X in the range 1 to 1.7 (depending on the thermoviscous parameters γ and Y), that $(A_0)_{max}$ will always have about the same magnitude ($\alpha/k_0 \approx \frac{1}{3}$), and that the peak in A_0 can be made to occur at any chosen actual frequency by suitable assignment of the viscosity number $\mathcal{V}$. [cf. (3c-72), (3c-85)]. In contrast with this behavior, a pure relaxation phenomenon would call for the sound speed to level off at the high-frequency limit given by K^{-1}, and would display a maximum in A_0 that increases in height and retreats toward higher frequencies as the speed increment $c^\infty - c^0$ increases and K varies from 1 toward zero.

Allusion has already been made to the established fact that measured values of attenuation usually exceed the "classical" prediction (3c-79*b*) and often exhibit one or more maxima at finite frequencies. As a matter of fact, even when the complete consequences of the classical theory are taken into account, and when the viscosity number is adjusted to make the predicted attenuation at low frequencies correspond with experiment, the classical viscothermal theory still fails to account for all the experimental facts, but *for a reason that is just the opposite of that usually advanced*, namely, because it then predicts *too much* attenuation at the resonance peak and at higher frequencies! In spite of this latent contradiction, the alleged failure of "classical" theory as represented by (3c-79*b*) (which is, after all, only *part* of an *approximate* solution of the *linearized first-order* equations) has stimulated widespread efforts to repair its deficiency by invoking a wide variety of relaxation and other theories,[2] many of which have been marred by an *ad hoc* flavor that renders them little more than examples of ingenuity in curve fitting.

Measurements of absorption and dispersion in rarefied helium gas over a wide range of the frequency variable S have confirmed in all essential details the pattern of behavior predicted by the *exact* viscothermal theory.[3] Unless the classical concepts of viscosity and heat conduction are to be abandoned altogether, therefore, logic demands that the *exact* viscothermal theory be accepted as the foundation on which to erect any more complete analysis of sound absorption in media less idealized than rarefied

[1] Jeans, "Dynamical Theory of Gases," 2d ed., pp. 260–262, Cambridge University Press, Cambridge, England, 1916.

[2] For reviews of what has been called the "exuberant literature" dealing with relaxation and other theories of sound absorption, see Kneser, *Ergeb. exakt. Naturwiss.* **22,** 121–185 (1949); Markham, Beyer, and Lindsay, *Revs. Modern Phys.* **23,** 353–411 (1951); Kittel, *Phys. Soc. (London), Repts. Progr. in Phys.* **11,** 205–247 (1948); see also, for background, W. T. Richards, *Revs. Modern Phys.* **11,** 36–64 (1939).

[3] Greenspan, *Phys. Rev.* **75,** 197–198 (1949); *J. Acoust. Soc. Am.* **22,** 568–571 (1950).

helium. A good many "honest" relaxation mechanisms do exist and must be accounted for, but in the accounting these effects should presumably be regarded as factors perturbing the fundamental thermoviscous behavior rather than the converse. The two-fluid-mixture theory of relaxation effects seems best adapted for inclusion in such a compound analysis, and a start in this direction has already been made.[1] Much remains to be done, however, before this basic acoustical problem can be said to be understood.

3c-10. Characteristic Acoustic Impedance of a Thermoviscous Medium. When the first-order sound pressure p_1 is put back into ($3c\text{-}70_2$) [by tracing its last term back through ($3c\text{-}25_{11}$)], this equation of motion can be rewritten at once in terms of the specific acoustic impedance, as follows:

$$
\begin{aligned}
&[j\omega\rho_0 - (\alpha + jk)^2\eta\mathcal{V}]u_1 - (\alpha + jk)p_1 = 0 \\
&\frac{p_1}{u_1} \equiv Z = jk\rho_0 c(\alpha + jk)^{-1} - \eta\mathcal{V}(\alpha + jk) \\
&\quad = \rho_0 c\left(1 - j\frac{\alpha}{k}\right)^{-1} - j\rho_0 c\,\frac{\omega\eta\mathcal{V}}{\rho_0 c_0^2}\left(\frac{c_0}{c}\right)^2\left(1 - j\frac{\alpha}{k}\right) \qquad (3c\text{-}87) \\
&\frac{p_1}{\rho_0 c u_1} \equiv z = \left(1 - j\frac{\alpha}{k}\right)^{-1} - jX\left(\frac{c_0}{c}\right)^2\left(1 - j\frac{\alpha}{k}\right)
\end{aligned}
$$

The normalized specific impedance, or *specific impedance ratio*, $(p_1/\rho_0 c u_1) \equiv z$, which would be unity in the nondissipative case, is now in a form to be evaluated by direct substitution of the series expansions (3c-76). After some manipulation, and retaining only terms through X^2 and Y^2, the impedance ratio can be put in the form

$$
\begin{aligned}
\frac{p_1}{\rho_0 c u_1} &= 1 - \frac{\alpha}{k}\left[\frac{\alpha}{k} + X\left(\frac{c_0}{c}\right)^2\right] + j\left[\frac{\alpha}{k} - X\left(\frac{c_0}{c}\right)^2\right] \\
&= 1 - \frac{1}{4}X^2[3 + 4(\gamma - 1)Y + (\gamma - 1)^2Y^2] + O(X^4) \\
&\qquad - j\left\{\frac{1}{2}X[1 - (\gamma - 1)Y] + O(X^3)\right\} \qquad (3c\text{-}88)
\end{aligned}
$$

It follows that sound pressure *lags* the particle velocity when $(\gamma - 1)\kappa/\eta\mathcal{V}C_p$ is less than unity, as it is for the common fluids under ordinary conditions; but pressure *leads* the particle velocity when the ratio of heat conductivity to viscosity is high enough to make $(\gamma - 1)\kappa > \eta\mathcal{V}C_p$.

3c-11. Thermal Noise in the Acoustic Medium. The mode of motion that is heat furnishes a restless background of noise that underlies all acoustical phenomena. The magnitude and nature of this thermal noise can be assessed by appealing to concepts drawn from such apparently unrelated sources as architectural acoustics, elementary quantum theory, and the classical kinetic theory of gases.

The scheme of analysis can be described simply: the thermoacoustic noise energy density, as measured by the mean-square sound pressure, is set equal to the density of the internal energy of thermal agitation associated with the translational degrees of freedom of the molecules composing the medium. It is then postulated that these molecular motions of thermal agitation can be regarded as a vector summation of the motions associated with a three-dimensional manifold of compressional standing waves, each behaving as it would in an ideal continuous medium having the same gross mechanical and elastic properties that characterize the actual medium. Each of these standing-wave systems thus constitutes an allowed, thermally excited, normal mode of vibration, or degree of freedom, to which can be assigned, in accordance with elementary quantum theory, the average energy

[1] Z. Sakadi, *Proc. Phys.-Math. Soc. Japan* (3) **23,** 208–213 (1941); Meixner, *Acustica* **2,** 101–109 (1952).

$$\frac{\text{Energy}}{\text{Mode}} = \frac{hf}{\exp(hf/kT) - 1} \tag{3c-89}$$

where h is Planck's constant, k is Boltzmann's constant, T is the absolute temperature, and f is the frequency in cycles per second.

The incremental number of such energy-bearing modes of vibration is given by the count of normal frequencies lying between f and $f + df$; and this is given, as in the theory of room acoustics,[1] by

$$dN = \left(\frac{4\pi Vf^2}{c^3} + \frac{\pi Sf}{2c^2} + \frac{L}{2c}\right) df \tag{3c-90}$$

where V is the volume, S the total surface, and L the sum of the three dimensions of the region under consideration, and where the three terms represent, respectively, the normal-frequency "points" distributed throughout the volume, over the coordinate planes, and along the coordinate axes of an octant of frequency space. If the three dimensions of the region are not too disparate, S can be approximated by $6V^{2/3}$, and L by $3V^{1/3}$, giving

$$dN = \frac{4\pi Vf^2 df}{c^3}\left[1 + \frac{3\lambda}{4V^{1/3}} + \frac{3\lambda^2}{8\pi V^{2/3}}\right] \tag{3c-91}$$

For sufficiently high frequencies, this reduces to the classical expression (Rayleigh, 1900; Jeans, 1905) for the distribution of normal frequencies,

$$dN = \frac{4\pi Vf^2 df}{c^3} \tag{3c-92}$$

an aymptotic form that can be shown (Weyl, 1911) to be independent of the shape of V and rigorously valid in the limit when $\lambda = c/f$ becomes small in comparison with $V^{1/3}$.

If attention is confined for the moment to finite frequency bands that do not include the lower frequencies, the incremental translational energy density of thermal agitation will be given by the product of (3c-89) and (3c-92). Then, by hypothesis, this can be set equal to the incremental energy density of the diffuse sound field, which is given by $d(\langle p^2\rangle/\rho c^2)$, where p is the rms sound pressure; thus

$$d\frac{\langle p^2\rangle}{\rho c^2} = \frac{(4\pi f^2 df/c^3)hf}{\exp(hf/kT) - 1} \tag{3c-93}$$

$$= \frac{(4\pi kT/c^3)f^2 df(hf/kT)}{\exp(hf/kT) - 1}$$

$$= \frac{4\pi kT}{c^3} f^2 df\left[1 - \frac{1}{2}\frac{hf}{kT} + \frac{1}{12}\left(\frac{hf}{kT}\right)^2 - \cdots\right], \quad \left(\frac{hf}{kT}\right)^2 < 4\pi^2 \tag{3c-94}$$

The total energy density associated with all the allowed modes of vibration is then to be found by extending the integral of (3c-94) over all frequencies less than the upper limiting frequency for which the mode count [by (3c-92)] is just equal to three times n_V, the total number of molecules in unit volume. This upper frequency limit, f_{lim}, is given, for either liquids or gases, by the integral of (3c-92);

$$\frac{N_{\text{lim}}}{V} = \frac{4\pi f_{\text{lim}}^3}{3c^3} = 3n_V = 3A\frac{\rho}{M} \qquad f_{\text{lim}}^3 = \frac{9c^3 A\rho}{4\pi M} \cdot \tag{3c-95}$$

where A is Avogadro's number (6.025×10^{26} molecules/kg mole), ρ is in kg/m³, and M is the molecular weight (numeric, $O_2 = 32$). At ordinary room temperature, $f_{\text{lim}} \approx 2 \times 10^{10}$ c/s for air, $\approx 4 \times 10^{12}$ c/s for water. These frequencies are well outside the range so far accessible for acoustical experimentation and need not be

[1] Maa, *J. Acoust. Soc. Am.* **10**, 235–238 (1939); Bolt, *J. Acoust. Soc. Am.* **10**, 228–234 (1939).

considered further except when the foregoing notions are used as the basis for a theory of specific heats, in which case it is necessary also to take into account vibrational and rotational degrees of freedom, and to reexamine the equilibrium statistics that underlie (3c-89). Note in passing that the *phonon* of specific-heat theory merely identifies the burden of internal energy carried by each of the normal modes of vibration postulated above.

Within the ranges of frequency and temperature ordinarily of interest in the assessment of thermal noise, the exponent hf/kT is so small that even the linear term in the series expansion of (3c-94) can be omitted. This amounts to a reversion to the classical analysis of energy partition in continuous media[1] and to the assignment of an energy kT to each allowed mode of vibration. With this simplification, (3c-94) can be integrated at once to yield the mean-square sound pressure, in the frequency band $f_2 - f_1$, as

$$\langle p^2 \rangle = \frac{4}{3} \pi kT \frac{\rho}{c} (f_2^3 - f_1^3) \qquad (\text{newtons/m}^2)^2 \qquad (3c\text{-}96)$$

in which Boltzmann's constant $k = 1.380 \times 10^{-23}$ joule/deg Kelvin, T is in degrees Kelvin, ρ in kg/m³, and c in m/sec. To facilitate computation, it is useful to rearrange (3c-96) in the following forms:

$$p_{\text{rms}} = 1.3 \times 10^{-12} \left(\frac{\rho}{c}\right)^{\frac{1}{2}} \left[\frac{T}{293} (f_2^3 - f_1^3)\right]^{\frac{1}{2}} \qquad \text{newtons/m}^2 \qquad (3c\text{-}97a)$$

$$(p_{\text{rms}})_{\text{air}} = 0.76 \times 10^{-10} \left[\frac{T}{293} (f_2^3 - f_1^3)\right]^{\frac{1}{2}} \qquad \text{dynes/cm}^2 = \mu\text{b} \qquad (3c\text{-}97b)$$

$$(p_{\text{rms}})_{\text{sea water}} = 10.6 \times 10^{-10} \left[\frac{T}{293} (f_2^3 - f_1^3)\right]^{\frac{1}{2}} \qquad \mu\text{b} \qquad (3c\text{-}97c)$$

in which the constants have been adjusted to make the temperature factor reduce to unity at 20°C, and where ρ/c has been taken as 0.00345 for air and 0.67 for sea water. It follows, for example, that the rms thermal noise pressure, for the wide-range audio-frequency band extending to 19 kc/s in air, is just equal to the reference sound pressure, $p_0 = 0.0002\ \mu$b.

The power spectrum of thermal noise can be deduced from either (3c-94) or (3c-97b) and may be expressed as a *sound spectrum level* by writing

$$\begin{aligned} \beta_{\text{noise}} &= 10 \log_{10} \left(\frac{d(\langle p^2 \rangle / p_0^2)}{df} \right) = 10 \log_{10} \frac{4\pi kTf^2\rho}{cp_0^2} \\ &= 10 \log_{10} \left[4.33 \times 10^{-7} (f_{\text{kc/s}})^2 \frac{T}{293} \right] \\ &= -63.6 + 20 \log_{10} f_{\text{kc/s}} + 10 \log_{10} \frac{T}{293} \quad \text{db} \qquad (3c\text{-}98) \end{aligned}$$

Note that this noise spectrum is *not* "white" but has instead a uniform positive slope of 6 db/octave, corresponding to an rms thermal-noise sound pressure that is directly proportional to frequency. On the other hand, for frequencies low enough to make the additive "correction" terms of (3c-91) significant, the noise spectrum level tends increasingly to lie *above* the +6 db/octave line as the frequency approaches the low-frequency cutoff at which only the gravest mode of vibration can be excited. The noise spectrum level can also be expected to vary erratically as the low-frequency limit is approached and the population of normal frequencies becomes sparse, in much the same way that the steady-state pressure response of small rooms varies irregularly with frequency when only a few normal modes of vibration are available for excitation. It does not follow, however, that thermal noise in such a small enclosure could be

[1] Jeans, "Dynamical Theory of Gases," 2d ed., pp. 381–391.

"quieted" by the application of sound absorbents. The boundary surfaces, without regard for their acoustical character, will always reach the same radiative equilibrium with the interior medium if both are at the same temperature; otherwise there would be a net flow of thermal "noise" energy across the boundaries in the guise of ordinary heat transfer.

The possibility that thermal noise might be the factor that limits human hearing acuity can be assessed with the help of (3c-98). If the critical-band theory of masking by wide-band noise continues to hold for subliminal stimuli, the effective masking level of thermal noise can be found by adding, at any frequency, the critical bandwidth (expressed as $10 \log_{10} \Delta f_c$) and the spectrum level given by (3c-98). Comparing this result with the binaural threshhold for random incidence then leads to the conclusion that thermal noise remains about 11 to 13 db below threshhold at the frequency of greatest vulnerability (ca. 3 to 5 kcs), even for young people with exceptionally acute hearing. On this basis human hearing might be assigned a "noise figure" of approximately 12 db. It is probable that some at least of this failure to achieve ideal function can be ascribed to internal noise of physiological origin. The near miss on thermal noise limiting gives comforting reassurance, however, that not more than a few decibels of additional hearing acuity could be utilized effectively by humans even if biological adaptation were to make it available.

3d. Acoustic Properties of Gases

LEO L. BERANEK

Bolt Beranek and Newman, Inc.

A number of the physical properties of a gas are important in determining its acoustic characteristics. These include density, pressure, temperature, specific heats, coefficients of viscosity, etc. These properties, and others, are presented and discussed below in detail.

3d-1. Density. The density ρ_0 of a number of common gases at standard temperature and pressure is given in Table 3d-1. The density at any temperature and pressure can be obtained from the expression

$$\rho = \rho_0 \left(\frac{P}{760}\right)\left(\frac{273.16}{T}\right)$$

where P is the barometric pressure in millimeters of mercury and T is the absolute temperature in degrees Kelvin.

3d-2. Atmospheric Pressure and Temperature. The atmospheric pressure and air temperatures, and consequently the air density, vary with elevation above the surface of the earth. Table 3d-2 gives the air pressure, temperature, and density as a function of elevation as compiled by Humphreys[1] and others where indicated.

[1] "Handbook of Chemistry and Physics," 37th ed. Chemical Rubber Publishing Company, Cleveland, 1954–1955.

TABLE 3d-1. DENSITY ρ_0 (0°C, 1 atm)

Gas	Formula	ρ_0, g/liter	ρ_0, lb/ft³
Air		1.2929	0.08071
		1.2920 S	0.0806 S
Ammonia	NH_3	0.7710	0.04813
		0.7598 S	0.04742 S
		0.7708 C	0.0482 C
Argon	A	1.7837	0.11135
		1.782 S	0.1112 S
		1.7828 C	0.1114 C
Carbon dioxide	CO_2	1.9769	0.12341
		1.9630 S	0.1225 S
Carbon monoxide	CO	1.2504	0.07806
		1.2492 S	0.0779 S
Chlorine	Cl_2	3.214	0.2006
		3.1638 S	0.1974 S
		3.2204 C	0.2011 C
Ethane	C_2H_6	1.3566	0.08469
Ethylene	C_2H_4	1.2604	0.07868
Helium	He	0.17847	0.01114
Hydrogen	H_2	0.08988	0.005611
Hydrogen sulfide	H_2S	1.539	0.09608
		1.5203 S	0.0949 S
Methane	CH_4	0.7168	0.04475
		0.7152 S	0.04462 S
Neon	Ne	0.90035	0.05621
		0.8713 C	0.0544 C
Nitric oxide	NO	1.3402	0.08367
		1.3388 S	0.0836 S
Nitrogen	N_2	1.25055	0.07807
		1.2568 S (atm)	0.07846 S
		1.2499 S (chem)	0.07803 S
Nitrous oxide	N_2O	1.9778	0.1235
Oxygen	O_2	1.42904	0.08921
		1.4277 S	0.08915 S
Propane	C_3H_8	2.0096	0.1254
		2.020 S	0.1261 S
Sulfur dioxide	SO_2	2.9269	0.1827
		2.858 S	0.1784 S
Steam (100°)	H_2O	0.5980	0.0373

S = Smithsonian Tables, 9th ed., 1954.
C = J. H. Perry, "Chemical Engineers' Handbook," 3d ed., McGraw-Hill Book Company, Inc., New York, 1950.

At 0°C a 760-mm column of mercury exerts a pressure of 1.01325×10^6 dynes/cm². This is standard atmospheric pressure. When determining the atmospheric pressure using a mercury barometer, account must be taken of the thermal expansion of mercury, and the thermal expansions of the glass container and metallic scale.

3d-3. Specific Heat. For several common gases the values of C_p, the specific heat at constant pressure, and γ, the ratio of C_p to C_v, are given in Table 3d-3. C_v is the specific heat at constant volume. C_p is expressed in calories per gram.

TABLE 3d-2. ATMOSPHERIC PRESSURE, TEMPERATURE, AND DENSITY AS A FUNCTION OF ELEVATION*†

Elevation		Summer			Winter		
Km	Miles	Temp., °C	Pressure, mm Hg	Density dry air, g/cm³	Temp., °C	Pressure, mm Hg	Density dry air, g/cm³
20.0	12.4	−51.0	44.1	0.000092	−57.0	39.5	0.000085
19.0	11.8	−51.0	51.5	0.000108	−57.0	46.3	0.000100
18.0	11.2	−51.0	60.0	0.000126	−57.0	54.2	0.000117
17.0	10.6	−51.0	70.0	0.000146	−57.0	63.5	0.000137
16.0	9.9	−51.0	81.7	0.000171	−57.0	74.0	0.000160
15.0	9.3	−51.0	95.3	0.000199	−57.0	87.1	0.000187
14.0	8.7	−51.0	111.1	0.000232	−57.0	102.1	0.000220
13.0	8.1	−51.0	129.6	0.000270	−57.0	119.5	0.000257
12.0	7.5	−51.0	151.2	0.000316	−57.0	140.0	0.000301
11.0	6.8	−49.5	176.2	0.000366	−57.0	164.0	0.000353
10.0	6.2	−45.5	205.1	0.000419	−54.5	192.0	0.000408
9.0	5.6	−37.8	237.8	0.000470	−49.5	224.1	0.000466
8.0	5.0	−29.7	274.3	0.000524	−43.0	260.6	0.000526
7.0	4.3	−22.1	314.9	0.000583	−35.4	301.6	0.000590
6.0	3.7	−15.1	360.2	0.000649	−28.1	347.5	0.000659
5.0	3.1	− 8.9	410.6	0.000722	−21.2	398.7	0.000735
4.0	2.5	− 3.0	466.6	0.000803	−15.0	455.9	0.000821
3.0	1.9	+ 2.4	528.9	0.000892	− 9.3	519.7	0.000915
2.5	1.6	+ 5.0	562.5	0.000942	− 6.7	554.3	0.000967
2.0	1.2	+ 7.5	598.0	0.000990	− 4.7	590.8	0.001023
1.5	0.9	+10.0	635.4	0.001043	− 3.0	629.6	0.001083
1.0	0.6	+12.0	674.8	0.001100	− 1.3	670.6	0.001146
0.5	0.3	+14.5	716.3	0.001157	0.0	714.0	0.001215
0.0	0.0	+15.7	760.0	0.001223	+ 0.7	760.0	0.001290

* "Handbook of Chemistry and Physics," 37th ed.
† See also Sec. 2m-8, pp. 2-127 to 2-128.

3d-4. Viscosity. The coefficient of viscosity η of a number of gases is given in Table 3d-4. The units of η are dyne-seconds per square centimeter or poises.

The ratio η/ρ of viscosity to density occurs frequently and is known as the kinematic viscosity coefficient. It is usually designated by the letter ν, and has the dimensions square centimeters per second, in the cgs system. For air, $\nu = 0.151$ cm²/sec at 18°C and 760 mm of mercury.

For a plane acoustic wave propagating in an unbounded gas a small attenuation will occur because of viscosity. The attenuation factor is $e^{-\alpha_\eta x}$ for the pressure (or particle velocity) and

$$\alpha_\eta = \frac{2}{3}\frac{\eta}{\rho}\frac{\omega^2}{c^3} = \frac{2}{3}\nu\frac{\omega^2}{c^3}$$

where c is the speed of sound and ω the angular frequency of the wave.

3d-5. Thermal Conductivity. The thermal conductivity κ of a number of gases is given in Table 3d-5. The units of κ are calories per centimeter-second-degree.

The quantity $\kappa/\rho C_v$ frequently appears in heat-conduction equations. It is often designated by the symbol α, and is called the coefficient of temperature exchange.

TABLE 3d-3. SPECIFIC HEAT AT CONSTANT PRESSURE C_p AND THE RATIO γ OF C_p TO THE SPECIFIC HEAT AT CONSTANT VOLUME C_v*

[C_p (cal/g deg); $\gamma = C_p/C_v$]

Gas	Temp., °C	C_p	Temp., °C	γ
Air	−120 (10 atm)	0.2719	−118 (1 atm)	1.415
	(20 atm)	0.3221		
	(40 atm)	0.4791	+ 17 (1 atm)	1.403
	(70 atm)	0.7771	− 78 (1 atm)	1.408
	− 50 (10 atm)	0.2440	− 79 (25 atm)	1.57
	(20 atm)	0.2521	− 79 (100 atm)	2.20
	(40 atm)	0.2741		
	(70 atm)	0.3121		
	0 (1 atm)	0.2398	0 (1 atm)	1.403
	(20 atm)	0.2484	0 (25 atm)	1.47
	(60 atm)	0.2652	0 (50 atm)	1.53
	50 (20 atm)	0.2480	0 (75 atm)	1.59
	(100 atm)	0.2719	17 (1 atm)	1.403
	(220 atm)	0.2961	20 (3 atm)	1.41
	100 (1 atm)	0.2404	100 (1 atm)	1.401
	(20 atm)	0.2471		
	(100 atm)	0.2600	200 (1 atm)	1.398
	(220 atm)	0.2841		
	400 (1 atm)	0.2430	400 (1 atm)	1.393
	1000 (1 atm)	0.2570	1000 (1 atm)	1.365
	1400 (1 atm)	0.2699	1400 (1 atm)	1.341
	1800 (1 atm)	0.2850	1800 (1 atm)	1.316
Ammonia	15 (1 atm)	0.5232	15 (1 atm)	1.310
Argon	15 (1 atm)	0.1253	15 (1 atm)	1.668
Carbon dioxide	15 (1 atm)	0.1989	15 (1 atm)	1.304
Carbon monoxide	15 (1 atm)	0.2478	15 (1 atm)	1.404
Chlorine	15 (1 atm)	0.1149	15 (1 atm)	1.355
Ethane	15 (1 atm)	0.3861	15 (1 atm)	1.22
Ethylene	15 (1 atm)	0.3592	15 (1 atm)	1.255
Helium	−180 (1 atm)	1.25	−180 (1 atm)	1.660
Hydrogen	15 (1 atm)	3.389	15 (1 atm)	1.410
Hydrogen sulfide	15 (1 atm)	0.2533	15 (1 atm)	1.32
Methane	15 (1 atm)	0.5284	15 (1 atm)	1.31
Neon	....	......	19 (1 atm)	1.64
Nitric oxide	15 (1 atm)	0.2329	15 (1 atm)	1.400
Nitrogen	15 (1 atm)	0.2477	15 (1 atm)	1.404
Nitrous oxide	15 (1 atm)	0.2004	15 (1 atm)	1.303
Oxygen	15 (1 atm)	0.2178	15 (1 atm)	1.401
Propane	....	......	16 (0.5 atm)	1.13
Steam	100 (1 atm)	0.4820	100 (1 atm)	1.324
Sulfur dioxide	15 (1 atm)	0.1516	15 (1 atm)	1.29

* "Handbook of Chemistry and Physics," 37th ed.

The reciprocal of α is often called diffusivity. In the cgs system the units of α are square centimeters per second. For air $\alpha = 0.27$ cm²/sec at 18°C and 760 mm of mercury.

A plane acoustic wave propagating in an unbounded gas will be attenuated slightly

TABLE 3d-4. COEFFICIENT OF VISCOSITY η FOR DIFFERENT GASES AS A FUNCTION OF TEMPERATURE*

Gas	Formula	Temp., °C	Viscosity, micropoises (dyne-sec/cm² $\times 10^{-6}$)
Air		−31.6	153.9
		0	170.8
		18	182.7
		40	190.4
		54	195.8
		74	210.2
		100	217.5
		150	238.5
		200	258.2
		300	294.6
		400	327.7
		500	358.3
Argon	A	0	209.6
		23	221.0
Carbon dioxide	CO_2	0	139.0
		20	148.0
		40	157.0
Carbon monoxide	CO	0	166
		15	172
		100	210
Helium	He	0	186.0
		20	194.1
Hydrogen	H_2	0	83.5
		20.7	87.6
Neon	Ne	20	311.1
Nitric oxide	NO	0	178
		20	187.6
Nitrogen	N_2	27.4	178.1
Nitrous oxide	N_2O	0	135
Oxygen	O_2	0	189
		19.1	201.8
		127.7	256.8

* "Handbook of Chemistry and Physics," 37th ed., and "International Critical Tables."

because of thermal-conduction effects. The attenuation constant α_T is

$$\alpha_T = \frac{\kappa(\gamma - 1)\omega^2}{\gamma \rho C_v c^3}$$

where $\kappa/\rho C_v$ is the coefficient of temperature exchange, γ the ratio of specific heats, c the propagation velocity, and ω the angular frequency of the wave.

3d-6. Speed (Velocity) of Propagation. The speed of sound for small sound amplitudes can be written exactly as[1]

$$c = \left[\frac{RT}{M}\left(f + \frac{gR}{hC_V^\infty}\right)\right]^{\frac{1}{2}}$$

where

$$f = -\frac{V^2}{RT}\left(\frac{\partial p}{\partial V}\right)_T$$

$$g = \left(\frac{V}{R}\frac{\partial p}{\partial T}\right)_V^2$$

$$h = \frac{C_v}{C_v^\infty} = 1 + \frac{T}{C_v^\infty}\int_\infty^V \left(\frac{\partial^2 p}{\partial T^2}\right)_v dV$$

C_v^∞ is the specified heat for constant volume as the volume approaches infinity; M, the molecular weight of the gas, has been substituted for ρV; and R, the gas constant, puts the equation in a useful form. The quantities f, g, h are dimensionless and differ only slightly from unity as determined by the imperfection of the gas.

TABLE 3d-5. THERMAL CONDUCTIVITY κ OF GASES AT 0°C*

Gas	Formula	Thermal conductivity κ at 0°C (cal/cm-sec-deg)
Air	....	0.0548×10^{-3}
Argon	A	0.0387×10^{-3}
Carbon dioxide	CO_2	0.0340×10^{-3}
Helium	He	0.344×10^{-3}
Hydrogen	H_2	0.416×10^{-3}
Neon	Ne	0.1104×10^{-3}
Nitrogen	N_2	0.0566×10^{-3}
Oxygen	O_2	0.0573×10^{-3}
Steam (100°C)	H_2O	0.0551×10^{-3} (100°C)

* Kennard, "Kinetic Theory of Gases," McGraw-Hill Book Company, Inc., New York, 1938.

Thus if the molecular weight, the specific heat, and the equation of state are known, the velocity of sound under any conditions can be calculated.

For an ideal gas, where $PV = RT$ one can write

$$c = \left[\frac{RT}{M} - \left(1 + \frac{R}{C_v}\right)\right]^{\frac{1}{2}} = \left(\frac{RT\gamma}{M}\right)^{\frac{1}{2}} = \left(\frac{\gamma p}{\rho}\right)^{\frac{1}{2}}$$

where $\gamma = \dfrac{C_p}{C_v}$

The accepted value of c_0, the velocity at standard conditions of temperature and pressure, for a number of gases is given in Table 3d-6.

The accepted value of the speed of sound in air, c, as calculated and checked on the average by several reported determinations is[1]

$$c_0 = 33{,}145 \pm 5 \text{ cm/sec}$$
$$c_0 = 1{,}087.42 \pm 0.16 \text{ fps}$$

under the conditions (1) audible frequency range, (2) temperature at 0°C, (3) 1 atm pressure, (4) 0.03 mole per cent content of CO_2, (5) 0 per cent water content. To

[1] See Hardy, Telfair, and Pielemeier, *J. Acoust. Soc. Am.* **13**, 226 (1942).

TABLE 3d-6. SPEED (VELOCITY) OF SOUND IN GASES*

Gas	Formula	Speed, m/sec at 0°C	Speed, fps at 0°C
Air	....	331.45	1,087.42
Ammonia	NH_3	415	1,361
Argon	A	319	1,046
Carbon monoxide	CO	337.1	1,106
Carbon dioxide	CO_2	258.0 (low freq.)	846 (low freq.)
		268.6 (high freq.)†	881 (high freq.)†
Carbon disulfide	CS_2	189	606
Chlorine	Cl_2	205.3	674
Ethylene	C_2H_4	314	1,030
Helium	He	970	3,182
Hydrogen	H_2	1,269.5	4,165
Illuminating gas		490.4	1,609
Methane	CH_4	432	1,417
Neon	Ne	435	1,427
Nitric oxide	NO	325	1,066
Nitrogen	N_2	337	1,096
Nitrous oxide	N_2O	261.8	859
Oxygen	O_2	317.2	1,041
Steam (100°C)	H_2O	404.8	1,328

* "Handbook of Chemistry and Physics," 37th ed., "International Critical Tables," and *J. Acoust. Soc. Am.*

† "High frequencies" means that the acoustic period is so short that the periodic changes in the vibrational heat constant cannot remain in phase with the other periodic changes as the sound wave passes through the gas.

calculate the speed of sound at various temperatures one can write

$$c = \left(\frac{R\gamma}{M} 273.16\right)^{\frac{1}{2}} \sqrt{\frac{T}{273.16}}$$

$$= 33{,}145 \sqrt{\frac{T}{273.16}} \quad \text{cm/sec}$$

$$= 33{,}145 \left(1 + \frac{°\text{C}}{273.16}\right) \quad \text{cm/sec} \qquad \left(\frac{°\text{C}}{273.16} \ll 1\right)$$

where T = absolute temperature

°C = temperature, °C

If the gas is made up of a mixture of gases or if water vapor is present the expression

$$c = \left[\frac{RT}{M}\left(1 + \frac{R}{C_v}\right)\right]^{\frac{1}{2}}$$

can still be used to calculate the velocity. The molecular weight M of the mixture can be calculated, or, realizing that $RT/M = p/\rho$, the density of the mixture can be used.

In addition to correcting M (or ρ) it is necessary to correct C_v also. It is incorrect to take the weighted average of the ratio of the specific heats, γ. The weighted average of the specific heats themselves must be used.

For rough calculations of the variation with humidity or composition, it is probably sufficient merely to correct for the density of the mixture.

3d-7. Characteristic Impedance. The characteristic impedance is equal to the ratio of the sound pressure to the particle velocity in a plane wave traveling in an unbounded medium. It is equal to the density times the velocity of propagation, that is, ρc. The variation of ρc with temperature can be calculated from the expression

$$\rho c = \rho_0 c_0 \left(\frac{273.16}{T}\right)^{\frac{1}{2}} \frac{P}{760} \quad \text{rayls}$$

where $\rho_0 c_0$ is the value at 0°C and 1 atm pressure. For air $\rho_0 c_0 = 42.86$ dyne sec/cm³. Table 3d-7 contains values of $\rho_0 c_0$ for several common gases.

TABLE 3d-7. CHARACTERISTIC IMPEDANCE $\rho_0 c$ OF COMMON GASES AT 0°C (273.16°K) TEMPERATURE AND 760 MM HG BAROMETRIC PRESSURE

Gas	Formula	$\rho_0 c_0$, dyne-sec/cm³ at 0°C, 760 mm Hg
Air	....	42.86
Argon	A	56.9
Carbon dioxide	CO_2	50.8
Carbon monoxide	CO	42.1
Helium	He	17.31
Hydrogen	H_2	11.41
Neon	Ne	38.5
Nitric oxide	NO	43.5
Nitrogen	N_2	42.1
Nitrous oxide	N_2O	51.8
Oxygen	O_2	45.3

3d-8. Attenuation. In addition to the dispersion of sound due to wind, turbulence in the atmosphere, and temperature gradients, two properties of the medium combine to attenuate a wave which is propagated in free space. The first of these attenuations is caused by molecular absorption and dispersion in polyatomic gases involving an exchange of translational and vibrational energy between colliding molecules. The second is due to viscosity and heat conduction in the medium.

Knudsen[1] says that "the attenuation of sound is greatly dependent upon location and weather conditions, that is, upon the humidity and temperature of the air. The cold air of the arctic is acoustically transparent; the attenuation of sound is not much more than that attributable to viscosity and heat conductivity; . . . for the hot and relatively dry summer air of the desert, such as at Greenland Ranch, Inyo County, California, where the relative humidity may drop as low as 2.4 per cent, the attenuation at 3000 cps is 0.14 db/m, and at 10,000 cycles it is 0.48 db/m."

Data on the absorption of audible sound in air are valuable because they are needed to calculate the reverberation time for high-frequency sound in rooms, for determining the amplification characteristics of public-address systems for use outdoors, and for predicting the range of effectiveness of apparatus for sound signaling and sound ranging in the atmosphere.

Kneser[1] has treated analytically the problem of absorption and dispersion of sound by molecular collision. He summarized his results in the form of a nomogram which has been reprinted along with comments by Pielemeier.[3] Pielemeier observes that for

[1] V. O. Knudsen, The Propagation of Sound in the Atmosphere—Attenuation and Fluctuations, *J. Acoust. Soc. Am.* **18**, 90–96 (1946).

[2] H. O. Kneser, The Interpretation of the Anomalous Sound-absorption in Air and Oxygen in Terms of Molecular Collisions, *J. Acoust. Soc. Am.* **5**, 122–126 (1933); A Nomogram for Determination of the Sound Absorption Coefficient in Air, *Akust. Z.* **5**, 256–257 (1940) (in German).

[3] W. H. Pielemeier, Kneser's Sound Absorption Nomogram and Other Charts, *J. Acoust. Soc. Am.* **16**, 273–274 (1945).

molecular absorption Kneser's theoretical values are lower than Knudsen's[1] experimental values for reasons not fully understood.

Kneser's nomogram is reproduced in Fig. 3d-1. By means of it, the attenuation due to the molecular absorption can readily be found for any ordinary set of conditions of temperature, humidity, and frequency. For example, if the temperature is 15°C, and relative humidity is 50 per cent, first locate 15° on the temperature axis, trace *left* to the 50 per cent mark, then upward to the middle of the shaded area (upper left), then to the right to the proper frequency curve (3 kc in this case), then downward to the K scale. Next begin another tracing at 15°C toward the *right* until the lower right curve is reached, then trace upward to the log $(M) + 7$ scale. Then join the

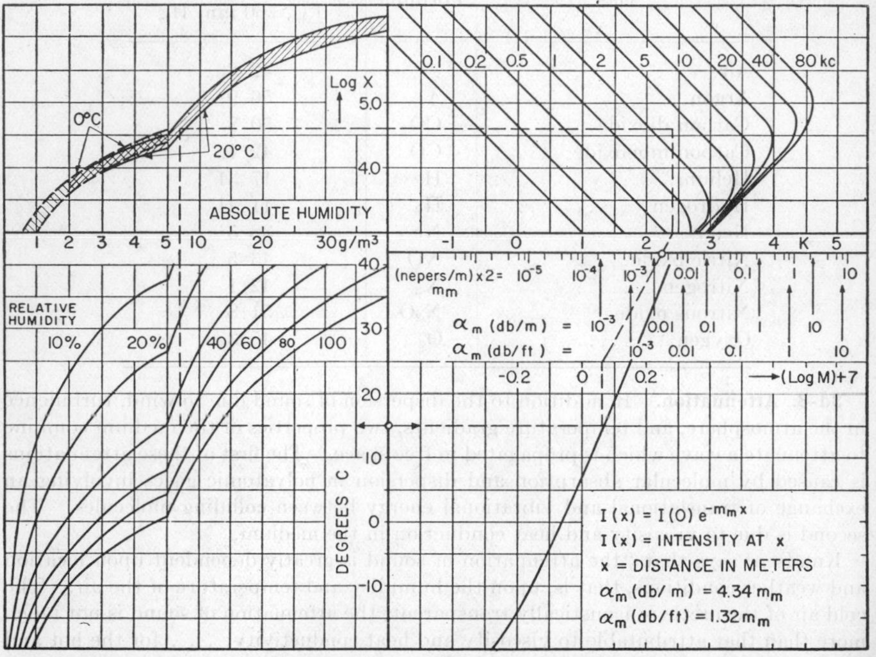

Fig. 3d-1. Nomogram for determining the attenuation in air caused by molecular absorption. *(From L. L. Beranek, "Acoustics Measurement," John Wiley & Sons, Inc., New York, 1949; after Kneser.)*

end points of the two tracings with a straight line. The value of the molecular attenuation α_m as read on that scale will be 12 db/km or 3.7×10^{-3} db/ft. The half width of the shaded band in the log X chart of Fig. 3d-1 represents the uncertainty in the log X values. Note that the band changes position slightly with temperature.

The attenuation caused by heat conduction and viscosity of the air α_c is not known so accurately. The classical absorption due to these causes has been thoroughly described by Lord Rayleigh[2] and was first derived by Kirchhoff and Stokes as the relation

$$\alpha_c = \alpha_\eta + \alpha_T = \frac{\omega^2}{2\rho_0 c^3}\left[\frac{4\eta}{3} + (\gamma - 1)\frac{\kappa}{C_p}\right] \quad \text{nepers/cm}$$

where $\omega/2\pi$ = frequency in cycles per second; ρ_0 = density in grams per centimeter

[1] V. O. Knudsen, The Absorption of Sound in Air, in Oxygen and in Nitrogen—Effects of Humidity and Temperature, *J. Acoust. Soc. Am.* **5**, 112–121 (1933).

[2] Lord Rayleigh, "Theory of Sound," The Macmillan Company, New York, 1929.

cubed; c = speed of sound in centimeters per second; η = coefficient of viscosity in poises; γ = ratio of specific heats; κ = coefficient of thermal conductivity in calories per second-degree-centimeter; and C_p is the specific heat at constant pressure in calories per gram-degree.

Recent papers by Sivian[1] and Krasnooshkin[2] have led to somewhat higher values for the absorption caused by viscosity. The data from these three sources are given by Fig. 3d-2 and the equations

For λ in feet, $$\alpha_c = 0.143 \frac{A}{\lambda^2} \quad \text{db/ft}$$

For λ in meters, $$\alpha_c = 0.0437 \frac{A}{\lambda^2} \quad \text{db/m}$$

where λ is the wavelength and A is given in the curve in Fig. 3d-2.

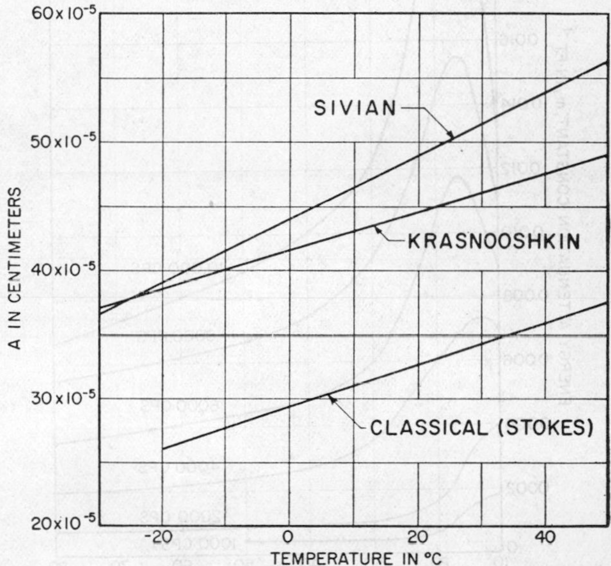

Fig. 3d-2. Plot of A in centimeters as a function of temperature: $A = \alpha_c\lambda^2/0.0437$, where λ = wavelength in meters, and α_c is the attenuation constant in db per meter for a free-traveling plane wave. The upper line (Sivian) obtained by multiplying the Stokes value by 1.5, lies closer to measured values than does either of the other two. *(From L. L. Beranek, "Acoustic Measurements," John Wiley & Sons, Inc., New York, 1949.)*

The total attenuation α_A due to both types of absorption is therefore

$$\alpha_A = \alpha_m + \alpha_c \quad \text{db/ft (or db/m)}$$

These high values of attenuation appear to come from the H_2O vapor content of the air, although they cannot be calculated accurately by the Kneser nomogram. At frequencies above 100 kc for undried air and at all frequencies for dried air, and oxygen and nitrogen, the measured attenuation is about 1.5 times that predicted by the Stokes relation.

[1] L. J. Sivian, High Frequency Absorption in Air and in Other Gases," *J. Acoust. Soc. Am.* **19**, 914–916 (1947).

[2] P. E. Krasnooshkin, On Supersonic Waves in Cylindrical Tubes and the Theory of the Acoustical Interferometer, *Phys. Rev.* **65**, 190 (1944). See also W. H. Pielemeier, Observed Classical Sound Absorption in Air, *J. Acoust. Soc. Am.* **17**, 24–28 (1945).

Some experimental values by Knudsen and Harris[1] for the total attenuation α_A at room temperature and for various values of relative humidity are given in Fig. 3d-3.

An empirical equation, which describes the measured values of Knudsen and Harris with good accuracy for relative humidities above 30 per cent and at a temperature of 20°C, is given by Cremer[2]

$$\alpha_A = \left(\frac{f}{1{,}000}\right)^{\frac{3}{2}} \frac{0.28}{20 + \phi_{20}} \qquad \text{db/m}$$

where ϕ_{20} is the relative humidity at 20°C and f is the frequency. For temperatures

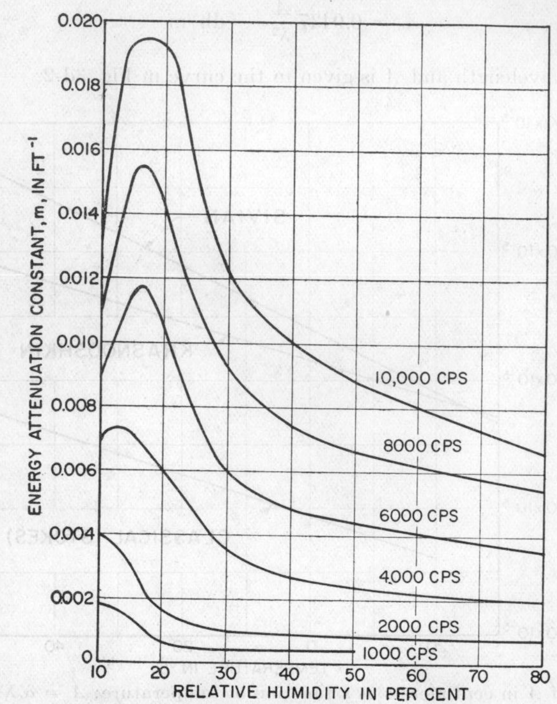

FIG. 3d-3. Measured values of the energy attenuation constant m as a function of relative humidity for different frequencies, $I(x) = I_0 \exp(-mx)$. The temperature is assumed to be about 68°F. (*From L. L. Beranek, "Acoustics," McGraw-Hill Book Company, Inc., New York, 1954: after* V. O. *Knudsen and C. M. Harris, Acoustical Designing in Architecture, p. 160, Fig. 8.10, John Wiley & Sons, Inc., New York, 1950.*)

differing slightly from 20°C, the measured value of relative humidity should be corrected to give a value of ϕ_{20} to be used in the above equation;

$$\phi_{20} = \phi_t(1 + 0.067\Delta t)$$

where Δt denotes temperature departure from 20°C. The quantity α_A is 4.34m, in the same units of distance.

[1] V. O. Knudsen and C. M. Harris, "Acoustical Designing in Architecture," p. 160 Fig. 8.10, John Wiley & Sons, Inc., New York, 1950.

[2] Lothar Cremer, "Die wissenschaftlichen Grundlagen der Raumakustik" (The Scientific Foundations of Room Acoustics), vol. III, S. Hirzel Verlag, Leipzig, 1950.

3e. Acoustic Properties of Liquids

R. D. FAY

Acoustics Laboratory
Massachusetts Institute of Technology

3e-1. Symbols and Definitions. Unless otherwise specified, cgs units are used.

ρ density
k adiabatic compressibility
f frequency
ω $2\pi f$
c speed of propagation of plane (or spherical) waves (velocity of sound), $c = (1/\rho k)^{\frac{1}{2}}$
ρc characteristic impedance
α coefficient of absorption, nepers/cm
For viscous absorption $\alpha \simeq \omega^2(2n + n')/2\rho c^3$ where n = shear viscosity and n' = dilatational viscosity.
α/f^2 absorption constant
db/dd intensity loss in decibels if distance from source is doubled. This unit is usually used only when loss is due to the geometry of the sound field as in spherical or cylindrical waves.

3e-2. Acoustical Comparison between Liquids and Gases. The acoustical behavior of liquids is fundamentally identical to that of gases, but the great differences in the magnitudes of the basic properties, density and compressibility, give rise to notable differences in the nature of practical sound fields in the two media. Thus the techniques which have been developed for the study of sound in gases cannot generally be applied successfully to the study of sound in liquids.

Numerically, the characteristic impedance ρc of liquids is three to four orders of magnitude greater than that of gases. Thus a liquid-gas interface appears as a substantially rigid boundary to a sound in the gas but as an effective pressure-release surface to a sound in the liquid. Even a thin film of gas, or a multiplicity of gaseous bubbles, generally prevents the existence of appreciable sound pressure in the neighboring liquid.

The compliance of solid boundaries is usually negligible compared with the compressibility of gases but is usually appreciable compared with the compressibility of liquids. Thus the simple types of sound field which are readily obtained in a gaseous medium by virtue of effectively rigid boundaries are extremely difficult to realize in a liquid medium. Types of sound fields from which acoustical properties of liquids can be determined have usually been obtained in the laboratory at high frequencies. Most of the published data on such properties were obtained in the megacycle frequency region.

3e-3. Sound Transmission in Large Bodies of Water. Sound transmission at sea is influenced largely by three factors: the geometry of the sound field, the nature of the upper and lower boundaries, and refraction. At short ranges, if source and receiver are at sufficient depths, spherical spreading of sonic energy is approximated and the intensity varies nearly as the inverse square of the range (6 db/dd). At long ranges, the field roughly approximates a two-dimensional continuum producing cylindrical spreading whereby the intensity tends to vary as the inverse first power of the range (3 db/dd). There is an intermediate range in which the controlling factor may be the interference between the direct sound and the sound reflected from the surface. For sinusoidal sound this interference produces the Lloyd-mirror effect. For broad bands the intensity tends to vary as the inverse fourth power of the range (12 db/dd).

These trends have been observed. They are dependent on such factors as source depth, receiver depth, depth of water, smoothness of surface, smoothness and reflectivity of bottom, frequency spectrum, and directivities of transducers. The trends are modified—sometimes completely masked—by the effects of refraction.

Refraction is caused by gradients in temperature, salinity, density, and currents. A major effect is a nonuniform distribution of sonic energy, frequently resulting in shadow zones and skip distances. At times sound channels are formed, i.e., layers within which the sound is trapped by virtue, for example, of downward refraction near the surface due to a temperature gradient and upward refraction in deeper water due to the density gradient.

Reverberation in water is produced by the scattering of sound by minute particles of suspended matter, marine life, and other inhomogeneities. Reverberation due to that portion of the sound which is scattered by the top and bottom surfaces is sometimes called "surface reverberation."

3e-4. Cavitation. The American Standard Acoustical Terminology gives the definition (Z24.1, 9.035): "Cavitation is the formation of local cavities in a liquid as a result of the reduction of total pressure." Cavitation may occur as the result of a sound-wave rarefaction, such as is produced in the negative pressure cycle of an underwater transmitting transducer, or as the result of the reduction of pressure due to hydrodynamic flow, such as is produced by the movement at high speed of a propeller underwater. Broad-band noise is generated by cavitation; a large amount of evidence indicates that this noise is associated with the collapse of cavitation bubbles. In many instances the noise of cavitation has been observed to begin before the cavitation bubbles have been visible to the unaided eye.

In shallow water depths, since atmospheric pressure corresponds to but a low hydraulic head in liquids, cavitation may occur at moderate sound intensities. Numerically, at a static pressure of N atm, the intensity of a sinusoidal plane (or spherical) wave in water at which the total pressure becomes zero at a negative peak is $I \simeq N^2/3$ watts/cm².

The observed cavitation threshold corresponds in many cases to a substantial negative pressure, usually reported to have a very variable value. Many degassed liquids show a tensile strength of the order of an atmosphere. Over very short time intervals this figure is much higher. The threshold of acoustically produced cavitation thus depends on the frequency. It also depends on gas content, ion content, and suspended matter (all cavity-producing nuclei), temperature, viscosity, cleanliness of the container, and the past history of the liquid.

Since cavitation bubbles reduce the sound that is radiated by a transducer, transformer oils and castor oil, which do not cavitate readily, are sometimes used to transmit sound from the transducer face to an outer radiating surface at which the intensity has been spreduced by reading.

3e-5. Dispersion. There is no firm evidence that the speed of propagation of sound in a simple liquid is dependent on frequency.

3e-6. Water and Aqueous Solutions. Table 3e-1, taken from the American Standards Association Acoustical Terminology (Z24.1-1951, Table 9.1), gives various properties of fresh and sea water under representative water conditions.

TABLE 3e-1. PROPERTIES OF FRESH AND SEA WATER

	Fresh water		Sea water			
Salinity (parts per 1,000)...........	0		30		36	
Temp., °C.........	4	25	5	20	15	25
Velocity, m/sec....	1,418.3	1,493.2	1,461.0	1,513.2	1,505.0	1,532.8
Density g/cm³....	1.00000	0.99707	1.02375	1.02099	1.02677	1.02412
Characteristic impedance $\times 10^{-5}$ (cgs units).......	1.4183	1.4888	1.4957	1.5450	1.5453	1.5698

Hydrostatic pressure increases the velocity by 0.018 m/second per meter of depth. It also increases the density by approximately 0.0000045 g/cm³ per meter of depth.

The velocities listed in Table 3e-1 are from Kuwaharara's tables.[1] More recent measurements indicate that the velocity in sea water is 3 to 4 m/sec higher.[2]

Up to 1,000 Mc, no measurable effect of frequency on velocity has been found.

The attenuation in the pressure amplitude of a plane progressive wave is expressed by $p(x) = p_0e^{-\alpha x}$. The theoretical value of α (Stokes-Kirchhoff) for viscous absorp-

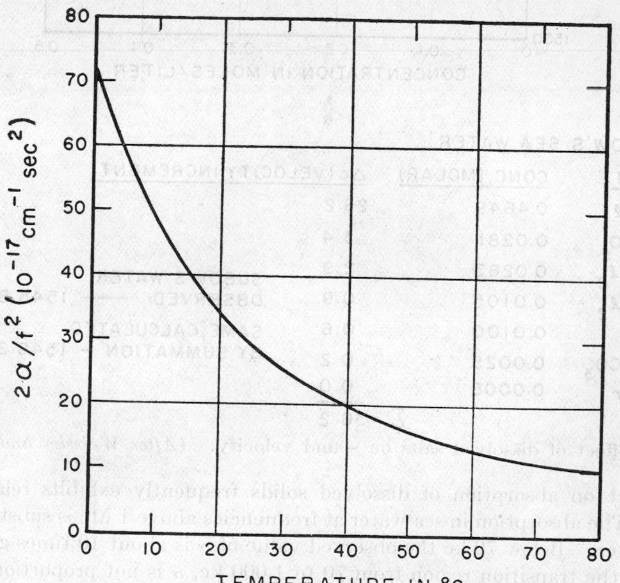

FIG. 3e-1. Theoretical absorption in water as a function of temperature. (*After Hall.*)

tion depends on f^2. The measured value of $\alpha/f^2 = 21.5 \times 10^{-17}$ cm^{-1} reported by Fox and Rock[3] for water has generally[4] been found to hold within experimental limits at room temperature over a very wide range of frequencies. This number has been

[1] Kuwahara, *Hydrographic Rev.* **16**, 123 (1939).
[2] Weissler and Del Grosso, *J. Acoust. Soc. Am.* **23**, 219 (1951).
[3] Fox and Rock, *J. Acoust. Soc. Am.* **12**, 505 (1941).
[4] Measured values have, however, been reported over 1,000 times greater than these.

shown by Hall[1] to correspond to the Stokes-Kirchhoff expression if bulk (dilatational) viscosity as well as shear viscosity is taken into account.

Hall's analysis includes the theoretical effect of temperature on attenuation. The values plotted in Fig. 3e-1 have been verified by several experiments.

Absorption in organic liquids shows no observable relation to the viscosity. The increments in sound velocity due to dissolved salts at the low concentrations found in sea water are found to be proportional to the molar concentration for each salt and to be additive (see Fig. 3e-2) for a number of salts.

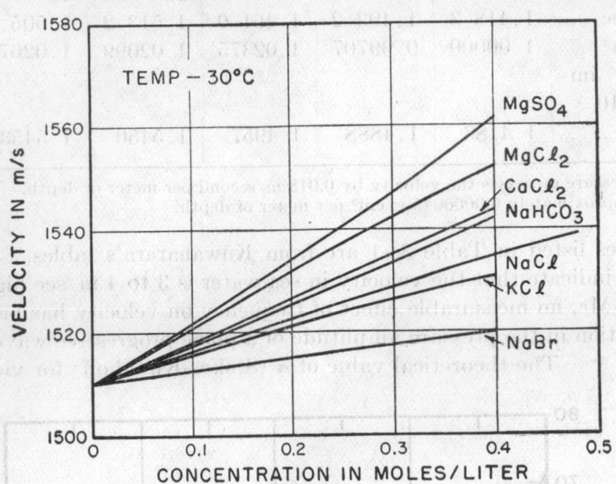

SUBOW'S SEA WATER

SALT	CONC. (MOLAR)	Δc (VELOCITY INCREMENT)
NaCl	0.4649	28.2
$MgSO_4$	0.0281	3.4
$MgCl_2$	0.0263	2.9
$CaCl_2$	0.0105	0.9
KCl	0.0100	0.6
$NaHCO_3$	0.0025	0.2
NaBr	0.0008	0.0
		Σ = 36.2

SUBOW'S WATER OBSERVED —— 1545.8 m/s

SAME, CALCULATED BY SUMMATION – 1546.2 m/s

Fig. 3e-2. Effect of dissolved salts on sound velocity. (*After Weissler and Del Grosso.*)

The effect on absorption of dissolved solids frequently exhibits relaxation phenomena. The absorption in sea water at frequencies above 1 Mc is substantially that in fresh water. Below 70 kc the observed value of α is about 10 times greater in sea water. In the transition region from 70 to 1,000 kc, α is not proportional to f^2 (see Fig. 3e-3). This additional attenuation has been variously attributed to the high concentration (and hence partial dissociation) of NaCl and to the presence of $MgSO_4$.[2]

Figure 3e-3 indicates the observed values of absorption in sea water in the transition range.

Sound velocity and absorption in liquid mixtures exhibit two distinct types of behavior. Mixtures of organic liquids tend to have values for c and for α which vary unidirectionally (not necessarily uniformly) with the relative proportions of the

[1] Hall *Phys. Rev.* **73,** 775 (1948).
[2] Liebermann, *J. Acoust. Soc. Am.* **20,** 868 1948).

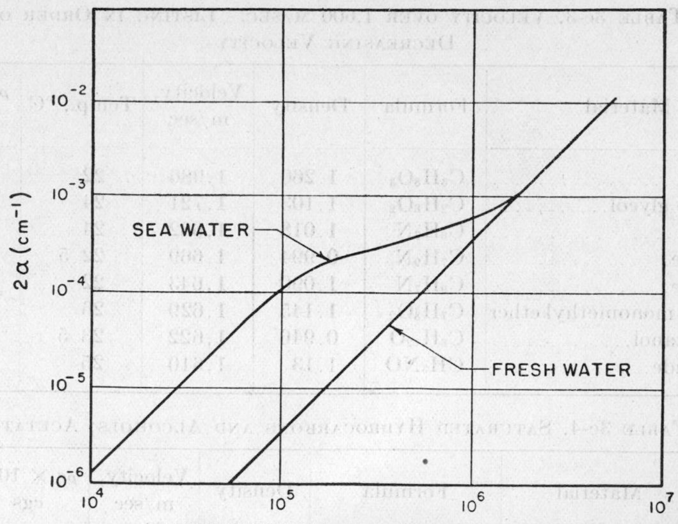

FIG. 3e-3. Sound absorption coefficients for sea water and fresh water. (*After Liebermann.*) To convert to decibels per kiloyard, multiply 2α by 3.97×10^5.

TABLE 3e-2. VELOCITY UNDER 1,100 M/SEC. LISTING IN ORDER OF INCREASING VELOCITY

Material	Formula	Density	Velocity, m/sec	Temp., °C	$\rho c \times 10^{-5}$ cgs
Ethyl bromide	C_2H_5Br	1.428	892	28	1.27
Carbon tetrachloride	CCl_4	1.596	928.5	23	1.48
Bromoform	$CHBr_3$	2.889	929	23.5	2.68
Butyl iodide (*n*)	C_4H_9I	1.616	959	28	1.55
Methylene bromide	CH_2Br_2	2.453	971	24	2.38
Methylene iodide	CH_2I_2	3.323	977	24	3.25
Butyl chloride	C_4H_9Cl	0.84	985	25	0.83
Chloroform	$CHCl_3$	1.487	1,001	23.5	1.49
Acetyl tetrabromide	$C_2H_2Br_4$	2.962	1,007	28	2.98
Ethylene bromide	$C_2H_4Br_2$	2.178	1,014	24	2.21
Butyl bromide (*n*)	C_4H_9Br	1.272	1,016	28	1.29
Acetylene dichloride	$C_2H_2Cl_2$	1.262	1,025	25	1.29
Pentane	C_5H_{12}	0.632	1,052	18	0.66
Allyl chloride	C_3H_5Cl	0.937	1,088	28	1.02

liquids. Solutions of organic liquids in water tend to show peaks in both c and α at some concentration. The velocity peaks are typically 5 to 10 per cent higher than that in either pure liquid, but the attenuation peak may show an increase of an order of magnitude over that of the organic liquid.[1]

Gases in actual solution in water are generally reported to have negligible effect on sound velocity and absorption.

[1] Willard, *J. Acoust. Soc. Am.* **12**, 438 (1941); Willis, *J. Acoust. Soc. Am.* **19**, 242 (1947); Burton, *J. Acoust. Soc. Am.* **20**, 186 (1948).

TABLE 3e-3. VELOCITY OVER 1,600 M/SEC. LISTING IN ORDER OF DECREASING VELOCITY

Material	Formula	Density	Velocity, m/sec	Temp., °C	$\rho c \times 10^{-5}$ cgs
Glycerin	$C_3H_8O_3$	1.260	1,986	22	2.50
Ethylene glycol	$C_2H_6O_2$	1.103	1,721	24	1.90
Aniline	C_6H_7N	1.018	1,682	24	1.71
Toluidine	C_7H_9N	0.994	1,669	22.5	1.66
Quinoline	C_9H_7N	1.090	1,643	22	1.79
Resorcin monomethyl ether	$C_7H_8O_2$	1.145	1,629	26	1.86
Cyclohexanol	$C_6H_{12}O$	0.946	1,622	23.5	1.53
Formamide	CH_3NO	1.13	1,610	25	1.82

TABLE 3e-4. SATURATED HYDROCARBONS AND ALCOHOLS; ACETATES

Material	Formula	Density	Velocity, m/sec	$\rho c \times 10^{-5}$ cgs
A. Saturated Hydrocarbons				
Pentane	C_5H_{12}	0.622	1,052	0.65
Hexane	C_6H_{14}	0.658	1,113	0.73
Heptane	C_7H_{16}	0.681	1,165	0.79
Octane	C_8H_{18}	0.702	1,238	0.87
B. Saturated Alcohols				
Methyl	CH_3OH	0.792	1,130	0.89
Ethyl	C_2H_5OH	0.786	1,207	0.95
Propyl	C_3H_7OH	0.801	1,234	0.99
Butyl	C_4H_9OH	0.808	1,315	1.06
Amyl	$C_5H_{11}OH$	0.813	1,347	1.09
C. Acetates				
Methyl	CH_3COOCH_3	0.928	1,211	1.12
Ethyl	$CH_3COOC_2H_5$	0.898	1,187	1.07
Propyl	$CH_3COOC_3H_7$	0.891	1,182	1.05
Butyl	$CH_3COOC_4H_9$	0.871	1,179	1.03
Amyl	$CH_3COOC_5H_{11}$	0.875	1,168	1.02

Gas bubbles in water are known to have a marked effect on both velocity and absorption.[1] The effect of air mixed in the surface water at sea by virtue of "white caps" has been found to persist after 48 hr of calm. Underwater sound measurements in the laboratory may be affected for many days by the air released from solution in tap water if not degassed.

3e-7. Acoustical Properties of Organic Liquids. The sound velocity in pure organic liquids covers little more than a 2:1 range; the lowest reported is for ethyl bromide (892 m/sec) and the highest is for glycerin (1,986 m/sec). With few excep-

[1] A. B. Wood, "A Textbook of Sound," The Macmillan Company, New York, 1941; D. T. Laird and P. M. Kendis, *J. Acoust. Soc. Am.* **24**, 29 (1952).

TABLE 3e-5. ABSOLUTE VALUES OF THE ABSORPTION CONSTANT FOR A NUMBER OF ORGANIC LIQUIDS. LISTING IN ORDER OF DECREASING ABSORPTION (Temperature between 23 and 27°C)

Material	Formula	Absorption $\alpha/f^2 \times 10^{15}$	Density	Velocity, m/sec	$\rho c \times 10^{-5}$ cgs
Carbon disulfide	CS_2	74	1.26	1,149	1.45
Glycerol	$C_3H_8O_3$	26	1.26	1,986	2.50
2, 3-Butanediol	$C_4H_{10}O_2$	20	1.05		
Benzene	C_6H_6	8.3(9.15)	0.87	1,295(1,310)	1.13
Carbon tetrachloride	CCl_4	5.7	1.59	930(928)	1.48
Cyclohexanol	$C_6H_{12}O$	5.0	0.96	1,622	1.56
Acetylene dichloride	$C_2H_2Cl_2$	4.0	1.26	1,025	1.29
Chloroform	$CHCl_3$	3.8(4.74)	1.49	995(1,001)	1.48
3-Methyl cyclohexanol resid	$C_7H_{14}O$	3.5	0.92	1,400	1.29
t-Amyl alcohol	$C_5H_{12}O$	3.3	0.81	1,204	0.975
Mesityl oxide	$C_6H_{10}O$	3.3	0.85	1,310	1.11
Bromoform	$CHBr_3$	2.3	2.89	908(929)	2.62
t-Butyl chloride	C_4H_9Cl	1.9	0.84	985	0.83
Chlorobenzene	C_6H_5Cl	1.7	1.10	1,302	1.43
Turpentine		1.5	0.88	1,255	1.10
Isopentane	C_5H_{12}	1.5	0.62	985	0.61
d-Fenchone	$C_{10}H_{16}O$	1.4	0.94	1,320	1.24
Ethyl ether	$C_4H_{10}O$	1.4(0.55)	0.71	985	0.70
Dioxane	$C_4H_8O_2$	1.3	1.03	1,380	1.42
Alkazene 13	$C_{15}H_{24}$	1.3	0.86	1,310	1.13
Kerosene		1.1	0.81	1,315	1.06
Methyl acetate	$C_3H_6O_2$	1.09	0.93	1,211	1.13
Ethyl acetate	$C_4H_8O_2$	1.1(0.77)	0.90	1,145(1,187)	1.03
Naphtha		1.0	0.76	1,225	0.93
Toluol	C_7H_8	0.9(0.85)	0.86	1,300(1,320)	1.12
Nitrobenzene	$C_6H_5NO_2$	0.9	1.20	1,490	1.79
1, 3-Dichloro-isobutane	$C_4H_8Cl_2$	0.9	1.14	1,230	1.40
Nitromethane	CH_3NO_2	0.9	1.13	1,335	1.51
Ethyl alcohol	C_2H_6O	0.9	0.79	1,150	0.91
Methyl alcohol	CH_4O	0.9	0.79	1,105(1,130)	0.87
Acetonitrile	CH_3CN	0.8	0.78	1,280(1,275)	1.00
m-Xylol	C_8H_{10}	0.78(0.74)	0.86	1,325(1,328)	1.14
Acetone	C_3H_6O	0.64(0.32)	0.79	1,170(1,203)	0.925
Alkazene 25	$C_{10}H_{12}Cl_2$	0.6	1.20	1,300	1.56
Formamide	CH_3NO	0.57	1.13	1,610	1.82
2, 5-Hexanedione	$C_6H_{10}O_2$	0.50	0.96	1,400	1.34
Water (distilled)	H_2O	0.33(0.25)	1.00	1,500(1,494)	1.50
Mercury	Hg*	0.66		1,450	

* Ring, Fitzgerald, and Hurdle, *Phys. Rev.*, **72**, 87 (1947).

tions, the range is from 1,000 to 1,500 m/sec. (It is a matter of interest that mercury also falls in this range, 1,450 m/sec.)

In contrast, the absorption constant α/f^2 varies over a wide range, about 300:1. Numerically the highest reported absorption constant for a simple liquid is about one order of magnitude lower than that for dry air.

The characteristic impedances of organic liquids ρc are distributed over the range from about 60,000 to 180,000 cgs units. Carbon tetrachloride with the ρc value of 148,000 and sound velocity of 930 m/sec is well suited for acoustic lenses in water in that the characteristic impedances are nearly matched and the velocity ratio is reasonably high, about 62:100.

The values of the properties of organic liquids reported from different sources are seldom in agreement within experimental errors. The discrepancies are presumably due to slight impurities; in the few cases in which mixtures have been investigated large effects from small concentrations have been observed.

The liquids which have been selected for tabulation are:

1. Liquids having sound velocities outside the range 1,100 to 1,600 m/sec.
2. Liquids in certain chemical groups
3. Liquids for which absorption data have been reported

The data for Tables 3e-2, 3e-3, and 3e-4 were taken from Bergman's "Ultrasonics," and for Table 3e-3 from an article by Willard.[1] It will be noted that all the organic liquids (except pentane) which have a sound velocity less than 1,100 m/sec are halogen compounds. Table 3e-2 shows that there are consistent trends within each group but inconsistent trends between groups.

In Table 3e-5 the absolute values of the absorption constant may be in error by a factor of 1.5. The relative values for liquids having nearly like properties (α/f^2 and c) should be correct within 10 per cent.

3f. Acoustic Properties of Solids

W. P. MASON

Bell Telephone Laboratories, Inc.

3f-1. Elastic Constants, Densities, Velocities, and Impedances. Solids are used for conducting acoustic waves in such devices as delay lines useful for storing information, and as resonating devices for controlling and selecting frequencies. Acoustic-wave propagation in solids has been used to determine the elastic constants of single crystals and polycrystalline materials. Changes in velocity with frequency and changes in attenuation with frequency have been used to analyze various intergrain, interdomain, and imperfection motions as discussed in Sec. 3f-2.

In an infinite isotropic solid and also in a finite solid for which the wave front is a large number of wavelengths, plane and nearly plane longitudinal and shear waves can

[1] G. W. Willard, *J. Acoust. Soc. Am.* **12**, 438 (1941).

exist which have the velocities

$$v_{\text{long}} = \sqrt{\frac{\lambda + 2\mu}{\rho}} \qquad v_{\text{shear}} = \sqrt{\frac{\mu}{\rho}} \tag{3f-1}$$

where μ and λ are the two Lamé elastic moduli, μ is the shearing modulus, and $\lambda + 2\mu$ has been called the plate modulus. For a rod whose diameter is a small fraction of a wavelength, extensional and torsional waves can be propagated with velocities

$$v_{\text{ext}} = \sqrt{\frac{Y_0}{\rho}} \qquad v_{\text{tor}} = \sqrt{\frac{\mu}{\rho}}$$

where

$$Y_0 = \mu\left(\frac{3\lambda + 2\mu}{\lambda + \mu}\right) \tag{3f-2}$$

For anisotropic media, three waves will, in general, be propagated, but it is only in special cases that the particle motions will be normal and perpendicular to the direction of propagation. The three velocities satisfy an equation[1]

$$\begin{vmatrix} \lambda_{11} - \rho v^2 & \lambda_{12} & \lambda_{13} \\ \lambda_{12} & \lambda_{22} - \rho v^2 & \lambda_{23} \\ \lambda_{13} & \lambda_{23} & \lambda_{33} - \rho v^2 \end{vmatrix} = 0 \tag{3f-3}$$

where ρ is the density, v the velocity, and the λ's are related to the elastic constants of the crystal by the formulas

$$\begin{aligned}
\lambda_{11} &= l^2c_{11} + m^2c_{66} + n^2c_{55} + 2mnc_{56} + 2nlc_{15} + 2lmc_{16} \\
\lambda_{12} &= l^2c_{16} + m^2c_{26} + n^2c_{45} + mn(c_{46} + c_{25}) + nl(c_{14} + c_{56}) + lm(c_{12} + c_{66}) \\
\lambda_{13} &= l^2c_{15} + m^2c_{46} + n^2c_{33} + mn(c_{45} + c_{36}) + nl(c_{13} + c_{55}) + lm(c_{14} + c_{56}) \\
\lambda_{23} &= l^2c_{56} + m^2c_{24} + n^2c_{34} + mn(c_{44} + c_{23}) + nl(c_{36} + c_{45})lm(c_{25} + c_{46}) \\
\lambda_{22} &= l^2c_{66} + m^2c_{22} + n^2c_{44} + 2mnc_{24} + 2nlc_{46} + 2lmc_{26} \\
\lambda_{33} &= l^2c_{55} + m^2c_{44} + n^2c_{33} + 2mnc_{34} + 2nlc_{35} + 2lmc_{45}
\end{aligned} \tag{3f-4}$$

In these formulas c_{11} to c_{66} are the 21 elastic constants and l, m, n the direction cosines of the direction of propagation with respect to the crystallographic x, y, and z axes which are related to the a, b, c crystallographic axes as discussed in an IRE publication.[2]

In Eq. (3f-3), we solve for the quantity ρv^2. It was shown by Christoffel[2] that the direction cosines for the particle motion ξ, i.e., α, β, γ, are related to the λ constants and a solution of ρv^2 by the equations

$$\alpha\lambda_{11} + \beta\lambda_{12} + \gamma\lambda_{13} = \alpha\rho v_i^2 \quad \alpha\lambda_{12} + \beta\lambda_{22} + \gamma\lambda_{23} = \beta\rho v_i^2 \quad \alpha\lambda_{13} + \beta\lambda_{23} + \gamma\lambda_{33} = \gamma\rho v_i^2 \tag{3f-5}$$

where $i = 1, 2, 3$. Hence, solutions of Eq. (3f-3) are related to particle motions by the equations of (3f-5).

Most metals crystallize in the cubic and hexagonal systems. Furthermore, when a metal is produced by rolling, an alignment of grains occurs such that the rolling direction is a unique axis. This type of symmetry, known as transverse isotropy, results in the same set of constants as that for hexagonal symmetry. For cubic crystals, the resulting elastic constants are

$$c_{11} = c_{22} = c_{33} \qquad c_{12} = c_{13} = c_{23} \qquad c_{44} = c_{55} = c_{66} \tag{3f-6}$$

while for hexagonal symmetry or transverse isotropy, the resulting elastic constants are

$$c_{11} = c_{22} \qquad c_{12} \qquad c_{13} = c_{23} \qquad c_{44} = c_{55} \qquad c_{66} = \frac{c_{11} - c_{12}}{2} \tag{3f-7}$$

[1] Love, "Theory of Elasticity," 4th ed., p. 298, Cambridge University Press, New York, 1934.

[2] Standards on Piezoelectric Crystals, *Proc. IRE* **37** (12), 1378–1395 (December, 1949).

For cubic symmetry, the waves transmitted along the [100] direction and the [110] direction have purely longitudinal and shear components with the elastic-constant values and particle direction ξ given by

[100] direction

$$v_{\text{long}} = \sqrt{\frac{c_{11}}{\rho}} \quad \xi \text{ along } [100] \qquad v_{\text{shear}} = \sqrt{\frac{c_{44}}{\rho}}$$

ξ along any direction in the [100] plane

[110] direction

$$v_{\text{long}} = \sqrt{\frac{c_{11} + c_{12} + 2c_{44}}{2\rho}} \qquad \xi \text{ along } [110]$$

$$v_{1\,\text{shear}} = \sqrt{\frac{c_{44}}{\rho}} \quad \xi \text{ along } [001] \qquad v_{2\,\text{shear}} = \sqrt{\frac{c_{11} - c_{12}}{2\rho}}$$

ξ along $[1\bar{1}0]$

For hexagonal or transverse isotropy, waves transmitted along the unique axis and any axis perpendicular to this will have the values

[001] direction

$$v_{\text{long}} = \sqrt{\frac{c_{33}}{\rho}} \quad \xi \text{ along } [001] \qquad v_{\text{shear}} = \sqrt{\frac{c_{44}}{\rho}}$$

ξ along any direction in the [001] plane

[100] direction

$$v_{\text{long}} = \sqrt{\frac{c_{11}}{\rho}} \quad \xi \text{ along } [100] \qquad v_{1\,\text{shear}} = \sqrt{\frac{c_{44}}{\rho}}$$

$$\xi \text{ along } [001] \qquad v_{2\,\text{shear}} = \sqrt{\frac{c_{11} - c_{12}}{2\rho}} \qquad \xi \text{ along } [010]$$

The fifth constant is measured by transmitting a wave 45 deg between the [100] and [001] directions, i.e., $l = n = 1/\sqrt{2}$; $m = 0$. For this case

$$\lambda_{11} = \frac{c_{11} + c_{44}}{2} \quad \lambda_{12} = \lambda_{23} = 0 \quad \lambda_{13} = \frac{c_{13} + c_{44}}{2} \quad \lambda_{22} = \frac{c_{11} - c_{12} + 2c_{44}}{4}$$

$$\lambda_{33} = \frac{c_{44} + c_{33}}{2} \tag{3f-8}$$

The three solutions of Eq. (3f-3) are

$$\rho v_1^2 = \frac{c_{11} - c_{12} + 2c_{44}}{4}$$

$$\rho v_{2,3}^2 = \frac{[(c_{11} + c_{33} + 2c_{44})/2] \pm \sqrt{[(c_{11} - c_{33})/2]^2 + (c_{13} + c_{44})^2}}{2} \tag{3f-9}$$

For these three velocities, the particle velocities have the direction cosines

For v_1, $\beta = 1$

For v_2, $$\alpha = \gamma \left\{ \frac{c_{11} - c_{33}}{2(c_{13} + c_{44})} + \sqrt{1 + \left[\frac{c_{11} - c_{33}}{2(c_{13} + c_{44})} \right]} \right\} \tag{3f-10}$$

For v_3, $$\alpha = -\gamma \left\{ \frac{c_{33} - c_{11}}{2(c_{13} + c_{44})} + \sqrt{1 + \left[\frac{(c_{11} - c_{33})}{2(c_{13} + c_{44})} \right]^2} \right\}$$

Hence, unless c_{11} is nearly equal to c_{33}, a longitudinal or shear crystal will generate both types of waves. Experimentally, however, it is found that a good discrimination can be obtained against the type of wave that is not primarily generated and a single velocity can be measured. A resonance technique can also be used to evaluate all the elastic constants of a crystalline material.

TABLE 3f-1. DENSITIES OF GLASSES, PLASTICS, AND METALS IN POLYCRYSTALLINE AND CRYSTALLINE FORM (X-RAY DENSITIES FOR CRYSTALS)*

Materials	Composition	Temp., °C	Density, kg/m³ × 10³ or g/cm³
Aluminum			
Hard-drawn		20	2.695
Crystal		25	2.697
Aluminum and copper	10 Al, 90 Cu	..	7.69
	5 Al, 95 Cu	..	8.37
	3 Al, 97 Cu	..	8.69
Beryllium		20	1.87
Crystal		18	1.871
Brass:			
Yellow	70 Cu, 30 Zn	..	8.5–8.7
Red	90 Cu, 10 Zn	..	8.6
White	50 Cu, 50 Zn	..	8.2
Bronze	90 Cu, 10 Sn	..	8.78
	85 Cu, 15 Sn	..	8.89
	80 Cu, 20 Sn	..	8.74
	75 Cu, 25 Sn	..	8.83
Chromium		20	6.92–7.1
Crystal		18	7.193
Cobalt		21	8.71
Crystal		..	8.788
Constantine	60 Cu, 40 Ni	..	8.88
Copper		..	8.3–8.93
Crystal		18	8.936
Duralumin	17ST = 4 Cu, 0.5 Mg, 0.5 Mn	..	2.79
Germanium		..	5.3
Crystal		20	5.322
German silver	26.3 Cu, 36.6 Zn, 36.8 Ni	..	8.30
	52 Cu, 26 Zn, 22 Ni	..	8.45
	59 Cu, 30 Zn, 11 Ni	..	8.34
	63 Cu, 30 Zn, 6 Ni	..	8.30
Gold		..	18.9–19.3
Crystal		20	19.32
Indium		..	7.28
Crystal		..	7.31
Invar	63.8 Fe, 36 Ni, 0.20 C		8.0
Iron		20	7.6–7.85
Crystal		20	7.87
Lead		20	11.36
Crystal		18	11.34
Lead and tin	87.5 Pb, 12.5 Sn	..	10.6
	84 Pb, 16 Sn	..	10.33
	72.8 Pb, 22.2 Sn	..	10.05
	63.7 Pb, 36.3 Sn		9.43
	46.7 Pb, 53.3 Sn		8.73
	30.5 Pb, 69.5 Sn	..	8.24

TABLE 3f-1. DENSITIES OF GLASSES, PLASTICS, AND METALS IN POLYCRYSTALLINE AND CRYSTALLINE FORM (X-RAY DENSITIES FOR CRYSTALS) (*Continued*)

Materials	Composition	Temp., °C	Density, kg/m³ × 10³ or g/cm³
Magnesium		..	1.74
Crystal		25	1.748
Manganese		..	7.42
Crystal		..	7.517
Mercury		20	13.546
Monel metal	71 Ni, 27 Cu, 2 Fe	..	8.90
Molybdenum		..	10.1
Crystal		25	10.19
Nickel		..	8.6–8.9
Crystal		25	8.905
Phosphor bronze	79.7 Cu, 10 Sn, 9.5 Sb, 0.8 P	..	8.8
Platinum		20	21.37
Crystal		18	21.62
Silicon		15	2.33
Crystal		25	2.332
Silver		..	10.4
Crystal		25	10.49
347 stainless steel		..	7.91
Tin		..	7–7.3
Crystal		..	7.3
Tungsten		..	18.6–19.1
Crystal		25	19.2
Zinc		..	7.04–7.18
Crystal		25	7.18
Fused silica		..	2.2
Pyrex glass (702)		..	2.32
Heavy silicate flint		..	3.879
Light borate crown		..	2.243
Lucite		..	1.182
Nylon 6-6		..	1.11
Polyethylene		..	0.90
Polystyrene		..	1.056

* See also Tables 26-1 through 26-13.

When a longitudinal or shear wave is reflected at an angle from a plane surface, both a longitudinal and a shear wave will in general be reflected from the surface, the angles of reflection and refraction satisfying Snell's law

$$\frac{\sin \beta}{v_S} = \frac{\sin \alpha}{v_l} \tag{3f-11}$$

where α and β are the angles of incidence and refraction with respect to a normal to the reflecting surface. Exceptions to this rule occur if a shear wave has its direction of particle displacement parallel to the reflecting surface, in which case only a pure shear wave is reflected, with the angle of reflection being equal to the angle of incidence. Use is made of this result in constructing delay lines which can be contained in a small volume. When the angle of incidence is 90 deg, the transmitted wave is reflected without change of mode. If the transmitting medium is connected to another medium with different properties, the transmission and reflection factors are determined by the relative impedances of the two media. The impedance is given by the formula

$$Z = \rho v = \sqrt{E\rho} \tag{3f-12}$$

where E is the appropriate elastic stiffness and ρ the density. The reflection and transmission coefficients between medium 1 and medium 2 are given by the equations

$$R = \frac{Z_1 - Z_2}{Z_1 + Z_2} \qquad T = 1 - R = \frac{2Z_2}{Z_1 + Z_2} \tag{3f-13}$$

Tables 3f-1 to 3f-4 list the densities, elastic constants, velocities, and impedances for a number of materials used in acoustic-wave propagation.

3f-2. Attenuation Due to Thermal Effects, Relaxations, and Scattering. When sound is propagated through a solid, it suffers a conversion of mechanical energy into heat. While all the causes of conversion are not known, a number of them are, and tables for these effects are given in this section.

3f-3. Loss Due to Heat Flow. When a sound wave is sent through a body, a compression or rarefaction occurs which heats or cools the body. This heat causes thermal expansions which alter slightly the elastic constants of the material. Since the compressions and rarefactions occur very rapidly, there is not time for much heat to flow and the elastic constants measured by sound propagation are the adiabatic constants. For an isotropic material, the adiabatic constants are related to the isothermal constants by the formulas[1]

$$\lambda^\sigma = \lambda^\theta + \frac{9\alpha^2 B^2 \Theta}{\rho C_v} \qquad \mu^\sigma = \mu^\theta \qquad Y_0{}^\sigma = Y_0{}^\theta + \left(\frac{\mu}{\lambda + \mu}\right)^2 \frac{9\alpha^2 B^2 \Theta}{\rho C_v} \tag{3f-14}$$

where the superscripts σ and θ indicate adiabatic and isothermal constants, α is the linear temperature coefficient of expansion, B the bulk modulus ($B = \lambda + \frac{2}{3}\mu$), Θ the absolute temperature in degrees Kelvin, ρ the density, and C_v the specific heat at constant volume. Table 3f-5 shows these quantities for a number of materials.

The difference between λ^σ and λ^θ should be taken account of when one compares the elastic constants measured by ultrasonic means with those measured by static means. From the data given in Table 3f-5, it is evident that this effect can produce errors as high as 10 per cent in the case of zinc. Adiabatic elastic constants are measured from frequencies somewhat greater than those for which thermal equilibrium is established during the cycle to a frequency[1] $f \doteq (\rho C_v v^2/2\pi K)$ for which wave propagation again takes place isothermally. This frequency is approximately 10^{12} cycles for most metals.

When account is taken of the energy lost by heat flow between the hot and cool parts, this adds an attenuation for longitudinal waves equal to

$$A = \frac{2\pi f^2}{\rho v^3}\left[\frac{K}{C_v}\left(\frac{E^\sigma - E^\theta}{E^\Theta}\right)\right] \quad \text{nepers/m} \tag{3f-15}$$

where f is the frequency, v the velocity, K the heat conductivity, and E the appropriate elastic constant for the mode of propagation considered. Since $Q = B/2A$, it becomes

$$Q = \frac{\rho C_v v^2}{2fK[(E^\sigma - E^\theta)/E^\Theta]} \tag{3f-16}$$

[1] W. P. Mason, "Piezoelectric Crystals and Their Application to Ultrasonics," pp. 480–481, D. Van Nostrand Company, Inc., New York, 1950.

Table 3f-2. Elastic Constants, Wave Velocities, and Characteristic Impedances of Metals, Glasses, and Plastics

Materials	Y_0, newton/m² × 10^{-10}	μ, newton/m² × 10^{-10}	λ, newton/m² × 10^{-10}	Poisson's ratio, σ	$V_l = \sqrt{(\lambda + 2\mu)/\rho}$, m/sec	$V_s = \sqrt{\mu/\rho}$, m/sec	$V_{ext} = \sqrt{Y_0/\rho}$ m/sec	$Z_l = \sqrt{\rho(\lambda + 2\mu)}$, kg/sec m² × 10^{-6}	$Z_s = \sqrt{\rho\mu}$, kg/sec m² × 10^{-6}
Aluminum, rolled	6.8–7.1	2.4–2.6	6.1	0.355	6,420	3,040	5,000	17.3	8.2
Beryllium	30.8	14.7	1.6	0.05	12,890	8,880	12,870	24.1	16.6
Brass, yellow, 70 Cu, 30 Zn	10.4	3.8	11.3	0.374	4,700	2,110	3,480	40.6	18.3
Copper, rolled	12.1–12.8	4.6	13.1	0.37	5,010	2,270	3,750	44.6	20.2
Duralumin 17S	7.15	2.67	5.44	0.335	6,320	3,130	5,150	17.1	8.5
Gold, hard-drawn	8.12	2.85	15.0	0.42	3,240	1,200	2,030	62.5	23.2
Iron electrolytic	20.6	8.2	11.3	0.29	5,950	3,240	5,120	46.4	25.3
Armco	21.2	8.24	11.35	0.29	5,960	3,240	5,200	46.5	25.3
Lead, rolled	1.5–1.7	0.54	3.3	0.43	1,960	690	1,210	22.4	7.85
Magnesium, drawn, annealed	4.24	1.62	2.56	0.306	5,770	3,050	4,940	10.0	5.3
Monel metal	16.5–18	6.18–6.86	12.4	0.327	5,350	2,720	4,400	47.5	24.2
Nickel	21.4	8.0	16.4	0.336	6,040	3,000	4,900	53.5	26.6
Platinum	16.7	6.4	9.9	0.303	3,260	1,730	2,800	69.7	37.0
Silver	7.5	2.7	8.55	0.38	3,650	1,610	2,680	38.0	16.7
347 Stainless steel	19.6	7.57	11.3	0.30	5,790	3,100	5,000	45.7	24.5
Tin, rolled	5.5	2.08	4.04	0.34	3,320	1,670	2,730	24.6	11.8
Tungsten, drawn	36.2	13.4	31.3	0.35	5,410	2,640	4,320	103	50.5
Zinc, rolled	10.5	4.2	4.2	0.25	4,210	2,440	3,850	30	17.3
Fused silica	7.29	3.12	1.61	0.17	5,968	3,764	5,760	13.1	8.29
Pyrex glass	6.2	2.5	2.3	0.24	5,640	3,280	5,170	13.1	7.6
Heavy silicate flint	5.35	2.18	1.77	0.224	3,980	2,380	3,720	15.4	9.22
Light borate crown	4.61	1.81	2.2	0.274	5,100	2,840	4,540	11.4	6.35
Lucite	0.40	0.143	0.562	0.4	2,680	1,100	1,840	3.16	1.3
Nylon 6-6	0.355	0.122	0.511	0.4	2,620	1,070	1,800	2.86	1.18
Polyethylene	0.076	0.026	0.288	0.458	1,950	540	920	1.75	0.48
Polystyrene	0.528	0.12	0.34	0.405	2,350	1,120	2,240	2.48	1.18

TABLE 3f-3. ELASTIC CONSTANTS OF CUBIC SINGLE CRYSTALS*

(s = compliance modulus, m²/newton; c = stiffness modulus, newtons/m²; for cgs units of dynes/cm², multiply the c constants by 10; divide the s constants by 10 to obtain cm²/dyne)

Crystal	$s_{11} \times 10^{11}$	$s_{12} \times 10^{11}$	$s_{44} \times 10^{11}$	$c_{11} \times 10^{-10}$	$c_{12} \times 10^{-10}$	$c_{44} \times 10^{-10}$	$B = [(c_{11} + 2c_{12})/3] \times 10^{-10}$	Anisotropy $2c_{44}/(c_{11} - c_{12})$
Ag	2.32	−0.993	2.29	11.9	8.94	4.37	9.93	2.95
Al	1.59	−0.58	3.52	10.82	6.13	2.85	7.69	1.24
Au	2.33	−1.07	2.38	19.6	16.45	4.20	17.5	2.67
Cu	1.49	−0.625	1.33	17.02	12.3	7.51	13.9	3.18
Fe	0.757	−0.282	0.862	23.7	14.1	11.6	17.3	2.37
Ge	0.964	−0.260	1.49	12.92	4.79	6.70	7.50	1.65
K	83.3	−37.0	38.0	0.416	0.333	0.263	0.361	6.34
Na	48.3	−20.9	16.85	0.615	0.469	0.592	0.518	8.11
Ni (sat.)	0.80	−0.312	0.844	25.0	16.0	11.85	19.0	2.63
Pb	9.30	−4.26	6.94	4.85	4.09	1.44	4.34	3.79
Si	0.768	−0.214	1.26	16.57	6.39	7.956	9.783	1.56
W	0.257	−0.073	0.66	50.2	19.9	15.15	30.0	1.0
Diamond†	0.0958	−0.01	0.174	107.6	12.5	57.6	44.2	1.21
NaCl	2.4	−0.50	7.8	0.49	0.124	0.126	0.25	0.688
KBr	4.0	−1.2	7.5	0.35	0.058	0.050	0.16	0.342
KCl	2.7	−0.3	15.6	0.40	0.062	0.062	0.17	0.361

Elastic Constants of Copper Alloys‡

Alloy	Atom % of second component	$s_{11} \times 10^{11}$	$s_{12} \times 10^{11}$	$s_{44} \times 10^{11}$	$c_{11} \times 10^{-10}$	$c_{12} \times 10^{-10}$	$c_{44} \times 10^{-10}$	$B = [(c_{11} + 2c_{12})/3] \times 10^{-10}$	Anisotropy $2c_{44}/(c_{11} - c_{12})$
CuZn	4.53	1.59	−0.671	1.348	16.34	11.92	7.42	13.39	3.36
CuAl	4.81	1.59	−0.674	1.335	16.58	12.16	7.49	13.63	3.39
	9.98	1.67	−0.711	1.305	15.95	11.77	7.66	13.16	3.66
CuGa	1.58	1.55	−0.65	1.346	16.49	11.93	7.43	13.45	3.25
	4.15	1.59	−0.672	1.349	16.51	12.10	7.41	13.57	3.36
CuSi	4.17	1.61	−0.685	1.336	16.78	12.42	7.48	13.87	3.43
	5.16	1.67	−0.709	1.335	16.09	11.88	7.49	13.28	3.56
	7.69	1.73	−0.745	1.350	16.64	12.60	7.41	13.95	3.67
CuGe	1.03	1.52	−0.637	1.333	16.66	12.00	7.50	13.62	3.29
	1.71	1.57	−0.663	1.333	16.30	11.83	7.50	13.32	3.35

* See also Tables 2f-1 through 2f-5.
† Recent data by W. L. Bond and H. J. McSkimin.
‡ Data from C. S. Smith.

TABLE 3f-4. ELASTIC CONSTANTS OF HEXAGONAL CRYSTALS

(s = compliance moduli, m^2/newton; c = stiffness moduli, newtons/m^2; for cgs units of dynes/cm^2 multiply the c constants by 10; divide the s constants by 10 to obtain cm^2/dyne)

Crystal	$s_{11} \times 10^{11}$	$s_{12} \times 10^{11}$	$s_{13} \times 10^{11}$	$s_{33} \times 10^{11}$	$s_{44} \times 10^{11}$	
Cd	1.23	−0.15	−0.93	3.55	5.40	
Mg	2.21	−0.77	−0.49	1.97	6.03	
Zn	0.84	+0.11	−0.78	2.87	2.64	
Co	0.473	−0.231	−0.07	0.319	1.325	
	$c_{11} \times 10^{-10}$	$c_{12} \times 10^{-10}$	$c_{13} \times 10^{-10}$	$c_{33} \times 10^{-10}$	$c_{44} \times 10^{-10}$	$B = \dfrac{1}{2(s_{11}+s_{12})+s_{33}+4s_{13}} \times 10^{-10}$
Cd	12.12	4.81	4.42	4.45	1.85	5.03
Mg	5.86	2.49	2.08	6.60	1.65	3.46
Zn	16.35	2.64	5.17	5.31	3.78	8.26
Co	30.71	16.5	10.27	35.81	7.55	19.01

TABLE 3f-5. ADIABATIC ISOTHERMAL [illegible]

Material	Density, kg/m³ × 10⁻³	C_v, joules/kg/°C × 10⁻³	α, × 10⁶/°C	K, watts/m²/m/°C × 10⁻²	λ^θ, newtons/m² × 10⁻¹⁰	μ, newtons/m² × 10⁻¹⁰	$\lambda^\sigma - \lambda^\theta$, newtons/m² × 10⁻⁹	$Y_0^\sigma - Y_0^\theta$, newtons/m² × 10⁻⁸	A/f^2, nepers/m
Aluminum	2.699	0.9	23.9	2.22	6.1	2.5	3.8	3.2	2.3×10^{-16}
Beryllium	1.82	2.17	12.4	1.58	1.6	14.7	1.4	11.4	2.1×10^{-18}
Copper	8.96	0.384	16.5	3.93	13.1	4.6	5.5	3.7	4.45×10^{-16}
Gold	19.32	0.13	14.2	2.97	15.0	2.85	6.1	1.5	1.95×10^{-15}
Iron	7.87	0.46	11.7	0.75	11.3	8.2	2.7	4.8	1.88×10^{-17}
Lead	11.4	0.128	29.4	0.344	3.3	0.54	2.12	0.36	2.95×10^{-15}
Magnesium	1.74	1.04	26	1.59	2.56	1.62	1.3	2.1	2.0×10^{-16}
Nickel	8.90	0.44	13.3	0.92	16.4	8.0	5.7	6.1	3.8×10^{-17}
Silver	10.49	0.234	19.7	4.18	8.55	2.7	4.5	2.6	1.95×10^{-15}
Tin	7.3	0.225	23	0.67	4.04	2.08	3.5	4.0	9.7×10^{-16}
Tungsten	19.3	0.134	4.3	2.0	31.3	13.4	3.1	2.8	5.0×10^{-17}
Zinc	7.1	0.382	29.7	1.12	4.2	4.2	4.3	10.7	3.8×10^{-16}
Fused silica	2.2	0.92	0.5	0.01	1.61	3.12	0.00045	0.002	2.6×10^{-22}

TABLE 3f-6. FACTORS GOVERNING INTERGRAIN HEAT FLOW IN METALS

Metal	Pb	Ag	Cu	Au	Fe	Al	W
R	0.065	0.031	0.031	0.014	0.022	0.0009	10^{-1}
$(C_p - C_v)/C_v$	0.067	0.040	0.028	0.038	0.016	0.046	0.006
Product	4.4×10^{-3}	1.2×10^{-3}	8.7×10^{-4}	5.3×10^{-4}	3.5×10^{-4}	4×10^{-5}	6×10^{-9}

TABLE 3f-7. RELATIVE SCATTERING FACTORS FOR LONGITUDINAL AND SHEAR WAVES IN POLYCRYSTALLINE METALS

Metal	Al	Au	Ag	Cu	Pb	Fe	Na	K	W	Mg	Zn	Cd
S_L	3×10^{-4}	1.78×10^{-3}	5×10^{-3}	7.4×10^{-3}	4.2×10^{-3}	6.7×10^{-3}	2.9×10^{-2}	1.7×10^{-2}	0	2.2×10^{-4}	5.6×10^{-2}	2.8×10^{-2}
S_S	3.3×10^{-3}	5.2×10^{-2}	6.1×10^{-2}	6.7×10^{-2}	7.2×10^{-2}	4.0×10^{-2}	1.25×10^{-1}	1.1×10^{-1}	0			

where Q is the ratio of 2π times the energy stored to energy dissipated per cycle and B is the phase shift per unit length. Table 3f-5 shows the attenuation for a number of solids due to thermal loss.

3f-4. Loss Due to Intergrain Heat Flow. A related thermal loss that occurs in polycrystalline material is the thermoelastic relaxation loss which arises from heat flow from grains that have received more compression or extension in the course of the wave motion than do adjacent grains. The Q from this source has been shown to be[1]

$$\frac{1}{Q} = \frac{C_p - C_v}{C_v} R \frac{f_0 f}{f_0^2 + f^2} \tag{3f-17}$$

where R is that fraction of the total strain energy which is associated with the fluctuations of dilations, and f_0, the relaxation frequency, is approximately

$$f_0 = \frac{D}{L_c^2} = \frac{K}{\rho C_p L_c^2} \tag{3f-18}$$

where L_c is the mean diameter of the crystallites and D the diffusion constant.

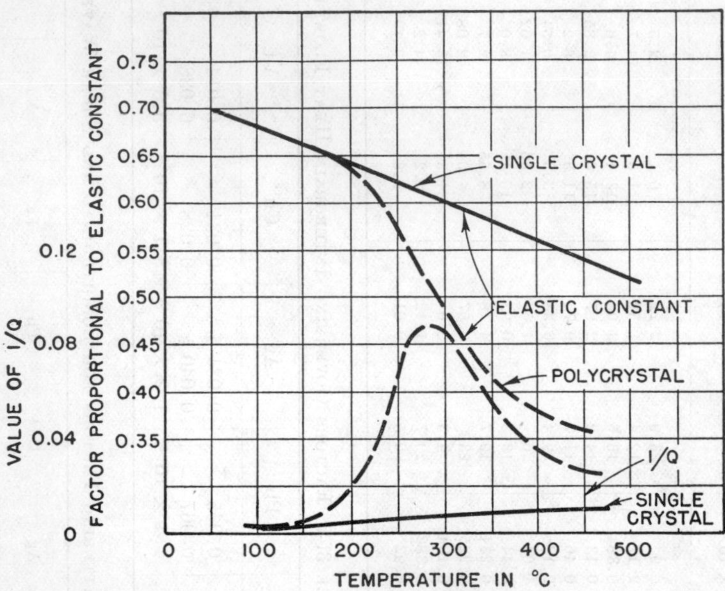

FIG. 3f-1. Elastic constants and Q for single-crystal and polycrystal aluminum. (*After Kê.*)

For most materials, the relaxation frequencies are under 100 kc. Table 3f-6 gives the product $[(C_p - C_v)/C_v]R$ for a number of metals.

3f-5. Loss Due to Grain Rotation. Another source of loss due to grain structure in metals is the loss due to the viscosity of the boundary layer between grains. This allows a relative rotation of grains provided the relaxation time is comparable with the time of the applied force. Figure 3f-1 shows the elastic modulus and the associated Q of a polycrystalline aluminum rod in torsional vibration at a frequency of 0.8 cycle as compared with similar measurements for a single crystal. The relaxation time for grain-boundary rotation is a function of temperature according to the equation

$$\tau = \tau_0 e^{H/kT} \tag{3f-19}$$

[1] C. Zener, "Elasticity and Anelasticity of Metals," p. 84, University of Chicago Press, Chicago, 1948.

where H, the activation energy, is of the same order as that found for creep and self-diffusion.

3f-6. Loss Due to Grain Scattering of Sound. Another effect of grain structure in solids is a loss of energy from the main wave due to the scattering of sound when the sound wavelength is of the same order as the grain size. This scattering occurs because adjacent grains have different orientations, and a reflection of sound occurs because of the resulting impedance difference between grains. An approximate formula[1] holding when the wavelength is larger than three times the grain size, and multiple scattering is neglected, is

$$\alpha_s \doteq \frac{8\pi^4 L_c^3 f^4}{9v^4} S \quad \text{nepers/m} \tag{3f-20}$$

where L_c is the average grain diameter, f the frequency, v the velocity, and S a scattering factor related to the anisotropy of the metal. Table 3f-7 shows a relative estimate of the scattering factors for longitudinal and shear waves for a number of metals. For shorter wavelengths, the attenuation changes less rapidly with frequency,[2] and for wavelengths shorter than the grain size, the loss is independent of the frequency. A formula applicable for all wavelengths is

$$\alpha_s = \frac{S}{2L_c}\left(\frac{Q_s}{A}\right) \tag{3f-21}$$

where Q_S/A is the ratio of the scattering area of the sphere to the actual cross-sectional area. For low frequencies $Q_S/A = \frac{16}{9}(\pi L_c/\lambda)^4 = \frac{16}{9}(\pi L_c f/v)^4$ while for very high frequencies $Q_S/A = 2$. Intermediate values of cross-sectional areas can be obtained from calculations given by Morse.[3] Because of elongations of grains in the direction of rolling, most materials have different scattering areas for propagation along the rolling axis and perpendicular to the axis.

3f-7. Acoustic Losses in Ferromagnetic and Ferroelectric Materials. Stresses in ferromagnetic and ferroelectric materials can cause motion of domain walls or rotation of domain directions. These occur in such a manner that domains are strengthened in directions parallel, antiparallel, or perpendicular to the direction of the stress. The increased polarization in the direction of the stress produces increased strains which are the same sign in both parallel and antiparallel domains since magnetostriction and electrostriction are square-law effects and hence the elastic stiffnesses of demagnetized materials are less than those of completely magnetized materials. For polarizations directed along cube axes, the difference in elastic constants for the saturated and depolarized states, i.e., the ΔE effect, is[4]

$$\frac{\Delta E}{E_D} = \frac{9\mu\lambda_s^2 E_s}{20\pi P_s^2} \tag{3f-22}$$

where μ is the initial permeability or dielectric constant, λ_s the saturated change in length along a polycrystalline rod, E_s and E_D the saturated and demagnetized elastic-stiffness constant and P_s the saturated magnetic or electric polarization. When the polarization lies along a cube diagonal—as in nickel—λ_s is replaced by $\frac{2}{3}\lambda_{111}[5c_{44}/(c_{11} - c_{12} + 3c_{44})]$ where λ_{111} is the saturated increase in length along the [111] direction and $5c_{44}/(c_{11} - c_{12} + 3c_{44})$ is a ratio of elastic constants.

[1] Mason, *op. cit.*, p. 422.

[2] R. B. Roney, "The Influence of Metal Grain Structure on the Attenuation of Ultrasonic Waves," Thesis, California Institute of Technology, 1950.

[3] Philip M. Morse, "Vibration and Sound," 2d ed., p. 355, McGraw-Hill Book Company, Inc., New York, 1948.

[4] R. M. Bozorth, "Ferromagnetism," p. 691, D. Van Nostrand Company, Inc., New York, 1951.

The motion of walls or the rotation of domains in metallic ferromagnetic materials generates eddy currents and hence causes an acoustic loss. It has been shown that the permeability follows a relaxation equation

$$\mu = \mu_0 \frac{(1 - jf/f_0)}{1 + f^2/f_0^2} \tag{3f-23}$$

where $f_0 \doteq 4R/25\mu_0 L_c^2$, R = resistivity, and L_c = domain diameter. For a distribution of domain sizes

$$\mu = \mu_0 \sum_{i=1}^{m} \frac{V_i}{V} \frac{1 - jf/f_i}{1 + f^2/f_i^2} \tag{3f-24}$$

where V_i is the volume occupied by domains of size L_i and V the total volume.

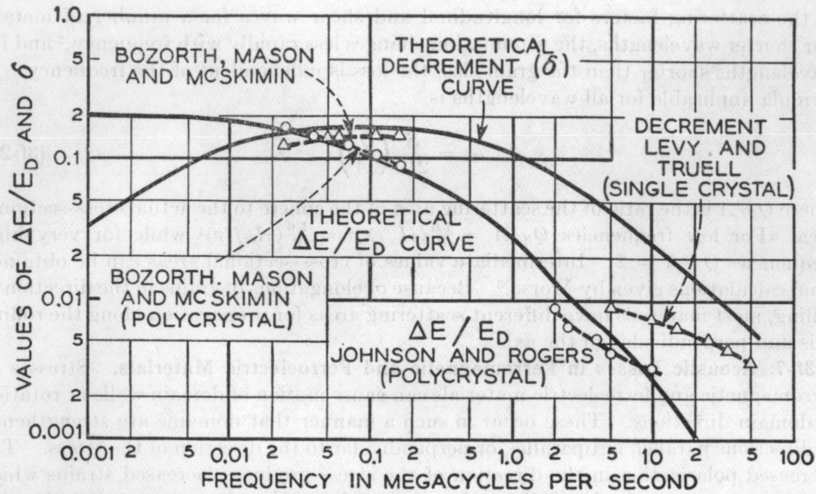

FIG. 3f-2. Decrement and ΔE effect for polycrystal nickel rod as a function of frequency. (*After Bozorth, Mason, and McSkimin; Johnson rnd Rogers; and Levy and Truell.*)

Inserting in Eq. (3f-22) the $\Delta E/E_D$ and Q are given by

$$\frac{\Delta E}{E_D} = \frac{9\lambda_s^2 E_s}{20\pi P_s^2}\left(\sum_{i=1}^{m} \frac{V_i/V}{1 + f^2/f_i^2}\right) \qquad \frac{1}{Q} = \frac{9\lambda_s^2 E_s}{20\pi P_s^2}\left[\sum \frac{(V_i/V)(f/f_i)}{1 + (f/f_i)^2}\right] \tag{3f-25}$$

Figure 3f-2 shows measurements of the ΔE effect and the decrement $\delta = \pi/Q$ plotted over a frequency range, for a polycrystalline nickel rod.

Another effect causing losses in ferromagnetic and ferroelectric materials is the microhysteresis effect. In this effect the domain walls or domain rotations lag behind the applied stress and produce a hysteresis loop. Hence the initial susceptibility has a hysteresis component which is a function of the amount of stress. Average values of the parameters can be written in the form

$$\mu = \mu_0[1 - jf(A)] \tag{3f-26}$$

where $f(A)$ is a function of the amplitide. Inserting this value of μ in Eq. (3f-22), the value of the microhysteresis loss is given. This type of loss is present in ferroelectric materials and is the principal cause of the low mechanical Q.

3f-8. Other Types of Losses. In addition to these recognized types of losses, other types exist which have not been accounted for quantitatively. Figure 3f-3 shows the Q of a number of materials measured in a frequency range for strains under 10^{-5}.[1] Except for nickel and iron rods whose decrease in Q with frequency is accounted for by microeddy-current effects, the materials have a Q independent of frequency. It has

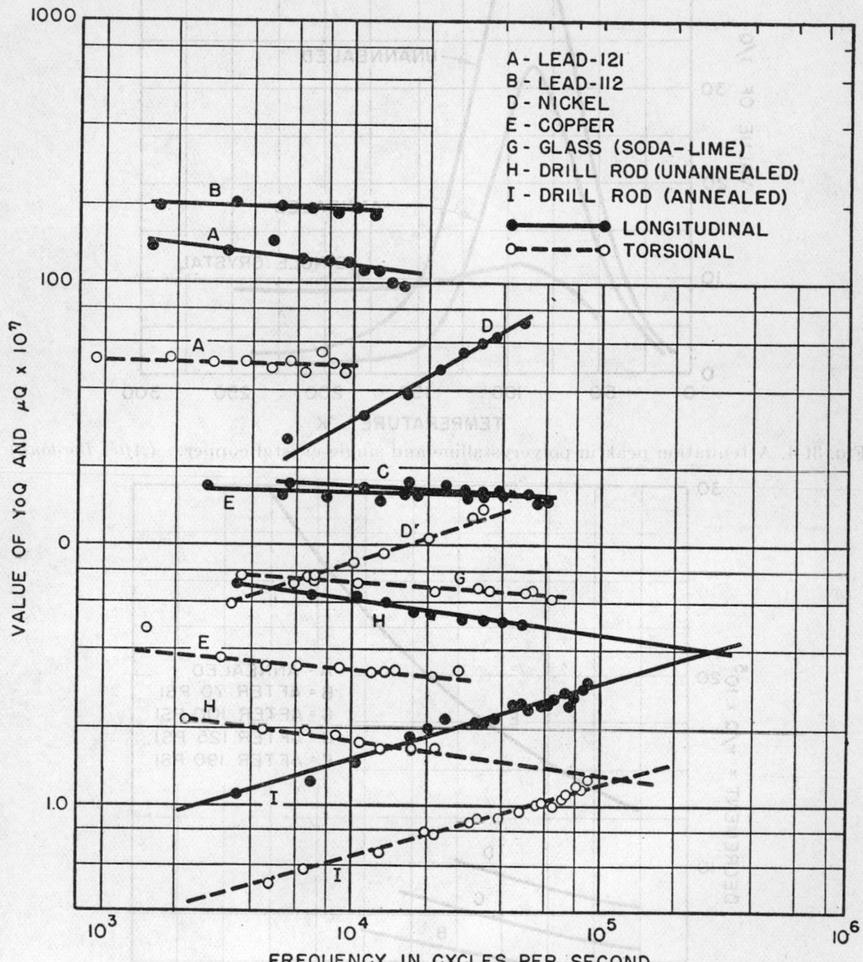

FIG. 3f-3. Values of Y_0/Q and μ/Q as a function of frequency for a number of polycrystalline materials. (*After Wegel and Walther.*)

been suggested that these losses are caused by elastic-hysteresis effects due to cyclic displacements of dislocations in the body or grain boundaries of metals. Some evidence[2] for this is shown in Fig. 3f-4, which shows the Q of a copper rod as a function of temperature and degree of annealing. Losses in annealed specimens having smaller numbers of dislocations are smaller than those in cold-worked specimens. At low

[1] R. L. Wegel and H. Walter, *Physics* **6**, 141 (1935).

[2] P. G. Bordoni, Assorbimento degli Ultrasuoni nei solidi, *Nuovo cimento* **7** (2), 144 (1950).

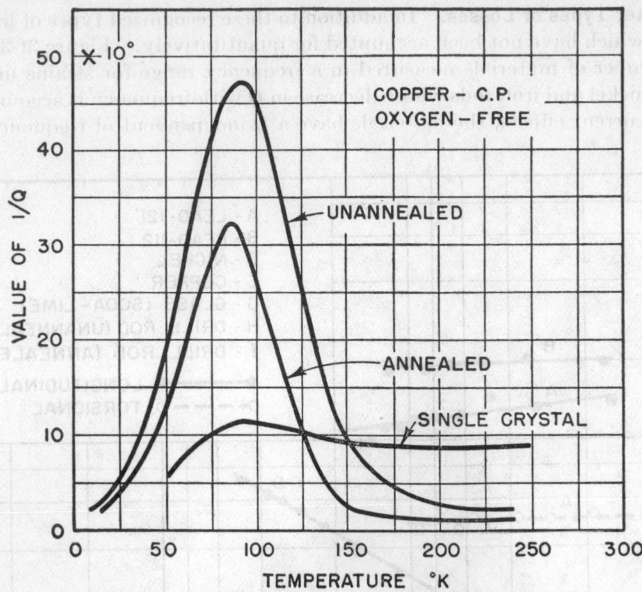

FIG. 3f-4. Attenuation peak in polycrystalline and single-crystal copper. (*After Bordoni.*)

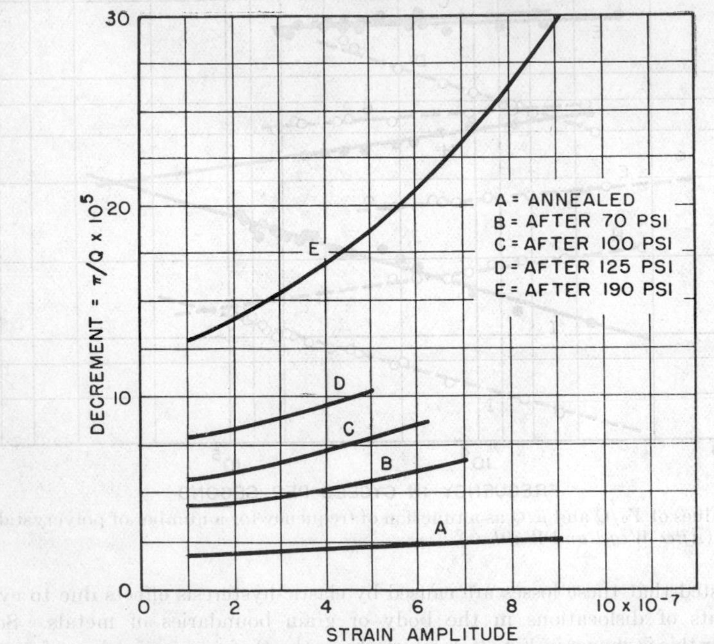

FIG. 3f-5. Decrement as a function of amplitude in a copper single crystal. (*After Nowick.*)

temperatures, a relaxation of dislocation motions appears to occur. Other work[1] shows that losses increase as a function of the amplitude, as shown by Fig. 3f-5. These losses have an activation energy similar to that shown by Fig. 3f-4 and are increased by cold work.

[1] A. S. Nowick, *Phys. Rev.* **80**, 249 (1950).

3g. Properties of Transducer Materials

W. P. MASON

Bell Telephone Laboratories, Inc.

To determine the acoustic properties of gases, liquids, and solids and to utilize them in acoustic systems, it is necessary to generate the appropriate waves by means of transducer materials which convert electrical energy into mechanical energy and vice versa. For liquids and solids, the most common types of materials are piezoelectric crystals, ferroelectric materials of the barium titanate type, and magnetostrictive materials.

3g-1. Piezoelectric Crystals. The static relations for a piezoelectric quartz crystal producing a single longitudinal mode are for rationalized mks units

$$S_2 = s_{22}{}^E T_2 + d_{21} E_x \qquad D_x = d_{21} T_2 + \epsilon_1{}^T E_x \tag{3g-1}$$

where S_2 and T_2 are the longitudinal strain and stress, respectively, $s_{22}{}^E$ the elastic compliance along the length measured at constant electric field, d_{21} the piezoelectric constant relating the strain with the applied field E_x, D_x the electric displacement, and $\epsilon_1{}^T$ the dielectric constant measured at constant stress. Equations of this type suffice to determine the static and low-frequency behavior of piezoelectric crystals. Using the first equation, one finds that the increase in length for no external stress and the external force for no increase in length are, respectively,

$$\Delta l = d_{21} \frac{Vl}{t}; \qquad F = T_2 tw = -d_{21} \frac{Vw}{s_{22}{}^E} \tag{3g-2}$$

where V is the applied potential, l, w, and t are the length, width, and thickness of the crystal, and F is the force which is considered positive for an extensional stress. From the second equation one finds that the open-circuit voltage and the short-circuited charge for a given applied force are, respectively,

$$V = -\left(\frac{d_{21}}{\epsilon^T}\right) \frac{lF}{tw} \qquad Q = \int_0^l \int_0^w D_x \, dl \, dw = d_{21} \frac{Fl}{t} \tag{3g-3}$$

Another important criterion for transducer use is the electromechanical-coupling factor k whose square is defined as the ratio of the energy stored in mechanical form to the total input electrical energy. Using Eqs. (3g-1), this can be shown to be

$$k^2 = \frac{d_{21}{}^2}{s_{22}{}^E \epsilon^T} \tag{3g-4}$$

It is readily shown that the clamped dielectric constant ϵ^S, obtained by setting $S_2 = 0$, and the constant-displacement elastic compliance s^D, obtained by setting $D_x = 0$, are related to the constant-stress dielectric constant ϵ^T and the constant-field elastic compliance $s_{22}{}^E$ by the equations

$$\frac{\epsilon_1{}^S}{\epsilon_1{}^T} = \frac{s_{22}{}^D}{s_{22}{}^E} = 1 - k^2 \tag{3g-5}$$

Equivalent circuits in which the properties of the crystal are expressed in terms of equivalent electrical elements are often useful (see Secs. 3l and 3m). An equivalent circuit for a piezoelectric crystal for static conditions is shown by Fig. 3g-1*A*. In this network the compliance $C_1 = s_{22}{}^E l/wt$ represents the compliance of the crystal with the electrodes short-circuited, the capacitance C_0 is the capacitance of the clamped crystal, i.e., $C_0 = lw\epsilon_1{}^S/t$, while the transformer shown is a perfect transformer, i.e., a transformer having no loss between zero frequency and the highest frequency for which the piezoelectric effect is operative, having a turns ratio of φ to 1 where

$$\varphi = -d_{21}\frac{w}{s_{22}{}^E} \tag{3g-6}$$

The fact that this equivalent circuit presents the same information as Eq. (3g-1) is readily verified by substitution and integration over the area of the crystal.

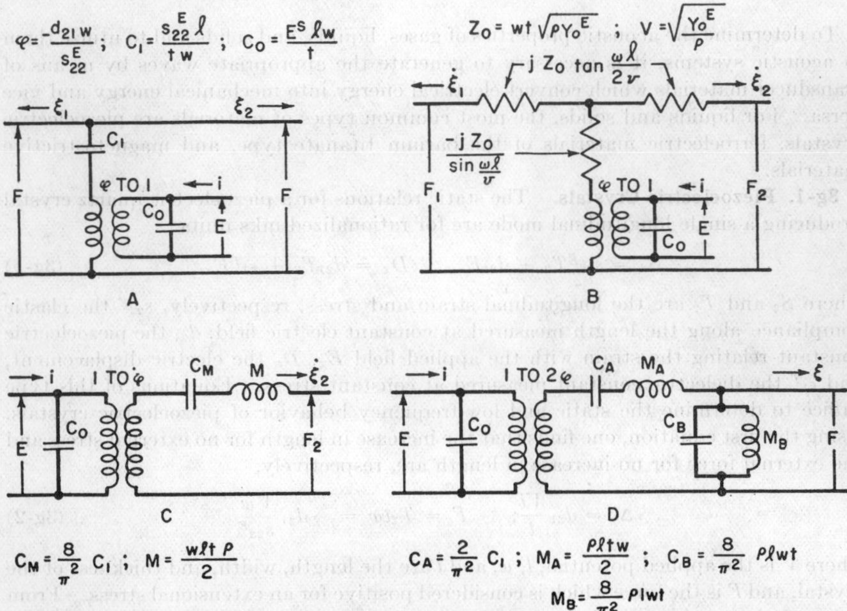

FIG. 3g-1. Equivalent circuit for a piezoelectric crystal for clamped and free conditions.

As an example of the use of such a network, one can calculate from it the efficiency of transformation of mechanical to electrical energy, or vice versa, under various conditions. Suppose that we clamp one end of the crystal and apply a force through the sending-end mechanical resistance R_M and receive the power generated into an electrical resistance R_E. Solving the network equations and obtaining the conditions for maximum power output, it is readily shown that the maximum power is obtained if

$$R_M = \frac{1}{\omega C_1 \sqrt{1-k^2}} \qquad R_E = \frac{\sqrt{1-k^2}}{\omega C_0} \tag{3g-7}$$

where $\omega = 2\pi$ times the frequency f. With these values the power in the termination is

$$P_0 = \frac{F^2k^4}{4\varphi^2 R_E} \tag{3g-8}$$

The available power that can be obtained from a source having an open-circuit force F with an internal impedance R_M is maximum when $\varphi^2 R_E = R_M$. This power is then

$$i_2{}^2 R_E = \frac{F^2}{4\varphi^2 R_E} \tag{3g-9}$$

and hence the power-conversion efficiency is

$$P_E = k^4 \tag{3g-10}$$

Hence, unless the coupling is high, the efficiency of conversion by static means is low.

This efficiency can be improved by resonating the capacity C_0 by an electric coil L_0 at the frequency of operation and can be further improved by mechanically resonating the static compliance of the crystal. The simplest way to analyze these circuits for their optimum conditions is to observe that, if the perfect transformer is moved to the end of the circuit, both equivalent sections are half sections of well-known filters. Equation (3g-11) gives the element values of the first filter resonated by an electrical coil, while Eq. (3g-14) gives the element values for the section tuned on both ends.

$$\begin{aligned} C_1' &= \frac{s_{22}{}^E l}{wt}\left(\frac{d_{21}w}{s_{22}{}^E}\right)^2 = \frac{lw}{t}\frac{d_{21}{}^2}{s_{22}{}^E} = \frac{f_1+f_2}{2\pi f_1 f_2 Z_0'} = \frac{1}{4\pi f_1 Z_0} \\ C_0 &= \frac{\epsilon^S lw}{t} = \frac{f_1}{2\pi f_2(f_2-f_1)Z_0'} = \frac{f_1}{2\pi(f_2{}^2-f_1{}^2)Z_0} \\ L_0 &= \frac{(f_2-f_1)Z_0'}{2\pi f_1 f_2} = \frac{(f_2{}^2-f_1{}^2)Z_0}{2\pi f_1 f_2{}^2} \end{aligned} \tag{3g-11}$$

where f_1 is the lower cutoff, f_2 the upper cutoff, Z_0 the mid-shunt impedance occurring on the electrical side, and Z_0' the mid-series impedance occurring on the mechanical side. Solving for f_1, f_2, Z_0, and $Z_0'(\varphi^2)$, i.e., the actual mechanical resistance, we find

$$f_2 = \frac{1}{2\pi\sqrt{L_0C_0}} \qquad f_1 = \frac{\sqrt{1-k^2}}{2\pi\sqrt{L_0C_0}} \qquad Z_0 = R_E = \frac{1-k^2}{2\pi f_1 C_0}$$

$$R_M = \varphi^2 Z_0' = \frac{1+\sqrt{1-k^2}}{2\pi f_1(ls_{22}{}^E/tw)} \tag{3g-12}$$

Hence, if there is no dissipation in the elements of the crystal, perfect power conversion can be obtained but only over a bandwidth of

$$\frac{f_2-f_1}{f_2} = 1-\sqrt{1-k^2} \tag{3g-13}$$

The other section of Fig. 3g-2 is a wider bandpass filter having the element values

$$C_1' = \frac{lw}{t}\frac{d_{21}{}^2}{s_{22}{}^E} = \frac{f_2-f_1}{2\pi f_1 f_2 Z_0} \qquad L_1' = \frac{\rho l t}{w}\left(\frac{s_{22}{}^E}{d_{21}}\right)^2 = \frac{Z_0}{2\pi(f_2-f_1)}$$

$$C_0 = \frac{\epsilon^S lw}{t} = \frac{1}{2\pi(f_2-f_1)Z_0} \qquad L_0 = \frac{(f_2-f_1)Z_0}{2\pi f_1 f_2} \tag{3g-14}$$

Solving for the bandwidth and the impedances

$$\frac{f_2-f_1}{f_m} = \frac{k}{\sqrt{1-k^2}} \qquad f_m = \sqrt{f_1 f_2} = \frac{1}{2\pi\sqrt{L_0C_0}} = \frac{1}{2\pi\sqrt{L_1C_1}}$$

$$Z_0 = R_E = \frac{\sqrt{1-k^2}}{2\pi f_m C_0 k} \qquad R_M = \varphi^2 Z_0 = \frac{k}{\sqrt{1-k^2}}\frac{1}{2\pi f_m s_{22}{}^E}\frac{wt}{l} \tag{3g-15}$$

This filter section can efficiently transform mechanical into electrical energy and vice versa with a loss determined only by the dissipation in the elements of the crystal.

The simplest method for mechanically resonating the crystal is to use it near its natural mechanical resonance. An exact equivalent circuit for a vibrating crystal is shown by Fig. 3g-1*B*. Near the first resonant frequency, the equivalent circuit for a clamped quarter-wave crystal is shown by Fig. 3g-1*C* while the equivalent circuit for a half-wave crystal is shown by Fig. 3g-1*D*. When the half-wave crystal resonated by a shunt coil is applied to converting electrical into mechanical energy, the same formulas given in Eqs. (3g-14) and (3g-15) and applicable except that $k^2/(1 - k^2)$ is replaced by $(8/\pi^2)[k^2/(1 - k^2)]$. By using the complete representation of Fig. 3g-1*B* the effect can be calculated by using various backing plates on the radiation from the front surface.

The general form of Eq. (3g-1) holds for any single mode whether it is longitudinal or transverse as long as the appropriate constants are used. For longitudinal thickness modes when the radiating surface is a number of wavelengths in diameter, $s_{22}{}^E$ is replaced by $1/c_{11}{}^E$ and d_{21} by $e_{21}/c_{11}{}^E$, the appropriate thickness piezoelectric constant. For a thickness shear mode, the appropriate shear stiffness (c_{44}, c_{55}, or c_{66})

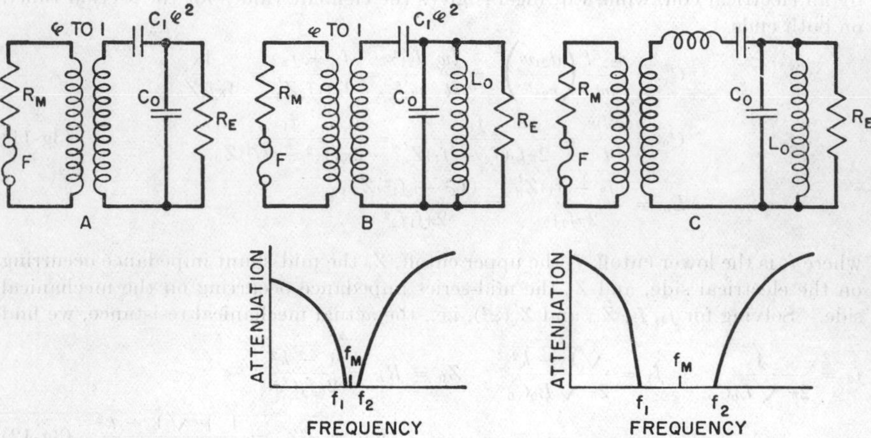

FIG. 3g-2. Use of equivalent circuit in determining the optimum conditions for energy transmission.

replaces $1/s_{22}$ and the appropriate shear piezoelectric constant replaces d_{21}. Table 3g-1 lists the constants in mks units for a number of standard crystal cuts.

3g-2. Electrostrictive and Magnetostrictive Materials. Other types of materials that have been used in transducers are ferroelectric crystals and ceramics of the barium titanate type and ferromagnetic crystals, polycrystals, and sintered materials of the ferrite type. All these materials have changes in lengths proportional to squares and even powers of the polarization and to obtain a linear response they have to be polarized. These polarized materials have relations between stresses, strains, electric and magnetic fields, and electric displacement and magnetic flux similar to those for a piezoelectric crystals shown by Eq. (3g-1) and hence these materials can be said to have "equivalent" constants which depend not only on the material but also on the degree of poling and in some cases on aging effects. The dielectric and permeability constants are those associated with the polarized medium as are also the elastic constants.

To obtain these equivalent piezoelectric and piezomagnetic constants, one can start with the more fundamental potential equations which have the same form for either electrostrictive or magnetostrictive materials. For polycrystalline or sintered materials, these potential equations can be written in the form

TABLE 3g-1. PROPERTIES OF PIEZOELECTRIC CRYSTALS IN MKS UNITS

Crystal and cut	Mode	Elastic constant, m^2/newton $\times 10^{11}$	Piezoelectric constant d, coulombs/newton $\times 10^{12}$	Dielectric capacitivity ϵ, farads/m $\times 10^{11}$	Electro-mechanical coupling k	Open-circuit voltage $g = d/\epsilon$, m^2/newton	Force factor d/s, newtons/volt $\times w$	Density, kg/m^3 $\times 10^{-3}$
Quartz X cut, length Y	L.L.	$s_{22}{}^E = 1.27$	$d_{21} = 2.25$	4.06	0.099	0.055	0.177	2.65
X cut	T.L.	$\frac{1}{c_{11}{}^E} = 1.16$	$\frac{e_{11}}{c_{11}{}^E} = -2.04$	4.06	0.093	0.050	0.175	2.65
Y cut	T.S.	$\frac{1}{c_{66}{}^E} = 2.57$	$\frac{e_{26}}{c_{66}{}^E} = +4.4$	4.06	0.137	0.108	0.171	2.65
Rochelle salt, 45-deg X cut	L.L.	$s'^E_{22} = 6.7$	$\frac{d_{14}}{2} = 435$	444.0	0.78	0.098	6.5	1.77
45-deg Y cut	L.L.	$s'^E_{11} = 9.89$	$\frac{d_{25}}{2} = -28.4$	9.85	0.288	0.29	0.287	1.77
ADP; 45-deg Z cut	L.L.	$s^{E'}_{11} = 5.3$	$\frac{d_{36}}{2} = 24.6$	13.8	0.29	0.178	0.465	1.804
KDP; 45-deg Z cut	L.L.	$s^{E'}_{11} = 4.85$	$\frac{d_{36}}{2} = 10.7$	19.6	0.12	0.058	0.22	2.31
EDT; Y cut, length X	L.L.	$s_{11}{}^E = 3.88$	$d_{21} = 11.3$	7.4	0.215	0.152	0.29	1.538
DKT; 45-deg Z cut	L.L.	$s^{E'}_{11} = 4.25$	$d'_{31} = -12.2$	5.8	0.245	0.21	0.287	1.988
L.H.; Y cut	T.L.	$\frac{1}{c_{22}{}^E} = 2$	$\frac{e_{22}}{c_{22}{}^E} = 15$	9.15	0.35	0.165	0.75	2.06
Hydrostatic	H.		$d_{21} + d_{22} + d_{23} = 13$	9.15		0.143		
Tourmaline, Z cut	T.L.	$\frac{1}{c_{33}{}^E} = 0.61$	$\frac{e_{33}}{c_{33}{}^E} = -1.84$	6.65	0.092	0.0275	0.3	3.1
Hydrostatic	H.		$d_{31} + d_{33} = -2.16$	6.65		0.0325		

Abbreviations: L.L. = length longitudinal; T.L. = thickness longitudinal; T.S. = thickness shear; ADP = ammonium dihydrogen phosphate; KDP = potassium dihydrogen phosphate; EDT = ethylene diamine tartrate; L.H. = lithium sulphate monohydrate.

$$G^* = -\tfrac{1}{2}[s_{11}{}^D(T_1{}^2 + T_2{}^2 + T_3{}^2) + 2s_{12}{}^D(T_1T_2 + T_1T_3 + T_2T_3) + 2(s_{11}{}^D - s_{12}{}^D)(T_4{}^2 + T_5{}^2 + T_6{}^2)] - \{Q_{11}(D_1{}^2T_1 + D_2{}^2T_2 + D_3{}^2T_3) + Q_{12}[T_1(D_2{}^2 + D_3{}^2) + T_2(D_1{}^2 + D_3{}^2) + T_3(D_1{}^2 + D_2{}^2)] + 2(Q_{11} - Q_{12})(T_4D_2D_3 + T_5D_1D_3 + T_6D_1D_2)\} + \tfrac{1}{2}\beta_{11}{}^T(D_1{}^2 + D_2{}^2 + D_3{}^2) + K_{11}{}^T(D_1{}^4 + D_2{}^4 + D_3{}^4) + K_{12}{}^T(D_1{}^2D_2{}^2 + D_1{}^2D_3{}^2 + D_2{}^2D_3{}^2) + K_{111}{}^T(D_1{}^6 + D_2{}^6 + D_3{}^6) + K_{112}{}^T[D_1{}^4(D_2{}^2 + D_3{}^2) + D_2{}^4(D_1{}^2 + D_3{}^2) + D_3{}^4(D_1{}^2 + D_2{}^2)] + K_{123}{}^TD_1{}^2D_2{}^2D_3{}^2 \quad (3g\text{-}16)$$

where T_1, T_2, T_3 are the three extensional stresses, T_4, T_5, T_6 the three shearing stresses, D_1, D_2, D_3 the three components of the electrical displacement for ferroelectric materials or the three components of the magnetic flux B for ferromagnetic materials, the s constants are the compliance constants for an isotropic material measured at constant electric or magnetic displacement, the Q's are the electrostrictive or magnetostrictive constants, $\beta_{11}{}^T$ the inverse of the initial dielectric constant or permeability measured at constant stress, and the K^T's are constants determining the total energy stored for higher polarizations. The static equations can be obtained by differentiation of G according to the relations

$$S_i = -\frac{\partial G}{\partial T_i} \qquad E_m = \frac{\partial G}{\partial D_m} \quad (3g\text{-}17)$$

Since linear equations are obtained only if a permanent polarization P_0 is introduced, we assume that

$$D_3 = P_0 + D_3{}^* \quad (3g\text{-}18)$$

where $D_3{}^*$ is a small variable component superposed on P_0. Also, D_1 and D_2 are small so that their squares and higher powers can be neglected compared with P_0. Introducing these into (3g-16) and differentiating, we have

$$\begin{aligned}
S_1 &= s_{11}{}^DT_1 + s_{12}{}^D(T_2 + T_1) + Q_{12}(P_0{}^2 + 2P_0D_3{}^*)\\
S_2 &= s_{11}{}^DT_2 + s_{12}{}^D(T_1 + T_3) + Q_{12}(P_0{}^2 + 2P_0D_3{}^*)\\
S_3 &= s_{11}{}^DT_3 + s_{12}{}^D(T_1 + T_2) + Q_{11}(P_0{}^2 + 2P_0D_3{}^*)\\
S_4 &= 2(s_{11}{}^D - s_{12}{}^D)T_4 + 2(Q_{11} - Q_{12})P_0D_2\\
S_5 &= 2(s_{11}{}^D - s_{12}{}^D)T_5 + 2(Q_{11} - Q_{12})P_0D_1\\
S_6 &= 2(s_{11}{}^D - s_{12}{}^D)T_6\\
E_1 &= -2(Q_{11} - Q_{12})P_0T_5 + D_1(\beta_{11}{}^T + 2K_{12}{}^TP_0{}^2 + 2K_{112}{}^TP_0{}^4)\\
E_2 &= -2(Q_{11} - Q_{12})P_0T_4 + D_2(\beta_{11}{}^T + 2K_{12}{}^TP_0{}^2 + 2K_{112}{}^TP_0{}^4)\\
E_3 &= -2Q_{11}P_0T_3 - 2Q_{12}P_0(T_1 + T_2) + D_3{}^*(\beta_{11}{}^T + 12K_{11}{}^TP_0{}^2 + 30K_{111}{}^TP_0{}^4)
\end{aligned} \quad (3g\text{-}19)$$

It is obvious that the variable components of Eq. (3g-19) follow the same rule as for a piezoelectric crystal. There are three longitudinal modes and a shearing mode. The length longitudinal mode has the following constants:

$$\text{L.L. mode} \quad s_{11}{}^E = s_{11}{}^D\left[1 + \frac{4Q_{12}{}^2P_0{}^2}{\beta_{33}{}^T(P_0)s_{11}{}^D}\right] \qquad d_{31} = \frac{2Q_{12}P_0}{\beta_{33}{}^T(P_0)}$$

$$\epsilon_{33}{}^T(P_0) = \frac{1}{\beta_{33}(P_0)} \quad (3g\text{-}20)$$

where $\beta_{33}{}^T(P_0) = (\beta_{11}{}^T + 12K_{11}{}^TP_0{}^2 + 30K_{111}{}^TP_0{}^4)$ is the dielectric impermeability of the ceramic when it has a permanent polarization P_0

$$\text{L.T. bar} \quad s_{11}{}^E = s_{11}{}^D\left[1 + \frac{4Q_{11}{}^2P_0{}^2}{\beta_{33}{}^T(P_0)s_{11}{}^D}\right] \qquad d_{33} = \frac{2Q_{11}P_0}{\beta_{33}{}^T(P_0)}$$

$$\epsilon_{33}{}^T(P_0) = \frac{1}{\beta_{33}{}^T(P_0)} \quad (3g\text{-}21)$$

* If higher-order terms than those considered here are used, second-order electrostrictive and magnetostrictive terms and the change in elastic constants with polarization can be taken care of. For example, see W. P. Mason, *Phys. Rev.* **82** (5), 715–723 (June 1, 1951).

TABLE 3g-2. PROPERTIES OF CERAMICS AT 25°C

Material	d_{31} eff, coulombs/newton $\times 10^{11}$	d_{33} eff, coulombs/newton $\times 10^{11}$	$\epsilon_3^T(P_0)$ farads/m $\times 10^{11}$	$Y_0^E = 1/s^E$ newtons/m² $\times 10^{11}$	Shear stiffness $G^E = \frac{1}{2(s_{11}^E - s_{12}^E)}$ newtons/m² $\times 10^{11}$	Numerics k_{31}	k_{33}	k_{15}	Energy stored $\frac{1}{2}(d_{33}^2/\epsilon)$ joules/m newton² $\times 10^{12}$	Open-circuit voltage $g = d_{33}/\epsilon^T$ volts $\times$ m/newton	Force factor $d_{33}Y_0^E \times 10^{22}$ newton/volts $\times$ m
Commercial $BaTiO_3$ ceramic	−(5.6)	13–16	1,200–1,500	1.18	0.46	0.17	0.45	0.41	0.85	0.0106	13.5
97% $BaTiO_3$, 3% $CaTiO_3$	−(5.3)	13.5	1,230	1.22	0.47	0.17	0.43	0.39	0.75	0.0111	11.0
96% $BaTiO_3$, 4% $PbTiO_3$	−(3.8)	10.5	880	1.14	0.44	0.14	0.39	0.34	0.63	0.012	9.2
90% $BaTiO_3$, 4% $PbTiO_3$, 6% $CaTiO_3$	−(4.0)	11.5	710	1.24	0.48	0.167	0.48	0.43	0.93	0.016	9.3
84% $BaTiO_3$, 8% $PbTiO_3$, 8% $CaTiO_3$	−(2.7)	8.0	530	1.31	0.50	0.124	0.4	0.35	0.60	0.015	6.1
80% $BaTiO_3$, 12% $PbTiO_3$, 8% $CaTiO_3$	−(2.0)	6.0	400	1.28	0.49	0.113	0.34	0.3	0.45	0.015	4.7
Data on Brush Ceramics*											
Ceramic A	−7.8	19.0	1,520	1.10	0.423	0.214	0.52	0.49	1.2	0.0126	20.9
5% $CaTiO_3$	−5.8	15.0	1,050	1.16	0.445	0.193	0.5	....	1.07	0.0142	17.4
5% $PbTiO_3$	−5.3	12.9	1,040	1.10	0.423	0.172	0.410	....	0.80	0.0124	14.2
9% $CaTiO_3$	−4.1	11.8	805	1.25	0.481	0.162	0.466	....	0.865	0.0147	14.8

* From H. Jaffe.

These formulas hold for a bar which is long in the direction of vibration compared with the cross-sectional dimensions. When a plate is used which is a number of wavelengths across, the sidewise motions S_1 and S_2 are zero and the constants are

$$\text{L.T. plate} \qquad \frac{1}{c_{11}{}^E} \qquad d'_{33} \qquad \epsilon'_{33}(P_0) \tag{3g-22}$$

where

$$\frac{1}{c_{11}{}^E} = \frac{1}{c_{11}{}^P} + d'^2_{33}\epsilon'_{33}(P_0) \qquad d'_{33} = 2P_0\left(Q_{11} - \frac{2s_{12}{}^D}{s_{11}{}^D + s_{12}{}^D}Q_{12}\right)\epsilon'_{33}(P_0)$$

$$\epsilon^{T'}_{33}(P_0) = \frac{1}{\beta_{33}{}^T(P_0) + [4Q_{12}{}^2P_0{}^2/(s_{11}{}^D + s_{12}{}^D)]} \qquad \text{and} \qquad c_{11}{}^D = \frac{s_{11}{}^D + s_{12}{}^D}{(s_{11}{}^D - s_{12}{}^D)(s_{11}{}^D + 2s_{12}{}^D)}$$

The thickness shear mode has the fundamental constants $2(s_{11}{}^E - s_{12}{}^E)$; d_{14}; $\epsilon_{11}{}^T(P_0)$,

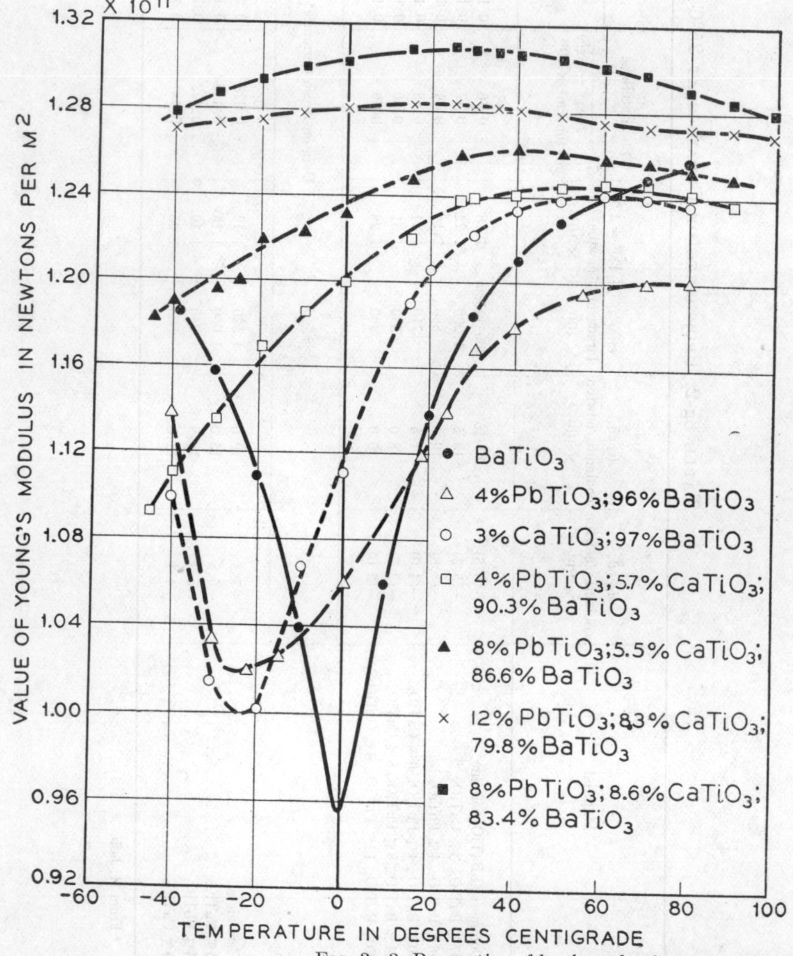

FIG. 3g-3. Properties of barium, lead, calcium titanate

i.e., the dielectric constant perpendicular to the poling direction, where

$$d_{14} = \frac{2(Q_{11} - Q_{12})P_0}{\epsilon_{11}{}^T(P_0)} \qquad 2(s_{11}{}^E - s_{12}{}^E) = 2(s_{11}{}^D - s_{12}{}^D) + \frac{4(Q_{11} - Q_{12})^2P_0{}^2}{\beta_{11}{}^T(P_0)}$$

$$\epsilon_{11}{}^T(P_0) = \frac{1}{(\beta_{11}{}^T + 2K_{12}{}^TP_0{}^2 + 2K_{112}{}^TP_0{}^4)} \qquad \text{(3g-23)}$$

Two other modes have been used in electrostrictive and magnetostrictive materials,

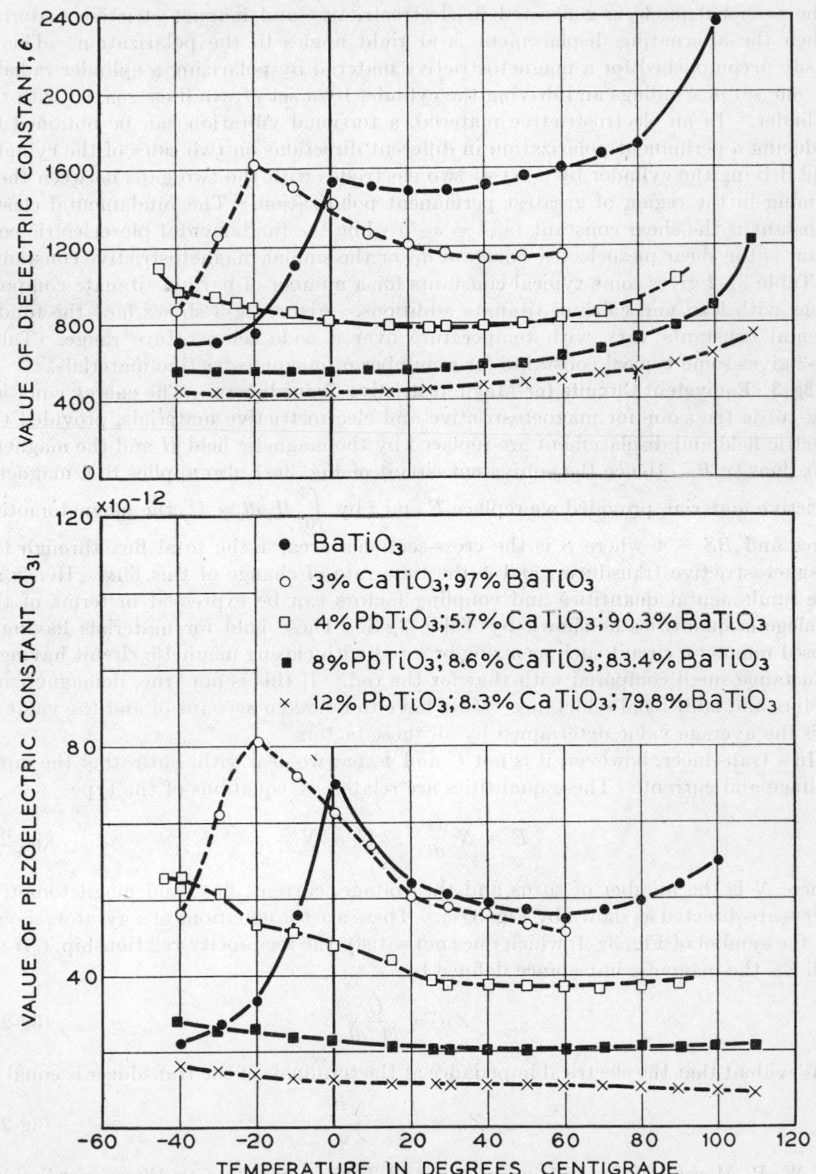

ceramics as functions of temperature and composition.

the radial mode and the torsional mode. The first is driven by polarizing the disk perpendicular to the major surface and involves the same fundamental constants as the length longitudinal mode of Eq. (3g-20). It has been shown[1] that the effective coupling and the resonant frequency of such disks are given by the equations

$$k^2 = \frac{2}{1-\sigma}\left(\frac{4Q_{11}{}^2P_0{}^2\epsilon^T(P_0)}{s_{11}{}^E}\right) \qquad f_R = \frac{2.03}{2\pi a}\sqrt{\frac{1}{s_{11}{}^E\rho(1-\sigma^2)}} \tag{3g-24}$$

where σ is Poisson's ratio which is approximately 0.3 for barium titanate ceramics. The torsional mode is generated in electrostrictive and magnetostrictive materials when the alternating displacement is at right angles to the polarization. This is easily accomplished for a magnetostrictive material by polarizing a cylinder radially by one set of windings and driving the cylinder by a set of windings coaxial with the cylinder. In an electrostrictive material, a torsional vibration can be obtained by inducing a permanent polarization in different directions on two sides of the cylinder and driving the cylinder by a set of two electrodes with the two gaps between them coming in the region of greatest permanent polarization. The fundamental elastic constant is the shear constant ($s_{44}{}^E = s_{55}{}^E$) while the fundamental piezoelectric constant is the shear piezoelectric constant d_{15} or the similar magnetostrictive constants.

Table 3g-2 gives some typical constants for a number of barium titanate compositions with lead and calcium titanate additions. Figure 3g-3 shows how the fundamental constants vary with temperature over a wide temperature range. Table 3g-3 gives some typical constants for a number of magnetostrictive materials.

3g-3. Equivalent Circuits for Magnetostrictive Transducers. The energy equation (3g-16) is the same for magnetostrictive and electrostrictive materials, provided the electric field and displacement are replaced by the magnetic field H and the magnetic flux density B. Hence the equivalent circuit of Fig. 3g-1 also applies to a magnetostrictive material, provided we replace E and i by $\int_0^l H_i\,dl = U$, the magnetomotive force and $\dot{B}S = \dot{\Phi}$ where S is the cross-sectional area, Φ the total flux through the magnetostrictive transducer, and $\dot{\Phi}$ the time rate of change of this flux. Hence all the fundamental quantities and coupling factors can be expressed in terms of the analogous quantities as shown by Table 3g-3. These hold for materials having a closed magnetic circuit such as a ring or a rod with closing magnetic circuit having a reluctance small compared with that for the rod. If this is not true, demagnetizing factors and additional reluctance values have to be taken account of and the value of Φ is the average value determined by all these factors.

In a transducer, however, it is not U and Φ that we deal with, but rather the input voltage and current. These quantities are related by equations of the type

$$E = N\frac{d\Phi}{dt} \qquad U = Ni \tag{3g-25}$$

where N is the number of turns and the voltage, current, flux, and magnetomotive forces are directed as shown by Fig. 3g-4. These are the equations of a gyrator, shown by the symbol of Fig. 3g-4, which does not satisfy the reciprocity relationship. If we call Z_M the magnetic impedance defined by

$$Z_M = \frac{U}{d\Phi/dt} \tag{3g-26}$$

it is evident that the electrical impedance at the terminals of the transducer is equal to

$$Z_E = \frac{E}{i} = \frac{N^2}{Z_M} \tag{3g-27}$$

[1] W. P. Mason, "Piezoelectric Crystals and Their Application to Ultrasonics," chap. XII, D. Van Nostrand Company, Inc., New York, 1950.

TABLE 3g-3. MAGNETOSTRICTIVE PROPERTIES OF METALS AND FERRITES
Data from C. M. Van der Burgt, *Phillips Research Repts.* **8,** 91–132, 1953

Material	$d_{33} \times 10^9$ webers/newton	$d_{14} \times 10^9$ webers/newton	Rev. per. long. $\mu^T(P_0) \times 10^4$ henrys/m	$Y_0{}^H = \frac{1}{s^H} \times 10^{-11}$ newtons/m²	k_{33}	Rev. per shear $\mu^T(P_0) \times 10^4$ henrys/m	Shear stiffness $G^E \times 10^{-11}$ newton/m²	Torsional coupling k_T	Energy stored $\frac{1}{2}(d_{33}{}^2/\mu^T) \times 10^{12}$ joules m/newton²	Density, kg/m³ $\times 10^{-3}$
99.9 nickel	−5.3	......	2.84	2.0	0.14	......	....	.....	0.05	8.9
50 Co; 0.5 Cr; 49.5 Fe	12.3	......	8.3	2.2	0.20	......	....	.....	0.09	8.2
35 Co; 0.5 Cr; 64.5 Fe	13.4	......	19.2	2.1	0.14	......	....	.....	0.047	8.1
NiO (15%); ZnO (35%); Fe_2O_3 (50%)	−11.1	−28.5	190	1.8	0.034	139	0.68	0.063	0.003	5.06
NiO (18%); ZnO (32%); Fe_2O_3 (50%)	−16.0	−39.5	77.5	1.62	0.073	74	0.62	0.115	0.0165	4.9
NiO (25%); ZnO (25%); Fe_2O_3 (50%)	−9.8	−20.3	22.0	1.53	0.082	20	0.59	0.110	0.022	4.85
NiO (32%); ZnO (18%); Fe_2O_3 (50%)	−8.7	−15.8	13.4	1.5	0.093	13.2	0.58	0.105	0.0282	4.85
NiO (40%); ZnO (10%); Fe_2O_3 (50%)	−5.9	−13.0	5.5	1.37	0.112	5.35	0.54	0.13	0.0315	4.76
NiO (50%); Fe_2O_3 (50%)	−4.4	......	2.8	0.93	0.08	2.4	0.36	0.09	0.0344	4.20

Data from R. M. Bozorth, E. A. Nesbit, and H. J. Williams

Material	Flux density B, webers/m²	Long. rev. per $\mu^T(P_0) \times 10^4$ henrys/m	Young's modulus $Y_0{}^A \times 10^{-11}$ newtons/m	Longitudinal coupling k_{33}	$d_{33} \times 10^9$ webers/newton	Energy stored $\frac{1}{2}(d_{33}{}^2/\mu^T) \times 10^{12}$ joules m/newton²	Density, kg/$m^3 \times 10^{-3}$
99.9% nickel	0.4	0.98	2.1	0.232	−5.0	0.127	8.9
	0.5	0.515	...	0.208	−3.26	0.103	
	0.55	0.317	...	0.177	−2.18	0.075	
45% Ni, 55% Fe, i.e., 45% Permalloy	0.722	8.94	1.6	0.154	11.5	0.074	8.17
	0.965	7.36	...	0.179	12.2	0.101	
	1.2	4.45	...	0.178	9.4	0.099	
	1.4	1.97	...	0.15	5.3	0.071	
2V Permindur, 2% V, 50% Co, 48% Fe	1.5	3.54	2.3	0.238	9.35	0.123	8.3
	1.6	2.61	...	0.222	7.5	0.108	
	1.8	2.23	...	0.202	6.3	0.089	
	2.0	1.14	...	0.18	4.0	0.07	

Hence the effect of the gyrator coupling is to invert all the elements of the equivalent circuit. Hence one should determine the element values of Fig. 3g-4 for the appropriate terminating conditions and then invert the values in accordance with Eq. (3g-27) to determine the elements of a magnetostrictive transducer. The values

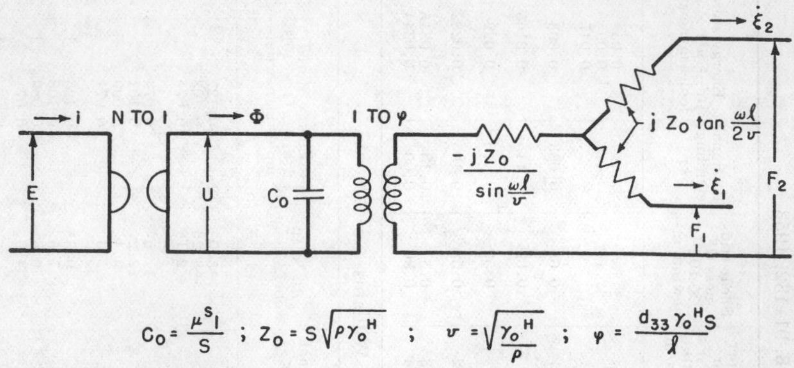

$$C_0 = \frac{\mu^S l}{S};\quad Z_0 = S\sqrt{\rho \gamma_0^H};\quad v = \sqrt{\frac{\gamma_0^H}{\rho}};\quad \varphi = \frac{d_{33}\gamma_0^H S}{l}$$

FIG. 3g-4. Equivalent circuit of a magnetostrictive rod.

given in Fig. 3g-4 are for a longitudinally vibrating rod where S is the cross-sectional area and l the length. μ^S is the average value of the permeability in the equations for the reluctance R

$$R = \frac{l}{\mu^S S} \tag{3g-28}$$

where μ^S is for the constant stress condition.

3h. Frequencies of Simple Vibrators. Musical Scales

ROBERT W. YOUNG

U.S. Navy Electronics Laboratory

3h-1. Strings. The fundamental frequency of vibration of an ideal string is

$$f_0 = \frac{1}{2l}\sqrt{\frac{F}{m}} \tag{3h-1}$$

where f_0 is the frequency, l is the free length, F is the force (tension) stretching the string, and m is the mass per unit length. Values of m for steel and gut strings are given in Table 3h-1.

In addition to the vibration in a single loop which gives rise to the fundamental frequency, the ideal string may vibrate in harmonics whose frequencies are

$$f_n = nf_0 \tag{3h-2}$$

TABLE 3h-1. MASS PER UNIT LENGTH OF STEEL AND GUT STRINGS*

Diam mm	Diam in.	Steel, g/m	Gut, g/m	Diam mm	Diam in.	Steel, g/m	Gut, g/m	Diam mm	Diam in.	Steel, g/m	Gut, g/m
0.20	0.0079	0.25	0.04	1.00	0.0394	6.15	1.10	1.80	0.0709	19.9	3.56
0.22	0.0087	0.30	0.05	1.02	0.0402	6.40	1.14	1.82	0.0717	20.4	3.64
0.24	0.0094	0.35	0.06	1.04	0.0409	6.65	1.19	1.84	0.0724	20.8	3.72
0.26	0.0102	0.42	0.07	1.06	0.0417	6.91	1.24	1.86	0.0732	21.3	3.80
0.28	0.0110	0.48	0.09	1.08	0.0425	7.17	1.28	1.88	0.0740	21.7	3.88
0.30	0.0118	0.55	0.10	1.10	0.0433	7.44	1.33	1.90	0.0748	22.2	3.97
0.32	0.0126	0.63	0.11	1.12	0.0441	7.71	1.38	1.92	0.0756	22.7	4.05
0.34	0.0134	0.71	0.13	1.14	0.0449	7.99	1.43	1.94	0.0764	23.1	4.14
0.36	0.0142	0.80	0.14	1.16	0.0457	8.27	1.48	1.96	0.0772	23.6	4.22
0.38	0.0150	0.89	0.16	1.18	0.0465	8.56	1.53	1.98	0.0780	24.1	4.31
0.40	0.0157	0.98	0.18	1.20	0.0472	8.86	1.58	2.00	0.0787	24.6	4.40
0.42	0.0165	1.08	0.19	1.22	0.0480	9.15	1.64	2.02	0.0795	25.1	4.49
0.44	0.0173	1.19	0.21	1.24	0.0488	9.46	1.69	2.04	0.0803	25.6	4.58
0.46	0.0181	1.30	0.23	1.26	0.0496	9.76	1.75	2.06	0.0811	26.1	4.67
0.48	0.0189	1.42	0.25	1.28	0.0504	10.1	1.80	2.08	0.0819	26.6	4.76
0.50	0.0197	1.54	0.27	1.30	0.0512	10.4	1.86	2.10	0.0827	27.1	4.85
0.52	0.0205	1.66	0.30	1.32	0.0520	10.7	1.92	2.12	0.0835	27.6	4.94
0.54	0.0213	1.79	0.32	1.34	0.0528	11.1	1.97	2.14	0.0843	28.2	5.04
0.56	0.0220	1.93	0.34	1.36	0.0535	11.4	2.03	2.16	0.0850	28.7	5.13
0.58	0.0228	2.07	0.37	1.38	0.0543	11.7	2.09	2.18	0.0858	29.2	5.23
0.60	0.0236	2.21	0.40	1.40	0.0551	12.1	2.16	2.20	0.0866	29.8	5.32
0.62	0.0244	2.36	0.42	1.42	0.0559	12.4	2.22	2.22	0.0874	30.3	5.42
0.64	0.0252	2.52	0.45	1.44	0.0567	12.8	2.28	2.24	0.0882	30.9	5.52
0.66	0.0260	2.68	0.48	1.46	0.0575	13.1	2.34	2.26	0.0890	31.4	5.62
0.68	0.0268	2.84	0.51	1.48	0.0583	13.5	2.41	2.28	0.0898	32.0	5.72
0.70	0.0276	3.01	0.54	1.50	0.0591	13.8	2.47	2.30	0.0906	32.5	5.82
0.72	0.0283	3.19	0.57	1.52	0.0598	14.2	2.54	2.32	0.0913	33.1	5.92
0.74	0.0291	3.37	0.60	1.54	0.0606	14.6	2.61	2.34	0.0921	33.7	6.02
0.76	0.0299	3.55	0.64	1.56	0.0614	15.0	2.68	2.36	0.0929	34.3	6.12
0.78	0.0307	3.74	0.67	1.58	0.0622	15.4	2.74	2.38	0.0937	34.8	6.23
0.80	0.0315	3.94	0.70	1.60	0.0630	15.7	2.81	2.40	0.0945	35.4	6.33
0.82	0.0323	4.14	0.74	1.62	0.0638	16.1	2.89	2.42	0.0953	36.0	6.44
0.84	0.0331	4.34	0.78	1.64	0.0646	16.5	2.96	2.44	0.0961	36.6	6.55
0.86	0.0339	4.55	0.81	1.66	0.0654	16.9	3.03	2.46	0.0968	37.2	6.65
0.88	0.0346	4.76	0.85	1.68	0.0661	17.4	3.10	2.48	0.0976	37.8	6.76
0.90	0.0354	4.98	0.89	1.70	0.0669	17.8	3.18	2.50	0.0984	38.4	6.87
0.92	0.0362	5.20	0.93	1.72	0.0677	18.2	3.25	2.52	0.0992	39.1	6.98
0.94	0.0370	5.43	0.97	1.74	0.0685	18.6	3.33	2.54	0.1000	39.7	7.09
0.96	0.0378	5.67	1.01	1.76	0.0693	19.0	3.41	2.56	0.1008	40.3	7.21
0.98	0.0386	5.91	1.06	1.78	0.0701	19.5	3.48	2.58	0.1016	40.9	7.32

* This table is based on a density of steel of 7.83 g/cm³. Density of gut is assumed to be 1.4 g/cm³, about one-sixth that of steel. This is only approximate, since the density of gut varies from sample to sample, and increases markedly with humidity. Brass wire has a density of 8.7 g/cm³, about 1.1 times that of steel.

where n is the integer denoting the particular mode of vibration. The length of each vibration loop is l/n. These successive lengths and the corresponding periods of vibration (i.e., the reciprocals of the frequencies) constitute a harmonic series according to the strict mathematical definition; nowadays, however, the frequencies themselves are usually said to make up a harmonic series.

The frequencies of actual strings depart somewhat from the frequencies computed from the simple formula because actual strings are stiff, they may be partially clamped at the ends, they are not infinitely thin, the tension increases with amplitude of vibration, the mass per unit length is not exactly uniform, there is internal damping and damping due to the surrounding air and supports, and the supports are not infinitely rigid. In the formulas which follow damping has been neglected.

For an actual string set

$$f = nf_0(1 + G) \tag{3h-3}$$

where the factor $(1 + G)$ is a measure of the departure (i.e., the inharmonicity) from the ideal harmonic values. Table 3h-2 lists values of G for various small perturbations. The approximations are valid only when G is small.

TABLE 3h-2. PERTURBATION IN FREQUENCY OF A STRING

Cause	G	Explanation
Stiffness	$\dfrac{n^2\pi^3 d^4 Y}{128 l^2 F}$	Y is Young's modulus, d is the diameter of the string
Yielding support	$\dfrac{4ml}{4\pi^2 n^2 M - K/f_0^2}$	The support consists of a mass M on a spring of transverse force constant K. Multiply by 2 if there are two such supports
Variable density	$-\dfrac{1}{l}\displaystyle\int_0^l g(x)\sin^2\frac{(\pi n x)}{l}\,dx$	The mass per unit length is $m = m_0[1 + g(x)]$ where m_0 is the mean value over the string and x is the distance from one end of the string; the function $g(x)$ must be small in comparison with unity

For musical purposes it is often convenient to give the inharmonicity in cents (hundredths of an equally tempered semitone) by setting

$$1 + G = 2^{\delta/1,200} = e^{\delta/1,731} \tag{3h-4}$$

where δ is the inharmonicity. To a usually acceptable approximation, $\delta = 1,731G$.

If the stiff string listed in Table 3h-2 is of steel music wire, $Y/\rho = 25.5 \times 10^6$ m²/sec², Y being Young's modulus and ρ the density. The tension is very nearly $F = l^2\rho f_0^2\pi d^2$. Thus for steel wire, and by virtue of the stiffness formula, the inharmonicity in cents is $\delta = 3.4 \times 10^{13} d^2/f_0^2 l^4$, provided that the diameter and length are in centimeters.

3h-2. Air Columns and Rods. The air within a simple tube of constant cross section, open at both ends or closed at both ends, vibrates freely at a frequency near

$$f = \frac{nc}{2l} \tag{3h-5}$$

where n is an integer (mode of vibration number), c is the speed of sound in the contained air, and l is the length of the tube (see Sec. 3d for speed of sound in air and its dependence on temperature). The diameter of the tube must be relatively small;

plane sound waves propagated longitudinally are assumed. The same formula applies to thin rods vibrating longitudinally and suitably supported (say, at distances $l/2n$ from the ends) so that the vibration is not inhibited (see Sec. 3f for speed of sound in solids).

Open organ pipe is an example of a doubly open tube of constant cross section. To calculate its frequency adequately it must be recognized, however, that the air beyond the physical ends of the tube partakes of the vibration and adds inertia to the vibrating system. (This does *not* mean, however, that there is a velocity antinode beyond the end of the tube.) The necessary corrections to the simple formula are usually introduced as empirical "end corrections" to be added to the geometrical length; thus

$$f = \frac{nc}{2(l + x_1 + x_2)} \tag{3h-6}$$

where $x_1 = 0.3d$ is the correction for the unimpeded end (d being the inside diameter of the pipe) and $x_2 = 1.4d$ is the correction for the mouth of the pipe. These are rough approximations; the literature on the end correction is extensive.[1]

The air inside a cylindrical tube that is closed at one end and open at the other vibrates at frequency

$$f = \frac{nc}{4(l + x)} \tag{3h-7}$$

where $x = x_1$ if the open end is unimpeded. In the case of the "closed" organ pipe (meaning closed at one end only), $x = x_2$.

The air in a conical tube is resonant in some cases at the same frequencies as a doubly open cylindrical tube of the same length, but there is the important difference that the contained sound waves are spherical rather than plane. Table 3h-3 gives equations[2] to be solved for each combination of end conditions; $k = 2\pi f/c$. "Closed-open," for example, means that the smaller end of the truncated cone is closed while the larger end is open; r_1 is the slant distance from the extrapolated apex of the cone to the smaller end and r_2 is the slant distance to the larger end. The slant length of the resonator is thus $r_2 - r_1$. When $r_1 = 0$, the length is r_2 and the cone is complete to the apex. Formulas for computing frequency when the cone is complete are shown at the right of Table 3h-3. As in the case of cylindrical tubes, the length should be

TABLE 3h-3. FREQUENCIES OF CONICAL RESONATORS

Ends	Equation	For $r_1 = 0$
Closed-closed	$kr_2 - \tan^{-1} kr_2 = kr_1 - \tan^{-1} kr_1$	$\tan kr_2 = kr_2$
Closed-open	$\tan k(r_2 - r_1) = -kr_1$	$f_1 = \frac{nc}{2r_2}$
Open-closed	$\tan k(r_2 - r_1) = kr_2$	$\tan kr_2 = kr_2$
Open-open	$f = \frac{nc}{2(r_2 - r_1)}$	$f = \frac{nc}{2r_2}$

slightly modified by end corrections. As the angle of the cone increases the correction decreases and may even become negative.[3]

3h-3. Volume Resonators. The Helmholtz resonator consists of a nearly closed cavity of volume V with an opening of acoustical conductance C. If the opening is

[1] E. G. Richardson, ed., "The Technical Aspects of Sound," vol. I, pp. 493–496, 578, Elsevier Publishing Company, Amsterdam, 1953; Harold Levine, *J. Acoust. Soc. Am.* **26**, 200–211 (1954).

[2] Eric J. Irons, *Phil. Mag.* **9,** 346–360 (1930).

[3] A. E. Bate and E. T. Wilson, *Phil. Mag.* **26,** 752–757 (1938).

in a thin wall the conductance is simply d, the diameter of the hole. If the opening is through a short neck of length l, approximately

$$C = \frac{\pi d^2}{4(l + 0.8d)} \tag{3h-8}$$

The natural frequency of the resonantor is

$$f = \frac{c}{2\pi}\sqrt{\frac{C}{V}} \tag{3h-9}$$

the velocity of sound in the opening being c. The equation is valid for wavelengths large in comparison with the dimensions of the resonator.

The ocarina may be recognized as an instrument of the resonator type because the *position* of an open hole of given size is immaterial; when the holes are all equal they may be opened in any order to give the same scale. The total conductance for use in the formula given above is the sum of the conductance of individual holes, provided that they are separated far enough that there is no interaction.

3h-4. Bars. A long thin bar clamped and/or free at the end(s) can vibrate transversely at the fundamental frequencies listed in Table 3h-4 under mode 1. The length of the bar is l, Y is Young's modulus, ρ is the density, and κ is the radius of gyration about the neutral axis of the cross section. For a round bar $\kappa = d/4$, where d is the diameter. For a flat bar of thickness t (in the plane of vibration) $\kappa = t/\sqrt{12}$; the width is immaterial. The frequency of a bar clamped at both ends is the same as that of a bar free at both ends. The frequency of a higher mode of vibration can be found by multiplying the fundamental frequency by the ratio indicated in Table 3h-4;

TABLE 3h-4. FREQUENCIES OF TRANSVERSE VIBRATION OF BARS

Ends	Frequency	Ratio			Cents		
	Mode → 1	2	3	4	2	3	4
Clamped-free	$f_1 = \frac{0.5597\kappa}{l^2}\sqrt{\frac{Y}{\rho}}$	6.267	17.548	34.387	3,177	4,960	6,124
Free-free, or clamped-clamped	$f_1 = \frac{3.561\kappa}{l^2}\sqrt{\frac{Y}{\rho}}$	2.756	5.404	8.933	1,755	2,921	3,791

the intervals in cents corresponding to these ratios are given at the extreme right of the table. These are the classic[1] values for thin bars; the frequencies of actual bars are lowered slightly as a consequence of rotatory inertia, lateral inertia, and shear.[2] For example, for a steel bar whose length is 40 times the thickness, the frequencies of the first four modes of vibration are expected to be 0.997, 0.992, 0.984, and 0.974 times the corresponding "thin" values (i.e., lowered 5, 14, 28, and 46 cents, respectively).

The simple tuning fork may be recognized as an example of dual clamped-free bars. The frequency of a tuning fork made of ordinary steel may be computed approximately from

$$f = \frac{80{,}000t}{l^2} \tag{3h-10}$$

[1] Lord Rayleigh, "Theory of Sound," vol. I, p. 280, Macmillan & Co., Ltd., London, 1894. The interval erroneously given as 2.4359 octaves has been corrected here to 2.4340 octaves = 2,921 cents.

[2] William T. Thomson, *J. Acoust. Soc. Am.* **11**, 199–204 (1939). There is an error: $m = \beta/[1 + \beta^2(k/L)^2]^{\frac{1}{4}}$, not $m = \beta/[1 + \beta^2(k/L)^2]^{\frac{1}{2}}$.

TABLE 3h-5. FREQUENCIES OF THE EQUALLY TEMPERED SCALE, BASED ON THE INTERNATIONAL STANDARD A = 440 CPS

Note	S	f	$2\pi f$	Note	S	f	$2\pi f$	Note	S	f	$2\pi f$
C_0	0	16.352	102.74	C_3	36	130.81	821.92	C_6	72	1,046.5	6,575.4
	1	17.324	102.74		37	138.59	870.79		73	1,108.7	6,966.4
D_0	2	18.354	115.32	D_3	38	146.83	922.58	D_6	74	1,174.7	7,380.6
	3	19.445	122.18		39	155.56	977.43		75	1,244.5	7,819.5
E_0	4	20.602	129.44	E_3	40	164.81	1,035.6	E_6	76	1,318.5	8,284.4
F_0	5	21.827	137.14	F_3	41	174.61	1,097.1	F_6	77	1,396.9	8,777.1
	6	23.125	145.30		42	185.00	1,162.4		78	1,480.0	9,299.0
G_0	7	24.500	153.93	G_3	43	196.00	1,231.5	G_6	79	1,568.0	9,851.9
	8	25.957	163.09		44	207.65	1,304.7		80	1,661.2	10,438
A_0	9	27.500	172.59	A_3	45	220.00	1,382.3	A_6	81	1,760.0	11,058
	10	29.135	183.06		46	233.08	1,464.5		82	1,864.7	11,716
B_0	11	30.868	193.95	B_3	47	246.94	1,551.6	B_6	83	1,975.5	12,413
C_1	12	32.703	205.48	C_4	48	261.63	1,643.8	C_7	84	2,093.0	13,151
	13	34.648	217.70		49	277.18	1,741.6		85	2,217.5	13,933
D_1	14	36.708	230.64	D_4	50	293.66	1,845.2	D_7	86	2,349.3	14,761
	15	38.891	244.36		51	311.13	1,954.9		87	2,489.0	15,639
E_1	16	41.203	258.89	E_4	52	329.63	2,071.1	E_7	88	2,637.0	16,569
F_1	17	43.654	274.28	F_4	53	349.23	2,194.3	F_7	89	2,793.8	17,554
	18	46.249	290.59		54	369.99	2,324.7		90	2,960.0	18,598
G_1	19	48.999	307.87	G_4	55	392.00	2,463.0	G_7	91	3,136.0	19,704
	20	51.913	326.18		56	415.30	2,609.4		92	3,322.4	20.875
A_1	21	55.000	345.58	A_4	57	440.00	2,764.6	A_7	93	3,520.0	22,117
	22	58.270	366.12		58	466.16	2,929.0		94	3,729.3	23,432
B_1	23	61.735	387.90	B_4	59	493.88	3,103.2	B_7	95	3,951.1	24,825
C_2	24	65.406	410.96	C_5	60	523.25	3,287.7	C_8	96	4,186.0	26,301
	25	69.296	435.40		61	554.37	3,483.2		97	4,434.9	27,865
D_2	26	73.416	461.29	D_5	62	587.33	3,690.3	D_8	98	4,698.6	29,522
	27	77.782	488.72		63	622.25	3,909.7		99	4,978.0	31,278
E_2	28	82.407	517.78	E_5	64	659.26	4,142.2	E_8	100	5,274.0	33,138
F_2	29	87.307	548.57	F_5	65	698.46	4,388.5	F_8	101	5,587.7	35,108
	30	92.499	581.19		66	739.99	4,649.5		102	5,919.9	37,196
G_2	31	97.999	615.74	G_5	67	783.99	4,926.0	G_8	103	6,271.9	39,408
	32	103.83	652.36		68	830.61	5,218.9		104	6,644.9	41,751
A_2	33	110.00	691.15	A_5	69	880.00	5,529.2	A_8	105	7,040.0	44,234
	34	116.54	732.25		70	932.33	5,858.0		106	7,458.6	46,864
B_2	35	123.47	775.79	B_5	71	987.77	6,206.3	B_8	107	7,902.1	49,651

Numerous subscript notations have been employed to distinguish the notes of one octave from those of another. The particular scheme used here assigns to C_0 a frequency which corresponds roughly to the lowest pitch. S is the number of semitones counted from this C_0.

provided that the thickness t and length l of the prongs are given in centimeters.

It is evident from Table 3h-4 that the different modes of vibration of a uniform bar are inharmonic. However, the cross section of the bar in the modern xylophone or marimba is often given an empirical lengthwise "undulation" such that the second mode of vibration of the free-free bar is changed in frequency to 3 or 4 times the fundamental frequency.[1] The frequencies of the higher modes of vibration are also modified

TABLE 3h-6. INTERVALS IN CENTS CORRESPONDING TO CERTAIN FREQUENCY RATIOS

Name of interval	Frequency ratio	Cents
Unison	1:1	0
Minor second or semitone	1.059463:1	100
Semitone	16:15	111.731
Minor tone or lesser whole tone	10:9	182.404
Major second or whole tone	1.122462:1	200
Major tone or greater whole tone	9:8	203.910
Minor third	1.189207:1	300
Minor third	6:5	315.641
Major third	5:4	386.314
Major third	1.259921:1	400
Perfect fourth	4:3	498.045
Perfect fourth	1.334840:1	500
Augmented fourth	45:32	590.224
Augmented fourth	1.414214:1	600
Diminished fifth	1.414214:1	600
Diminished fifth	64:45	609.777
Perfect fifth	1.498307:1	700
Perfect fifth	3:2	701.955
Minor sixth	1.587401:1	800
Minor sixth	8:5	813.687
Major sixth	5:3	884.359
Major sixth	1.681793:1	900
Harmonic minor seventh	7:4	968.826
Grave minor seventh	16:9	996.091
Minor seventh	1.781797:1	1,000
Minor seventh	9:5	1,017.597
Major seventh	15:8	1,088.269
Major seventh	1.887749:1	1,100
Octave	2:1	1,200.000

by variation in cross section for special purposes such as the simulation of the sound of a bell.[2]

3h-5. Musical Scales. By international agreement the standard tuning frequency for musical performance is the A of 440 cps. The frequencies of the equally tempered scale based on this frequency appear in Table 3h-5. Middle C thus has a frequency of 261.6 cps. The C of 256 cps, frequently used in the past for demonstrations in physics, has never been adopted for practical musical performance.

[1] See U.S. Pats. 1,838,502 (1931) and 1,632,751 (1927).

[2] See U.S. Pats. 2,273,333 (1942), 2,516,725 (1950), 2,536,800 (1951), and 2,606,474 (1952).

For many calculations with musical intervals it is convenient to deal with logarithmic units that can be added instead of the ratios which must be multiplied. The octave is equal to 1,200 logarithmic cents, and the equally tempered semitone is 100 cents. The interval in cents corresponding to any two frequencies f_1 and f_2 is 1,200 $\log_2 (f_2/f_1) = 3{,}986 \log_{10} (f_2/f_1)$. Table 3h-6 lists certain common intervals in cents, and the corresponding ratios; the frequency ratios for intervals up to 100 cents are given in Table 3h-7.

TABLE 3h-7. RATIOS FOR INTERVALS TO 100 CENTS

Cents	Ratio	Cents	Ratio	Cents	Ratio	Cents	Ratio
0	1.000000	25	1.014545	50	1.029302	75	1.044274
1	1.000578	26	1.015132	51	1.029896	76	1.044877
2	1.001158	27	1.015718	52	1.030492	77	1.045481
3	1.001734	28	1.016305	53	1.031087	78	1.046085
4	1.002313	29	1.016892	54	1.031683	79	1.046689
5	1.002892	30	1.017480	55	1.032079	80	1.047294
6	1.003472	31	1.018068	56	1.032876	81	1.047899
7	1.004052	32	1.018656	57	1.033473	82	1.048505
8	1.004632	33	1.019244	58	1.034070	83	1.049111
9	1.005212	34	1.019833	59	1.034667	84	1.049717
10	1.005793	35	1.020423	60	1.035265	85	1.050323
11	1.006374	36	1.021012	61	1.035863	86	1.050930
12	1.006956	37	1.021602	62	1.036462	87	1.051537
13	1.007537	38	1.022192	63	1.037060	88	1.052145
14	1.008120	39	1.022783	64	1.037660	89	1.052753
15	1.008702	40	1.023374	65	1.038259	90	1.053361
16	1.009285	41	1.023965	66	1.038859	91	1.053970
17	1.009868	42	1.024557	67	1.039459	92	1.054579
18	1.010451	43	1.025149	68	1.040060	93	1.055188
19	1.011035	44	1.025741	69	1.040661	94	1.055798
20	1.011619	45	1.026334	70	1.041262	95	1.056408
21	1.012204	46	1.026927	71	1.041864	96	1.057018
22	1.012789	47	1.027520	72	1.042466	97	1.057629
23	1.013374	48	1.028114	73	1.043068	98	1.058240
24	1.013959	49	1.028708	74	1.043671	99	1.058851

3i. Radiation of Sound

FRANK MASSA

Massa Laboratories, Incorporated

3i-1. Introduction. Radiation of sound may take place in a number of ways but, basically, all sound generators cause an alternating pressure to be set up in the fluid medium within which the sound energy is established. The sound energy that is set up in a medium depends not only on the physical characteristics of the medium and the oscillatory volume displacement of the fluid set up by the vibrating source but also upon the size and shape of the generator. The acoustic power generated by any vibrating source can be expressed by

$$P = U^2 R_A \times 10^{-7} \quad \text{watts} \tag{3i-1}$$

where U = rate of volume displacement of the fluid, cc/sec
R_A = acoustic radiation resistance of the source, acoustic ohms

If the rate of volume displacement is taken in peak cc/sec, Eq. (3i-1) will yield peak watts of power. If the volume displacement is taken in rms cc/sec, the power will be given in rms watts.

Of the many possible methods for generating sound, two types of generators will effectively serve to classify most of them. These basic generators are (1) pulsating sphere, and (2) vibrating piston.

Each type of generator has a different acoustic impedance characteristic which depends on the dimensions of the source and on the frequency of vibration.

3i-2. Acoustic Impedance. *Pulsating Sphere.* The specific acoustic impedance of a pulsating sphere is given by

$$z = \frac{\rho c}{1 + [1/(\pi D/\lambda)]^2} + j\frac{\rho c/(\pi D/\lambda)}{1 + [1/(\pi D/\lambda)]^2} \quad \text{acoustic ohms/cm}^2 \tag{3i-2}$$

where ρ = density of the medium, g/cc
c = velocity of sound in the medium, cm/sec
D = diameter of the sphere, cm
$\lambda = c/f$
f = frequency, cps

It can be seen from inspection that at high frequencies, where D/λ becomes very large, the specific acoustic impedance becomes a pure resistance equal to ρc and the reactance term vanishes. At low frequencies, where D/λ is small, the specific acoustic impedance becomes

$$z = \rho c \left(\frac{\pi D}{\lambda}\right)^2 + j\rho c \frac{\pi D}{\lambda} \quad \text{acoustic ohms/cm}^2 \tag{3i-3}$$

A plot of the specific acoustic resistance and reactance of a pulsating sphere as a function of D/λ is shown in Fig. 3i-1. To obtain the total acoustic radiation resistance

R_A of the sphere, it is necessary to divide the specific acoustic resistance by the total surface area of the sphere in cm². The value of R_A thus determined, when substituted in Eq. (3i-1), will give the actual acoustic watts being generated by the spherical source.

Vibrating Piston. The specific acoustic impedance of a circular piston set in an infinite rigid baffle and radiating sound from one of its surfaces is given by

$$z = \rho c \left[1 - \frac{J_1(2\pi D/\lambda)}{\pi D/\lambda} \right] + j\rho c \frac{K_1(2\pi D/\lambda)}{2(\pi D/\lambda)^2} \quad \text{acoustic ohms/cm}^2 \qquad (3i\text{-}4)$$

where D is the diameter of the piston in centimeters, J_1 and K_1 are Bessel functions, and the remaining symbols are defined under Eq. (3i-2).

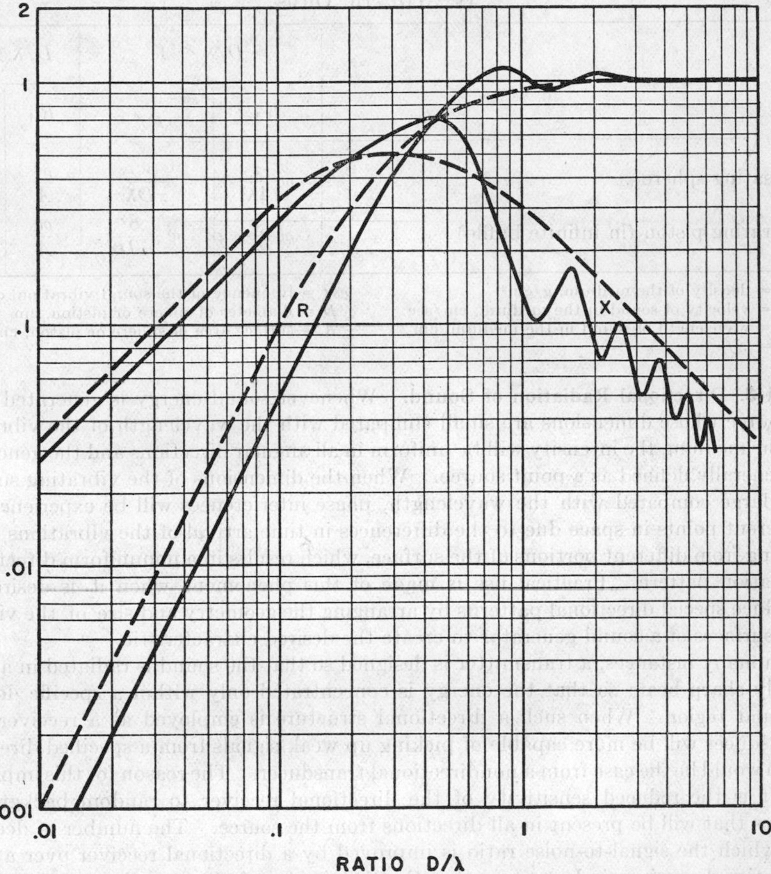

FIG. 3i-1. Specific acoustic resistance R and reactance X of a pulsating sphere (dashed curves) and a vibrating piston set in an infinite baffle (solid curves). To obtain magnitude of R or X multiply ordinates by ρc of the medium.

At high frequencies, where D/λ is large, Eq. (3i-4) reduces to a pure resistance equal to ρc. At low frequencies, where D/λ is small, the specific acoustic impedance for a piston set in an infinite baffle with one side radiating becomes

$$z = \frac{\rho c(\pi D/\lambda)^2}{2} + j\rho c \frac{8D}{3\lambda} \quad \text{acoustic ohms/cm}^2 \qquad (3i\text{-}5)$$

A plot of the specific acoustic resistance and reactance for a vibrating piston mounted in an infinite baffle is shown in Fig. 3i-1. To obtain the total acoustic radiation resistance of the piston, it is necessary to divide the specific resistance by the piston area in cm². The value of R_A so determined, when substituted in Eq. (3i-1), will give the actual acoustic watts being generated by a piston.

Summary of Radiation Impedance Characteristics. In Table 3i-1 are shown the magnitudes of the acoustic radiation resistance and reactance for a sphere and piston for both low-frequency (D/λ small) and high-frequency (D/λ large) operation.

TABLE 3i-1. TABULATED VALUES OF THE TOTAL ACOUSTIC RADIATION RESISTANCE AND REACTANCE OF A SPHERE AND PISTON IN ACOUSTIC OHMS

	$D/\lambda \ll 1$		$D/\lambda \gg 1$	
	R_A	X_A	R_A	X_A
Pulsating sphere............................	$\rho c \frac{\pi}{4\lambda^2}$	$\frac{\rho c}{\pi D\lambda}$	$\frac{\rho c}{A}$	0
Vibrating piston (in infinite baffle)............	$\rho c \frac{\pi}{2\lambda^2}$	$\rho c \frac{8}{3\pi D\lambda}$	$\frac{\rho c}{A}$	0

ρ = density of the medium, g/cm²
c = velocity of sound in the medium, cm/sec
λ = wavelength of sound in the medium, cm
$\lambda = c/f$
f = frequency of the sound vibration, cps
D = diameter of sphere or pistion, cm
A = surface area of sphere or piston, cm²

3i-3. Directional Radiation of Sound. Whenever sound energy is generated from a source whose dimensions are small compared with the wavelength of the vibration in the medium, the intensity will be uniform in all angular directions and the generator is generally defined as a point source. When the dimensions of the vibrating surface are large compared with the wavelength, phase interferences will be experienced at different points in space due to the differences in time arrival of the vibrations originating from different portions of the surface, which results in a nonuniform directional radiation pattern. Practical use is made of this phenomena when it is desired to produce special directional patterns by arranging the geometry and size of the vibrating surfaces of a sound generator to create the desired characteristic.

In many instances, a transmitter is designed so that the sound is radiated in a relatively sharp beam so that the energy is concentrated only within a specific desired angular region. When such a directional structure is employed as a receiver, the transducer will be more capable of picking up weak signals from a specified direction than would be the case from a nondirectional transducer. The reason for this improvement is the reduced sensitivity of the directional receiver to random background noises that will be present in all directions from the source. The number of decibels by which the signal-to-noise ratio is improved by a directional receiver over a nondirectional receiver is known as the *directivity index* of the transducer. It will be defined more fully later. The following will show the directional radiation characteristics of several common structures.

Uniform Line Source. If a uniform long line is vibrating at uniform amplitude, the radiated sound intensity will be a maximum in a plane which is the perpendicular bisector of the line. At angles removed from the perpendicular bisector of the line, the intensity will fall off to a series of nulls and secondary maxima of diminishing amplitudes as the angle of incidence to the axis of the line deviates from the normal bisector of the line. For a line of length L vibrating uniformly over its entire length at a frequency corresponding to a wavelength of sound λ in the medium, the ratio of the sound pressure p_Θ produced at an angle Θ removed from the normal axis of maximum response to the sound pressure p_0 on the normal axis is given by

$$\frac{p_\Theta}{p_0} = \frac{\sin[(\pi L/\lambda)\sin\Theta]}{(\pi L/\lambda)\sin\Theta} \tag{3i-6}$$

If L is large compared with λ, the response as a function of Θ will go through a series of nulls and secondary maxima of successively diminishing amplitudes.

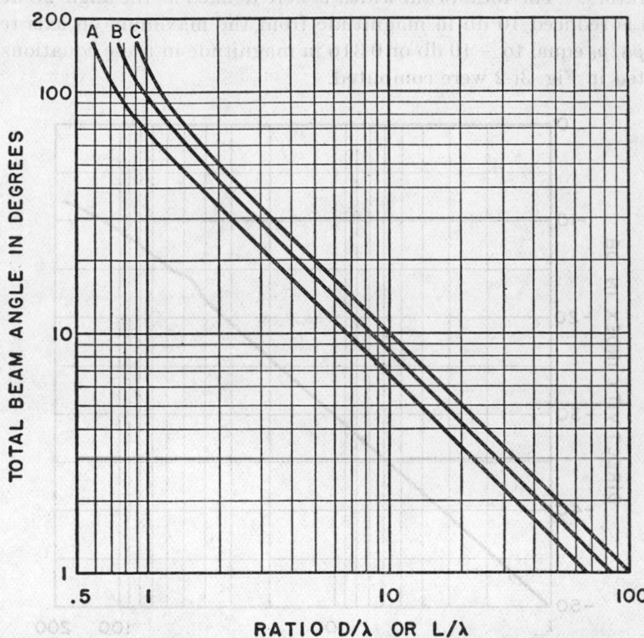

FIG. 3i-2. Total beam angle for a piston, ring, and line source as a function of size of source to wavelength of sound being radiated. A, thin ring of diameter D. B, uniform line of length L. C, piston of diameter D. (*Curves A and C from Massa, "Acoustic Design Charts," The Blakiston Division, McGraw-Hill Book Company, Inc., New York, 1942.*)

Circular Piston in Infinite Baffle. The directional radiation pattern from a large circular piston vibrating at constant amplitude and phase and set into an infinite rigid baffle may be obtained from the expression

$$\frac{p_\Theta}{p_0} = \frac{2J_1[(\pi D/\lambda)\sin\Theta]}{(\pi D/\lambda)\sin\Theta} \tag{3i-7}$$

where p_Θ = sound pressure at an angle Θ from the normal axis of the piston
p_0 = sound pressure on normal axis of piston
D = diameter of piston
λ = wavelength of sound
J_1 = Bessel function of order 1

From this equation, it can be seen that, as D/λ increases, the beam width becomes smaller and the sound pressure goes through a series of nulls and secondary maxima as Θ progressively departs from the normal axis to the piston.

Thin Circular Ring. The directional radiation pattern from a large narrow circular ring of diameter D vibrating at constant amplitude and fitted into an infinite plane baffle may be obtained from the expression

$$\frac{p_\Theta}{p_0} = J_0\left(\frac{\pi D}{\lambda}\sin\Theta\right) \tag{3i-8}$$

where J_0 = Bessel function of order zero and all other symbols are defined under Eq. (3i-7).

Beam Width for Line, Piston, and Ring. From Eqs. (3i-6), (3i-7), and (3i-8), the total beam width has been computed for the radiation from each of the three types of sound generators. The total beam width is here defined as the angle 2Θ at which the pressure p_Θ is reduced 10 db in magnitude from the maximum on axis response p_0. By setting p_Θ/p_0 equal to -10 db or 0.316 in magnitude in these equations, the three curves plotted in Fig. 3i-2 were computed.

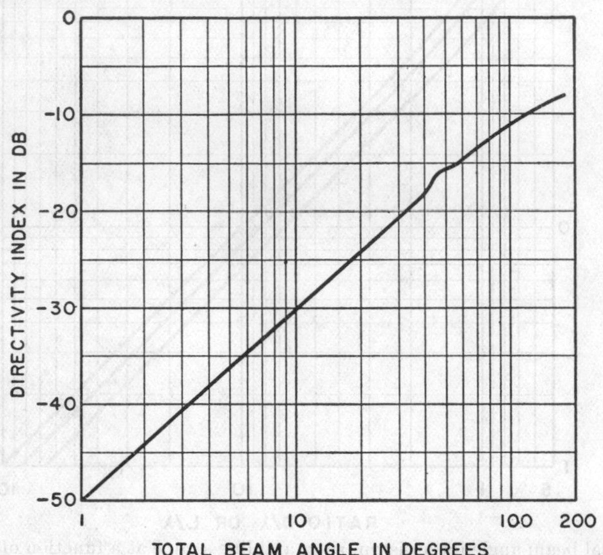

FIG. 3i-3. Directivity index of a piston or ring as a function of total beam angle where beam angle is defined as the included angle of the main beam between the 10-decibel-down points in the directional response. *(Computed from Massa, "Acoustic Design Charts," The Blakiston Division, McGraw-Hill Book Company, Inc., New York, 1942.)*

3i-4. Directivity Index. It has already been mentioned that a directional transducer has an advantage over a nondirectional structure whenever it is desired to send or receive signals from a particular localized direction only. The fact that the directional transducer is less sensitive to sounds coming from random undesired directions makes it possible for it to detect weaker signals than would be possible with a nondirectional unit. The measure of this improvement in decibels corresponds to the *directivity index* of the transducer. The directivity index of a transducer is defined as the ratio of the total power radiated by a transducer to the total power required by a nondirectional transducer to produce the same peak intensity as is produced by the directional transducer on its axis of maximum response.

The directivity index of a transducer is expressed in decibels, and a plot of the directivity index as a function of beam width for a piston or ring is shown in Fig. 3i-3.

3j. Architectural Acoustics

CYRIL M. HARRIS

Columbia University

3j-1. Sound-absorptive Materials. When sound waves strike a surface, the energy may be divided into three portions: the incident, reflected, and absorbed energy. Suppose plane waves are incident on a surface of infinite extent. For this case, the absorption coefficient α of the surface may be defined as

$$\alpha = \frac{\int_s \mathbf{I}_p \cdot \mathbf{ds}}{\int_s \mathbf{I}_A \cdot \mathbf{ds}} \tag{3j-1}$$

where I_p is the time average of the intensity vector of the sound field at the absorptive surface; ds is the vector surface element—the positive direction being into the material from the incident side; and I_A is the time average of the intensity vector which would exist at the surface element if the surface were removed. The absorption coefficient defined above is a function of angle of incidence and frequency.

For acoustical designing in architecture it is convenient to use an "average" absorption coefficient α which is assumed to depend only on the physical characteristics of the material and not on the sound field. These are the values of absorption that are given in this section. A surface having an absorption coefficient α and area S square feet is said to have an absorption of αS sabins. Thus the *sabin* (sometimes called a square-foot unit of absorption) is the absorption equivalent of 1 sq ft of material having an absorption coefficient of unity.

A quantity which describes the acoustical properties of a material that is more fundamental than absorption coefficient is its *acoustic impedance*, defined as the complex ratio of sound pressure to the corresponding particle velocity at the surface of the material. Because of the complexities involved in the solutions to problems of room acoustics by boundary-value theory in terms of boundary impedances,[1] the simpler concept of absorption coefficient is usually employed in calculating the acoustical properties of rooms, as indicated in the following section.

Most manufactured acoustical materials depend largely on their porosity for their acoustic absorption, the sound waves being converted into heat as they are propagated into the interstices of the material and also by vibration of the small fibers of the material. Another important mechanism of absorption is panel vibration; when sound waves force a panel into motion the resulting flexual vibration converts a fraction of the incident sound energy into heat.

The average value of absorption coefficient of a material varies with frequency. Tables usually list the values of α at 125, 250, 500, 1,000, and 4,000 cps, or at 128, 256,

[1] P. M. Morse, "Vibration and Sound," chap. VIII, McGraw-Hill Book Company, Inc., New York, 1948.

512, 1,024, 2,048, and 4,096 cps, which for practical purposes are identical. In comparing materials which are used for noise-reduction purposes in offices, banks, corridors, etc., it is sometimes useful to employ a single figure called the noise-reduction coefficient (abbreviated NRC) of the material which is the average of the absorption coefficients at 250, 500, 1,000, and 2,000 cps, to the nearest multiple of 0.05.

Figures 3j-1 through 3j-4 give the absorption coefficient vs. frequency for several types of acoustical material.[1] The absorption-frequency characteristics of regularly perforated cellulose fiber tile $\frac{3}{4}$ in. thick is shown in Fig. 3j-1. These curves represent average coefficients for materials of the same type, thickness, and method of mounting but of different manufacture. Similar data are shown in Fig. 3j-2 for fissured mineral tile $\frac{13}{16}$ in. thick. Values of noise-reduction coefficient are shown to the right of the graph. Values of absorption coefficient for various types of building materials are

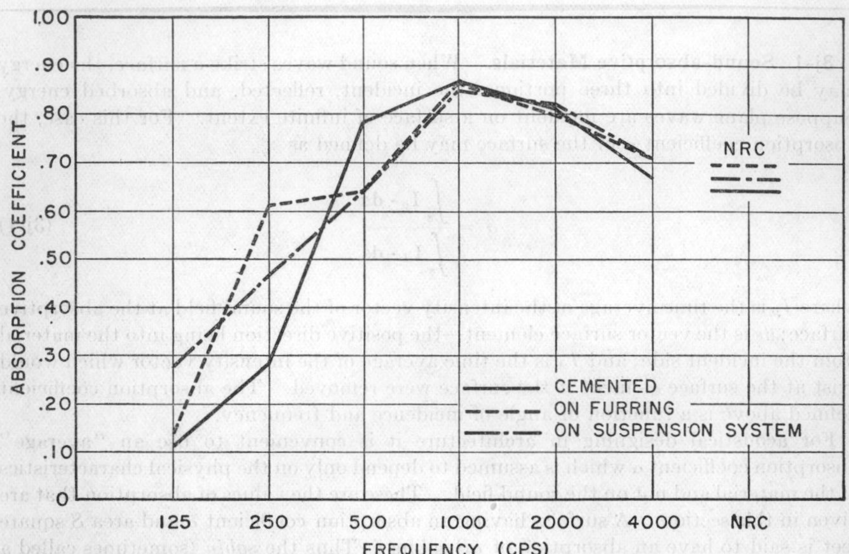

FIG. 3j-1. The absorption vs. frequency characteristic for regularly perforated cellulose fiber acoustical tile. These data represent average values for $\frac{3}{4}$-in. tile having the same thickness and mounted in the same way but of different manufacture. (*After H. J. Sabine.*)

given in Table 3j-1.[2] The equivalent absorption of individuals and seats, expressed in sabins, is given in Table 3j-2. More complete data, and data for other types of material, are given in Knudsen and Harris.[3] Sound-absorptive materials and structures may be classified in the following way: (1) prefabricated units, including acoustical tile, tile boards, and certain mechanically perforated units backed with absorptive material; (2) acoustical plasters; (3) acoustical blankets, consisting of mineral wool, glass fibers, hair felt, or wood fibers held together in blanket form by a suitable binder; (4) panel absorbers, including panels of plywood, paperboard, and pressed-wood fiber; (5) membrane absorbers consisting of a membrane of negligible stiffness backed by an enclosed air space; (6) resonator absorbers of the Helmholtz type; and (7) special types.

[1] C. M. Harris, "Handbook of Noise Control," chapter by H. J. Sabine, McGraw-Hill Book Company, Inc., New York, in preparation.

[2] Acoustical Materials Association, *Bull.* XV, New York, 1955.

[3] V. O. Knudsen and C. M. Harris, "Acoustical Designing in Architecture," John Wiley & Sons, Inc., New York, 1950.

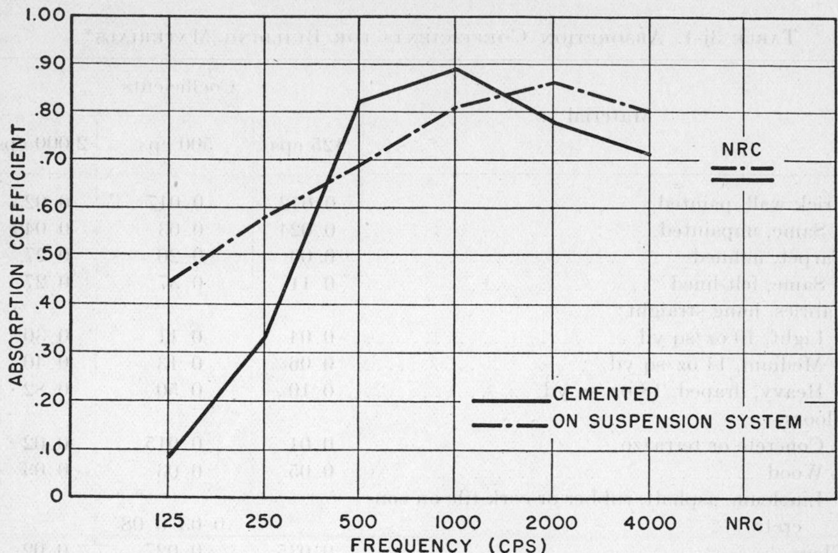

FIG. 3j-2. The absorption vs. frequency characteristic for fissured mineral tile. These data represent average values for $\frac{13}{16}$-in. tile having the same thickness and mounted in the same way but of different manufacture. (*After H. J. Sabine.*)

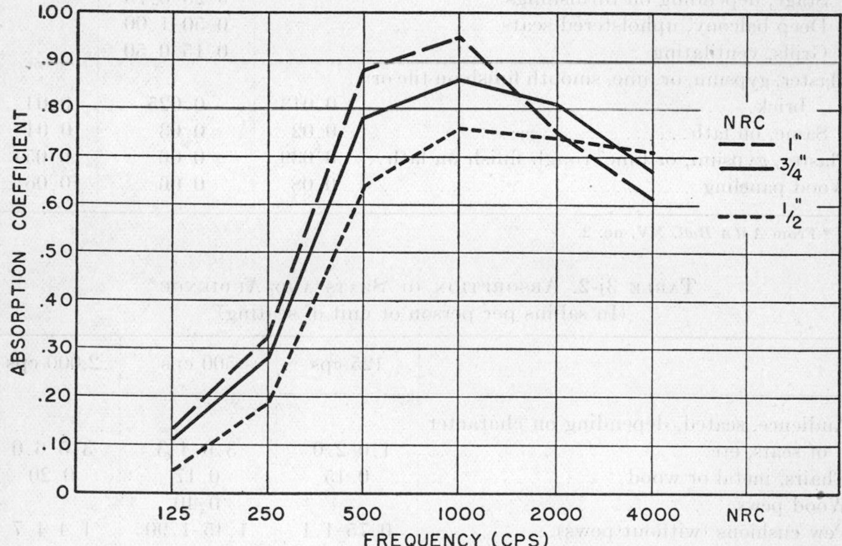

FIG. 3j-3. The absorption vs. frequency characteristic for regularly perforated cellulose fiber acoustical tile which has been spot-cemented to a rigid surface. These data represent the average value for tiles of different manufacture, mounted in the same way and having different thickness. (*After H. J. Sabine.*)

3j-2. Reverberation-time Calculations. After sound has been produced in or enters an enclosed space it will be reflected by the boundaries of the enclosure. Although some energy is lost at each reflection, several seconds may elapse before the sound decays to inaudibility. This prolongation of sound after the original source has stopped is called *reverberation,* a certain amount of which is found to add a pleasing

TABLE 3j-1. ABSORPTION COEFFICIENTS FOR BUILDING MATERIALS*

Material	Coefficients 125 cps	500 cps	2,000 cps
Brick wall, painted	0.012	0.017	0.023
Same, unpainted	0.024	0.03	0.049
Carpet, unlined	0.09	0.20	0.27
Same, felt-lined	0.11	0.37	0.27
Fabrics, hung straight:			
Light, 10 oz/sq yd	0.04	0.11	0.30
Medium, 14 oz/sq yd	0.06	0.13	0.40
Heavy, draped, 18 oz/sq yd	0.10	0.50	0.82
Floors:			
Concrete or terrazzo	0.01	0.015	0.02
Wood	0.05	0.03	0.03
Linoleum, asphalt, rubber or cork tile on concrete		0.03–0.08	
Glass	0.035	0.027	0.02
Marble or glazed tile	0.01	0.01	0.015
Openings:			
Stage, depending on furnishings		0.25–0.75	
Deep balcony, upholstered seats		0.50–1.00	
Grills, ventilating		0.15–0.50	
Plaster, gypsum, or lime, smooth finish on tile or brick	0.013	0.025	0.04
Same, on lath	0.02	0.03	0.04
Plaster, gypsum, or lime, rough finish on lath	0.039	0.06	0.054
Wood paneling	0.08	0.06	0.06

* From *AMA Bull.* XV, no. 2.

TABLE 3j-2. ABSORPTION OF SEATS AND AUDIENCE*
(In sabins per person or unit of seating)

	125 cps	500 cps	2,000 cps
Audience, seated, depending on character of seats, etc	1.0–2.0	3.0–4.3	3.5–6.0
Chairs, metal or wood	0.15	0.17	0.20
Wood pews		0.40	
Pew cushions (without pews)	0.75–1.1	1.45–1.90	1.4–1.7
Theater and auditorium chairs:			
Wood-veneer seat and back		0.25	
Upholstered in leatherette		1.6	
Heavily upholstered in plush or mohair		2.6–3.0	

* From *AMA Bull.* XV, no. 2.

characteristic to the acoustical qualities of a room. On the other hand, excessive reverberation can ruin the acoustical properties of an otherwise well-designed room.

Because of the importance of the proper control of reverberation in rooms, a standard of measure called *reverberation time* (abbreviated t_{60}) has been established. It is one of the important parameters in architectural acoustics. This is the time required for a specified sound to die away to one-thousandth of its initial pressure, a drop in sound pressure level of 60 db. It is given by the following equation:

$$t_{60} = \frac{0.049V}{S[-2.30 \log_{10}(1 - \bar{\alpha})] + 4mV} \quad \text{sec} \tag{3j-2}$$

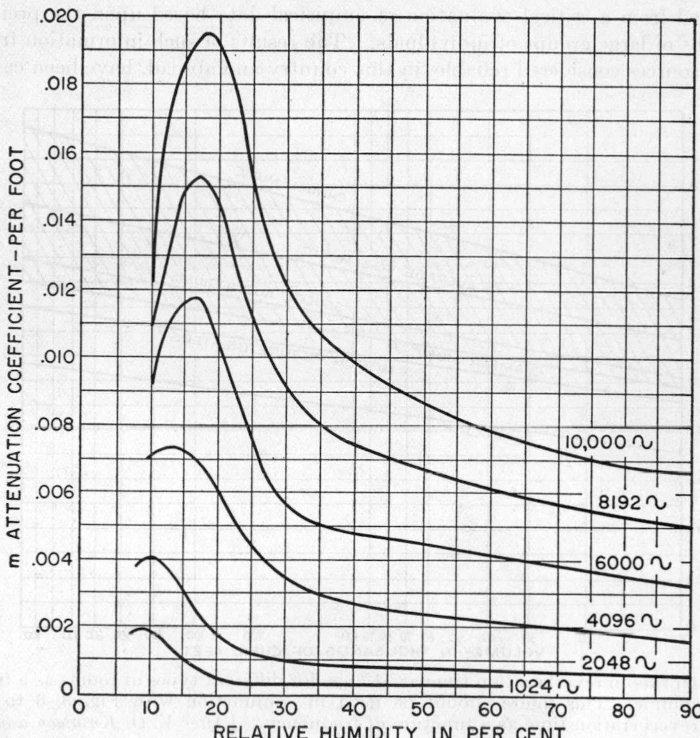

FIG. 3j-4. Values of the attenuation coefficient m as a function of relative humidity for different frequencies. (*After V. O. Knudsen and C. M. Harris.*)

and when $\bar{\alpha}$ is small compared with unity,

$$t_{60} = \frac{0.049V}{S\bar{\alpha} + 4mV} \quad \text{sec} \tag{3j-3}$$

where V = volume of the room, cu ft

S = total surface area, sq ft

$\bar{\alpha}$ = average absorption coefficient given by

$$\bar{\alpha} = \frac{\alpha_1 S_1 + \alpha_2 S_2 + \alpha_3 S_3 + \cdots}{S_1 + S_2 + S_3 + \cdots} = \frac{a}{S} \tag{3j-4}$$

α_1 = absorption coefficient of area S_1, etc.

a = total absorption in the room, sabins

The quantity m is the attenuation coefficient for air given by Fig. 3j-4.[1] For relatively small auditoriums and frequencies below 2,000 cps, the mV term can usually be neglected so that Eq. (3j-3) reduces to

$$t_{60} = \frac{0.049V}{S\bar{\alpha}} \quad \text{sec} \tag{3j-5}$$

3j-3. Optimum Reverberation Time. A certain amount of reverberation in a room adds a pleasing quality to music. Since the reverberation time one would consider to be optimum is a matter of personal preference, it is not a quantity that can be calculated from a formula. On the other hand, useful engineering-design data may be obtained from a critical evaluation of empirical data based upon the preference evaluations of large groups of individuals. The results of such information from all available sources considered reliable, in this country and abroad, have been carefully

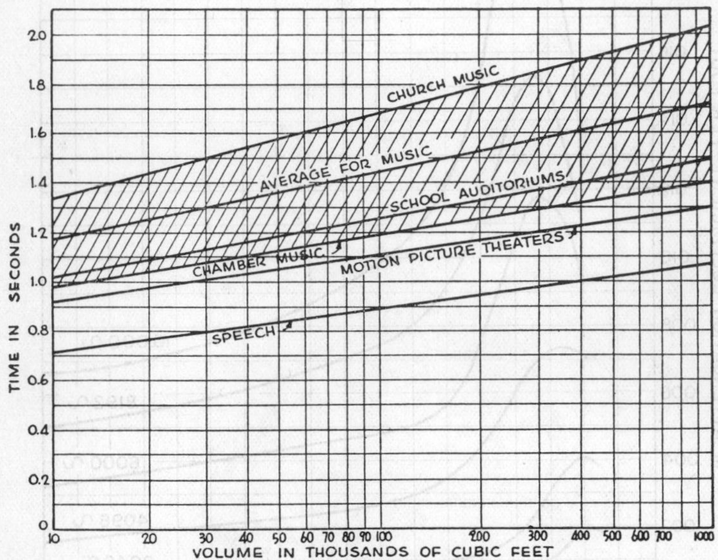

FIG. 3j-5. Optimum reverberation time at 512 cps for different types of rooms as a function of room volume. This figure should be used in conjunction with Fig. 3j-6 to obtain optimum reverberation time as a function of frequency. (*After V. O. Knudsen and C. M. Harris.*)

evaluated by Knudsen and Harris,[1] who have published the curves for optimum reverberation time shown in Figs. 3j-5 and 3j-6. The data in Fig. 3j-5 give the optimum reverberation times at 512 cps as a function of volume for rooms and auditoriums that are used for different purposes. Since the optimum reverberation time for music depends on the type of music, it is represented by a broad band. The optimum reverberation time for a room used primarily for speech is considerably shorter; a reverberation time longer than those shown results in a decrease in speech intelligibility.

The optimum reverberation times at frequencies other than 512 cps is obtained by multiplying the values given in Fig. 3j-5 by the ratio R from Fig. 3j-6 for the desired frequency. These data indicate that below 512 cps the optimum reverberation time may fall anywhere in a wide range shown by the crosshatched band; smaller rooms usually have preferred ratios that are in the lower part of the band.

[1] *Ibid.*

3j-4. Air-borne Sound Transmission through Partitions. The fraction of incident sound energy transmitted through a partition is called its transmission coefficient τ. In rating the noise-insulating value of partitions, windows, and doors, it is generally convenient to employ a logarithmic quantity, transmission loss T.L., which is equal to the number of decibels by which sound energy that is incident on a partition is reduced in transmission through it. The two quantities are related by the equation

$$\text{T.L.} = 10 \log \frac{1}{\tau} \quad \text{db} \tag{3j-6}$$

Air-borne sound is transmitted through a so-called "rigid" partition, such as a wall of concrete or brick, by forcing it into vibration; then the vibrating partition becomes a secondary source, radiating sound to the side opposite the original source. Over a large portion of the audible range, such a partition, on the average, approximates a mass-controlled system so that its transmission loss should increase 6 db each time the weight of the partition is doubled. In most actual partitions the increase is usually less, say 4 to 5 db for the average frequency range between 128 and 2,048 cps.

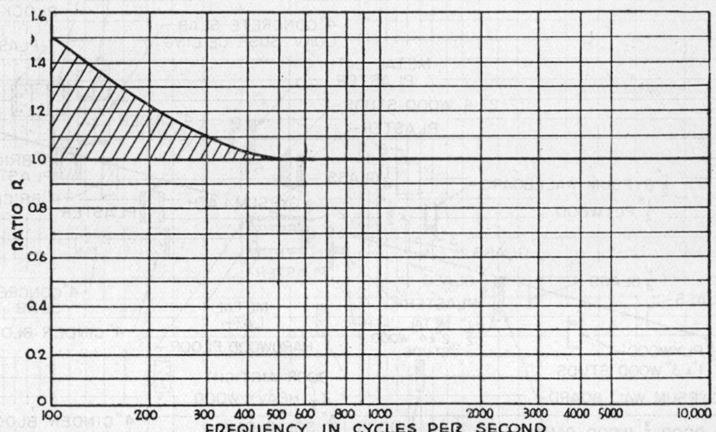

FIG. 3j-6. Chart for computing optimum reverberation time as a function of frequency. The time at any frequency is given in terms of a ratio R which should be multiplied by the optimum time at 512 cps (from Fig. 3j-5) to obtain the optimum time at that frequency. (*After V. O. Knudsen and C. M. Harris.*)

This is illustrated by Fig. 3j-7, which gives the transmission loss (averaged over frequency in the range from 128 to 4,096 cps) as a function of weight of the partition in pounds per square foot of surface area. The straight line represents the calculated transmission loss assuming that the values of T.L. increase 6 db for each doubling of the weight. The transmission loss for a partition is not constant with frequency, increasing usually 3 to 6 db/octave.

Note that a compound-wall construction can yield relatively high sound insulation with relatively low mass per unit wall area. The double-wall construction is one such example. It is important that the separation between the walls be as complete as possible—structural ties will greatly reduce the effectiveness of such a structure.

Values of transmission loss for various types of walls and floors employed in ordinary building construction are given in Table 3j-3 and Fig. 3j-7.[1]

3j-5. Noise Level within a Room. The sound level of noise which is transmitted into a room from the outside depends on (1) the noise-insulating properties of its

[1] Knudsen and Harris, *op. cit.;* Sound Insulation of Wall and Floor Constructions, Building Materials and Structures, *Natl. Bur. Standards* (*U.S.*) *Rept.* 144 (1955).

bounding surfaces, (2) the total absorption in the room, and (3) the characteristics of the noise source. The following formula gives a rating of the over-all noise reduction provided by the enclosure. It represents, approximately, the difference between the noise level outside a room and the noise level inside a room.

$$\text{Noise-insulation factor} = 10 \log \frac{a}{T} \quad \text{db} \tag{3j-7}$$

where a represents the total absorption in the room in sabins defined by Eq. (3j-4), and T represents the total transmittance of the enclosure given by

$$T = \tau_1 S_1 + \tau_2 S_2 + \tau_3 S_3 + \cdots \tag{3j-8}$$

where τ_1 is equal to the transmission coefficient of area S_1, etc.

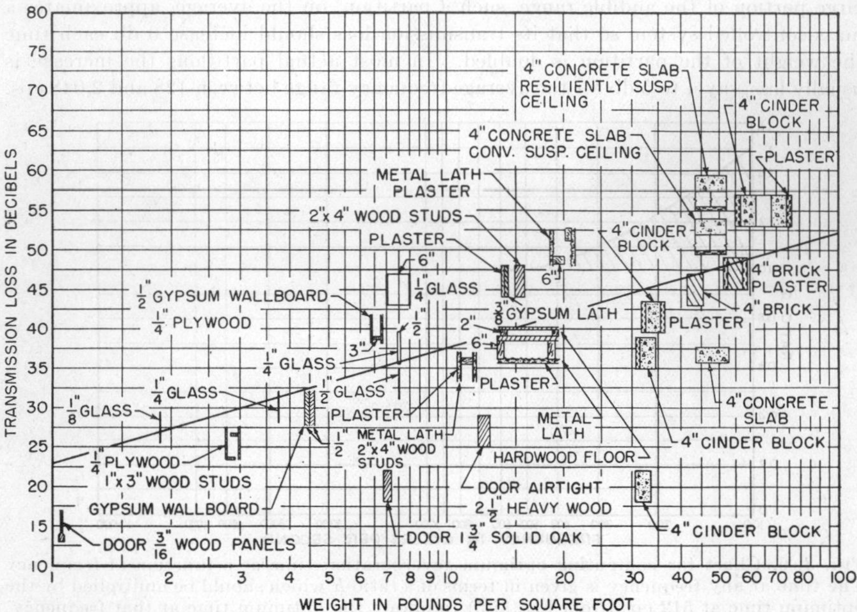

FIG. 3j-7. Transmission loss, average over frequency in the range from 128 to 4,096 cps, as a function of weight of the parts in pounds per square foot of surface area.

If a source of noise is within a room, then at distances near to the source the sound pressure decreases inversely with increasing distance from the source; there is a decrease in sound pressure level of 6 db for each doubling of the distance from the source, just as if the source were in the open air. However, at every point in the room there will be an additional contribution to the total pressure as a result of reflections from the walls. As one recedes from the source the reflected contributions become more and more important until direct sound from the source becomes negligible by comparison.

Then if the sound field is diffuse (perfect diffusion is said to exist if the sound pressure everywhere in the room is the same, and it is equally probable that the waves are traveling in every direction) the sound pressure level in the room will be given approximately by

$$L_p = 10 \log \frac{W}{a} + 136.4 \quad \text{db} \tag{3j-9}$$

if a value of $\rho c = 40.8$ rayls is assumed for air, and

where W = power of the sound source, watts
a = total absorption of the room, sabins.

A consideration of the above formula shows that, if the acoustic-power output of the noise source remains constant, and if the total absorption in the room is increased from a_1 to a_2 the reduction in noise level is given by

$$\text{Noise reduction} = 10 \log \frac{a_2}{a_1} \text{ db} \qquad (3j\text{-}10)$$

TABLE 3j-3. VALUES OF TRANSMISSION LOSS T.L. VS. FREQUENCY FOR VARIOUS TYPES OF WALL AND FLOOR CONSTRUCTION*

Construction	Weight, lb/sq ft	Average, 128–4,096	128 cps	256 cps	512 cps	1,024 cps	2,048 cps	4,096 cps	Authority†
Wood studs 2 by 4 in., 16 in. o.c.:									
With lime plaster $\frac{7}{8}$ in. thick on metal lath	19.8	44	26	41	44	52	56	58	N.B.S.
With gypsum plaster $\frac{1}{2}$ in. thick on $\frac{3}{4}$-in. gypsum lath	15.2	41	33	31	39	46	49	66	N.B.S.
Wood studs, 2 by 4 in., staggered; $\frac{7}{8}$-in. gypsum plaster on metal lath	19.8	50	44	47	47	50	52	63	N.B.S.
Staggered wood studs 1 by 3 in., $\frac{1}{4}$-in. plywood glued to both sides	2.6	26	14	20	28	33	40	30	N.B.S.
Two sets of 2- by 2-in. wood studs, $\frac{1}{4}$-in. plywood sheet inserted in $\frac{1}{4}$-in. space between studs, $\frac{1}{4}$-in. plywood faces, slightly compressed paper-backed mineral wood inserted in both air spaces, total panel thickness $4\frac{3}{4}$ in.	5.1	37	20	31	37	41	49	50	N.B.S.
Steel studs, 3 in., 16 in. o.c., $\frac{7}{8}$-in. gypsum plaster on expanded metal lath	19.6	37	30	28	35	40	43	53	N.B.S.
Brick, laid on edge; gypsum plaster on both sides	31.6	42		40	37	49	59		N.B.S.
Tile, hollow partition, 4 in. thick, pumice-cement block, two cells 4 by 8 by 16 in., no plaster	15.5	11	8	5	9	14	19	17	N.B.S.
Same, but one side plastered	20.4	35	31	27	35	36	40	47	N.B.S.
Same, but both sides plastered	25.3	37	32	34	36	39	42	52	N.B.S.
Cinder block, hollow partition 3 by 8 by 16 in., plaster on both sides	32.2	45	34	37	42	51	57	64	N.B.S.
Multiple-block partition; two leaves, each of 3-in. hollow blocks, separated by 2-in. cavity and built on opposite sides of gap separating rooms; outer faces plastered (two partitions of nominally the same construction)	28	9	54	38	47	49	69	77	N.P.L.
Wood joints, 2 by 8 in., $\frac{1}{2}$-in. fiberboard lath and $\frac{1}{2}$-in. gypsum plaster ceiling; 1-in. pine subflooring and 1-in. pine finish flooring	14.3	45	23	34	47	55	54	69	N.B.S.
Same joists and ceiling as above; 1-in. pine subfloor; $\frac{1}{2}$-in. fiberboard, 1- by 3-in. sleepers, and 1-in. pine finish floor	16.2	50	30	37	50	57	65	79	N.B.S.

* For the average values for other types of construction, and for windows and doors, also see Fig. 3j-7.
† N.B.S. denotes National Bureau of Standards; N.P.L. denotes National Physical Laboratory.

According to this equation, which should be regarded as an engineering approximation to actual conditions, if the absorption in a room is increased by a factor of 4 the noise reduction will be 6 db. It shows that the addition of absorption level in a room will provide substantial noise reduction in average level in a room that is relatively bare but little decrease level in a highly damped room. The reduction will be different at different frequencies since the total absorption is a function of frequency. However it is sometimes convenient to employ the noise-reduction coefficient of a material to obtain a single noise-reduction figure. Besides reducing the steady-state level, the addition of absorptive treatment in a room also provides beneficial effects by reducing the reverberation time in the room and by localizing the source of noise to the area in which it originates—thereby minimizing unexpected noises.

TABLE 3j-4. RECOMMENDED ACCEPTABLE AVERAGE NOISE LEVELS IN UNOCCUPIED ROOMS*

	Decibels
Radio, recording, and television studios	25–30
Music rooms	30–35
Legitimate theaters	30–35
Hospitals	35–40
Motion-picture theaters, auditoriums	35–40
Churches	35–40
Apartments, hotels, homes	35–45
Classrooms, lecture rooms	35–40
Conference rooms, small offices	40–45
Courtrooms	40–45
Private offices	40–45
Libraries	40–45
Large public offices, banks, stores, etc	45–55
Restaurants	50–55

The levels given in this table are "weighted"; i.e., they are the levels measured with a standard sound-level meter incorporating an "A" (40-db) frequency-weighting network.

* V. O. Knudsen and C. M. Harris, "Acoustical Designing in Architecture," John Wiley & Sons, Inc., New York, 1950.

3j-6. Acceptable Noise Levels for Various Types of Room. Table 3j-4 gives values of recommended acceptable average noise levels for unoccupied rooms with the ventilation system in operation. These values are used for design purposes, for example, in computing the amount of over-all noise insulation that should be provided for a room. They hold for typical room-noise spectra. Although even lower noise levels than those which are listed may provide some advantage under certain circumstances, and may be desirable if cost is not a factor, this table gives values which represent a combination of acceptability and economic practicality. For certain types of room the values which are recommended are lower than those which are commonly found.

3k. Speech and Hearing

EDWIN B. NEWMAN[1]

Harvard University

The data concerning hearing are, without exception, empirical in derivation. Consequently, the values reported always represent some parameter of a population, most often a mean, and the reader is warned to bear constantly in mind the many sources of variability that attach to any particular measurement.

3k-1. Physical Dimensions of the Ear

TABLE 3k-1. PHYSICAL DIMENSIONS OF THE EAR*

Pinna:
- Mean length, young men, 65.0 mm
- Range, 52–79 mm

Auditory meatus:
- Cross section, 0.3–0.5 cm^2
- Diameter, 0.7 cm
- Length, 2.7 cm
- Volume, 1.0 cc

Tympanic membrane:
- Area, 0.5–0.9 cm^2 (roughly circular)
- Thickness, about 0.1 mm
- Volume elasticity for 10 cps, equivalent to about 8 cc air
- Displacement amplitude for 1,000-cps tone (at threshold), 10^{-9} cm
- Displacement amplitude for low-frequency tones (threshold of feeling), about 10^{-2} cm

Middle ear:
- Total volume, about 2 cc
- Malleus:
  - Weight, 23 mg
  - Length, 5.5–6.0 mm
- Incus: weight, 27 mg
- Stapes:
  - Weight, 215 mg
  - Length of footplate, 3.2 mm
  - Width of footplate, 1.4 mm
  - Area of footplate, 3.2 mm^2
  - Width of elastic ligament, 0.015–0.1 mm

Cochlea:
- Length of cochlear channels, 35 mm
- Height of scala vestibuli or scala tympani, about 1 mm (great variability)
- Round window: area, 2 mm^2
- Basilar membrane:
  - Width at stapes, 0.04 mm
  - Width at helicotrema, 0.5 mm
- Helicotrema: area of opening, 0.25–0.4 mm^2

* S. S. Stevens, ed., "Handbook of Experimental Psychology," John Wiley & Sons, Inc., New York, 1951.

3k-2. Acoustic Impedance of the Ear. Reasonable agreement on measurements below 1,000 cps has been obtained. The reference point for measurements is just

[1] This section benefited from the advice and assistance of Dr. S. S. Stevens and Mrs. Nancy C. Waugh.

TABLE 3k-2. ACOUSTIC IMPEDANCE OF THE EAR IN ACOUSTIC OHMS, MEASURED JUST WITHIN THE MEATUS

Frequency	Total impedance	Resistive component	Reactive component
250	200	50	−190
350	150	40	−145
500	125	35	−115
700	70	25	−65
1,000	55	25	−50

Above 1,000 cycles, measurements depend increasingly on the method of measurement.

TABLE 3k-3. MINIMUM AUDIBLE PRESSURE AT ENTRANCE TO EXTERNAL EAR CANAL (MAC), IN DECIBELS SPL

	Frequency									
	80	125	250	500	1,000	2,000	4,000	6,000	8,000	10,000
Threshold....	43.5	30.0	18.5	11.5	9.0	8.0	9.5	13.0	17.0	21.0

The following corrections may be applied if it is desired to find thresholds for other conditions:

a. MAC to Threshold Pressure at Eardrum[a]

	Frequency								
	125	250	500	1,000	2,000	4,000	6,000	8,000	10,000
Add........	0.0	0.0	−0.5	−1.0	−4.5	−10.5	−4.0	−2.5	

b. MAC to Equivalent Coupler Calibration of Various Earphones[a,b,c]

	Frequency									
	125	250	500	1,000	2,000	4,000	6,000	8,000	10,000	Coupler
Add for PDR-8 with MX-41/AR	+8.0	+4.0	+0.5	+1.0	+1.5	+4.5	+12.0	−3.0	..	NBS-9A
Add for WE 705A......	+13.0	+4.0	+0.5	+1.0	+4.5	+5.0	−0.5	−7.0	..	NBS-9A
Add for STC 4026A......	+14.5	+11.0	+0.5	−3.5	+1.0	+0.5	−4.0	−7.5	..	NPL[b]

[a] F. M. Wiener and D. A. Ross, The Pressure Distribution in the Auditory Canal in a Progressive Sound Field, *J. Acoust. Soc. Am.* **18**, 401–408 (1946).

[b] L. J. Wheeler and E. D. D. Dickson, The Determination of the Threshold of Hearing, *J. Laryngol. Otol.* **66**, 379–395 (1952).

[c] E. L. R. Corliss, R. F. Brown, Jr., M. D. Burkhard, R. P. Thompson, Jr., and J. F. Mullen, Methods for Calibration of Hearing Diagnostic Instruments, *Natl. Bur. Standards (U.S.) Rept.* 1470, 1–43 (1952).

TABLE 3k-3. MINIMUM AUDIBLE PRESSURE AT ENTRANCE TO EXTERNAL EAR CANAL (MAC), IN DECIBELS SPL (*Continued*)

c. MAC to Free Field (MAF) (plane wave, 0° azimuth in absence of head)[d]

	Frequency								
	125	250	500	1,000	2,000	4,000	6,000	8,000	10,000
Add..........	+1.0	+0.5	−2.0	−4.0	−11.0	−12.5	−7.0	−3.0	−3.0

d. Mean Monaural to Mean Binaural Listening[e]

	Frequency				
	125–2,000	4,000	6,000	8,000	10,000
Add......................	−2.0	−3.0	−4.0	−5.0	−6.0

e. Reference Age Group (18–25) to Older Age Groups[f]

	Frequency					
	125–1,000	2,000	4,000	6,000	8,000	10,000
Add for:						
Men 30–39.........	+1.0	+2.0	+5.0	+6.0	+6.0	+7.0
Men 40–49.........	+2.0	+5.0	+13.0	+13.0	+11.0	+13.0
Men 50–59.........	+5.0	+13.0	+27.0	+32.0	+35.0	+35.0
Women 30–39......	+1.0	+2.0	+3.0	+4.0	+4.0	+4.0
Women 40–49......	+3.0	+5.0	+6.0	+8.0	+9.0	+9.0
Women 50–59......	+5.0	+9.0	+13.0	+18.0	+20.0	+22.0

[d] L. J. Sivian and S. D. White, On Minimum Audible Sound Fields, *J. Acoust. Soc. Am.* **4,** 288–321 (1933).

[e] H. Fletcher, "Speech and Hearing in Communication," p. 131, D. Van Nostrand Company, Inc., New York, 1953.

[f] J. C. Steinberg, H. C. Montgomery and M. B. Gardner, Results of the World's Fair Hearing Tests, *J. Acoust. Soc. Am.* **12,** 291–301 (1940); J. C. Webster, H. W. Himes, and M. Lichtenstein, San Diego County Fair Hearing Survey, *J. Acoust. Soc. Am.* **22,** 473–483 (1950).

within the external meatus. The values in Table 3k-2 are representative but are subject to wide variations among individuals.[1]

3k-3. Minimum Audible Sound. The best recent measurements use as their point of reference the sound pressure level of a tone, heard one-half the time, and measured at the entrance to the external meatus. The observations were made on healthy young men, eighteen to twenty-five years of age, tested individually with earphones, one ear at a time. Sound pressures were determined with a probe-tube microphone and are given in decibels above 0.0002 dyne/cm². $N = 1{,}200$ ears.[2]

[1] E. Waetzmann and L. Keibs, Hörschwellenbestimmungen mit dem Thermophon und Messungen am Trommelfell, *Ann. Physik* **26,** 141–144 (1936); O. Metz, The Acoustic Impedance Measured on Normal and Pathological Ears, *Acta Oto-Laryngol., Suppl.* 63, 1–254 (1946); A. H. Inglis, C. H. G. Gray, and R. T. Jenkins, A Voice and Ear for Telephone Measurements, *Bell System Tech. J.* **11,** 293–317 (1932).

[2] R. S. Dadson and J. H. King, A Determination of the Normal Threshold of Hearing and Its Relation to the Standardization of Audiometers, *J. Laryngol. Otol.* **66,** 366–378 (1952); L. J. Wheeler and E. D. D. Dickson, The Determination of the Threshold of Hearing, *J. Laryngol. Otol.* **66,** 379–395 (1952).

3k-4. Threshold of Feeling or Discomfort. The upper limit for a tolerable intensity of sound rises substantially with increasing habituation. Moreover, a variety of subjective effects are reported, such as discomfort, tickle, pressure, and pain, each at a slightly different level. As a simple engineering estimate it can be said that naïve listeners reach a limit at about 125 db SPL and experienced listeners at 135 to 140 db. These are over-all measures of sound falling within the audible range and are roughly independent of frequency.

3k-5. Differential Thresholds for Pure Tones and Noise. A differential threshold represents a careful determination by laboratory methods of the ability of a subject

TABLE 3k-4. DIFFERENTIAL THRESHOLD FOR INTENSITY, IN DECIBELS

Sensation level, db above absolute threshold	Pure tones, frequency in cps							
	35	70	200	1,000	4,000	7,000	10,000	White noise
5	....	....	4.75	3.03	2.48	4.05	4.72	1.80
10	7.24	4.22	3.44	2.35	1.70	2.83	3.34	1.20
20	4.31	2.38	1.93	1.46	0.97	1.49	1.70	0.47
30	2.72	1.52	1.24	1.00	0.68	0.90	1.10	0.44
40	1.76	1.04	0.86	0.72	0.49	0.68	0.86	0.42
50	....	0.75	0.68	0.53	0.41	0.61	0.75	0.41
60	....	0.61	0.53	0.41	0.29	0.53	0.68	0.41
70	....	0.57	0.45	0.33	0.25	0.49	0.61	
80	....	....	0.41	0.29	0.25	0.45	0.57	
90	....	....	0.41	0.29	0.21	0.41		
100	....	....	....	0.25	0.21			
110	....	....	....	0.25				

TABLE 3k-5. DIFFERENTIAL THRESHOLD FOR FREQUENCY, IN $\Delta F/F$*

Sensation level, db above absolute threshold	Pure tones, frequency in cps						
	60	125	250	500	1,000	2,000	4,000
5	0.0252	0.0110	0.0097	0.0065	0.0049	0.0040	0.0077
10	0.0140	0.0060	0.0053	0.0035	0.0027	0.0022	0.0042
15	0.0092	0.0040	0.0035	0.0024	0.0018	0.0014	0.0028
20	0.0073	0.0032	0.0028	0.0019	0.0014	0.0012	0.0022
30		0.0032	0.0028	0.0019	0.0014	0.0011	0.0022

* J. D. Harris, Pitch Discrimination, *J. Acoust. Soc. Am.* **24**, 750–755 (1952).

to just detect, and report, a difference in any specific property of a sound, all other factors presumably being held constant.

The method for determining the differential threshold for intensity of pure tones employed one tone beating with a second tone at 3 beats per second.[1] Much evidence is available to support what should be kept always in mind, that thresholds determined

[1] R. R. Reisz, Differential Intensity Sensitivity of the Ear for Pure Tones, *Phys. Rev.* **31**, 867–875 (1928).

by other methods are a function of numerous psychological parameters and will differ systematically from the values in Table 3k-4. A more conventional method was used to determine the thresholds for white noise, with the results given in the last column.[1]

The ability to distinguish pitch is subject to a greater range of individual variability than other functions reported here. The data given are for three trained listeners and have been smoothed in both directions. Untrained listeners usually require a greater frequency difference than that reported here. Note also that individual listeners commonly show idiosyncrasies at particular frequencies.

3k-6. Masking. Masking refers to our inability to hear a weak sound in the presence of a louder sound. It is usually measured by the amount of change in the threshold of the weaker sound, i.e., how much more intense must the weak sound be made in order to be heard over the masking sound, than it needed to be when the masking sound was not present. The masking of one pure tone by another is a complex function of the particular frequencies and of the absolute level of the respective tones. See any standard text on hearing for the curves describing this relationship.

The masking of a pure tone by a noise with a reasonably flat and continuous spectrum is a linear function (except at levels below 10 db) of the total intensity within a "critical band" centered on the masked tone. The width of the critical band of frequencies whose total energy is just equal to the energy of the masked tone is given by Table 3k-6.

TABLE 3k-6. WIDTH OF "CRITICAL BAND" ΔF AS A FUNCTION OF CENTER FREQUENCY F (10 log ΔF)*

	Frequency							
	100	250	500	1,000	2,000	4,000	8,000	10,000
ΔF, db	19.4	17.1	17.1	18.0	19.9	23.1	27.7	29.2

* N. R. French and J. C. Steinberg, Factors Governing the Intelligibility of Speech Sounds, *J. Acoust. Soc. Am.* **19,** 90–119 (1947).

The masking of one continuous noise by another can be thought of as a case of differential sensitivity to change in the intensity of a noise (see last column of Table 3k-4). Thus, above 40 db SPL, if a weak noise is more than 10 db less intense than a very similar masking noise, the weak noise will not be heard; its presence or absence does not produce a discriminable difference in intensity. If the spectral composition of the two noises, masking and masked, are quite different, then the critical-band concept must be employed.

3k-7. Sounds of Short Duration. Acoustic disturbances of very short duration, i.e., less than 0.0001 sec, are heard only to the extent that they transmit energy to the ear. Short pulses at ultrasonic frequencies are generally not heard unless they are rectified. Impulse or step functions excite the ear, but not efficiently.

At the opposite extreme, tones, or continuous noise, of duration greater than from 0.2 to 0.5 sec, are generally heard independently of duration. Between these limits relatively complex relations are found.[2]

As a first approximation for both tones and noise, the effective intensity of short sounds is a function of total energy integrated over the duration of the sound. More

[1] G. A. Miller, Sensitivity to Changes in the Intensity of White Noise and Its Relation to Masking and Loudness, *J. Acoust. Soc. Am.* **19,** 609–619 (1947).

[2] S. S. Stevens, ed., "Handbook of Experimental Psychology," pp. 1020–1021, John Wiley & Sons, Inc., New York, 1951.

accurately, the threshold is defined by[1]

$$I_t = kIt^{0.8} \tag{3k-1}$$

For some short tones and for many types of impulse noise, account must be taken of the frequency distribution of energy. Inasmuch as the ear varies in sensitivity as a function of frequency, any change in the shape or duration of a short acoustic pulse will also change its effectiveness because of the altered spectral composition.

3k-8. Loudness. Loudness and pitch are ways in which a listener reacts to sounds. Furthermore, within limits, a listener can use numbers to describe how much of a response he makes to the sound. These numbers usefully describe how loud, or how high in pitch, a sound seems to be. It is then necessary to relate how loud it is (subjective response) to how intense it is in physical terms. The loudness of a pure tone of 1,000 cps is described by the following relationship:

$$\log L = 0.0301N - 1.204 \tag{3k-2}$$

in which L is the loudness measured in sones and N is the loudness level in phons (equal to the sound pressure level of the tone in decibels above 0.0002 dyne/cm²).[2] Another way of putting this is to say that loudness doubles for each 10-db change in sound pressure level.

TABLE 3k-7. LOUDNESS LEVEL AS A FUNCTION OF SOUND PRESSURE LEVEL AND FREQUENCY*

Sound pressure level	Frequency							
	125	250	500	1,000	2,000	4,000	8,000	10,000
10	.....	.....	.....	10.0	18.0	18.0		
20	.....	6.3	16.0	20.0	28.0	28.0	11.0	
30	4.0	18.0	26.5	30.0	37.0	36.5	20.5	17.0
40	17.0	31.0	38.5	40.0	45.5	45.0	29.5	26.0
50	34.0	45.5	52.0	50.0	55.0	54.0	38.0	35.0
60	52.0	59.5	64.5	60.0	64.0	63.5	47.0	43.5
70	70.0	72.5	76.0	70.0	73.5	72.5	56.0	53.5
80	86.0	84.5	86.0	80.0	84.5	83.0	66.0	63.5
90	98.0	95.5	96.0	90.0	95.0	94.5	77.0	73.5
100	108.0	105.5	105.0	100.0	106.0	106.0	88.0	85.5
110	118.0	115.5	113.0	110.0	117.0	117.5	101.5	98.0

* American Standard for Noise Measurement, ASA Z24.2—1942.

There is some evidence that the loudness of a noise grows more rapidly than that of a tone with an increase in sound pressure level, especially at low levels. The exact relations are less well known than those for a tone.

The loudness of tones at other frequencies than 1,000 cps is given by determining the loudness level in the manner described below and converting to tones by Eq. (3k-2).

3k-9. Loudness Level. The loudness level of a tone of 1,000 cps, expressed in phons, is defined as the sound pressure level in decibels above the reference level of 0.0002 dyne/cm².

The loudness level of tones of other frequencies is given by the empirical relations in Table 3k-7.

[1] D. B. Yntema, "The Probability of Hearing a Short Tone Near Threshold," Ph.D. Dissertation, Harvard University, 1954, 43 pp.

[2] S. S. Stevens, The Measurement of Loudness, *J. Acoust. Soc. Am.* **27**, 815–829 (1955).

Note that this table is based on the ASA standard and presumes the "free-field" measurement of sound pressure. This requires a measurement of a plane progressive wave at the listener's position before the listener is placed in the field. More meaningful measurements would doubtless be obtained from pressure measurements at the ear. For this purpose, apply the corrections contained in Table 3k-3*c* to the ear canal pressures before entering Table 3k-7.

To enter the table with sound pressure levels measured under other conditions, first add the corrections in Table 3k-3*c*, then subtract rather than adding corrections in Tables 3k-3*a* through 3k-3*d*. Note, however, that corrections given for presbycusis in Table 3k-3*e* may give quite misleading results because of recruitment at high frequencies in some elderly people.

3k-10. Pitch. The relation between frequency and the subjective magnitude of perceived pitch is shown by Table 3k-8. By definition, the pitch of a tone of 1,000 cps at 40 db SPL is 1,000 mels.[1]

TABLE 3k-8. PITCH OF A PURE TONE, IN MELS, AS A FUNCTION OF FREQUENCY

Frequency	Mels	Frequency	Mels	Frequency	Mels
20	0	350	460	1,750	1,428
30	24	400	508	2,000	1,545
40	46	500	602	2,500	1,771
60	87	600	690	3,000	1,962
80	126	700	775	3,500	2,116
100	161	800	854	4,000	2,250
150	237	900	929	5,000	2,478
200	301	1,000	1,000	6,000	2,657
250	358	1,250	1,154	7,000	2,800
300	409	1,500	1,296	10,000	3,075

3k-11. Localization of Sound. The localization of complex sounds is primarily a function of time differences of arrival at the two ears, and, to a first approximation, such differences may be calculated by assuming the ears on either end of the diameter of a sphere of 7.5 cm radius.

The localization of tones of low frequency (below 1,500 cps) is possible on the basis of phase differences, which may be interpreted in terms of time differences.

The localization of tones of high frequency is possible on the basis of intensity differences resulting from the sound shadow of the head. Exact measurements here are difficult at best.

Sound localization is greatly aided when the head or body can be rotated, or moved about, in the sound field, while the observer hears the appropriate sequence of sounds.[2]

Sound localization in reverberant rooms or with so-called "stereophonic-sound sources" depends critically upon a "precedence effect," by which the localization determined by the primary sound or sound from the nearer of two sound sources is overriding in its effect.[3]

In experiments where time differences are used to balance out intensity differences

[1] S. S. Stevens and J. Volkmann, The Relation of Pitch to Frequency: a Revised Scale, *Am. J. Psychol.* **53,** 329–353 (1940).

[2] H. Wallach, Ueber die Wahrnehmung der Schallrichtung, *Psychol. Forsch.* **22,** 238–266 (1938).

[3] H. Wallach, E. B. Newman, and M. R. Rosenzweig, The Precedence Effect in Sound Localization, *Am. J. Psychol.* **62,** 313–336 (1949).

in the opposite direction, 1.0×10^{-5} sec priority offsets a 6-db difference in intensity; 2.3×10^{-5} sec offsets a 14-db difference in intensity between the two ears.[1]

3k-12. Speech Power. The total radiated speech power, averaged over a 15-sec interval for a sample including both men and women at conversational levels used for telephone talking, has been estimated as 32 microwatts.

When measured at the face of a telephone transmitter, this power produces the sound pressure levels given in Table 3k-9 for different distances from the mouth of the speaker.[2]

TABLE 3k-9. AVERAGE SOUND PRESSURE LEVEL PRODUCED BY CONVERSATIONAL SPEECH AS A FUNCTION OF DISTANCE FROM LIPS TO MICROPHONE

	Distance, cm								
	Touching	0.5	1.0	2.5	5.0	10.0	25.0	50.0	100.0
Sound pressure level.......	104	102	99	95	90	85	78	72	66

A second source of variability lies in the essentially statistical distribution of speech power in time. If speech power is measured in successive $\frac{1}{8}$-sec intervals (a time slightly shorter than a syllable, and slightly longer than a phoneme), a distribution is obtained with the mean values given in Table 3k-9 and variability that can be attributed to time sampling equal to a standard deviation of 7.0 db.[3] The distribution is badly skewed so that the value 7.0 db indicates only a rough order of magnitude. The variability is also greater when particular frequency bands are measured.

A third source of variability is the variation in effort expended by the person who is talking. As a rough approximation, a raised voice level is 6 db above conversational level, the loudest level that can be maintained is 12 db above conversational level, and the loudest shout is 18 db above conversational level. In the other direction, a whisper may be 20 db below conversational level.

[1] J. H. Shaxby and F. H. Gage, Studies in the Localization of Sound. A. The Localization of Sounds in the Median Plane: An Experimental Investigation of the Physical Processes Concerned, *Med. Research Council (Brit.) Spec. Rept. Ser.* no. 166 (1932), 32 pp.

[2] M. H. Abrams, S. J. Goffard, J. Miller, F. H. Sanford, and S. S. Stevens, The Effect of Microphone Position on the Intelligibility of Speech in Noise, *OSRD Rept.* 4023 (1944), 16 pp.

[3] H. K. Dunn and S. D. White, Statistical Measurements on Conversational Speech, *J. Acoust. Soc. Am.* **11**, 278–288 (1940).

3k-13. Speech Sounds

TABLE 3k-10. CHARACTERISTICS OF SOUNDS IN GENERAL AMERICAN SPEECH

Symbol	Example	Power,* db re long time average†	Relative frequency of sound, %‡	Formant frequencies for men and women¶					
				First		Second		Third	
				M	W	M	W	M	W
u	cool	+0.6	1.60	300	370	870	950	2,240	2,670
ʊ	cook	+2.3	0.69	440	470	1,020	1,160	2,240	2,680
o	cone	+2.5	0.33	500	. . .	820			
ɔ	talk	+4.1	1.26	570	590	840	920	2,410	2,710
ɒ	cloth	+3.7	2.81	730	850	1,090	1,220	2,440	2,810
ɑ	calm		0.49						
a	ask	+2.5	3.95	660	860	1,720	2,050	2,410	2,850
æ	bat								
ɛ	bet	+1.6	3.44	530	610	1,840	2,330	2,480	2,990
e	tape	+1.4	1.84						
ɪ	bit	0.0	8.53	390	430	1,990	2,480	2,550	3,070
i	beet	0.0	2.12	270	310	2,290	2,790	3,010	3,310
ɝ	bird	−0.5	0.53	490	500	1,350	1,640	1,690	1,960
ə	sofa	. . . . .	4.63						
ʌ	bun	+2.9	2.33	640	760	1,190	1,400	2,390	2,780
eɪ	laid	+1.4	see e						
aɪ	bite	+2.5	1.59						
ju	you	+0.6	0.31						
oʊ	soap	+2.5	1.30						
aʊ	about	+2.3	0.59						
ɔɪ	boil	+3.0	0.09						

* The power measurements do not represent the peak instantaneous power but the average over the sustained portion of the phoneme where such a period can be defined. In this case, as with the formant frequencies, the absolute values are highly variable, but intercomparisons among the various sounds are generally more reliable.

† H. Fletcher, "Speech and Hearing in Communication," p. 86, D. Van Nostrand Company, Inc., New York, 1953.

‡ G. Dewey, "Relative Frequency of English Speech Sounds," Harvard University Press, Cambridge, Mass., 1923.

¶ E. G. Richardson, ed., "Technical Aspects of Sound," pp. 215–217, Elsevier Press, Inc., New York, 1953.

TABLE 3k-10. CHARACTERISTICS OF SOUNDS IN GENERAL AMERICAN SPEECH (*Continued*)

Symbol	Example	Power,* db re long time average†	Relative frequency of sound, %‡	Formant frequencies for men and women¶			
				First	Second	Third	Fourth
l	lip	−3.0	3.74	450	1,000	2,550	2,950
m	me	−5.8	2.78	140	1,250	2,250	2,750
n	nip	−7.4	7.24	140	1,450	2,300	2,750
ŋ	sing	−4.4	0.96	140	2,350	2,750	
w	we	0.0	2.08				
r	rip	−1.0	6.35	500	1,350	1,850	3,500
j	yes	0.0	0.60	270	2,040		
p	pie	−15.2	2.04	...	800	1,350	
t	tie	−11.2	7.13	...	1,700	2,450	
k	key	−11.9	2.71	...	Variable		
b	by	−14.6	1.81	140	800	1,350	
d	die	−14.6	4.31	140	1,700	2,450	
g	guy	−11.2	0.74	140	Variable		
v	vie	−12.2	2.28	140	1,150	2,500	3,650
f	foe	−16.0	1.84	...	1,150	2,500	3,650
θ	thin	−23.0	0.37	...	1,450	2,550	
ð	then	−12.6	3.43	140	1,450	2,550	
s	sip	−11.0	4.55	...	2,000	2,700	
z	is	−11.0	2.97	140	2,000	2,700	
ʃ	shy	−4.0	0.82	...	2,150	2,650	
ʒ	measure	−10.0	0.05	140	2,150	2,650	
h	hit	−13.0	1.81				
tʃ	chop	−6.8	0.52				
dʒ	Joe	−9.4	0.44				

* The power measurements do not represent the peak instantaneous power but the average over the sustained portion of the phoneme where such a period can be defined. In this case, as with the formant frequencies, the absolute values are highly variable, but intercomparisons among the various sounds are generally more reliable.

† H. Fletcher, "Speech and Hearing in Communication," p. 86, D. Van Nostrand Company, Inc., New York, 1953.

‡ G. Dewey, "Relative Frequency of English Speech Sounds," Harvard University Press, Cambridge, Mass., 1923.

¶ E. G. Richardson, ed., "Technical Aspects of Sound," pp. 215–217, Elsevier Press, Inc., New York, 1953.

3k-14. Articulation Index. The articulation index is a set of numbers that makes possible the prediction of the efficiency of some types of voice-communication systems by the addition of suitably chosen values. The operations involve (1) dividing the speech spectrum into a series of bands having an equal possible contribution ΔA to the total efficiency, and (2) determining what proportion of the ΔA each band will contribute under the particular noise and speech conditions being tested.

Under (1) it is customary to use no more than 20 such bands. The frequency limits of 20 such bands are given in Table 3k-11.

TABLE 3k-11. TWENTY FREQUENCY BANDS CONTRIBUTING EQUALLY TO EFFICIENCY OF SPEECH COMMUNICATION*

Band No.	Frequency range	Band No.	Frequency range	Band No.	Frequency range
1	395	8	1,250–1,425	15	2,930–3,285
2	395–540	9	1,425–1,620	16	3,285–3,700
3	540–675	10	1,620–1,735	17	3,700–4,200
4	675–810	11	1,735–2,075	18	4,200–4,845
5	810–950	12	2,075–2,335	19	4,845–5,790
6	950–1,095	13	2,335–2,620	20	5,790
7	1,095–1,250	14	2,620–2,930		

* H. Fletcher, "Speech and Hearing in Communication," D. Van Nostrand Company, Inc., New York, 1953.

For conditions where substantial wide-band noise is present, the second requirement may be approximated by the formula

$$w_i = \tfrac{1}{30}(S_i - N_i + 6) \tag{3k-3}$$

in which w_i is a weight having a maximum value of 1.0, S_i is the signal level in band i in decibels, N_i is the noise level in the same band i in decibels referred to the same base as S_i.[1]

TABLE 3k-12. ARTICULATION SCORES AS A FUNCTION OF ARTICULATION INDEX*

Articulation index	CVC syllables, %	Monosyllabic words (PB lists), %
0.10	7	7
0.20	22	22
0.30	38	40
0.40	55	61
0.50	68	77
0.60	79	87
0.70	87	93
0.80	93	96
0.90	96	98
1.00	98	99

* E. G. Richardson, ed., "Technical Aspects of Sound," Elsevier Press, Inc., New York, 1953.

The articulation index A is then described by the summation

$$A = \frac{1}{n} \sum_{i=1}^{i=n} w_i \tag{3k-4}$$

Articulation scores are related to the articulation index according to the Table 3k-12.

[1] N. R. French and J. C. Steinberg, Factors Governing the Intelligibility of Speech Sounds, *J. Acoust. Soc. Am.* **19**, 90–119 (1947).

31. Classical Electro-dynamical Analogies

HARRY F. OLSON

RCA Laboratories

Analogies are useful when it is desired to compare an unfamiliar system with one that is better known. The relations and actions are more easily visualized, the mathematics more readily applied, and the analytical solutions more readily obtained in the familiar system. Analogies make it possible to extend the line of reasoning into unexplored fields. In view of the tremendous amount of study which has been directed toward the solution of circuits, particularly electric circuits, and the engineer's familiarity with electric circuits, it is logical to apply this knowledge to the solutions of vibration problems in other fields by the same theory as that used in the solution of electric circuits. The objective in this section is the establishment of analogies between electrical, mechanical, and acoustical systems.

31-1. Resistance. *Electric Resistance.* Electric energy is changed into heat by the passage of an electric current through an electric resistance. Electric resistance R_E, in abohms, is defined as

$$R_E = \frac{e}{i} \tag{31-1}$$

where e = voltage across the electric resistance, abvolts

i = current through the electric resistance, abamp

Mechanical Rectilineal Resistance. Mechanical rectilineal energy is changed into heat by a rectilinear motion which is opposed by mechanical rectilineal resistance (friction). Mechanical rectilineal resistance (termed mechanical resistance when there is no ambiguity) R_M, in mechanical ohms, is defined as

$$R_M = \frac{f_M}{u} \tag{31-2}$$

where f_M = applied mechanical force, dynes

u = velocity at the point of application of the force, cm/sec

Mechanical Rotational Resistance. Mechanical rotational energy is changed into heat by a rotational motion which is opposed by a rotational resistance (rotational friction). Mechanical rotational resistance (termed rotational resistance when there is no ambiguity) R_R, in rotational ohms, is defined as

$$R_R = \frac{f_R}{\Omega} \tag{31-3}$$

where f_R = applied torque, dyne-cm

Ω = angular velocity about the axis at the point of the torque, radians/sec

Acoustic Resistance. Acoustic energy is changed into heat either by a motion in a fluid which is opposed by acoustic resistance due to a fluid resistance incurred by viscosity or by the radiation of sound. Acoustic resistance R_A, in acoustical ohms, is defined as

$$R_A = \frac{p}{U} \tag{31-4}$$

where p = pressure, dynes/sq cm
U = volume velocity, cu cm/sec

31-2. Inductance, Mass, Moment of Inertia, Inertance. *Inductance.* Electromagnetic energy is associated with inductance. Inductance is the electric-circuit element that opposes a change in current. Inductance L, in abhenrys, is defined as

$$e = L\frac{di}{dt} \tag{31-5}$$

where e = voltage, emf, or driving force, abvolts
$\frac{di}{dt}$ = rate of change of current, abamp/sec

Mass. Mechanical rectilineal inertial energy is associated with mass in the mechanical rectilineal system. Mass is the mechanical element which opposes a change in velocity. Mass m, in grams, is defined as

$$f_M = m\frac{du}{dt} \tag{31-6}$$

where $\frac{du}{dt}$ = acceleration, cm/sec/sec
f_M = driving force, dynes

Moment of Inertia. Mechanical rotational energy is associated with moment of inertia in the mechanical rotational system. Moment of inertia is the rotational element which opposes a change in angular velocity. Moment of inertia I, in gram (centimeter)^2, is defined as

$$f_R = I\frac{d\Omega}{dt} \tag{31-7}$$

where $\frac{d\Omega}{dt}$ = angular acceleration, radians/sec/sec
f_R = torque, dyne-cm

Inertance. Acoustic inertial energy is associated with inertance in the acoustic system. Inertance is the acoustic element which opposes a change in volume velocity. Inertance M, in grams per (centimeter)^4, is defined as

$$p = M\frac{dU}{dt} \tag{31-8}$$

where $\frac{dU}{dt}$ = rate of change of volume velocity, cu cm/sec/sec
p = driving pressure, dynes/sq cm

31-3. Electric Capacitance, Rectilineal Compliance, Rotational Compliance, Acoustic Capacitance. *Electric Capacitance.* Electric capacitance is associated with capacitance. Electric capacitance is the electric-circuit element which opposes a change in voltage. Electric capacitance C_E, in abfarads, is defined as

$$i = C_E\frac{de}{dt} \tag{31-9}$$

$$e = \frac{1}{C_E}\int i\,dt = \frac{Q}{C_E} \tag{31-10}$$

where Q = charge on the electrical capacitance, abcoulombs
e = emf, abvolts

Rectilineal Compliance. Mechanical rectilineal potential energy is associated with the compression of a spring or compliant element. Rectilineal compliance is the mechanical element which opposes a change in the applied force. Rectilineal compliance (termed compliance when there is no ambiguity) C_M, in centimeters per dyne, is defined as

$$f_M = \frac{x}{C_M} \tag{3l-11}$$

where x = displacement, cm
f_M = applied force, dynes

Rotational Compliance. Mechanical rotational potential energy is associated with the twisting of a spring or compliant element. Rotational compliance is the mechanical element that opposes a change in the applied torque. Rotational compliance C_R, in radians per centimeter per dyne, is defined as

$$f_R = \frac{\phi}{C_R} \tag{3l-12}$$

where ϕ = angular displacement, radians
f_R = applied torque, dyne-cm

Acoustic Capacitance. Acoustic potential energy is associated with the compression of a fluid or a gas. Acoustic capacitance is the acoustic element which opposes a change in the applied pressure. The acoustic capacitance C_A, in (centimeters)^5 per dyne, is defined as

$$p = \frac{X}{C_A} \tag{3l-13}$$

where X = volume displacement, cu cm
p = pressure, dynes/sq cm

3l-4. Representation of Electrical, Mechanical Rectilineal, Mechanical Rotational, and Acoustical Elements. Electrical, mechanical rectilineal, mechanical rotational,

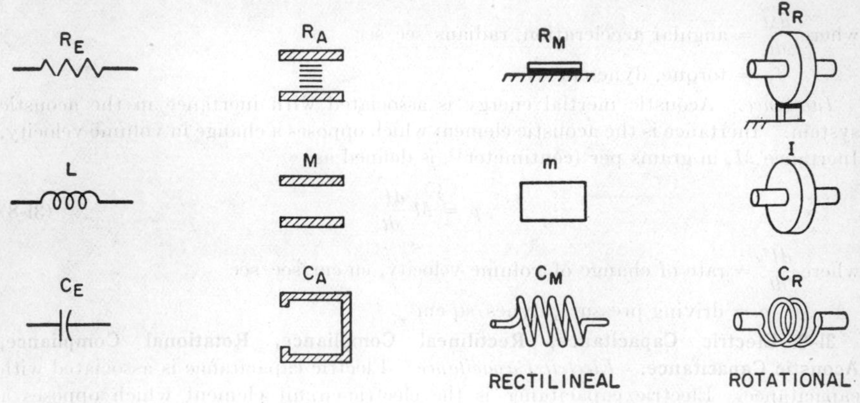

FIG. 3l-1. Graphical representation of the three basic elements in electrical, mechanical rectilineal, mechanical rotational, and acoustical systems.

and acoustical elements have been defined in the preceding sections. Figure 3l-1 illustrates schematically the three elements in each of the four systems.

The electrical elements, electric resistance, inductance, and electric capacitance are represented by the conventional symbols.

Mechanical rectilineal resistance is represented by sliding friction which causes dissipation. Mechanical rotational resistance is represented by a wheel with a sliding-friction brake which causes dissipation. Acoustic resistance is represented by narrow slits which causes dissipation due to viscosity when fluid is forced through the slits. These elements are analogous to electric resistance in the electrical system.

Inertia in the mechanical rectilineal system is represented by a mass. Moment of inertia in the mechanical rotational system is represented by a flywheel. Inertance in the acoustical system is represented as the fluid contained in a tube in which all the particles move with the same phase when actuated by a force due to pressure. These elements are analogous to inductance in the electrical system.

Compliance in the mechanical rectilineal system is represented as a spring. Rotational compliance in the mechanical rotational system is represented as a spring. Acoustic capacitance in the acoustical system is represented as a volume which acts as a stiffness or spring element. These elements are analogous to electric capacitance in the electrical system.

Table 31-1 shows the quantities, units, and symbols in the four systems.

31-5. Description of Systems of One Degree of Freedom. An electrical, mechanical rectilineal, mechanical rotational, and acoustical system of one degree of freedom are shown in Fig. 31-2. In one degree of freedom the activity in every element of the

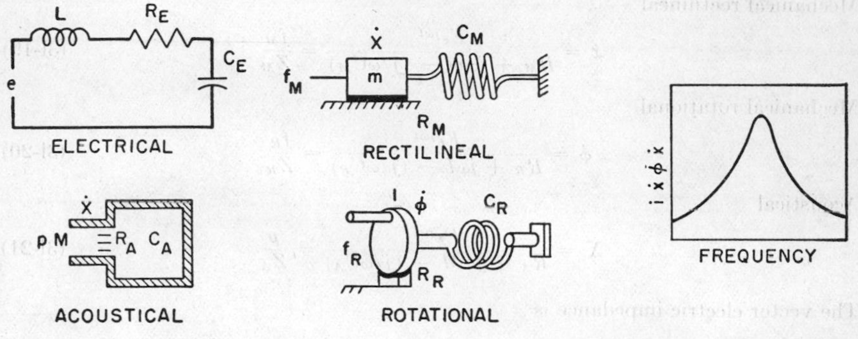

FIG. 31-2. Electrical, mechanical rectilineal, mechanical rotation, and acoustical systems of one degree of freedom and the current, velocity, angular velocity and volume velocity response characteristics.

system may be expressed in terms of one variable. In the electrical system an electromotive force e acts upon an inductance L, an electric resistance R_E, and an electric capacitance C_E connected in series. In the mechanical rectilineal system a driving force f_M acts upon a particle of mass m fastened to a spring of compliance C_M and sliding upon a plate with a frictional force which is proportional to the velocity and designated as the mechanical rectilineal resistance R_M. In the mechanical rotational system a driving torque f_R acts upon a flywheel of moment of inertia I connected to a spring or rotational compliance C_R and the periphery of the wheel sliding against a brake with a frictional force which is proportional to the velocity and designated as the mechanical rotational resistance R_R. In the acoustical system, an impinging sound wave of pressure p acts upon an inertance M and an acoustic resistance R_A comprising the air in the tubular opening which is connected to the volume or acoustical capacitance C_A. The acoustic resistance R_A is due to viscosity.

The differential equations describing the four systems of Fig. 31-2 are as follows:
Electrical

$$L\ddot{q} + R_E\dot{q} + \frac{Q}{C_E} = E\epsilon^{j\omega t} \tag{31-14}$$

Mechanical rectilineal

$$m\ddot{x} + R_M\dot{x} + \frac{x}{C_M} = F_M\epsilon^{j\omega t} \tag{31-15}$$

Mechanical rotational

$$I\ddot{\phi} + R_R\dot{\phi} + \frac{\phi}{C_R} = F_R\epsilon^{j\omega t} \tag{31-16}$$

Acoustical

$$M\ddot{X} + R_A\dot{X} + \frac{X}{C_A} = P\epsilon^{j\omega t} \tag{31-17}$$

E, F_M, F_R, and P are the amplitudes of the driving forces in the four systems. $E\epsilon^{j\omega t} = e$, $F_M\epsilon^{j\omega t} = f_M$, $F_R\epsilon^{j\omega t} = f_R$ and $P\epsilon^{j\omega t} = p$.

The steady-state solutions of Eqs. (31-14) to (31-17) are:

Electrical

$$\dot{q} = i = \frac{E\epsilon^{j\omega t}}{R_E + j\omega L - (j/\omega C_E)} = \frac{e}{Z_E} \tag{31-18}$$

Mechanical rectilineal

$$\dot{x} = \frac{F\epsilon^{j\omega t}}{R_M + j\omega m - (j/\omega C_M)} = \frac{f_M}{Z_M} \tag{31-19}$$

Mechanical rotational

$$\dot{\phi} = \frac{F\epsilon^{j\omega t}}{R_R + j\omega I - (j/\omega C_R)} = \frac{f_R}{Z_R} \tag{31-20}$$

Acoustical

$$\dot{X} = \frac{P\epsilon^{j\omega t}}{R_A + j\omega M - (j/\omega C_A)} = \frac{p}{Z_A} \tag{31-21}$$

The vector electric impedance is

$$Z_E = R_E + j\omega L - \frac{j}{\omega C_E} \tag{31-22}$$

The vector mechanical rectilineal impedance is

$$Z_M = R_M + j\omega m - \frac{j}{\omega C_M} \tag{31-23}$$

The vector mechanical rotational impedance is

$$Z_R = R_R + j\omega I - \frac{j}{\omega C_R} \tag{31-24}$$

The vector acoustic impedance is

$$Z_A = R_A + j\omega M - \frac{j}{\omega C_A} \tag{31-25}$$

TABLE 3l-1. QUANTITIES, UNITS, AND SYMBOLS FOR ELECTRICAL, MECHANICAL RECTILINEAL, MECHANICAL ROTATIONAL, AND ACOUSTICAL ELEMENTS

Electrical			Mechanical rectilineal		
Quantiy	Unit	Symbol	Quantity	Unit	Symbol
Electromotive force	Volts × 10^8	e	Force	Dynes	f_M
Charge or quantity	Coulombs × 10^{-1}	Q	Linear displacement	Centimeters	x
Current	Amperes × 10^{-1}	i	Linear velocity	Centimeters per second	$\dot{x}$ or u
Electric impedance	Ohms × 10^9	Z_E	Mechanical impedance	Mechanical ohms	Z_M
Electric resistance	Ohms × 10^9	R_E	Mechanical resistance	Mechanical ohms	R_M
Electric reactance	Ohms × 10^9	X_E	Mechanical reactance	Mechanical ohms	X_M
Inductance	Henry × 10^9	L	Mass	Grams	m
Electric capacitance	Farads × 10^{-9}	C_E	Compliance	Centimeters per dyne	C_M
Power	Ergs per second	P_E	Power	Ergs per second	P_M

Mechanical rotational			Acoustical		
Quantity	Unit	Symbol	Quantity	Unit	Symbol
Torque	Dyne-centimeter	f_R	Pressure	Dynes per square centimeter	p
Angular displacement	Radians	ϕ	Volume displacement	Cubic centimeters	X
Angular velocity	Radians per second	$\dot{\phi}$ or Ω	Volume velocity	Cubic centimeters per second	$\dot{X}$ or U
Rotational impedance	Rotational ohms	Z_R	Acoustic impedance	Acoustic ohms	Z_A
Rotational resistance	Rotational ohms	R_R	Acoustic resistance	Acoustic ohms	R_A
Rotational reactance	Rotational ohms	X_R	Acoustic reactance	Acoustic ohms	X_A
Moment of inertia	(Gram) (centimeter)^2	I	Inertance	Grams per (centimeter)^4	M
Rotational compliance	Radians per dyne per centimeter	C_R	Acoustic capacitance	(Centimeter)^5 per dyne	C_A
Power	Ergs per second	P_R	Power	Ergs per second	P_A

3m. The Mobility and Classical Impedance Analogies[1]

FLOYD A. FIRESTONE

Editor, The Journal of the Acoustical Society of America

3m-1. Introduction. An *analogy* is a recognized relationship of consistent mutual similarity between the equations and structures appearing within two or more fields of knowledge, and an identification and association of the quantities and structural elements which play mutually similar roles in these equations and structures, for the purpose of facilitating transfer of knowledge of mathematical procedures of analysis and behavior of the structures between these fields.

The theory of analogies is still developing, as evidenced by the recent publications of Olson, Raymond, Bloch, Trent, Le Corbeiller, Bauer, Beranek, and others (see references on page 3-177). This section sets forth the author's recommendations for a useful problem-solving technique as presented in his paper, 'Twixt Earth and Sky with Rod and Tube, *J. Acoust. Soc. Am.* **26,** 140 (1954) (abstract only).

Instead of drawing an analogous electric circuit, the author recommends that *mechanical* and *acoustical* schematic diagrams be drawn, utilizing the mechanical and acoustical symbols shown below. Such a schematic diagram can be drawn directly from an inspection of the structure and is a record of our determinations of the functions and connections of its parts. The mechanical and acoustical symbols here presented are distinctive but similar to their electrical analogues so that their shape indicates to one familiar with electrical schematics the algebraic operations which are to be performed in the analysis. Then the problem is solved using mechanical or acoustical units. Even if an analogous electric circuit is drawn, there is advantage in understanding in detail the mechanical or acoustical analogue of each straight line, junction, and element on the diagram, as set forth in the mobility and impedance analogy tables which follow.

Schematic diagrams based on analogies are most useful in solving those mechanical and acoustical problems where it is known at the outset that the parts are constrained to move in one line only. Problems involving several degrees of freedom for each mass require the construction of a separate schematic diagram for each degree of freedom, usually with coupling between these diagrams.

In the *mobility analogy,* mechanical mobility (complex velocity amplitude divided by complex force amplitude) is analogous to electric impedance, velocity to voltage, and force to current. In the *impedance analogy,* mechanical *impedance* is analogous to electric impedance, force to voltage, and velocity to current.

3m-2. Wires, Rods, and Tubes. In an electric circuit, connections between distant terminals are made by slim wires which, when idealized on a schematic diagram, are assumed to be free of inductance, resistance, and capacitance to ground. Ofttimes a number of wires are soldered together to form a (soldered) *junction* which

[1] The author wishes to acknowledge with pleasure many interesting and instructive conversations on this subject, as well as a voluminous correspondence, with Dr. Horace M. Trent.

ensures equal voltages at all the terminals connected by the tree of wires. But it will also be useful to introduce the *isocurrent junction* (or electric mesher) which ensures equal currents in all the wires coming to it; structurally it is a set of similar ideal transformers with one side of each primary grounded and all secondaries connected in series, the schematic symbol being abbreviated to that of a junction with a circle around it indicating the series of secondaries. The isocurrent junction is the electric example of that broad class of junctions which we shall call "meshers" because they have the effect of connecting all the attached circuits into the same mesh.

In a mechanical system, on the other hand, the connections between distant moving terminals are in practice made by either or both of *two* "slim" devices, *rods* or *tubes*. Ideally, the rods are free from mass, friction, or compliance. Ideally the hydraulic tubes are held stationary and are filled with ideal fluid free from mass, viscosity, or compressibility. Ofttimes a number of rods are bolted together to form a *rigid junction* which ensures equal velocities of all the terminals connected by the tree of rods. Also, ofttimes a number of tubes are joined in a small common chamber to form a *hydraulic junction* which ensures equal pressures (and forces if all tubes are of the same area) at all the terminals connected by the tree of tubes. However, rods can be joined in a hydraulic junction which will ensure equal forces in the rods, if the rods are provided with equal-area pistons hydraulically connected. Similarly, by means of connected pistons, tubes can be joined in a rigid junction.

Since mechanical systems are customarily connected by two kinds of slim devices (rods and tubes) while electric systems are connected by only one kind of slim device (wires), it is not possible in general to draw a correct schematic diagram by either the mobility or impedance analogies *alone* which will correspond completely to the apparent geometry of the mechanical structure. A mobility schematic is a rod diagram (each straight line represents a rod), and it will correspond with the geometry of all parts of the mechanical structure which are rigidly connected by rods. An impedance schematic is a tubing diagram (each connecting line represents a hydraulic tube), and it will correspond with the geometry of all parts of the mechanical structure which are hydraulically connected by tubes.

3m-3. Ground, Earth, and Sky. In a mobility schematic or rod diagram, the reference symbol which is analogous to the ground symbol in an electrical wiring diagram is a frame of reference called the *earth*, whereas in an impedance schematic or tubing diagram the reference symbol is a force (or pressure) of reference called the *sky*. The sky is the dual of the earth. Structurally, the sky consists of a bowl, a lake, or an atmosphere of ideal fluid maintained under a constant pressure of reference. In a mobility schematic or rod diagram one terminal of every mass is the earth relative to which the velocity of the mass is measured, while in an impedance schematic or tubing diagram one terminal of every spring is the sky relative to which the force in the spring is measured; these concepts are necessary in order that either type of schematic diagram may be drawn by inspection. The earth has zero mobility and infinite mass, while the sky has zero impedance and infinite compliance.

3m-4. Analogues of the Condenser and the Capacitor. In addition to the mechanical analogues of the inductor and the resistor, the analogues of *two* classes of capacitive elements must be considered, which we shall distinguish by the names *condenser* and *capacitor*. The condenser is the parallel-plate device which can be connected either in a high wire or to ground, while the capacitor is typified by the isolated sphere in free space as discussed in electrostatics, one terminal only being free while the other terminal is permanently grounded.

In the mobility analogy, every mass is analogous to the capacitor, not the condenser, in the sense that one terminal of the mass is the body of the mass while the other terminal is always the earth relative to which the velocity of the mass is measured. It is this drawing of an earth symbol near each mass which makes closed circuits in a mobility schematic and permits the drawing of a correct rod diagram of any rod-connected system in a straightforward intuitive manner. There is also an unusual structure called a *transinertor* which is a combination of two masses and a mesher, and which is analogous to the condenser; it can be connected either in series with the high rod or to ground.

In the impedance analogy, every spring is analogous to the capacitor, not the condenser, in the sense that one terminal of the spring is the body of the spring while the other terminal is always the sky relative to which the force of the spring is measured. It is this drawing of a sky symbol near each spring which makes closed circuits in an impedance schematic and permits the drawing of a correct tubing diagram of any tube-connected system in a straightforward intuitive manner.

3m-5. The Dotted Arrow. Alongside each rod diagram is drawn a dotted arrow, usually toward the right, which indicates the direction of motion which is considered positive. This is analogous to marking the plus and minus signs on our voltmeters. A solid arrow superimposed on a rod indicates the direction in which impulse is flowing, such as would increase the momentum of a mass in the direction of the dotted arrow. If the solid arrow is in the direction of the dotted arrow, the rod is in compression; if the arrows are in opposite directions, the rod is in tension; if the arrows are at right angles, the rod is in shear. In a rotational system, the rotational velocity is considered positive if it is clockwise when looking in the direction of the dotted arrow placed beside the rotational schematic diagram; a solid arrow superimposed on a shaft then indicates the direction of flow of torsional impulse such as would increase the positive angular momentum of any inertor into which it flows.

In a tubing diagram only the solid arrow is used, superimposed on a tube. It indicates the direction of positive fluid velocity or volume velocity.

3m-6. Rationale of the Schematic Symbols Proposed for the Elements. In both analogies, the mechanical and acoustical schematic symbols are similar in appearance to their analogous electrical symbols. On a rod diagram, the symbols for a mechanical spring and responsor have $1\frac{1}{2}$ "wiggles," the acoustic elastor and responsor have $2\frac{1}{2}$ wiggles, the torsional spring and responsor have $2\frac{1}{2}$ wiggles but are tapered, while the electrical inductor and resistor have $3\frac{1}{2}$ wiggles as usual. Similarly a torsional inertor is tapered.

On an impedance schematic, the symbols are similar to those for the mobility schematic though dual in meaning, and each impedance schematic symbol has a line drawn beside it.

3m-7. Method of Drawing Schematic Diagrams. (1) Choose your analogy, either for life or for the problem at hand, remembering that the mobility analogy is the most convenient for rod-connected systems while the impedance analogy is the most convenient for hydraulic tube-connected systems. (2) Identify the functions performed by each part of the given structure. (3) Choose the schematic symbols which represent these functions. (4) Identify the terminals of each element, coupler, and vibrator of the structure. (5) Connect in the schematic diagram by means of appropriate connectors and rigid or hydraulic junctions those terminals which are connected in the structure.

The identification of the terminals of each element will include the assignment of the earth symbol as one terminal of each mass in a mobility schematic or rod diagram, or the assignment of the sky symbol as one terminal of each spring in an impedance schematic or tubing diagram; this will result in closed meshes and correct series and parallel connections in each diagram.

A single hydraulic tube fitted with pistons at its two ends (of equal areas for mechanical systems but not necessarily equal for acoustic systems) performs the same functions as a rod; so both rod and tube may be represented by a straight line and are interchangeable in a series. It is where several rods join, or tubes join, that there is a difference of function, a *rigid junction* of rods ensuring equal velocities while a *hydraulic junction* of tubes ensures equal forces or sound pressures. Either analogy may therefore be used for diagraming a system connected by rods and/or tubes by first determining whether a given structural connection performs the function of a rigid junction or of a hydraulic junction, then designating by means of the symbols below whether the connection constitutes a *simple junction* (analogous to a soldered junction of wires) or a *mesher* (analogous to the isocurrent junction mentioned in Sec. 3m-2). That analogy will be best for a given problem which brings in a minimum number of meshers with which we are not so familiar. Thus the mobility analogy will be best for rod-connected systems and the impedance analogy best for tube-connected systems.

3m-8. Types of Schematic Diagram. 1. The mobility schematic diagram or rod diagram. Because most mechanical systems are rod-connected and have no tubes, a mobility schematic diagram or rod diagram will be most convenient and can usually be drawn by inspection of the structure, using the mobility-analogy symbols given on left pages. Even an acoustic system of the kind where there are no side branches and the elements are of equal cross-sectional areas and lie in a series, as when a piezoelectric crystal radiates plane waves into a delay line, may be most conveniently represented by a mobility schematic since the contact of the adjacent faces of the elements ensures their equal volume velocities as if they were connected by acoustic rods.

2. The impedance schematic diagram or tubing diagram. If we have a hydraulically operated mechanical system which is tube-connected or an acoustic filter connected by tubes with side branches, an impedance schematic or tubing diagram will be most convenient and can be drawn by inspection using the impedance-analogy symbols given on right pages, provided that the sky is introduced as one terminal of each spring.

3. The two-analogy schematic diagram. Complete correspondence between the schematic diagram and the geometry of the structure can be obtained by diagraming the rod-connected parts by the mobility analogy and the tube-connected parts by the impedance analogy, appropriate couplers being indicated where rod and tube portions adjoin. Using this technique, the schematic diagram of the system can be drawn by inspection of the original structure, using the appropriate mechanical or acoustical symbols given below, including the analogy connectors on page 3-176.

3m-9. Mechanical Mobility z vs. Mechanical Admittance Y_M. Why should the new term *mechanical mobility* z be introduced when it is of the same *magnitude* as the established term *mechanical admittance* Y_M?

$$\text{Mechanical mobility } z = \frac{\hat{v} \text{ across}}{\hat{F} \text{ through}} \text{ while mechanical admittance } Y_M = \frac{\hat{v} \text{ through}}{\hat{F} \text{ across}}.$$

Thus while the magnitudes of the mechanical mobility and mechanical admittance are equal, the words *through* and *across* are inverted in the definitions, because mobility belongs in a rod-connected system and mechanical admittance belongs in a tube-connected system.

Mechanical mobility z is indigenous to a rod-connected system, and when a number of springs or other elements are connected in series, the mobility of the combination is the sum of the individual mobilities: $z = z_1 + z_2 + z_3$. It would be *unanalogous*, though correct, to say that the mechanical admittance of the elements in *series* is the sum of the individual mechanical admittances; this lack of analogy is avoided by introducing with the rod diagram the new term *mobility* and having it associated with the letter z. Mechanical admittance is indigenous to a tube-connected system and the above-mentioned *series* of structural elements would turn out to be a *parallel* combination of elements in a *tubing* diagram; the mechanical admittance of the

[*Text continued on page 3-177; tables, over.*]

THE MOBILITY ANALOGY

Symbols for Constructing Mechanical, Acoustical, and Electrical Schematic Diagrams Based on the Mobility Analogy

Symbols for rod diagrams			Symbols for the analogous wiring diagrams
Rectilineal mechanical systems	Rotational mechanical systems	Acoustic systems (preferably rigidly connected)	Electric circuits (preferably with soldered junctions)
Connectors			
1 rod 2	1 shaft 2	1 acoustic rod 2	1 wire 2
Ideal massless, incompressible, frictionless rod, *not* necessarily of uniform cross section, which connects movable terminals 1 and 2 so that	Ideal inertialess, uncompliant, frictionless shaft, *not* necessarily of uniform cross section, which connects movable terminals 1 and 2 so that	Ideal inertanceless, uncompliant, frictionless acoustic rod which connects two wavefronts 1 and 2, *not* necessarily of the same areas, by any means which function the same as a pivoted lever driving pistons 1 and 2 at lever arms equal to the reciprocal of the piston areas, so that	Ideal capacitanceless, inductanceless, resistanceless wire, *not* necessarily of uniform cross section, which connects terminals 1 and 2 so that
velocity $v_1 = v_2$ and force $F_1 = F_2$	angular velocity $v_{R1} = v_{R2}$ and torque $F_{R1} = F_{R2}$	the volume velocity $U_1 = U_2$ and the sound pressure $p_1 = p_2$	voltage $E_1 = E_2$ and current $I_1 = I_2$
Propagation in any type of ideal rod is considered instantaneous		Frequent special case, equal areas in contact. 1 2 $l_1A_1 = l_2A_2 = 1$ Prototypal structure of acoustic rod	Propagation in an ideal wire is considered instantaneous

THE IMPEDANCE ANALOGY (Classical Analogy)
Symbols for Constructing Mechanical, Acoustical, and Electrical Schematic Diagrams Based on the Impedance Analogy

Symbols for tubing diagrams			Symbols for the analogous wiring diagrams
Rectilineal mechanical systems	Rotational mechanical systems	Acoustic systems (preferably tube-connected)	Electric circuits (preferably with soldered junctions)
Connectors			
1 —— 2 tube	1 —— 2 tube	1 —— 2 acoustic tube	1 —— 2 wire
Stationary tube of *unit area* of cross section, filled with ideal, massless, incompressible, inviscid fluid, often terminating in unit-area pistons; or any mechanism of equivalent function. Dead-end tubes are closed unless connected to *sky*.	Stationary tube filled with ideal fluid, and having at every end *identical* fluid motors for transducing lineal fluid motion to rotation of a solid or fluid member (example, the Sperry Exactor hydraulic control); or any mechanism of equivalent function.	Stationary tube, *not* necessarily of uniform cross section, filled with ideal fluid (tube diameter being small compared with the wavelength in the actual medium). The speed of sound in an ideal acoustic tube is infinite.	Stationary ideal, capacitanceless, inductanceless, resistanceless wire, *not* necessarily of uniform cross section. Propagation along an ideal wire is considered instantaneous.
It connects terminals 1 and 2 so that force $F_1 = F_2$ and velocity $v_1 = v_2$	It connects terminals 1 and 2 so that torque $F_{R1} = F_{R2}$ and angular velocity $v_{R1} = v_{R2}$	It connects terminals 1 and 2 so that sound pressure $p_1 = p_2$ and volume velocity $U_1 = U_2$	It connects terminals 1 and 2 so that voltage $E_1 = E_2$ and current $I_1 = I_2$

THE MOBILITY ANALOGY

Rectilineal mechanical	Rotational mechanical	Acoustic	Electric
Symbols Indicating the Signs of the Variables			
+ - - → or + (vertical)	+ - - →	+ - - → or + (vertical)	+
Dotted arrow shows direction of positive velocity v relative to the earth.	Clockwise rotation v_R looking in the direction of the dotted arrow is positive relative to the earth.	Dotted arrow shows direction of positive volume velocity U relative to the earth.	The + sign near the wire indicates a positive voltage relative to ground.
Small arrow on rod shows direction of positive flow of force F and impulse Q_M. If impulse flows into a mass, its momentum in the direction of the dotted arrow is increased. Both arrows in the same direction indicates compression; at right angles, shear.	Small arrow on shaft shows direction of positive flow of torque F_R and torsional impulse Q_R.	Small arrow shows direction of flow of force per unit area (sound pressure p) and impulse per unit area (acoustic impulse Q_A). Both arrows in the same direction indicates compression; at right angles, shear.	Arrow shows direction of flow of positive current I and charge Q.
+ - - → compression; shear; tension	+ - - → clockwise torque (chain, belt, or gears, 1 to 1); counter-clockwise torque	+ - - → compression; shear; rarefaction	+ current right; current downward; current left
Rigid connector offset	Rigid connector offset	Rigid connector offset (rare)	Offset connector
compression everywhere	clockwise torque everywhere	compression everywhere	same as above
Flexible connector	Flexible shaft	Flexible connector (similar to tube of small d/λ)	Offset connector

THE IMPEDANCE ANALOGY

Rectilineal mechanical	Rotational mechanical	Acoustic	Electric
Symbols Indicating the Signs of the Variables			
The + sign indicates positive pressure in the tube (relative to the sky) and is assumed to be associated with positive force F The arrow shows the direction of the velocity v (relative to the tubing)	The + sign indicates positive pressure in the tube (relative to the sky) and is assumed to be associated with positive torque F_R The arrow shows the direction of fluid motion which is associated with positive clockwise angular velocity v_R	The + sign indicates a positive sound pressure p (relative to the sky, P_0) The arrow shows the direction of a positive volume velocity U	The + sign indicates a positive voltage (relative to the ground) The arrow shows the direction of flow of a positive historical current I
Rounded corners are recommended for tubes v Stationary tube with bends; direction of positive velocity v and displacement s is shown by arrows	v_R Stationary tube with changes of direction; positive clockwise angular velocity v_R and angular displacement s_R are shown by arrows	U Stationary tube with bends; direction of positive volume velocity U and volume displacement S_A is shown by arrows	I Offset connector; wire with bends; direction of positive current I and flow of charge Q is shown by arrows

THE MOBILITY ANALOGY

Rectilineal mechanical	Rotational mechanical	Acoustic	Electric
Simple junctions. The *across* variables are equal. The sum of the *through* variables toward the junction is zero			
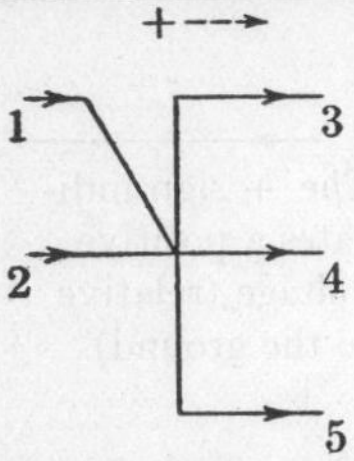 Rigid junction (welded rods of any cross-sectional area)	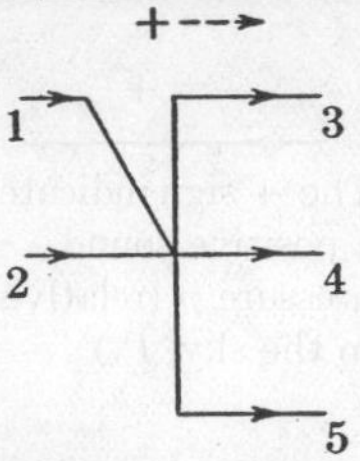 Rigid junction (1 to 1 gearbox with shafts of any cross-sectional area)	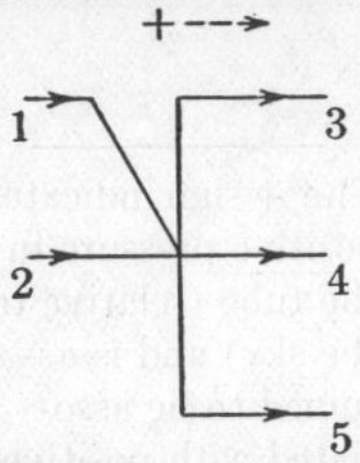 Rigid acoustic junction, connecting wavefronts 1 to 5, *not* necessarily of equal areas, by any means which functions the same as a pivoted lever driving pistons 1 to 5 at lever arms equal to the reciprocals of the piston areas (as if the levers of individual acoustic rods were rigidly connected) $1 = l_1A_1 = l_2A_2 = \text{etc.}$	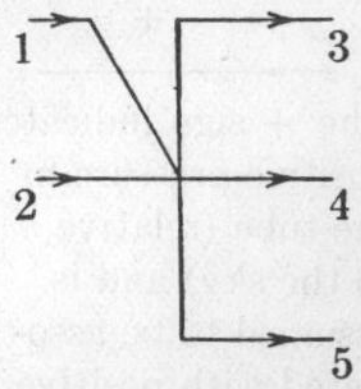 Junction (soldered wires of any cross-sectional area)
$v_1 = v_2 = \text{etc.}$ $F_1 + F_2 - F_3 - F_4 - F_5 = 0$	$v_{R1} = v_{R2} = \text{etc.}$ $F_{R1} + F_{R2} - F_{R3} - F_{R4} - F_{R5} = 0$	$U_1 = U_2 = \text{etc.}$ $p_1 + p_2 - p_3 - p_4 - p_5 = 0$	$E_1 = E_2 = \text{etc.}$ $I_1 + I_2 - I_3 - I_4 - I_5 = 0$

THE IMPEDANCE ANALOGY

Rectilineal mechanical	Rotational mechanical	Acoustic	Electric
Simple junctions. The *across* variables are equal. The sum of the *through* variables toward the junction is zero			
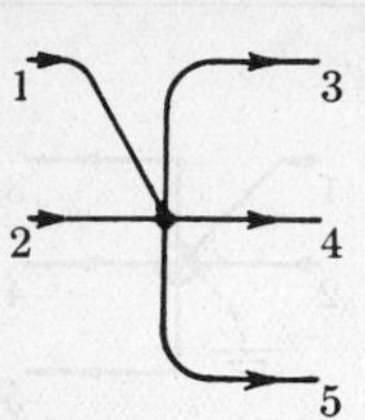 Hydraulic junction, having unit terminal areas 1 to 5	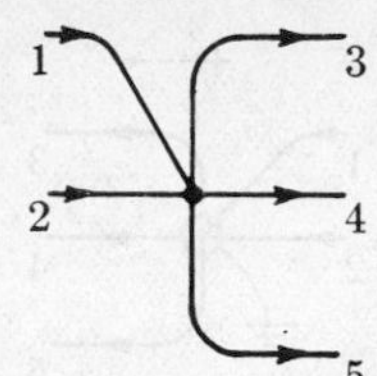 Hydraulic junction; (differential gear-box 1:1)	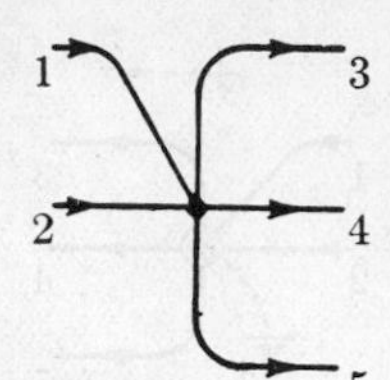 Hydraulic acoustic junction of tubes *not* necessarily of equal areas	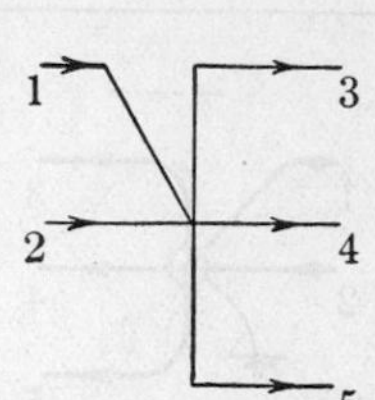 Junction (soldered wires of any cross-sectional area)
$F_1 = F_2 =$ etc. $v_1 + v_2 - v_3 - v_4 - v_5 = 0$	$F_{R1} = F_{R2} =$ etc. $v_{R1} + v_{R2} - v_{R3} - v_{R4} - v_{R5} = 0$	$p_1 = p_2 =$ etc. $U_1 + U_2 - U_3 - U_4 - U_5 = 0$	$E_1 = E_2 =$ etc. $I_1 + I_2 - I_3 - I_4 - I_5 = 0$

THE MOBILITY ANALOGY

Rectilinear mechanical	Rotational mechanical	Acoustic	Electric
Meshers. The *through* variables (in the direction of the dotted arrow) are equal. The sum of the *across* variables (with sign changed where through arrow points away from junction) is zero			
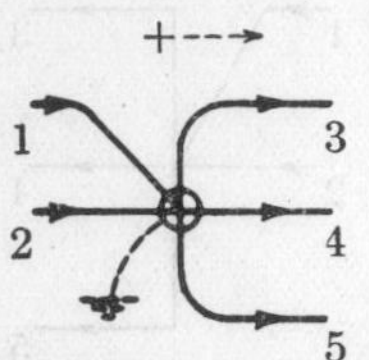	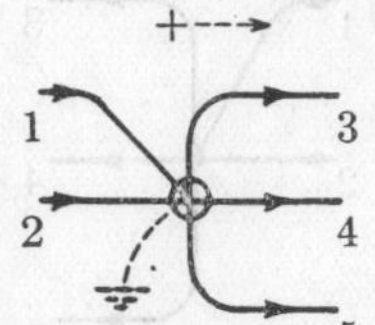	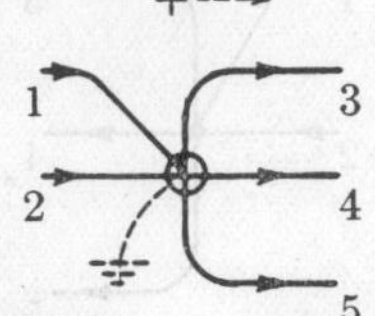	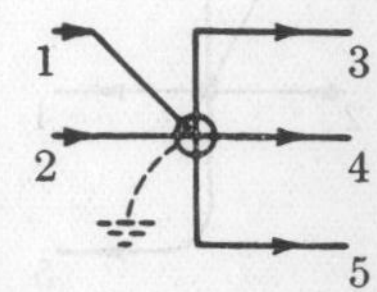
Hydraulic junction; mesher (see below) $F_1 = F_2 =$ etc. $v_1 + v_2 - v_3 - v_4 - v_5 = 0$ The earth connection is not necessary when equal numbers of forces flow *to* and *from* the mesher.	Hydraulic junction; mesher (see below) $F_{R1} = F_{R2} =$ etc. $v_{R1} + v_{R2} - v_{R3} - v_{R4} - v_{R5} = 0$ The earth connection is not necessary when equal numbers of torques flow *to* and *from* the mesher.	Hydraulic acoustic junction; mesher $p_1 = p_2 =$ etc. $U_1 + U_2 - U_3 - U_4 - U_5 = 0$ The acoustic earth connection is not necessary when equal numbers of sound pressures flow *to* and *from* the mesher.	Isocurrent junction; mesher (see below) $I_1 = I_2 =$ etc. $E_1 + E_2 - E_3 - E_4 - E_5 = 0$ The ground connection is not necessary when equal numbers of currents flow *to* and *from* the mesher.
Typical hydraulic junction structure (see symbol above):	Typical hydraulic junction structure (see symbol above):	Typical hydraulic junction structure (see symbol above):	Typical mesher structure (see symbol above):
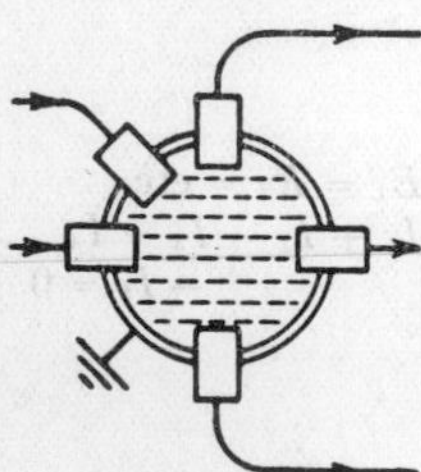	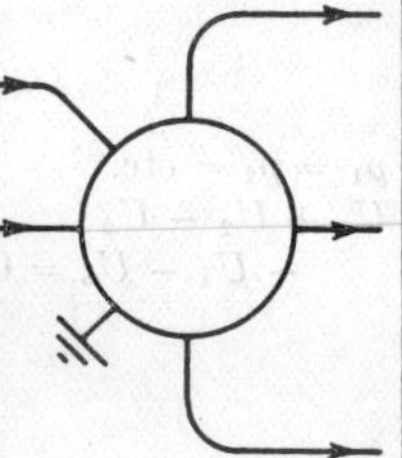	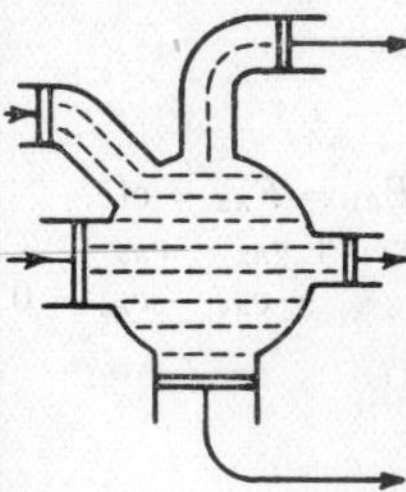	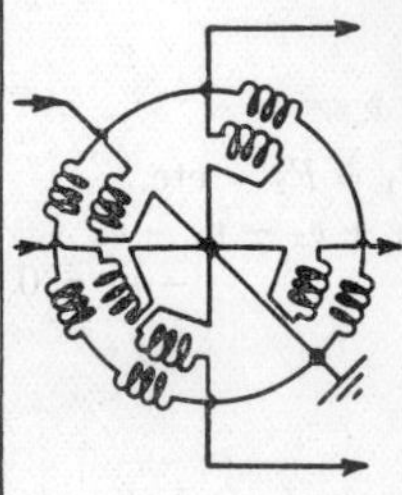
Equal-area pistons with common liquid, or any set of levers which will ensure equal forces of compression	Differential gearbox giving equal torques	Acoustic rods, generally of different wavefront (piston) areas, entering a small chamber containing ideal fluid	Similar ideal transformers (on separate cores) with secondaries in series. Phased as shown by arrows

THE IMPEDANCE ANALOGY

Rectilinear mechanical	Rotational mechanical	Acoustic	Electric
Meshers. The *through* variables (as indicated by the arrows) are equal. The sum of the *across* variables (with sign changed where through variable arrow points away from junction) is zero			
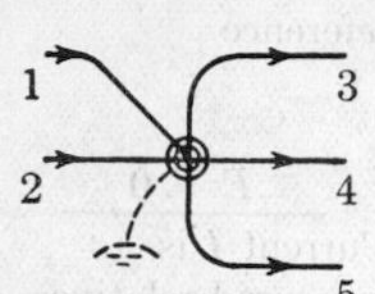	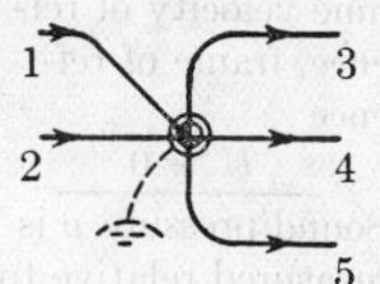	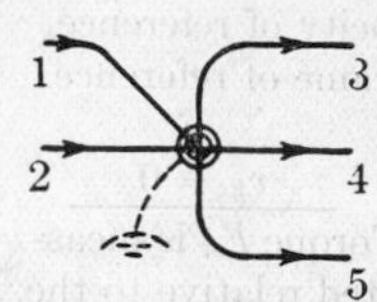	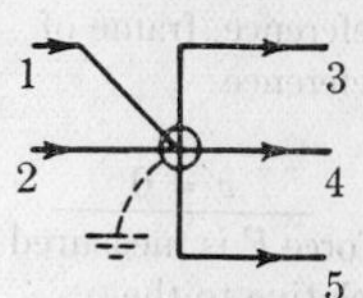
Rigid junction; mesher (see below) $v_1 = v_2 =$ etc. $F_1 + F_2 - F_3 - F_4 - F_5 = 0$	Rigid (geared) junction; mesher $v_{R1} = v_{R2} =$ etc. $F_{R1} + F_{R2} - F_{R3} - F_{R4} - F_{R5} = 0$	Rigid acoustic junction; mesher $U_1 = U_2 =$ etc. $p_1 + p_2 - p_3 - p_4 - p_5 = 0$	Isocurrent junction; mesher $I_1 = I_2 =$ etc. $E_1 + E_2 - E_3 - E_4 - E_5 = 0$
The sky connection is not necessary when equal numbers of velocities flow *to* and *from* the mesher.	The sky connection is not necessary when equal numbers of rotational velocities flow *to* and *from* the mesher.	The acoustic sky connection is not necessary when equal numbers of volume velocities flow *to* and *from* the mesher.	The ground connection is not necessary when equal numbers of currents flow *to* and *from* the mesher.
Typical rigid junction structure (see symbol above):	Typical rigid junction structure (see symbol above):	Typical rigid acoustic junction structure:	Typical mesher structure:
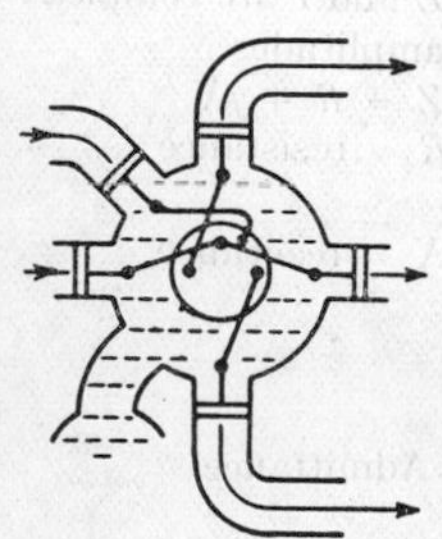	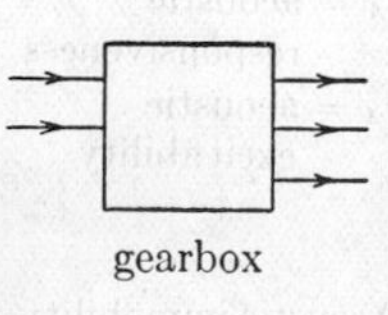	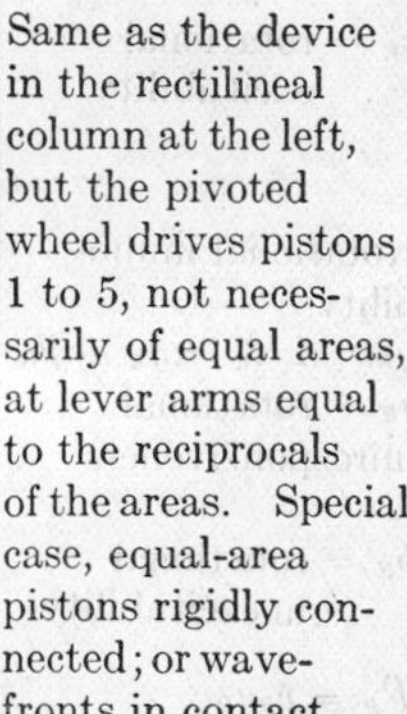 Same as the device in the rectilineal column at the left, but the pivoted wheel drives pistons 1 to 5, not necessarily of equal areas, at lever arms equal to the reciprocals of the areas. Special case, equal-area pistons rigidly connected; or wavefronts in contact	Same as on opposite page
A multiplicity of rigidly connected equal-area pistons which ensure equal fluid velocities in all tubes; or a number of rods bolted together	Gears, belts, chains, or levers, which ensure equal rotations of shafts		

THE MOBILITY ANALOGY

Rectilineal mechanical	Rotational mechanical	Acoustic	Electric
Referents			
or	or	or	
Earth, velocity of reference, frame of reference	Earth, angular velocity of reference, frame of reference	Acoustic earth, volume velocity of reference, frame of reference	Ground, voltage of reference
$v = 0$	$v_R = 0$	$U = 0$	$E = 0$
Force F is measured relative to the force in the surrounding empty space (no symbol)	Torque F_R is measured relative to the torque in the surrounding empty space (no symbol)	Sound pressure p is measured relative to the pressure P_0 in the surrounding atmosphere (no symbol)	Current I is measured relative to the current in the surrounding empty space (no symbol)
Passive Elements			
z	z_R	z_A	Z
A mechanical mobility z. $z \equiv \dfrac{\hat{v} \text{ across}}{\hat{F} \text{ through}}$ $\hat{v}$ and $\hat{F}$ are complex amplitudes. $z = r + jx$ r = responsiveness x = excitability	A rotational mobility z_R. $z_R \equiv \dfrac{\hat{v}_R \text{ across}}{\hat{F}_R \text{ through}}$ $\hat{v}_R$ and $\hat{F}_R$ are complex amplitudes. $z_R = r_R + jx_R$ r_R = rotational responsiveness x_R = rotational excitability	An acoustic mobility z_A. $z_A \equiv \dfrac{\hat{U} \text{ across}}{\hat{p} \text{ through}}$ $\hat{U}$ and $\hat{p}$ are complex amplitudes. $z_A = r_A + jx_A$ r_A = acoustic responsiveness x_A = acoustic excitability	An electric impedance Z. $Z \equiv \dfrac{\hat{E} \text{ across}}{\hat{I} \text{ through}}$ $\hat{E}$ and $\hat{I}$ are complex amplitudes. $Z = R + jX$ R = resistance X = reactance
Mechanical immobility $y = 1/z = g + jb$ g = unresponsiveness b = unexcitability	Rotational immobility $y_R = 1/z_R = g_R + jb_R$ g_R = rotational unresponsiveness b_R = rotational unexcitability	Acoustic immobility $y_A = 1/z_A = g_A + jb_A$ g_A = acoustic unresponsiveness b_A = acoustic unexcitability	Admittance $Y = 1/Z = G + jB$ G = conductance B = susceptance
$\hat{F} = \hat{v}y$ $\hat{v} = \hat{F}z$ $P = vF$ $P = v\|F\| \cos \varphi_z$ $= F\|^2 r$	$\hat{F}_R = \hat{v}_R y_R$ $\hat{v}_R = \hat{F}_R z_R$ $P_i = v_R F_R$ $P = v_R\|F_R\| \cos \varphi_{zR}$ $= F_R\|^2 r_R$	$\hat{p} = \hat{U} y_A$ $\hat{U} = \hat{p} z_A$ $P_i = Up$ $P = U\|p\| \cos \varphi_{zA}$ $= p\|^2 r_A$	$\hat{I} = \hat{E}Y$ $\hat{E} = \hat{I}Z$ $P_i = EI$ $P = E\|I\| \cos \varphi_Z$ $= I\|^2 R$

THE IMPEDANCE ANALOGY

Rectilineal mechanical	Rotational mechanical	Acoustic	Electric
Referents			
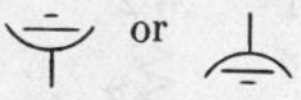 or Sky, force of reference, (a reservoir of ideal fluid maintained at constant pressure) $F = 0$	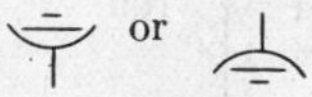 or Sky, torque of reference, (a reservoir of ideal fluid maintained at constant pressure) $F_R = 0$	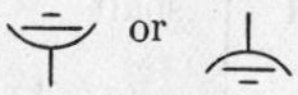 or Sky, pressure of reference, (usually an atmosphere of fluid at constant pressure P_0) $p = 0$	 Ground, voltage of reference, (a source of charge at constant voltage) $E = 0$
Velocity v is measured relative to the surrounding tubing or full space (no symbol)	Angular velocity v_R is measured relative to the surrounding tubing or full space (no symbol)	Volume velocity U is measured relative to the surrounding tubing or full space (no symbol)	Current I is measured relative to the current in the surrounding empty space (no symbol)
Passive Elements			
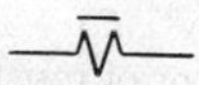 Z_M A mechanical impedance Z_M. $Z_M \equiv \frac{\hat{F} \text{ across}}{\hat{v} \text{ through}}$	 Z_R A rotational impedance Z_R. $Z_R \equiv \frac{\hat{F}_R \text{ across}}{\hat{v}_R \text{ through}}$	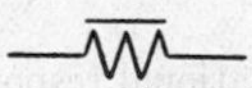 Z_A An acoustic impedance Z_A. $Z_A \equiv \frac{\hat{p} \text{ across}}{\hat{U} \text{ through}}$	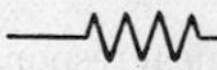 Z An electric impedance Z. $Z \equiv \frac{\hat{E} \text{ across}}{\hat{I} \text{ through}}$
$Z_M = R_M + jX_M$ R_M = mechanical resistance X_M = mechanical reactance	$Z_R = R_R + jX_R$ R_R = rotational resistance X_R = rotational reactance	$Z_A = R_A \pm jX_A$ R_A = acoustic resistance X_A = acoustic reactance	$Z = R + jX$ R = resistance X = reactance
Mechanical admittance $Y_M = 1/Z_M$ $= G_M + jB_M$ G_M = mechanical conductance B_M = mechanical susceptance	Rotational admittance $Y_R = 1/Z_R$ $= G_R + jB_R$ G_R = rotational conductance B_R = rotational susceptance	Acoustic admittance $Y_A = 1/Z_A$ $= G_A + jB_A$ G_A = acoustic conductance B_A = acoustic susceptance	Admittance $Y = 1/Z = G + jB$ G = conductance B = susceptance
$\hat{v} = \hat{F}Y_M$ $\hat{F} = \hat{v}Z_M$ $P_i = Fv$ $P = F\|v\| \cos \varphi_{ZM}$ $P = v\|^2 R_M$	$\hat{v}_R = \hat{F}_R Y_R$ $\hat{F}_R = \hat{v}_R Z_R$ $P_i = F_R v_R$ $P = F_R\|v_R\| \cos \varphi_{ZR}$ $P = v_R\|^2 R_R$	$\hat{U} = \hat{p}Y_A$ $\hat{p} = \hat{U}Z_A$ $P_i = pU$ $P = p\|U\| \cos \varphi_{ZA}$ $P = U\|^2 R_A$	$\hat{I} = \hat{E}Y$ $\hat{E} = \hat{I}Z$ $P_i = EI$ $P = E\|I\| \cos \varphi_Z$ $P = I\|^2 R$

THE MOBILITY ANALOGY

Rectilineal mechanical	Rotational mechanical	Acoustic	Electric
+ ---> 1 rod 3 2 z earth	+ ---> 1 shaft 3 2 z_R earth	+ ---> 1 rod 3 2 z_A earth	wire 1 2 3 Z ground
Three-terminal mobility z including (rigid) junction. $\hat{v}_1 = \hat{v}_2 = \hat{v}_3 = \hat{v}$ $\hat{F}_3 = \hat{F}_1 - \hat{F}_2$ $\hat{F}_2 = \hat{v}/z$	Three-terminal rotational mobility z_R including (rigid) junction. $\hat{v}_{R1} = \hat{v}_{R2} = \hat{v}_{R3} = \hat{v}$ $\hat{F}_{R3} = \hat{F}_{R1} - \hat{F}_{R2}$ $\hat{F}_{R2} = \hat{v}_R/z_R$	Three-terminal acoustic mobility z_A including (rigid) junction. $\hat{U}_1 = \hat{U}_2 = \hat{U}_3 = \hat{U}$ $\hat{p}_3 = \hat{p}_1 - \hat{p}_2$ $\hat{p}_2 = \hat{U}/z_A$	Three-terminal impedance Z including junction. $\hat{E}_1 = \hat{E}_2 = \hat{E}_3 = \hat{E}$ $\hat{I}_3 = \hat{I}_1 - \hat{I}_2$ $\hat{I}_2 = \hat{E}/Z$
r Mechanical responsor of responsiveness r	r_R Rotational responsor of rotational responsiveness r_R	r_A Acoustic responsor of acoustic responsiveness r_A	R Resistor of resistance R
Typical structure: viscous oil between plates attached to the terminals	Typical structure: viscous oil between concentric rotating cones attached to the terminals	Typical structure: viscous oil leaking through holes in piston in movable cylinder	Typical structure: a length of resistive wire
$r \equiv \dfrac{v \text{ across}}{F \text{ through}} = \dfrac{\hat{v}}{\hat{F}}$ $z = r$ $v = Fr$ $\hat{v} = \hat{F}r$ $P = \|F\|^2 r = \|v\|^2/r$ Displacement $s = \int v\, dt = rQ_M$ where impulse $Q_M = \int F\, dt$	$r_R \equiv \dfrac{v_R \text{ across}}{F_R \text{ through}} = \dfrac{\hat{v}_R}{\hat{F}_R}$ $z_R = r_R$ $v_R = F_R r_R$ $\hat{v}_R = \hat{F}_R r_R$ $P = \|F_R\|^2 r_R = \|v_R\|^2/r_R$ Rotational displacement $\theta = \int v_R\, dt = r_R Q_R$ where torsional impulse $Q_R = \int f_R\, dt$	$r_A \equiv \dfrac{U \text{ across}}{p \text{ through}} = \dfrac{\hat{U}}{\hat{p}}$ $z_A = r_A$ $U = pr_A$ $\hat{U} = \hat{p}r_A$ $P = \|p\|^2 r_A = \|U\|^2/r_A$ Volume displacement $S = \int U\, dt = r_A Q_A$ where acoustic impulse $Q_A = \int p\, dt$	$R \equiv \dfrac{E \text{ across}}{I \text{ through}} = \dfrac{\hat{E}}{\hat{I}}$ $Z = R$ $E = IR$ $\hat{E} = \hat{I}R$ $P = \|I\|^2 R = \|E\|^2/R$ Voltage impulse $S = \int E\, dt = RQ$ where charge $Q = \int I\, dt$

THE IMPEDANCE ANALOGY

Rectilineal mechanical	Rotational mechanical	Acoustic	Electric
tube 1 2 3 Z_M sky	tube 1 2 3 Z_R sky	tube 1 2 3 Z_A sky	wire 1 2 3 Z ground
Three-terminal mechanical impedance Z_M including hydraulic junction.	Three-terminal rotational impedance Z_R including hydraulic junction.	Three-terminal acoustic impedance Z_A including hydraulic junction.	Three-terminal impedance Z including junction.
$\hat{F}_1 = \hat{F}_2 = \hat{F}_3 = \hat{F}$ $\hat{v}_3 = \hat{v}_1 - \hat{v}_2$ $\hat{v}_2 = \hat{F}/Z_M$	$\hat{F}_{R1} = \hat{F}_{R2} = \hat{F}_{R3} = \hat{F}_R$ $v_{R3} = v_{R1} - v_{R2}$ $\hat{v}_{R2} = \hat{F}_R/Z_R$	$\hat{p}_1 = \hat{p}_2 = \hat{p}_3 = \hat{p}$ $\hat{U}_3 = \hat{U}_1 - \hat{U}_2$ $\hat{U}_2 = \hat{p}/Z_A$	$\hat{E}_1 = \hat{E}_2 = \hat{E}_3 = \hat{E}$ $\hat{I}_3 = \hat{I}_1 - \hat{I}_2$ $\hat{I}_2 = \hat{E}/Z$
R_M	R_R	R_A	R
Mechanical resistor of resistance R_M	Rotational resistor of rotational resistance R_R	Acoustic resistor of acoustic resistance R_A	Resistor of resistance R
Typical structure: a length of viscous fluid moving in a stationary tube of unit cross-sectional area	Typical structure: an annulus of viscous liquid between a rotating cone and a stationary cone; or a coil of tubing containing viscous fluid	Typical structure: a length of viscous fluid moving in a stationary tube of any cross-sectional area	Typical structure: a length of resistive wire
$R_M \equiv \dfrac{F \text{ across}}{v \text{ through}} = \dfrac{\hat{F}}{\hat{v}}$ $Z_M = R_M$ $F = vR_M$ $\hat{F} = \hat{v}R_M$ $P = \|v\|^2 R_M = \|F\|^2/R_M$	$R_R \equiv \dfrac{F_R \text{ across}}{v_R \text{ through}} = \dfrac{\hat{F}_R}{\hat{v}_R}$ $Z_R = R_R$ $F_R = v_R R_R$ $\hat{F}_R = \hat{v}_R R_R$ $P = \|v_R\|^2 R_R = \|f_R\|^2/R_R$	$R_A \equiv \dfrac{p \text{ across}}{U \text{ through}} = \dfrac{\hat{p}}{\hat{U}}$ $Z_A = R_A$ $p = UR_A$ $\hat{p} = \hat{U}R_A$ $P = \|U\|^2 R_A = \|p\|^2/R_A$	$R \equiv \dfrac{E \text{ across}}{I \text{ through}} = \dfrac{\hat{E}}{\hat{I}}$ $Z = R$ $E = IR$ $\hat{E} = \hat{I}R$ $P = \|I\|^2 R = \|E\|^2/R$
Impulse $Q_M = \int F\,dt = R_M s$ where displacement $s = \int v\,dt$	Torsional impulse $Q_R = \int F_R\,dt = R_R\theta$ where displacement $\theta = \int v_R\,dt$	Acoustic impulse $Q_A = \int p\,dt = R_A S_A$ where volume displacement $S_A = \int U\,dt$	Voltage impulse $S = \int E\,dt = RQ$ where charge $Q = \int I\,dt$

THE MOBILITY ANALOGY

Rectilinear mechanical	Rotational mechanical	Acoustic	Electric
rod 1 3 2 r earth	shaft 1 3 2 r_R earth	rod 1 3 2 r_A earth	wire 1 2 3 R ground
Three-terminal mechanical responsor r including junction.	Three-terminal rotational responsor r_R including junction.	Three-terminal acoustic responsor r_A including (rigid) junction.	Three-terminal resistor R including (soldered) junction.
$v_1 = v_2 = v_3 = v$ $F_3 = F_1 - F_2$ $\hat{F}_2 = \hat{v}/r$	$v_{R1} = v_{R2} = v_{R3} = v_R$ $F_{R3} = F_{R1} - F_{R2}$ $\hat{F}_{R2} = \hat{v}_R/r_R$	$U_1 = U_2 = U_3 = U$ $p_3 = p_1 - p_2$ $\hat{p}_2 = \hat{U}/r_A$	$E_1 = E_2 = E_3 = E$ $I_3 = I_1 - I_2$ $\hat{I}_2 = \hat{E}/R$
C_M (or L_M)	C_R (or L_R)	C_A (or L_A)	L
Spring of compliance C_M (or L_M)	Torsional spring of rotational compliance C_R (or L_R)	Acoustic spring of acoustic compliance C_A (or L_A)	Inductor of inductance L
$v = C_M\, dF/dt$ $z = j\omega C_M$ (or $j\omega L_M$) $\hat{v} = \hat{F}z$ $W = C_M F^2/2$ Displacement $s = \int v\, dt = C_M F$	$v_R = C_R\, dF_R/dt$ $z_R = j\omega C_R$ $\hat{v}_R = \hat{F}_R z_R$ $W = C_R F_R{}^2/2$ Angular displacement $\theta = \int v_R\, dt = C_R F_R$	$U = C_A\, dp/dt$ $z_A = j\omega C_A$ $\hat{U} = \hat{p} z_A$ $W = C_A p^2/2$ Volume displacement $X = \int U\, dt = C_A p$ A closed volume V of gas at pressure P_0 has $C_A = V/\gamma P_0$	$E = L\, dI/dt$ $Z = j\omega L$ $\hat{E} = \hat{I}Z$ $W = LI^2/2$ Voltage impulse $S = \int E\, dt = LI$

THE IMPEDANCE ANALOGY

Rectilineal mechanical	Rotational mechanical	Acoustic	Electric
tube; 1, 2, 3; R_M; sky	tube; 1, 2, 3; R_R; sky	tube; 1, 2, 3; R_A; sky	wire; 1, 2, 3; R; ground
Three-terminal mechanical resistor R_M including hydraulic junction.	Three-terminal rotational resistor R_R including hydraulic junction.	Three-terminal acoustic resistor R_A including hydraulic junction.	Three-terminal impedance Z including (soldered) junction.
$F_1 = F_2 = F_3 = F$ $v_3 = v_1 - v_2$ $\hat{v}_2 = \hat{F}/R_M$	$F_{R1} = F_{R2} = F_{R3} = F_R$ $v_{R3} = v_{R1} - v_{R2}$ $\hat{v}_{R2} = \hat{F}_{R2}/R_R$	$p_1 = p_2 = p_3 = p$ $U_3 = U_1 - U_2$ $\hat{U}_2 = \hat{p}/R_A$	$E_1 = E_2 = E_3 = E$ $I_3 = I_1 - I_2$ $\hat{I}_2 = E/R$
m	J	M	L
A mass, of mass m	A rotational inertor of polar moment of inertia J	An acoustic inertor of inertance M (or M_A). $M = m/A^2$	An inductor of inductance L
Typical structure: a length of massive fluid contained in a unit-area tube	Typical structure: a coil of stationary tubing containing a massive fluid	Typical structure: a mass m of gas in a stationary tube or neck of area A	Typical structure: a coil of wire
$F = m\,dv/dt = ma$ $Z_M = j\omega m$ $\hat{F} = \hat{v}Z_M$ $W = mv^2/2$ Impulse equals momentum	$F_R = J\,dv_R/dt = J\alpha$ $Z_R = j\omega J$ $\hat{F}_R = \hat{v}_R Z_R$ $W = Jv_R^2/2$ Torsional impulse equals angular momentum	$p = M\,dU/dt = pA_A$ $Z_A = j\omega M$ $\hat{p} = \hat{U}Z_A$ $W = MU^2/2$ Acoustic impulse equals acoustic momentum	$E = L\,dI/dt$ $Z = j\omega L$ $\hat{E} = \hat{I}Z$ $W = LI^2/2$ Voltage impulse
$Q_M = \int F\,dt = mv$	$Q_R = \int F_R\,dt = Jv_R$	$Q_A = \int p\,dt = MU$	$S = \int E\,dt = LI$

THE MOBILITY ANALOGY

Rectilineal mechanical	Rotational mechanical	Acoustic	Electric
rod 1 3 2 C_M earth	shaft 1 3 2 C_R earth	rod 1 3 2 C_A earth	wire 1 3 2 L ground
Three-terminal spring (elastor) of compliance C_M, including junction.	Three-terminal torsional spring (elastor) of rotational compliance C_R, including junction.	Three-terminal acoustic spring (elastor) of acoustic compliance C_A, including junction.	Three-terminal inductor of inductance L, including junction.
$v_1 = v_2 = v_3 = v$ $F_3 = F_1 - F_2$ $\hat{F}_2 = \hat{v}/j\omega C_M$	$v_{R1} = v_{R2} = v_{R3} = v_R$ $F_{R3} = F_{R1} - F_{R2}$ $\hat{F}_{R2} = \hat{v}_R/j\omega C_R$	$U_1 = U_2 = U_3 = U$ $p_3 = p_1 - p_2$ $\hat{p}_2 = \hat{U}/j\omega C_A$	$E_1 = E_2 = E_3 = E$ $I_3 = I_1 - I_2$ $\hat{I}_2 = \hat{E}/j\omega L$
m	J	M	C or
A mass of mass m	A rotational inertor of polar moment of inertia J	An acoustic inertor of inertance M (or M_A). $M = m/A^2$	A capacitor of capacitance C.
One terminal permanently earthed. Typical structure: a solid block constrained to lineal motion	One terminal permanently earthed. Typical structure: a flywheel	One terminal permanently earthed. Typical structure: a mass of gas in a constriction	One terminal permanently grounded. Typical structure: an isolated metal sphere in free space
$F = m\, dv/dt = ma$ $z = -j/\omega m$ $\hat{v} = \hat{F}z$ $W = mv^2/2$	$F_R = J\, dv_R/dt = J\alpha$ $Z_R = -j/\omega J$ $\hat{v}_R = \hat{F}_R z_R$ $W = Jv_R^2/2$	$p = M\, dU/dt = MA_A$ $Z_A = -j/\omega M$ $\hat{U} = \hat{p} z_A$ $W = MU^2/2$	$I = C\, dE/dt$ $Z = -j/\omega C$ $\hat{E} = \hat{I}Z$ $W = CE^2/2$
Impulse equals momentum	Torsional impulse equals angular momentum	Acoustic impulse equals acoustic momentum	Charge equals capacitance times voltage
$Q_M = \int F\, dt = mv$	$Q_R = \int F_R\, dt = Jv_R$	$Q_A = \int p\, dt = MU$	$Q = \int I\, dt = CE$

THE IMPEDANCE ANALOGY

Rectilineal mechanical	Rotational mechanical	Acoustic	Electric
1 2 3 m sky	1 2 3 J sky	1 2 3 M sky	1 2 3 L ground
Three-terminal mass m including hydraulic junction.	Three-terminal rotational inertor J including hydraulic junction.	Three-terminal acoustic inertor M including hydraulic junction.	Three-terminal inductor L including junction.
$F_1 = F_2 = F_3 = F$ $v_3 = v_1 - v_2$ $\hat{v}_2 = \hat{F}/Z_M$	$F_{R1} = F_{R2} = F_{R3} = F_R$ $v_{R3} = v_{R1} - v_{R2}$ $\hat{v}_{R2} = \hat{F}_R/Z_R$	$p_1 = p_2 = p_3 = p$ $U_3 = U_1 - U_2$ $\hat{U}_2 = \hat{p}/Z_A$	$E_1 = E_2 = E_3 = E$ $I_3 = I_1 - I_2$ $\hat{I}_2 = \hat{E}/Z$
C_M sky	C_R sky	C_A sky	C or C ground
Spring of compliance C_M. One terminal permanently skyed	Torsional spring of rotational compliance C_R. One terminal permanently skyed	Acoustic spring of acoustic compliance C_A. $C_A = V/\gamma P_0$. One terminal permanently skyed	Capacitor of capacitance C. One terminal permanently grounded
Typical structure: a bubble of gas in a rigid container, or ideal fluid in a shielded flexible container	Typical structure: a torsional spring reacting against its rigid support	Typical structure: compliant gas in a rigid container of volume V	Typical structure: an isolated metal sphere in free space
$v = C_M\, df/dt$ $Z_M = -j/\omega C_M$ $\hat{F} = \hat{v}Z_M$ $W = C_M F^2/2$	$v_R = C_R\, dF_R/dt$ $Z_R = -j/\omega C_R$ $\hat{F}_R = \hat{v}_R Z_R$ $W = C_R F_R^2/2$	$U = C_A\, dp/dt$ $Z_A = -j/\omega C_A$ $\hat{p} = \hat{U}Z_A$ $W = C_A p^2/2$	$I = C\, dE/dt$ $Z = -j/\omega C$ $\hat{E} = \hat{I}Z$ $W = CE^2/2$
Displacement	Rotational displacement	Volume displacement	Charge
$s = \int v\, dt = C_M F$	$\theta = \int v_R\, dt = C_R F_R$	$S = \int U\, dt = C_A p$	$Q = \int I\, dt = CE$

THE MOBILITY ANALOGY

Rectilineal mechanical	Rotational	Acoustic	Electric
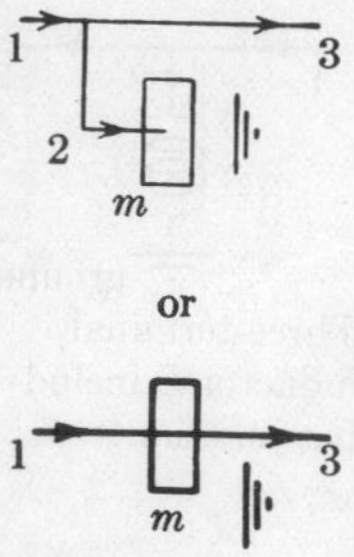	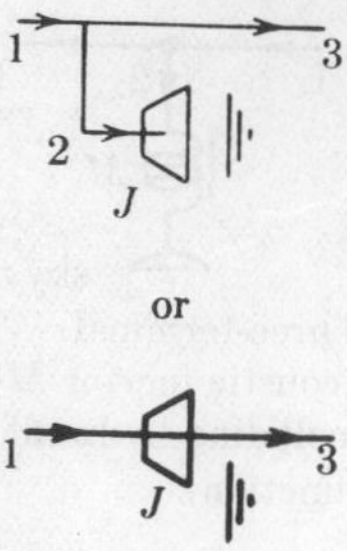	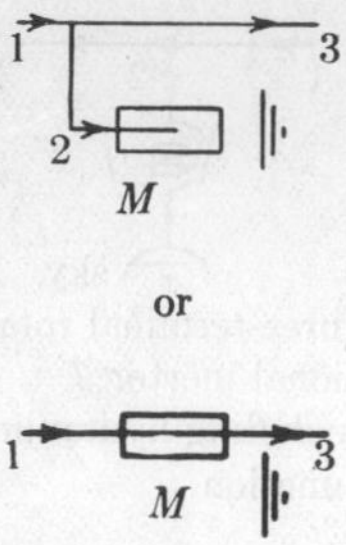	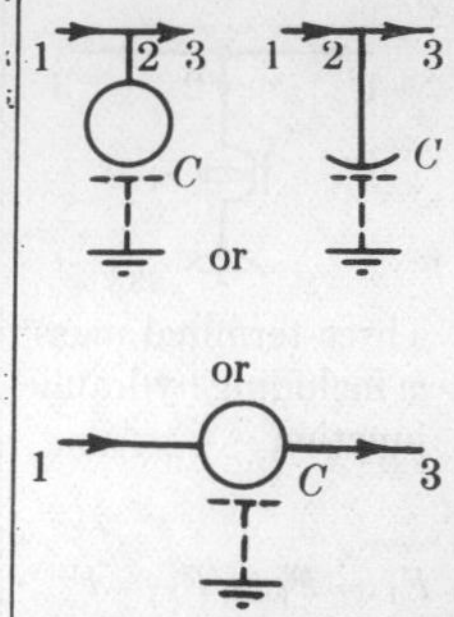
Three-terminal mass m including junction	Three-terminal rotational inertor J including junction	Three-terminal acoustic inertor M including junction	Three-terminal capacitor C including junction
$v_1 = v_2 = v_3 = v$ $F_3 = F_1 - F_2$ $\hat{F}_3 = j\omega m\hat{v}$	$v_{R1} = v_{R2} = v_{R3} = v_R$ $F_{R3} = F_{R1} - F_{R2}$ $\hat{F}_{R2} = j\omega J\hat{v}_R$	$U_1 = U_2 = U_3 = U$ $p_3 = p_1 - p_2$ $\hat{p}_2 = j\omega M\hat{U}$	$E_1 = E_2 = E_3 = E$ $I_3 = I_1 - I_2$ $\hat{I}_2 = j\omega C\hat{E}$
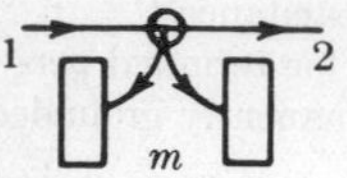 m	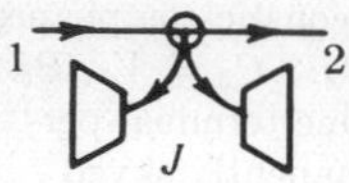 J	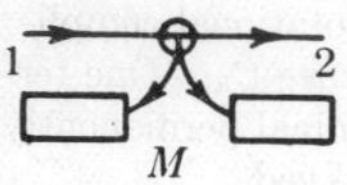 M	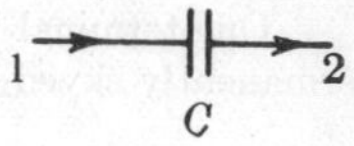
Transinertor of mass m	Rotational transinertor of moment of inertia J	Acoustic transinertor of inertance M	Condenser of capacitance C
$F_1 = F_2$	$F_{R1} = F_{R2}$	$p_1 = p_2$	$I_1 = I_2$
Connectible either in series with a hot rod, or to earth	Connectible either in series with a high shaft, or to earth	Connectible either in series with a high rod, or to earth	Connectible either in series with a high wire, or to ground
Typical structure: floating levers or a hydraulic junction which ensure equal forces in the rod and on the two masses, each of mass $2m$	Typical structure: differential gears or a hydraulic junction which ensure equal torques in the shaft and on the two inertors, each of moment of inertia $2J$	Typical structure: a hydraulic junction which ensures equal sound pressures in the main rod and on the two inertors, each of inertance $2M$	Typical structure: parallel plates between which there is a displacement current. There is no direct analogous mechanical phenomenon through *empty* space

THE IMPEDANCE ANALOGY

Rectilineal mechanical	Rotational mechanical	Acoustic	Electric
1, 3, 2, C_M or 1, 3, C_M	1, 3, or 1, 3, C_R	1, 3, C_A or 1, 3, C_A	1, 2, 3, C or 1, 2, 3, C or 1, 3, C
Three-terminal spring C_M including hydraulic junction.	Three-terminal torsional spring C_R including hydraulic junction.	Three-terminal acoustic spring C_A including hydraulic junction.	Three-terminal capacitor including soldered junction.
$F_1 = F_2 = F_3 = F$ $v_3 = v_1 - v_2$ $\hat{v}_2 = j\omega C_M \hat{F}$	$F_{R1} = F_{R2} = F_{R3} = F_R$ $v_{R3} = v_{R1} - v_{R2}$ $\hat{v}_{R2} = j\omega C_R \hat{F}_R$	$p_1 = p_2 = p_3 = p$ $U_3 = U_1 - U_2$ $\hat{U}_2 = j\omega C_A \hat{p}$	$E_1 = E_2 = E_3 = E$ $I_3 = I_1 - I_2$ $\hat{I}_2 = j\omega C \hat{E}$
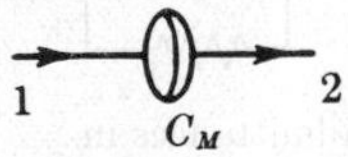 1, 2, C_M	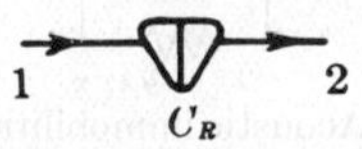 1, 2, C_R	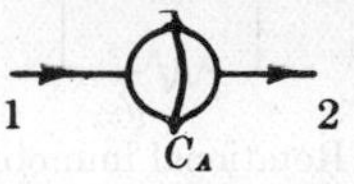 1, 2, C_A	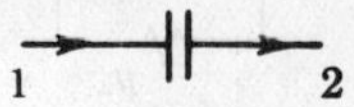 1, 2
Elaster of compliance C_M	Torsional elaster of rotational compliance C_R	Acoustic elaster of acoustic compliance C_A	Condenser of capacitance C
$v_1 = v_2$ Connectible either in series with a high tube, or to sky	$v_{R1} = v_{R2}$ Connectible either in series with a high tube, or to sky	$U_1 = U_2$ Connectible either in series with a high tube, or to sky	$I_1 = I_2$ Connectible either in series with a high wire, or to ground
Typical structure: a compliant diaphragm separating two chambers filled with ideal fluid	Typical structure: a torsional spring reacting against a stationary support	Typical structure: a compliant diaphragm separating two chambers filled with ideal fluid	Typical structure: parallel plates between which there is a displacement current

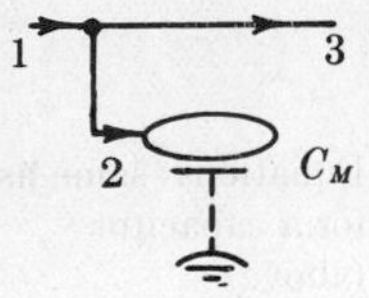

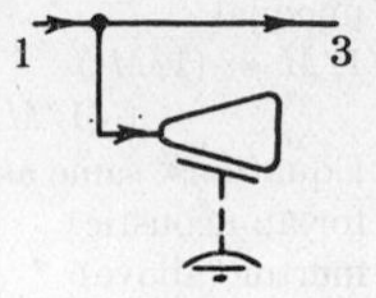

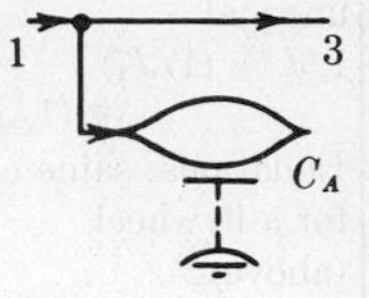

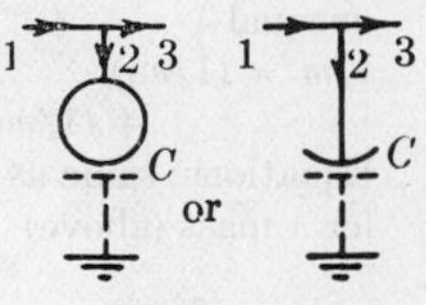

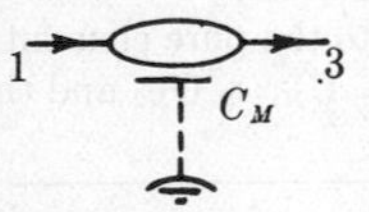

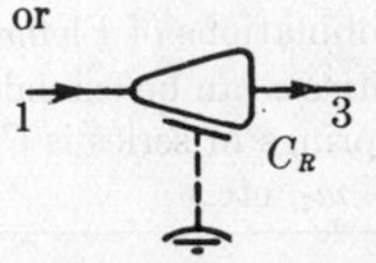

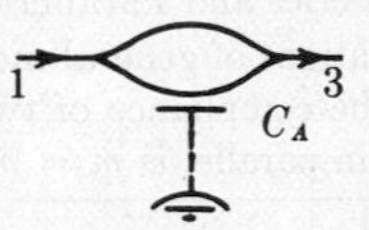

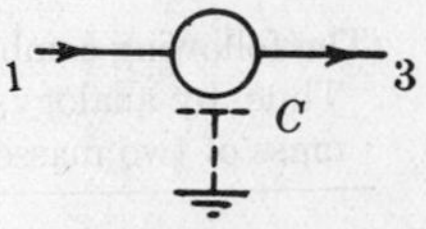

THE MOBILITY ANALOGY

Rectilineal mechanical	Rotational mechanical	Acoustic	Electric
If the masses are unequal $1/m = (1/m_1) + (1/m_2)$ Equations: same as for a mass (above)	If the inertors are unequal $1/J = (1/J_1) + (1/J_2)$ Equations: same as for a flywheel (above)	If the inertors are unequal $1/M = (1/M_1) + (1/M_2)$ Equations: same as for an acoustic inertor (above)	Equations: same as for a capacitor (above)

Series and Parallel Combinations of Elements

(The following combinations of general mobilities z can be extended to the pure elements. Thus, by analogy, the compliance of two springs in series is $C_M = C_{M1} + C_{M2}$ and the mass of two masses in parallel is $m = m_1 + m_2$, etc.)

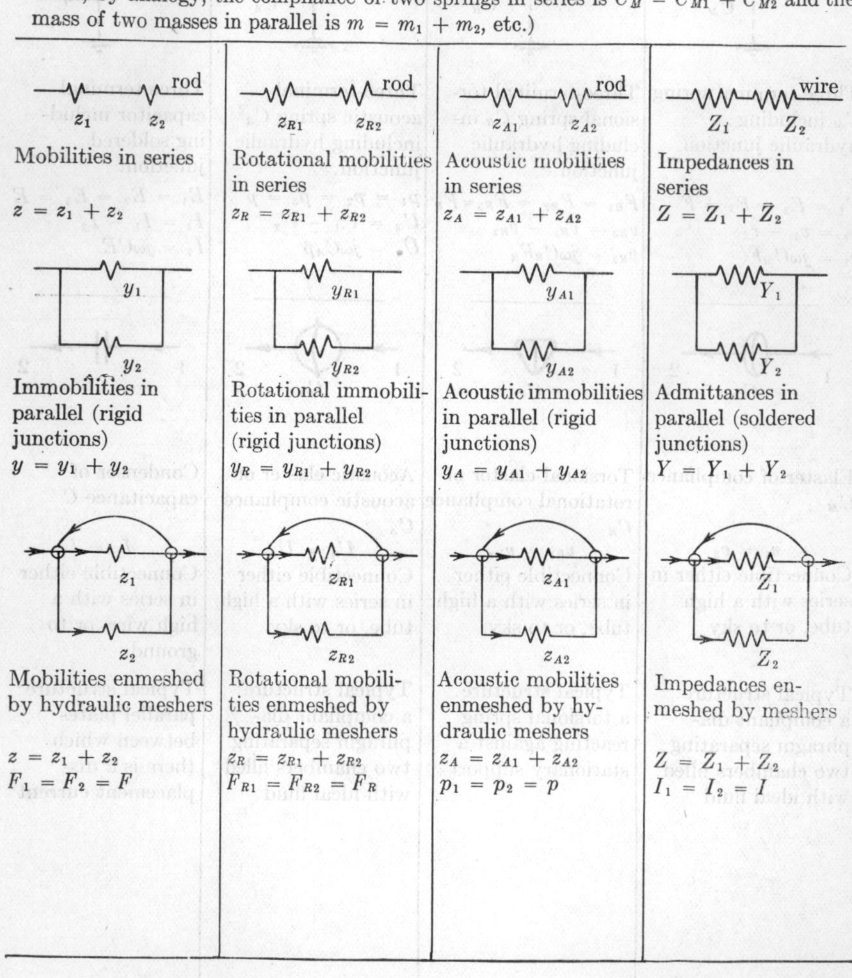

Rectilineal mechanical	Rotational mechanical	Acoustic	Electric
rod, z_1, z_2 Mobilities in series $z = z_1 + z_2$	rod, z_{R1}, z_{R2} Rotational mobilities in series $z_R = z_{R1} + z_{R2}$	rod, z_{A1}, z_{A2} Acoustic mobilities in series $z_A = z_{A1} + z_{A2}$	wire, Z_1, Z_2 Impedances in series $Z = Z_1 + Z_2$
y_1, y_2 Immobilities in parallel (rigid junctions) $y = y_1 + y_2$	y_{R1}, y_{R2} Rotational immobilities in parallel (rigid junctions) $y_R = y_{R1} + y_{R2}$	y_{A1}, y_{A2} Acoustic immobilities in parallel (rigid junctions) $y_A = y_{A1} + y_{A2}$	Y_1, Y_2 Admittances in parallel (soldered junctions) $Y = Y_1 + Y_2$
z_1, z_2 Mobilities enmeshed by hydraulic meshers $z = z_1 + z_2$ $F_1 = F_2 = F$	z_{R1}, z_{R2} Rotational mobilities enmeshed by hydraulic meshers $z_R = z_{R1} + z_{R2}$ $F_{R1} = F_{R2} = F_R$	z_{A1}, z_{A2} Acoustic mobilities enmeshed by hydraulic meshers $z_A = z_{A1} + z_{A2}$ $p_1 = p_2 = p$	Z_1, Z_2 Impedances enmeshed by meshers $Z = Z_1 + Z_2$ $I_1 = I_2 = I$

THE IMPEDANCE ANALOGY

Rectilineal mechanical	Rotational mechanical	Acoustic	Electric
Equations: same as for a spring (above)	Equations: same as for a torsional spring (above)	Equations: same as for an acoustic spring (above)	Equations: same as for a capacitor (above)

Series and Parallel Combinations of Elements

(The following combinations of general impedances can be extended to the pure elements. Thus, by analogy, the mass of two masses in series is $m = m_1 + m_2$ and the compliance of two elasters in parallel is $C_M = C_{M1} + C_{M2}$, etc.)

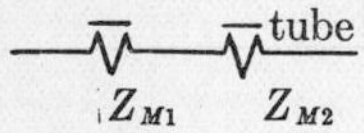 tube Z_{M1} Z_{M2} Mechanical impedances in series $Z_M = Z_{M1} + Z_{M2}$	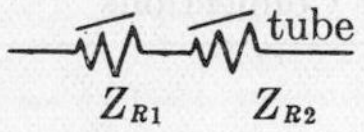 tube Z_{R1} Z_{R2} Rotational impedances in series $Z_R = Z_{R1} + Z_{R2}$	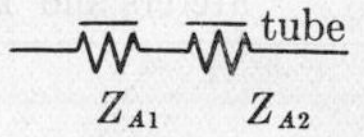 tube Z_{A1} Z_{A2} Acoustic impedances in series $Z_A = Z_{A1} + Z_{A2}$	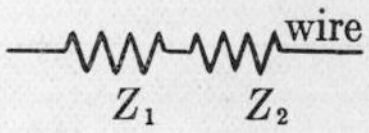 wire Z_1 Z_2 Impedances in series $Z = Z_1 + Z_2$
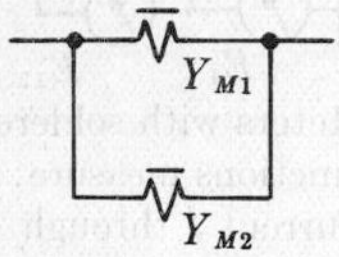 Y_{M1} Y_{M2} Mechanical admittances in parallel (hydraulic junctions) $Y_M = Y_{M1} + Y_{M2}$	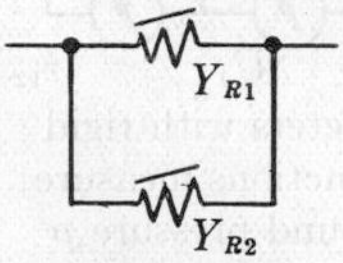 Y_{R1} Y_{R2} Rotational admittances in parallel (hydraulic junctions) $Y_R = Y_{R1} + Y_{R2}$	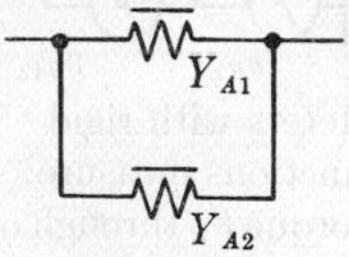 Y_{A1} Y_{A2} Acoustic admittances in parallel (hydraulic junctions) $Y_A = Y_{A1} + Y_{A2}$	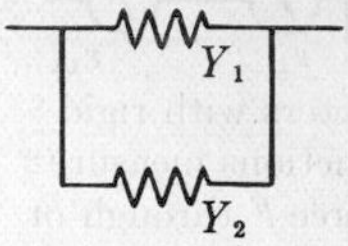 Y_1 Y_2 Admittances in parallel (soldered junctions) $Y = Y_1 + Y_2$
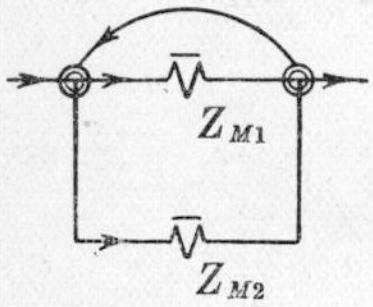 Z_{M1} Z_{M2} Mechanical impedances enmeshed by rigid meshers $Z_M = Z_{M1} + Z_{M2}$ $v_1 = v_2 = v$	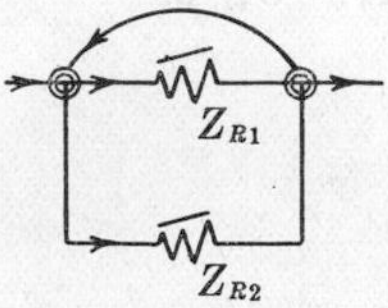 Z_{R1} Z_{R2} Rotational impedances enmeshed by rigid meshers $Z_R = Z_{R1} + Z_{R2}$ $v_{R1} = v_{R2} = v_R$	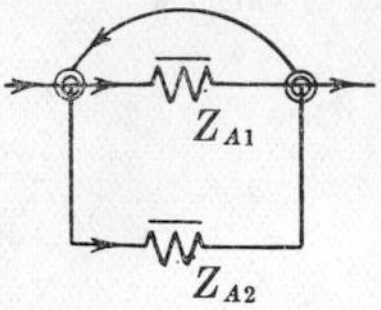 Z_{A1} Z_{A2} Acoustic impedances enmeshed by rigid meshers $Z_A = Z_{A1} + Z_{A2}$ $U_1 = U_2 = U$	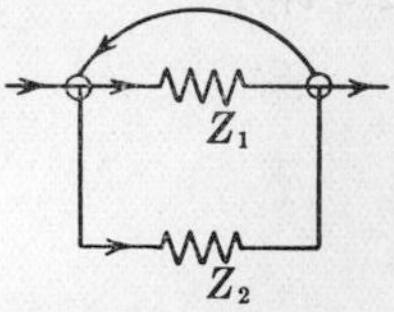 Z_1 Z_2 Impedances enmeshed by meshers $Z = Z_1 + Z_2$ $I_1 = I_2 = I$

THE MOBILITY ANALOGY

Rectilineal mechanical	Rotational mechanical	Acoustic	Electric
Vibrators			Generators
+ - - → − + v or F	+ - - → − + v_R or F_R	+ - - → − + U or p	− + E or I
A vibrator having a vibromotive velocity v or vibromotive force F as marked	A rotational vibrator having a rotatomotive velocity v_R or rotatomotive torque F_R as marked	An acoustic vibrator having an acoustomotive volume velocity U or acoustomotive sound pressure p as marked	A generator having an electromotive force E or current I as marked
Meters and Their Connections			
1 z 2 F − + + − v_1 v_{12}	1 2 F_R z_R − + + − v_{R1} v_{R12}	1 2 p z_A − + + − U_1 U_{12}	1 2 I Z − + + − E_1 E_{12}
Meters with rigid junctions measure: Force F through or into z Velocity v_1 at or of terminal 1 Velocity v_{12} across z $z = \hat{v}_{12}/\hat{F}$	Meters with rigid junctions measure: Torque F_R through or into z_R Velocity v_{R1} at or of terminal 1 Angular velocity v_{R12} across z_R $z_R = \hat{v}_{R12}/\hat{F}_R$	Meters with rigid junctions measure: Sound pressure p through or into z_A Volume velocity U_1 at or of terminal 1 Volume velocity U_{12} across z_A $z_A = \hat{U}_{12}/\hat{p}$	Meters with soldered junctions measure: Current I through or into Z Voltage E_1 at or of terminal 1 Voltage E_{12} across Z $Z = \hat{E}_{12}/\hat{I}$

THE IMPEDANCE ANALOGY

Rectilineal mechanical	Rotational mechanical	Acoustic	Electric
Vibrators			Generators
F or v	F_R or v_R	p or U	E or I
A vibrator pumping a vibromotive force F or velocity v as marked	A rotational vibrator having a rotatomotive torque F_R or angular velocity v_R as marked	An acoustic vibrator having an acoustomotive sound pressure p or volume velocity U as marked	A generator having an electromotive force E or current I as marked
Meters and Their Connections			
Z_M; 1; 2; v; F_1; F_{12}	Z_R; 1; 2; v_R; F_{R1}; F_{R12}	Z_A; 1; 2; U; p_1; p_{12}	Z; 1; 2; I; E_1; E_{12}
Meters with hydraulic junctions measure: Velocity v through or into Z_M Force F_1 at or of terminal 1 Force F_{12} across Z_M	Meters with hydraulic junctions measure: Angular velocity v_R through or into Z_R Torque F_{R1} at or of terminal 1 Torque F_{R12} across Z_R	Meters with hydraulic junctions measure Volume velocity U through or into Z_A Sound pressure p_1 at or of terminal 1 Sound pressure p_{12} across Z_A	Meters with soldered junctions measure: Current I through or into Z Voltage E_1 at or of terminal 1 Voltage E_{12} across Z
$Z_M = \hat{F}_{12}/\hat{v}$	$Z_R = \hat{F}_{R12}/\hat{v}_R$	$Z_A = \hat{p}_{12}/\hat{U}$	$Z = \hat{E}_{12}/\hat{I}$

Erratum: The lower left symbol in each of the above diagrams in the first three columns should be a sky, not an earth.

THE MOBILITY ANALOGY

Rectilineal mechanical	Rotational mechanical	Acoustic	Electric
Mutual Couplers. Only analogues of mutual inductance are shown though analogues of mutual resistance and mutual capacitance can be built using ideal transformers			
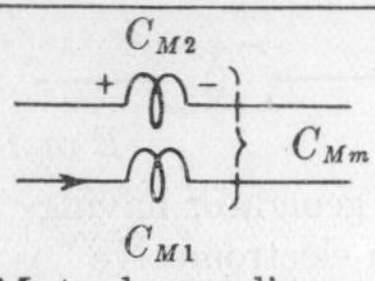	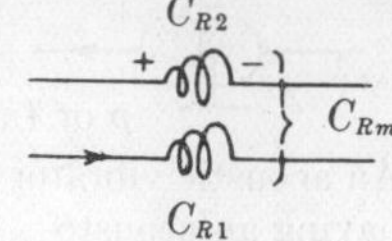	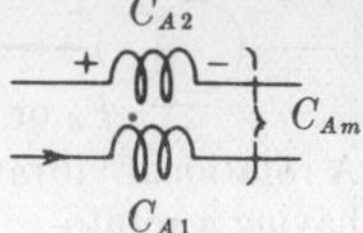	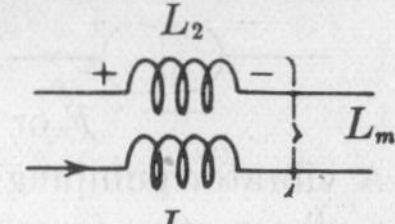
Mutual compliance C_{Mm} between springs of self-compliances C_{M1} and C_{M2}.	Mutual rotational compliance C_{Rm} between torsional springs of self-compliances C_{R1} and C_{R2}.	Mutual acoustic compliance C_{Am} between acoustic springs of self-compliances C_{A1} and C_{A2}.	Mutual inductance L_m between coils of self-inductances L_1 and L_2.
$v_2 = C_{Mm}\, dF_1/dt$ $v_1 = C_{Mm}\, dF_2/dt$ $\hat{v}_2 = -j\omega C_{Mm}\hat{F}_1$ etc. Coefficient of coupling $k = C_{Mm}/\sqrt{C_{M1}C_{M2}}$.	$v_{R2} = C_{Rm}\, dF_{R1}/dt$ $v_{R1} = C_{Rm}\, dF_{R2}/dt$ $\hat{v}_{R2} = -j\omega C_{Rm}\hat{F}_{R1}$ etc. Coefficient of coupling $k = C_{Rm}/\sqrt{C_{R1}C_{R2}}$.	$U_2 = C_{Am}\, dp_1/dt$ $U_1 = C_{Am}\, dp_2/dt$ $\hat{U}_2 = -j\omega C_{Am}\hat{p}_1$ Coefficient of coupling $k = C_{Am}/\sqrt{C_{A1}C_{A2}}$.	$E_2 = L_m\, dI_1/dt$ $E_1 = L_m\, dI_2/dt$ $\hat{E}_2 = -j\omega L_m\hat{I}_1$ etc. Coefficient of coupling $k = L_m/\sqrt{L_1L_2}$.
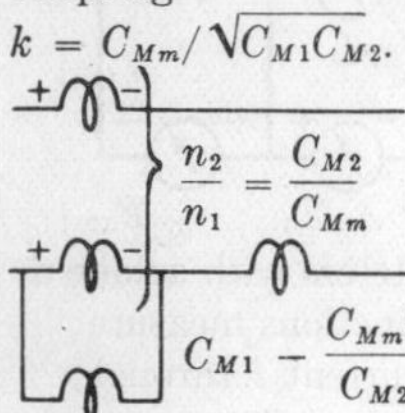	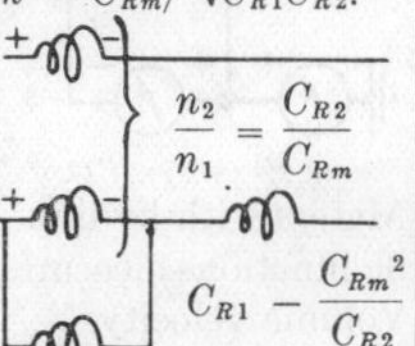	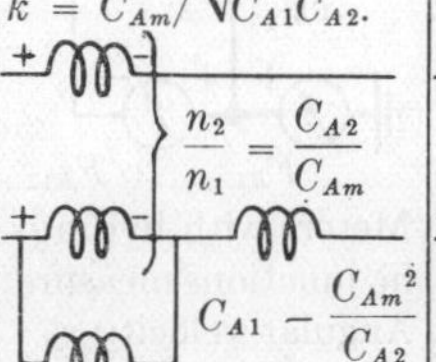	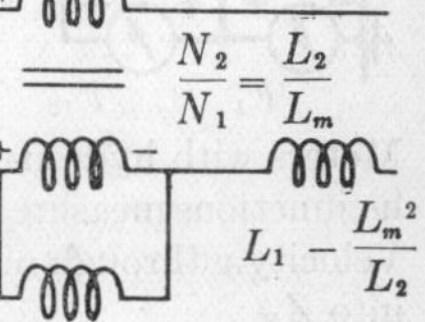
C_{Mm}^2/C_{M2} Ideal transformer with springs, equivalent to mutual springs above.	C_{Rm}^2/C_{R2} Ideal transformer with springs, equivalent to mutual springs above.	C_{Am}^2/C_{A2} Ideal transformer with acoustic springs, equivalent to mutual springs above.	L_m^2/L_2 Ideal transformer with inductors, equivalent to mutual inductors above.
Typical structure: 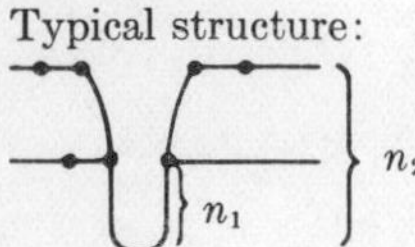 A compliant hairpin with lever ratio n_2/n_1.	Typical structure: As above; springs in series and parallel with primary differential, geared to secondary differential.	Typical structure: 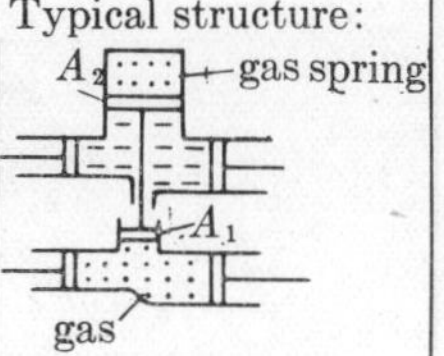 Gas spring on coupling member between fluid filled differentials.	Typical structure: 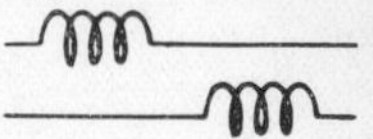 Proximate coils with air or iron core.

THE IMPEDANCE ANALOGY

Rectilineal mechanical	Rotational mechanical	Acoustic	Electric
Mutual Couplers. Only analogues of mutual inductance are shown though analogues of mutual resistance and mutual capacitance can be built using ideal transformers			
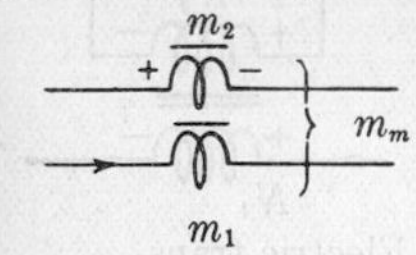 m_2, m_m, m_1	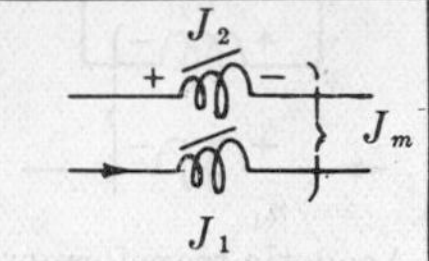 J_2, J_m, J_1	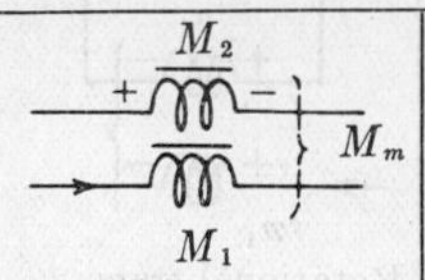 M_2, M_m, M_1	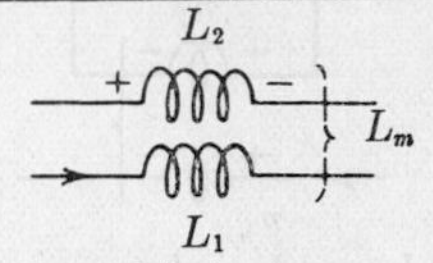 L_2, L_m, L_1
Mutual mass m_m between masses of self-masses m_1 and m_2.	Mutual moment of inertia J_m between rotational inertors of moments of inertia J_1 and J_2.	Mutual inertance M_m between acoustic inertors of inertances M_1 and M_2.	Mutual inductance L_m between coils of self-inductances L_1 and L_2.
$F_2 = m_m\, dv_1/dt$ $F_1 = m_m\, dv_2/dt$ $\widehat{F}_2 = -j\omega m_m \widehat{v}_1$ etc.	$F_{R2} = J_m\, dv_{R1}/dt$ $F_{R1} = J_m\, dv_{R2}/dt$ $\widehat{F}_{R2} = -j\omega J_m \widehat{v}_{R1}$ etc.	$p_2 = M_m\, dU_1/dt$ $p_1 = M_m\, dU_2/dt$ $\widehat{p}_2 = -j\omega M_m \widehat{U}_1$ etc.	$E_2 = L_m\, dI_1/dt$ $E_1 = L_m\, dI_2/dt$ $\widehat{E}_2 = -j\omega L_m \widehat{I}_1$ etc.
Coefficient of coupling $k = m_m/\sqrt{m_1 m_2}$.	Coefficient of coupling $k = J_m/\sqrt{J_1 J_2}$.	Coefficient of coupling $k = M_m/\sqrt{M_1 M_2}$.	Coefficient of coupling $k = L_m/\sqrt{L_1 L_2}$.
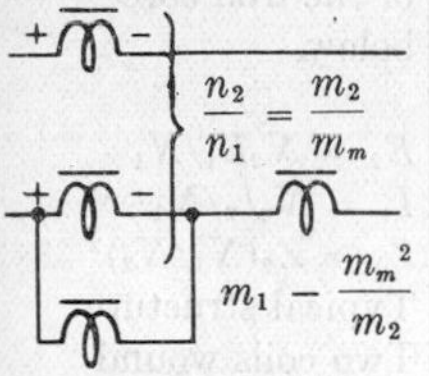 $\frac{n_2}{n_1} = \frac{m_2}{m_m}$ $m_1 - \frac{m_m^2}{m_2}$ m_m^2/m_2	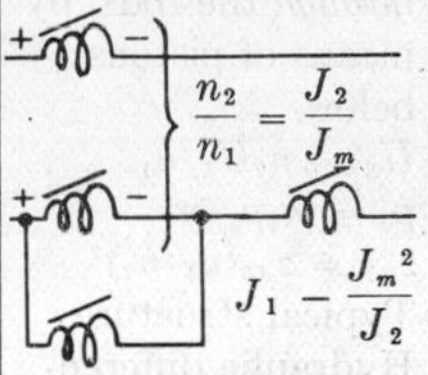 $\frac{n_2}{n_1} = \frac{J_2}{J_m}$ $J_1 - \frac{J_m^2}{J_2}$ J_m^2/J_2	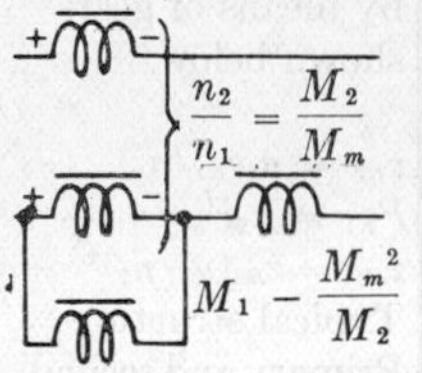 $\frac{n_2}{n_1} = \frac{M_2}{M_m}$ $M_1 - \frac{M_m^2}{M_2}$ M_m^2/M_2	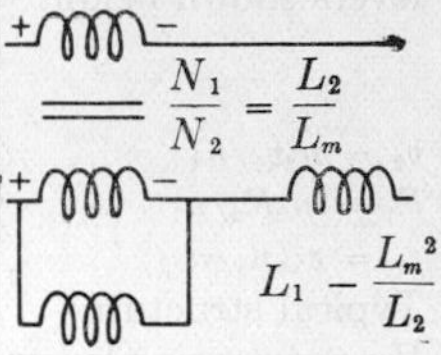 $\frac{N_1}{N_2} = \frac{L_2}{L_m}$ $L_1 - \frac{L_m^2}{L_2}$ L_m^2/L_2
Ideal transformer with masses, equivalent to mutual masses above.	Ideal transformer with inertors, equivalent to mutual inertors above.	Ideal transformer with acoustic inertors, equivalent to mutual inertors above.	Ideal transformer with inductors, equivalent to mutual inductors above.
Typical structure: 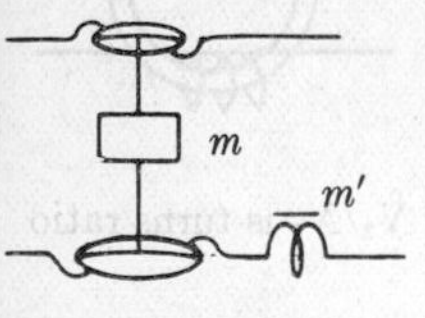 m, m'	Typical structure: 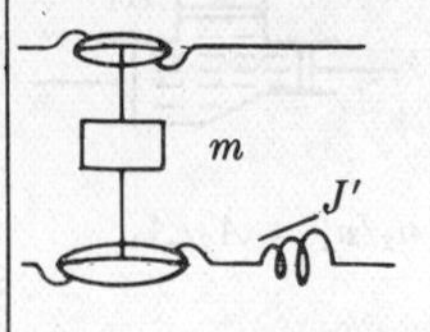 m, J'	Typical structure: 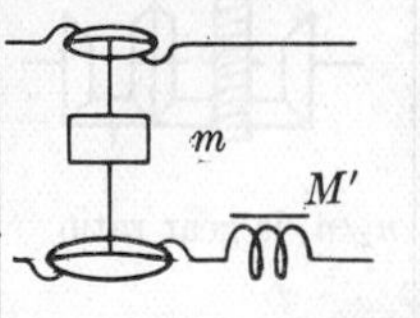 m, M'	Typical structure: 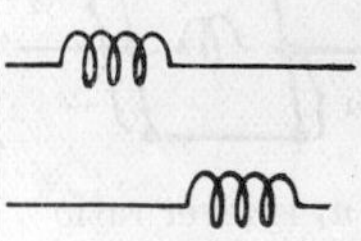
Inertia on connector between differentials, plus series mass m'.	Inertia on connector between differentials, plus series inertor J'.	Inertia on connector between differentials, plus series inertor M'.	Proximate coils with air or iron core.

THE MOBILITY ANALOGY

Rectilineal	Rotational	Acoustic	Electric
	Ideal Transformers		
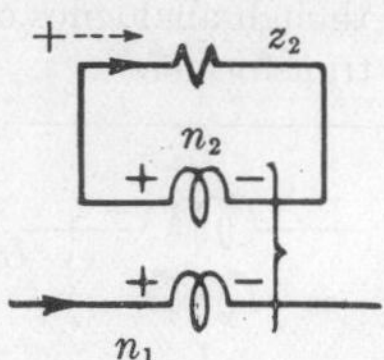	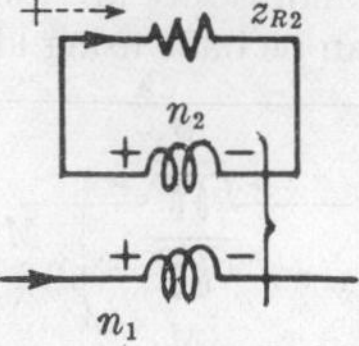	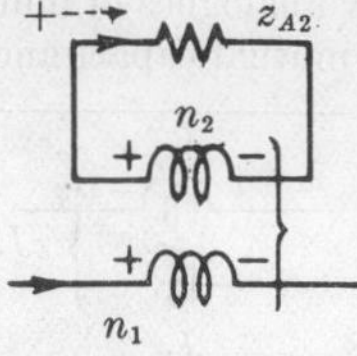	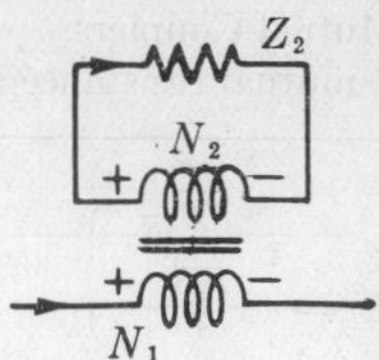
Lineal transformer with load The bracketed springs of great compliance symbolize the coupling of the velocities *across* primary and secondary, and the force *through* the rods, by means of levers shown below.	Rotational transformer with load The bracketed springs of great compliance symbolize the coupling of the angular velocities *across* primary and secondary and the torque *through* the shafts, by means of gears shown below.	Acoustic transformer with load The bracketed acoustic springs of great compliance symbolize the coupling of the volume velocities *across* primary and secondary, and the sound pressures *through* the rods, by means of pistons below.	Electric transformer with load The inductors of great inductance symbolize the coupling of the voltages *across* the primary and the secondary, and the currents *through* the wires, by means of the iron core below.
$v_2 = n_2v_1/n_1$ $F_1 = n_2F_2/n_1$ $z_1 = z_2(n_1/n_2)^2$ Typical structure: Hinged floating levers multiply the velocities across primary and secondary	$v_{R2} = n_2v_{R1}/n_1$ $F_{R1} = n_2F_{R2}/n_1$ $z_{R1} = z_{R2}(n_1/n_2)^2$ Typical structure: Primary and secondary differentials with propeller shafts geared together	$U_2 = n_2U_1/n_1$ $p_1 = n_2p_2/n_1$ $z_{A1} = z_{A2}(n_1/n_2)^2$ Typical structure: Hydraulic differentials with cross-connected pistons	$E_2 = N_2E_1/N_1$ $I_1 = N_2I_2/N_1$ $Z_1 = Z_2(N_1/N_2)^2$ Typical structure: Two coils wound on a laminated iron ring
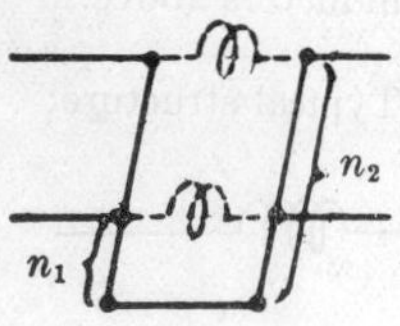	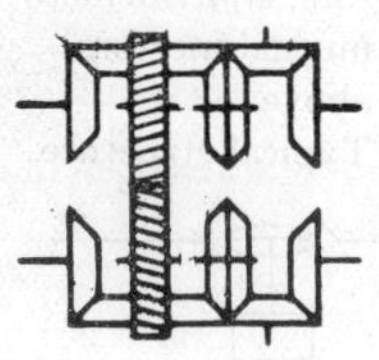	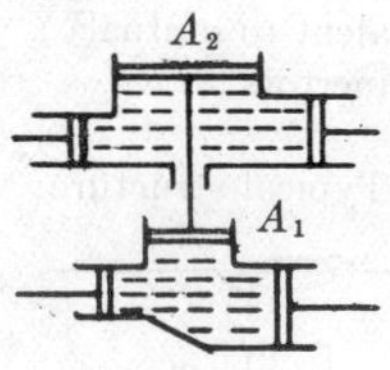	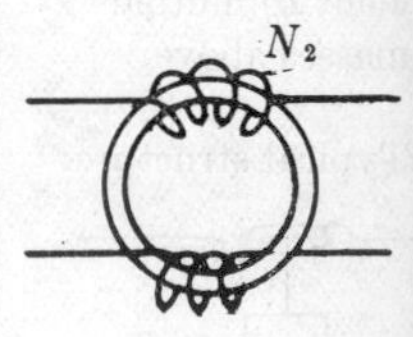
n_2/n_1 is lever ratio	n_2/n_1 is gear ratio	$n_2/n_1 = A_2/A_1$	N_2/N_1 is turns ratio
Very compliant dotted spring *s may* pass *constant* primary force with no secondary force; not ideal at zero frequency.	Analogous possibility	Analogous possibility	The primary *may* pass a *constant* current with no secondary current; not ideal at zero frequency

THE IMPEDANCE ANALOGY

Rectilineal	Rotational	Acoustic	Electric
Ideal Transformers			
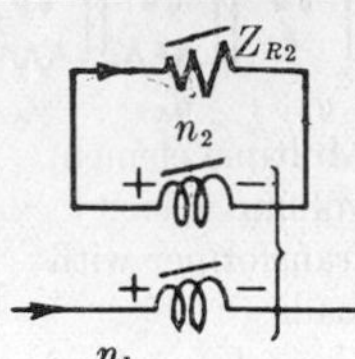	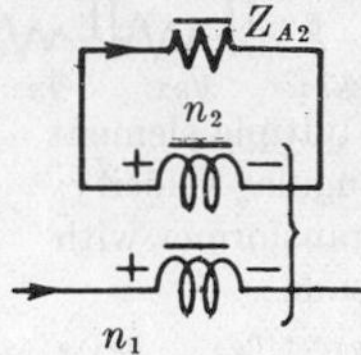	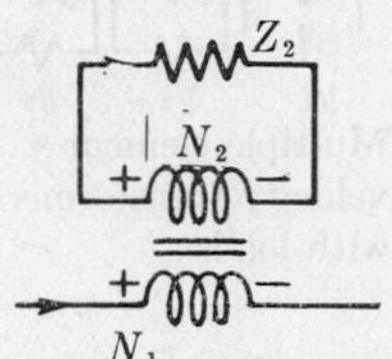	
Lineal transformer with load The bracketed masses of great mass symbolize the coupling of the forces *across* the primary and secondary, and the velocities *through* the tubes, by auxiliary mechanism as shown below.	Rotational transformer with load The bracketed rotational inertors of great moments of inertia symbolize the coupling of the torques *across* the primary and secondary, and the angular velocities *through* the tubes, by auxiliary mechanism as shown below.	Acoustic transformer with load The bracketed acoustic inertors of great inertances symbolize the coupling of the sound pressures *across* the primary and secondary, and the volume velocities *through* the tubes, by auxiliary mechanism as shown below.	Electric transformer with load The inductors of great inductance symbolize the coupling of the voltages *across* the primary and secondary, and the currents *through* the wires, by an iron core shown below.
$F_2 = n_2F_1/n_1$ $v_1 = n_2v_2/n_1$ $Z_{M1} = Z_{M2}(n_1/n_2)^2$ Typical structure: Two differential diaphragms or pistons, of different areas, actuated by the forces across primary and secondary, are connected by the dotted rod	$F_{R2} = n_2F_{R1}/n_1$ $v_{R1} = n_2v_{R2}/n_1$ $Z_{R1} = Z_{R2}(n_1/n_2)^2$ Typical structure: Two differentials actuated by the torques across primary and secondary are rigidly interconnected by the dotted shaft	$p_2 = n_2p_1/n_2$ $U_1 = n_2U_2/n_1$ $Z_{A1} = Z_{A2}(n_1/n_2)^2$ Typical structure: Same as the rectilineal transformer but the terminal tubes are of any areas	$E_2 = N_2E_1/N_1$ $I_1 = N_2I_2/N_1$ $Z_1 = Z_2(N_1/N_2)^2$ Typical structure: Two coils wound on an iron ring
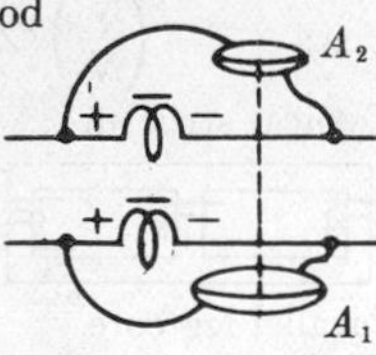	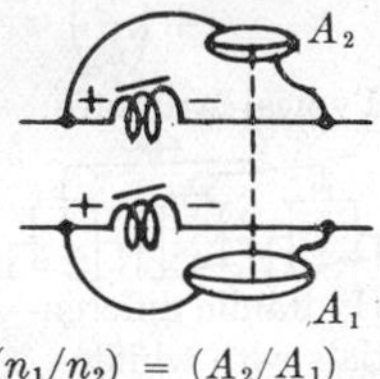	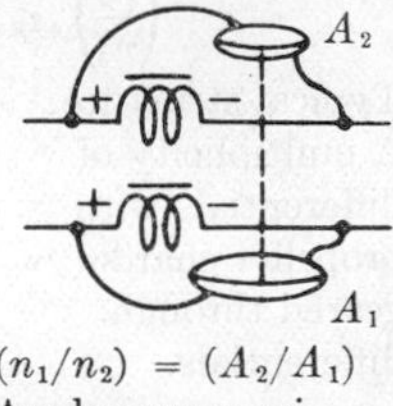	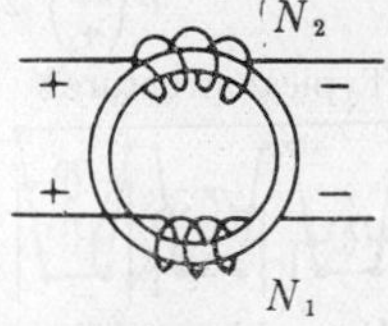
$(n_1/n_2) = (A_2/A_1)$ The large mass(es) *may* pass *constant* primary velocity with no secondary velocity; not necessarily ideal at zero frequency	$(n_1/n_2) = (A_2/A_1)$ Analogous possibility	$(n_1/n_2) = (A_2/A_1)$ Analogous possibility	N_1/N_2 is turns ratio The primary *may* pass a *constant* current with no secondary current, not ideal at zero frequency

THE MOBILITY ANALOGY

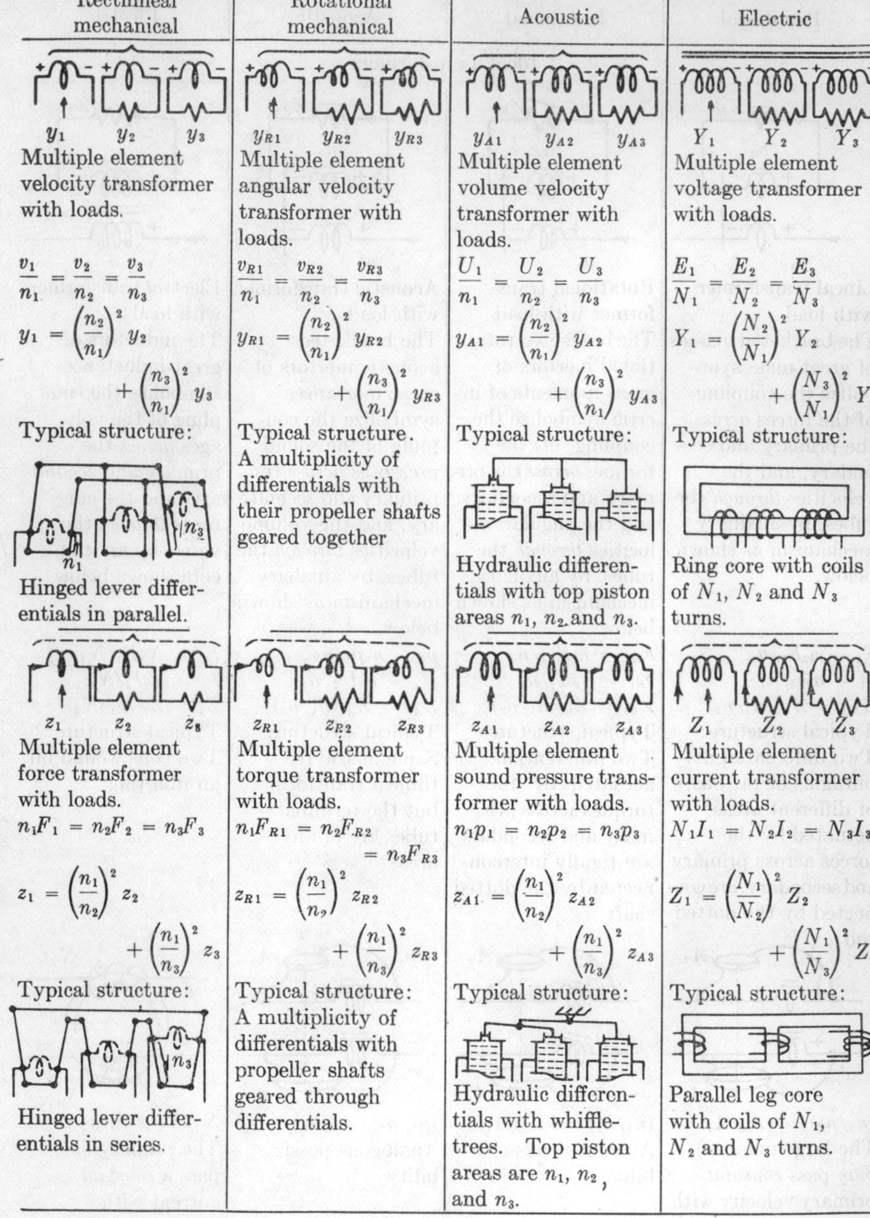

Rectilineal mechanical	Rotational mechanical	Acoustic	Electric
y_1 y_2 y_3	y_{R1} y_{R2} y_{R3}	y_{A1} y_{A2} y_{A3}	Y_1 Y_2 Y_3
Multiple element velocity transformer with loads.	Multiple element angular velocity transformer with loads.	Multiple element volume velocity transformer with loads.	Multiple element voltage transformer with loads.
$\frac{v_1}{n_1} = \frac{v_2}{n_2} = \frac{v_3}{n_3}$	$\frac{v_{R1}}{n_1} = \frac{v_{R2}}{n_2} = \frac{v_{R3}}{n_3}$	$\frac{U_1}{n_1} = \frac{U_2}{n_2} = \frac{U_3}{n_3}$	$\frac{E_1}{N_1} = \frac{E_2}{N_2} = \frac{E_3}{N_3}$
$y_1 = \left(\frac{n_2}{n_1}\right)^2 y_2 + \left(\frac{n_3}{n_1}\right)^2 y_3$	$y_{R1} = \left(\frac{n_2}{n_1}\right)^2 y_{R2} + \left(\frac{n_3}{n_1}\right)^2 y_{R3}$	$y_{A1} = \left(\frac{n_2}{n_1}\right)^2 y_{A2} + \left(\frac{n_3}{n_1}\right)^2 y_{A3}$	$Y_1 = \left(\frac{N_2}{N_1}\right)^2 Y_2 + \left(\frac{N_3}{N_1}\right)^2 Y_3$
Typical structure: n_1 n_3 Hinged lever differentials in parallel.	Typical structure. A multiplicity of differentials with their propeller shafts geared together	Typical structure: Hydraulic differentials with top piston areas n_1, n_2 and n_3.	Typical structure: Ring core with coils of N_1, N_2 and N_3 turns.
z_1 z_2 z_3	z_{R1} z_{R2} z_{R3}	z_{A1} z_{A2} z_{A3}	Z_1 Z_2 Z_3
Multiple element force transformer with loads.	Multiple element torque transformer with loads.	Multiple element sound pressure transformer with loads.	Multiple element current transformer with loads.
$n_1F_1 = n_2F_2 = n_3F_3$	$n_1F_{R1} = n_2F_{R2} = n_3F_{R3}$	$n_1p_1 = n_2p_2 = n_3p_3$	$N_1I_1 = N_2I_2 = N_3I_3$
$z_1 = \left(\frac{n_1}{n_2}\right)^2 z_2 + \left(\frac{n_1}{n_3}\right)^2 z_3$	$z_{R1} = \left(\frac{n_1}{n_2}\right)^2 z_{R2} + \left(\frac{n_1}{n_3}\right)^2 z_{R3}$	$z_{A1} = \left(\frac{n_1}{n_2}\right)^2 z_{A2} + \left(\frac{n_1}{n_3}\right)^2 z_{A3}$	$Z_1 = \left(\frac{N_1}{N_2}\right)^2 Z_2 + \left(\frac{N_1}{N_3}\right)^2 Z_3$
Typical structure: n_3 Hinged lever differentials in series.	Typical structure: A multiplicity of differentials with propeller shafts geared through differentials.	Typical structure: Hydraulic differentials with whiffletrees. Top piston areas are n_1, n_2, and n_3.	Typical structure: Parallel leg core with coils of N_1, N_2 and N_3 turns.

THE IMPEDANCE ANALOGY

Rectilineal mechanical	Rotational mechanical	Acoustic	Electric
 Y_{M1} Y_{M2} Y_{M3}	 Y_{R1} Y_{R2} Y_{R3}	 Y_{A1} Y_{A2} Y_{A3}	 Y_1 Y_2 Y_3
Multiple element force transformer with loads.	Multiple element torque transformer with loads.	Multiple element sound pressure transformer with loads.	Multiple element voltage transformer with loads.
$\frac{F_1}{n_1} = \frac{F_2}{n_2} = \frac{F_3}{n_3}$	$\frac{F_{R1}}{n_1} = \frac{F_{R2}}{n_2} = \frac{F_{R3}}{n_3}$	$\frac{p_1}{n_1} = \frac{p_2}{n_2} = \frac{p_3}{n_3}$	$\frac{E_1}{N_1} = \frac{E_2}{N_2} = \frac{E_3}{N_3}$
$Y_{M1} = \left(\frac{n_2}{n_1}\right)^2 Y_{M2} + \left(\frac{n_3}{n_1}\right)^2 Y_{M3}$	$Y_{R1} = \left(\frac{n_2}{n_1}\right)^2 Y_{R2} + \left(\frac{n_3}{n_1}\right)^2 Y_{R3}$	$Y_{A1} = \left(\frac{n_2}{n_1}\right)^2 Y_{A2} + \left(\frac{n_3}{n_1}\right)^2 Y_{A3}$	$Y_1 = \left(\frac{N_2}{N_1}\right)^2 Y_2 + \left(\frac{N_3}{N_1}\right)^2 Y_3$
Typical structure: 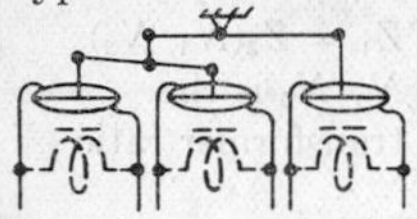	Typical structure: 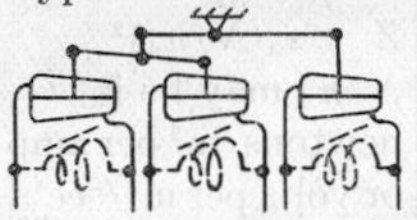	Typical structure: 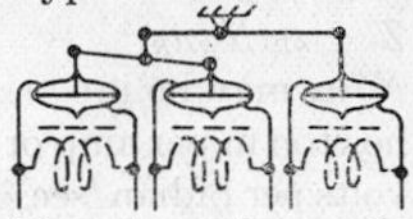	Typical structure: 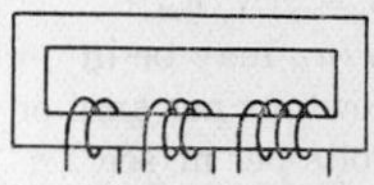
The n's are inversely proportional to piston areas.	The n's are inversely proportional to the piston areas.	The n's are inversely proportional to the piston areas.	The N's are proportional to the numbers of turns.
 Z_{M1} Z_{M2} Z_{M3}	 Z_{R1} Z_{R2} Z_{R3}	 Z_{A1} Z_{A2} Z_{A3}	 Z_1 Z_2 Z_3
Multiple element velocity transformer with loads.	Multiple element angular velocity transformer with loads.	Multiple element volume velocity transformer with loads.	Multiple element current transformer with loads.
$n_1 v_1 = n_2 v_2 = n_3 v_3$	$n_1 v_{R1} = n_2 v_{R2} = n_3 v_{R3}$	$n_1 U_1 = n_2 U_2 = n_3 U_3$	$N_1 I_1 = N_2 I_2 = N_3 I_3$
$Z_{M1} = \left(\frac{n_1}{n_2}\right)^2 Z_{M2} + \left(\frac{n_1}{n_3}\right)^2 Z_{M3}$	$Z_{R1} = \left(\frac{n_1}{n_2}\right)^2 Z_{R2} + \left(\frac{n_1}{n_3}\right)^2 Z_{R3}$	$Z_{A1} = \left(\frac{n_1}{n_2}\right)^2 Z_{A2} + \left(\frac{n_1}{n_3}\right)^2 Z_{A3}$	$Z_1 = \left(\frac{N_1}{N_2}\right)^2 Z_2 + \left(\frac{N_1}{N_3}\right)^2 Z_3$
Typical structure: 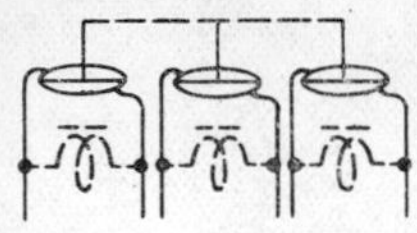	Typical structure: 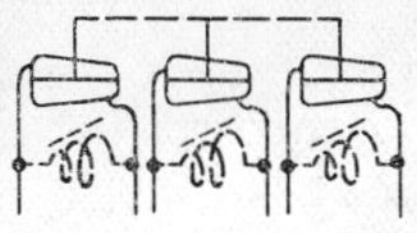	Typical structure: 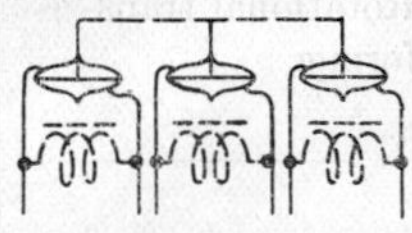	Typical structure: 
The n's are inversely proportional to piston areas.	The n's are inversely proportional to the piston areas.	The n's are inversely proportional to the piston areas.	The N's are proportional to the numbers of turns.

THE MOBILITY ANALOGY

Rectilineal mechanical	Rotational mechanical	Acoustic	Electric
The Conservative Ideal Direct Transducers and Transformers, Which Couple Through Variables to Through Variables, and Across Variables to Across Variables			
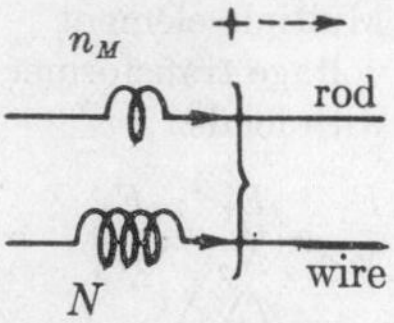 n_M rod wire N Electromechanical current-force transducer $E/N = v/n_M$ $NI = n_M F$ $Z = z(N/n_M)^2$ N/n_M may be in newtons per amp or volts per m/sec	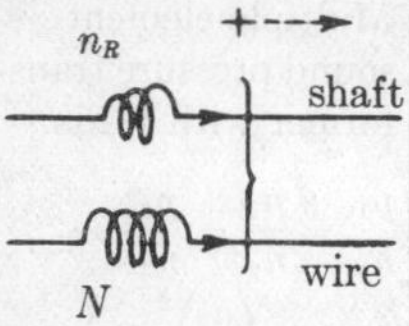 n_R shaft wire N Electrorotational current-torque transducer $E/N = v_R/n_R$ $NI = n_R F_R$ $Z = z_R(N/n_R)^2$ N/n_R may be in newton m per amp or volts per radian/sec	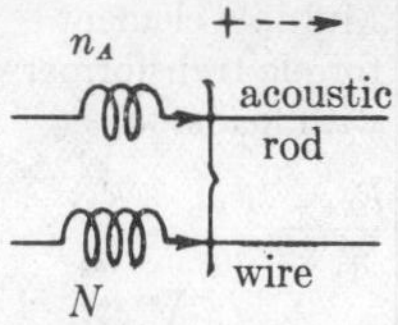 n_A acoustic rod wire N Electroacoustic current-sound pressure transducer $E/N = U/n_A$ $NI = n_A p$ $Z = z_A(N/n_A)^2$ N/n_A may be in newtons/m^2 per amp or volts per m^3/sec	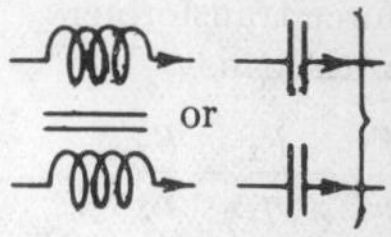 or Electric transformer $E_1/N_1 = E_2/N_2$ $N_1 I_1 = N_2 I_2$ $Z_1 = Z_2(N_1/N_2)$ N_1/N_2 is the transformer ratio
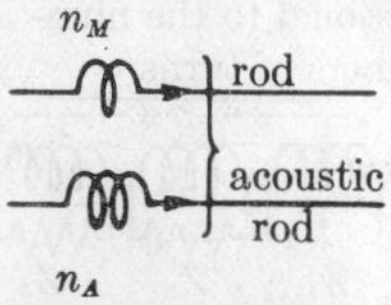 n_M rod acoustic rod n_A Acoustomechanical sound pressure-force transducer	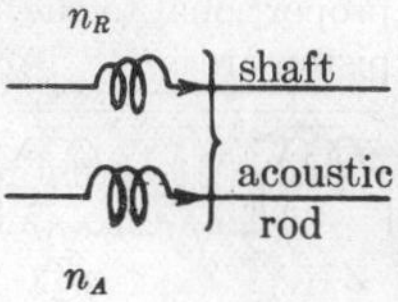 n_R shaft acoustic rod n_A Acoustorotational sound pressure-torque transducer	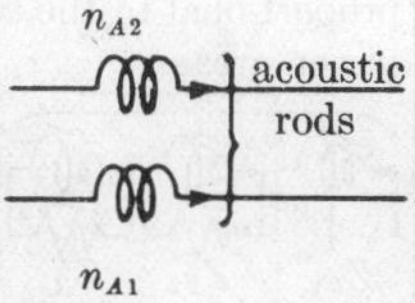 n_{A2} acoustic rods n_{A1} Acoustic transformer	
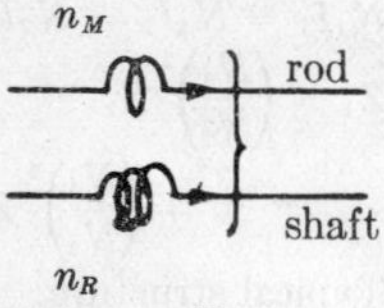 n_M rod shaft n_R Rotato-rectilineal torque-force transducer	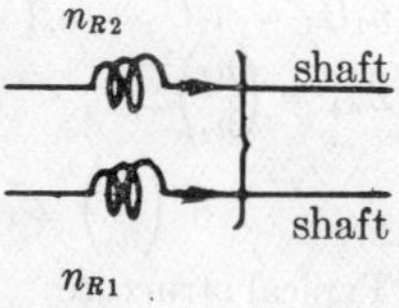 n_{R2} shaft shaft n_{R1} Rotational transformer	All these transducers and transformers have equations and units of the form given in the top row	
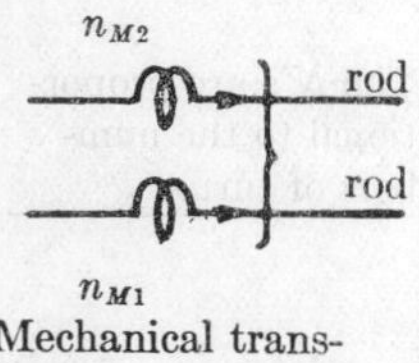 n_{M2} rod rod n_{M1} Mechanical transformer			

THE IMPEDANCE ANALOGY

Rectilineal mechanical	Rotational mechanical	Acoustic	Electric
The Conservative Ideal Direct Transducers and Transformers, Which Couple Through Variables to Through Variables, and Across Variables to Across Variables			
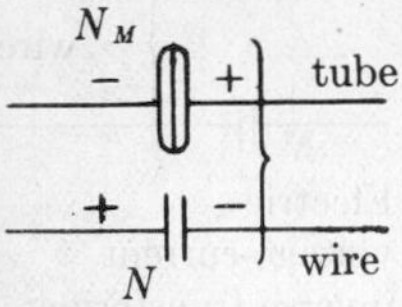 N_M – + tube; + – wire; N Electromechanical voltage-force transducer $E/N = F/N_M$ $NI = N_M v$ $Z = Z_M(N/N_M)^2$ N/N_M may be in volts per newton or m/sec per amp	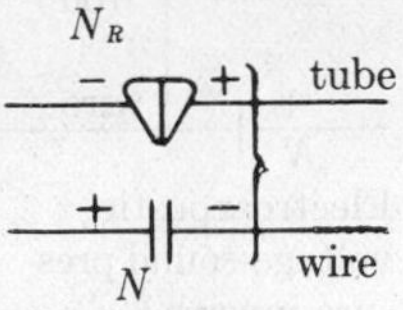 N_R – + tube; + – wire; N Electrorotational voltage-torque transducer $E/N = F_R/N_R$ $NI = N_R v_R$ $Z = Z_R(N/N_R)^2$ N/N_M may be in volts per newton m or radians/sec per amp	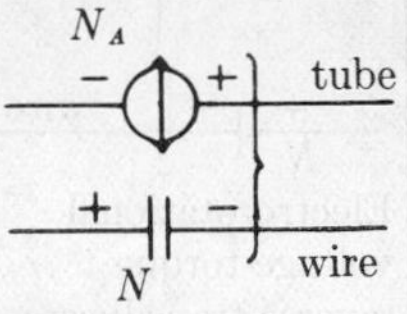 N_A – + tube; + – wire; N Electroacoustic voltage-sound pressure transducer $E/N = p/N_A$ $NI = N_A U$ $Z = Z_A(N/N_A)^2$ N/N_A may be in volts per newton/m² or m²/sec per amp	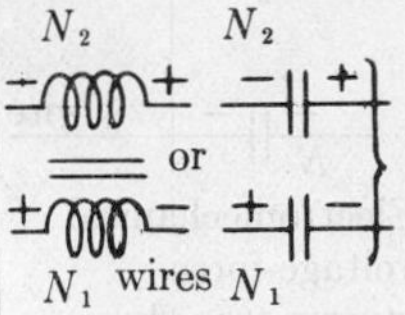 N_2 + or N_2 – +; + – N_1 wires N_1 Electric (voltage-voltage) transformer $E_1/N_1 = E_2/N_2$ $N_1 I_1 = N_2 I_2$ $Z_1 = Z_2(N_1/N_2)^2$ N_1/N_2 is the transformer ratio
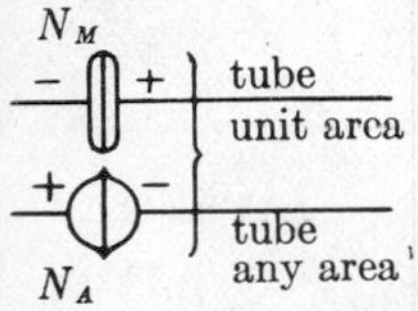 N_M – + tube unit area; + – tube any area; N_A Acoustomechanical sound pressure-force transducer	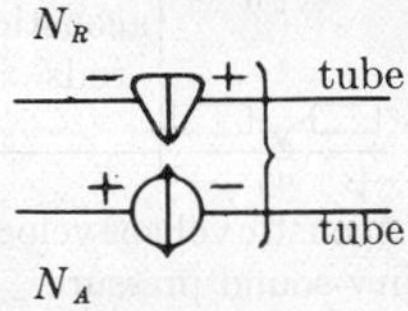 N_R – + tube; + – tube; N_A Acoustorotational sound pressure-torque transducer	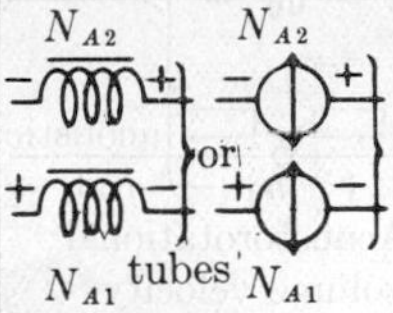 N_{A2} + or N_{A2} – +; + – N_{A1} tubes N_{A1} Acoustic transformer	
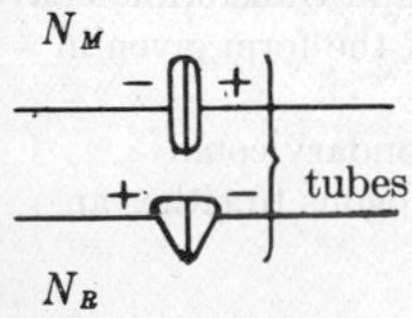 N_M – + ; + – tubes; N_R Rotato-rectilineal torque-force transducer	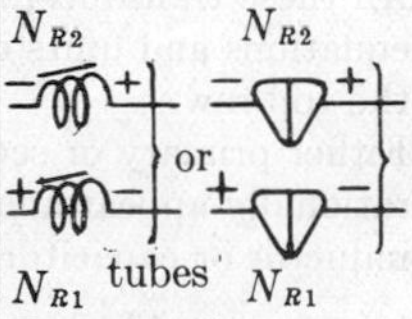 N_{R2} + or N_{R2} – +; + – N_{R1} tubes N_{R1} Rotational transducer	All these transducers and transformers have equations and units of the form given in the top row. Two styles of symbol are rational for each of these elements since mutual-capacitance transformers and mutual-inductance transformers are equivalent in function	
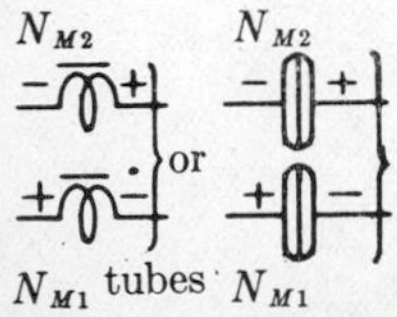 N_{M2} – + or N_{M2} – +; + – N_{M1} tubes N_{M1} Mechanical transformer			

THE MOBILITY ANALOGY

Rectilineal mechanical	Rotational mechanical	Acoustic	Electric
The Conservative Ideal Inverse Transducers and Transformers, Which Couple Through Variables to Across Variables			
n_M + rod + − wire N Electromechanical voltage-force inverse transducer $E/N = n_M F$ $NI = v/n_M$ $Z = y(Nn_M)^2$ Nn_M may be in volts per newton or m/sec per amp	n_R + shaft + − wire N Electrorotational voltage-torque inverse transducer $E/N = n_R F_R$ $NI = v_R/n_R$ $Z = y_R(Nn_R)^2$ Nn_R may be in volts per newton m or radian/sec per amp	n_A + acoustic rod + − wire N Electroacoustic voltage-sound pressure inverse transducer $E/N = n_A p$ $NI = U/n_A$ $Z = y_A(Nn_A)^2$ Nn_A may be in volts per newton/m² or m³/sec per amp	N_2 wires + − N_1 Electric voltage-current inverse transformer. A gyrator $E_1/N_1 = N_2 I_2$ $N_1 I_1 = E_2/N_2$ $Z_1 = Y_2(N_1 N_2)^2$ $N_1 N_2$ is the transfer impedance in ohms, or volts/amp
n_M rod acoustic rod + n_A − Acoustomechanical volume velocity-force inverse transducer	n_R shaft acoustic rod + n_A − Acoustorotational volume velocity-torque inverse transducer	n_{A2} acoustic rods + n_A − Acoustic volume velocity-sound pressure inverse transformer. An acoustic gyrator	
n_M rod shaft + n_R − Rotato-rectilineal angular velocity-force inverse transducer	n_{R2} shafts + n_{R1} − Rotational angular velocity-torque inverse transformer. A gyroscope	All these transducers and transformers have equations and units of the form given in the top row. Either primary or secondary could rationally appear analogous to either an inductor or capacitor	
n_{M2} rods + − n_{M1} Mechanical velocity-force inverse transducer. A lineal gyrator			

THE IMPEDANCE ANALOGY

Rectilineal mechanical	Rotational mechanical	Acoustic	Electric
The Conservative Ideal Inverse Transducers and Inverse Transformers, Which Couple Through Variables to Across Variables			
N_M − + tube wire N Electromechanical current-force inverse transducer $E/N = N_M v$ $NI = F/N_M$ $Z = Y_M(NN_M)^2$ NN_M may be in newtons per amp or volts per m/sec	N_R − + tube wire N Electrorotational current-torque inverse transducer $E/N = N_R v_R$ $NI = F_R/N_R$ $Z = Y_R(NN_R)^2$ NN_R may be in newton m per amp or volts per radian/sec	N_A − + tube wire N Electroacoustic current-sound pressure inverse transducer $E/N = N_A U$ $NI = p/N_A$ $Z = Y_A(NN_A)^2$ NN_A may be in newtons/m² per amp or volts per m³/sec	N_2 − + wires N_1 Electric current-voltage inverse transformer. A gyrator $E_1/N_1 = N_2 I_2$ $N_1 I_1 = E_2/N_2$ $Z_1 = Y_2(N_1 N_2)^2$ $N_1 N_2$ is the transfer impedance in ohms, or volts/amp
N_M − + tube unit area tube N_A any area Acoustomechanical volume velocity-force inverse transducer	N_R − + tube unit area tube N_A any area Acoustorotational volume velocity-torque inverse transducer	N_{A2} − + tubes any area N_{A1} Acoustic volume velocity-sound pressure inverse transformer. An acoustic gyrator	
N_M − + tube tube N_R Rotato-rectilineal angular velocity-force inverse transducer	N_{R2} − + tubes N_R Rotational angular velocity-torque inverse transducer. A gyroscope	All these transducers and transformers have equations and units of the form given in the top row. Either primary or secondary could rationally appear analogous to either an inductor or capacitor	
N_{M2} − + tubes N_{M1} Mechanical velocity-force inverse transformer. A lineal gyrator			

THE MOBILITY AND IMPEDANCE ANALOGIES

Rectilineal mechanical	Rotational mechanical	Acoustic	Electric
The Conservative Ideal Inverse Autotransformers for Connecting a Rod Diagram to a Tubing Diagram at a Change of Analogy. Through Variables Are Coupled to Across Variables			
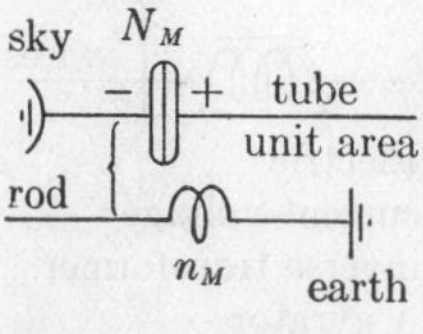 sky N_M − + tube unit area rod n_M earth	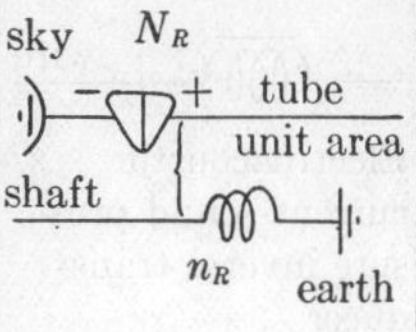 sky N_R − + tube unit area shaft n_R earth	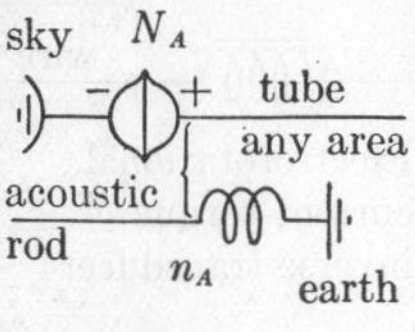 sky N_A − + tube any area acoustic rod n_A earth	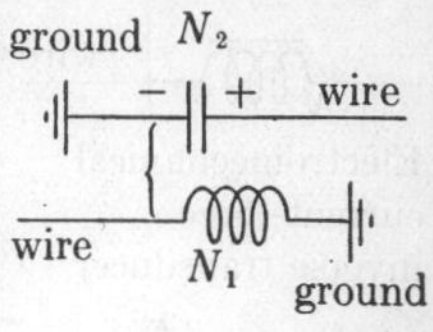 ground N_2 − + wire wire N_1 ground
$\frac{v \text{ across}}{n_M} = N_M v \text{ thru}$	$\frac{v_R \text{ across}}{n_R} = N_R v_R \text{thru}$	$\frac{U \text{ across}}{n_A} = N_A U \text{thru}$	$\frac{E_1 \text{ across}}{N_1} = N_2 I_2 \text{ thru}$
$n_M F \text{ thru} = \frac{F \text{ across}}{N_M}$	$n_R F_R \text{ thru} = \frac{F_R \text{ across}}{N_R}$	$n_A p \text{ thru} = \frac{p \text{ across}}{N_A}$	$N_1 I_1 \text{ thru} = \frac{E_2 \text{ across}}{N_2}$
$z = Y_M(n_M N_M)^2$ $n_M N_M$ is the transformer factor, reciprocal of piston area, often unity	$z_R = Y_R(n_R N_R)^2$ $n_R N_R$ is the transformer factor, often unity	$z_A = Y_A(n_A N_A)^2$ $n_A N_A$ is the transformer factor, often unity	$Z_1 = Y_2(N_1 N_2)^2$ $N_1 N_2$ is the transfer impedance in ohms, or volts/amp.
Typical structure: 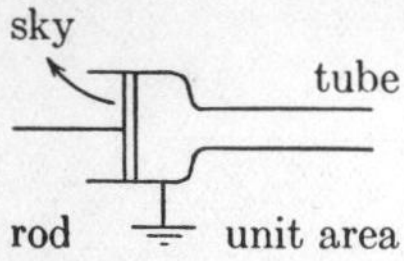 sky tube rod unit area	Typical structure: 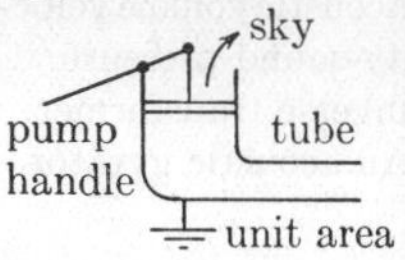 sky pump handle tube unit area	Typical structure: 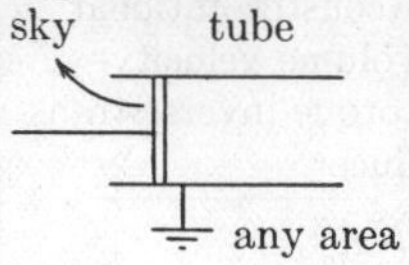 sky tube any area	Typical structure: A moving coil transducer connected mechanically to an electrostatic transducer

References

Olson, Harry F.: "Dynamical Analogies," D. Van Nostrand Company, Inc., New York, 1943. Standard reference book on the classical impedance analogy.

Beranek, Leo L.: "Acoustics," chap. 3, etc., McGraw-Hill Book Company, Inc., New York, 1954. Expounds and utilizes both the mobility and impedance analogies.

Raymond, F.: Analogies électriques et mécaniques, *Rev. gén. élec.* **61**, 465–475 (October, 1952). Both analogies. In the impedance analogy, "le *bâti* (frame of reference) *en mécanique* n'est nullement l'analogue de la *terre* en électricité."

Bloch, A.: Electromechanical Analogies and Their Use for the Analysis of Mechanical and Electromechanical Systems, *J. Inst. Elec. Engrs.* (*London*) **92**, 157–169 (1945, pt. I). Unfortunately, calls the mobility analogy the *inverse analogy*.

Bloch, A.: On Methods for the Construction of Networks Dual to Non-planar Networks, *Proc. Phys. Soc.* (*London*) **58**, 677–694 (1946).

Bauer, Benjamin B.: Transformer Couplings for Equivalent Network Synthesis, *J. Acoust. Soc. Am.* **25**, 837–840 (1953). Connects each element through a transformer, then gets rid of the transformers.

Trent, Horace M.: Isomorphisms between Oriented Linear Graphs and Lumped Physical Systems, *J. Acoust. Soc. Am.* **27**, 500–527 (1955). Draws mobility schematic by setting up the networks of meters required to measure F and v, etc.

Le Corbeiller, P., and Ying-Wa Yueng: Duality in Mechanics, *J. Acoust. Soc. Am.* **24**, 643–648 (November, 1950). Recommends the mobility analogy.

Firestone, Floyd A.: The Mobility Method of Computing the Vibration of Linear Mechanical and Acoustical Systems: Mechanical and Electrical Analogies, *J. Appl. Phys.* **9**, 373–387 (1938).

Firestone, Floyd A.: A New Analogy between Mechanical and Electrical Systems, *J. Acoust. Soc. Am.* **4**, 249–267 (1933). Introduces the concept of mobility and discriminates through and across variables.

Hähnle, Walter: Die Darstellung elektromechanischer Gebilde durch rein elektrische Schaltbilder, *Wissen. Veröff. Siemens-Konzern* **XI**, 1–23 (1932). Expounds both analogies.

Darrieus, M.: Les Modeles mécaniques en electrotechnique, leur application aux problemes de stabilité, *Bull. soc. franç. élec.* 96, 794–809 (August, 1929). **First mention of the force-current analogy.**

Circuit Theory. See Sec. 5b-14 (pp. 5-79 to 5-85) of this book.

[*Text continued from page 3-143.*]

parallel combination of these elements would with perfect analogy be the sum of the individual mechanical admittances: $Y_M = Y_{M1} + Y_{M2} + Y_{M3}$.

3m-10. Couplers: Transformers and Transducers. A coupler introduces a constraint between circuits or between different portions of the same circuit. It specifies relationships between variables at different places, a more complicated type of relationship than the 1 to 1 specified by connectors, which might be considered as simplified couplers. Ideal passive couplers transmit energy but store none. Direct couplers couple through variables to through variables and across to across, while inverse couplers couple through variables to across variables. Transformers and transducers couple like and unlike system types, respectively. In general, a transformer consists of a subtracter operated by the difference between the values of a variable at two points, actuating a multiplier, the multiplied value then being impressed as a difference between the values of a variable at two other points.

3m-11. Units. While any consistent system of units may be used in computations with analogies, the mks system is particularly advantageous since the watt will then be the unit of power in both the acoustic, mechanical, and electric portions of a transducer. Thus velocity v is in m/sec, force F in newtons, mobility z in m/sec per newton; angular velocity v_R is in radians/sec, torque F_R in newton m, rotational mobility z_R in radians/sec per newton m; volume velocity U is in m^3/sec, sound pressure p in newtons/m^2, acoustic mobility z_A in m^3/sec per newton/m^2; voltage E is in volts, current I in amperes, impedance Z in ohms. Power P is in watts and energy W in joules, throughout.

3n. Selected References on Acoustics

LEO L. BERANEK

Bolt Beranek and Newman, Inc.

Bartholomew, W.: "Acoustics of Music," Prentice-Hall, Inc., New York, 1946.
Beranek, L. L.: "Acoustics," McGraw-Hill Book Company, Inc., New York, 1954.
Beranek, L. L.: "Acoustic Measurements," John Wiley & Sons, Inc., New York, 1949.
Crede, C. E.: "Vibration and Shock Isolation," John Wiley & Sons, Inc., New York, 1951.
Cremer, L.: "Die wissenschaftlichen Grundlagen der Raumakustik," Band I, S. Hirzel Verlag, Zurich, 1949.
Cremer, L.: "Die wissenschaftlichen Grundlagen der Raumakustik," Band III, S. Hirzel Verlag, Leipzig, 1950.
Cullum, D. J. W.: "The Practical Application of Acoustic Principles," E. and F. N. Spon, Ltd., London, 1949.
Culver, C. A.: "Musical Acoustics," Blakiston Division, McGraw-Hill Book Company, Inc., New York, 1949.
Davis, H.: "Hearing and Deafness," Murray Hill Books, Inc., New York, 1947.
Frayne, J. G., and H. Wolfe: "Sound Recording," John Wiley & Sons, Inc., New York, 1949.
Hansen, H. M., and P. F. Chenea: "Mechanics of Vibration," John Wiley & Sons, Inc., New York, 1952.
Hirsch, I. J.: "The Measurement of Hearing," McGraw-Hill Book Company, Inc., New York, 1952.
Heuter, T. F., and R. H. Bolt: "Sonics," John Wiley & Sons, Inc., New York, 1955.
Hunt, F. V.: "Electroacoustics," Harvard University Press and John Wiley & Sons, Inc., New York, 1954.
Kinsler, L. E., and A. R. Frey: "Fundamentals of Acoustics," John Wiley & Sons, Inc., New York, 1950.
Knudsen, V.: "Architectural Acoustics," John Wiley & Sons, Inc., New York, 1932.
Knudsen, V., and C. Harris: "Acoustical Designing in Architecture, John Wiley & Sons, Inc., New York, 1950.
Lamb, H.: "Hydrodynamics," 6th ed., Dover Publication, New York, 1945.
Mason, W. P.: "Electro-mechanical Transducers and Wave Filters," D. Van Nostrand Company, Inc., New York, 1943.
Miller, G. A.: "Language and Communication," McGraw-Hill Book Company, Inc., New York, 1951.
Morse, P. M.: "Vibration and Sound," 2d ed., McGraw-Hill Book Company, Inc., New York, 1948.
Olson, H. F.: "Elements of Acoustical Engineering," D. Van Nostrand Company, Inc., New York, 1947.
Olson, H. F.: "Dynamical Analogies," D. Van Nostrand Company, Inc., New York, 1943.
Olson, H. F.: "Musical Engineering," McGraw-Hill Book Company, Inc., New York, 1952.
Peterson, A. P. G., and L. L. Beranek: "Handbook of Noise Measurement," General Radio Company, Cambridge, Mass., 1954.

Raes, A. C.: "Acustica Arquitectónica," Editorial Victor Leru, Buenos Aires, 1953.
Lord Rayleigh: "The Theory of Sound," vols. 1 and 2, Dover Publications, New York, 1945.
Richardson, E. G.: "Technical Aspects of Sound," Elsevier Press, Inc., New York, 1953.
Skudrzyk, E.: "Die Grundlagen der Akustik, Springer-Verlag OHG, Vienna, 1954.
Stephens, R., and A. E. Bate: "Wave Motion and Sound," Edward Arnold & Co., London, 1950.
Stevens, S. S., ed.: "Handbook of Experimental Psychology," John Wiley & Sons, Inc., New York, 1951.
Stevens, S. S., and H. Davis: "Hearing," John Wiley & Sons, Inc., New York, 1938.
Stewart, G. W., and R. B. Lindsay: "Acoustics," D. Van Nostrand Company, Inc., New York, 1930.
Swenson, G. W., Jr.: "Principles of Modern Acoustics," D. Van Nostrand Company, Inc., New York, 1953.
Wood, A.: "Acoustics," Interscience Publishers, Inc., New York, 1941.
Zwikker, C., and C. W. Kosten: "Sound Absorbing Materials," Elsevier Press, Inc., New York, 1949.

Section 4

HEAT

MARK W. ZEMANSKY, Editor

The City College of New York

CONTENTS

4a. Temperature Scales, Thermocouples, and Resistance Thermometers...... 4-2
4b. Very Low Temperature Data. Properties of Paramagnetic Salts........ 4-14
4c. Critical Constants........ 4-21
4d. High-pressure Effects........ 4-24
4e. Heat Capacities........ 4-39
4f. Thermal Expansion........ 4-51
4g. Thermal Conductivity........ 4-65
4h. Thermodynamic Properties of Gases........ 4-80
4i. Pressure-Volume-Temperature Relationships of Fluids. Viral Coefficients. 4-118
4j. Temperature, Pressure, Heat, and Entropy Change of Transition, Fusion, and Vaporization........ 4-130

4a. Temperature Scales, Thermocouples, and Resistance Thermometers

R. E. WILSON

Hughes Research and Development Laboratories

Data on optical pyrometry and thermal radiation are given in Sec. 6.

TABLE 4a-1. EQUATIONS RELATING THE COMMON TEMPERATURE SCALES

Celsius—Fahrenheit

$$t°\text{C} = \tfrac{5}{9}(t°\text{F} - 32) \qquad \text{or} \qquad 9(t°\text{C} + 40) = 5(t°\text{F} + 40)$$

where °C = °Celsius (international scale)
°F = °Fahrenheit

Celsius—Kelvin (Absolute Thermodynamic)

$$T°\text{K} = t°\text{C} + T_0 + \epsilon_c$$

where °K = °Kelvin
T_0 = temperature of the ice point on the absolute thermodynamic scale (273.16°K)
ϵ_c = correction term in Celsius degrees

Fahrenheit—Rankine

$$T°\text{R} = \tfrac{9}{5}T°\text{K} \qquad \text{or} \qquad T°\text{R} = t°\text{F} + T_0 + \epsilon_F$$

where °R = °Rankine
T_0 = temperature of the ice point on the absolute thermodynamic scale [$\frac{9}{5}(273.16) - 32 = 459.69°\text{R}$]
ϵ_F = correction term in Fahrenheit degrees

TABLE 4a-2. DEFINITION OF THE INTERNATIONAL TEMPERATURE SCALE OF 1948*

Temp. range	Fixed points, under standard pressure of 1 atm (1,013,250 dynes/cm²)	Standard instruments	Interpolation equations
−182.97 to 630.5°C	Oxygen boiling point (−182.970°C) Ice point (0°C) Steam point (100°C) Sulfur boiling point (444.600°C)	Platinum resistance thermometers (four-lead type)	$R_t = R_0(1 + At + Bt^2)$ (above 0°C) $R_t = R_0[(1 + At + Bt^2 + C(t - 100)t^3]$ (below 0°C) where R_t = resistance of the platinum coil at temperature t R_0 = resistance of the platinum coil at the ice point, 0°C t = temperature, °Celsius A, B, C = constants
630.5 to 1063.0°C	Antimony freezing point or equivalent temperature (630.5°C) as determined with a platinum resistance thermometer Silver freezing point (960.8°C) Gold freezing point (1063.0°C)	Platinum vs. platinum–10% rhodium thermocouple	$E = a + bt + ct^2$ where E = electromotive force a, b, c = constants
1063.0°C up	Gold freezing point (1063.0°C)	Optical pyrometer	$\frac{J_t}{J_{Au}} = \frac{e^{\frac{c_2}{\lambda(t_{Au}+T_0)}} - 1}{e^{\frac{c_2}{\lambda(t+T_0)}} - 1}$ where J_t and J_{Au} = radiant energies per unit wavelength interval at wavelength λ emitted per unit time by unit area of a black body at the temperature t and at the gold point t_{Au}, respectively c_2 = 1.438 cm deg T_0 = temperature of the ice point, °K λ = a wavelength of the visible spectrum e = base of Naperian logarithms

* H. F. Stimson, The International Temperature Scale of 1948, *J. Research Natl. Bur Standards* **42,** 209 (1949).

TABLE 4a-3. CORRESPONDING TEMPERATURES ON THE INTERNATIONAL TEMPERATURE SCALES OF 1948 AND 1927*

[Degrees C (int.)]

1948	1927	1948	1927
630.50	630.50	2100	2107
650	649.92	2200	2208
700	699.76	2300	2310
750	749.65	2400	2411
800	799.58	2500	2512
850	849.57	2600	2613
900	899.60	2700	2715
950	949.68	2800	2816
960.80	960.50	2900	2918
1000	999.80	3000	3020
1050	1049.95	3100	3122
1063.00	1063.00	3200	3223
1100	1100.2	3300	3325
1200	1200.6	3400	3428
1300	1301.1	3500	3530
1400	1401.7	3600	3632
1500	1502.3	3700	3735
1600	1603.0	3800	3837
1700	1703.8	3900	3940
1800	1804.6	4000	4043
1900	1905.5	4100	4146
2000	2006.4	4200	4249

* Robert J. Corruccini, Differences between the International Temperature Scales of 1948 and 1927, *J. Research, Natl. Bur. Standards* **43,** 133 (1949), RP2014.

TABLE 4a-4. SECONDARY FIXED POINTS UNDER THE PRESSURE OF 1 STANDARD ATMOSPHERE (EXCEPT FOR THE TRIPLE POINTS)*

	Temp. (°*C*) (*Int.* 1948)
Temperature of equilibrium between solid carbon dioxide and its vapor..	−78.5

$$t_p = -78.5 + 12.12\left(\frac{p}{p_0} - 1\right) - 6.4\left(\frac{p}{p_0} - 1\right)^2$$

Temperature of freezing mercury..................................	−38.87
Temperature of equilibrium between ice, water, and its vapor (triple point)	+0.0100
Temperature of transition of sodium sulfate decahydrate...............	32.38
Temperature of triple point of benzoic acid..........................	122.36
Temperature of equilibrium between naphthalene and its vapor.........	218.0

$$t_p = 218.0 + 44.4\left(\frac{p}{p_0} - 1\right) - 19\left(\frac{p}{p_0} - 1\right)^2$$

Temperature of freezing tin..	231.9
Temperature of equilibrium between benzophenone and its vapor......	305.9

$$t_p = 305.9 + 48.8\left(\frac{p}{p_0} - 1\right) - 21\left(\frac{p}{p_0} - 1\right)^2$$

Temperature of freezing cadmium...................................	320.9
Temperature of freezing lead..	327.3
Temperature of equilibrium between mercury and its vapor...........	356.58

$$t_p = 356.58 + 55.552\left(\frac{p}{p_0} - 1\right) - 23.03\left(\frac{p}{p_0} - 1\right)^2 + 14.0\left(\frac{p}{p_0} - 1\right)^3$$

Temperature of freezing zinc...	419.5
Temperature of freezing antimony....................................	630.5
Temperature of freezing aluminum...................................	660.1
Temperature of freezing copper in a reducing atmosphere............	1083
Temperature of freezing nickel.......................................	1453
Temperature of freezing cobalt.......................................	1492
Temperature of freezing palladium...................................	1552
Temperature of freezing platinum....................................	1769
Temperature of freezing rhodium.....................................	1960
Temperature of freezing iridium......................................	2443
Temperature of melting tungsten.....................................	3380

* H. F. Stimson, The International Temperature Scale of 1948, *J. Research Natl. Bur. Standards* **42** (1949), RP1962.

TABLE 4a-5. THERMAL EMF OF CHEMICAL ELEMENTS RELATIVE TO PLATINUM*

Temp., °C	Lithium, mv	Sodium, mv	Potassium, mv	Rubidium, mv	Cesium, mv	Calcium, mv	Cerium, mv
−200	−1.12	+1.00	+1.61	+1.09	+0.22		
−100	−1.00	+0.29	+0.78	+0.46	−0.13		
0	0	0	0	0	0	0	0
+100	+1.82	......	......	......		−0.51	+1.14
200	......	......				−1.13	2.46
300	......	......				−1.85	

Temp., °C	Magnesium, mv	Zinc, mv	Cadmium, mv	Mercury, mv	Indium, mv	Thallium, mv	Aluminum, mv
−200	+0.37	−0.07	−0.04	......	......	......	+0.45
−100	−0.09	−0.33	−0.31	......	......	......	−0.06
0	0	0	0	0	0	0	0
+100	+0.44	+0.76	+0.90	−0.60	+0.69	+0.58	+0.42
200	+1.10	1.89	2.35	−1.33	......	1.30	1.06
300	......	3.42	4.24	......	......	2.16	1.88
400	......	5.29	......	......	......	......	2.84
500	......	......	......	......	......	......	3.93
600	......	......	......	......	......	......	5.15

Temp., °C	Carbon, mv	Silicon, mv	Germanium, mv	Tin, mv	Lead, mv	Antimony, mv	Bismuth, mv
−200	......	+63.13	−46.00	+0.26	+0.24	......	+12.39
−100	......	+37.17	−26.62	−0.12	−0.13	......	+7.54
0	0	0	0	0	0	0	0
+100	+0.70	−41.56	+33.9	+0.42	+0.44	+4.89	−7.34
200	1.54	−80.58	72.4	1.07	1.09	10.14	−13.57
300	2.55	−110.09	91.8	......	1.91	15.44	
400	3.72	......	82.3	......	......	20.53	
500	5.15	......	63.5	......	......	25.10	
600	6.79	......	43.9	......	......	28.88	
700	8.84	......	27.9				
800	11.01						
900	13.59						
1000	16.51						
1100	19.49						

See page 4–7 for footnotes.

TABLE 4a-5. THERMAL EMF OF CHEMICAL ELEMENTS RELATIVE TO PLATINUM*
(Continued)

Temp., °C	Copper, mv	Silver, mv	Gold, mv	Iron, mv	Cobalt, mv	Nickel, mv
−200	−0.19	−0.21	−0.21	−3.10	......	+2.28
−100	−0.37	−0.39	−0.39	−1.94	......	+1.22
0	0	0	0	0	0	0
+100	+0.76	+0.74	+0.78	+1.98	−1.33	−1.48
200	1.83	1.77	1.84	3.69	−3.08	−3.10
300	3.15	3.05	3.14	5.03	−5.10	−4.59
400	4.68	4.57	4.63	6.08	−7.24	−5.45
500	6.41	6.36	6.29	7.00	−9.35	−6.16
600	8.34	8.41	8.12	8.02	−11.28	−7.04
700	10.49	10.75	10.13	9.34	−12.88	−8.10
800	12.84	13.36	12.29	11.09	−14.00	−9.35
900	15.41	16.20	14.61	13.10	−14.49	−10.69
1000	18.20	......	17.09	14.64	−14.20	−12.13
1100	......	......	......	......	−12.98	−13.62
1200	......	......	......	......	−10.68	

Temp., °C	Iridium, mv	Rhodium, mv	Palladium, mv	Molybdenum, mv	Tungsten, mv	Tantalum, mv	Thorium, mv
−200	−0.25	−0.20	+0.81	......	+0.43	+0.21	
−100	−0.35	−0.34	+0.48	......	−0.15	−0.10	
0	0	0	0	0	0	0	0
+100	+0.65	+0.70	−0.57	+1.45	+1.12	+0.33	−0.13
200	1.49	1.61	−1.23	3.19	2.62	0.93	−0.26
300	2.47	2.68	−1.99	5.23	4.48	1.79	−0.40
400	3.55	3.91	−2.82	7.57	6.70	2.91	−0.50
500	4.78	5.28	−3.84	10.20	9.30	4.30	−0.53
600	6.10	6.77	−5.03	13.13	12.26	5.95	−0.45
700	7.56	8.40	−6.41	16.35	15.60	7.87	−0.21
800	9.12	10.16	−7.98	19.87	19.30	10.05	+0.22
900	10.80	12.04	−9.72	23.69	23.36	12.49	+0.87
1000	12.59	14.05	−11.63	27.80	27.80	15.20	+1.73
1100	14.48	16.18	−13.70	32.21	32.60	18.17	+2.80
1200	16.47	18.42	−15.89	36.91	37.78	21.41	+4.04
1300	18.47	20.70	−18.12	......	......	......	+5.42
1400	20.48	23.00	−20.41				
1500	22.50	25.35	−22.74				

* A positive sign means that in a simple thermoelectric circuit the resultant emf as given is in such a direction as to produce a current from the element to the platinum at the reference junction (0°C).

The values below 0°C, in most cases, have not been determined on the same samples as the values above 0°C.

American Institute of Physics, "Temperature, Its Measurement and Control in Science and Industry," pp. 1308–1310, Reinhold Publishing Corporation, New York, 1941.

TABLE 4a-6. THERMAL EMF OF IMPORTANT THERMOCOUPLE MATERIALS RELATIVE TO PLATINUM*

Temp., °C	Chromel P, mv	Alumel, mv	Copper, mv	Iron, mv	Constantan, mv
−200	−3.36	+2.39	−0.19	−2.92	+5.35
−100	−2.20	+1.29	−0.37	−1.84	+2.98
0	0	0	0	0	0
+100	+2.81	−1.29	+0.76	+1.89	−3.51
200	5.96	−2.17	1.83	3.54	−7.45
300	9.32	−2.89	3.15	4.85	−11.71
400	12.75	−3.64	4.68	5.88	−16.19
500	16.21	−4.43	6.41	6.79	−20.79
600	19.62	−5.28	8.34	7.80	−25.47
700	22.96	−6.18	10.49	9.12	−30.18
800	26.23	−7.08	12.84	10.86	−34.86
900	29.41	−7.95	15.41	12.84	−39.45
1000	32.52	−8.79	18.20	14.30	−43.92
1100	35.56	−9.58			
1200	38.51	−10.34			
1300	41.35	−11.06			
1400	44.04	−11.77			

* American Institute of Physics, "Temperature, Its Measurement and Control in Science and Industry," pp. 1308–1310, Reinhold Publishing Corporation, New York, 1941.

TABLE 4a-7. THERMAL EMF OF SOME ALLOYS RELATIVE TO PLATINUM*

Temp., °C	Manganin, mv	Gold-chromium, mv	Copper-beryllium, mv	Yellow brass, mv	Phosphor bronze, mv	Solder 50 Sn–50 Pb, mv	Solder 96.5 Sn–3.5 Ag, mv
0	0	0	0	0	0	0	0
+100	+0.61	−0.17	+0.67	+0.60	+0.55	+0.46	+0.45
200	1.55	−0.32	1.62	1.49	1.34		
300	2.77	−0.44	2.81	2.58	2.34		
400	4.25	−0.55	4.19	3.85	3.50		
500	5.95	−0.63	......	5.30	4.81		
600	7.84	−0.66	......	6.96	6.30		

Temp., °C	18-8 stainless steel, mv	Spring steel, mv	80 Ni 20 Cr, mv	60 Ni–24 Fe–16 Cr, mv	Copper coin (95 Cu–4 Sn–1 Zn), mv	Nickel coin (75 Cu–25 Ni), mv	Silver coin (90 Ag–10 Cu), mv
0	0	0	0	0	0	0	0
+100	+0.44	+1.32	+1.14	+0.85	+0.60	−2.76	+0.80
200	1.04	2.63	2.62	2.01	1.48	−6.01	1.90
300	1.76	3.81	4.34	3.41	2.60	−9.71	3.25
400	2.60	4.84	6.25	5.00	3.91	−13.78	4.81
500	3.56	5.80	8.31	6.76	5.44	−18.10	6.59
600	4.67	6.86	10.53	8.68	7.14	−22.59	8.64
700	5.93	......	12.91	10.78			
800	7.37	......	15.44	13.06			
900	8.99	......	18.11	15.50			
1000	......		20.91	18.10			

* American Institute of Physics, "Temperature, Its Measurement and Control in Science and Industry," pp. 1308–1310, Reinhold Publishing Corporation, New York, 1941.

TABLE 4a-8. PLATINUM VS. PLATINUM–10% RHODIUM THERMOCOUPLES*
[Emf, absolute millivolts; temp., °C (int. 1948); reference junctions at 0°C]

°C	0	10	20	30	40	50	60	70	80	90	100
0	0.000	0.056	0.113	0.173	0.235	0.299	0.364	0.431	0.500	0.571	0.643
100	0.643	0.717	0.792	0.869	0.946	1.025	1.106	1.187	1.269	1.352	1.436
200	1.436	1.521	1.607	1.693	1.780	1.868	1.956	2.045	2.135	2.225	2.316
300	2.316	2.408	2.499	2.592	2.685	2.778	2.872	2.966	3.061	3.156	3.251
400	3.251	3.347	3.442	3.539	3.635	3.732	3.829	3.926	4.024	4.122	4.221
500	4.221	4.319	4.419	4.518	4.618	4.718	4.818	4.919	5.020	5.122	5.224
600	5.224	5.326	5.429	5.532	5.635	5.738	5.842	5.946	6.050	6.155	6.260
700	6.260	6.365	6.471	6.577	6.683	6.790	6.897	7.005	7.112	7.220	7.329
800	7.329	7.438	7.547	7.656	7.766	7.876	7.987	8.098	8.209	8.320	8.432
900	8.432	8.545	8.657	8.770	8.883	8.997	9.111	9.225	9.340	9.455	9.570
1000	9.570	9.686	9.802	9.918	10.035	10.152	10.269	10.387	10.505	10.623	10.741
1100	10.741	10.860	10.979	11.098	11.217	11.336	11.456	11.575	11.695	11.815	11.935
1200	11.935	12.055	12.175	12.296	12.416	12.536	12.657	12.777	12.897	13.018	13.138
1300	13.138	13.258	13.378	13.498	13.618	13.738	13.858	13.978	14.098	14.217	14.337
1400	14.337	14.457	14.576	14.696	14.815	14.935	15.054	15.173	15.292	15.411	15.530
1500	15.530	15.649	15.768	15.887	16.006	16.124	16.243	16.361	16.479	16.597	16.716
1600	16.716	16.834	16.952	17.069	17.187	17.305	17.422	17.539	17.657	17.774	17.891
1700	17.891	18.008	18.124	18.241	18.358	18.474	18.590				

* Henry Shenker, John I. Lauritzen, Jr., and Robert J. Corruccini, Reference Tables for Thermocouples, *Natl. Bur. Standards (U.S.) Circ.* 508 (May 7, 1951).

TABLE 4a-9. PLATINUM VS. PLATINUM–13% RHODIUM THERMOCOUPLES*
[Emf, absolute millivolts; temp., °C (int. 1948); reference junctions at 0°C]

°C	0	10	20	30	40	50	60	70	80	90	100
0	0.000	0.055	0.112	0.172	0.234	0.298	0.363	0.431	0.500	0.572	0.645
100	0.645	0.721	0.798	0.877	0.957	1.039	1.121	1.205	1.290	1.377	1.465
200	1.465	1.553	1.643	1.734	1.826	1.918	2.012	2.107	2.202	2.298	2.395
300	2.395	2.493	2.591	2.690	2.790	2.890	2.991	3.092	3.194	3.296	3.399
400	3.399	3.502	3.607	3.712	3.817	3.923	4.029	4.134	4.241	4.348	4.455
500	4.455	4.563	4.672	4.782	4.893	5.004	5.115	5.226	5.338	5.450	5.563
600	5.563	5.677	5.792	5.907	6.022	6.137	6.252	6.368	6.485	6.602	6.720
700	6.720	6.838	6.957	7.076	7.195	7.315	7.436	7.557	7.679	7.801	7.924
800	7.924	8.047	8.170	8.294	8.419	8.544	8.669	8.795	8.921	9.047	9.175
900	9.175	9.303	9.431	9.559	9.687	9.816	9.946	10.077	10.208	10.339	10.471
1000	10.471	10.603	10.735	10.869	11.003	11.138	11.273	11.408	11.544	11.681	11.817
1100	11.817	11.954	12.090	12.227	12.365	12.503	12.641	12.779	12.917	13.055	13.193
1200	13.193	13.332	13.471	13.610	13.749	13.888	14.027	14.165	14.304	14.443	14.582
1300	14.582	14.721	14.860	14.999	15.138	15.276	15.415	15.553	15.692	15.831	15.969
1400	15.969	16.108	16.247	16.386	16.524	16.663	16.802	16.940	17.079	17.217	17.355
1500	17.355	17.493	17.631	17.768	17.906	18.043	18.179	18.316	18.453	18.590	18.727
1600	18.727	18.864	19.001	19.137	19.273	19.409	19.545	19.682	19.818	19.954	

* Henry Shenker, John L. Lauritzen, Jr., and Robert J. Corruccini, Reference Tables for Thermocouples, *Natl. Bur. Standards (U.S.) Circ.* 508 (May 7, 1951).

TABLE 4a-10. COPPER VS. CONSTANTAN THERMOCOUPLES*

[Emf, absolute millivolts; temp., °C, (int. 1948); reference junctions at 0°C]

°C	0	10	20	30	40	50	60	70	80	90	100
−100	−3.349	−3.624	−3.887	−4.138	−4.377	−4.603	−4.817	−5.018	−5.205	−5.379	
(−)0	0.000	−0.380	−0.751	−1.112	−1.463	−1.804	−2.135	−2.455	−2.764	−3.062	−3.349
(+)0	0.000	0.389	0.787	1.194	1.610	2.035	2.467	2.908	3.357	3.813	4.277
100	4.277	4.749	5.227	5.712	6.204	6.703	7.208	7.719	8.236	8.759	9.288
200	9.288	9.823	10.363	10.909	11.459	12.015	12.575	13.140	13.710	14.285	14.864
300	14.864	15.447	16.035	16.626	17.222	17.821	18.425	19.032	19.642	20.257	20.874

* Henry Shenker, John L. Lauritzen, Jr., and Robert J. Corruccini, Reference Tables for Thermocouples, *Natl. Bur. Standards (U.S.) Circ.* 508 (May 7, 1951).

TABLE 4a-11. IRON VS. CONSTANTAN THERMOCOUPLES*

[Emf, absolute millivolts; temp., °C, (int. 1948); reference junctions at 0°C]

°C	0	10	20	30	40	50	60	70	80	90	100
−100	− 4.63	− 5.05	− 5.42	− 5.80	− 6.16	− 6.50	− 6.82	− 7.12	− 7.40	− 7.66	
(−)0	0.00	− 0.50	− 1.00	− 1.48	− 1.96	− 2.43	− 2.89	− 3.34	− 3.78	− 4.21	− 4.63
(+)0	0.00	0.50	1.02	1.54	2.06	2.58	3.11	3.65	4.19	4.73	5.27
100	5.27	5.81	6.36	6.90	7.45	8.00	8.56	9.11	9.67	10.22	10.78
200	10.78	11.34	11.89	12.45	13.01	13.56	14.12	14.67	15.22	15.77	16.33
300	16.33	16.88	17.43	17.98	18.54	19.09	19.64	20.20	20.75	21.30	21.85
400	21.85	22.40	22.95	23.50	24.06	24.61	25.16	25.72	26.27	26.83	27.39
500	27.39	27.95	28.52	29.08	29.65	30.22	30.80	31.37	31.95	32.53	33.11
600	33.11	33.70	34.29	34.88	35.48	36.08	36.69	37.30	37.91	38.53	39.15
700	39.15	39.78	40.41	41.05	41.68	42.32	42.96	43.60	44.25	44.89	45.53
800	45.53	46.18	46.82	47.46	48.09	48.73	49.36	49.98			

* Robert J. Corruccini and Henry Shenker, Modified 1913 Reference Tables for Iron-Constantan Thermocouples, *J. Research Natl. Bur. Standards* **50,** 229 (1953), RP2415.

TABLE 4a-12. CHROMEL VS. ALUMEL THERMOCOUPLES*
[Emf, absolute millivolts; temp., °C, (int. 1948); reference junction at 0°C]

°C	0	10	20	30	40	50	60	70	80	90	100
−100	− 3.49	− 3.78	− 4.06	− 4.32	− 4.58	− 4.81	− 5.03	− 5.24	− 5.43	− 5.60	
(−)0	− 0.00	− 0.39	− 0.77	− 1.14	− 1.50	− 1.86	− 2.20	− 2.54	− 2.87	− 3.19	− 3.49
(+)0	0.00	0.40	0.80	1.20	1.61	2.02	2.43	2.85	3.26	3.68	4.10
100	4.10	4.51	4.92	5.33	5.73	6.13	6.53	6.93	7.33	7.73	8.13
200	8.13	8.54	8.94	9.34	9.75	10.16	10.57	10.98	11.39	11.80	12.21
300	12.21	12.63	13.04	13.46	13.88	14.29	14.71	15.13	15.55	15.98	16.40
400	16.40	16.82	17.24	17.67	18.09	18.51	18.94	19.36	19.79	20.22	20.65
500	20.65	21.07	21.50	21.92	22.35	22.78	23.20	23.63	24.06	24.49	24.91
600	24.91	25.34	25.76	26.19	26.61	27.03	27.45	27.87	28.29	28.72	29.14
700	29.14	29.56	29.97	30.39	30.81	31.23	31.65	32.06	32.48	32.89	33.30
800	33.30	33.71	34.12	34.53	34.93	35.34	35.75	36.15	36.55	36.96	37.36
900	37.36	37.76	38.16	38.56	38.95	39.35	39.75	40.14	40.53	40.92	41.31
1000	41.31	41.70	42.09	42.48	42.87	43.25	43.63	44.02	44.40	44.78	45.16
1100	45.16	45.54	45.92	46.29	46.67	47.04	47.41	47.78	48.15	48.52	48.89
1200	48.89	49.25	49.62	49.98	50.34	50.69	51.05	51.41	51.76	52.11	52.46
1300	52.46	52.81	53.16	53.51	53.85	54.20	54.54	54.88			

* Henry Shenker, John L. Lauritzen, Jr., and Robert J. Corruccini, Reference Tables for Thermocouples, *Natl. Bur. Standards (U.S.) Circ.* 508 (May 7, 1951).

TABLE 4a-13. CHROMEL VS. CONSTANTAN THERMOCOUPLES*
[Emf, absolute millivolts; temp., °C (int. 1948); reference junctions at 0°C]

°C	0	10	20	30	40	50	60	70	80	90	100
−100	−5.18	−5.62	−6.04	−6.44	−6.83	−7.20	−7.55	−7.87	−8.17	−8.45	−8.71
(−)0	0.00	−0.58	−1.14	−1.70	−2.24	−2.77	−3.28	−3.78	−4.26	−4.73	−5.18
(+)0	0.00	0.59	1.19	1.80	2.41	3.04	3.68	4.33	4.99	5.65	6.32
100	6.32	7.00	7.69	8.38	9.08	9.79	10.51	11.23	11.95	12.68	13.42
200	13.42	14.17	14.92	15.67	16.42	17.18	17.95	18.72	19.49	20.26	21.04
300	21.04	21.82	22.60	22.39	24.18	24.97	25.76	26.56	27.35	28.15	28.95
400	28.95	29.75	30.55	31.36	32.16	32.96	33.77	34.58	35.39	36.20	37.01
500	37.01	37.82	38.62	39.43	40.24	41.05	41.86	42.67	43.48	44.29	45.10
600	45.10	45.91	46.72	47.53	48.33	49.13	49.93	50.73	51.54	52.34	53.14
700	53.14	53.94	54.74	55.53	56.33	57.12	57.92	58.71	59.50	60.29	61.08
800	61.08	61.86	62.65	63.43	64.21	64.99	65.77	66.54	67.31	68.08	68.85
900	68.85	69.62	70.39	71.15	71.92	72.68	73.44	74.20	74.95	75.70	76.45

* Henry Shenker, John L. Lauritzen, Jr., and Robert J. Corruccini, Reference Tables for Thermocouples, *Natl. Bur. Standards (U.S.) Circ.* 508, (May 7, 1951).

TABLE 4a-14. ELECTRICAL RESISTIVITY OF SOME ELEMENTS AND ALLOYS AS A FUNCTION OF TEMPERATURE*

[At 0°C both the relative (R_t/R_0) and actual resistivity (microhm-cm) are given]

Temp., °C	Platinum (R_t/R_0)	Copper (R_t/R_0)	Nickel (R_t/R_0)	Iron (R_t/R_0)	Silver (R_t/R_0)	90 Pt–10 Rh (R_t/R_0)	87 Pt–13 Rh (R_t/R_0)
−200	0.177	0.117	.....	.....	0.176		
−100	0.599	0.557	.....	.....	0.596		
0	1.000	1.000	1.000	1.000	1.000	1.000	1.000
	(9.83)	(1.56)	(6.38)	(8.57)	(1.50)	(18.4)	(19.0)
+100	1.392	1.431	1.663	1.650	1.408	1.166	1.156
200	1.773	1.862	2.501	2.464	1.827	1.330	1.308
300	2.142	2.299	3.611	3.485	2.256	1.490	1.456
400	2.499	2.747	4.847	4.716	2.698	1.646	1.601
500	2.844	3.210	5.398	6.162	3.150	1.798	1.744
600	3.178	3.695	5.882	7.839	3.616	1.947	1.885
700	3.500	4.208	6.327	9.790	4.094	2.093	2.023
800	3.810	4.752	6.751	12.009	4.586	2.234	2.157
900	4.109	5.334	7.156	12.790	5.091	2.370	2.287
1000	4.396	5.960	7.542	13.070	.....	2.503	2.414
1100	4.671	.....	.....	.....	.....	2.633	2.538
1200	4.935	.....	.....	.....	.....	2.761	2.660
1300	5.187	.....	.....	.....	.....	2.887	2.780
1400	5.427	.....	.....	.....	.....	3.011	2.898
1500	5.655	.....	.....	.....	.....	3.133	3.014

Temp., °C	80 Ni–20 Cr (R_t/R_0)	60 Ni–24 Fe–16 Cr (R_t/R_0)	50 Fe–30 Ni–20 Cr (R_t/R_0)	Chromel P (90 Ni–10 Cr (R_t/R_0)	Alumel 95 Ni–bal. Al Si and Mn (R_t/R_0)	Constantan (55 Cu–45 Ni) (R_t/R_0)	Manganin (R_t/R_0)
0	1.000	1.000	1.000	1.000	1.000	1.000	1.000
	(107.6)	(111.6)	(99.0)	(70.0)	(28.1)	(48.9)	(48.2)
100	1.021	1.025	1.037	1.041	1.239	0.999	1.002
200	1.041	1.048	1.073	1.086	1.428	0.996	0.996
300	1.056	1.071	1.107	1.134	1.537	0.994	0.991
400	1.068	1.092	1.137	1.187	1.637	0.994	0.983
500	1.073	1.108	1.163	1.222	1.726	1.007	
600	1.071	1.115	1.185	1.248	1.814	1.024	
700	1.067	1.119	1.204	1.275	1.899	1.040	
800	1.066	1.127	1.221	1.304	1.982	1.056	
900	1.071	1.138	1.237	1.334	2.066	1.074	
1000	1.077	1.149	1.251	1.365	2.150	1.092	
1100	1.083	.....	.....	1.397	2.234	1.110	
1200	.....	.....	.....	1.430	2.318		

* The values below 0°C, in most cases, were not determined on the same samples as the values above 0°C. American Institute of Physics, "Temperature, Its Measurement and Control in Science and Industry," p. 1312, Reinhold Publishing Corporation, New York, 1941.

4b. Very Low Temperature Data. Properties of Paramagnetic Salts

RALPH P. HUDSON

The National Bureau of Standards

Table 4b-1 summarizes the principal properties of 10 paramagnetic salts. Detailed data are given in the rest of the section.

TABLE 4b-1. PROPERTIES OF PARAMAGNETIC SALTS

Paramagnetic salt	Gram-ionic weight, M (g)	Density, $\rho \left(\frac{g}{cm^3}\right)$	Curie const. $C \left(\frac{emu}{gram\text{-}ion}\right)$	Specific heat const. $\frac{A}{R}$ (deg²)	Splitting factor $\frac{\delta}{k}$ (°K)
1. Cerium magnesium nitrate $2Ce(NO_3)_3 \cdot 3Mg(NO_3)_2 \cdot 24H_2O$	765		0.318	7.5×10^{-6}	
2. Chromium potassium alum $Cr_2(SO_4)_3 \cdot K_2SO_4 \cdot 24H_2O$	499	1.83	1.88	0.017	0.25
3. Chromium methylammonium alum $Cr_2(SO_4)_3 \cdot (CH_3NH_3)_2SO_4 \cdot 24H_2O$	492	1.645	1.88	0.019	0.27
4. Copper potassium sulfate $CuSO_4 \cdot K_2SO_4 \cdot 6H_2O$	442	2.22	(0.445)	6.0×10^{-4}	——
5. Iron ammonium alum $Fe_2(SO_4)_3 \cdot (NH_4)_2SO_4 \cdot 24H_2O$	482	1.71	4.38	0.0143	0.23
6. Gadolinium sulfate $Gd_2(SO_4)_3 \cdot 8H_2O$	373	3.010	7.88	0.32	1.35
7. Manganese ammonium sulfate $MnSO_4 \cdot (NH_4)_2SO_4 \cdot 6H_2O$	391	1.83	4.38	0.033	0.24
8. Titanium cesium alum $Ti_2(SO_4)_3 \cdot Cs_2SO_4 \cdot 24H_2O$	589	~2	(0.118)	3.9×10^{-5}	——
9. Cobalt ammonium sulfate $CoSO_4 \cdot (NH_4)_2SO_4 \cdot 6H_2O$	395	1.902	3.00 0.873 1.77	4.30×10^{-3}	——
10. Copper sulfate pentahydrate $CuSO_4 \cdot 5H_2O$	250	2.284	(0.457 $\Delta = -0.65$)		——

Note: Average values for C, measured for anisotropic salts in powder form, are quoted in parentheses.

1. Cerium Magnesium Nitrate. $2Ce(NO_3)_3 \cdot 3Mg(NO_3)_2 \cdot 24H_2O$; gram-ionic weight, 765; Ce^{3+}; $4f^1$; $^2F_{\frac{5}{2}}$.

The next lowest level to the ground state, $^2F_{\frac{7}{2}}$, lies about 2,500 cm^{-1} above the $^2F_{\frac{5}{2}}$ ground level. The latter is assumed by Cooke, Duffus, and Wolf[1] to be split into doublets characterized to a first approximation by $J_Z = \pm\frac{1}{2}, \pm\frac{3}{2}, \pm\frac{5}{2}$.

Cooke et al. find $A/C = 1{,}970$, $g_\perp = 1.84$, $g_\parallel = 0.25 \pm 0.05$. Taking $C = 0.318$ emu per g ion, $A/R = 7.5 \times 10^{-6}$ deg². (Owing to the smallness of the magnetic

[1] A. H. Cooke, H. J. Duffus, and W. P. Wolf, *Phil. Mag.* **44**, (7), 623 (1953).

specific heat, the contribution to the specific heat from the lattice is not negligible at 1°K and may be estimated to become comparable with the magnetic specific heat at about 0.5°K.)

Daniels and Robinson[1] find $A/R = 6.4 \times 10^{-6}$, and that $T^* = T$ down to 0.006°K. Their data are given in Table 4b-2.

TABLE 4b-2. TEMPERATURE DATA ON CERIUM MAGNESIUM NITRATE (DANIELS AND ROBINSON)

S/R	T 10^{-3} °K	T^* 10^{-3} °	S/R	T 10^{-3} °K	T^* 10^{-3} °	S/R	T 10^{-3} °K	T^* 10^{-3} °
0.100	3.08	3.20	0.450	3.12	3.66	0.560	4.50	4.90
0.300	3.08	3.20	0.475	3.23	3.88	0.570	4.79	5.09
0.350	3.08	3.28	0.500	3.43	4.09	0.580	5.12	5.32
0.400	3.08	3.38	0.525	3.76	4.35	0.590	5.46	5.56
0.425	3.08	3.49	0.550	4.25	4.72	0.600	5.86	5.86

2. Chromium Potassium Alum. $Cr_2(SO_4)_3 \cdot K_2SO_4 \cdot 24H_2O$; gram- ionic weight, 499; density, 1.83; Cr^{3+}; $3d^3$; ${}^4F_{\frac{3}{2}}$.

An orbital singlet is lowest—some 10^4 cm^{-1} below the first triplet. This spin quadruplet remains degenerate in a cubic field but splits into two Kramers doublets in any field of lower symmetry. $g = 2$. Paramagnetic-resonance experiments by Bleaney[2] indicate two distinct values of the splitting δ below 160°K, and the situation is very confused. (Adiabatic-demagnetization experiments lead to a rms value of δ.)

De Klerk[3] finds $A/R = 0.0192$ deg², and $\delta/k = 0.27$ deg for a powder specimen. His data are given in Table 4b-3.

TABLE 4b-3. TEMPERATURE DATA ON CHROMIUM POTASSIUM ALUM (DE KLERK)

H_i, gauss	T_i, °K	$\ln 4 - S/R$	T_f^*	T_f, °K
628	1.174	0.0102	0.946	0.944
823	1.184	0.0124	0.877	0.875
1,022	1.177	0.0154	0.784	0.782
1,209	1.174	0.0189	0.701	0.699
1,645	1.158	0.0296	0.570	0.566
1,905	1.157	0.0369	0.508	0.502
2,183	1.155	0.0461	0.453	0.448
2,762	1.152	0.0687	0.365	0.359
3,572	1.149	0.1085	0.288	0.280
4,152	1.153	0.1380	0.251	0.242
5,805	1.148	0.2480	0.178	0.166
8,120	1.142	0.4180	0.124	0.108
10,310	1.143	0.5710	0.095	0.077

For two single crystals, $\delta/k = 0.263$ deg and 0.251 deg respectively.[4]

In Table V-IV of the reference, de Klerk lists corresponding values of T^*, $\ln 4 - S/R$, and T ranging between the values 0.064 and 0.033 deg, 0.801 and 0.987 deg, and

[1] J. M. Daniels and F. N. H. Robinson, *Phil. Mag.* **44**, (7), 630 (1953).
[2] B. Bleaney, *Proc. Roy. Soc.* (*London*), ser. A, **204**, 203 (1950).
[3] D. de Klerk, Thesis, p. 52, Leiden, 1948.
[4] *Ibid.*, pp. 54, 89.

0.035 and 0.0039 deg, respectively. This table is not internally consistent, however, and one cannot say which part of the data listed is in error. Assuming the T values to be correct and the error to lie elsewhere, there is marked disagreement between these results and those of Daniels and Kurti[1] given in Table 4b-4, for a compressed-powder specimen. The latter authors find absolute temperatures greater than de Klerk's values by a factor of 3 at the lowest entropies.

TABLE 4b-4. TEMPERATURE DATA ON CHROMIUM POTASSIUM ALUM (DANIELS AND KURTI)

$\ln 4 - S/R$	T, °K	$\ln 4 - S/R$	T, °K
0.487	0.0728	0.906	0.011_5
0.550	0.0515	1.096	0.011_5
0.630	0.0354	1.136	0.010_7
0.731	0.0232	1.178	0.009_0
0.848	0.0127	1.236	0.007_0

$$\left(\frac{S}{R}\right)_{T_0} = 0.40 \qquad \frac{H}{T} = 16 \times 10^3$$

The most reliable measurements above 0.1°K are those of Bleaney[2] given in Table 4b-5.

TABLE 4b-5. TEMPERATURE DATA ON CHROMIUM POTASSIUM ALUM (BLEANEY)

T, °K	T^*	T, °K	T^*	T, °K	T^*
1.000	1.000	0.280	0.291	0.120	0.138
0.600	0.604	0.240	0.252	0.100	0.121
0.480	0.485	0.200	0.215	0.080	0.103
0.400	0.406	0.180	0.195	0.060	0.086
0.360	0.368	0.160	0.174	0.050	0.079
0.320	0.330	0.140	0.156	0.045	0.075

3. Chromium Methylammonium Alum. $Cr_2(SO_4)_3(CH_3 \cdot NH_3)_2SO_4 \cdot 24H_2O$; gram-ionic weight, 492; density, 1.645 (see chromium potassium alum).

Discussion is the same as for the potassium alum except that paramagnetic-resonance experiments[3] indicate a unique value for the splitting δ. The following values of δ/k from demagnetization experiments have been reported: de Klerk and Hudson[4] (powder specimen), 0.275 deg; Gardner and Kurti[5] (compressed powder), 0.27; Hudson and McLane[6] (single crystal), 0.269 ± 0.003. The paramagnetic-resonance value is smaller than these values, and the discrepancy is probably due to some anisotropic exchange interaction.

The absolute temperature measurements of Gardner and Kurti are summarized in Table 4b-6.

[1] J. M. Daniels and N. Kurti, *Proc. Roy. Soc.* (*London*), ser. A, **221**, 243 (1954).
[2] B. Bleaney, *Proc. Roy. Soc. London*, ser. A., **204**, 216 (1950).
[3] B. Bleaney, *Proc. Roy. Soc.* (*London*), ser. A., **204**, 203 (1950).
[4] D. de Klerk and R. P. Hudson, *Phys. Rev.* **91**, 278 (1953).
[5] W. E. Gardner and N. Kurti, *Proc. Roy. Soc.* (*London*), A, **223**, 542 (1954).
[6] R. P. Hudson and C. K. McLane, *Phys. Rev.*, **95**, 932, (1954).

TABLE 4b-6. TEMPERATURE DATA ON CHROMIUM METHYLAMMONIUM ALUM (GARDNER AND KURTI)

S/R	T^*	T, °K	S/R	T^*	T, °K	S/R	T^*	T, °K
1.325	0.404	0.396	1.000	0.143	0.122	0.650	0.071	0.032
1.300	0.336	0.326	0.950	0.132	0.109	0.600	0.061	0.028
1.250	0.266	0.254	0.900	0.121	0.096	0.550	0.053	0.023
1.200	0.224	0.210	0.850	0.111	0.077	0.500	0.051	0.020
1.150	0.196	0.180	0.800	0.102	0.065	0.450	0.051	0.018
1.100	0.175	0.157	0.750	0.092	0.048	0.400	0.052	0.016
1.050	0.157	0.137	0.700	0.083	0.039	0.350	0.053	0.013

The results of Hudson and McLane are summarized in Table 4b-7.

TABLE 4b-7. TEMPERATURE DATA ON CHROMIUM METHYLAMMONIUM ALUM (HUDSON AND MCLANE)

H/T, gauss/deg	$\ln 4 - S/R$	T^*	T, °K	H/T, gauss/deg	$\ln 4 - S/R$	T^*	T, °K
1,000	0.0180	0.724	0.719	4,000	0.1668	0.232	0.216
1,250	0.0242	0.624	0.618	4,500	0.2034	0.208	0.191
1,500	0.0317	0.544	0.538	5,000	0.2422	0.189	0.170
1,750	0.0404	0.482	0.474	6,000	0.3234	0.160	0.138
2,000	0.0505	0.431	0.422	7,000	0.4064	0.138	0.114
2,500	0.0739	0.355	0.344	8,000	0.4885	0.120	0.0938
3,000	0.1013	0.302	0.289	9,000	0.5677	0.105	0.0763
3,500	0.1325	0.262	0.248				

T_i assumed T_i to be $\sim$1.15°K $\left(\frac{S}{R}\right)_{T_c} = 0.53$ $\frac{H}{T} = 13.4 \times 10^3$ $T_c \sim 0.02$°K

4. Copper Potassium Sulfate. $CuSO_4 \cdot K_2SO_4 \cdot 6H_2O$; gram-ionic weight, 442; density = 2.22; For spectroscopic data, see copper sulfate.

Bleaney, Bowers, and Ingram[1] find that $g_\parallel = 2.45$, $g_\perp = 2.14$. Benzie and Cooke[2] obtain $A/R = 6.0 \times 10^{-4}$ deg^2, in agreement with that found by Garrett[3] from demagnetization experiments, and a Curie-Weiss Δ of 0.034 deg. De Klerk[4] has published demagnetization data for a powder specimen taking a g value of 2; he also gives some corresponding values of T and T^*, T being measured via a potassium chromic alum thermometer. The Curie-Weiss Δ was found to be 0.052 deg and $A/R = 6.8 \times 10^{-4}$ deg^2; the contribution from magnetic interaction was calculated to be 1.35×10^{-4}.

Further demagnetization experiments by Steenland and others,[5] in which g was taken to be 2.18, report approximate absolute-temperature measurements in the range 0.0046 to 0.025°K [$(S/R)_{T_c} = 0.46$, $H/T = 11.5 \times 10^3$, $T_c = 0.05$°K]. The lowest values have been criticized by Daniels as being incompatible with the entropy and hyperfine structure.

[1] B. Bleaney, K. D. Bowers, and D. J. E. Ingram, *Proc. Phys. Soc.* (*London*), ser. A, **64,** 758 (1951).

[2] R. J. Benzie and A. H. Cooke, *Proc. Phys. Soc.* (*London*), ser. A, **63,** 201, 213 (1950).

[3] C. G. B. Garrett, *Proc. Roy. Soc.* (*London*), ser. A, **203,** 375 (1950).

[4] D. de Klerk, *Physica* **12,** 513 (1946).

[5] M. J. Steenland, D. de Klerk, J. A. Beun, and C. J. Gorter, *Physica* **17,** 161 (1951).

The contribution of nuclear hyperfine structure to A/R has been found to be 1.3×10^{-4} from demagnetization determinations,[1] 1.1×10^{-4} from relaxation experiments,[2] and 1.40×10^{-4} from the resonance spectrum.[3]

Reekie[4] obtained a Curie constant of 0.445 emu/g ion for a powdered sample.

5. Iron Ammonium Alum. $Fe_2(SO_4)_3 \cdot (NH_4)_2SO_4 \cdot 24H_2O$; gram-ionic weight, 482.2; density, 1.71; Fe^{3+} $3d^5$; $^6S_{\frac{5}{2}}$.

The free ion is in an S state and interaction with the crystalline electric field is abnormally small. The 6-fold degenerate level is split by a cubic field into a doublet and quadruplet. The measurements of Benzie and Cooke,[5] however, are more consistent with a splitting into three equally spaced doublets (and this has been confirmed by Meier[6]); their value for the over-all splitting is $\delta/k = 0.23$ deg (for the doublet-quadruplet pattern they calculate $\delta/k = 0.20$ deg). $A/R = 0.0143$ deg^2. The g values are all 2 within less than 1 per cent.[7] Cooke[8] reports low-temperature $T^* - T$ correlation, made by Kurti and Simon, given in graphical presentation; $T_c = 0.042$°K. The same data, for the region below 0.2°K, are summarized in Table 4b-8.

TABLE 4b-8. TEMPERATURE DATA ON IRON AMMONIUM ALUM (KURTI AND SIMON)

T, °K	T^*	T, °K	T^*	T, °K	T^*
0.015	0.0720	0.043	0.0850	0.090	0.1390
0.020	0.0702	0.045	0.0910	0.100	0.149
0.025	0.0683	0.050	0.0970	0.120	0.168
0.030	0.0670	0.055	0.1008	0.140	0.183
0.035	0.0666	0.060	0.1050	0.160	0.198
0.040	0.0666	0.070	0.1150	0.180	0.214
0.042	0.0668	0.080	0.1273	0.200	0.229

Steenland[9] and others obtain $T_c = 0.030$°K, $(S/R)_{T_c} = 0.65$, $H/T = 11.5 \times 10^3$.

De Klerk[10] finds $A/R = 0.0128$ deg,^{2} $\delta/k = 0.183$ deg, and the data in Table 4b-9.

TABLE 4b-9. TEMPERATURE DATA ON IRON AMMONIUM ALUM (DE KLERK)

H, gauss	T_i, °K	T_f, °K	$\ln 6 - S/R$
615	1.164	0.76	0.0071
825	1.164	0.62	0.0127
1,055	1.172	0.51	0.0203
1,260	1.173	0.44	0.0288
2,180	1.162	0.269	0.0844

[1] C. G. B. Garrett, *Proc. Roy. Soc.* (*London*), ser. A., **203**, 375 (1950).
[2] R. J. Benzie and A. H. Cooke, *Nature* **164**, 837 (1949).
[3] A. Abragam and M. H. L. Pryce, *Proc. Roy. Soc.* (*London*), ser. A, **206**, 164 (1951).
[4] J. Reekie, *Proc. Roy. Soc.* (*London*), ser. A, **173**, 367 (1939).
[5] R. J. Benzie and A. H. Cooke, *Proc. Phys. Soc.* (*London*), ser. A, **63**, 213 (1950).
[6] P. H. E. Meier, *Physica* **17**, 899 (1951).
[7] J. Ubbink, J. A. Poulis, and C. J. Gorter, *Physica* **17**, 213 (1951); C. A. Whitmer and R. T. Weidner, *Phys. Rev.* **84**, 159 (1951).
[8] A. H. Cooke, *Proc. Phys. Soc.* (*London*), ser. A, **62**, 269 (1949).
[9] M. J. Steenland, D. de Klerk, M. L. Potters, and C. J. Gorter, *Physica* **17**, 149 (1951).
[10] D. de Klerk, Thesis, p. 50, Leiden, 1948.

6. Gadolinium Sulfate. $Gd_2(SO_4)_3{\cdot}8H_2O$; gram-ionic weight, 373; density, 3.010; Gd^{3+}; $4f^7$; $^8S_{\frac{7}{2}}$.

Bleaney and others[1] report paramagnetic resonance experiments on gadolinium ethylsulfate and note that the spectrum is of the same nature in gadolinium sulfate. For the former, g is isotropic and equal to 1.993.

A/R has been found from paramagnetic-relaxation measurements e.g., 0.28 (de Haas and du Pre[2]), 0.33 (Bijl[3]) and 0.32 (Benzie and Cooke[4]). (By direct calorimetry in the liquid-helium range van Dijk and Auer[5] obtained 0.32.)

Hebb and Purcell's analysis[6] shows that the 8-fold ground level is split by a cubic field into two doublets and a quadruplet. van Dijk[7,8] finds that $\delta/k = 1.35$ deg gives the best agreement with the published data.

Giauque and MacDougall[9] used this substance for their first demagnetizations in 1933, reaching a lowest T^* of 0.24 deg. Van Dijk[7] measured absolute temperatures calorimetrically down to $T^* = 0.27$ deg ($T = 0.22$°K).

7. Manganese Ammonium Sulfate. $MnSO_4{\cdot}(NH_4)_2SO_4{\cdot}6H_2O$; gram-ionic weight, 391; density, 1.83; Mn^{++}; $3d^5$; $^6S_{\frac{5}{2}}$.

This is a Tutton salt similar to cobalt ammonium and copper potassium sulfates. The free ion is in an S state and the interaction with the crystalline electric field is very small. Resonance experiments[10] show that $g = 2.000$ and is isotropic to $\sim$1 in 10^4.

Relaxation measurements show that $A/R = 0.033$ (Benzie and Cooke[11]) and 0.034 (Bijl[3]).

Demagnetization experiments by Cooke and Hull[12] give $A/R = 0.033$, $T_c = 0.14$°K, $(S/R)_{T_c} = 1.27$, $H/T = 6.2 \times 10^3$ gauss/deg. Steenland and others[13] made absolute-temperature measurements in the region of and below T_c, the latter being found to be 0.10°K.

A surprisingly large hyperfine structure is observed[10] and has been explained by Abragam and Pryce.[14] Contributions to A/R are: Stark splitting + hyperfine structure 0.0154, dipole interaction 0.0092. This leaves 0.009, which must be ascribed to exchange.

8. Titanium Cesium Alum. $Ti_2(SO_4)_3{\cdot}Cs_2SO_4{\cdot}24H_2O$; gram-ionic weight, 589; Ti^{3+}; $3d^1$; $^2D_{\frac{3}{2}}$.

The orbital triplet (with 2-fold spin degeneracy) is split into three Kramers doublets by the action of the trigonal component of the crystal field and spin-orbit coupling. The separations are only a few hundred cm^{-1}. At low temperatures, only one doublet is populated, with effective $S = \frac{1}{2}$. Owing to the nearness of two higher states, the g value departs markedly from 2 and is anisotropic.

Bogle and Cooke (unpublished) found $g_\parallel = 1.25$, $g_\perp = 1.14$. Benzie and Cooke[15] find (for a powder): Curie constant, $C = 0.118$ emu per g ion, $g = 1.12$ (and estimate

[1] B. Bleaney, R. J. Elliott, H. E. D. Scovil, and R. S. Trenam, *Phil. Mag.* **42**, 1062 (1951).
[2] W. J. de Haas and F. K. du Pre, *Physica* **6**, 705 (1939).
[3] D. Bijl, *Physica* **16**, 269 (1950).
[4] R. J. Benzie and A. H. Cooke, *Proc. Phys. Soc.* (*London*), ser. A, **63**, 201, 213 (1950).
[5] H. van Dijk and W. V. Auer, *Physica* **9**, 785 (1942).
[6] M. H. Hebb and E. M. Purcell, *J. Chem. Phys.* **5**, 338 (1937).
[7] H. van Dijk, *Physica* **9**, 729 (1942).
[8] H. van Dijk, *Physica* **12**, 371 (1946).
[9] W. F. Giauque and D. P. MacDougall, *Phys. Rev.* **43**, 768 (1933).
[10] B. Bleaney and D. J. E. Ingram, *Proc. Roy. Soc.* (*London*), ser. A, **205**, 336 (1951).
[11] R. J. Benzie and A. H. Cooke, *Proc. Phys. Soc.* (*London*), ser. A, **201**, 213 (1950).
[12] A. H. Cooke, *Proc. Phys. Soc.* (*London*), ser. A, **62**, 269 (1949).
[13] M. J. Steenland, L. C. van der Marel, D. de Klerk, and C. J. Gorter, *Physica* **15**, 906 (1949).
[14] A. Abragam and M. H. L. Pryce, *Proc. Roy. Soc.* (*London*), ser. A, **205**, 135 (1951).
[15] R. J. Benzie and A. H. Cooke, *Proc. Roy. Soc.* (*London*), ser. A, **209**, 269 (1951).

$g_\parallel = 1.40, g_\perp = 0.96$), $A/C = 2.7 \times 10^4$ (± 10 per cent), and hence $A/R = 3.9 \times 10^{-5}$. Dilution experiments showed that nuclear hyperfine structure in the odd isotopes contributes 0.4×10^{-5} to A/R, and dipole interaction accounts for 0.3×10^{-5}. The balance (3.2×10^{-5}) must be due to exchange.

Adiabatic-demagnetization experiments[1] showed $(S/R)_{T_c} = 0.22$ for $H/T = 2.6 \times 10^3$ gauss/deg.

9. Cobalt Ammonium Sulfate. $CoSO_4 \cdot (NH_4)_2SO_4 \cdot 6H_2O$; gram-ionic weight, 395.2; density, 1.902; Co^{++}; $3d^7$; $^4F_{\frac{9}{2}}$.

In a cubic field the 7-fold orbital state is split into two triplets and a singlet, with one triplet the lowest. This triplet, with its 4-fold spin degeneracy, is then split into a number of doublets by the combined effect of the spin-orbit coupling and a tetragonal or trigonal field. For the lowest doublet (effective $S = \frac{1}{2}$) $g_\parallel = 6.45$, $g_\perp = 3.05$.[2]

There are two ions in unit cell, their tetragonal axes lying in the K_1K_3 plane and inclined at 33° to the K_1 axis, on opposite sides of it. Because of the anisotropy, C varies markedly for the K_1, K_2, and K_3 axes: $C_1 = 3.00$, $C_2 = 0.873$, and $C_3 = 1.77$ emu per g ion.

Garrett,[3] taking $g_\parallel = 6.2$, $g_\perp = 3.0$, obtained $S - T^* - T$ data for the K_1, K_2, and K_3 axes. $A/R = 4.30 \times 10^{-3}$ deg². The critical temperature is found to be 0.084°K.

Malaker[4] found 1.61×10^{-3} for the nuclear contribution to A/R, which is in good agreement with the resonance-experiments value[5] of 1.66×10^{-3}. The dipolar contribution is 1.9×10^{-3}.

10. Copper Sulfate. $CuSO_4 \cdot 5H_2O$; gram-ionic weight, 249.7; density, 2.279; Cu^{++}; $3d^9$; $^2D_{\frac{5}{2}}$.

In a cubic field the orbital levels split into an upper triplet and a lower doublet. In a tetragonal or rhombic field the doublet is further split into two singlets. The latter are still spin-degenerate and, at low temperatures, effectively $S = \frac{1}{2}$. In this salt there is a considerable exchange interaction. The specific heat is rather complicated with a pronounced minimum at 1.37°K, a small anomaly at 0.75°K, and a further peak below 0.25°K[6].

There are two ions in unit cell, the angle between their tetragonal axes being approximately 80 deg. Benzie and Cooke[7] measured the susceptibility along the magnetic axis χ_a and perpendicular to it χ_e and found

$$\chi_a = \frac{0.407}{T + 0.6} \qquad (= \chi_\perp)$$

$$\chi_e = \frac{0.480}{T + 0.6} \qquad \left(= \frac{\chi_\parallel + \chi_\perp}{2} \right)$$

[1] N. Kurti, P. Laine, and F. Simon, *Compt. rend.* **204**, 675 (1937).
[2] B. Bleaney and D. H. E. Ingram, *Proc. Roy. Soc.* (*London*), ser. A, **208**, 143 (1951).
[3] C. G. B. Garrett, *Proc. Roy. Soc.* (*London*), ser. A, **206**, 242 (1951).
[4] S. F. Malaker, *Phys. Rev.* **84**, 133 (1951).
[5] A. H. Cooke, H. J. Duffus, and W. P. Wolf, *Phil. Mag.* **44**, (7), 623 (1953).
[6] T. H. Geballe and W. F. Giauque, *J. Amer. Chem. Soc.* **74**, 3513 (1952).
[7] R. J. Benzie and A. H. Cooke, *Proc. Phys. Soc.* (*London*), ser. A, **64**, 124 (1951).

4c. Critical Constants

DAVID WHITE

The Ohio State University

Table 4c-1, which is presented in this section, was compiled from the review article by K. A. Kobe and R. E. Lynn, Jr.,[1] where references may be found. Kelvin temperatures can be calculated from the relation

$$T°K = t°C + 273.16$$

TABLE 4c-1. CRITICAL TEMPERATURE, PRESSURE, AND DENSITY OF ELEMENTS AND COMPOUNDS

	t_c, °C	P_c, atm	ρ_c, g/cm³
Inorganic:			
Ammonia	132.35	111.3	0.235
Argon	−122.44	48.00	0.5308
Boron tribromide	300	......	0.90
Boron trichloride	178.8	38.2	
Boron trifluoride	−12.3	49.2	
Bromine	311	102	1.18
Carbon dioxide	31.04	72.85	0.468
Carbon disulfide	279	78	0.441
Carbon monoxide	−140.2	34.5	0.3010
Carbonyl sulfide	105	61	
Chlorine	144.0	76.1	0.573
Chlorotrifluorosilane	34.48	34.20	
Cyanogen	127	59	
Deuterium (equilibrium)	−234.90	16.28	0.0668
Deuterium (normal)	−234.81	16.43	
Dichlorodifluorosilane	95.77	35.54	
Germanium tetrachloride	276.9	38	
Helium³	−269.82	1.15	
Helium⁴	−267.95	2.26	0.0693
Hydrazone	380	145	
Hydrogen (equilibrium)	−240.22	12.77	0.0308
Hydrogen (normal)	−239.92	12.80	0.03102
Hydrogen bromide	89.80	84.00	
Hydrogen chloride	51.4	81.5	0.423
Hydrogen cyanide	183.5	53.2	0.195

See page 4–23 for footnotes.

[1] *Chem. Rev.* **52**, 117–236 (1953).

TABLE 4c-1. CRITICAL TEMPERATURE, PRESSURE, AND DENSITY OF ELEMENTS AND COMPOUNDS (*Continued*)

	t_c, °C	P_c, atm	ρ_c, g/cm³
Hydrogen deuteride	−237.25	14.65	0.0481
Hydrogen fluoride	230.2		
Hydrogen iodide	150.0	80.8	
Hydrogen selenide	138	88	
Hydrogen sulfide	100.4	88.9	0.3488
Iodine	553		
Krypton	−63.77	54.27	0.9085
Neon	−228.72	26.86	0.4835
Nitric acid	−92.9	64.6	0.52
Nitrogen	−146.9	33.54	0.3110
Nitrogen peroxide	158	100	0.56
Nitrous oxide	36.5	71.65	0.459
Oxygen	−118.38	50.14	0.41
Oxygen fluoride*	−58.0	48.9	0.553
Ozone†	12.1	54.6	
Phosgene	182	56	0.52
Phosphine	51.3	64.5	
Phosphonium chloride	49.1	72.7	
Silane	−3.5	47.8	
Silicon tetrachloride	233.6		
Silicon tetrafluoride	−14.15	36.66	
Stannic chloride	318.7	36.95	0.7419
Sulfur	1040	116	
Sulfur dioxide	157.5	77.79	0.524
Sulfur hexafluoride	45.55	37.11	0.7517
Sulfur trioxide	218.2	83.8	0.633
Trichlorofluorosilane	165.26	35.33	
Uranium hexafluoride	230.2	45.5	
Water	374.2	218.3	0.326
Xenon	16.590	58.0	1.105
Organic:			
Acetic acid	321.6	57.1	0.351
Acetic anhydride	296	46.2	
Acetone	235.5	46.6	0.273
Acetylene	36.3	61.6	0.231
Benzene	289.5	48.6	0.300
Bromobenzene	397.7	44.6	0.458
n-Butane	152.01	37.47	0.228
1-Butene	146.4	39.7	0.234
Carbon tetrachloride	283.2	44.97	0.558
Chlorobenzene	359.2	44.6	0.365
Chlorodifluoromethane	96.4	48.48	0.525
Chloroform	263.4	54	0.496
Chlorotrifluoromethane	28.86	38.2	0.578
Cyclohexane	281.0	40.57	0.273
Cyclopentane	238.6	44.55	0.27

See page 4–23 for footnotes.

TABLE 4c-1. CRITICAL TEMPERATURE, PRESSURE, AND DENSITY OF ELEMENTS AND COMPOUNDS (*Concluded*)

	t_c, °C	P_c, atm	ρ_c, g/cm³
Dibromomethane	309.8	70.6	
Dichlorodifluoromethane	111.5	39.6	0.555
Dichlorofluoromethane	178.5	51.0	0.522
Diethyl ether	194.6	35.6	0.265
Dimethyl amine	164.5	52.4	
Dimethyl ether	126.9	52.6	0.246
Ethane	32.27	48.20	0.203
Ethyl alcohol	243	63.0	0.276
Ethyl amine	183.2	55.54	
Ethyl bromide	230.7	61.5	0.507
Ethyl chloride	187.2	51.72	
Ethyl fluoride	102.16	46.62	
Ethyl formate	235.3	46.8	0.323
Ethyl sulfide	225.5	54.2	0.300
Ethylene	9.90	50.50	0.227
Ethylene oxide	195.8	70.97	0.32
Fluorobenzene	286.55	44.6	0.354
n-Hexane	234.7	29.94	0.234
Iodobenzene	448	44.6	0.581
Methane	−82.1	45.80	0.162
Methyl alcohol	240.0	78.47	0.272
Methyl amine	156.9	73.6	
Methyl bromide	191		
Methyl chloride	143.12	65.93	0.353
Methyl fluoride	44.55	58.0	0.300
Methyl formate	214.0	59.2	0.349
Methyl iodide	255		
Methyl sulfide	229.9	54.6	0.309
Methylene chloride	237.0	59.97	
Nitromethane	62.3	......	0.352
n-Pentane	196.62	33.31	0.232
Phenol	419.2	60.5	
Propane	96.80	42.01	0.220
Propene	91.8	45.6	0.233
n-Propyl alcohol	264.1	50.2	0.273
Propyne	128	52.8	
Toluene	320.8	41.6	0.29
Trichlorofluoromethane	198.0	43.2	0.554

* R. Anderson, J. G. Schnizlein, R. C. Toole, and T. D. O'Brien, *J. Phys. Chem.* **56,** 473–474 (1952).
† A. C. Jenkins and C. M. Birdsall, *J. Chem. Phys.* **20,** 1158–1161 (1952).

4d. High-pressure Effects

P. W. BRIDGMAN

Harvard University

Critical phenomena and data for gases are not treated here but will be found in other sections. The literature dealing with the effects of pressure on liquids and solids is very extensive, and only a typical selection can be attempted. The data presented here have been selected to cover as wide a range as possible, both of pressure and of the nature of the material. References to the general subject are:

Bridgman, P. W.: "The Physics of High Pressure," George Bell & Sons, Ltd.; London, 1949.

Bridgman, P. W.: Recent Work in the Field of High Pressures, *Rev. Modern Phys.* **18**, 1–93 (1946).

Timmermans, J.: "Les Constantes physiques des composés organiques cristallises," Masson et Cie, Paris, 1953.

In the following, single phases are treated first, and then systems of two phases. The data for single-phase systems consist mostly of volume as a function of pressure, at several temperatures when the data have been determined, but in a number of cases at only a single temperature. From these data, compressibilities may be found and also thermal expansions if the volumes are known for more than one temperature. Other thermodynamic parameters, such as specific heats, have been directly determined as a function of pressure in very few cases and have to be inferred from the volume relations by indirect methods. No attempt is made here to give any of these values.

For the two-phase systems, the melting curves are given first, including, when known, the other parameters necessary to completely characterize the melting thermodynamically; these are change of volume and latent heat. Finally, the transition parameters for a few systems exhibiting polymorphism under pressure are given. The phase diagrams of these substances are also given for greater clarity. In most cases the various transition lines are sufficiently characterized by the parameters at the triple points, which are indicated in the tables.

TABLE 4d-1. SPECIFIC VOLUME OF WATER*
(In cm^3/g; in the range 200 to 1000°C and 100 to 2,500 bars)

Temp., °C	Pressure, bars						
	100	200	500	1,000	1,500	2,000	2,500
200	1.14830	1.13899	1.1145	1.0811	1.0533	1.0258	1.0027
300	1.39704	1.35992	1.2869	1.2131	1.1639	1.1257	1.0946
400	26.31	9.96	1.745	1.4443	1.3284	1.2591	1.2092
500	32.35	14.77	3.890	1.8794	1.5653	1.4402	1.3566
600	37.78	18.11	6.114	2.6802	1.9496	1.6630	1.5252
700	42.517	20.973	7.7651	3.5829	2.449	1.980	1.7346
800	46.082	23.391	9.0925	4.4338	2.994	2.350	2.000
900	49.54	25.74	10.28	5.208	3.531	2.738	2.296
1000	52.90	27.84	11.30	5.900	4.035	3.123	2.589

* G. C. Kennedy, *Am. J. Sci.* **248,** 540 (1950).

TABLE 4d-2. SPECIFIC VOLUME OF WATER*
(In cm^3/g; between 0 and 95°C and up to 11,000 kg/cm^2)

Pressure, kg/cm^2	Temp., °C		
	0	50	95
1	1.0001	1.0121	1.0396
500	0.9772		
1,000	0.9568	0.9742	0.9985
1,500	0.9397	0.9583	0.9813
2,000	0.9249	0.9440	0.9662
3,000	0.8997	0.9202	0.9410
4,000	0.8796	0.8998	0.9195
5,000	0.8627	0.8825	0.9010
6,000	......	0.8669	0.8850
7,000	......	0.8531	0.8706
8,000	......	0.8408	0.8578
9,000	......	0.8297	0.8462
10,000	......	0.8193	0.8353
11,000	......	......	0.8257

* P. W. Bridgman, *Proc. Am. Acad. Arts Sci.* **66,** 185 (1931).

TABLE 4d-3. RELATIVE VOLUMES OF MERCURY, ETHYL ALCOHOL, AND ETHYL ETHER AT SEVERAL TEMPERATURES*

(To 12,000 kg/cm². Relative volumes in terms of volume at 0°C and atmospheric pressure)

Pressure kg/cm²	Mercury		Ethyl alcohol			Ethyl ether		
	0°C	22°C	20°C	50°C	80°C	20°C	50°C	80°C
1	1.00000	1.00398	1.0212	1.0557	1.0934	1.0315		
500	....	....	0.9794	1.0044	1.0334	0.9681	1.0011	1.0387
1,000	0.99626	1.00007	0.9506	0.9707	0.9944	0.9363	0.9616	0.9906
1,500	....	....	0.9267	0.9440	0.9640	0.9093	0.9291	0.9516
2,000	0.99261	0.99627	0.9081	0.9235	0.9407	0.8871	0.9038	0.9223
3,000	0.98905	0.99264	0.8786	0.8919	0.9055	0.8530	0.8670	0.8812
4,000	0.98561	0.98909	0.8545	0.8668	0.8787	0.8275	0.8400	0.8552
5,000	0.98231	0.98571	0.8343	0.8461	0.8568	0.8071	0.8186	0.8284
6,000	0.97914	0.98246	0.8178	0.8291	0.8387	0.7916	0.8023	0.8112
7,000	0.97607	0.97934	0.8038	0.8142	0.8229	0.7773	0.7869	0.7953
8,000	....	0.97637	0.7917	0.8013	0.8094	0.7645	0.7732	0.7813
9,000	....	0.97356	0.7807	0.7893	0.7973	0.7525	0.7606	0.7687
10,000	....	0.97088	0.7703	0.7785	0.7863	0.7418	0.7496	0.7574
11,000	....	0.96835	0.7606	0.7693	0.7765	0.7312	0.7388	0.7469
12,000	....	0.96596	0.7521	0.7600	0.7682	0.7216	0.7289	0.7365

* P. W. Bridgman, *Proc. Am. Acad. Arts Sci.* **47,** 347 (1911) (mercury); **49,** 1 (1913) (ethyl alcohol, ethyl ether).

TABLE 4d-4. RELATIVE VOLUMES OF CS_2 AND *n*-PENTANE AT SEVERAL TEMPERATURES*

(To 12,000 kg/cm². Relative volumes in terms of volume at 0°C and atmospheric pressure)

Pressure, kg/cm²	CS_2			*n*-Pentane		
	20°C	50°C	80°C	0°C	50°C	95°C
1	1.0235	1.0630	1.1092	1.0000	(1.0837)	(1.1869)
500	0.9865	1.0158	1.0473			
1,000	0.9586	0.9829	1.0083	0.9021	0.9395	0.9768
1,500	0.9358	0.9571	0.9787			
2,000	0.9173	0.9362	0.9552	0.8546	0.8820	0.9078
3,000	0.8877	0.9033	0.9185	0.8229	0.8454	0.8671
4,000	0.8647	0.8770	0.8902	0.7997	0.8193	0.8371
5,000	0.8453	0.8570	0.8676	0.7811	0.7985	0.8125
6,000	0.8295	0.8406	0.8501	0.7647	0.7807	0.7933
7,000	0.8147	0.8257	0.8347	0.7506	0.7657	0.7775
8,000	0.8022	0.8131	0.8220	0.7381	0.7520	0.7641
9,000	0.7911	0.8020	0.8107	0.7281	0.7409	0.7527
10,000	0.7805	0.7910	0.7997	0.7192	0.7316	0.7433
11,000	0.7715	0.7809	0.7894			
12,000	0.7638	0.7710	0.7795			

* P. W. Bridgman, *Proc. Am. Acad. Arts Sci.* **49,** 1, (1913) (CS_2); **66,** 185 (1931) (*n*-pentane).

TABLE 4d-5. RELATIVE VOLUMES OF *n*-OCTANE, BENZENE, AND GLYCERINE AT SEVERAL TEMPERATURES*
(To 12,000 kg/cm². Relative volumes in terms of volume at 0°C and atmospheric pressure)

Pressure, kg/cm²	*n*-Octane			Benzene, C_6H_6		Glycerine		
	0°C	50°C	95°C	50°C	95°C	0°C	50°C	95°C
1	1.0000	1.0595	1.1230	1.0630	1.1295	1.0000	1.0266	
500	0.9572	1.0005	......	1.0160	......	0.9900	1.0136	
1,000	0.9311	0.9654	0.9943	0.9841	1.0201	0.9806	1.0025	1.0240
1,500	......	......	......	0.9591	0.9916	0.9721	0.9930	1.0125
2,000	0.8924	0.9200	0.9422	......	0.9684	0.9641	0.9843	1.0024
3,000	0.8640	0.8882	0.9068	......	0.9325	0.9501	0.9688	0.9853
4,000	......	0.8639	0.8802	......	......	0.9373	0.9548	0.9700
5,000	......	0.8428	0.8592	......	......	0.9264	0.9423	0.9565
6,000	......	0.8251	0.8416	......	......	0.9157	0.9310	0.9447
7,000	......	0.8103	0.8267	......	......	0.9057	0.9211	0.9342
8,000	......	......	0.8134	......	......	0.8958	0.9121	0.9244
9,000	......	......	0.8014	......	......	0.8867	0.9036	0.9152
10,000	......	......	0.7915	......	......	0.8783	0.8955	0.9070
11,000	......	......	......	......	......	0.8712	0.8879	0.8994
12,000	......	......	......	......	......	0.8648	0.8800	0.8925

* P. W. Bridgman, *Proc. Am. Acad. Arts Sci.* **66**, 185 (1931) (*n*-octane benzene); **67**, 1 (1932) (glycerine).

TABLE 4d-6. VOLUME OF SOLID HELIUM AT 0°K*

Pressure, kg/cm²	Volume, ml/mole	Compressibility $(1/v)(\partial v/\partial p)_T$
52	19.0	184×10^{-5}
91	18.0	135
141	17.0	100
207	16.0	73
305	15.0	52
475	14.0	37
718	13.0	25
1,105	12.0	16
1,715	11.0	12
2,240	10.5	10

* J. S. Dugdale and F. E. Simon, *Proc. Roy. Soc.* (*London*) **218**, 291 (1953).

TABLE 4d-7. FRACTIONAL CHANGE OF VOLUME AT 25°C OF RELATIVELY INCOMPRESSIBLE METALS*

Pressure, kg/cm²	$\Delta V/V_0$						
	W	Pt	Fe	Cu	Ag	Au	Al
5,000	0.00155	0.00176	0.00289	0.00353	0.00473	0.00281	0.00668
10,000	0.00309	0.00351	0.00575	0.00696	0.00938	0.00558	0.01312
15,000	0.00475	0.00526	0.00856	0.01039	0.01385	0.00831	0.01932
20,000	0.00634	0.00701	0.01133	0.01370	0.01820	0.01101	0.02520
25,000	0.00797	0.00877	0.01407	0.01695	0.02236	0.01367	0.03090
30,000	0.00959	0.01048	0.01676	0.02010	0.02619	0.01626	0.03642

* P. W. Bridgman, *Proc. Am. Acad. Arts Sci.* **77**, 187 (1949).

TABLE 4d-8. RELATIVE VOLUMES OF VARIOUS SOLIDS AT 25°C*

Pressure, kg/cm²	Lucite	Cellulose acetate	Bakelite	Hard rubber	Nylon 6–10	Teflon	Orthoclase
1	1.0000	1.0000	1.0000	1.0000	1.0000	1.0000	1.0000
2,500	0.9633	0.9532	0.9760	0.9684	0.9615	0.9473	
5,000	0.9329	0.9216	0.9562	0.9390	0.9345	0.9153	
10,000	0.8903	0.8811	0.9240	0.8955	0.8940	0.8547	0.9829
15,000	0.8613	0.8514	0.8978	0.8655	0.8652	0.8306	
20,000	0.8329	0.8283	0.8765	0.8427	0.8430	0.8125	0.9667
30,000	0.8051	0.7935	0.8436	0.8083	0.8100	0.7857	0.9512
40,000	0.7816	0.7682	0.8188	0.7834	0.7861	0.7661	0.9366

Pressure, kg/cm²	Calcite	Garnet	Iodoform	Urea nitrate	Potassium phosphate	Potassium alum
1	1.0000	1.0000	1.0000	1.0000	1.0000	1.0000
5,000	......	......	0.9451	0.9628	0.9821	0.9718
10,000	0.9866	0.9929	0.9079	0.9358	0.9665	0.9486
15,000	tr.	......	0.8806	0.9145	0.9526	0.9296
20,000	0.9275	0.9862	0.8586	0.8966	0.9401	0.9131
30,000	0.9113	0.9800	0.8241	0.8669	0.9183	0.8843
40,000	0.8981	0.9743	0.7966	0.8431	0.9004	0.8607

* P. W. Bridgman, *Proc. Am. Acad. Arts Sci.* **76**, 71 (1948).

TABLE 4d-9. RELATIVE VOLUMES OF SOME OF THE MORE COMPRESSIBLE ELEMENTS, SALTS, AND OTHER SOLIDS AT 25°C*

Pressure, kg/cm²	Li	Na	K	Rb	Cs	Ca	Sr	Ba	C
1	1.000	1.000	1.000	1.000	1.000	1.000	1.000	1.000	1.000
10,000	0.928	0.889	0.814	0.802	0.761	0.942	0.925	0.914	
20,000	0.874	0.816	0.723	0.708	0.656	0.897	0.878	0.841^{tr}	
30,000	0.833	0.770	0.668	0.652	0.571^{tr}	0.861	0.828^{tr}	0.789^{tr}	0.940
40,000	0.801	0.737	0.628	0.612	0.521	0.832	0.791	0.747	0.929
50,000	0.773	0.708	0.595	0.578	0.431^{tr}	0.805	0.761	0.712	0.919
60,000	0.748	0.683	0.568	0.551	0.409	0.780	0.734	0.682^{tr}	0.911
70,000	0.727	0.661	0.546	0.528	0.392	0.748^{tr}	0.702^{tr}	0.639	0.903
80,000	0.707	0.641	0.528	0.507	0.381	0.732	0.683	0.618	0.896
90,000	0.689	0.623	0.513	0.489	0.375	0.716	0.665	0.598	0.890
100,000	0.672	0.606	0.500	0.473	0.368	0.702	0.648	0.580	0.885

* P. W. Bridgman, *Proc. Am. Acad. Arts Sci.* **76**, 55, 71 (1948); **74**, 425 (1942).

TABLE 4d-10. RELATIVE VOLUMES OF SOLIDS AT 25°C*

Pressure, kg/cm²	Mg	Sn	Pb	Bi	S	NaCl	NaI	CsCl	CsI
1	1.000	1.000	1.000	1.000	1.000	1.000	1.000	1.000	1.000
10,000	.....	0.982	0.978	0.972	0.917	0.962	0.944	0.952	0.935
20,000	.....	0.966	0.959	0.948	0.869	0.932	0.902	0.914	0.887
30,000	0.935	0.951	0.941	0.842^{tr}	0.837	0.907	0.868	0.882	0.849
40,000	0.919	0.936	0.925	0.826	0.812	0.885	0.840	0.856	0.818
50,000	0.904	0.923	0.901	0.808^{tr}	0.792	0.865	0.816	0.834	0.792
60,000	0.890	0.909	0.898	0.795	0.775	0.848	0.795	0.816	0.770
70,000	0.878	0.897	0.885	0.778^{tr}	0.760	0.832	0.777	0.801	0.751
80,000	0.866	0.886	0.874	0.768	0.747	0.817	0.761	0.788	0.734
90,000	0.856	0.875	0.864	0.760	0.736	0.803	0.747	0.777	0.719
100,000	0.847	0.864	0.855	0.739^{tr}	0.726	0.790	0.734	0.767	0.706

Pressure, kg/cm²	$NaNO_3$	PbS	PbTe	Quartz crystal	Quartz glass	Pyrex glass
1	1.000	1.000	1.000	1.000	1.000	1.000
10,000	0.966	0.980	0.978	0.976	0.970	0.969
20,000	0.938	0.962	0.961	0.955	0.939	0.938
30,000	0.914	0.928^{tr}	0.939	0.939	0.909	0.907
40,000	0.893	0.918	0.930	0.926	0.885	0.885
50,000	0.873	0.909	0.884^{tr}	0.914	0.864	0.867
60,000	0.846	0.900	0.869	0.902	0.847	0.851
70,000	0.833^{tr}	0.892	0.855	0.892	0.832	0.838
80,000	0.820	0.886	0.842	0.883	0.819	0.827
90,000	0.809	0.881	0.831	0.875	0.808	0.817
100,000	0.799	0.876	0.820	0.868	0.798	0.809

*P. W. Bridgman, *Proc. Am. Acad. Arts Sci.* **76**, 55. 71 (1948); **74**, 425 (1942).

TABLE 4d-11. MELTING OF HYDROGEN AND HELIUM*

Temp., °K	Hydrogen pressure, kg/cm²	Helium				
		Pressure, kg/cm²	Entropies, cal/mole deg		Volumes, ml/mole	
			Solid	Fluid	Solid	Fluid
5	.....	196	0.23	1.70	16.21	17.14
10	.....	595	0.48	2.00	13.45	14.13
15	4	1,150	0.66	2.26	12.08	12.65
20	213	1,800	0.86	2.54	11.10	11.61
25	438	2,540	1.04	2.82	10.25	10.72
30	706	3,350				
40	1,370	5,260				
55	2,200					
60	3,180					
70	4,330					
80	5,630					

* F. Simon, *Z. Elektrochem.* **35,** 618 (1929); F. Simon, M. Ruhemann, and W. A. M. Edwards, *Z. physik. Chem.* **5,** 331 (1930); J. S. Dugdale and F. E. Simon, *Proc. Roy. Soc.* (*London*) **218,** 291 (1953).

TABLE 4d-12. MELTING PARAMETERS OF NITROGEN AND ARGON*

Pressure, kg/cm²	Nitrogen			Argon		
	Temp., °K	ΔV, cm³/g	Latent heat, kg cm/g	Temp., °K	ΔV, cm³/g	Latent heat, kg cm/g
1	63.1	(0.072)	(218)	83.9	0.0795	280
1,000	82.3	0.058	271	106.3	0.0555	280
2,000	98.6	0.047	302	126.4	0.0425	279
3,000	113.0	0.040	334	144.9	0.0340	277
4,000	125.8	0.033	335	162.0	0.0280	275
5,000	137.8	0.029	342	178.0	0.0240	276
6,000	149.2	0.026	346	193.1	0.0210	277

* P. W. Bridgman, *Phys. Rev.* **46,** 930 (1934).

TABLE 4d-13. MELTING PARAMETERS OF VARIOUS SUBSTANCES*

Pressure, kg/cm²	Mercury			Carbon dioxide			Sodium			Potassium		
	Temp., °C	ΔV, cm³/g	Latent heat kg cm/g	Temp., °C	ΔV, cm³/g	Latent heat kg cm/g	Temp., °C	ΔV, cm³/g	Latent heat, kg cm/g	Temp., °C	ΔV, cm³/g	Latent heat, kg cm/g
1	−38.9	0.00253	118	−56.6	......	.....	97.6	0.0279	1,180	62.5	0.0268	551
1,000	−33.8	0.00253	119	−37.3	......	.....	105.9	0.0256	1,174	78.7	0.0237	581
2,000	−28.6	0.00253	122	−20.5	......	.....	113.9	0.0236	1,171	92.4	0.0211	602
3,000	−23.5	0.00252	124	− 5.5	0.1071	1,668	121.5	0.0220	1,168	104.7	0.0188	615
4,000	−18.4	0.00251	126	+ 8.5	0.0979	1,688	128.8	0.0207	1,169	115.8	0.0168	622
5,000	−13.4	0.00250	128	21.4	0.0896	1,689	135.8	0.0197	1,176	126.0	0.0150	621
6,000	− 8.3	0.00249	130	33.1	0.0822	1,679	142.5	0.0187	1,189	135.4	0.0135	612
7,000	− 3.2	0.00247	132	44.2	0.0755	1,655	148.9	0.0179	1,207	144.1	0.0121	600
8,000	+ 1.8	0.00245	133	55.2	0.0697	1,630	155.1	0.0171	1,221	152.5	0.0107	585
9,000	6.9	0.00241	134	65.8	0.0644	1,610	161.0	0.0163	1,227	160.1	0.0095	567
10,000	11.9	0.00238	135	75.4	0.0602	1,603	166.7	0.0156	1,226	167.0	0.0084	543
11,000	16.9	0.00234	135	84.6	0.0564	1,604	172.2	0.0148	1,218	173.6	0.0074	516
12,000	22.0	0.00229	135	93.5	0.0531	1,612	177.5	0.0140	1,207	179.6	0.0064	483
23,000	75.3											

See page 4-33 for footnotes.

TABLE 4d-13. MELTING PARAMETERS OF VARIOUS SUBSTANCES* (*Continued*)

Pressure, kg/cm²	Carbon tetrachloride			Benzene			Phosphorus			Bismuth		
	Temp., °C	ΔV, cm³/g	Latent heat, kg cm/g	Temp., °C	ΔV, cm³/g	Latent heat, kg cm/g	Temp., °C	ΔV, cm³/g	Latent heat, kg cm/g	Temp., °C	ΔV, cm³/g	Latent heat, kg cm/g
1	−22.6	0.0258	167	5.4	0.1317	1,288	44.2	0.0193	209	271.0	0.00345	549
1,000	+14.2	0.0201	150	32.5	0.1026	1,294	72.7	0.0179	227	267.5	0.00354	536
2,000	45.9	0.0165	141	56.5	0.0872	1,306	99.3	0.0167	241	263.8	0.00362	524
3,000	75.8	0.0140	134	77.7	0.0759	1,324	124.4	0.0155	252	260.0	0.00370	511
4,000	102.7	0.0120	127	96.6	0.0675	1,347	148.2	0.0144	263	256.0	0.00378	498
5,000	126.8	0.0102	120	114.6	0.0614	1,370	170.5	0.0133	272	251.9	0.00386	485
6,000	149.5	0.0086	113	131.2	0.0564	1,390	191.9	0.0122	278	247.6	0.00394	472
7,000	171.0	0.0073	104	147.2	0.0522	1,405	.....	......	...	243.2	0.00401	459
8,000	192.1	0.0062	95	162.2	0.0485	1,415	.....	......	...	238.6	0.00407	444
9,000	211.9	0.0054	88	176.7	0.0451	1,420	.....	......	...	233.8	0.00413	430
10,000	......	......	...	190.7	0.0422	1,421	.....	......	...	228.8	0.00419	416
11,000	......	......	...	204.2	0.0394	1,420	.....	......	...	223.6	0.00424	401
12,000	......	......	...	.....	......	.....	.....	......	...	218.3	0.00429	388

See page 4-33 for footnotes.

TABLE 4d-13. MELTING PARAMETERS OF VARIOUS SUBSTANCES* (*Continued*)

Pressure, kg/cm²	Ethyl alcohol			*n*-Butyl alcohol			Chloroform			Tin	Carbon bisulfide			Lead
	Temp., °C	ΔV, cm³/g	Latent heat, kg cm/g	Temp., °C	ΔV, cm³/g	Latent heat, kg cm/g	Temp., °C	ΔV, cm³/g	Latent heat, kg cm/g	temp., °C	Temp., °C	ΔV, cm³/g	Latent heat, kg cm/g	temp., °C
1	−117.3	......	.....	−89.8	......	.....	−63.5	......	.....	232	−111.6	......	.....	327
5,000	− 76	......	.....	−33	......	.....	+10	0.0430	870	247	− 51	......	.....	363
10,000	− 39	......	.....	+12	0.0478	1,690	76	0.0354	980	261	0	0.0285	820	396
15,000	− 5	0.0443	1,850	49	0.0432	2,050	137	0.0301	1,070	275	+ 46	0.0247	900	428
20,000	+ 25	0.0435	2,200	80	0.0399	2,430	192	0.0262	1,160	287	89	0.0222	960	458
25,000	54	0.0428	2,480	108	0.0373	2,730	243	0.0231	1,240	298	130	0.0205	1,030	486
30,000	82	0.0420	2,700	132	0.0352	3,040	......	......	.....	309	170	0.0195	1,110	512
35,000	109	0.0412	2,910	155	0.0333	3,390	......	......	.....	319	209	0.0187	1,190	537

* P. W. Bridgman, *Proc. Am. Acad. Arts Sci.* **47,** 347 (1911); **74,** 399 (1942); *Phys. Rev.* **3,** 126, 153 (1914); **6,** 1, 94 (1915); V. P. Butuzov and M. G. Gonikberg, *Doklady Akad. Nauk SSSSR* **91,** 1083 (1953).

TABLE 4d-14. TRANSITION PARAMETERS OF WATER AND ICE (See also Fig. 4d-1)

Pressure, kg/cm²	Temp., °C	ΔV, cm³/g	Latent heat, kg cm/g	Triple point
		I-liquid		
1	0	0.0900	3,410	
1,130	−10.0	0.1122	2,900	
2,115	−22.0	0.1352	2,390	T.P.
		I-III		
2,115	−22.0	0.1818	220	T.P.
2,170	−34.7	0.1963	90	T.P.
		Liquid-III		
2,115	−22.0	0.0466	−2,170	T.P.
3,530	−17.0	0.0241	−2,620	T.P.
		I-II		
2,170	−34.7	0.2178	−430	T.P.
1,794	−75.0	0.2146	−380	
		III-II		
2,170	−34.7	0.0215	−520	T.P.
3,510	−24.3	0.0145	−720	T.P.
		Liquid-V		
3,530	−17.0	0.0788	−2,660	T.P.
6,380	+.16	0.0527	−2,990	T.P.
		III-V		
3,530	−17.0	0.0547	−40	T.P.
3,510	−24.3	0.0546	−40	T.P.
		II-V		
3,510	−24.3	0.0401	680	T.P.
4,200	−34.0	0.0401	660	
		V-VI		
6,380	+0.16	0.0389	−10	T.P.
6,365	−20	0.0381	−10	
		Liquid-V		
6,380	+0.16	0.0916	−3,000	T.P.
10,590	30.0	0.0663	−3,360	
16,000	57.2	0.0478	−3,430	
22,400	81.6	0.0330	−3,610	T.P.
		VI-VII		
22,000	0.0	0.0567	−290	
22,350	+40.0	0.0573	−60	
22,400	81.6	0.0580	0	T.P.
		Liquid-VII		
22,400	81.6	0.0910	−3,610	T.P.
28,000	124.1	0.0817	−4,840	
34,000	161.1	0.0738	−5,650	
40,000	192.3	0.0674	−6,550	

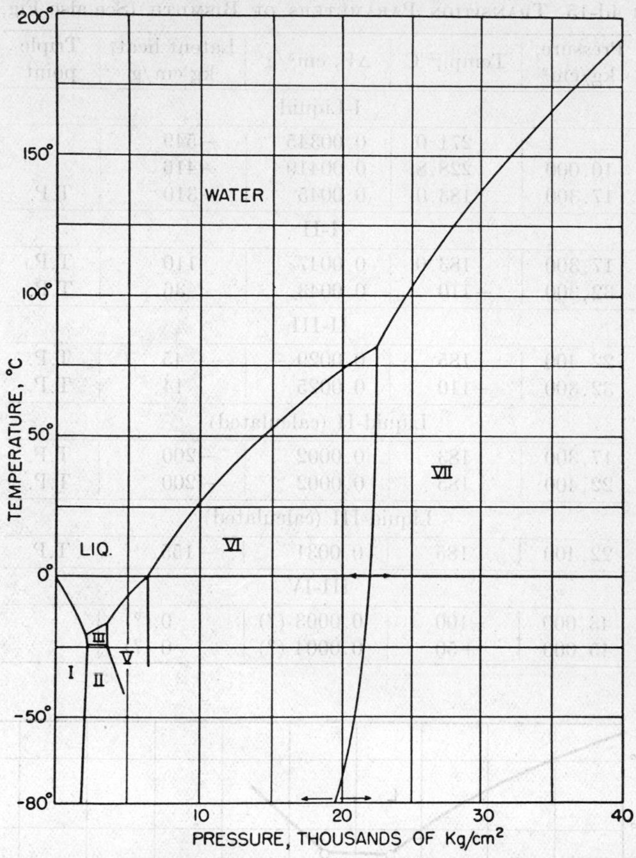

FIG. 4d-1. Phase diagram of water.

TABLE 4d-15. TRANSITION PARAMETERS OF BISMUTH (See also Fig. 4d-2)

Pressure, kg/cm²	Temp., °C	ΔV, cm³/g	Latent heat, kg cm/g	Triple point
		I-Liquid		
1	271.0	0.00345	−549	
10,000	228.8	0.00419	−416	
17,300	183.0	0.0045	−310	T.P.
		I-II		
17,300	183.0	0.0047	110	T.P.
32,300	−110	0.0043	36	T.P.
		II-III		
22,400	185	0.0029	45	T.P.
32,300	−110	0.0025	14	T.P.
		Liquid-II (calculated)		
17,300	183	0.0002	−200	T.P.
22,400	185	0.0002	−200	T.P.
		Liquid-III (calculated)		
22,400	185	0.0031	−155	T.P.
		III-IV		
43,000	−100	0.0003 (?)	0 (?)	
45,000	+50	0.0004 (?)	0 (?)	

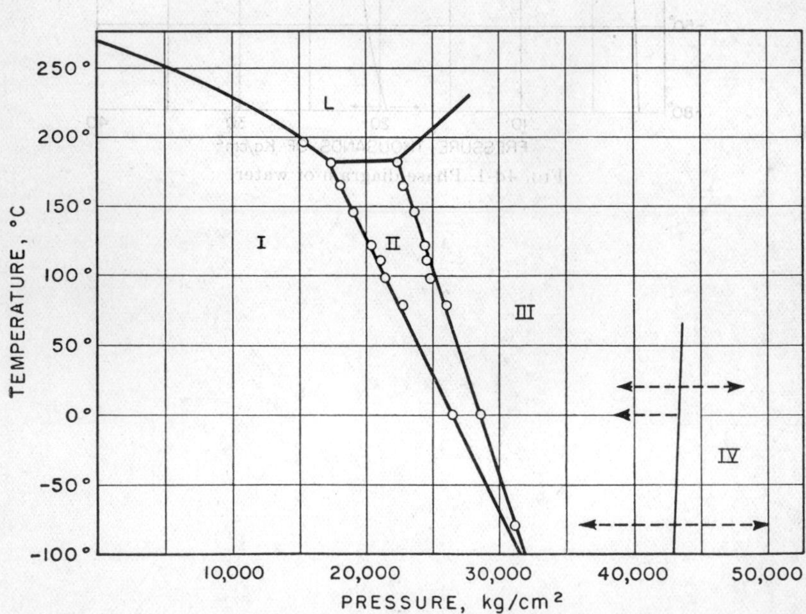

FIG. 4d-2. Phase diagram of bismuth.

Table 4d-16. Transition Parameters of Urethane ($C_3H_7NO_2$)
(See also Fig. 4d-3)

Pressure, kg/cm²	Temp., °C	ΔV, cm³/g	Latent heat, kg cm/g	Triple point
		Liquid-I		
1	47.9	0.0599	−1,740	
2,350	66.2	0.0253	−1,620	T.P.
		I-II		
2,350	66.2	0.0102	90	T.P.
3,400	25.5	0.0092	70	T.P.
		Liquid-II		
2,350	66.2	0.0355	−1,530	T.P.
4,230	76.8	0.0184	−1,470	T.P.
		Liquid-III		
4,230	76.8	0.0640	−1,730	T.P.
8,000	119.0	0.0500	−1,950	
12,000	156.7	0.0378	−1,830	
		II-III		
4,230	76.8	0.0456	−260	T.P.
3,400	25.5	0.0482	−235	T.P.
		I-III		
3,400	25.5	0.0574	−165	T.P.
3,160	0	0.0572	−150	

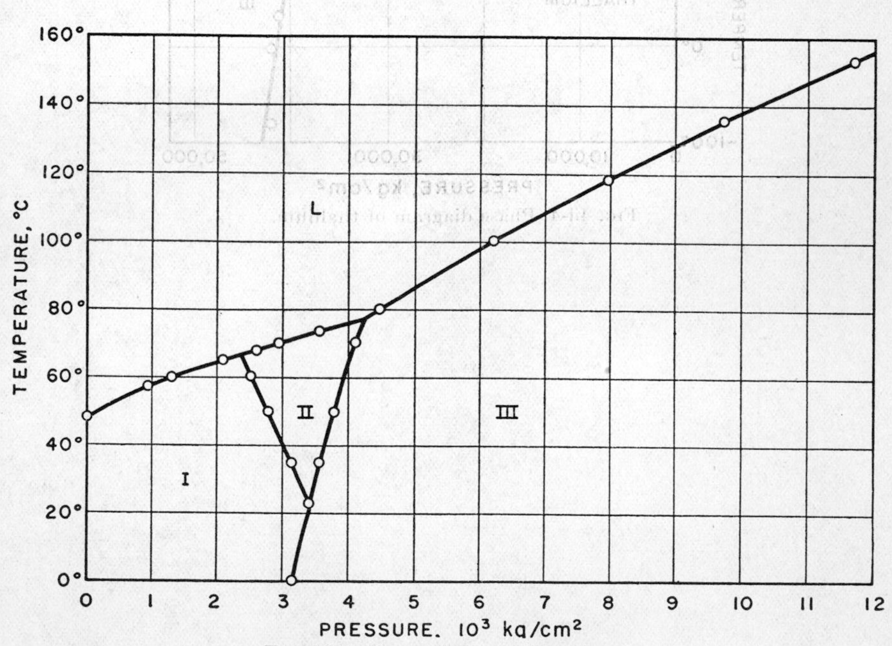

Fig. 4d-3. Phase diagram of urethane.

TABLE 4d-17. TRANSITION PARAMETERS OF THALLIUM (See also Fig. 4d-4)

Pressure, kg/cm²	Temp., °C	ΔV, cm³/g	Latent heat, kg cm/g	Triple point
		II-I		
1	227	0.00004 (?)		
39,000	153	0.00024	41.7	T.P.
		II-III		
39,000	153	0.00053	2.7	
43,000	−100	0.00039	1.1	T.P.
		I-III (calculated)		
39,000	153	0.00029	−39.0	T.P.

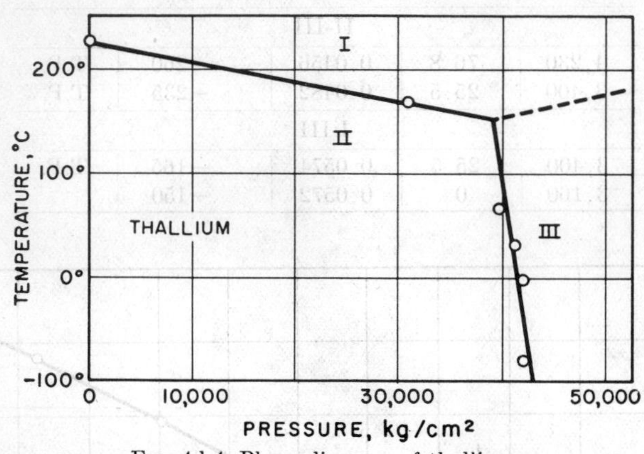

FIG. 4d-4. Phase diagram of thallium.

4e. Heat Capacities

G. T. FURUKAWA

The National Bureau of Standards

T. B. DOUGLAS

The National Bureau of Standards

TABLE 4e-1. MOLAR HEAT CAPACITY AT CONSTANT PRESSURE OF ELEMENTAL SUBSTANCES AT LOW TEMPERATURES*

	10	15	20	25	30	50	70	100	150	200	250	298.16
Aluminum Al 26.98	0.01	0.02	0.05	0.11	0.20	0.91	1.85	3.12	4.43	5.16	5.56	5.82
Antimony Sb 121.76	(0.06)	(0.20	(0.48)	(0.80)	(1.18)	(2.99)	4.10	4.92	5.55	5.82	5.93	6.03
Argon A 39.944	0.90	1.89	2.82	3.70	4.39	5.93	6.96 (c)	4.97 (g)	4.97	4.97	4.97	4.97
Arsenic As 74.91	(0.03)	(0.10)	(0.21)	(0.35)	(0.59)	(1.88)	2.88	3.99	4.94	5.43	5.75	5.89
Beryllium Be 9.013	0.0006	0.002	0.004	0.01	0.02	0.05	0.15	0.41	1.26	2.38	3.37	4.26
Bismuth Bi 209.00	0.52	1.20	1.77	2.43	2.95	4.27	4.99	5.46	5.83	5.98	6.05	6.10
Boron (amorphous) B 10.82	....	....	0.02	0.01	0.01	0.04	0.12	0.33	0.86	1.55	2.22	2.86
Boron (crystalline) B 10.82	....	....	0.006	0.009	0.006	0.02	0.08	0.26	0.77	1.45	2.11	2.65
Bromine Br_2 159.832	(0.74)	1.83	3.28	4.12	5.82	8.14	9.70	10.51	11.75	12.87	13.84 (c)	17.0 (l)
Cadmium Cd 112.41	0.22	0.60	1.15	1.71	2.26	3.90	4.67	5.32	5.73	5.93	6.08	6.19
Calcium Ca 40.08	0.04	0.15	0.35	0.62	0.94	2.60	3.64	4.66	5.49	5.91	6.12	6.28
Carbon (graphite) C 12.010	(0.004)	0.01	0.02	0.03	0.04	0.12	0.23	0.40	0.77	1.18	1.63	2.04
Carbon (diamond) C 12.010	....	....	(0.0003)	(0.001)	(0.002)	0.005	0.015	0.059	0.24	0.56	0.99	1.46
Cerium Ce 140.13	1.05*	1.14*	1.76	2.46	3.08	3.10	5.83	6.46	6.71*	6.90		
Chlorine Cl_2 70.914	(0.30)	0.89	1.85	2.89	3.99	6.99	8.68	10.10	12.20 (c)	15.95 (l)	15.63 (l)	8.07 (g)
Chromium Cr 52.01	(0.01)	(0.02)	(0.04)	(0.06)	(0.12)	0.47	1.20	2.39	3.94	4.81	5.30	5.58
Cobalt Co 58.94	0.02	0.04	0.07	0.14	0.24	0.98	2.04	3.34	4.60	5.33	5.75	5.98
Copper Cu 63.54	0.01	0.04	0.11	0.23	0.41	1.49	2.62	3.85	4.90	5.43	5.72	5.85
Fluorine F_2 38.00	....	1.75	3.10	4.61	6.03 (c_1)	11.79 (c_2)	13.56 (l)	6.96 (g)	6.99	7.10	7.28	7.49
Gallium Ga 69.72	(0.15)	0.31	0.54	0.84	1.19	2.45	3.47	4.43	5.26	5.69	5.95	6.23
Germanium Ge 72.60	0.02	0.08	0.22	0.42	0.64	1.50	2.28	3.31	4.45	4.99		
Gold Au 197.2	(0.12)	0.35	0.77	1.24	1.76	3.41	4.39	5.12	5.62	5.84	5.96	6.07
Hafnium Hf 178.6	(0.03)	0.05	0.13	0.31	0.60	3.90*	10.2*	5.40	5.80	6.00	6.08	6.15
Helium He 4.003	4.97 (g)	4.97	4.97	4.97	4.97	4.97	4.97	4.97	4.97	4.97	4.97	4.97
n-Hydrogen H_2 2.016	....	3.50 (l)	....	....	4.97 (g)	4.98	5.06	5.39	6.07	6.52	6.77	6.89
		99.8% para										
n-Deuterium D_2 4.032	....	1.66 (c)	5.49 (l)	....	5.06 (g)	5.95	6.89	7.19	7.03	6.98	6.98	6.98
		97.8% ortho										
Indium In 114.76	0.43	1.01	1.67	2.36	2.94	4.41	5.08	5.58	5.99	6.17	6.31	(6.43)
Iodine I_2 253.82	0.93	....	....	5.12	....	8.79	....	10.96	11.86	12.42	....	13.14
Iron Fe 55.85	0.02	0.03	0.06	0.10	0.18	0.73	1.61	2.88	4.33	5.13	5.63	5.97
Krypton Kr 83.80	1.46	2.90	3.67	4.43	5.01	6.01	6.57	7.55 (c)	4.97 (g)	4.97	4.97	4.97
Lanthanum La 138.92	0.26	0.80	1.48	2.20	2.81	4.41	5.12	5.64	6.04			
Lead Pb 207.21	0.67	1.74	2.62	3.36	3.94	5.10	5.54	5.84	6.04	6.18	6.30	6.41
Lithium Li 6.940	(0.03)	0.05	0.10	0.17	0.27	1.00	1.88	3.05	4.42	5.17	5.60	5.90

Magnesium Mg 24.32	0.01	0.03	0.08	0.19	0.35	1.41	2.50	3.77	4.90	5.38	5.63	5.71
Manganese (α) Mn 54.93	(0.05)	0.09	0.13	(0.21)	0.33	1.16	2.24	3.52	4.79	5.51	5.97	6.29
Mercury Hg 200.61	1.06	1.75	2.46	3.04	3.53	4.76	5.36	5.80	6.19	6.52 (c)	6.78 (l)	6.69
Molybdenum Mo 95.95	(0.01)	(0.03)	0.06	0.13	0.22	0.94	1.92	3.19	4.47	5.09	5.45	5.61
Neodymium Nd 144.27	1.26	1.79	2.45*	2.85	3.39	5.16	5.99	6.36	6.77			
Neon (C) Ne 20.183	1.48	2.87	4.27 (c)	(8.36) (l)				4.97 (g)	4.97	4.97	4.97	4.97
Nickel Ni 58.69	0.02	0.04	0.08	0.14	0.23	0.96	1.95	3.26	4.80	5.37	5.83	6.23
Nitrogen N_2 28.016	(1.06)	2.87	4.50	6.50	8.26 (c_1)	9.92 (c_2)	13.4 (l)	6.96 (g)	6.96	6.96	6.96	6.96
Oxygen O_2 32	(0.60)	1.59	3.27 (c_1)	5.30 (c_2)	6.72 (c_2)	11.0 (c_3)	12.7 (l)	6.96 (g)	6.96	6.96	6.98	7.02
Palladium Pd 106.7	0.05	0.13	0.24	0.41	0.66	1.93	3.10	4.26	5.30	5.79	6.06	6.21
Platinum Pt 195.23	0.05	0.16	0.35	0.65	0.99	2.56	3.68	4.69	5.56	5.95	6.11	6.20
Potassium K 39.100	(0.49)	1.56	2.19	3.01	3.65	5.01	5.52	5.89	6.22	6.48	6.75	6.97
Praseodymium Pr 140.92	0.99	2.02	3.18	4.36	5.07	6.18*	6.30	6.22	6.42			
Rhenium Re 186.31			0.15	0.32	0.54	1.89	3.08	4.31	5.33	5.80	6.08	6.14
Selenium Se 78.96	(0.18)	0.45	0.83	1.17	1.51	2.62	3.42	4.34	5.18	5.58	5.80	6.07
Silicon Si 28.09	(0.00)	(0.01)	0.03	0.06	0.10	0.48	1.07	1.74	2.87	3.74	4.37	4.73
Silver Ag 107.880	0.05	0.17	0.40	0.75	1.14	2.78	3.90	4.82	5.49	5.80	6.00	6.09
Sodium Na 22.997	0.14	0.46	0.91	1.45	2.00	3.82	4.75	5.42	5.92	6.24	6.53	6.79
Sulfur (monoclinic) S 32.066	(0.10)	(0.31)	(0.61)	(0.86)	(1.08)	1.77	2.36	3.10	4.06	4.80	5.29	5.64
Sulfur (rhombic) S 32.066	(0.10)	0.31	0.61	0.86	1.08	1.77	2.35	3.06	3.96	4.64	5.08	5.40
Tantalum Ta 180.88	(0.5)	(0.15)	(0.34)	(0.59)	(0.90)	2.60	3.80	4.78	5.48	5.78	5.95	6.05
Tellurium Te 127.61	(0.21)	0.62	1.09	1.57	2.00	3.55	4.47	5.09	5.69	5.91	6.07	6.14
Thallium Tl 204.39	(0.81)	1.59	2.40	3.18	3.80	5.01	5.60	5.84	6.06	6.15	6.23	6.29
Thorium Th 232.12			1.11	1.80	2.40	4.05	4.88	5.48	5.97	6.22	6.39	6.53
Tin (gray) Sn 118.70	(0.16)	0.50	0.89	1.24	1.58	2.69	3.70	4.67	5.44	5.81	6.02	6.16
Tin (white) Sn 118.70	0.22	0.64	1.11	1.65	2.20	3.68	4.53	5.35	5.85	6.08	6.20	6.30
Titanium Ti 47.90	(0.02)	0.04	0.08	0.16	0.28	1.14	2.15	3.43	4.68	5.32	5.71	5.98
Tungsten W 183.92	0.02	0.06	0.08	0.21	0.36	1.47	2.68	3.90	5.00	5.51	5.79	5.97
Uranium U 238.07		0.42	0.81	1.33	1.94	3.70	4.60	5.35	5.90	6.21	6.44	6.57
Vanadium V 50.95	(0.01)	(0.03)	(0.06)	(0.13)	(0.23)	0.96	1.85	3.23	4.61	5.28	5.64	5.90
Xenon Xe 131.3	1.94	3.24	4.00	4.73	5.19	5.99	6.32	6.75	8.04 (c)	4.97 (g)	4.97	4.97
Zinc Zn 65.38	0.04	0.17	0.49	0.77	1.16	2.65	3.68	4.59	5.38	5.70	5.94	6.07
Zirconium Zr 91.22	(0.03)	(0.10)	0.27	0.49	0.78	2.21	3.37	4.46	5.30	5.69	5.92	6.01

* The compilations of (1) K. K. Kelley, Contributions to the Data on Theoretical Metallurgy XI. Entropies of Inorganic Substances, Revision (1948) of Data and Methods of Calculation, *U.S. Bur. Mines Bull.* 477; and (2) C. A. Shiffman, "The Heat Capacities of the Elements below Room Temperature," General Electric Company Research Publication Services (1952) were used extensively in the construction of this table. Most of the references may be found in these two publications.

Temperatures are given in degrees absolute (°K). The formula weight accompanies the symbol for each element. The heat capacity is given in calories per degree centigrade per gram-formula weight. The values given are for the elements in the crystalline state unless indicated otherwise. The letters c, l, and g, denoting the crystalline, liquid, and gaseous states, respectively, indicate changes of state. The values in parentheses are extrapolations either above or below the temperature range of experimental data. The asterisks (*) indicate that the values given are in the region of sharp transitions and may contain large errors.

TABLE 4e-2. MOLAR HEAT CAPACITY AT CONSTANT PRESSURE OF THE CHEMICAL ELEMENTS AT HIGHER THAN ROOM TEMPERATURE*

Element	298.16°	400°	500°	600°	700°	800°	1000°	1200°	1500°	2000°	2500°	3000°
Aluminum Al 26.98	5.82 (c)	6.12	6.42	6.72	7.01	7.31 (c)	7.00 (l)	7.00 (l)				
Antimony Sb 121.76	6.03 (c)	6.21	6.38	6.55	6.73	6.90 (c)	7.50 (l)	7.50 (l)				
Argon A 39.944	4.97 (g)	4.97	4.97	4.97	4.97	4.97	4.97	4.97	4.97	4.97	4.97	4.97 (g)
Arsenic As 74.91	5.89 (c)	6.12	6.34	6.56	6.78	7.01	7.45 (c)					
Beryllium Be 9.013	4.26 (c)	4.77	5.25	5.58	5.84	6.06	6.52	7.04 (c)				
Bismuth Bi 209.00	6.10 (c)	6.65	7.19 (c)	7.50 (l)	7.50	7.50	7.50	7.50 (l)				
Boron (crystalline) B 10.82	2.65 (c)	3.30	3.74	4.18	4.62	5.06	5.94	6.82 (c)				
Bromine Br_2 159.832	8.62 (g)	8.81	8.89	8.94	8.96	8.98	9.00	9.01	9.02 (g)			
Cadmium Cd 112.41	6.19 (c)	6.78	7.07 (c)	7.10 (l)	7.10	7.10	7.10 (l)					
Calcium Ca 40.08	6.28 (α)	6.64	6.99	7.34 (α)	7.27 (β)	7.41	7.69 (β)					
Carbon (graphite) C 12.010	2.04	3.20	3.77	4.13	4.38	4.59	4.91	5.18	5.54	6.09		
Carbon (diamond) C 12.010	1.46	2.52	3.17	3.67	4.09	4.48	5.19	5.87				
Cerium Ce 140.13	6.19 (c)	6.80	7.40	8.00	8.60	9.20 (c)						
Cesium Cs 132.91	7.42 (c)	8.00 (l)	8.00									
Chlorine Cl_2 70.914	8.08 (g)	8.42	8.58	8.67	8.72	8.76	8.81	8.84	8.88	8.92	8.96	8.99 (g)
Chromium Cr 52.01	5.55 (c)	6.23	6.67	7.02	7.31	7.59	8.11	8.61	9.34 (c)	9.40 (l)		
Cobalt Co 58.94	6.00 (α)	6.44	6.87	7.30	7.73 (α)	7.99 (β)	9.16	10.33 (β)	9.60 (γ)	8.30 (l)		
Columbium (niobium) Cb (Nb) 92.91	5.95 (c)	6.04	6.14	6.24	6.33	6.43	6.62	6.81	7.10 (c)			
Copper Cu 63.54	5.86 (c)	6.01	6.16	6.31	6.46	6.61	6.91	7.21 (c)	7.50 (l)			
Fluorine F_2 38.00	7.49 (g)	7.89	8.19	8.41	8.56	8.68	8.84	8.94	9.06	9.18	9.27	9.34 (g)
Gallium Ga 69.72	6.24 (c)	6.81 (l)										
Gold Au 197.2	6.03 (c)	6.16	6.28	6.40	6.53	6.65	6.90	7.15 (c)	7.00 (l)			
Helium He 4.003	4.97 (g)	4.97	4.97	4.97	4.97	4.97	4.97	4.97	4.97	4.97	4.97	4.97 (g)
Hydrogen (normal) H_2 2.016	6.89 (g)	6.98	6.99	7.01	7.04	7.09	7.22	7.42	7.72	8.20	8.53	8.86 (g)
Indium In 114.76	6.56 (c)	6.81 (c)	7.50 (l)									
Iodine I_2 253.82	13.14 (c)	19.20 (l)	8.89 (g)	8.89	8.89	8.89	8.89	8.89	8.89 (g)			
Iridium Ir 193.1	5.98 (c)	6.13	6.27	6.41	6.55	6.70	6.98	7.26	7.69 (c)			
Iron Fe 55.85	5.97 (α)	6.48	7.09	7.75	8.43	9.12	10.51 (α)	8.45 (γ)	9.35 (γ)	10.00 (l)		
Krypton Kr 83.80	4.97 (g)	4.97	4.97	4.97	4.97	4.97	4.97	4.97	4.97	4.97	4.97	4.97 (g)
Lanthanum La 138.92	6.65 (c)	6.81	6.97	7.13	7.29	7.45 (c)						
Lead Pb 207.21	6.32 (c)	6.56	6.79	7.02 (c)	7.25 (l)	7.17	7.03	6.88 (l)				
Lithium Li 6.940	5.89 (c)	6.60 (c)	7.20 (l)	7.06	6.93	6.92	6.89	6.87 (l)				
Magnesium Mg 24.32	5.71 (c)	6.25	6.58	6.82	7.03	7.22 (c)	7.40 (l)					
Manganese Mn 54.93	6.29 (α)	6.82	7.24	7.63	7.99	8.34 (α)	8.99 (β)	9.12 (β)	11.30 (δ)	11.00 (l)		
Mercury Hg 200.61	6.67 (l)	6.55	6.49	6.49 (l)	4.97 (g)	4.97	4.97	4.97	4.97	4.97	4.97	4.97 (g)

Molybdenum Mo 95.95	5.87 (c)	6.00	6.13	6.26	6.39	6.52	6.78	7.04	7.43 (c)			
Neodymium Nd 144.27	7.20 (c)	7.75	8.28	8.81	9.35	9.88 (c)						
Neon Ne 20.183	4.97 (g)	4.97	4.97	4.97	4.97	4.97	4.97	4.97	4.97	4.97	4.97	4.97 (g)
Nickel Ni 58.69	6.23 (α)	6.88	7.58	8.28 (α)	7.26 (β)	7.44	7.80	8.16	8.70 (β)	9.20 (l)		
Nitrogen N_2 28.016	6.96 (g)	7.07	7.17	7.27	7.37	7.48	7.68	7.88	8.19	8.70	9.21 (g)	
Osmium Os 190.2	5.95 (c)	6.04	6.13	6.22	6.31	6.39	6.57	6.75	7.01 (c)			
Oxygen O_2 32.000	7.01 (g)	7.31	7.50	7.65	7.78	7.90	8.12	8.33	8.64	9.15	9.55	10.16 (g)
Ozone O_3 48.000	9.11 (g)	10.02	10.56	10.97	11.31	11.62	12.19	12.72	13.49	14.75 (g)		
Palladium Pd 106.7	6.21 (c)	6.35	6.49	6.63	6.77	6.90	7.18	7.46	7.87 (c)			
Phosphorus (white) P_4 123.90	22.50 (c)	23.50 (l)										
Phosphorus (red) P 30.975	5.90	6.30	6.69	7.08	7.47	7.86						
Platinum Pt 195.23	6.20 (c)	6.34	6.45	6.57	6.70	6.83	7.09	7.36	7.75 (c)			
Potassium K 39.100	6.97 (c)	7.53 (l)	7.34	7.20	7.13	7.11	7.26 (l)					
Radon Rn 222	4.97 (g)	4.97	4.97	4.97	4.97	4.97	4.97	4.97	4.97	4.97	4.97	4.97 (g)
Rhenium Re 186.31	6.10 (c)	6.18	6.31	6.44	6.57	6.70	6.96	7.22	7.61 (c)			
Rhodium Rh 102.91	6.10 (c)	6.31	6.52	6.73	6.93	7.14	7.55	7.96	8.58 (c)			
Rubidium Rb 85.48	7.27 (c)	7.80 (l)										
Ruthenium Ru 101.7	5.70 (α)	5.85	6.00	6.15	6.30	6.45	6.75	7.05 (α)	7.20 (γ)	7.50 (δ)		
Selenium Se 78.96	6.07 (c)	6.82 (c)	8.40 (l)	8.40 (l)								
Silicon Si 28.09	4.73 (c)	5.33	5.63	5.83	5.96	6.07	6.24	6.38 (c)				
Silver Ag 107.880	6.10 (c)	6.13	6.25	6.41	6.59	6.78	7.17	7.56 (c)	7.30 (l)			
Sodium Na 22.997	6.72 (c)	7.53 (l)	7.30	7.13	7.00	6.92	6.92	7.12 (l)				
Sulfur S 32.066	5.44 (rh)	7.40 (l,λ)	7.90	8.40	8.90 (l,λ)							
Tantalum Ta 180.88	6.05 (c)	6.13	6.21	6.29	6.37	6.44	6.60	6.76	6.99 (c)			
Tellurium Te 127.61	6.14 (c)	6.29	6.44	6.59	6.74 (c)							
Thallium Tl 204.39	6.29 (α)	6.64	6.99 (α)	7.50 (l)	7.50	7.50 (l)						
Thorium Th 232.12	7.70 (c)	7.84	8.07	8.34	8.61	8.90	9.19	9.48	9.79 (c)			
Tin (white) Sn 118.70	6.30 (c)	6.94	7.57 (c)	7.30 (l)	7.30	7.30	7.30	7.30 (l)				
Titanium Ti 47.90	6.00 (α)	6.26	6.51	6.76	7.01	7.27	7.77 (α)	7.50 (β)	7.50 (β)			
Tungsten (wolfram) W 183.92	5.97 (c)	6.04	6.12	6.20	6.27	6.35	6.50	6.65	6.88	7.26 (c)		
Uranium U 238.07	6.57 (α)	7.04	7.68	8.39	9.14	9.92 (α)	10.18 (β)	9.20 (γ)				
Vanadium V 50.95	6.00 (c)	6.20	6.40	6.60	6.80	7.00	7.40	7.80	8.40 (c)			
Xenon Xe 131.3	4.97 (g)	4.97	4.97	4.97	4.97	4.97	4.97	4.97	4.97	4.97	4.97	4.97 (g)
Zinc Zn 65.38	6.07 (c)	6.31	6.55	6.79 (c)	7.50 (l)	7.50	7.50	7.50 (l)				
Zirconium Zr 91.22	6.01 (c)	6.27	6.55	6.90	7.27	7.66 (c)						

* The heat capacity is given in calories per gram-formula-weight per degree centigrade. The physical state of the element (crystalline, liquid, or gaseous) is indicated in parentheses by the proper letter. When two or more crystalline forms of the element are known, these are distinguished as α, β, γ, etc. The numbers accompanying the symbols of the elements are the formula weights. All temperatures heading the columns are in degrees absolute (°K).

Most of the values in this table were computed from the equations given in the comprehensive compilation by K. K. Kelley, High-temperature Heat-content, Heat-capacity, and Entropy Data for Inorganic Compounds, *U.S. Bur. Mines Bull.* 476, 1949, where specific references to these measurements may be found.

The contribution to the molar heat capacity at constant volume C_v of a solid due to lattice vibrations is given by Debye's equation

$$C_v = 3R\left[12\left(\frac{T}{\Theta}\right)^3\int_0^{\Theta/T}\frac{y^3\,dy}{e^y - 1} - 3\frac{\Theta/T}{e^{\Theta/T} - 1}\right] \tag{4e-1}$$

where R is the universal gas constant and Θ is the Debye temperature. Values of C_v for many different values of Θ/T are given in Table 4e-3. The molar internal energy E of a solid due to lattice vibrations is equal to $\int_0^T C_v\,dT$. Values of E/T as a function of Θ/T are given in Table 4e-4. The molar entropy S of a solid due to lattice vibrations is equal to $\int_0^T (C_v/T)\,dT$. Values of S as a function of Θ/T are given in Table 4e-5.

TABLE 4e-3. VALUES OF THE DEBYE C_v AS A FUNCTION OF Θ/T*

$\frac{\Theta}{T}$	0.0	0.1	0.2	0.3	0.4	0.5	0.6	0.7	0.8	0.9
0	5.955	5.95	5.94	5.93	5.91	5.88	5.85	5.81	5.77	5.72
1	5.670	5.61	5.55	5.48	5.41	5.34	5.26	5.18	5.09	5.01
2	4.918	4.83	4.74	4.64	4.54	4.45	4.35	4.25	4.15	4.05
3	3.948	3.85	3.75	3.65	3.56	3.46	3.36	3.27	3.18	3.09
4	2.996	2.91	2.82	2.74	2.65	2.57	2.50	2.42	2.34	2.27
5	2.197	2.13	2.06	1.99	1.93	1.87	1.81	1.75	1.69	1.63
6	1.582	1.53	1.48	1.43	1.39	1.34	1.30	1.26	1.21	1.18
7	1.137	1.100	1.065	1.031	0.998	0.966	0.935	0.906	0.878	0.850
8	0.823	0.798	0.774	0.750	0.727	0.704	0.683	0.662	0.642	0.623
9	0.604	0.588	0.570	0.552	0.537	0.521	0.507	0.492	0.478	0.465
10	0.452	0.439	0.427	0.415	0.404	0.394	0.383	0.373	0.363	0.353
11	0.345	0.335	0.324	0.319	0.310	0.303	0.295	0.287	0.280	0.273
12	0.267	0.260	0.254	0.248	0.242	0.237	0.231	0.226	0.221	0.216
13	0.211	0.206	0.202	0.197	0.193	0.188	0.184	0.180	0.176	0.172
14	0.169	0.165	0.162	0.159	0.155	0.152	0.149	0.146	0.143	0.140
15	0.137	0.135	0.132	0.130	0.127	0.125	0.122	0.120	0.118	0.116

$\frac{\Theta}{T}$	C	$\frac{\Theta}{T}$	C	$\frac{\Theta}{T}$	C
16	0.113	21	0.0502	26	0.0264
17	0.0945	22	0.0436	27	0.0236
18	0.0796	23	0.0382	28	0.0212
19	0.0677	24	0.0336	29	0.0190
20	0.0581	25	0.0298	30	0.0172

* From "Handbuch der Physik," vol. 10, p. 367.

TABLE 4e-4. VALUES OF $\frac{E}{T} = \frac{1}{T}\int_0^T C_v\,dT$ AS A FUNCTION OF Θ/T *

$\frac{\Theta}{T}$	0.00	0.01	0.02	0.03	0.04	0.05	0.06	0.07	0.08	0.09
0.1	5.733	5.710	5.688	5.667	5.646	5.625	5.604	5.583	5.562	5.541
0.2	5.520	5.500	5.480	5.459	5.438	5.417	5.396	5.375	5.354	5.333
0.3	5.312	5.291	5.271	5.250	5.230	5.210	5.190	5.170	5.150	5.130
0.4	5.110	5.091	5.071	5.051	5.031	5.012	4.992	4.972	4.952	4.933
0.5	4.913	4.893	4.874	4.855	4.836	4.817	4.788	4.779	4.760	4.741
0.6	4.722	4.704	4.685	4.666	4.647	4.628	4.610	4.592	4.574	4.555
0.7	4.536	4.518	4.500	4.483	4.465	4.447	4.429	4.412	4.394	4.376
0.8	4.358	4.341	4.324	4.307	4.290	4.273	4.255	4.238	4.221	4.203
0.9	4.186	4.169	4.152	4.135	4.118	4.101	4.084	4.067	4.050	4.033
1.0	4.017	4.001	3.985	3.968	3.952	3.935	3.918	3.902	3.886	3.870
1.1	3.854	3.838	3.822	3.806	3.790	3.774	3.758	3.742	3.726	3.710
1.2	3.695	3.680	3.665	3.650	3.635	3.620	3.605	3.590	3.575	3.560
1.3	3.545	3.530	3.515	3.500	3.486	3.471	3.457	3.442	3.428	3.413
1.4	3.399	3.385	3.371	3.357	3.343	3.329	3.315	3.301	3.287	3.273
1.5	3.259	3.245	3.231	3.217	3.203	3.190	3.176	3.163	3.150	3.136
1.6	3.123	3.110	3.096	3.082	3.069	3.056	3.043	3.030	3.017	3.004
1.7	2.992	2.979	2.966	2.953	2.940	2.927	2.915	2.902	2.890	2.877
1.8	2.864	2.851	2.839	2.826	2.814	2.801	2.789	2.776	2.764	2.752
1.9	2.739	2.727	2.716	2.704	2.692	2.681	2.670	2.659	2.648	2.637

$\frac{\Theta}{T}$	0.0	0.1	0.2	0.3	0.4	0.5	0.6	0.7	0.8	0.9
0	5.955	5.7330	5.5195	5.3122	5.1100	4.9130	4.7220	4.5364	4.3578	4.1862
1	4.0168	3.8536	3.6951	3.5450	3.3991	3.2592	3.1229	2.9920	2.8640	2.7395
2	2.6266	2.5138	2.4068	2.3047	2.2044	2.1078	2.0166	1.9288	1.8446	1.7642
3	1.6873	1.6131	1.5423	1.4756	1.4118	1.3492	1.2917	1.2364	1.1825	1.1314
4	1.0921	1.0361	0.9931	0.9517	0.9118	0.8733	0.8361	0.8002	0.7654	0.7317
5	0.7009	0.6712	0.7438	0.6187	0.5944	0.5708	0.5478	0.5255	0.5037	0.4824
6	0.4618	0.4437	0.4259	0.4088	0.3926	0.3787	0.3652	0.3519	0.3387	0.3257
7	0.3128	0.3017	0.2908	0.2803	0.2702	0.2605	0.2513	0.2423	0.2340	0.2263
8	0.2195	0.2135	0.2077	0.2017	0.1959	0.1905	0.1855	0.1797	0.1744	0.1691
9	0.1639	0.1588	0.1536	0.1485	0.1435	0.1384	0.1336	0.1289	0.1242	0.1195
10	0.1149	0.1107	0.1070	0.1028	0.1009	0.0983	0.0957	0.0953	0.0907	0.0886
11	0.0866	0.0845	0.0824	0.0804	0.0783	0.0763	0.0742	0.0722	0.0704	0.0686
12	0.0671	0.0655	0.0640	0.0625	0.0610	0.0595	0.0580	0.0565	0.0552	0.0540
13	0.0526	0.0514	0.0502	0.0491	0.0481	0.0471	0.0461	0.0451	0.0441	0.0431
14	0.0420	0.0411	0.0403	0.0395	0.0388	0.0380	0.0373	0.0365	0.0358	0.0350
15	0.0343	0.0335	0.0328	0.0320	0.0313	0.0308	0.0303	0.0298	0.0293	0.0288

* "Handbuch der Physik," vol. 10, p. 368.

Table 4e-5. Values of $S = \int_0^T \frac{C_v}{T}\,dT$ as a Function of Θ/T*

$\frac{\Theta}{T}$	0.00	0.01	0.02	0.03	0.04	0.05	0.06	0.07	0.08	0.09
0.1	21.65	21.16	20.69	20.23	19.79	19.37	18.99	18.62	18.26	17.79
0.2	17.53	17.23	16.98	16.73	16.47	16.22	15.97	15.74	15.52	15.31
0.3	15.12	14.93	14.76	14.59	14.42	14.25	14.08	13.91	13.74	13.58
0.4	13.42	13.27	13.13	13.00	12.86	12.73	12.60	12.47	12.35	12.22
0.5	12.06	11.98	11.86	11.75	11.64	11.53	11.41	11.32	11.22	11.12
0.6	11.03	10.93	10.84	10.75	10.65	10.56	10.47	10.38	10.29	10.21
0.7	10.14	10.04	9.96	9.88	9.80	9.73	9.66	9.58	9.51	9.45
0.8	9.364	9.291	9.229	9.162	9.094	9.027	8.959	8.892	8.825	8.756
0.9	8.689	8.630	8.564	8.495	8.440	8.379	8.320	8.263	8.206	8.150
1.0	8.094	8.039	7.984	7.928	7.873	7.818	7.762	7.707	7.653	7.601
1.1	7.549	7.498	7.447	7.396	7.346	7.302	7.249	7.201	7.153	7.105
1.2	7.060	7.015	6.970	6.925	6.880	6.835	6.791	6.748	6.706	6.663
1.3	6.621	6.579	6.537	6.496	6.455	6.413	6.373	6.333	6.295	6.256
1.4	6.218	6.185	6.144	6.107	6.069	6.032	5.995	5.958	5.921	5.885
1.5	5.849	5.813	5.778	5.743	5.709	5.675	5.640	5.607	5.574	5.540
1.6	5.507	5.475	5.442	5.410	5.379	5.347	5.316	5.285	5.253	5.222
1.7	5.191	5.160	5.130	5.100	5.070	5.041	5.012	4.982	4.953	4.924
1.8	4.895	4.867	4.840	4.811	4.783	4.755	4.728	4.700	4.672	4.645
1.9	4.617	4.590	4.565	4.539	4.513	4.488	4.463	4.438	4.414	4.390

$\frac{\Theta}{T}$	0.0	0.1	0.2	0.3	0.4	0.5	0.6	0.7	0.8	0.9
0	......	21.6510	17.5293	15.1233	13.4213	12.1051	11.0354	10.1357	9.3643	8.6892
1	8.0934	7.5484	7.0601	6.6206	6.2183	5.8491	5.5068	5.1906	4.8947	4.6176
2	4.3680	4.1296	3.9084	3.7020	3.5055	3.3202	3.1484	2.9861	2.8332	2.7493
3	2.5538	2.4253	2.3042	2.1913	2.0849	1.9816	1.8871	1.7976	1.7115	1.6306
4	1.5529	1.4810	1.4141	1.3502	1.2892	1.2309	1.1750	1.1214	1.0698	1.0202
5	0.9748	0.9317	0.8914	0.8548	0.8195	0.7854	0.7525	0.7206	0.6897	0.6595
6	0.6306	0.6050	0.5799	0.5562	0.5334	0.5138	0.4950	0.4765	0.4583	0.4403
7	0.4225	0.4072	0.3922	0.3777	0.3639	0.3506	0.3381	0.3258	0.3144	0.3033
8	0.2946	0.2865	0.2786	0.2704	0.2626	0.2551	0.2484	0.2406	0.2334	0.2263
9	0.2193	0.2124	0.2054	0.1985	0.1918	0.1850	0.1785	0.1722	0.1659	0.1596
10	0.1535	0.1478	0.1428	0.1386	0.1347	0.1312	0.1277	0.1242	0.1210	0.1182
11	0.1155	0.1127	0.1099	0.1072	0.1044	0.1017	0.0989	0.0963	0.0939	0.0915
12	0.0895	0.0873	0.0853	0.0833	0.0813	0.0793	0.0773	0.0753	0.0736	0.0720
13	0.0701	0.0686	0.0669	0.0655	0.0641	0.0628	0.0615	0.0601	0.0588	0.0575
14	0.0560	0.0548	0.0537	0.0527	0.0517	0.0506	0.0497	0.0487	0.0477	0.0467

* "Handbuch der Physik," vol. 10, p. 369.

Once Θ is known, C_v, E, and S may be obtained at any desired T. Table 4e-6 contains values of Θ for nonmetals.

At low temperatures, the molar heat capacity of metals varies with the temperature according to the equation

$$C_v = \frac{464}{\Theta^3} T^3 + \gamma T \tag{4e-2}$$

where Θ is the Debye temperature and γ is the electronic constant. Table 4e-7 contains values of Θ and γ for 39 metals. This table is the result of a critical evaluation of the latest low-temperature calorimetric work. The starred values of γ were not obtained calorimetrically but were calculated thermodynamically from superconducting threshold field curves. For references, see page 210 of "Progress in Low Temperature Physics," C. J. Gorter, ed., Interscience Publishers, Inc., New York, North-Holland Publishing Co., Amsterdam; 1955.

Table 4e-6. Debye Temperatures for Nonmetals

Substance	Θ, °K	Substance	Θ, °K
A	85	KBr	177
AgBr	144	KCl	227
AgCl	183	KI	115–200
CaF_2	474	LiF	607–750
Cl	115	MgO	750–890
D(H^2)	97	NaCl	281
Diamond	1860	N	68
FeS_2	645	Ne	63
H	105	O	91
He	28–36	RbBr	120–135
He II	15.5	RbI	100–118
I	106		

Substance	Θ, °K	Reference
Germanium	250–400	I. Esterman and J. R. Weertman, *J. Chem. Phys.* **20,** 972 (1952)
Silicon	658 [but $f(t)$]	Pearlman and Keesom, *Phys. Rev.* **88,** 398 (1952)
Gray tin	260	Hill and Parkins, *Phil. Mag.* **43,** 309 (1952)
TiO_2	318	C. H. Shomate, *J. Am. Chem. Soc.* **69,** 218 (1947)
PbS	194	R. L. Petritz and W. W. Scanlon
PbSe	135–160	D. H. Parkinson and J. E. Quarrington, *Proc. Phys. Soc. (London)*, ser. A, **67,** 569 (1954)
PbTe	124–135	D. H. Parkinson and J. E. Quarrington, *Proc. Phys. Soc. (London)*, ser. A, **67,** 569 (1954)
UO_2	160	Long, Jones, and Gordon, *U.S. Bur. Mines Rept.* A-329 (Oct. 28, 1942)
ZnS	300	Calculated by F. A. Kroger from Wooster, *Acta Cryst.* **4,** 191 (1951); Meijer and Polder, *Physica* **19,** 255 (1953) Table 1
C (graphite)	~1000	J. A. Krumhansl and H. Brooks, *J. Chem. Phys.* **21,** 1663 (1953)

TABLE 4e-7. DEBYE TEMPERATURES AND ELECTRONIC CONSTANTS FOR METALS
(Starred values were obtained magnetically)

Metal	Θ, °K	γ, 10^{-4} cal/mole deg²	Metal	Θ, °K	γ, 10^{-4} cal/mole deg²
Ag	229	1.45–1.60	Na	160	4.3
Al	375	3.27–3.48	Nb	252	17.5–20.4
Au	164	1.67	Ni	413	17.4
Ba	116	....	Os	.....	5.62
Be	1160	0.53	Pb	96.3	7.48–8.0
Bi	117	0.114–0.186	Pd	275	22.4–31.0
Ca	220	2.9	Pr	.....	22
Cd	165	1.5–1.7	Pt	233	16.1–16.5
Co	385	12.0	Rb	59	....
Cr	418	3.7–3.8	Re	275	5.85
Cs	43	....	Rh	350	10.0–11.7
Cu	343	1.60–1.80	Ru	.....	8.0
Fe	355	12.0	Sb	140	....
Ga	240	1.2	Sn	195	4.18–4.46
Gd	152	16	Sr	148	....
Hf	213	6.3–6.8	Ta	230	13.0–14.0
Hg	75	5.3*	Th	168	11.2–13.3
In	109	4.0–4.33	Ti	430	8.0–8.5
Ir	285	7.5–7.6	Tl	100	3.5
K	100	....	U	200	26
La	132	16–21	V	338	21.1–22.1
Li	430	....	W	270	1.8–5.0
Mg	342	3.15–3.25	Zn	235	1.25–1.50
Mn	410	32.9–43	Zr	265	6.92–7.25
Mo	360	5.05–5.25			

The calorimetric quantities Θ and γ are given separately for the superconducting metals in Table 4e-8, along with the zero-field transition temperature T_0 and the threshold field at absolute zero H_0.

TABLE 4e-8. SUPERCONDUCTING TRANSITION TEMPERATURES, ELECTRONIC CONSTANTS, AND DEBYE TEMPERATURES FOR SUPERCONDUCTORS
(Starred values were obtained magnetically)

Metal	T_0, °K	γ, 10^{-4} cal/mole deg²	Θ, °K	H_0, oersted	References
Al......	1.175	3.27–3.48	375	106	D2, G1, G2, K8, S7
Cd......	0.56–0.65	1.5–1.7	165	27–28.8	G1, G2, K9, S1, S10, S12, T1
Ga......	1.103	1.2	240	47–50.3	G1, G2, S7
Hf......	0.37	6.3–6.8	213	....	K9, S10
Hg......	4.160	5.3*	69	400–419	D3, D4, M1, M6, P2, R1, R2, S3, S4
In......	3.374–3.432	4.0–4.33	109	269–275	C1, C3, C4, D3, M6
La......	4.8, 5.8	16–21	132	....	J2, M4, P1, S5, Z1, Z2
Nb......	8.7–8.9	17.5–20.4	252	1960	C5, D3, D4, J1
Os......	0.71	5.62	....	65	G1
Pb......	7.22	7.48–8.0	96.3	800	C2, D3, D4, H2, J3, O1, P3, S2
Re......	1.70	5.85	210	188	A4, D5
Rh......	0.9	10.0–11.7	350	....	
Ru......	0.47	8.0	....	46	G1
Sn......	3.74	4.18–4.46	195	304–310	A2, A3, D3, D4, H1, K6, K7, L1, M2, M3, S2, W3
Ta......	4.38	13.0–14.0	230	860	D3, D4, K2, M5, P4, W1, W5
Tc......	11.2	....	....	....	T2
Th......	1.388–1.40	11.2–13.3	168	131	S6, S7
Ti......	0.39	8.0–8.5	430	100	D1, E1, S7, S10, S11, S13, W2
Tl......	2.392	3.5	100	171	D3, K4, K5, M6
U.......	1.1	26	200	....	A1, A4, G3, S7, S8
V.......	4.89	21.1–22.1	338	1340	W3, W4
Zn......	0.93	1.25–1.50	235	42–52.5	D2, D9, G1, G2, K1, K3, S7, S9
Zr......	0.55	6.92–7.25	265	46.6	E1, K9, S10

References for Table 4e-8

A1. Alekseyevsky, N., and L. Migunov: *J. Phys.* (*U.S.S.R.*) **11,** 95 (1947).
A2. Allen, Dawton, Lock, Pippard, and Shoenberg: *Nature* **166,** 1071 (1950).
A3. Allen, Dawton, Bar, Mendelssohn, and Olsen: *Nature* **166,** 1071 (1950).
A4. Aschermann, G., and E. Justi: *Physik. Z.* **43,** 207 (1942).
B1. Brown, Zemansky, and Boorse: *Phys. Rev.* **86,** 134 (1952).
C1. Clement, J. R., and E. H. Quinnell: *Phys. Rev.* **79,** 1028 (1950).
C2. Clement, J. R., and E. H. Quinnell: *Phys. Rev.* **85,** 502 (1952).
C3. Clement, J. R., and E. H. Quinnell: *Phys. Rev.* **92,** 258 (1953).
C4. Clusiou, K., and L. Schachinger: *Z. angew. Phys.* **4,** 442 (1952).
C5. Cook, Zemansky, and Boorse: *Phys. Rev.* **80,** 737 (1950).
D1. Daunt, J. G., and C. V. Heer: *Phys. Rev.* **76,** 715 (1949).
D2. Daunt, J. G., and C. V. Heer: *Phys. Rev.* **76,** 1324 (1949).

D3. Daunt, Horseman, and Mendelssohn: *Phil. Mag.* **27**, 754 (1939).
D4. Daunt and Mendelssohn: *Proc. Roy. Soc.* (*London*), ser. A, **160**, 127 (1937).
D5. Daunt and Smith: *Phys. Rev.* **88**, 309 (1952).
E1. Estermann, Friedberg, and Goldman: *Phys. Rev.* **87**, 582 (1952).
G1. Goodman: *Nature* **167**, 111 (1951).
G2. Goodman and Mendoza: *Phil. Mag.* **42**, 594 (1951).
G3. Goodman and Shoenberg: *Nature* **165**, 441 (1950).
H1. de Haas and Engelkes: *Physica* **4**, 325 (1937).
H2. Horowitz, Silvidi, Malaker, and Daunt: *Phys. Rev.* **88**, 1182 (1952).
J1. Jackson and Preston-Thomas: *Phil. Mag.* **41**, 1284 (1950).
J2. James, Legvold, and Spedding: *Phys. Rev.* **88**, 1092 (1952).
J3. Justi: *Physik. Z.* **42**, 325 (1941).
K1. Keesom: *Physica* **1**, 123 (1933).
K2. Keesom and Desirant: *Physica* **8**, 273 (1941).
K3. Keesom and van den Ende: *Leid. Comm.* 219b.
K4. Keesom and Kok: *Physica* **1**, 175 (1934).
K5. Keesom and Kok: *Physica* **1**, 503 (1934).
K6. Keesom and van Laer: *Physica* **4**, 487 (1937).
K7. Keesom and van Laer: *Physica* **5**, 193 (1938).
K8. Kok and Keesom: *Physica* **4**, 835 (1937).
K9. Kurti and Simon: *Proc. Roy. Soc.* (*London*), ser. A, **151**, 610 (1935).
L1. Lock, Pippard, and Shoenberg: *Proc. Cambridge Phil. Soc.* **47**, 811 (1951).
M1. Maxwell: *Phys. Rev.* **78**, 477 (1950).
M2. Maxwell: *Phys. Rev.* **79**, 173 (1950).
M3. Maxwell: *Phys. Rev.* **86**, 235 (1952).
M4. Mendelssohn and Daunt: *Nature* **139**, 473 (1937).
M5. Mendelssohn and Moore: *Phil. Mag.* **21**, 532 (1936).
M6. Misener: *Proc. Roy. Soc.* (*London*), ser. A, **174**, 262 (1940).
O1. Olsen: *Nature* **168**, 245 (1951).
P1. Parkinson, Simon, and Spedding: *Proc. Roy. Soc.* (*London*), ser. A, **207**, 137 (1951).
P2. Pickard and Simon: *Proc. Phys. Soc.* (*London*) **61**, 1 (1948).
P3. Preston-Thomas: *Can. J. Phys.* **30**, 626 (1952).
P4. Preston-Thomas: *Phys. Rev.* **88**, 325 (1952).
R1. Reynolds, Serin, and Nesbitt: *Phys. Rev.* **84**, 691 (1951).
R2. Reynolds, Serin, Wright, and Nesbitt: *Phys. Rev.* **78**, 487 (1950).
S1. Samoilov, *Dokl. Akad. Nauk SSSR* **81**, 79 (1951).
S2. Serin, Reynolds, and Lohman: *Phys. Rev.* **86**, 162 (1952).
S3. Serin, Reynolds, and Nesbitt: *Phys. Rev.* **78**, 813 (1950).
S4. Serin, Reynolds, and Nesbitt: *Phys. Rev.* **80**, 761 (1950).
S5. Shoenberg: *Proc. Cambridge Phil. Soc.* **36**, 84 (1940).
S6. Shoenberg: *Nature* **142**, 874 (1938).
S7. Shoenberg: *Proc. Cambridge Phil. Soc.* **36**, 84 (1940).
S8. Shoenberg: *Nature* **159**, 303 (1947).
S9. Silvidi and Daunt: *Phys. Rev.* **77**, 125 (1950).
S10. Smith and Daunt: *Phys. Rev.* **88**, 1172 (1952).
S11. Smith, Gager, and Daunt: *Phys. Rev.* **89**, 654 (1953).
S12. Steele and Hein: *Phys. Rev.* **87**, 908 (1952).
S13. Steele and Hein: *Phys. Rev.* **92**, 243 (1953).
T1. Tuyn: *Leid. Comm.* 196b.
T2. Daunt and Cobble: *Phys. Rev.* **92**, 507 (1953).
W1. Webber: *Phys. Rev.* **72**, 1241 (1947).
W2. Webber and Reynolds: *Phys. Rev.* **73**, 640 (1948).
W3. Webber, Reynolds, and McG ire: *Phys. Rev.* **76**, 293 (1949).
W4. Wexler and Corak: *Phys. Rev.* **85**, 85 (1952).
W5. Worley, Zemansky, and Boorse: *Phys. Rev.* **91**, 1567 (1953).
Z1. Ziegler: *J. Chem. Phys.* **16**, 838 (1948).
Z2. Ziegler: *J. Am. Chem. Soc.* **75**, 1215 (1953).

4f. Thermal Expansion[1]

PETER HIDNERT AND H. S. KRIDER

The National Bureau of Standards

TABLE 4f-1. COEFFICIENTS OF LINEAR* THERMAL EXPANSION OF CHEMICAL ELEMENTS (POLYCRYSTALLINE)†

Element	Temp. or temp. range, °C	Coefficient of linear thermal expansion × 10⁶ per °C
Aluminum	−191 to 0	18.0
	+ 20 to 100	23.8
	20 to 300	25.7
	20 to 600	28.7
Antimony‡	−190 to 20	8. to 10.
	+ 20 to 100	8.4 to 11.0
	20 to 300	9.2 to 11.4
	20 to 500	9.5 to 11.6
Arsenic	40	5.6
Barium	0 to 300	18.1 to 21.0
Beryllium	−120 to 0	8.1
	+ 20 to 100	12.3
	20 to 300	14.0
	20 to 700	16.8
	1200	23.7
Bismuth‡	−190 to 17	13 to 17
	− 15 to 100	13 to 14
	+ 75 to 265	17.4
Boron	20 to 750	8.3
Cadmium	−220	20.6
	−160	27.4
	+ 10	29.7
	20 to 100	31.8
Calcium	−150	18.0
	− 50	20.9
	+ 30	22.5
	20 to 100	25.2
	0 to 300	22.0
Carbon:		
Diamond	−180 to 0	0.4
	0 to 78	1.2
	0 to 400	2.8
	0 to 750	4.5
Graphite	20 to 100	0.6 to 4.3
	20 to 400	1.3 to 4.8
	20 to 800	1.8 to 5.3
Chromium	−216 to 0	4.1
	−100 to 0	5.1
	0 to 100	5.7 to 8.3
	0 to 300	7.8 to 8.9
	0 to 700	9.1 to 10.3
Cobalt	20 to 100	12.4
	20 to 400	14.0
Copper	−253 to 10	11.7
	−191 to 16	14.1
	+ 25 to 100	16.8
	25 to 300	17.8
	0 to 500	18.2
	0 to 1000	20.3

See page 4-53 for footnotes.

[1] All tables except 4f-7 and 4f-8 reprinted by permission from "Smithsonian Physical Tables," 9th ed. Data or references to publications on thermal expansion of other materials may be obtained from the National Bureau of Standards.

TABLE 4f-1. COEFFICIENTS OF LINEAR* THERMAL EXPANSION OF CHEMICAL ELEMENTS (POLYCRYSTALLINE)† (*Continued*)

Element	Temp. or temp. range, °C	Coefficient of linear thermal expansion × 10⁶ per °C	Element	Temp. or temp. range, °C	Coefficient of linear thermal expansion × 10⁶ per °C
Germanium	20 to 230	6.0	Molybdenum¶	−190 to 0	4.2
	230 to 450	7.3		−100 to 0	4.8
	450 to 840	7.5		20 to 100	3.7 to 5.3
				25 to 500	4.7 to 5.8
Gold	−190 to 16	13.1		27 to 2127	7.2
	0 to 100	14.2			
	0 to 400	14.9	Neodymium	100 to 260	0.4
	0 to 700	15.8			
	0 to 900	16.5			
			Nickel	−253 to 10	8.1
				−192 to 16	10.0
Indium	−180 to 20	26.7		0 to 100	13.1
	+ 20 to 100	30.5		0 to 300	14.4
				25 to 600	15.5
Iridium	−183 to 19	5.7		25 to 900	16.3
	+ 18 to 100	6.6			
	0 to 1000	7.9			
	0 to 1700	8.7	Niobium	−212 to 0	5.8
				−100 to 0	6.9
				0 to 100	7.2
Iron	−182 to 0	9.1		0 to 300	7.5
	−100 to 0	10.4		20 to 1500	10.0
	0 to 20	11.6			
	20 to 100	12.1			
	20 to 300	13.4	Osmium	40	6.6
	20 to 600	14.7			
	20 to 900	15.0	Palladium	−191 to 16	10.3
				+ 16 to 100	12.4
				16 to 500	12.8
Lead	−190 to 20	26.7		16 to 1000	13.8
	+ 20 to 100	29.2			
	20 to 200	30.0			
	20 to 300	31.3	Platinum	−191 to 16	8.0
				− 90 to 0	8.7
Lithium	−178	17.0		0 to 100	9.0
	− 98	36.3		0 to 300	9.2
	− 3	45.7		0 to 500	9.6
	0 to 95	56		0 to 1000	10.2
Magnesium	−190 to 20	21.3	Potassium	0 to 50	85
	20 to 100	25.9			
	20 to 300	28.0	Rhodium	−174	5.0
	20 to 500	29.8		− 92	7.4
				− 28	7.9
Manganese:				0 to 100	8.4
Alpha phase	−190 to 0	15.9		0 to 500	9.7
	−183 to 0	17.6		0 to 1000	10.8
	0 to 20	22.3		0 to 1500	12.1
	0 to 100	22.8			
	0 to 300	25.2	Rubidium	− 98 to 19	66
Beta phase	−183 to 0	12.8 to 20.4			
	0 to 20	18.7 to 24.9	Ruthenium	+ 13 to 32	6.8
Gamma phase	− 70 to 0	13.6		40	9.6
	0 to 20	14.8		50	9.9

See page 4–53 for footnotes.

TABLE 4f-1. COEFFICIENTS OF LINEAR* THERMAL EXPANSION OF CHEMICAL ELEMENTS (POLYCRYSTALLINE)† (*Continued*)

Element	Temp. or temp. range, °C	Coefficient of linear thermal expansion × 10⁶ per °C	Element	Temp. or temp. range, °C	Coefficient of linear thermal expansion × 10⁶ per °C
Selenium:			Thallium	0 to 100	29.4
Polycrystalline	− 78 to 19	20.3		0 to 200	30.0
	+ 20 to 100	22.9	Thorium	−216 to 20	9.8
	205	45.2		+ 20 to 100	11.3
Amorphous	− 78 to 0	42.7		20 to 300	12.1
	0 to 21	48.7		20 to 600	13.7
Amorphous; melted and cast	−160 to 0	37.3	Tin	−183 to 20	15.8 to 22.6
	0	43.9		+ 18 to 100	23.8 to 27.0
				25 to 200	24
Silicon	−172	−0.4	Titanium	−195 to 20	6.8
	− 87	+0.9		+ 20 to 200	8.9
	+ 20 to 50	2.4		20 to 400	9.4
	100	2.0		20 to 600	9.9
	500	3.0		20 to 800	10.1
	1000	3.3			
			Tungsten (wolfram)	−190 to 0	3.8
Silver	−250 to 0	14.9		−100 to 0	4.2
	−191 to 16	17.0		0 to 100	4.4
	0 to 100	19.4		0 to 300	4.6
	20 to 300	20.2		0 to 650	4.6
	20 to 500	20.7		27 to 1000	4.7
	0 to 900	22.4		27 to 1750	5.2
				27 to 2400	5.8
Sodium	−193 to 0	59.8	Vanadium	−183 to 0	6.6
	0 to 17	68.2		0 to 40	7.8
	0 to 50	70			
	0 to 95	71	Zinc‡	−183 to 18	9 to 10
				+ 20 to 100	17 to 40
Tantalum	−190 to 20	6.2		20 to 200	30 to 40
	+ 20 to 100	6.6		20 to 300	34 to 39
	20 to 300	6.6			
	20 to 500	6.6	Zirconium	−183 to 0	4.0 to 5.1
	27 to 1400	7.3		0 to 20	4.6 to 5.9
	27 to 2400	7.8		+ 20 to 200	5.4
				20 to 400	6.1
Tellurium	40	16.8		20 to 700	7.1

* The coefficient of cubical expansion of an isotropic solid element may be taken as 3 times the coefficient of linear expansion within a high degree of approximation (see Table 4f-3 for measured coefficients of cubical expansion of some chemical elements).

† For references, see "Smithsonian Physical Tables," 9th ed.

‡ The coefficients of expansion depend upon the orientation of the constituent crystals.

¶ The coefficients of expansion depend upon coarseness of grains and treatment of metal.

TABLE 4f-2. COEFFICIENTS OF LINEAR* THERMAL EXPANSION OF CHEMICAL ELEMENTS (CRYSTALS)

Element	Temp. or temp. range, °C	Coefficient of linear thermal expansion per °C	
		Parallel to axis	Perpendicular to axis
Antimony	−215 to +20	16.0×10^{-6}	7.0×10^{-6}
	+ 15 to 25	15.6	
	0 to 100	16.8	
	20 to 200	....	8.4
	20 to 400	....	8.1
Arsenic	30 to 75	3.2 to 6.8	
Beryllium	−150	1.6	2.8
	+ 10	8.6	11.7
	18 to 220	10.4	15.0
	18 to 454	13.1	15.7
Bismuth	−140	15.9	10.5
	+ 30	16.2	11.6
	20 to 260	16.5	
	20 to 240	....	12.0
Cadmium	−190 to 18	48.2	18.5
	+ 20 to 100	50.4	18.9
Carbon:			
Graphite	−195 to 0		4.8
	0 to 40		6.6
	0 to 500	17.2	1.3
	0 to 1000	18.8	1.8
	0 to 1500	20.7	2.0
	0 to 2300	23.1	2.4
	20 to 870	26.7	
Cobalt	33 to 100	16.1	12.6
Indium	− 17 to 9	56	13
	+ 23 to 87	45.0	11.7
Magnesium	20 to 100	26.4	25.6
	20 to 200	27.7	26.6
Mercury	−190 to −160	42.6	33.4
	−188 to −79	47.0	37.5
	−120	49.6	37.5

See page 4-55 for footnote.

TABLE 4f-2. COEFFICIENTS OF LINEAR* THERMAL EXPANSION OF CHEMICAL ELEMENTS (CRYSTALS) (*Continued*)

Element	Temp. or temp. range, °C	Coefficient of linear thermal expansion per °C	
		Parallel to axis	Perpendicular to axis
Osmium	+ 50	5.8×10^{-6}	4.0×10^{-6}
	250	6.6	4.6
	500	8.3	5.8
Rhenium	20 to 1917	12.4	4.7
Ruthenium	50	8.8	5.9
	250	9.8	6.4
	550	11.7	7.6
Selenium	15 to 55	−17.9	
	20 to 60	.....	74.1
Tellurium	20	− 1.6	27.2
	20 to 60	− 1.7	27.0
Thallium	32 to 91	+72	9
Tin	−195 to 20	25.9	14.1
	0 to 20	29.0	15.8
	+ 14 to 25	32.2	16.8
	34 to 194	45.8	25.7
Zinc	−190 to 18	49.5	11.3
	+ 20 to 100	64.0	14.1
	0 to 250	56	15
	20 to 400	59	16
Zirconium	0 to 100	4	13

* If there is random orientation of the crystals in a polycrystalline element such as antimony or cadmium, the coefficient of linear expansion of the polycrystalline element may be computed from the following equation:

$$a = \frac{1}{3}(a\| + 2a\perp)$$

where $a\|$ is the coefficient of linear expansion of the crystal parallel to its axis, and $a\perp$ is the coefficient of linear expansion of the crystal in the direction perpendicular to its axis (see Table 4f-1 for measured coefficients of linear expansion of polycrystalline elements).

TABLE 4f-3. COEFFICIENTS OF CUBICAL THERMAL EXPANSION OF CHEMICAL ELEMENTS

Element	Temp. or temp. range, °C	Coefficient of cubical thermal expansion $\times 10^6$ per °C	Element	Temp. or temp. range, °C	Coefficient of cubical thermal expansion $\times 10^6$ per °C
Cadmium	100	91	Potassium	0 to 55	240
	210	105			
	250	110	Rubidium	0 to 38	270
Carbon:			Selenium:		
Diamond	27	3.2	Compressed	0 to 100	175
	25 to 650	9.1	Not compressed	0 to 100	198
Cesium	0 to 23	291	Sodium	−186 to 17	186
				0 to 53	207
Cobalt	100	35.6		0 to 79	208
	300	39.4		20 to 95	226
Gallium	− 78 to 18	53	Sulfur:		
	0 to 29.6	55	Rhombic	−273 to 18	139
				−195 to 18	164
Iodine	−195 to 25	204 to 251		− 79 to 18	180
	+ 10 to 40	264	Crystallized	0 to 100	354
			Sicilian	0 to 100	260
Lithium	0 to 100	162			
	0 to 178	170	Tin	80	68
				140	78
Nickel	100	38.2		190	89
	200	41.9			
	300	46.5	Zinc	50	89
				200	104
Phosphorus	−273 to 19	317		300	110
	−195 to 19	398			
	− 79 to 19	362			
	0 to 44	372			

TABLE 4f-4. COEFFICIENTS OF LINEAR THERMAL EXPANSION OF SOME ALLOYS*

Alloy†	Temp. or temp. range, °C	Coefficient‡ of linear thermal expansion × 10^6 per °C
Aluminum-beryllium, 4.2 to 32.7 Be	20 to 100	22.4 to 17.8
	20 to 500	26.6 to 22.2
Aluminum-copper, 9.9 Cu	20 to 100	22.0
	20 to 300	23.8
33.2 Cu	20 to 100	19.7
	20 to 300	20.8
Aluminum-nickel, 3.4 Ni	20 to 100	21.9
	20 to 300	23.7
19.5 Ni	20 to 100	18.2
	20 to 300	19.5
Aluminum-silicon, 4.2 to 12.6 Si	20 to 100	22.2 to 19.4
	20 to 300	24.8 to 22.1
19.7 Si	20 to 100	18.5
	20 to 300	19.0
40 Si	20 to 100	14.7
	20 to 300	17.1
Aluminum-zinc, 0 to 50 Zn	20 to 100	23.6 to 26.5
Brass, 3 to 40 Zn	25 to 100	16.9 to 19.7
	25 to 300	17.7 to 21.2
Bronze, 4.2 to 10.1 Sn	25 to 100	17.1 to 17.8
	25 to 300	17.8 to 19.0
Cast iron	20 to 100	8.7 to 11.1
	20 to 400	11.5 to 12.7
Cobalt-iron-chromium, 53.0 to 55.5 Co, 35.0 to 37.5 Fe, 9.0 to 10.5 Cr	20 to 60	−1.1 to +1.7
Copper-beryllium, 3.0 Be	20 to 100	15.9 to 17.3
	20 to 300	16.4 to 17.4
Copper-nickel, 19.5 Ni	−182 to 0	13.0
	0 to 40	14.7
49.8 Ni	−182 to 0	11.8
	0 to 40	13.7
Copper-tin (see Bronze)		

See page 4-60 for footnotes.

TABLE 4f-4. COEFFICIENTS OF LINEAR THERMAL EXPANSION OF SOME ALLOYS* (*Continued*)

Alloy†	Temp. or temp. range, °C	Coefficient‡ of linear thermal expansion × 10^6 per °C
Copper-zinc (see Brass)		
Dumet:		
Axial	20 to 300	6.1 to 6.8
Radial	20 to 300	8.0 to 10.0
Duralumin	20 to 100	21.9 to 23.8
	20 to 500	25.4 to 27.6
Fernico, 54 Fe, 31 Ni, 15 Co	25 to 300	5.0
Invar, 64 Fe, 36 Ni	0 to 100	0 to 2
Iron-aluminum, 0.5 to 10.5 Al	20 to 100	11.6 to 12.2
Iron-chromium, 1 to 40 Cr	20 to 100	12.4 to 9.4
Iron-cobalt 9.9 to 49.4 Co	30 to 100	11.2 to 9.3
Iron-manganese, 2.8 to 14.4 Mn	20 to 100	12.7 to 16.9
Iron-nickel, 3.6 Ni	20 to 100	10.9
34.5 Ni	20 to 100	3.7
36 Ni	0 to 100	0 to 2
40 to 50 Ni	30 to 100	4.1 to 9.7
Iron-nickel-chromium, 6.6 to 74.7 Fe, 1.3 to 70.1 Ni, 4.9 to 26.7 Cr	20 to 100	8.7 to 18.4
	20 to 1000	13.1 to 20.6
Iron-nickel-cobalt, 62.5 to 64.0 Fe, 30.5 to 34.0 Ni, 3.5 to 6.0 Co	20	0.0 to 0.5
61.3 Fe, 31.8 Ni, 6.0 Co	20 to 100	0.9
	20 to 240	2.4
58.7 Fe, 32.4 Ni, 8.2 Co	20 to 200	1.7
	20 to 295	2.6
Iron-silicon, 1.0 to 8.4 Si	20 to 100	12.2 to 11.3
Kanthal (A, A-1, and D)¶	20 to 100	11.4 to 11.7
	20 to 900	13.9 to 15.1
Kovar (see Fernico)		

See page 4–60 for footnotes.

TABLE 4f-4. COEFFICIENTS OF LINEAR THERMAL EXPANSION OF SOME ALLOYS* (*Continued*)

Alloy†	Temp. or temp. range, °C	Coefficient‡ of linear thermal expansion × 10^6 per °C
Lead-antimony, 2.9 to 39.6 Sb	20 to 100	28.2 to 20.4
Magnesium-aluminum, 10.4 Al	20 to 100	25.9
	20 to 200	27.2
30 Al	0 to 100	23.7
	0 to 200	25.1
Magnesium-tin, 20.4 Sn	30 to 100	24.3
	30 to 300	24.7
46.3 Sn	30 to 100	21.1
	30 to 300	21.3
Magnesium-zinc, 20 Zn	40 to 100	29.5
50 Zn	40 to 100	30.2
Manganin	20 to 100	18.1
	0 to 400	18.9
	0 to 800	21.1
Monel metal	25 to 100	13.5 to 14.5
	25 to 600	15.9 to 16.7
Nickel-chromium, 20.4 Cr	20 to 100	13.0
	20 to 1000	17.2
47.7 Cr	20 to 100	13.5
	20 to 1000	17.7
Nickel silver, 62.0 to 63.2 Cu, 10.0 to 20.2 Ni, 17.4 to 27.1 Zn	0 to 100	14.8 to 15.4
	0 to 400	16.8 to 17.4
Platinum-iridium, 20 Ir	−190 to 0	7.5
	0 to 100	8.3
	0 to 1000	9.6
	0 to 1600	10.5
Platinum-rhodium, 20 Rh	0 to 500	9.6
	0 to 1000	10.4
	0 to 1400	11.0
SAE carbon steels§	20 to 100	8.8 to 14.4
SAE stainless chromium irons	20 to 100	9.4 to 10.7

See page 4–60 for footnotes.

TABLE 4f-4. COEFFICIENTS OF LINEAR THERMAL EXPANSION OF SOME ALLOYS* (*Continued*)

Alloy†	Temp. or temp. range, °C	Coefficient‡ of linear thermal expansion × 10^6 per °C
Speculum metal	20 to 100	16.0
Stainless steel, 12 Cr	20 to 100	10.0
18 Cr, 8 Ni	20 to 100	16.4
Stellite, 55 to 80 Co, 20 to 40 Cr, 0 to 10 W, 0 to 2 C	20 to 100	11.0 to 14.1
	20 to 600	13.6 to 16.5
Tantalum carbide	20 to 2377	8.2
Tungsten carbide +5.9 Co	20 to 100	4.5
	20 to 400	5.2
+13.0 Co	20 to 100	5.2
	20 to 400	6.0
Zinc-aluminum, 22.6 Al	20 to 100	26.0
	20 to 200	28.3
50 Al	20 to 100	26.5
	20 to 200	27.6

* For references, see "Smithsonian Physical Tables," 9th ed.
† Chemical composition is given in per cent by weight.
‡ Coefficient of expansion varies with composition and treatment.
¶ Composition of Kanthal: A: 68.5 Fe, 23.4 Cr, 6.2 Al, 1.9 Co, 0.06 C; A-1: 69.0 Fe, 23.4 Cr, 5.7 Al, 1.9 Co, 0.06 C; D: 70.9 Fe, 22.6 Cr, 4.5 Al, 2.0 Co, 0.09 C.
§ Coefficients of expansion of other SAE steels (free-cutting, manganese, nickel, nickel-chromium, molybdenum, chromium, chromium-vanadium, and chromium-nickel austenitic steels) are given in "Metals Handbook" for the American Society for Metals.

Table 4f-5. Coefficients of Linear Thermal Expansion of Some Miscellaneous Materials*

Material	Temp. or temp. range, °C	Coefficient of linear thermal expansion × 10⁶ per °C
Alum:		
Ammonium	20 to 50	9.5
Ammonium chrome	20 to 50	10.6
Potassium	20 to 50	11.0
Thallium	20 to 50	13.1
Amber	0 to 50	53
Bakelite	20 to 60	21 to 33
Beryl	20 to 100	0.3 to 1.6
Brick, clay building	− 10 to 40	3.0 to 12.4
Carborundum	0 to 500	7.3
	0 to 1000	8.4
	0 to 1800	9.2
Concrete	− 13 to 27	6.8 to 12.7
	− 13 to 88	7.5 to 14.0
Dental amalgam	+ 20 to 50	22 to 28
Glass:		
Miscellaneous	0 to 300	0.8 to 12.8
Pyrex	20 to 100	3.1 to 3.5
	20 to 300	3.0 to 3.6
Granites (American)	− 20 to 60	4.8 to 8.3
Ice	−250	−6.1
	−200	+0.8
	−150	16.8
	−100	33.9
	− 50	45.6
	0	52.7
Magnesia	+ 20 to 500	12.4
	20 to 1000	13.7
Marble	25 to 100	5 to 16
Mica, muscovite:		
∥ to cleavage plane	0 to 100	8.5
⊥ to cleavage plane†	20 to 300	8 to 25
Mica, phlogopite:		
∥ to cleavage plane	0 to 100	13.5
⊥ to cleavage plane †	20 to 100	1 to 179
Porcelain	20 to 200	1.6 to 19.6
Quartz, crystalline		
∥ to axis	0 to 100	8.0
	0 to 300	9.6
	0 to 500	12.2
⊥ to axis	0 to 100	14.4
	0 to 300	16.9
	0 to 500	20.9
Quartz, fused (silica)	20 to 100	0.5
	20 to 1000	0.5
Rocks (American):		
Igneous	20 to 100	3.4 to 11.9
Sedimentary	20 to 100	2.7 to 12.2
Metamorphic	20 to 100	2.3 to 11.0
Rubber (hard)‡	¶	50 to 84
Slate	20 to 100	6.3 to 8.3
Tooth:		
Root	20 to 50	8.3
Across crown	20 to 50	11.4
Root and crown	20 to 50	7.8
Wood:		
Along grain	¶	1 to 11
Across grain	¶	32 to 73

* For references, see "Smithsonian Physical Tables," 9th ed.
† With load of 30 psi.
‡ Includes terms "ebonite" and "vulcanite."
¶ Various temperature ranges between 0 and 100°C.

Table 4f-6. Cubical Expansion of Liquids

(If V_0 is the volume at 0° then at t° the expansion formula is $V_t = V_0(1 + \alpha t + \beta t^2 + \gamma t^3)$. The table gives values of α, β and γ and k, the true coefficient of cubical expansion at 20° for some liquids and solutions. Δt is the temperature range of the observation.)

Liquid	Δt, °C	$\alpha\ 10^3$	$\beta\ 10^6$	$\gamma\ 10^8$	$k\ 10^3$ at 20°C
Acetic acid	16 to 107	1.0630	0.12636	1.0876	1.071
Acetone	0 to 54	1.3240	3.8090	−0.87983	1.487
Alcohol:					
Amyl	−15 to 80	0.9001	0.6573	1.18458	0.902
Ethyl, 30% by vol	18 to 39	0.2928	10.790	−11.87	
Ethyl, 50% by vol	0 to 39	0.7450	1.85	0.730	
Ethyl, 99.3% vol	27 to 46	1.012	2.20	....	1.12
Ethyl, 500 atm pressure	0 to 40	0.866			
Ethyl, 3,000 atm pressure	0 to 40	0.524			
Methyl	0 to 61	1.1342	1.3635	0.8741	1.199
Benzene	11 to 81	1.17626	1.27776	0.80648	1.237
Bromine	0 to 59	1.06218	1.87714	−0.30854	1.132
Calcium chloride:					
5.8% solution	18 to 25	0.07878	4.2742	....	0.250
40.9% solution	17 to 24	0.42383	0.8571	....	0.458
Carbon disulfide	−34 to 60	1.13980	1.37065	1.91225	1.218
500 atm pressure	0 to 50	0.940			
3,000 atm pressure	0 to 50	0.581			
Carbon tetrachloride	0 to 76	1.18384	0.89881	1.35135	1.236
Chloroform	0 to 63	1.10715	4.66473	−1.74328	1.273
Ether	−15 to 38	1.51324	2.35918	4.00512	1.656
Glycerin		0.4853	0.4895	....	0.505
Hydrochloric acid, 33.2% solution	0 to 33	0.4460	0.215	....	0.455
Mercury	0 to 100	0.18182	0.0078	....	0.18186
Olive oil	....	0.6821	1.1405	−0.539	0.721
Pentane	0 to 33	1.4646	3.09319	1.6084	1.608
Petroleum, density 0.8467	24 to 120	0.8994	1.396	....	0.955
Potassium chloride, 24.3% solution	16 to 25	0.2695	2.080	....	0.353
Phenol	36 to 157	0.8340	0.10732	0.4446	1.090
Sodium chloride, 20.6% solution	0 to 29	0.3640	1.237	....	0.414
Sodium sulfate, 24% solution	11 to 40	0.3599	1.258	....	0.410
Sulfuric acid:					
10.9% solution	0 to 30	0.2835	2.580	....	0.387
100.0%	0 to 30	0.5758	−0.432	....	0.558
Turpentine	−9 to 106	0.9003	1.9595	−0.44998	0.973
Water	0 to 33	−0.06427	8.5053	−6.7900	0.207

TABLE 4f-7. COEFFICIENTS OF LINEAR EXPANSION* OF SOME SEMICONDUCTORS, (°C)$^{-1}$

Material	Coefficient†	Reference
CdS (‖)	4×10^{-6} at 25°C	R. Seiwert, *Ann. Physik* **6,** 241 (1949)
CdS (⊥)	6×10^{-6} at 25°C	
Germanium	5.5×10^{-6} at 25°C	M. E. Fine, *J. Appl. Phys.* **24,** 338 (1953)
PbS	19×10^{-6} at 40°C	S. S. Sharma, *Proc. Indian Acad. Sci.* **A34,** 72 (1951)
PbSe	20×10^{-6}	T. S. Moss, "Photoconductivity, in the Elements," pp. 66 and 67, Butterworth & Co. (Publishers), Ltd., London, 1952
PbTe	27×10^{-6}	
ZnS	7×10^{-6}	
Gray tin	5.3×10^{-6}, −163 to 18°C	ASM "Metals Handbook," p. 1070, American Society for Metals (1948)
TiO_2	9×10^{-6}	Von Hippel, Breckenridge, Chesley, and Tisza, *Ind. Eng. Chem.* **38,** 1097 (1946)
UO_2	11.5×10^{-6}, 20 to 720°C	J. Thewliss, *Acta Cryst.* **5,** 790 (1952)

* Compiled by Mark W. Zemansky, The City College of New York.
† Temperature or temperature range for coefficients of PbSE, PbTe, ZnS, and TiO_2 not indicated in the publications cited.

An approximate relation between the coefficient of volume expansion,

$$\beta = (1/v)\,(\partial v/\partial T)_P$$

and the temperature is given by Grüneisen's equation

$$\beta = \frac{C_v}{Q_0[1 - k(E/Q_0)]^2} \tag{4f-1}$$

where C_v is the molar heat capacity at constant volume, E is the energy of the lattice vibrations, and Q_0 and k are constants. If the Debye temperature Θ is known, both C_v and E may be calculated at any value of T from the equations

$$C_v = 3R\left[12\left(\frac{T}{\Theta}\right)^3 \int_0^{\Theta/T} \frac{y^3\,dy}{e^y - 1} - 3\,\frac{\Theta/T}{e^{\Theta/T} - 1}\right] \tag{4f-2}$$

$$E = \int_0^T C_v\,dT \tag{4f-3}$$

Values of C_v for many values of Θ/T are given in Table 4e-3, and values of E in Table 4e-4. Thus, if Θ, Q_0, and k are known, β can be calculated. Table 4f-8 lists the values of Θ, Q_0, and k for 24 metals which are consistent with the experimentally determined values of β measured by Adenstedt,[1] Erfling,[2] and Nix and MacNair.[3] The values of Θ listed in Table 4f-8 are not in perfect agreement with those determined from low-temperature heat capacities. (For the most reliable values of Θ obtained from low-temperature heat capacities, see Table 4e-7.)

Another consequence of Grüneisen's theory of the solid state is the approximate proportionality of Q_0 with the melting temperature T_m. Values of T_m are listed in the last column of Table 4f-8.

[1] H. Adenstedt, *Ann. Physik* **26,** 69 (1936).
[2] H. D. Erfling, *Ann. Physik* **34,** 136 (1939); **41,** 467 (1942).
[3] F. C. Nix and D. MacNair, *Phys. Rev.* **60,** 597 (1941); **61,** 74 (1942).

TABLE 4f-8. CONSTANTS* IN GRÜNEISEN'S EQUATION FOR THERMAL EXPANSION

Metal	Θ, °K	Q_0 kcal/mole	k	T_m, °K
Ag	215	108.8	2.42	1234
Al	400	83.6	2.7	933
Au	190	148.8	3.4	1336
Be	1000	106.0	2.4	1623
Bi	147	150.0	0.5	544
Ca	220	96.0	3.8	1083
Cr	430	277.0	1.7	
	490	294	2.0	1888
Cu	315	120	2.8	1357
Fe	420	166.7	3.7	1806
βMn	330	85.0	3.3	1533
Mo	390	363.0	3.0	2893
Nb	280	290.5	7.0	2773
Ni	400	151.5	4	1725
Pb	88	77.84	3.19	601
Pd	300	163.7	0.49	1825
Pt	230	221	2.21	2042
Rh	350	229.5	2.5	2233
Sb	201	179.0	0.4	904
Sn	180	112.0	6.0	505
Ta	252	292.4	0.2924	3278
Th	200	184.5	2.0	2118
V	450	215.5	6.5	2008
W	310	471.2	30.63	3653
Zn	235	68.6	3.33	693

* Compiled by Mark W. Zemansky, The City College of New York.

4g. Thermal Conductivity

W. E. FORSYTHE[1]

The Smithsonian Institution

ROBERT L. POWELL[2]

NBS-AEC Cryogenic Engineering Laboratory

[1] High-temperature thermal conductivities reprinted by permission from the "Smithsonian Physical Tables," 9th ed.

[2] Low-temperature thermal conductivities.

Table 4g-1. Conversion Factors for Thermal Conductivity

	Watts cm^{-2} $°K^{-1}$ cm	Watts $in.^{-2}$ $°F^{-1}$ in.	Watts $meter^{-2}$ $°K^{-1}$ meter	Calories sec^{-1} cm^{-2} $°K^{-1}$ cm	Calories sec^{-1} $in.^{-2}$ $°F^{-1}$ in.	K calories hr^{-1} $meter^{-2}$ $°K^{-1}$ meter	Btu hr^{-1} ft^{-2} $°F^{-1}$ in.	Btu hr^{-1} ft^{-2} $°F^{-1}$ ft	Btu sec^{-1} $in.^{-2}$ $°F^{-1}$ in.	Btu hr^{-1} $in.^{-2}$ $°F^{-1}$ in.
$\frac{\text{Watt-cm}}{\text{cm}^2\ °\text{K}}$ =	1.000	1.411	100.0	0.2389	0.3371	86.00	693.46	57.79	1.338×10^{-3}	4.816
$\frac{\text{Watts-in.}}{\text{in.}^2 - °\text{F}}$ =	0.7087	1.000	70.87	0.1693	0.2389	60.95	491.4	40.95	9.480×10^{-4}	3.413
$\frac{\text{Watts-meter}}{\text{meter}^2\ °\text{K}}$ =	0.01	1.411×10^{-2}	1.000	2.389×10^{-3}	3.371×10^{-3}	0.860	6.935	0.5779	1.338×10^{-5}	4.816×10^{-2}
$\frac{\text{Calories-cm}}{\text{sec-cm}^2\ °\text{K}}$ =	4.1858	5.907	418.58	1.000	1.411	360	2,902.7	241.9	5.602×10^{-3}	20.16
$\frac{\text{Calories-in.}}{\text{sec-in.}^2\ °\text{F}}$ =	2.966	4.1858	296.6	0.7087	1.000	255.1	2,057.0	171.4	3.968×10^{-3}	14.28
$\frac{\text{K calories-meter}}{\text{hr-meter}^2\text{-}°\text{K}}$ =	1.162×10^{-2}	1.641×10^{-2}	1.163	2.778×10^{-3}	3.920×10^{-3}	1.000	8.059	0.6721	1.556×10^{-5}	5.599×10^{-2}
$\frac{\text{Btu-in.}}{\text{hr-ft}^2\text{-}°\text{F}}$ =	1.442×10^{-3}	2.035×10^{-3}	0.1442	3.445×10^{-4}	4.861×10^{-4}	0.1242	1.000	8.33×10^{-2}	1.929×10^{-6}	6.944×10^{-3}
$\frac{\text{Btu-ft}}{\text{hr-ft}^2\text{-}°\text{F}}$ =	1.730×10^{-2}	2.442×10^{-2}	1.730	4.135×10^{-3}	5.834×10^{-3}	1.489	12	1.000	2.315×10^{-5}	8.333×10^{-2}
$\frac{\text{Btu-in.}}{\text{sec-in.}^2\text{-}°\text{F}}$ =	747.38	1,054.8	7.4738×10^4	178.5	252.0	6.428×10^4	5.184×10^5	4.3191×10^4	1.000	3,600
$\frac{\text{Btu-in.}}{\text{hr-in.}^2\text{-}°\text{F}}$ =	0.2076	0.2930	20.76	4.960×10^{-2}	7.002×10^{-2}	17.86	144	12	2.778×10^{-4}	1.000

Table 4g-2. Thermal Conductivity of Metals and Alloys

Substance	t°C	cal cm/sec cm² °C	α
Aluminum	−190	0.497	
Aluminum	30	0.497	+0.0030
Aluminum	76.4	0.550	
Antimony	0	0.0442	−0.00104
Antimony	100	0.0396	
Bismuth	−186	0.025	
Bismuth	18	0.0194	−0.0021
Bismuth	100	0.0161	
Brass	−160	0.181	
Brass	17	0.260	
Brass, yellow	0	0.204	+0.0024
Brass, red	0	0.246	+0.0015
Cadmium, pure	−160	0.239	
Cadmium, pure	18	0.222	−0.00038
Cadmium, pure	100	0.215	
Constantan	18	0.0540	+0.00227
(60 Cu + 40 Ni)	100	0.0640	
Copper,* pure	−160	1.079	
Copper,* pure	18	0.918	−0.00013
Copper,* pure	100	0.908	
German silver	0	0.070	+0.0027
Gold	−190	0.793	−0.00007
Gold	17	0.705	
Graphite	17	0.037	+0.0003
Iridium	17	0.141	−0.0005
Iron,† pure	18	0.161	−0.0008
Iron,† pure	100	0.151	
Iron, wrought	−160	0.152	
Iron, polycrystalline	30	0.173	
Iron, polycrystalline	100	0.163	
Iron, polycrystalline	200	0.147	−0.0008
Iron, polycrystalline	800	0.071	
Iron, steel, 1% C	18	0.108	−0.0001
Iron, steel, 1% C	100	0.107	
Lead, pure	−160	0.092	
Lead, pure	18	0.083	−0.0001
Lead, pure	100	0.081	
Magnesium	0 to 100	0.376	
Manganin	−160	0.035	
Manganin (84 Cu	18	0.0519	+0.0026
+ 4 Ni 12 Mn)	100	0.0630	
Mercury	0	0.0148	+0.0055
Mercury	50	0.0189	

Substance	t°C	cal cm/sec cm² °C	α
Molybdenum	17	0.346	−0.0001
Nickel	−160	0.129	
Nickel	18	0.1420	
Nickel	0	0.1425	−0.00032
Nickel	100	0.1380	
Nickel	200	0.1325	−0.00095
Nickel	700	0.069	
Nickel	1000	0.064	−0.00047
Nickel	1200	0.058	
Palladium	18	0.1683	+0.0010
Palladium	100	0.182	
Platinum	18	0.1664	+0.00051
Platinum	100	0.1733	
Pt 10% Ir	17	0.074	+0.0002
Pt 10% Rh	17	0.072	+0.0002
Platinoid	18	0.060	
Potassium	5.0	0.232	−0.0013
Potassium	57.4	0.216	
Rhodium	17	0.210	−0.0010
Silver, pure	−160	0.998	
Silver	18	1.006	−0.00017
Silver	100	0.992	
Sodium	5.7	0.321	−0.0012
Sodium	88.1	0.288	
Steel	18	0.110	
Tantalum	17	0.130	−0.0001
Tantalum	1700	0.174	
Tantalum	1900	0.186	+0.00032
Tantalum	2100	0.198	
Tin	0	0.155	−0.00069
Tin	100	0.145	
Tin, pure	−160	0.192	
Tungsten	17	0.476	−0.0001
Tungsten	1600	0.249	+0.00023
Tungsten	2000	0.272	
Tungsten	2400	0.294	+0.00016
Tungsten	2800	0.313	
Wood's alloy	......	0.319	
Zinc, pure	−160	0.278	
Zinc, polycrystalline	0	0.280	
Zinc, polycrystalline	200	0.250	
Zinc, polycrystalline	400	0.231	
Zinc, liquid	500	0.144	

The coefficient k is the quantity of heat in small calories which is transmitted per second through a plate 1 cm thick per square centimeter of its surface when the difference of temperature between the two faces of the plate is 1°C. The coefficient k is found to vary with the absolute temperature of the plate, and is expressed approximately by the equation $k_t = k_0[1 + a(t - t_0)]$. k_0 is the conductivity at t_0, the lower temperature of the bracketed pairs in the table, k_t that at temperature t, and a is a constant.

* Copper: 100 to 197°C, k_t = 1.043; 100 to 268°, 0.969; 100 to 370°, 0.931; 100 to 541°, 0.902.

† Iron: 100 to 727°C, k_t = 0.202; 100 to 912°, 0.184; 100 to 1245°, 0.191.

TABLE 4g-3. THERMAL CONDUCTIVITY OF INSULATING MATERIALS*

Material	Density g/cm³	t°C	Conductivity watt cm/(cm² °C)	Conductivity cal cm/(sec cm² °C)
Air, 76 cm Hg	0.00129	0	0.00023	0.000055
Asbestos wool	0.40	−100	0.00068	0.000162
Asbestos wool	0.40	0	0.00090	0.000215
Asbestos wool	0.40	+100	0.00101	0.00024
Asbestos with 85% MgO	0.3	30	0.00075	0.000179
Brick, very porous, dry	0.71	20	0.00174	0.00042
Brick, machine-made, dry	1.54	0	0.00038	0.000091
Brick, machine-made, moist, 1.2% vol	....	50	0.00096	0.00023
Calorox, fluffy mineral matter	0.064	30	0.00032	0.000076
Celluloid, white	1.4	30	0.00021	0.000050
Cement mortar	2.0	90	0.0055	0.0013
Chalk	....	.....	0.0092	0.0022
Charcoal	0.18	20	0.00055	0.00013
Coke dust	1.0	20	0.0015	0.00036
Concrete	1.6	0	0.008	0.002
Cork	0.05	0	0.00032	0.000076
Cork	0.05	100	0.00041	0.000098
Cork	0.35	0	0.00061	0.000146
Cork	0.35	100	0.00079	0.000189
Cotton, tightly packed	0.08	−150	0.00038	0.000091
Cotton, tightly packed	0.08	0	0.00056	0.000133
Cotton, tightly packed	0.08	+150	0.00076	0.00018
Cotton wool, tightly packed	0.08	30	0.00042	0.00010
Diatomite (binders may increase 100%)	0.20	0	0.00052	0.00012
Diatomite (binders may increase 100%)	0.20	400	0.00094	0.00022
Diatomite (binders may increase 100%)	0.50	0	0.00086	0.00021
Diatomite (binders may increase 100%)	0.50	400	0.00157	0.00037
Ebonite	1.19	−190	0.00138	0.00033
Ebonite	1.19	− 78	0.00157	0.00038
Ebonite	1.19	0	0.00160	0.00038
Felt, flax fibers	0.18	30	0.00047	0.00011
Felt, hair	0.27	30	0.00036	0.000086
Felt, wool	0.15	40	0.00063	0.000151
Felt, wool	0.33	30	0.00052	0.000124
Flannel	....	.....	....	0.000023
Fuller's earth	0.53	30	0.00101	0.00024
Glass, lead	....	15	0.0060	0.00143
Glass, soda	2.59	20	0.0072	0.00172
Glass, soda	2.59	100	0.0076	0.00182

*** Compiled from the "International Critical Tables"; see original for more complete data.**

TABLE 4g-3. THERMAL CONDUCTIVITY OF INSULATING MATERIALS (*Continued*)

Material	Density g/cm³	t°C	Conductivity watt cm / cm² °C	Conductivity cal cm / sec cm² °C
Glass, wool	0.22	50	0.00042	0.000100
Glass, wool	0.22	100	0.00050	0.000120
Glass, wool	0.22	200	0.00065	0.000155
Glass, wool	0.22	300	0.00081	0.000195
Graphite, 100 mesh	0.48	40	0.0018	0.00044
Graphite, 40 mesh	0.42	40	0.0038	0.00093
Graphite, 20 to 40 mesh	0.70	40	0.0129	0.0031
Horsehair, compressed	0.17	20	0.00051	0.000122
Ice	0.92	0	0.022	0.0053
Leather, chamois	....	85	0.00063	0.000151
Leather, cowhide	....	85	0.00176	0.000421
Leather, sole	1.0	30	0.0016	0.00038
Linen	....	20	0.00086	0.00021
Linoleum, cork	0.54	20	0.00080	0.000191
Mica, average	....	50	0.0050	0.0012
Micanite	....	30	0.0021–0.0042	0.000050–0.00010
Mineral wool	0.15	30	0.00042	0.00010
Mineral wool	0.30	.....	0.00052	0.00012
Paper, rice	....	40	0.00046	0.00011
Paper, blotting	....	20	0.00063	0.00015
Paraffin wax	0.89	30	0.0023	0.00055
Peat, dry	0.19	30	0.00052	0.00012
Peat, blocks	0.84	20	0.0017	0.00041
Porcelain	....	90	0.0104	0.0025
Rocks:				
Basalt	....	20	0.020	0.0048
Chalk	....	.....	0.0092	0.0022
Granite	2.8	.....	0.022	0.0053
Limestone, very variable	2.0	20	0.010	0.0024
Slate, ⊥ to cleavage	....	95	0.014	0.0033
Slate, ‖ to cleavage	....	95	0.025	0.0060
Sandstone, air-dried	2.2	20	0.013	0.00031
Sandstone, freshly cut	2.3	20	0.017	0.00041
Rubber, rigid sponge, hard	0.09	25	0.00037	0.000088
Rubber, sponge, vulcanized	0.22	20	0.00054	0.00013
Rubber, commercial, 40% rubber	....	25	0.0028	0.00067
Rubber, commercial, 92% rubber	....	25	0.0016	0.00038
Sawdust	0.20	30	0.00060	0.000143
Shellac	....	.....	0.0023	0.0006
Silk	....	.....	0.00040	0.00010
Silk scrap from spinning mill	0.10	−200	0.00023	0.000055
Silk scrap from spinning mill	0.10	−100	0.00037	0.000088

Table 4g-3. Thermal Conductivity of Insulating Materials (*Continued*)

Material	Density g/cm³	t°C	Conductivity watt cm / cm² °C	Conductivity cal cm / sec cm² °C
Silk scrap from spinning mill	0.10	0	0.000495	0.000118
Silk scrap from spinning mill	0.10	50	0.00056	0.000134
Snow	0.25	0	0.0016	0.00038
Steel wool	0.15	55	0.00080	0.000191
Steel wool	0.08	55	0.00090	0.00022
Woods:				
Ash ⊥ to grain	0.74	20	0.0017	0.00041
Ash ∥ to grain	0.74	20	0.0031	0.00074
Balsa ⊥ to grain	0.11	30	0.00045	0.000084
Boxwood	0.90	20	0.0015	0.00036
Cedar ⊥ to grain	0.48	.....	0.0011	0.00027
Cypress ⊥ to grain	0.46	30	0.00096	0.00023
Fir ⊥ to grain	0.54	20	0.0014	0.00033
Fir ∥ to grain	0.54	20	0.0035	0.00081
Lignum vitae	1.16	20	0.0025	0.00060
Lignum vitae	1.16	100	0.0030	0.00072
Mahogany, ⊥ to grain	0.70	20	0.0016	0.00038
Mahogany, ∥ to grain	0.70	20	0.0031	0.00074
Oak, ⊥ to grain	0.82	15	0.0021	0.00050
Oak, ∥ to grain	0.82	15	0.0036	0.00086
Pine, pitch, ⊥ to grain	.....	30	0.0015	0.00036
Pine, Virginia, ⊥ to grain	0.55	30	0.0014	0.00033
Pine, white, ⊥ to grain	0.45	60	0.0011	0.00026
Pine, white, ∥ to grain	0.45	60	0.0026	0.00062
Spruce, ⊥ to grain	0.41	.....	0.0011	0.00026
Teak, ⊥ to grain	0.64	15	0.00175	0.00042
Teak, ∥ to grain	0.64	15	0.0038	0.00091
Walnut, ⊥ to grain	0.65	20	0.0014	0.00033
Wool, pure	0.09	30	0.00036	0.000086
Wool, pure, very loose packing	0.04	30	0.00042	0.00010

Table 4g-4. Thermal Conductivity of Water*

Temp., °C	k, 10^{-5} watt/cm °C	Temp., °C	k, 10^{-5} watt/cm °C	Temp., °C	k, 10^{-5} watt/cm °C
0	554	100	680	200	666
10	576	110	684	210	659
20	598	120	686	220	652
30	615	130	687	230	644
40	630	140	686	240	635
50	643	150	685	250	624
60	654	160	682	260	614
70	665	170	680	270	602
80	671	180	676	280	590
90	676	190	672	290	576
100	680	200	666	300	564

* E. Schmidt and W. Sellschopp, *Forsch, Gebiete Ingenieurw.* **3**, 277–286 (1932).

TABLE 4g-5. THERMAL CONDUCTIVITY OF ORGANIC MATERIALS

Substance	°C	k_t, cal cm/sec cm² °C	Substance	°C	k_t, cal cm/sec cm² °C	Substance	°C	k_t, cal cm/sec cm² °C
Acetic acid......	9–15	0.0_3472	Carbon disulfide	0	0.0_3387	Olive........	....	0.0_3395
Alcohols:			Chloroform.....	9–15	0.0_3288	Castor........	....	0.0_3425
Methyl........	11	0.0_352	Ether..........	9–15	0.0_3303	Toluene........	0	0.0_3349
Ethyl..........	11	0.0_346	Glycerin.......	25	0.0_368	Vaseline........	25	0.0_344
Amyl..........	0	0.0_3345	Oils:			Xylene.........	0	0.0_3343
Aniline..........	0	0.0_3434	Petroleum ...	13	0.0_3355			
Benzene.........	9–15	0.0_3333	Turpentine...	13	0.0_3325			

Substance	Temp., °C	Conductivity at 1 atm watt cm/cm² °C	Substance	Temp., °C	Conductivity at 1 atm watt cm/cm² °C
Normal pentane.....	30	1.347×10^{-3}	Carbon disulfide.....	30	1.599×10^{-3}
	75	1.285		75	1.515
Sulfuric ether........	30	1.377	Petroleum ether.....	30	1.306
	75	1.347		75	1.264
Acetone............	30	1.795	Kerosene...........	30	1.494
	75	1.687		75	1.394

TABLE 4g-6. THERMAL CONDUCTIVITY OF GASES

The conductivity of gases, $k_t = \frac{1}{4}(9\gamma - 5)\mu C_v$, where γ is the ratio of the specific heats, C_p/C_v, and μ is the viscosity coefficient (Jeans, "Dynamical Theory of Gases," 1916). Theoretically k_t should be independent of the density and has been found to be so by Kundt and Warburg and others within a wide range of pressure below 1 atm. It increases with the temperature.

Gas	t°C	k_t, 10^{-5} cal cm/sec cm² °C	Gas	t°C	k_t, 10^{-5} cal cm/sec cm² °C	Gas	t°C	k_t, 10^{-5} cal cm/sec cm² °C
Air*........	−191	1.80	CO_2.....	100	4.96	Hg......	203	1.85
Air........	0	5.66	C_2H_4....	0	3.95	N_2......	−191	1.83
Air........	100	7.19	He......	−193	14.6	N_2......	0	5.68
A.........	−183	1.42	He......	0	34.4	N_2......	100	7.18
A.........	0	3.88	He......	100	39.8	O_2......	−191	1.72
A.........	100	5.09	H_2.....	−192	13.3	O_2......	0	5.70
CO........	0	5.42	H_2......	0	41.6	O_2......	100	7.43
CO_2.......	− 78	2.19	H_2......	100	49.9	NO.....	8	4.6
CO_2.......	0	3.32	CH_4.....	0	7.20	N_2O.....	0	3.53

* Air: k_0 = 5.22 (10^{-5}) cal cm^{-1} sec^{-1} °C^{-1}; 5.74 at 22°; temp. coef. = 0.0029.

TABLE 4g-7. THERMAL CONDUCTIVITY OF CUBIC CRYSTALS*

Crystal	Temp, °C	Thermal conductivity, 10^{-4} cal cm/sec cm² °C
AgCl	0	26
BaF_2	52	27.1
	38	170
	68	140
CaF_2	−190	932
	−78	360
	0	246.8
	36	232
CsBr	100	191.0
	45	22
	65	26
KBr	0	87
	46	115
KCl	−252	1400
	−250	1170
	−190	502
	−78	248.5
	0	166.5
	42	156
	72	153
	100	117.6
KI	−190	303
	−78	(110)
	0	73.1
	25	(65)
	100	(50)
LiF (vacuum grown)	34	280
LiF (air grown)	36	249
LiF	105	61.3
	249	93.2
	384	122.0
	499	138.0
MgO	−78	930
	0	830
	25	800
	34	290
	72	340
	100	700
NaCl	−190	636
	−78	249.5
	0	166.7
	35	147
	70	130
	100	115.9

* For references see Alexander Smakula, "Physical Properties of Optical Crystals," O.T.S. Document PB No. 111053, 1952.

TABLE 4g-7. THERMAL CONDUCTIVITY OF CUBIC CRYSTALS (*Continued*)

Crystal	Temp, °C	Thermal conductivity, 10^{-4} cal cm/sec cm² °C
NaCl (from melt)	−190	809
	0	213
NaCl (from solution)	−190	902.5
	0	902.5
	0	228
NaF	−190	1,240
	0	252
	25	220
TlBr	0	19
TlCl	0	23
KRS-5	54	21.3
KRS-6	56	17.1
	35	330
	60	260
$MgO \cdot Al_2O_3$ (spinel)	120	80
	300	100
	500	150

TABLE 4g-8. THERMAL CONDUCTIVITY OF NONCUBIC CRYSTALS*

Crystal	Temp., °C	Parallel to *c* axis, 10^{-4} cal cm/sec cm² °C	Perpendicular to *c* axis, 10^{-4} cal cm/sec cm² °C
Al_2O_3 (sapphire)	105	.....	61.3
	249	.....	93.2
	384	.....	122
	499	.....	138
$CaCO_3$ (calcite)	−190	730	440
	−78	.....	137.7
	0	129	102
	25		98
	100	.....	85.2
SiO_2 (crystalline quartz)	−252	.....	6,800
	−250	.....	5,100
	−190	1,170	586
	−78	467	240.9
	0	325	173.1
	100	215	133.3
	145	174	
	236	153	
	260	.....	89
	308	137	
	383	.....	104
	468	.....	106
	475	123	

* References for this table may be found in Alexander Smakula, "Physical Properties of Optical Crystals," O.T.S. Document PB No. 111053, 1952.

TABLE 4g-9. THERMAL CONDUCTIVITY OF SiO_2 (FUSED QUARTZ)

Temp., °C	*Thermal conductivity* k, 10^{-4} *cal cm/sec cm² °C*
−270.7	1.5
−268.2	2.7
−263.2	2.8
−253.2	3.5
−233.2	5.8
−213.7	9.0
−193.2	14.2
− 78	22.7
0	35.2
41	28.2
60	33.0
120	34.1
180	35.3
240	36.4

TABLE 4g-10. DIFFUSIVITIES

Material	Diffusivity, cm²/sec	Material	Diffusivity cm²/sec
Aluminum	0.860	Coal	0.002
Antimony	0.135	Concrete (cinder)	0.0032
Bismuth	0.069	Concrete (stone)	0.0048
Brass (yellow)	0.339	Concrete (light slag)	0.006
Cadmium	0.467	Cork (ground	0.0017
Copper	1.140	Ebonite	0.0010
Gold	1.209	Glass (ordinary)	0.0057
Iron (wrought, also mild steel)	0.173	Granite	0.0127
		Ice	0.0112
Iron (cast, also 1% carbon steel)	0.121	Limestone	0.0081
		Marble (white)	0.0097
Lead	0.245	Paraffin	0.00098
Magnesium	0.932	Rock material (earth avg)	0.0118
Mercury	0.45	Rock material (crustal rocks)	0.0064
Nickel	0.155		
Palladium	0.261	Sandstone	0.0113
Platinum	0.243	Snow (fresh)	0.0033
Silver	1.700	Soil (clay or sand, slightly damp)	0.005
Tin	0.407		
Zinc	0.413	Soil (very dry)	0.0031
Air 1 atm	0.179	Water	0.0017
Asbestos (loose)	0.0025	Wood (pine, cross grain)	0.00068
Brick (avg fire)	0.0052	Wood (pine with grain)	0.0023
Brick (avg building)	0.0044		

The diffusivity of a substance $= h^2 = k/c\rho$, where k is the thermal conductivity, c the specific heat, and ρ the density. The values are mostly for room temperature, about 18°C.

TABLE 4g-11. THERMAL CONDUCTIVITY—LIQUIDS, PRESSURE EFFECT*

No.†	Liquid	°C	Conductivity at 0 kg/cm^2 (cgs)	Conductivity relative to unity (0 kg/cm^2) as function of pressure in kg/cm^2							
				1,000	2,000	4,000	6,000	8,000	10,000	11,000	12,000
1	Methyl alcohol........	30	0.000505	1.201	1.342	1.557	1.724	1.864	1.986	2.043	2.097
		75	0.000493	1.212	1.365	1.601	1.785	1.939	2.072	2.133	2.191
2	Ethyl alcohol.........	30	0.000430	1.221	1.363	1.574	1.744	1.888	2.014	2.070	2.122
		75	0.000416	1.233	1.400	1.650	1.845	2.007	2.152	2.217	2.278
3	Isopropyl alcohol.....	30	0.000367	1.205	1.352	1.570	1.743	1.894	2.028	2.091	2.150
		75	0.000363	1.230	1.399	1.638	1.812	1.962	2.093	2.154	2.211
4	Normal butyl alcohol..	30	0.000400	1.181	1.307	1.495	1.648	1.780	1.900	1.955	2.008
		75	0.000391	1.218	1.358	1.559	1.720	1.859	1.985	2.043	2.099
5	Isoamyl alcohol.......	30	0.000354	1.184	1.320	1.524	1.686	1.828	1.955	2.013	2.069
		75	0.000348	1.207	1.348	1.557	1.724	1.868	1.998	2.063	2.126
6	Ether..............	30	0.000329	1.305	1.509	1.800	2.009	2.177	2.322	2.388	2.451
		75	0.000322	1.313	1.518	1.814	2.043	2.231	2.394	2.469	2.537
7	Acetone.............	30	0.000429	1.184	1.315	1.511	1.659	1.786	1.900	Freezes	
		75	0.000403	1.181	1.325	1.554	1.738	1.891	2.024	2.083	2.137
8	Carbon bisulfide......	30	0.000382	1.174	1.310	1.512	1.663	1.783	1.880	1.923	1.962
		75	0.000362	1.208	1.366	1.607	1.789	1.935	2.054	2.107	2.154
9	Ethyl bromide........	30	0.000286	1.193	1.327	1.517	1.657	1.768	1.858	1.895	1.928
		75	0.000273	1.230	1.390	1.609	1.772	1.907	2.022	2.073	2.121
10	Ethyl iodide..........	30	0.000265	1.125	1.232	1.394	1.509	1.592	1.662	1.694	1.724
		75	0.000261	1.148	1.265	1.442	1.570	1.671	1.757	1.799	1.837
11	Water...............	30	0.00144	1.058	1.113	1.210	1.293	1.366	1.428	1.456	Freezes
		75	0.00154	1.065	1.123	1.225	1.308	1.379	1.445	1.476	1.506
12	Toluol..............	30	0.000364	1.159	1.286	1.470	1.604	1.716	.....	(2.394‡)	
		75	0.000339	1.210	1.355	1.573	1.738	1.872	1.987	2.039	2.089
13	Normal pentane......	30	0.000322	1.281	1.483	1.777	1.987	2.163	2.325	2.404	2.481
		75	0.000307	1.319	1.534	1.855	2.112	2.335	2.543	2.642	2.740
14	Petroleum ether.......	30	0.000312	1.266	1.460	1.752	1.970	2.143	2.279	2.333	2.379
		75	0.000302	1.268	1.466	1.780	2.026	2.232	2.409	2.488	2.561
15	Kerosene............	75	0.000333	1.185	1.314	1.502	1.654	1.792	1.925	1.990	2.054

* P. W. Bridgman, *Proc. Am. Acad. Arts Sci.* **59**, 158 (1923).

† 1, 2, 6, 8, 12, 13, extreme purity; 3, 4, 5, 7, 9, 10, 11, very pure; 14, 15, commercial.

‡ Toluol freezes at 9,900 kg/cm^2 at 30°. The figure at 11,000 is for the solid.

Table 4g-12. Thermal Conductivity of Optical Materials*

Material	Temp., °C	k, cal/sec cm °C	Material	Temp., °C	k, cal/sec cm °C
Barium fluoride	−49	4.8×10^{-2}	Cesium bromide	−49	2.9×10^{-3}
	−38	4.0		−23	2.4
	−14	3.2		+25	2.3
	+13	2.8		45	2.2
	32	2.6		98	2.0
	63	2.5			
	95	2.5			
Cesium iodide	8	2.8×10^{-3}	Fused silica	−49	3.1×10^{-3}
	25	2.7		−24	3.0
	40	2.65		+14	2.85
	59	2.6		42	2.8
	90	2.5		104	2.8
Sodium chloride	−37	1.8×10^{-2}	Spinel	−29	4.1×10^{-2}
	−30	1.7		−21	3.7
	+16	1.55		+6	3.0
	35	1.5		21	2.8
	70	1.3		68	2.6
	98	1.2		100	2.5
Arsenic sulfide glass	10	3.9×10^{-4}	Rutile:		
	22	4.3	∥ to optic axis	16	2.8×10^{-2}
	42	4.8		36	3.0
	57	5.2	⊥ to optic axis	18	2.1
	80	6.0		44	1.8
	90	6.2			
	102	6.4			
Thallium bromide iodide	−37	1.1×10^{-3}	Thallium bromide chloride	−31	1.1×10^{-3}
(KRS-5)	−18	1.1	(KRS-6)	−20	1.1
	0	1.2		+11	1.2
	20	1.3		24	1.4
	36	1.7		56	1.7
	54	2.1		98	2.2
	99	3.8			
Sapphire:†			Ammonium dihydrogen		
∥ to optic axis	21	6.0×10^{-2}	phosphate:		
	50	5.0	∥ to optic axis	46	1.7×10^{-3}
⊥ to optic axis	21	5.5		66	1.7
	49	4.5	⊥ to optic axis	40	3.0
				69	3.2

* Measured by S. S. Ballard and K. A. McCarthy, *Rev. Sci. Instr.* **21**, 905 (1950); *J. Opt. Soc. Am.* **41** 1062 (1951).

† See also J. L. Weeks and R. L. Seifert, *J. Am. Ceram. Soc.* **35**, 15 (1952).

Table 4g-13. Thermal Conductivity of Some Semiconductors
(At room temperature unless noted)

Material	Conductivity, cal/sec cm °C	Reference
Germanium	0.14, 25°C 0.11, 100°C	A. Grieco and H. C. Montgomery, *Phys. Rev.* **86,** 570 (1952)
Silicon	0.20	1948 "Metals Handbook"
PbS	0.0016	Lees, *Phil. Trans.* **A191,** 399 (1938)
PbSe	0.01	E. H. Putley, *Proc. Phys. Soc.* (*London*) **B65,** 991 (1952)
PbTe	0.012	E. H. Putley, *Proc. Phys. Soc.* (*London*) **B67,** (1954)
Mg_2Sn	0.03	H. P. R. Frederikse, NBS
C (graphite)	See references	A. W. Smith, *Phys. Rev.* **95,** 1095 (1954); R. Berman, *Proc. Phys. Soc.* (*London*), **A65,** 1029 (1952)

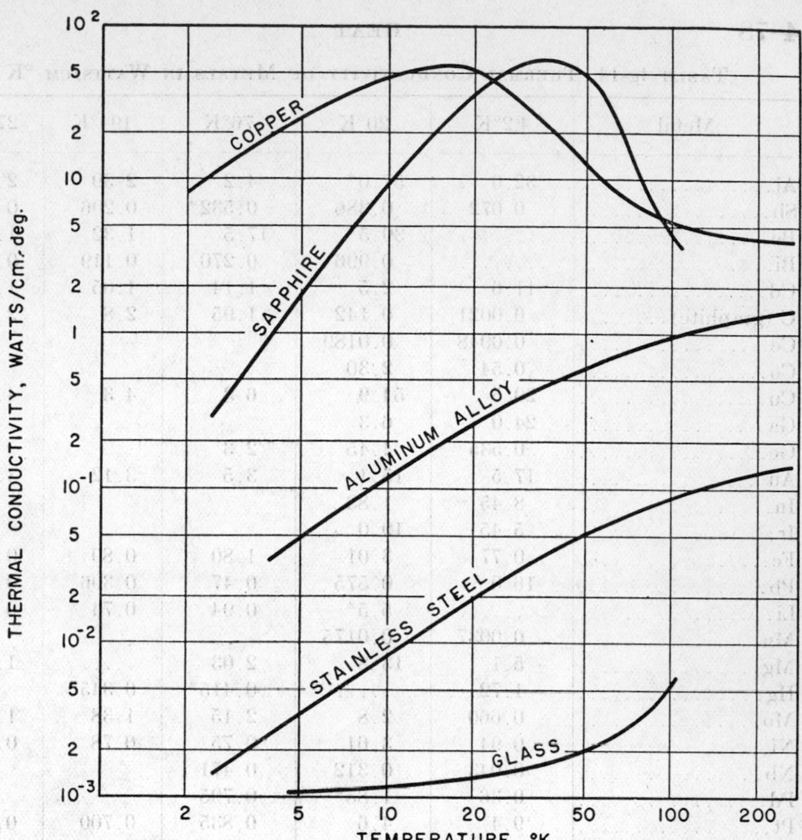

FIG. 4g-1. Typical curves showing low-temperature dependence of thermal conductivity.

It is generally assumed that thermal conductivity is not a function of temperature gradient but is a function of temperature itself. It also is assumed that the conductivity is not size- or shape-dependent, though this last is not strictly true for dielectric crystals at very low temperatures. Five representative curves are given in Fig. 4g-1, showing the temperature dependence of a typical metal, nonferrous alloy, ferrous alloy, dielectric crystal, and disordered dielectric. Impurities in the metals or dielectric crystals will cause a lowering or removal of the maximum in the conductivity. The values of thermal conductivity given in the following tables are expressed in the unit watts/cm deg Kelvin.

The thermal conductivity of solids at liquid helium (4.2°K), liquid hydrogen (20°K), liquid nitrogen (76°K), solid CO_2 (194°K), and ice (273°K) temperatures are given in Tables 4g-14 to 4g-17. The values of conductivity for solids are broken up into four main groups: metals, alloys, dielectric crystals, and disordered dielectrics. The numbers marked with an asterisk are extrapolated. The author references and more exact values may be obtained by referring to *National Bureau of Standards Circular* 556. Three survey references to literature and data in this field are:

Berman, R.: The Thermal Conductivity of Dielectric Solids at Low Temperatures, *Adv. Physics* (suppl. to *Phil. Mag.*) **2,** 103–140 (1953).

Olsen, J. L., and H. M. Rosenberg: The Thermal Conductivity of Metals at Low Temperatures, *Adv. Physics* **2,** 28–66 (1953).

Powell, R. L., and W. A. Blanpied, The Thermal Conductivity of Metals and Alloys at Low Temperatures, Published as *Natl. Bur. Standards* (*U.S.*) *Circ.* 556, 1954.

TABLE 4g-14. THERMAL CONDUCTIVITY OF METALS IN WATTS/CM °K

Metal	4.2°K	20°K	76°K	194°K	273°K
Al	32.0	57.0*	4.2	2.39	2.38*
Sb	0.072	0.386	0.532*	0.296	0.245
Be	....	39.5*	17.5	1.32	1.57
Bi	....	0.996	0.270	0.119	0.112
Cd	11.6	2.5	1.14	1.05	1.05
C (graphite)	0.0021	0.142	1.95	2.8	2.51
Ce	0.0048	0.0189			
Co	0.54	2.30			
Cu	20.5	54.9	6.3	4.3	4.16
Ga	24.0	6.3			
Ge	0.535	4.45	2.3		
Au	17.5	15.1	3.5	3.12	3.11
In	8.45	1.83			
Ir	5.45	19.0			
Fe	0.77	3.01	1.80	0.89	0.82
Pb	16.0	0.575	0.47	0.396	0.350
Li	....	5.5*	0.94	0.74	0.702
Mn	0.0037	0.0175			
Mg	5.1	13.8	2.03	......	1.72
Hg	1.72	......	0.415*	0.345	
Mo	0.660	2.8	2.15	1.38	1.38
Ni	0.94	3.61	0.75	0.78	0.76
Nb	0.043	0.312	0.471		
Pd	0.36	1.85*	0.795		
Pt	9.4	4.6	0.835	0.700	0.699
K	....	....	....	......	0.990
Rh	2.7	11.2			
Ag	144.3	51.0	5.2	4.2	4.17
Na	31.5*	5.5	1.55	1.22	1.40
Ta	0.225	0.629	0.599		
Te			0.034*	0.0215	0.018
Tl	8.95	0.711	0.645*	0.531	0.506
Sn	74.0	2.3	0.86*	0.72	0.666
Ti	0.048	0.23			
W	0.718	54.5	2.6	1.78	1.69
U	0.046	0.151	0.231	0.257	0.286
V	0.0135	0.0619			
Zn	11.3	7.3	1.53	1.40	1.25
Zr	0.127	0.461			

*** Extrapolated.**

TABLE 4g-15. THERMAL CONDUCTIVITY OF ALLOYS IN WATTS/CM °K

Alloy	4.2°K	20°K	76°K	194°K	273°K
Aluminum:					
Duralumin	......	0.300	0.91		
J51	......	......	2.41	2.00	2.10
4S	......	......	0.79	1.22	1.49
75S	......	......	0.63	1.04	
24S	......	......	0.575	0.99	1.11
Copper:					
Brass	......	......	.....	0.92	1.05
Constantan 40% Ni	0.0091	0.088	0.190	0.225	0.239
Cu-Au 50.1% Au	......	0.42	1.05		
Cu-Ni 10% Ni	0.013	0.155	0.38		
German silver	0.013	0.158	0.168	0.207	0.235
Manganin	......	......	.....	0.170	0.209
Platnoid	......	......	.....	0.200	0.245
Silver bronze	0.012	0.052			
Ferrous:					
Carbon steel SAE 1020	0.125	0.200*	0.58	0.651	0.645
Stainless	0.0027	0.0205	0.082	0.125	0.140
Nickel:					
Contracid	......	0.0154	0.072	0.095	0.113
Inconel	0.0051	0.041	0.118	0.134	0.150
Monel	0.009	0.072	0.167	0.197	0.219

* Extrapolated.

TABLE 4g-16. THERMAL CONDUCTIVITY OF DIELECTRIC CRYSTALS IN WATTS/CM °K

Crystal	4.2°K	20°K	76°K	194°K	273°K
Alumina	0.00495	0.232	1.5	0.46	
Beryilla	0.0026	0.155	2.80		
Diamond	0.76	16.0	34.0	8.6	6.59
KBr	1.22	0.488	0.140		
KCl	2.74	1.30	0.370		
Quartz	4.20	7.6	0.66		
Sapphire	1.13	35.0	10.9		

TABLE 4g-17. THERMAL CONDUCTIVITY OF DISORDERED DIELECTRICS IN MW/CM °K

Dielectric	4.2°K	20°K	76°K	194°K	273°K
Perspex	0.575	0.74			
Phoenix glass	0.92	1.51	3.7		
Pyrex			4.6*	8.75	10.2
Quartz glass	1.02	1.60	4.85		

* Extrapolated.

4h. Thermodynamic Properties of Gases

JOSEPH HILSENRATH

The National Bureau of Standards

The Thermodynamic Properties of Air, Argon, Carbon Dioxide, Hydrogen, Nitrogen, Oxygen, and Steam. Tables 4h-3 through 4h-37 are an abridged version of a collection of tables computed and published at the National Bureau of Standards.[1] The tables of compressibility and density were computed from equations of state which were fitted to the existing *PVT* data. In most instances the method of fitting permitted simultaneous consideration of other experimental data, such as Joule-Thomson coefficients, specific heat, and sound-velocity measurements. The tables for entropy, enthalpy, and specific heats were obtained by combining these properties of the ideal gas with corrections for the gas imperfection obtained, through the thermodynamic identities, from the equation of state. A fuller discussion and more extensive tabulations in the temperature argument are to be found in the above-cited circular of the National Bureau of Standards.

The tables are presented in dimensionless form. Conversion factors given in Tables 4h-1 and 4h-2 permit ready conversion to some of the more frequently used units. Values of the gas constant R are listed for frequently used units in order to facilitate the use of the tables of the compressibility factor in calculating, by means of the equation $Z = PV/RT$, the pressure P, the specific volume V (or density $1/V$), or the temperature T, when any two of these are known. The molecular weights given in Table 4h-2 permit extension of the tabulated values of R to still other units.

Pressure entries have been chosen to facilitate four-point Lagrangian interpolation, when linear interpolation is not valid. A convenient rule of thumb for determining the adequacy of linear interpolation is the following: "The error introduced by linear interpolation is approximately $\frac{1}{8}$ of the second difference." Where the error greatly exceeds the uncertainty of the table, nonlinear interpolation is recommended.

TABLE 4h-1. VALUES OF THE GAS CONSTANT R IN VARIOUS UNITS

P	V	T	R
atm	cm³/mole	°K	82.0567 atm cm³/mole °K
kg/cm²	cm³/mole	°K	84.7832 (kg/cm²)cm³/mole °K
bars*	cm³/mole	°K	83.1440 bars cm³/mole °K
mm Hg	cm³/mole	°K	62,363.1 (mm Hg)cm³/mole °K
atm	liters/mole	°K	0.0820544 atm liters/mole °K
kg/cm²	liters/mole	°K	0.0847809 (kg/cm²) liters/mole °K
mm Hg	liters/mole	°K	62.3613 (mm Hg) liters/mole °K
atm	ft³/(lb)mole	°R	0.730228 atm ft³/mole °R
mm Hg	ft³/(lb)mole	°R	554.973 (mm Hg) ft³/mole °R

* 10^6 dynes/cm².

[1] Joseph Hilsenrath et al., Tables of Thermal Properties of Gases, *Natl. Bur. Standards (U.S.) Circ.* 564, 1955.

TABLE 4h-2. CONVERSION FACTORS FOR TABLES 4h-4 THROUGH 4h-37

To convert tabulated value of	To	Having the dimensions indicated below	Air	Argon	CO_2	H_2	N_2	O_2	Steam
			Multiply by						
$(H - E_0°)/RT_0$	$(H - E_0°)$	cal mole^{-1}	542.821	542.821	542.821	542.821	542.821	542.821	542.821
		cal g^{-1}	18.7399	13.5896	12.3340	269.256	19.3754	16.9632	30.1299
		joules g^{-1}	78.4079	56.8589	51.6056	1126.57	81.0669	70.9742	126.064
		Btu (lb mole)$^{-1}$	976.437	976.437	976.437	976.437	976.437	976.437	976.437
		Btu lb^{-1}	33.7098	24.4451	22.1867	484.344	34.8528	30.5137	54.1893
C_p/R, S/R	C_p, S	cal mole^{-1} °K^{-1} (or °C^{-1})	1.98719	1.98719	1.98719	1.98719	1.98719	1.98719	1.98719
		cal g^{-1} °K^{-1} (or °C^{-1})	0.0686042	0.0497494	0.0451531	0.985709	0.0709305	0.0620997	0.110301
		joules g^{-1} °K^{-1} (or °C^{-1})	0.287041	0.208152	0.188921	4.12422	0.296774	0.259826	0.461500
		Btu (lb mole)$^{-1}$ °R^{-1} (or °F^{-1})	1.98588	1.98588	1.98588	1.98588	1.98588	1.98588	1.98588
		Btu lb^{-1} °R^{-1} (or °F^{-1})	0.0685590	0.0497166	0.0451234	0.985060	0.0708838	0.0620588	0.110229
ρ/ρ_0 and for steam of ρ in g cm^{-3}	ρ	g cm^{-3}	1.29304×10^{-3}	1.78377×10^{-3}	1.9770×10^{-3}	8.98854×10^{-5}	1.25046×10^{-3}	1.42900×10^{-3}	1
		mole cm^{-3}	4.46400×10^{-5}	4.46568×10^{-5}	4.4922×10^{-5}	4.45860×10^{-5}	4.46338×10^{-5}	4.46562×10^{-5}	0.055506
		g liter^{-1}	1.29308	1.78382	1.9771	8.98879×10^{-2}	1.25050	1.42904	1.00003×10^{3}
		lb in^{-3}	4.67143×10^{-5}	6.44432×10^{-5}	7.1424×10^{-5}	3.24734×10^{-6}	4.51760×10^{-5}	5.16262×10^{-5}	3.61275×10^{-2}
		lb ft^{-3}	8.07223×10^{-2}	0.111358	0.12342	5.61140×10^{-3}	7.80641×10^{-2}	8.92101×10^{-2}	62.4283
Molecular weight..			28.966	39.944	44.010	2.016	28.016	32.000	18.016

Table 4h-3. Compressibility Factor for Air, $Z = \frac{PV}{RT}$

T, °K	1 atm	4 atm	7 atm	10 atm	40 atm	70 atm	100 atm
100	0.98090						
200	0.99767	0.99067	0.98367	0.97666	0.9080	0.8481	0.8105
300	0.99970	0.99879	0.99797	0.99717	0.99135	0.9900	0.9933
400	1.00019	1.00079	1.00141	1.00205	1.00946	1.0188	1.0299
500	1.00034	1.00137	1.00242	1.00348	1.01454	1.0265	1.0393
600	1.00038	1.00152	1.00267	1.00385	1.01574	1.0281	1.0408
700	1.00038	1.00153	1.00268	1.00385	1.01558	1.0275	1.0397
800	1.00037	1.00148	1.00259	1.00371	1.01493	1.0263	1.0379
900	1.00035	1.00140	1.00246	1.00351	1.01411	1.0248	1.0356
1000	1.00033	1.00132	1.00231	1.00331	1.01325	1.0233	1.0333
1100	1.00031	1.00124	1.00218	1.00311	1.01245	1.0218	1.0312
1200	1.00029	1.00117	1.00205	1.00293	1.01170	1.0205	1.0292
1300	1.00028	1.00110	1.00193	1.00275	1.01100	1.0192	1.0275
1400	1.00026	1.00104	1.00182	1.00259	1.01037	1.0181	1.0259
1500	1.00024	1.00098	1.00171	1.00245	1.00978	1.0171	1.0244
1600	1.00023	1.00094	1.00163	1.00233	1.0093	1.0162	1.0232
1700	1.00023	1.00090	1.00157	1.00223	1.0088	1.0154	1.0220
1800	1.00024	1.00087	1.00152	1.00213	1.0083	1.0146	1.0208
1900	1.00027	1.00085	1.00146	1.00204	1.0079	1.0138	1.0198
2000	1.00035	1.00085	1.00140	1.00196	1.0076	1.0132	1.0188
2100	1.0006	1.0010	1.0014	1.0019	1.0073	1.0126	1.0180
2200	1.0008	1.0010	1.0014	1.0019	1.0070	1.0121	1.0172
2300	1.0014	1.0013	1.0016	1.0020	1.0067	1.0116	1.0165
2400	1.0023	1.0017	1.0019	1.0022	1.0067	1.0113	1.0160
2500	1.0036	1.0024	1.0024	1.0026	1.0066	1.0110	1.0155
2600	1.0056	1.0034	1.0031	1.0032	1.0067	1.0108	1.0151
2700	1.0086	1.0048	1.0042	1.0041	1.0068	1.0107	1.0148
2800	1.0124	1.0068	1.0057	1.0053	1.0071	1.0108	1.0145
2900	1.0178	1.0096	1.0079	1.0071	1.0079	1.0111	1.0147
3000	1.0252	1.0133	1.0107	1.0095	1.0092	1.0119	1.0151

TABLE 4h-4. RELATIVE DENSITY OF AIR, ρ/ρ_0

T, °K	1 atm	4 atm	7 atm	10 atm	40 atm	70 atm	100 atm
100	2.7830						
200	1.3681	5.511	9.713	13.976	60.13	112.66	168.40
300	0.9102	3.644	6.383	9.125	36.72	64.34	91.61
400	0.6823	2.7277	4.771	6.811	27.043	46.89	66.27
500	0.5458	2.1809	3.813	5.441	21.526	37.23	52.53
600	0.4548	1.8171	3.176	4.532	17.917	30.977	43.71
700	0.3898	1.5575	2.7226	3.885	15.360	26.567	37.51
800	0.3411	1.3629	2.3825	3.400	13.449	23.274	32.879
900	0.3032	1.2115	2.1180	3.023	11.964	20.720	29.290
1000	0.2729	1.0905	1.9065	2.721	10.777	18.675	26.419
1100	0.24809	0.9914	1.7334	2.474	9.805	17.001	24.066
1200	0.22742	0.9089	1.5892	2.268	8.994	15.605	22.103
1300	0.20993	0.8390	1.4671	2.094	8.308	14.422	20.438
1400	0.19494	0.7791	1.3625	1.945	7.720	13.406	19.007
1500	0.18195	0.7272	1.2718	1.815	7.209	12.525	17.766
1600	0.17058	0.6818	1.1924	1.702	6.762	11.753	16.675
1700	0.16054	0.6417	1.1223	1.602	6.367	11.070	15.712
1800	0.15162	0.6061	1.0600	1.513	6.016	10.463	14.857
1900	0.14364	0.5742	1.0043	1.434	5.702	9.921	14.089
2000	0.13645	0.5455	0.9541	1.362	5.419	9.430	13.398
2100	0.12992	0.5194	0.9087	1.297	5.162	8.986	12.770
2200	0.12399	0.4958	0.8674	1.239	4.929	8.582	12.199
2300	0.11852	0.4741	0.8295	1.185	4.716	8.213	11.676
2400	0.11348	0.4542	0.7947	1.135	4.520	7.873	11.195
2500	0.10880	0.4357	0.7625	1.089	4.339	7.560	10.753
2600	0.10441	0.4185	0.7327	1.047	4.172	7.271	10.343
2700	0.10024	0.4024	0.7048	1.007	4.017	7.003	9.963
2800	0.09630	0.3873	0.6786	0.970	3.872	6.752	9.610
2900	0.09249	0.3729	0.6538	0.935	3.736	6.517	9.277
3000	0.08876	0.3592	0.6302	0.901	3.607	6.295	8.964

TABLE 4h-5. SPECIFIC HEAT OF AIR, C_p/R

T, °K	1 atm	4 atm	7 atm	10 atm	40 atm	70 atm	100 atm
100	3.5824						
200	3.5062	3.5495	3.5950	3.6427	4.256	5.132	6.079
300	3.5059	3.5220	3.5383	3.5546	3.722	3.889	4.046
400	3.5333	3.5416	3.5500	3.5583	3.640	3.717	3.788
500	3.5882	3.5932	3.5983	3.6032	3.652	3.697	3.739
600	3.6626	3.6660	3.6693	3.6726	3.705	3.735	3.763
700	3.7455	3.7479	3.7502	3.7525	3.775	3.797	3.817
800	3.828	3.830	3.832	3.834	3.851	3.867	3.882
900	3.906	3.908	3.909	3.910	3.924	3.936	3.947
1000	3.979	3.980	3.982	3.983	3.993	4.003	4.012
1100	4.046	4.047	4.048	4.049	4.057	4.065	4.072
1200	4.109	4.110	4.111	4.111	4.118	4.125	4.130
1300	4.171	4.172	4.172	4.173	4.179	4.184	4.189
1400	4.230	4.231	4.231	4.232	4.236	4.241	4.245
1500	4.289	4.290	4.290	4.290	4.294	4.298	4.302
1600	4.352	4.351	4.351	4.351	4.354	4.357	4.361
1700	4.418	4.414	4.413	4.414	4.416	4.419	4.421
1800	4.487	4.480	4.479	4.478	4.477	4.479	4.481
1900	4.566	4.549	4.544	4.543	4.540	4.540	4.542
2000	4.662	4.626	4.617	4.613	4.603	4.604	4.605
2100	4.781	4.715	4.699	4.692	4.674	4.670	4.671
2200	4.947	4.823	4.791	4.780	4.745	4.738	4.734
2300	5.179	4.969	4.918	4.893	4.828	4.814	4.806
2400	5.484	5.149	5.067	5.026	4.922	4.897	4.886
2500	5.882	5.373	5.247	5.186	5.028	4.987	4.971
2600	6.40	5.661	5.474	5.389	5.152	5.088	5.062
2700	7.06	6.019	5.753	5.634	5.295	5.203	5.172
2800	7.87	6.455	6.088	5.930	5.467	5.341	5.297
2900	8.86	6.993	6.497	6.300	5.668	5.496	5.434
3000	9.96	7.605	6.991	6.724	5.906	5.678	5.602

TABLE 4h-6. ENTHALPY OF AIR, $(H - E_0^\circ)/RT_0$

T, °K	1 atm	4 atm	7 atm	10 atm	40 atm	70 atm	100 atm
100	1.2552						
200	2.5465	2.5281	2.5094	2.4908	2.2922	2.0794	1.8734
300	3.8292	3.8204	3.8118	3.8034	3.7194	3.6411	3.5699
400	5.1167	5.1125	5.1079	5.1039	5.0623	5.0252	4.9926
500	6.4195	6.4176	6.4154	6.4137	6.3951	6.3795	6.3670
600	7.7463	7.7459	7.7454	7.7449	7.7408	7.7388	7.7390
700	9.1023	9.1027	9.1035	9.1037	9.1096	9.1168	9.1253
800	10.489	10.490	10.491	10.492	10.505	10.519	10.534
900	11.904	11.906	11.908	11.909	11.928	11.947	11.968
1000	13.348	13.350	13.352	13.354	13.377	13.400	13.424
1100	14.817	14.819	14.822	14.824	14.851	14.877	14.904
1200	16.310	16.312	16.316	16.318	16.347	16.376	16.405
1300	17.826	17.828	17.832	17.834	17.866	17.897	17.928
1400	19.363	19.365	19.370	19.373	19.407	19.440	19.471
1500	20.922	20.924	20.929	20.932	20.968	21.003	21.036
1600	22.504	22.506	22.511	22.514	22.551	22.587	22.621
1700	24.110	24.112	24.116	24.118	24.156	24.193	24.228
1800	25.740	25.740	25.744	25.746	25.784	25.821	25.857
1900	27.397	27.392	27.394	27.396	27.434	27.472	27.509
2000	29.086	29.071	29.070	29.072	29.108	29.146	29.183
2100	30.813	30.781	30.774	30.775	30.806	30.844	30.881
2200	32.592	32.527	32.510	32.509	32.530	32.566	32.603
2300	34.443	34.318	34.286	34.279	34.282	34.315	34.349
2400	36.393	36.169	36.107	36.093	36.067	36.092	36.123
2500	38.470	38.093	37.994	37.961	37.888	37.901	37.927
2600	40.713	40.110	39.955	39.895	39.750	39.744	39.764
2700	43.172	42.246	42.008	41.911	41.661	41.627	41.638
2800	45.901	44.528	44.173	44.026	43.630	43.556	43.554
2900	48.960	46.985	46.474	46.262	45.666	45.539	45.518
3000	52.403	49.655	48.940	48.650	47.784	47.583	47.537

TABLE 4h-7. ENTROPY OF AIR, S/R

T, °K	1 atm	4 atm	7 atm	10 atm	40 atm	70 atm	100 atm
100	20.049						
200	22.497	21.091	20.513	20.139	18.551	17.767	17.184
300	23.917	22.524	21.958	21.594	20.138	19.513	19.095
400	24.929	23.539	22.976	22.616	21.194	20.602	20.214
500	25.723	24.335	23.773	23.414	22.006	21.428	21.056
600	26.383	24.995	24.434	24.077	22.677	22.104	21.736
700	26.954	25.567	25.006	24.649	23.253	22.685	22.320
800	27.460	26.073	25.512	25.155	23.762	23.196	22.833
900	27.915	26.528	25.968	25.610	24.219	23.655	23.293
1000	28.330	26.944	26.384	26.025	24.634	24.071	23.709
1100	28.713	27.327	26.767	26.408	25.018	24.454	24.093
1200	29.068	27.682	27.122	26.763	25.373	24.809	24.448
1300	29.399	28.013	27.453	27.093	25.702	25.138	24.777
1400	29.711	28.324	27.764	27.404	26.013	25.448	25.087
1500	30.005	28.618	28.058	27.698	26.306	25.741	25.380
1600	30.284	28.897	28.337	27.977	26.585	26.020	25.659
1700	30.549	29.162	28.602	28.242	26.850	26.287	25.926
1800	30.804	29.416	28.856	28.496	27.104	26.542	26.181
1900	31.048	29.660	29.100	28.740	27.348	26.785	26.424
2000	31.284	29.896	29.335	28.974	27.582	27.019	26.658
2100	31.514	30.124	29.563	29.201	27.808	27.245	26.884
2200	31.740	30.346	29.784	29.421	28.027	27.463	27.102
2300	31.964	30.563	29.999	29.636	28.240	27.676	27.314
2400	32.191	30.778	30.212	29.847	28.447	27.883	27.520
2500	32.423	30.992	30.422	30.055	28.650	28.084	27.721
2600	32.663	31.208	30.632	30.263	28.849	28.281	27.918
2700	32.917	31.428	30.844	30.471	29.046	28.476	28.111
2800	33.188	31.654	31.059	30.681	29.242	28.669	28.302
2900	33.481	31.889	31.279	30.895	29.438	28.861	28.491
3000	33.799	32.136	31.507	31.114	29.634	29.052	28.678

TABLE 4h-8. COMPRESSIBILITY FACTOR FOR ARGON, $Z = PV/RT$

T, °K	1 atm	4 atm	7 atm	10 atm	40 atm	70 atm	100 atm
100	0.9782	0.9079					
200	0.99706	0.98818	0.97923	0.97023	0.8778	0.7838	0.6917
300	0.99937	0.99750	0.99565	0.99382	0.9773	0.9643	0.9553
400	0.99998	0.99991	0.99986	0.99982	1.0002	1.0022	1.0057
500	1.00018	1.00072	1.00127	1.00183	1.0079	1.0147	1.0224
600	1.00025	1.00101	1.00178	1.00255	1.0105	1.0190	1.0279
700	1.00027	1.00111	1.00194	1.00278	1.0113	1.0201	1.0292
800	1.00028	1.00111	1.00195	1.00279	1.0113	1.0199	1.0288
900	1.00027	1.00109	1.00191	1.00273	1.0110	1.0194	1.0279
1000	1.00026	1.00104	1.00183	1.00261	1.0105	1.0185	1.0265
1100	1.00025	1.00100	1.00174	1.00249	1.0100	1.0176	1.0252
1200	1.00024	1.00095	1.00166	1.00237	1.0095	1.0167	1.0239
1300	1.00023	1.00090	1.00158	1.00225	1.0090	1.0158	1.0226
1400	1.00021	1.00085	1.00149	1.00213	1.0085	1.0149	1.0213
1500	1.00020	1.00081	1.00142	1.00203	1.0081	1.0142	1.0203
1600	1.00019	1.00077	1.00135	1.00193	1.0077	1.0135	1.0193
1700	1.00018	1.00073	1.00128	1.00183	1.0073	1.0128	1.0183
1800	1.00018	1.00070	1.00123	1.00175	1.0070	1.0123	1.0175
1900	1.00017	1.00067	1.00117	1.00167	1.0067	1.0117	1.0167
2000	1.00016	1.00064	1.00111	1.00159	1.0064	1.0111	1.0159
2100	1.00015	1.00061	1.00107	1.00153	1.0061	1.0107	1.0153
2200	1.00015	1.00058	1.00102	1.00146	1.0058	1.0102	1.0146
2300	1.00014	1.00056	1.00098	1.00140	1.0056	1.0098	1.0140
2400	1.00014	1.00054	1.00095	1.00135	1.0054	1.0095	1.0135
2500	1.00013	1.00052	1.00091	1.00130	1.0052	1.0091	1.0130
2600	1.00013	1.00050	1.00088	1.00125	1.0050	1.0088	1.0125
2700	1.00012	1.00048	1.00084	1.00120	1.0048	1.0084	1.0120
2800	1.00012	1.00046	1.00081	1.00116	1.0046	1.0081	1.0116
2900	1.00011	1.00045	1.00078	1.00112	1.0045	1.0078	1.0112
3000	1.00011	1.00043	1.00076	1.00108	1.0043	1.0076	1.0108
3100	1.00011	1.00042	1.00074	1.00105	1.0042	1.0074	1.0105
3200	1.00011	1.00041	1.00072	1.00102	1.0041	1.0072	1.0102
3300	1.00010	1.00039	1.00069	1.00098	1.0039	1.0069	1.0098
3400	1.00010	1.00038	1.00067	1.00096	1.0038	1.0067	1.0096
3500	1.00009	1.00037	1.00065	1.00093	1.0037	1.0065	1.0093
3600	1.00009	1.00036	1.00063	1.00090	1.0036	1.0063	1.0090
3700	1.00009	1.00035	1.00062	1.00088	1.0035	1.0062	1.0088
3800	1.00009	1.00034	1.00060	1.00085	1.0034	1.0060	1.0085
3900	1.00008	1.00033	1.00058	1.00083	1.0033	1.0058	1.0083
4000	1.00008	1.00032	1.00057	1.00081	1.0032	1.0057	1.0081
4100	1.00008	1.00032	1.00055	1.00079	1.0032	1.0055	1.0079
4200	1.00008	1.00031	1.00054	1.00077	1.0031	1.0054	1.0077
4300	1.00008	1.00030	1.00053	1.00075	1.0030	1.0053	1.0075
4400	1.00007	1.00029	1.00051	1.00073	1.0029	1.0051	1.0073
4500	1.00007	1.00028	1.00050	1.00071	1.0028	1.0050	1.0071
4600	1.00007	1.00028	1.00049	1.00070	1.0028	1.0049	1.0070
4700	1.00007	1.00027	1.00048	1.00068	1.0027	1.0048	1.0068
4800	1.00007	1.00026	1.00046	1.00066	1.0026	1.0046	1.0066
4900	1.00007	1.00026	1.00046	1.00065	1.0026	1.0046	1.0065
5000	1.00006	1.00025	1.00044	1.00063	1.0025	1.0044	1.0063

TABLE 4h-9. RELATIVE DENSITY OF ARGON, ρ/ρ_0

T, °K	1 atm	4 atm	7 atm	10 atm	40 atm	70 atm	100 atm
100	2.79	12.02					
200	1.3685	5.5232	9.754	14.064	62.18	121.9	197.3
300	0.91023	3.6477	6.3954	9.1531	37.23	66.03	95.22
400	0.68226	2.7292	4.7764	6.8237	27.28	47.65	67.84
500	0.54570	2.1816	3.8157	5.4480	21.66	37.65	53.38
600	0.45471	1.8175	3.1781	4.5367	18.00	31.25	44.25
700	0.38975	1.5577	2.7237	3.8877	15.42	26.75	37.88
800	0.34103	1.3630	2.3832	3.4017	13.49	23.41	33.16
900	0.30314	1.2116	2.1185	3.0239	12.00	20.82	29.50
1000	0.27283	1.0905	1.9068	2.7219	10.80	18.76	26.59
1100	0.24803	0.99136	1.7336	2.4747	9.825	17.07	24.20
1200	0.22736	0.90879	1.5893	2.2688	9.011	15.66	22.21
1300	0.20987	0.83893	1.4671	2.0945	8.322	14.47	20.53
1400	0.19489	0.77904	1.3625	1.9451	7.731	13.44	19.09
1500	0.18189	0.72714	1.2717	1.8156	7.219	12.56	17.83
1600	0.17053	0.68172	1.1923	1.7023	6.770	11.78	16.73
1700	0.16050	0.64164	1.1223	1.6023	6.375	11.09	15.76
1800	0.15158	0.60601	1.0600	1.5134	6.022	10.48	14.90
1900	0.14361	0.57414	1.0042	1.4339	5.707	9.938	14.13
2000	0.13643	0.54544	0.95408	1.3623	5.423	9.447	13.43
2100	0.12993	0.51949	0.90868	1.2975	5.167	9.000	12.80
2200	0.12403	0.49589	0.86742	1.2386	4.933	8.595	12.23
2300	0.11863	0.47434	0.82974	1.1848	4.720	8.225	11.70
2400	0.11369	0.45458	0.79520	1.1355	4.524	7.885	11.22
2500	0.10914	0.43641	0.76342	1.0902	4.344	7.572	10.78
2600	0.10495	0.41963	0.73408	1.0483	4.178	7.283	10.37
2700	0.10106	0.40410	0.70692	1.0095	4.024	7.016	9.987
2800	0.097452	0.38967	0.68169	0.9735	3.881	6.768	9.635
2900	0.094092	0.37624	0.65820	0.93997	3.747	6.536	9.306
3000	0.090956	0.36371	0.63628	0.90868	3.623	6.320	8.999
3100	0.088022	0.35198	0.61576	0.87939	3.507	6.117	8.712
3200	0.085271	0.34098	0.59653	0.85193	3.397	5.927	8.442
3300	0.082688	0.33066	0.57847	0.82614	3.295	5.749	8.189
3400	0.080256	0.32093	0.56147	0.80187	3.198	5.581	7.950
3500	0.077964	0.31177	0.54544	0.77898	3.107	5.423	7.725
3600	0.075798	0.30311	0.53030	0.75737	3.021	5.273	7.513
3700	0.073749	0.29492	0.51597	0.73691	2.940	5.131	7.311
3800	0.071809	0.28716	0.50240	0.71754	2.863	4.997	7.121
3900	0.069968	0.27980	0.48953	0.69916	2.790	4.870	6.940
4000	0.068219	0.27281	0.47730	0.68169	2.720	4.749	6.768
4100	0.066555	0.26616	0.46567	0.66508	2.654	4.634	6.604
4200	0.064970	0.25982	0.45458	0.64925	2.591	4.524	6.448
4300	0.063459	0.25378	0.44402	0.63417	2.531	4.419	6.299
4400	0.062018	0.24802	0.43393	0.61977	2.474	4.320	6.157
4500	0.060640	0.24251	0.42429	0.60601	2.419	4.224	6.022
4600	0.059321	0.23724	0.41507	0.59284	2.366	4.133	5.891
4700	0.058059	0.23219	0.40625	0.58024	2.316	4.045	5.767
4800	0.056850	0.22736	0.39779	0.56816	2.268	3.961	5.648
4900	0.055689	0.22272	0.38967	0.55657	2.222	3.881	5.533
5000	0.054576	0.21826	0.38189	0.54545	2.178	3.804	5.424

TABLE 4h-10. SPECIFIC HEAT OF ARGON, C_p/R

T, °K	1 atm	4 atm	7 atm	10 atm	40 atm	70 atm	100 atm
100	2.6077	3.016	3.55				
200	2.5154	2.5626	2.612	2.663	3.31	4.2	5.2
300	2.5057	2.5230	2.5404	2.5581	2.74	2.93	3.12
400	2.5029	2.5118	2.5206	2.5294	2.61	2.70	2.79
500	2.5018	2.5071	2.5124	2.5176	2.570	2.621	2.670
600	2.5012	2.5047	2.5082	2.5117	2.546	2.579	2.611
700	2.5008	2.5033	2.5058	2.5082	2.532	2.555	2.578
800	2.5006	2.5025	2.5043	2.5062	2.524	2.541	2.558
900	2.5005	2.5020	2.5033	2.5047	2.519	2.531	2.544
1000	2.5004	2.5015	2.5026	2.5037	2.515	2.525	2.536
1100	2.5003	2.5012	2.5021	2.5030	2.512	2.520	2.528
1200	2.5002	2.5010	2.5017	2.5024	2.510	2.516	2.523
1300	2.5002	2.5008	2.5014	2.5020	2.508	2.514	2.519
1400	2.5002	2.5007	2.5012	2.5017	2.507	2.512	2.516
1500	2.5001	2.5006	2.5010	2.5014	2.506	2.510	2.513
1600	2.5001	2.5005	2.5009	2.5012	2.505	2.509	2.511
1700	2.5001	2.5004	2.5007	2.5011	2.504	2.507	2.511
1800	2.5001	2.5004	2.5006	2.5009	2.504	2.506	2.509
1900	2.5001	2.5003	2.5006	2.5008	2.503	2.506	2.508
2000	2.5001	2.5003	2.5005	2.5007	2.503	2.505	2.507
2100	2.5001	2.5002	2.5004	2.5006	2.502	2.504	2.506
2200	2.5001	2.5002	2.5004	2.5005	2.502	2.504	2.505
2300	2.5000	2.5002	2.5003	2.5005	2.502	2.503	2.505
2400	2.5000	2.5002	2.5003	2.5004	2.502	2.503	2.504
2500	2.5000	2.5002	2.5003	2.5004	2.502	2.503	2.504
2600	2.5000	2.5001	2.5002	2.5003	2.501	2.502	2.503
2700	2.5000	2.5001	2.5002	2.5003	2.501	2.502	2.503
2800	2.5000	2.5001	2.5002	2.5003	2.501	2.502	2.503
2900	2.5000	2.5001	2.5002	2.5003	2.501	2.502	2.503
3000	2.5000	2.5001	2.5002	2.5002	2.501	2.502	2.502

TABLE 4h-11. ENTHALPY OF ARGON, $(H - E_0^\circ)/RT_0$

T, °K	1 atm	4 atm	7 atm	10 atm	40 atm	70 atm	100 atm
100	0.8935	0.8220	0.7413				
200	1.8236	1.8029	1.7819	1.7606	1.53	1.3	
300	2.7422	2.7319	2.7217	2.7114	2.610	2.512	2.42
400	3.6590	3.6532	3.6476	3.6418	3.586	3.533	3.48
500	4.5750	4.5718	4.5686	4.5654	4.535	4.506	4.48
600	5.4907	5.4891	5.4874	5.4859	5.471	5.457	5.445
700	6.4063	6.4057	6.4052	6.4047	6.400	6.397	6.395
800	7.3218	7.3220	7.3222	7.3226	7.326	7.330	7.335
900	8.2372	8.2380	8.2388	8.2396	8.249	8.258	8.268
1000	9.1525	9.1538	9.1551	9.1564	9.170	9.184	9.198
1100	10.0679	10.0696	10.0712	10.0729	10.090	10.107	10.125
1200	10.9832	10.9852	10.9871	10.9891	11.009	11.029	11.049
1300	11.8985	11.9007	11.9029	11.9051	11.927	11.950	11.972
1400	12.8138	12.8162	12.8186	12.8210	12.845	12.869	12.894
1500	13.7291	13.7316	13.7342	13.7367	13.763	13.788	13.815
1600	14.6443	14.6470	14.6497	14.6524	14.680	14.707	14.735
1700	15.5595	15.5624	15.5652	15.5680	15.597	15.625	15.654
1800	16.4749	16.4778	16.4808	16.4837	16.513	16.543	16.572
1900	17.3901	17.3931	17.3962	17.3992	17.430	17.460	17.491
2000	18.3053	18.3085	18.3116	18.3147	18.346	18.377	18.409
2100	19.2206	19.2238	19.2269	19.2301	19.262	19.294	19.326
2200	20.1358	20.1390	20.1423	20.1456	20.178	20.211	20.243
2300	21.0510	21.0543	21.0576	21.0609	21.094	21.127	21.160
2400	21.9662	21.9696	21.9729	21.9763	22.010	22.044	22.077
2500	22.8815	22.8849	22.8884	22.8918	22.926	22.960	22.994
2600	23.7967	23.8002	23.8036	23.8071	23.842	23.876	23.911
2700	24.7120	24.7154	24.7189	24.7224	24.757	24.792	24.827
2800	25.6272	25.6307	25.6342	25.6377	25.673	25.708	25.743
2900	26.5424	26.5459	26.5495	26.5530	26.589	26.624	26.659
3000	27.4576	27.4612	27.4647	27.4683	27.504	27.540	27.575

TABLE 4h-12. ENTROPY OF ARGON, S/R

T, °K	1 atm	4 atm	7 atm	10 atm	40 atm	70 atm	100 atm
100	15.8425	14.328	13.62				
200	17.6069	16.2012	15.6218	15.245	13.64	12.83	12.2
300	18.6245	17.2308	16.6637	16.2995	14.8389	14.2067	13.781
400	19.3449	17.9548	17.3913	17.0308	15.6067	15.0118	14.618
500	19.9032	18.5146	17.9527	17.5937	16.1850	15.6037	15.2261
600	20.3593	18.9715	18.4104	18.0522	16.6513	16.0776	15.7072
700	20.7449	19.3575	18.7969	18.4391	17.0426	16.4732	16.1070
800	21.0787	19.6917	19.1313	18.7739	17.3802	16.8134	16.4498
900	21.3733	19.9864	19.4263	19.0690	17.6772	17.1122	16.7503
1000	21.6368	20.2500	19.6900	19.3328	17.9423	17.3785	17.0179
1100	21.8751	20.4884	19.9285	19.5715	18.1819	17.6190	17.2592
1200	22.0926	20.7060	20.1462	19.7892	18.4003	17.8381	17.4789
1300	22.2927	20.9062	20.3464	19.9895	18.6010	18.0394	17.6807
1400	22.4780	21.0916	20.5318	20.1749	18.7869	18.2256	17.8673
1500	22.6505	21.2640	20.7043	20.3474	18.9597	18.3988	18.0408
1600	22.8119	21.4254	20.8657	20.5089	19.1214	18.5607	18.2029
1700	22.9635	21.5771	21.0174	20.6606	19.2733	18.7128	18.3552
1800	23.1064	21.7200	21.1603	20.8035	19.4165	18.8561	18.4987
1900	23.2415	21.8551	21.2955	20.9387	19.5518	18.9915	18.6343
2000	23.3698	21.9834	21.4238	21.0670	19.6802	19.1201	18.7630
2100	23.4917	22.1053	21.5457	21.1890	19.8022	19.2422	18.8851
2200	23.6080	22.2217	21.6620	21.3053	19.9187	19.3587	19.0017
2300	23.7192	22.3329	21.7732	21.4165	20.0299	19.4701	19.1131
2400	23.8256	22.4393	21.8797	21.5229	20.1364	19.5766	19.2197
2500	23.9276	22.5413	21.9817	21.6249	20.2385	19.6787	19.3218
2600	24.0257	22.6394	22.0798	21.7231	20.3366	19.7769	19.4201
2700	24.1200	22.7337	22.1741	21.8174	20.4310	19.8713	19.5145
2800	24.2109	22.8246	22.2650	21.9083	20.5219	19.9623	19.6055
2900	24.2987	22.9124	22.3528	21.9961	20.6098	20.0501	19.6934
3000	24.3834	22.9971	22.4375	22.0808	20.6945	20.1349	19.7782

TABLE 4h-13. COMPRESSIBILITY FACTOR FOR CARBON DIOXIDE, $Z = PV/RT$

T, °K	1 atm	4 atm	7 atm	10 atm	40 atm	70 atm	100 atm
300	0.99501	0.9798	0.9644	0.9486	0.7611		
400	0.99817	0.99267	0.98714	0.9815	0.9252	0.8697	0.8155
500	0.99927	0.99711	0.99496	0.99281	0.9721	0.9531	0.9365
600	0.99975	0.99903	0.99832	0.99763	0.9916	0.9874	0.9850
700	0.99998	0.99996	0.99995	0.99996	1.0008	1.0031	1.0068
800	1.0001	1.0004	1.0008	1.0011	1.0054	1.0108	1.0172
900	1.0001	1.0007	1.0012	1.0018	1.0079	1.0147	1.0224
1000	1.0002	1.0008	1.0015	1.0022	1.0092	1.0167	1.0248
1100	1.0002	1.0009	1.0016	1.0024	1.0098	1.0177	1.0260
1200	1.0002	1.0009	1.0017	1.0024	1.0101	1.0181	1.0263
1300	1.0002	1.0010	1.0017	1.0025	1.0102	1.0181	1.0262
1400	1.0002	1.0010	1.0017	1.0025	1.0101	1.0179	1.0258
1500	1.0002	1.0010	1.0017	1.0025	1.0100	1.0176	1.0253

TABLE 4h-14. RELATIVE DENSITY OF CARBON DIOXIDE, ρ/ρ_0

T, °K	1 atm	4 atm	7 atm	10 atm	40 atm	70 atm	100 atm
300	0.9088	3.6916	6.5637	9.532	47.52		
400	0.6794	2.7329	4.8095	6.909	29.321	54.600	83.17
500	0.5429	2.1766	3.8173	5.465	22.327	39.848	57.937
600	0.45227	1.8104	3.1704	4.5323	18.238	32.054	45.904
700	0.38757	1.5503	2.7130	3.8758	15.489	27.044	38.491
800	0.33908	1.3558	2.3719	3.3871	13.491	23.483	33.335
900	0.30138	1.2048	2.1073	3.0088	11.962	20.793	29.483
1000	0.27123	1.0842	1.8961	2.7069	10.752	18.677	26.470
1100	0.24657	0.9855	1.7235	2.4604	9.768	16.963	24.038
1200	0.22585	0.9034	1.5798	2.2551	8.952	15.544	22.028
1300	0.20863	0.8339	1.4582	2.0816	8.262	14.348	20.335
1400	0.19373	0.7743	1.3541	1.9329	7.673	13.325	18.890
1500	0.18081	0.7227	1.2638	1.8041	7.162	12.441	17.639

TABLE 4h-15. SPECIFIC HEAT OF CARBON DIOXIDE, C_p/R

T, °K	1 atm	4 atm	7 atm	10 atm	40 atm	70 atm	100 atm
300	4.513	4.624	4.739	4.862	7.45		
400	4.984	5.027	5.070	5.115	5.615	6.225	6.960
500	5.374	5.396	5.418	5.440	5.669	5.875	6.014
600	5.696	5.708	5.721	5.734	5.873	6.020	6.173
700	5.964	5.972	5.981	5.989	6.078	6.171	6.267
800	6.188	6.194	6.200	6.206	6.266	6.326	6.387
900	6.376	6.380	6.384	6.389	6.433	6.476	6.518
1000	6.533	6.536	6.540	6.543	6.577	6.609	6.640
1100	6.665	6.668	6.671	6.674	6.700	6.725	6.749
1200	6.776	6.779	6.781	6.783	6.805	6.825	6.844
1300	6.872	6.874	6.876	6.878	6.896	6.912	6.928
1400	6.952	6.954	6.955	6.957	6.972	6.986	6.999
1500	7.021	7.022	7.024	7.025	7.038	7.050	7.061

TABLE 4h-16. ENTHALPY OF CARBON DIOXIDE, $(H - E_0^\circ)/RT_0$

T, °K	1 atm	4 atm	7 atm	10 atm	40 atm	70 atm	100 atm
300	4.135	4.079	4.023	3.965	3.25		
400	5.876	5.846	5.816	5.785	5.466	5.128	4.771
500	7.774	7.755	7.737	7.717	7.522	7.315	7.081
600	9.802	9.789	9.777	9.764	9.635	9.497	9.333
700	11.938	11.929	11.921	11.912	11.824	11.729	11.609
800	14.164	14.157	14.151	14.145	14.084	14.016	13.925
900	16.464	16.459	16.456	16.451	16.409	16.360	16.287
1000	18.828	18.824	18.822	18.819	18.791	18.755	18.696
1100	21.245	21.243	21.241	21.239	21.222	21.197	21.147
1200	23.706	23.704	23.704	23.703	23.695	23.677	23.635
1300	26.204	26.204	26.204	26.203	26.202	26.192	26.156
1400	28.735	28.735	28.736	28.736	28.741	28.736	28.705
1500	31.293	31.294	31.295	31.296	31.306	31.305	31.279

TABLE 4h-17. ENTROPY OF CARBON DIOXIDE, S/R

T, °K	1 atm	4 atm	7 atm	10 atm	40 atm	70 atm	100 atm
300	25.715	24.293	23.698	23.305	21.43		
400	27.080	25.678	25.103	24.732	23.183	22.449	21.904
500	28.235	26.840	26.273	25.908	24.436	23.783	23.316
600	29.244	27.853	27.288	26.927	25.488	24.870	24.437
700	30.143	28.753	28.190	27.830	26.409	25.809	25.395
800	30.954	29.565	29.003	28.645	27.233	26.643	26.240
900	31.695	30.307	29.745	29.387	27.982	27.398	27.001
1000	32.375	30.987	30.426	30.069	28.667	28.087	27.694
1100	33.004	31.616	31.055	30.698	29.300	28.723	28.332
1200	33.589	32.202	31.641	31.284	29.887	29.312	28.923
1300	34.135	32.748	32.187	31.831	30.436	29.862	29.474
1400	34.647	33.260	32.700	32.343	30.949	30.377	29.990
1500	35.129	33.742	33.182	32.825	31.431	30.858	30.475

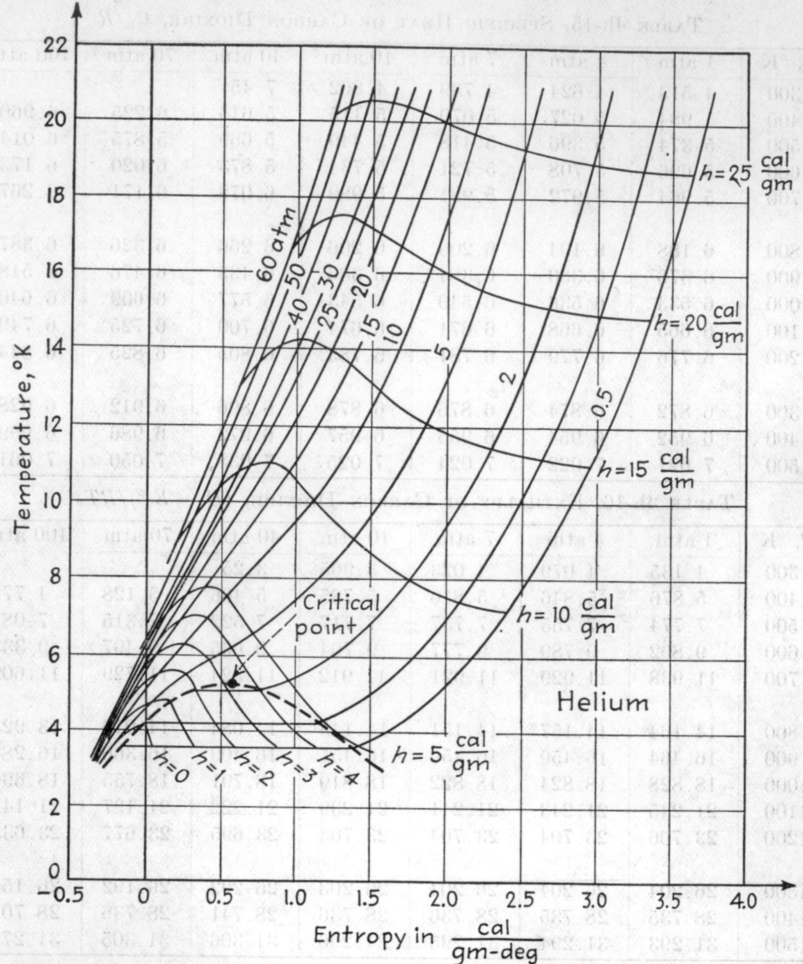

FIG. 4h-1. Temperature-entropy diagram for helium. (*Zelmanov.*)

TABLE 4h-18. COMPRESSIBILITY FACTOR FOR HYDROGEN, $Z = PV/RT$

T, °K	1 atm	4 atm	7 atm	10 atm	40 atm	70 atm	100 atm
40	0.9845	0.9362	0.8853	0.8317			
60	0.9955	0.9822	0.9691	0.9564	0.8757	0.8700	0.9395
80	0.9986	0.9946	0.9908	0.9872	0.9682	0.9782	1.0174
100	0.9998	0.9992	0.9987	0.9983	1.0029	1.0222	1.0560
120	1.0003	1.0012	1.0021	1.0030	1.0176	1.0405	1.0726
140	1.0005	1.0020	1.0036	1.0052	1.0243	1.0488	1.0786
160	1.0006	1.0024	1.0043	1.0062	1.0271	1.0516	1.0798
180	1.0007	1.0028	1.0048	1.0067	1.0283	1.0523	1.0785
200	1.0007	1.0028	1.0048	1.0068	1.0283	1.0513	1.0760
220	1.0007	1.0028	1.0048	1.0067	1.0276	1.0497	1.0730
240	1.0007	1.0027	1.0047	1.0066	1.0269	1.0480	1.0698
260	1.0006	1.0024	1.0044	1.0064	1.0259	1.0459	1.0667
280	1.0006	1.0024	1.0042	1.0061	1.0247	1.0439	1.0636
300	1.0006	1.0024	1.0042	1.0059	1.0238	1.0420	1.0607
320	1.0006	1.0024	1.0041	1.0057	1.0229	1.0402	1.0579
340	1.0005	1.0021	1.0037	1.0054	1.0217	1.0384	1.0553
360	1.0005	1.0020	1.0036	1.0052	1.0209	1.0367	1.0529
380	1.0005	1.0020	1.0035	1.0050	1.0201	1.0353	1.0507
400	1.0005	1.0020	1.0034	1.0048	1.0193	1.0339	1.0486
420	1.0005	1.0019	1.0033	1.0046	1.0185	1.0325	1.0466
440	1.0004	1.0017	1.0030	1.0045	1.0180	1.0314	1.0448
460	1.0004	1.0016	1.0029	1.0043	1.0172	1.0301	1.0431
480	1.0004	1.0016	1.0028	1.0041	1.0165	1.0289	1.0415
500	1.0004	1.0016	1.0028	1.0040	1.0160	1.0280	1.0400
520	1.0004	1.0016	1.0028	1.0039	1.0155	1.0271	1.0385
540	1.0004	1.0016	1.0026	1.0037	1.0148	1.0260	1.0372
560	1.0004	1.0015	1.0026	1.0036	1.0144	1.0252	1.0360
580	1.0003	1.0013	1.0024	1.0035	1.0140	1.0244	1.0348
600	1.0003	1.0012	1.0023	1.0034	1.0136	1.0237	1.0337

TABLE 4h-19. RELATIVE DENSITY OF HYDROGEN, ρ/ρ_0

T, °K	1 atm	4 atm	7 atm	10 atm	40 atm	70 atm	100 atm
40	6.9408	29.195	54.029	82.160			
60	4.5761	18.552	32.905	47.632	208.08	366.53	484.88
80	3.4214	13.740	24.138	34.609	141.15	244.49	335.82
100	2.7338	10.942	19.158	27.379	109.01	187.17	258.83
120	2.2771	9.0999	15.910	22.709	89.532	153.23	212.36
140	1.9514	7.7937	13.617	19.422	76.240	130.30	181.01
160	1.7073	6.8167	11.907	16.978	66.528	113.71	158.21
180	1.5174	6.0569	10.578	15.084	59.067	101.01	140.80
200	1.3657	5.4512	9.5206	13.574	53.160	90.995	127.01
220	1.2415	4.9557	8.6551	12.341	48.361	82.849	115.79
240	1.1381	4.5431	7.9347	11.314	44.361	76.068	106.46
260	1.0506	4.1949	7.3265	10.446	40.988	70.358	98.553
280	0.97559	3.8953	6.8045	9.7026	38.105	65.457	91.780
300	0.91055	3.6356	6.3509	9.0575	35.596	61.204	85.896
320	0.85364	3.4084	5.9546	8.4931	33.401	57.479	80.740
340	0.80351	3.2088	5.6065	7.9959	31.473	54.192	76.178
360	0.75887	3.0309	5.2956	7.5532	29.748	51.265	72.110
380	0.71893	2.8714	5.0174	7.1571	28.204	48.632	68.458
400	0.68298	2.7278	4.7670	6.8006	26.815	46.286	65.165
420	0.65046	2.5982	4.5404	6.4780	25.558	44.120	62.181
440	0.62095	2.4806	4.3353	6.1842	24.408	42.160	59.457
460	0.59396	2.3729	4.1473	5.9165	23.365	40.377	56.964
480	0.56921	2.2741	3.9749	5.6711	22.407	38.740	54.675
500	0.54644	2.1831	3.8159	5.4448	21.522	37.223	52.563
520	0.52542	2.0991	3.6691	5.2359	20.704	35.823	50.615
540	0.50596	2.0214	3.5339	5.0430	19.951	34.533	48.801
560	0.48789	1.9494	3.4077	4.8634	19.246	33.326	47.113
580	0.47112	1.8826	3.2908	4.6961	18.590	32.202	45.541
600	0.45541	1.8200	3.1815	4.5400	17.977	31.150	44.070

TABLE 4h-20. SPECIFIC HEAT OF HYDROGEN, C_p/R

T, °K	0 atm	1 atm	10 atm	100 atm
20	2.500			
40	2.501	2.564	3.463	
60	2.519	2.544	2.780	3.957
80	2.591	2.605	2.723	3.564
100	2.714	2.722	2.790	3.295
120	2.857	2.862	2.905	3.242
140	2.993	2.996	3.026	3.264
160	3.108	3.111	3.135	3.326
180	3.204	3.206	3.226	3.377
200	3.280	3.282	3.296	3.413
220	3.340	3.341	3.355	3.454
240	3.387	3.388	3.399	3.486
260	3.424	3.425	3.433	3.504
280	3.450	3.451	3.458	3.516
300	3.469	3.470	3.476	3.526
320	3.483	3.484	3.489	3.532
340	3.494	3.495	3.499	3.536
360	3.501	3.502	3.506	3.539
380	3.507	3.508	3.510	3.539
400	3.510	3.511	3.514	3.539
420	3.513	3.514	3.516	3.539
440	3.515	3.516	3.518	3.538
460	3.516	3.517	3.519	3.538
480	3.518	3.518	3.520	3.537
500	3.519	3.519	3.521	3.536
520	3.521	3.521	3.523	3.536
540	3.522	3.522	3.524	3.536
560	3.524	3.524	3.526	3.536
580	3.525	3.525	3.527	3.536
600	3.527	3.527	3.529	3.536

Table 4h-21. Enthalpy of Hydrogen, $(H - E_0^\circ)/RT_0$

°K	0.01 atm	0.1 atm	1 atm	10 atm	100 atm
60	1.0175	1.0172	1.0142	0.9833	0.7818
80	1.2042	1.2040	1.2021	1.1837	1.0577
100	1.3981	1.3980	1.3968	1.3852	1.3059
120	1.6020	1.6020	1.6012	1.5936	1.5449
140	1.8163	1.8163	1.8158	1.8108	1.7825
160	2.0398	2.0398	2.0394	2.0365	2.0234
180	2.2710	2.2710	2.2708	2.2695	2.2690
200	2.5085	2.5085	2.5084	2.5083	2.5178
220	2.7509	2.7509	2.7510	2.7519	2.7692
240	2.9973	2.9973	2.9975	2.9993	3.0236
260	3.2467	3.2467	3.2470	3.2495	3.2792
280	3.4983	3.4984	3.4986	3.5017	3.5363
300	3.7517	3.7517	3.7521	3.7556	3.7941
320	4.0063	4.0063	4.0067	4.0106	4.0525
340	4.2617	4.2617	4.2622	4.2664	4.3114
360	4.5178	4.5178	4.5183	4.5229	4.5705
380	4.7743	4.7744	4.7748	4.7797	4.8296
400	5.0312	5.0312	5.0317	5.0368	5.0887
420	5.2883	5.2883	5.2889	5.2941	5.3478
440	5.5455	5.5456	5.5461	5.5516	5.6067
460	5.8029	5.8030	5.8035	5.8091	5.8659
480	6.0604	6.0605	6.0610	6.0669	6.1249
500	6.3180	6.3181	6.3187	6.3246	6.3839
520	6.5757	6.5758	6.5764	6.5824	6.6427
540	6.8335	6.8336	6.8342	6.8404	6.9015
560	7.0915	7.0915	7.0921	7.0984	7.1606
580	7.3495	7.3496	7.3502	7.3565	7.4194
600	7.6077	7.6078	7.6084	7.6147	7.6784

TABLE 4h-22. ENTROPY OF HYDROGEN, S/R

T, °K	0.01 atm	0.1 atm	1 atm	10 atm	100 atm
60	15.554	13.251	10.938	8.535	5.557
80	16.287	13.984	11.676	9.324	6.642
100	16.878	14.575	12.269	9.937	7.400
120	17.386	15.083	12.778	10.456	7.996
140	17.836	15.533	13.229	10.913	8.496
160	18.244	15.941	13.637	11.324	8.935
180	18.616	16.313	14.009	11.699	9.331
200	18.958	16.655	14.352	12.043	9.688
220	19.273	16.970	14.667	12.359	10.015
240	19.566	17.263	14.960	12.653	10.317
260	19.838	17.535	15.232	12.926	10.596
280	20.093	17.790	15.487	13.182	10.857
300	20.331	18.029	15.726	13.421	11.100
320	20.556	18.254	15.951	13.646	11.328
340	20.768	18.465	16.162	13.858	11.542
360	20.967	18.665	16.362	14.058	11.744
380	21.157	18.854	16.552	14.248	11.936
400	21.337	19.034	16.731	14.428	12.117
420	21.508	19.206	16.903	14.600	12.290
440	21.671	19.369	17.066	14.763	12.454
460	21.828	19.525	17.223	14.919	12.612
480	21.977	19.675	17.372	15.069	12.762
500	22.121	19.818	17.515	15.213	12.906
520	22.260	19.957	17.655	15.352	13.046
540	22.392	20.090	17.787	15.484	13.179
560	22.520	20.218	17.915	15.612	13.308
580	22.644	20.341	18.038	15.736	13.431
600	22.764	20.461	18.158	15.856	13.552

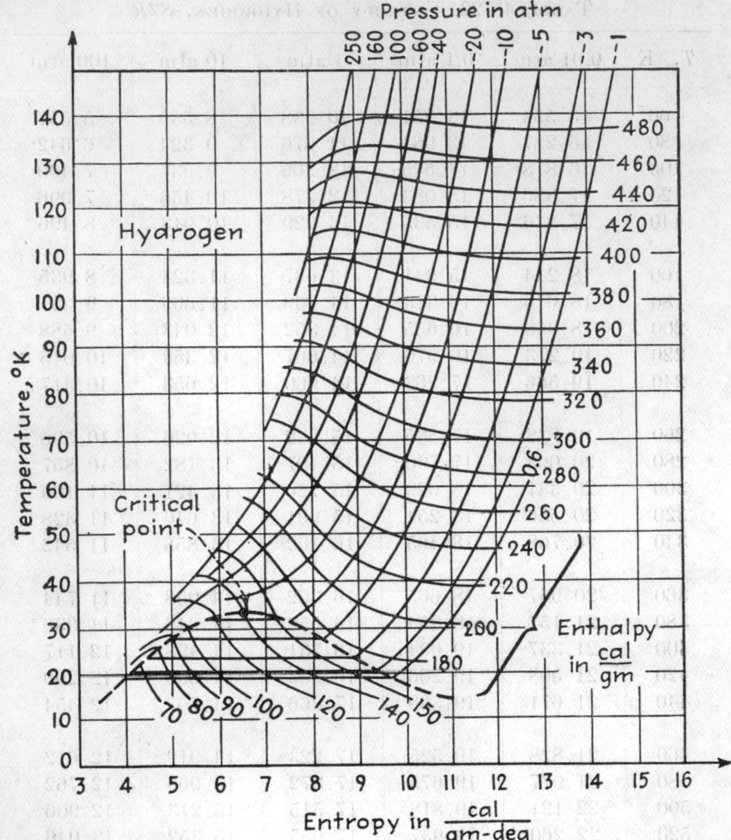

Fig. 4h-2. Temperature-entropy diagram for hydrogen. (*Woolley, Scott, and Brickwedde.*)

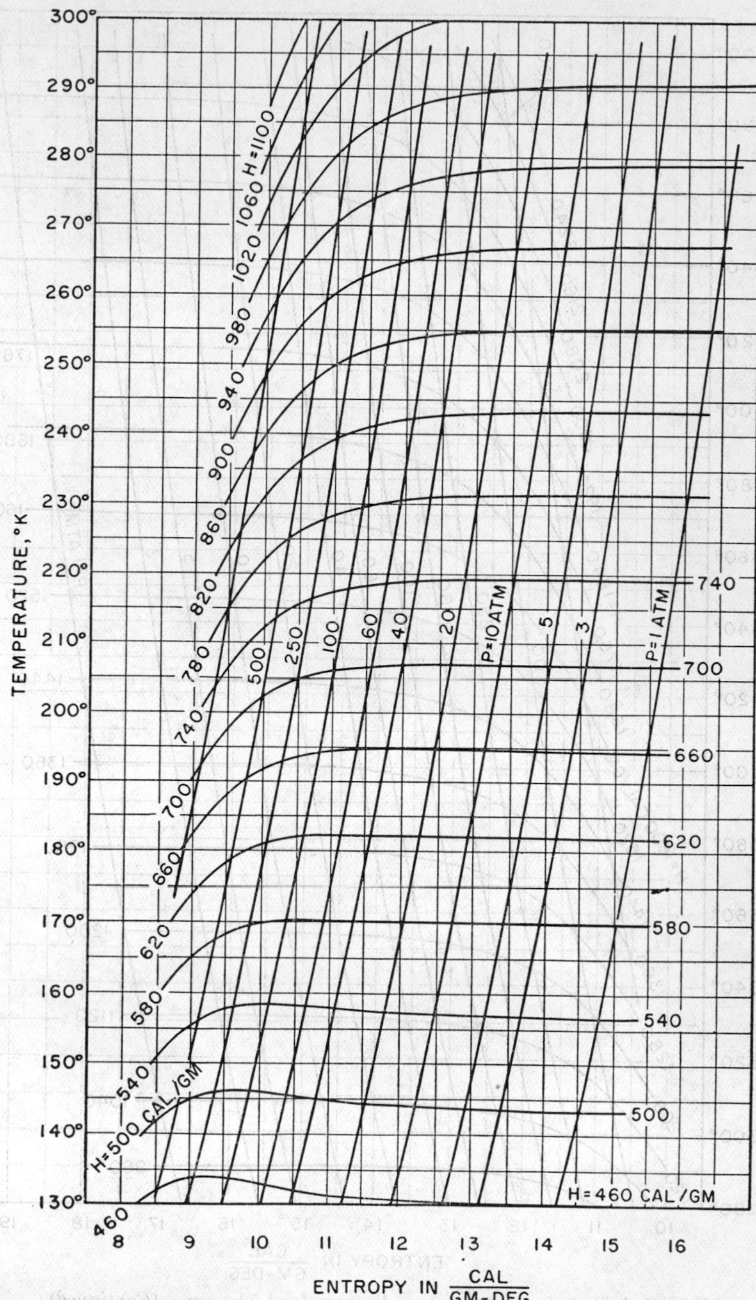

FIG. 4h-3. Temperature-entropy diagram for hydrogen. (*Continued*)

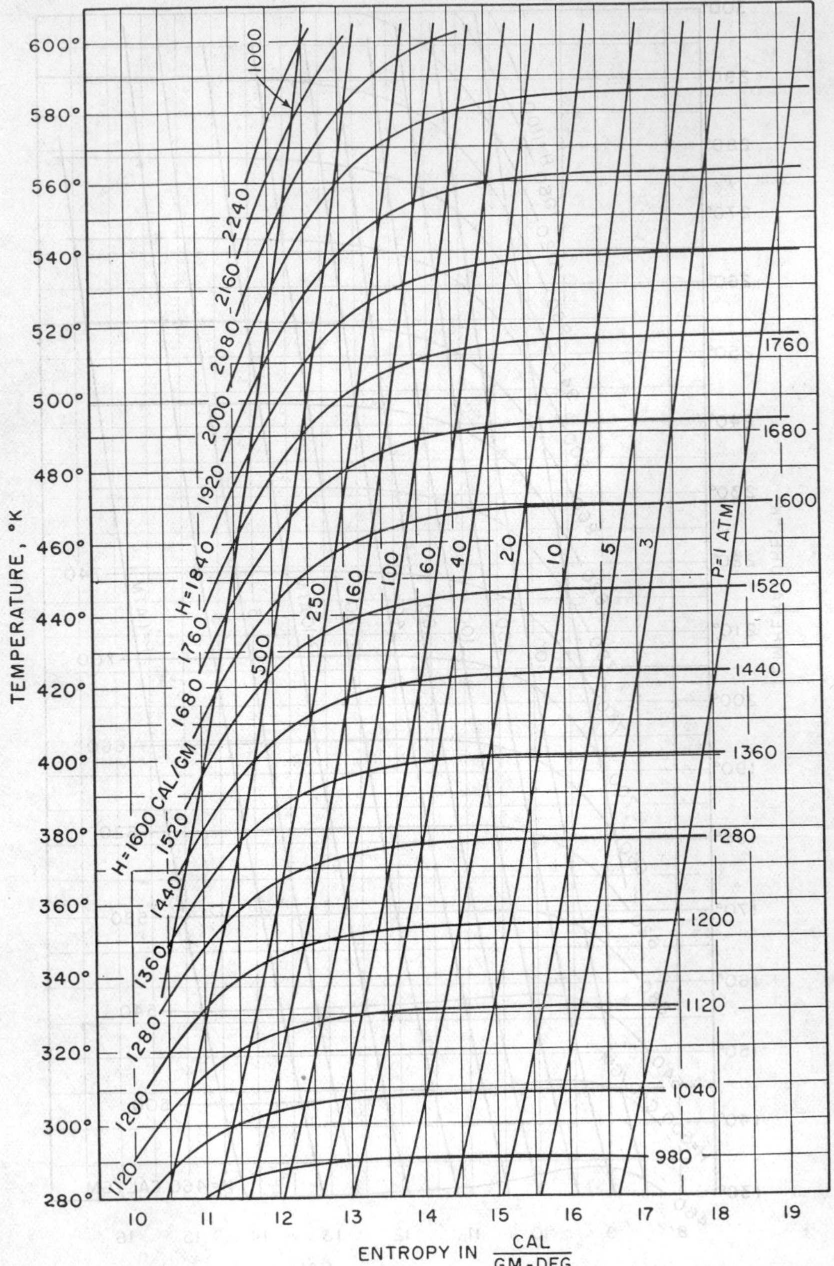

FIG. 4h-4. Temperature-entropy diagram for hydrogen. *(Continued)*

TABLE 4h-23. COMPRESSIBILITY FACTOR FOR NITROGEN, $Z = PV/RT$

T, °K	1 atm	4 atm	7 atm	10 atm	40 atm	70 atm	100 atm
100	0.981	0.909	0.783				
200	0.99788	0.99150	0.98514	0.9788	0.9185	0.8705	0.844
300	0.99982	0.99930	0.99882	0.99838	0.9962	0.9984	1.0054
400	1.00028	1.00113	1.00201	1.00290	1.01292	1.0248	1.0383
500	1.00041	1.00164	1.00289	1.00414	1.01726	1.0313	1.0461
600	1.00044	1.00174	1.00306	1.00439	1.01795	1.0320	1.0465
700	1.00043	1.00171	1.00301	1.00430	1.01744	1.0309	1.0446
800	1.00041	1.00163	1.00286	1.00409	1.0165	1.0292	1.0420
900	1.00038	1.00154	1.00269	1.00384	1.0155	1.0273	1.0391
1000	1.00036	1.00144	1.00252	1.00360	1.0145	1.0255	1.0365
1100	1.00034	1.00135	1.00236	1.00337	1.0135	1.0238	1.0341
1200	1.00032	1.00126	1.00221	1.00316	1.0127	1.0223	1.0319
1300	1.00030	1.00119	1.00208	1.00297	1.0119	1.0209	1.0299
1400	1.00028	1.00112	1.00195	1.00279	1.0112	1.0196	1.0280
1500	1.00026	1.00105	1.00184	1.00263	1.0105	1.0185	1.0264
1600	1.00025	1.00100	1.00174	1.00249	1.0100	1.0175	1.0250
1700	1.00024	1.00094	1.00165	1.00235	1.0094	1.0165	1.0236
1800	1.00022	1.00089	1.00156	1.00223	1.0089	1.0156	1.0223
1900	1.00021	1.00085	1.00148	1.00212	1.0085	1.0148	1.0212
2000	1.00020	1.00081	1.00141	1.00202	1.0081	1.0141	1.0202
2100	1.00019	1.00077	1.00135	1.00193	1.0077	1.0135	1.0193
2200	1.00018	1.00074	1.00129	1.00184	1.0074	1.0129	1.0184
2300	1.00018	1.00070	1.00123	1.00176	1.0070	1.0123	1.0176
2400	1.00017	1.00068	1.00118	1.00169	1.0068	1.0118	1.0169
2500	1.00016	1.00065	1.00113	1.00162	1.0065	1.0113	1.0162
2600	1.00016	1.00062	1.00109	1.00156	1.0062	1.0109	1.0156
2700	1.00015	1.00060	1.00105	1.00150	1.0060	1.0105	1.0150
2800	1.00015	1.00058	1.00102	1.00145	1.0058	1.0102	1.0145
2900	1.00014	1.00056	1.00097	1.00139	1.0056	1.0097	1.0139
3000	1.00014	1.00054	1.00095	1.00135	1.0054	1.0095	1.0135

TABLE 4h-24. RELATIVE DENSITY OF NITROGEN, ρ/ρ_0

T, °K	1 atm	4 atm	7 atm	10 atm	40 atm	70 atm	100 atm
100	2.783	12.010	24.40				
200	1.36809	5.50755	9.7004	13.947	59.45	109.77	161.7
300	0.91029	3.64304	6.3783	9.1160	36.543	63.810	90.523
400	0.68240	2.72729	4.76856	6.8061	26.955	46.625	65.741
500	0.54585	2.18072	3.81150	5.4382	21.472	37.065	52.200
600	0.45486	1.81708	3.17571	4.5307	17.881	30.866	43.484
700	0.38989	1.55755	2.72218	3.8838	15.334	26.485	37.339
800	0.34116	1.36296	2.38226	3.3990	13.429	23.212	32.754
900	0.30326	1.21163	2.11792	3.0223	11.949	20.673	29.195
1000	0.27294	1.09058	1.90645	2.7206	10.765	18.631	26.342
1100	0.24813	0.99152	1.73342	2.4737	9.796	16.971	24.003
1200	0.22746	0.90898	1.58920	2.2681	8.987	15.579	22.049
1300	0.20997	0.83912	1.46715	2.0940	8.302	14.401	20.393
1400	0.19497	0.77923	1.36253	1.9448	7.714	13.389	18.971
1500	0.18198	0.72733	1.27183	1.8155	7.205	12.510	17.734
1600	0.17061	0.68191	1.19246	1.7022	6.758	11.739	16.648
1700	0.16057	0.64184	1.12242	1.6023	6.364	11.060	15.690
1800	0.15165	0.60621	1.06016	1.5135	6.014	10.455	14.837
1900	0.14367	0.57433	1.00444	1.4340	5.699	9.912	14.072
2000	0.13649	0.54563	0.95428	1.3625	5.416	9.423	13.381
2100	0.12999	0.51967	0.90890	1.2977	5.161	8.980	12.755
2200	0.12409	0.49606	0.86763	1.2388	4.927	8.576	12.186
2300	0.11869	0.47451	0.82996	1.1850	4.715	8.208	11.665
2400	0.11375	0.45475	0.79542	1.1357	4.519	7.870	11.187
2500	0.10920	0.43658	0.76364	1.0904	4.340	7.559	10.747
2600	0.10500	0.41980	0.73430	1.0485	4.174	7.271	10.340
2700	0.10111	0.40426	0.70713	1.0097	4.020	7.005	9.963
2800	0.09750	0.38983	0.68190	0.9737	3.878	6.757	9.611
2900	0.09414	0.37639	0.65842	0.9402	3.745	6.527	9.286
3000	0.09100	0.36385	0.63648	0.9089	3.620	6.310	8.980

TABLE 4h-25. SPECIFIC HEAT OF NITROGEN, C_p/R

T, °K	1 atm	4 atm	7 atm	10 atm	40 atm	70 atm	100 atm
100	3.613						
200	3.5146	3.5569	3.6009	3.6466	4.1865	4.860	5.64
300	3.5083	3.5243	3.5404	3.5565	3.7195	3.878	4.021
400	3.5207	3.5289	3.5372	3.5454	3.6260	3.7023	3.773
500	3.5595	3.5645	3.5694	3.5744	3.6225	3.6680	3.7104
600	3.6225	3.6258	3.6292	3.6324	3.6642	3.6944	3.7229
700	3.6998	3.7021	3.7045	3.7067	3.7293	3.7506	3.7709
800	3.7812	3.7829	3.7846	3.7863	3.8029	3.8188	3.8338
900	3.8600	3.8614	3.8627	3.8640	3.8766	3.8888	3.9004
1000	3.9329	3.9340	3.9350	3.9361	3.9460	3.9556	3.9647
1100	3.9985	3.9993	4.0001	4.0010	4.0089	4.0166	4.0239
1200	4.0564	4.0571	4 0578	4.0584	4.0649	4.0712	4.0772
1300	4.1074	4.1079	4.1085	4.1091	4.1144	4.1197	4.1247
1400	4.1520	4.1524	4.1529	4.1533	4.1578	4.1621	4.1663
1500	4.1910	4.1914	4.1918	4.1922	4.1960	4.1995	4.2031
1600	4.2253	4.2256	4.2260	4.2263	4.2295	4.2326	4.2356
1700	4.2555	4.2558	4.2561	4.2563	4.2591	4.2618	4.2644
1800	4.2822	4.2824	4.2827	4.2829	4.2852	4.2875	4.2896
1900	4.3058	4.3060	4.3062	4.3064	4.3084	4.3103	4.3122
2000	4.3269	4.3270	4.3272	4.3274	4.3292	4.3309	4.3325
2100	4.3458	4.3459	4.3461	4.3462	4.3478	4.3492	4.3507
2200	4.3627	4.3629	4.3630	4.3632	4.3645	4.3658	4.3671
2300	4.3780	4.3782	4.3783	4.3784	4.3796	4.3807	4.3818
2400	4.3920	4.3921	4.3922	4.3924	4.3934	4.3944	4.3953
2500	4.4047	4.4048	4.4049	4.4050	4.4059	4.4068	4.4076
2600	4.4163	4.4164	4.4165	4.4166	4.4174	4.4182	4.4189
2700	4.4270	4.4271	4.4272	4.4272	4.4280	4.4287	4.4293
2800	4.4369	4.4370	4.4370	4.4371	4.4377	4.4384	4.4389
2900	4.4460	4.4461	4.4461	4.4462	4.4467	4.4473	4.4478
3000	4.4545	4.4546	4.4546	4.4547	4.4551	4.4556	4.4561

TABLE 4h-26. ENTHALPY OF NITROGEN, $(H - E_0°)/RT_0$

T, °K	1 atm	4 atm	7 atm	10 atm	40 atm	70 atm	100 atm
100	1.2589						
200	2.5535	2.5358	2.5179	2.4999	2.3140	2.125	1.94
300	3.8385	3.8302	3.8221	3.8140	3.7351	3.662	3.596
400	5.1244	5.1203	5.1164	5.1125	5.0756	5.0426	5.013
500	6.4194	6.4178	6.4162	6.4147	6.4005	6.3891	6.3802
600	7.7334	7.7333	7.7332	7.7331	7.7332	7.7354	7.7393
700	9.0735	9.0744	9.0752	9.0762	9.0861	9.0977	9.1103
800	10.4428	10.4444	10.4460	10.4477	10.4647	10.4829	10.5020
900	11.8416	11.8438	11.8459	11.8482	11.8705	11.8937	11.9177
1000	13.2683	13.2708	13.2734	13.2760	13.3025	13.3296	13.3573
1100	14.7203	14.7232	14.7261	14.7290	14.7588	14.7891	14.8197
1200	16.1950	16.1982	16.2014	16.2046	16.2369	16.2697	16.3029
1300	17.6894	17.6929	17.6963	17.6997	17.7343	17.7691	17.8043
1400	19.2014	19.2050	19.2086	19.2122	19.2486	19.2851	19.3221
1500	20.7288	20.7325	20.7363	20.7400	20.7779	20.8159	20.8542
1600	22.2695	22.2734	22.2773	22.2812	22.3203	22.3597	22.3992
1700	23.8219	23.8259	23.8299	23.8340	23.8742	23.9146	23.9550
1800	25.3848	25.3889	25.3930	25.3971	25.4382	25.4795	25.5209
1900	26.9568	26.9610	26.9652	26.9693	27.0113	27.0533	27.0954
2000	28.5370	28.5413	28.5455	28.5498	28.5924	28.6352	28.6779
2100	30.1246	30.1290	30.1333	30.1376	30.1808	30.2241	30.2674
2200	31.7187	31.7230	31.7274	31.7318	31.7755	31.8193	31.8632
2300	33.3187	33.3231	33.3275	33.3319	33.3761	33.4203	33.4647
2400	34.9240	34.9284	34.9329	34.9374	34.9819	35.0266	35.0712
2500	36.5342	36.5387	36.5432	36.5477	36.5926	36.6377	36.6827
2600	38.1488	38.1533	38.1579	38.1624	38.2076	38.2530	38.2983
2700	39.7676	39.7722	39.7767	39.7813	39.8268	39.8723	39.9179
2800	41.3901	41.3947	41.3993	41.4039	41.4496	41.4954	41.5413
2900	43.0160	43.0206	43.0252	43.0298	43.0758	43.1218	43.1678
3000	44.6452	44.6499	44.6545	44.6591	44.7053	44.7514	44.7976

TABLE 4h-27. ENTROPY OF NITROGEN, S/R

T, °K	1 atm	4 atm	7 atm	10 atm	40 atm	70 atm	100 atm
100	19.1705	17.607	16.55				
200	21.6249	20.2208	19.6431	19.2682	17.6905	16.932	16.382
300	23.0482	21.6549	21.0884	20.7248	19.2706	18.6461	18.230
400	24.0586	22.6687	22.1055	21.7454	20.3246	19.7322	19.3448
500	24.8479	23.4595	22.8977	22.5390	21.1322	20.5532	20.1781
600	25.5020	24.1144	23.5534	23.1953	21.7958	21.2236	20.8548
700	26.0662	24.6790	24.1184	23.7607	22.3654	21.7970	21.4319
800	26.5656	25.1786	24.6183	24.2609	22.8682	22.3022	21.9396
900	27.0154	25.6286	25.0685	24.7113	23.3203	22.7561	22.3949
1000	27.4260	26.0393	25.4793	25.1223	23.7323	23.1693	22.8094
1100	27.8039	26.4173	25.8574	25.5004	24.1114	23.5491	23.1899
1200	28.1543	26.7678	26.2080	25.8511	24.4627	23.9010	23.5424
1300	28.4811	27.0947	26.5349	26.1780	24.7901	24.2289	23.8707
1400	28.7872	27.4007	26.8410	26.4842	25.0965	24.5357	24.1779
1500	29.0751	27.6887	27.1290	26.7721	25.3848	24.8242	24.4666
1600	29.3467	27.9603	27.4006	27.0438	25.6567	25.0964	24.7390
1700	29.6037	28.2173	27.6577	27.3009	25.9140	25.3537	24.9965
1800	29.8477	28.4613	27.9017	27.5449	26.1582	25.5981	25.2410
1900	30.0799	28.6936	28.1339	27.7772	26.3905	25.8306	25.4736
2000	30.3013	28.9150	28.3553	27.9986	26.6120	26.0522	25.6953
2100	30.5129	29.1266	28.5670	28.2102	26.8238	26.2640	25.9072
2200	30.7154	29.3291	28.7695	28.4128	27.0264	26.4667	26.1100
2300	30.9097	29.5234	28.9638	28.6071	27.2207	26.6611	26.3043
2400	31.0963	29.7100	29.1504	28.7937	27.4074	26.8478	26.4911
2500	31.2759	29.8896	29.3300	28.9733	27.5870	27.0275	26.6708
2600	31.4488	30.0625	29.5029	29.1462	27.7600	27.2004	26.8438
2700	31.6157	30.2294	29.6698	29.3131	27.9269	27.3674	27.0108
2800	31.7769	30.3906	29.8310	29.4743	28.0882	27.5287	27.1721
2900	31.9327	30.5464	29.9868	29.6301	28.2440	27.6846	27.3280
3000	32.0836	30.6973	30.1377	29.7810	28.3949	27.8355	27.4790

TABLE 4h-28. COMPRESSIBILITY FACTOR FOR OXYGEN, $Z = PV/RT$

T, °K	1 atm	4 atm	7 atm	10 atm	40 atm	70 atm	100 atm
100	0.97724						
200	0.99701	0.98796	0.97880	0.96956	0.8734	0.7764	0.6871
300	0.99939	0.99759	0.99580	0.99402	0.97731	0.9636	0.9541
400	1.00001	1.00006	1.00012	1.00019	1.00161	1.0042	1.0079
500	1.00022	1.00088	1.00154	1.00222	1.00942	1.0173	1.0256
600	1.00029	1.00116	1.00204	1.00292	1.01205	1.0216	1.0314
700	1.00031	1.00124	1.00218	1.00312	1.01275	1.0227	1.0328
800	1.00031	1.00124	1.00218	1.00311	1.01265	1.0224	1.0323
900	1.00030	1.00121	1.00211	1.00302	1.01223	1.0216	1.0312
1000	1.00029	1.00115	1.00202	1.00288	1.01167	1.0206	1.0296
1100	1.00027	1.00109	1.00192	1.00274	1.01107	1.0195	1.0281
1200	1.00026	1.00104	1.00182	1.00260	1.01047	1.0184	1.0265
1300	1.00025	1.00098	1.00172	1.00246	1.00991	1.0174	1.0250
1400	1.00023	1.00093	1.00163	1.00233	1.00938	1.0165	1.0237
1500	1.00022	1.00088	1.00155	1.00221	1.00890	1.0156	1.0224
1600	1.00021	1.00084	1.00147	1.00210	1.00845	1.0149	1.0213
1700	1.00020	1.00080	1.00140	1.00200	1.00803	1.0141	1.0202
1800	1.00019	1.00076	1.00133	1.00190	1.00765	1.0134	1.0193
1900	1.00018	1.00072	1.00127	1.00181	1.00728	1.0128	1.0183
2000	1.00017	1.00069	1.00121	1.00173	1.00696	1.0122	1.0175
2100	1.00017	1.00066	1.00116	1.00166	1.00666	1.0117	1.0167
2200	1.00016	1.00063	1.00111	1.00159	1.00638	1.0112	1.0161
2300	1.00015	1.00061	1.00107	1.00152	1.00610	1.0107	1.0153
2400	1.00015	1.00058	1.00102	1.00146	1.00586	1.0103	1.0147
2500	1.00014	1.00056	1.00098	1.00141	1.00564	1.0099	1.0142
2600	1.00014	1.00054	1.00095	1.00135	1.00543	1.0095	1.0136
2700	1.00013	1.00052	1.00091	1.00130	1.00523	1.0092	1.0131
2800	1.00013	1.00050	1.00088	1.00126	1.00505	1.0089	1.0127
2900	1.00012	1.00049	1.00085	1.00122	1.00488	1.0086	1.0122
3000	1.00012	1.00047	1.00082	1.00117	1.00471	1.0083	1.0118

TABLE 4h-29. RELATIVE DENSITY OF OXYGEN, ρ/ρ_0

T, °K	1 atm	4 atm	7 atm	10 atm	40 atm	70 atm	100 atm
100	2.79257						
200	1.36860	5.5245	9.7584	14.073	62.4	123	198.5
300	0.91023	3.6474	6.39455	9.151	37.231	66.082	95.34
400	0.68225	2.72885	4.77519	6.8212	27.246	47.557	67.69
500	0.54568	2.18129	3.81474	5.4459	21.628	37.556	53.217
600	0.45470	1.81723	3.17736	4.5351	17.9767	31.165	44.098
700	0.38974	1.55750	2.72307	3.8864	15.3980	26.684	37.747
800	0.34102	1.36282	2.38269	3.4006	13.4746	23.355	33.045
900	0.30313	1.21143	2.11809	3.0231	11.9823	20.776	29.404
1000	0.27282	1.09035	1.90646	2.7211	10.7901	18.717	26.505
1100	0.24802	0.99129	1.73331	2.4741	9.8150	17.034	24.131
1200	0.22736	0.90872	1.58903	2.26828	9.0024	15.631	22.154
1300	0.20987	0.83887	1.46694	2.09409	8.3145	14.443	20.480
1400	0.19488	0.77899	1.36228	1.94476	7.7247	13.423	19.041
1500	0.18189	0.72710	1.27157	1.81533	7.2131	12.539	17.794
1600	0.17053	0.68168	1.19219	1.70206	6.7653	11.764	16.700
1700	0.16050	0.64161	1.12214	1.60210	6.3700	11.080	15.735
1800	0.15158	0.60599	1.05987	1.51324	6.0184	10.472	14.874
1900	0.14361	0.57412	1.00415	1.43373	5.7037	9.927	14.105
2000	0.13643	0.54543	0.95400	1.36215	5.4202	9.436	13.410
2100	0.12993	0.51947	0.90862	1.29737	5.1637	8.991	12.781
2200	0.12403	0.49587	0.86736	1.23849	4.9303	8.587	12.208
2300	0.11863	0.47432	0.82968	1.18473	4.7173	8.217	11.686
2400	0.11369	0.45457	0.79515	1.13543	4.5218	7.878	11.206
2500	0.10915	0.43640	0.76337	1.09007	4.3419	7.566	10.763
2600	0.10495	0.41962	0.73404	1.04820	4.1758	7.278	10.355
2700	0.10106	0.40409	0.70688	1.00943	4.0219	7.010	9.976
2800	0.09745	0.38966	0.68165	0.97342	3.8790	6.762	9.624
2900	0.09409	0.37623	0.65817	0.93989	3.7458	6.531	9.296
3000	0.09096	0.36370	0.63625	0.90861	3.6216	6.315	8.990

TABLE 4h-30. SPECIFIC HEAT OF OXYGEN, C_p/R

T, °K	1 atm	4 atm	7 atm	10 atm	40 atm	70 atm	100 atm
200	3.519	3.5681	3.6196	3.6739	4.415	5.66	7.6
300	3.5403	3.5584	3.5766	3.5951	3.7862	3.981	4.165
400	3.6243	3.6335	3.6427	3.6520	3.7453	3.836	3.921
500	3.7415	3.7470	3.7526	3.7582	3.8134	3.8677	3.920
600	3.8611	3.8648	3.8685	3.8722	3.9087	3.9445	3.980
700	3.9681	3.9707	3.9733	3.9759	4.0016	4.0266	4.052
800	4.0583	4.0603	4.0622	4.0641	4.0830	4.1017	4.120
900	4.1332	4.1347	4.1361	4.1376	4.1521	4.1664	4.180
1000	4.1952	4.1964	4.1975	4.1987	4.2101	4.2213	4.232
1100	4.2472	4.2481	4.2491	4.2500	4.2591	4.2681	4.277
1200	4.2915	4.2922	4.2930	4.2937	4.3012	4.3085	4.316
1300	4.3302	4.3308	4.3315	4.3321	4.3382	4.3442	4.350
1400	4.3653	4.3658	4.3663	4.3669	4.3721	4.3771	4.382
1500	4.3976	4.3981	4.3985	4.3990	4.4034	4.4076	4.412
1600	4.4283	4.4287	4.4291	4.4295	4.4332	4.4369	4.440
1700	4.4579	4.4582	4.4586	4.4589	4.4621	4.4652	4.468
1800	4.4869	4.4872	4.4875	4.4878	4.4905	4.4933	4.496
1900	4.5154	4.5156	4.5159	4.5161	4.5185	4.5209	4.523
2000	4.5437	4.5439	4.5441	4.5443	4.5464	4.5485	4.551
2100	4.5716	4.5717	4.5719	4.5721	4.5739	4.5758	4.578
2200	4.5993	4.5995	4.5997	4.5999	4.6016	4.6032	4.605
2300	4.6268	4.6269	4.6271	4.6272	4.6287	4.6301	4.631
2400	4.6540	4.6542	4.6543	4.6544	4.6558	4.6570	4.658
2500	4.6808	4.6810	4.6811	4.6812	4.6824	4.6835	4.685
2600	4.7071	4.7072	4.7073	4.7074	4.7085	4.7095	4.710
2700	4.7328	4.7329	4.7330	4.7331	4.7341	4.7349	4.736
2800	4.7579	4.7580	4.7581	4.7582	4.7590	4.7598	4.761
2900	4.7824	4.7825	4.7826	4.7826	4.7834	4.7841	4.785
3000	4.8062	4.8063	4.8064	4.8064	4.8072	4.8077	4.808

TABLE 4h-31. ENTHALPY OF OXYGEN, $(H - E_0°)/RT_0$

T, °K	1 atm	4 atm	7 atm	10 atm	40 atm	70 atm	100 atm
100	1.254						
200	2.5523	2.5308	2.5091	2.4871	2.248	1.972	1.659
300	3.8424	3.8319	3.8213	3.8108	3.705	3.602	3.505
400	5.1523	5.1464	5.1406	5.1349	5.078	5.023	4.971
500	6.5000	6.4968	6.4936	6.4905	6.460	6.431	6.403
600	7.8919	7.8903	7.8888	7.8873	7.873	7.860	7.848
700	9.3254	9.3250	9.3245	9.3242	9.321	9.319	9.318
800	10.7951	10.7956	10.7960	10.7965	10.802	10.807	10.814
900	12.2949	12.2960	12.2970	12.2981	12.309	12.321	12.333
1000	13.8198	13.8213	13.8228	13.8243	13.840	13.857	13.874
1100	15.3653	15.3672	15.3691	15.3710	15.391	15.411	15.431
1200	16.9285	16.9307	16.9329	16.9351	16.958	16.981	17.004
1300	18.5067	18.5092	18.5116	18.5141	18.539	18.565	18.591
1400	20.0985	20.1012	20.1038	20.1065	20.134	20.161	20.189
1500	21.7025	21.7054	21.7082	21.7111	21.740	21.769	21.799
1600	23.3181	23.3211	23.3241	23.3271	23.358	23.388	23.419
1700	24.9447	24.9479	24.9510	24.9541	24.986	25.018	25.050
1800	26.5820	26.5852	26.5885	26.5917	26.625	26.658	26.691
1900	28.2299	28.2333	28.2366	28.2399	28.274	28.308	28.342
2000	29.8880	29.8915	29.8949	29.8983	29.933	29.968	30.003
2100	31.5566	31.5601	31.5636	31.5671	31.602	31.638	31.674
2200	33.2353	33.2389	33.2424	33.2460	33.282	33.318	33.355
2300	34.9239	34.9275	34.9312	34.9348	34.971	35.008	35.045
2400	36.6229	36.6266	36.6303	36.6340	36.671	36.708	36.745
2500	38.3314	38.3352	38.3389	38.3426	38.380	38.418	38.455
2600	40.0500	40.0537	40.0575	40.0613	40.099	40.137	40.175
2700	41.7778	41.7816	41.7854	41.7892	41.827	41.866	41.904
2800	43.5151	43.5189	43.5227	43.5266	43.565	43.604	43.643
2900	45.2614	45.2653	45.2691	45.2730	45.312	45.351	45.390
3000	47.0165	47.0204	47.0243	47.0282	47.067	47.107	47.146

TABLE 4h-32. ENTROPY OF OXYGEN, S/R

T, °K	1 atm	4 atm	7 atm	10 atm	40 atm	70 atm	100 atm
100	20.794						
200	23.2553	21.8488	21.2686	20.8908	19.2709	18.431	17.74
300	24.6839	23.2899	22.7224	22.3579	20.8928	20.2555	19.825
400	25.7127	24.3224	23.7587	23.3980	21.9719	21.3733	20.9789
500	26.5337	25.1450	24.5830	24.2239	22.8139	22.2311	21.8517
600	27.2266	25.8387	25.2775	24.9193	23.5176	22.9429	22.5712
700	27.8299	26.4425	25.8819	25.5241	24.1272	23.5571	23.1900
800	28.3659	26.9788	26.4185	26.0610	24.6670	24.0999	23.7357
900	28.8484	27.4615	26.9013	26.5440	25.1521	24.5869	24.2246
1000	29.2872	27.9005	27.3404	26.9833	25.5926	25.0287	24.6678
1100	29.6896	28.3029	27.7430	27.3859	25.9963	25.4334	25.0733
1200	30.0610	28.6744	28.1146	27.7576	26.3685	25.8064	25.4471
1300	30.4061	29.0196	28.4598	28.1029	26.7144	26.1527	25.7939
1400	30.7283	29.3419	28.7821	28.4252	27.0372	26.4760	26.1176
1500	31.0307	29.6442	29.0845	28.7276	27.3399	26.7790	26.4209
1600	31.3155	29.9290	29.3693	29.0125	27.6250	27.0644	26.7067
1700	31.5848	30.1984	29.6387	29.2819	27.8946	27.3342	26.9766
1800	31.8404	30.4540	29.8943	29.5375	28.1505	27.5902	27.2328
1900	32.0838	30.6974	30.1377	29.7810	28.3941	27.8339	27.4767
2000	32.3161	30.9297	30.3701	30.0133	28.6265	28.0664	27.7094
2100	32.5385	31.1521	30.5925	30.2358	28.8490	28.2890	27.9320
2200	32.7518	31.3655	30.8058	30.4491	29.0625	28.5025	28.1456
2300	32.9568	31.5705	31.0108	30.6541	29.2675	28.7077	28.3508
2400	33.1543	31.7680	31.2083	30.8516	29.4651	28.9053	28.5485
2500	33.3449	31.9586	31.3990	31.0422	29.6558	29.0960	28.7393
2600	33.5289	32.1426	31.5830	31.2263	29.8399	29.2802	28.9235
2700	33.7071	32.3208	31.7612	31.4045	30.0181	29.4585	29.1018
2800	33.8796	32.4933	31.9337	31.5770	30.1907	29.6310	29.2744
2900	34.0470	32.6607	32.1011	31.7444	30.3581	29.7985	29.4419
3000	34.2096	32.8233	32.2637	31.9070	30.5207	29.9612	29.6047

TABLE 4h-33. COMPRESSIBILITY FACTOR FOR STEAM, $Z = PV/RT$

T, °K	1 atm	10 atm	20 atm	40 atm	60 atm	80 atm	100 atm	120 atm
380	0.98591							
400	0.98912							
420	0.99133							
440	0.99294							
460	0.99415	0.93377						
480	0.99509	0.94617						
500	0.99583	0.95528	0.90274					
520	0.99642	0.96223	0.91953					
540	0.99690	0.96768	0.93215	0.84838				
560	0.99730	0.97207	0.94198	0.87379	0.79031			
580	0.99763	0.97565	0.94983	0.89295	0.82692	0.74683		
600	0.99790	0.97862	0.95622	0.90792	0.85386	0.79194	0.7180	0.6214
620	0.99814	0.98111	0.96152	0.91995	0.87462	0.82458	0.7682	0.7025
640	0.99834	0.98323	0.96596	0.92980	0.89115	0.84955	0.8043	0.7542
660	0.99852	0.98503	0.96969	0.93787	0.90432	0.86877	0.8309	0.7902
680	0.99867	0.98659	0.97292	0.94472	0.91530	0.88451	0.85218	0.81809
700	0.99880	0.98795	0.97570	0.95060	0.92463	0.89772	0.86977	0.84068
720	0.99892	0.98913	0.97813	0.95568	0.93263	0.90893	0.88453	0.85939
740	0.99902	0.99018	0.98026	0.96011	0.93955	0.91854	0.89708	0.87513
760	0.99911	0.99110	0.98213	0.96399	0.94558	0.92688	0.90787	0.88855
780	0.99919	0.99192	0.98379	0.96742	0.95086	0.93413	0.91722	0.90011
800	0.99927	0.99265	0.98527	0.97045	0.95553	0.94051	0.92538	0.91015
820	0.99933	0.99330	0.98659	0.97315	0.95966	0.94614	0.93256	0.91893
840	0.99939	0.99389	0.98778	0.97556	0.96335	0.95113	0.93891	0.92667

TABLE 4h-33. COMPRESSIBILITY FACTOR FOR STEAM, $Z = PV/RT$ (*Continued*)

T, °K	140 atm	160 atm	180 atm	200 atm	220 atm	240 atm	260 atm	280 atm	300 atm
620	0.6209								
640	0.6979	0.6315	0.5464						
660	0.7461	0.6975	0.6428	0.5790	0.4987	0.3751			
680	0.78194	0.7433	0.7018	0.6566	0.6065	0.5499	0.484	0.4066	0.3323
700	0.81031	0.77850	0.74508	0.70978	0.6723	0.6324	0.5895	0.5435	0.4944
720	0.83343	0.80660	0.77882	0.74999	0.72005	0.6889	0.6565	0.6227	0.5876
740	0.85266	0.82965	0.80606	0.78186	0.75704	0.7316	0.7054	0.6786	0.6512
760	0.86891	0.84892	0.82859	0.80790	0.78684	0.7654	0.7436	0.7215	0.6990
780	0.88280	0.86528	0.84756	0.82962	0.81147	0.7931	0.7745	0.7557	0.7368
800	0.89480	0.87933	0.86375	0.84804	0.83220	0.8162	0.8001	0.7839	0.7676
820	0.90525	0.89151	0.87771	0.86384	0.84989	0.8359	0.8218	0.8076	0.7933
840	0.91442	0.90214	0.88985	0.87752	0.86515	0.8527	0.8403	0.8278	0.8152

TABLE 4h-34. DENSITY OF STEAM, ρ IN G/CM³

T, °K	1 atm	10 atm	20 atm	40 atm	60 atm	80 atm
380	0.00058604					
400	0.00055493					
420	0.00052732					
440	0.00050254					
460	0.00048010	0.0051115				
480	0.00045966	0.0048343				
500	0.00044095	0.0045967	0.0097284			
520	0.00042374	0.0043880	0.0091835			
540	0.00040785	0.0042016	0.0087236	0.01917		
560	0.00039313	0.0040333	0.0083242	0.017947	0.029765	
580	0.00037944	0.0038799	0.0079708	0.016957	0.027467	0.040549
600	0.00036670	0.0037392	0.0076536	0.016121	0.025713	0.036965
620	0.00035478	0.0036094	0.0073659	0.015397	0.024293	0.034356
640	0.00034363	0.0034891	0.0071029	0.014758	0.023098	0.032305
660	0.00033315	0.0033771	0.0068611	0.014188	0.022071	0.030633
680	0.00032331	0.0032726	0.0066372	0.013671	0.021165	0.029203
700	0.00031403	0.0031748	0.0064292	0.013198	0.020353	0.027951
720	0.00030527	0.0030829	0.0062351	0.012763	0.019618	0.026839
740	0.00029699	0.0029964	0.0060534	0.012361	0.018947	0.025841
760	0.00028915	0.0029148	0.0058829	0.011987	0.018331	0.024934
780	0.00028171	0.0028377	0.0057224	0.011638	0.017762	0.024106
800	0.00027464	0.0027648	0.0055709	0.011312	0.017233	0.023344
820	0.00026793	0.0026956	0.0054278	0.011006	0.016740	0.022639
840	0.00026154	0.0026298	0.0052922	0.010717	0.016279	0.021984

TABLE 4h-34. DENSITY OF STEAM, ρ IN G/CM³ (*Continued*)

T, °K	100 atm	120 atm	140 atm	160 atm	180 atm	200 atm
600	0.05096	0.07066				
620	0.04610	0.06049	0.07985			
640	0.04265	0.05458	0.06882	0.08692	0.113	
660	0.040036	0.05052	0.06242	0.07631	0.09315	0.1149
680	0.037888	0.04736	0.057808	0.06949	0.08281	0.09835
700	0.036061	0.044771	0.054190	0.064463	0.075773	0.088380
720	0.034475	0.04258	0.051224	0.060489	0.070477	0.081318
740	0.033074	0.040684	0.048715	0.057219	0.066255	0.075895
760	0.031820	0.039015	0.046546	0.054448	0.062757	0.071516
780	0.030689	0.037526	0.044639	0.052049	0.059779	0.067858
800	0.029658	0.036184	0.042939	0.049937	0.057192	0.064724
820	0.028711	0.034965	0.041408	0.048053	0.054910	0.061991
840	0.027838	0.033847	0.040017	0.046357	0.052871	0.059572

TABLE 4h-34. DENSITY OF STEAM, ρ IN G/CM³ (*Continued*)

T, °K	220 atm	240 atm	260 atm	280 atm	300 atm
660	0.1468	0.2128			
680	0.1171	0.1409	0.1734	0.2223	0.2915
700	0.1026	0.1190	0.1383	0.1616	0.1903
720	0.093169	0.1062	0.1208	0.1371	0.1557
740	0.086221	0.09733	0.1094	0.1224	0.1367
760	0.080773	0.09058	0.1010	0.1121	0.1240
780	0.076313	0.08518	0.09449	0.1043	0.1146
800	0.072552	0.08070	0.08918	0.09803	0.1073
820	0.069309	0.07688	0.08471	0.09283	0.1013
840	0.066465	0.07357	0.08037	0.08841	0.09619

TABLE 4h-35. SPECIFIC HEAT OF STEAM, C_p/R

T, °K	1 atm	10 atm	20 atm	40 atm	60 atm	80 atm	100 atm
380	4.462						
400	4.355						
420	4.312						
440	4.291						
460	4.282	5.614					
480	4.285	5.231					
500	4.294	4.994	6.211				
520	4.308	4.842	5.703				
540	4.326	4.744	5.378	7.432			
560	4.346	4.681	5.164	6.602	9.131		
580	4.367	4.641	5.019	6.074	7.725	10.574	
600	4.391	4.618	4.921	5.723	6.886	8.619	11.513
620	4.416	4.606	4.854	5.481	6.338	7.527	9.215
640	4.442	4.603	4.808	5.311	5.966	6.826	7.970
660	4.467	4.606	4.779	5.190	5.704	6.351	7.172
680	4.495	4.615	4.762	5.104	5.518	6.020	6.634
700	4.522	4.627	4.754	5.043	5.383	5.785	6.259
720	4.550	4.642	4.752	4.999	5.284	5.610	5.987
740	4.578	4.659	4.756	4.970	5.211	5.482	5.789
760	4.607	4.680	4.765	4.951	5.158	5.387	5.641
780	4.636	4.701	4.776	4.939	5.118	5.314	5.528
800	4.665	4.724	4.792	4.937	5.094	5.264	5.448
820	4.694	4.748	4.809	4.939	5.078	5.227	5.387
840	4.724	4.772	4.828	4.944	5.069	5.201	5.342

TABLE 4h-36. ENTHALPY OF STEAM, $(H - E_0^\circ)/RT_0$

T, °K	1 atm	10 atm	20 atm	40 atm	60 atm	80 atm	100 atm
380	5.482						
400	5.804						
420	6.121						
440	6.436						
460	6.750	6.306					
480	7.063	6.702					
500	7.377	7.075	6.665				
520	7.692	7.435	7.180				
540	8.008	7.786	7.505	6.811			
560	8.326	8.131	7.890	7.322	6.592		
580	8.645	8.472	8.263	7.785	7.204	6.471	
600	8.965	8.811	8.627	8.216	7.736	7.165	6.462
620	9.288	9.148	8.984	8.625	8.219	7.753	7.210
640	9.612	9.485	9.338	9.020	8.669	8.277	7.836
660	9.938	9.822	9.689	9.404	9.095	8.758	8.388
680	10.266	10.160	10.038	9.781	9.506	9.211	8.892
700	10.596	10.498	10.386	10.152	9.905	9.642	9.364
720	10.928	10.838	10.734	10.520	10.295	10.059	9.811
740	11.262	11.178	11.082	10.885	10.679	10.465	10.242
760	11.599	11.520	11.431	11.248	11.059	10.863	10.660
780	11.937	11.863	11.780	11.610	11.435	11.254	11.069
800	12.278	12.208	12.130	11.971	11.808	11.641	11.470
820	12.620	12.555	12.482	12.333	12.181	12.025	11.867
840	12.965	12.903	12.834	12.695	12.552	12.407	12.260

TABLE 4h-37. ENTROPY OF STEAM, S/R

T, °K	1 atm	10 atm	20 atm	40 atm	60 atm	80 atm	100 atm
380	23.628						
400	23.854						
420	24.065						
440	24.265						
460	24.456	21.945					
480	24.638	22.175					
500	24.813	22.383	21.513				
520	24.982	22.576	21.746				
540	25.145	22.757	21.954	20.981			
560	25.302	22.928	22.146	21.235	20.539		
580	25.455	23.092	22.324	21.457	20.833	20.260	
600	25.604	23.249	22.493	21.657	21.080	20.582	20.092
620	25.748	23.400	22.653	21.840	21.296	20.845	20.427
640	25.889	23.546	22.806	22.011	21.491	21.072	20.699
660	26.026	23.688	22.954	22.173	21.670	21.274	20.931
680	26.159	23.825	23.096	22.326	21.838	21.459	21.137
700	26.290	23.959	23.234	22.473	21.996	21.630	21.323
720	26.418	24.090	23.368	22.615	22.146	21.790	21.495
740	26.543	24.217	23.498	22.751	22.290	21.942	21.657
760	26.665	24.342	23.625	22.883	22.428	22.087	21.809
780	26.786	24.643	23.749	23.012	22.561	22.226	21.954
800	26.903	24.583	23.870	23.137	22.690	22.360	22.093
820	27.019	24.700	23.989	23.259	22.816	22.489	22.227
840	27.132	24.814	24.105	23.378	22.938	22.615	22.356

4i. Pressure-Volume-Temperature Relationships of Gases Virial Coefficients

ABRAHAM S. FRIEDMAN

U.S. Atomic Energy Commission

Many empirical and semiempirical relations have been used to describe the pressure-volume-temperature relationships of gases and liquids. Among those most frequently used are the equations of van der Waals, Dieterici, Berthelot, Clausius, and Beattie and Bridgeman. It is most convenient, however, and more satisfactory from the theoretical standpoint, to use the Kamerlingh Onnes equation of state or any of the other simple variations of the virial equation:

$$PV = RT\left(1 + \frac{B_v}{V} + \frac{C_v}{V^2} + \frac{D_v}{V^3} + \frac{E_v}{V^4} + \cdots\right)$$
$$PV = RT(1 + B_pP + C_pP^2 + D_pP^3 + E_pP^4 + \cdots)$$

The virial coefficients are temperature-dependent and are expressed in units of powers of volume or reciprocal pressure, depending on the forms of equations used. The coefficients of these equations may be interrelated as follows:

$$B_v = B_pRT$$
$$C_v = (C_p + B_p^2)(RT)^2$$
$$D_v = (D_p + 3C_pB_p + B_p^3)(RT)^3$$
$$E_v = (E_p + 4D_pB_p + 6C_pB_p^2 + 2C_p^2 + B_p^4)(RT)^4$$

. . . .

$$B_p = \frac{B_v}{RT}$$
$$C_p = \frac{C_v - B_v^2}{(RT)^2}$$
$$D_p = \frac{D_v - 3B_vC_v + 2B_v^3}{(RT)^3}$$
$$E_p = \frac{E_v - 2C_v^2 - 4B_vD_v + 10B_v^2C_v - 5B_v^4}{(RT)^4}$$

. . . .

The workers at the van der Waals Laboratory generally express their PVT data in terms of the density in amagat units ρ_A, which is a relative scale, the reference volume usually being taken as the value at 0°C and 1 atm pressure. The equation of state takes the form

$$PV = A + B\rho_A + C\rho_A^2 + D\rho_A^3 + E\rho_A^4 + \cdots$$

It is also possible to express the equations of van der Waals, Dieterici, etc., as virial expansions, in which case the virial coefficients are those given in tabular form below.

	B_v	C_v	D_v
van der Waals: $(P + a/V^2)(V - b) = RT$	$b - \frac{a}{RT}$	b^2	b^3
Dieterici: $(Pe^{a/RTV})(V - b) = RT$	$b - \frac{a}{RT}$	$b^2 - \frac{ab}{RT} + \frac{a^2}{2(RT)^2}$	$b^3 - \frac{ab^2}{RT} + \frac{a^2b}{2(RT)^2} - \frac{a^3}{6(RT)^3}$
Berthelot: $(P + a/V^2T)(V - b) = RT$	$b - \frac{a}{RT^2}$	b^2	b^3
Clausius: $[P + a/(V + c)^2T](V - b) = RT$	$b - \frac{2ac}{RT^2}$	$b^2 - \frac{3ac^2}{RT^2}$	$b^3 - \frac{4ac^3}{RT^2}$

Data of state have been selected and assembled for several gases. These have been fitted to virial equations by the various investigators, and the coefficients of these equations are tabulated. The form of the virial equations and the units used are, in most cases, those of the original investigators. No attempt has been made to include all the available *PVT* data of these gases. Several excellent bibliographies of *PVT* properties of fluids exist,[1] and abstracts of research papers in this field are published in *Chemical Abstracts*.

In the tables given below, the virial coefficients B, C, etc., are those of the expansion in terms of amagat densities, the coefficients B_v, C_v, etc., are the coefficients of the polynomial in $1/V$, and the coefficients B_p, C_p, etc., are the coefficients of the polynomial in P.

TABLE 4i-1. VIRIAL COEFFICIENTS FOR HELIUM (He)*

T, °C	$B \times 10^3$	$C \times 10^6$	$D \times 10^9$
0	0.5292	0.1500	0.218
25	0.5710	0.1564	0.239
50	0.6105	0.1699	0.268
75	0.6494	0.2402	−0.070
100	0.6909	0.2456	−0.126
125	0.7299	0.2716	−0.283
150	0.7645	0.3376	−0.554

Pressure range: 10 to 300 atm.
Density in amagats (1 amagat = 4.4589×10^{-5} moles He/cc).
* Michels and Wouters, *Physica* **8**, 923 (1941); Wouters, Dissertation, University of Amsterdam, 1941.

[1] See, for example, D. M. Newitt, "High Pressure Plant and Fluids at High Pressures," Oxford University Press, New York, 1940; S. Gratch, *Trans. ASME* **70**, 631 (1948); L. C. Nelson and E. F. Obert, *Trans. ASME* **76**, 1057 (1954).

TABLE 4i-2. VIRIAL COEFFICIENTS FOR HELIUM (He^3 AND He^4)*

T, °K	He^4 B_v, cc/mole	He^3 B_v, cc/mole	T, °K	He^4 B_v, cc/mole	He^3 B_v, cc/mole
0.3	−2,715.4	−375.1	3.6	−88.71	−64.72
0.4	−1,712.8	−348.6	3.8	−83.12	−60.80
0.5	−1,203.2	−320.0	4.0	−78.11	−57.25
0.6	− 906.6	−293.5	4.2	−73.58	−54.01
0.7	− 717.6	−269.9	4.4	−69.47	−51.04
0.8	− 589.0	−249.1	4.6	−65.72	−48.32
0.9	− 497.2	−230.7	4.8	−62.29	−45.81
1.0	− 428.9	−214.4	5.0	−59.14	−43.49
1.2	− 335.2	−187.08	6.0	−46.53	−34.11
1.4	− 274.6	−165.13	7.0	−37.53	−27.29
1.6	− 232.34	−147.21	8.0	−30.78	−22.11
1.8	− 201.25	−132.36	10.0	−21.34	−14.75
2.0	− 177.39	−119.89	12.0	−15.04	− 9.78
2.2	− 158.47	−109.29	15.0	− 8.77	− 4.77
2.4	− 143.06	−100.18	19.64	....	0.00
2.6	− 130.26	− 92.28	20.0	− 2.53	0.28
2.8	− 119.42	− 85.38	23.18	0.00	
3.0	− 110.13	− 79.29	25.0	1.15	3.29
3.2	− 102.06	− 73.88	30.0	3.57	5.28
3.4	− 94.98	− 69.05	40.0	6.49	7.70
			50.0	8.16	9.07
			60.0	9.20	9.93

Second virial coefficients calculated from the force constants of a Lennard-Jones six-twelve potential function.

* Kilpatrick, Keller, Hammel, and Metropolis, *Phys. Rev.* **94**, 1103 (1954).

TABLE 4i-3. VIRIAL COEFFICIENTS FOR NEON (Ne)*

T, °C	$B_p \times 10^3$ (m Hg)$^{-1}$	$C_p \times 10^6$ (m Hg)$^{-2}$	$E_p \times 10^9$ (m Hg)$^{-4}$
−207.9	−5.1522	7.4076	3.7425
−182.5	−1.4468	11.722	
−150	+0.0129	5.239	
−100	0.5976	1.353	
− 50	0.6553	0.748	
0	0.6261	0.490	
+100	0.5098	0.538	
200	0.4425	0.189	
300	0.3853		
400	0.3273		

Pressure range: 0 to 75 m Hg.

* Holborn and Otto, *Z. Physik* **33**, 1 (1925); **38**, 359 (1926).

TABLE 4i-4. VIRIAL COEFFICIENTS FOR ARGON (A)*

T, °K	B_p, atm^{-1}	$C_p \times 10^3$, atm^{-2}	$D_p \times 10^9$, atm^{-3}	$E_p \times 10^{11}$, atm^{-4}	$F_p \times 10^{13}$, atm^{-5}
80	−0.03919	−1.82			
90	−0.02836	−0.885			
100	−0.02127	−0.4677			
110	−0.01640	−0.2634			
120	−0.01292	−0.1555			
130	−0.01036	−0.09513			
140	−0.008432	−0.05973			
150	−0.006938	−0.03816			
200	−0.002941	−0.00391	28.47	−5.16	1.58
250	−0.001370	0.00069	23.66	−7.76	2.03
300	−0.000631	0.00120	11.61	−6.60	1.40
350	−0.000244	0.00104	2.75	−0.87	0.02
400	−0.000026	0.00081	0.42	−0.10	
450	0.000101	0.00061			
500	0.000178	0.00046			
550	0.000224	0.00035			
600	0.000252	0.00027			
650	0.000268	0.00021			
700	0.000276	0.00016			
750	0.000279	0.00013			
800	0.000278	0.00010			
1000	0.000261	0.00004			
1500	0.000203				
2000	0.000159				
2500	0.000130				
3000	0.000108				
3500	0.000093				
4000	0.000081				
4500	0.000071				
5000	0.000063				

* J. Hilsenrath et al., *Natl. Bur. Standards (U.S.) Cir.* 564, 1955.

TABLE 4i-5. VIRIAL COEFFICIENTS FOR KRYPTON (Kr)*

T, °C	B_v, liters/mole	C_v, (liters/mole)^2	$E_v \times 10^5$ (liters/mole)^4
0	−0.06296	0.002758	−0.1184
25	−0.05236	0.002611	−0.1627
50	−0.04278	0.002259	−0.01800
75	−0.03521	0.002077	0.03923
100	−0.02886	0.001944	0.07865
125	−0.02347	0.001843	0.1074
150	−0.01882	0.001758	0.1351
175	−0.01473	0.001670	0.1705
200	−0.01111	0.001581	0.2197
225	−0.008404	0.001640	0.1372
250	−0.005694	0.001625	0.1004
275	−0.003168	0.001562	0.1404
300	−0.001154	0.001611	0.05625

Density range: 1 to 10 moles/liter.
* Beattie, Brierley, and Barriault, *J. Chem. Phys.* **20,** 1615 (1952).

TABLE 4i-6. SECOND VIRIAL COEFFICIENTS FOR XENON (Xe)*

T, °K	B_v, liters/mole
289.80	−0.1378
298.15	−0.1302
323.15	−0.1106
348.15	−0.0945
373.16	−0.0812
398.17	−0.0701
423.18	−0.0607
448.20	−0.0526
473.21	−0.0454
498.23	−0.0391
523.25	−0.0332
548.26	−0.0280
573.28	−0.0235

* Beattie, Barriault, and Brierley, *J. Chem. Phys.* **19,** 1222 (1951).

TABLE 4i-7. VIRIAL COEFFICIENTS FOR XENON (Xe)*

	0°C	25°C	30°C	40°C	50°C	75°C	100°C	125°C	150°C
$A = RT$	1.006986	1.099150	1.117583	1.154449	1.191314	1.283479	1.375643	1.467807	1.559971
$B \times 10^3$	−6.97642	−6.459542	−6.352	−6.150	−5.950758	−5.499720	−5.046321	−4.656402	−4.297573
$C \times 10^5$	1.27147	1.453417	1.371080	1.312370	1.259808	1.210478	0.986975	0.961896	0.974894
$D \times 10^8$	0	−5.203863	−3.197344	−1.682540	−0.756664	−0.193922	3.180954	3.038628	2.627841
$E \times 10^{10}$	0.52738	7.9112101	5.6735824	3.5985523	2.3616596	1.2120539	−1.8827796	−1.7862985	−1.5295443
$F \times 10^{12}$	0	−5.02072017	−3.85933320	−2.66879840	−1.95159793	−1.15745852	0.39740876	0.43469633	0.4141180
$G \times 10^{15}$	0	14.4812871	11.4672576	8.2400434	6.3137947	4.0736364	0.0609279	−0.0846543	−0.1328780
$H \times 10^{18}$	0	−18.8255152	−14.9707903	−10.7594517	−8.2980748	−5.4181185	−0.2735897	−0.1520461	−0.0902496
$I \times 10^{21}$	0	9.3353921	7.3909181	5.2451016	4.0251896	2.6149050	0	0	0
Density range	d = 0–66 Am.	d = 0–515 Am.	d = 0–515 Am.	d = 0–515 Am.	d = 0–515 Am.	d = 0–515 Am.	d = 0–515 Am.	d = 0–486 Am.	d = 0–486 Am.

Density in amagats (1 amagat = 4.4927×10^{-5} mole Xe per cc).

* A. Michels et al., *Physica* **20,** 99 (1954).

TABLE 4i-8. VIRIAL COEFFICIENTS FOR HYDROGEN (H_2)*

T, °K	B_v, cc	C_v, cc²	D_v, cc³	$E_v \times 10^{-3}$ cc⁴	$F_v \times 10^{-4}$, cc⁵
20.59	−140.980				
22.58	−122.630				
24.65	−108.020				
26.75	− 95.995				
28.83	− 90.275	2,200.0			
30.86	− 80.734	2,078.0	−30,000		
33.00	− 73.439	2,050.0	−21,700		
35.10	− 64.300	1,700.0	−16,200	−270	2,810
37.61	− 56.950	1,510.0	−13,200	−260	2,650
40.09	− 51.520	1,400.0	−10,400	−250	2,510
45.10	− 41.380	1,181.0	− 6,000	−240	2,282
50.09	− 33.720	1,038.0	− 3,700	−220	2,130
55.09	− 28.070	925.0	− 345	−210	1,930
60.03	− 22.900	841.0	1,500	−196	1,724
63.96	− 19.650	763.0	4,100	−175	1,490
69.00	− 16.200	685.0	8,500	−140	834
75.01	− 12.460	612.0	10,600	− 90	540
80.02	− 9.760	553.0	11,300	− 55	380
90.04	− 5.170	462.2	12,980	− 5	100
100.02	− 1.900	412.0	13,000	30	40
104.0	0.000				
125.03	3.830	318.3	14,000	120	10
150.04	7.630	269.0	13,000	150	
175.02	10.330	257.0	11,000	120	
200.11	11.930	254.0	8,850	60	
249.99	14.000	252.0	7,500	20	
273.16	14.193				
299.99	15.010	250.0	6,000	5	

Pressure range: 0 to 200 atm.
* H. L. Johnston *et al.*, Ohio State University Cryogenic Laboratory.

TABLE 4i-9. VIRIAL COEFFICIENTS FOR HYDROGEN (H_2)*

T, °C	A	$B \times 10^3$	$C \times 10^6$	$D \times 10^9$
0	0.99939	0.6015	1.834	−16.838
25	1.09086	0.6606	2.521	−20.206
50	1.18233	0.7308	2.606	−16.249
75	1.27379	0.8030	3.588	−40.836
100	1.36526	0.8841	2.619	−17.798
125	1.45673	0.9314	4.348	−43.290
150	1.54820	1.0010	4.337	−36.189

Pressure range: 0 to 50 atm.
Density in amagat units.
* Michels and Goudeket, *Physica* **8**, 347 (1941).

TABLE 4i-10. VIRIAL COEFFICIENTS FOR DEUTERIUM (D_2)*

T, °C	A	$B \times 10^3$	$C \times 10^6$	$D \times 10^9$
0	0.99945	0.57884	4.47087	−61.9635
25	1.09092	0.64317	2.0572	−24.291
50	1.18239	0.68055	5.0292	−60.984
75	1.27387	0.74937	5.9227	−76.729
100	1.36536	0.83057	5.1521	−59.138
125	1.45682	0.90211	5.2563	−60.585
150	1.54829	0.97838	5.3152	−62.845

Pressure range: 0 to 50 atm.
Density in amagat units.
* Michels and Goudeket, *Physica* **8**, 353 (1941).

TABLE 4i-11. VIRIAL COEFFICIENTS FOR NITROGEN (N_2)*

T, °K	B_v, cm³	$C_v \times 10^{-2}$, cm⁶	$D_v \times 10^{-4}$, cm⁹	$E_v \times 10^{-5}$, cm¹²	$F_v \times 10^{-7}$, cm¹⁵
326	0				
300	− 3.54	7.437	16.65	− 22.19	−87.538
273.16	− 9.50	8.20	15.60	− 75.00	−16.00
250	− 16.19	10.00	14.00	−100.00	21.50
200	− 34.33	12.00	13.96	−117.75	36.40
175	− 49.44	15.70	13.20	−120.76	45.50
150	− 71.16	21.86	12.52	−122.75	41.00
125.2	−106.92	42.00	− 4.50		
120	−114.62	48.00	− 26.60		
110	−131.80	65.00	− 200.0		
100	−162.10	85.00	− 600		
90	−200.50	135.00	−1000		
80	−250.80	210.00	−2000		

Pressure range: 0 to 200 atm.
* H. L. Johnston et al., Ohio State University Cryogenic Laboratory.

TABLE 4i-12. VIRIAL COEFFICIENTS FOR NITROGEN (N_2)*

T, °K	B_P, atm^{-1}	C_P, atm^{-2}	D_P, atm^{-3}
150	−0.(2)5586	−0.(4)2490	−0.(7)10394
200	−0.(2)2125	−0.(7)801	0.(7)5727
250	−0.(3)790	0.(5)235	0.(7)1484
300	−0.(3)183	0.(5)208	0.(8)298
350	0.(3)120	0.(5)156	−0.(9)21
400	0.(3)279	0.(5)114	−0.(9)97
450	0.(3)364	0.(6)838	−0.(8)103
500	0.(3)408	0.(6)623	−0.(9)89
550	0.(3)429	0.(6)471	−0.(9)73
600	0.(3)435	0.(6)360	−0.(9)58
650	0.(3)434	0.(6)279	−0.(9)46
700	0.(3)428	0.(6)219	−0.(9)36
750	0.(3)419	0.(6)174	−0.(9)29
800	0.(3)408	0.(6)139	−0.(9)23
1000	0.(3)360	0.(7)61	−0.(9)10
1500	0.(3)263	0.(7)10	
2000	0.(3)202		
2500	0.(3)162		
3000	0.(3)135		

Pressure range 0 to 100 atm.
Numbers in parentheses indicate zeros immediately to right of decimal point.
* J. Hilsenrath et al., *Natl. Bur. Standards (U.S.) Circ.* 564, 1955.

TABLE 4i-13. VIRIAL COEFFICIENTS FOR OXYGEN (O_2)*

T, °K	B_P, atm^{-1}	C_P, atm^{-2}	D_P, atm^{-3}
50			
100	−0.(1)218811	−0.(3)49949	−0.(3)3826
150	−0.(2)71105	−0.(4)4404	−0.(6)9312
200	−0.(2)29842	−0.(5)660	+0.(7)5150
250	−0.(2)13644	−0.(6)59	+0.(7)2683
300	−0.(3)6051	0.(6)60	0.(8)8649
350	−0.(3)2091	0.(6)78	0.(8)1828
400	+0.(4)119	0.(6)72	−0.(9)5143
450	0.(3)1403	0.(6)62	−0.(8)1209
500	0.(3)2167	0.(6)52	−0.(8)1306
750	0.(3)3112	0.(6)22	−0.(9)6111
1000	0.(3)2875	0.(6)11	−0.(9)2577
1500	0.(3)2208	0.(7)4	−0.(10)647
2000	0.(3)1731	0.(7)2	−0.(10)228
2500	0.(3)1406	0.(7)1	−0.(11)99
3000	0.(3)1174	0.(7)1	−0.(11)49

Pressure range: 0 to 100 atm.
Numbers in parentheses indicate zeros immediately to right of decimal point.
* J. Hilsenrath et al., *Natl. Bur. Standards (U.S.) Circ.* 564, 1955.

TABLE 4i-14. VIRIAL COEFFICIENTS FOR CARBON MONOXIDE (CO)*

	Series coefficients for carbon monoxide						
	0°C	25°C	50°C	75°C	100°C	125°C	150°C
A	1.00062	1.09220	1.18379	1.27537	1.36695	1.45853	1.55011
$B \times 10^3$	−0.609570	−0.387728	−0.173710	0.060129	0.279123	0.499249	0.703395
$C \times 10^6$	2.74732	3.13199	3.60123	3.26131	3.26204	2.99544	3.31613
$D \times 10^9$	6.10453	2.81560	−1.08194	4.59805	5.87388	10.7319	8.29195
$E \times 10^{11}$	−2.23472	0.029516	2.47553	−0.281361	−0.421188	−2.60066	−0.770897
$F \times 10^{14}$	7.66630	1.36450	−5.13513	2.52046	2.46871	7.94417	2.50096
$G \times 10^{17}$	−7.38468	1.15574	9.52599	−0.953864	−0.587082	−7.37101	0.322446
$H \times 10^{20}$	3.20596	−1.37431	−5.60470	−0.069931	−0.358606	2.91011	−1.32504

Pressure range: 40 to 3,000 atm.
Density in amagat units (1 amagat = 4.4643×10^{-5} moles CO per cc).
* A. Michels et al., *Physica* **18,** 121 (1952).

T, °C	A	$B \times 10^3$	$C \times 10^6$
0	1.00062	−0.633991	3.55228
25	1.09220	−0.403802	3.64460
50	1.18379	−0.179705	3.75360
75	1.27537	0.051373	3.67000
100	1.36695	0.274208	3.64751
125	1.45853	0.489526	3.67394
150	1.55011	0.695124	3.88893

Pressure range: 20 to 50 atm.
Density in amagat units.

TABLE 4i-15. VIRIAL COEFFICIENTS FOR CARBON MONOXIDE (CO)*

T, °K	B_P, atm^{-1}	C_P, atm^{-2}
200	−0.(2)2701	0.(5)4485
250	−0.(2)1087	0.(5)4200
300	−0.(3)345	0.(5)2803
350	+0.(4)31	0.(5)1847
400	0.(3)232	0.(5)1269
450	0.(3)343	0.(6)903
500	0.(3)404	0.(6)652
750	0.(3)443	0.(6)146
1000	0.(3)387	0.(7)36
1500	0.(3)287	
2000	0.(3)221	
2500	0.(3)178	
3000	0.(3)148	

Pressure range: 0 to 100 atm.
Numbers in parentheses indicate zeros immediately to right of decimal point.
* J. Hilsenrath et al., *Natl. Bur. Standards (U.S.) Circ.* 564, 1955.

TABLE 4i-16. VIRIAL COEFFICIENTS FOR AIR*

	0°C	25°C	50°C	75°C
$A = RT$	1.000596	1.092176	1.183755	1.275334
$B \times 10^3$	−0.579305	−0.374396	−0.172469	0.029083
$C \times 10^6$	2.505321	2.815469	3.013159	3.192234
$D \times 10^9$	3.838577	1.956272	1.578322	0.729456
$E \times 10^{11}$	−1.133777	−0.040178	0.311958	0.962308
$F \times 10^{14}$	3.932747	1.618943	0.951103	0
$G \times 10^{17}$	−2.761489	−0.479369	0	0
$H \times 10^{21}$	8.738907	0	0	0
Density range	0–642 Am.	0–505 Am.	0–406 Am.	0–182 Am.

	0°C	25°C	50°C	75°C
A	1.000596	1.092176	1.183755	1.275334
$B \times 10^3$	−0.600117	−0.391219	−0.181245	0.026432
$C \times 10^6$	3.14759	3.33556	3.33203	3.28972
Density range	0–51 Am.			

* Michels et al., *Appl. Sci. Research* (**A**)**4,** 52 (1953).

TABLE 4i-17. VIRIAL COEFFICIENTS FOR AIR*

T, °K	B_v, cm³/mole	C_v cm⁶/mole²	$D_v \times 10^4$, cm⁹/mole³
50	−527.60		
100	−153.15	−3253.5	9.40
150	− 72.681	944.9	7.00
200	− 38.241	1323.5	5.46
250	− 19.327	1332.7	4.36
300	− 7.480	1288.5	3.46
350	+ 0.575	1239.1	2.75
400	6.367	1194.2	2.16
450	10.701	1154.4	1.72
500	14.048	1119.2	1.40
750	23.241	990.4	0.4
1000	27.129	904.30	
1500	30.138	789.45	

Pressure range: 0 to 100 atm.
* J. Hilsenrath et al., *Natl. Bur. Standards* (*U.S.*) *Circ.* 564, 1955.

A statistical mechanical treatment permits the expression of the virial coefficients of spherically symmetrical molecules in terms of the intermolecular potential energy and the distance between the molecules. The second virial coefficient is then given by

$$B_v = 2\pi N \int_0^\infty (1 - e^{-\epsilon(r)/kT}) r^2 \, dr$$

Various models have been proposed for the intermolecular potential energy function $\epsilon(r)$. One of the most frequently used models for nonpolar gases is that due to Lennard-Jones:

$$\epsilon(r) = \epsilon_0 \left[\frac{m}{n-m} \left(\frac{r_0}{r}\right)^n - \frac{n}{n-m} \left(\frac{r_0}{r}\right)^m \right]$$

where the repulsive exponent n is generally taken as 12 and the attractive exponent m is taken as 6. The Lennard-Jones six-twelve potential function is then

$$\epsilon(r) = \epsilon_0 \left[\left(\frac{r_0}{r}\right)^{12} - 2 \left(\frac{r_0}{r}\right)^6 \right]$$

or

$$\epsilon(r) = 4\epsilon_0 \left[\left(\frac{d}{r}\right)^{12} - \left(\frac{d}{r}\right)^6 \right]$$

where ϵ_0 is the energy at the minimum of the potential-energy well and r_0 is the intermolecular separation at this energy. The intermolecular separation at $\epsilon(r) = 0$ is given by d, where $d = r_0(m/n)^{\frac{1}{n-m}} = r_0(\frac{1}{2})^{\frac{1}{6}}$. The constant ϵ_0 is often expressed in units of temperature by dividing by the Boltzmann constant k.

Table 4i-18. Constants in the Lennard-Jones Potential Function

Gas	$\epsilon_0 \times 10^{16}$, ergs	ϵ_0/k, °K	r_0, A	d, A	Ref.
He	10.22	7.40	2.65	2.36	1
He*	14.03	10.16	2.87	2.56	2
Ne	48.2	34.9	3.12	2.78	3
A	165.0	119.5	3.84	3.42	4
Kr	238.4	172.7	4.03	3.59	5
Xe	309.9	224.5	4.56	4.06	6
H_2	42.36	30.69	3.35	2.98	7
D_2	45.93	33.27	3.39	3.02	1
H_2, D_2*	50.75	36.76	3.28	2.92	2
N_2	132.4	95.93	4.15	3.69	7
O_2	163	118	3.88	3.46	8
CO	140.3	101.6	4.26	3.79	9

* Calculated with quantum corrections.

References

1. White, D., and H. L. Johnston: *Phys. Rev.* **79**, 236 (1950).
2. deBoer, J., and A. Michels: *Physica* **5**, 945 (1938).
3. Holborn, L., and J. Otto: *Z. Physik* **33**, 1 (1925).
4. Hilsenrath, J., et al.: *Natl. Bur. Standards (U.S.) Circ.* 564, 1955.
5. Beattie, Brierley, and Barriault: *J. Chem. Phys.* **20**, 1615 (1952).
6. Beattie, Barriault, and Brierley: *J. Chem. Phys.* **19**, 1222 (1951).
7. White, D., A. S. Friedman, and H. L. Johnston: *Phys. Rev.* **79**, 235 (1950).
8. Holborn, L., and J. Otto: *Z. Physik* **10**, 367 (1922).
9. Michels, A., et al.: *Physica* **18**, 121 (1952).

4j. Temperature, Pressure, Heat, and Entropy Change of Transition, Fusion, and Vaporization

D. D. WAGMAN

The National Bureau of Standards

The following table, 4j-1, is based upon a more extensive compilation, *Natl. Bur. Standards* (*U.S.*) *Circ.* 500, in which all references may be found. In this table c = crystal, liq = liquid, g = gas, ΔH = heat, ΔS = entropy change, and ΔC_p = change of heat capacity.

TABLE 4j-1. PHASE TRANSITION DATA FOR ELEMENTS AND COMPOUNDS

Substance	Type of process	Phase Initial	Phase Final	Pressure, mm Hg	Temp., °K	ΔH, kcal/mole	ΔS, cal/mole deg	ΔC_p, cal/mole deg
A	Fusion	c	liq	516.5	83.85	0.281	3.35	2.16
	Vaporization	liq	g	516.5	83.85			
	Vaporization	liq	g	760	87.29	1.558	17.85	−5.08
Ag	Fusion	c	liq	....	1234.0	2.70	2.19	0.7
	Vaporization	liq	g	760	2466	60.72	24.62	
AgBr	Transition	c, II	c, I	....	532			
	Fusion	c, I	liq	....	703	2.18	3.10	−3.6
	Vaporization	liq	g	760	1806	37.0	20.5	
AgCl	Fusion	c	liq	....	728	3.05	4.19	−2.31
	Vaporization	liq	g	760	1830	43.7	23.9	
AgCN	Fusion	c	liq	....	623	2.8	4.5	
AgI	Transition	c, II	c, I	....	420	1.47	3.50	
	Fusion	c, I	liq	....	831	2.25	2.71	
	Vaporization	liq	g	760	1777	34.4	19.4	
$AgNO_3$	Transition	c, II	c, I	....	433	0.66	1.52	−0.06
	Fusion	c, I	liq	....	483	2.76	5.71	4.5
Ag_2S	Transition	c, II	c, I	....	452	1.05	2.32	1.2
	Fusion	c, I	liq	....	1115	3.36	3.01	
Ag_2SO_4	Transition	c, II	c, I	....	685	1.9	2.8	
	Fusion	c, I	liq	....	933	4	4	
Al	Fusion	c	liq	....	933.3	2.6	2.8	
	Vaporization	liq	g	760	2600	67.9	26	
Al_2Br_6	Fusion	c	liq	....	370.7	5.4	14.6	
	Vaporization	liq	g	760	530	11	21	
Al_2Cl_6	Sublimation	c	g	760	453.3	26.7	58.9	
	Sublimation	c	g	1,625	465	26.5	57.0	
	Fusion	c	liq	1,625	465	16.9	36.3	
Al_2O_3	Fusion	c	liq	....	2307	26	11	
As	Sublimation	c, metallic	g, As_4	760	883	7.75	8.78	
	Fusion	c, metallic	liq	27,200	1090			
	Vaporization	liq	g	27,200	1090			

TABLE 4*j*-1. PHASE TRANSITION DATA FOR ELEMENTS AND COMPOUNDS (*Continued*)

Substance	Type of process	Phase		Pressure, mm Hg	Temp., °K	ΔH, kcal/mole	ΔS, cal/mole deg	ΔC_p, cal/mole deg
		Initial	Final					
$AsBr_3$	Fusion	c	liq	.....	304.4	2.81	9.23	
	Vaporization	liq	g	760	494	10	20	
$AsCl_3$	Fusion	c	liq	.....	257	2.42	9.42	
	Vaporization	liq	g	760	403	7.5	18.6	
AsF_3	Fusion	c	liq	.....	267.21	2.486	9.304	
	Vaporization	liq	g	142.6	292.50	8.566	29.285	
AsF_5	Fusion	c	liq	149	192.9	2.71	14.0	
	Vaporization	liq	g	149	192.9			
	Vaporization	liq	g	760	220.6	4.96	22.5	
AsH_3	Fusion	c	liq	24.6	156.9	0.56	3.6	
	Vaporization	liq	g	24.6	156.9			
	Vaporization	liq	g	760	210.7	4.18	19.8	
As_4O_6	Sublimation	c, octahedral	g	28	547	26.1	47.7	
	Fusion	c, octahedral	liq	28	547	11.9	21.8	
	Sublimation	c, monoclinic	g	67	586	23.0	39.2	
	Fusion	c, monoclinic	liq	67	586	8.8	15.0	
	Vaporization	liq	g	760	733	14.2	19.4	
Au	Fusion	c	liq	.....	1336.16	3.03	2.27	−0.53
	Vaporization	liq	g	760	2933	74.21	25.30	−2.0
B	Fusion	c	liq	.....	2313			
B_2O_3	Fusion	c	liq	.....	723	5.27	7.29	
	Vaporization	liq	g	2	1523	77	50	
BCl_3	Fusion	c	liq	.....	166			
	Vaporization	liq	g	760	285.6	5.7	20.0	
BF_3	Sublimation	c	g	54	144.5	5.7	39	
	Fusion	c	liq	54	144.5	1.0	7	
	Vaporization	liq	g	54	144.5	4.7	33	
	Vaporization	liq	g	760	174	4.3	25	

TABLE 4j-1. PHASE TRANSITION DATA FOR ELEMENTS AND COMPOUNDS (*Continued*)

Substance	Type of process	Phase Initial	Phase Final	Pressure, mm Hg	Temp., °K	ΔH, kcal/mole	ΔS, cal/mole deg	ΔC_p, cal/mole deg
B_2H_6	Fusion	c	liq	....	108.30	1.069	9.87	
	Vaporization	liq	g	760	180.32	3.412	18.89	
Ba	Transition	c, II	c, I	....	648			
	Sublimation	c, I	g	0.0063	990	41.1	41.5	
	Fusion	c, I	liq	....	990			
	Vaporization	liq	g	760	1911	35.7	18.7	
$BaCl_2$	Transition	c, II	c, I	....	1193			
	Fusion	c, I	liq	....	1233	5.4	4.4	
	Vaporization	liq	g	6.3	1462	57	39	
$BaCO_3$	Transition	c, III	c, II	....	1083	4.5	4.1	7.93
	Transition	c, II	c, I	....	1241	0.7	0.6	
BaF_2	Fusion	c	liq	....	1593	3.0	1.9	
	Vaporization	liq	g	42	2072	83	40	
BaO	Sublimation	c	g	0.00076	1650	89	54	
	Fusion	c	liq	....	2190			
$BaSO_4$	Transition	c, II	c, I	....	1422			
	Fusion	c, I	liq	....	1623	9.7	6.0	
$BaTiO_3$	Transition	c, II	c, I	....	385.8			
Be	Sublimation	c	g	0.034	1556	75.2	48.3	
	Fusion	c	liq	0.034	1556	2.3	1.5	
$BeCl_2$	Sublimation	c	g, $BeCl_2$	2	678	29.2	43.1	
	Vaporization	liq	g, $BeCl_2$	2	678	26.2	38.6	
	Vaporization	liq	g, $BeCl_2$	760	820	25	30	
	Sublimation	c	g, Be_2Cl_4	127	678	15.4	22.7	
BeO	Sublimation	c	g	0.00076	2327	147.4	63.3	
	Sublimation	c	g	0.196	2823	145.4	51.5	
	Fusion	c	liq	0.196	2823			
Bi	Fusion	c	liq	....	544.2	2.63	4.83	
	Vaporization	liq	g	760	1693			

TABLE 4j-1. PHASE TRANSITION DATA FOR ELEMENTS AND COMPOUNDS (*Continued*)

Substance	Type of process	Phase Initial	Phase Final	Pressure, mm Hg	Temp., °K	ΔH, kcal/mole	ΔS, cal/mole deg	ΔC_p, cal/mole deg
$BiCl_3$	Fusion	c	liq	....	505	2.6	5.1	
	Vaporization	liq	g	760	714	17.35	24.30	
Bi_2O_3	Fusion	c	liq	......	1090	6.8	6.2	
Br_2	Fusion	c	liq	......	265.9	2.52	9.48	2.0
	Vaporization	liq	g	214	298.16	7.34	24.6	
C	Sublimation	c, graphite	g, std. state	760	298.16	171.698	36.4002	
	Sublimation	c, graphite	equilibrium gas	760	4620			
CBr_4	Transition	c, II	c, I	....	320.1	1.5	4.7	
	Fusion	c, I	liq	....	363.3	0.98	2.70	
	Vaporization	liq	g	760	460	10.4	22.6	
CCl_4	Transition	c, II	c, I	....	225.5	1.09	4.8	
	Fusion	c, I	liq	....	250.3	0.60	2.4	1.1
	Vaporization	liq	g	760	349.9	7.17	20.5	
CF_4	Transition	c, II	c, I	....	76.23	0.35	4.6	
	Fusion	c, I	liq	....	89.47	0.167	1.87	
	Vaporization	liq	g	760	145.14	3.01	20.7	
$CFCl_3$	Fusion	c	liq	....	162.68	1.648	10.13	
	Vaporization	liq	g	760	296.8	5.96	20.1	−10.4
CF_2Cl_2	Fusion	c	liq	....	118	0.99	8.4	
	Vaporization	liq	g	760	242.7	4.85	20.0	
$CHBr_3$	Fusion	c	liq	......	281.21	2.65	9.42	
	Vaporization	liq	g	22	323	10.4	32.2	
	Vaporization	liq	g	760	422.7			
$CHCl_3$	Fusion	c	liq	......	209.7	2.2	10.5	
	Vaporization	liq	g	760	334.4	7.02	20.99	
CH_2Cl_2	Fusion	c	liq	......	176	1.1	6	
	Vaporization	liq	g	760	313	6.69	21.4	
CH_2I_2	Fusion	c, II	liq	......	278.76	3.02	10.8	
	Fusion	c, I	liq	......	279.26	2.88	10.3	
	Vaporization	liq	g	330	425			

TABLE 4j-1. PHASE TRANSITION DATA FOR ELEMENTS AND COMPOUNDS (*Continued*)

Substance	Type of process	Phase Initial	Phase Final	Pressure, mm Hg	Temp., °K	ΔH, kcal/mole	ΔS, cal/mole deg	ΔC_p, cal/mole deg
CH_2O (formaldehyde)	Fusion	c	liq	......	154.9			
	Vaporization	liq	g	760	253.9	5.85	23.0	
CH_2O_2 (formic acid)	Fusion	c	liq	18	281.46	3.03	10.8	8.8
	Vaporization	liq	g	18	281.46			
	Vaporization	liq	g	760	373.7	5.32	14.24	
CH_3Br	Transition	c, II	c, I	......	173.79	0.113	0.650	
	Fusion	c, I	liq	......	179.48	1.429	7.96	
	Vaporization	liq	g	760	276.72	5.715	20.65	
CH_3Cl	Fusion	c	liq	65.66	175.44	1.537	8.76	1.5
	Vaporization	liq	g	65.66	175.44			
	Vaporization	liq	g	760	248.94	5.15	20.7	
CH_3F	Fusion	c	liq	......	131.4			
	Vaporization	liq	g	760	195.1	4.23	21.7	
CH_3I	Fusion	c	liq	.....	206.7			
	Vaporization	liq	g	760	315.6	6.7	21.2	
CH_3O_2N (nitromethane)	Fusion	c	liq	.....	244.78	2.319	9.47	
	Vaporization	liq	g	36.7	298.16	9.147	30.68	
	Vaporization	liq	g	760	374.0			
CH_4	Fusion	c	liq	87.7	90.68	0.225	2.48	
	Vaporization	liq	g	87.7	90.68			
	Vaporization	liq	g	760	111.67	1.955	17.51	
CH_4O	Transition	c, II	c, I	.....	157.4	0.154	0.98	
	Fusion	c, I	liq	.....	175.26	0.757	4.32	4.2
	Vaporization	liq	g	124.0	298.16	8.94	29.98	
	Vaporization	liq, std.	g, std.	760	298.16	8.94	26.48	
	Vaporization	liq	g	760	337.9	8.43	24.95	
CH_4ON_2 (urea)	Fusion	c	liq	.....	405.8	3.60	8.9	
CH_4S	Transition	c, II	c, I	.....	137.6	0.052	0.38	
	Fusion	c, I	liq	.....	150.16	1.411	9.40	4.8
	Vaporization	liq	g	760	279.12	5.872	21.04	

TABLE 4*j*-1. PHASE TRANSITION DATA FOR ELEMENTS AND COMPOUNDS (*Continued*)

Substance	Type of process	Phase: Initial	Phase: Final	Pressure, mm Hg	Temp., °K	ΔH, kcal/mole	ΔS, cal/mole deg	ΔC_p, cal/mole deg
CH_5N (methylamine)	Fusion	c	liq	.....	179.70	1.466	8.16	
	Vaporization	liq	g	760	266.84	6.17	23.1	
C_2H_5Cl	Fusion	c	liq	.....	134.83	1.064	7.89	1.52
	Vaporization	liq	g	760	285.43	5.9	21	
C_2H_2	Sublimation	c	g	760	189.2	5.1	27	
	Fusion	c	liq	900	191.7	0.9	5	
	Vaporization	liq	g	900	191.7	4.2	22	
C_2H_4	Fusion	c	liq	0.9	103.97	0.8008	7.702	
	Vaporization	liq	g	0.9	103.97			
	Vaporization	liq	g	760	169.45	3.237	19.10	
C_2H_4O (acetaldehyde)	Fusion	c	liq	.....	155	0.77	5.0	
	Vaporization	liq	g	760	293.3	6.5	22.2	− 9.3
C_2H_4O (ethylene oxide)	Fusion	c	liq		160.71	1.236	7.69	3.45
	Vaporization	liq	g	760	283.72	6.101	21.50	− 9.7
$C_2H_4O_2$ (acetic acid)	Fusion	c, I	liq	760	289.77	2.80	9.66	9.4
	Transition	c, I	c, II	155,000	328.9	0.11	0.3	
	Fusion	c, I	liq	155,000	328.9	2.78	8.5	
	Fusion	c, II	liq	155,000	328.9	2.89	8.8	
	Vaporization	liq	g, equilibrium	760	391.4	5.83	14.9	
C_2H_6	Fusion	c	liq	0.006	89.89	0.6834	7.603	2.2
	Vaporization	liq	g	0.006	89.89			
	Vaporization	liq	g	760	184.53	3.517	19.06	−11.5
C_2H_6O (dimethyl ether)	Fusion	c	liq	....	131.66	1.180	8.96	6.8
	Vaporization	liq	g	760	248.34	5.141	20.70	−10.6
C_2H_6O (ethanol)	Fusion	c	liq	....	158.6	1.200	7.57	5.70
	Vaporization	liq	g	58.6	298.16	10.12	33.94	
	Vaporization	liq, std.	g, std.	760	298.16	10.12	28.99	
	Vaporization	liq	g	760	351.7	9.22	26.22	
C_2H_7N (ethylamine)	Fusion	c	liq	....	192.2			
	Vaporization	liq	g	760	289.7	6.7	23	−14.4

TABLE 4j-1. PHASE TRANSITION DATA FOR ELEMENTS AND COMPOUNDS (*Continued*)

Substance	Type of process	Phase Initial	Phase Final	Pressure, mm Hg	Temp., °K	ΔH, kcal/mole	ΔS, cal/mole deg	ΔC_p, cal/mole deg
C_2H_7N (dimethylamine)	Fusion	c	liq	....	180.97	1.420	7.85	9.81
	Vaporization	liq	g	760	280.0	6.33	22.6	−17.1
C_2N_2	Fusion	c	liq	553.6	245.32	1.938	7.900	5.29
	Vaporization	liq	g	553.6	245.32			
	Vaporization	liq	g	760	252.01	5.576	22.126	
CO	Transition	c, II	c, I	....	61.53	0.151	2.45	− 3.2
	Fusion	c, I	liq	115.3	68.10	0.200	2.94	1.9
	Vaporization	liq	g	115.3	68.10			
	Vaporization	liq	g	760	81.66	1.444	17.68	
CO_2	Sublimation	c	g	760	194.68	6.031	30.98	
	Fusion	c	liq	....	217.0	1.99	9.2	
$COCl_2$	Fusion	c	liq	....	140.37	1.371	9.43	
	Vaporization	liq	g	760	280.72	5.832	20.78	
CS_2	Fusion	c	liq	....	161.1	1.05	6.52	
	Vaporization	liq	g	760	319.41	6.40	20.0	
Ca	Transition	c, II	c, I	....	723	0.2	0.3	−0.5
	Sublimation	c, I	g	0.35	1123	44.0	39.2	
	Fusion	c, I	liq	....	1123	2.2	2.0	
CaC_2	Transition	c, II	c, I	....	720	1.33	1.85	−1.20
$CaCl_2$	Sublimation	c	g	0.018	934.6	54	58	
	Fusion	c	liq	....	1055	6.78	6.43	
$CaCrO_4$	Fusion	c	liq	....	2433			
CaF_2	Transition	c, II	c, I	....	1424	1.14	0.80	
	Fusion	c, I	liq	....	1691	7.1	4.2	
	Vaporization	liq	g	11	2145	83	39	
CaO	Fusion	c	liq	....	2873	12	4.2	
$CaSO_4$	Transition	c, II	c, I	....	1466			
	Fusion	c, I	liq	....	1573	6.7	4.3	
$CaSiO_3$	Transition	c, II	c, I	....	1463			
	Fusion	c, I	liq	....	1803			

TABLE 4j-1. PHASE TRANSITION DATA FOR ELEMENTS AND COMPOUNDS (*Continued*)

Substance	Type of process	Phase Initial	Phase Final	Pressure, mm Hg	Temp., °K	ΔH, kcal/mole	ΔS, cal/mole deg	ΔC_p, cal/mole deg
Ca_2SiO_4	Transition	c, III	c, II	....	948	0.35	0.37	0.58
	Transition	c, II	c, I	....	1673	0.77	0.46	
	Fusion	c, I	liq	....	2393			
$CaTiO_3$	Transition	c, II	c, I	....	1530	0.55	0.36	−0.23
Cd	Sublimation	c	g	0.11	594.1	26.28	44.23	
	Fusion	c	liq	0.11	594.1	1.46	2.46	
	Vaporization	liq	g	760	1040	23.86	22.94	
$CdBr_2$	Sublimation	c	g	0.0032	638	38.2	59.9	
	Fusion	c	liq	....	841	5.0	6.0	
	Vaporization	liq	g	760	863			
$CdCl_2$	Sublimation	c	g	0.966	841	41.2	49.0	
	Fusion	c	liq	0.966	841	5.3	6.3	
	Vaporization	liq	g	760	1253	29.4	23.5	
CdF_2	Fusion	c	liq	....	1322	5.4	4.1	
	Vaporization	liq	g	760	2020	56.0	27.7	
CdI_2	Sublimation	c	g	0.48	660	32	48	
	Fusion	c	liq	0.48	660	8	12	
CdO	Sublimation	c	g	760	1832	53.8	29.4	
CdS	Sublimation	c	g	0.0126	958	51.4	53.7	
Ce	Transition	c, IV	c, III	....	140			
	Transition	c, III	c, II	....	666			
	Transition	c, II	c, I	....	713			
	Fusion	c, I	liq	....	1048	2.1	2.0	
Cl_2	Fusion	c	liq	....	172.16	1.531	8.89	2.75
	Vaporization	liq	g	....	172.16			
	Vaporization	liq	g	760	239.10	4.878	20.40	− 8.76
ClF	Vaporization	liq	g	760	172.9	5.34	30.88	
ClF_3	Vaporization	liq	g	760	284.6	5.74	20.2	

TABLE 4j-1. PHASE TRANSITION DATA FOR ELEMENTS AND COMPOUNDS (*Continued*)

Substance	Type of process	Phase Initial	Phase Final	Pressure, mm Hg	Temp., °K	ΔH, kcal/mole	ΔS, cal/mole deg	ΔC_p, cal/mole deg
Co	Transition	c, III	c, II	....	723	0.005	0.007	
	Transition	c, II	c, I	....	1398	0.07	0.05	
	Fusion	c, I	liq	....	1765	3.7	2.1	
	Vaporization	liq	g	760	3373			
$CoCl_2$	Fusion	c	liq	....	997	7.4	7.4	
	Vaporization	liq	g	760	1323	27.2	20.6	
CoO	Fusion	c	liq	....	2078			
CoS	Fusion	c	liq	....	1373			
Cr	Fusion	c	liq	....	2173	3.5	1.6	
$CrCl_2$	Sublimation	c	g	0.61	1088	60.1	55.2	
	Fusion	c	liq	0.61	1088	7.7	7.1	
Cr_2O_3	Transition	c, II	c, I	....	306.0			
	Fusion	c, I	liq	....	2538			
Cs	Sublimation	c	g	1.2×10^{-6}	301.9	18.82	62.34	
	Fusion	c	liq	1.2×10^{-6}	301.9	0.50	1.6	
	Vaporization	liq	g	760	963	16.32	16.95	
CsBr	Fusion	c	liq	....	909	1.7	1.9	
	Vaporization	liq	g	....	1573	35.99	22.88	
CsCl	Transition	c, II	c, I	....	718	1.8	2.5	
	Fusion	c, I	liq	....	918	3.60	3.92	
	Vaporization	liq	g	760	1573	35.69	22.69	
CsF	Fusion	c	liq	....	955	2.45	2.56	
	Vaporization	liq	g	....	1524	34.3	22.5	
$CsNO_3$	Transition	c, II	c, I	....	429			
	Fusion	c, I	liq	....	690	3.25	4.71	
CsOH	Transition	c, II	c, I	....	496	1.76	3.55	
	Fusion	c, I	liq	....	545.5	1.61	2.93	
Cs_2SO_4	Transition	c, II	c, I	....	933			
	Fusion	c, I	liq	....	1292			
Cu	Fusion	c	liq	....	1356.2	3.11	2.29	0.5
	Vaporization	liq	g	760	2855	72.8	25.4	

TABLE 4j-1. PHASE TRANSITION DATA FOR ELEMENTS AND COMPOUNDS (*Continued*)

Substance	Type of process	Phase		Pressure, mm Hg	Temp., °K	ΔH, kcal/mole	ΔS, cal/mole deg	ΔC_p, cal/mole deg
		Initial	Final					
CuBr	Fusion	c	liq	....	761			
CuCl	Fusion	c	liq	....	703	2.4	3.4	
Cu_2O	Fusion	c	liq	....	1502	13.4	8.9	
Cu_2S	Transition	c, II	c, I	....	376	1.34	3.6	0.2
	Fusion	c, I	liq	....	1400	5.5	3.9	
$ErCl_3$	Fusion	c, γ	liq	....	1047			
F_2	Fusion	c	liq	1.66	53.54	0.122	2.28	
	Vaporization	liq	g	760	85.02	1.562	18.4	−6.90
Fe	Transition	c, α	c, β	....	1033	0.0	0.0	0.0
	Transition	c, β	c, γ	....	1180	0.217	0.184	1.40
	Sublimation	c, γ	g	5.4×10^{-5}	1473	94.4	64.1	
	Transition	c, γ	c, δ	....	1673	0.15	0.09	1
	Fusion	c, δ	liq	....	1808	3.6	2.0	−2.8
	Vaporization	liq	g	760	3073			
$FeBr_2$	Fusion	c	liq	....	957			
$FeCl_2$	Fusion	c	liq	......	950	10.28	10.82	3.63
	Vaporization	liq	g	760	1299	30.21	23.26	
$FeCl_3$	Sublimation	c	$\frac{1}{2}Fe_2Cl_6$(g)	582	577	16.5	28.6	
	Fusion	c	$\frac{1}{2}Fe_2Cl_6$(liq)	582	577	10.3	17.8	−4
	Vaporization	liq	$\frac{1}{2}Fe_2Cl_6$(g)	582	577	6.24	10.81	
	Vaporization	liq	$\frac{1}{2}Fe_2Cl_6$(g)	760	592	6.02	10.17	
$Fe(CO)_5$	Fusion	c	liq	....	252	3.25	12.90	
	Vaporization	liq	g	760	378	8.9	23.5	
FeI_2	Fusion	c	liq	....	860			
$Fe_{0.95}O$	Fusion	c	liq	....	1641	7.5	4.6	
Fe_2O_3	Transition	c, II	c, I	....	1303			
Fe_3O_4	Fusion	c	liq	....	1867	33	18	
FeS	Transition	c, II	c, I	....	411	1.05	2.55	−4.89
	Fusion	c	liq	....	1468	7.73	5.26	
Ga	Transition	c, I	c, II	8.86×10^6	275.6	0.51	1.85	
	Fusion	c, I	liq	8.86×10^6	275.6	1.23	4.46	

TABLE 4j-1. PHASE TRANSITION DATA FOR ELEMENTS AND COMPOUNDS (*Continued*)

Substance	Type of process	Phase Initial	Phase Final	Pressure, mm Hg	Temp., °K	ΔH, kcal/mole	ΔS, cal/mole deg	ΔC_p, cal/mole deg
Ga	Fusion	c, II	liq	8.86×10^6	275.6	0.72	2.61	
	Fusion	c, I	liq	....	309.940	1.336	4.31	0.38
	Vaporization	liq	g	0.0006	1210	63.8	52.7	
Ga_2O_3	Fusion	c	liq	....	2013			
GaS	Fusion	c	liq	....	1218			
Ge	Fusion	c	liq	....	1233	8.3	6.7	
	Vaporization	liq	g	760	2960	81.6	28	
$GeBr_4$	Fusion	c	liq	....	299.3			
	Vaporization	liq	g	760	460.3	9.9	21.5	
$GeCl_4$	Fusion	c	liq	....	223.7			
	Vaporization	liq	g	760	356.3	7.9	22.2	
GeH_4	Transition	c, III	c, II	....	73.2	0.050	0.68	
	Transition	c, II	c, I	....	76.5	0.086	1.12	
	Fusion	c, I	liq	....	107.26	0.200	1.86	2.0
	Vaporization	liq	g	760	184.80	3.361	18.19	
GeO_2	Transition	c, II, insoluble	c, I, soluble	....	1306			
	Fusion	c, II, insoluble	liq	....	1359			
	Fusion	c, I, soluble	liq	....	1389			
HBr	Fusion	c	liq	....	186.28	0.575	3.09	1.64
	Vaporization	liq	g	....	186.28			
	Vaporization	liq	g	760	206.43	4.210	20.39	− 7.37
HCl	Transition	c, II	c, I	....	98.38	0.284	2.89	1.15
	Fusion	c, I	liq	....	158.94	0.476	2.99	2.10
	Vaporization	liq	g	760	188.11	3.86	20.5	− 7.14
HCN	Transition	c, II	c, I	....	170.41	0.004	0.02	
	Fusion	c, I	liq	140.4	259.92	2.009	7.73	1.7
	Vaporization	liq	g	140.4	259.92			
	Vaporization	liq	g	760	298.86	6.027	20.17	
HF	Fusion	c	liq	....	190.09	1.094	5.756	2.55
	Vaporization	liq	g	760	293.1	1.8	6.1	−10.9

TABLE 4j-1. PHASE TRANSITION DATA FOR ELEMENTS AND COMPOUNDS (*Continued*)

Substance	Type of process	Phase Initial	Phase Final	Pressure, mm Hg	Temp., °K	ΔH, kcal/mole	ΔS, cal/mole deg	ΔC_p, cal/mole deg
HI	Fusion	c	liq	......	222.36	0.686	3.08	1.10
	Vaporization	liq	g	......	222.36			
	Vaporization	liq	g	760	237.80	4.724	19.86	− 7.14
HNO_3	Fusion	c	liq	......	231.56	2.503	10.81	10.55
	Vaporization	liq	g	48	293	9.43	32.2	
H_2	Fusion	c	liq	52.8	13.84	0.028	2.0	1.9
	Vaporization	liq	g	52.8	13.84			
	Vaporization	liq	g	760	20.26	0.215	10.6	
H_2O	Fusion	c	liq	760	273.16	1.4363	5.2581	8.911
	Vaporization	liq	g	4.58	273.17	10.767	39.415	−10.184
	Vaporization	liq	g	23.75	298.16	10.514	35.263	− 9.971
	Vaporization	liq	g	760	373.16	9.7171	26.0400	−10.021
	Vaporization	liq, std.	g, std.	760	298.16	10.520	28.390	
H_2S	Transition	c, III	c, II	......	103.54	0.366	3.53	1.20
	Transition	c, II	c, I	......	126.24	0.108	0.86	− 0.65
	Fusion	c, I	liq	173.9	187.63	0.568	3.03	1.59
	Vaporization	liq	g	173.9	187.63			
	Vaporization	liq	g	760	212.82	4.463	20.97	− 8.34
H_2SO_4	Fusion	c	liq	......	283.53	2.36	8.32	6.218
$H_2SO_4 \cdot H_2O$	Fusion	c	liq	......	281.65	4.63	16.44	25.04
H_2Se	Transition	c, III	c, II	......	82.3	0.309	3.75	1.5
	Transition	c, II	c, I	......	172.54	0.267	1.55	− 1.9
	Fusion	c, I	liq	205.4	207.43	0.601	2.90	1.95
	Vaporization	liq	g	205.4	207.43	5.34	25.72	
	Vaporization	liq	g	760	231.9	4.62	19.93	
H_2Te	Fusion	c	liq	......	222	1.0	4.5	
	Vaporization	liq	g	760	270.9	5.55	20.49	
H_3PO_3	Fusion	c	liq	......	343.3	3.07	8.94	
H_3PO_4	Fusion	c	liq	......	315.51	2.52	7.99	

TABLE 4j-1. PHASE TRANSITION DATA FOR ELEMENTS AND COMPOUNDS (*Continued*)

Substance	Type of process	Phase		Pressure, mm Hg	Temp., °K	ΔH, kcal/mole	ΔS, cal/mole deg	ΔC_p, cal/mole deg
		Initial	Final					
$^1H^2H$	Fusion	c	liq	93	16.60	0.038	2.3	2.0
	Vaporization	liq	g	93	16.60	0.265	16.0	
	Vaporization	liq	g	760	22.13			
$^1H^2HO$	Vaporization	liq	g	22.0	298.16	10.652	35.726	
$^1H_2$	Fusion	c	liq	52.8	13.84	0.028	2.0	1.9
	Vaporization	liq	g	52.8	13.84			
	Vaporization	liq	g	760	20.26	0.215	10.6	
$^2H_2$	Fusion	c	liq	128	18.63	0.0471	2.53	2.2
	Vaporization	liq	g	128	18.63			
	Vaporization	liq	g	760	23.59	0.2937	12.45	
^2H_2O	Fusion	c	liq	....	276.98	1.501	5.419	9.48
	Vaporization	liq	g	20.78	298.16	10.193	34.186	
	Vaporization	liq, std.	g, std.	760	298.16	10.850	29.22	
He	Fusion	c	liq, I	78,300	3.5	0.005	1.5	
	Transition	liq, II	liq, I	38.3	2.186	0.00	0.00	−19
	Vaporization	liq, I	g	760	4.216	0.020	4.7	
Hf	Transition	c, II	c, I	....	1773			
	Fusion	c, I	liq	....	2500			
HfO_2	Fusion	c	liq	....	3050			
Hg	Sublimation	c	g	2.5×10^{-6}	234.29	15.20	64.9	
	Fusion	c	liq	2.5×10^{-6}	234.29	0.549	2.34	
	Vaporization	liq	g	0.00209	298.16	14.65	49.13	
	Vaporization	liq	g, equilibrium	760	629.88	14.13	22.43	
$HgBr_2$	Sublimation	c	g	116	514	18.82	36.6	
	Fusion	c	liq	116	514	3.96	7.7	
	Vaporization	liq	g	760	592	14.08	23.8	
$HgCl_2$	Sublimation	c	g	418	550	18.50	33.6	
	Fusion	c	liq	418	550	4.15	7.5	
	Vaporization	liq	g	760	577	14.08	24.4	

TABLE 4j-1. PHASE TRANSITION DATA FOR ELEMENTS AND COMPOUNDS (*Continued*)

Substance	Type of process	Phase		Pressure, mm Hg	Temp., K	ΔH, kcal/mole	ΔS, cal/mole deg	ΔC_p, cal/mole deg
		Initial	Final					
HgI_2	Transition	c, II, red	c, I, yellow	0.195	402	0.601	1.50	
	Sublimation	c, I, yellow	g	8.8	530	19.86	37.5	
	Fusion	c, I, yellow	liq	8.8	530	4.53	8.6	
	Vaporization	liq	g	760	627	14.26	22.7	
HgS	Transition	c, II, red	c, I, black	80	659	1.0	1.5	
ICl	Fusion	c	liq	33.2	300.5	1.83	6.09	
	Vaporization	liq	g	33.2	300.5	9.93	33.06	
I_2	Fusion	c	liq	....	386.8	3.74	9.67	
	Sublimation	c	g	0.31	298.16	14.88	49.91	
In	Fusion	c	liq	....	429.6	0.78	1.81	
	Vaporization	liq	g	0.007	1200	55.7	46.4	
Ir	Fusion	c	liq	....	2716			
	Vaporization	liq	g	760	4623			
K	Fusion	c	liq	....	336.4	0.554	1.65	−0.23
	Vaporization	liq	g, equilibrium	760	1030			
$KAl(SO_4)_2 \cdot 12H_2O$	Transition	c, II	c, I	....	57.9	0.047	0.8	
	Fusion	c, I	liq	....	364	6.7	18.4	
KBr	Sublimation	c	g	0.3	1008	48.9	48.5	
	Fusion	c	liq	0.3	1008	7	7	
	Vaporization	liq	g	760	1656	37.1	22.4	
KCl	Sublimation	c	g	0.40	1045	49.5	47.4	
	Fusion	c	liq	0.40	1045	6.1	5.8	0.61
	Vaporization	liq	g	760	1680	38.8	23.1	
KCN	Transition	c, II	c, I	....	168.3	0.30	1.8	
	Fusion	c, I	liq	....	833	3.5	4.0	
KF	Fusion	c	liq	....	1129	6.8	6.0	1.5
	Vaporization	liq	g	760	1775	41.3	23.3	
$KHSO_4$	Transition	c, III	c, II	....	437.4	0.49	1.12	
	Transition	c, II	c, I	....	453.7	0.095	0.21	
	Fusion	c, I	liq	....	491.8			

TABLE 4j-1. PHASE TRANSITION DATA FOR ELEMENTS AND COMPOUNDS (*Continued*)

Substance	Type of process	Phase Initial	Phase Final	Pressure, mm Hg	Temp., °K	ΔH, kcal/mole	ΔS, cal/mole deg	ΔC_p, cal/mole deg
KI	Sublimation	c	g	0.36	958	47.2	49.3	
	Fusion	c	liq	0.36	958			
	Vaporization	liq	g	760	1597	34.7	21.7	
KNO_3	Transition	c, IV	c, III	2.84×10^6	294.5	− 0.512	− 1.74	
	Transition	c, IV	c, II	2.84×10^6	294.5	− 0.381	− 1.29	
	Transition	c, III	c, II	2.84×10^6	294.5	0.131	0.445	
	Transition	c, III	c, II	61,500	401.18	− 0.502	− 1.25	
	Transition	c, III	c, I	61,500	401.18	0.558	1.39	
	Transition	c, II	c, I	61,500	401.18	1.060	2.64	
	Transition	c, II	c, I	760	400.9	1.3	3.2	2.9
	Fusion	c, I	liq	....	610	2.8	4.6	0.7
KOH	Transition	c, II	c, I	....	522	1.52	2.91	
	Fusion	c, I	liq	....	673	1.8	2.6	
	Vaporization	liq	g	760	1600	30.8	19.3	
K_2CO_3	Transition	c, IV	c, III	....	523			
	Transition	c, III	c, II	....	701			
	Transition	c, II	c, I	....	895			
	Fusion	c, I	liq	....	1169	7.8	6.8	
K_2SO_4	Transition	c, II	c, I	....	856	1.94	2.27	−4.79
	Fusion	c, I	liq		1342	8.76	6.53	−6.49
Kr	Fusion	c	liq	549	115.95	0.391	3.37	2.01
	Vaporization	liq	g	549	115.95			
	Vaporization	liq	g	760	119.93	2.158	17.99	−5.67
La	Transition	c, IV	c, III	....	110			
	Transition	c, III	c, II	....	821			
	Transition	c, II	c, I	....	982			
	Fusion	c, I	liq	....	1193			
Li	Transition	c, II	c, I	....	77			
	Fusion	c, I	liq	....	453.7	0.723	1.594	0.39
	Vaporization	liq	g, equilibrium	....	1599			
LiBr	Fusion	c	liq	....	823	2.9	3.5	
	Vaporization	liq	g	760	1583	35.4	22.4	
LiCl	Sublimation	c	g	0.014	883	46.2	52.3	
	Fusion	c	liq	0.014	883	3.2	3.6	
	Vaporization	liq	g	760	1655	36.0	21.8	

TABLE 4j-1. PHASE TRANSITION DATA FOR ELEMENTS AND COMPOUNDS (*Continued*)

Substance	Type of process	Phase Initial	Phase Final	Pressure, mm Hg	Temp., °K	ΔH, kcal/mole	ΔS, cal/mole deg	ΔC_p, cal/mole deg
LiF	Fusion	c	liq	...	1118	2.4	2.1	
	Vaporization	liq	g	760	1954	51.0	26.1	
LiI	Fusion	c	liq	...	722			
	Vaporization	liq	g	760	1444	40.8	28.2	
LiOH	Fusion	c	liq	...	735			
Li_2CO_3	Fusion	c	liq	...	1008			
$LiNO_3$	Fusion	c	liq	...	527	6.1	11.6	0.45
Li_2SO_4	Transition	c, II	c, I	...	848	6.8	8.0	
	Fusion	c, I	liq	...	1132	3.0	2.6	
$LuCl_3$	Fusion	c, γ	liq	...	1165			
Mg	Fusion	c	liq	3	923	2.2	2.4	
	Vaporization	liq	g	760	1393	31.5	22.6	
$MgCl_2$	Fusion	c	liq	...	987	10.3	10.4	
	Vaporization	liq	g	760	1691	32.7	19.3	
$MgCl_2 \cdot 6H_2O$	Fusion	c	liq	...	390	8.2	21.0	
MgO	Fusion	c	liq	...	3173	18.5	5.8	
$MgSO_4$	Fusion	c	liq	...	1400	3.5	2.5	
Mg_3N_2	Transition	c, II	c, I	...	1061	0.26	0.24	
	Transition	c, III	c, II	...	823	0.22	0.27	
Mn	Transition	c, IV	c, III	...	1000	0.54	0.54	
	Transition	c, III	c, II	...	1374	0.54	0.39	
	Transition	c, II	c, I	...	1410	0.43	0.30	
	Fusion	c, I	liq	...	1517	3.50	2.31	
	Vaporization	liq	g	760	2360	53.7	22.8	
$MnBr_2$	Fusion	c	liq	...	971			
$MnCl_2$	Fusion	c	liq	...	923	9.0	9.7	
	Vaporization	liq	g	760	1463	28.8	19.7	
MnO	Fusion	c	liq	...	2053			
Mn_2O_3	Transition	c, II	c, I	...	873			
Mn_3O_4	Transition	c, II	c, I	...	1445	4.5	3.1	
	Fusion	c, I	liq	...	1833			
MnS	Fusion	c	liq	...	1803	6.2	3.4	

TABLE 4j-1. PHASE TRANSITION DATA FOR ELEMENTS AND COMPOUNDS (*Continued*)

Substance	Type of process	Phase		Pressure, mm Hg	Temp., °K	ΔH, kcal/mole	ΔS, cal/mole deg	ΔC_p, cal/mole deg
		Initial	Final					
Mo	Fusion	c	liq	......	2883			
$Mo(CO)_6$	Sublimation	c	g	48	375	16.3	43.5	
MoF_6	Sublimation	c	g	406	290.7	8.3	28.6	
	Fusion	c	liq	406	290.7	2.2	7.6	
	Vaporization	liq	g	760	308	6.0	19.5	
MoO_3	Sublimation	c	g	0.3	973	65	67	
	Fusion	c	liq	10	1068.4	12.54	11.74	
	Vaporization	liq	g	760	1428	33	23	
Na	Fusion	c	liq	......	371.0	0.622	1.68	0.12
	Vaporization	liq	g, equilibrium	760	1162			
NaBr	Sublimation	c	g	0.40	1023	49.3	48.2	
	Fusion	c	liq	0.40	1023	6.1	5.9	
	Vaporization	liq	g	760	1665	38.7	23.2	
NaCN	Transition	c, III	c, II	......	172.1	0.15	0.87	
	Transition	c, II	c, I	......	288.5	0.70	2.43	
	Fusion	c, I	liq	......	835	4	5	
	Vaporization	liq	g	760	1770	37	21	
Na_2CO_3	Transition	c, IV	c, III	......	629	0.20	0.32	
	Transition	c, III	c, II	......	759	0.45	0.59	
	Transition	c, II	c, I	......	891			
	Fusion	c, I	liq	......	1127	8	7	
NaCl	Sublimation	c	g	0.5	1081	51.5	47.6	
	Fusion	c	liq	0.5	1081	6.8	6.3	0.8
	Vaporization	liq	g	760	1738	40.8	23.5	
NaF	Sublimation	c	g	0.5	1268	63	49	
	Fusion	c	liq	0.5	1268	7.8	6.2	0.65
	Vaporization	liq	g	760	1977	50	25	
NaI	Fusion	c	liq	......	935	5.2	5.6	
	Vaporization	liq	g	760	1577	38.2	24.2	
Na_2MoO_4	Transition	c, II	c, I	......	713	14.6	20.5	
	Fusion	c, I	liq	......	960	3.6	3.8	

TABLE 4j-1. PHASE TRANSITION DATA FOR ELEMENTS AND COMPOUNDS (*Continued*)

Substance	Type of process	Phase		Pressure, mm Hg	Temp., °K	ΔH, kcal/mole	ΔS, cal/mole deg	ΔC_p, cal/mole deg
		Initial	Final					
$NaNO_3$	Transition	c, II	c, I	....	548			
	Fusion	c, I	liq	....	583	3.8	6.5	0.3
NaOH	Transition	c, II	c, I	....	566.0	1.514	2.67	
	Fusion	c, I	liq	....	592.2	1.518	2.57	1.2
$NaOH·H_2O$	Fusion	c	liq	....	337.4			
$Na_4P_2O_7$	Fusion	c	liq	....	1243	14	11	
Na_2SO_4	Transition	c, II	c, I	....	513			
	Fusion	c, I	liq	....	1163	5.8	5.0	
Na_2SiO_3	Fusion	c	liq	....	1362	12.5	9.2	−1.07
Na_2TiO_3	Transition	c, II	c, I	....	560	0.4	0.7	−1.31
	Fusion	c, I	liq	....	1303	16.8	12.9	−1.2
Nb	Sublimation	c	g	0.00017	2500	181	72	
	Fusion	c	liq	....	2760			
$NbCl_5$	Sublimation	c	g	330	483	20.4	42.2	
	Fusion	c	liq	330	483	8.5	17.6	
	Vaporization	liq	g	760	519	11.8	22.7	
Nb_2O_5	Fusion	c	liq	....	1785	24.59	13.78	
Nb_2O_3	Fusion	c	liq	....	2045			
Nd	Transition	c, IV	c, III	....	109			
	Transition	c, III	c, II	....	781			
	Transition	c, II	c, I	....	987			
	Fusion	c, I	liq	....	1113			
Ne	Fusion	c	liq	324	24.57	0.080	3.26	2.42
	Vaporization	liq	g	324	24.57	0.431	17.54	−3.42
NH_3	Fusion	c	liq	45.57	195.40	1.351	6.914	
	Vaporization	liq	g	45.57	195.40			
	Vaporization	liq	g	760	239.73	5.581	23.28	
NH_4Br	Transition	c, II	c, I	735	411.0	0.77	1.87	
	Fusion	c, I	liq	....	815			
NH_4Cl	Transition	c, II	c, I	760	457.6	1.06	2.32	
	Fusion	c, I	liq	2.62×10^4	793			
	Vaporization	liq	g	2.62×10^4	793			
NH_4I	Transition	c, II	c, I	760	260	0.70	2.7	
	Fusion	c, I	liq	....	824			

TABLE 4j-1. PHASE TRANSITION DATA FOR ELEMENTS AND COMPOUNDS (*Continued*)

Substance	Type of process	Phase		Pressure, mm Hg	Temp., °K	ΔH, kcal/mole	ΔS, cal/mole deg	ΔC_p, cal/mole deg
		Initial	Final					
NH_4NO_3	Transition	c, V	c, IV	760	255	0.13	0.51	
	Transition	c, IV	c, III	760	305.3	0.38	1.23	
	Transition	c, III	c, II	6.32×10^5	336.5	0.20	0.59	
	Transition	c, IV	c, III	6.32×10^5	336.5	0.32	0.95	
	Transition	c, IV	c, II	6.32×10^5	336.5	0.52	1.54	
	Transition	c, III	c, II	760	357.4	0.32	0.90	
	Transition	c, II	c, I	760	398.4	1.01	2.54	
	Transition	c, IV	c, II	6.73×10^6	442.4	0.96	2.16	
	Transition	c, IV	c, VI	6.73×10^6	442.4	0.98	2.21	
	Transition	c, II	c, VI	6.73×10^6	442.4	0.02	0.05	
	Fusion	c, I	liq	760	442.8	1.3	2.94	
	Transition	c, VI	c, I	6.63×10^6	459.9	0.99	2.15	
	Transition	c, II	c, VI	6.63×10^6	459.9	0.03	0.06	
	Transition	c, II	c, I	6.63×10^6	459.9	1.02	2.21	
NO	Fusion	c	liq	164.4	109.51	0.550	5.02	6.0
	Vaporization	liq	g	164.4	109.51			
	Vaporization	liq	g	760	121.39	3.293	27.13	11.8
N_2	Transition	c, II	c, I	....	35.62	0.055	1.54	
	Fusion	c, I	liq	94	63.18	0.172	2.72	
	Vaporization	liq	g	94	63.18			
	Vaporization	liq	g	760	77.34	1.333	17.24	
N_2H_4	Fusion	c	liq	....	274.69	3.025	11.01	8.0
	Vaporization	liq	g	764	386.7	9.70	25.1	
N_2O	Fusion	c	liq	658.9	182.30	1.563	8.574	4.67
	Vaporization	liq	g	658.9	182.30			
	Vaporization	liq	g	760	184.68	3.956	21.42	
Ni	Transition	c, II	c, I	....	626	0.092	0.15	− 0.71
	Fusion	c, I	liq	....	1726	4.2	2.4	0.0
	Vaporization	liq	g	760	3073	91.0	29.6	
$NiCl_2$	Sublimation	c	g	760	1260	48.36	38.38	
	Fusion	c	liq	....	1300.8	18.47	14.18	
$Ni(CO)_4$	Fusion	c	liq	....	248			
	Vaporization	liq	g	760	315.6	7.0	22.2	
NiO	Sublimation	c	g	1.14×10^{-5}	1500	111.4	74.2	
	Fusion	c	liq	....	2223			
NiS	Fusion	c	liq	....	1070			

TABLE 4j-1. PHASE TRANSITION DATA FOR ELEMENTS AND COMPOUNDS (*Continued*)

Substance	Type of process	Phase		Pressure, mm Hg	Temp., °K	ΔH, kcal/mole	ΔS, cal/mole deg	ΔC_p, cal/mole deg
		Initial	Final					
Np	Fusion	c	liq	....	913			
$NpCl_3$	Fusion	c	liq	....	1075			
$NpCl_4$	Fusion	c	liq	....	811			
NpF_6	Fusion	c	liq	....	326			
O_2	Transition	c, III	c, II	....	23.89	0.022	0.92	0.3
	Transition	c, II	c, I	....	43.80	0.178	4.07	−0.14
	Fusion	c, I	liq	1.14	54.36	0.106	1.95	1.74
	Vaporization	liq	g	1.14	54.36			
	Vaporization	liq	g	760	90.19	1.630	18.07	−6.00
O_3	Vaporization	liq	g	760	162.65	2.59	15.92	
Os	Fusion	c	liq	....	2973			
	Vaporization	liq	g	760	4673			
OsO_4	Fusion	c, I	liq	....	313.3	3.41	10.9	
	Vaporization	liq	g	760	403	9.5	23.6	
P	Transition	c, IV, white	c, III, white	760	196			
	Transition	c, IV, white	c, III, white	4.41×10^6	270.8	1.35	4.09	
	Transition	c, III, white	c, II, red	....	298.16	− 4.4		
	Transition	c, III, white	c, I, black	....	298.16	−10.3		
	Fusion	c, III, white	liq	760	317.4	0.15	0.47	
	Vaporization	liq	g, P_4	760	553	2.97	5.37	
	Fusion	c, II, red	liq	32,760	863	4.85	5.62	
	Vaporization	liq	g, P_4	32,760	863	2.50	2.90	
PBr_3	Fusion	c	liq	....	232.7			
	Vaporization	liq	g	760	446.4	9.28	20.79	
PBr_5	Sublimation	c	g	210	357.0	13.0	36.4	
PCl_3	Fusion	c	liq	....	181			
	Vaporization	liq	g	760	349	7.28	20.9	
PCl_5	Sublimation	c	g, mixt. equilibrium	760	432	16.1	37.3	
	Fusion	c	liq	....	433			
PF_3	Fusion	c	liq	....	121.7			
	Vaporization	liq	g	760	172.0	3.43	19.9	

TABLE 4j-1. PHASE TRANSITION DATA FOR ELEMENTS AND COMPOUNDS (*Continued*)

Substance	Type of process	Phase Initial	Phase Final	Pressure, mm Hg	Temp., °K	ΔH, kcal/mole	ΔS, cal/mole deg	ΔC_p, cal/mole deg
PF_5	Fusion	c	liq	427	179.4	2.8	15.6	
	Sublimation	c	g	427	179.4	6.9	38.5	
	Vaporization	liq	g	760	188.7	4.1	21.7	
PH_3	Transition	c, IV	c, III	....	30.31	0.0197	0.650	
	Transition	c, III	c, II	....	49.44	0.186	3.76	
	Transition	c, II	c, I	....	88.12	0.116	1.32	
	Fusion	c, I	liq	27.33	139.38	0.270	1.94	
	Vaporization	liq	g	27.33	139.38			
	Vaporization	liq	g	760	185.42	3.490	18.82	
P_4O_{10}	Sublimation	c, II	g	760	632	17.6	27.8	
	Fusion	c, II	liq	3,700	693	5	7.2	
	Fusion	c, I	liq	570	845	11.5	13.6	
	Vaporization	liq	g	570	845	16.8	19.9	
$PaCl_5$	Fusion	c	liq	....	574			
Pb	Fusion	c	liq	....	600.5	1.14	1.90	0.29
	Vaporization	liq	g	760	2023	43.0	21.3	
$PbBr_2$	Fusion	c	liq	....	643.2	5	7.8	
	Vaporization	liq	g	760	1187	27.7	23.3	
$PbCl_2$	Fusion	c	liq	....	771	5.7	7.4	
	Vaporization	liq	g	760	1227	29.6	24.1	
PbF_2	Fusion	c, I	liq	....	1095	1.8	1.6	
	Vaporization	liq	g	760	1563	38.3	24.5	
$PbH_{12}C_4$ (tetramethyllead)	Fusion	c	liq	....	245.7			
	Vaporization	liq	g	760	379.3	8.0	21.1	
$PbH_{20}C_8$ (tetraethyllead)	Fusion	c	liq	....	137			
	Vaporization	liq	g	609.7	450.0	11.87	26.38	
PbO	Transition	c, II, red	c, I, yellow	....	762			
	Fusion	c, I, yellow	liq	....	1159	2.8	2.4	
	Vaporization	liq	g	760	1745	51	29	
PbS	Sublimation	c	g	10	1238	55	44	
	Fusion	c	liq	....	1387	4.2	3.0	

TABLE 4j-1. PHASE TRANSITION DATA FOR ELEMENTS AND COMPOUNDS (*Continued*)

Substance	Type of process	Phase Initial	Phase Final	Pressure, mm Hg	Temp., °K	ΔH, kcal/mole	ΔS, cal/mole deg	ΔC_p, cal/mole deg
$PbSO_4$	Transition	c, II	c, I	....	1139	4.06	3.56	
	Fusion	c, I	liq	....	1360	9.6	7.1	
Pd	Fusion	c	liq	....	1825	4	2	
	Vaporization	liq	g	760	3833			
Pt	Fusion	c	liq	....	2042	5.2	2.5	
	Vaporization	liq	g	760	4283			
$PuCl_3$	Sublimation	c	g	0.0017	1033	65	63	
	Vaporization	liq	g	0.0017	1033	59.7	57.8	
PuF_3	Sublimation	c	g	0.00036	1329	96.9	72.9	
	Vaporization	liq	g	0.079	1562	80.9	51.8	
Ra	Fusion	c	liq	....	973			
Rb	Transition	c, II	c, I	....	243			
	Sublimation	c, I	g	0.01	312.0	20.47	65.61	
	Fusion	c, I	liq	0.01	312.0	0.52	1.67	
	Vaporization	liq	g	760	952	18.11	19.02	
RbBr	Fusion	c	liq	....	953	3.7	3.9	
	Vaporization	liq	g	760	1625	37.12	22.84	
RbCl	Fusion	c	liq	....	990	4.40	4.44	
	Vaporization	liq	g	760	1654	36.92	22.32	
RbF	Fusion	c	liq	....	1048	4.13	3.94	
	Vaporization	liq	g	760	1681	39.51	23.50	
RbI	Fusion	c	liq	....	913	2.99	3.27	
	Vaporization	liq	g	760	1577	35.96	22.80	
$RbNO_3$	Transition	c, IV	c, III	....	438			
	Transition	c, III	c, II	....	498			
	Transition	c, II	c, I	....	564			
	Fusion	c, I	liq	....	589	1.34	2.28	
RbOH	Transition	c, II	c, I	....	518	1.70	3.28	
	Fusion	c, I	liq	....	574	1.62	2.82	
Rb_2CO_3	Fusion	c	liq	....	1108			

TABLE 4j-1. PHASE TRANSITION DATA FOR ELEMENTS AND COMPOUNDS (*Continued*)

Substance	Type of process	Phase		Pressure, mm Hg	Temp., °K	ΔH, kcal/mole	ΔS, cal/mole deg	ΔC_p, cal/mole deg
		Initial	Final					
Re	Fusion	c	liq	....	3420			
Re_2O_7	Fusion	c	liq	....	573.5	15.3	26.7	
	Vaporization	liq	g	760	635.5	18.1	28.5	
Rh	Fusion	c	liq	....	2233			
	Vaporization	liq	g	....	4233			
Rn	Fusion	c	liq	....	202	0.693	3.43	
	Vaporization	liq	g	760	211	3.92	18.6	
Ru	Transition	c, IV	c, III	....	1308	0.034	0.026	
	Transition	c, III	c, II	....	1473			
	Transition	c, II	c, I	....	1773	0.23	0.13	
	Fusion	c, I	liq	....	2773			
	Vaporization	liq	g	760	4383			
S	Transition	c, II, rhombic	c, I, monoclinic	0.0047	368.6	0.09	0.25	0.24
	Sublimation	c, II, rhombic	g, S_8	0.0047	368.6	3.01	8.17	
	Sublimation	c, I, monoclinic	g, S_8	0.0047	368.6	2.92	7.93	
	Fusion	c, I, monoclinic	liq, λ	....	392	0.293	0.75	1.6
	Vaporization	equilibrium liq, λ, μ	g	760	717.76	2.5	3.5	
SF_6	Transition	c, II	c, I	....	94.26	0.384	4.07	− 1.98
	Sublimation	c, I	g	760	209.5	5.46	26.04	
	Fusion	c, I	liq	1,700	222.5	1.20	5.40	− 1.7
	Vaporization	liq	g	1,700	222.5	4.08	18.34	
SO_2	Fusion	c	liq	12.56	197.68	1.769	8.95	4.50
	Vaporization	liq	g	12.56	197.68			
	Vaporization	liq	g	760	263.14	5.955	22.63	−11.84
Sb	Transition	c, III	c, II	....	367.8			
	Transition	c, II	c, I	....	690			
	Fusion	c, I	liq	....	903.7	4.8	5.3	
	Vaporization	liq	g, equilibrium	760	1713			
$SbBr_3$	Fusion	c	liq	....	369.8	3.51	9.49	
	Vaporization	liq	g	749	561			

TABLE 4j-1. PHASE TRANSITION DATA FOR ELEMENTS AND COMPOUNDS (*Continued*)

Substance	Type of process	Phase Initial	Phase Final	Pressure, mm Hg	Temp., °K	ΔH, kcal/mole	ΔS, cal/mole deg	ΔC_p, cal/mole deg
$SbCl_3$	Fusion	c	liq	....	346.4	3.03	8.74	
	Vaporization	liq	g	760	494	10.80	21.86	
$SbCl_5$	Fusion	c	liq	....	276.2	2.4	8.7	
	Vaporization	liq	g	21	349.7	11.5	32.9	
SbH_3	Fusion	c	liq	....	185			
	Vaporization	liq	g	760	256			
Sb_4O_6	Transition	c, II	c, I	0.525	830	3.24	3.91	
	Fusion	c, I	liq	8.5	928	29.49	31.78	
	Vaporization	liq	g	8.5	928			
	Vaporization	liq	g	760	1729	17.83	10.31	
Sc	Fusion	c	liq	....	1673			
	Vaporization	liq	g	760	4173			
$ScCl_3$	Sublimation	c	g	684	1233	61.1	49.6	
	Fusion	c	liq	684	1233			
Se	Transition	vitreous	c, I, gray	....	398	1.05	2.64	2.2
	Transition	c, III, red	c, I, gray	....	423	0.18	0.43	0.2
	Fusion	c, I, gray	liq	0.0043	490.6	1.25	2.56	2.7
	Vaporization	liq	g, Se_6	0.0043	490.6	4.31	8.79	
	Vaporization	liq	g, Se_6	760	1009	3.43	3.40	
	Vaporization	liq	g, $Se_{4.37}$	760	958.0	5.10	5.32	
	Vaporization	liq	g, Se_2	760	1027	12.80	12.46	
SeF_6	Sublimation	c	g	760	226.6	6.27	27.68	
	Fusion	c	liq	1,500	238.6	1.70	7.14	
	Vaporization	liq	g	1,500	238.6	4.38	18.34	
SeO_2	Sublimation	c	g	760	595	21.1	35.4	
Si	Fusion	c	liq	.....	1683	11	6.5	
$SiBr_4$	Fusion	c	liq	....	278.4			
	Vaporization	liq	g	760	426.0	9.1	21.4	
$SiCl_4$	Fusion	c	liq	....	205	1.84	9.0	
	Vaporization	liq	g	760	330.2	7.0	21.2	

TABLE 4j-1. PHASE TRANSITION DATA FOR ELEMENTS AND COMPOUNDS (*Continued*)

Substance	Type of process	Phase Initial	Phase Final	Pressure, mm Hg	Temp., °K	ΔH, kcal/mole	ΔS, cal/mole deg	ΔC_p, cal/mole deg
SiF_4	Sublimation	c	g	760	177.7	6.15	34.6	
	Fusion	c	liq	1,320	182.9	1.69	9.2	
	Vaporization	liq	g	1,320	182.9	4.46	24.4	
SiH_4	Transition	c, II	c, I	.....	63.5	0.147	2.32	
	Fusion	c, I	liq	.....	88.5	0.159	1.80	1.3
	Vaporization	liq	g	760	161.8	2.9	18	
SiO_2	Transition	quartz, c, III	quartz, c, II	.....	91			
	Transition	quartz, c, II	quartz, c, I	.....	846	0.15	0.18	−5.6
	Transition	quartz, c, I	tridymite, c, I	.....	1140	0.12	0.11	
	Fusion	quartz, c, I	liq	.....	1883	2.04	1.08	
	Transition	tridymite, c, IV	tridymite, c, III	.....	390	0.07	0.18	
	Transition	tridymite, c, III	tridymite, c, II	.....	436	0.04	0.09	
	Transition	tridymite, c, II	tridymite, c, I	.....	598	0.05	0.08	
	Transition	tridymite, c, I	cristobalite, c, I	.....	1743	0.05	0.03	
	Fusion	tridymite, c, I	liq	.....	1953			
	Transition	cristobalite, c, II	cristobalite, c, I	.....	515	0.31	0.60	
	Fusion	cristobalite, c, I	liq	.....	2001	1.84	0.92	
Sn	Transition	c, III, gray	c, II, white	.....	291	0.6	2.1	
	Transition	c, II, white	c, I	.....	476.0	0.002	0.004	
	Fusion	c, I	liq	.....	505.1	1.69	3.35	
	Vaporization	liq	g	760	2600			
$SnBr_2$	Fusion	c	liq	.....	505	1.7	3.4	
	Vaporization	liq	g	760	911	22	24	
$SnBr_4$	Transition	c, II	c, I	.....	267			
	Fusion	c, I	liq	.....	303	3.0	9.9	
	Vaporization	liq	g	760	478	10	21	
$SnCl_2$	Fusion	c	liq	.....	520	3.0	5.8	
	Vaporization	liq	g	760	896	21	23	
$SnCl_4$	Fusion	c	liq	.....	239.9	2.19	9.13	
	Vaporization	liq	g	760	386	8.3	21.5	

TABLE 4j-1. PHASE TRANSITION DATA FOR ELEMENTS AND COMPOUNDS (*Continued*)

Substance	Type of process	Phase Initial	Phase Final	Pressure, mm Hg	Temp., °K	ΔH, kcal/mole	ΔS, cal/mole deg	ΔC_p, cal/mole deg
SnO_2	Transition	c, II	c, I	....	683	0.45	0.66	
SnS	Fusion	c	liq	....	1153			
Sr	Fusion	c	liq	....	1043	2.2	2.1	
	Vaporization	liq	g	760	1657	33.8	20.4	
$SrCl_2$	Fusion	c	liq	....	1148	4.1	3.6	
$SrCO_3$	Transition	c, II	c, I	....	1197	4.7	3.9	
	Fusion	c, I	liq	....	1770			
SrF_2	Fusion	c	liq	....	1673	4.3	2.6	
SrO	Fusion	c	liq	....	2688			
$SrSO_4$	Transition	c, II	c, I	....	1425			
	Fusion	c, I	liq	....	1878			
Ta	Sublimation	c	g	8.6×10^{-6}	2500	180	72	
	Fusion	c	liq	....	3250			
TaC	Fusion	c	liq	....	4100			
$TaCl_5$	Sublimation	c	g	415	484	22.7	46.9	
	Fusion	c	liq	415	484	11.1	22.9	
	Vaporization	liq	g	760	508	11.5	22.6	
Ta_2O_5	Fusion	c	liq	....	2163			
Te	Transition	c, II	c, I	....	621	0.13	0.21	
	Fusion	c, I	liq	0.18	723	4.28	5.92	2.0
	Vaporization	liq	g, Te_2	0.18	723	13.3	18.4	
	Vaporization	liq	g, Te_2	760	1360	11.9	8.75	
TeF_6	Transition	c, II	c, I	60	199.7	0.5	2.5	
	Sublimation	c, I	g	760	234.6	6.47	27.6	
	Fusion	c, I	liq	800	235.5	2.1	9.0	
	Vaporization	liq	g	800	235.5	4.3	18.4	
Th	Transition	c, I	c, II	....	498			
	Fusion	c	liq	....	1968			
ThO_2	Fusion	c	liq	....	3493			
Ti	Transition	c, II	c, I	....	1157			
	Sublimation	c, I	g	0.036	2085	106.5	51.0	
	Fusion	c, I	liq	0.036	2085			

TABLE 4j-1. PHASE TRANSITION DATA FOR ELEMENTS AND COMPOUNDS (*Conitnued*)

Substance	Type of process	Phase		Pressure, mm Hg	Temp., °K	ΔH, kcal/mole	ΔS, cal/mole deg	ΔC_p, cal/mole deg
		Initial	Final					
$TiBr_4$	Transition	c, II	c, I	......	258			
	Fusion	c, I	liq	......	311.7	2.1	6.7	
	Vaporization	liq	g	760	503			
$TiCl_4$	Fusion	c	liq	......	250	2.24	9.0	
	Vaporization	liq	g	760	409.0	8.4	20.5	
TiI_4	Fusion	c	liq	......	423			
	Vaporization	liq	g	760	650.3	13.6	20.9	
TiO	Transition	c, II	c, I	......	1264	0.82	0.65	
TiO_2	Transition	c, III, β, anatase	c, II, α, anatase	......	915	0.3	0.3	
	Fusion	c, I, rutile	liq	......	2108			
Tl	Transition	c, I	c, III	2.87×10^7	426	− 0 19	− 0.45	
	Transition	c, II	c, III	2.87×10^7	426	0.01	0.02	
	Transition	c, II	c, I	2.87×10^7	426	0.20	0.47	
	Transition	c, II	c, I	......	508.3	0.082	0.16	0.18
	Fusion	c, I	liq	......	576.8	1.03	1.79	0.43
	Vaporization	liq	g	28	1350	40.1	29.7	
	Vaporization	liq	g	760	1730			
TlBr	Sublimation	c	g	2.11	732	31.4	42.9	
	Fusion	c	liq	2.11	732	3.6	4.9	
	Vaporization	liq	g	760	1089	24.6	22.7	
TlCl	Sublimation	c	g	1.12	702	29	41	
	Fusion	c	liq	1.12	702	4.0	5.6	
	Vaporization	liq	g	760	1079	24.8	23.0	
TlI	Transition	c, II, yellow	c, I, red	......	438			
	Sublimation	c, I, red	g	1.00	713	30.0	42.1	
	Fusion	c, I, red	liq	1.00	713	2.7	3.8	
	Vaporization	liq	g	760	1098	24.9	22.6	
Tl_2O	Fusion	c	liq	......	573			
	Vaporization	liq	g	760	773			
	Fusion	c	liq	......	990			
Tl_2O_3	Fusion	c	liq	......	990			
Tm	Vaporization	liq	g	760	3773			

TABLE 4j-1. PHASE TRANSITION DATA FOR ELEMENTS AND COMPOUNDS (*Continued*)

Substance	Type of process	Phase		Pressure, mm Hg	Temp., °K	ΔH, kcal/mole	ΔS, cal/mole deg	ΔC_p, cal/mole deg
		Initial	Final					
U	Transition	c, III	c, II	....	935	0.714	0.763	
	Transition	c, II	c, I	....	1049	1.165	1.110	
	Fusion	c, I	liq	....	1405			
UBr_4	Sublimation	c	g	4.78	792	49.9	63.0	
	Vaporization	liq	g	4.78	792	43.8	55.3	
	Vaporization	liq	g	760	1039	31.0	29.8	
UCl_4	Sublimation	c	g	15.5	863	46.3	53.6	
	Vaporization	liq	g	15.5	863	36.0	41.7	
UF_6	Sublimation	c	g	760	329	11.8	35.9	
	Sublimation	c	g	1,133	337.2	11.8	35.0	
	Fusion	c	liq	1,133	337.2	4.59	13.61	8.81
	Vaporization	liq	g	1,133	337.2	7.2	21.4	
V	Fusion	c	liq	....	2003			
	Sublimation	c	g	6.1×10^{-5}	1800	120.4	66.9	
VCl_4	Fusion	c	liq	....	247.5			
	Vaporization	liq	g	760	425	9.1	21.4	
V_2O_3	Fusion	c	liq	....	2250			
V_2O_4	Transition	c, II	c, I	....	345	2.05	5.94	6.9
	Fusion	c, I	liq	....	1815	27.21	15.0	10.1
V_2O_5	Fusion	c	liq	....	943	15.56	16.50	2.9
W	Fusion	c	liq	....	3653			
WCl_6	Transition	c, III	c, II	....	442			
	Transition	c, II	c, I	38	500.1	3.4	6.8	
	Sublimation	c, II	g	38	500.1	21.0	42.0	
	Sublimation	c, I	g	233	557.2	17.4	31.2	
	Fusion	c, I	liq	233	557.2	2.3	4.1	
	Vaporization	liq	g	760	609.7	14.9	24.4	
WF_6	Transition	c, II	c, I	....	265.0	1.6	6.0	
	Fusion	c, I	liq	420	275.7	0.5	1.8	

TABLE 4j-1. PHASE TRANSITION DATA FOR ELEMENTS AND COMPOUNDS (*Continued*)

Substance	Type of process	Phase		Pressure, mm Hg	Temp., °K	ΔH, kcal/mole	ΔS, cal/mole deg	ΔC_p, cal/mole deg
		Initial	Final					
WO_2	Sublimation	c	g	0.0058	1375	112	81	
	Fusion	c	liq	....	1743			
Xe	Fusion	c	liq	611	161.3	0.549	3.40	2.13
	Vaporization	liq	g	611	161.3			
	Vaporization	liq	g	760	165.1	3.021	18.29	−5.71
Y	Fusion	c	liq	....	1773			
	Vaporization	liq	g	760	4373			
$YbCl_3$	Fusion	c, γ	liq	....	1127			
Zn	Fusion	c	liq	....	692.7	1.595	2.303	
	Vaporization	liq	g	760	1180	27.43	23.24	
$ZnCl_2$	Fusion	c	liq	....	548	5.5	10	
	Vaporization	liq	g	760	1029	30.9	30.0	
ZnO	Fusion	c	liq	....	2248			
ZnS	Sublimation	c, II	g	0.01	1127	64.3	57.1	
	Transition	c, II	c, I	....	1293			
	Sublimation	c, I	g	760	1455			
Zr	Transition	c, II	c, I	....	1135	0.7	0.6	
	Sublimation	c, I	g	1.5×10^{-6}	2000	137.7	68.9	
	Fusion	c, I	liq	....	2125			
ZrC	Fusion	c	liq	....	3765			
$ZrCl_4$	Sublimation	c	g	760	604	25.3	41.9	
	Fusion	c	liq	....	710			
ZrN	Fusion	c	liq	....	3225			
ZrO_2	Transition	c, III	c, II	....	1478	1.42	0.96	
	Transition	c, II	c, I	....	2173			
	Fusion	c, I	liq	....	2988	20.8	7.0	

Figure 4j-1 presents vapor-pressure curves for approximately 40 elements and compounds.

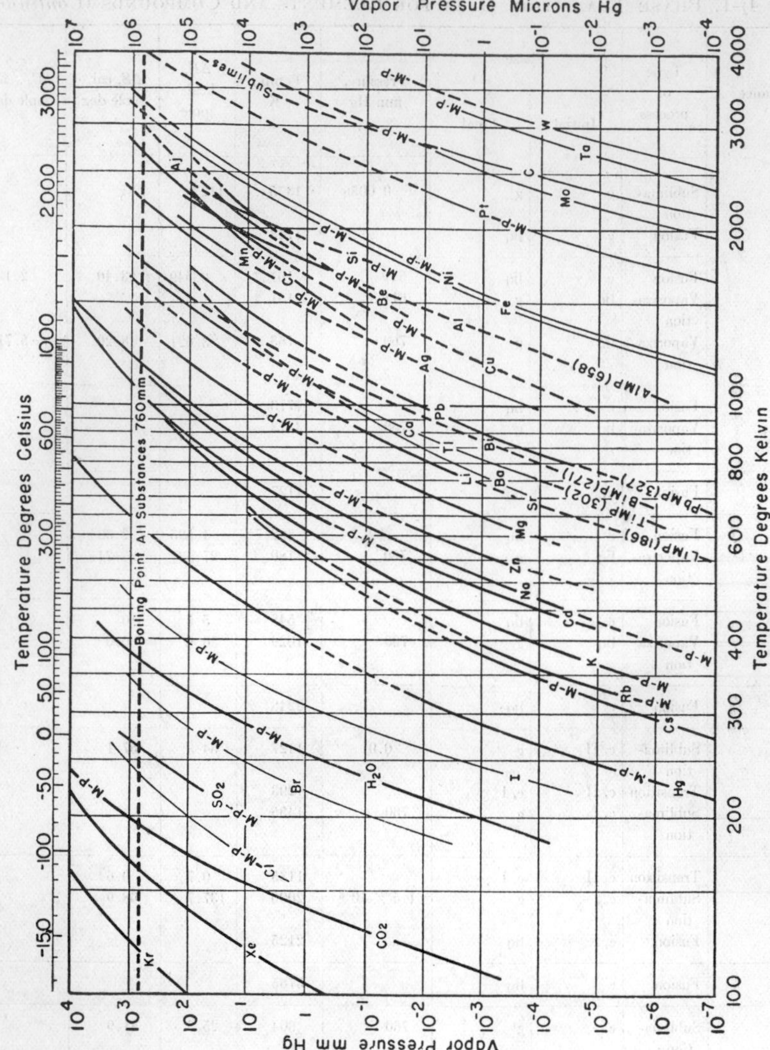

Fig. 4j-1. Vapor-pressure data. [*Compiled by R. R. Law, Rev. Sci. Instr.* **19**, 920 (1948).]

Section 5

ELECTRICITY AND MAGNETISM

D. F. BLEIL, Editor

U.S. Naval Ordnance Laboratory, White Oak, Md.

CONTENTS

5a. Definitions, Units, Nomenclature, Symbols, Conversion Tables 5-2
5b. Formulas 5-12
5c. Electrical Standards 5-105
5d. Properties of Dielectrics 5-114
5e. Properties of Semiconductors 5-157
5f. Properties of Nonmetallic Conductors 5-166
5g. Properties of Metallic Conductors 5-197
5h. Magnetic Properties of Materials 5-206
5i. Electrical Power Practices 5-245
5j. Electrochemical Information 5-268
5k. Electric and Magnetic Properties of the Earth and Stars 5-283

5a. Definitions, Units, Nomenclature, Symbols, Conversion Tables

W. R. SMYTHE

California Institute of Technology

5a-1. Fundamental Definitions Based on Mechanical Measurements

Capacitivity or Dielectric Constant. The capacitivity in farads per meter is the ratio of the force between two charged conductors measured in vacuum to that measured when the vacuum is replaced by a homogeneous fluid insulating medium, multiplied by 8.85434×10^{-12}. In a homogeneous solid it is the product of 8.85434×10^{-12} by the ratio of the force on a given small charge measured at the center of a thin disk-shaped evacuated cavity placed normal to a uniform electric field to that on the same charge measured at the center of a thin needle-shaped evacuated cavity aligned with the same field.

Charge. One coulomb is that charge which, when carried by each of two bodies whose distance apart r in meters is very large compared with their dimensions, produces in a vacuum a mutual repulsion of $8.98740r^{-2} \times 10^{9}$ newton. A charge of one coulomb is transported by a current of one ampere in one second. There are two kinds of charge. Electrons carry a negative charge and protons a positive charge.

Current. An ampere is that current which, flowing in the same direction in each of two identical coaxial circular loops of wire whose distance apart r in meters is very large compared with their radius a, produces in a vacuum a mutual attraction of $6\pi^2a^4r^{-4} \times 10^{-7}$ newton. A current of one ampere transports one coulomb of charge per second. Current direction is defined as that in which a positive charge moves.

Electric Intensity. The electric intensity in volts per meter is the vector force in newtons acting on a very small body carrying a very small positive charge placed at the field point, divided by the charge in coulombs. In a homogeneous solid the measurement is carried out at the center of a thin evacuated needle-shaped cavity aligned so that the force lies along the axis.

Electromotance or Electromotive Force. The electromotance in volts around a closed path is the work in joules required to carry a very small positive charge around that path, divided by the charge in coulombs.

Magnetic Induction or Magnetic Flux Density. The magnetic induction in webers per square meter is a vector whose direction is that in which the axis of a small circular current-carrying test loop that rests in stable equilibrium at the field point would advance if it were a right-hand screw rotated in the sense of the current circulation and whose magnitude equals the torque in newton meters on the loop when its axis is normal to the induction, divided by the product of loop current by loop area. In a homogeneous solid the measurement is carried out at the center of a thin evacuated disk-shaped cavity oriented so that the induction is normal to its faces.

Permeability. The permeability in henrys per meter is the ratio of the force between two linear circuits carrying fixed current measured in a homogeneous fluid insulating medium to that measured in a vacuum, multiplied by $4\pi \times 10^{-7}$. In a homogeneous solid it is the product of $4\pi \times 10^{-7}$ by the ratio of the magnetic induction at the center of a thin evacuated disk-shaped cavity oriented so that the induction is normal to its faces to that at the center of a thin evacuated needle-shaped cavity oriented so that the induction is directed along its axis.

Potential. The potential in volts at a point in an electrostatic field is the work in joules done in bringing a very small positive charge to the point from a point arbitrarily chosen at zero potential, divided by the charge in coulombs.

5a-2. Basic Laws

Ampere's Law. At any field point near a linear circuit, each circuit element contributes to the magnetic induction an amount inversely proportional to the square of the distance $\mathbf{r}$ from it to the point, directly proportional to its length, current, and the sine of the angle between $\mathbf{ds}$ and $\mathbf{r}$, and in the direction of $\mathbf{ds} \times \mathbf{r}$.

Coulomb's Law. The force in a homogeneous isotropic medium of infinite extent between two point charges is proportional to the product of their magnitudes divided by the square of the distance between them.

Faraday's Law of Induction. The electromotance induced in a circuit is proportional to the rate of change of the magnetic flux linking the circuit.

Joule's Law. The rate of production of heat in a constant-resistance electric circuit is proportional to the square of the current.

Kirchhoff's Laws. (1) The algebraic sum of the currents flowing into any point in a network is zero. (2) The algebraic sum of the products of current by resistance around any closed path in a network equals the algebraic sum of the electromotances in that path.

Lenz's Law. The current induced in a circuit due to a change in the magnetic flux through it or to its motion in a magnetic field is so directed as to oppose the change in flux or to exert a mechanical force opposing the motion.

Ohm's Law. The current in an electric circuit is directly proportional to the electromotance in it.

5a-3. Definitions of Some Descriptive Terms. For quantitative terms, see Table 5a-1.

Anode. The positive electrode in such devices as the arc, vacuum tube, and electrolytic cell.

Antiferroelectric Materials. Those in which spontaneous electric polarization occurs in lines of ions; adjacent lines are polarized in an antiparallel arrangement.

Antiferromagnetic Materials. Those in which spontaneous magnetic polarization occurs in equivalent sublattices; the polarization in one sublattice is aligned antiparallel to the other.

Cathode. The negative electrode in such devices as the arc, vacuum tube, and electrolytic cell.

Coercive Force. The value of the reverse magnetic intensity needed to destroy the magnetic moment of the specimen.

Conductors. Bodies in which differences of potential, if not maintained by some driving electromotance, disappear rapidly with a flow of current.

Curie Point. The point, as the temperature increases, at which the transition from ferromagnetic to paramagnetic properties of a substance is complete.

Diamagnetic Bodies. Those which, when placed in an inhomogeneous magnetic field, tend to move toward its weaker regions.

Dielectric Bodies. Those which can support an electric strain and in which differences of potential disappear very slowly or not at all because of current flow.

Eddy or *Foucault Currents.* Circulating currents set up in conducting masses or sheets by varying magnetic fields.

Edison or *Richardson Effect.* The thermionic emission of electrons from hot bodies at a rate which increases rapidly with temperature.

Electric Circuit. The path taken by an electric current. Elements of the circuit which possess the properties of capacitance, inductance, resistance, etc., (Table 5a-1) are known as capacitors, inductors, resistors, etc., respectively.

Electric Lines of Force. Curves in an electric field whose tangents at any point give the direction of the field at that point.

Electric Tubes of Flux. Charge-free regions in isotropic space whose sides are everywhere tangent to the electric intensity and whose ends terminate on charges or charged areas or may meet to form closed rings.

Electrodes. Terminals by which current may enter or leave a region.

Electrolysis. The process of passing current through a substance when so doing liberates one or more of its constituents at the electrodes.

Electrolyte. A substance capable of electrolysis.

Electrostriction. The change of dimensions of a dielectric body when placed in an electric field.

Ettinghausen Effect. The phenomenon observed when a conductor carries current in a transverse magnetic field and a temperature gradient appears in a direction normal to both.

Ferrimagnetic Materials. Those in which spontaneous magnetic polarization occurs in nonequivalent sublattices; the polarization in one sublattice is aligned antiparallel to the other.

Ferroelectric Materials. Those in which the electric polarization (see Table 5a-1) is produced by cooperative action between groups or domains of collectively oriented molecules.

Ferromagnetic Materials. Those in which the magnetization is produced by cooperative action between groups or domains of collectively oriented molecules.

Gyromagnetic Effects. The phenomena of magnetization by rotation (Barnett effect) and rotation by magnetization (Einstein–de Haas effect).

Hall Effect. The production of a transverse potential gradient in a material by a steady electric current which has a component normal to a magnetic field.

Hysteresis Curves. These show the steady-state relation between the magnetic induction in a material and the steady-state alternating magnetic intensity (see Table 5a-1) that produces it.

Image Force. The force on a charge due to that charge or polarization which it induces on neighboring conductors or dielectrics.

Magnetic Lines of Force. Curves in a magnetic field whose tangents at any point give the direction of the magnetic intensity there.

Magnetic Saturation. A condition in which further increases in the magnetizing field produce no increase in magnetization.

Magnetic Tubes of Flux. Regions in space whose sides are everywhere tangent to the magnetic induction and whose ends may meet to form closed rings.

Magnetostriction. The change in dimensions of a body when placed in a magnetic field.

Nernst Effect. The production of a transverse electric field by a heat current.

Parallel Connections. These are so arranged that current divides between elements, no portion passing through more than one element.

Paramagnetic Bodies. When placed in an inhomogeneous magnetic field, these bodies tend to move toward its stronger regions.

Peltier Effect. The phenomenon of absorption or generation of heat according to the direction of passage of current across a junction of two conductors.

Permanent Magnets. Strongly magnetized bodies whose magnetization is little affected by the action of internal or external magnetic fields or by moderate mechanical shocks.

Photoconductivity. The property of a material which causes its resistivity (see Table 5a-1) to change when light falls upon it.

Photoelectric Effect. The liberation of electrons from a surface when light falls upon it.

Piezoelectric Effects. The phenomena of separation of charge in a crystal by mechanical stresses and the converse.

Proximity Effect. The distortion of alternating-current flow in one conductor due to that in neighboring conductors.

Pyroelectric Effect. The phenomenon of separation of charge in a crystal by heating.

Rectifiers. Devices which offer higher resistance (see Table 5a-1) to current passing in one direction than the other.

Seebeck or *Thermoelectric Effect.* The flow of current in a circuit consisting of two or more conductors caused by temperature differences at the junctions.

Semiconductor. A rather poor conductor whose conductivity may be changed radically by small changes in its physical condition.

Series Connections. These are so arranged that current must pass through all the elements in succession.

Skin Effect. The concentration of high-frequency alternating current near the surface of a conductor.

Thomson Effects. Phenomena in which potential gradients are produced in a material by differences of temperature.

Triboelectricity. The electric charges separated by friction between bodies.

Volta or *Contact-potential Effect.* The appearance of opposite charges on two dissimilar uncharged metals when placed in contact and the existence of a difference of potential between them.

Work Function. The energy needed to carry a charge across a metal vacuum boundary.

Note on Tables 5a-2, 5a-3, *and* 5a-4. These tables are presented to facilitate transposition of formulas from one system of units into another. In such systems as the Gaussian, the formula to be transposed must be written for a medium in which μ and ϵ are not unity before using the tables. For example, the force on a moving charge in static fields is

$$\mathbf{F} = Q\mathbf{E} + c^{-1}Q(\mathbf{v} \times \mathbf{B}') \qquad \text{(Gaussian)}$$

where $\mathbf{F}$ is in dynes, Q and $\mathbf{E}$ in esu, $\mathbf{v}$ in cm/sec, $\mathbf{B}'$ in emu or gauss, and $c \approx 3 \times 10^{10}$ cm/sec. The equivalent formula in cgs emu is found from Table 5a-3 where, using primes for emu quantities, we write according to directions, cQ' for Q, $c^{-1}\mathbf{E}'$ for $\mathbf{E}$ and obtain

$$\mathbf{F}' = Q'\mathbf{E}' + Q'(\mathbf{v} \times \mathbf{B}') \qquad \text{(cgs emu)}$$

For mks units, written with a double prime, we use the same table but write $10^{-5}\mathbf{F}''$ for $\mathbf{F}$, $10Q''$ for Q', $10^{-2}\mathbf{v}''$ or $10^{-2}\mathbf{l}''/t$ for $\mathbf{v}$ or $\mathbf{l}/t$ and $10^{-4}\mathbf{B}''$ for $\mathbf{B}'$, giving, after cancellation of 10^{-5} throughout,

$$\mathbf{F}'' = Q''\mathbf{E}'' + Q''(\mathbf{v}'' \times \mathbf{B}'') \qquad \text{(mks)}$$

In this formula $\mathbf{F}''$ is in newtons, Q'' in coulombs, $\mathbf{E}''$ in volts per meter, $\mathbf{v}''$ in meters per second, and $\mathbf{B}''$ in webers per square meter.

TABLE 5a-1. SYMBOLS. MKS UNIT NAMES. SYMBOLIC DEFINITIONS. DIMENSIONS[a]

Quantity	Symbol	Mks unit	Equivalents	Dimensions
Admittance	$\check{Y}$	mho	$\check{Z}^{-1} = G + jB$	$m^{-1}l^{-2}tQ^2$
Attenuation		decibels	$10 \log (A_1/A_2)$	0
Attenuation constant	α	parts/m	$(x_2 - x_1)^{-1} \ln (A_1/A_2)$	l^{-1}
Capacitance	C	farad	QV^{-1}	$m^{-1}l^{-2}t^2Q^2$
Mutual	C_m, C_{rs}	farad	$Q_sV_r^{-1}$ if $V_t = 0,\ t \neq r$	$m^{-1}l^{-2}t^2Q^2$
Self	C, C_{rr}	farad	$Q_rV_r^{-1}$ if $V_t = 0,\ t \neq r$	$m^{-1}l^{-2}t^2Q^2$
Capacitivity	ϵ	farad/m	Defined in 5a-1	$m^{-1}l^{-3}t^2Q^2$
Capacitivity of vacuum	ϵ_v	farad/m	8.85434×10^{-12}	$m^{-1}l^{-3}t^2Q^2$
Capacitivity, relative	K_e, K	ratio	$\epsilon\epsilon_v^{-1}$	0
Charge	$Q, \check{Q}, q$	coulomb	Fundamental	Q
Charge density, line	λ	coulomb/m	dQ/ds	$l^{-1}Q$
Surface	$\sigma, (\rho_s)$	coulomb/m²	dQ/dS	$l^{-2}Q$
Volume	ρ	coulomb/m³	dQ/dv	$l^{-3}Q$
Conductance	G	mho	$R^{-1} = IV^{-1}$	$m^{-1}l^{-2}tQ^2$
Conductivity	$\gamma, (\sigma)$	mho/m	$\mathbf{iE}^{-1}$	$m^{-1}l^{-3}tQ^2$
Surface	$\gamma', (\sigma')$	mho	$\mathbf{i}'_s\mathbf{E}_s^{-1}$	$m^{-1}l^{-2}tQ^2$
Current	$I, \check{I}$	ampere	Defined in 5a-1	$t^{-1}Q$
Current density	$\mathbf{i}, \check{\mathbf{i}}, \mathbf{J}$	ampere/m²	$\gamma\mathbf{E}, \gamma\check{\mathbf{E}}$	$l^{-2}t^{-1}Q$
Surface	$\mathbf{i}', \check{\mathbf{i}}', \mathbf{J}'$	ampere/m	$\gamma'\mathbf{E}_s, \gamma'\check{\mathbf{E}}_s$	$l^{-1}t^{-1}Q$
Dielectric constant	ϵ	farad/m	Defined in 5a-1	$m^{-1}l^{-3}t^2Q^2$
Displacement, electric	$\mathbf{D}, \check{\mathbf{D}}$	coulomb/m²	$\epsilon\mathbf{E}, \epsilon\check{\mathbf{E}}, \epsilon_v\mathbf{E} + \mathbf{P}$	$l^{-2}Q$
Elastance	S	daraf	C^{-1}, VQ^{-1}	$ml^2t^{-2}Q^{-2}$
Mutual	S_m, S_{rs}	daraf	$V_sQ_r^{-1}$ if $Q_t = 0,\ t \neq r$	$ml^2t^{-2}Q^{-2}$
Self	S, S_{rr}	daraf	$V_rQ_r^{-1}$ if $Q_t = 0,\ t \neq r$	$ml^2t^{-2}Q^{-2}$
Elastivitity	σ	daraf-m	ϵ^{-1}	$ml^3t^{-2}Q^{-2}$
Electromotance (electromotive force)	$\mathcal{E}, \check{\mathcal{E}}$	volt	Defined in 5a-1	$ml^2t^{-2}Q^{-1}$
Electronic charge	e	coulomb	1.6020×10^{-19}	Q
Energy	W	joule	$I\Phi, QV, \frac{1}{2}\int \mathbf{E} \cdot \mathbf{D}\, dv, \frac{1}{2}\int \mathbf{H} \cdot \mathbf{B}\, dv$	ml^2t^{-2}
Flux, electric	ψ	coulomb	$\int \mathbf{n} \cdot \mathbf{D}\, dS$	Q
Flux, magnetic	Φ	weber	$\int \mathbf{n} \cdot \mathbf{B}\, dS$	$ml^2t^{-1}Q^{-1}$
Force	$\mathbf{F}$	newton	$Q\mathbf{E}, \int \mathbf{i} \times \mathbf{B}\, dv$	mlt^{-2}
Frequency	ν	cycle/sec	$v\lambda^{-1}, \omega(2\pi)^{-1}$	t^{-1}
Frequency, angular	ω	radian/sec	$2\pi\nu, 2\pi v\lambda^{-1}$	t^{-1}
Impedance	$\check{Z}$	ohm	$\check{\mathcal{E}}\check{I}^{-1}, R + jX$	$ml^2t^{-1}Q^{-2}$
Intrinsic, vacuum	η	ohm	$\mu_v^{\frac{1}{2}}\epsilon_v^{-\frac{1}{2}} \approx 120\pi$	$ml^2t^{-1}Q^{-2}$
Mutual	$\check{Z}_m, \check{Z}_{rs}$	ohm		$ml^2t^{-1}Q^{-2}$
Self	$\check{Z}, \check{Z}_{rr}$	ohm	....	$ml^2t^{-1}Q^{-2}$
Inductance	L	henry	....	ml^2Q^{-2}
Mutual	M, L_m, L_{rs}	henry	$(I_1I_2)^{-1}\int \mathbf{B}_2 \cdot \mathbf{n}\, dS_1$	ml^2Q^{-2}
Self	L, L_{rr}	henry	$(\mu I^2)^{-1}\int B^2\, dv$	ml^2Q^{-2}
Induction, magnetic	$\mathbf{B}, \check{\mathbf{B}}$	weber/m²	Defined in 5a-1	$mt^{-1}Q^{-1}$
Intensity, electric	$\mathbf{E}, \check{\mathbf{E}}$	volt/m	Defined in 5a-1	$mlt^{-2}Q^{-1}$

[a] Space vectors are printed in boldface. Phasors, which are complex numbers used in solving algebraically for the steady-state value of a sinusoidally time-dependent quantity, are designated by a flat v over the symbol. For conjugate phasors, an inverted flat v is used. The symbol j is used for $(-1)^{\frac{1}{2}}$.

TABLE 5a-1. SYMBOLS. MKS UNIT NAMES. SYMBOLIC DEFINITIONS. DIMENSIONS (*Continued*)

Quantity	Symbol	Mks unit	Equivalents	Dimensions
Intensity, magnetic	$\mathbf{H}, \check{\mathbf{H}}$	amp-turn/m	$\mu^{-1}\mathbf{B}$, $\mu_v^{-1}\mathbf{B} - \mathbf{M}$	$l^{-1}t^{-1}Q$
Length	l	meter	Fundamental	l
Magnetization (loop)	$\mathbf{M}$	amp-turn/m	$(K_m - 1)\mathbf{H}$	$l^{-1}t^{-1}Q$
Magnetization (dipole)	$\mathbf{M}$	weber/m²	$(K_m - 1)\mu_v\mathbf{H}$	$mt^{-1}Q^{-1}$
Magnetomotance (magnetomotive force)	$\mathfrak{F}$	amp-turn	$\mu^{-1}\oint\mathbf{B}\cdot\mathbf{ds}$, $\oint\mathbf{H}\cdot\mathbf{ds}$	$t^{-1}Q$
Mass	m	kilogram	Fundamental	m
Moment, electric	$\mathbf{p}, \check{\mathbf{p}}$	coulomb-m	$Q\,\mathbf{ds}$	lQ
Moment, magnetic loop	$\mathbf{m}, \check{\mathbf{m}}$	amp-m²	$\pi a^2 I\mathbf{n}$	$l^2t^{-1}Q$
Moment, magnetic (dipole)	$\mathbf{m}$	weber-m	$m\,\mathbf{ds}$	$ml^3t^{-1}Q^{-1}$
Period	T	second	$\omega^{-1}2\pi, \nu^{-1}, \lambda v^{-1}$	t
Permeance	$\mathcal{P}$	henry	$\mathcal{R}^{-1}, \mathfrak{F}^{-1}\Phi$	ml^2Q^{-2}
Permeability	μ	henry/m	Defined in 5a-1	mlQ^{-2}
Vacuum	μ_v	henry/m	$4\pi \times 10^{-7}$	mlQ^{-2}
Relative	K_m		$\mu_v^{-1}\mu$	0
Phase angle	φ	radian	....	0
Phase constant (see Wave number)				
Polarization, electric	$\mathbf{P}$	coulomb/m²	$(K_e - 1)\epsilon_v\mathbf{E}$	$l^{-2}Q$
Polarization, magnetic (see Magnetization)				
Pole strength	m	weber	....	$ml^2t^{-1}Q^{-1}$
Potential, electrostatic	V	volt	Defined in 5a-1	$ml^2t^{-2}Q^{-1}$
Electrodynamic	$\Phi, \check{\Phi}$	volt	$\mathbf{E} = -\nabla\Phi - d\mathbf{A}/dt$	$ml^2t^{-2}Q^{-1}$
Vector magnetic	$\mathbf{A}, \check{\mathbf{A}}$	weber/m	$\mathbf{B} = \nabla \times \mathbf{A}$	$mlt^{-1}Q^{-1}$
Power	P	watt	dW/dt	ml^2t^{-3}
Poynting vector	$\mathbf{\Pi}$	watt/m²	$\mu^{-1}\mathbf{E} \times \mathbf{B}$	mt^{-3}
Propagation constant	$\Gamma, (\check{\gamma})$	parts/m	$\alpha + j\beta$	l^{-1}
Quality factor	Q	a ratio	ωLR^{-1}	0
Reactance	X	ohm	$\omega L - (\omega C)^{-1}$	$ml^2t^{-1}Q^{-2}$
Reluctance	$\mathcal{R}$	amp-turn/weber	$\mathfrak{F}\Phi^{-1}$	$m^{-1}l^{-2}Q^2$
Reluctivity	ν	m/henry	μ^{-1}	$m^{-1}l^{-1}Q^2$
Resistance	R	ohm	VI^{-1}	$ml^2t^{-1}Q^{-2}$
Resistivity	ρ	ohm-m	$\mathbf{Ei}^{-1}$	$ml^3t^{-1}Q^{-2}$
Susceptance	B	mho	$\check{Y} = G + jB$	$m^{-1}l^{-2}tQ^2$
Susceptibility, electric	χ_e	....	K_e^{-1}	0
Magnetic	χ_m	....	K_m^{-1}	0
Time	t	second	Fundamental	t
Time constant	τ	second	LR^{-1}, RC	t
Velocity of light	c	m/sec	2.99790×10^8	lt^{-1}
Wavelength	λ	meter	$2\pi\beta^{-1}, 2\pi v\omega^{-1}$	l
Wave number (phase constant)	β, k	radian/m	$2\pi\lambda^{-1}, \omega v^{-1}$, $\gamma = \alpha + j\beta$	l^{-1}
Work	W	joule	$\oint\mathbf{F}\cdot\mathbf{ds}$	ml^2t^{-2}

TABLE 5a-2. REDUCTION OF FORMULA TO CGS ESU[a]

Quantity	Esu	Emu	Practical cgs and rationalized mks	
Capacitance	C	$c^{-2}C$	$9^{-1}10^{-11}C$ farad	
Capacitivity	ϵ	$c^{-2}\epsilon$	$9^{-1}10^{-11}\epsilon(4\pi$ farad)/cm	$\epsilon_v\epsilon$ farad/m
Charge, quantity	Q	$c^{-1}Q$	$3^{-1}10^{-9}Q$ coulomb	
Conductance	G	$c^{-2}G$	$9^{-1}10^{-11}G$ mho	
Conductivity, area	γ'	$c^{-2}\gamma'$	$9^{-1}10^{-11}\gamma'$ mho	
Conductivity, volume	γ	$c^{-2}\gamma$	$9^{-1}10^{-11}\gamma$ mho/cm	$9^{-1}10^{-9}\gamma$ mho/m
Current	I	$c^{-1}I$	$3^{-1}10^{-9}I$ amp	
Current density, area	$\mathbf{i}'$	$c^{-1}\mathbf{i}'$	$3^{-1}10^{-9}\mathbf{i}'$ amp/cm	$3^{-1}10^{-7}\mathbf{i}'$ amp/m
Current density, volume	$\mathbf{i}$	$c^{-1}\mathbf{i}$	$3^{-1}10^{-9}\mathbf{i}$ amp/cm^2	$3^{-1}10^{-5}\mathbf{i}$ amp/m^2
Displacement	$\mathbf{D}$	$c^{-1}\mathbf{D}$	$3^{-1}10^{-9}\mathbf{D}$ $(4\pi$ coulomb)/cm^2	$3\epsilon_v 10^4\mathbf{D}$ coulomb/m^2
Elastance	S	c^2S	$9 \times 10^{11}S$ daraf	
Electromotance	$\mathcal{E}$	$c\mathcal{E}$	$300\mathcal{E}$ volt	
Energy	W	W	W erg	$10^{-7}W$ joule
Force	$\mathbf{F}$	$\mathbf{F}$	$\mathbf{F}$ dyne	$10^{-5}\mathbf{F}$ newton
Impedance	$\check{Z}$	$c^2\check{Z}$	$9 \times 10^{11}\check{Z}$ ohm	
Inductance	L	c^2L	$9 \times 10^{11}L$ henry	
Intensity, electric	$\mathbf{E}$	$c\mathbf{E}$	$300\mathbf{E}$ volt/cm	$30{,}000\mathbf{E}$ volt/m
Length	l	l	l centimeter	$10^{-2}l$ meter
Mass	m	m	m gram	$10^{-3}m$ kilogram
Polarization, electric	$\mathbf{P}$	$c^{-1}\mathbf{P}$	$3^{-1} \times 10^{-9}\mathbf{P}$ coulomb/cm^2	$3^{-1} \times 10^{-5}\mathbf{P}$ coulomb/m^2
Potential, electric	V	cV	$300V$ volt	
Power	P	P	P erg/sec	$10^{-7}P$ watt
Reactance	X	c^2X	$9 \times 10^{11}X$ ohm	
Resistance	R	c^2R	$9 \times 10^{11}R$ ohm	
Resistivity, area	σ	$c^2\sigma$	$9 \times 10^{11}\sigma$ ohm	
Resistivity, volume	ρ	$c^2\rho$	$9 \times 10^{11}\rho$ ohm-cm	$9 \times 10^{9}\rho$ ohm-m

[a] A formula given in emu, unrationalized practical cgs or rationalized mks units, in which the capacitivity or permeability, if relevant, appears explicitly, is expressed in cgs esu by replacing each symbol by the value given in the emu, practical cgs or rationalized mks column, respectively. Each line may be read as an equation relating the size of the units involved. Here c is 2.9979×10^{10}. For precise work the 3 and 9 factors should be replaced by 2.9979 and 8.9874.

TABLE 5a-3. REDUCTION OF FORMULA TO CGS EMU[a]

Quantity	Emu	Esu	Practical cgs and rationalized mks
Capacitance	C	c^2C^*	10^9C farad
Charge, quantity	Q	cQ^*	$10Q$ coulomb
Conductance	G	c^2G^*	10^9G mho
Conductivity, area	γ'	$c^2\gamma'^*$	$10^9\gamma'$ mho
Conductivity, volume	γ	$c^2\gamma^*$	$10^9\gamma$ mho/cm; $10^{11}\gamma$ mho/m
Current	I	cI^*	$10I$ amp
Current density, area	i'	$c\mathrm{i}'^*$	$10\mathrm{i}'$ amp/cm; $10^3\mathrm{i}'$ amp/m
Current density, volume	i	$c\mathrm{i}^*$	$10\mathrm{i}$ amp/cm²; $10^5\mathrm{i}$ amp/m²
Elastance	S	$c^{-2}S^*$	$10^{-9}S$ daraf
Electromotance	$\mathcal{E}$	$c^{-1}\mathcal{E}^*$	$10^{-8}\mathcal{E}$ volt
Energy	W	W	W erg; $10^{-7}W$ joule
Flux, magnetic	Φ^*	$c^{-1}\Phi$	Φ maxwell; $10^{-8}\Phi$ weber
Force	$\mathbf{F}$	$\mathbf{F}$	$\mathbf{F}$ dyne; $10^{-5}\mathbf{F}$ newton
Impedance	$\check{Z}$	$c^{-2}\check{Z}^*$	$10^{-9}\check{Z}$ ohm
Inductance	L	$c^{-2}L^*$	$10^{-9}L$ henry
Induction, magnetic	$\mathbf{B}^*$	$c^{-1}\mathbf{B}$	$\mathbf{B}$ gauss; $10^{-4}\mathbf{B}$ weber/m²
Intensity, electric	$\mathbf{E}$	$c^{-1}\mathbf{E}^*$	$10^{-8}\mathbf{E}$ volt/cm; $10^{-6}\mathbf{E}$ volt/m
Intensity, magnetic	$\mathbf{H}^*$	$c\mathbf{H}$	$\mathbf{H}$ oersted; $(4\pi)^{-1}10^3\mathbf{H}$ amp-turn/m
Length	l	l	l centimeter; $10^{-2}l$ meter
Magnetic moment (dipole)	$\mathbf{m}'^*$	$c^{-1}\mathbf{m}'$	$4\pi\mathbf{m}'$ maxwell-cm; $4\pi10^{-10}\mathbf{m}'$ weber-m
Magnetic moment (loop)	$\mathbf{m}^*$	$c\mathbf{m}$	$10\mathbf{m}$ amp-cm²; $10^{-3}\mathbf{m}$ amp-m²
Magnetization (dipole)	$\mathbf{M}'^*$	$c^{-1}\mathbf{M}'$	$4\pi\mathbf{M}'$ maxwell/cm²; $4\pi10^{-4}\mathbf{M}'$ weber/m²
Magnetization (loop)	$\mathbf{M}^*$	$c\mathbf{M}$	$10\mathbf{M}$ amp/cm; $1000\mathbf{M}$ amp/m
Magnetomotance	$\mathcal{F}^*$	$c\mathcal{F}$	$\mathcal{F}$ gilbert; $(4\pi)^{-1}10\mathcal{F}$ amp-turn
Mass	m	m	m gram; $10^{-3}m$ kilogram
Permeability	μ^*	$c^{-2}\mu$	μ gauss/oersted; $4\pi10^{-7}\mu$ henry/m
Pole strength, magnetic	m^*	$c^{-1}m$	$4\pi m$ maxwell; $4\pi10^{-8}m$ weber
Potential, electric	V	$c^{-1}V^*$	$10^{-8}V$ volt
Potential, vector	$\mathbf{A}^*$	$c^{-1}\mathbf{A}$	$\mathbf{A}$ gauss-cm; $10^{-6}\mathbf{A}$ weber/m
Power	P	P	P erg/sec; $10^{-7}P$ watt
Reactance	X	$c^{-2}X^*$	$10^{-9}X$ ohm
Reluctance	$\mathcal{R}^*$	$c^2\mathcal{R}$	$\mathcal{R}$ gilbert/max; $(4\pi)^{-1}10^9\mathcal{R}$ amp-turn/web
Resistance	R	$c^{-2}R^*$	$10^{-9}R$ ohm
Resistivity, area	σ	$c^{-2}\sigma^*$	$10^{-9}\sigma$ ohm
Resistivity, volume	ρ	$c^{-2}\rho^*$	$10^{-9}\rho$ ohm-cm; $10^{-11}\rho$ ohm-m

[a] A formula given in esu, Gaussian (starred), unrationalized practical cgs, or rationalized mks units, in which the capacitivity or permeability, if relevant, appears explicitly, is expressed in cgs emu by replacing each symbol by the value given in the esu, starred, practical cgs, or rationalized mks columns, respectively. Each line may be read as an equation relating the size of the units involved. Here c is 2.9979×10^{10}.

Table 5a-4. Reduction of Formula to Rationalized mks Units[a]

Quantity	(a) Practical cgs (b) mks	Emu	Esu
Capacitance	C farad	$10^{-9}C$	$9 \times 10^{11}C^*$
Capacitivity	(a) ϵ (4π farad)/cm	$10^{-9}\epsilon$	$9 \times 10^{11}\epsilon^*$
	(b) ϵ farad/m	$4\pi 10^{-11}\epsilon$	$\epsilon_v^{-1}\epsilon^*$
Charge, quantity	Q coulomb	$10^{-1}Q$	$3 \times 10^{9}Q^*$
Conductance	G mho	$10^{-9}G$	$9 \times 10^{11}G^*$
Conductivity, area	γ' mho	$10^{-9}\gamma'$	$9 \times 10^{11}\gamma'^*$
Conductivity, volume	(a) γ mho/cm	$10^{-9}\gamma$	$9 \times 10^{11}\gamma^*$
	(b) γ mho/m	$10^{-11}\gamma$	$9 \times 10^{9}\gamma^*$
Current	I ampere	$10^{-1}I$	$3 \times 10^{9}I^*$
Current density, area	(a) i′ amp/cm	10^{-1}i′	3×10^{9}i′*
	(b) i′ amp/m	10^{-3}i′	3×10^{7}i′*
Current density, volume	(a) i amp/cm²	10^{-1}i	3×10^{9}i*
	(b) i amp/m²	10^{-5}i	3×10^{5}i*
Displacement, electric	(a) **D** (4π coulomb)/cm²	10^{-1}**D**	3×10^{9}**D***
	(b) **D** coulomb/m²	$4\pi 10^{-5}$**D**	$(3\epsilon_v)^{-1}10^{-4}$**D***
Elastance	S daraf	$10^{9}S$	$9^{-1}10^{-11}S^*$
Electromotance	$\mathcal{E}$ volt	$10^{8}\mathcal{E}$	$(300)^{-1}\mathcal{E}^*$
Energy	(a) W erg	W	W
	(b) W joule	$10^{7}W$	$10^{7}W$
Flux, magnetic	(a) Φ maxwell	Φ^*	$3^{-1}10^{-10}\Phi$
	(b) Φ weber	$10^{8}\Phi^*$	$(300)^{-1}\Phi$
Force	(a) **F** dyne	**F**	**F**
	(b) **F** newton	10^{5}**F**	10^{5}**F**
Impedance	$\check{Z}$ ohm	$10^{9}\check{Z}$	$9^{-1}10^{-11}\check{Z}^*$
Inductance	L henry	$10^{9}L$	$9^{-1}10^{-11}L^*$
Induction, magnetic	(a) **B** gauss	**B***	$3^{-1}10^{-10}$**B**
	(b) **B** weber/m²	10^{4}**B***	$3^{-1}10^{-6}$**B**
Intensity, electric	(a) **E** volt/cm	10^{8}**E**	$(300)^{-1}$**E***
	(b) **E** volt/m	10^{6}**E**	$3^{-1}10^{-4}$**E***
Intensity, magnetic	(a) **H** oersted	**H***	3×10^{10}**H**
	(b) **H** amp-turn/m	$4\pi 10^{-3}$**H***	$12\pi 10^{7}$**H**
Length	(a) l centimeter	l	l
	(b) l meter	$10^{2}l$	$10^{2}l$
Magnetic moment (dipole)	(a) m′ maxwell-cm	$(4\pi)^{-1}$m′*	$(12\pi)^{-1}10^{-10}$m′
	(b) m′ weber-m	$(4\pi)^{-1}10^{10}$m′*	$(12\pi)^{-1}$m′
Magnetic moment (loop)	(a) m amp-cm²	10^{-1}m*	3×10^{9}m
	(b) m amp-m²	10^{3}m*	3×10^{13}m
Magnetization (dipole)	(a) **M**′ maxwell/cm²	$(4\pi)^{-1}$**M**′*	$(12\pi)^{-1}10^{-10}$**M**′
	(b) **M**′ weber/m²	$(4\pi)^{-1}10^{4}$**M**′*	$(12\pi)^{-1}10^{-6}$**M**′
Magnetization (loop)	(a) **M** amp/cm	10^{-1}**M***	3×10^{9}**M**
	(b) **M** amp/m	10^{3}**M***	3×10^{7}**M**

[a] A formula given in cgs emu, cgs esu, or Gaussian (starred) units, in which the capacitivity or permeability, if relevant, appears explicitly, may be expressed in (a) unrationalized cgs practical units or (b) rationalized mks units by replacing each symbol with its value in the emu, esu, or starred column, respectively. Each line may be read as an equation relating the size of the units involved. In precise work, replace 3 by 2.9979 and 9 by 8.9874.

TABLE 5a-4. REDUCTION OF FORMULA TO RATIONALIZED MKS UNITS (*Continued*)

Quantity	(*a*) Practical cgs (*b*) mks	Emu	Esu
Magnetomotance.........	(*a*) $\mathfrak{F}$ gilbert	$\mathfrak{F}^*$	$3 \times 10^{10}\mathfrak{F}$
	(*b*) $\mathfrak{F}$ amp-turn	$4\pi 10^{-1}\mathfrak{F}^*$	$12\pi \times 10^{9}\mathfrak{F}$
Mass....................	(*a*) m gram	m	m
	(*b*) m kilogram	$10^3 m$	$10^3 m$
Permeability.............	(*a*) μ gauss/oersted	μ^*	$9^{-1}10^{-20}\mu$
	(*b*) μ henry/m	$(4\pi)^{-1}10^7\mu^*$	$(36\pi)^{-1}10^{-13}\mu$
Polarization, electric......	(*a*) $\mathbf{P}$ coulomb/cm²	$10^{-1}\mathbf{P}$	$3 \times 10^9\mathbf{P}^*$
	(*b*) $\mathbf{P}$ coulomb/m²	$10^{-5}\mathbf{P}$	$3 \times 10^5\mathbf{P}^*$
Pole strength............	(*a*) m maxwell	$(4\pi)^{-1}m^*$	$(12\pi)^{-1}10^{-10}m$
	(*b*) m weber	$(4\pi)^{-1}10^8 m^*$	$(1200\pi)^{-1}m$
Potential, electric.........	V volt	$10^8 V$	$(300)^{-1}V^*$
Potential, vector..........	(*a*) $\mathbf{A}$ gauss-cm	$\mathbf{A}^*$	$3^{-1}10^{-10}\mathbf{A}$
	(*b*) $\mathbf{A}$ weber/m	$10^6\mathbf{A}^*$	$3^{-1}10^{-4}\mathbf{A}$
Power....................	(*a*) P erg/sec	P	P
	(*b*) P watt	$10^7 P$	$10^7 P$
Reactance...............	X ohm	$10^9 X$	$9^{-1}10^{-11}X^*$
Reluctance...............	(*a*) $\mathfrak{R}$ gilbert/max	$\mathfrak{R}^*$	$9 \times 10^{20}\mathfrak{R}$
	(*b*) $\mathfrak{R}$ amp-turn/weber	$4\pi 10^{-9}\mathfrak{R}^*$	$36\pi \times 10^{11}\mathfrak{R}$
Resistance................	R ohm	$10^9 R$	$9^{-1}10^{-11}R^*$
Resistivity, area..........	σ ohm	$10^9\sigma$	$9^{-1}10^{-11}\sigma^*$
Resistivity, volume.......	(*a*) ρ ohm-cm	$10^9\rho$	$9^{-1}10^{-11}\rho^*$
	(*b*) ρ ohm-m	$10^{11}\rho$	$9^{-1}10^{-9}\rho^*$

5b. Formulas

W. R. SMYTHE[1]

California Institute of Technology

S. SILVER, J. R. WHINNERY, AND D. J. ANGELAKOS[2]

University of California

D. F. BLEIL[3]

U.S. Naval Ordnance Laboratory, White Oak, Md.

STATIC-FIELD FORMULAS

Note. In the following formulas $\approx$ designates an approximate equality, $K(k)$ and $E(k)$ are complete elliptic integrals of modulus k, $F(\phi,k)$ and $E(\phi,k)$ are incomplete elliptic integrals, $\ln x$ is the natural logarithm of x, δ_n^m is the Kronecker delta which is zero unless m equals n when it is one, $J_n(x)$ is a Bessel function, $\Gamma(x)$ is a gamma function, $(2n-1)!!$ means $1 \cdot 3 \cdot 5 \cdots (2n-1)$, $(2n)!!$ means $2 \cdot 4 \cdot 6 \cdots (2n)$. Vectors are written boldface unless only the strength or magnitude is involved when the same symbol is used without boldface. The positive value of a difference $x - y$ is indicated by $|x - y|$.

5b-1. Capacitance Formulas in MKS Units

Single Body Remote from Earth

Sphere of radius a $\quad C = 4\pi\epsilon a \approx 1.1128 \times 10^{-10} a$

Oblate spheroid of semiaxes a and c, $a > c$ $\quad C = 4\pi\epsilon(a^2 - c^2)^{\frac{1}{2}}[\tan^{-1}(a^2c^{-2} - 1)^{\frac{1}{2}}]^{-1}$

Prolate spheroid of semiaxes a and b, $a > b$ $\quad C = 4\pi\epsilon(a^2 - b^2)^{\frac{1}{2}}[\tanh^{-1}(1 - b^2a^{-2})^{\frac{1}{2}}]^{-1}$

Ellipsoid of semiaxes a, b, and c, $a > b > c$

$$C = 4\pi\epsilon(a^2 - c^2)^{\frac{1}{2}}[F(k,\phi)]^{-1}$$

where $\phi = \sin^{-1}(1 - c^2a^{-2})^{\frac{1}{2}}$ and $k = (a^2 - b^2)^{\frac{1}{2}}(a^2 - c^2)^{-\frac{1}{2}}$.

Circular disk of radius a $\quad C = 8\epsilon a$

Elliptic disk of semiaxes a and b, $a > b$ $\quad C = 4\pi\epsilon a\{K[(1 - b^2a^{-2})^{\frac{1}{2}}]\}^{-1}$

Two spheres of radius a in contact $\quad C = 8\pi\epsilon a \ln 2$

Two spheres of radii a and b in contact

$$C = -4\pi\epsilon ab(a+b)^{-1}\{2\gamma + \psi[b(a+b)^{-1}] + \psi[a(a+b)^{-1}]\}$$

where $\psi(z) = \Gamma'(z)/\Gamma(z)$ and γ is Euler's constant 0.5772.

[1] Static-field formulas.
[2] Dynamic-field equations.
[3] Some solid-state formulas.

Two spheres of radius a, distance between centers c, connected by thin wire

$$C = 8\pi\epsilon a \sinh \beta \sum_{n=1}^{\infty} (-1)^{n+1} \operatorname{csch} m\beta$$

where $\cosh \beta = \frac{1}{2}ca^{-1}$.
Two spheres of radii a and b, distance between centers c, connected by thin wire

$$C = 8\pi\epsilon ab \sinh \alpha \sum_{n=1}^{\infty} \{(c \sinh n\alpha)^{-1} + [a \sinh n\alpha + b \sinh (n-1)\alpha]^{-1}\}$$

where $\cosh \alpha = \frac{1}{2}a^{-1}b^{-1}(c^2 - a^2 - b^2)$.
Two spherical caps with a common rim which meet at an external angle π/m where m is a positive integer

$$C = 4\pi\epsilon a\{1 + \sin \alpha \sum_{s=1}^{\infty} [\csc (m^{-1}s\pi + \alpha) - \csc (m^{-1}s\pi)]\}$$

The sphere of which the flatter cap is a portion has a radius a and the rim subtends an angle α at its center.
Same as above but with external angle $3\pi/2$.[1]

$$C = 4\pi\epsilon 3^{-\frac{1}{2}}a \sin \alpha\{3^{\frac{1}{2}} - 3^{-1}4 + [2 \sin \tfrac{1}{3}\alpha(\sin \tfrac{1}{3}\alpha + \sin \tfrac{1}{3}\pi)]^{-1} + [2 \cos \tfrac{1}{3}\alpha(\cos \tfrac{1}{3}\alpha + \cos \tfrac{1}{3}\pi)]^{-1}\}$$

Spherical bowl whose chord, drawn from center to rim, subtends an angle α at the center of the sphere of radius a on which it lies

$$C = 4\epsilon a(\alpha + \sin \alpha)$$

Torus formed by rotation of a circle of radius a about a coplanar line a distance b from its center

$$C = 8\pi\epsilon b(1 - a^2b^{-2})^{\frac{1}{2}} \sum_{n=1}^{\infty} (2 - \delta_n^0) \frac{Q_n}{P_n}$$

where $P_0 = 2k^{\frac{1}{2}}K(k')$, $Q_0 = 2k^{\frac{1}{2}}K(k)$, $P_1 = 2k^{-\frac{1}{2}}E(k')$, and $Q_1 = 2k^{-\frac{1}{2}}[K(k) - E(k)]$ and the moduli of the complete elliptic functions are given by

$$k = a[b + (b^2 - a^2)^{\frac{1}{2}}]^{-1} = (1 - k'^2)^{\frac{1}{2}}$$

When $n > 1$, the following recurrence formula may be used to find both P_n and Q_n

$$(2n + 1)P_{n+1} - 4na^{-1}bP_n + (2n - 1)P_{n-1} = 0$$

A capacitance table is given in *Australian J. Phys.* [**7**, 350 (1954)].
Torus formed by rotation of a circle of diameter d about a tangent line

$$C = 8\pi\epsilon d \sum_{n=1}^{\infty} [J_1(k_nd)]^{-1} S_{0,0}(k_nd) \approx 0.970 \times 10^{-10}d$$

where $S_{0,0}(k_nd)$ is a Lommel function and $J_0(k_nd) = 0$.

[1] For additional intersecting sphere-capacitance formulas, see Snow, *J. Research Natl. Bur. Standards* **43**, 377–407 (1949).

Aichi's formula for a nearly spherical surface

$$C \approx 3.139 \times 10^{-11} S^{\frac{1}{2}}$$

where S is surface area.
Cube of side a. Close lower limit

$$C \approx 0.7283 \times 10^{-10} a$$

Figure of rotation, $z = a(\cos u + k \cos 2u)$, $\rho = a(\sin u - k \sin 2u)$, $0 < k < \frac{1}{2}$

$$C \approx 1.11278 \times 10^{-10} a (1 - 0.06857k^2 - 0.00559k^4)$$

Flat circular annulus, with edges at $\rho = a$, $\rho = b$. $a < b$

$$C \approx 4.510 \times 10^{-11} b \left[\cos^{-1} \frac{a}{b} + \left(1 - \frac{a^2}{b^2}\right)^{\frac{1}{2}} \tanh^{-1} \frac{a}{b} \right] \left(1 + \frac{0.0143b}{a} \tan^3 \frac{1.28a}{b}\right)$$

Error varies from about $\pm 0.001C$ at $b = 1.1a$ to zero at $b = a$.

$$C \approx 17.48 \times 10^{-12} (a + b) \{\ln [16(a + b)(b - a)^{-1}]\}^{-1}$$

Error varies from about $\pm 0.001C$ at $b = 1.1a$ to zero at $b = a$.
Thin torus generated by rotation of a circle of radius a about a coplanar line a distance b from its center

$$C \approx 3.49066 \times 10^{-10} b \left(\ln \frac{8b}{a} \right)^{-1}$$

Capacitance between Two Bodies Remote from All Others and Carrying Equal and Opposite Charges

Two spheres of radii a and b with distance r between centers

$$C = (c_{11} c_{22} - c_{12}^2)(c_{11} + c_{22} + 2c_{12})^{-1}$$

where c_{11} or $c_{22} = 4\pi\epsilon ab \sinh \alpha \sum_{n=1}^{\infty} [(b \text{ or } a) \sinh n\alpha + (a \text{ or } b) \sinh (n - 1)\alpha]$.

$$c_{12} = -4\pi\epsilon abr^{-1} \sinh \alpha \sum_{n=1}^{\infty} \operatorname{csch} n\alpha \qquad \text{and} \qquad \cosh \alpha = \tfrac{1}{2}(r^2 - a^2 - b^2)a^{-1}b^{-1}$$

Two equal spheres of radius a with distance r between centers

$$C = 2\pi\epsilon a \sinh \beta \sum_{n=1}^{\infty} [\operatorname{csch} (2n - 1)\beta + \operatorname{csch} 2n\beta]$$

where $\cosh \beta = \frac{1}{2} r a^{-1}$.
Kirchhoff's formula for two identical plane parallel coaxial circular disks of thickness t and radius r with square edges and a distance d between adjacent faces

$$C \approx 8.855 \times 10^{-12} (\pi r^2 d^{-1} + r\{-1 + \ln [16\pi r d^{-1}(1 + t d^{-1})] + 4\pi t d^{-1} \ln (1 + t^{-1} d)\})$$

Two identical oppositely charged plane parallel coaxial infinitely thin circular disks at a distance c apart

$$C \approx 8.855 \times 10^{-12} \{\pi r^2 d^{-1} + r[\ln (16\pi r d^{-1}) - 1]\}$$

Two thin oppositely charged coaxial rings generated by rotating two coplanar circles of radius a about a line parallel to and at a distance b from the line of length c that joins their centers

$$C \approx 1.7480 \times 10^{-10} \left\{ \frac{1}{2b} \ln \frac{8b}{a} + \frac{1}{(4a^2 + c^2)^{\frac{1}{2}}} K[(1 + 4c^2b^{-2})^{-\frac{1}{2}}] \right\}^{-1}$$

Capacitance between Two Bodies, One Enclosing the Other

Concentric spheres of radii a and b, $a < b$ $\quad C = 4\pi\epsilon ab(b - a)^{-1}$
Spheres of radii a and b with distance c between centers

$$C = 4\pi\epsilon ab \sinh \alpha \sum_{s=0}^{\infty} [b \sinh n\alpha - a \sinh (n - 1)\alpha]^{-1}$$

where $\cosh \alpha = \frac{1}{2}(a^2 + b^2 - c^2)(ab)^{-1}$.
Confocal ellipsoids with semiaxes $a > b > c$, $a' > b' > c'$, and $a > a'$

$$C = 4\pi\epsilon a'(a - a')^{-1}(a^2 - c^2)^{\frac{1}{2}}\{F[(a^2 - b^2)^{\frac{1}{2}}(a^2 - c^2)^{-\frac{1}{2}}, \sin^{-1} (1 - c^2a^{-2})^{\frac{1}{2}}]\}^{-1}$$

Small sphere of radius a midway between planes a distance $2c$ apart

$$C \approx 1.1128 \times 10^{-10} \left(\frac{1}{a} - \frac{1}{c} \ln 2\right)^{-1}$$

Two-dimensional Formulas for Capacitance per Meter Length

Let $U + jV = f(x + jy)$, then if V_1 and V_2 form two closed curves in the xy plane such that all U lines originate inside one and terminate inside the other and are continuous in the intermediate regions, V_1 and V_2 are sections of two cylindrical conductors and the capacitance per meter between them is

$$C_1 = \epsilon[U]|V_2 - V_1|^{-1}$$

where $[U]$ is the increment in U in passing once around V_1 or V_2 in the positive direction.
Two circular cylinders of radii a and b with a distance c between centers

$$C_1 = 2\pi\epsilon \left(\cosh^{-1} \frac{|c^2 - a^2 - b^2|}{2ab}\right)^{-1}$$

One cylinder may enclose the other or they may be mutually external.
Cylinder of radius a and plane at a distance c from its center

$$C_1 = 2\pi\epsilon[\cosh^{-1} (ca^{-1})]^{-1}$$

Coaxial circular cylinders of radii a and b, $b > a$

$$C_1 = 2\pi\epsilon \ln (a^{-1}b)$$

Confocal elliptic cylinders semiaxes a, b and a', b', $b > a$, $b' > a'$, $a > a'$

$$C_1 = 2\pi\epsilon[\tanh^{-1} (b^{-1}a) - \tanh^{-1} (b'^{-1}a')]^{-1}$$

Two identical infinite parallel coplanar strips with near-edge distance $2a$ and far-edge distance $2b$

$$C_1 = \epsilon K[(1 - b^{-2}a^2)^{\frac{1}{2}}][K(b^{-1}a)]^{-1}$$

Two identical infinite parallel flat strips of width $2a$ at a distance $2b$ apart in position to form opposite faces of a rectangular prism[1]

$$C_1 = \epsilon K[(1 - k^2)^{\frac{1}{2}}][K(k)]^{-1} = \epsilon K(k')[K(k)]^{-1}$$

where k must be chosen to satisfy

$$\frac{a}{b} = \frac{K(k')E\{\cos^{-1}[E(k')/K(k')], k'\} - E(k')F\{\cos^{-1}[E(k')/K(k')], k'\}}{E(k')K(k) - (k/k')^2E(k)K(k')}$$

Approximate formula for above

$$C_1 \approx \epsilon b^{-1}a\{1 + b(\pi a)^{-1}[1 + \ln(2\pi b^{-1}a)]\}$$

Square coaxial line with faces of inner square section of width $2a$ parallel to faces of outer square section of width $2b$

$$C_1 = 2\epsilon \frac{K[(k_1^2 - k_2^2)^{\frac{1}{2}}k_1^{-1}(1 - k_2^2)^{-\frac{1}{2}}]}{K[k_2(1 - k_1^2)^{\frac{1}{2}}k_1^{-1}(1 - k_2^2)^{-\frac{1}{2}}]}$$

where k_1 and k_2 are found from

$$\frac{K(k_1)}{K[(1 - k_1^2)^{\frac{1}{2}}]} = \frac{K[(1 - k_2^2)^{\frac{1}{2}}]}{K(k_2)} = \frac{b + a}{b - a}$$

Strip of width b coplanar with and parallel to the edge of a semi-infinite grounded sheet with a gap a between them

$$C_1 = 2\epsilon K[b^{\frac{1}{2}}(a + b)^{-\frac{1}{2}}]\{K[a^{\frac{1}{2}}(a + b)^{-\frac{1}{2}}]\}^{-1}$$

Circular cylinder of radius a midway between earthed parallel plates at a distance $2b$ apart

$$C_1 \approx 4\epsilon K(\sin\theta)[K(\cos\theta)]^{-1}$$

where θ must be chosen to satisfy

$$\sin\theta = \tanh[\pi a\theta(2b\theta - \pi a)^{-1}]$$

This is an upper limit which is about 0.1 per cent above the true value when $a = \frac{1}{2}b$ and approaches the true value as a/b diminishes.

Small wire of radius a parallel to and at a distance c from the nearer of two parallel earthed plates at a distance b apart. $a \ll c$

$$C_1 \approx 2\pi\epsilon\left[\ln\left(\frac{2b}{\pi a}\sin\frac{\pi c}{b}\right)\right]^{-1}$$

Rectangular prism of n sides, each side of width a, coaxial with and inside circular cylinder of radius b. $b \gg a$

$$C_1 \approx 2\pi\epsilon[\ln(a^{-1}bN)]^{-1}$$

where $N = 2\pi n^{-1}\Gamma(1 + 2n^{-1})[\Gamma(1 + n^{-1})]^{-2}$.

Capacitance Edge Corrections. Consider a thin, charged semi-infinite plate with straight edge parallel to and halfway between two infinite conducting plates at potential zero spaced a distance b apart. Increased capacitance per unit length of edge due to bulging of field is equivalent to adding strip of width $\pi^{-1}b \ln 2$ to the edge and assuming no bulging.

[1] For other two-strip configurations see A. E. H. Love, *Proc. London Math. Soc.* **22**, 339–369 (1923).

Same as above but infinite plates a distance $2B$ apart and central plates of thickness $2A$ with square edge. Increased capacitance per unit length due to bulging of field equivalent to adding to central plate a strip of thickness $2A$ and width

$$\frac{2}{\pi}\left\{B \ln \frac{2B - A}{B - A} - A \ln \frac{[A(2B - A)]^{\frac{1}{2}}}{B - A}\right\}$$

and assuming no bulging or charge on edge.

Parallel-plate capacitor with rectangular step in one plate, spacing on one side of step a and on other b. $b > a$. Additional capacitance per unit length of step above that from assumption of uniform field on each side of step is

$$2\pi\epsilon\left(\frac{a^2 + b^2}{ab} \ln \frac{b + a}{b - a} + 2 \ln \frac{b^2 - a^2}{4ab}\right)^{-1}$$

Two infinite sheets, each of which has one half bent at right angles to the other, are placed with the edges of the bends parallel so that the distance between sheets on one side of the bend is a and on the other b. The additional capacitance per unit length of bend over that given by the assumption of a uniform field over each a half of the inner sheet and no field in the corner rectangle is

$$\frac{2\epsilon}{\pi}\left(\ln \frac{a^2 + b^2}{4ab} + \frac{a}{b} \tan^{-1} \frac{b}{a} + \frac{b}{a} \tan^{-1} \frac{a}{b}\right)$$

Capacitance and Elastance Coefficients

In a system of n conductors the charge on conductor m is

$$Q_m = c_{1m}V_1 + c_{2m}V_2 + \cdots + c_{mm}V_m + \cdots + c_{nm}V_n$$

In a system of n conductors the potential of conductor m is

$$V_m = s_{1m}Q_1 + s_{2m}Q_2 + \cdots + s_{mm}Q_m + \cdots + s_{nm}Q_n$$

The force or torque tending to increase distance or angle x is

$$-\frac{1}{2}\sum_{p=1}^{n}\sum_{q=1}^{n} \frac{\partial c_{pq}}{\partial x} Q_pQ_q = +\frac{1}{2}\sum_{p=1}^{n}\sum_{q=1}^{n} \frac{\partial s_{pq}}{\partial x} V_pV_q$$

The energy of a system of n conductors is

$$W = \tfrac{1}{2}\sum_{p=1}^{n}\sum_{q=1}^{n} c_{pq}V_pV_q = \tfrac{1}{2}\sum_{p=1}^{n}\sum_{q=1}^{n} s_{pq}Q_pQ_q$$

For two distant conductors

$$s_{pq} = s_{qp} \approx (4\pi\epsilon r)^{-1}$$

If conductor 2 encloses conductor 1 only, then

$$c_{11} = -c_{12} \quad \text{and} \quad s_{1r} = s_{2r}$$

where $1 < r$.

For two spheres of radii a_1 and a_2 with centers a distance c apart, far from all other bodies

$$c_{11} = 4\pi\epsilon a_1a_2 \sinh \alpha \sum_{n=1}^{\infty} [a_2 \sinh n\alpha \pm a_1 \sinh (n - 1)\alpha]^{-1}$$

where $\cosh \alpha = \frac{1}{2}|c^2 - a^2 - b^2|a^{-1}b^{-1}$ and the upper sign is used unless a_2 encloses a_1. If spheres are mutually external

$$c_{12} = -4\pi\epsilon a_1 a_2 c^{-1} \sinh \alpha \sum_{n=1}^{\infty} \operatorname{csch} n\alpha$$

If the capacitances to earth of two distant bodies when alone are C_1 and C_2, the capacitance coefficients are approximately

$$c_{11} \approx \frac{16\pi^2\epsilon^2 r^2 C_1}{16\pi^2\epsilon^2 r^2 - C_1C_2} \qquad c_{12} = c_{21} \approx -\frac{C_1C_2}{4\pi\epsilon r} \qquad c_{22} \approx \frac{16\pi^2\epsilon^2 r^2 C_2}{16\pi^2\epsilon^2 r^2 - C_1C_2}$$

5b-2. Electrostatic-force Formulas. The force in the direction of the unit vector $\mathbf{m}$ on a conductor with surface charge density σ in a dielectric of capacitivity ϵ is

$$F_m = \tfrac{1}{2}\epsilon^{-1} \int_S \sigma^2 \mathbf{m} \cdot \mathbf{n}\, dS$$

where $\mathbf{n}$ is a unit vector normal to the surface.
When a uniform isotropic dielectric body of capacitivity ϵ occupies the volume v, where, before its advent, the field due to a fixed distribution of charge was $\mathbf{E}$ and after its advent $\mathbf{E}'$, its energy is

$$W = \tfrac{1}{2} \int_v (\epsilon_v - \epsilon)\mathbf{E} \cdot \mathbf{E}'\, dv$$

The force or torque tending to increase the distance or angle x of the above body is

$$F_x = -\frac{\partial W}{\partial x}$$

The torque tending to increase the angle α which the normal to a disk of radius a makes with a field that would be uniform and of strength E except for the disk is

$$T = \frac{8}{3}\epsilon a^3 E^2 \sin 2\alpha$$

The torque tending to increase the angle α between the field and the major axis of an oblate dielectric spheroid of capacitivity ϵ with semiaxes a and b, where $b > a$, placed in a field that would be uniform and of strength E except for the spheroid is

$$T = \frac{2\pi\epsilon_v(K-1)^2 b^2 a E^2 (3P - 2)\sin 2\alpha}{3[(K-1)^2P^2 + (K-1)(2-K)P - 2K]}$$

where $P = A[(1 + A^2)\cot^{-1} A - A]$, $A = a(b^2 - a^2)^{-\frac{1}{2}}$, and $K = \epsilon\epsilon_v^{-1}$.
If the above oblate spheroid is conducting, the torque is

$$T = \frac{2\pi\epsilon_v b^2 a E^2 (3P - 2)\sin 2\alpha}{3P(P-1)}$$

The torque tending to increase the angle α between the field and the major axis of a prolate dielectric spheroid of capacitivity ϵ with semiaxes a and b where $b < a$ placed in a field that would be uniform and of strength E except for the spheroid is

$$T = \frac{2\pi\epsilon_v(K-1)^2 b^2 a E^2 (2 - 3Q)\sin 2\alpha}{3[(K-1)^2Q^2 + (K-1)(2-K)Q - 2K]}$$

where $Q = C[(1 - C^2)\coth^{-1} C + C]$. $C = a(a^2 - b^2)^{-\frac{1}{2}}$ and $K = \epsilon\epsilon_v^{-1}$.

If the above prolate spheroid is conducting, the torque becomes[1]

$$T = \frac{2\pi\epsilon_v b^2 a E^2 (2 - 3Q) \sin 2\alpha}{3Q(Q - 1)}$$

Two parallel cylinders of radii a and b carry charges $+Q$ and $-Q$ and their axes are a distance c apart. The force per unit length tending to increase c is

$$F_1 = \frac{\pm Q^2 c}{2\pi\epsilon[(c^2 - a^2 - b^2)^2 - 4a^2b^2]^{\frac{1}{2}}}$$

The plus sign is used if one cylinder encloses the other and the minus sign if they are mutually external.

Two identical coplanar parallel strips carry charges $+Q$ and $-Q$, the distance between their nearer edges being $2a$ and between their far edges $2b$. The attractive force per unit length between them is

$$F_1 = \frac{\pi b Q^2}{8\epsilon a(a + b)[K(a/b)]^2}$$

Two identical infinite coplanar parallel conducting strips carry equal positive charges Q, the distance between their near edges being $2a$ and between their far edges $2b$. The repulsive force per unit length between them is

$$F_1 = \frac{Q^2}{2\pi\epsilon(a + b)}$$

The force on a point charge at a distance b from the center of a sphere of radius a at zero potential is

$$F = \frac{abQ^2}{4\pi\epsilon(a^2 - b^2)^2}$$

When $b > a$, the force is toward the center; and when $b < a$, it is away from the center. The repulsive force between a point charge q at a distance b from the center of a sphere of radius a carrying a total charge Q is, when $b > a$,

$$F = \frac{q}{4\pi\epsilon b^2}\left[Q + \frac{a^3(a^2 - 2b^2)q}{b(b^2 - a^2)^2}\right]$$

At the point x_0, y_0, z_0 inside a rectangular conducting box bounded by the planes $x = 0,a$, $y = 0,b$, $z = 0,c$, the image force on a charge Q is

$$F_z = -\frac{2Q^2}{\epsilon ab}\sum_{n=1}^{\infty}\sum_{m=1}^{\infty}\frac{\sinh A_{mn}(c - 2z_0)}{\sinh A_{mn}c}\sin^2\frac{n\pi x_0}{a}\sin^2\frac{m\pi y_0}{b}$$

in the z direction where $A_{mn} = \pi(ab)^{-1}(m^2a^2 + n^2b^2)^{\frac{1}{2}}$. The other force components are given by cyclic permutation of the symbols x, y, z; a, b, c; and x_0, y_0, z_0. At a distance c from one of two parallel uncharged plates at a distance b apart, the image force on a charge Q is

$$F = \frac{Q^2}{16\pi\epsilon a^2}\left[\zeta\left(2, \frac{1}{2} - \frac{c}{b}\right) - \zeta\left(2, \frac{c}{b}\right)\right]$$

where $\zeta(z,a)$ is a Riemann zeta function.

[1] For torque on general ellipsoid, see Stratton, "Electromagnetic Theory," p. 215, McGraw-Hill Book Company, Inc., New York, 1941.

On the axis and at a distance b from the center of a conducting disk of radius a carrying a charge Q, the repulsive force on a point charge q is

$$F = \frac{q}{4\pi\epsilon(a^2 + b^2)}\left[Q - \frac{a(3b^2 + a^2)q}{2\pi b(a^2 + b^2)} + \frac{3b^2 - a^2}{2\pi b^2} q \tan^{-1}\frac{a}{b}\right]$$

At a distance c from the center of an uncharged dielectric sphere of radius a and relative capacitivity K, the attractive force on a charge Q is

$$F = \frac{(K-1)Q^2}{4\pi\epsilon_v c^2}\sum_{n=1}^{\infty}\frac{n(n+1)}{Kn + n + 1}\left(\frac{a}{c}\right)^{2n+1}$$

At a distance c from the plane face of an infinite block of dielectric of relative capacitivity K, the attractive force on a point charge Q is

$$F = \frac{Q^2}{16\pi\epsilon_v c^2}\frac{K-1}{K+1}$$

The attractive force on a point charge Q at a distance a from the plane face of a dielectric slab of thickness c and relative capacitivity K is

$$F = \frac{\beta Q^2}{16\pi\epsilon_v}\left[\frac{1}{a^2} - (1-\beta^2)\sum_{n=1}^{\infty}\frac{\beta^{2(n-1)}}{(a+nc)^2}\right]$$

where $\beta = (K-1)(K+1)^{-1}$.

The attractive force per unit length on a line charge of strength λ per unit length parallel to and at a distance c from the axis of an uncharged circular cylinder of radius a and relative capacitivity K is

$$F_1 = \frac{K-1}{K+1}\frac{\lambda^2 a^2}{2\pi\epsilon_v c(c^2 - a^2)}$$

For a conductor, $K = \infty$; so the first factor is unity.

The force toward the wall per unit length on a line charge of strength λ per unit length parallel to and at a distance c from the axis of a circular cylindrical hole of radius a in an infinite block of dielectric of relative capacitivity K is

$$F_1 = \frac{K-1}{K+1}\frac{c\lambda^2}{2\pi\epsilon_v(a^2 - c^2)}$$

For a conductor, $K = \infty$; so the first factor is unity.

The attractive force per unit length on a line charge of strength λ per unit length parallel to and at a distance a from the nearer face of a dielectric slab of thickness a and relative capacitivity K is

$$F_1 = \frac{\beta\lambda^2}{4\pi\epsilon_v}\left[\frac{1}{a} - (1-\beta^2)\sum_{n=1}^{\infty}\frac{\beta^{2(n-1)}}{a+nc}\right]$$

where $\beta = (K-1)(K+1)^{-1}$.

In the foregoing case, if $a = mc$ where m is an integer, the force per unit length is expressible in finite terms; thus

$$F_1 = \frac{\beta\lambda^2}{4\pi\epsilon_v c}\left\{\frac{1}{m} - \frac{1-\beta^2}{\beta^{2(m+1)}}\left[\ln(1-\beta^2) + \sum_{n=1}^{m}\frac{\beta^{2n}}{n}\right]\right\}$$

The attractive force per unit length on a line charge of strength λ per unit length parallel to and at a distance a from an uncharged conducting plane is

$$F_1 = \frac{\lambda^2}{4\pi\epsilon a}$$

The attractive force between a line charge of strength λ per unit length and an uncharged conducting sphere of radius a whose center is at a distance b from it is

$$F = \frac{\lambda^2 a^2}{\pi\epsilon_v b(b^2 - a^2)^{\frac{1}{2}}} \sin^{-1}\frac{a}{b}$$

The attractive force between a line charge of strength λ per unit length and an uncharged dielectric sphere of relative capacitivity K and radius a is

$$F = \frac{(K-1)\lambda^2}{\pi\epsilon_v} \sum_{n=1}^{\infty} \frac{n(2n-2)!!}{(2n-1)!!(Kn+n+1)} \left(\frac{a}{b}\right)^{2n+1}$$

5b-3. Multipole Formulas. The potential of a point charge Q is

$$V = \frac{Q}{4\pi\epsilon r}$$

where r is the distance from the charge to the field point.
The force on a point charge in a field of electric intensity $\mathbf{E}$ is

$$\mathbf{F} = Q\mathbf{E}$$

The potential of a dipole of moment $\mathbf{p}$ is

$$V = \frac{p\cos\theta}{4\pi\epsilon r^2} = \frac{\mathbf{p}\cdot\mathbf{r}}{4\pi\epsilon r^3}$$

where $\mathbf{r}$ is measured from the dipole to the field point.
The force on a dipole in a field $\mathbf{E}$ is $\mathbf{F} = (\mathbf{p}\cdot\nabla)\mathbf{E}$.
The torque on a dipole in a field $\mathbf{E}$ is $\mathbf{T} = \mathbf{p}\times\mathbf{E}$.
The mutual energy of two dipoles of moment $\mathbf{p}_1$, $\mathbf{p}_2$ which make angles θ_1 and θ_2 with the vector $\mathbf{r}$ that joins them and whose planes intersect along $\mathbf{r}$ at an angle ψ is

$$W = \frac{p_1 p_2}{4\pi\epsilon r^3}(\sin\theta_1 \sin\theta_2 \cos\psi - 2\cos\theta_1 \cos\theta_2)$$

The components of force and torque between two dipoles are

$$F_r = -\frac{\partial W}{\partial r} \qquad T_\alpha = -\frac{\partial W}{\partial \alpha}$$

The potential of a multipole of the nth order and moment strength $p^{(n)}$ is

$$V_n = \frac{(-1)^n p^{(n)}}{4\pi\epsilon n!} \frac{\partial^n}{\partial l_1 \cdots \partial l_n}\left(\frac{1}{r}\right)$$
$$= \sum_{m=0}^{n} (a_{nm}\cos m\varphi + b_{nm}\sin m\varphi) r^{-n-1} P_n{}^m(\cos\theta)$$

5b-4. Dielectric-boundary Formulas. If V' and V'' are the electrostatic potentials in the dielectrics ϵ' and ϵ'', then at their uncharged interface

$$V' = V'' \qquad \text{and} \qquad \epsilon' \frac{\partial V'}{\partial n} = \epsilon'' \frac{\partial V''}{\partial n}$$

where n is a coordinate normal to the interface.

The normal stress, directed from ϵ'' to ϵ', on the above interface is

$$F_n = \frac{\epsilon'' - \epsilon'}{2\epsilon'} \left(\frac{D_t'^2}{\epsilon'} + \frac{D_n'^2}{\epsilon''} \right)$$

where D_t' and D_n' are the tangential and normal components of the displacement in ϵ'.

5b-5. Dielectric Bodies in Electrostatic Fields. A sphere of radius a and capacitivity ϵ is placed in a uniform field of intensity **E**. The uniform field intensity inside and the potential outside due to its polarization are, respectively,

$$\mathbf{E}_i = \frac{3\epsilon_v \mathbf{E}}{\epsilon + 2\epsilon_v} \qquad V_p = E \frac{\epsilon_v - \epsilon}{\epsilon + 2\epsilon_v} \frac{a^3}{r^2} \cos\theta$$

where r is measured from the center of the sphere and **E** is directed along $\theta = 0$.

An oblate dielectric spheroid of capacitivity ϵ whose minor (rotational) axis on $\theta = 0$ is $2a$ and whose focal circle is of radius c is placed in a uniform electric field **E** parallel to $\theta = 0$. The uniform field inside and the potential outside due to its polarization are, respectively,

$$\mathbf{E}_i = \mathbf{E}\,\epsilon_v c^3 M \qquad V_p = M(\epsilon - \epsilon_v)a(a^2 + c^2)E(\cot^{-1}\zeta - \zeta^{-1})r\cos\theta$$

where $M = \{a(\epsilon_v - \epsilon)[(a^2 + c^2)\cot^{-1}(c^{-1}a) - ac] + \epsilon c^3\}^{-1}$

and $\zeta^2 = \tfrac{1}{2}c^{-2}\{r^2 - c^2 + [(r^2 - c^2)^2 + 4r^2c^2\cos^2\theta]^{\frac{1}{2}}\}$

The above spheroid is placed in a field $\mathbf{E}'$ in the $\varphi = 0$ direction, normal to the $\theta = 0$ axis. The uniform field intensity inside and the potential outside due to its polarization are, respectively,

$$\mathbf{E}_i' = 2\mathbf{E}'\epsilon_v c^3 M' \qquad V_p' = M'(\epsilon - \epsilon_v)a(c^2 + a^2)E'[\cot^{-1}\zeta - \zeta(1 + \zeta^2)^{-1}]r\sin\theta\cos\varphi$$

where $M' = \{a(\epsilon - \epsilon_v)[(a^2 + c^2)\cot^{-1}(c^{-1}a) - ac] + 2\epsilon_v c^3\}^{-1}$

The above spheroid is placed in a uniform field $\mathbf{E}_0$ which makes an angle α with its rotational $\theta = 0$ axis. The uniform field inside and the potential outside due to its polarization are, respectively,

$$\mathbf{E}_{0i} = \mathbf{E}_0\epsilon_v c^3[M\cos\alpha + M'\sin\alpha] \qquad V_{0p} = E_0[V_pE^{-1}\cos\alpha + V_p'E'^{-1}\sin\alpha]$$

where V_p', V_p, **E**, and $\mathbf{E}'$ are given in the preceding formulas.

A prolate spheroid of capacitivity ϵ whose major (rotational) axis on $\theta = 0$ is $2b$ and whose focal distance is $2c$ is placed in a uniform electric field **E** parallel to $\theta = 0$. The uniform field intensity inside and the potential outside due to its polarization are, respectively,

$$\mathbf{E}_i = \mathbf{E}\epsilon_v c^3 N \qquad V_p = N(\epsilon - \epsilon_v)b(c^2 - b^2)E(\coth^{-1}\eta - \eta^{-1})r\cos\theta$$

where $N = \{b(\epsilon_v - \epsilon)[(c^2 - b^2)\coth^{-1}(c^{-1}b) + bc] + \epsilon c^3\}^{-1}$

and $\eta^2 = \tfrac{1}{2}c^{-2}\{r^2 + c^2 + [(r^2 + c^2)^2 - 4c^2r^2\cos^2\theta]^{\frac{1}{2}}\}$

The above spheroid is placed in a field $\mathbf{E}'$ in the $\varphi = 0$ direction normal to the $\theta = 0$ axis. The uniform field inside and the potential outside due to its polarization are, respectively,

$$\mathbf{E}_i = \mathbf{E}'\epsilon_v c^3 N' \qquad V_p' = N'(\epsilon - \epsilon_v)b(b^2 - c^2)E'[\coth^{-1}\eta - \eta(1 - \eta^2)^{-1}]r\sin\theta\cos\varphi$$

where $N' = \{b(\epsilon_v - \epsilon)[(b^2 - c^2)\coth^{-1}c^{-1}b - bc] + 2\epsilon_v c^3\}^{-1}$.

The above prolate spheroid is placed in a uniform field $\mathbf{E}_0$ which makes an angle α with its rotational $\theta = 0$ axis. The uniform field inside and the potential outside due to its polarization are, respectively,

$$\mathbf{E}_{0i} = \mathbf{E}_0 \epsilon_v c^3 [N \cos \alpha + N' \sin \alpha] \qquad V_{0p} = E_0 [V_p E^{-1} \cos \alpha + V'_p E'^{-1} \sin \alpha]$$

where V_p, V'_p, $\mathbf{E}$, and $\mathbf{E}'$ are given in the foregoing formulas.

5b-6. Static-current-flow Formulas. *Linear-circuit Formulas.* See steady-state alternating-current formulas.

Currents in Extended Media (Three Dimensions). The following formulas assume the medium to be uniform, homogeneous, and isotropic and to have a resistivity ρ which obeys Ohm's law.

The resistance between a single perfectly conducting electrode immersed in an infinite medium and the concentric infinite sphere is related to the capacitance of the same electrode by the formula

$$R = \rho \epsilon_v C^{-1}$$

where the capacitance C for a sphere, prolate or oblate spheroid, ellipsoid, circular disk, elliptic disk, two spheres in contact, two spheres connected by a wire, two spheres intersecting at an angle π/m, a spherical bowl, torus, cube, and circular plane annulus are given in the electrostatic section. The resistance between widely separated source and sink electrodes immersed in an infinite medium is

$$R_{12} \approx R_1 + R_2 - \rho(2\pi r)^{-1}$$

where R_1 and R_2 are the resistances to infinity of each alone and r, the distance between them, is large compared with their dimensions. The resistance to infinity of a single electrode, sunk into the plane surface of a semi-infinite medium such as the earth in such a way that the submerged part, if combined with its mirror image in the surface, would form one of the above electrodes is

$$R = 2\rho \epsilon_v C^{-1}$$

When both source and sink electrodes are half submerged in the plane face just described, the resistance between them is

$$R = R_{12} \approx 2[R_1 + R_2 - \rho(2\pi r)^{-1}]$$

where R_{12}, R_1, and R_2 have the same significance as before and r, the distance between them, is much larger than the electrode dimensions. In the preceding case, if the medium has a resistivity ρ_1 to a depth a and ρ_2 below this depth, then the resistance between electrodes is

$$R \approx 2\left\{R_1 + R_2 - \frac{\rho_1}{2\pi r} + \frac{\rho_1}{\pi} \sum_{n=1}^{\infty} \left[\frac{(-\beta)^n}{2na} - \frac{(-\beta)^n}{(4n^2a^2 + r^2)^{\frac{1}{2}}}\right]\right\}$$

where $\beta = (\rho_1 - \rho_2)(\rho_1 + \rho_2)^{-1}$ and both a and r are large compared with the electrode dimensions.

Two perfectly conducting disk electrodes of radii a and b are applied to the plane horizontal face of a semi-infinite homogeneous medium whose horizontal and vertical resistivities are ρ_1 and ρ_2. If the electrode spacing r is much greater than a and b, the resistance between them is

$$R \approx (\rho_1\rho_2)^{\frac{1}{2}}[(4a)^{-1} + (4b)^{-1} - (\pi r)^{-1}]$$

Two conical perfectly conducting electrodes of half angle β with an angle α between their axes pass normally through a spherical shell of thickness b and resistivity ρ.

The resistance between them is rigorously

$$R = \rho(\pi b)^{-1} \cosh^{-1} (\csc \beta \sin \tfrac{1}{2}\alpha)$$

A cylindrical column of length l and radius a of material of resistivity ρ connects normally the plane faces of two semi-infinite masses of the same resistivity. The resistance R between the infinite hemispherical perfectly conducting electrodes bounding the masses lies within the limits

$$\frac{\rho l}{\pi a^2} + \frac{\rho}{2a} < R < \frac{\pi\rho}{2[\pi a - l \ln (1 + \pi a/l)]}$$

This formula is most accurate for small values of l/a and is exact at $l = 0$. For large values of l

$$R \approx \rho a^{-1}(0.31831 l a^{-1} + 0.522)$$

Perfectly conducting disk electrodes of radius b are applied concentrically to the ends of a solid right circular cylinder of radius a, length c, and resistivity ρ. The resistance between them is

$$R \approx 2\rho(\pi a^2)^{-1}[c + f(b)]$$

where $f(0.25a) = 2.05164a$, $f(0.50a) = 0.5336a$, and $f(0.75a) = 0.1060a$. The errors are less than 0.05 per cent if c is greater than $4a$.

Currents in Extended Media (Two Dimensions). The resistance between perfectly conducting plane electrodes covering the ends and orthogonal to the sides of a bar of rectangular section, resistivity ρ, and thickness b bent in a circular arc with inner radius a and outer radius c, which subtends an angle α at the center, is

$$R = \rho\alpha b^{-1}[\ln (a^{-1}c)]^{-1}$$

The resistance between two small cylindrical electrodes of radius r passing normally through a strip of width a, thickness b, and resistivity ρ at a distance $2c$ apart on a line midway between its edges is, if $r \ll a$ and $r \ll c$,

$$R \approx \frac{\rho}{\pi b} \ln \frac{a \sinh 2\pi a^{-1}c}{\pi r}$$

The resistance between the electrodes in the above strip when they are equidistant from its center on a line normal to its edges is

$$R \approx \frac{\rho}{\pi b} \ln \frac{2a \tan \pi a^{-1}c}{\pi r}$$

In the following six configurations the bars of resistivity ρ have rectangular cross sections and are of uniform thickness b. Perfectly conducting electrodes cover the ends which are at right angles to the sides. For 1 per cent accuracy the interval between each end and the beginning of the boundary perturbation should exceed about twice the width of the intervening straight bar.

A bar of width a has an infinitely narrow cut of depth c normal to one side. The additional resistance due to the cut is

$$\Delta R = -4\rho(\pi b)^{-1} \ln \cos \tfrac{1}{2}\pi a^{-1}c$$

One side of a bar is straight and the other has a rectangular step in it. The width on one side of the step is a and on the other c where $a > c$. The additional resistance due to the distortion of the flow near the step over the sum of the resistances of the two straight portions alone is

$$\Delta R = \frac{\rho}{\pi b}\left(\frac{a^2 + c^2}{ac} \ln \frac{a + c}{a - c} + 2 \ln \frac{a^2 - c^2}{4ac}\right)$$

In the preceding case the corner of the step is cut off at 45 deg so that the width increases linearly from c to a. The additional resistance due to the tapered section over that of the two straight portions alone is

$$\Delta R = \frac{2\rho}{\pi b}\left(\frac{a^2 + c^2}{ac} \tanh^{-1} \frac{c}{a} + \frac{a^2 - c^2}{ac} \tan^{-1} \frac{c}{a} + \ln \frac{a^4 - c^4}{8a^2c^2}\right)$$

A straight rectangular bar has a right-angle bend, the width on one side of the bend being a and on the other c. The increase of resistance over the sum of the resistances of the two straight portions alone, the corner rectangle common to both being excluded, is

$$\Delta R = \frac{2\rho}{\pi b} \ln\left(\frac{a^2 + c^2}{4ac} + \frac{a}{c} \tan^{-1} \frac{c}{a} + \frac{c}{a} \tan^{-1} \frac{a}{c}\right)$$

A straight rectangular bar of width a has a hole drilled through it equidistant from its edges. The increase in resistance due to the hole is less than

$$\Delta R \approx -2\rho c(ab\theta)^{-1} \ln \cos \theta$$

where θ is a parameter chosen so that $\sin \theta = \tanh [\pi c\theta(a\theta - \pi c)^{-1}]$. These formulas are practically exact for small holes far from the ends. When the diameter of the hole is half the strip width R is about 0.1 per cent too large. For small values of c/a the parameter is given by

$$\theta \approx \frac{2\pi c}{a}\left(1 - \frac{\pi^2 c^2}{3a^2} + \frac{\pi^4 c^4}{3a^4}\right)$$

The value of ΔR given above is unchanged if the hole is replaced by two semicircular notches of the same radius in opposite edges of the strip.

Perfectly conducting electrodes are applied to a block of thickness b, width a, length c, and resistivity ρ in such a way as to cover the full thickness over a band of width w at the center of opposite ends. The resistance between the electrodes lies between the limits

$$\frac{2\rho}{\pi b} \cosh^{-1} \frac{\cosh \frac{1}{2}\pi a^{-1} c}{\sin \frac{1}{2}\pi a^{-1} w} > R > \frac{2}{\pi b} \sinh^{-1} \frac{\sinh \frac{1}{2}\pi a^{-1} c}{\sin \frac{1}{2}\pi a^{-1} w}$$

5b-7. Static-magnetic-field Formulas. *Magnetic Field of Various Circuit Configurations.* The magnetic induction due to a current density **i** flowing in a volume v is

$$\mathbf{B} = \frac{\mu}{4\pi} \nabla \times \int_v \frac{\mathbf{i}\, dv}{r}$$

The magnetic induction of a thin linear circuit with total current I is

$$B = \frac{\mu I}{4\pi} \oint \frac{\sin \theta \, ds}{r^2}$$

where θ is the angle between **ds** and **r** and **B** is normal to the plane of **ds** and **r**. The magnetic induction due to a long straight cylinder carrying current parallel to its axis, when both current density and permeability are independent of the azimuth angle θ, is $B_\theta = \mu_a I_a (2\pi a)^{-1}$ where a is distance of field point from axis, I_a is current inside radius a, and μ is the permeability at the field point.

The edges of a flat strip lie at $x = a$ and $x = -a$ and it carries a uniformly distributed current I in the z direction. The distances of a field point in the positive quadrant from the near and far edges are, respectively, r_1 and r_2 and the angle between r_1 and r_2

is α. The magnetic induction components are

$$B_y = \frac{\mu I}{4\pi a} \ln \frac{r_2}{r_1} \qquad B_x = -\frac{\mu I}{4\pi a} \alpha$$

A conductor of rectangular section of area A is bounded by the planes $x = a$, $x = -a$, $y = b$, and $y = -b$ and carries a uniformly distributed current I in the z direction. The distances from a field point in the positive quadrant to the corners, starting with the nearest and proceeding clockwise about the z axis, are r_1, r_2, r_3, and r_4. The angles between successive r's are α_1, α_2, α_3, and α_4, and the x and y components of r_1 and r_3 are x_1, y_1 and x_3, y_3. If all the above quantities are taken positive, the magnetic-induction components are

$$B_x = -\frac{1}{2} \mu I(\pi A)^{-1} \left(y_3\alpha_4 - y_1\alpha_1 + x_3 \ln \frac{r_3}{r_2} - x_1 \ln \frac{r_4}{r_1} \right)$$

$$B_y = \frac{1}{2} \mu I(\pi A)^{-1} \left(x_3\alpha_2 - x_1\alpha_3 + y_3 \ln \frac{r_3}{r_4} - y_1 \ln \frac{r_2}{r_1} \right)$$

The space inside and outside the conductor has the same permeability μ.

The magnetic induction outside the conductors of a long bifilar line that consists of a cylinder whose axis is $y = a$ which carries a uniformly distributed x-directed current I and another cylinder whose axis is $y = -a$ that carries the same current in the opposite direction is

$$B_y = \tfrac{1}{2}\pi^{-1}\mu I z(r_2^{-2} - r_1^{-2}) \qquad B_z = -\tfrac{1}{2}\pi^{-1}\mu I[r_2^{-2}(y + a) - r_1^{-2}(y - a)]$$

where r_1 and r_2 are the distances from positive and negative wire axes, respectively, and μ is the permeability of the conductors and surrounding space.

The magnetic induction of bifilar lines composed of flat strips or rectangular bars can be found by taking the vector sum of the inductions already given for each conductor alone.

A long circular conducting cylinder of radius b has a longitudinal hole of radius a whose axis is displaced a distance c from the cylinder axis. If a longitudinal current I is uniformly distributed over the conducting area, the induction **B** in the hole is uniform and normal to c and its magnitude is

$$B = \mu c I[2\pi(b^2 - a^2)]^{-1}$$

A circular loop of wire lies at $z = 0$, $\rho = a$ and carries a current clockwise about the z axis. The magnetic-induction components are

$$B_z = A(I_1 - a^{-1}\rho I_2) \qquad B_\rho = A a^{-1} z I_2$$

where[1] $I_1 = \pi^{-1} \int_0^\pi (1 - b \cos\theta)^{-\frac{3}{2}}\, d\theta$, $I_2 = \pi^{-1} \int_0^\pi (1 - b \cos\theta)^{\frac{3}{2}} \cos\theta\, d\theta$, $A = \frac{1}{2}\mu I a^2(a^2 + z^2 - \rho^2)^{-\frac{3}{2}}$, and $b = 2a\rho(a^2 + z^2 - \rho^2)^{-1}$.

Two coaxial wire loops of radius a at a distance a apart carry currents I in the same direction and constitute a Helmholtz coil which gives a nearly uniform field on the axis midway between them. For a small distance r around this point the field varies as $(r/a)^4$. The induction there is

$$B = 8\mu I 5^{-\frac{3}{2}} a^{-1}$$

Accurate values of B may be found by a superposition of the fields calculated separately by the preceding formula for a single loop.

[1] Six-place tables of I_1 and I_2 suitable for linear interpolation are given by C. L. Bartberger, *J. Appl. Phys.* **21**, 1108 (1950).

The magnetic-induction components at a great distance from a small loop of wire at $\theta = \frac{1}{2}\pi$, $r = a$ which carries a current I are

$$B_r = \tfrac{1}{2}\mu I r^{-3} a^2 \cos\theta \qquad B_\theta = \tfrac{1}{4}\mu I r^{-3} a^2 \sin\theta$$

A rectangular loop of wire lies at $x = \pm a$, $y = \pm b$ and carries a current I clockwise about the z axis. The distances of the field point at x, y, z in the positive octant from successive corners, starting with the nearest, are r_1, r_2, r_3, and r_4 and the components of r_1 and r_3 are x_1, y_1, z and x_3, y_3, z. The components of the magnetic induction are

$$\begin{aligned}
B_x &= \tfrac{1}{4}\pi^{-1}\mu I z\{[r_1(r_1 - y_1)]^{-1} + [r_3(r_3 + y_3)]^{-1} - [r_4(r_4 + y_3)]^{-1} - [r_2(r_2 - y_1)]^{-1}\} \\
B_y &= \tfrac{1}{4}\pi^{-1}\mu I z\{[r_3(r_3 + x_3)]^{-1} + [r_1(r_1 - x_1)]^{-1} - [r_4(r_4 - x_1)]^{-1} - [r_2(r_2 + x_3)]^{-1}\} \\
B_z &= \tfrac{1}{4}\pi^{-1}\mu I\{x_1[r_1(r_1 - y_1)]^{-1} - x_1[r_4(r_4 + y_3)]^{-1} + x_3[r_2(r_2 - y_1)]^{-1} - x_3[r_3(r_3 + y_3)]^{-1} \\
&\quad + y_1[r_1(r_1 - x_1)]^{-1} - y_1[r_2(r_2 + x_3)]^{-1} + y_3[r_4(r_4 - x_1)]^{-1} - y_3[r_3(r_3 + x_3)]^{-1}\}
\end{aligned}$$

All lengths are to be taken positive. If the single wire of the preceding formulas is replaced by N wires, the fields may be found rigorously by superimposing N solutions of the type given, one for each wire, or by integration over the section. In case the area of this section is small compared with other coil dimensions, a sufficiently accurate result is often given by substitution of NI for I in these formulas and the use of the dimensions of the center turn for that of the loop.

A helix of pitch α is wound on a cylinder of radius a. The angles between the positive axis and vectors drawn from the field point to the ends of the helix wire are β_1 and β_2. The axial component of the induction is then given rigorously by

$$B_a = \tfrac{1}{4}\mu I \cot\alpha(\pi a)^{-1}(\cos\beta_2 - \cos\beta_1)$$

There is also a component normal to the axis which becomes negligible when α is small.

The axial component of the induction on the axis of a solenoid with n turns per unit length is, using the notation of the preceding formula,

$$B_a = \tfrac{1}{2}\mu n I(\cos\beta_2 - \cos\beta_1)$$

The induction approaches uniformity everywhere inside an infinitely long solenoid as the pitch decreases and its limiting value is $B_2 = n\mu I$.

When any figure, such as a torus, generated by the rotation of a closed curve about a coplanar external line, is closely and uniformly wound with N turns of wire so that each turn nearly coincides with one position of the generating curve, then, when carrying a current I, the exterior induction is zero and the interior induction is

$$B_\varphi = \tfrac{1}{2}\mu N I(\pi r)^{-1}$$

A coil of N circular turns wound closely over the entire surface of an oblate spheroid whose major and minor semiaxes are a and b will give a uniform induction B inside, provided that the projections of these turns on the b axis are uniformly spaced. The total number of ampere-turns needed is

$$NI = \frac{B}{4\pi\mu}\left[\frac{a^2 - b^2}{b - a^2(a^2 - b^2)^{-\frac{1}{2}}\cos^{-1}(b/a)}\right]$$

When $b = a$, this becomes $NI = bB/(4\pi\mu)$.

A coil of N circular turns wound closely over the entire surface of a prolate spheroid whose major and minor semiaxes are b and a will give a uniform induction B inside, provided that the projections of these turns on the b axis are uniformly spaced. The total number of ampere-turns needed is

$$NI = \frac{B}{4\pi\mu}\left[\frac{b^2 - a^2}{b - a^2(b^2 - a^2)^{-\frac{1}{2}}\cosh^{-1}(b/a)}\right]$$

Self- and Mutual Inductance for Static Fields. The mutual inductance between two circuits is given by the formulas

$$M = L_{12} = 10^{-7} \oint_1 \oint_2 r^{-1}\, \mathbf{ds}_1 \cdot \mathbf{ds}_2 = \tfrac{1}{4}\pi^{-1} 10^7 \int_v \mathbf{B}_1 \cdot \mathbf{B}_2\, dv$$

where $\mathbf{ds}_1$ and $\mathbf{ds}_2$ are elements of circuit 1 and circuit 2 and $\mathbf{B}_1$ and $\mathbf{B}_2$ are their separate magnetic inductions for unit current. One line integral covers each circuit and the volume integral covers the whole field region.

The self-inductance of a circuit is a special case of the above formula

$$L = \tfrac{1}{4}\pi^{-1} 10^7 \int_v B^2\, dv$$

where B is the magnetic induction per unit current and v includes the entire field region.

The energy in the field of n circuits carrying currents $I_1, I_2, \ldots, I_n$ is

$$W = \tfrac{1}{2} \sum_{p=0}^{n} \sum_{q=0}^{n} L_{pq} I_p I_q$$

Note. In the following material there are many references to Grover. These refer to F. W. Grover, "Inductance Calculations," D. Van Nostrand Company, Inc., New York, 1946. In this book most inductances are given in microhenrys and lengths in centimeters. In the following formulas mks units are used; so the inductances are in henrys and the lengths in meters. Unless otherwise stated, the permeability throughout is that of a vacuum.

The self-inductance of a round wire of relative permeability K_m and length l in a vacuum is

$$L \approx 2l[\ln (2a^{-1}l) - 1 + \tfrac{1}{4}K_m] \times 10^{-7}$$

The self-inductance of a rectangular bar of perimeter p is

$$L \approx 2l[\ln (4p^{-1}l) + \tfrac{1}{2} + 0.1118 l^{-1}p] \times 10^{-7}$$

The self-inductance of a bar of elliptical section, semiaxes a and b, is

$$L \approx 2l\{\ln [2l(a+b)^{-1}] - 0.05685\} \times 10^{-7}$$

The self-inductance of a tube of external and internal radii a and b is

$$L \approx 2l\left[\ln \frac{2l}{a} + \frac{b^4}{(a^2-b^2)^2} \ln \frac{a}{b} + \frac{7b^2 - 5a^2}{4(a^2-b^2)}\right] \times 10^{-7}$$

Note. In the following formulas for bifilar lines the inductance per unit length is found by setting $l = 1$. In all cases l is supposed to be much greater than the pair spacing. The current densities are taken uniform. The current goes out on one element and returns on the other.

The self-inductance of two parallel cylinders of radii a and b and length l with a distance d between axes is

$$L = l\{1 + 2 \ln [(ab)^{-1}d^2]\} \times 10^{-7}$$

The self-inductance of two similar parallel wires of radius a and relative permeability K_m with a distance d between axes is

$$L \approx l[4 \ln (a^{-1}d) + K_m - 4d] \times 10^{-7}$$

The self-inductance of two similar parallel rectangular wires of perimeter p with a distance d between centers is

$$L \approx [4l \ln (2p^{-1}d) + 6l + 0.447p - 4d] \times 10^{-7}$$

The self-inductance of two similar parallel tubes, external radius a, internal radius b, with a distance d between centers is

$$L \approx l\left[4 \ln \frac{d}{a} + \frac{4b^4}{(a^2 - b^2)^2} \ln \frac{a}{b} + \frac{3b^2 - a^2}{a^2 - b^2}\right] \times 10^{-7}$$

The self-inductance of a coaxial line when the external radii of the inside conductor, insulation space, and outside conductor are c, b, and a, respectively, and the relative permeabilities K_m, K'_m, and K''_m and when the length l is great compared with a is

$$L = 2l\left\{\frac{1}{4}K_m + K'_m \ln \frac{b}{c} + \frac{1}{4}K''_m\left[\frac{4a^4}{(a^2 - b^2)^2} \ln \frac{a}{b} - \frac{3a^2 - b^2}{a^2 - b^2}\right]\right\} \times 10^{-7}$$

If $K_m = K'_m = K''_m$, this formula also holds for a noncoaxial line provided the axes are parallel.

The self-inductance of a wire of radius r and relative permeability K_m which is bent into a circular loop of mean radius a, neglecting small terms in r^4/a^4, is

$$L \approx 4\pi a\left[\left(1 + \frac{r^2}{8a^2}\right) \ln \frac{8a}{r} + \frac{r^2}{24a^2} - 2 + \frac{1}{4}K_m\right] \times 10^{-7}$$

The self-inductance of a wire of radius r and relative permeability K_m which is bent into a rectangular loop with sides a and b and diagonal $d = (a^2 + b^2)^{\frac{1}{2}}$ is[1]

$$L \approx 4\left[a \ln \frac{2ab}{r(a + d)} + b \ln \frac{2ab}{r(b + d)} + 2d - \left(2 - \frac{1}{4}K_m\right)(a + b)\right] \times 10^{-7}$$

The self-inductance of a wire with rectangular section of perimeter p which is bent into a rectangular loop with sides a and b and diagonal d, is

$$L \approx 4\left[a \ln \frac{4ab}{p(a + d)} + b \ln \frac{4ab}{p(b + d)} + 2d + \frac{1}{2}(a + b) + 0.223p\right] \times 10^{-7}$$

The self-inductance of a thin band of radius a and width b is

$$L \approx 4\pi a[\ln (8b^{-1}a) - \tfrac{1}{2}] \times 10^{-7}$$

The mutual inductance of two thin coaxial circular loops of radii a and b, when r_1 and r_2 are the farthest and nearest distances between the loops, is given in terms of complete elliptic integrals by[2]

$$\begin{aligned} M &= 8\pi k^{-1}a^{\frac{1}{2}}b^{\frac{1}{2}}[(1 - \tfrac{1}{2}k^2)K(k) - E(k)] \times 10^{-7} \\ &= 8\pi k_1^{-1}a^{\frac{1}{2}}b^{\frac{1}{2}}[K(k_1) - E(k_1)] \times 10^{-7} \end{aligned}$$

where $k^2 = r_1^{-2}(r_1^2 - r_2^2)$ and $k_1^2 = (r_1 - r_2)(r_1 + r_2)^{-1}$.

The mutual inductance between a long straight wire and a loop of radius a whose diameter it intersects at right angles at a distance c from the loop center is

$$\begin{aligned} M &= 4\pi[c \sec \alpha - (c^2 \sec^2 \alpha - a^2)^{\frac{1}{2}}] \times 10^{-7} \qquad c > a \\ M &= 4\pi c \tan (\tfrac{1}{4}\pi - \tfrac{1}{2}\alpha) \times 10^{-7} \qquad c < a \end{aligned}$$

[1] Tables are given by Grover, pp. 59–65.
[2] Grover gives tables on pp. 77–87.

where α is the acute angle between the plane of the loop and the plane defined by its center and the straight wire.

The mutual inductance of two parallel coaxial identical rectangular loops whose sides are a and b and which are spaced so that the distance from any corner of one loop to the most distant corner of the other is d, is[1]

$$M = 4\left[a \ln \frac{(a+A)B}{(a+D)d} + b \ln \frac{(b+B)A}{(b+D)d} + 8(D - A - B + d)\right] \times 10^{-7}$$

where $A^2 = a^2 + d^2$, $B^2 = b^2 + d^2$ and $D^2 = a^2 + b^2 + d^2$.

The mutual inductance between two circular loops of wire whose axes intersect at an angle γ at a point where the radius a of one loop subtends an angle α and the radius b of the other an angle β is

$$M = 4\pi^2 a \sum_{n=1}^{\infty} \frac{a^n \sin\alpha \sin\beta}{n(n+1)b^n} P_n{}^1(\cos\alpha) P_n{}^1(\cos\beta) P_n(\cos\gamma) \times 10^{-7}$$

where the last terms include two associated Legendre functions and one polynomial.[2]

The mutual inductance of two circular loops with parallel axes can be calculated from tables in Grover, pages 177 to 192.

Note. The self- or mutual inductance of thin coils whose cross section is small compared with other dimensions is given approximately by insertion of the factor N^2 or N_1N_2, respectively, where N is the total number of turns, in the corresponding loop formula and the use of the mean coil dimensions for the corresponding loop dimensions.

A circular ring encircles or is encircled by a coaxial helix, the larger radius being A and the smaller a. The distances from the plane of the ring to the farther and nearer ends of the helix are b_1 and b_2 and n is the number of turns per meter on the helix. The mutual inductance is

$$M = 2\pi n(A + a)\{c[k_1{}^{-1}(K_1 - E_1) \pm k_2{}^{-1}(K_2 - E_2)] + (A - a)(b_1{}^{-1}\psi_1 \pm b_2{}^{-1}\psi_2)\} \times 10^{-7}$$

where the subscript 1 or 2 indicates the use of b_1 or b_2 for b in the following formulas:

$$k^2 = 4Aa[(A+a)^2 + b^2]^{-1} \quad k' = (1 - k^2) \quad c^2 = 4Aa(A+a)^{-2} \quad k' \sin\beta = (1 - c^2)^{\frac{1}{2}}$$

$$\psi = K(k)E(k',\beta) - [K(k) - E(k)]F(k',\beta) - \tfrac{1}{2}\pi$$

The upper sign in the $\pm$ is taken when the plane of the ring cuts the helix; otherwise the lower sign is used. Complete elliptic integrals of modulus k are indicated by K or $K(k)$ and E or $E(k)$ and $E(k',\beta)$ and $F(k',\beta)$ are incomplete elliptic integrals of modulus k' and amplitude β.[3]

Note. The following current-sheet formulas assume that the current density on the shell is uniform and flows around the cylinder normal to the axis in an infinitely thin sheet. A correction may be added to take account of the fact that the current is actually concentrated in wires of definite radius and spacing as in Grover, pages 148 to 150, but is often not needed for close windings. By a process equivalent to integration of the preceding formula, an exact formula for the mutual inductance between a cylindrical current sheet or helix and a coaxial concentric current sheet can be derived.[4]

[1] For tables, see Grover, pp. 66–69.

[2] For tables, see Grover, pp. 193–208.

[3] For tables, see Grover, pp. 114–118.

[4] Louis Cohen, *Bull. Natl. Bur. Standards* **3**, 298 (1907). **For practical purposes, tables given in Grover, pp. 122–141, are better.**

The self-inductance of a current sheet of radius a, length b, and diagonal $d = (4a^2 + b^2)^{\frac{1}{2}}$ having a total number of turns N is[1]

$$L = \tfrac{4}{3}\pi b^{-2}N^2[d(4a^2 - b^2)E(k) - b^2dK(k) - 8a^3] \times 10^{-7}$$

where $k = 2d^{-1}a$.

A current sheet is wound on the surface of the toroid formed by the rotation in the φ direction of a plane area S about an external line. If there are N turns and if the current density is independent of φ and has no φ component, then the self-inductance is

$$L = 2K_mN^2 \int_S r^{-1}\, dS \times 10^{-7}$$

where K_m is the relative permeability inside the current sheet and r is the distance of the area element dS from the rotational axis. The self-inductance in the above case, if S is a circle of radius a whose center is at a distance b from the rotational axis, is

$$L = 4\pi K_mN^2[b - (b^2 - a^2)^{\frac{1}{2}}] \times 10^{-7}$$

The self-inductance, if S is a rectangular section with sides parallel to the axis of length a and sides normal to it of length b and with the inside surface a distance R from the axis, is

$$L = 2N^2aK_m \ln\,(1 + R^{-1}b) \times 10^{-7}$$

The self-inductance of a circular coil of N turns and circular section is

$$L \approx 4\pi N^2a[(1 + \tfrac{1}{8}r^2a^{-2}) \ln\,(8r^{-1}a) + r^2(24a^2)^{-1} - 1.75] \times 10^{-7}$$

where r is the radius of the section, a the radius of the axis of the section, and $(r/a)^n$ is neglected when $n > 2$. The self-inductance of the above coil if it has a square section of side c is, if $c \ll a$,

$$L \approx 4\pi aN^2\{\tfrac{1}{2}[1 + c^2(24a^2)^{-1}] \ln\,(32c^{-2}a^2) - 0.84834 + 0.051a^{-2}c^2\} \times 10^{-7}$$

The self-inductance of coils of rectangular section can be calculated from tables given in Grover, pages 94 to 113.

The mutual inductance of coils of rectangular section and parallel axes can be calculated from tables given in Grover, pages 225 to 235. The mutual inductance of coils of rectangular section with inclined axes can be found from tables given by Grover on pages 209 to 214.

The increase in self-inductance of a circuit due to the placement of a sphere of radius a and relative permeability K_m in a position near it where the induction B per unit current is nearly uniform is

$$\Delta L \approx a^3B^2(K_m - 1)(K_m + 2)^{-1} \times 10^7$$

The increase of self-inductance of a loop of radius a due to the insertion concentrically of a sphere of radius b and infinite permeability is

$$\Delta L = 8\pi a^{-2}b^3K(a^{-2}b^2) \times 10^{-7}$$

The mutual inductance between two coaxial loops of radii a and b when the distance between centers is c and there is an infinite slab of thickness t and relative permeability K_m between and parallel to them, is

$$M = 8\pi(ab)^{\frac{1}{2}}(1 - \beta^2) \sum_{n=0}^{\infty} k_n^{-1}\beta^{2n}[(1 - k_n^2)K(k_n) - E(k_n)]$$

$$k_n^2 = 4ab[(a + b)^2 + (c + 2nt)^2]^{-1} \qquad \beta = (K_m - 1)(K_m + 2)^{-1}$$

[1] For most purposes the tables given in Grover, pp. 142–162, are more practical than the formula.

Magnetic Forces on Circuits. The component of force in newtons tending to displace one of a pair of circuits in the x direction, the other being fixed, is

$$F_x = I_1 I_2 \frac{\partial M}{\partial x}$$

where I_1 and I_2 are the currents and M is the mutual inductance. The torque in newton meters tending to rotate one of a pair of circuits through an angle α, the other being fixed, is

$$T_\alpha = I_1 I_2 \frac{\partial M}{\partial \alpha}$$

Thus any desired forces or torques may be computed from the mutual-inductance formulas of the last few pages by differentiation, provided that it is possible to express M explicitly in terms of x or α. When this is not possible the difference in the mutual-inductance values calculated for the position x or α and the position $x + dx$ or $\alpha + d\alpha$ using the Grover tables may be multiplied by $I_1 I_2$ and divided by dx or $d\alpha$. In many cases the tabular intervals are small enough so this will give adequate accuracy; in other cases careful interpolation will be needed. Notice that in Grover's tables distances are in centimeters.

The force per unit length between two long parallel circular cylinders or tubes carrying uniformly distributed currents I_1 and I_2 is

$$F_1 = 2I_1 I_2 a^{-1} \times 10^{-7}$$

The force is attractive when I_1 and I_2 have the same direction; otherwise it is repulsive.

The force per unit length between two parallel strips[1] of width a symmetrically placed with their faces a uniform distance b apart and carrying currents I_1 and I_2 is

$$4I_1 I_2 a^{-1}[\tan^{-1}(b^{-1}a) - \tfrac{1}{2}a^{-1}b \ln(1 + b^{-2}a^2)] \times 10^{-7}$$

The force is attractive when I_1 and I_2 have the same direction; otherwise it is repulsive.

The force between two coaxial loops of radii a and b with centers at a distance c apart that carry currents I_1 and I_2 is

$$F = I_1 I_2 \pi c k [a^{\frac{1}{2}} b^{\frac{1}{2}} (1 - k^2)]^{-1} [(2 - k^2)E(k) - 2(1 - k^2)K(k)] \times 10^{-7}$$

where $k^2 = 4ab[(a + b)^2 + c^2]^{-1}$. The force is attractive when I_1 and I_2 encircle the axis in the same direction.

The axial force between a circular loop of radius a and a coaxial helix of radius b (a may be greater or less than b) and n turns per meter is

$$F = I_1 I_2 n(M - M') \times 10^{-7}$$

The loop center may lie inside or outside the helix. Here M and M' are the mutual inductances between a loop of radius a and coaxial loops of radius b whose planes pass through the extreme near end and extreme far end of the helix, respectively. The force is toward the center of the helix if the currents circle the axis in the same direction.

The force between a helix and a coaxial circular coil of mean radius a, square section of side c, and N turns is given approximately by the foregoing formula if NI_1 is used for I_1 and $a[1 + c^2(24a^2)^{-1}]$ for a. The force between two coaxial single-layer coils may be calculated by a formula in Grover on page 258 and a table on page 115.

The torque on a circular coil of rectangular section with internal and external radii a and b and any length which carries a current I, has N turns, and whose axis makes

[1] The force between two parallel rectangular bus bars is given by B. Hague, "Electromagnetic Problems in Electrical Engineering," p. 338, Oxford University Press, New York, 1929.

an angle α with a uniform field of induction **B** is

$$T = \tfrac{1}{3}\pi BNI(a^2 + ab + b^2)\sin\alpha$$

The torque on the above coil if it has a circular section of radius b whose center is at a distance a from the axis is

$$T = \tfrac{1}{4}\pi BNI(4a^2 - b^2)\sin\alpha$$

The torque on one of two concentric circular loops of wire of radii a and b which carry currents I_1 and I_2 is

$$T = 4\pi^2 aI_1I_2 \times 10^{-7} \sum_{n=0}^{\infty} \frac{2n+2}{2n+1}\left[\frac{(2n+1)!!}{(2n+2)!!}\right]^2 \left(\frac{a}{b}\right)^{2n+1} P_{2n+1}{}^1(\cos\alpha)$$

where α is the angle between their axes and $P_{2n+1}{}^1(\cos\alpha)$ is a Legendre function. It is directed so as to set one current parallel to the other.

The force on any circuit near the plane face of a semi-infinite block of material having a uniform relative permeability K_m which is independent of field strength equals the force between the circuit carrying a current I and its mirror-image circuit in the plane face carrying a current $I' = (K_m - 1)(K_m + 1)^{-1}I$. The direction of I', if K_m is greater than one, is such that the projections of I and I' on the interface coincide in position and direction. It is evident that if $K_m \gg 1$ then $I \approx I'$ and the exact value of K_m need not be known.

The force per unit length on an infinite wire carrying a current I parallel to the walls of an infinite evacuated rectangular conduit of infinite permeability is

$$F_x = 4\pi b^{-1}I^2 \times 10^{-7} \sum_{m=1}^{\infty} \operatorname{csch}(m\pi ab^{-1}) \sinh[m\pi b^{-1}(2c - a)] \cos^2(m\pi db^{-1})$$

where the walls of the conduit are at $x = 0$, $x = a$ and $y = 0$, $y = b$. The wire lies at $x = c$, $y = d$. To get F_y, interchange a with b and c with d. The series converges very rapidly unless the wire is near the wall. The force per unit length toward the nearest wall on an infinite wire parallel to and at a distance c from the axis of an evacuated cylindrical hole of radius a in a block of material of relative permeability K_m is

$$F_1 = 2(a^2 - c^2)^{-1}cI^2(K_m - 1)(K_m + 1)^{-1} \times 10^{-7}$$

Permeable Bodies in Magnetic Fields. The energy of an unmagnetized body of volume v when placed in a field of induction **B** produced by fixed sources in a region of constant permeability μ is

$$W = \tfrac{1}{2}\int_v (\mu^{-1} - \mu_i^{-1})\mathbf{B}\cdot\mathbf{B}_i\,dv$$

where $\mathbf{B}_i$ and μ_i are the final values of the magnetic induction and permeability in the volume element dv inside the body and the integration is over the volume of the body. The torque tending to decrease the angle α between **B** and the major axis of an oblate permeable spheroid of relative permeability K_m with semiaxes a and b, where $b > a$, placed in a uniform field of induction **B** produced by fixed sources in a vacuum is

$$T = \frac{(K_m - 1)^2 b^2 aB^2(3P - 2)\sin 2\alpha}{6[(K_m - 1)^2P^2 + (K_m - 1)(2 - K_m)P - 2K_m]} \times 10^7$$

where $P = A[(1 + A^2)\cot^{-1}A - A]$ and $A = a(b^2 - a^2)^{-\frac{1}{2}}$.

The torque tending to decrease the angle α between **B** and the major axis of a prolate permeable spheroid of relative permeability K_m with semiaxis a and b where $b < a$ placed in a uniform field of induction **B** produced by fixed sources in a vacuum is

$$T = \frac{(K_m - 1)^2 b^2 a B^2 (2 - 3Q) \sin 2\alpha}{6[(K_m - 1)^2 Q^2 + (K_m - 1)(2 - K_m)Q - 2K_m]} \times 10^7$$

where $Q = c[(1 - c^2) \coth^{-1} c + c]$ and $c = a(a^2 - b^2)^{-\frac{1}{2}}$.

The attractive force between a long cylinder carrying a uniformly distributed current I and an external sphere of relative permeability K_m and radius a whose center is at a distance b from the cylinder axis is

$$F = 4I^2 \times 10^{-7} \sum_{n=1}^{\infty} \frac{(2n - 2)!!n(K_m - 1)}{(2n - 1)!!(nK_m + n + 1)} \left(\frac{a}{b}\right)^{2n+1}$$

If the permeability is very large in the above case, the force is

$$F = 4I^2 a^2 b^{-1} (b^2 - a^2)^{-\frac{1}{2}} \sin^{-1} (b^{-1}a) \times 10^7$$

Magnetic Shielding. Two long wires of a bifilar lead at $\rho = c$, $\varphi = 0$ and $\rho = c$, $\varphi = \pi$ carry currents I and $-I$ and are shielded by a cylinder of relative permeability K_m of internal and external radius a and b. The components of the induction outside the shield are

$$B_\rho = -16I \times 10^{-7} \sum_{n=0}^{\infty} \frac{b^{4n+2} c^{2n+1} \rho^{-2n-2} \sin (2n + 1)\theta}{(K_m + 1)^2 b^{4n+2} - (K_m - 1)^2 a^{4n+2}}$$

$$B_\varphi = 16I \times 10^{-7} \sum_{n=0}^{\infty} \frac{b^{4n+2} c^{2n+1} \rho^{-2n-2} \cos (2n + 1)\theta}{(K_m + 1)^2 b^{4n+2} - (K_m - 1)^2 a^{4n+2}}$$

A long cylindrical shield of internal and external radius a and b and relative permeability K_m is placed across a uniform field of induction **B**. The induction $\mathbf{B}_i$ inside is uniform and of magnitude

$$B_i = \frac{4K_m b^2 B}{4K_m b^2 + (K_m - 1)^2 (b^2 - a^2)}$$

A spherical shield of internal and external radius a and b and relative permeability K_m is placed in a uniform field of induction **B**. The induction $\mathbf{B}_i$ inside is uniform and its magnitude is

$$B_i = \frac{9K_m b^3 B}{9K_m b^3 + 2(K_m - 1)^2 (b^3 - a^3)}$$

The Magnetic Circuit. The reluctance $\mathcal{R}$ of a magnetic circuit is well defined only when all the magnetic flux Φ links all N turns of the magnetizing coils which when carrying a current I generate the magnetomotance $\mathcal{F}$. Then

$$\mathcal{F} = \mathcal{R}\Phi = NI$$

The reluctance of a toroid of such high and uniform relative permeability K_m that there is no flux leakage can be calculated regardless of the position of the magnetizing coil from the current-sheet self-inductance formulas for N turns already given for toroids of various sections. Thus

$$\mathcal{R} = N^2 L^{-1}$$

The change in reluctance of a closed magnetic plane circuit of thickness b, rectangular section and uniform relative permeability K_m so high that leakage is negligible due to the presence of corners, steps, tapered sections, and circular holes can be calculated from the formulas already given for resistance change ΔR for two-dimensional current flow in media of resistivity ρ. Thus

$$\Delta\mathfrak{R} = 4\pi \times 10^7 K_m \rho^{-1} \Delta R$$

If a gap of uniform width a is cut out of a magnetic circuit of high relative permeability K_m, normal to the induction **B**, and if a is small compared with all dimensions of the section of area A cut, then the increase in reluctance is

$$\Delta\mathfrak{R} \approx 4\pi a A^{-1}(K_m - 1) \times 10^{-7}$$

where the surrounding space is empty and the fringing field at the edge of the gap is neglected.

The fringing field may be calculated when the region of negative x is filled with an infinitely permeable medium except for a gap bounded by $y = \frac{1}{2}a$ and $y = -\frac{1}{2}a$ which extends to $x = -\infty$. A magnetomotance is applied across the gap so that far from the edge the induction is B_0. The induction B_y anywhere on the x axis is then given implicitly by

$$x = \pi^{-1}a[B_0 B_y^{-1} - \tanh^{-1}(B_y B_0^{-1})]$$

where $0 < B_y < B_0$.

If the magnetomotance across a gap with faces at $z = \frac{1}{2}b$ and $z = -\frac{1}{2}b$ in an infinitely permeable cylinder bounded by $\rho = a$ is $\mathfrak{F}_0$, then the magnetomotance in the gap, when $\rho < a$ is

$$\mathfrak{F} \approx \mathfrak{F}_0 \left[\frac{z}{b} + \sum_{n=1}^{\infty} C_n \frac{I_0(\frac{1}{2}n\pi\rho/b)}{I_0(\frac{1}{2}n\pi a/b)} \sin\frac{n\pi z}{2b} \right]$$

where $C_1 = -0.17232$ and when $n > 1$,

$$C_n = \frac{(-1)^n}{n}\left[0.5836 \frac{0.1775 \cdot 1.1775 \cdots (n - 0.8225)}{0.8225 \cdot 1.8225 \cdots (n - 0.1775)} - 0.0201 n^{-2}\right]$$

The induction is $\mathbf{B} = -4\pi \times 10^{-7} \nabla \mathfrak{F}$. This formula assumes that the field across the edge of the gap is two-dimensional. If this is the only gap in an infinitely permeable circuit, then $\mathfrak{F}_0 = NI$ where N is the number of turns of the magnet coil and I is its current.[1]

Permanent Magnets. In the following formulas it is assumed that the magnetization M of a permanent magnet is absolutely rigid and that any magnetization induced in it by external fields is negligible compared with M. The energy of such a magnet when placed in an external field of induction **B** in a vacuum is $W = -\int \mathbf{M} \cdot \mathbf{B}\, dv$, where the integration is over the volume of the magnet and the "loop" definition of **M** is used rather than the "pole" definition. The forces and torques acting on the magnet are

$$F_x = \frac{\partial W}{\partial x} \qquad T = \frac{\partial W}{\partial \theta}$$

The moment of a magnet is $\mathbf{m} = \int \mathbf{M}\, dv$ where the integration is over the magnet volume.

The mutual (apparently potential) energy of two thin needles magnetized lengthwise at a distance a apart large compared with their length and having loop moments of magnitude m_1 and m_2, when immersed in a medium of relative permeability K_m, is

$$W = m_1 m_2 K_m^{-1} r^{-3}(\sin\theta_1 \sin\theta_2 \cos\psi - 2\cos\theta_1 \cos\theta_2) \times 10^{-7}$$

[1] Tables of $\frac{1}{2}C_n$ are given by W. R. Smythe, *Revs. Modern Phys.* **20**, 176 (1948).

where θ_1 and θ_2 are the angles between $\mathbf{m}_1$ and $\mathbf{m}_2$, respectively, and $\mathbf{r}$. The angle between the planes that contain $\mathbf{m}_1$ and $\mathbf{m}_2$ and intersect in $\mathbf{r}$ is ψ. The repulsive force between two needles is $-\partial W/\partial r$ and if α is the azimuth angle about any line the torque on either magnet about that line is $-\partial W/\partial \alpha$, the other magnet being fixed. In a vacuum where K_m is unity this formula applies to magnets of moments $\mathbf{m}_1$ and $\mathbf{m}_2$ of any shape provided their dimensions are small compared with $\mathbf{r}$. In other media the mutual energy depends on the shape.

Uniformly magnetized bodies may be replaced by their equivalent current sheets for the purpose of calculating fields and mutual torques in a vacuum. The current sheet coincides with the surface of the body and the current density encircles the body in a path normal to the direction x of magnetization and is uniform in terms of x and numerically equal to M. Thus the fields of thin disks magnetized normal to their faces and the torques and forces between them are identical with those between circular loops already given, if I_1 and I_2 are replaced by M_1 and M_2. Similarly, in a vacuum the fields and forces involving uniformly magnetized bars may be calculated from the formulas already given for solenoids provided nI, where n is the number of turns per meter, is replaced by M. The mutual-inductance tables given by Grover and already referred to may be used.

A right circular cylinder of length b and radius a uniformly magnetized lengthwise with an intensity M, when placed with its flat end against an infinitely permeable flat surface, adheres with a force

$$F = 8\pi abM^2\{k^{-1}[K(k) - E(k)] - k_1^{-1}[K(k_1) - E(k_1)]\} \times 10^{-7}$$

where the moduli of the complete elliptic integrals are $k = 2a(4a^2 + b^2)^{-\frac{1}{2}}$ and $k_1 = a(a^2 + b^2)^{-\frac{1}{2}}$. If M is very large, this gives, approximately

$$F \approx 2\pi^2a^2M^2 \times 10^{-7}$$

The same force is experienced by two identical cylindrical magnets placed N to S. The same force, but repulsive, appears if they are placed N to N or S to S.

A long straight bar of uniform cross-sectional area S has a uniform lengthwise magnetization M. The flat end, when placed in contact with an infinitely permeable flat block, adheres with a force

$$F \approx 2\pi SM^2 \times 10^{-7}$$

The above bar bent in the shape of a horseshoe with coplanar ends will, if the magnetization remains uniform, adhere with twice this force.

The torque on a sphere with uniform magnetization M immersed in a medium of relative permeability K_m in a field of induction B such that the angle between B and M is α is

$$T = \frac{4\pi a^3MB \sin \alpha}{2K_m + 1}$$

The torque on any body of volume v with a uniform magnetization M when placed in a uniform field of induction B in a vacuum so that the angle between B and M is α is

$$T = BMv \sin \alpha$$

DYNAMIC-FIELD EQUATIONS

5b-8. Field Equations

Equations of Continuity between Currents and Charges

Integral Formulations. VOLUME DISTRIBUTIONS: Consider a region V, bounded by a surface S, in which the net positive charge at time t is $Q(t)$; $I(t)$ is the net current flowing out from the region across the boundary S; then

$$I(t) = -\frac{\partial Q}{\partial t} \tag{5b-1}$$

Let $\mathbf{J}(x,y,z,t)$ designate the current-density vector, $\rho(x,y,z,t)$ the charge density, and $\mathbf{n}$ the unit vector at a point on S directed outward from the region V. The equation of continuity in terms of the density functions is

$$\oiint \mathbf{J} \cdot \mathbf{n}\, dS = -\frac{\partial}{\partial t} \iiint_V \rho\, dv \tag{5b-2}$$

SURFACE DISTRIBUTIONS: In the discussion of time-varying fields it is useful to consider limiting cases of volume distributions confined to thin layers as surface distributions. Let A be an area of a surface S on which there is a surface current density $\mathbf{J}'$ and surface charge density ρ_s. Let Γ be the curve on S bounding the area A. Equation (5b-1) applies with the interpretation that $I(t)$ is the net current flowing out from A across the boundary Γ and $Q(t)$ is the charge on the area A. In terms of the source functions

$$\oint_\Gamma \mathbf{J}' \cdot \mathbf{n}_1\, dl = -\frac{\partial}{\partial t} \iint_A \rho_s\, dS \tag{5b-3}$$

where $\mathbf{n}_1$ is the unit vector in the tangent plane at a point on Γ, normal to Γ and directed outward from the area A.

MAGNETIC SOURCES: While magnetic charges and currents do not exist per se, certain time-varying field phenomena can be interpreted most conveniently formally in terms of equivalent magnetic distributions. The source functions will be designated by $\mathbf{J}_m$, ρ_m for volume distributions, and $\mathbf{J}'_m$, ρ_{sm} for surface distributions. The source functions are related by equations of continuity of the same forms as Eqs. (5b-2) and (5b-3).

Differential Formulations. VOLUME DISTRIBUTIONS:

$$\nabla \cdot \mathbf{J} + \frac{\partial \rho}{\partial t} = 0 \tag{5b-4}$$

$$\nabla \cdot \mathbf{J}_m + \frac{\partial \rho_m}{\partial t} = 0 \tag{5b-5}$$

SURFACE DISTRIBUTIONS: Suppose the equations of the surface S to be given in terms of generalized coordinates u_1, u_2 by

$$x = x(u_1,u_2) \qquad y = y(u_1,u_2) \qquad z(u_1,u_2)$$

Let $\mathbf{a}_1$ and $\mathbf{a}_2$ be *unit* vectors in the tangent plane to the surface such that $\mathbf{a}_1$ is in the direction of increasing u_1 (tangent to the curve u_2 = constant) and $\mathbf{a}_2$ is in the direction of increasing u_2 (tangent to the curve u_1 = constant), and let the corresponding components of the current be J'_1 and J'_2, i.e.,

$$\mathbf{J}' = J'_1\mathbf{a}_1 + J'_2\mathbf{a}_2$$

Further let E, F, G be the differential parameters of the surface defined by

$$E = \left(\frac{\partial x}{\partial u_1}\right)^2 + \left(\frac{\partial y}{\partial u_1}\right)^2 + \left(\frac{\partial z}{\partial u_1}\right)^2$$

$$F = \frac{\partial x}{\partial u_1}\frac{\partial x}{\partial u_2} + \frac{\partial y}{\partial u_1}\frac{\partial y}{\partial u_2} + \frac{\partial z}{\partial u_1}\frac{\partial z}{\partial u_2}$$

$$G = \left(\frac{\partial x}{\partial u_2}\right)^2 + \left(\frac{\partial y}{\partial u_2}\right)^2 + \left(\frac{\partial z}{\partial u_2}\right)^2$$

The differential form of the surface equation of continuity is

$$\frac{1}{\sqrt{g}}\left[\frac{\partial}{\partial u_1}\left(J'_1\sqrt{\frac{g}{E}}\right)+\frac{\partial}{\partial u_2}\left(J'_2\sqrt{\frac{g}{G}}\right)\right]+\frac{\partial \rho_s}{\partial t}=0 \tag{5b-6}$$

with $g = EG - F^2$.

EQUATIONS IN TERMS OF THE VELOCITY FIELD: In dealing with problems of electron beams or more generally with charged particles, the currents are defined by the charge densities and the velocities of flow. Let $\mathbf{v}(x,y,z,t)$ be the velocity of the charge at instant t at the point x,y,z; then

$$\mathbf{J} = \rho\mathbf{v} \qquad \mathbf{J}_m = \rho_m\mathbf{v}$$

The equations of continuity take the form

$$\rho\nabla\cdot\mathbf{v} + \mathbf{v}\cdot\nabla\rho + \frac{\partial\rho}{\partial t} = \rho\nabla\cdot\mathbf{v} + \frac{D\rho}{Dt} = 0$$

$$\rho_m\nabla\cdot\mathbf{v} + \mathbf{v}\cdot\nabla\rho_m + \frac{\partial\rho_m}{\partial t} = \rho_m\nabla\cdot\mathbf{v} + \frac{D\rho_m}{Dt} = 0$$

The derivative D/Dt is known as the flow derivative. These equations are hydrodynamical expressions of the continuity between charge and current.

Field Vectors and Constitutive Parameters

The electromagnetic field is comprised of two electric vectors **E** and **D** and two magnetic vectors **B** and **H**. The relationship between the members of the respective pairs of field vectors in a given medium may be characterized by the constitutive parameters of the medium, ϵ, the capacitivity, and μ, the permeability. The interpretation of these quantities for a time-varying field will be made more precise subsequently.

Isotropic Media. The constitutive parameters are scalar quantities:

$$\mathbf{D} = \epsilon\mathbf{E} \tag{5b-7}$$

$$\mathbf{B} = \mu\mathbf{H} \tag{5b-8}$$

Anisotropic Media. The vectors **D** and **E** and respectively the vectors **B** and **H** are not collinear but are linear vector functions of one another. The constitutive parameters ϵ and μ constitute tensors of second rank. Let D_i, etc., represent the components of the vectors and [ ] a column matrix of the components; ϵ_{ij}, μ_{ij} represent the components of the constitutive tensors and ( ) the square matrix of these components. The constitutive relations for an anisotropic medium have the form

$$[\mathbf{D}] = (\epsilon)[\mathbf{E}] \tag{5b-9}$$

$$[\mathbf{B}] = (\mu)[\mathbf{H}] \tag{5b-10}$$

or, in component form,

$$D_i = \sum_{j=1}^{3} \epsilon_{ij}E_j \tag{5b-11}$$

$$B_i = \sum_{j=1}^{3} \mu_{ij}H_j \tag{5b-12}$$

Both symmetric and antisymmetric forms of the constitutive tensors may be encountered.

Conductivity Parameters. A conducting medium is characterized by a linear relation between the current density and the electric vector **E**,

$$\mathbf{J} = \sigma \mathbf{E} \tag{5b-13}$$

In an isotropic medium σ, the conductivity is a scalar; in an anisotropic medium σ is a tensor of second rank and Eq. (5b-13) is to be read as a matrix equation of the same form as Eqs. (5b-11) and (5b-12).

Time-periodic Fields. Time-periodic phenomena in which all the field vectors and source functions are periodic functions of time are dealt with most conveniently by using the complex time representation $e^{j\omega t}$, where ω is the angular frequency $= 2\pi\nu$, ν being the frequency in cycles per second. Each quantity can be expressed in the form

$$F = \mathfrak{F} e^{j\omega t} \tag{5b-14}$$

where $\mathfrak{F}$, the complex amplitude, is a function of position only. The amplitude is a complex number

$$\mathfrak{F} = \mathfrak{F}_r + j\mathfrak{F}_i \tag{5b-15}$$

and Eq. (5b-14) has the meaning that the instantaneous value of the quantity F at a time t at the point (x,y,z) in space is

$$\text{Re } \mathfrak{F} e^{j\omega t} = \mathfrak{F}_r \cos \omega t - \mathfrak{F}_i \sin \omega t \tag{5b-16}$$

The complex representation is applicable to each component of a time-periodic vector quantity. A time-periodic vector **F** can accordingly be represented by

$$\mathbf{F} = \boldsymbol{\mathfrak{F}} e^{j\omega t} \tag{5b-17}$$

where the amplitude $\boldsymbol{\mathfrak{F}}$ is a complex vector function of position,

$$\boldsymbol{\mathfrak{F}} = \boldsymbol{\mathfrak{F}}_r + j\boldsymbol{\mathfrak{F}}_i \tag{5b-18}$$

The constitutive relationships (5b-9) and (5b-10) are strictly definable only for time-periodic phenomena; the relationships become relationships between the respective complex amplitudes

$$[\boldsymbol{\mathfrak{D}}] = (\epsilon)[\boldsymbol{\mathcal{E}}] \tag{5b-19}$$
$$[\boldsymbol{\mathfrak{B}}] = (\mu)[\boldsymbol{\mathcal{H}}] \tag{5b-20}$$

with the matrix components ϵ_{ij} and μ_{ij} being complex numbers that are functions of the frequency ω. The frequency dependence of the constitutive parameters is known as the dispersive property of the medium. The conductivity parameter σ is in general also frequency-dependent.

The relations (5b-7) and (5b-8) are applicable to other than time-periodic time-varying fields only when over the significant part of the frequency spectrum covered by the Fourier components of the time dependence the constitutive parameters ϵ and μ are sensibly independent of frequency.

Polarization Vectors. The role of a material medium in an electromagnetic field is expressed by distributions of electric and magnetic dipoles. The medium can be characterized by two polarization density functions **P**, electric dipole moment per unit volume, and **M**, magnetic dipole moment per unit volume. The polarization may be induced under action of the field from other sources, or it may be virtually permanent and independent of external fields. The permanent polarizations will be designated by $\mathbf{P}_0$ and $\mathbf{M}_0$. The relationships between the field vectors and the polarization vectors are

$$\mathbf{D} = \epsilon_v \mathbf{E} + \mathbf{P} + \mathbf{P}_0 \tag{5b-21}$$
$$\mathbf{B} = \mu_v(\mathbf{H} + \mathbf{M} + \mathbf{M}_0) \tag{5b-22}$$

where ϵ_v and μ_v are the constitutive parameters of free space.

Maxwell's Equations

The basic equations relating the field vectors to physically realizable sources are as follows:

Integral Forms. Let Γ be a closed curve spanned by an arbitrary surface S, both stationary in the observer's frame of reference; let $\mathbf{n}$ be a unit vector normal to S

$$\oint_\Gamma \mathbf{E} \cdot d\mathbf{l} = -\frac{\partial}{\partial t} \iint_S \mathbf{B} \cdot \mathbf{n}\, dS \tag{5b-23}$$

$$\oint_\Gamma \mathbf{H} \cdot d\mathbf{l} = \iint_S \left[\mathbf{J} + \frac{\partial \mathbf{D}}{\partial t} \right] \cdot \mathbf{n}\, dS \tag{5b-24}$$

Associated with these relations are "Gauss's laws" relating the net outward flux of $\mathbf{D}$ and $\mathbf{B}$ through a closed surface to the charges contained within:

$$\oiint \mathbf{D} \cdot \mathbf{n}\, dS = Q = \iiint \rho\, dv \tag{5b-25}$$

$$\oiint \mathbf{B} \cdot \mathbf{n}\, dS = 0 \tag{5b-26}$$

Differential Forms

$$\nabla \times \mathbf{E} = -\frac{\partial \mathbf{B}}{\partial t} \tag{5b-27}$$

$$\nabla \times \mathbf{H} = J + \frac{\partial \mathbf{D}}{\partial t} \tag{5b-28}$$

$$\nabla \cdot \mathbf{D} = \rho \tag{5b-29}$$

$$\nabla \cdot \mathbf{B} = 0 \tag{5b-30}$$

Equations (5b-26) and (5b-30) express the nonexistence of free magnetic charges.

Inclusion of Magnetic Sources. The field equations corresponding to both electric and magnetic sources would have the more general forms

$$\oint \mathbf{E} \cdot d\mathbf{l} = -\iint_S \left[\mathbf{J}_m + \frac{\partial \mathbf{B}}{\partial t} \right] \cdot \mathbf{n}\, dS \tag{5b-31}$$

$$\oint \mathbf{H} \cdot d\mathbf{l} = \iint_S \left[\mathbf{J} + \frac{\partial \mathbf{D}}{\partial t} \right] \cdot \mathbf{n}\, dS \tag{5b-32}$$

$$\oiint \mathbf{D} \cdot \mathbf{n}\, dS = Q = \iiint_V \rho\, dv \tag{5b-33}$$

$$\oiint \mathbf{B} \cdot \mathbf{n}\, dS = Q_m = \iiint_V \rho_m\, dv \tag{5b-34}$$

These are useful in the treatment of problems in which magnetic sources enter as formalisms into the analysis. The corresponding differential forms are

$$\nabla \times \mathbf{E} = -\mathbf{J}_m - \frac{\partial \mathbf{B}}{\partial t} \tag{5b-35}$$

$$\nabla \times \mathbf{H} = \mathbf{J} + \frac{\partial \mathbf{D}}{\partial t} \tag{5b-36}$$

$$\nabla \cdot \mathbf{D} = \rho \tag{5b-37}$$

$$\nabla \cdot \mathbf{B} = \rho_m \tag{5b-38}$$

Representation of Media as Equivalent Distributions. The equations can be reduced to equivalent systems involving appropriate current and charge distributions in a medium having constitutive parameters ϵ_v, μ_v. Thus,

$$\nabla \times \mathbf{E} = -\mu_v \frac{\partial \mathbf{H}}{\partial t} - \left(\mathbf{J}_m + \mu_v \frac{\partial \mathbf{M}}{\partial t} \right) \tag{5b-39}$$

$$\nabla \times \mathbf{H} = \mathbf{J} + \frac{\partial \mathbf{P}}{\partial t} + \epsilon_v \frac{\partial \mathbf{E}}{\partial t} \tag{5b-40}$$

Time-varying polarizations are thus equivalent to current distributions,

$$\mu_v \frac{\partial \mathbf{M}}{\partial t} \to \mathbf{J}_m$$

$$\frac{\partial \mathbf{P}}{\partial t} \to \mathbf{J}$$

Further,

$$\nabla \cdot \mathbf{E} = \frac{\rho - \nabla \cdot \mathbf{P}}{\epsilon_v} \quad (5b\text{-}41)$$

$$\nabla \cdot \mathbf{H} = -\nabla \cdot \mathbf{M} \quad (5b\text{-}42)$$

so that the equivalent charge distributions are

$$\rho_p = -\nabla \cdot \mathbf{P}$$

$$\rho_m = -\nabla \cdot \mathbf{M}$$

Time-periodic Fields. All quantities have time dependence $e^{j\omega t}$. The time factor can be suppressed and the equations become relations between complex amplitudes. For the differential forms:

$$\nabla \times \mathbf{E} = -\mathbf{J}_m - j\omega \mathbf{B} \quad (5b\text{-}43)$$

$$\nabla \times \mathbf{H} = \mathbf{J} + j\omega \mathbf{D} \quad (5b\text{-}44)$$

$$\nabla \cdot \mathbf{D} = \rho \quad (5b\text{-}45)$$

$$\nabla \cdot \mathbf{B} = \rho_m \quad (5b\text{-}46)$$

Force Law

The force law, which from an experimental point of view is basically the defining expression for **E** and **B**, is

$$\mathbf{F} = \iiint [\rho \mathbf{E} + (\mathbf{J} \times \mathbf{B})]\, dV \quad (5b\text{-}47)$$

where **F** is the resultant force acting on the charge and current distribution within a region V. The force density is

$$\mathbf{f} = \rho \mathbf{E} + (\mathbf{J} \times \mathbf{B}) \quad (5b\text{-}48)$$

or

$$\mathbf{f} = \rho \mathbf{E} + \rho \mathbf{v} \times \mathbf{B} \quad (5b\text{-}49)$$

Boundary Conditions

Boundaries between Media. Let S be a surface separating two media having constitutive parameters ϵ_1, μ_1, σ_1, and ϵ_2, μ_2, σ_2, respectively; let **n** be the unit vector normal to S directed from medium 1 into medium 2. The conditions at the boundary are:

1. Tangential components of the electric vector **E** are continuous,

$$\mathbf{n} \times (\mathbf{E}_2 - \mathbf{E}_1) = 0 \quad (5b\text{-}50)$$

2. Discontinuity in the normal component of the vector **D** equals the surface charge density of the boundary,

$$\mathbf{n} \cdot (\mathbf{D}_2 - \mathbf{D}_1) = \rho_s \quad (5b\text{-}51)$$

3. Tangential components of the vector **H** are continuous,

$$\mathbf{n} \times (\mathbf{H}_2 - \mathbf{H}_1) = 0 \quad (5b\text{-}52)$$

provided that neither σ_1 nor σ_2 is infinite.

4. Normal component of the vector **B** is continuous,

$$\mathbf{n} \cdot (\mathbf{B}_2 - \mathbf{B}_1) = 0 \quad (5b\text{-}53)$$

When the conductivity of one of the media is infinite, the fields inside that medium vanish and there is correspondingly a discontinuity in the tangential component of the magnetic field associated with a surface sheet; if $\sigma_1 = \infty$,

$$\mathbf{n} \times \mathbf{H} = \mathbf{J}'$$

where **H** is the total magnetic field in region 2.

The boundary conditions (5b-50) and (5b-53) are applicable to total fields. In diffraction theory it is convenient to work with partial fields for which there may be discontinuities across surfaces in the region under consideration. These can be associated with equivalent magnetic sources and the appropriate relations are

$$\mathbf{n} \times (\mathbf{E}_2 - \mathbf{E}_1) = \mathbf{J}_m'$$
$$\mathbf{n} \cdot (\mathbf{B}_2 - \mathbf{B}_1) = \rho_{sm}$$

Boundary Conditions at Infinity. The field associated with a finite distribution of sources must satisfy conditions at infinity which pertain to the energy radiated by the sources. For a time-periodic field in a homogeneous medium the conditions at infinity take the form

$$\lim_{R \to \infty} R \left[\mathbf{H} - \left(\frac{\epsilon}{\mu}\right)^{\frac{1}{2}} (\mathbf{a}_R \times \mathbf{E}) \right] = 0$$

$$\lim_{R \to \infty} R\mathbf{E} \text{ is finite}$$

where R is the radial distance from an arbitrary origin in the neighborhood of the sources and $\mathbf{a}_R$ is a unit vector directed from the origin in the radial direction.

The Wave Equations for the Field Vectors

The field vectors satisfy second-order differential equations which characterize wave phenomena. The equations for *homogeneous isotropic* media are as follows:

$$\nabla \times \nabla \times \mathbf{E} + \mu\epsilon \frac{\partial^2 \mathbf{E}}{\partial t^2} = -\mu \frac{\partial \mathbf{J}}{\partial t} - \nabla \times \mathbf{J}_m$$
$$\nabla \times \nabla \times \mathbf{H} + \mu\epsilon \frac{\partial^2 \mathbf{H}}{\partial t^2} = -\epsilon \frac{\partial \mathbf{J}_m}{\partial t} + \nabla \times \mathbf{J} \qquad (5b\text{-}54)$$

When the vectors are expressed componentwise in a rectangular-coordinate system, the equations can be put in the form

$$\nabla^2 \mathbf{E} - \mu\epsilon \frac{\partial^2 \mathbf{E}}{\partial t^2} = \frac{1}{\epsilon} \nabla \rho + \mu \frac{\partial \mathbf{J}}{\partial t} + \nabla \times \mathbf{J}_m \qquad (5b\text{-}55)$$

$$\nabla^2 \mathbf{H} - \mu\epsilon \frac{\partial^2 \mathbf{H}}{\partial t^2} = \frac{1}{\mu} \nabla \rho_m + \epsilon \frac{\partial \mathbf{J}_m}{\partial t} - \nabla \times \mathbf{J} \qquad (5b\text{-}56)$$

where ∇^2 is the conventional Laplacian operator.

Poynting Vector and Poynting's Theorem

The Poynting vector

$$\mathbf{\Pi} = \mathbf{E} \times \mathbf{H} \qquad (5b\text{-}57)$$

serves to describe the flow of energy associated with an electromagnetic field. The energy flowing out per second from a volume V bounded by a surface S is

$$P = \int \mathbf{\Pi} \cdot \mathbf{n} \, dS \qquad (5b\text{-}58)$$

where **n** is the unit vector normal to dS directed outward from the region V.

When dealing with time-periodic fields it is useful to introduce the complex Poynting vector

$$\breve{\mathbf{\Pi}} = \mathbf{E} \times \mathbf{H}^* \qquad (5b\text{-}59)$$

where the complex representation of the time-periodic quantities is implied and the asterisk denotes the complex conjugate. The *real part* of the complex Poynting vector then represents the average value of the power flow over a cycle of the time variation; precisely

$$\langle \mathbf{\Pi} \rangle = \tfrac{1}{2} \operatorname{Re} \breve{\mathbf{\Pi}} = \tfrac{1}{2} \operatorname{Re} \mathbf{E} \times \mathbf{H}^* \tag{5b-60}$$

The Poynting theorem is the equation of continuity for the energy associated with the field.

Differential Form

$$\nabla \cdot \mathbf{\Pi} + \mathbf{E} \cdot \mathbf{J} = -\frac{\partial}{\partial t}(w_e + w_m) \tag{5b-61}$$

where

$$w_e = \tfrac{1}{2}\mathbf{E} \cdot \mathbf{D} \tag{5b-62}$$

$$w_m = \tfrac{1}{2}\mathbf{B} \cdot \mathbf{H} \tag{5b-63}$$

are the electric and magnetic energy per unit volume, respectively. The theorem is written here for the total field and the magnetic-source formalisms accordingly are not included.

Integral Form. Given a volume V bounded by a surface S,

$$\int \mathbf{\Pi} \cdot \mathbf{n}\, dS + \int (\mathbf{E} \cdot \mathbf{J})\, dv = -\frac{\partial}{\partial t}\int (w_e + w_m)\, dv \tag{5b-64}$$

The time-average energy relationships in case of a time-periodic field in an isotropic medium are given by the complex Poynting theorem:

$$\nabla \cdot \breve{\mathbf{\Pi}} = -(\sigma + \omega\epsilon_i)\frac{\mathbf{E} \cdot \mathbf{E}^*}{2} - \sigma\frac{\mathbf{E} \cdot \mathbf{E}_0^*}{2} - \omega\mu_i\frac{\mathbf{H} \cdot \mathbf{H}^*}{2} - 2j\omega\left(\mu_r\frac{\mathbf{H} \cdot \mathbf{H}^*}{4} - \epsilon_r\frac{\mathbf{E} \cdot \mathbf{E}^*}{4}\right) \tag{5b-65}$$

The current density $\mathbf{J}$ has been expressed in terms of the electric field

$$\mathbf{J} = \sigma(\mathbf{E} + \mathbf{E}_0)$$

where $\mathbf{E}_0$ represents impressed electric-field intensity. The constitutive parameters ϵ and μ enter into Eq. (5b-65) as complex quantities. The subscripts designate real and imaginary parts in the obvious manner. One-half the *real* part of Eq. (5b-65) expresses the time-average energy flow and dissipation; one-half the imaginary part represents the mean value of the energy stored in the field.

The Vector and Scalar Potentials

An electromagnetic field can, in general, be divided into two parts, one associated with electric-type sources $\mathbf{J}$ and ρ, the other associated with magnetic-type sources $\mathbf{J}_m$ and ρ_m. Each part can be developed by means of vector and scalar potentials as follows:

$$\mathbf{E}_e = -\nabla\phi_e - \frac{\partial \mathbf{A}_e}{\partial t} \tag{5b-66}$$

$$\mathbf{B}_e = \nabla \times \mathbf{A}_e \tag{5b-67}$$

$$\mathbf{D}_m = -\nabla \times \mathbf{A}_m \tag{5b-68}$$

$$\mathbf{H}_m = -\nabla\phi_m - \frac{\partial \mathbf{A}_m}{\partial t} \tag{5b-69}$$

The general representation of the field in terms of potentials is accordingly

$$\mathbf{E} = -\nabla\phi_e - \frac{\partial \mathbf{A}_e}{\partial t} - \frac{1}{\epsilon}\nabla \times \mathbf{A}_m \tag{5b-70}$$

$$\mathbf{H} = \frac{1}{\mu}\nabla \times \mathbf{A}_e - \nabla\phi_m - \frac{\partial \mathbf{A}_m}{\partial t} \tag{5b-71}$$

For homogeneous isotropic media the differential equations relating the potentials to the source functions are[1]

$$\nabla^2\mathbf{A}_e - \mu\epsilon\frac{\partial^2\mathbf{A}_e}{\partial t^2} = -\mu\mathbf{J} \tag{5b-72}$$

$$\nabla^2\phi_e - \mu\epsilon\frac{\partial^2\phi_e}{\partial t^2} = -\frac{\rho}{\epsilon} \tag{5b-73}$$

$$\nabla^2\mathbf{A}_m - \mu\epsilon\frac{\partial^2\mathbf{A}_m}{\partial t^2} = -\epsilon\mathbf{J}_m \tag{5b-74}$$

$$\nabla^2\phi_m - \mu\epsilon\frac{\partial^2\phi_m}{\partial t^2} = -\frac{\rho_m}{\mu} \tag{5b-75}$$

Subject to the auxiliary conditions

$$\nabla\cdot\mathbf{A}_e + \mu\epsilon\frac{\partial\phi_e}{\partial t} = 0 \tag{5b-76}$$

$$\nabla\cdot\mathbf{A}_m + \mu\epsilon\frac{\partial\phi_m}{\partial t} = 0 \tag{5b-77}$$

The solutions to the differential equation appropriate to all space when the source distributions are themselves bounded in extent are

$$\mathbf{A}_e = \frac{\mu}{4\pi}\int_V \frac{[\mathbf{J}]}{r}\,dv \tag{5b-78}$$

$$\phi_e = \frac{1}{4\pi\epsilon}\int_V \frac{[\rho]}{r}\,dv \tag{5b-79}$$

$$\mathbf{A}_m = \frac{1}{4\pi\epsilon}\int_V \frac{[\mathbf{J}_m]}{r}\,dv \tag{5b-80}$$

$$\phi_m = \frac{1}{4\pi\mu}\int_V \frac{[\rho_m]}{r}\,dv \tag{5b-81}$$

where r is the distance from the element of volume dv to the field point P and the bracketed source quantities denote retarded values; i.e., for a given instant t at the field point P the corresponding values of the source functions at time $t' = t - r/c$, $c = (\mu\epsilon)^{-\frac{1}{2}}$, are to be used. For time-periodic fields the complex amplitudes are

$$\mathbf{A}_e = \frac{\mu}{4\pi}\int_V \mathbf{J}\frac{e^{-jkr}}{r}\,dv \tag{5b-82}$$

$$\phi_e = \frac{1}{4\pi\epsilon}\int_V \rho\frac{e^{-jkr}}{r}\,dv \tag{5b-83}$$

$$\mathbf{A}_m = \frac{1}{4\pi\epsilon}\int_V \mathbf{J}_m\frac{e^{-jkr}}{r}\,dv \tag{5b-84}$$

$$\phi_m = \frac{1}{4\pi\mu}\int_V \rho_m\frac{e^{-jkr}}{r}\,dv \tag{5b-85}$$

where $k = 2\pi/\lambda = \omega(\mu\epsilon)^{\frac{1}{2}}$.

References

Schelkunoff, S. A.: "Electromagnetic Waves," D. Van Nostrand Company, Inc., New York, 1943.

Smythe, W. R.: "Static and Dynamic Electricity," 2d ed., McGraw-Hill Book Company, Inc., New York, 1950.

Stratton, J. A.: "Electromagnetic Theory," McGraw-Hill Book Company, Inc., New York, 1941.

[1] In Eqs. (5b-72) and (5b-74), ∇^2 is the conventional Laplacian operator, provided that the vectors are expressed componentwise with respect to a rectangular-coordinate reference frame.

5b-9. Basic Wave Functions for Time-periodic Fields. This section is a collection of basic sets of solutions to Maxwell's equations in a homogeneous isotropic region, free from generators, which are appropriate to the rectangular, cylindrical (circular), and spherical coordinate systems. They are particularly useful for boundary-value problems in regions bounded by surfaces which correspond to coordinate surfaces of the various systems.

Plane Wave Functions

A plane wave is specified by the complex amplitude of either **E** or **H** and the propagation vector **k**. The propagation vector may be real or complex,

$$\mathbf{k} = \mathbf{k}_r - j\mathbf{k}_i \tag{5b-86}$$

and in the case of a complex **k** the real and imaginary parts may be collinear or in different directions. In all cases the propagation vector must satisfy the relation

$$\mathbf{k} \cdot \mathbf{k} = k^2 = \omega^2 \mu \epsilon_T \tag{5b-87}$$

The constitutive parameter ϵ_T here signifies the effective complex capacitivity.

$$\epsilon_T = \epsilon_r - j\left(\epsilon_i + \frac{\sigma}{\omega}\right) \tag{5b-88}$$

including the effects of both dielectric and conductive dissipation factors.[1]

Let $\mathbf{E}_0$ and $\mathbf{H}_0$ be the complex amplitudes of the respective field vectors; the basic wave function is

$$\mathbf{E} = \mathbf{E}_0 e^{-j\mathbf{k}\cdot\mathbf{r}} \tag{5b-89}$$

$$\mathbf{H} = \mathbf{H}_0 e^{-j\mathbf{k}\cdot\mathbf{r}} \tag{5b-90}$$

with

$$\mathbf{H}_0 = \frac{1}{\omega\mu}(\mathbf{k} \times \mathbf{E}_0) \tag{5b-91}$$

$$\mathbf{E}_0 = -\frac{1}{\omega\epsilon_T}(\mathbf{k} \times \mathbf{H}_0) \tag{5b-92}$$

and **r** the position vector, expressed in rectangular coordinates by

$$\mathbf{r} = x\mathbf{a}_x + y\mathbf{a}_y + z\mathbf{a}_z$$

TEM Waves.[2] The vectors $\mathbf{k}_r$ and $\mathbf{k}_i$ are collinear; $\mathbf{E}_0$ and $\mathbf{H}_0$ are mutually orthogonal and lie in a plane normal to the direction of **k**. If $\mathbf{E}_0$ is linearly polarized, $\mathbf{H}_0$ is likewise linearly polarized.

TE Waves.[2] The vectors $\mathbf{k}_r$ and $\mathbf{k}_i$ are not collinear; $\mathbf{E}_0$ is perpendicular to the plane defined by $\mathbf{k}_r$ and $\mathbf{k}_i$ and $\mathbf{H}_0$ lies in the plane defined by $\mathbf{k}_r$ and $\mathbf{k}_i$. For a given linearly polarized $\mathbf{E}_0$ the magnetic vector $\mathbf{H}_0$ is elliptically polarized.

TM Waves.[2] The vectors $\mathbf{k}_r$ and $\mathbf{k}_i$ are not collinear; $\mathbf{H}_0$ is perpendicular to the plane defined by $\mathbf{k}_r$ and $\mathbf{k}_i$ and $\mathbf{E}_0$ lies in the plane defined by $\mathbf{k}_r$ and $\mathbf{k}_i$. For a given linearly polarized $\mathbf{H}_0$ the electric vector $\mathbf{E}_0$ is elliptically polarized.

Cylindrical Wave Functions

The circular cylindrical wave functions are expressed in terms of the cylindrical coordinates r, θ, z; r and θ being polar coordinates in the xy plane. There are three distinct types of basic function characterized by the relationship between the field vectors and the z axis.

[1] When μ and ϵ_T are complex, the propagation constant k and the propagation vector **k** are multivalued. The choice of the branch of the function is determined by such physical considerations as that the sense of attenuation must correspond with the sense of propagation of the wave.

[2] See Sec. 5b-10.

TEM Waves. The vectors **E** and **H** are wholly transverse to the z axis and are related by

$$\mathbf{H} = \frac{k}{\omega\mu} (\mathbf{a}_z \times \mathbf{E}) \tag{5b-93}$$

$$\mathbf{E} = -\frac{k}{\omega\epsilon} (\mathbf{a}_z \times \mathbf{H}) \tag{5b-94}$$

The complex propagation constant k has the value given by Eq. (5b-87). Two general groups of solutions can be distinguished:

(1) $$E_r = \frac{\partial U_n}{\partial r} \qquad E_\theta = \frac{1}{r}\frac{\partial U_n}{\partial \theta} \tag{5b-95}$$

(2) $$H_r = \frac{\partial U_n}{\partial r} \qquad H_\theta = \frac{1}{r}\frac{\partial U_n}{\partial \theta} \tag{5b-96}$$

where U_n is a separable solution of Laplace's equation in two dimensions; explicitly

$$U_0 = (A_0\theta + B_0)(C_0 \ln r + D_0) \tag{5b-97}$$

$$U_n = (C_n r^n + D_n r^{-n})e^{-jn\theta} \tag{5b-98}$$

TE Waves

$$\begin{aligned} E_r &= -\frac{n\omega\mu}{r}\psi_n & H_r &= -jh\frac{\partial \psi_n}{\partial r} \\ E_\theta &= j\omega\mu\frac{\partial \psi_n}{\partial r} & H_\theta &= -\frac{nh}{r}\psi_n \\ E_z &= 0 & H_z &= (k^2 - h^2)\psi_n \end{aligned} \tag{5b-99}$$

TM Waves

$$\begin{aligned} E_r &= -jh\frac{\partial \psi_n}{\partial r} & H_r &= \frac{nk^2}{\omega\mu}\frac{\psi_n}{r} \\ E_\theta &= -\frac{nh}{r}\psi_n & H_\theta &= \frac{jk^2}{\omega\mu}\frac{\partial \psi_n}{\partial r} \\ E_z &= (k^2 - h^2)\psi_n & H_z &= 0 \end{aligned} \tag{5b-100}$$

The function ψ_n is

$$\psi_n = Z_n(\Lambda r)e^{-jhz}e^{-jn\theta} \tag{5b-101}$$

$$\Lambda = (k^2 - h^2)^{\frac{1}{2}} \tag{5b-102}$$

where $Z_n(\Lambda r)$ is a suitable linear combination of two linearly independent solutions to the Bessel differential equation of order n. The function may be multivalued corresponding to the multivalued definition of Λ; the choice of the branch of the function is governed by the physical conditions of the problem. The parameters h and n may take on real and complex values according to the requirements of a particular problem.

Spherical Wave Functions

The spherical wave functions are expressed in terms of the spherical coordinates r, θ, ϕ; where θ is the colatitude angle with respect to the pole axis and ϕ is the azimuthal angle. The functions again fall into three classes characterized by the relationship between the field vectors and the radial direction.

TEM Waves

$$E_r = H_r = 0$$

$$E_\phi = \frac{e^{\pm jkr}}{r \sin\theta} \qquad H_\phi = \pm\left(\frac{\epsilon}{\mu}\right)^{\frac{1}{2}} E_\theta \tag{5b-103}$$

TE Waves

$$\begin{aligned} E_r &= 0 & H_r &= \frac{\partial^2}{\partial r^2}(r\psi_{nm}) + k^2(r\psi_{nm}) \\ E_\theta &= -\frac{j\omega\mu}{r\sin\theta}\frac{\partial}{\partial\phi}(r\psi_{nm}) & H_\theta &= \frac{1}{r}\frac{\partial^2}{\partial r\,\partial\theta}(r\psi_{nm}) \\ E_\phi &= \frac{j\omega\mu}{r}\frac{\partial}{\partial\theta}(r\psi_{nm}) & H_\phi &= \frac{1}{r\sin\theta}\frac{\partial^2}{\partial r\,\partial\phi}(r\psi_{nm}) \end{aligned} \tag{5b-104}$$

TM Waves

$$E_r = \frac{\partial^2}{\partial r^2}(r\psi_{nm}) + k^2(r\psi_{nm}) \qquad H_r = 0$$

$$\begin{aligned} E_\theta &= \frac{1}{r}\frac{\partial^2}{\partial r\,\partial\theta}(r\psi_{nm}) & H_\theta &= \frac{j\omega\epsilon}{r\sin\theta}\frac{\partial}{\partial\phi}(r\psi_{nm}) \\ E_\phi &= \frac{1}{r\sin\theta}\frac{\partial^2}{\partial r\,\partial\phi}(r\psi_{nm}) & H_\phi &= \frac{j\omega\epsilon}{r}\frac{\partial}{\partial\theta}(r\psi_{nm}) \end{aligned} \tag{5b-105}$$

where
$$\psi_{nm} = \mathcal{Z}_n(kr)\mathcal{L}_n{}^m(\cos\theta)e^{-jm\phi} \tag{5b-106}$$

The function $\mathcal{Z}_n(kr)$ is a spherical function defined in terms of a general cylinder function $Z_{n+\frac{1}{2}}(kr)$ by

$$\mathcal{Z}_n(kr) = \left(\frac{\pi}{2kr}\right)^{\frac{1}{2}} Z_{n+\frac{1}{2}}(kr) \tag{5b-107}$$

the cylinder function being a suitable linear combination of two linearly independent solutions to the Bessel differential equation of order $n + \frac{1}{2}$. The function $\mathcal{L}_n{}^m(\cos\theta)$ is a general solution of the associated Legendre differential equation; it is a linear combination of the functions $P_n{}^m(\cos\theta)$, $Q_n{}^m(\cos\theta)$. Note that

$$\frac{\partial^2}{\partial r^2}(r\psi_{nm}) + k^2(r\psi_{nm}) = \frac{n(n+1)}{r}\mathcal{Z}_n(kr)\mathcal{L}_n{}^m(\cos\theta)e^{-jm\phi} \tag{5b-108}$$

References

Schelkunoff, S. A.: "Electromagnetic Waves," D. Van Nostrand Company, Inc., New York, 1943.

Stratton, J. A.: "Electromagnetic Theory," McGraw-Hill Book Company, Inc., New York, 1941.

5b-10. Waves Guided by Conductors. If guides of electromagnetic waves are restricted to those of arbitrary but uniform cross section, i.e., cylindrical in shape, and if a harmonic time dependence of the form $e^{j\omega t}$ is assumed, then the axial dependence of all the field components is of the form $e^{\mp\gamma z}$. The propagation constant may be written

$$\gamma = \alpha + j\beta$$

Basic Wave Types

Waves containing neither an electric nor a magnetic field component in the direction of propagation are called *transverse electromagnetic waves* (*TEM*). These transmission-line waves along a multiconductor guide are also known as *principal waves.*

Waves containing an electric-field but not a magnetic-field component in the direction of propagation are called *transverse magnetic* (*TM*) waves, *E* waves, or waves of *electric type.*

Waves containing a magnetic-field but not an electric-field component in the direction of propagation are called *transverse electric* (*TE*) waves, *H* waves, or waves of *magnetic type.*

Conventional Transmission Lines

For a two-conductor uniform line, the differential equations for the voltage V and current I are

$$\frac{\partial V}{\partial z} = -L\frac{\partial I}{\partial t} - RI$$
$$\frac{\partial I}{\partial z} = -C\frac{\partial V}{\partial t} - GV$$

where L, C, R, and G are the inductance, capacitance, resistance, and conductance, respectively, all per unit length z of the line.

Table 5b-1. Some Constants of Coaxial, Parallel-wire, Shielded Pairs and Parallel-bar Transmission Lines*

	Coaxial (r_o, r_i)	Parallel-wire (s, d)	Shielded pair ($p = \frac{s}{d}$, $q = \frac{s}{D}$; D, d, s, 2, 3)	Parallel-bar (a, b) Formulas for $a \ll b$
Capacitance C, farads/m	$\dfrac{2\pi\epsilon}{\ln\left(\dfrac{r_0}{r_i}\right)}$	$\dfrac{\pi\epsilon}{\cosh^{-1}\left(\dfrac{s}{d}\right)}$	. . . .	$\dfrac{\epsilon b}{a}$
External inductance L, henrys/m	$\dfrac{\mu}{2\pi}\ln\left(\dfrac{r_0}{r_i}\right)$	$\dfrac{\mu}{\pi}\cosh^{-1}\left(\dfrac{s}{d}\right)$	. . . .	$\mu\dfrac{a}{b}$
Conductance G, mhos/m	$\dfrac{2\pi\sigma}{\ln\left(\dfrac{r_0}{r_i}\right)} = \dfrac{2\pi\omega\epsilon_v\epsilon_r''}{\ln\left(\dfrac{r_0}{r_i}\right)}$	$\dfrac{\pi\sigma}{\cosh^{-1}\left(\dfrac{s}{d}\right)} = \dfrac{\pi\omega\epsilon_v\epsilon_r''}{\cosh^{-1}\left(\dfrac{s}{d}\right)}$	. . . .	$\dfrac{\sigma b}{a} = \dfrac{\omega\epsilon_v\epsilon_r' b}{a}$
Resistance R, ohms/m	$\dfrac{R_s}{2\pi}\left(\dfrac{1}{r_0} + \dfrac{1}{r_i}\right)$	$\dfrac{2R_s}{\pi d}\left[\dfrac{s/d}{\sqrt{(s/d)^2 - 1}}\right]$	$\dfrac{2R_{s2}}{\pi d}\left[1 + \dfrac{1 + 2p^2}{4p^4}(1 - 4q^2)\right] + \dfrac{8R_{s3}}{\pi D} q^2\left[1 + q^2 - \dfrac{1 + 4p^2}{8p^4}\right]$	$\dfrac{2R_s}{b}$
Internal inductance L_i, henrys/m (for high frequency)	← $\dfrac{R}{\omega}$ → (all columns)			

Characteristic impedance at high frequency Z_0, ohms	$\frac{\eta}{2\pi} \ln \left(\frac{r_0}{r_i}\right)$	$\frac{\eta}{\pi} \cosh^{-1} \left(\frac{s}{d}\right)$	$\frac{\eta_1}{\pi} \left\{ \ln \left[2p \left(\frac{1 - q^2}{1 + q^2}\right) \right] - \frac{1 + 4p^2}{16p^4} (1 - 4q^2) \right\}$	$\eta \frac{a}{b}$
Z_0 for air dielectric	$60 \ln \left(\frac{r_0}{r_i}\right)$	$120 \cosh^{-1} \left(\frac{s}{d}\right) \cong 120 \ln \left(\frac{2s}{d}\right)$ if $s/d \gg 1$	$120 \left\{ \ln \left[2p \frac{(1 - q^2)}{(1 + q^2)} \right] - \frac{1 + 4p^2}{16p^4} (1 - 4q^2) \right\}$	$120\pi \frac{a}{b}$
Attenuation due to conductor α_c	← $\frac{R}{2Z_0}$ →			
Attenuation due to dielectric α_d	← $\frac{GZ_0}{2} = \frac{\sigma\eta}{2} = \frac{\pi \sqrt{\epsilon_r'\mu_r'}}{\lambda_0} \left(\frac{\epsilon''_r}{\epsilon'_r}\right)$ →			
Total attenuation, db/m	← $8.686(\alpha_c + \alpha_d)$ →			
Phase constant for low-loss lines β	← $\omega \sqrt{\mu\epsilon} = \frac{2\pi}{\lambda}$ →			

All units above are mks.
For the dielectric:

$\epsilon = \epsilon_r'\epsilon_v$ = dielectric constant, farads/m
$\mu = \mu_r'\mu_v$ = permeability, henrys/m
$\eta = \sqrt{\mu/\epsilon}$ ohms

ϵ_r'' = loss factor of dielectric $= \sigma/\omega\epsilon_v$
R_s = skin-effect surface resistivity of conductor, ohms
λ = wavelength in dielectric $= \lambda_0/\sqrt{\epsilon_r'\mu_r'}$

* Ramo and Whinnery, "Fields and Waves in Modern Radio," 2d ed., John Wiley & Sons, Inc., New York, 1953. Formulas for shielded pair obtained from Green, Leibe, and Curtis, *Bell System Tech. J.* **15**, 248–284 (April, 1936).

TABLE 5b-2. SEVERAL IMPORTANT FORMULAS FOR SOME COMMON TRANSMISSION LINES*

Quantity	General line	Ideal line	Approximate results for low-loss lines
Propagation constant $\gamma = \alpha + j\beta$	$\sqrt{(R + j\omega L)(G + j\omega C)}$	$j\omega \sqrt{LC}$	(See α and β below)
Phase constant β	$Im(\gamma)$	$\omega \sqrt{LC} = \frac{\omega}{v} = \frac{2\pi}{\lambda}$	$\omega \sqrt{LC} \left(1 - \frac{RG}{4\omega^2 LC} + \frac{G^2}{8\omega^2 C^2} + \frac{R^2}{8\omega^2 L^2}\right)$
Attenuation constant α	$Re(\gamma)$	0	$\frac{R}{2Z_0} + \frac{GZ_0}{2}$
Characteristic impedance Z_0	$\sqrt{\frac{R + j\omega L}{G + j\omega C}}$	$\sqrt{\frac{L}{C}}$	$\sqrt{\frac{L}{C}}\left[1 + j\left(\frac{G}{2\omega C} - \frac{R}{2\omega L}\right)\right]$
Input impedance Z_i	$Z_0 \left(\frac{Z_L \cosh \gamma l + Z_0 \sinh \gamma l}{Z_0 \cosh \gamma l + Z_L \sinh \gamma l}\right)$	$Z_0 \left(\frac{Z_L \cos \beta l + jZ_0 \sin \beta l}{Z_0 \cos \beta l + jZ_L \sin \beta l}\right)$	
Impedance of shorted line	$Z_0 \tanh \gamma l$	$jZ_0 \tan \beta l$	$Z_0 \left(\frac{\alpha l \cos \beta l + j \sin \beta l}{\cos \beta l + j\alpha l \sin \beta l}\right)$
Impedance of open line	$Z_0 \coth \gamma l$	$-jZ_0 \cot \beta l$	$Z_0 \left(\frac{\cos \beta l + j\alpha l \sin \beta l}{\alpha l \cos \beta l + j \sin \beta l}\right)$
Impedance of quarter-wave line	$Z_0 \left(\frac{Z_L \sinh \alpha l + Z_0 \cosh \alpha l}{Z_0 \sinh \alpha l + Z_L \cosh \alpha l}\right)$	$\frac{Z_0{}^2}{Z_L}$	$Z_0 \left(\frac{Z_0 + Z_L \alpha l}{Z_L + Z_0 \alpha l}\right)$
Impedance of half-wave line	$Z_0 \left(\frac{Z_L \cosh \alpha l + Z_0 \sinh \alpha l}{Z_0 \cosh \alpha l + Z_L \sinh \alpha l}\right)$	Z_L	$Z_0 \left(\frac{Z_L + Z_0 \alpha l}{Z_0 + Z_L \alpha l}\right)$
Voltage alone line $V(z)$	$V_i \cosh \gamma z - I_i Z_0 \sinh \gamma z$	$V_i \cos \beta z - jI_i Z_0 \sin \beta z$	
Current along line $I(z)$	$I_i \cosh \gamma z - \frac{V_i}{Z_0} \sinh \gamma z$	$I_i \cos \beta z - j \frac{V_i}{Z_0} \sin \beta z$	
Reflection coefficient K_R	$\frac{Z_L - Z_0}{Z_L + Z_0}$	$\frac{Z_L - Z_0}{Z_L + Z_0}$	
Standing-wave ratio	$\frac{1 + \|K_R\|}{1 - \|K_R\|}$	$\frac{1 + \|K_R\|}{1 - \|K_R\|}$	

R, L, G, C = distributed resistance, inductance, conductance, capacitance per unit length
l = length of line
Subscript i denotes input end quantities.
Subscript L denotes load end quantities.

z = distance along line from input end
λ = wavelength measured along line
v = phase velocity of line equals velocity of light in dielectric of line for an ideal line

* Ramo and Whinnery, "Fields and Waves in Modern Radio," 2d ed., John Wiley & Sons, Inc., New York, 1953.

If steady-state sinusoidal conditions of the form $e^{j\omega t}$ are considered, then the equations become

$$\frac{dV}{dz} = -(R + j\omega L)I$$

$$\frac{dI}{dz} = -(G + j\omega C)V$$

and $d^2V/dz^2 = \gamma^2 V$ where $\omega = 2\pi\nu$, ν is the frequency, and γ is the propagation constant

$$\gamma = \sqrt{(R + j\omega L)(G + j\omega C)} = \alpha + j\beta \tag{5b-109}$$

The real and imaginary parts of this constant are the attenuation constant and the wave number, respectively.

The solution for the voltage along the line is of the form

$$V = Ae^{-\gamma z} + Be^{+\gamma z} \tag{5b-110}$$

The current then is

$$I = \frac{1}{Z_0}[Ae^{-\gamma z} - Be^{\gamma z}] \tag{5b-111}$$

where $Z_0 = (R + j\omega L)/\gamma = \sqrt{(R + j\omega L)/(G + j\omega C)}$ and is called the characteristic or surge impedance. Tables 5b-1 and 5b-2 summarize constants for some common lines and some important formulas for transmission lines.

Velocities of Wave Propagation. The *phase velocity*, $v_p = \omega/\beta$, for the loss-free transmission line is $v_p = 1/\sqrt{LC}$.

The *group velocity* is that velocity of the envelope of a high-frequency wave whose amplitude varies at a low-frequency rate

$$v_g = \frac{d\omega}{d\beta} = \frac{v_p}{1 - (\omega/v_p)(dv_p/d\omega)} \tag{5b-112}$$

Measurement of Load Impedance. A method of determining the impedance which terminates a transmission line[1] consists in the measurement of the following:

1. Position of voltage (or electric-field intensity) minimum as measured from the load in electrical degrees, $\beta d_{\min}$ where $\beta = 2\pi/\lambda$.
2. Standing-wave ratio $S = V_{\max}/V_{\min}$. Then, the load impedance is

$$Z_L = Z_0 \frac{1 - j\,S \tan \beta d_{\min}}{S - j \tan \beta d_{\min}} \tag{5b-113}$$

Impedance Matching. In order to reduce a given standing-wave ratio to unity, either a closed stub or an open stub, both of less than a quarter of a wavelength, may be used (Fig. 5b-1). Figure 5b-2 is a set of curves[2] which simplifies matching.

OPEN- AND CLOSED-STUB MATCHING:

l_c = length of closed stub
d_c = location of closed stub measured from $V_{\min}$ toward *load*
l_o = length of open stub
d_o = location of open stub measured from $V_{\min}$ toward *transmitter*

[1] King, Mimno, and Wing, "Transmission Lines, Antennas, and Wave Guides," p. 41, McGraw-Hill Book Company, Inc., New York, 1945; D. King, "Measurements at Centimeter Wavelength," Chap. 6, D. Van Nostrand Company, Inc., New York, 1952; Montgomery, "Technique of Microwave Measurements, vol. 11, MIT Radiation Laboratory Series, McGraw-Hill Book Company, Inc., New York, 1947; "Handbook of Microwave Measurements," vols. 1, 2, Polytechnic Institute of Brooklyn, 1954.

[2] "Reference Data for Radio Engineers," 3d ed., p. 331, Federal Telephone and Radio Corp., New York.

Standard Radio-frequency Cables. Table 5b-3 contains data[1] on standard flexible solid-dielectric radio-frequency cables. Figure 5b-3 illustrates the attenuation characteristics of cables listed according to their standard number.

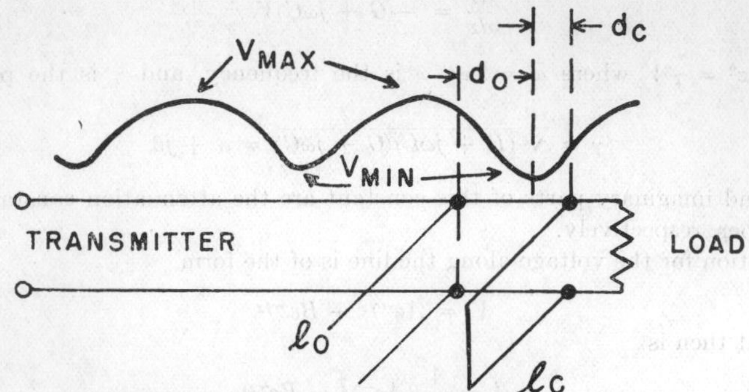

FIG. 5b-1. Impedance matching with a stub.

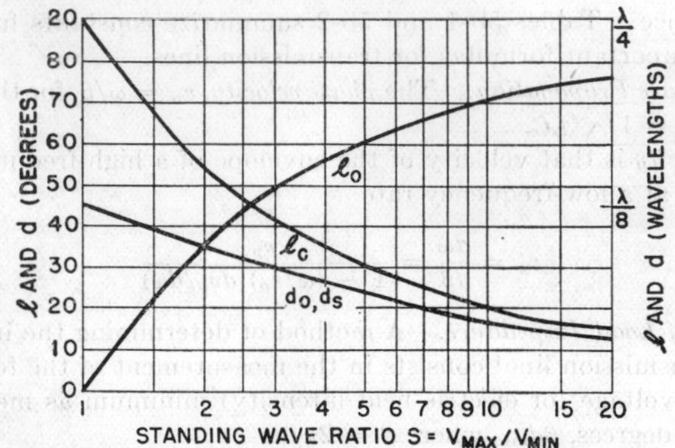

FIG. 5b-2. Impedance-matching curves.

Waves in Bounded Regions. Maxwell's equations for uniform guiding systems in terms of a propagation factor $e^{(j\omega t - \gamma z)}$ may be stated in terms of the field components in the direction of propagation z for:

RECTANGULAR COORDINATES:

$$
\begin{aligned}
H_x &= \frac{1}{\gamma^2 + k^2}\left(j\omega\epsilon \frac{\partial E_z}{\partial y} - \gamma \frac{\partial H_z}{\partial x}\right) \\
H_y &= -\frac{1}{\gamma^2 + k^2}\left(j\omega\epsilon \frac{\partial E_z}{\partial x} + \gamma \frac{\partial H_z}{\partial y}\right) \\
E_x &= -\frac{1}{\gamma^2 + k^2}\left(\gamma \frac{\partial E_z}{\partial x} + j\omega\mu \frac{\partial H_z}{\partial y}\right) \\
E_y &= \frac{1}{\gamma^2 + k^2}\left(-\gamma \frac{\partial E_z}{\partial y} + j\omega\mu \frac{\partial H_z}{\partial x}\right)
\end{aligned}
\tag{5b-114}
$$

[1] Listed by the Armed Services Index of R.F. Transmission Lines and Fittings, Armed Services Electro Standards Agency ASEA 49-2B, Fort Monmouth, N.J.

TABLE 5b-3. LIST OF STANDARD RADIO-FREQUENCY CABLES

Class of cables	JAN type	Inner conductor	Dielectric material*	Nominal diam of dielectric, in.	Shielding braid	Protective covering	Nominal over-all diam, in.	Weight, lb/ft	Approx. impedance,† ohms	Nominal capacitance, $\mu\mu$f/ft	Max operating voltage (rms)	Remarks
General purpose	RG-5A/U RG-5B/U‡	16 Awg silvered copper	A	0.181	Silver-coated copper, double braid	Noncontaminating synthetic resin	0.332	0.087	50.0	28.5	3,000	Small-sized microwave cable
	RG-8/U RG-8A/U‡	7/21 Awg copper	A	0.285	Copper, single braid	Synthetic resin	0.405	0.106	50.0	29.5	4,000	Medium-sized flexible cable
	RG-9A/U RG-9B/U‡	7/21 Awg silvered copper	A	0.280	Silver-coated copper, double braid	Noncontaminating synthetic resin	0.420	0.150	50.0	30.0	4,000	Special medium-sized flexible cable
	RG-10/U RG-10A/U‡	7/21 Awg copper	A	0.285	Copper, single braid	Noncontaminating synthetic resin and armor	0.475 max	0.146	50.0	29.5	4,000	Same as RG-8/U and RG-8A/U but with armor
	RG-14/U RG-14A/U‡	10 Awg copper	A	0.370	Copper, double braid	Noncontaminating synthetic resin	0.545	0.216	50.0	29.5	5,500	Medium-sized power-transmission cable
	RG-17/U RG-17A/U‡	0.188-in. copper	A	0.680	Copper, single braid	Noncontaminating synthetic resin	0.870	0.460	50.0	29.5	11,000	Large-sized, low-attenuation, high-power-transmission cable
	RG-18/U RG-18A/U‡	0.188-in. copper	A	0.680	Copper, single braid	Noncontaminating synthetic resin and armor	0.945 max	0.585	50.0	29.5	11,000	Same as RG-17/U and RG-17A/U but with armor
	RG-19/U RG-19A/U‡	0.250-in. copper	A	0.910	Copper, single braid	Noncontaminating synthetic resin	1.120	0.740	50.0	29.5	14,000	Very large, low-attenuation, high-power-transmission cable
	RG-20/U RG-20A/U‡	0.250-in. copper	A	0.910	Copper, single braid	Noncontaminating synthetic resin and armor	1.195 max	0.925	50.0	29.5	14,000	Same as RG-19/U and RG-19A/U but with armor
	RG-55/U	20 Awg copper	A	0.116	Tinned copper, double braid	Polyethylene	0.206 max	0.034	50.0	28.5	1,900	Small-sized flexible cable
	RG-58A/U RG-58C/U‡	19/0.0068 in. tinned copper	A	0.116	Tinned copper, single braid	Synthetic resin	0.195	0.025	50.0	28.5	1,900	Small-sized flexible cable
	RG-74/U RG-74A/U‡	10 Awg copper	A	0.370	Copper, double braid	Noncontaminating synthetic resin and armor	0.615 max	0.310	50.0	29.5	5,500	Same as RG-14/U and RG-14A/U but with armor
	RG-59/U RG-59A/U‡	22 Awg copper-covered steel	A	0.146	Copper, single braid	Synthetic resin	0.242	0.032	70.0	21.0	2,300	General-purpose small-sized video cable

TABLE 5b-3. LIST OF STANDARD RADIO-FREQUENCY CABLES (*Continued*)

Class of cables	JAN type	Inner conductor	Dielectric material*	Nominal diam of dielectric, in.	Shielding braid	Protective covering	Nominal over-all diam, in.	Weight, lb/ft	Approx. impedance,† ohms	Nominal capacitance, $\mu\mu$f/ft	Max operating voltage (rms)	Remarks
	RG-11/U RG-11A/U‡	7/26 Awg tinned copper	*A*	0.285	Copper, single braid	Synthetic resin	0.405	0.096	70.0	20.5	4,000	Medium-sized flexible video and communication cable
	RG-35/U RG-35A/U‡	9 Awg copper	*A*	0.680	Copper, single braid	Noncontaminating synthetic resin and armor	0.945 max	0.525	70.0	21.5	10,000	Large-sized high-power low-attenuation video and communication cable
	RG-6/U RG-6A/U‡	21 Awg copper-covered steel	*A*	0.185	Inner: silver-coated copper; outer: copper	Noncontaminating synthetic resin	0.332	0.082	70.0	20.0	2,700	Small-sized video and communication cable
	RG-13/U RG-13A/U‡	7/26 Awg tinned copper	*A*	0.280	Copper, double braid	Synthetic resin	0.420	0.126	70.0	20.5	4,000	Medium-sized flexible video and communication cable
	RG-12/U RG-12A/U‡	7/26 Awg tinned copper	*A*	0.285	Copper, single braid	Noncontaminating synthetic resin	0.475 max	0.141	75.0	20.5	4,000	Similar to RG-11/U but with armor
	RG-84/U RG-84A/U‡	9 Awg copper	*A*	0.680	Copper, single braid	Noncontaminating synthetic resin	1.000	1.325	71.0	21.5	10,000	Same as RG-35/U except lead sheath instead of armor for subterranean installations
	RG-85/U RG-85A/U‡	9 Awg copper	*A*	0.680	Copper, single braid	Noncontaminating synthetic resin	1.565 max	2.910	71.0	21.5	10,000	Same as RG-84/U with special armor for subterranean installations
High temperature	RG-87A/U	7/20 Awg silvered copper	*F* (solid)	0.280	Silver-coated copper, double braid	Teflon-tape moisture seal, two braids fiber glass, silicone-varnish impregnated	0.425	......	50.0	29.5	4,000	Semiflexible cable, operating at temp. −55 to 250°C
	RG-115/U	7/21 Awg silvered copper	*F* (tape)	0.250	Silver-coated copper, double braid	Teflon-tape moisture seal, two braids fiber glass, silicone-varnish impregnated	0.370	......	50.0	29.5	4,000	Semiflexible cable, operating at temp. −55 to 250°C
	RG-116/U	7/20 Awg silvered copper	*F* (solid)	0.280	Silver-coated copper, double braid	Teflon-tape moisture seal, two braids fiber glass, silicone-varnish impregnated and armor	0.475	......	50.0	29.5	4,000	Same as RG-87A/U but with armor
	RG-117/U	0.188-in. copper	*F* (solid)	0.620	Copper, single braid	Teflon-tape moisture seal, two braids fiber glass,	0.730	......	50.0	29.0	22,000	Semiflexible cable, operating at temp. −55 to 250°C

						silicone-varnish impregnated						
	RG-118/U	0.188-in. copper	*F* (solid)	0.620	Copper, single braid	Teflon-tape moisture seal, two braids fiber glass, silicone-varnish impregnated and armor	0.780	0.610	50.0	29.0	22,000	Same as RG-117/U but with armor
	RG-119/U	0.102-in. copper	*F* (solid)	0.328	Copper, double braid	Teflon-tape moisture seal, two braids fiber glass, silicone-varnish impregnated	0.465	......	50.0	29.0	12,000	Semiflexible cable, operating at temp. −55 to 250°C
	RG-120/U	0.102-in. copper	*F* (solid)	0.328	Copper, double braid	Teflon-tape moisture seal, two braids fiber glass, silicone-varnish impregnated and armor	0.515	......	50.0	29.0	12,000	Same as RG-119/U but with armor
	RG-81/U	0.062-in. copper	*G*	0.321	Copper tube		0.375	0.172	50.0	37.0	3,000	Small, semirigid cable, operating at temp. to 250°C
	RG-82/U	0.125-in. copper	*G*	0.650	Copper tube		0.750	0.698	50.0	36.0	4,000	Large semirigid cable, operating at temp. to 250°C
Pulse¶	RG-25/U	19/0.0117-in. tinned copper	*D*	0.308	Tinned copper, double braid	Synthetic rubber	0.565	0.205	50.0	50.0	8,000 peak	Special cable for twist application
	RG-26/U	19/0.0117-in. tinned copper	*D*	0.308	Tinned copper, single braid	Synthetic rubber and armor	0.525 max	0.189	50.0	50.0	8,000 peak	Medium-sized cable
	RG-27/U	19/0.0185-in. tinned copper	*D*	0.455	Tinned copper, single braid	Synthetic resin and armor	0.675 max	0.304	50.0	50.0	15,000 peak	Large-sized cable
	RG-28/U	19/0.0185-in. tinned copper	*D*	0.455	Inner: tinned copper; outer: galvanized steel	Synthetic rubber	0.805	0.370	50.0	50.0	15,000 peak	Large-sized cable
	RG-64/U	190/.0117-in. tinned copper	*D*	0.308	Tinned copper, double braid	Synthetic rubber	0.495	0.205	50.0	50.0	8,000 peak	Medium-sized cable
	RG-78/U RG-78A/U‡	19/0.0117-in. tinned copper	*E*	0.288	Tinned copper, single braid	Polyethylene	0.385 max	......	50.0	50.0	8,000 peak	High-voltage cable
	RG-88/U RG-88A/U‡	19/0.0117-in. tinned copper	*E*	0.288	Tinned copper, four braids	Polyethylene	0.490 max	......	50.0	50.0	8,000	Replaces RG-77/U in aircraft applications
Special characteristics	RG-22A/U RG-22B/U‡	Each conductor 7/0.0152-in. copper	*A*	0.285	Tinned copper, double braid	Noncontaminating Synthetic resin	0.420	0.151	95.0	16.0	1,000	Small-sized balanced twin-conductor cable

TABLE 5b-3. LIST OF STANDARD RADIO-FREQUENCY CABLES (*Continued*)

Class of cables	JAN type	Inner conductor	Dielectric material*	Nominal diam of dielectric, in.	Shielding braid	Protective covering	Nominal over-all diam, in.	Weight, lb/ft.	Approx. impedance,† ohms	Nominal capacitance, μμf/ft	Max operating voltage (rms)	Remarks
	RG-57/U RG-57A/U‡	Each conductor 7/21 Awg copper	*A*	0.472	Tinned copper, single braid	Synthetic resin	0.625	0.225	95.0	17.0	3,000	Large-sized twin-conductor cable
	RG-111/U RG-111A/U‡	Each conductor 7/0.0152-in. copper	*A*	0.285	Tinned copper, double braid	Noncontaminating synthetic resin and armor	0.490 max	0.146	95.0	16.0	1,000	Same as RG-22/U and RG-22A/U but with armor
	RG-21/U RG-21A/U‡	16 Awg resistance wire	*A*	0.185	Silver-coated copper, double braid	Noncontaminating synthetic resin	0.332	0.087	50.0	29.0	2,700	Special high-attenuation cable with small temp. coefficient of attenuation
	RG-62/U RG-62A/U‡	22 Awg copper-covered steel	*A*	0.146	Copper, single braid	Synthetic resin	0.242	0.0382	93.0	13.5	750	Small-sized low-capacitance air-spaced cable
	RG-62B/U‡	7/32 Awg copper-covered steel	*A*	0.146	Copper, single braid	Noncontaminating synthetic resin	0.242	0.0283	93.0	13.5	750	Same as RG-62/U and RG-62A/U except inner conductor is stranded
	RG-71/U	22 Awg copper-covered steel	*A*	0.146	Tinned copper, double braid	Polyethylene	0.250 max	0.0457	93.0	13.5	750	Small-sized low-capacitance air-spaced cable
	RG-63/U RG-63B/U‡	22 Awg copper-covered steel	*A*	0.285	Copper, single braid	Synthetic resin	0.405	0.0832	125.0	10.0	1,000	Medium-sized low-capacitance air-spaced cable
	RG-79/U RG-79B/U‡	22 Awg copper-covered steel	*A*	0.285	Copper, single braid	Synthetic resin and armor	0.475 max	0.136	125.0	10.0	1,000	Same as RG-63/U and RG-63B/U but with armor
	RG-65/U RG-65A/U‡	No. 32 formex, *F*, 0.128-in. diam meter (helix)	*A*	0.285	Copper, single braid	Synthetic resin	0.405	0.096	950.0	44.0	1,000	High-impedance video cable, high delay line

Note 1. The detail requirements for the cable types listed herein are covered by Specification JAN-C-17A.
Note 2. Power rating and attenuation characteristics of these cables will be available in the Armed Services Index of R. F. Transmission Lines and Fittings.
* Dielectric materials:
A. Stabilized polyethylene.
D. Layer of synthetic rubber between two layers of conducting rubber.
E. Layer of conducting rubber plus two layers of synthetic rubber.
F. Polytetrafluoroethylene (teflon).
G. Magnesium oxide.
† See individual specifications for nominal impedances and allowable tolerances.
‡ This cable is mechanically and electrically the same as the one listed with it but has the improved, noncontaminating, low-temperature synthetic resin jacket. This cable is preferred for all Signal Corps procurements.
¶ In pulse cable, the nominal diameter of dielectric is the diameter over the outer layer of conducting or synthetic rubber.

CYLINDRICAL COORDINATES:

$$\begin{aligned}
H_r &= \frac{1}{\gamma^2 + k^2}\left(\frac{j\omega\epsilon}{r}\frac{\partial E_z}{\partial \phi} - \gamma\frac{\partial H_z}{\partial r}\right)\\
H_\phi &= -\frac{1}{\gamma^2 + k^2}\left(j\omega\epsilon\frac{\partial E_z}{\partial r} + \frac{\gamma}{r}\frac{\partial H_z}{\partial \phi}\right)\\
E_r &= -\frac{1}{\gamma^2 + k^2}\left(\gamma\frac{\partial E_z}{\partial r} + \frac{j\omega\mu}{r}\frac{\partial H_z}{\partial \phi}\right)\\
E_\phi &= \frac{1}{\gamma^2 + k^2}\left(-\frac{\gamma}{r}\frac{\partial E_z}{\partial \phi} + j\omega\mu\frac{\partial H_z}{\partial r}\right)
\end{aligned} \qquad (5b\text{-}115)$$

where $k^2 = \omega^2\mu\epsilon$.

If the dielectric has finite conductivity σ substitute $\epsilon(1 + \sigma/j\omega\epsilon)$ for ϵ in the above expressions.[1]

For a wave traveling in the negative z direction, substitute $-\gamma$ for γ above.

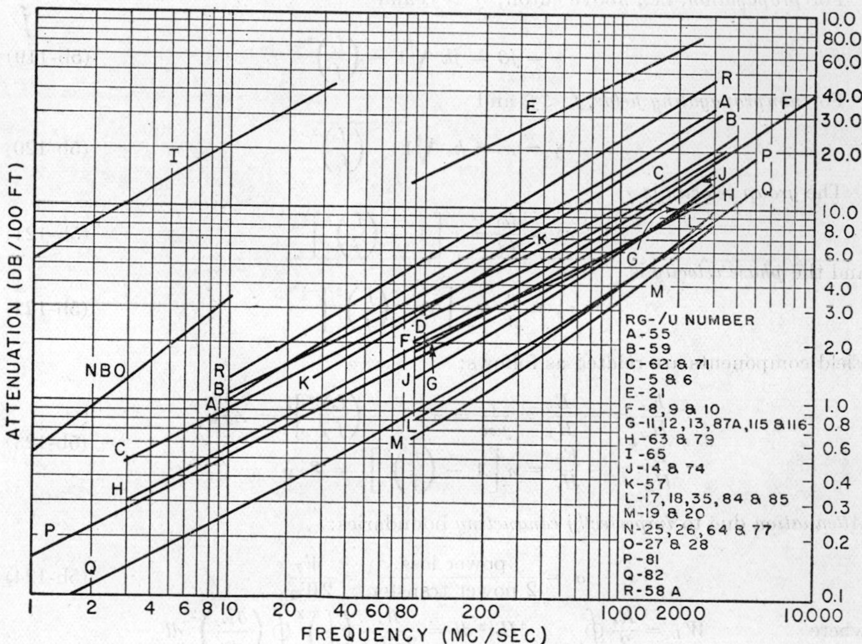

FIG. 5b-3. Attenuation of standard r-f cables vs. frequency.

Wave Types. TRANSVERSE ELECTROMAGNETIC WAVES (*TEM*): The longitudinal components E_z and H_z are zero. This requires that $\gamma^2 + k^2 = 0$, whence

$$\gamma = \pm jk = \pm\frac{j\omega}{v} = \pm j\omega\sqrt{\mu\epsilon} \qquad (5b\text{-}116)$$

The wave equation, for the electric field

$$\nabla_{xy}{}^2\mathbf{E} = -(\gamma^2 + k^2)\mathbf{E} \qquad (5b\text{-}117)$$

[1] Ramo and Whinnery, "Fields and Waves in Modern Radio," 2d ed., pp. 305–307, John Wiley & Sons, Inc., New York, 1953.

reduces to $\nabla_{xy}^2\mathbf{E} = 0$ and for the magnetic field, $\nabla_{xy}^2\mathbf{H} = 0$, where ∇_{xy}^2 is the two-dimensional Laplacian (∇_t^2) in the plane transverse to z, representing contributions to ∇^2 from derivatives in this plane.

TRANSVERSE MAGNETIC WAVES (TM): The longitudinal component H_z of the magnetic field is zero. The wave equation is $\nabla_t^2 E_z = -k_c^2 E_z$, where

$$k_c^2 = (\gamma^2 + k^2) = \gamma^2 + \omega^2\mu\epsilon \tag{5b-118}$$

The *propagation constant* is $\gamma = \sqrt{k_c^2 - k^2}$ where k_c is determined from the solution of the wave equation subject to the boundary condition that $E_z = 0$ on the conducting boundary. The allowable values of k_c are called *characteristic values*, or *eigen values*, and any one of the values determines a particular TM *mode* for the given guide.

$$k_c = \frac{2\pi}{\lambda_c} = 2\pi f_c \sqrt{\mu\epsilon}$$

where λ_c and f_c are the cutoff wavelength and frequency, respectively.

For *propagation*, i.e., above cutoff, $f > f_c$ and

$$\gamma = j\beta = jk\sqrt{1 - \left(\frac{f_c}{f}\right)^2} \tag{5b-119}$$

For *nonpropagating fields*, $f < f_c$ and

$$\gamma = \alpha = k_c\sqrt{1 - \left(\frac{f}{f_c}\right)^2} \tag{5b 120}$$

The *group velocity* is

$$v_g = \frac{d\omega}{d\beta} = v\left[1 - \left(\frac{f_c}{f}\right)^2\right]^{\frac{1}{2}} \tag{5b-121}$$

and the *phase velocity* is

$$v_p = \frac{\omega}{\beta} = v\left[1 - \left(\frac{f_c}{f}\right)^2\right]^{-\frac{1}{2}} \tag{5b-122}$$

Field components are related as follows:

$$\begin{aligned} \frac{E_x}{H_y} = -\frac{E_y}{H_x} = \frac{\gamma}{j\omega\epsilon} = \eta\left[1 - \left(\frac{f_c}{f}\right)^2\right]^{\frac{1}{2}} = Z_{TM} \\ \frac{E_r}{H_\phi} = -\frac{E_\phi}{H_r} = \eta\left[1 - \left(\frac{f_c}{f}\right)^2\right]^{\frac{1}{2}} = Z_{TM} \end{aligned} \tag{5b-123}$$

Attenuation due to *imperfectly conducting* boundaries:

$$\alpha = \frac{\text{power loss}}{2\text{ power transfer}} = \frac{W_L}{2W_T} \tag{5b-124}$$

where $$W_L = \frac{R_s}{2}\oint_{\text{bound}} |H_t|^2\,dl = \frac{R_s}{2\eta^2 k_c^2}\left(\frac{f}{f_c}\right)^2 \oint \left(\frac{\partial E_z}{\partial n}\right)^2 dl$$

and $$W_T = \frac{Z_{TM}}{2}\int_{\substack{\text{cross}\\\text{section}}} |H_t|^2\,dS = \frac{Z_{TM}}{2\eta^2}\left(\frac{f}{f_c}\right)^2 \int_{\substack{\text{cross}\\\text{section}}} E_z^2\,dS$$

$|H_t|^2 = H_x^2 + H_y^2$ is the square of the total transverse magnetic field, $\partial/\partial n$ is the normal derivative at the bounding conductor wall, $R_s = \sqrt{\pi f\mu/\sigma_c}$ is the surface resistance, and σ_c is the conductivity of the boundary conductor.

Attenuation due to *imperfect dielectric:*

$$\alpha_d = \frac{\sigma_d \eta}{2\sqrt{1 - (f_c/f)^2}} \tag{5b-125}$$

where σ_d is the conductivity of the dielectric.

TRANSVERSE ELECTRIC WAVES (TE): The longitudinal component E_z of the electric field is zero.

The wave equation is $\nabla_t^2 H_z = k_c^2 H_z$, where k_c and γ are identical with the values defined for the TM waves above except that the wave equation is now subject to the boundary condition that the normal derivative of H_z is zero at the conducting boundary (e.g., $\partial H_z/\partial x = 0$ along y).

The allowable values of k_c determine the particular *TE modes* for the given guide.

For propagation, $f > f_c$ and γ is given by Eq. (5b-119).

For nonpropagation, $f < f_c$ and γ is given by Eq. (5b-120).

v_g and v_p are given by Eq. (5b-121) and Eq. (5b-122), respectively. Field components are related as follows:

$$\frac{E_x}{H_y} = -\frac{E_y}{H_x} = \frac{j\omega\mu}{\gamma} = \eta\left[1 - \left(\frac{f_c}{f}\right)^2\right]^{-\frac{1}{2}} = Z_{TE}$$
$$\frac{E_r}{H_\phi} = -\frac{E_\phi}{H_r} = \eta\left[1 - \left(\frac{f_c}{f}\right)^2\right]^{-\frac{1}{2}} = Z_{TE} \qquad \text{(5b-126)}$$

Attenuation due to *imperfectly conducting* boundaries:

$$\alpha = \frac{W_L}{2W_T} = \frac{\dfrac{R_s}{2}\oint\left\{H_z^2 + \left(\dfrac{f}{f_c}\right)^2 \dfrac{[1-(f_c/f)^2]}{k_c^2}\left[\dfrac{\partial H_z}{\partial l}\right]^2\right\} dl}{\dfrac{\eta^2 (f/f_c)^2}{Z_{TE}} \displaystyle\int_{\substack{\text{cross}\\ \text{section}}} H_z^2\, dS} \qquad \text{(5b-127)}$$

where $\partial H_z/\partial l$ is the tangential component of the transverse gradient along the boundary of the transverse plane.

Attenuation due to *imperfect dielectrics:*

α_d as given by Eq. (5b-125)

Common Waveguides. Rectangular Waveguides: See Fig. 5b-4.

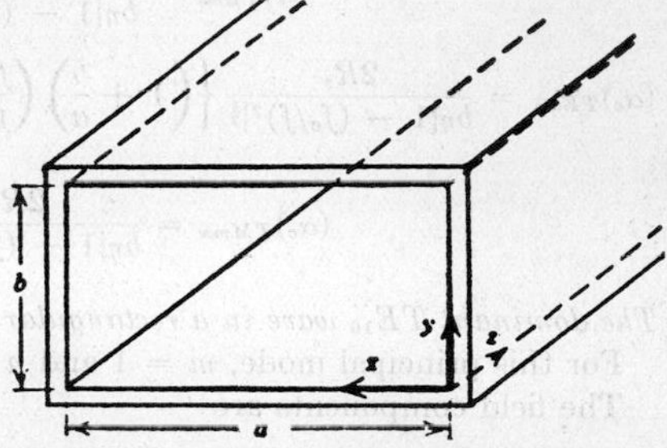

FIG. 5b-4. Coordinate system for rectangular guide.

a. No *TEM* wave is possible within the guide.

b. TM_{mn} waves:

$$E_z = E_0 \sin\left(\frac{m\pi}{a}x\right)\sin\left(\frac{n\pi}{b}y\right)$$
$$H_x = j\frac{(n\pi/b)f}{k_c\eta f_c}E_0 \sin\left(\frac{m\pi}{a}x\right)\cos\left(\frac{n\pi}{b}y\right) \qquad \text{(5b-128a)}$$
$$H_y = -j\frac{(m\pi/a)f}{k_c\eta f_c}E_0 \cos\left(\frac{m\pi}{a}x\right)\sin\left(\frac{n\pi}{b}y\right)$$
$$E_x = Z_{TM}H_y$$
$$E_y = -Z_{TM}H_x$$

c. TE_{mn} waves:

$$H_z = H_0 \cos\left(\frac{m\pi}{a}x\right)\cos\left(\frac{n\pi}{b}y\right)$$
$$E_x = j\frac{\eta(n\pi f/b)}{k_c f_c}H_0 \cos\left(\frac{m\pi}{a}x\right)\sin\left(\frac{n\pi}{b}y\right)$$
$$E_y = -j\frac{\eta(m\pi f/a)}{k_c f_c}H_0 \sin\left(\frac{m\pi}{a}x\right)\cos\left(\frac{n\pi}{b}y\right) \qquad \text{(5b-128b)}$$
$$H_x = \frac{-E_y}{Z_{TE}}$$
$$H_y = \frac{E_x}{Z_{TE}}$$

The propagation factor $e^{(j\omega t-\gamma z)}$ is understood for a wave traveling in a positive z direction where γ, Z_{TM}, and Z_{TE} are given by Eqs. (5b-119) to (5b-123).

For a negatively traveling wave, $e^{(j\omega t+\gamma z)}$ is used and the signs of Z_{TM} and Z_{TE} are reversed.

The characteristics determined from the dimensions of the waveguide are

$$(k_c)mn = \sqrt{\left(\frac{m\pi}{a}\right)^2 + \left(\frac{n\pi}{b}\right)^2} \tag{5b-129}$$

Cutoff wavelength $$(\lambda_c)mn = \frac{2\pi}{k_c} = \frac{2}{\sqrt{(m/a)^2 + (n/b)^2}}$$

Cutoff frequency $$(f_c)_{mn} = \frac{k_c}{2\pi\sqrt{\mu\epsilon}} = \frac{1}{2\sqrt{\mu\epsilon}}\sqrt{\left(\frac{m}{a}\right)^2 + \left(\frac{n}{b}\right)^2}$$

Guide wavelength $$(\lambda_g)_{mn} = \frac{\lambda}{\sqrt{1 - [(f_c)_{mn}/f]^2}}$$

The allowable values of m and n are

TE_{mn}: m, n are integers; either m or n may be zero, but not both.

TM_{mn}: m, n are integers; neither m nor n can be zero.

Attenuation above cutoff due to *imperfect conductivity:*

$$(\alpha_c)_{TEmo} = \frac{R_s}{b\eta[1 - (f_c/f)^2]^{\frac{1}{2}}}\left[1 + \frac{2b}{a}\left(\frac{f_c}{f}\right)^2\right] \tag{5b-130}$$

$$(\alpha_c)_{TEmn} = \frac{2R_s}{b\eta[1 - (f_c/f)^2]^{\frac{1}{2}}}\left\{\left(1 + \frac{b}{a}\right)\left(\frac{f_c}{f}\right)^2 + \left[1 - \left(\frac{f_c}{f}\right)^2\right]\frac{(b/a)[(b/a)m^2 + n^2]}{(b^2m^2/a^2) + n^2}\right\} \tag{5b-131}$$

$$(\alpha_c)_{TMmn} = \frac{2R_s}{b\eta[1 - (f_c/f)^2]^{\frac{1}{2}}}\left[\frac{m^2(b/a)^3 + n^2}{m^2(b/a)^3 + n^2}\right] \tag{5b-132}$$

The dominant TE_{10} wave in a rectangular guide:

For this principal mode, $m = 1$ and $n = 0$

The field components are

$$H_z = H_0 \cos\left(\frac{\pi x}{a}\right)$$

$$E_y = -j\frac{\eta 2a}{\lambda} H_0 \sin\left(\frac{\pi}{a}x\right) \qquad E_x = 0 \tag{5b-133}$$

$$H_x = -\frac{E_y}{Z_{TE_{10}}} = \frac{j\eta 2a}{\lambda Z_{TE_{10}}} H_0 \sin\left(\frac{\pi}{a}x\right) \qquad H_y = 0$$

$$Z_{TE_{10}} = \frac{\eta}{\sqrt{1 - (\lambda/2a)^2}}$$

$$v_p = \frac{1}{\sqrt{\mu\epsilon}\sqrt{1 - (\lambda/2a)^2}} \quad \text{phase velocity}$$

$$v_g = \frac{1}{\sqrt{\mu\epsilon}}\sqrt{1 - \left(\frac{\lambda}{2a}\right)^2} \quad \text{group velocity}$$

$$\lambda_c = 2a \quad \text{cutoff wavelength}$$

$$f_c = \frac{1}{2a\sqrt{\mu\epsilon}} \quad \text{cutoff frequency}$$

The *waveguide wavelength* is

$$\lambda_g = \frac{\lambda}{\sqrt{1 - (\lambda/2a)^2}} = \frac{1}{\sqrt{f^2\mu\epsilon - (1/2a)^2}} \tag{5b-134}$$

TABLE 5b-4. SUMMARY OF WAVE TYPES FOR RECTANGULAR GUIDES*

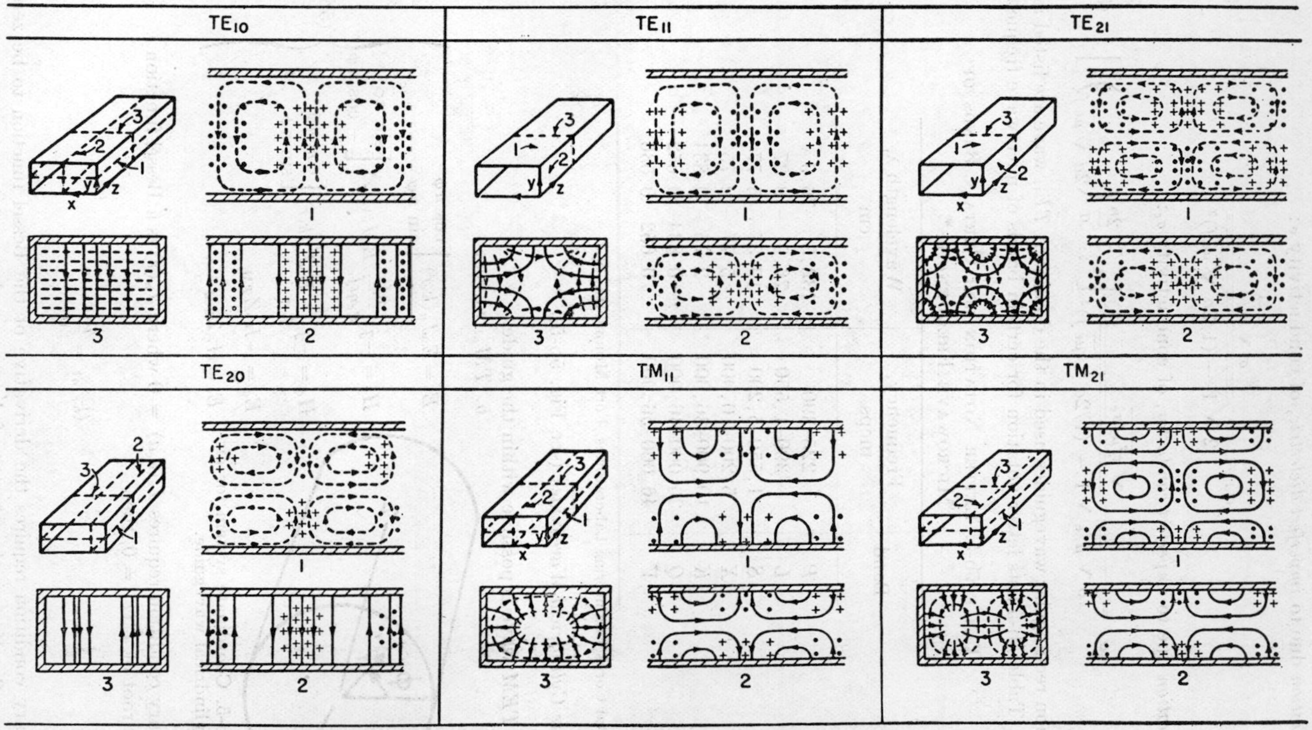

* The solid dots represent vectors coming out of the paper, and the crosses represent vectors going into the paper.

Attenuation due to *imperfect dielectric*, of conductivity σ:

$$\alpha_d = \frac{\sigma \sqrt{\mu/\epsilon}}{2\sqrt{1 - (1/2a\sqrt{\mu\epsilon}f)^2}} \tag{5b-135}$$

Attenuation due to *imperfect conductor*, of conductivity σ_c:

$$\alpha_c = \frac{\sqrt{\pi f \mu/\sigma_c}}{b\sqrt{\mu/\epsilon}\sqrt{1 - (1/2a\sqrt{\mu\epsilon}f)^2}} \left[1 + \frac{2b}{a}\left(\frac{1}{2a\sqrt{\mu\epsilon}f}\right)^2\right] \tag{5b-136}$$

Common rectangular waveguides used in the dominant TE_{10} wave are listed in Table 5b-4. Table 5b-5 lists letter notation for certain bands of microwave frequencies.

TABLE 5b-5. LETTER NOTATION FOR CERTAIN BANDS OF MICROWAVE FREQUENCIES*

Band	Frequency, mcps	Wavelength λ, cm
P	225–390	133.3 –76.9
L	390–1,550	76.9 –19.37
S	1,550–5,200	19.37 – 5.77
X	5,200–10,900	5 77 – 2.75
K	10,900–36,000	2.75 – 0.834
Q	36,000–46,000	0.834– 0.652
V	46,000–56,000	0.652– 0.536

* Signal Corps Engineering Laboratories, Fort Monmouth, N.J.

Circular Cylindrical Waveguides (see Fig. 5b-5.)

a. No *TEM* wave is possible within the guide.

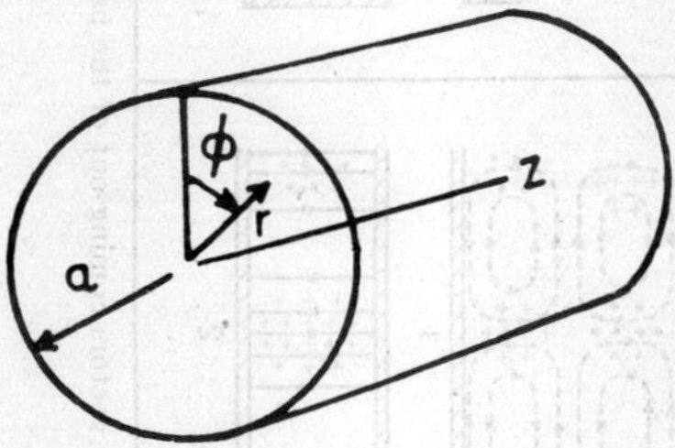

FIG. 5b-5. Coordinate system for circular cylindrical waveguide.

b. TM_{nl} waves:

$$\left.\begin{aligned}
E_z &= E_0 J_n(k_c r) \begin{bmatrix} \cos n\phi \\ \sin n\phi \end{bmatrix} \\
H_r &= -j\frac{nf}{k_c \eta r f_c} E_0 J_n(k_c r) \begin{bmatrix} \sin n\phi \\ -\cos n\phi \end{bmatrix} \\
H_\phi &= -j\frac{f}{f_c \eta} E_0 J_n'(k_c r) \begin{bmatrix} \cos n\phi \\ \sin n\phi \end{bmatrix} \\
E_\phi &= -H_r Z_{TM} \\
E_r &= H_\phi Z_{TM}
\end{aligned}\right\} \tag{5b-137a}$$

Boundary condition requires $J_n(k_c a) = 0$ where $J_n(x)$ is a Bessel function.[1] If p_{nl} is the lth root of $J_n(x) = 0$, then

$$(k_c)_{nl} = \frac{p_{nl}}{a}$$

Boundary condition requires the derivative of the Bessel function to be zero, i.e., $J_n'(k_c a) = 0$. If p_{nl}' is the lth root of $J_n'(x) = 0$, then

$$(k_c)_{nl} = \frac{p_{nl}'}{a}$$

[1] Jahnke and Emde, "Tables of Functions," Dover Publications, New York, 1943

c. TE_{nl} waves

$$
\left.
\begin{aligned}
H_z &= H_0 J_n(k_c r) \begin{bmatrix} \cos n\phi \\ \sin n\phi \end{bmatrix} \\
E_r &= j\,\frac{n\eta f}{k_c r f_c}\,H_0 J_n(k_c r) \begin{bmatrix} \sin n\phi \\ -\cos n\phi \end{bmatrix} \\
E_\phi &= j\eta\,\frac{f}{f_c}\,H_0 J_n'(k_c r) \begin{bmatrix} \cos n\phi \\ \sin n\phi \end{bmatrix} \\
H_\phi &= \frac{E_r}{Z_{TE}} \\
H_r &= -\,\frac{E_\phi}{Z_{TE}}
\end{aligned}
\right\} \qquad (5b\text{-}137b)
$$

$$(\lambda_c)_{TM_{nl}} = \frac{2\pi a}{p_{nl}} \qquad (\lambda_c)_{TE_{nl}} = \frac{2\pi a}{p_{nl}'} \qquad \text{cutoff wavelength}$$

$$(f_c)_{TM_{nl}} = \frac{p_{nl}}{2\pi a\sqrt{\mu\epsilon}} \qquad (f_c)_{TE_{nl}} = \frac{p_{nl}'}{2\pi a\sqrt{\mu\epsilon}} \qquad \text{cutoff frequency}$$

$$(\lambda_g)_{nl} = \frac{\lambda}{\sqrt{1-[(f_c/f)nl]^2}} \qquad \text{guide wavelength} \qquad (5b\text{-}138)$$

The allowable values of n and l are

TE_{nl}: n, l are integers; n can be zero but not l.

TM_{nl}: n, l are integers; n can be zero but not l.

TABLE 5b-6. SUMMARY OF WAVE TYPES FOR CIRCULAR GUIDES

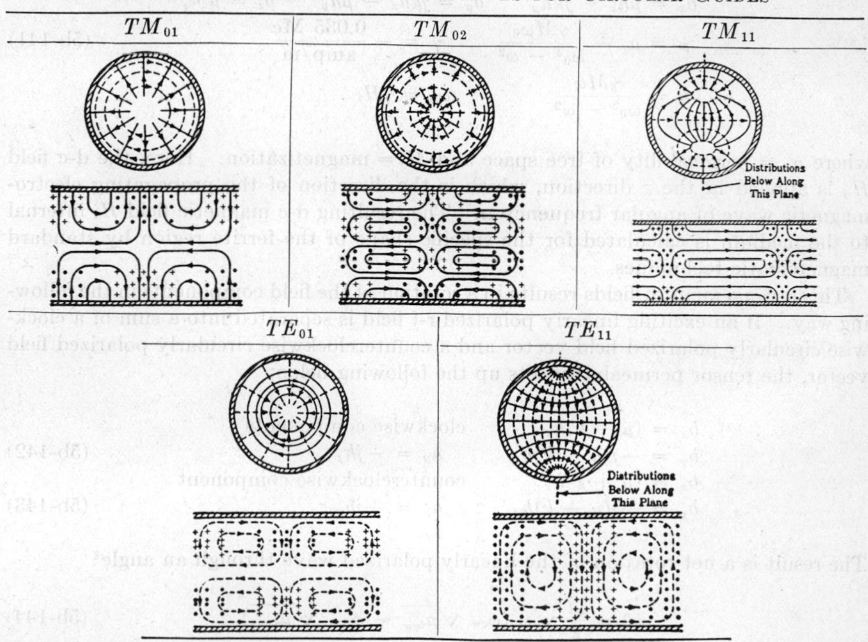

Attenuation due to *imperfect conducting walls:*

$$(\alpha_c)_{TMnl} = \frac{R_s}{a\eta\sqrt{1-(f_c/f)^2}} \qquad \text{nepers/m} \qquad (5b\text{-}139)$$

$$(\alpha_c)_{TE_{nl}} = \frac{R_s}{a\eta\sqrt{1-(f_c/f)^2}}\left[\left(\frac{f_c}{f}\right)^2 + \frac{n^2}{(p_{nl}')^2 - n^2}\right] \qquad (5b\text{-}140)$$

The expressions for γ, Z_{TM}, Z_{TE} are the same as described under the general considerations of waves in bounded regions and are used with the cutoff frequencies determined above.

Waveguide Discontinuities

Discontinuities in waveguides and their scattering properties may be represented by equivalent networks and conventional transmission lines.[1]

For example, a symmetrical obstacle strip of small thickness with its edges perpendicular to the electric field (TE_{10} mode) in rectangular guide is represented by a capacitance across the line, whereas a strip parallel to the electric field is represented by an inductance across the line.

Anisotropic Wave-propagation Systems

The use of ferrites (Sec. 5h-10) at microwave frequencies is possible because of their high resistivity (typical values from 10^{+4} to 10^{+6} ohm-m as compared with 10^{-3} ohm-m for iron). These ferrites have typical relative dielectric constants ranging in value from 9 to 20.

The tensor permeability property of the ferrite is what makes the ferrite so useful at microwave frequencies. This property is used in many ways, among which the following two are more common.

Faraday Rotation at Microwave Frequencies. Polder[2] has shown that a ferrite region which is uniformly magnetized and saturated and subjected to uniform r-f fields will have the following uniform flux densities:

$$b_x = \mu h_x - jkh_y \qquad b_y = jkh_x - \mu h_y \qquad b_z = \mu_v h_z$$

$$\mu = \mu_v - \frac{\gamma M \omega_0}{\omega_0^2 - \omega^2} \qquad \gamma = -\frac{0.035 \text{ Mc}}{\text{amp/m}} \tag{5b-141}$$

$$k = \frac{\gamma M \omega}{\omega_0^2 - \omega^2} \qquad \omega_0 = \gamma H_i$$

where μ_v = permeability of free space and M = magnetization. Here, the d-c field H_a is applied in the z direction, which is the direction of the propagating electromagnetic wave of angular frequency ω. The resulting d-c magnetic field H_i internal to the medium is calculated for the specific shape of the ferrite region by standard magnetostatic techniques.

This arrangement of fields results in a rotation of the field components in the following way. If an exciting linearly polarized r-f field is separated into a sum of a clockwise circularly polarized field vector and a counterclockwise circularly polarized field vector, the tensor permeability sets up the following fields:

$$\begin{aligned} b_x &= (\mu - k)h_x && \text{clockwise components} \\ b_y &= -j(\mu - k)h_x && h_y = -jh_x \end{aligned} \tag{5b-142}$$

$$\begin{aligned} b_x &= (\mu + k)h_x && \text{counterclockwise component} \\ b_y &= +j(\mu + k)h_x && h_y = +jh_x \end{aligned} \tag{5b-143}$$

The result is a net rotation of the linearly polarized wave through an angle[3]

$$\theta = \frac{\omega l}{2} \sqrt{\epsilon_e} \left(\phi_{cw} \sqrt{\mu_{e_{cw}}} - \phi_{ccw} \sqrt{\mu_{e_{ccw}}}\right) \tag{5b-144}$$

[1] Marcuvitz, "Waveguide Handbook," pp. 101–413, MIT Radiation Laboratory Series, McGraw-Hill Book Company, Inc., New York.

[2] D. Polder, On the Theory of Electromagnetic Resonance, *Phil. Mag.* **40**, 99–115 (1949).

[3] Fox, Miller, and Weiss, Behavior and Applications of Ferrites in the Microwave Region, *Bell System Tech. J.* XXXIV-5 (January, 1955).

where $\omega = 2\pi\nu$

l = length of ferrite sample

ϵ_e = effective relative dielectric constant of composite thin ferrite rod and cross-sectional region of the guiding system

ϕ_{cw} = cutoff factor of the clockwise rotating component of the total linearly polarized r-f field

ϕ_{ccw} = cutoff factor of the counterclockwise rotating component of the total linearly polarized r-f field

$\mu_{e_{cw}}$ and $\mu_{e_{ccw}}$ are the effective relative permeabilities of the composite system for the clockwise and counterclockwise components, respectively.

A ferrite loaded round guide propagating the TE_{11} mode and having an axial d-c magnetic field is generally used to obtain the Faraday rotation.

Transversely Applied D-C Magnetic Field. If a transverse d-c magnetic field is applied to a ferrite region in a rectangular waveguide, the properties of the dominant mode are affected in the following way:

1. Phase constants for the two directions of transmission are different.
2. The attenuation constants for the two directions of transmission may be different.
3. The electric- and magnetic-field configurations in the waveguide are different for the two directions of propagation.

Any one or combinations of these effects can be used to obtain a nonreciprocal behavior.

5b-11. Resonant Cavities. Resonant cavities are used at high frequencies in place of lumped-circuit elements, primarily because they eliminate radiation and in general possess very high Q's.

The Q of a resonator is defined as follows:

$$Q = \frac{2\pi\nu_{\text{resonance}}\text{ (energy stored in circuit)}}{\text{average power loss}} = \frac{\omega_0 U}{W_L} \qquad \text{(5b-145)}$$

The Q may be estimated from a measurement of the $1/\sqrt{2}$ amplitude points on each side of resonance; then $1/Q = \Delta\nu/\nu_0$.

Common Resonators

Rectangular Resonators. The modes are designated by TE_{mnp} or TM_{mnp} where the letters m, n, p represent number of variations in x, y, z directions, respectively.

SIMPLE TE_{101} MODE (see Fig. 5b-6)

$$\begin{aligned} E_y &= E_0 \sin\frac{\pi x}{a}\sin\frac{\pi z}{d} \\ H_x &= -j\frac{E_0\lambda}{\eta 2d}\sin\frac{\pi x}{a}\cos\frac{\pi z}{d} \\ H_z &= j\frac{E_0}{\eta}\frac{\lambda}{2a}\cos\frac{\pi x}{a}\sin\frac{\pi z}{d} \\ \eta &= \sqrt{\frac{\mu}{\epsilon}} \end{aligned} \qquad \text{(5b-146)}$$

$$Q = \frac{\pi\eta}{4R_s}\left[\frac{2b(a^2+d^2)^{\frac{3}{2}}}{ad(a^2+d^2)+2b(a^3+d^3)}\right] \qquad \text{(5b-147)}$$

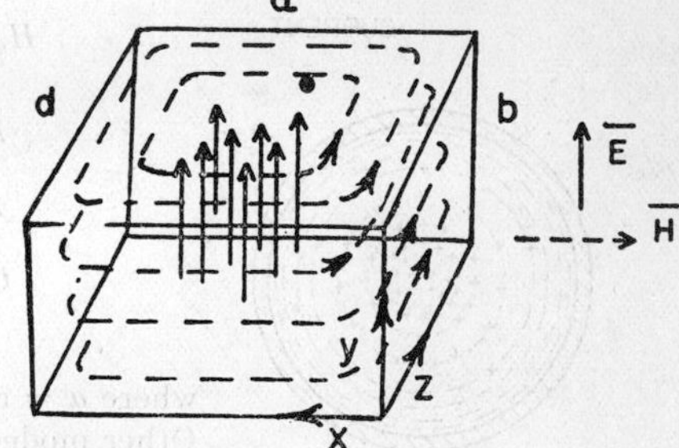

FIG. 5b-6. Electric and magnetic fields in rectangular resonator with TE_{101} mode.

For silver: $R_s = 2.52 \times 10^{-7}\sqrt{\nu}$
For copper: $R_s = 2.61 \times 10^{-7}\sqrt{\nu}$
For brass: $R_s = 3.26 \times 10^{-7}\sqrt{\nu}$
For air: $\eta = 377$ ohms

For dielectric constant ϵ_r: $$\eta = \frac{377}{\sqrt{\epsilon_r}}$$

TE_{mnp} MODE:

$$
\begin{aligned}
H_z &= C \cos\frac{m\pi x}{a}\cos\frac{n\pi y}{b}\sin\frac{p\pi z}{d}\\
H_y &= -\frac{C}{k_c^2}\left(\frac{p\pi}{d}\right)\left(\frac{n\pi}{b}\right)\cos\frac{m\pi x}{a}\sin\frac{n\pi y}{b}\cos\frac{p\pi z}{d}\\
H_x &= -\frac{C}{k_c^2}\left(\frac{p\pi}{d}\right)\left(\frac{m\pi}{a}\right)\sin\frac{m\pi x}{a}\cos\frac{n\pi y}{b}\cos\frac{p\pi z}{d}\\
E_x &= \frac{j\omega\mu C}{k_c^2}\left(\frac{n\pi}{b}\right)\cos\frac{m\pi x}{a}\sin\frac{n\pi y}{b}\sin\frac{p\pi z}{d}\\
E_y &= -\frac{j\omega\mu C}{k_c^2}\left(\frac{m\pi}{a}\right)\sin\frac{m\pi x}{a}\cos\frac{n\pi y}{b}\sin\frac{p\pi z}{d}
\end{aligned}
\tag{5b-148}
$$

TM_{mnp} MODE:

$$
\begin{aligned}
E_z &= D \sin\frac{m\pi x}{a}\sin\frac{n\pi y}{b}\cos\frac{p\pi z}{d}\\
E_x &= -\frac{D}{k_c^2}\left(\frac{p\pi}{d}\right)\left(\frac{\pi}{a}\right)\cos\frac{m\pi x}{a}\sin\frac{n\pi y}{b}\sin\frac{p\pi z}{d}\\
E_y &= -\frac{D}{k_c^2}\left(\frac{p\pi}{d}\right)\left(\frac{n\pi}{b}\right)\sin\frac{m\pi x}{a}\cos\frac{n\pi y}{b}\sin\frac{p\pi z}{d}\\
H_x &= \frac{j\omega\epsilon D}{k_c^2}\left(\frac{n\pi}{b}\right)\sin\frac{m\pi x}{a}\cos\frac{n\pi y}{b}\cos\frac{p\pi z}{d}\\
H_y &= -\frac{j\omega\epsilon D}{k_c^2}\left(\frac{m\pi}{a}\right)\cos\frac{m\pi x}{a}\sin\frac{n\pi y}{b}\cos\frac{p\pi z}{d}
\end{aligned}
\tag{5b-149}
$$

Note:
$$k_c^2 = \left(\frac{m\pi}{a}\right)^2 + \left(\frac{p\pi}{b}\right)^2 = \left(\frac{2\pi}{\lambda_c}\right)^2$$
$$k = \frac{2\pi}{\lambda} = \left[\left(\frac{m\pi}{a}\right)^2 + \left(\frac{n\pi}{b}\right)^2 + \left(\frac{p\pi}{d}\right)^2\right]^{\frac{1}{2}}$$

Circular Cylindrical Resonator

A simple mode (TM_{010}) exists and is shown in Fig. 5b-7.

$$
\begin{aligned}
E_z &= E_0 J_0(kr)\\
H_\phi &= j\frac{E_0}{\eta}J_1(kr)\\
k &= \frac{p_{01}}{a} = \frac{2.405}{a}\\
\lambda &= 2.61a \text{ (resonant wavelength)}\\
Q &= \frac{\eta}{R_s}\frac{2.405}{2[a/h+1]}
\end{aligned}
\tag{5b-150}
$$

where a = radius and h = length of cavity. Other modes are shown in Fig. 5b-8.

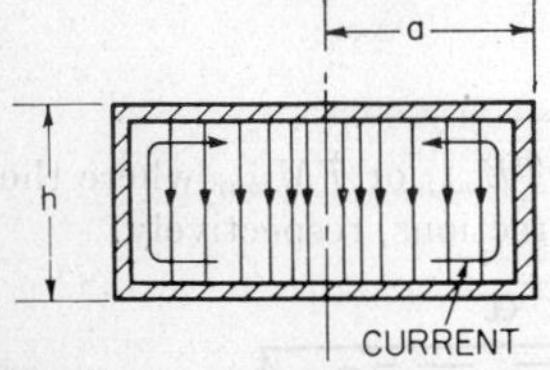

FIG. 5b-7. Simple TM_{010} mode in a cylindrical cavity.

Spherical Resonators

Figures 5b-9 and 5b-10 show the field patterns for the TM_{101} and TE_{101} modes, respectively.

General Considerations. DEGENERATE MODES: Modes with different field distributions but with the same resonant frequency are called *degenerate* modes.

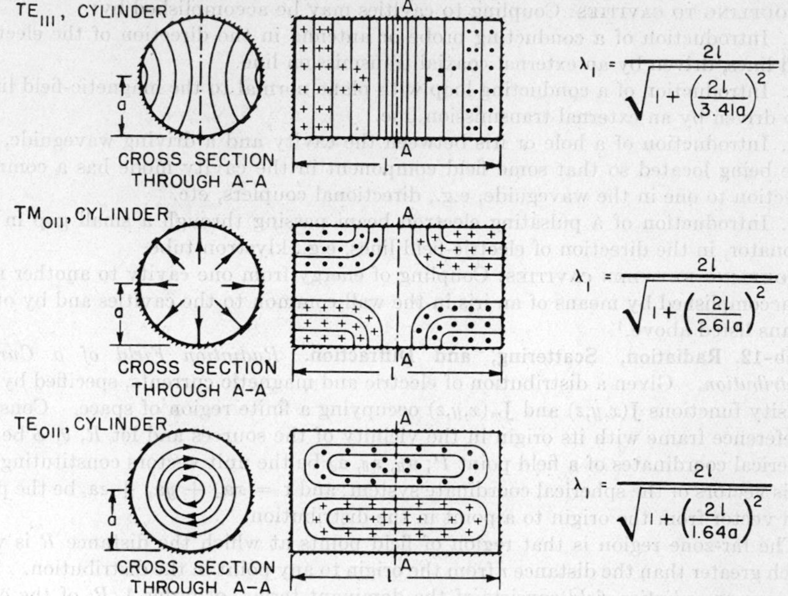

FIG. 5b-8. Other modes in a cylindrical cavity.

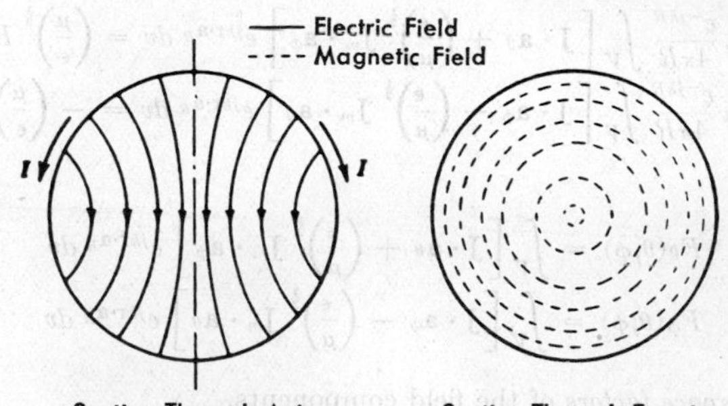

FIG. 5b-9. Field patterns for simple TM_{101} mode in spherical resonator. $Q = \eta/R_s$, $\lambda = 2.29a$.

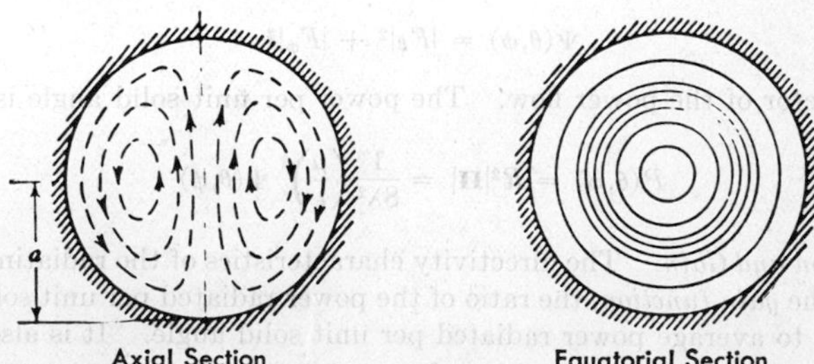

FIG. 5b-10. Field patterns for TE_{101} mode in spherical resonator. Resonant wavelength $\lambda = 1.39a$.

COUPLING TO CAVITIES: Coupling to cavities may be accomplished by:

1. Introduction of a conducting probe or antenna in the direction of the electric-field lines, driven by an external coaxial transmission line.
2. Introduction of a conducting loop with plane normal to the magnetic-field lines, also driven by an external transmission line.
3. Introduction of a hole or iris between the cavity and a driving waveguide, the hole being located so that some field component in the cavity mode has a common direction to one in the waveguide, e.g., directional couplers, etc.
4. Introduction of a pulsating electron beam passing through a small gap in the resonator, in the direction of electric-field lines, e.g., klystron tube.

COUPLING BETWEEN CAVITIES: Coupling of energy from one cavity to another may be accomplished by means of an iris in the wall common to the cavities and by other means listed above.[1]

5b-12. Radiation, Scattering, and Diffraction. *Radiation Field of a Current Distribution.* Given a distribution of electric and magnetic currents, specified by the density functions $\mathbf{J}(x,y,z)$ and $\mathbf{J}_m(x,y,z)$ occupying a finite region of space. Consider a reference frame with its origin in the vicinity of the sources and let R, θ, ϕ be the spherical coordinates of a field point P; $\mathbf{a}_R$, $\mathbf{a}_\theta$, $\mathbf{a}_\phi$ be the unit vectors constituting the basis vectors of the spherical coordinate system; and $\mathbf{r} = x\mathbf{a}_x + y\mathbf{a}_y + z\mathbf{a}_z$ be the position vector from the origin to a point in the distribution.

The far-zone region is that region of field points at which the distance R is very much greater than the distance r from the origin to any point in the distribution. The *far-zone* or *radiation field* consists of the dominant terms, of order $1/R$, of the components of the field vectors. To order $1/R$ the field is transverse to the radial direction and its components in the spherical-coordinate basis system are

$$E_\theta = -j\omega\mu \frac{e^{-jkR}}{4\pi R} \int_V \left[\mathbf{J} \cdot \mathbf{a}_\theta + \left(\frac{\epsilon}{\mu}\right)^{\frac{1}{2}} \mathbf{J}_m \cdot \mathbf{a}_\phi \right] e^{jk\mathbf{r}\cdot\mathbf{a}_R}\, dv = \left(\frac{\mu}{\epsilon}\right)^{\frac{1}{2}} H_\phi \tag{5b-151}$$

$$E_\phi = -j\omega\mu \frac{e^{-jkR}}{4\pi R} \int_V \left[\mathbf{J} \cdot \mathbf{a}_\phi - \left(\frac{\epsilon}{\mu}\right)^{\frac{1}{2}} \mathbf{J}_m \cdot \mathbf{a}_\theta \right] e^{jk\mathbf{r}\cdot\mathbf{a}_R}\, dv = -\left(\frac{\mu}{\epsilon}\right)^{\frac{1}{2}} H_\theta \tag{5b-152}$$

The quantities

$$F_\theta(\theta,\phi) = \int_V \left[\mathbf{J} \cdot \mathbf{a}_\theta + \left(\frac{\epsilon}{\mu}\right)^{\frac{1}{2}} \mathbf{J}_m \cdot \mathbf{a}_\phi \right] e^{jk\mathbf{r}\cdot\mathbf{a}_R}\, dv \tag{5b-153}$$

$$F_\phi(\theta,\phi) = \int_V \left[\mathbf{J} \cdot \mathbf{a}_\phi - \left(\frac{\epsilon}{\mu}\right)^{\frac{1}{2}} \mathbf{J}_m \cdot \mathbf{a}_\theta \right] e^{jk\mathbf{r}\cdot\mathbf{a}_R}\, dv \tag{5b-154}$$

are the *complex space factors* of the field components.

The Poynting vector—the time average intensity of power flow—is

$$\breve{\mathbf{\Pi}} = \frac{1}{2} \operatorname{Re} (\mathbf{E} \times \mathbf{H}^*) = \frac{1}{8\lambda^2 R^2} \left(\frac{\mu}{\epsilon}\right)^{\frac{1}{2}} \Psi(\theta,\phi)\mathbf{a}_R \tag{5b-155}$$

where

$$\Psi(\theta,\phi) = |F_\theta|^2 + |F_\phi|^2 \tag{5b-156}$$

is the space factor of the power flow. The power per unit solid angle is

$$P(\theta,\phi) = R^2|\mathbf{\Pi}| = \frac{1}{8\lambda^2} \left(\frac{\mu}{\epsilon}\right)^{\frac{1}{2}} \Psi(\theta,\phi) \tag{5b-157}$$

Gain Function and Gain. The directivity characteristics of the radiating system are expressed by the *gain function,* the ratio of the power radiated per unit solid angle in a direction (θ,ϕ) to average power radiated per unit solid angle. It is also referred to

[1] J. C. Slater, "Microwave Electronics," pp. 135–168, D. Van Nostrand Company, Inc., New York, 1950.

as the gain function with respect to an isotropic radiator radiating the same total power. Thus,

$$G(\theta,\phi) = \frac{P(\theta,\phi)}{\frac{1}{4\pi}\int_0^{2\pi}\int_0^{\pi} P(\theta,\phi)\sin\theta\,d\theta\,d\phi} = \frac{4\pi\Psi(\theta,\phi)}{\int_0^{2\pi}\int_0^{\pi}\Psi(\theta,\phi)\sin\theta\,d\theta\,d\phi} \tag{5b-158}$$

The *absolute gain* is the maximum value of the gain function. The *directivity* is the absolute gain expressed in decibels:

$$\text{Directivity} = 10\log_{10}[G(\theta,\phi)]_{\max} \tag{5b-159}$$

The directivity characteristics may also be specified in a more detailed manner in terms of the power associated with each of the orthogonal components E_θ and E_ϕ:

$$G_\theta = \frac{4\pi|F_\theta|^2}{\int_0^{2\pi}\int_0^{\pi}\Psi(\theta,\phi)\sin\theta\,d\theta\,d\phi} \tag{5b-160}$$

$$G_\phi = \frac{4\pi|F_\phi|^2}{\int_0^{2\pi}\int_0^{\pi}\Psi(\theta,\phi)\sin\theta\,d\theta\,d\phi} \tag{5b-161}$$

It is evident that

$$G(\theta,\phi) = G_\theta(\theta,\phi) + G_\phi(\theta,\phi) \tag{5b-162}$$

The Electric Dipole. A short linear structure designed so that the current distribution is uniform over its extent is equivalent to an oscillating electric dipole of moment

$$p = \frac{Il}{j\omega} \tag{5b-163}$$

where I is the current and l is the length of the structure.

If the dipole is taken to be at the origin of the coordinate system and the dipole axis is taken as the polar axis of a spherical-coordinate system, the components of the field are

$$E_R = \frac{1}{2\pi\epsilon}\left(\frac{1}{R^3} + \frac{jk}{R^2}\right)\cos\theta\, p_0 e^{-jkR} \tag{5b-164}$$

$$E_\theta = \frac{1}{4\pi\epsilon}\left(\frac{1}{R^3} + \frac{jk}{R^2} - \frac{k^2}{R}\right)\sin\theta\, p_0 e^{-jkR} \tag{5b-165}$$

$$H_\phi = \frac{j\omega}{4\pi}\left(\frac{1}{R^2} + \frac{jk}{R}\right)\sin\theta\, p_0 e^{-jkR} \tag{5b-166}$$

where p_0 is the amplitude of the time-varying dipole moment.

$$p = p_0 e^{j\omega t} \tag{5b-167}$$

The Poynting vector—intensity of power flow—is

$$\mathbf{\Pi} = \frac{\omega k^3}{32\pi^2\epsilon}|p_0|^2\frac{\sin^2\theta}{R^2}\mathbf{a}_R \tag{5b-168}$$

and the gain function is

$$G(\theta,\phi) = \tfrac{3}{2}\sin^2\theta \tag{5b-169}$$

The Magnetic Dipole. A small current loop encompassing an area A and carrying a current I is the equivalent of an oscillating magnetic dipole of moment

$$m = IA \tag{5b-170}$$

The magnetic moment is normal to the area A. Taking again the dipole at the origin and the dipole axis as the polar axis of a spherical-coordinate system we have for the field components

$$E_\phi = \frac{k^2}{4\pi}\left(\frac{\mu}{\epsilon}\right)^{\frac{1}{2}}\left(\frac{1}{R} - \frac{j}{kR^2}\right) \sin\theta\ m_0 e^{-jkR} \tag{5b-171}$$

$$H_R = \frac{1}{2\pi}\left(\frac{1}{R^3} + \frac{jk}{R^2}\right) \cos\theta\ m_0 e^{-jkR} \tag{5b-172}$$

$$H_\theta = \frac{1}{4\pi}\left(\frac{1}{R^3} + \frac{jk}{R^2} - \frac{k^2}{R}\right) \sin\theta\ m_0 e^{-jkR} \tag{5b-173}$$

where m_0 is the amplitude of the time-varying magnetic moment.

The gain function is the same as that of an electric dipole.

Scattering and Absorption. The scattering and absorption characteristics of a system in otherwise free space are formulated in terms of the interaction of the system with a homogeneous plane wave. From a wave-theory standpoint the elements are as follows: Under the action of the primary incident wave $\mathbf{E}_i$, $\mathbf{H}_i$ the system is excited and produces a secondary field $\mathbf{E}_s$, $\mathbf{H}_s$. The Poynting vector of the resultant field is then

$$\begin{aligned}\breve{\mathbf{\Pi}} &= \tfrac{1}{2}\,\mathrm{Re}\,[(\mathbf{E}_i + \mathbf{E}_s) \times (\mathbf{H}_i^* + \mathbf{H}_s^*)] \\ &= \tfrac{1}{2}\,\mathrm{Re}\,(\mathbf{E}_i \times \mathbf{H}_i^*) + \tfrac{1}{2}\,\mathrm{Re}\,[(\mathbf{E}_i \times \mathbf{H}_s^*) + (\mathbf{E}_s \times \mathbf{H}_i^*)] + \tfrac{1}{2}\,\mathrm{Re}\,(\mathbf{E}_s \times \mathbf{H}_s)\end{aligned} \tag{5b-174}$$

or

$$\mathbf{\Pi} = \mathbf{\Pi}_i + \mathbf{\Pi}_{is} + \mathbf{\Pi}_s \tag{5b-175}$$

The subscripts make the obvious identification of the parts of (5b-175) with those of (5b-174). The term $\mathbf{\Pi}_{is}$ is the representation of the interaction between the primary and secondary fields. The term $\mathbf{\Pi}_s$ is the intensity of power flow that is formally associated with the secondary field regarded as an independent entity.

The integral of the normal component of the *resultant* Poynting vector over a closed surface enclosing the scattering system measures the energy transferred from the incident wave to the system. The net contribution of $\mathbf{\Pi}_i$ in this computation is zero, and thus

$$\int_{\substack{\text{enclosing}\\\text{surface}}} (\mathbf{\Pi}\cdot\mathbf{n})\,dS = \int_{\substack{\text{enclosing}\\\text{surface}}} (\mathbf{\Pi}_{is}\cdot\mathbf{n})\,dS + \int_{\substack{\text{enclosing}\\\text{surface}}} (\mathbf{\Pi}_s\cdot\mathbf{n})\,dS \le 0 \tag{5b-176}$$

with $\mathbf{n}$ the unit vector normal to the surface directed outward from the region occupied by the system. If the system is such that it absorbs no energy from the incident wave, the net power flow out from the region must be zero; whereas if the system absorbs energy, the net power flow out from the region must be negative. That is,

$$P_{\text{abs}} = -\int_{\substack{\text{enclosing}\\\text{surface}}} (\mathbf{\Pi}_{is}\cdot\mathbf{n})\,dS - \int_{\substack{\text{enclosing}\\\text{surface}}} (\mathbf{\Pi}_s\cdot\mathbf{n})\,dS \tag{5b-177}$$

The surface integral of the normal component of the Poynting vector $\mathbf{\Pi}_s$ associated with the secondary field alone is necessarily positive since the secondary field must take the form of an outgoing wave from the system. This quantity is defined to be the power scattered by the system

$$P_{\text{scat}} = \int_{\substack{\text{enclosing}\\\text{surface}}} (\breve{\mathbf{\Pi}}_s\cdot\mathbf{n})\,dS = \int_{\substack{\text{enclosing}\\\text{surface}}} [\mathbf{n}\cdot\tfrac{1}{2}\,\mathrm{Re}\,(\mathbf{E}_s \times \mathbf{H}_s^*)]\,dS \tag{5b-178}$$

The complete exchange of energy is expressed accordingly,

$$P_{\text{abs}} + P_{\text{scat}} = -\int_{\substack{\text{enclosing}\\ \text{surface}}} \{\mathbf{n} \cdot [\tfrac{1}{2} \operatorname{Re} (\mathbf{E}_i \times \mathbf{H}_s^*) + (\mathbf{E}_s \times \mathbf{H}_i^*)]\}\, dS \qquad (5b\text{-}179)$$

The *absorption cross section* is defined as the ratio of the power absorbed to the incident power intensity:

$$P_{\text{abs}} = |\mathbf{\Pi}_i| A_{\text{abs}} \qquad (5b\text{-}180)$$

When applied to antennas the absorption cross section is referred to more commonly as the receiving cross section A_R.

The *scattering cross section* is defined as the ratio of the power scattered to the incident power intensity:

$$P_{\text{scat}} = |\mathbf{\Pi}_i| A_s \qquad (5b\text{-}181)$$

The sum $A_a + A_s$ is the total cross section of the system.

The scattering cross section defined in the foregoing is the total scattering cross section for the particular direction of incidence of the plane wave. It is also customary to speak of the *differential cross section* which is the ratio of the power scattered per unit solid angle in a given direction to the incident power intensity; thus

$$\sigma = \frac{R^2 |\mathbf{\Pi}_s|}{|\mathbf{\Pi}_i|} \qquad (5b\text{-}182)$$

All the cross sections which have been defined are functions of the direction of incidence of the primary wave. The functional dependance of the receiving cross section of an antenna is referred to as the receiving pattern of the antenna.

The polarization of the incident wave must be specified when the cross sections are discussed. In particular, when values are given for the receiving cross section of an antenna it is implied that the polarization of the incident wave is that for which the response is a maximum. If the antenna radiates linear polarization in a given direction when transmitting, the incident plane wave, on reception, is considered to be polarized correspondingly; if the antenna on transmission radiates elliptical polarization, the cross section is referred to an incident plane with proper sense of elliptical polarization (opposite in sense to the transmission characteristic) with corresponding ellipticity. Separate cross sections may be defined corresponding to the separate components E_θ and E_ϕ of the transmitting pattern. The total cross section corresponding to a given direction of incidence is, however, not in general equal to the sum of the component cross sections.

Reciprocity Theorem and Universal Average Absorption Cross Section. The reciprocity theorem states that the transmitting and receiving patterns of an antenna system are the same when the external medium, the antenna structure, and its associated networks are linear and bilateral (the constitutive parameters of all media are either scalars or symmetric tensors).

The receiving cross section of an antenna is dependent on the impedance relationships between the antenna and its associated networks (transmission line and detector). The maximum value is attained when the system is matched, i.e., the input impedance to the antenna is the conjugate of the input impedance of the associated networks as viewed from the antenna terminals.

The average value of the absorption cross section of a matched system over all aspects is a universal constant:

$$\bar{A}_r = \frac{\lambda^2}{4\pi} \qquad (5b\text{-}183)$$

The reciprocity theorem is embodied in the relationship

$$A_r(\theta,\phi) = G(\theta,\phi)\,\frac{\lambda^2}{4\pi} \tag{5b-184}$$

between the cross section presented to a plane wave incident from a given direction (θ,ϕ) and the gain function of the antenna system on transmission in that same direction.

Fourier-transform Relation between Far-zone Field and Current Distribution. The vector potential of a current distribution in the far-zone region of the distribution [cf. (5b-78)] assumes the form

$$\mathbf{A} = \frac{\mu}{4\pi R}\, e^{-jkR} \int_V \mathbf{J} e^{jk\mathbf{r}\cdot\mathbf{a}_R}\, dv \tag{5b-185}$$

The radiation-field components are simply related to the vector potential by

$$E_\theta = -j\omega\mathbf{A}\cdot\mathbf{a}_\theta = -j\omega A_\theta \tag{5b-186}$$
$$E_\phi = -j\omega\mathbf{A}\cdot\mathbf{a}_\phi = -j\omega A_\phi \tag{5b-187}$$

The complex space factors F_θ and F_ϕ are thus the corresponding components of the vector quantity

$$\mathbf{F} = \int_V \mathbf{J} e^{jk\mathbf{r}\cdot\mathbf{a}_r}\, dv \tag{5b-188}$$

Let the propagation vector $\mathbf{k}$ be defined by

$$\mathbf{k} = k\mathbf{a}_r \tag{5b-189}$$

Then we have a vector function

$$\mathbf{F}(\mathbf{k}) = \int_V \mathbf{J} e^{j\mathbf{k}\cdot\mathbf{r}}\, dv \tag{5b-190}$$

Except for constants the vector function $\mathbf{F}(\mathbf{k})$ is the Fourier transform of the current distribution. It is the equivalent of the transform encountered in X-ray diffraction theory. The transform is defined for values of $\mathbf{k}$ embracing all possible values of its components. The radiation pattern is associated with only those vectors $\mathbf{k}$ for which the components satisfy the relations

$$k_1^2 + k_2^2 + k_3^2 = k^2 = \frac{4\pi^2}{\lambda^2} \tag{5b-191}$$

The current distribution is in turn the transform of vector function $\mathbf{F}$, namely,

$$\mathbf{J}(\mathbf{r}) = \frac{1}{(2\pi)^3} \int_{-\infty}^{\infty}\int_{-\infty}^{\infty}\int_{-\infty}^{\infty} \mathbf{F}(\mathbf{k}) e^{-j\mathbf{k}\cdot\mathbf{r}}\, dk_1\, dk_2\, dk_3 \tag{5b-192}$$

with, of course,

$$\mathbf{k}\cdot\mathbf{r} = k_1x + k_2y + k_3z \tag{5b-193}$$

This transform relationship is useful in the general theory of radiating systems.

Development of a Field from Boundary Values—Huygens-Fresnel Principle. Given a surface S enclosing the sources and the values of $\mathbf{E}$ and $\mathbf{H}$ over the surface S. The field at a point P outside the region of the surfaces is given by

$$\mathbf{E}_p = \frac{1}{4\pi}\int_s [-j\omega\mu(\mathbf{n}\times\mathbf{H})\psi + (\mathbf{n}\times\mathbf{E})\times\nabla\psi + (\mathbf{n}\cdot\mathbf{E})\nabla\psi]\, dS \tag{5b-194}$$

$$\mathbf{H}_p = \frac{1}{4\pi}\int_s [j\omega\epsilon(\mathbf{n}\times\mathbf{E})\psi + (\mathbf{n}\times\mathbf{H})\times\nabla\psi + (\mathbf{n}\cdot\mathbf{H})\nabla\psi]\, dS \tag{5b-195}$$

where $\mathbf{n}$ is the unit vector normal to S directed outward from the region of the sources; $\psi = e^{-jkr}/r$ with r the distance from dS to P; ∇ the gradient in terms of the coordinates on S.

Equivalent representations are

$$\mathbf{E}_p = -\frac{1}{4\pi}\int_S \left[\psi \frac{\partial \mathbf{E}}{\partial n} - \mathbf{E}\frac{\partial \psi}{\partial n}\right] dS \tag{5b-196}$$

$$\mathbf{H}_p = -\frac{1}{4\pi}\int_S \left[\psi \frac{\partial \mathbf{H}}{\partial n} - \mathbf{H}\frac{\partial \psi}{\partial n}\right] dS \tag{5b-197}$$

and

$$\mathbf{E}_p = \frac{1}{4\pi j\omega\epsilon}\int_S [(\mathbf{n}\times\mathbf{H})\cdot\nabla(\nabla\psi) + k^2(\mathbf{n}\times\mathbf{H})\psi]\,dS \tag{5b-198}$$

$$\mathbf{H}_p = \frac{1}{4\pi j\omega\mu}\int_S [(\mathbf{n}\times\mathbf{E})\cdot\nabla(\nabla\psi) + k^2(\mathbf{n}\times\mathbf{E})\psi]\,dS \tag{5b-199}$$

The representations are transformable one into the other only when *closed surfaces* are considered.

Representations (5b-194), (5b-195) and (5b-198), (5b-199) are forms corresponding to equivalent distributions,

$$\begin{aligned} &\text{Surface electric current} && \mathbf{J}' = \mathbf{n}\times\mathbf{H} \\ &\text{Surface magnetic current} && \mathbf{J}_m' = -\mathbf{n}\times\mathbf{E} \\ &\text{Surface electric charge} && \rho_s = \epsilon(\mathbf{n}\cdot\mathbf{E}) \\ &\text{Surface magnetic charge} && \rho_{s_m} = \mu(\mathbf{n}\cdot\mathbf{H}) \end{aligned} \tag{5b-200}$$

When the surface S is an equiphase surface of the wave field the representations constitute the mathematical expression of the Huygens-Fresnel principle for the electromagnetic field. The equivalent source functions (5b-200) are in toto the appropriate system of Huygens' sources to be associated with an element of surface dS.

The representations (5b-198) and (5b-199) embody the required equation of continuity between the current and charge distributions on a surface. The development of the field is thus based on just two fundamental source functions $\mathbf{J}'$ and $\mathbf{J}_m'$.

Large-aperture Systems—Reflectors, Lenses, Horns. The formation of beams by reflectors, lenses, and horns in which the aperture is the dominant factor is by a process of diffraction. When the aperture involved is large compared with the wavelength the radiation process can be treated reasonably well by the following line of analysis. The field over the aperture is related in the most simple way possible to the primary sources—in the case of lenses and reflectors, by the use of geometrical optics; in the case of horns, by considering the field distribution which would exist over the aperture plane of the horn extended to infinity. All Huygens' sources are considered to be negligible in comparison with those over the aperture plane associated with the simple aperture field. The field appropriate to those Huygens' sources over the aperture is then

$$\mathbf{E}_p = \frac{1}{4\pi j\omega\epsilon}\int_{\text{aperture}} [(\mathbf{n}\times\mathbf{H})\cdot\nabla(\nabla\psi) + k^2(\mathbf{n}\times\mathbf{H})\psi]\,dS \tag{5b-201}$$

$$\mathbf{H}_p = \frac{1}{4\pi j\omega\mu}\int_{\text{aperture}} [(\mathbf{n}\times\mathbf{E})\cdot\nabla(\nabla\psi) + k^2(\mathbf{n}\times\mathbf{E})\psi]\,dS \tag{5b-202}$$

with the quantities having the definition given in the previous section. It is to be noted that in the present case the integration is carried out over an open surface in contrast with that of the previous section.

When the aperture field is obtained by the simple considerations stated before, there is an elementary relation between the tangential components of the electric and magnetic vectors over the aperture. For the *particular case* of a plane aperture and conditions such that the aperture is virtually an equiphase surface the relationship has the form

$$\mathbf{H} = \alpha(\mathbf{n} \times \mathbf{E}) \tag{5b-203}$$

where α is a constant for the particular system. In the case of lenses and reflectors $\alpha = (\epsilon/\mu)^{\frac{1}{2}}$ whereas in the case of a horn it is the transverse wave admittance corresponding to the infinite horn.

The far-zone field of the system of Huygens' sources is then

$$\mathbf{E}_p = \frac{-jke^{-jkR}}{4\pi R} \mathbf{a}_R \times \left[\left(\mathbf{n} + \alpha\left(\frac{\mu}{\epsilon}\right)^{\frac{1}{2}} \mathbf{a}_R\right) \times \mathbf{N}\right] \tag{5b-204}$$

where $\mathbf{N}$ is the *radiation vector*

$$\mathbf{N} = \int_{Ap} \mathbf{E} e^{jk(x \sin\theta \cos\phi + y \sin\theta \sin\phi)}\, dx\, dy \tag{5b-205}$$

with $\mathbf{a}_R$ a unit vector in the radial direction from an origin in the aperture, R, θ, ϕ spherical coordinates of the field point (the polar axis being normal to the aperture plane) and $\mathbf{E}$ the electric-field vector in the aperture. Componentwise:

$$E_\theta = \frac{jke^{-jkR}}{4\pi R}\left[1 + \alpha\left(\frac{\mu}{\epsilon}\right)^{\frac{1}{2}} \cos\theta\right](N_x \cos\phi + N_y \sin\phi) = \left(\frac{\mu}{\epsilon}\right)^{\frac{1}{2}} H_\phi \tag{5b-206}$$

$$E_\phi = \frac{jke^{-jkR}}{4\pi R}\left[\cos\theta + \alpha\left(\frac{\mu}{\epsilon}\right)^{\frac{1}{2}}\right](N_x \sin\phi - N_y \cos\phi) = -\left(\frac{\mu}{\epsilon}\right)^{\frac{1}{2}} H_\theta \tag{5b-207}$$

References

Schelkunoff, S. A.: "Electromagnetic Waves," D. Van Nostrand Company, Inc., New York, 1943.

Schelkunoff, S. A.: "Advanced Antenna Theory," John Wiley & Sons, Inc., New York, 1952.

Schelkunoff, S. A., and H. T. Friis: "Antennas, Theory and Practice," John Wiley & Sons, Inc., New York, 1952.

Silver, S., ed., "Microwave Antenna Theory and Design," MIT Radiation Laboratory Series, vol. 12, McGraw-Hill Book Company, Inc., New York, 1949.

Stratton, J. A.: "Electromagnetic Theory," McGraw-Hill Book Company, Inc., New York, 1941.

5b-13. Waves in Space-charge Regions. *Plasma Oscillations.* Langmuir and Tonks[1] observed the phenomenon of oscillation in a plasma consisting of approximately equal density of electrons and positive ions, and showed the angular frequency to be

$$\omega_p = \left(\frac{\rho\eta}{\epsilon_v}\right)^{\frac{1}{2}} \tag{5b-208}$$

where ρ = charge density, coulombs/m³

η = charge-to-mass ratio, coulombs/kg

ϵ_v = capacitivity of space, 8.854×10^{-12} farad/m

For electrons, $\eta = 1.759 \times 10^{11}$, oscillation frequency is

$$\nu_p = 8.979 N^{\frac{1}{2}} \text{ cps}$$

where N = number of electrons/m³

Oscillations of ions in the plasma have also been observed[2] but the frequency is lower by the square root of charge-to-mass ratio.

The mechanism of plasma oscillation has been studied in detail for both the longi-

[1] I. Langmuir and L. Tonks, *Phys. Rev.* **33,** 195 (1929).

[2] R. Rompe and H. Steenbeck, *Ergeb. exakt. Naturwiss.* **18,** 303 (1939).

tudinal (irrotational) oscillations,[1] which do not radiate, and the transverse oscillation,[2] which do radiate.

The general dispersion relation giving wave number $\mathbf{k}$ as a function of angular frequency ω in a region having a distribution of velocities following a given distribution function $f(\mathbf{v})$ is[3]

$$1 = \frac{\rho\eta}{\epsilon_v} \int \frac{f(\mathbf{v})\, dv}{(\omega - \mathbf{k} \cdot \mathbf{v})^2} \tag{5b-209}$$

Space-charge Waves in a Drifting Stream. Hahn[4] and Ramo[5] studied electromagnetic-wave phenomena along an electron stream drifting with a constant d-c velocity (much greater than the thermal velocities) in the axial direction. All d-c fields in the drift region were neglected (as when the beam is neutralized by positive ions) and alternating current and velocity were assumed small compared with the d-c values. Assuming time and axial variations as $\exp [j(\omega t - \beta z)]$, the following differential equation applies within the beam:

$$\nabla_t^2 E = (\beta^2 - k^2) \left[1 - \frac{\omega_p^2}{(\omega - \beta v_0)^2} \right] E \tag{5b-210}$$

where ∇_t^2 = transverse part of div grad
k = free-space wave number, ω/c
ω_p = as in Eq. (5b-208)
v_0 = d-c electron velocity
E = axial component of a-c electric field

For a one-dimensional stream, $\nabla_t^2 E = 0$, four values of β result from Eq. (5b-210), two field waves in this simple case completely uncoupled from the electrons, and two space-charge waves which correspond to plasma oscillations in the moving-coordinate system.

Field waves: $$\beta = \pm k \tag{5b-211}$$

Space-charge waves: $$\beta = \frac{\omega \pm \omega_p}{v_0} \tag{5b-212}$$

If transverse variations in the a-c solutions are allowed and the beam is enclosed by a perfectly conducting cylinder, the field waves are only slightly perturbed from the waveguide solutions for the corresponding hollow cylinder. Space-charge waves occur in pairs bracketing the d-c electron velocity. For $\omega \gg \omega_p$, the phase constant corresponding to the nth eigen value of Eq. (5b-210) may be written

$$\beta_n = \frac{\omega \pm \omega_{qn}}{v_0} \tag{5b-213}$$

ω_{q_n} is an effective plasma frequency, reduced from ω_p by the image charges on the drift-tube walls. Curves of ω_{q_n}/ω_p for $n = 1, \mathbf{2}$ are given in Fig. 5b-11 applying to a circularly cylindrical beam of radius b in a perfectly conducting drift tube of radius a.

A-C velocity and current vary along the beam as follows, in terms of the initial value for the nth mode:

$$\begin{aligned} i_n(z) &= i_n(0) \cos \beta_n z + j \frac{\rho_0 \omega}{\omega_{qn}} v_n(0) \sin \beta_n z \\ v_n(z) &= v_n(0) \cos \beta_n z + j \frac{\omega_{qn}}{\rho_0 \omega} i_n(0) \sin \beta_n z \end{aligned} \tag{5b-214}$$

where ρ_0 = magnitude of d-c charge density

[1] D. Bohm and E. P. Gross, *Phys. Rev.* **75,** 1851, 1864 (1948).

[2] H. R. Mimno, *Revs. Modern Phys.* **9,** 1 (1937); H. Lassen, *Ann. Physik* **1,** 415 (1947); H. Margenau, *Phys. Rev.* **73,** 297 (1948).

[3] Bohm and Gross, *loc. cit.*

[4] W. C. Hahn, *Gen. Elec. Rev.* **42,** 258 (1939).

[5] S. Ramo, *Phys. Rev.* **56,** 276 (1939).

Growing Waves. The a-c space-charge waves may grow along the electron stream because of various interaction processes which transfer energy from the kinetic energy of the beam to the a-c fields. These processes are important for producing practical microwave amplifiers of the beam type, but also in the amplifications of noise

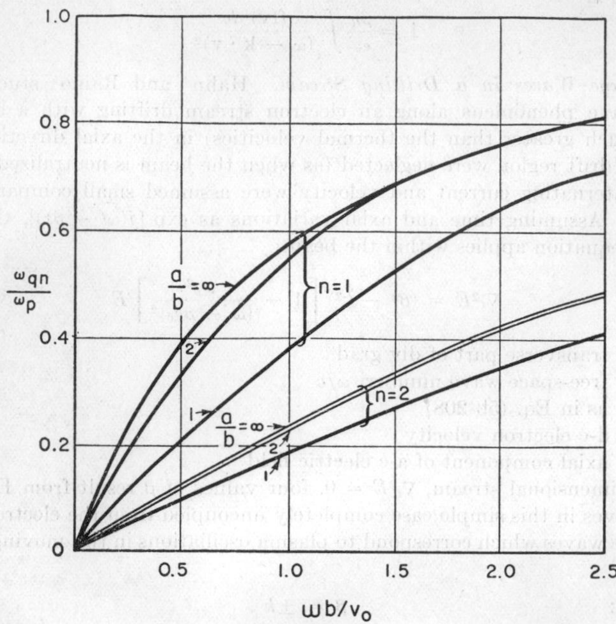

FIG. 5b-11. Effective plasma-frequency reduction factor for circular cylindrical solid electron beam of radius b in perfectly conducting drift tube of radius a, for modes 1 and 2. [*From C. K. Birdsall and J. R. Whinnery, Waves in an Electron Stream with General Admittance Walls, J. Appl. Phys.* **24,** 314 (1953).]

fluctuations in electron tubes, gaseous-discharge devices, and possibly in stellar atmospheres. Some of the basic interactions which produce growing waves are

1. Traveling-wave interaction[1]
2. Multiple-velocity stream interaction[2]
3. Inductive-wall interaction[3]
4. Resistive-wall interaction[4]
5. Velocity-jump interaction[5]
6. Rippled-wall and rippled-stream interaction[6]
7. Magnetron-type amplification[7]
8. Slipping-stream amplification[8]

[1] J. R. Pierce, "Traveling-wave Tubes," D. Van Nostrand Company, Inc., New York, 1950; R. Kompfner, *Wireless World* **52,** 369 (1946).

[2] J. R. Pierce and W. B. Hebenstreit, *Bell System Tech. J.* **28,** 33 (1949); A. V. Haeff, *Proc. IRE* **37,** 4 (1949).

[3] L. R. Walker as described by Pierce, *op. cit.*, p. 195; C. K. Birdsall and J. R. Whinnery, *J. Appl. Phys.* **24,** 314 (1953).

[4] J. R. Pierce, *Bell System Tech. J.* **30,** 626 (1951); C. K. Birdsall, G. R. Brewer, and A. V. Haeff, *Proc. IRE* **41,** 865 (1953).

[5] P. K. Tien and L. M. Field, *Proc. IRE* **40,** 694 (1952).

[6] S. Bloom and R. W. Peter, *RCA Rev.* **15,** 95 (1954); C. K. Birdsall, *Proc. IRE* **42,** 1628 (1954).

[7] R. Warnecke, W. Kleen, A. Lerbs, O. Doehler, and H. Huber, *Proc. IRE* **38,** 486 (1950).

[8] G. G. MacFarlane and H. G. Hay, *Proc. Phys. Soc.* (*London*) **B63,** 409 (1950); R. Warnecke, H. Huber, P. Guenard, and O. Doehler, *Compt. rend.* **235,** 470 (1952).

Technical applications of traveling-wave interaction, in which an electron stream interacts with a circuit having a slow wave in approximate synchronism with the electron velocity, are the most important of the above. Pierce[1] has shown that gain of a traveling-wave device may be written

$$G = A + BCN \quad \text{db} \tag{5b-215}$$

where N = number of guide wavelengths in interaction circuit
C = Pierce gain parameter = $(I_0K/4V_0)^{\frac{1}{3}}$
I_0 = d-c beam current
V_0 = d-c beam velocity
K = interaction impedance = $(E^2/2\beta^2P)$
E = effective electric-field magnitude acting on electrons
β = phase constant
P = average power flow in the slow wave

A and B are functions of loss, space-charge effects, and departure from synchronism of beam and circuit. Limiting values for negligible loss and space charge, and with operation in synchronism are $A = -9.54$, $B = 47.3$. More complete values are given by Pierce[1] and Cutler.[2] Technical applications of the traveling-wave magnetron[3] also seem very promising for power applications, since in this type the beam is focused by crossed electric and magnetic fields, and the r-f energy comes from the potential energy of the crossed field, and not from an average slowing down of the beam. The beam may thereby stay in synchronism with the circuit over a greater distance and higher efficiency is expected.

A special case of traveling-wave interaction, for which the wave on the slow-wave circuit has oppositely directed phase and group velocities, was shown by Kompfner[4] to have practical application in producing amplifiers and oscillators with a wide range (one or more octaves) of electric tuning. Warnecke[5] has also described this, giving results on backward-wave interaction in crossed electric and magnetic fields (M-type Carcinotron), where the higher efficiency of the crossed-field devices was observed.

Space-charge Waves in Accelerated Streams. The differential equation[6] governing small-signal space-charge waves in unidirectional flow for a general d-c velocity variation $v_0(z)$ is

$$I_1'' + I_1'\left(\frac{2j\omega}{v_0} + \frac{3}{v_0}\frac{dv_0}{dz}\right) + I_1\left(\frac{\eta I_0}{\epsilon_v v_0^3} + \frac{2j\omega}{v_0^2}\frac{dv_0}{dz} - \frac{\omega^2}{v_0^2}\right) = \frac{-j\omega\eta I_0}{v_0^3}E \tag{5b-216}$$

where I_1 = a-c density
I_0 = d-c density
η = electronic charge-to-mass ratio
E = impressed a-c electric field

Primes denote derivatives with distance z.

The case studied in greatest detail[7] is that for a d-c potential distribution corresponding to that consistent with the d-c space-charge effects in the stream. The most useful form of the relations between first-order a-c quantities is that given by Llewellyn and Peterson.[8]

1 "Traveling-wave Tubes," D. Van Nostrand Company, Inc., New York, 1950.
2 C. C. Cutler, *Proc. IRE* **39**, 914 (1951).
3 Warnecke, Kleen, Lerbs, Doehler, and Huber, *loc. cit.*
4 R. Kompfner and N. T. Williams, *Proc. IRE* **41**, 1602 (1953).
5 R. Warnecke, *Ann. radioélec. compagn. franç. assoc. T.S.F.* **9**, 286 (1954).
6 L. D. Smullin, *J. Appl. Phys.* **22**, 1496 (1951).
7 W. E. Benham, *Phil. Mag.* **5**, 641 (1928); J. Muller, *Hochfreq. u. Elek.* **41**, 156 (1933); F. B. Llewellyn, *Bell System Tech. J.* **14**, 1632 (1935).
8 F. B. Llewellyn and L. C. Peterson, *Proc. IRE* **32**, 144 (1944).

General Equations for a Parallel-plane Region

$$
\begin{aligned}
V_b - V_a &= A^*I + B^*q_a + C^*v_a \\
q_b &= D^*I + E^*q_a + F^*v_a \\
v_b &= G^*I + H^*q_a + I^*v_a
\end{aligned}
\qquad (5b\text{-}217)
$$

where $V_b - V_a$ = first-order a-c voltage between a and b planes
I = first-order a-c density
q_a = first-order alternating convection current at a plane
q_b = first-order alternating convection current at b plane
v_a = first-order a-c velocity at a plane
v_b = first-order a-c velocity at b plane

The Constants in the Above Equations

$$A^* = \frac{I}{\epsilon}(u_a + u_b)\frac{T^2}{2}\frac{1}{\beta}\left[1 - \frac{\zeta}{3}\left(1 - \frac{12S}{\beta^3}\right)\right]$$

$$B^* = \frac{1}{\epsilon}\frac{T^2}{\beta^3}[u_a(P - \beta Q) - u_bP + \zeta(u_a + u_b)P]$$

$$C^* = -\frac{1}{\eta}2\zeta(u_a + u_b)\frac{P}{\beta^2}$$

$$D^* = 2\zeta\left(\frac{u_a + u_b}{u_b}\right)\frac{P}{\beta^2}$$

$$E^* = \frac{1}{u_b}[u_b - \zeta(u_a + u_b)]\,e^{-\beta}$$

$$F^* = \frac{\epsilon}{\eta}\frac{2\zeta}{T^2}\left(\frac{u_a + u_b}{u_b}\right)\beta e^{-\beta}$$

$$G^* = \frac{\eta}{\epsilon}\frac{T^2}{\beta^3}\frac{1}{u_b}[u_b(P - \beta Q) - u_aP + \zeta(u_a + u_b)P]$$

$$H^* = -\frac{\eta}{\epsilon}\frac{T^2}{2}\left(\frac{u_a + u_b}{u_b}\right)(1 - \zeta)\frac{e^{-\beta}}{\beta}$$

$$I^* = \frac{1}{u_b}[u_a - \zeta(u_a + u_b)]e^{-\beta}$$

where
$$
\begin{aligned}
P &= 1 - (1 + \beta)e^{-\beta} \doteq \beta^2/2 - \beta^3/3 + \beta^4/8 + \cdots \\
Q &= 1 - e^{-\beta} \doteq \beta - \beta^2/2 + \beta^3/6 - \beta^4/24 + \cdots \\
S &= 2 - \beta - (2 + \beta)e^{-\beta} \doteq -\beta^3/6 + \beta^4/12 - \beta^5/40 + \beta^6/180 + \cdots \\
\beta &= j\theta = j\omega T
\end{aligned}
$$

D-C Equations

Limiting current density:

$$I_m = 2.33 \times 10^{-6}\frac{[(V_{0a})^{\frac{1}{2}} + (V_{0b})^{\frac{1}{2}}]^3}{d^2}$$

Definition of space-charge factor:

$$\frac{I_D}{I_m} = \frac{9}{4}\zeta\left(1 - \frac{\zeta}{3}\right)^2$$

Transit time: $$T = \frac{T_0}{1 - \zeta/3}$$

where $T_0 = \dfrac{2d}{u_a + u_b}$ = transit time in absence of space charge

D-C velocity: $$u = (2\eta V_D)^{\frac{1}{2}}$$

Distance equation: $$x = \left(1 - \frac{\zeta}{3}\right)(u_a + u_b)\frac{T}{2}$$

where $\eta = e/m = 1.76 \times 10^{11}$ coulombs/kg
I_D = density of direct current
$\epsilon = 1/(36\pi \times 10^9)$ farads/m
V_D = d-c potential
$\eta/\epsilon = 2 \times 10^{22}$

Space-charge Waves of Noise. Shot-noise fluctuations[1] at the cathode excite space-charge waves of noise in an electron beam, as observed experimentally by Cutler and Quate.[2] The ratio of maximum to minimum noise amplitude in the noise waves may be modified by "space-charge-wave transducers,"[3] such as jumps in d-c velocity, to minimize noise figures of practical electron tubes. The absolute minimum that may be obtained[4] will depend upon the degree of correlation between velocity and current fluctuations in the beam passing the potential minimum.

Energy Relations in Space-charge Waves. Tonks[5] displayed a form of the Poynting theorem suitable for regions containing electric charges having a single-valued velocity function $v(x,y,z)$.

$$\int_S (\mathbf{E} \times \mathbf{H}) \cdot d\mathbf{S} + \frac{\partial}{\partial t}\int_V \frac{1}{2}[\mathbf{E} \cdot \mathbf{D} + \mathbf{H} \cdot \mathbf{B}]\, dV + \frac{\partial}{\partial t}\int_V \frac{nmv^2}{V^2}\, dV + \int_S \frac{mv^2}{2} n\mathbf{v} \cdot d\mathbf{S} = 0 \quad \text{(5b-218)}$$

$n(x,y,z)$ = volume density of particles of mass m

The first term represents the usual Poynting flow of electromagnetic energy out of the surface surrounding the region, the second the rate of change of stored energy in the electromagnetic field, the third the rate of change of kinetic energy within the region, and the fourth the net kinetic power flow through the surface. Gabor[6] has studied applications to electronic devices.

The complex form[7] of the above appropriate to the first-order a-c solution in one-dimensional space-charge waves is

$$\int_S (\mathbf{E}_1 \times \mathbf{H}_1^*) \cdot d\mathbf{S} + j\omega \int_V [\mu \mathbf{H}_1 \cdot \mathbf{H}_1^* - \epsilon \mathbf{E}_1 \cdot \mathbf{E}_1^*]\, dV + \frac{j\omega}{\eta}\int_V \rho_0 \mathbf{v}_1 \cdot \mathbf{v}_1^*\, dV + \int_{\text{cross section}} [U_1(z_2)i_1^*(z_2) - U_1(z_1)i_1^*(z_1)]\, dS = 0 \quad \text{(5b-219)}$$

where $U_1 = -\dfrac{v_0 v_1}{\eta}$
v_0 = d-c velocity
v_1 = a-c velocity
i_1 = a-c density
ρ_0 = d-c charge density

The real part of $\frac{1}{2}U_1 i_1^*$ thus represents the average of the a-c kinetic power flow across a cross section.

5b-14. Circuit Theory. *Basis of Circuit Theory.* The basic circuit problem is the special case of the electromagnetic-field problem with currents flowing in nearly filamentary paths, and the field interaction largely localized. Thus the field analysis of the various parts may be made separately to obtain macroscopic parameters to be

[1] W. Schottky, *Physik. Z.* **15,** 526 (1914); A. J. Rack, *Bell System Tech. J.* **17,** 592 (1938).
[2] C. C. Cutler and C. F. Quate, *Phys. Rev.* **80,** 875 (1950).
[3] D. A. Watkins, *Proc. IRE* **40,** 65 (1952); R. W. Peter, *RCA Rev.* **13,** 345 (1952).
[4] J. R. Pierce, *J. Appl. Phys.* **25,** 931 (1954).
[5] L. Tonks, *Phys. Rev.* **54,** 863 (1938).
[6] D. Gabor, *J. Inst. Elec. Engrs.* (*London*) **91:3,** 178 (1944).
[7] J. R. Pierce, *Bell System Tech. J.* **33,** 1343 (1954); originally given by L. J. Chu in unpublished work.

combined according to certain rules (called the network equations) in order to obtain the over-all behavior of the system.

In the topological form of a typical circuit or network (Fig. 5b-12) a junction of current paths (as a) is called a *node* or *branch point;* the path between two nodes (as ab) is called a *branch;* a complete closed path taken along various branches (as $abcda$) is called a *mesh;* a pair of terminals across which voltage may be applied or input current measured (as aa') is called a *terminal pair.*

Kirchhoff's two laws form the basis of circuit theory:

1. *The algebraic sum of the currents meeting at a junction is zero.*
2. *In any closed-circuit path the algebraic sum of applied and induced voltages is zero.*

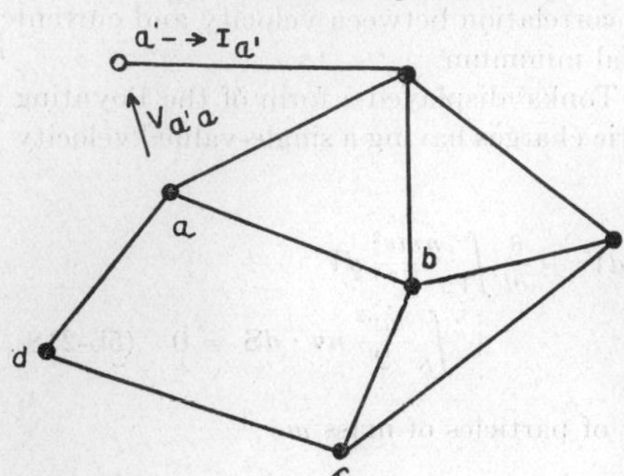

Fig. 5b-12. A typical circuit or network.

For stationary current flow, the first Kirchhoff law expresses the continuity of current, and the second law the conservative property of a stationary electric field. For systems with time-varying currents, the basis of the two laws lies in Maxwell's equations. The first law is correct if total current, displacement plus convection or conduction current, is used, and the basis is the continuity of this total current. The second law is correct if the applied and induced voltages are interpreted by the following equation, obtained by integrating the vector-potential form of the field equations (see Sec. 5b-8) about a circuit path following surfaces of conductors:[1]

$$\int_1^2 \mathbf{E}_0 \cdot d\mathbf{l} - \int_1^2 \frac{\mathbf{i}}{\sigma} \cdot d\mathbf{l} - \int_1^2 \frac{\partial \mathbf{A}}{\partial t} \cdot d\mathbf{l} - \int_1^2 \nabla\phi \cdot d\mathbf{l} = 0 \qquad \text{(5b-220)}$$

The terms may be considered as follows: the first an applied voltage about the path produced by an applied electric-field vector $\mathbf{E}_0$; the second an induced voltage from ohmic and internal-inductance effects within the conductor; the third an induced voltage arising primarily from magnetic effects of the circuit; the fourth an induced voltage arising primarily from electric charges of the circuit.

To apply Eq. (5b-220) in general, it is necessary to have a solution of the field problem in order to perform the indicated integrations. The last two terms, in the general case, will contribute to radiation fields (see Sec. 5b-12) as well as local fields. However, the great usefulness of the approach, as indicated in the first paragraph, comes when fields may be considered as localized and individual parts of the circuit considered separately. Equation (5b-220) may then be written for current as a function of time, $I(t)$, in a single-mesh circuit with applied voltage $V_0(t)$,

$$V_0(t) - RI(t) - L\frac{dI(t)}{dt} - \frac{1}{C}\int_0^t I(\tau)d\tau = 0 \qquad \text{(5b-221)}$$

$$R = \int_1^2 \frac{dl}{\sigma A} \qquad \text{(5b-222)}$$

where A = cross-sectional area of conductor (not skin effect)

$$L = \frac{1}{I}\int_1^2 \mathbf{A} \cdot d\mathbf{l} = \text{magnetic flux enclosed per unit current} \qquad \text{(5b-223)}$$

$$C = \frac{\phi_2 - \phi_1}{\int_0^t I(\tau)d\tau} = \text{scalar-potential difference per unit charge} \qquad \text{(5b-224)}$$

[1] J. R. Carson, *Bell System Tech. J.* **6**, 1 (1927).

R, L, and C are resistance, inductance, and capacitance coefficients, respectively. In the approximation of localized fields and negligible retardation effects, capacitance and inductance are the same as the coefficients defined for the electrostatic and magnetostatic cases, respectively, so that the extensive formulas and curves of Secs. 5b-1 to 5b-4 may be used for these. The resistance coefficient is modified from the low-frequency value by skin effect (see Sec. 5b-15).

Couplings to other parts of the system may also be included in the circuit approach by means of mutual resistances, inductances, and capacitances when the couplings are localized. For the ith current in a system of N currents,

$$V_{0i} - \sum_{j=1}^{N} \left[R_{ij} I_j + L_{ij} \frac{dI_j}{dt} + \frac{1}{C_{ij}} \int_0^t I_j(\tau)\, d\tau \right] = 0 \qquad \text{(5b-225)}$$

Equation (5b-225) may be applied to a mesh, provided that the currents of the system are mesh currents, or to a branch, provided that the currents are branch currents.

Steady-state Sinusoids: N-Terminal-pair Networks. If steady-state sinusoidal voltages and currents are represented by the complex phasors $\check{V}$ and $\check{I}$ where

$$V(t) = \operatorname{Re} \check{V} e^{j\omega t}$$

and $I(t) = \operatorname{Re} \check{I}\, e^{j\omega t}$, Eq. (5b-225) may be written

$$\check{V}_i - \sum_{j=1}^{N} Z_{ij} \check{I}_j = 0 \qquad \text{(5b-226)}$$

where

$$Z_{ij}(\omega) = R_{ij} + j[\omega L_{ij} - (\omega C_{ij})^{-1}] \qquad \text{(5b-227)}$$

Some network theorems of importance are:[1]

1. *Superposition Theorem. The current that flows in a linear network, or the potential difference that exists between any two points in such a network, resulting from the simultaneous application of a number of voltages distributed in any manner whatsoever throughout the network is the sum of the component currents at the first point (or the component potential differences between the two points) that would be caused by the individual voltages acting separately.*

2. *Reciprocity Theorem. In any network composed of linear impedances, if an electromotive force E applied between two terminals produces a current I at some branch in the network, then the same voltage E acting at the second point in the circuit will produce the same current I at the first point.*

3. *Thevenin's Theorem. Any linear network containing one or more sources of voltage and having two terminals behaves, in so far as a load impedance connected across the terminals is concerned, as though the network and its generators were equivalent to a simple generator having an internal impedance Z and a generated voltage E, where E is the voltage that appears across the terminals when no load impedance is connected and Z is the impedance that is measured between the terminals when all sources of voltage in the network are short-circuited.*[2]

4. *Compensation Theorem. If an impedance ΔZ is inserted in a branch of a network, the resulting current increment produced at any point in the network is equal to the current that would be produced at that point by a compensating voltage acting in series with the*

[1] F. E. Terman, "Radio Engineers' Handbook," p. 198, McGraw-Hill Book Company, Inc., New York, 1943.

[2] When the sources of energy in the network are constant-current generators, instead of constant-voltage generators, the internal impedance Z is the impedance observed between the terminals when all constant-current generators are open-circuited.

modified branch, whose value is $-I\Delta Z$, where I is the original current that flowed where the impedance was inserted before the insertion was made.

The form of Eq. (5b-226) also applies to the N terminal pairs of a network and represents a set of N linear equations relating the N terminal voltages to the N currents at those terminals. Sign convention is as in Fig. 5b-12. Solving (5b-226) for the currents gives an alternative form in terms of the admittance parameters.

$$\check{I}_i - \sum_{j=1}^{N} Y_{ij}\check{V}_j = 0 \tag{5b-228}$$

where

$$Y_{ij} = \frac{M_{ji}}{\det Z} \tag{5b-229}$$

$\det Z$ = determinant of Z_{ij} coefficients
M_{ji} = cofactor of Z_{ji} in the above determinant

Another form useful for networks to be connected to transmission lines or waveguides at the N terminals is in terms of the scattering matrix coefficients:[1]

$$b_i - \sum_{j=1}^{N} S_{ij}a_j = 0 \tag{5b-230}$$

where

$$a_i = \tfrac{1}{2}Z_{0i}^{-\frac{1}{2}}(\check{V}_i + Z_{0i}\check{I}_i) \tag{5b-231}$$

$$b_i = \tfrac{1}{2}Z_{0i}^{-\frac{1}{2}}(V_i - Z_{0i}I_i) \tag{5b-232}$$

Z_{0i} is a normalization parameter, usually taken as the characteristic impedance of the transmission system to be joined to the ith terminal pair, so that a_i and b_i represent, respectively, incident and reflected voltage amplitudes in the ith transmission system. In matrix form

$$[S] = ([Z] - [U])([Z] + [U])^{-1} \tag{5b-233}$$

where $[U]$ = unit matrix.

One-terminal-pair Networks. For a one-terminal-pair, passive, linear network, the input-impedance function $Z(\omega) = R(\omega) + jX(\omega)$ has these properties for real ω:

1. $R(\omega) \geq 0$ (equality holds only for loss-free networks).
2. $R(\omega)$ is even function of ω.
3. $X(\omega)$ is odd function of ω.
4. X is positive if time-average stored energy in magnetic fields is greater than that in electric field, negative if stored energy in electric field is greater, and zero (resonant) if the two stored energies have equal time averages.
5. If $R = 0$, $dX/d\omega > 0$.

Real and imaginary parts of the admittance function $Y(\omega) = Z^{-1}$ have identical properties to real and imaginary parts, respectively, of the impedance function.

Considered as function of a complex variable, $Z(\sigma + j\omega)$ or $Y(\sigma + j\omega)$ have no singularities but simple poles, and all poles and zeros lie in the negative half plane, $\sigma \leq 0$. Since Z is meromorphic, by the Mittag-Leffler theorem, it may be expanded in "partial fractions."[2]

$$Z(\omega) = \frac{ja_0}{\omega} + j\omega L_\infty + \sum_{n=1}^{N} \frac{2j\omega a_n}{\omega^2 - \omega_n^2} \tag{5b-234}$$

[1] C. G. Montgomery, R. H. Dicke, and E. M. Purcell, "Principles of Microwave Circuits," MIT Radiation Laboratory Series, vol. 8, p. 146, McGraw-Hill Book Company, Inc., New York, 1948.

[2] S. A. Schelkunoff, *Proc. IRE* **32,** 83 (1944).

where ω_n = nth pole of $Z(\omega)$

a_n = residue at the nth pole $= -\dfrac{1}{[dY/jd\omega]_{\omega=\omega_n}}$

a_0 = residue at $\omega = 0$

If Eq. (5b-234) is not convergent, or is slowly convergent, a convergence factor may be added.

$$Z(\omega) = j\omega L_0 + j\frac{a_0}{\omega} + \sum_{n=1}^{\infty} 2j\omega a_n \left[\frac{1}{\omega^2 - \omega_n^2} + \frac{1}{\omega_n^2}\right] \qquad \text{(5b-235)}$$

A similar expression applies to $Y(\omega)$ in terms of its poles and residues.

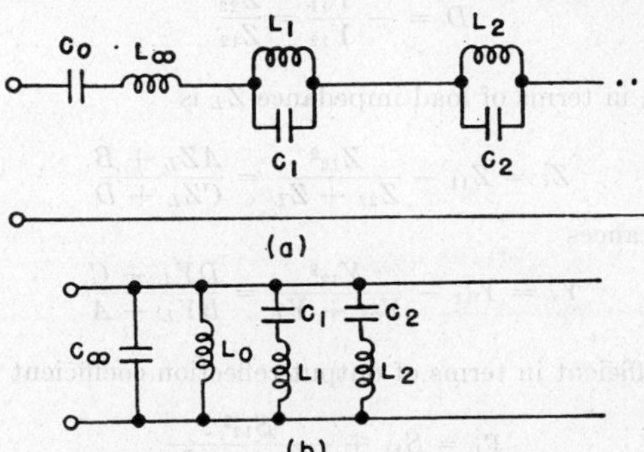

FIG. 5b-13. Canonical Foster forms for lossless one-terminal pairs.

If no convergence term is needed, as in (5b-234), the circuit may be interpreted for the loss-free case in terms of the first Foster canonical form[1] (Fig. 5b-13a); the similar expression for admittance Y leads to the second Foster form[1] (Fig. 5b-13b); if one convergence term is retained in Eq. (5b-235), the equivalent circuit[2] is as in Fig. 5b-14 and convergence is faster. The first and second canonical Cauer forms[3] (Figs. 5b-15a,b) are obtained by continued fraction expansion of Z and Y, respectively.

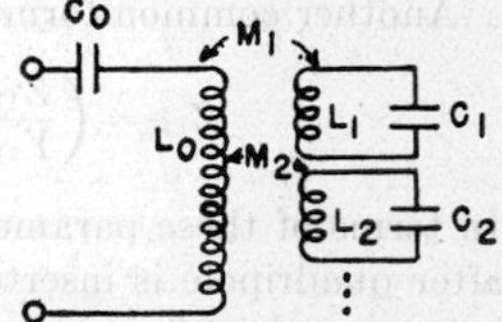

FIG. 5b-14. Equivalent circuit for one-terminal pair with rapid convergence.

Two-terminal-pair Networks. The most important class of linear networks is the *two-terminal-pair* network, sometimes called *four-terminal network*, *quadripole*, or *transducer* (Fig. 5b-16). Either the form (5b-226) or (5b-228) or (5b-230) may be used,

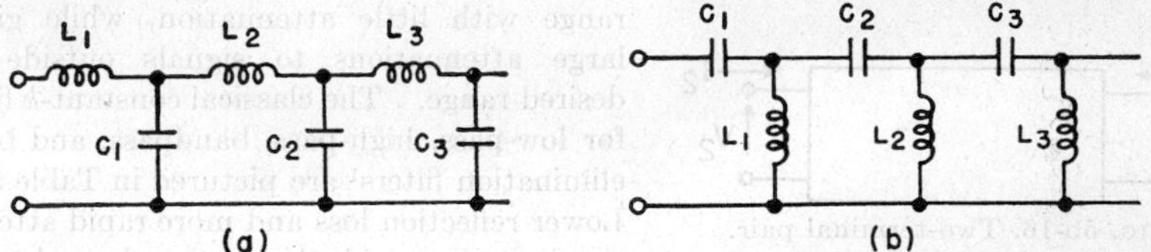

FIG. 5b-15. Canonical Cauer forms for lossless one-terminal pairs.

or a number of other forms.[4] Of these, the most useful for cascaded networks are the transfer parameters.

[1] R. M. Foster, *Bell System Tech. J.* **3**, 259 (1924).

[2] Schelkunoff, *loc. cit.*

[3] Cauer, *Arch. Elektrotech.* **17**, 355 (1927).

[4] E. Guillemin, "Communication Networks," vol. II, John Wiley & Sons, Inc., New York, 1935.

$$\begin{bmatrix} \check{V}_1 \\ \check{I}_1 \end{bmatrix} = \begin{bmatrix} A & B \\ C & D \end{bmatrix} \begin{bmatrix} \check{V}_2 \\ -\check{I}_2 \end{bmatrix} \tag{5b-236}$$

$AD - BC = 1$ for a network satisfying reciprocity

$$A = -\frac{Y_{22}}{Y_{12}} = \frac{Z_{11}}{Z_{12}}$$
$$B = -\frac{1}{Y_{12}} = \frac{\det Z}{Z_{12}}$$
$$C = -\frac{\det Y}{Y_{12}} = \frac{1}{Z_{12}}$$
$$D = -\frac{Y_{11}}{Y_{12}} = \frac{Z_{22}}{Z_{12}} \tag{5b-237}$$

Input impedance Z_i in terms of load impedance Z_L is

$$Z_i = Z_{11} - \frac{Z_{12}^2}{Z_{22} + Z_L} = \frac{AZ_L + B}{CZ_L + D} \tag{5b-238}$$

Similarly for admittances

$$Y_i = Y_{11} - \frac{Y_{12}^2}{Y_{22} + Y_L} = \frac{DY_L + C}{BY_L + A} \tag{5b-239}$$

Input reflection coefficient in terms of output reflection coefficient is

$$\Gamma_1 = S_{11} + \frac{S_{12}^2}{(1/\Gamma_2) - S_{22}} \tag{5b-240}$$
$$\Gamma_1 = \frac{b_1}{a_1} \qquad \Gamma_2 = \frac{a_2}{b_2}$$

Another common formulation utilizes image impedances and transfer functions

$$Z_{i1} = \left(\frac{Z_{11}}{Y_{11}}\right)^{\frac{1}{2}} \qquad Z_{i2} = \left(\frac{Z_{22}}{Y_{22}}\right)^{\frac{1}{2}} \qquad \theta = \cosh^{-1} (Y_{11}Z_{11})^{\frac{1}{2}} \tag{5b-241}$$

In terms of these parameters, the insertion loss, or ratio of current through receiver after quadripole is inserted between source and receiver to current through receiver before quadripole is inserted, is

$$\frac{I_2}{I_{20}} = \frac{(Z_R + Z_s)(Z_{i1}Z_{i2})^{\frac{1}{2}}}{(Z_sZ_{i2} + Z_RZ_{i1}) \cosh \theta + (Z_RZ_S + Z_{i1}Z_{i2}) \sinh \theta} \tag{5b-242}$$

Z_s is source impedance and Z_R receiver impedance.

Many two-terminal pairs are used as filters, to pass signals over a desired frequency range with little attenuation, while giving large attenuations to signals outside the desired range. The classical constant-k filters for low-pass, high-pass, bandpass, and band-elimination filters[1] are pictured in Table 5b-7. Lower reflection loss and more rapid attenuation increase outside the pass band are obtained by adding half sections of m-derived[2] filters at each end. The corresponding m-derived sections are also pictured in Table 5b-7.

FIG. 5b-16. Two-terminal pair.

The lattice network in Fig. 5b-17 gives more flexibility in achieving desired response characteristics. It is the most general symmetrical two-terminal pair in the sense

[1] O. J. Zobel, *Bell System Tech. J.* **2**, 1 (1923); T. E. Shea, "Transmission Networks and Wave Filters," D. Van Nostrand & Company, Inc., New York, 1939.
[2] O. J. Zobel, *Bell System Tech. J.* **10**, 284 (1931).

that *if a symmetrical two-terminal-pair reactive network is realizable at all, it is realizable in the lattice form.* Image impedance and transfer constants are

$$Z_{i1} = Z_{i2} = (Z_a Z_b)^{\frac{1}{2}} \qquad \theta_x = 2 \tanh^{-1} \left(\frac{Z_a}{Z_b}\right)^{\frac{1}{2}} \tag{5b-243}$$

Thus for purely reactive elements, pass bands occur when Z_a and Z_b are of opposite sign, and attenuation bands when Z_a and Z_b are of like sign. Attenuation is infinite when $Z_a = Z_b$.

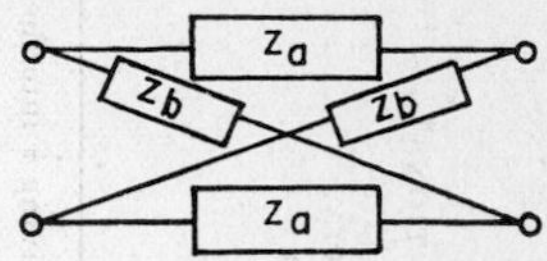

Fig. 5b-17. Lattice network.

The approximation problem in network synthesis is to arrive at physically realizable Z_a and Z_b to give response curves agreeing with the desired curves within certain specified tolerances. The errors may be either oscillatory[1] or monotonic.[2] Potential-analogue methods are also useful in the approximation problem.[3]

5b-15. Skin Effect. *Definition of the Effect.* An applied high-frequency field near the surface of a conductor causes current to concentrate on the surface near the applied field, the decay into the conductor being approximately exponential. This concentration increases as frequency, conductivity, or permeability increases. The result is an increased resistance and decreased internal inductance at frequencies for which the effect is significant. The localized joule heating which results causes little temperature gradient throughout the conductor because of the high thermal conductivity of the metal. The current changes in phase as well as in magnitude as one progresses into the conductor.

The results given neglect displacement current within the conductors, an assumption well justified for good conductors, but results should consequently not be used for materials with appreciable dielectric losses.

Steady-state Formulas for a Plane Solid. For a plane semi-infinite solid extending from $x = 0$ to $x = \infty$ and with an applied field E_0 in the z direction at $x = 0$, current density varies with depth x as

$$\check{J}_z = \sigma \check{E}_0 e^{-x/\delta} e^{-jx/\delta} \qquad \text{amp/m}^2 \tag{5b-244}$$

δ, the *skin depth* or *depth of penetration*, is defined as

$$\delta = \left(\frac{\omega\mu\sigma}{2}\right)^{-\frac{1}{2}} \qquad \text{m} \tag{5b-245}$$

The surface impedance Z_s is the ratio of (complex) applied electric field at the surface to (complex) current flow per unit width. It is found to be

$$Z_s = \frac{\check{E}_0}{\check{J}'_z} = (1 + j)R_s \tag{5b-246}$$

where R_s, the surface resistivity, is

$$R_s = \frac{1}{\sigma\delta} = \left(\frac{\omega\mu}{2\sigma}\right)^{\frac{1}{2}} \qquad \text{ohms/square} \tag{5b-247}$$

Power loss per unit area is

$$P_L = \tfrac{1}{2} R_s \check{\mathbf{J}}' \cdot \check{\mathbf{J}}'^* \qquad \text{watts/m}^2 \tag{5b-248}$$

[1] Cauer, *Siebschaltungen* V.D.I. Verlag, 1931; Cauer, *Z. angew. Math. Mech.* **10,** 425 (1930).

[2] H. W. Bode, *J. Math. Phys.* **13,** 275 (1934).

[3] W. W. Hansen and O. C. Lundstrum, *Proc. IRE* **33,** 528 (1945).

TABLE 5b-7. DESIGN OF LOW-PASS, HIGH-PASS AND BAND-PASS FILTER SECTIONS*

Fundamental Relations

R_1 = load resistance f_1 = cut-off frequency (lowest frequency transmitted) f_∞ = a frequency of very high attenuation

$$L_k = \frac{R}{4\pi f_1} \qquad C_k = \frac{1}{4\pi f_1 R} \qquad m = \sqrt{1 - \left(\frac{f_\infty}{f_1}\right)^2}$$

Design of Sections

Type	Attenuation characteristic	*A.* Filters having T intermediate sections		*B.* Filters having π intermediate sections	
		Configuration	Formulas	Configuration	Formulas
End (m of approximately 0.6)	Attenuation, Frequency, f_∞, f_1	$2C_1$, $2L_2$, $\frac{1}{2}C_2$; Intermediate T sections	$C_1 = \frac{C_k}{m}$ $C_2 = \frac{4m}{1-m^2}C_k$ $L_2 = \frac{L_k}{m}$	$\frac{1}{2}L_1$, $2C_1$, $2L_2$; Intermediate π sections	$L_1 = \frac{4m}{1-m^2}L_k$ $C_1 = \frac{C_k}{m}$ $L_2 = \frac{L_k}{m}$
I	Attenuation, Frequency, f_∞, f_1	$2C_1$, L_2, C_2	$C_1 = \frac{C_k}{m}$ $C_2 = \frac{4m}{1-m^2}C_k$ $L_2 = \frac{L_k}{m}$	L_1, C_1, $2L_2$	$L_1 = \frac{4m}{1-m^2}L_k$ $C_1 = \frac{C_k}{m}$ $L_2 = \frac{L_k}{m}$
II $f_\infty = 0$	Attenuation, Frequency, f_1	$2C_1$, L_2	$C_1 = C_k$ $L_2 = L_k$	$2L_2$, C_1	$C_1 = C_k$ $L_2 = L_k$

*From F. E. Terman, "Radio Engineers' Handbook, pp. 228–231, McGraw-Hill Book Company, New York, 1943.

Table 5b-7. Design of Low-pass, High-pass and Band-pass Filter Sections (*Continued*)

Fundamental Relations

R = load resistance f_2 = cut-off frequency (highest frequency transmitted) f_∞ = a frequency of very high attenuation

$$L_k = \frac{R}{\pi f_2} \qquad C_k = \frac{1}{\pi f_2 R} \qquad m = \sqrt{1 - \left(\frac{f_2}{f_\infty}\right)^2}$$

Design of Sections

Type	Attenuation characteristic	A. Filters having T intermediate sections: Configuration	A. Filters having T intermediate sections: Formulas	B. Filters having π intermediate sections: Configuration	B. Filters having π intermediate sections: Formulas
End (m of approximately 0.6)	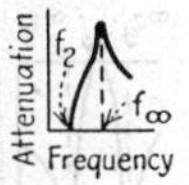	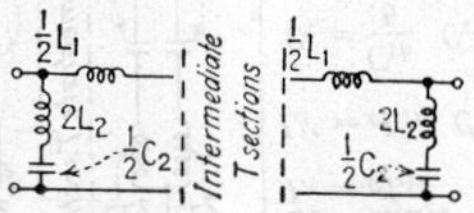	$L_1 = mL_k$ $L_2 = \frac{1 - m^2}{4m} L_k$ $C_2 = mC_k$	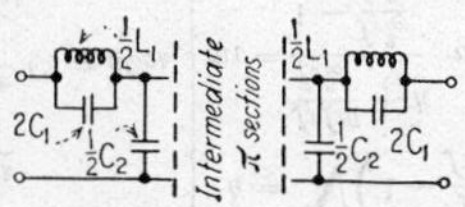	$L_1 = mL_k$ $C_1 = \frac{1 - m^2}{4m} C_k$ $C_2 = mC_k$
I	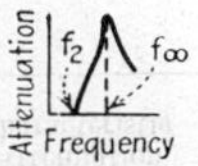	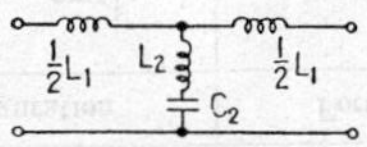	$L_1 = mL_k$ $L_2 = \frac{1 - m^2}{4m} L_k$ $C_2 = mC_k$	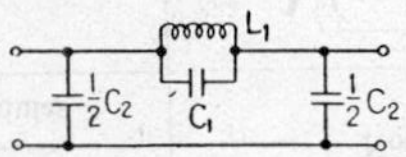	$L_1 = mL_k$ $C_1 = \frac{1 - m^2}{4m} C_k$ $C_2 = mC_k$
II ($f_\infty = \infty$)	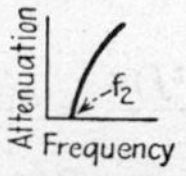	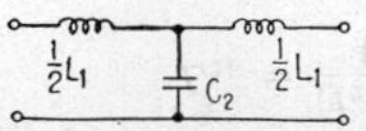	$L_1 = L_k$ $C_2 = C_k$	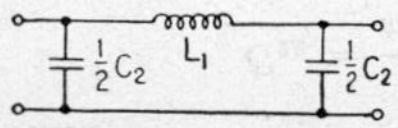	$L_1 = L_k$ $C_2 = C_k$

TABLE 5b-7. DESIGN OF LOW-PASS, HIGH-PASS AND BAND-PASS FILTER SECTIONS (*Continued*)

Fundamental Relations

R = load resistance

f_1 = lower frequency limit of pass band

f_2 = higher frequency limit of pass band

$f_{1\infty}$ = a frequency of very high attenuation in low-frequency attenuating band

$f_{2\infty}$ = a frequency of very high attenuation in high-frequency attenuating band

$$L_{1k} = \frac{R}{\pi(f_2 - f_1)} \qquad L_{2k} = \frac{(f_2 - f_1)R}{4\pi f_1 f_2} \qquad C_{1k} = \frac{f_2 - f_1}{4\pi f_1 f_2 R} \qquad C_{2k} = \frac{1}{\pi(f_2 - f_1)R}$$

Design of Sections

Type	Attenuation characteristic	A. Filters having T intermediate sections: Configuration	A. Formulas	B. Filters having π intermediate sections: Configuration	B. Formulas	Notation for both T and π sections
End ($m_1 = m_2$ = approximately 0.6)			$L_1 = m_1 L_{1k}$ $L_2 = aL_{1k}$ $L_2' = cL_{1k}$ $C_1 = \frac{C_{1k}}{m_2}$ $C_2 = \frac{C_{1k}}{b}$ $C_2' = \frac{C_{1k}}{d}$		$L_1 = \frac{L_{2k}}{b}$ $L_1' = \frac{L_{2k}}{d}$ $L_2 = \frac{L_{2k}}{m_2}$ $C_1 = aC_{2k}$ $C_1' = cC_{2k}$ $C_2 = m_1 C_{2k}$	$g = \sqrt{\left(1 - \frac{f_{1\infty}^2}{f_1^2}\right)\left(1 - \frac{f_{1\infty}^2}{f_2^2}\right)}$ $h = \sqrt{\left(1 - \frac{f_1^2}{f_{2\infty}^2}\right)\left(1 - \frac{f_2^2}{f_{2\infty}^2}\right)}$ $m_1 = \frac{\frac{f_1 f_2 g}{f_{2\infty}^2} + h}{1 - \frac{f_{1\infty}^2}{f_{2\infty}^2}}$ $m_2 = \frac{g + \frac{f_{1\infty}^2}{f_1 f_2} h}{1 - \frac{f_{1\infty}^2}{f_{2\infty}^2}}$ $a = \frac{(1-m_1^2) f_{2\infty}^2}{4g f_1 f_2}\left(1 - \frac{f_{1\infty}^2}{f_{2\infty}^2}\right) = \frac{(1-m_2^2) f_1 f_2}{4g f_{1\infty}^2}\left(1 - \frac{f_{1\infty}^2}{f_{2\infty}^2}\right)$ $b = \frac{(1-m_2^2)}{4g}\left(1 - \frac{f_{1\infty}^2}{f_{2\infty}^2}\right)$ $c = \frac{(1-m_1^2)}{4h}\left(1 - \frac{f_{1\infty}^2}{f_{2\infty}^2}\right)$ $d = \frac{(1-m_1^2) f_{2\infty}^2}{4h f_1 f_2}\left(1 - \frac{f_{1\infty}^2}{f_{2\infty}^2}\right) = \frac{(1-m_2^2) f_1 f_2}{4h f_{1\infty}^2}\left(1 - \frac{f_{1\infty}^2}{f_{2\infty}^2}\right)$ when ($m_1 = m_2$), $g = h$, $a = d$, $b = c$, $f_{1\infty} = \frac{f_1 f_2}{f_{2\infty}}$, $m_1 = m_2 = \frac{h}{1 - \frac{f_1 f_2}{f_{2\infty}^2}}$ and $f_{2\infty}^2 = \frac{f_1^2 + f_2^2 - 2m^2 f_1 f_2}{2(1-m^2)} + \left[\left(\frac{f_1^2 + f_2^2 - 2m^2 f_1 f_2}{2(1-m^2)}\right)^2 - f_1^2 f_2^2\right]^{1/2}$ These formulas apply for both end and Type I sections
I			$L_1 = m_1 L_{1k}$ $L_2 = aL_{1k}$ $L_2 = cL_1.$ $C_1 = \frac{C_{1k}}{m_2}$ $C_2 = \frac{C_{1k}}{b}$ $C_2 = \frac{C_{1k}}{d}$		$L_1 = \frac{L_{2k}}{b}$ $L_1 = \frac{L_{2k}}{d}$ $L_2 = \frac{L_{2k}}{m_2}$ $C_1 = aC_{2k}$ $C_1 = cC_{2k}$ $C_2 = m_1 C_{2k}$	(see above)
II $f_{1\infty} = 0$ $f_{2\infty} = f_2$			$L_1 = \frac{f_1 R}{\pi f_2 (f_2 - f_1)}$ $L_2 = \frac{(f_1 + f_2) R}{4\pi f_1 f_2}$ $C_1 = C_{1k}$		$C_1 = \frac{f_1 + f_2}{4\pi f_1 f_2 R}$ $C_2 = \frac{f_1}{\pi f_2 (f_2 - f_1) R}$ $L_2 = L_{2k}$	

III $f_{1\infty} = f_1$ $f_{2\infty} = \infty$	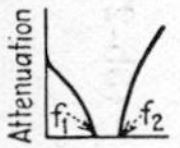	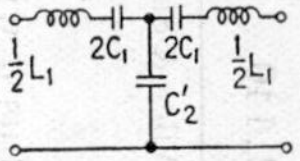	$L_1 = L_{1k}$ $C_2 = \dfrac{1}{\pi(f_1+f_2)R}$ $C_1 = \dfrac{f_2 - f_1}{4\pi f_1^2 R}$	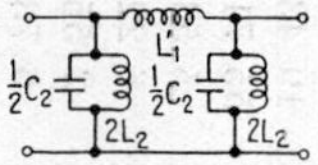	$L_1' = \dfrac{R}{\pi(f_1+f_2)}$ $L_2 = \dfrac{(f_2 - f_1)R}{4\pi f_1^2}$ $C_2 = C_{2k}$	
IV $f_{1\infty} = 0$ $f_{2\infty} = \infty$		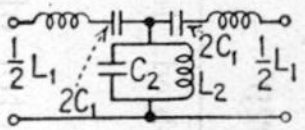	$L_1 = L_{1k}$ $L_2 = L_{2k}$ $C_1 = C_{1k}$ $C_2 = C_{2k}$	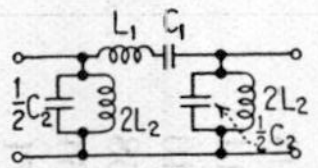	$L_1 = L_{1k}$ $L_2 = L_{2k}$ $C_1 = C_{1k}$ $C_2 = C_{2k}$	
V $f_{2\infty} = f_2$	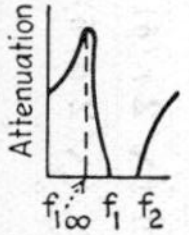	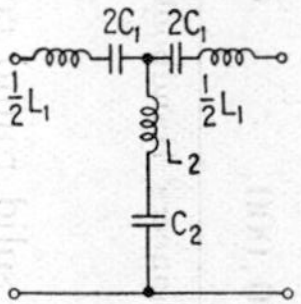	$L_1 = m_2 L_{1k}$ $L_2 = \dfrac{(1 - m_1^2)}{4m_1} L_{1k}$ $C_1 = \dfrac{C_{1k}}{m_2}$ $C_2 = \dfrac{4m_2}{1 - m_2^2} C_{1k}$ See notation for m_1 and m_2	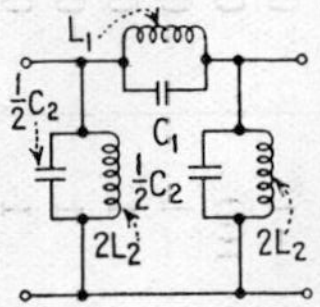	$L_1 = \dfrac{4m_2}{1 - m_2^2} L_{2k}$ $L_2 = \dfrac{L_{2k}}{m_2}$ $C_1 = \dfrac{(1 - m_1^2)}{4m_1} C_{2k}$ $C_2 = m_1 C_{2k}$ See notation for m and m_2	$m_1 = \dfrac{f_1}{f_2} m_2$ $m_2 = \sqrt{\dfrac{1 - \dfrac{f_{1\infty}^2}{f_1^2}}{1 - \dfrac{f_{1\infty}^2}{f_2^2}}}$
VI $f_{1\infty} = f_1$	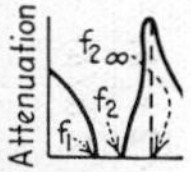	Same circuit as above for Type V	Same formulas as above for Type V See notation for m_1 and m_2	Same circuit as above for Type V	Same formulas as above for Type V See notation for m_1 and m_2	$m_1 = \sqrt{\dfrac{1 - \dfrac{f_2^2}{f_{2\infty}^2}}{1 - \dfrac{f_1^2}{f_{2\infty}^2}}}$ $m_2 = \dfrac{f_1}{f_2} m_1$
VII $f_{1\infty} = 0$	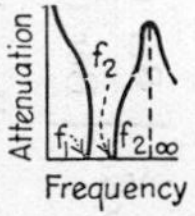	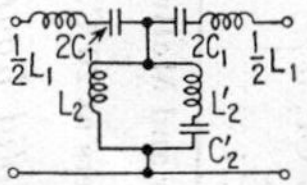	$L_1 = m_1 L_{1k}$ $L_2 = a L_{1k}$ $L_2' = \dfrac{(1 - m_1^2)}{4h} L_{1k}$ $C_1 = C_{1k}$ $C_2' = \dfrac{h}{a} C_{1k}$	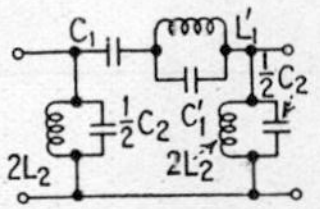	$L_1' = \dfrac{h}{a} L_{2k}$ $L_2 = L_{2k}$ $C_1 = aC_{2k}$ $C_2 = m_1 C_{2k}$ $C_1' = \dfrac{(1 - m_1^2)}{4h} C_{2k}$	$h = \sqrt{\left(1 - \dfrac{f_1^2}{f_{2\infty}^2}\right)\left(1 - \dfrac{f_2^2}{f_{2\infty}^2}\right)}$ $m_1 = \dfrac{f_1 f_2}{f_{2\infty}^2} + h$ $a = \dfrac{(1 - m_1^2) f_{2\infty}^2}{4 f_1 f_2}$
VIII $f_{2\infty} = \infty$	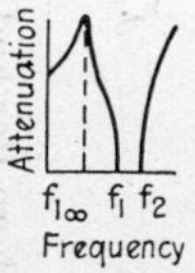	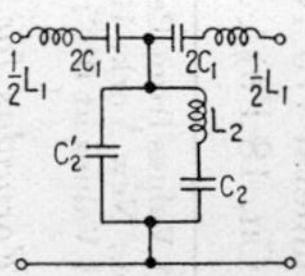	$L_1 = L_{1k}$ $L_2 = \dfrac{d}{g} L_{1k}$ $C_1 = \dfrac{C_{1k}}{m_2}$ $C_2 = \dfrac{4g}{1 - m_2^2} C_{1k}$ $C_2' = \dfrac{C_{1k}}{d}$	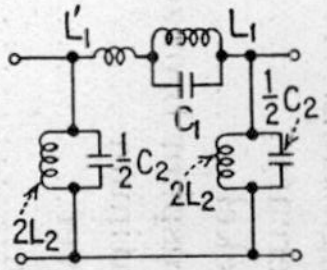	$L_1 = \dfrac{4g}{1 - m_2^2} L_{2k}$ $L_2 = \dfrac{L_{2k}}{m_2}$ $L_1' = \dfrac{L_{2k}}{d}$ $C_1 = \dfrac{d}{g} C_{2k}$ $C_2 = C_{2k}$	$g = \sqrt{\left(1 - \dfrac{f_{1\infty}^2}{f_1^2}\right)\left(1 - \dfrac{f_{1\infty}^2}{f_2^2}\right)}$ $m_2 = g + \dfrac{f_{1\infty}^2}{f_1 f_2}$ $d = \dfrac{(1 - m_2^2) f_1 f_2}{4 f_{1\infty}^2}$

In terms of the surface magnetic intensity **H** and a unit vector **n** normal to the surface, current per unit width is

$$\mathbf{J} = \mathbf{n} \times \mathbf{H} \qquad (5b\text{-}249)$$

Formulas for δ and R_s as functions of frequency are given for several common materials in Table 5b-8.

TABLE 5b-8. SKIN-EFFECT QUANTITIES FOR CONDUCTORS

Metal	Resistivity* (ohm-m)10^8	Relative* permeability at 0.002 weber/m²	$\delta\sqrt{\nu}$ δ = depth of penetration, m, ν = frequency, cps	$10^7 R_s/\sqrt{\nu}$ R_s = surface resistivity, ohms/m²
Aluminum	2.828	1	0.085	3.33
Brass (65.8 Cu, 34.2 Zn)	6.29†	1	0.126	4.99
Brass (90.9 Cu, 9.1 Zn)	3.65†	1	0.096	3.79
Graphite	1,000	1	1.592	62.81
Chromium	2.6†	1	0.081	3.21
Copper	1.724	1	0.066	2.61
Gold	2.22†	1	0.075	2.96
Lead	22	1	0.236	9.32
Magnesium	4.6	1	0.108	4.26
Mercury	95.8†	1	0.493	19.43
Nickel	7.8	100	0.014	55.71
Phosphor bronze	7.75†	1	0.140	5.54
Platinum	9.83†	1	0.158	6.22
Silver	1.629	1	0.064	2.55
Tin	11.5	1	0.171	6.73
Tungsten	5.51	1	0.118	4.67
Zinc	5.38†	1	0.117	4.60
Magnetic iron	10	200	0.011	90.9
Permalloy (78.5 Ni, 21.5 Fe)	16	8,000	0.0022	727
Supermalloy (5 Mo, 79 Ni, 16 Fe)	60	10^5	0.0012	4,880
Mumetal (75 Ni, 2 Cr, 5 Cu, 18 Fe)	62	20,000	0.0029	2,140

* Values from Pender and McIlwain, "Electrical Engineers' Handbook," 4th ed., John Wiley & Sons, Inc., New York, 1950.

† Values at 0°C; others at 20°C.

Formulas for a Solid Round Wire. For a solid round conductor of radius a with applied axial electric field E_0 at the surface, current density at radius r is

$$\check{J}_z = \sigma \check{E}_0 \left[\frac{\text{Ber}\,(\sqrt{2}\,r/\delta) + j\,\text{Bei}\,(\sqrt{2}\,r/\delta)}{\text{Ber}\,(\sqrt{2}\,a/\delta) + j\,\text{Bei}\,(\sqrt{2}\,a/\delta)} \right] \quad \text{amp/m}^2 \qquad (5b\text{-}250)$$

where Ber and Bei[1] are Bessel functions.

$$\text{Ber}\,x + j\,\text{Bei}\,x = J_0(j^{-\frac{1}{2}}x)$$

[1] Defined by Lord Kelvin and tabulated in H. B. Dwight, "Tables of Integrals," rev. ed., The Macmillan Company, New York, 1947; or McLachlan, "Bessel Functions for Engineers," Oxford University Press, New York, 1934.

Internal impedance (resistance and internal reactance) per unit length is

$$Z_i = R + j\omega L_i = \frac{jR_s}{\sqrt{2}\,a\pi}\left[\frac{\text{Ber}\,(\sqrt{2}\,a/\delta) + j\,\text{Bei}\,(\sqrt{2}\,a/\delta)}{\text{Ber}'\,(\sqrt{2}\,a/\delta) + j\,\text{Bei}'\,(\sqrt{2}\,a/\delta)}\right] \quad \text{ohm/m} \quad (5b\text{-}251)$$

where $\text{Ber}'\,x + j\,\text{Bei}'\,x = d(\text{Ber}\,x + j\,\text{Bei}\,x)/dx$ is also tabulated. A low-frequency approximation to Eq. (5b-251) valid for $a/\delta < 1$ is

$$Z_i \approx \left\{\frac{1}{\pi a^2 \sigma}\left[1 + \frac{1}{48}\left(\frac{a}{\delta}\right)^4\right] + j\frac{\omega\mu}{8\pi}\right\} \quad \text{ohm/m} \quad (5b\text{-}252)$$

A high-frequency approximation to Eq. (5b-251) valid for $a/\delta > 10$ is

$$Z_i \approx (1 + j)\frac{R_s}{2\pi a} \quad \text{ohm/m} \quad (5b\text{-}253)$$

Curves of R/R_0, $\omega L_i/R_s$, and $L_i/(L_i)_0$ are given in Fig. 5b-18 as functions of a/δ. R_0 is d-c resistance and $(L_i)_0$ the internal inductance at zero frequency,

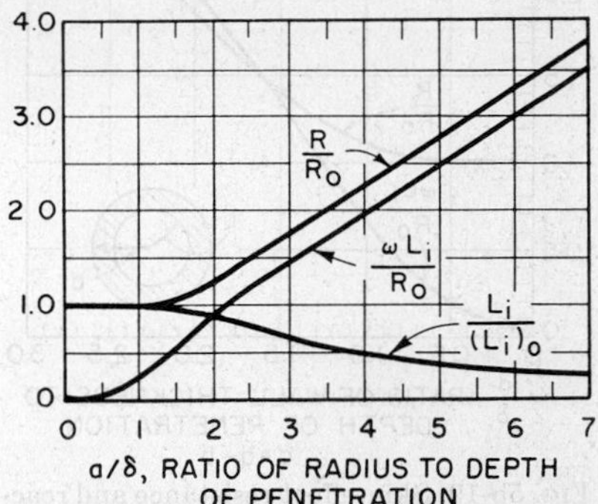

FIG. 5b-18. Skin effects for solid round conductors.

$$R_0 = \frac{1}{\pi a^2 \sigma} \quad \text{ohm/m} \qquad (L_i)_0 = \frac{\mu}{8\pi} \quad \text{henrys/m}$$

Tubular Conductor. For a tubular conducting cylinder of internal radius b and external radius a, and with an applied field at the external radius, impedance per unit length is

$$R_i + j\omega L_i = \frac{R_s}{\sqrt{2j}\,\pi a}\left[\frac{J_0(Ta)H_0^{(1)\prime}(Tb) - J_0'(Tb)H_0^{(1)}(Ta)}{J_0'(Ta)H_0^{(1)\prime}(Tb) - J_0'(Tb)H_0^{(1)\prime}(Ta)}\right] \quad \text{ohms/m} \quad (5b\text{-}254)$$

where T is the complex quantity $(-j\omega\mu\sigma)^{\frac{1}{2}}$. The real and imaginary parts of the first Hankel function $H_0^{(1)}$ of complex argument $(j^{-\frac{1}{2}}x)$ are given in Jahnke and Emde.[1] Note that

$$H_0^{(1)\prime}(x) = \frac{d}{dx}H_0^{(1)}(x) = -H_1^{(1)}(x)$$

If the applied field is at the inner radius (as when the tubular conductor is used as the outer conductor of a coaxial transmission system), interchange a and b in Eq. (5b-254).

For a thin-walled tubular conductor[2] with thickness $d = a - b$, an approximation to Eq. (5b-254) is

$$R = \frac{R_s}{2\pi a}\left[\frac{\sinh\,(2d/\delta) + \sin\,(2d/\delta)}{\cosh\,(2d/\delta) - \cos\,(2d/\delta)}\right] \quad \text{ohm/m} \quad (5b\text{-}255)$$

$$\omega L_i = \frac{R_s}{2\pi a}\left[\frac{\sinh\,(2d/\delta) - \sin\,(2d/\delta)}{\cosh\,(2d/\delta) - \cos\,(2d/\delta)}\right] \quad \text{ohm/m} \quad (5b\text{-}256)$$

Figure 5b-19 shows R/R_0 and $\omega L_i/R_0$ as functions of d/δ where R_0 is d-c resistance, $R_0^{-1} = \pi(a^2 - b^2)\sigma$.

[1] Jahnke and Emde, "Tables of Functions," Dover Publications, New York, 1945.

[2] More complete curves for the thick-walled tubular conductor are given in H. B. Dwight, A Precise Method of Calculating Skin Effect on Isolated Tubes, *J. Am. Inst. Elec. Engrs.* **42**, 827 (August, 1923).

Conductors of Other Shapes. For a conductor of arbitrary shape, solution of the following equation yields current distribution

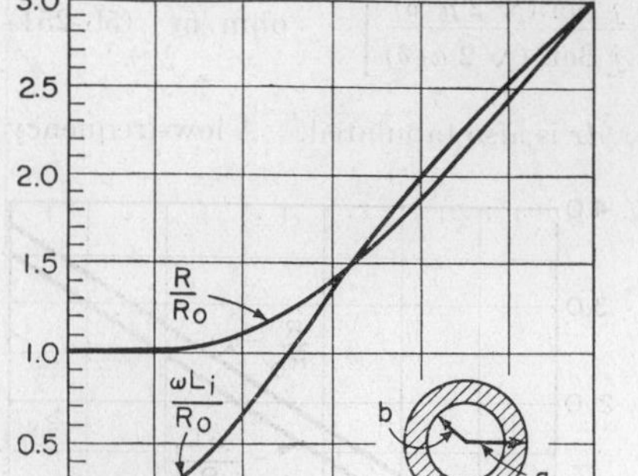

Fig. 5b-19. Skin-effect resistance and reactance for thin-walled tubular conductors.

$$\nabla^2 \check{J} = j\omega\mu\sigma \check{J} \qquad \text{(5b-257)}$$

with boundary conditions at the surface of $\mathbf{n} \cdot \mathbf{J} = 0$ and $\mathbf{J} = \sigma \mathbf{E}_0$ where $\mathbf{E}_0$ is the applied field at the surface. Solutions are not available for many shapes. Figure 5b-20 shows resistance compared with d-c resistance for a conducting cylinder of rectangular cross section[1] determined mostly by experimental methods.

For any conductor at frequencies high enough so that thickness and all radii of curvature are large compared with skin depth defined by Eq. (5b-245), the planar analysis may be used as a good approximation. Internal impedance (resistance and internal reactance) for a length l and width w over which fields are uniform are then

$$Z \approx (1 + j) \frac{R_s l}{w} \qquad \text{ohms} \qquad \text{(5b-258)}$$

For a given surface magnetic field, power loss per unit area may then be found approxi-

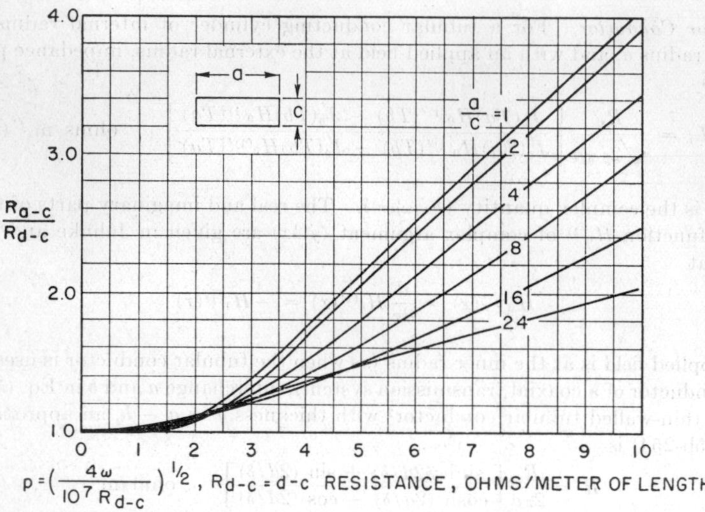

Fig. 5b-20. A-C resistance of rectangular conductors. [*From Terman, "Radio Engineer's Handbook," p. 43, McGraw-Hill Book Company, Inc., New York, 1943, as extended from data of S. J. Haefner, Proc. IRE* **25**, 434 *(April, 1937).*]

mately by Eqs. (5b-248) and (5b-249). A very general method of determining the skin resistance of certain polygons has been given by Wheeler.[2]

Similitude is useful in the study of skin effect in arbitrarily shaped conductors. If

[1] S. J. Haefner, Alternating Current Resistance of Rectangular Conductors, *Proc. IRE* **25**, 434 (April, 1937).

[2] H. A. Wheeler, Skin Resistance of a Transmission-line Conductor of Polygon Cross Section, *Proc. IRE* **43**, 805 (July, 1955).

two systems are geometrically similar, distribution of currents in the two systems will be similar, provided that linear dimensions are in the same ratio as skin depth for the materials of the two systems. Impedance of the two systems will then be inversely as the ratio of linear dimensions. Tests made on a small system at high frequencies may then be used to predict results for a large system at lower frequencies.

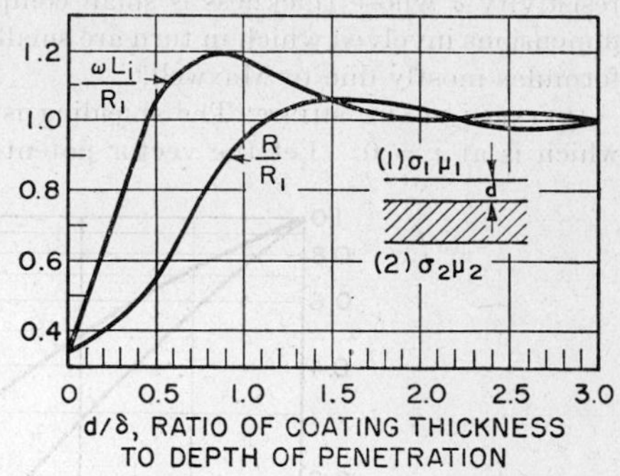

FIG. 5b-21. Skin-effect resistance and reactance for coated conductor with $\sqrt{\mu_2\sigma_1/\mu_1\sigma_2} = 0.34$.

Coated and Laminated Conductors. If a coating of one conducting material is placed on another material, resistance and internal reactance will be nearly the same as for a solid of the coating material, provided that coating thickness is large compared with δ for that material; resistance and internal reactance will be nearly the same as for a solid of the base material if coating thickness is very small compared with δ for the coating material. For a semi-infinite solid of constants σ_2, μ_2 coated with a sheet of depth d of a material with constants σ_1, μ_1, internal impedance for the general thickness is

$$Z_i = (1 + j)R_{s_1}\left\{\frac{\sinh[(1 + j)d/\delta_1] + (R_{s2}/R_{s1})\cosh[(1 + j)d/\delta_1]}{\cosh[(1 + j)d/\delta_1] + (R_{s2}/R_{s1})\sinh[(1 + j)d/\delta_1]}\right\} \quad \text{ohms/m} \tag{5b-259}$$

Surface resistivity R_s and skin depth δ are as defined in Eqs. (5b-245) and (5b-247). Figure 5b-21 shows the way in which resistance and internal reactance vary with d/δ_1 for a particular case of the coating of a poorer high-frequency conductor than the base, $R_{s_2}/R_{s_1} = 0.34$; Fig. 5b-22 shows curves for the particular case of $R_{s_2}/R_{s_1} = 1.6$, the coating being the better high-frequency conductor.

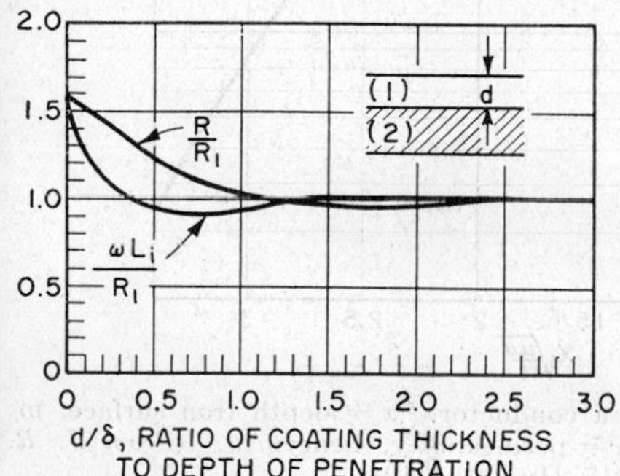

FIG. 5b-22. Skin-effect resistance and reactance for coated conductors with $\sqrt{\mu_2\sigma_1/\mu_1\sigma_2} = 1.6$.

An important use of laminated conductor interspersed with insulating layers to produce more efficient use of the current-carrying cross section has been given by Clogston.[1]

Transient Penetration in the Plane Solid. If a constant magnetic field H_0 is suddenly applied at time $t = 0$ to the surface of a semi-infinite plane solid, field at depth x, time $t > 0$ is

$$H(x,t) = H_0\left[1 - erf\left(\frac{x}{2}\sqrt{\frac{\mu\sigma}{t}}\right)\right] \quad \text{amp/m} \tag{5b-260}$$

If the applied field increases linearly with time, $H(0,t) = Ct$ for $t > 0$,

$$H(x,t) = Ct\left\{\left(1 + \frac{\mu\sigma x^2}{2t}\right)\left[1 - erf\left(\frac{x}{2}\sqrt{\frac{\mu\sigma}{t}}\right)\right] - x\sqrt{\frac{\mu\sigma}{\pi t}}\exp\left(\frac{-\mu\sigma x^2}{4t}\right)\right\} \tag{5b-261}$$

Universal curves of $H(x,t)/H(0,t)$ are given in Fig. 5b-23 for the two cases.

[1] A. M. Clogston, *Bell System Tech. J.* **30**, 491 (1951).

Thin-sheet Shielding Formulas.[1] The shielding effect on both transient and steady-state time-varying fields of plane, spherical, or cylindrical conducting sheets of area resistivity σ whose thickness is small compared with the skin depth and with other dimensions involved which in turn are small compared with a wavelength are given by formulas mostly due to Maxwell.

INFINITE PLANE SHEET: The shielding is independent of the position of the sheet which is at $z = 0$. Let the vector potential of the source, located in the region of

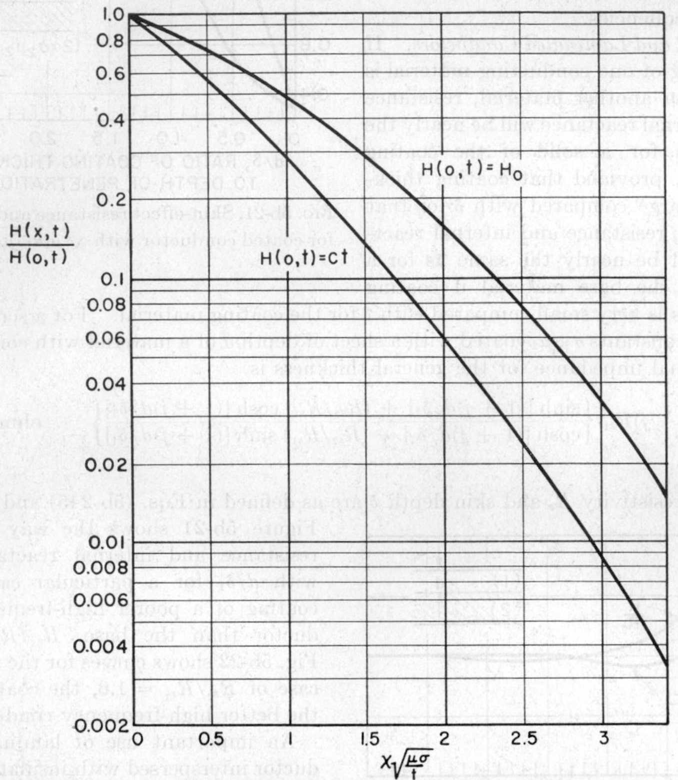

FIG. 5b-23. Penetration of pulsed fields into a conductor. x = depth fron surface, m; t = time, sec; σ = conductivity, mhos/m; μ = permeability, henrys/m. *(From J. R. Whinnery, General Electric Co. Data Folder* 46217, *Oct.* 20, 1942).

positive z, be given without the sheet by $f(t,x,y,z)$. After the sheet is introduced the vector potential in the region of negative z is given by

$$A = \frac{2\sigma}{\mu_v}\frac{\partial}{\partial z}\int_0^\infty f\left(t - \tau, x, y, z - \frac{2\sigma}{\mu_v}\tau\right) d\tau \qquad \text{(5b-262)}$$

The instantaneous rate of dissipation of energy in the sheet is

$$P = \frac{2\sigma}{\mu_v}\int_{-\infty}^{\infty}\int_{-\infty}^{\infty}\left[\frac{\partial^2}{\partial t\,\partial z}\int_0^\infty f_0\left(t - \tau, x, y, -z - \frac{2\sigma}{\mu_v}\tau\right) d\tau\right]_{z=0}^2 dx\,dy \qquad \text{(5b-263)}$$

where f_0 is the component of f parallel to the sheet.

[1] Material supplied by W. R. Smythe.

SPHERICAL SHELL: Let the vector potential at $r = a$ without the shell due to an axially symmetrical field be $\Sigma C_n P_n^1(\cos\theta) f_n(t)$. After the shell is placed at $r = a$, the vector potential inside due to external sources is

$$A_\phi = -\frac{\sigma}{\mu_v a} \sum (2n+1) r^n a^{-n} C_n P_n^1 (\cos\theta) \int_0^\infty f_n(t-\tau) e^{-(2n+1)\sigma\tau/\mu_v a}\, d\tau \quad \text{(5b-264)}$$

The vector potential outside due to internal sources is the same but with $(a/r)^{n+1}$ substituted for $(r/a)^n$. The instantaneous energy-dissipation rate in the shell is

$$P = \frac{4\pi\sigma}{\mu_v^2 a} \sum n(n+1)(2n+1) C_n^2 \left[\frac{\partial}{\partial t} \int_0^\infty f(t-\tau) e^{-(2n+1)\sigma\tau/\mu_v a}\, d\tau\right]^2 \quad \text{(5b-265)}$$

CYLINDRICAL SHELL: Let the vector potential at $\rho = a$ without the shell of sources which consist of currents parallel to the z axis be

$$\Sigma C_n \cos(n\phi + \alpha_n) f_n(t)$$

When the shell is placed at $\rho = a$, the vector potential inside due to external sources is

$$A_z = -\frac{2\sigma}{\mu_v a} \sum n \rho^n a^{-n} C_n \cos(n\phi + \alpha_n) \int_0^\infty f_n(t-\tau) e^{-2n\sigma\tau/\mu_v a}\, d\tau \quad \text{(5b-266)}$$

The vector potential outside due to internal sources is given by writing a/ρ for ρ/a. The instantaneous rate of energy dissipation per unit length is given by

$$P = \frac{4\pi\sigma}{\mu_v^2 a} \sum n^2 C_n^2 \left[\frac{\partial}{\partial t} \int_0^\infty f(t-\tau) e^{-2n\sigma\tau/\mu_v a}\, d\tau\right]^2 \quad \text{(5b-267)}$$

EDDY-CURRENT HEATING OF SPHERE: When the wavelength is very long compared with the radius a of a sphere of conductivity σ and relative permeability $K_m = \mu/\mu_v$ which is placed in a uniform alternating magnetic field of flux density B and angular frequency ω, the rate of energy dissipation is

$$\frac{3\pi a^5 \omega^2 K_m^2 \sigma [1/2u(S+s) - C + c] B^2}{U^2[(pa^2+1)C + (pa^2-1)c - u(S+s)] + Upa^2 u(S-s) + p^2 a^4 (C-c)} \quad \text{(5b-268)}$$

where $U = K_m - 1$, $p = \sigma\mu\omega$, $u = (2p)^{\frac{1}{2}} a$, $S = \sinh u$, $C = \cosh u$, $s = \sin u$, and $c = \cos u$. Note that, when the relative permeability is one, all the terms in the denominator except the last vanish.

SOME SOLID-STATE FORMULAS

5b-16. Electrical Conductivity. In a solid where ohmic conduction occurs, the current density $\mathbf{J}$ is given by

$$\mathbf{J} = \sigma \mathbf{E}$$

where σ is the conductivity and $\mathbf{E}$ the applied electric field. In a homogeneous isothermal crystal σ is a tensor having the symmetry of the crystal. The current density may be written as

$$\mathbf{J} = ne\mathbf{v}_D$$

where n is the density of charge carriers and $\mathbf{v}_D$ is their drift velocity. The drift velocity depends on the distribution function assumed for dynamic equilibrium[1]

[1] See ref. I, chap. IV, also ref. II. General references, given at the end of this section, are designated by roman numerals.

Metals (Free-electron Theory)

$$\sigma = \frac{4}{3}\frac{ne^2\lambda}{(2\pi mkT)^{\frac{1}{2}}} \quad \text{Maxwell-Boltzmann statistics} \tag{5b-269}$$

$$\sigma = \frac{ne^2\lambda(W_F)}{mv(W_F)} \quad \text{Fermi-Dirac statistics} \tag{5b-270}$$

m is the electronic mass, k the Boltzmann constant, λ is the mean free path of the electrons, $\lambda(W_F)$ is a function of the Fermi energy, and $v(W_F)$ is the velocity of the electrons near the Fermi level

$$W_F \cong W_F{}^0\left[1 - \frac{\pi^2}{12}\left(\frac{kT}{W_F{}^0}\right)^2\right]$$

where

$$W_F{}^0 = \frac{\hbar^2}{2m}(3\pi^2 n)^{\frac{2}{3}} = \frac{h^2}{2m}\left(\frac{3n}{8\pi}\right)^{\frac{2}{3}}$$

Equation (5b-269) gives the correct magnitude of the conductivity at room temperature if λ is taken as the interatomic distance; however, the temperature dependence is not T^{-1} as is found by experiment. Equation (5b-270) requires that $\lambda(W_F)$ be 10 to 100 times the interatomic distance to match room-temperature data and approach infinity as $T \to 0$. An empirical relation given by Grüneisen[1]

$$\rho = \frac{1}{\sigma} = AT^5 \int_0^{\theta/T} \frac{x^5\,dx}{(e^x - 1)(1 - e^{-x})}$$

gives the proper temperature dependence for some simple metals.[2]

Semiconductors. When electrons (see Sec. 5e) are the only charge carriers

$$\sigma = \frac{J}{E} = ne\mu_n \tag{5b-271}$$

where n is the density of electrons in the conduction band and $\mu_n = v_D/E$ is the mobility of the electrons. The drift velocity is frequently written

$$\mathbf{v}_D = -\frac{e\tau}{m}\mathbf{E}$$

where τ is mean free time. In terms of τ

$$\mu_n = \frac{e\tau_n}{m_n}$$

and

$$\sigma_n = \frac{ne^2\tau_n}{m_n}$$

If holes are the only charge carriers,

$$\sigma = pe\mu_p = \frac{pe^2\tau_p}{m_p} \tag{5b-272}$$

where p is the density of the holes in the valence band and μ_p is the hole mobility. In a mixed semiconductor (electrons and holes)

$$\sigma = e(n\mu_n + p\mu_p) \tag{5b-273}$$

The values of n, p, and μ depend on both the model used and the temperature.[3] At

[1] E. Grüneisen, *Ann. Physik* **16,** 530 (1933).

[2] For a detailed discussion of the conductivity in metals see ref. I, chap. XV; refs. II, III, and J. Bardeen, *J. Appl. Phys.* **11,** 88 (1940).

[3] See ref. VI, chap. 11.

temperatures for which the Fermi-Dirac statistics can be replaced by the classical case, i.e.,

$$T > \left(\frac{3}{\pi}\right)^{\frac{2}{3}} \frac{h^2}{8km} n^{\frac{2}{3}}$$

Equation (5b-269) may be used for σ in Eqs. (5b-271), (5b-272), and (5b-273) with the proper substitution for n and λ.

Electron Conduction (n Type) *Hole Conduction (p Type)*

$$\sigma = \frac{4}{3} \frac{ne^2\lambda_n}{(2\pi m_n kT)^{\frac{1}{2}}} \qquad \sigma = \frac{4}{3} \frac{pe^2\lambda}{(2\pi m_p kT)^{\frac{1}{2}}} \tag{5b-274}$$

Ionic Conductors. Ionic conductivity, in most cases (see Sec. 5f-6), at high temperatures can be represented by

$$\sigma = \frac{Ne^2D}{kT} e^{-W/kT} = Ae^{-W/kT} \tag{5b-275}$$

The factor A, derived by Einstein,[1] is the contribution to the conductivity from electrolytic migration of a given atom. N is the number of diffusing atoms per cubic centimeter, D is the diffusion coefficient in zero field, and W is the activation energy which depends on the transport mechanism involved in the conduction.

5b-17. Thermoelectric, Thermomagnetic, and Galvanomagnetic Effects. *Thermionic Emission.* The current density of electrons emitted from a metal at a temperature T is

$$J = AT^2(1 - r)e^{-\varphi/kT} \exp\left(-\sqrt{E}\, e^{\frac{3}{2}}/kT\right) \tag{5b-276}$$

where $A = 4\pi mek^2/h^3 = 120$ amp/cm²/deg², r is the reflection coefficient representing the probability that an electron with sufficient energy to exceed the surface barrier will be reflected back, φ is the work function, $\sqrt{E}\, e^{\frac{3}{2}}$ is the maximum potential near the surface due to an electric field E at the surface.

Thompson Coefficient. If a homogeneous conductor carries a current of density J_x and has a uniform temperature gradient dT/dx, then the heat per second developed per unit volume

$$\frac{dH}{dt} = \rho J_x^2 - \sigma_T J_x \frac{dT}{dx}$$

The Thompson coefficient[2] is

$$\sigma_T = -\frac{\pi k^2 T}{3e}\left(\frac{1}{W_F{}^0} + \frac{1}{\lambda}\frac{d\lambda}{dW_F{}^0}\right) \tag{5b-277}$$

A knowledge of the mean free path λ as a function of the energy is required to evaluate σ_T. For example, Sommerfeld and Frank[3] considered the number of free electrons per unit volume to be independent of the temperature and the mean free path of the electrons independent of their velocity. These assumptions give for metals

$$\sigma_T = \frac{2\pi^2 mk^2 T\lambda_B}{3eh^2}$$

where λ_B is the de Broglie wavelength of those electrons which have the critical velocity of the Fermi distribution. Johnson and Lark-Horovitz[4] have calculated the Thompson coefficient for a two-carrier model of a semiconductor for the intrinsic,

[1] F. Seitz, "Physics of Metals," p. 183, McGraw-Hill Book Company, Inc., New York, 1943.

[2] See ref. I, p. 179.

[3] A. Sommerfeld and N. H. Frank, *Revs. Modern Phys.* **3**, 1 (1931).

[4] V. A. Johnson and K. Lark-Horovitz, *Phys. Rev.* **92**, 226 (1953).

impurity, and transition ranges. For the intrinsic range

$$\sigma_T = -\frac{T}{e}\frac{d}{dT}\left\{\frac{2k(b-1)}{b+1}\right\} + \frac{T}{e}\frac{k(b-1)}{b+1}\frac{d}{dT}\left(\frac{-E_g}{2kT}\right)$$

where $b = \mu_n/\mu_p$ and $E_g = E_0 + \alpha T$ is the energy gap at the temperature T.

Absolute Thermoelectric Power. When a temperature gradient is applied to a homogeneous electronic conductor in which no electric current flows, a thermal emf ϵ, called absolute thermoelectric power, is given by

$$\epsilon = \frac{1}{e}\frac{d\bar{\mu}}{dT} \tag{5b-278}$$

where $\bar{\mu}$ is the electrochemical potential of the free electrons. For metals

$$\epsilon = \int_0^T \frac{\sigma_T}{T}\,dT \tag{5b-279}$$

When two conductors form a couple and the temperature difference across the junctions is small, T and $T + dT$, the thermoelectric power Q is given by

$$Q = \int \frac{\sigma_{T_2} - \sigma_{T_1}}{T}\,dT \tag{5b-280}$$

Seebeck Effect. When two metals form a closed circuit through a potentiometer ($J = 0$) and their junctions are maintained at different temperatures T_1 and T_2, a Seebeck emf $\mathcal{E}_s$ results which is given by

$$\mathcal{E}_s = \int_{T_1}^{T_2} (\epsilon_1 - \epsilon_2)\,dT \tag{5b-281}$$

Peltier Effect. When a current I passes through the junction of two conductors, the junction will be heated or cooled. When the current is reversed the junction is cooled or heated. The heat per second at the junction is

$$H_{12} = \Pi_{12} I$$

Π_{12} is called the Peltier coefficient ($\Pi_{21} = -\Pi_{12}$)

$$\Pi_{12} = T\int \frac{\sigma_{T_2} - \sigma_{T_1}}{T}\,dT = T(\epsilon_2 - \epsilon_1) \tag{5b-282}$$

Isothermal Hall Effect. When a magnetic field is applied to a conductor carrying a current density **J**, an electric field $\mathbf{E}_H$ (Hall field) is developed given by the relation

$$\mathbf{E}_H = R\mathbf{J} \times \mathbf{B} \tag{5b-283}$$

R is called the Hall coefficient. When the current density is in the long direction of the sample (J_x) and the field is in the z direction, the Hall coefficient is (see Sec. 5e-2)

$$R = -\frac{1}{ne} = -\frac{\mu}{\sigma} \tag{5b-284}$$

where n = carriers/m³, $e = 1.60 \times 10^{19}$ coulombs, μ = m²/volt sec, and σ = (ohm-m)⁻¹.

The Hall coefficient for a semiconductor depends on the charge carrier involved

$$(n\text{ type})\ R = -\frac{3\pi}{8e}\frac{1}{n} \qquad (p\text{ type})\ R = \frac{3\pi}{8e}\frac{1}{p}$$

$$(\text{mixed})\ R = -\frac{3\pi}{8e}\left[\frac{nb^2 - p}{(nb+p)^2}\right] \tag{5b-285}$$

where $b = \mu_n/\mu_p$. In ferromagnetic materials an effective field

$$\mathbf{H}_{\text{eff}} = \mathbf{H} + 4\pi\alpha\mathbf{M}$$

is substituted for the applied field (see Sec. 5h-12).

Nernst Effect. If a temperature gradient is maintained in an electronic conductor ($\mathbf{J} = 0$) in the presence of a transverse magnetic field a transverse electric field develops which is given by

$$\mathbf{E}_t = Q\nabla T \times \mathbf{H} \tag{5b-286}$$

Q is called the Nernst coefficient. For semiconductors the isothermal Nernst coefficient[1] at temperatures high enough for classical statistics to apply is

$$\begin{array}{cc} (n\ Type) & (p\ Type) \\ Q_n = -\dfrac{3\pi}{16}\dfrac{k}{e}\mu_n & Q_p = -\dfrac{3\pi}{16}\dfrac{k}{e}\mu_p \end{array} \tag{5b-287}$$

Ettingshausen Effect. If a temperature difference is maintained across an electronic conductor perpendicular to a current of density $\mathbf{J}$ in the presence of a magnetic field, a transverse temperature gradient is established. The heat current $q = 0$

$$\nabla_t T = P\mathbf{J} \times \mathbf{H} \tag{5b-288}$$

P is called the Ettingshausen coefficient.

Righi-Leduc Effect. If a difference in temperature is maintained in an electronic conductor in the presence of a magnetic field in which $\mathbf{J} = 0$, a transverse temperature gradient is established

$$\nabla_t T = S\mathbf{H} \times \nabla T \tag{5b-289}$$

S is called the Righi-Leduc coefficient.

Magnetoresistance. The resistance of a metal or semiconductor is altered by the presence of a magnetic field. A calculation[2] of the change in resistance due to the application of a magnetic field, based on the free-electron theory, provides the expression

$$\frac{\Delta\rho}{\rho} = \frac{BH^2}{1 + CH^2} \tag{5b-290}$$

This expression agrees with the form of the experimentally determined curve of $\Delta\rho/\rho$ vs. H, i.e., for low fields $CH^2 \ll 1$

$$\frac{\Delta\rho}{\rho} \sim H^2$$

and for very high fields a saturation is approached

$$\frac{\Delta\rho}{\rho} = A \text{ (const)}$$

The values of B and C in Eq. (5b-290) do not agree quantitatively, indicating that the free-electron theory is too simple.[3]

Cyclotron Resonance of Electrons and Holes. Current carriers in a solid, when accelerated by a microwave electric field perpendicular to an externally applied static

[1] For a summary of thermoelectric and galvanomagnetic formulas for semiconductors, see E. H. Putley, *Proc. Phys. Soc.* (*London*) **B68**, 22, 35 (1955).

[2] See ref. I, p. 184.

[3] For a more extensive treatment, consult the literature. H. Jones and C. Zener, *Proc. Roy. Soc.* (*London*) **145**, 268 (1934); L. David, *Phys. Rev.* **56**, 93(1939); F. Seitz, *Phys. Rev.* **79**, 372 (1950); C. Herring, *Bell System Tech. J.* **34**, 237 (1955).

magnetic field H, will spiral about the magnetic field. Under certain conditions[1] a resonance absorption is observed when the angular frequency of the electron is related to the magnetic field by the cyclotron equation

$$\omega_c = \frac{\pm eH}{m^*c} \tag{5b-291}$$

where the $\pm$ sign refers to the sign of the carrier (+ for holes), m^* is the effective mass, and c is the velocity of light. The technique provides a direct measurement of the effective mass of electrons and holes.

5b-18. Types of Magnetism. *Diamagnetism.* Substances whose magnetic susceptibility

$$\chi = \frac{M}{H}$$

is negative are called diamagnetic. The Langevin-Pauli formula for the diamagnetic susceptibility of an atom is (ref. VIII)

$$\chi = -\frac{Ne^2}{6mc^2} \sum \bar{r}^2 \tag{5b-292}$$

where $\bar{r}^2$ is the mean square distance of the electron from the nucleus and the summation is over all the electrons in the atom.

Paramagnetism. Substances whose magnetic susceptibility is positive are called paramagnetic. Langevin made a classical statistical analysis of an ensemble of dipole moments in thermal equilibrium in a magnetic field. The magnetization is given by

$$M = N\mu L\left(\frac{\mu H}{kT}\right) \tag{5b-293}$$

where N is the number of atoms per unit volume and μ is their dipole moment. The Langevin function is

$$L(a) = \coth a - \frac{1}{a}$$

If $\mu H \ll kT$, the Langevin formula reduces to the Curie law

$$\chi = \frac{N\mu^2}{3kT} = \frac{C}{T} \tag{5b-294}$$

Introduction of the quantum theory into the statistics for atoms with total angular momentum quantum number J gives

$$M = NgJ\mu_B B_J\left(\frac{gJ\mu_B H}{kT}\right) \tag{5b-295}$$

where g is the Landé factor, μ_B is the Bohr magneton, $eh/4\pi mc = -0.927 \times 10^{-20}$ ergs/oersted, and the Brillouin function is

$$B_J(x) = \frac{2J+1}{2J} \coth \frac{(2J+1)x}{2J} - \frac{1}{2J} \coth \frac{x}{2J} \tag{5b-296}$$

For $x \ll 1$ susceptibility becomes

$$\chi = NJ(J+1)\,\frac{g^2\mu_B{}^2}{3kT} \tag{5b-297}$$

Note. The above equations were derived on the assumption that the atoms are free and therefore do not in general apply to solids. For details, see ref. VIII.

[1] G. Dresselhaus, A. F. Kip, and C. Kittel, *Phys. Rev.* **98**, 368 (1955).

Ferromagnetism. Ferromagnetic substances are characterized by the onset of a spontaneous magnetization (in a zero applied field) at temperatures for which $T < Tc$ where Tc is called the Curie temperature.

i. WEISS MOLECULAR FIELD: Consider the magnetic field applied to the dipoles in the Langevin function to consist of the applied field plus an internal field which is proportional to the magnetization. The effective field is

$$H_e = H_a + qM$$

The magnetization is

$$M = N\mu L\left(\frac{H_a + qM}{kT}\right) \tag{5b-298}$$

A nonvanishing solution for M exists for $H_a = 0$ when $T \leq T_c$, where

$$T_c = \frac{N\mu^2 q}{3k} \tag{5b-299}$$

For $T > T_c$ the susceptibility is

$$\chi = \frac{N\mu^2}{3k(T - T_c)} = \frac{C}{T - T_c} \tag{5b-300}$$

This equation is called the Curie-Weiss law. It is usually written

$$\chi = \frac{C}{T - \theta}$$

where θ, called the paramagnetic Curie point, is found by experiment to be slightly larger than T_c when $T \gg T_c$ (see 5h-13).

ii. HEISENBERG EXCHANGE COUPLING: Heisenberg replaces[1] the molecular field assumption with the idea that the interaction between a pair of atoms i and j has the form

$$V_{ij} = -2\mathcal{J}\mathbf{S}_i \cdot \mathbf{S}_j \tag{5b-301}$$

where $\mathbf{S}_i$ and $\mathbf{S}_j$ are quantum-mechanical spin operators and $\mathcal{J}$ is the exchange energy. This problem has not been solved exactly; the most usual approximations are to consider interactions only between nearest neighbors and to assume that all states of the crystal with the same total spin have the same energy. For these approximations, the Heisenberg results can be taken over directly from (i) with the following substitutions:

$$\mu \to g\mu_B S \qquad \mu^2 \to g^2\mu_B{}^2 S(S+1)$$
$$L(x) \to B_S(x)$$
$$q \to \frac{2z\mathcal{J}}{Ng^2\mu_B{}^2}$$

where the z is the number of nearest neighbors of a given atom. These procedures and results usually go by the name of "the first Heisenberg approximation." The literature (see ref. VIII) should be consulted for information about other approximate solutions of the spin-operator problem. The magnetization in this approximation is

$$M = gNS\mu_B B_S(x) \tag{5b-302}$$

where $x = \dfrac{gS\mu_B}{kT}(H + qM)$

The Curie temperature is

$$T_c = \frac{2z\mathcal{J}S(S+1)}{3k} \tag{5b-303}$$

For $T > T_c$

$$\chi = \frac{4N\mu_B{}^2 S(S+1)}{3k(T - T_c)} \tag{5b-304}$$

[1] W. Heisenberg, *Z. Physik* **49**, 619 (1928).

Antiferromagnetism. Antiferromagnetic substances are those in which the magnetic ions can be divided into equivalent sublattices which become spontaneously magnetized in an antiparallel arrangement below some temperature T_c. The antiparallel alignment occurs because of a large negative exchange integral. Van Vleck[1] considered two simple interpenetrating cubic lattices and nearest-neighbor interactions. Call one sublattice A and the other B. The effective field on an ion of lattice A is due to the ions of B; thus

$$H_{e_A} = H_a - qM_B$$
$$H_{e_B} = H_a - qM_A$$

where q is the same as in the ferromagnetic case except that $\mathcal{J}$ is now negative. The susceptibility for $T > T_c$ is

$$\chi = \frac{g^2 N \mu_B{}^2 S(S+1)}{3k(T+\theta)} = \frac{C}{T+\theta} \tag{5b-305}$$

where $\theta = cT_c$ and $c = 1$ for the simple model.[2] The susceptibility below the Curie temperature for this simple model consists of two parts; the susceptibility parallel ($\chi_\parallel$) and perpendicular ($\chi_\perp$) to the antiferromagnetic axis. $\chi_\parallel$ decreases and becomes zero as $T \to 0$; thus the susceptibility at absolute zero is

$$\chi_{T=0} = \tfrac{2}{3}\chi_{T=T_c} \tag{5b-306}$$

Ferrimagnetism. Ferrimagnetic substances are those in which the magnetic ions can be divided into nonequivalent sublattices which become spontaneously magnetized in an antiparallel arrangement below some temperature T_c. A ferrite, i.e., $NiFe_2O_4$, is used as an example. It is a spinel structure having a close-packed cubic oxygen lattice in which there are 8 tetrahedral and 16 octahedral sites occupied by magnetic ions. The sites are labeled A and B, respectively. Néel,[3] using the Weiss theory, gave the effective fields at the A and B sites as

$$H_A = H_a + \gamma_{AA}M_A - \gamma_{AB}M_B$$
$$H_B = H_a - \gamma_{AB}M_A + \gamma_{BB}M_B$$

where

$$\gamma_{ij} = \frac{2z_{ij}\mathcal{J}_{ij}}{N_j g^2 \mu_B{}^2}$$

z_{ij} is the number of nearest neighbors on the j sublattice to an atom on the i sublattice, $\mathcal{J}_{ij}$ is the exchange coupling between the electrons of those atoms, and N_j is the total number of magnetic ions on the j sublattice.

For $T > T_c$

$$\chi = \frac{C}{T - T_c}\,\frac{T-\theta'}{T-T_c'} \tag{5b-307}$$

where $C = \dfrac{Ng^2\mu_B{}^2S(S+1)}{3k}$ $\qquad \lambda = \dfrac{N_A}{N} \qquad \mu = \dfrac{N_B}{N}$

$$T_c = \tfrac{1}{2}C[\lambda\gamma_{AA} + \mu\gamma_{BB} + \sqrt{(\lambda\gamma_{AA} - \mu\gamma_{BB})^2 + 4\lambda\mu\gamma_{AB}{}^2}]$$
$$T_c' = \tfrac{1}{2}C[\lambda\gamma_{AA} + \mu\gamma_{BB} - \sqrt{(\lambda\gamma_{AA} - \mu\gamma_{BB})^2 + 4\lambda\mu\gamma_{AB}{}^2}]$$
$$\theta' = \lambda\mu C[\gamma_{AA} + \gamma_{BB} + 2\gamma_{AB}]$$

For $T < T_c$

[1] J. H. Van Vleck, *J. Chem. Phys.* **9,** 85 (1941).
[2] For other models, see J. Samuel Smart, *Phys. Rev.* **86,** 968 (1952).
[3] L. Néel, *Ann. Phys.* **3,** 137 (1948).

$$M_A = N_A g \mu_B S y_A \qquad M_B = N_B g \mu_B S y_B \tag{5b-308}$$

where $y_A = B_S \dfrac{Ng^2\mu_B{}^2S^2}{3kT}(\lambda\gamma_{AA}y_A - \mu\gamma_{AB}y_B)$

$$y_B = B_S \frac{Ng^2\mu_B{}^2S}{3kT}(-\lambda\gamma_{AB}y_A + \mu\gamma_{BB}y_B)$$

where $B_S(x)$ is the Brillouin function.

5b-19. Gyromagnetic Effects. *Gyromagnetic Ratio.* The magnetic moment of an amperian current loop is proportional to its angular momentum

$$\boldsymbol{\mu} = \frac{g'e}{2mc}\mathbf{j} = \gamma'\mathbf{j} \tag{5b-309}$$

or summed over an entire body

$$\mathbf{M} = \gamma'\mathbf{J} \tag{5b-310}$$

where **J** is the total angular momentum corresponding to the magnetic moment **M**. A change in either **J** or **M** produces a corresponding change in the other.

BARNETT[1] EFFECT: Change of magnetization by rotation.

EINSTEIN–DE HASS EFFECT:[2] Change of rotation by magnetization.

Measurements by these methods yields values of $g' \leq 2$ indicating that the electron spin is the predominant source of magnetism. Kittel (see ref. IV) gives the relation $g - 2 \cong 2 - g'$, where g is the spectroscopic splitting factor.

Spin Resonance. A substance with a magnetic moment in a static magnetic field H will absorb energy from an oscillating magnetic field of small intensity at right angles to the static field. The peak of the absorption curve occurs at the angular frequency

$$\omega = \frac{2\pi g\mu H}{h} = \gamma H \tag{5b-311}$$

where μ is the appropriate unit for the magnetic moment and g is the spectroscopic splitting factor.

PROTONS. μ is the nuclear magneton $\mu_P = eh/4\pi M_P c$ and $g = 5.58$

$$\frac{\omega}{2\pi} = \nu\ (\text{kc/sec}) = 4.26H\ (\text{oersteds}) \tag{5b-312}$$

FREE ELECTRONS:

$$\mu = \mu_B \quad \text{and} \quad g = 2$$

$$\nu\ (\text{Mc/sec}) = 2.80H\ (\text{oersteds}) \tag{5b-313}$$

PARAMAGNETIC SALTS:[3] The equation of motion, treating the body as a whole, may be obtained[4] by the use of Eq. (5b-310), $\mathbf{M} = \gamma\mathbf{J}$, and the torque $d\mathbf{J}/dt = \mathbf{M} \times \mathbf{H}$,

$$\frac{d\mathbf{M}}{dt} = \gamma(\mathbf{M} \times \mathbf{H}) \tag{5b-314}$$

where the components of **H** are

$$H_x = 2H_1 \cos \omega t \qquad H_y = 0 \qquad H_z = \text{static field}$$

the amplitude of the oscillatory field is small compared with the static field, and the resonance frequency is

$$\omega_0 = \gamma H_z \tag{5b-315}$$

[1] S. J. Barnett, *Revs. Modern Phys.* **7**, 129 (1935).
[2] A. Einstein and W. J. de Hass, *Verhandl. deut. physik. Ges.* **17**, 152 (1915).
[3] For metals, see Freeman J. Dyson, *Phys. Rev.* **98**, 349 (1955).
[4] F. Bloch, *Phys. Rev.* **70**, 460 (1946).

FERROMAGNETIC RESONANCE: Kittel[1] has shown that the above equations hold for ferromagnetic resonance if all demagnetizing effects are included. For example, the resonance frequency becomes

$$\omega = \gamma (BH)^{\frac{1}{2}} \tag{5b-316}$$

for a specimen in the form of a thin disk with the static field parallel to the disk.

ANTIFERROMAGNETIC RESONANCE: Above the Curie temperature, paramagnetic resonance is found. Below the Curie temperature, the effective field[2] becomes

$$H_{\text{eff}} = [H_A(2H_E + H_A)]^{\frac{1}{2}} \tag{5b-317}$$

where H_A is the effective anisotropy field of one sublattice and H_E is the exchange field.

FERRIMAGNETIC RESONANCE: The individual sublattices must be considered in the resonance equation. An effective splitting factor[3] for the combined sublattices is given by

$$g_{\text{eff}} \frac{e}{2mc} = \frac{|\mathbf{M}|}{|\mathbf{S}|} = \frac{|\Sigma \mathbf{M}_i|}{|\Sigma(\mathbf{M}_i/\gamma_i)|} \tag{5b-318}$$

where M_i is the magnetization of the individual sublattice and $\gamma_i = g_i(e/2mc)$ describes its gyromagnetic ratio.

General References

I. Seitz, F.: "The Modern Theory of Solids," McGraw-Hill Book Company, Inc., New York, 1940.
II. Wilson, A. H.: "Theory of Metals," 2d ed., Cambridge University Press, New York, 1953.
III. Mott, N. F., and H. Jones: "Theory of the Properties of Metals and Alloys," Oxford University Press, New York, 1936.
IV. Kittel, C.: "Introduction to Solid State Physics," John Wiley & Sons, Inc., New York, 1953.
V. Mott, N. F., and R. W. Gurney: "Electronic Processes in Ionic Crystals," 2d ed., Oxford University Press, New York, 1948.
VI. Shockley, W.: "Electrons and Holes in Semiconductors," D. Van Nostrand Company, Inc., New York, 1950.
VII. Lark-Horovitz, Karl: The New Electronics, "The Present State of Physics," AAAS, Washington, D.C., 1954.
VIII. Van Vleck, J. H.: "The Theory of Electric and Magnetic Susceptibilities," Oxford University Press, New York, 1932.
IX. Bozorth, Richard M.: "Ferromagnetism," D. Van Nostrand Company, Inc., New York, 1951.

[1] C. Kittel, *Phys. Rev.* **71,** 270 (1947); **73,** 155 (1948).
[2] C. Kittel, *Phys. Rev.* **82,** 565 (1951).
[3] Roald K. Wangsness, *Phys. Rev.* **93,** 68 (1954).

5c. Electrical Standards

F. K. HARRIS

The National Bureau of Standards

5c-1. Fundamental Considerations. The standards in terms of which electrical quantities are evaluated are derived from absolute measurements which serve to establish the magnitudes of the electrical units in terms of the basic mechanical units. The relations between the fundamental mechanical units and the electrical units derived from them are required to satisfy two conditions: (1) the electrical watt should equal the mechanical watt; and (2) in a rationalized system the unit of resistance must be such as to make the wave impedance of free space numerically equal to $\mu_v c$, where μ_v is the conventionally assigned value of the permeability of free space and c is the velocity of the electromagnetic wave.[1] The first condition fixes the *product* of the volt and the ampere (the watt), while the second fixes their *quotient* (the ohm).

Two types of absolute measurements have been used in assigning values to the electrical units. In one type of experiment an inductor (either self or mutual) is constructed of such form that its inductance can be computed from its measured dimensions together with the conventionally assumed permeability of the space around it. This inductor is then supplied with a periodically varying current, and its reactance at the known frequency is compared with the resistance of a standard resistor.[2] In this *absolute ohm* experiment a value is assigned to the resistor in terms of length, frequency, and permeability.

In a second type of experiment, a pair of coils is so arranged that the force or torque exerted between them when they carry a current can be measured accurately. This arrangement is called a *current balance.* The current, thus measured in absolute amperes, is passed through a resistor whose value is known in absolute ohms. The resulting voltage drop is opposed to the electromotive force of a standard cell, and its emf is determined in *absolute volts.*[3]

Values having been assigned to physical standards of resistance and voltage on the basis of absolute measurements, the values of the other electrical units can be derived from them using appropriate relationships. Thus the *ohm* and *volt* become the basic units of electrical measurement, and their physical embodiments in resistance coils and standard cells become the fundamental electrical standards.

5c-2. History of Electrical Standards. The British Association ohm (1864), resulting from the work of a committee under the leadership of Maxwell, represented the first concerted attempt by a responsible organization to realize an electrical standard based on absolute measurements correlating a mechanical and electrical system of units. At that time the Daniell cell was commonly used as the standard of emf. Later the Clark cell (1872) and its modification by Lord Rayleigh (1884) were used. Still more recently (by international agreement in 1908) the cadmium

[1] F. B. Silsbee, *Instruments* **26,** 1522 (1953).
[2] Thomas, Peterson, Cooter, and Kotter, *J. Research Natl. Bur. Standards* **43,** 291 (1949).
[3] Curtis, Driscoll, and Critchfield, *J. Research Natl. Bur. Standards* **28,** 133 (1942).

cell, invented by Weston (1891), has entirely replaced the Clark cell and is in use today as the standard of emf.

Although the assignment of values to electrical standards on the basis of an absolute system of units has been generally recognized as desirable since the initial proposal of the British Association, the difficulties encountered in absolute measurements led to rather large uncertainties in the values of the standards. This resulted in the adoption (1894) of an auxiliary set known as the "international" units, which were a "reasonable approximation" of the absolute units and which could, it was hoped, be experimentally reproduced with sufficient accuracy for measurement purposes. These units were defined by the resistance of a uniform column of mercury of specified length and mass, and by the current required for the deposition of silver at a specified rate from a silver nitrate solution. The units defined in terms of the "mercury" ohm and the "silver" ampere could be established easily within a few hundredths of a per cent, but presently there was need for greater accuracy in measurements. Fortunately the techniques needed in absolute measurement also improved and it became possible to establish values of the electrical units within about 10 parts in a million by absolute methods.

Accordingly, on Jan. 1, 1948, the "international" system of units was formally abandoned and the "absolute" system was universally adopted. This required small changes in the values assigned to the various units, because of differences between the magnitudes of the "international" units last assigned in 1910 and the newly determined "absolute" units. Table 5c-1 may be used to compute the value in "absolute" units of any quantity that is known in the "international" units used in the United States. Corresponding tables based on the "international" units maintained by other countries would be slightly different because each country maintained its own standards, and small differences developed over the years between the units of one country and another.

TABLE 5c-1. UNITED STATES VALUES

1 international ohm = 1.000495 absolute ohms
1 international volt = 1.000330 absolute volts
1 international ampere = 0.999835 absolute ampere
1 international coulomb = 0.999835 absolute coulomb
1 international henry = 1.000495 absolute henrys
1 international farad = 0.999505 absolute farad
1 international watt = 1.000165 absolute watts
1 international joule = 1.000165 absolute joules

5c-3. Maintenance of the Electrical Units. The National Bureau of Standards in Washington, D.C., is assigned the task of maintaining the electrical units defined by an Act of Congress and used in science and technology in the United States. It also plays an active part in disseminating accurate values of the various electrical quantities by the measurement and certification of electrical standards belonging to other laboratories.[1]

The absolute measurements which are made to assign values to the ohm and the volt require much care and skill and are so time-consuming that they can be justified only at intervals of several years. In the intervals between absolute measurements, values of the ohm and volt are maintained by groups of wire-wound resistors and of standard cells. These groups constitute the *primary* electrical standards of the country and, in effect, all values of the various electrical quantities are derived from them.

[1] This service is voluntary on the part of the organization requesting certification, as the bureau has no police powers. Also, with certain exceptions, a fee is charged covering the cost of certification.

5c-4. Standards of Resistance. The *primary* standard of resistance in the United States is a group of ten 1-ohm resistors of special construction. The present group comprising the primary standard are of the Thomas[1] type, made in 1933. They were wound of No. 12 Awg manganin wire, vacuum annealed at 550°C, and sealed in air in double-walled containers. The individual members of the group are intercompared annually. The maximum net change in any member of the group, with respect to the group average, has been 3.7 parts per million and the average change 1.2 ppm during the 22 years (to 1955) that have elapsed since the group was set up. They can be intercompared or can be compared with other similar standards to about one part in 10^7. By suitable comparisons (successively in series and in parallel) ratios of resistance can be established to a few parts in 10^7, and the primary group of standards can be used to extend the range of measurement to higher and lower values of resistance.

Secondary standards of resistance can be calibrated (or assigned values) stepwise from the primary group up to a maximum of perhaps 1 megohm, and to a minimum of 10 microhms or less. Almost without exception manganin is used as the alloy in resistance standards, as sheet material for resistors of low value and wire for resistors of high value. Manganin has two advantages in this application: (1) its temperature coefficient of resistance at ordinary room temperatures is very low, a few parts in 10^6, and (2) its thermal emf against copper is small, 2 to 3 μv per degree centigrade. Manganin is, however, a strain-sensitive material, and also it oxidizes to some extent at ordinary temperatures. Hence the stability of a resistance standard depends on its construction, the extent to which initial strains have been relieved by annealing, its freedom from strain in use, and its protection from air and moisture. These factors vary considerably for standards of various types and values. The construction used in the Thomas-type standards which make up the primary group probably represents the best approach yet made to the ideal: the complete elimination of initial strain by a high-temperature anneal; practically strain-free mounting in use; a reasonably large ratio of volume to surface area; and protection by sealing from atmospheric effects. The stability of these standards is better by a factor of 10 or even 100 times than that of the usual resistance standard. No general statement is possible concerning the stability of standards, except that those of higher value are usually less stable, because of both more unrelieved strain and more exposed surface area per unit volume of the material.

5c-5. Standards of Electromotive Force. The *primary* standard consists of a group of 47 saturated cadmium (Weston) cells which are maintained at a temperature of 28°C, held constant to within 0.01°C. Of these cells, 33 are of the acid type, sulfuric acid being present in the electrolyte at a concentration of 0.03–0.05N. The remainder of the group are neutral in the sense that no acid has been added. The presence of acid prevents hydrolysis of the mercurous sulfate in the cell and decreases the solvent action of the electrolyte on the glass container. Thus it contributes to the constancy of emf of the cell. However, the emf of an acid cell is lower than that of a neutral cell by an amount proportional to the concentration of the acid (30 μv for 0.05 normal acid).[2] Of the cells which make up the primary standard, 12 have been in the group since 1906 and 2 since 1913. Of the remainder 7 made in 1932, and 26 made in 1949 were added in 1955. New cells are made periodically, employing carefully purified materials, and are used to supplement the primary group.[3] The cells of the primary standard are intercompared periodically and the group average is used as the

[1] Thomas, *J. Research Natl. Bur. Standards* **5**, 295 (1930); **36**, 107 (1946).

[2] The initial small decrease of emf usually observed in a neutral cell during the first few months after it is made is believed to result from the formation of acid in the electrolyte.

[3] These supplementary groups are kept under the same conditions as the primary group and are regularly compared with them. Thus, if a cell in the primary group should fail, another cell having a known history of constancy could be used to replace it.

standard of emf. An international intercomparison made in 1955 indicated that, at that time, the United States standard differed by 0.7 μv from that maintained by the International Bureau of Weights and Measures at Sevres, France.

Secondary standards of emf may be cadmium cells of either the saturated or unsaturated type. Most modern cells, both saturated and unsaturated, are of the "acid" type, containing sulfuric acid at a normality of about 0.05. Saturated cells maintain a more nearly constant emf over long periods of time than do unsaturated cells and are being used to an increasing extent as reference standards by many laboratories. The temperature coefficient of emf of the saturated cell is considerably larger than that of the unsaturated cell, and its temperature must be held constant to within about 0.02°C if the emf is to be constant to 1 μv. Temperature control for saturated cells may be maintained by a thermostatically regulated oil bath or air bath. If oil is used it should be clear, of medium viscosity, acid-free, and without appreciable vapor pressure. An air bath for maintaining standard cells at a constant temperature[1] is used in a number of laboratories. It consists of a thick-walled aluminum box which is enclosed by and thermally insulated from a second aluminum box. The outer box is again protected by thermal insulation and is maintained at a constant temperature somewhat above ambient (usually about 35°C ± 0.01). Temperature fluctuations within the inner compartment are attenuated to less than 0.001°C. The international formula (adopted in 1908) relating the emf of a saturated cadmium cell to its temperature is

$$E_t = E_{20} - 0.000040(t - 20) - 0.00000095(t - 20)^2 + 0.00000001(t - 20)^3$$

where E_t is the emf at temperature t and E_{20} is the emf at 20°C. This formula is stated to apply to either acid or neutral cells, and holds to within 1 μv for temperatures between 0 and 40°C.

Unsaturated cells (becoming saturated at 4°C) are used almost universally as working standards of emf in this country.[2] Their temperature coefficient of emf (approximately −5 μv/°C) is much lower than that of the saturated cell; and they will withstand parcel-post or express shipment (the solid electrode material being held in place by porous plugs) whereas saturated cells cannot be shipped but must be hand-carried. However, the emf of unsaturated cells generally decreases with time, usually between 50 and 100 μv per year, so that their life span is limited to about 10 years. Because of this change of emf with time, it is advisable that unsaturated cells be checked periodically against a stable standard. For accurate work they should be certified once a year, and discarded when their emf has dropped to 1.0183 volts.

Certain precautions should always be observed in using standard cells.

1. They should be protected from large or sudden changes in temperature, because of the large temporary change in emf that accompanies a sudden temperature change. This "hysteresis" and the cell's recovery time vary considerably in different cells. Its cause is not understood, but there is evidence that the effect is larger in old than in new cells.

2. Cells should not be exposed to nearby sources of heat that may produce temperature inequalities in the two limbs. This would cause a large change in emf since the temperature coefficients of the individual electrodes are quite large (one positive and one negative) and annul each other only if their temperatures are equal. Many cells are equipped with a copper-lined protective case to reduce temperature inequalities between the limbs.

3. Temperatures above 40°C and below 4°C should be avoided. The 10 per cent amalgam generally used in cells solidifies at a temperature slightly below this lower

[1] Mueller and Stimson, *J. Research Natl. Bur. Standards* **13**, 699 (1933).

[2] Saturated cells are used extensively for this purpose in Great Britain.

limit and gives rise to abnormal changes in emf, while the cadmium sulfate has a transition point only a little higher (at 43.6°C) than the recommended upper limit. The monohydrate formed at the transition temperature is undesirable and persists as a metastable form when the temperature is again lowered.

4. The elements of a cell should not be exposed to strong light, as the mercurous sulfate is photosensitive. Cells with exposed elements usually have a band of black paint covering the mercurous sulfate layer.

5. The internal resistance of a standard cell is about 500 ohms in the high-resistance type, and 100 ohms in the low-resistance type. The latter should be used with a deflection potentiometer. Loss of sensitivity in potentiometer measurements, which is traced to the standard-cell circuit, may indicate the presence of a gas bubble forming in the negative limb of the cell. Such a cell should be discarded.

6. Current drawn from a cell which is used as an emf standard should be kept small and should be drawn only for very short periods of time, a few seconds at most. Currents should never exceed 100 μa. A standard cell that has been short-circuited may be presumed to have been permanently damaged, and should be discarded. Laboratory conditions should be avoided which will result in moisture condensation on the cell case and a lowering of the insulation resistance between terminals.

7. Cells which have been shipped or otherwise roughly handled may not be dependable. A recovery period of a week should be allowed before the cell is used as a reference standard.

8. The emf of an unsaturated cell should be checked periodically. When it falls to 1.0183 the cell should be discarded, as it is no longer a reliable standard.

5c-6. Capacitance Standards. Capacitors whose values can be computed accurately from their measured dimensions are necessarily small, perhaps 150 picofarads[1] at most. Their geometry must be simple: concentric spheres, coaxial cylinders, or parallel plates. The dielectric is usually air. The problem is complicated by the fact that solid dielectric must be used to support one or both electrodes of the system. The presence of solid dielectric in the electric field of the capacitor precludes its exact computation and introduces losses so that the current does not lead the impressed voltage by exactly 90 deg in a-c applications. These complications can be largely avoided by appropriate design, using a three-electrode guard-ring capacitor with the solid insulation so located that it is not exposed to the field of the working capacitor. The coplanarity of the guarded electrode with its guard ring is critical in a computable standard because a displacement of this electrode results in the exposure of a sharp edge with consequent field concentration. Moon[2] has built a series of computable parallel-plate guard-ring capacitors in the range from 5 to 0.1 picofarads, and

[1] A list of prefixes, sponsored by the International Union of Physics and approved by the International Electrotechnical Commission (05-35-080 in IEC Publication 80), which represent the most common powers of 10 has been accepted in several countries and is used somewhat in the United States. The prefixes and the corresponding powers of 10 are given in the table below.

Prefix	Value	Prefix	Value
Tera	10^{12}	Deci	10^{-1}
Giga	10^{9}	Centi	10^{-2}
Mega	10^{6}	Milli	10^{-3}
Kilo	10^{3}	Micro	10^{-6}
Hecto	10^{2}	Nano	10^{-9}
Deka	10^{1}	Pico	10^{-12}

[2] Moon and Sparks, *J. Research Natl. Bur. Standards* **41**, 497 (1948).

has estimated that his accuracy was limited to 0.1 per cent for the 1-pf capacitor by the accuracy with which mechanical dimensions could be measured. Taking advantage of the fact that the field is concentrated at an exposed sharp edge, he also constructed a series of computable "guard-well" capacitors[1] in which the working electrode is recessed behind the plane of the guard ring. In this construction the capacitance is a function of the depth of the recess, and the capacitance can be as small as desired while linear dimensions remain large enough for precise construction and measurement. Moon estimated that the uncertainty in his guard-well capacitors was 0.5 per cent at 0.01 pf and 2 per cent at 0.001 pf.

Air capacitors consisting of groups of interleaved parallel plates have been built for use as secondary standards up to 0.01 μf; and adjustable air capacitors (up to about 10^3 pf) in which a group of movable parallel plates rotates with respect to a group of fixed interleaved parallel plates. The values of such capacitors can be determined stepwise by comparison with computable standards in a suitable capacitance bridge or may be determined in terms of resistance and frequency in a Maxwell bridge. The losses (and hence the phase-defect angles), which are always small in such capacitors, depend largely on the extent to which solid dielectric is present in the working field, and to a very much lesser extent[2] on the presence of surface films on the electrodes. The accuracy of adjustable air capacitors depends on the closeness with which the angular position of the movable plates with respect to the fixed plates can be set and reproduced, and on the quality of the bearings on which the electrode system rotates.

Solid-dielectric capacitors, in which thin mica sheets are interleaved with metal foil, are used as working standards up to about 1 μf. The assembly is impregnated with wax to eliminate voids and air pockets and is compressed through massive end plates to squeeze out excess wax. The quality and constancy of such a standard depends critically on the construction, being a function of the assembly pressure as well as the quality of the mica. Absorption and losses are always present in such capacitors. The phase-defect angles of the best mica capacitors may amount to 1 to 2 minutes throughout the audio-frequency range, and their capacitance values may be expected to remain constant within 0.01 or 0.02 per cent over a period of many years. Mica is the only solid dielectric material that has been successfully used in standard capacitors.

5c-7. Inductance Standards. Self and mutual inductors, whose values may be computed from measured dimensions, have been built at the National Bureau of Standards and at other national laboratories for use in absolute-ohm measurements. Computable self-inductors are single-layer solenoids wound on marble, porcelain, low-expansion-glass, or fused-silica forms. In some instances an accurate screw thread has been cut into the cylindrical form to control the spacing of the winding.[3] Computable mutual inductors have been built following a design of Campbell[4] or Wenner's modification[5] of it. In each of these designs the primary consists of single-layer helical windings on a marble or porcelain cylinder, the sections of the winding being spaced in such a way that a relatively large annular space is available around the central portion of the cylinder, within which the field is very small. The multilayer secondary winding is located in this space, and since the field is small, the exact location of the secondary becomes relatively less critical. Such mutual inductors can be computed as accurately as can the self-inductance standards. However, both types of inductor, apart from being very difficult and expensive to build and compute,

[1] Snow, *J. Research Natl. Bur. Standards* **42**, 287 (1949).
[2] Koops, *Philips Tech. Rev.* **5**, 300 (1940).
[3] Curtis, Moon, and Sparks, *J. Research Natl. Bur. Standards* **21**, 371 (1938).
[4] Campbell, *Proc. Roy. Soc.* (*London*), ser. A, **79**, 428 (1907).
[5] Thomas, Peterson, Cooter, and Kotter, *J. Research Natl. Bur. Standards* **43**, 325 (1949).

have relatively low time constants and are not generally useful for work outside the special field (absolute measurements) for which they are designed.

Self-inductance standards for laboratory work are usually multilayer coils of such shape that their inductance is maximum for a given size and length of wire.[1] Their accurate computation from measured dimensions is not possible and their values are usually established from electrical measurements in terms of other inductors, or a combination of resistance and capacitance. Laboratory mutual inductors also are usually designed to achieve a maximum time constant.

Higher inductance in a given volume or with a given amount of copper can be obtained if the winding is on a core of high-permeability material. Special ferromagnetic alloys are used for this purpose in sheet or strip form, or as a bonded granular or powder material. The gain in time constant is achieved at the expense of some nonlinearity in the inductor, since the permeability of the core is a function of the current in the winding. Also increased losses are to be expected from eddy currents and from hysteresis in the iron. By proper construction and the use of suitable core materials, these defects can be kept small, so that "iron-cored" inductance standards of moderate accuracy and stability are practicable.

Inductors wound as multilayer cylindrical coils of rectangular cross section, to achieve maximum time constant, set up an external field and, conversely, are subject to "pickup" from stray fields in which they are placed. These effects are considerably reduced by dividing the coil into two equal sections wound in opposite directions so that the emfs induced in them by a changing external field tend to cancel. Such an arrangement is called *astatic*. A much greater degree of astaticism is attained when the coil is toroidal, with the winding uniformly distributed around the torus.

Adjustable standards of self and mutual inductance are of two general kinds: the cross-coil type, in which the plane of a movable coil is turned to make various angles with the plane of the fixed coil; and the parallel-coil type, in which the plane of the movable coil is always parallel to the plane of the fixed coil. A familiar example of the cross-coil type is the Ayrton and Perry inductometer, in which the fixed and movable coils are zones of concentric spheres, with the movable coil pivoted on the common polar axis. Probably the best example of the parallel-coil type is the Brooks inductometer with three pairs of link-shaped coils, designed to provide a uniform scale over most of its range. The coil dimensions are such that, at the maximum reading, the conditions for maximum time constant are approximately met. Also, the system is arranged to be nearly astatic. The rotor, holding the movable pair of coils, turns on a shaft between pairs of fixed parallel coils. The coils are all connected in series when the instrument is used as a self-inductor, and for use as a mutual inductor the circuits of the fixed and movable coils are separated.

All inductors are to some extent frequency-sensitive as a result of distributed self-capacitance, eddy currents, and imperfect insulation between turns and layers of the winding. The effect of distributed capacitance is to increase both the effective resistance and inductance above their low-frequency values. At values well below resonance the following formulas hold approximately:

$$R_{\text{eff}} = R_0(1 + 2\omega^2 L_0 C) \quad \text{and} \quad L_{\text{eff}} = L_0(1 + \omega^2 L_0 C)$$

where R_0 and L_0 are the values at zero frequency, and C is the equivalent capacitance considered to be connected across the terminals of the inductor. The effect of eddy currents is to increase the effective resistance and to decrease the effective inductance in accordance with the following formulas:

$$R_{\text{eff}} = R_0 + \frac{M^2 \rho \omega^2}{\rho^2 + l^2\omega^2} \quad \text{and} \quad L_{\text{eff}} = L_0 - \frac{M^2 l \omega^2}{\rho^2 + l^2\omega^2}$$

[1] Brooks, *J. Research Natl. Bur. Standards* **7**, 293 (1931).

where ρ and l are, respectively, the equivalent resistance and self-inductance of the eddy-current circuit, and M is its coupling with the inductor. The effect of imperfect insulation (equivalent to a shunt resistance across the terminals of the inductor) is to decrease the effective inductance. However, it may increase or decrease the effective resistance[1] depending on conditions. If the leakage resistance ρ is very high compared with the coil resistance, the following formulas hold:

$$L_{\text{eff}} = L_0\left(1 - \frac{\omega^2 L_0{}^2}{\rho^2}\right) \quad \text{and} \quad R_{\text{eff}} = R_0\left(1 + \frac{\omega^2 L_0{}^2}{R_0\rho}\right)$$

It must be borne in mind that ρ is the a-c resistance of the insulation and therefore may itself be a function of frequency.

5c-8. Frequency Standards. All standards of frequency are derived from the standard of time, the second, which is derived in turn from the motion of the earth. The standard second is the 1/86,400 part of a mean solar day, the average interval (throughout the year) between passages of the sun through a given meridian. The United States Naval Observatory checks and regulates the standard of time from observations of the passage of fixed stars through the vertical meridian.

The *primary* standard of frequency is a 100-kc quartz-crystal oscillator maintained under constant temperature and pressure conditions by the National Bureau of Standards. It is checked for constancy by using it to operate a clock that is compared with Naval Observatory time. A large number of frequencies are obtained from this crystal through multiplier and divider circuits. Standard frequencies, monitored against the primary standard, are continuously broadcast from the NBS radio transmitter WWV at Beltsville, Md., near Washington, D.C.[2] These frequencies include 2.5, 5, 10, 15, and 25 Mc/sec, each modulated at 440 cps (A above middle C on the international musical scale) or at 600 cps. These audio frequencies are given in alternate 5-min periods. In addition, second signals are given on each carrier frequency, consisting of a 5-cycle pulse at a frequency of 1 kc. This pulse is omitted at the beginning of the last second of each minute. The second signals are accurate to 1 μsec, and the standard frequencies (including the audio frequencies) to 1 part in 50 million.[3]

Quartz crystals are used in vast numbers to control the frequencies of oscillators throughout much of the radio spectrum, in both measurement and communication applications. Their constancy depends on the closeness with which their temperature and pressure are controlled.

Tuning forks may be used as laboratory standards at power and audio frequencies. A precision fork, operating at a constant temperature, may have a frequency that is stable to 10 ppm and, when corrected for barometric pressure, to 1 ppm. A battery-driven fork without temperature control may have a temperature coefficient less than −0.015 per cent/°C, and a voltage coefficient less than 0.01 per cent/volt. It should provide a frequency known to better than 0.1 per cent under any specified laboratory condition.

The frequency of 60-cps power in most localities affords a convenient reference point. However, even where power is supplied from a network that includes generating sta-

[1] Campbell and Childs, "Measurement of Inductance, Capacitance, and Frequency," p. 191, D. Van Nostrand Company, Inc., New York, 1935.

[2] Standard frequencies and time signals are also broadcast from the bureau's auxiliary station WWVH in Hawaii. Signals either from Beltsville or from Hawaii can usually be received anywhere in the world.

[3] This is the error in transmission. The error in reception may amount instantaneously to as much as 1 ppm as a result of motions of reflecting layers of the ionosphere. The standard oscillators by which the broadcast frequencies are monitored are themselves accurate to 3 parts in 10^9, actually more nearly constant than the rate of rotation of the earth itself.

tions over an area of many hundreds of square miles, the frequency is not continuously held precisely to 60 cps. It may depart by as much as 0.1 or 0.2 cps, occasionally even more. Also the frequency can be corrected only very slowly because of the large inertia of the system, perhaps as much as half an hour being required. The average frequency will be very close to 60 cps over an extended time period and synchronous clocks will usually keep time within a few seconds. However, a commercial power source cannot be reliably employed as a frequency standard to much better than 1 per cent.

5c-9. Deflecting Instruments. Instruments customarily used for the measurement of current, voltage, or power are made in a number of accuracy classes. The best grades, called "laboratory standards" may be in the $\frac{1}{10}$ (or $\frac{1}{20}$) per cent class, meaning that, over the useful part of the scale, no marked point is in error by more than $\frac{1}{10}$ (or $\frac{1}{20}$) per cent of the full-scale value. These are large instruments and must be carefully leveled to ensure good performance. Smaller portable instruments are made in accuracy classes of 0.2, 0.5, and $\frac{3}{4}$ per cent. The class of an instrument is usually stated in the maker's catalogue. Switchboard instruments are generally in a 1 per cent class, and panel instruments in the 1, 2, or even 5 per cent class. D-c ammeters and voltmeters are almost universally permanent-magnet moving-coil instruments, while the construction of a-c instruments depends on the intended application. Moving-iron or electrodynamic instruments are used at power frequencies and, if suitably compensated, in the lower audio-frequency range. Thermocouple ammeters are useful from low frequencies up to many megacycles per second, while thermocouple voltmeters are generally applicable only at power and audio frequencies unless they have special multipliers designed for high-frequency operation. Electrostatic voltmeters have no frequency limitations other than that imposed by low impedance at very high frequencies, and many vacuum-tube voltmeters are designed to operate from power frequencies up to many megacycles per second without serious error.

Depending on operating principle and construction, deflecting instruments are subject to errors of various types: temperature, magnetic field, frequency, waveform, spring hysteresis, use in other than the intended position, and others.[1]

References

Curtis: "Electrical Measurements," McGraw-Hill Book Company, Inc., New York, 1937.

Campbell and Childs: "Measurement of Inductance, Capacitance, and Frequency," D. Van Nostrand Company, Inc., New York, 1935.

Electrochemical Constants, *Natl. Bur. Standards (U.S.) Circ.* 524 (1953).

Establishment and Maintenance of the Electrical Units, *Natl. Bur. Standards (U.S.) Circ.* 475 (1949).

Extension and Dissemination of Electrical and Magnetic Units by the National Bureau of Standards, *Natl. Bur. Standards (U.S.) Circ.* 531 (1952).

Golding: "Electrical Measurements," Pitman Publishing Corporation, New York, 1946.

Harris: "Electrical Measurements," John Wiley & Sons, Inc., New York, 1952.

Drysdale and Jolley: "Electrical Measuring Instruments," 2d ed., John Wiley & Sons, Inc., New York, 1952.

Keinath: "Die Technik electrischer Messgerate," R. Oldenbourg-Verlag, Munich, 1928.

Palm: "Electrische Messgerate," Springer-Verlag OHG, Berlin, 1948.

Vinal: "Primary Batteries," John Wiley & Sons, Inc., New York, 1950.

[1] Standard C-39 of the American Standards Association lists the types of errors and their expected magnitudes for a number of types of instruments in various accuracy classes. For more complete information on the errors of deflecting instruments a good text on instruments or measurements should be consulted.

Historical Reports of the Committee on Electrical Standards Appointed by the British Association for the Advancement of Science, Cambridge University Press, London, 1913.
U.S. Law of 1894 (Public Law 105, 53d Cong.) 28 Stat., Ch. 131, p. 102.
U.S. Law of 1949 (Public Law 619, 81st Cong., Ch. 486, 2d Sess.), Title 15, U.S.C.A. 221.

5d. Properties of Dielectrics

S. O. MORGAN,[1] D. EDELSON,[2] AND W. MCMAHON[3]
Bell Telephone Laboratories, Inc.

W. J. MERZ[4]
RCA Laboratories

5d-1. Dielectric Constants of Crystalline Solids. Crystalline solids are divided into inorganic (Table 5d-1) and organic (Table 5d-2) groups. Compounds are listed alphabetically in the first column and the chemical formula is given in the second. The column headed mp, °C under Organic Solids gives the melting point in degrees centigrade. The columns headed t, °C give the temperature of the measurements in degrees centigrade, the columns headed $\nu \sim$/sec give the frequency of the measurement in cycles per second, the columns headed ϵ/ϵ_v gives the dielectric constant (relative capacitivity) and the final columns the reference to the source of the information.

Figures 5d-1 and 5d-2, taken from ref. 21.2, display data for typical crystalline solids whose molecules can rotate in the solid state above a transition temperature. High values of dielectric constant are thus observed for polar compounds in a certain range of temperatures. Below the transition point the dielectric constant decreases to approximately the same value for each substance and is typical of most organic solids where dipole rotation is impossible. For one type of compound, illustrated by camphor and its derivatives, this decrease is sharp and independent of frequency. For the other type, illustrated by the hexachlorobenzenes, this decrease is gradual and frequency-dependent. Other examples of this behavior will be found in refs. 21.2, and 32 through 42 on page 5-119.

[1] Dielectric constants of crystalline solids.
[2] Dielectric constants of amorphous solids and of gases.
[3] Dielectric constants of pure liquids.
[4] Piezoelectric and pyroelectric constants, ferroelectric and antiferroelectric properties.

TABLE 5d-1. INORGANIC SOLIDS—CRYSTALLINE

Name	Formula	*t*, °C	ν~/sec	ϵ/ϵ_v	Ref.*
Alums:					
Ammonium alum	$Al(NH_4)(SO_4)_2 \cdot 12H_2O$	r.t.	10^{12}	6	18
Cesium alum	$CsAl(SO_4)_2 \cdot 12H_2O$	....	10^{12}	5.0	18
Potassium alum	$KAl(SO_4)_2 \cdot 12H_2O$	....	aud.	6.5	5
Rubidium alum	$RbAl(SO_4)_2 \cdot 12H_2O$	....	10^{12}	5.1	18
Rubidium chrome alum	$RbCr(SO_4)_2 \cdot 12H_2O$	....	10^{12}	5.0	18
Aluminum phosphate	$AlPO_4$	r.t.	10^3	6.05	21
Ammonium bromide	NH_4Br	r.t.	10^{12}	7.3	18
Ammonium chloride	NH_4Cl	r.t.	2×10^6	6.96	13
Ammonium tartrate	$(NH_4)_2(C_4H_4O_6)$	r.t.	10^3	6.45	21
Barium carbonate	$BaCO_3$	18	2×10^5	8.53	27
Barium chloride	$BaCl_2$	....	....	9.81	15
Barium chloride dihydrate	$BaCl_2 \cdot 2H_2O$	....	....	9.00	15
Barium fluoride	BaF_2	....	2×10^6	7.33	13
Barium formate	$Ba(COOH)_2$	r.t.	10^3	7.9	21
Barium nitrate	$Ba(NO_3)_2$	19	2×10^5	4.95	27
Barium oxide	BaO	−25 to 60	60~ to 6×10^7	34	1
Barium peroxide	BaO_2	r.t.	2×10^6	10.7	11
Barium sulfate	$BaSO_4$	15	10^8	11.4	
Beryllium carbonate	$BeCO_3$	18	2×10^5	9.7	27
Beryllium oxide	BeO	18	2×10^6	7.35	13
Bismuth trioxide	Bi_2O_3	r.t.	2×10^6	18.2	11
Cadmium bromide	$CdBr_2$	20	5×10^5	8.6	8
Cadmium malonate	$Cd(C_3H_2O_4)$	20	5×10^5	4.5	8
Calcium carbonate	$CaCO_3$	18	2×10^5	9.15	27
Calcium fluoride	CaF_2	....	10^5	6.76	14, 18, 24, 25
			aud.	6.85	5, 23, 28, 22
Calcium nitrate	$Ca(NO_3)_2$	19	2×10^5	6.54	27
Calcium oxide	CaO	10	2×10^6	11.8	13
Ceric oxide	CeO_2	r.t.	2×10^6	7.0	11
Cesium bromide	CsBr	....	2×10^6	6.51	13
Cesium carbonate	Cs_2CO_3	18	2×10^5	6.53	27
Cesium chloride	CsCl	19	2×10^5	6.34	27
Cesium iodide	CsI	25	1×10^6	5.65	13, 12
Chromic oxide	Cr_2O_3	r.t.	2×10^6	12.0	11
Cupric oxide	CuO	r.t.	2×10^6	18.1	11
Cupric sulfate pentahydrate	$CuSO_4 \cdot 5H_2O$	....	....	6.60	15
Cuprous bromide	CuBr	20	5×10^5	8.0	8
Cuprous chloride	CuCl	20	5×10^5	10.0	8, 13
Cuprous oxide	Cu_2O	r.t.	2×10^6	12.0	11
Dextrose sodium bromide	$C_6H_{12}O_6 \cdot NaBr$	....	10^3	4.0	21
Diamond	C	....	....	5.5	26.1
Ferrous oxide	FeO	r.t.	2×10^6	14.2	11
Iodic acid	HIO_3	....	10^3	7.5	21
Iodine	I_2	....	10^8	4.0	18
Lead acetate	$Pb(C_2H_3O_2)_2$	17–22	10^6	2.6	
Lead bromide	$PbBr_2$	20	$0.5\text{–}3 \times 10^6$	>30	8
Lead carbonate	$PbCO_3$	15	10^8	18.6	
Lead chloride	$PbCl_2$	20	$0.5\text{–}3 \times 10^6$	33.5	8
Lead iodide	PbI_2	20	$0.5\text{–}3 \times 10^6$	20.8	8
Lead molybdate (wulfenite)	$PbMoO_4$	....	3×10^8	26.8‖	26.1
Lead nitrate	$Pb(NO_3)_2$	....	$0.5\text{–}3 \times 10^6$	16.8	8
Lead oxide	PbO	r.t.	2×10^6	25.9	11
Lead sulfate	$PbSO_4$	17–22	10^6	14.3	
Lithium bromide	LiBr	....	2×10^6	12.1	13
Lithium chloride	LiCl	....	2×10^6	11.05	8
Lithium carbonate	Li_2CO_3	18	2×10^5	4.9	27

TABLE 5d-1. INORGANIC SOLIDS—CRYSTALLINE (*Continued*)

Name	Formula	t, °C	ν∼/sec	ε/εv	Ref.*
Lithium fluoride	LiF	20	10^6	9.27	13
		25	10^2–10^7	9.00	31
		80	10^2–10^7	9.11	31
Lithium iodide	LiI		2×10^6	11.03	13
Lithium sulfate monohydrate	$Li_2SO_4 \cdot H_2O$		10^3	5.6	21
Lithium trisodium chromate	$LiNa_3CrO_4 \cdot 6H_2O$		10^3	8.0	21
Lithium trisodium molybdate	$LiNa_3MoO_4 \cdot 6H_2O$	....	10^3	8.1	21
Magnesium carbonate	$MgCO_3$	18	2×10^5	8.1	27
Magnesium malonate	$Mg(C_3H_2O_4)$	20	5×10^5	5.8	8
Magnesium oxalate	$Mg(C_2O_4)$	20	5×10^5	5.2	8
Magnesium oxide	MgO	25	10^2–10^8	9.65	31
Magnesium sulfate	$MgSO_4$	20	5×10^5	8.2	8
Magnesium sulfate heptahydrate	$MgSO_4 \cdot 7H_2O$		....	5.46	15
Mercuric chloride	$HgCl_2$	....	10^{12}	6.5	18
Mercurous chloride	HgCl		10^{12}	14.0⊥	18
Mica—ruby, muscovite	....	26	10^2–3×10^9	5.4	31
Mica—Canadian	....	25	10^2–10^4	6.9⊥	31
		25	10^4	7.3‖	31
Nickel sulfate hexahydrate	$NiSO_4 \cdot 6H_2O$	....	10^3	6.2	21
Phosphorus, red	P	....	10^8	4.1	
Yellow	....	....	10^8	3.6	26.1
Potassium bromate	$KBrO_3$	r.t.	2×10^6	7.3	29
Potassium bromide	KBr	r.t.	2×10^6	4.78	13
Potassium carbonate	K_2CO_3	18	2×10^5	4.96	27
Potassium chlorate	$KClO_3$	r.t.	2×10^6	5.1	29
Potassium chloride	KCl	29.5	10^6	4.64	12
		80	10^6	4.80	12
Potassium chromate	K_2CrO_4	....	6×10^7	7.3	
Potassium cyanide	KCN	r.t.	2×10^6	6.15	29
Potassium dihydrogen arsenate	KH_2AsO_4	r.t.	2×10^6	31	29
Potassium dihydrogen phosphate	KH_2PO_4	....	10^3	46	21
Potassium fluoride	KF	....	2×10^6	6.05	13
Potassium iodate	KIO_3	r.t.	2×10^6	16.85	29
Potassium iodide	KI	....	2×10^6	4.94	13
Potassium nitrate	KNO_3	20	2×10^5	4.37	27
Potassium perchlorate	$KClO_4$	r.t.	2×10^6	5.9	29
Potassium orthophosphate	K_3PO_4	r.t.	2×10^6	7.75	29
Potassium monohydrogen orthophosphate	K_2HPO_4	r.t.	2×10^6	9.05	29
Potassium dihydrogen orthophosphate	KH_2PO_4	r.t.	2×10^6	>31	29
Potassium sulfate	K_2SO_4	r.t.	2×10^6	6.4	29
Potassium thiocyanate	KSCN	r.t.	2×10^6	7.9	29
Rubidium bromide	RbBr	....	2×10^6	5.0	13
Rubidium carbonate	Rb_2CO_3	19	2×10^5	6.73	27
Rubidium chloride	RbCl	....	2×10^6	5.0	13
Rubidium fluoride	RbF	....	2×10^6	5.91	13
Rubidium iodide	RbI	....	2×10^6	5.0	13
Selenium	Se	25	3×10^8	11.0	31
		25	3×10^9	10.4	31
		25	2×10^{10}	7.5	31
Selenium, amorphous	Se	25	10^2–10^{10}	6.00	31
Silver bromide	AgBr	....	2×10^6	13.1	13, 8
Silver chloride	AgCl	....	2×10^6	12.3	13, 8
Silver cyanide	AgCN	....	10^6	5.6	
Silver nitrate	$AgNO_3$	20	5×10^5	9.0	8
Sodium ammonium tartrate tetrahydrate	$NaNH_4(C_4H_4O_6) \cdot 4H_2O$	....	10^3	9.0	21
Sodium bromide	NaBr	....	2×10^6	5.99	13
Sodium carbonate	Na_2CO_3	18	2×10^5	8.75	27
Sodium carbonate decahydrate	$Na_2CO_3 \cdot 10H_2O$	....	6×10^7	5.3	15

TABLE 5d-1. INORGANIC SOLIDS—CRYSTALLINE (*Continued*)

Name	Formula	*t*, °C	ν~/sec	ϵ/ϵ_v	Ref.*
Sodium chlorate	$NaClO_3$	....	....	5.28	16
Sodium chloride	NaCl	20	2×10^6	5.62	13
		25	10^2–10^7	5.9	31
		85	10^4–10^7	5.98	31
Sodium cyanide	NaCN	20	10^5	7.55	32
Sodium fluoride	NaF	19	2×10^6	6.0	13
Sodium iodide	NaI	....	2×10^6	6.60	13
Sodium nitrate	$NaNO_3$	19	2×10^5	6.85	27
Sodium perchlorate	$NaClO_4$	....	10^3	5.76	21
Sodium sulfate	Na_2SO_4	....	....	7.90	15
Sodium sulfate decahydrate	$Na_2SO_4 \cdot 10H_2O$	....	....	5.0	15
Strontium carbonate	$SrCO_3$	18	2×10^5	8.85	27
Strontium chloride	$SrCl_2$	....	....	9.19	15
Strontium chloride hexahydrate	$SrCl_2 \cdot 6H_2O$	....	....	8.52	15
Strontium fluoride	SrF_2	....	2×10^6	7.69	13
Strontium formate dihydrate	$Sr(COOH)_2 \cdot 2H_2O$	....	10^3	6.1	21
Strontium nitrate	$Sr(NO_3)_2$	19	2×10^5	5.33	27
Strontium oxide	SrO	....	2×10^6	13.3	13
Sulfur (100)	S	25	10^2–10^3	3.75	31
(010)		25	10^2–10^3	3.95	31
(001)		25	10^2–10^3	4.44	31
Sublined		25	10^2–10^3	3.69	31
Tantalum oxide	Ta_2O_5	r.t.	2×10^6	11.6	11
Thallous bromide	TlBr	25	10^3–10^7	30.3	31
Thallous chloride	TlCl	....	2×10^6	31.9	13
Thallous iodide	TlI	25	10^3–10^7	21.8	31
		193	10^7	37.3	31
Thallous nitrate	$TlNO_3$	20	5×10^5	16.5	8
Thallous sulfate	Tl_2SO_4	20	5×10^5	25.5	8
Thorium oxide	ThO_2	r.t.	2×10^6	10.6	11
Zinc malonate	$Zn(C_3H_2O_4)$	20	5×10^5	5.6	8
Zinc sulfide	ZnS	....	10^{12}	8.2	19
Zirconium oxide	ZrO_2	r.t.	2×10^6	12.5	11

* References are on p. 5-119.

TABLE 5d-2. ORGANIC SOLIDS—CRYSTALLINE

Name	Formula	mp, °C	*t*, °C	ν~/sec	ϵ/ϵ_0	Ref.*
Acetoxime	C_3H_7NO	61	23	10^5	3.00	35
p-Amino benzoic acid	$C_7H_7NO_2$	187	12	10^5	3.1	35
				10^3	6.7	35
Anethole	$C_{10}H_{12}O$	32.5	−30	10^5	3.0	35
Benzamide	C_7H_7NO	130	29	10^5	3.0	35
Benzaphenone	$C_{13}H_{10}O$	48.5	25	10^5	3.2	35
Benzene	C_6H_6	5	0	10^5	2.44	21.1
Benzene hexachloride	$C_6H_6Cl_6$	157	28	10^5	2.7	35
Borneol	$C_{10}H_{18}O$	208.6	25	10^5	2.78	34
			90	10^5	3.85	34
d-Camphene	$C_{10}H_{16}$	42.7	25	10^5	2.36	35
d-Camphor	$C_{10}H_{16}O$	179	25	10^5	11.2	34
l-Camphor	$C_{10}H_{16}O$	180	25	10^5	11.35	35
dl-Camphor	$C_{10}H_{16}O$	174	25	10^5	10.3	34
Carbon tetrachloride	CCl_4	−22.5	−30	10^5	2.43	21.1
Chloroform	$CHCl_3$	−63.2	−70	10^5	2.40	21.1
Cholestrol	$C_{27}H_{46}O$	148.5	27	10^5	2.86	35
Cyclohexanol	$C_6H_{12}O$	24	20	10^5	16.0	33
Cyclohexyl adipate	$C_{18}H_{30}O_4$	35.5	25	10^5	2.56	35
Dibenzyl	$C_{14}H_{14}$	52.5	23	10^5	2.59	35
p-Dichlorobenzene	$C_6H_4Cl_2$	53	20	10^5	2.88	21.1
1,4-Bromochloronaphthalene	$C_{10}H_6BrCl$	......	26	10^5	2.86	35
2,3-Dichlorodioxane	$C_{10}H_6Cl_2$	37	10	10^5	3.06	35
1,2-Dichloronaphthalene	$C_{10}H_6Cl_2$	107	25	10^5	2.6	35
1,5-Dichloronaphthalene	$C_{10}H_6Cl_2$	135	25	10^5	2.26	35
2,6-Dichloronaphthalene	$C_4H_6O_2Cl_2$	29	20	10^5	2.90	35
o-Dinitrobenzene	$C_6H_4N_2O_4$	116.5	24	10^5	3.5	35
Dioxane	$C_4H_8O_2$	12	0	10^5	2.28	35
Ethylene bromide	$C_2H_4Br_2$	10	0	10^5	2.80	32
Ethylene chloride	$C_2H_4Cl_2$	−35.5	−40	10^5	4.65	32
Ethylene cyanide	$C_4H_4N_2$	54.2	25	10^5	65.9	32
Ethylene diamine	$C_2H_8N_2$	10	6.7	10^5	5.9	32
Ethylene iodide	$C_2H_4I_2$	82	26	10^5	3.45	35
Ethylene thiocyanate	$C_2H_4(SCN)_2$	89.8	25	10^5	3.33	32
β-Fluoronaphthalene	$C_{10}H_7F$	59	25	10^5	3.0	35
Naphthalene	$C_{10}H_8$	80.1	25	10^3–3×10^9	2.85	31
Nonachlorobiphenyl	$C_{12}HCl_9$	......	25	10^2–10^7	2.64	31
Pentachlorobenzene	C_6HCl_5	85	25	10^5	3.05	35
Pentaerythritol	$C_5H_{12}O_4$	253	29	10^5	2.44	35
Phenanthraquinone	$C_{14}H_8O_2$	207	25	10^5	3.45	35
Phenyl urethane	$C_9H_{11}NO_2$	52	22.5	10^5	2.71	35
Quinone	$C_6H_4O_2$	115.7	23	10^5	2.66	35
Succinic acid	$C_4H_6O_4$	185	25	10^5	2.40	35
Tartaric acid	$C_4H_6O_6$	170	21	10^5	6.0	35
				10^3	9.7	35
o-Terphenyl	$C_{18}H_{14}$	......	25	10^2–10^7	2.8	31
m-Terphenyl	$C_{18}H_{14}$	186	25	10^3–10^9	2.86	31
p-Terphenyl	$C_{18}H_{14}$	213	25	3×10^9	2.95	31
Thiocamphor	$C_{10}H_{16}S$	139	25	10^5	9.7	35
o,p-Toluene sulfonamide	$C_7H_8O_3S$	......	25	2.5×10^{10}	3.21	31
Tri-*o*-cresyl phosphate	$C_{21}H_{21}O_4P$	......	−46	10^5	3.0	35
Tri-*m*-cresyl phosphate	$C_{21}H_{21}O_4P$	......	−46	10^5	3.1	35
Tri-*p*-cresyl phosphate	$C_{21}H_{21}O_4P$	......	25	10^5	2.9	35
Triphenyl phosphate	$C_{18}H_{15}O_4P$	49.9	25	10^5	2.8	35

* References are on p. 5-119.

References

1. Bever and Sproull: *Phys. Rev.* **83,** 801 (1951).
2. Blandin: *Compt. rend.* **231,** 828 (1950).
3. Boltzmann: *Sitzber. Akad. Wiss. Wien Math. naturw. Kl.* **68II,** 81 (1873).
4. Borel: *Compt. rend.* **116,** 1509 (1893); *Arch. sci. phys. nat.* **30,** 131, 181, 219, 327, 422 (1893).
5. Curie: *Ann. chim. et de phys.* **17,** 385 (1889).
6. Errera and Brasseur: *Physik. Z.* **34,** 368 (1933).
7. Errera and Ketelaar: *J. phys. radium* **3** (7), 239 (1932).
8. Eucken and Buchner: *Z. physik. Chem.* **27** (B), 321 (1934).
9. Fellinger: *Ann. Physik* **60,** 181 (1919).
10. Fellinger: *Ann. Physik* **7,** 333 (1902).
11. Guntherschultze and Keller: *Z. Physik* **75,** 78 (1932).
12. Højendahl: *Z. physik. Chem.* **20** (B), 54 (1933).
13. Højendahl: *Kgl. Danske Videnskab. Selskab Mat.-fys. Medd.* **16,** 1–132 (1938).
14. Jaeger: *Ann. Physik* **53,** 409 (1917).
15. Kamiyoshi and Miyamoto: *Science Repts. Research Insts. Tôhoku Univ.*, ser. A, **2,** 370 (1950).
16. Kiriyama: *Science (Japan)* **17,** 239 (1947).
17. Kyropolous: *Z. Physik* **63,** 849 (1930).
18. Liebisch and Rubens: *Sitzber. preuss. Akad. Wiss., Physik-math. Kl.* **1919,** 876.
19. Liebisch and Rubens: *Sitzber. preuss. Akad. Wiss., Physik-math. Kl.* **1921,** 211.
20. Malone and Ferguson: *J. Chem. Phys.* **2,** 99 (1934).
21. Mason: "Piezoelectric Crystals," D. Van Nostrand Company, Inc., New York, 1950.

21.1. Morgan and Lowry: *J. Phys. Chem.* **34,** 2385 (1930).

21.2. Morgan and Yager: *Ind. Eng. Chem.* **32,** 1519 (1940).

22. Naragamo Rao: *Proc. Indian Acad. Sci.* **30A,** 82 (1949).

22a. Pirani: Dissertation, Berlin, 1903.

23. Romich and Nowak: *Sitzber. Akad. Wiss. Wien, Math. naturw. Kl.* **70II,** 380 (1875).
24. Rubens: *Sitzber. preuss. Akad. Wiss., Physik-math. Kl.* **1915,** I, 4.
25. Rubens: *Z. Physik* **1,** 11 (1920).
26. Schmidt: *Ann. Physik* **9,** 919 (1902).

26.1. Schmidt: *Ann. Physik* **11,** 114 (1903).

27. Schupp: *Z. Physik* **75,** 84 (1932).
28. Starke: *Ann. Physik* **60,** 629 (1897).

28.1. Starke: *Ann. Physik* **61,** 804 (1897).

29. Steulmann: *Z. Physik* **77,** 114 (1932).
30. Voigt: "Lehrbuch der Kristallphysik," p. 459.
31. Von Hippel: "Dielectric Materials and Applications," John Wiley & Sons, Inc., New York, 1954.
32. White and Morgan: *J. Chem. Phys.* **5,** 655 (1937).
33. White and Morgan: *J. Am. Chem. Soc.* **57,** 2078 (1935).
34. Yager and Morgan: *J. Am. Chem. Soc.* **57,** 2071 (1935).
35. Yager and White: unpublished results of Bell Telephone Laboratories.
36. Smyth and Hitchcock: *J. Am. Chem. Soc.* **55,** 1830 (1933).
37. Smyth: *Chem. Rev.* **19,** 329 (1936).
38. Baker and Smyth: *J. Am. Chem. Soc.* **60,** 1229 (1938); **61,** 1695, 2063, 2798 (1939).
39. White and Bishop: *J. Am. Chem. Soc.* **62,** 8 (1940).
40. White, Biggs, and Morgan: *J. Am. Chem. Soc.* **62,** 16 (1940).
41. Hoffman and Smyth: *J. Am. Chem. Soc.* **72,** 171 (1950).
42. Crowe and Smyth: *J. Am. Chem. Soc.* **73,** 5401, 5404 (1951).

5d-2. Dielectric Properties of Amorphous Solids

TABLE 5d-3. DIELECTRIC PROP
(Values for tan δ are multiplied

Ceramic	T, °C		Frequency						
			1×10^2	1×10^3	1×10^4	1×10^5	1×10^6	1×10^7	1×10^8
Steatite bodies:									
AlSiMag A-35[1]	23	ϵ'/ϵ_v	6.10	5.96	5.89	5.86	5.84	5.80	5.75
		tan δ	150	100	70	50	38	35	37
	85	ϵ'/ϵ_v	6.84	6.37	6.11	5.96	5.86	5.80	5.75
		tan δ	890	370	175	103	77	50	50
AlSiMag A-196[1]	25	ϵ'/ϵ_v	5.90	5.88	5.84	5.80	5.70	5.65	5.60
		tan δ	30	59	79.5	55	30.5	19	16
	81	ϵ'/ϵ_v	5.90	5.88	5.84	5.80	5.70	5.65	5.60
		tan δ	58	40	46.5	70.5	66	40.5	24
AlSiMag 211[1]	25	ϵ'/ϵ_v	6.00	5.98	5.98	5.97	5.97	5.96	5.96
		tan δ	92	34	12	6	5	4	4
AlSiMag 228[1]	81	ϵ'/ϵ_v	6.52	6.46	6.40	6.40	6.36	6.30	.....
		tan δ	35.6	22	18	21.5	18.4	11.8	......
Steatite type 302[2]	25	ϵ'/ϵ_v	5.80	5.80	5.80	5.80	5.80	5.80	5.80
		tan δ	32	20	16	13	12	12	12
Steatitc body 7292[3]	25	ϵ'/ϵ_v	6.55	6.55	6.54	6.53	6.53	6.53	6.53
		tan δ	14	7	4.8	3.9	4.9	5.2	6.2
Crolite No. 29[4]	24	ϵ'/ϵ_v	6.04	6.04	6.04	6.04	6.04	6.04	......
		tan δ	25	19	15	13	11	10	......
Forsterite bodies:									
AlSiMag 243[1]	85	ϵ'/ϵ_v	6.37	6.37	6.37	6.36	6.32	6.28	.....
		tan δ	21	13.7	8.0	<9	3.7	3.5	......
Titania and titanate bodies:									
Ceramic NPOT 96[1]	25	ϵ'/ϵ_v	29.5	29.5	29.5	29.5	29.5	29.5	29.5
		tan δ	12	4.9	3.3	2.5	1.6	1.7	2
Ceramic N750T96[1]	25	ϵ'/ϵ_v	83.4	83.4	83.4	83.4	83.4	83.4	83.4
		tan δ	5.7	4.5	3.5	2.5	2.2	2.3	4.6
Ceramic N1400T110[1]	25	ϵ'/ϵ_v	131	130.8	130.7	130.5	130.2	130.2	130.0
		tan δ	6.7	5.5	3.3	1.4	3.0	5.5	7.0
Body T106[1]	25	ϵ'/ϵ_v	1,518	1,508	1,480				
		tan δ	31	87	99				
Porcelains:									
Zircon porcelain Zi-4[5]	25	ϵ'/ϵ_v	6.44	6.40	6.35	6.32	6.32	6.30	6.30
		tan δ	59	40	31	27	23	21	25
Electrical porcelain, wet process[6]	25	ϵ'/ϵ_v	6.47	6.24	6.08	5.98	5.87	5.82	5.80
		tan δ	280	180	130	105	90	115	135
Electrical porcelain, dry process[6]	25	ϵ'/ϵ_v	5.50	5.36	5.23	5.14	5.08	5.04	5.04
		tan δ	220	140	105	85	75	70	78
Coors AI-200—high alumina[5]	25	ϵ'/ϵ_v	8.83	8.83	8.82	8.80	8.80	8.80	8.80
		tan δ	14	5.7	4.8	3.8	3.3	3.2	3.0
Porcelain No. 4462—high alumina[7]	25	ϵ'/ϵ_v	8.99	8.95	8.95	8.95	8.95	8.95	8.95
		tan δ	22	9.1	6.0	3.0	2.0	2.0	4.0
Coors AB-2—high alumina[5]	25	ϵ'/ϵ_v	8.22	8.18	8.17	8.17	8.16	8.16	8.16
		tan δ	20	13.4	11.4	10.5	9.0	7.5	9.0
AlSiMag 491—high alumina[1]	25	ϵ'/ϵ_v	....	....	....	......	8.74	......	......
		tan δ	....	....	....	......	22	......	......

Manufactured by:

1. American Lava.
2. Centralab.
3. General Ceramics and Steatite.
4. Crowley.
5. Coors.
6. Knox.
7. Frenchtown Porcelain.

* Data taken from Tables of Dielectric Materials, vol. IV, Laboratory for Insulation Research, MIT Technical Report 57; and Chart 501, American Lava Co.

† Frequency = 1×10^9.

ERTIES OF SELECTED CERAMICS*
by 10^4; frequency given in cps)

Frequency				Volume resistivity, ohm-cm					
3×10^8	3×10^9	1×10^{10}	2.5×10^{10}	25°C	100°C	300°C	500°C	700°C	900°C
....	5.60	......	5.36	$>10^{14}$	2.1×10^{12}	6.0×10^7	3.2×10^5	2.3×10^4	7.0×10^3
....	41	.....,	58						
....	5.50								
....	47								
....	5.42	5.24	5.18	$>10^{14}$	1.0×10^{13}	6.5×10^9	4.0×10^7	1.8×10^6	3.0×10^5
....	18	26	38						
....	5.42								
....	18								
....	.....	5.90		$>10^{14}$	3.0×10^{13}		3.5×10^{10}		
....	.....	14	.....			....			
....	5.95	......	.....	$>10^{14}$	$>10^{14}$	8.0×10^{10}	3.0×10^8	5.0×10^6	4.0×10^5
....	11								
....	5.8	5.8	.....	$>7 \times 10^{14}$	4.0×10^{13}				
....	19	36							
6.53	6.52	6.51							
6.8	9	10.9							
....	5.90	5.71	.....	$>10^{15}$	$>10^{14}$				
....	24	30							
....	5.88	......	.....	$>10^{14}$	5.0×10^{13}	7.0×10^{11}	1.2×10^{10}	1.0×10^8	3.0×10^6
....	6								
....	.....	28.9							
....	.....	20							
....	.....	83.4							
....	.....	14.6							
6.30	6.23	6.18	.....	7×10^{14}	7×10^{14}				
27	45	57							
5.75	.....	5.51							
140	.....	155							
5.02	.....	4.74							
98	.....	156							
....	8.79	8.79	.....	7×10^{14}	9×10^{13}				
....	10	18							
8.93†	8.90	8.80							
9†	11	14							
....	8.14	8.08		$>10^{14}$					
....	16	27	.....						
....	8.60	8.50	.....	$>10^{14}$	$>10^{14}$	1.7×10^{11}	2.0×10^7	6.2×10^5	8.0×10^4
....	17	23							

TABLE 5d-4. PROPERTIES OF SELECTED GLASSES*
(Values for tan δ are multiplied by 10^4; frequency given in cps)

Glass	T, °C		Frequency											$\log_{10}$ volume resistivity		
			1×10^2	1×10^3	1×10^4	1×10^5	1×10^6	1×10^7	1×10^8	3×10^8	3×10^9	1×10^{10}	2.5×10^{10}	25°C	250°C	350°C
Corning 0010 (potash, soda, lead)	24	ϵ'/ϵ_v	6.68	6.63	6.57	6.50	6.43	6.39	6.33	.....	6.1	5.96	5.87	>17	8.9	7.0
		tan δ	77.5	53.5	35	23	16.5	15	23	.....	60	90	110			
Corning 0014 (lead, barium)	25	ϵ'/ϵ_v	6.78	6.77	6.76	6.75	6.73	6.72	6.70	6.69	....	6.64				
		tan δ	23.1	17.2	14.4	12.2	12.4	13.8	17.0	19.5	....	70				
Corning 0080 (soda lime)	23	ϵ'/ϵ_v	8.30	7.70	7.35	7.08	6.90	6.82	6.75	.....	6.71	6.71	6.62	12.4	6.4	5.1
		tan δ	780	400	220	140	100	85	90	.....	126	170	180			
Corning 0090 (potash, lead, silicate)	20	ϵ'/ϵ_v	9.15	9.15	9.15	9.14	9.12	9.10	9.02	.....	8.67	8.45	8.25			
		tan δ	12	8	7	7	8	12	18	.....	54	103	122			
Corning 0100 (potash, soda, barium, silicate)	25	ϵ'/ϵ_v	7.18	7.17	7.16	7.14	7.10	7.10	7.07	.....	7.00	6.95	6.87			
		tan δ	24	16	13.5	13	14	17	24	.....	44	63	106			
Corning 0120 (potash, soda, lead)	23	ϵ'/ϵ_v	6.75	6.70	6.66	6.65	6.65	6.65	6.65	.....	6.64	6.60	6.51	>17	10.1	8.0
		tan δ	46	30	20	14	12	13	18	.....	41	63	127			
Corning 1770 (soda lime)	25	ϵ'/ϵ_v	6.25	6.16	6.10	6.03	6.00	6.00	6.00	.....	5.95	5.83	5.44			
		tan δ	49.5	42	33	26	27	34	38	.....	56	84	140			
Corning 1990 (iron-sealing glass)	24	ϵ'/ϵ_v	8.40	8.38	8.35	8.32	8.30	8.25	8.20	.....	7.99	7.94	7.84			
		tan δ	4	4	3	4	5	7	9	.....	19.9	42	112			
Corning 1991 (iron-sealing glass)	24	ϵ'/ϵ_v	8.10	8.10	8.08	8.08	8.08	8.06	8.00	.....	7.92	7.83				
		tan δ	12	9	6	5	5	7	12	.....	38	51				
Corning 3320 (soda, potash, borosilicate)	24	ϵ'/ϵ_v	5.00	4.93	4.88	4.82	4.79	4.78	4.77	.....	4.74	4.72	4.7			
		tan δ	80	58	43	34	30	30	32	.....	55	73	120			
Corning 7040 (soda, potash, borosilicate)	25	ϵ'/ϵ_v	4.84	4.82	4.79	4.77	4.73	4.70	4.68	.....	4.67	4.64	4.52			
		tan δ	50	34	25.5	20.5	19	22	27	.....	44	57	73			
Corning 7050 (soda, borosilicate)	25	ϵ'/ϵ_v	4.88	4.84	4.82	4.80	4.78	4.76	4.75	.....	4.74	4.71	4.64	16	8.8	7.2
		tan δ	81	56	43	33	27	28	35	.....	52	61	83			
Corning 7052 (soda, potash, lithia, borosilicate)	23	ϵ'/ϵ_v	5.20	5.18	5.14	5.12	5.10	5.10	5.09	.....	5.04	4.93	4.85	17	9.2	7.4
		tan δ	68	49	34	26	24	28	34	.....	58	81	114			
Corning 7055	25	ϵ'/ϵ_v	5.45	5.41	5.38	5.33	5.31	5.30	5.27	5.25	....	5.08				
		tan δ	45	36	30	28	28	29	38	49	....	130				
Corning 7060 (soda, borosilicate)	25	ϵ'/ϵ_v	5.02	4.97	4.92	4.86	4.84	4.84	4.84	.....	4.82	4.80	4.65			
		tan δ	89	55	42	40	36	30	30	.....	54	98	90			
Corning 7070 (potash, lithia, borosilicate)	23	ϵ'/ϵ_v	4.00	4.00	4.00	4.00	4.00	4.00	4.00	4.00	4.00	4.00	3.9	>17	11.2	9.1
		tan δ	6	5	5	6	8	11	12	12	12	21	31			
	100	ϵ'/ϵ_v	4.17	4.16	4.15	4.14	4.13	4.10	.....	.....	4.00	4.00				

Material	T, °C															
		tan δ	50	22	13	10		11	.....	.....	19	21				
Corning 7230 (aluminum borosilicate)	25	ϵ'/ϵ_v	3.88	3.86	3.85	3.85	3.85	3.85	.....	.....	3.76					
		tan δ	33	23	16	13	11	12	.....	.....	22					
Corning 7570	25	ϵ'/ϵ_v	14.58	14.56	14.54	14.53	14.52	14.50	14.42	14.4	.....	14.2				
		tan δ	11.5	13.5	15.9	16.5	19.0	23.5	33	44	.....	98				
Corning 7720 (soda, lead, borosilicate)	24	ϵ'/ϵ_v	4.74	4.70	4.67	4.64	4.62	4.61	.....	.....	.....	4.59	......	16	8.8	7.2
		tan δ	78	42	29	22	20	23	.....	.....	.....	43				
Corning 7740 (soda, borosilicate)	25	ϵ'/ϵ_v	4.80	4.73	4.70	4.60	4.55	4.52	4.52	.....	.....	4.52	4.50	15	8.1	6.6
		tan δ	128	86	65	54	49	45	45	.....	.....	85	96			
Corning 7750 (soda, borosilicate)	25	ϵ'/ϵ_v	4.45	4.42	4.39	4.38	4.38	4.38	.....	.....	4.38	4.38				
		tan δ	45	33	24	20	18	19	.....	.....	43	54				
Corning 7900 (96% silica)	20	ϵ'/ϵ_v	3.85	3.85	3.85	3.85	3.85	3.85	.....	3.85	3.84	3.82	3.82	17	9.7	8.1
		tan δ	6	6	6	6	6	6	.....	6	6.8	9.4	13			
	100	ϵ'/ϵ_v	3.85	3.85	3.85	3.85	3.85	3.85	.....	3.85	3.84	3.82				
		tan δ	37	17	12	10	8.5	7.5	.....	7.5	10	13				
Corning 7911 (96% silica)	25	ϵ'/ϵ_v	....	....	....	....	....	....	.....	.....	.....	3.82	......	>17	11.7	9.6
		tan δ	....	....	....	....	....	....	.....	.....	.....	6.5				
Corning 8460 (barium, borosilicate)	25	ϵ'/ϵ_v	8.35	8.30	8.30	8.30	8.30	8.30	8.30	.....	8.10	8.06	8.05			
		tan δ	11	9	7.5	7	8	10	16	.....	40	57	60			
Corning 8830	25	ϵ'/ϵ_v	5.38	5.28	5.20	5.11	5.05	5.01	5.00	4.97	.....	4.83				
		tan δ	204	130	91	73	60	54	57	63	.....	99				
Corning 8871 (alkaline lead silicate)	25	ϵ'/ϵ_v	8.45	8.45	8.45	8.45	8.45	8.43	.....	8.40	8.34	8.05	7.82			
		tan δ	18	13	9	7	6	7	.....	14	26	49	70			
Corning 9010	25	ϵ'/ϵ_v	6.51	6.49	6.48	6.45	6.44	6.43	6.42	6.40	.....	6.27				
		tan δ	50.5	36.2	26.7	22.7	21.5	22.6	30	41	.....	91				
Foamglas (Pittsburgh-Corning) (soda lime)	23	ϵ'/ϵ_v	90.0	82.5	68.0	44.0	17.5	9.0	.....	.....	.....	5.49				
		tan δ	1,500	1,600	2,380	3,200	3,180	1,960	.....	.....	.....	455				
Fused silica 915c	25	ϵ'/ϵ_v	3.78	3.78	3.78	3.78	3.78	3.78	3.78	3.78	.....	3.78				
		tan δ	6.6	2.6	1.1	0.4	0.1	0.1	0.3	0.5	....	1.7				
Glass-bonded micas:																
Mycalex 400	25	ϵ'/ϵ_v	7.47	7.45	7.42	7.40	7.39	7.38	.....	.....	....	7.12				
		tan δ	29	19	16	14	13	13	.....	.....	....	33				
	80	ϵ'/ϵ_v	7.64	7.59	7.54	7.52	7.50	7.47	.....	.....	....	7.32				
		tan δ	150	85	50	25	16	14	.....	.....	....	57				
Mycalex K10	24	ϵ'/ϵ_v	9.5	9.3	9.2	9.1	9.0	9.0	.....	.....	11.3†	11.3†				
		tan δ	170	125	76	42	26	21	.....	.....	40	40				
Mykroy grade 8	25	ϵ'/ϵ_v	6.87	6.81	6.76	6.74	6.73	6.73	6.72	.....	6.68‡	6.96‡	6.66			
		tan δ	95	66	43	31	26	24	25	.....	38	48	81			
Mykroy grade 38	25	ϵ'/ϵ_v	7.71	7.69	7.64	7.61	7.61	7.61	.....	.....	7.68‡	8.35‡				
		tan δ	43	33	27	24	21	14	.....	.....	35	40				

* Taken from Tables of Dielectric Materials, vol. IV, Laboratory for Insulation Research, MIT Technical Report 57; and Properties of Commercial Glasses, Bull. B-83, Corning Glass Works.
† Not corrected for variations in density.
‡ Samples nonhomogeneous.

TABLE 5d-5. DIELECTRIC PROPERTIES OF SELECTED PLASTICS AND RUBBERS*
(Values for tan δ are multiplied by 10^4)

Material	T, °C		Frequency, cps									
			1×10^2	1×10^3	1×10^4	1×10^5	1×10^6	1×10^7	1×10^8	3×10^8	3×10^9	1×10^{10}	2.5×10^{10}
Plastics													
Phenol-formaldehyde:													
Bakelite BM-120 (not pre-	27	ϵ'/ϵ_v	5.50	5.15	4.90	4.65	4.45	4.30	...	...	3.70	3.55	
formed or preheated)		tan δ	740	460	345	320	350	415	...	...	400	500	
	57	ϵ'/ϵ_v	7.80	6.35	5.70	5.30	4.90	4.65	4.5	...	4.15		
		tan δ	2,950	1,150	530	380	430	470	480	...	530		
	88	ϵ'/ϵ_v	18.2	8.5	6.5	5.7	5.2	5.0	4.7	...	4.40		
		tan δ	7,600	3,700	1,400	600	400	420	470	...	700		
Bakelite BM-16981 (not	25	ϵ'/ϵ_v	7.6	6.1	5.4	5.1	4.9	4.8	4.7	...	4.6	4.5	
preformed or preheated)		tan δ	2,300	1,000	500	300	200	130	100	...	100	120	
Formica XX (field ⊥ to	26	ϵ'/ϵ_v	5.23	5.15	4.96	4.78	4.60	4.32	4.04	...	3.57	3.55	
laminate)		tan δ	230	165	170	230	340	490	570	...	600	700	
Formica LE (field ⊥ to	26	ϵ'/ϵ_v	6.50	5.70	5.30	5.00	4.75	4.35	3.95	...	3.35	3.25	
laminate)		tan δ	1,350	600	430	400	410	480	500	...	400	460	
Dilecto (hot punching)	25	ϵ'/ϵ_v	14.7	8.61	6.68	5.76	5.05	4.60	4.10	3.78	3.45	3.35	
XXX-P-26 (field ∥ sheet)		tan δ	6,420	2,970	1,380	840	720	705	690	680	500	480	
Phenol-aniline-formaldehyde:													
Formica grade MF-66	25	ϵ'/ϵ_v	4.53	4.50	4.43	4.38	4.31	4.24	4.11	4.09	3.90	3.88	3.85
Fiberglas		tan δ	106	95	107	102	95	109	160	195	260	290	300
	79	ϵ'/ϵ_v	4.94	4.75	4.66	4.59	4.51	4.44	4.35	...	4.20	4.10	
		tan δ	350	192	135	110	105	110	130	...	346	702	
Melamine-formaldehyde:													
Formica grade FF-41	26	ϵ'/ϵ_v	6.15	6.00	5.95	5.85	5.75	5.65	5.5				
(sheet stock)		tan δ	400	119	86	93	115	165	200				
Melmac resin 592	27	ϵ'/ϵ_v	6.70	6.25	5.85	5.50	5.20	4.90	4.70	...	4.67	4.59	
		tan δ	590	470	410	375	347	326	360	...	410	434	
	57	ϵ'/ϵ_v	8.15	6.95	6.35	5.85	5.40	5.10	4.90	...	4.75		
		tan δ	1,250	750	490	400	350	320	350	...	480		
	88	ϵ'/ϵ_v	21.8	11.8	8.0	6.5	6.0	5.8	5.5	...	4.90		
		tan δ	7,400	3,400	1,650	750	520	470	380	...	520		

Material	T, °C												
Melmac type 1077	28	ϵ'/ϵ_v	7.00	6.90	6.75	6.50	6.20	5.90	......	......	4.8	4.7	
(ivory WB 48)		tan δ	240	130	140	190	280	440	......	......	900	1,000	
Panelyte 140 (field ⊥ to	24	ϵ'/ϵ_v	6.15	6.05	6.00	5.93	5.82	5.70	5.55	5.5	......	4.70	4.62
laminate)		tan δ	135	93	120	155	155	170	215	260	......	360	260
Urea-formaldehyde:													
Plaskon urea, natural	24	ϵ'/ϵ_v	7.1	6.7	6.4	6.2	6.0	5.7	5.2	5.1	4.79	4.65	
		tan δ	380	280	220	220	310	410	500	530	694	782	
	80	ϵ'/ϵ_v	8.8	7.8	7.4	7.1	6.8	6.6	......	......	5.54	4.27	
		tan δ	940	600	420	320	300	350	......	......	819	1,630	
Polyamide resins:													
Nylon 66	25	ϵ'/ϵ_v	3.88	3.75	3.60	3.45	3.33	3.24	3.16	......	3.03		
		tan δ	144	193	233	254	257	244	210	......	128		
Nylon 610	25	ϵ'/ϵ_v	3.60	3.50	3.35	3.24	3.14	3.05	3.0	......	2.84	......	2.73
		tan δ	155	186	208	221	218	205	200	......	117	......	105
	84	ϵ'/ϵ_v	13.5	11.2	9.0	6.3	4.4	3.7	3.4	......	2.94		
		tan δ	2,350	1,400	1,580	2,030	1,720	1,150	670	......	356		
Cellulose derivatives:													
Acetates:													
Tenite I 008A H_4	26	ϵ'/ϵ_v	4.55	4.48	4.33	4.14	3.90	3.63	3.40	......	3.25	3.16	3.11
		tan δ	80	175	270	345	393	405	380	......	310	300	300
Tenite II 205A H_2	26	ϵ'/ϵ_v	3.54	3.50	3.44	3.38	3.28	3.18	3.05	......	2.80		
		tan δ	78	107	158	174	178	180	190	......	267		
Nitrate													
Pyralin	27	ϵ'/ϵ_v	10.8	8.4	7.5	7.0	6.6	6.1	5.2	......	3.74	3.32	
		tan δ	6,400	1,000	450	400	640	930	1,030	......	1,650	1,310	
	78	ϵ'/ϵ_v	......	7.5	6.7	6.3	6.2	6.1	5.2	......	4.0		
		tan δ	......	7,000	1,500	600	640	930	1,030	......	1,620		
Methyl cellulose													
Methocel	22	ϵ'/ϵ_v	7.6	6.8	6.4	6.1	5.7	4.9	4.3	......	3.35		
		tan δ	1,280	570	330	400	650	1,020	1,000	......	550		
Ethyl cellulose													
Ethocel LT5	25	ϵ'/ϵ_v	3.11	3.09	3.05	3.02	3.01	2.96	2.90	2.77	2.74	2.70	
		tan δ	75	65	63	76	113	150	160	170	210	250	
Silicone resins													
Formica G6	25	ϵ'/ϵ_v	3.99	3.91	3.87	3.85	3.82	3.82	3.82	3.81	3.79	3.74	
(field ∥ laminate)		tan δ	210	110	96	130	46	22	27	37	51	61	
(field ⊥ laminate)	25	ϵ'/ϵ_v	3.79	3.79	3.79	3.79	3.79	3.79					
		tan δ	13	11.5	10.5	10	10.5	13.3					

TABLE 5d-5. DIELECTRIC PROPERTIES OF SELECTED PLASTICS AND RUBBERS* (*Continued*)

Material	T, °C		Frequency, cps										
			1 × 10²	1 × 10³	1 × 10⁴	1 × 10⁵	1 × 10⁶	1 × 10⁷	1 × 10⁸	3 × 10⁸	3 × 10⁹	1 × 10¹⁰	2.5 × 10¹⁰
Polyvinyl resins:													
Polyethylene:													
Milled 3 min, 125°C	23	ϵ'/ϵ_v	2.25	2.25	2.25	2.25	2.25	2.25	2.25	....	2.25	2.24	
		tan δ	<2	<2	<2	<2	<2	<2	<2	....	5.8	6.6	
Milled 30 min, 125°C	23	ϵ'/ϵ_v	2.26	2.26	2.26	2.26	2.26	2.26	2.26	2.26	2.25	2.25	
		tan δ	<5	5	6	7	8	9	10	10.6	11.7	11.9	
Milled 30 min, 190°C	−12	ϵ'/ϵ_v	2.38	2.37	2.36	2.35	2.35	2.34	2.33	....	2.32	2.30	
(no antioxidant)		tan δ	24	21	19	18	21	28	39	....	36	22	
	23	ϵ'/ϵ_v	2.38	2.37	2.36	2.36	2.35	2.34	2.33	2.33	2.32	2.31	
		tan δ	28	28	27	27	28	30	42	51	50	44	
Polyisobutylene	25	ϵ'/ϵ_v	2.23	2.23	2.23	2.23	2.23	2.23	2.23	....	2.23		
		tan δ	4	1	1	<2	1	1	3	....	4.7		
Polyvinyl chloride acetate:													
Vinylite QYNA (unmodified polyvinyl chloride)	20	ϵ'/ϵ_v	3.18	3.10	3.02	2.96	2.88	2.87	2.85	....	2.84		
		tan δ	130	185	225	210	160	115	81	....	55		
	47	ϵ'/ϵ_v	3.60	3.52	3.41	3.28	3.14	3.02	2.92	....	2.81		
		tan δ	100	166	240	261	228	162	110	....	77		
	76	ϵ'/ϵ_v	3.92	3.83	3.68	3.3	3.0	2.87	2.8	2.8			
		tan δ	180	220	320	400	350	270	190	175			
	96	ϵ'/ϵ_v	6.60	5.30	4.40	3.7	3.3	2.8	2.7	2.7	....	2.6	
		tan δ	1,500	1,400	1,200	980	740	500	320	280	....	180	
	110	ϵ'/ϵ_v	9.9	8.6	6.8	5.6							
		tan δ	1,030	1,330	1,780	1,900							
Vinylite VG-5544	25	ϵ'/ϵ_v	7.72	7.20	6.40	5.25	4.13	3.45	3.05	2.99	2.94	2.82	2.80
		tan δ	570	640	1,060	1,500	1,550	1,200	650	460	185	159	150
Vinylite VG-5901, black	25	ϵ'/ϵ_v	6.5	5.5	4.6	3.9	3.4	3.1	3.0	2.94	2.88	2.83	
		tan δ	1,020	1,180	1,190	1,000	740	500	280	200	106	105	
Vinylite VU-1900, clear	24	ϵ'/ϵ_v	6.55	5.65	4.70	3.90	3.30	2.95	2.80	....	2.65	2.62	2.62
		tan δ	1,000	1,150	1,300	1,180	880	560	310	....	131	104	110
	79	ϵ'/ϵ_v	10.3	8.15	7.5	6.5	5.5	4.3	3.4	....	2.84	2.60	
		tan δ	7,300	1,250	720	800	1,550	2,700	1,550	....	498	351	

Vinylite VYHH	22	ϵ'/ϵ_v	3.20	3.12	3.06	3.00	2.91	2.88	2.83	…	2.79		
(acetate copolymer)		tan δ	100	130	155	150	140	110	90	…	76		
	47	ϵ'/ϵ_v	3.56	3.48	3.38	3.27	3.16	3.02	2.9	…	2.79		
		tan δ	110	142	190	227	206	152	114	…	92		
Vinylite VYNW	20	ϵ'/ϵ_v	3.20	3.15	3.05	2.96	2.90	2.84	2.8	…	2.74		
(acetate copolymer)		tan δ	135	165	197	190	150	110	80	…	59		
Geon 2046	23	ϵ'/ϵ_v	6.95	6.10	5.05	4.13	3.55	3.15	3.00	2.97	2.89	2.83	
		tan δ	820	1,100	1,320	1,200	890	570	300	211	116	116	
	80	ϵ'/ϵ_v	9.1	8.8	8.3	7.6	6.5	5.0	4.0	…	3.06	2.90	
		tan δ	250	300	410	680	1,540	2,800	1,500	…	484	328	
Lucoflex	25	ϵ'/ϵ_v	…	…	…	…	…	…	2.75				
		tan δ	…	…	…	…	…	…	170				
Polyvinyl chloride 1006	25	ϵ'/ϵ_v	6.1	…	4.55	…	3.3						
		tan δ	760	…	1,100	…	760						
Polyvinylidene and vinyl chloride:													
Saran B-115	23	ϵ'/ϵ_v	4.88	4.65	4.17	3.60	3.18	2.97	2.82	…	2.71	2.70	
		tan δ	450	630	885	845	570	310	180	…	72	51	
	84	ϵ'/ϵ_v	5.13	4.94	4.85	4.71	4.40	3.75	3.2	…	2.76		
		tan δ	800	210	130	320	780	1,300	900	…	242		
Polychlorotrifluoroethylene:													
Kel-F grade 300	25	ϵ'/ϵ_v	2.82	2.76	2.65	2.50	2.46	2.42	2.36	2.35	2.34	2.33	
		tan δ	148	225	212	140	96	75	54	51	66	59	
Polytetrafluoroethylene:													
Teflon	22	ϵ'/ϵ_v	2.1	2.1	2.1	2.1	2.1	2.1	2.1	2.1	2.1	2.08	2.08
		tan δ	<5	<3	<3	<3	<2	<2	<2	1.5	1.5	3.7	6
	100	ϵ'/ϵ_v	2.04	2.04	2.04	2.04	2.04	2.04	…	…	…	2.04	
		tan δ	10	4	2	<3	<2	<2	…	…	…	5.1	
Polyvinyl alcohol acetate:													
Elvanol 51A-05	25	ϵ'/ϵ_v	8.2	7.8	7.2	6.2	5.2	4.5	…	…	3.74	3.50	3.46
		tan δ	430	440	580	720	900	1,000	…	…	550	502	620
	85	ϵ'/ϵ_v	400	100	33	16	10	7.3	…	…	4.67		
		tan δ	15,000	13,000	9,000	3,600	2,300	2,000	…	…	1,770		
Polyvinyl acetals:													
Formvar, type E	26	ϵ'/ϵ_v	3.16	3.12	3.08	3.00	2.92	2.85	…	…	2.76	…	2.7
		tan δ	54	100	154	190	190	165	…	…	113	…	115
	88	ϵ'/ϵ_v	3.55	3.5	3.4	3.25	3.1	2.95	2.85	…	2.80		
		tan δ	60	83	102	145	213	310	300	…	227		
Butvar 55/98	27	ϵ'/ϵ_v	3.04	3.02	2.98	2.94	2.86	2.75	2.67	…	2.62		
		tan δ	41	59	108	161	215	216	177	…	172		

TABLE 5d-5. DIELECTRIC PROPERTIES OF SELECTED PLASTICS AND RUBBERS* (*Continued*)

Material	T, °C		Frequency, cps										
			1×10^2	1×10^3	1×10^4	1×10^5	1×10^6	1×10^7	1×10^8	3×10^8	3×10^9	1×10^{10}	2.5×10^{10}
Polyacrylates:													
Lucite HM-119 (now replaced by HM-140)	−12	ϵ'/ϵ_v	3.0	2.9	2.8	2.7	2.63	2.60	2.59	....	2.58	2.57	
		tan δ	330	250	190	140	102	70	55	....	35.4	34	
	23	ϵ'/ϵ_v	3.20	2.84	2.75	2.68	2.63	2.60	2.58	....	2.58	2.57	2.57
		tan δ	620	440	315	220	145	100	67	....	51.3	49	32
	81	ϵ'/ϵ_v	3.97	3.45	3.08	2.86	2.72	2.62	2.59	....	2.58	2.57	
		tan δ	600	820	720	540	380	220	130	....	77	95	
Plexiglas	27	ϵ'/ϵ_v	3.40	3.12	2.95	2.84	2.76	2.71	....	2.66	2.60	2.59	
		tan δ	605	465	300	200	140	100	....	62	57	67	
	80	ϵ'/ϵ_v	4.30	3.80	3.34	3.00	2.80	2.70	....	....	2.56		
		tan δ	700	895	800	520	320	210	....	....	79		
Polystyrene:													
Polystyrene (commercially molded) sheet stock	25	ϵ'/ϵ_v	2.56	2.56	2.56	2.56	2.56	2.56	2.55	2.55	2.55	2.54	2.54
		tan δ	<0.5	<0.5	<0.5	0.5	0.7	<2	<1	3.5	3.3	4.3	12
	80	ϵ'/ϵ_v	2.54	2.54	2.54	2.54	2.54	2.54	2.54	2.54	2.54	2.53	
		tan δ	9	2	<1	<2	<2	<2	<3	2.7	4.5	5.3	
Styron 475 (high impact)	25	ϵ'/ϵ_v	2.62	2.61	2.59	2.56	2.56	2.55	2.55	2.53†	2.53	2.53	
		tan δ	3.6	3.0	2.4	2.6	4.2	7.6	11	19†	36	17	
Styron 666	25	ϵ'/ϵ_v	2.54	2.54	2.54	2.54	2.54	2.54	2.54	2.54†	2.53	2.52	
		tan δ	1.75	1.1	<1	<1	0.7	1.2	2	2.7†	3.1	3.4	
Styrofoam 103.7	25	ϵ'/ϵ_v	1.03	1.03	1.03	1.03	1.03	1.03	....	....	1.03	1.03	
		tan δ	<2	<1	<1	<1	<2	<2	....	....	1	1.5	
Styrene copolymers, linear:													
Styrene-acrylonitrile copolymer	25	ϵ'/ϵ_v	2.96	2.95	2.92	2.87	2.80	2.78	2.77	2.77†	2.77	2.76	
		tan δ	59	63	67	67	64	50	41	40†	41	45	
Styrene copolymers, cross-linked:													
Rexolite 1422	25	ϵ'/ϵ_v	2.55	2.55	2.55	2.55	2.55	2.55	2.55	2.55†	2.54	2.54	
		tan δ	2.1	1.1	1	1.1	1.3	2	3.8	4.6†	4.8	4.7	
Polyesters:													
Laminac 4115	25	ϵ'/ϵ_v	3.24	3.22	3.20	3.17	3.12	3.07	2.94	2.87†	2.83	2.82	
		tan δ	37.5	43.2	68.3	113	135	147	141	107†	93	88	

Material	T, °C											
Marco resin MR-21C	25	ϵ'/ϵ_v	3.37	3.35	3.31	3.25	3.16	3.08	....	2.90	2.84	2.82
		tan δ	53	51	65	102	150	170	....	149	106	123
Paraplex P13 (flexible)	25	ϵ'/ϵ_v	4.02	4.00	3.92	3.92	3.65	3.32	3.08	2.89†	2.77	2.77
		tan δ	73	108	184	310	530	590	600	440†	320	290
Paraplex P43 (rigid)	25	ϵ'/ϵ_v	3.23	3.22	3.19	3.16	3.11	3.04	2.98	2.89†	2.85	2.85
		tan δ	33	43	68	98	130	160	160	110†	100	80
Selectron 5003	25	ϵ'/ϵ_v	....	3.4	....	....	3.1	3.1				
		tan δ	....	53	....	....	150	160				
Stypol 507E	25	ϵ'/ϵ_v	....	4.3	....	....	4.0	3.7				
		tan δ	....	190	....	....	230	290				
Alkyd resins:												
Alkyd, diisocyanate, foamed	25	ϵ'/ϵ_v	1.223	1.223	1.223	1.223	1.218	1.205	1.20	....	1.20	1.19
		tan δ	19.8	14.7	22.7	33.5	41	42	38	....	34	22
Red glyptal No. 1201	25	ϵ'/ϵ_v	4.9	4.5	4.1	4.0	3.9	3.8				
		tan δ	760	600	500	400	320	290				
Plaskon alkyd 422	25	ϵ'/ϵ_v	5.47	5.26	5.14	5.01	4.92	4.85	4.77	4.75†	4.75	4.72
(clay-filled)		tan δ	365	213	151	134	120	113	110	100†	104	126
Plaskon alkyd 440	25	ϵ'/ϵ_v	5.13	5.04	4.95	4.85	4.73	4.61	4.50	4.42†	4.38	4.33
(glass-filled)		tan δ	191	151	154	185	196	188	172	133†	137	146
Epoxy resins:												
Araldite casting resin	25	ϵ'/ϵ_v	3.67	3.67	3.67	3.65	3.62	3.49	3.35	3.28	3.09	3.01
CN-501		tan δ	17	24	50	110	190	270	340	340	270	220
Araldite E-134 (flexible)	25	ϵ'/ϵ_v	7.3	6.1	5.3	4.7	4.4	4.1	3.7	3.5	3.2	3.1
		tan δ	1,200	1,050	920	760	770	1,000	1,300	750	460	390
Hysol 6020	25	ϵ'/ϵ_v	3.96	3.90	3.82	3.67	3.54	3.42	3.29	....	3.01	2.99
		tan δ	68	113	206	260	272	266	299	....	274	252
Epon resin 828	25	ϵ'/ϵ_v	3.64	3.63	3.61	3.57	3.52	3.44	3.32	3.13†	3.04	2.91
		tan δ	31	38	68	111	142	191	264	220†	210	184
Rubbers												
Natural rubber:												
Hevea rubber, vulcanized	27	ϵ'/ϵ_v	2.94	2.94	2.93	2.88	2.74	2.52	2.42	....	2.36	
		tan δ	48	24	62	220	446	410	180	....	47	
Hevea rubber compound	27	ϵ'/ϵ_v	....	36	27	14	9.0	7.0	6.8	....	6.3	
		tan δ	....	25,000	12,000	4,000	2,500	1,600	850	....	234	
Gutta-percha	25	ϵ'/ϵ_v	2.61	2.60	2.58	2.55	2.53	2.50	2.47	2.45	2.40	2.38
		tan δ	5	4	9	21	42	80	120	110	60	50
Balata	25	ϵ'/ϵ_v	2.50	2.50	2.50	2.50	2.50	2.47	2.42	2.41	2.40	2.39
		tan δ	9	5	4	5	15	33	62	63	37	30
Buna rubber, GR-S (Buna S)	26	ϵ'/ϵ_v	2.66	2.66	2.66	2.65	2.56	2.52	2.52	....	2.49	2.44
compound		tan δ	7	9	25	60	120	160	95	....	56	50

TABLE 5d-5. DIELECTRIC PROPERTIES OF SELECTED PLASTICS AND RUBBERS* (*Continued*)

Material	T, °C		Frequency, cps										
			1×10^2	1×10^3	1×10^4	1×10^5	1×10^6	1×10^7	1×10^8	3×10^8	3×10^9	1×10^{10}	2.5×10^{10}
Butyl rubber, GR-I	25	ϵ'/ϵ_v	2.43	2.42	2.41	2.40	2.40	2.40	2.39	....	2.38	2.38	
compound		tan δ	50	60	58	38	22	15	10	....	9.3	9.9	
Nitrile rubber, Royalite	25	ϵ'/ϵ_v	5.41	5.20	5.12	4.87	4.41	3.62	....	3.18†	3.13	3.03	
149-11		tan δ	320	165	250	590	1,080	900	....	260†	200	190	
Neoprene	24	ϵ'/ϵ_v	6.70	6.60	6.54	6.47	6.26	5.54	4.5	4.24	4.00	4.00	4
		tan δ	160	110	115	150	380	1,190	900	636	339	261	250
Thiokol, type FA compound	23	ϵ'/ϵ_v	....	2,260	515	200	110	70	30	24	16	14	13.6
		tan δ	....	12,900	8,000	5,100	3,900	3,200	2,800	2,800	2,200	1,500	1,000
Silicone rubbers:													
Silastic 181	25	ϵ'/ϵ_v	3.36	3.30	3.26	3.23	3.20	3.19	3.18	3.16	3.11	3.09	
		tan δ	62	67	65	58	37	28	29	36	100	174	
Silastic 250	25	ϵ'/ϵ_v	3.19	3.18	3.17	3.16	3.10	3.07	3.05	3.04	3.02	3.00	
		tan δ	55	30	69	106	64	29	28	44	190	200	
SE-450	25	ϵ'/ϵ_v	3.09	3.08	3.08	3.08	3.07	3.06	3.05	3.00†	2.97	2.88	
		tan δ	16	7.2	5.3	7	11	17	30	74†	158	183	
SE-460	25	ϵ'/ϵ_v	3.14	3.12	3.11	3.10	3.10	3.09	3.07	3.05†	3.02	2.94	
		tan δ	56	54	44	25	12	15	23	57†	98	180	
SE-550	25	ϵ'/ϵ_v	3.14	3.12	3.10	3.10	3.10	3.08	3.06	3.02†	3.00	2.94	
		tan δ	13	7.8	6.5	7	9.5	16	31	84†	143	195	

* Taken from Tables of Dielectric Materials, vol. IV, Laboratory for Insulation Research, MIT Technical Report 57.
† Frequency = 1×10^9.

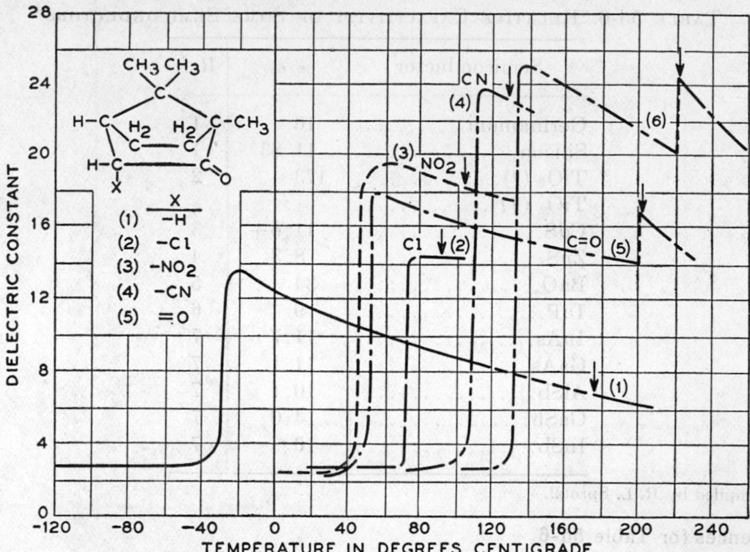

FIG. 5d-1. Dielectric constant of camphor (1), chlorocamphor (2), nitrocamphor (3), cyanocamphor (4), camphor quinone (5), and camphoric anhydride (6). Heavy arrow indicates the melting point; values are independent of frequency below 100 kc (see ref. 21.2).

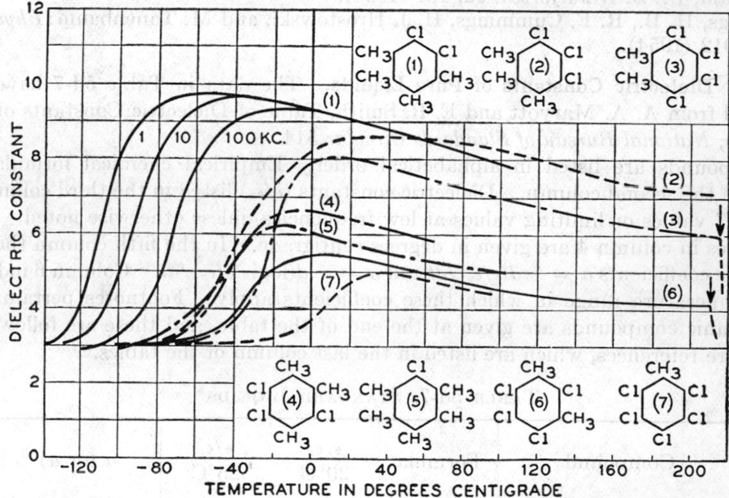

FIG. 5d-2. Dielectric constant of polar hexa-substituted chloromethylbenzenes at 100 kc. (1) dichlorophrenitene, (2) trichlorohemimellitene, (3) tetrachloro-*o*-xylene, (4) trichloropseudocumene, (5) pentamethylchlorobenzene, (6) tetrachloro-*m*-xylene, (7) pentachlorotoluene (see ref. 33).

TABLE 5d-6. RELATIVE CAPACITIVITY OF SOME SEMICONDUCTORS*

Semiconductor	ϵ/ϵ_v	Ref.
Germanium	16	1
Silicon	11.83	1
TiO_2 (*1*)	173	2
TiO_2 (*11*)		
CdS	11.6+	3
ZnS	8.3	4
BaO	34	5
InP	9	6
InAs	11.7	7
GaAs	11.1	7
AlSb	10.1	7
GaSb	14.0	7
InSb	16	7

* Compiled by R. L. Sproull.

References for Table 5d-6

1. Briggs, H. B.: *Phys. Rev.* **77,** 287 (1950).
2. Schmidt, W.: *Ann. Physik* **9,** 919 (1902); **11,** 114 (1903).
3. Kroger, F. A., and H. J. Vink: Philips, Eindhoven.
4. Hohendahl, K.: *Kgl. Danske Videnskab. Selskab, Mat.-fys. Medd.* **16** (2) (1938).
5. Bever, R. S., and R. L. Sproull: *Phys. Rev.* **83,** 801 (1951).
6. Oswald, F.: *Z. Naturforsch.* **9a,** 181 (1954).
7. Briggs, H. B., R. F. Cummings, H. J. Hrostowski, and M. Tanenbaum: *Phys. Rev.* **93,** 912 (1954).

5d-3. Dielectric Constants of Pure Liquids. The data in Table 5d-7 have been selected from A. A. Maryott and E. R. Smith, Table of Dielectric Constants of Pure Liquids, *National Bureau of Standards Circular* 514.

Compounds are listed in alphabetical order. Empirical chemical formulas are given in the second column. Dielectric constants (ϵ/ϵ_v) listed in the third column are "static" values or limiting values at low frequencies unless otherwise noted. Temperatures in column 4 are given in degrees centigrade. In the fifth column the temperature coefficients $a = -d(\epsilon/\epsilon_v)/dt$ and $\alpha = -d(\log_{10} \epsilon/\epsilon_v)/dt$. Column 6 indicates the temperature range in which these coefficients apply. Footnotes pertaining to the organic compounds are given at the end of the table, and these are followed by literature references, which are listed in the last column of the tables.

TABLE 5d-7. STANDARD LIQUIDS*

Compound	Formula	ϵ/ϵ_v 20°C	ϵ/ϵ_v 25°C	a (or α)
Benzene	C_6H_6	2.284	2.274	0.0020
Cyclohexane	C_6H_{12}	2.023	2.015	0.0016
Chlorobenzene	C_6H_5Cl	5.708	5.621	0.00133(α)

* These liquids are recommended as reference standards. They may be used to calibrate dielectric measuring cells.

Table 5d-8. Inorganic Liquids

Compound	Formula	ϵ/ϵ_v	t, °C	a (or α) $\times 10^2$	Range t_1, t_2	Ref.
Ammonia	NH_3	25	−77.7			103
		22.4	−33.4			98
		18.9	5			117
		17.8	15			
		16.9	25			
		16.3	35			
Argon	A	1.53_8[a]	−191	0.34	−191, −184	58
Bromine	Br_2	3.09	20	0.7	0, 50	45, 62, 150
Carbon dioxide	CO_2	1.60[b]	20			96
Chlorine	Cl_2	2.10_1	−50	0.31	−65, −33	128
Deuterium	D_2	1.277	20°K	0.4	18.8, 21.2°K	169
Deuterium oxide	D_2O	78.25	25	[d]	0.4, 98	140
Dinitrogen oxide	N_2O	1.97	−90			9, 66
Dinitrogen tetroxide	N_2O_4	2.5_6[c]	15			17
Fluorine	F_2	1.54	−202	0.19	−216, −190	128
Helium	He	1.055_5	2.06°K			29, 51, 52
		1.055_9	2.30[f]			
		1.055_3	2.63			
		1.053_9	3.09			
		1.051_8	3.58			
		1.048	4.19			
Hydrogen	H_2	1.228	20.4°K	0.34	14, 21°K	30, 83, 145, 152, 169
Hydrogen bromide	HBr	7.00	−85	0.26(α)	−85, −70	94
		3.8[e]	25			19
Hydrogen chloride	HCl	6.35	−15	0.288(α)	−85, −15	115
		12.	−113			73, 94, 128
		4.6	28			19
Hydrogen fluoride	HF	17_5	−73			53
		13_4	−42			
		11_1	−27			
		84	0			
Hydrogen iodide	HI	3.39	−50	0.8	−51, −37	94
		2.9[e]	22			19
Hydrogen peroxide	H_2O_2	84.2	0	[g]	−30, 20	196
Hydrogen sulfide	H_2S	9.26	−85.5			103
		9.05	−78.5			110
Iodine	I_2	$11._1$	118			82
		$11._7$	140			
		$13._0$	168			
Nitrogen	N_2	1.454	−203	0.29	−210, −195	36, 136, 152
Oxygen	O_2	1.507	−193	0.24	−218, −183	41, 128, 148
Phosphorus	P	4.10	34			88
		4.06	46			
		3.86	85			
Selenium	Se	5.40	250	0.25	237, 301	139
Sulfur	S	3.52	118	[h]		87
		3.48	231			
Sulfur dioxide	SO_2	17.6	−20	0.287(α)		201
		15.0_8	0			199
		$14._1$	20	7.7	14, 140	3, 8, 13
		2.1_0	154[i]			
Sulfur trioxide	SO_3	3.11	18			131
Water	H_2O	78.54	25	[j]	0, 100	64, 71, 140
		34.5_9	200	[k]	100, 370	143, 75, 80, 83

[a] Depressed numbers indicate uncertainty in that number.
[b] At pressure of 50 atm.
[c] $\nu = 3.6 \times 10^8$ cps.
[d] $\epsilon = 78.25[1 - 4.617(10^{-3})(t - 25) + 1.22(10^{-5})(t - 25)^2 - 2.7(10^{-8})(t - 25)^3]$; average deviation $\pm 0.04\%$.
[e] $\nu = 4 \times 10^8$ cps.
[f] Liquid transition and discontinuity in variation of dielectric constant with temperature at 2.295°K. Values reported in ref. 290 agree closely with those listed.
[g] $g = 84.2 - 0.62t + 0.0032t^2$.
[h] Graphical data in the range 118 to 350°C show a minimum near 160° and a broad maximum near 200°.
[i] Critical temperature.
[j] $\epsilon/\epsilon_v = 78.54[1 - 4.579(10^{-3})(t - 25) + 1.19(10^{-5})(t - 25)^2 - 2.8(10^{-8})(t - 25)^3]$; average deviation $\pm 0.03\%$.
[k] $\epsilon/\epsilon_v = 5321/T + 233.76 - 0.9297T + 0.001417T^2 - 0.0000008292T^3$.

TABLE 5d-9. ORGANIC LIQUIDS

Compound	Formula	ϵ/ϵ_v	t, °C	a (or α) $\times 10^2$	Range t_1, t_2	Ref.
Acetaldehyde	C_2H_4O	21.$_8$[a]	10			5
		21.1[a]	21			
Acetic acid	$C_2H_4O_2$	6.15	20			68, 137
		6.29	40			
		6.62	70			
Acetic anhydride	$C_4H_6O_3$	22.$_4$	1			20
		20.$_7$	19			
Acetone	C_3H_6O	20.7$_0$	25	0.205(α)	−60, 40	160, 187, 105, 122
		17.7	56			
Acetonitrile	C_2H_3N	37.5	20	16.	15, 25	11, 20, 26, 86
		26.$_6$	82			
Acetophenone	C_8H_8O	17.39	25	4.	At 25	95, 175, 26
		8.64	202			
Acetyl acetone (2,4-pentanedione)	$C_5H_8O_2$	25.$_7$[a]	20			5, 15, 16
Amyl acetate	$C_7H_{14}O_2$	4.75	20	1.2	At 20	5, 6, 8, 39
Aniline	C_6H_7N	6.89	20	0.148(α)	0, 50	4, 46, 85, 106, 113, 171
		5.93	70			129
		4.54	184.6			26
Anisole (methoxybenzene)	C_7H_8O	4.33	25	1.1	20, 40	46, 98, 175, 188
		3.89	70			129
Benzaldehyde	C_7H_6O	19.$_7$	0			20, 38
		17.$_8$	20			
Benzene	C_6H_6	2.284	20	0.200	10, 60	10, 54, 95, 125, 170, 178, 186, 193, 197
		2.073	129			14
		1.966	182			
Benzonitrile	C_7H_5N	25.20	25	0.157(α)	0, 25	60, 95
		24.02	40			
		22.10	70			
Benzylamine	C_7H_9N	5.5	1			20
		4.6	21			
		4.3	50			
Benzyl alcohol	C_7H_8O	13.1	20			20, 38
		9.47	70			129
		6.6	132			82
Bromal	C_2HBr_3O	7.6[n]	20			21
m-Bromoaniline	C_6H_6BrN	13.$_0$[n]	19			21
p-Bromoanisole	C_7H_7BrO	7.06	30	1.6	30, 40	175
Bromobenzene	C_6H_5Br	5.40	25	0.115(α)	0, 70	42, 43, 61, 129, 185
1-Bromobutane	C_4H_9Br	7.07	20	0.150(α)	10, 90	69, 163, 185
		11.1	−90			
		9.26	−50			
		7.88	−10			
2-Bromobutane		8.64	25	3.30	1, 55	185
1-Bromo-1-butene[q] (bp 86°C)	C_4H_7Br	5.0$_5$	*ca.* 20			31
1-Bromo-1-butene[q] (bp 98°C)		5.8$_9$	*ca.* 20			31
2-Bromo-2-butene[r]		6.7$_6$	*ca.* 20			31
2-Bromo-2-butene[s]		5.3$_8$	*ca.* 20			31
1-Bromo-2-chlorobenzene	C_6H_4BrCl	6.8$_0$	20			58
1-Bromo-3-chlorobenzene		4.5$_8$	20			58
1-Bromo-2-chloroethane	C_2H_4BrCl	7.14	20	0.140(α)	10, 90	78
		7.98	−10			
cis-1-Bromo-2-chloroethylene	C_2H_2BrCl	7.3$_1$	17			32
trans-1-Bromo-2-chloroethylene		2.5$_0$	17			32

Footnotes appear at end of table.

TABLE 5d-9. ORGANIC LIQUIDS (*Continued*)

Compound	Formula	ϵ/ϵ_v	t, °C	a (or α) $\times 10^2$	Range t_1, t_2	Ref.
Bromocyclohexane	$C_6H_{11}Br$	7.92	25			185
		11.$_0$	−65			158
1-Bromodecane	$C_{10}H_{21}Br$	4.44	25	1.07	25, 55	185
		4.75	1			
Bromoform	$CHBr_3$	4.39	20	0.105(α)	10, 70	69, 105, 107
Bromoethane	C_2H_5Br	9.39	20	0.196(α)	−30, 30	23, 49, 67, 89, 185
		16.1	−90			
		13.6	−60			
4-Bromoheptane	$C_7H_{15}Br$	6.81	22			65
1-Bromohexadecane	$C_{16}H_{33}Br$	3.71	25	0.7	25, 55	185, 198
1-Bromohexane	$C_6H_{13}Br$	5.82	25	1.73	25, 55	185
		6.30	1			
Bromomethane	CH_3Br	9.82	0	[k]	−80, 0	67
1-Bromo-2-methylpropane	C_4H_9Br	7.18	25	2.8	1, 55	185
2-Bromo-2-methylpropane		10.1$_5$	25	5.20	−15, 55	142, 163, 185
1-Bromonaphthalene	$C_{10}H_7Br$	4.83	25	0.87	25, 55	185
1-Bromononane	$C_9H_{19}Br$	5.42	−20	1.3	−35, 16	195
		4.74	25	1.13	1, 55	185
1-Bromooctadecane	$C_{18}H_{37}Br$	3.53	30	0.5	27, 58	198
1-Bromoctane	$C_8H_{17}Br$	6.35	−50	1.9	−55, −39	195
		5.00	25	1.33	1, 55	185
1-Bromopentadecane	$C_{15}H_{31}Br$	3.89	20			195
1-Bromopentane	$C_5H_{11}Br$	6.32	25	0.152(α)	−45, 55	141, 185
		9.90	−90			
1-Bromopropane	C_3H_7Br	8.09	25	3.35	1, 55	185
2-Bromopropane		9.46	25	4.40	1, 55	185
		16.1	−85			141
3-Bromo-1-propene	C_3H_5Br	7.4	1			20
		7.0	19			
1-Bromotetradecane	$C_{14}H_{29}Br$	3.84	25	0.80	1, 55	185
o-Bromotoluene	C_7H_7Br	4.28	58			43
m-Bromotoluene		5.36	58			43
p-Bromotoluene		5.49	58			43
1-Bromotridecane	$C_{13}H_{27}Br$	4.20	10			195
1,4-Butanediol	$C_4H_{10}O_2$	32.$_9$	15			157
		30.$_2$	30			
1-Butanol	$C_4H_{10}O$	17.8	20	0.300(α)	−40, 20	56, 146, 189
		17.1	25	0.335(α)	25, 70	190
		8.2	118			26
2-Butanol		15.8	25			146
2-Butanone	C_4H_8O	18.5$_1$	20	0.207(α)	−60, 60	160
Butyl ether	$C_8H_{18}O$	3.06	25			98, 132
Butyraldehyde	C_4H_8O	13.4	26			26
		10.8	77			
Butyronitrile	C_4H_7N	20.$_3$[b]	21			11
Carbon dioxide	CO_2	1.604[c]	0			96
Carbon disulfide	CS_2	2.641	20	0.268	−90, 130	14, 100, 124, 130, 135, 161, 197
		3.001	−110			
		2.19	180			
Carbon tetrachloride	CCl_4	2.238	20	0.200	−10, 60	100, 111, 154, 161, 165, 197
Chloral	C_2HCl_3O	4.9$_4$	20	0.17(α)	15, 45	27
		7.6	−40			
		4.2	62			
m-Chloroaniline	C_6H_6ClN	13.$_4$[n]	19			21
Chlorobenzene	C_6H_5Cl	5.708	20			42, 95, 112, 171
		5.621	25			

TABLE 5d-9. ORGANIC LIQUIDS (*Continued*)

Compound	Formula	ϵ/ϵ_v	t, °C	a (or α) $\times 10^2$	Range t_1, t_2	Ref.
Chlorobenzene (*Continued*)		5.71	20			26, 48, 49, 61, 86, 92, 123, 129, 137
		7.28	−50			
		6.30	−20			
		4.21	130			
1-Chlorobutane	C_4H_9Cl	7.39	20	0.173(α)	−10, 70	69, 162
		12.2	−90			
		9.94	−50			
		9.07	−30			
3-Chloro-1, 2-epoxy-propane(epichlorohydrin)	C_3H_5ClO	25.$_6$	1			20
		22.$_6$	22			
Chloroethane	C_2H_5Cl	6.2$_9$	170			13
		6.0$_6$	179			
		5.1$_3$	183			
		4.6$_8$	185.5[h]			
Chloroform	$CHCl_3$	4.806	20	0.160(α)	0, 50	60, 100, 111
		6.76	−60			49, 67, 123
		6.12	−40			
		5.61	−20			
		3.7$_1$	100			
		3.3$_3$	140			
		2.9$_3$	180			
4-Chloroheptane	$C_7H_{15}Cl$	6.54	22			
Chloromethane	CH_3Cl	12.6	−20	t	−70, −20	67, 86
1-Chloro-2-methyl propane	C_4H_9Cl	12.2	−120			167
		10.1	−89			
		7.87	−38			
		6.49	14			
2-Chloro-2-methyl propane		10.9$_5$	0	0.225(α)	−23, 30	77, 142
1-Chloronaphthalene	$C_{10}H_7Cl$	5.04	25	1.07	1, 55	185
1-Chloro-2-nitrobenzene	$C_6H_4ClNO_2$	37.$_7$	50			118
		31.$_8$	80			
		27.$_3$	110			
		23.$_7$	140			
		21.$_6$	163			
1-Chloro-3-nitrobenzene		20.$_9$	50			118
		18.$_1$	80			
		15.$_9$	110			
		14.$_1$	140			
		13.$_0$	160			
1-Chloro-4-nitrobenzene		8.0$_9$	120	0.16(α)	85, 160	
1-Chlorooctane	$C_8H_{17}Cl$	5.05	25	1.70	1, 55	185
1-Chloropentane	$C_5H_{11}Cl$	6.6	11			1
o-Chlorophenol	C_6H_5ClO	6.31	25	2.7	25, 58	39, 43, 176
p-Chlorophenol		9.47	55	3.7	55, 65	43, 176
1-Chloropropane	C_3H_7Cl	7.7[n]	20			21
3-Chloro-1,2-propanediol	$C_3H_7ClO_2$	37	3			20
		31	19			
1-Chloro-2-propanone	C_3H_5ClO	30[n]	19			21
3-Chloro-1-propane	C_3H_5Cl	8.7	1			20
		8.2	20			
α-Chlorotoluene	C_7H_7Cl	7.0	13			1
o-Chlorotoluene	C_7H_7Cl	4.45	20			58
		4.16	58			43
m-Chlorotoluene		5.55	20			58
		5.04	58			43
p-Chlorotoluene		6.08	20			58
		5.55	58			43

TABLE 5d-9. ORGANIC LIQUIDS (*Continued*)

Compound	Formula	ϵ/ϵ_v	t, °C	a (or α) $\times 10^2$	Range t_1, t_2	Ref.
Cinnamaldehyde	C_9H_8O	16.9	24			76
o-Cresol	C_7H_8O	11.5	25	11	25, 30	176
m-Cresol		11.8	25	0.41(α)	15, 50	38, 99, 176
p-Cresol		9.9_1	58			43
Cyanogen	C_2N_2	2.5_2	23			12
1,3-Cyclohexadiene	C_6H_8	2.6_6	−89			158
1,4-Cyclohexadione	$C_6H_8O_2$	4.4_0	78			158
Chlorocyclohexane	$C_6H_{11}Cl$	7.6	25			70
		$10._9$	−47			158
Cyclohexanol	$C_6H_{12}O$	15.0	25	0.437(α)	20, 66	24, 70, 137
		7.2_4	100			
		4.8_8	150			
Cyclohexanone	$C_6H_{10}O$	18.3	20			24, 70
		$19._9$	−40			158
Cyclohexyltrifluoromethane	$C_7H_{11}F_3$	$11._9$	−85			158
Cyclopentanol	$C_5H_{10}O$	$18._0$	20	0.38(α)	At 20	153
		$25._5$	−20			158
Cyclopentanone	C_5H_8O	$16._3$	−51			158
Decanol	$C_{10}H_{22}O$	8.1	20			97
m-Dibromobenzene	$C_6H_4Br_2$	4.80	20			37, 58
o-Dibromobenzene		7.35	20			37, 58
p-Dibromobenzene		2.5_7	95			37
dl-2,3-Dibromobutane	$C_4H_8Br_2$	5.75_8	25			159
meso-2,3-Dibromobutane	$C_4H_8Br_2$	6.24_5	25			159
1,2-Dibromoethane	$C_2H_4Br_2$	4.78	25	0.60	10, 55	10, 98, 105,
		4.09	131			133, 185, 26
cis-1,2-Dibromoethylene	$C_2H_2Br_2$	7.7_2	0			101
		7.0_8	25			
trans-1,2-Dibromoethylene		2.9_7	0			101
		2.8_8	25			
1,2-Dibromoheptane	$C_7H_{14}Br_2$	3.77	25			102
Dibromomethane	CH_2Br_2	7.77	10			69
		6.68	40			
1,2-Dibromo-2-methyl propane	$C_4H_8Br_2$	4.1^n	20			21
1,2-Dibromopropane	$C_3H_6Br_2$	4.3^n	20			21
Dibutyl phthalate	$C_{16}H_{22}O_4$	6.43_6	30	1.98	30, 35	200
Dibutyl sebacate	$C_{18}H_{34}O_4$	4.54_0	30	1.07	30, 35	200
1,4-Dichlorobutane	$C_4H_8Cl_2$	8.90	25	3.07	1, 55	185
m-Dichlorobenzene	$C_6H_4Cl_2$	5.04	25	0.120(α)	0, 50	48
o-Dichlorobenzene		9.93	25	0.194(α)	0, 50	48
p-Dichlorobenzene		2.41	50	0.18	50, 80	37, 67
β,β'-Dichlorodiethyl ether	$C_4H_8Cl_2O$	21.2	20			105
1,1-Dichloroethane	$C_2H_4Cl_2$	$10._0$	18			95, 112, 178
1,2-Dichloroethane		10.65	20			86, 92
		10.36	25			172, 185
		10.36^x	25			
		12.7	−10			
1,1-Dichloroethylene	$C_2H_2Cl_2$	4.6_7	16			32
cis-1,2-Dichloroethylene		9.20	25			151
trans-1,2-Dichloroethylene		2.14	25			130, 151
Dichloromethane	CH_2Cl_2	9.08	20	*i*	−80, 25	67, 194
1,2-Dichloro-2-methyl propane	$C_4H_8Cl_2$	14.0	−100			167
		10.8	−60			
		8.71	−20			
		7.22	20			
1,2-Dichloropropane	$C_3H_6Cl_2$	8.93	26			76
2,2-Dichloropropane		10.1_9	20	0.247(α)	−33, 20	155

TABLE 5d-9. ORGANIC LIQUIDS (*Continued*)

Compound	Formula	ϵ/ϵ_v	t, °C	a (or α) $\times 10^2$	Range t_1, t_2	Ref.
1,1-Dichloro-2-propanone	$C_3H_4Cl_2O$	$14._6^{n}$	20			21
2,5-Dichlorostyrene	$C_8H_6Cl_2$	2.58	25			190
Diethyl sebacate	$C_{14}H_{26}O_4$	5.00	30	1.2	30, 40	175
m-Diiodobenzene	$C_6H_4I_2$	4.2_5	25			37
o-Diiodobenzene		5.7	20			37
p-Diiodobenzene		2.8_8	120			37
cis-1,2-Diiodoethylene	$C_2H_2I_2$	4.4_6	83			31
trans-1,2-Diiodoethylene		3.1_9	83			31
Diiodomethane	CH_2I_2	5.32	25			69
Dimethoxymethane (methylal)	$C_3H_8O_2$	2.7^a	20			15
Dimethylamine	C_2H_7N	6.32	0			182
		5.26	25			
Dioctyl phthalate	$C_{24}H_{38}O_4$	5.1	25			181
Dioctyl sebacate	$C_{26}H_{50}O_4$	4.01	26			190
Diphenyl	$C_{12}H_{10}$	2.53	75	0.18	75, 155	47
Dodecanol	$C_{12}H_{26}O$	6.5	25			192
Epichlorohydrin (3-chloro-1,2-epoxypropane)	C_3H_5ClO	$22._6$	22			20
		$25._6$	1			
Erythritol (1,2,3,4-butanetetrol)	$C_4H_{10}O_4$	$28._2$	120			91, 97
1,2-Ethanediamine	$C_2H_8N_2$	14.2	20	10	10, 27	133
Ethanethiol	C_2H_6S	6.9_1	15			157
Ethanol	C_2H_6O	24.30	25			79, 116
		24.3^x	25	0.270(α)	−5, 70	79, 80, 137
		41.0^x	−60	0.297(α)	−110, −20	56
Ethylamine	C_2H_7N	6.94	10	^{o}	−20,10	86
Ethyl alcohol (see Ethanol)						
(Ethylene) glycol	$C_2H_6O_2$	$37._7$	25	0.224(α)	20, 100	80
Ethylene oxide	C_2H_4O	$13._9$	−1			20
Ethyl ether	$C_4H_{10}O$	4.335	20	2.0	At 20	10, 24, 44, 68, 171
		4.34^x	20	0.217(α)	−40, 30	137
		10.4	−116			120
		3.97	40	0.170(α)	40, 140	14
		2.1_2	180			
		1.8_9	190			
		1.5_3	193.3^h			
Ethyl mercaptan (see Ethanethiol)						
Ethyl nitrate	$C_2H_5NO_3$	$19._4$	20	9	0, 50	5, 15, 20
Fenchone	$C_{10}H_{16}O$	$12._8$	21			153
Fluorobenzene	C_6H_5F	5.42	25			104, 174, 58
		4.76	60			
1-Fluoropentane	$C_5H_{11}F$	4.24	20			163
o-Fluorotoluene	C_7H_7F	4.22	30			174
		3.88	60			
m-Fluorotoluene		5.42	30			174
		4.90	60			
p-Fluorotoluene		5.86	30			174
		5.34	60			
Formamide	CH_3NO	109	20	72	18, 25	183, 191
Formic acid	CH_2O_2	$58._5^a$	16			5
Furfural	$C_5H_4O_2$	$46._9$	1			20
		$41._9$	20			
		$34._9$	50			
Glycerol	$C_3H_8O_3$	42.5	25	0.208(α)	0, 100	25, 80, 122
Glycolonitrile	C_2H_3NO	68^a	20			15
Guaiacol (see *o*-Methoxyphenol)						
Heptaldehyde	$C_7H_{14}O$	9.07	2			65

TABLE 5d-9. ORGANIC LIQUIDS (*Continued*)

Compound	Formula	ϵ/ϵ_v	t, °C	a (or α) × 10²	Range t_1, t_2	Ref.
Heptane	C_7H_{16}	1.924	20	0.140	−50, 50	50, 63, 197
		2.074	−90			
		1.850	70			
4-Heptanol	$C_7H_{16}O$	6.17	22			65
4-Heptanone	$C_7H_{14}O$	12.5_8	20	0.205(α)	0, 100	65, 160
		15.1	−20			
		8.00	120			
Hexachloro-1,3-butadiene	C_4Cl_6	2.55	25			190
1-Hexadecanol	$C_{16}H_{34}O$	3.82	50	1.7	48, 67	126, 134
1-Hexanol	$C_6H_{14}O$	13.3	25	0.35(α)	15, 35	74, 119
		8.5_5	75			
Hydrocyanic acid	HCN	$158._1$	0	[i]	−13, 18	173
		$114._9$	20	0.63(α)	18, 26	
Iodobenzene	C_6H_5I	4.63	20			163, 58
1-Iodobutane	C_4H_9I	6.22	20	0.135(α)	0, 80	26, 69, 162
		8.89	−80			
		7.53	−40			
		4.52	130			
Iodoethane	C_2H_5I	7.82	20	0.150(α)	−20, 70	56, 137
		12.3	−90			
		10.2	−50			
1-Iodohexadecane	$C_{16}H_{33}I$	3.50	20			162
1-Iodohexane	$C_6H_{13}I$	5.37	20			162
Iodomethane	CH_3I	7.00	20	[m]	−70, 40	67
1-Iodo-2-methyl propane	C_4H_9I	6.47	20			162
2-Iodo-2-methyl propane		8.42	20			162
		10.5	−33			142
1-Iodooctane	$C_8H_{17}I$	4.62	25	1.17	1,55	162, 185
1-Iodopentane	$C_5H_{11}I$	5.81	20			162
1-Iodopropane	C_3H_7I	7.00	20			162
2-Iodopropane		8.19	20			162
p-Iodotoluene	C_7H_7I	4.4	35			22
Isobutyronitrile	C_4H_7N	20.4[b]	24			11
Isocapronitrile	$C_6H_{11}N$	15.5[b]	22			11
Isoquinoline	C_9H_7N	10.7	25			106
Lactonitrile	C_3H_5NO	38[a]	20			15
Linoleic acid	$C_{18}H_{32}O_2$	2.61	0			138, 156, 177
		2.71	20			
		2.70	70			
		2.60	120			
1-α-Menthol	$C_{10}H_{20}O$	3.95	42			158
Menthone	$C_{10}H_{18}O$	8.8[b]	18			18, 153
		$11._8$	−35			
Methane	CH_4	1.70	−173	0.2	−181, −159	66
Methanol	CH_4O	32.63	25	0.264(α)	5, 55	143, 179
		64	−113			7
		54	−80			
		40	−20			
Methoxybenzene (anisole)	C_7H_8O	4.33	25	1.1	20, 40	46, 98, 175, 188
		3.89	70			
2-Methoxyethanol	$C_3H_8O_2$	$16._0$	30			129, 176
o-Methoxyphenol (guaiacol)	$C_7H_8O_2$	$11._7$[n]	28			21
Methyl alcohol (see Methanol)						
Methylamine	CH_5N	11.4	−10	0.26(α)	−30, −10	86
		9.4	25			182
N-Methylaniline	C_7H_9N	5.97	22			106, 113, 12, 20
4-Methylcyclohexanol	$C_7H_{14}O$	$13._3$	20	0.41(α)	At 20	153

TABLE 5d-9. ORGANIC LIQUIDS (*Continued*)

Compound	Formula	ϵ/ϵ_v	t, °C	a (or α) $\times 10^2$	Range t_1, t_2	Ref.
2-Methylcyclohexanone	$C_7H_{12}O$	16.$_4$	−15			158
		14.$_0$	20			153
Methyl ether	C_2H_6O	5.02	25	2.38	25, 100	108
		2.97	110			
		2.64	120			
		2.37	125			
		2.26	126.1			
		1.90	127.6[p]			
Methyl nitrate	CH_3NO_3	23.$_5$[b]	18			12
2-Methyl-1-propanol	$C_4H_{10}O$	17.7	25	0.377(α)	20, 90	10, 60, 74, 80, 146
		34.	−80			
		26.	−34			
2-Methyl-2-propanol		10.9	30			77
		8.49	50			
		6.89	70			
2-Methylpyridine (α-picoline)	C_6H_7N	9.8[b]	20			12
Morpholine	C_4H_9NO	7.33	25			149
Naphthalene	$C_{10}H_8$	2.54	85			130, 166
1-Naphthonitrile	$C_{11}H_7N$	16.$_0$[b]	70	0.16(α)	22, 70	12
o-Nitroaniline	$C_6H_6N_2O_2$	34.$_5$	90	3	90, 110	175
p-Nitroaniline		56.$_3$	160	6	160, 180	175
Nitrobenzene	$C_6H_5NO_2$	34.82	25	0.225(α)	10, 80	6 , 95
		20.8	130	0.164(α)	130, 211	
		24.9	90			
		22.7	110			
m-Nitrobenzyl alcohol	$C_7H_7NO_3$	22.[n]	20			21
Nitromethane	CH_3NO_2	35.8$_7$	30	0.189(α)	12, 92	55, 200
o-Nitrophenol	$C_6H_5NO_3$	17.3	50	6.4	50, 60	176
1-Nitropropane	$C_3H_7NO_2$	23.2$_4$	30	10.1	30, 35	200
2-Nitropropane		25.5$_2$	30	10.9	30, 35	200
o-Nitrotoluene	$C_7H_7NO_2$	27.4	20	15.	At 20	10, 60
		21.$_6$	58			43
		11.8	222			26
m-Nitrotoluene		23.$_8$	20			35
		21.$_9$	58			43
p-Nitrotoluene		22.$_2$	58			43
Octadecanol	$C_{18}H_{38}O$	3.42	58			192
		3.35	63			
1-Octanol	$C_8H_{18}O$	10.3$_4$	20	0.410(α)	20, 60	56, 57
		13.3	−10			
		11.3	10			
2-Octanone	$C_8H_{16}O$	10.3$_9$	20	0.215(α)	0, 60	160
		12.5	−20			
		7.42	100			
		6.10	160			
Olcic acid	$C_{18}H_{34}O_2$	2.46	20			93, 121, 138, 156, 177
		2.45	60			
		2.41	100			
Palmitic acid	$C_{16}H_{32}O_2$	2.30	71			121, 127
Pentachloroethane	C_2HCl_5	3.73	20			28, 39, 105
2,4-Pentanedione (acetylacetone)	$C_5H_8O_2$	25.$_7$[a]	20			5, 15, 16
1-Pentanol	$C_5H_{12}O$	13.9	25	0.23(α)	15, 35	97, 119, 146
2-Pentanone	$C_5H_{10}O$	15.4$_5$	20	0.195(α)	−40, 80	160
		22.0	−60			
3-Pentanone		17.0$_0$	20	0.225(α)	0, 80	160
		19.4	−20			
		19.8	−40			

TABLE 5d-9. ORGANIC LIQUIDS (*Continued*)

Compound	Formula	ϵ/ϵ_v	t, °C	a (or α) $\times 10^2$	Range t_1, t_2	Ref.
Phenol	C_6H_6O	9.78	60	0.32(α)	40, 70	43, 86, 99, 129
Phenyl ether	$C_{12}H_{10}O$	3.65	30	0.7	30, 50	46, 175
Phosgene	CCl_2O	4.7_2^b	0			34
		4.3_4^b	22			
α-Picoline (see 2-Methylpyridine)						
Piperidine	$C_5H_{11}N$	5.8^b	22			12
Propane	C_3H_8	1.61	0	0.20	−90, 15	114
1,2-Propanediol	$C_3H_8O_2$	$32._0$	20	0.27(α)	At 20	153
1,3-Propanediol		$35._0$	20	0.23(α)	At 20	153
1-Propanol	C_3H_8O	20.1	25	0.293(α)	20, 90	80, 146, 190
		38.	−80			
		29	−34			
2-Propanol		18.3	25	0.310(α)	20, 70	80, 146
Propene	C_3H_6	1.87_5	20			108
		1.79_5	45			
		1.69_0	65			
		1.53_0	85			
		1.44_1	90			
		1.33_1	91.9^h			
Propionaldehyde	C_3H_6O	$18._5^a$	17			5
Propionitrile	C_3H_5N	$31._0$	0			11, 15, 20
		$27._2$	20			
		$24._3$	50			
Propyl alcohol (normal, see 1-Propanol, iso, see 2-Propanol)						
Propyl butyrate	$C_7H_{14}O_2$	4.3^n	20			21
Propyl ether	$C_6H_{14}O$	3.3_9	26			76
Pyridine	C_5H_5N	12.3	25			83, 35, 106, 26
		9.4	116			
Quinoline	C_9H_7N	9.00	25			26, 105, 106
		5.05	238			
Salicylaldehyde	$C_7H_6O_2$	$17._1$	30	7	30, 40	176
Siloxanes	$(C_2H_6OSi)_n$					
Octamethylcyclotetrasiloxane	$n = 4$	2.39	20			180
Decamethylcyclopentasiloxane	$n = 5$	2.50	20			180
Dodecamethylcyclohexasiloxane	$n = 6$	2.59	20			180
Tetradecamethylcycloheptasiloxane	$n = 7$	2.68	20			180
Hexadecamethylcyclooctasiloxane	$n = 8$	2.74	20			180
$C_6H_{18}OSi_2(CH_3)_3SI[OSi(CH_3)_2]_nCH_3$						
Hexamethyldisiloxane	$n = 1$	2.17	20			180
Octamethyltrisiloxane	$n = 2$	2.30	20			180
Decamethyltetrasiloxane	$n = 3$	2.39	20			180
Dodecamethylpentasiloxane	$n = 4$	2.46	20			180
Tetradecamethylhexasiloxane	$n = 5$	2.50	20			180
	$n = 66^w$	2.72	20			180
Stearic acid	$C_{18}H_{36}O_2$	2.29	70			47, 121, 127
		2.26	100			177
Styrene (phenylethylene)	C_8H_8	2.43	25			109, 130, 190
		2.32	75			
Succinonitrile	$C_4H_4N_2$	56.5	57.4			133
		53.6	67.7			
		52.3	78.2			
1,1,2,2-Tetrabromoethane	$C_2H_2Br_4$	8.6	3			20
		7.0	22			
1,1,2,2-Tetrachloroethane	$C_2H_2Cl_4$	8.2_0	20			35
Tetrachloroethylene	C_2Cl_4	2.30	25	0.20	25, 90	72, 130, 190
1-Tetradecanol	$C_{14}H_{30}O$	4.72	38			
		4.40	48			192

TABLE 5d-9. ORGANIC LIQUIDS (*Continued*)

Compound	Formula	ϵ/ϵ_v	t, °C	a (or α) $\times 10^2$	Range t_1, t_2	Ref.
Toluene	C_7H_8	2.438	0	0.0455(α)	−90, 0	14, 42, 63, 130
		2.379	25	0.243	0, 90	147, 152
		2.15_7	127			
		2.04_2	181			
o-Toluidine	C_7H_9N	6.34	18			113
		5.71	58			43
		4.00	200			26
m-Toluidine		5.95	18			113
		5.45	58			43
p-Toluidine		4.98	54			22, 43, 99
o-Tolunitrile	C_8H_7N	$18._5$[b]	23			11
1,2,3,-Tribromopropane	$C_3H_5Br_3$	6.45	20			164
Trichloroacetic acid	$C_2HCl_3O_2$	4.6	60			20
1,1,1-Trichloroethane	$C_2H_3Cl_3$	7.1_0	0	3.6	−33, 2	155
		7.5_2	20			105
Trichloroethylene	C_2HCl_3	3.4_2	*ca.* 16			28
α,α,α-Trichlorotoluene	$C_7H_5Cl_3$	6.9[n]	21			18, 21
Tricresyl phosphate	$C_{21}H_{21}O_4P$	6.9	40			144
Trifluoroacetic acid	$C_2HF_3O_2$	$39._5$	20	−50	0, 28	201a
		$26._2$	−11			
α,α,α-Trifluorotoluene	$C_7H_5F_3$	9.18	30			174
		8.09	60			
2-Undecanone	$C_{11}H_{22}O$	8.4	14.5			59
Vinyl ether	C_4H_6O	3.94	20			84
o-Xylene	C_8H_{10}	2.568	20	0.266	−20, 130	2, 76, 81, 130
m-Xylene		2.374	20	0.195	−40, 170	2, 10, 14, 24, 76, 81, 137, 152
p-Xylene		2.270	20	0.160	20, 130	44, 76, 81, 90, 130, 168, 184

[a] $\nu = 4 \times 10^8$ cps.
[b] $\nu = 3.6 \times 10^8$ cps.
[c] At pressure of 50 atm.
[h] Critical temperature.
[i] $\log_{10} \epsilon = 2.199 - 0.0079t + 0.00005t^2$.
[j] $\epsilon/\epsilon_v = (3{,}320/T) - 2.24$.
[k] $\epsilon/\epsilon_v = (3{,}320/T) - 2.34$.
[l] $\epsilon/\epsilon_v = 12.6 - 0.061(t + 20) + 0.0005(t + 20)^2$.
[m] $\epsilon/\epsilon_v = (2{,}160/T) - 0.39$.
[n] $\nu = 5 \times 10^8$ cps.
[o] $\epsilon/\epsilon_v = 6.94 - 0.036(t - 10) + 0.0004(t - 10)^2$.
[p] Critical temperature = 126.9°C.
[q] cis-trans isomers.
[r] Br and CH_3 trans.
[s] Br and CH_3 cis.
[w] Silicone oil of average molecular weight corresponding to this formula.
[x] Value chosen to conform with the remainder of the tabulated data for this substance.

References

1. Jahn, H., and G. Möller: *Z. physik. Chem.* **13,** 385 (1894).
2. Nernst, W.: *Z. physik. Chem.* **14,** 622 (1894).
3. Linde, F.: *Ann. Physik* **56,** 546 (1895).
4. Ratz, F.: *Z. physik. Chem.* **19,** 94 (1896).
5. Drude, P.: *Z. physik. Chem.* **23,** 267 (1897).
6. Löwe, K. F.: *Ann. Physik* **66,** 390 (1898).
7. Abegg, R., and W. Seitz: *Z. physik. Chem.* **29,** 242 (1899).
8. Coolidge, W. D.: *Ann. Physik* **69,** 130 (1899).
9. Hasenoehrl, F.: *Proc. Koninkl. Ned. Akad. Wetenschap.* **2,** 211 (1900); *Commun. Phys. Lab. Univ. Leiden* **52** (1900).

10. Turner, B. B.: *Z. physik. Chem.* **35**, 385 (1900).
11. Schlundt, H.: *J. Phys. Chem.* **5**, 157 (1901).
12. Schlundt, H.: *J. Phys. Chem.* **5**, 503 (1901).
13. Eversheim, P.: *Ann. Physik* **8**, 539 (1902).
14. Tangl, K.: *Ann. Physik* **10**, 748 (1903).
15. Walden, P.: *Z. physik. Chem.* **46**, 103 (1903).
16. Eggers, H. E.: *J. Phys. Chem.* **8**, 14 (1904).
17. Schlundt, H.: *J. Phys. Chem.* **8**, 122 (1904).
18. Mathews, J. H.: *J. Phys. Chem.* **9**, 641 (1905).
19. Schaefer, O. C., and H. Schlundt: *J. Phys. Chem.* **13**, 669 (1909).
20. Walden, P.: *Z. physik. Chem.* **70**, 569 (1910).
21. Dobroserdov, D. K.: *J. Russ. Phys.-Chem. Soc.* **43**, 73 (1911).
22. Cauwood, J. D., and W. E. S. Turner: *J. Chem. Soc.* **107**, 276 (1915).
23. Harrington, E. A.: *Phys. Rev.* **8**, 581 (1916).
24. Richards, T. W., and J. W. Shipley: *J. Am. Chem. Soc.* **41**, 2002 (1919).
25. Graffunder, W.: *Ann. Physik* **70**, 225 (1923).
26. Grimm, F. V., and W. A. Patrick: *J. Am. Chem. Soc.* **45**, 2794 (1923).
27. Meyer, E. H. L.: *Ann. Physik* **75**, 801 (1924).
28. Walden, P., and O. Werner: *Z. physik. Chem.* **111**, 465 (1924).
29. Wolfke, M., and H. K. Onnes: *Proc. Koninkl. Ned. Akad. Wetenschap.* **27**, 627 (1924); *Commun. Phys. Lab. Univ. Leiden* **171b** (1924).
30. Wolfke, M., and H. K. Onnes: *Proc. Koninkl. Ned. Akad. Wetenschap.* **27**, 621 (1924); *Commun. Phys. Lab. Univ. Leiden* **171c** (1924).
31. Errera, J., and M. Lepingale: *Bull. classe sci. Acad. roy. Belg.* **2**, 150 (1925).
32. Errera, J.: *J. phys. radium* **6**, 390 (1925).
33. Lange, L.: *Z. Physik* **33**, 169 (1925).
34. Schlundt, H., and A. F. O. Germann: *J. Phys. Chem.* **29**, 353 (1925).
35. Walden, P., H. Ulich, and O. Werner: *Z. physik. Chem.* **116**, 261 (1925).
36. Ebert, L., and W. H. Keesom: *Proc. Koninkl. Ned. Akad. Wetenschap.* **29**, 1188 (1926); *Commun. Phys. Lab. Univ. Leiden* **182d** (1926).
37. Errera, J.: *Physik. Z.* **27**, 764 (1926).
38. Kerr, R. N.: *J. Chem. Soc.* **1926**, 2796.
39. Sayce, L. A., and H. V. A. Briscoe: *J. Chem. Soc.* **1926**, 2623.
40. Werner, W., and W. H. Keesom: *Proc. Koninkl. Ned. Akad. Wetenschap.* **29**, 34 (1926); *Commun. Phys. Lab. Univ. Leiden* **178a** (1926).
41. Werner, W., and W. H. Keesom: *Proc. Koninkl. Ned. Akad. Wetenschap.* **29**, 306 (1926); *Commun. Phys. Lab. Univ. Leiden* **178c** (1926).
42. Williams, J. W., and I. J. Krchma: *J. Am. Chem. Soc.* **48**, 1888 (1926).
43. Kerr, R. N., *Phil. Mag.* **3**, 330 (1927).
44. Krchma, I. J., and J. W. Williams: *J. Am. Chem. Soc.* **49**, 2408 (1927).
45. Anderson, A. I.: *Proc. Phys. Soc.* (*London*) **40**, 62 (1928).
46. Esterman, J.: *Z. physik. Chem.* **B1**, 134 (1928).
47. Lautsch, W.: *Z. physik. Chem.* **B1**, 115 (1928).
48. Smyth, C. P., S. O. Morgan, and J. C. Boyce: *J. Am. Chem. Soc.* **50**, 1536 (1928).
49. Smyth, C. P., and S. O. Morgan: *J. Am. Chem. Soc.* **50**, 1547 (1928).
50. Smyth, C. P., and W. N. Stoops: *J. Am. Chem. Soc.* **50**, 1883 (1928).
51. Wolfke, M., and W. H. Keesom: *Proc. Koninkl. Ned. Akad. Wetenschap.* **31**, 81 (1928); *Commun. Phys. Lab. Univ. Leiden* **190a** (1928).
52. Wolfke, M., and W. H. Keesom: *Proc. Koninkl. Ned. Akad. Wetenschap.* **31**, 800 (1928); *Commun. Phys. Lab. Univ. Leiden* **192a** (1928).
53. Fredenhagen, K., and J. Dahmlos: *Z. anorg. u. allgem. Chem.* **178**, 272 (1929).
54. Hartshorn, L., and D. A. Oliver: *Proc. Roy. Soc.* (*London*), ser. A, **123**, 664 (1929).
55. Lattey, R. T., and O. Gatty, *Phil. Mag.* **7**, 985 (1929).
56. Smyth, C. P., and W. N. Stoops: *J. Am. Chem. Soc.* **51**, 3312 (1929).
57. Smyth, C. P., and W. N. Stoops: *J. Am. Chem. Soc.* **51**, 3330 (1929).
58. Walden, P., and L. Werner: *Z. physik. Chem.* **B2**, 10 (1929).
59. Wolf, K. L.: *Z. physik. Chem.* **B2**, 39 (1929).
60. Ball, A. O.: *J. Chem. Soc.* **1930**, 570.
61. Das, L. M., and S. C. Roy: *Indian J. Phys.* **5**, 441 (1930).

62. Doborzynski, D.: *Z. Physik* **66**, 657 (1930).
63. Dornte, R. W., and C. P. Smyth: *J. Am. Chem. Soc.* **52**, 3546 (1930).
64. Drake, F. H., G. W. Pierce, and M. T. Dow: *Phys. Rev.* **35**, 613 (1930).
65. Errera, J., and M. L. Sherrill: *J. Am. Chem. Soc.* **52**, 1993 (1930).
66. McLennan, J. C., R. C. Jacobsen, and J. O. Wilhelm: *Trans. Roy. Soc. Can.* **24**, 37 (1930).
67. Morgan, S. O., and H. H. Lowry: *J. Phys. Chem.* **34**, 2385 (1930).
68. Smyth, C. P., and H. E. Rogers: *J. Am. Chem. Soc.* **52**, 1824 (1930).
69. Smyth, C. P., and H. E. Rogers: *J. Am. Chem. Soc.* **52**, 2227 (1930).
70. Williams, J. W.: *J. Am. Chem. Soc.* **52**, 1831 (1930).
71. Wyman, J.: *Phys. Rev.* **35**, 623 (1930).
72. Bretscher, E.: *Physik. Z.* **32**, 765 (1931).
73. Cone, R. M., G. H. Denison, and J. D. Kemp: *J. Am. Chem. Soc.* **53**, 1278 (1931).
74. Danforth, W. E.: *Phys. Rev.* **38**, 1224 (1931).
75. Lattey, R. T., O. Gatty, and W. G. Davies: *Phil. Mag.* **12**, 1019 (1931).
76. Pyle, W. R.: *Phys. Rev.* **38**, 1057 (1931).
77. Smyth, C. P., and R. W. Dornte: *J. Am. Chem. Soc.* **53**, 545 (1931).
78. Smyth, C. P., R. W. Dornte, and E. B. Wilson: *J. Am. Chem. Soc.* **53**, 4242 (1931).
79. Wyman, J.: *J. Am. Chem. Soc.* **53**, 3292 (1931).
80. Åkerlöf, G.: *J. Am. Chem. Soc.* **54**, 4125 (1932).
81. Heil, L. M.: *Phys. Rev.* **39**, 666 (1932).
82. Jagielski, A.: *Bull. intern. acad. polon. sci., Classe sci. math. et nat.* **A1932**, 327 (1932).
83. Linton, E. P., and O Maass: *J. Am. Chem. Soc.* **54**, 1863 (1932).
84. Smyth, C. P., and W. S. Walls: *J. Am. Chem. Soc.* **54**, 3230 (1932).
85. Smyth, C. P., and C. S. Hitchcock: *J. Am. Chem. Soc.* **54**, 4631 (1932).
86. Ulich, H., and W. Nespital: *Z. physik. Chem.* **B16**, 221 (1932).
87. Curtis, H. J.: *J. Chem. Phys.* **1**, 160 (1933).
88. Dobinski, S.: *Z. Physik* **83**, 129 (1933).
89. Fairbrother, F.: *J. Chem. Soc.* **1933**, 1541.
90. Fairbrother, F.: *Proc. Roy. Soc.* (*London*), ser. A, **142**, 173 (1933).
91. Girard, P., and P. Abadie: *Compt. rend.* **197**, 146 (1933).
92. Højendahl, K.: *Z. physik. Chem.* **B20**, 54 (1933).
93. Oncley, J. L., and J. W. Williams: *Phys. Rev.* **43**, 341 (1933).
94. Smyth, C. P., and C. S. Hitchcock: *J. Am. Chem. Soc.* **55**, 1830 (1933).
95. Sugden, S.: *J. Chem. Soc.* **1933**, 768.
96. Uhlig, H. H., J. G. Kirkwood, and F. G. Keyes: *J. Chem. Phys.* **1**, 155 (1933).
97. Girard, P.: *Trans. Faraday Soc.* **30**, 763 (1934).
98. Hooper, G. S., and C. A. Kraus: *J. Am. Chem. Soc.* **56**, 2265 (1934).
99. Howell, O. R., and W. Jackson: *Proc. Roy. Soc.* (*London*), ser. A, **145**, 539 (1934).
100. Jenkins, H. O.: *J. Chem. Soc.* **1934**, 480.
101. Olson, A. R., and W. Maroney: *J. Am. Chem. Soc.* **56**, 1320 (1934).
102. Sherrill, M. L., M. E. Smith, and D. D. Thompson: *J. Am. Chem. Soc.* **56**, 611 (1934).
103. Smyth, C. P., and C. S. Hitchcock: *J. Am. Chem. Soc.* **56**, 1084 (1934).
104. Snoek, J. L.: *Physik. Z.* **35**, 196 (1934).
105. Earp, D., and S. Glasstone: *J. Chem. Soc.* **1935**, 1709.
106. Le Fevre, R. J. W.: *J. Chem. Soc.* **1935**, 773.
107. Le Fevre, C. G., and R. J. W. Le Fevre: *J. Chem. Soc.* **1935**, 1747.
108. Marsden, J., and O. Maass: *Can. J. Research* **B13**, 296 (1935).
109. Otto, M. M., and H. H. Wenzke: *J. Am. Chem. Soc.* **57**, 294 (1935).
110. Bickford, W. G.: *Iowa State Coll. J. Sci.* **11**, 35 (1936).
111. Davies, R. M.: *Phil. Mag.* **21**, 1 (1936).
112. Davies, R. M.: *Phil. Mag.* **21**, 1008 (1936).
113. Freymann, R.: *Compt. rend.* **202**, 952 (1936).
114. Glockler, G., and R. E. Peck: *J. Chem. Phys.* **4**, 624 (1936).
115. Glockler, G., and R. E. Peck: *J. Chem. Phys.* **4**, 658 (1936).
116. Gore, R. C., and H. T. Briscoe: *J. Phys. Chem.* **40**, 619 (1936).

117. Grubb, H. M., J. E. Chittum, and H. Hunt: *J. Am. Chem. Soc.* **58,** 776 (1936).
118. Jagielski, A.: *Bull. intern. acad. polon. sci., Classe sci. math. et nat.* **A1936,** 451 (1936).
119. Keutner, E.: *Ann. Physik* **29** (1936).
120. McNeight, S. A., and C. P. Smyth: *J. Am. Chem. Soc.* **58,** 1718 (1936).
121. Piekara, B.: *Physik. Z.* **37,** 624 (1936).
122. Albright, P. S.: *J. Am. Chem. Soc.* **59,** 2098 (1937).
123. Coop, I. E.: *Trans. Faraday Soc.* **33,** 583 (1937).
124. Cowley, E. G., and J. R. Partington: *J. Chem. Soc.* **1937,** 130.
125. Hadamard, J.: *Compt. rend.* **204,** 1234 (1937).
126. Higasi, K., and M. Kubo: *Bull. Chem. Soc. Japan* **12,** 326 (1937).
127. Hrynakowski, K., and A. Zochowski: *Ber. deut. chem. Ges.* **70B,** 1739 (1937).
128. Kanda, E.: *Bull. Chem. Soc. Japan* **12,** 473 (1937).
129. Martin, A. R.: *Trans. Faraday Soc.* **33,** 191 (1937).
130. Müller, F. H.: *Physik. Z.* **38,** 283 (1937).
131. Smits, A., and N. F. Moerman: *Rec. trav. chim.* **56,** 169 (1937).
132. Thomas, G.: *J. Chem. Soc.* **1937,** 1051.
133. White, A. H., and S. O. Morgan: *J. Chem. Phys.* **5,** 655 (1937).
134. Baker, W. O., and C. P. Smyth: *J. Am. Chem. Soc.* **60,** 1229 (1938).
135. Guillien, R.: *Compt. rend.* **206,** 1001 (1938).
136. Guillien, R.: *Compt. rend.* **207,** 393 (1938).
137. Le Fevre, R. J. W.: *Trans. Faraday Soc.* **34,** 1127 (1938).
138. Paranjpe, G. R., and D. J. Davar: *Indian J. Phys.* **12,** 283 (1938).
139. Wesolowski, J.: *Bull. intern. acad. polon. sci., Classe sci. math. et nat.* **A1938,** 290 (1938).
140. Wyman, J., and E. N. Ingalls: *J. Am. Chem. Soc.* **60,** 1182 (1938).
141. Baker, W. O., and C. P. Smyth: *J. Am. Chem. Soc.* **61,** 1695 (1939).
142. Baker, W. O., and C. P. Smyth: *J. Am. Chem. Soc.* **61,** 2798 (1939).
143. Davies, R. M., and T. T. Jones: *Phil. Mag.* **28,** 307 (1939).
144. Fuoss, R. M.: *J. Am. Chem. Soc.* **61,** 2334 (1939).
145. Guillien, R.: *Rev. sci.* **77,** 575 (1939).
146. Larson, R. G., and H. Hunt: *J. Phys. Chem.* **43,** 417 (1939).
147. Lewis, G. L., and C. P. Smyth: *J. Chem. Phys.* **7,** 1085 (1939).
148. Lewis, G. L., and C. P. Smyth: *J. Am. Chem. Soc.* **61,** 3062 (1939).
149. Lewis, G. L., and C. P. Smyth: *J. Am. Chem. Soc.* **61,** 3067 (1939).
150. Plotnikov, V. A., I. A. Sheka, and Z. A. Yankelevich: *J. Gen. Chem. (U.S.S.R.)* **9,** 868 (1939).
151. Wood, R. E., and R. G. Dickinson: *J. Am. Chem. Soc.* **61,** 3259 (1939).
152. Guillien, R.: *J. phys. radium* **1,** 29 (1940).
153. Morgan, S. O., and W. A. Yager: *Ind. Eng. Chem.* **32,** 1519 (1940).
154. Rodebush, W. H., C. R. Eddy, and L. D. Eubank: *J. Chem. Phys.* **8,** 889 (1940).
155. Turkevich, A., and C. P. Smyth: *J. Am. Chem. Soc.* **62,** 2468 (1940).
156. Volarovich, M. P., and N. M. Stepanenko: *Acta Physicochim. U.R.S.S.* **13,** 647 (1940).
157. Wang, Y. L.: *Z. physik. Chem.* **B45,** 323 (1940).
158. White, A. H., and W. S. Bishop: *J. Am. Chem. Soc.* **62,** 8 (1940).
159. Winstein, S., and R. E. Wood: *J. Am. Chem. Soc.* **62,** 548 (1940).
160. Cole, R. H.: *J. Chem. Phys.* **9,** 251 (1941).
161. Skinner, L. A.: Dissertation, Duke University, Durham, N.C.
162. Audsley, A., and F. R. Goss: *J. Chem. Soc.* **1942,** 358.
163. Audsley, A., and F. R. Goss: *J. Chem. Soc.* **1942,** 497.
164. de Kreuk, L. J.: *Rec. trav. chim.* **61,** 819 (1942).
165. Miller, J. G.: *J. Am. Chem. Soc.* **64,** 117 (1942).
166. Sambursky, S., and G. Wolfsohn: *Phys. Rev.* **62,** 357 (1942).
167. Turkevich, A., and C. P. Smyth: *J. Am. Chem. Soc.* **64,** 737 (1942).
168. van Arkel, A. E., P. Meerburg, and C. R. v.d. Handel: *Rec. trav. chim.* **61,** 767 (1942).
169. van Itterbeek, D. A., and J. Spaepen: *Physica* **9,** 339 (1942).
170. Backer, H. J., and W. G. Perdok: *Rec. trav. chim.* **62,** 533 (1943).

171. Clay, J., A. J. Dekker, and J. Hemelrijk: *Physica* **10**, 178 (1943).
172. Watanabe, I., S. Midzushima, and Y. Masiko: *Sci. Papers Inst. Phys. Chem. Research (Tokyo)* **40**, 425 (1943).
173. Coates, G. E., and J. E. Coates: *J. Chem. Soc.* **1944**, 77.
174. Deal, C. H.: Dissertation, Duke University, Durham, N.C.
175. Phadke, S. R., S. D. Gokhale, N. L. Phalnikar, and B. V. Bhide: *J. Indian Chem. Soc.* **22**, 235 (1945).
176. Phadke, S. R., N. L. Phalnikar, and B. V. Bhide: *J. Indian Chem. Soc.* **22**, 239 (1945).
177. Stephanenko, N., and T. Novikova: *Acta Physicochim. U.R.S.S.* **20**, 653 (1945).
178. Vernon, A. A., J. Wyman, and R. A. Avery: *J. Am. Chem. Soc.* **67**, 1422 (1945).
179. Albright, P. S., and L. J. Gosting: *J. Am. Chem. Soc.* **68**, 1061 (1946).
180. Sauer, R. O., and D. J. Mead: *J. Am. Chem. Soc.* **68**, 1794 (1946).
181. Elliott, M. A., A. R. Jones, and L. B. Lockhart: *Anal. Chem.* **19**, 10 (1947).
182. Le Fevre, R. J., and P. Russell: *Trans. Faraday Soc.* **43**, 374 (1947).
183. Vasenko, E. N.: *J. Phys. Chem. (U.S.S.R.)* **21**, 361 (1947).
184. Fairbrother, F.: *J. Chem. Soc.* **1948**, 1051.
185. Heston, W. A., E. T. Hennelly, and C. P. Smyth: *Tech. Rept.* 10, ONR Contract N6ori-105, Task Order IV; also *J. Am. Chem. Soc.* **72**, 2071 (1950).
186. Mouradoff-Fouquet, L.: *Compt. rend.* **226**, 1970 (1948).
187. Reynolds, M. B., and C. A. Kraus: *J. Am. Chem. Soc.* **70**, 1709 (1948).
188. Strobel, H. A., and H. C. Eckstrom: *J. Chem. Phys.* **16**, 817 (1948).
189. Stroble, H. A., and H. C. Eckstrom: *J. Chem. Phys.* **16**, 827 (1948).
190. von Hipple, A.: Tables of Dielectric Materials, vol. III, Technical Report X, Laboratory for Insulation Research, Massachusetts Institute of Technology, Cambridge, Mass.
191. Burdun, G. D., and P. B. Kantor: *Doklady Akad. Nauk U.S.S.R.* **67**, 985 (1949).
192. Hoffman, J. D., and C. P. Smyth: *J. Am. Chem. Soc.* **71**, 431 (1949).
193. van der Maesen, F.: *Physica* **15**, 481 (1949).
194. Barclay, G. A., and R. J. W. Le Fevre: *J. Chem. Soc.* **1950**, 556.
195. Crowe, R. W., and C. P. Smyth: *J. Am. Chem. Soc.* **72**, 4427 (1950).
196. Gross, P. M., Jr., and R. C. Taylor: *J. Am. Chem. Soc.* **72**, 2075 (1950).
197. Heston, W. M., and C. P. Smyth: *J. Am. Chem. Soc.* **72**, 99 (1950).
198. Hoffman, J. D., and C. P. Smyth: *J. Am. Chem. Soc.* **72**, 171 (1950).
199. Le Fevre, R. J. W., and I. G. Ross: *J. Chem. Soc.* **1950**, 283.
200. Malmberg, C. G., and A. A. Maryott: Unpublished data, National Bureau of Standards.
201. Vierk, A. L.: *Z. anorg. Chem.* **261**, 283 (1950).
201a. Simons, J. H., and K. H. Lorentzen: *J. Am. Chem. Soc.* **72**, 1426 (1950).

TABLE 5d-10. REPRESENTATIVE VALUES OF DIELECTRIC CONSTANT OF MISCELLANEOUS COMMERCIAL DIELECTRICS

Material	T, °C	ν, cps	ϵ/ϵ_v
Asphalt	26	1×10^3	2.66
		1×10^6	2.58
		1×10^{10}	2.55
Asbestos	25	1×10^3	4.8
Castor oil	15	1×10^3	4.7
	23	3×10^9	2.68
Castor oil, hydrogenated	24	1×10^3	10.3
	24	1×10^6	3.2
Chlorinated diphenyl:			
54% chlorine	25	1×10^3	5.05
42% chlorine	25	1×10^3	6.70
Chlorinated naphthalene (hot-molded)	25	1×10^3	3.78
	25	1×10^6	3.70
	25	3×10^9	2.57
Hydrocarbon oils:			
Transformer oil	25	1×10^3	2.22
	25	3×10^9	2.18
Cable oil	25	1×10^3	2.25
Mineral oil	25	1×10^3	2.15
Hydrocarbon waxes:			
Paraffin	25	1×10^3	2.20
	27	3×10^9	2.20
Biwax	25	1×10^3	2.5
Ceresin	25	1×10^3	2.2
Superla No. 8	25	1×10^3	2.34
	25	3×10^9	2.26
Mica, clear ruby muscovite	25	10^3–10^6	7.0
Polyisobutylenes:			
Vistanex	21	2×10^3	2.20
Vistac	25	1×10^3	2.22

5d-4. Dielectric Properties of Gases

TABLE 5d-11. DIELECTRIC CONSTANTS OF REFERENCE GASES*
(At 20°C and 1 atm)

	$(\epsilon'/\epsilon_v - 1) \times 10^6$
Helium	65.0 ± 0.4
Hydrogen	253.8 ± 0.3
Oxygen	494.7 ± 0.2
Argon	517.2 ± 0.4
Air (dry, CO_2-free)	536.4 ± 0.3
Nitrogen	548.0 ± 0.5
Carbon dioxide	922 ± 1

* Taken from Maryott and Buckley, *Natl. Bur. Standards (U.S.) Circ.* 537. Dielectric constants of other gases may be calculated from dipole moment and molar refraction data given in the above reference.

Table 5d-12. Relative Dielectric Strengths of Various Gases and Nitrogen-Vapor Mixtures*

Gas or N_2 vapor mixture saturated at 23°C and 760 mm Hg total pressure	Pressure of vapor, mm Hg	Relative dielectric strength
Fluorotrichloromethane, CCl_3F	725	3.0
Tetrafluorodichloroethane, $C_2Cl_2F_4$	760	2.8
Trifluorotrichloroethane, $C_2Cl_3F_3$	306	2.6
Sulfur hexafluoride, SF_6	760	2.41†
Difluorodichloromethane, CCl_2F_2	760	2.4
Boron trichloride, BCl_3	760	2.3
Methyl iodide, CH_3I	370	2.2
Sulfur dioxide, SO_2	760	1.9
Phosphorus trichloride, PCl_3	113	1.9
Thionyl chloride, $SOCl_2$	110	1.65
Carbon tetrachloride, CCl_4	105	1.65
Chloroform, $CHCl_3$	180	1.58
Sulfuryl chloride, SO_2Cl_2	......	1.56
Chlorine, Cl_2	760	1.55
Carbon disulfide, CS_2	330	1.50
Fluorodichloromethane, $CHCl_2F$	760	1.33
Hydrogen sulfide, H_2S	760	1.30
Ethylene, C_2H_4	760	1.21
Titanium tetrachloride, $TiCl_4$	12	1.17
Methyl formate, $HCOOCH_3$	570	1.16
Trichloroethylene, $CHCl{:}CCl_2$	65	1.15
Nitrous oxide, N_2O	760	1.14
Phosphoryl chloride, $POCl_3$	34	1.11
Dichloromethane, CH_2Cl_2	400	1.11
Acetylene, C_2H_2	760	1.10
Trichloroethane, $CH_2ClCHCl_2$	......	1.08
Ethyl amine, $C_2H_5NH_2$	760	1.06
Chloromethane, CH_3Cl	760	1.06
Dimethyl amine, $(CH_3)_2NH$	760	1.04
Acetaldehyde, CH_3CHO	760	1.03
Fluorochloromethane, CH_2ClF	......	1.03
Carbon monoxide, CO	760	1.02
Tetrachloroethane, $CHCl_2CHCl_2$	6.8	1.02
Sulfur dichloride, S_2Cl_2	12.5	1.02
Nitrobenzene, $C_6H_5NO_2$	0.3	1.02
Methyl bromide, CH_3Br	760	1.02
Ethyl ether, $(C_2H_5)_2O$	495	1.00
Methane, CH_4	760	1.00
Ethyl alcohol, C_2H_5OH	52	1.00
Dichloroethane, CH_2ClCH_2Cl	70	1.00
Ethyl chloride, C_2H_5Cl	760	1.00
Nitromethane, CH_3NO_2	34	1.00
Benzoyl chloride, C_6H_5COCl	est. 0.2	1.00

TABLE 5d-12. RELATIVE DIELECTRIC STRENGTHS OF VARIOUS GASES AND NITROGEN-VAPOR MIXTURES (*Continued*)

Gas or N_2 vapor mixture saturated at 23°C and 760 mm Hg total pressure	Pressure of vapor, mm Hg	Relative dielectric strength
Thioacetic acid, CH_3COSH	....	1.00
Acetone, CH_3COCH_3	210	0.98
Dibromoethane, CH_2BrCH_2Br	12.5	0.98
Air	760	0.97‡
Methyl acetate, CH_3COOCH_3	195	0.95
Ethylene oxide, $CH_2\;CH_2$ (└─O─┘)	760	0.95
Benzaldehyde, C_6H_5CHO	0.6	0.95
Acetic acid, CH_3COOH	14	0.94
Methyl alcohol, CH_3OH	110	0.94
Formaldehyde, CH_2O	760	0.93
Bromobenzene, C_6H_5Br	*ca.* 4	0.93
Ethyl acetate, $CH_3COOC_2H_5$	86	0.91
Tetrachloroethylene, $CCl_2{:}CCl_2$	*ca.* 18	0.90
Carbon dioxide, CO_2	760	0.88
Aniline, $C_6H_5NH_2$	*ca.* 0.3	0.87
Oxygen, O_2	760	0.86‡
Toluene, $C_6H_5CH_3$	25	0.86
Benzene, C_6H_6	85	0.84
Ammonia, NH_3 (over NH_4OH)	....	0.82
Chlorobenzene, C_6H_5Cl	10.5	0.81
Methylamine, CH_3NH_2	760	0.81
Diethyl amine, $(C_2H_5)_2NH$	215	0.78
Difluoromethane, CH_2F_2	....	0.69
Hydrogen, H_2	760	0.54‡

* The relative dielectric strength is defined as the ratio of dielectric strength of the gas or nitrogen-vapor mixture to that of nitrogen at atmospheric pressure and room temperature, when measured in the same gap. Taken from Charlton and Cooper, *Gen. Elec. Rev.* **40,** 438 (1937).

† Hochberg and Sandberg, *J. Tech. Phys.* (*U.S.S.R.*) **12,** 65 (1942).

‡ Landolt-Börnstein, "Physikalisch-Chemischen Tabellen," vol. III, p. 1264.

5d-5. Piezoelectric and Pyroelectric Constants

TABLE 5d-13. PIEZOELECTRIC STRAIN CONSTANTS

Substance	Formula	d_{11}	d_{14}	d_{25}	d_{36}	Ref.
1. Aluminum phosphate	$AlPO_4$	±3.3	±1.5	......	......	11*
		+1.4	Small	......	......	5*
2. Ammonium dihydrogen arsenate	$NH_4H_2AsO_4$	......	+41	......	+31	5*
3. Ammonium dihydrogen phosphate	$NH_4H_2PO_4$	......	−1.5	......	+48	5*
			+1.5	......	−45.6	18
			+1.7	......	+49	11*
4. Ammonium ditartrate	$NH_4HC_4H_4O_6$	......	−1.6	7.0	0.4	17
5. Barium formate	$Ba(HCOO)_2$	......	±4.0	±2.7	±4.7	11*
6. Benzil	$C_{14}H_{10}O_2$	+8.0	......	......	......	20
7. Beryllium sulfate tetrahydrate	$BeSO_4{:}4H_2O$	......	7	......	......	5*
8. Cesium tartrate	$Cs_2C_4H_4O_6$	2.7	0.17	......	......	5*
9. Deutero ammonium dideuterium phosphate	$ND_4D_2PO_4$	......	10	......	75	13
10. Dextrose plus sodium bromide	$C_6H_{12}O_6$ 2 NaBr	−3.7	−1.8	......	......	11*
11. Dextrose plus sodium chloride	$C_6H_{12}O_6$ 2 NaCl	−7.0	+.3	......	......	11*
12. Dextrose plus sodium iodide	$C_6H_{12}O_6$	−3.8	+.7	......	......	11*
	2 NaI	3.4	......	......	......	5*
13. Heavy rochelle salt	$KNaC_4D_2H_2O_6{\cdot}4D_2O$	......	Very large	−73	+13.3	12
		......	See Table 5d-14			
14. Iodic acid	HIO_3	......	±18.9	±15.3	±23.5	11*
15. Lithium ammonium tartrate monohydrate	$LiNH_4C_4H_4O_6{\cdot}H_2O$	......	±4.4	±6.5	±4.9	11*
			7.7	−5.3	6.8	17
16. Lithium potassium tartrate monohydrate	$LiKC_4H_4O_6{\cdot}H_2O$	......	+3.2	+11.2	±7.6	11*
			+2.0	−9.4	+6.6	17
			2.1	10.0	6.8	5*
17. Magnesium sulfate heptahydrate	$MgSO_4{\cdot}7H_2O$	......	−2.1	−2.7	−3.8	18
18. Nickel sulfate heptahydrate	$NiSO_4{\cdot}7H_2O$	......	−2.0	−2.9	−3.2	18
19. Nickel sulfate hexahydrate	$NiSO_4{\cdot}6H_2O$	......	−5.3	......	......	18
			±6.0	......	......	11*
20. Patchouli camphor	$C_{15}H_{26}O$	+0.05	......	......	......	20
21. Potassium dihydrogen arsenate	KH_2AsO_4	......	+23.5	......	+22	5*
			26.6	......	22.4	15
22. Potassium dihydrogen phosphate	KH_2PO_4	......	+1.3	......	−20.9	18
			1.4		23	11*
			+1.3	......	+21	5*
23. Potassium ditartrate	$KHC_4H_4O_6$	......	−4.3	3.4	−1.0	17
24. Potassium dithionate	$K_2S_2O_6$	1.4	2.0	......	......	5*
25. Quartz	SiO_2	+2.31	−0.73	......	......	2
		+2.3	−0.67	......	......	6, 18
		−2.25	+0.85	......	......	11*
26. Rochelle salt	$KNaC_4H_4O_6{\cdot}4H_2O$	......	Very large	−56	+11.8	11
			See Table 5d-14	−53	+11.7	6
27. Rubidium dihydrogen phosphate	RbH_2PO_4	......	4.5	......	37	5*
28. Rubidium tartrate	$Rb_2C_4H_4O_6$	+2.7	......	......	......	20
29. Sodium ammonium tetrahydrate	$NaNH_4C_4H_4O_6{\cdot}4H_2O$	......	+18.7	−49.8	+9.4	10
			±19	±31.7	±10.3	11
30. Sodium bromate	$NaBrO_3$	......	−2.6	......	......	2
			−2.4	......	......	18
			+2.7	......	......	11*
31. Sodium chlorate	$NaClO_3$	......	−1.75	......	......	18, 2
			+2.0	......	......	11*
32. Strontium formate dihydrate	$Sr(HCOO)_2{\cdot}2H_2O$	......	±8.5	±11.5	±2.3	11*
33. Zinc blende	ZnS	......	−3.2	......	......	9
34. Zinc sulfate heptahydrate	$ZnSO_4{\cdot}7H_2O$	......	−1.9	−3.5	−3.1	18

TABLE 5d-13. PIEZOELECTRIC STRAIN CONSTANTS (*Continued*)

Substance	Formula	d_{15}	d_{22}	d_{24}	d_{31}	d_{32}	d_{33}	Ref.
35. Ammonium pentaborate tetrahydrate	$NH_4B_5O_8 \cdot 4H_2O$	+13		+6.7	−6.6	−1.9	+6.9	5*
36. Barium antimonyl tartrate	$Ba(SbO)_2(C_4H_4O_6)_2 \cdot H_2O$						+3.7	20
37. Barium titanate	$BaTiO_3$				−37		84	7*
38. Barium titanate ceramic	$BaTiO_3$	283			−78		190	5*
39. Lithium trisodium chromate hexahydrate	$LiNa_3(CrO_4)_2 \cdot 6H_2O$		±2.9					11*
40. Lithium trisodium molybdate hexahydrate	$LiNa_3(MoO_4)_2 \cdot 6H_2O$		±2.5		±1.3		±1.9	11*
41. Potassium lithium sulfate	$KLiSO_4$	+0.9			−2.35		+5.2	5*
42. Potassium pentaborate tetrahydrate	$KB_5O_8 \cdot 4H_2O$	+9.5		+1.7	−5.4		+5.6	5*
43. Sodium lithium sulfate	$NaLiSO_4$		0.85		+0.01		+0.3	5*
44. Tourmaline	Variable	+3.7	−0.23		+0.25		+1.9	16
		−3.6	−0.33		−0.34		−1.8	11*

Substance	Formula	d_{14}	d_{16}	d_{21}	d_{22}	d_{23}	d_{25}	d_{34}	d_{36}	Ref.
45. Cane sugar	$C_{12}H_{22}O_{11}$	+1.2	−2.4	+1.5	−3.3	+0.7	−0.9	−4.2	+0.4	8
46. Diammonium tartrate	$(NH_4)_2C_4H_4O_6$	+3.1	−2.8	+5.9	−8.7	+0.6	−2.0	−4.7	+1.9	18
		+3.3	+1.7	−6.7	+8.6	−0.6	+2.4	+1.8	+2.0	5*
47. Dipotassium tartrate hemihydrate	$K_2C_4H_4O_6 \cdot \frac{1}{2}H_2O$	+7.9	+3.5	−0.8	+4.5	−5.3	−6.5	−12.3	−23.2	4*
48. Ethylene diamine tartrate	$C_6H_{14}O_6N_2$	−10.0	−12.2	+10.1	+2.2	−11.3	−18.0	−17.0	−18.4	1*
49. Guanidine tartrate	$C_5H_{11}O_6N_3$			+2.6		−3.9	+3.3			5*
50. Lithium sulfate monohydrate	$Li_2SO_4 \cdot H_2O$	+0.76	−2.0	−3.6	+16.3	+1.7	−5.0	−2.1	−4.2	3*
51. Rhamnose	$C_6H_{12}O_5 \cdot H_2O$	+0.7	+5.0	+2.7	−3.0	−5.0	+12.2	−12.0	+1.1	14
52. Sorbitol hexa-acetate	$C_{18}H_{26}O_{12}$	1.4	23	0.5	−8	0.8		2	2	5
53. Tartaric acid	$C_4H_6O_6$	−12.2	+9.5	+2.0	−2.2	+0.65	+1.3	+9.3	−8.0	19
		+8.0	+5.3	−0.8	−2.2	−2.1	+0.4	−10.8	+11.7	11*

*According to the standards on piezoelectric crystals of the IRE [*Proc. IRE* **37**, 1378 (1949)], we define the piezoelectric strain constants $d_{ik} = \frac{\partial D_i}{(\partial T_k)_E}$ or $d_{ik} = \frac{\partial S_k}{(\partial E_i)_T}$ where $i = 1, 2, 3$ and $k = 1$ to 6; T_k = stress; S_k = strain; D_i = electric displacement; and E_i = electric field. The units are coulomb/newton or meter/volt (rationalized mks). The listed numbers have to be multiplied by 10^{-12}. In all cases marked by an asterisk, the IRE convention of tension being a positive stress has been followed. For the other values quoted the convention used is somewhat uncertain, although pressure is usually taken as positive.

References

1. Bechmann, R.: *Proc. Phys. Soc.* (*London*) **63B**, 577 (1950).
2. Bechmann, R.: *Proc. Phys. Soc.* (*London*) **64B**, 323 (1951).
3. Bechmann, R.: *Proc. Phys. Soc.* (*London*) **65B**, 375 (1952).
4. Bechmann, R., and S. Ayers: *Proc. Phys. Soc.* (*London*) **67B**, 422 (1954).
5. Brush Laboratories Company, Cleveland, Ohio: reports.
6. Cady, W.: "Piezoelectricity," McGraw-Hill Book Company, Inc., New York, 1946.
7. Caspari, M. E., and W. J. Merz: *Phys. Rev.* **80**, 1082 (1950).
8. Holman, W. F.: *Ann. Phys.* **29**, 160 (1909).
9. Knol, K. S.: *Konink. Akad. Wetenschap. Amsterdam* **35**, 99 (1932).
10. Mandell, W.: *Proc. Roy. Soc.* (*London*) **121**, 130 (1928).
11. Mason, W. P.: "Piezoelectric Crystals and Their Application to Ultrasonics," D. Van Nostrand Company, Inc., New York, 1950.
12. Mason, W. P., and A. N. Holden: *Phys. Rev.* **57**, 54 (1940).
13. Mason, W. P., and B. T. Matthias: *Phys. Rev.* **88**, 477 (1952).
14. Meyer, G.: Dissertation, Göttingen, 1937.
15. Niemiec, T.: *Phys. Rev.* **75**, 215 (1949).
16. Riecke, E., and W. Voigt: *Wied. Ann. Phys.* **45**, 523 (1892).
17. Scholz, H.: Dissertation, Göttingen, 1941.
18. Spitzer, F.: Dissertation, Göttingen, 1938.
19. Tamaru, T.: *Phys. Z.* **6**, 379 (1905).
20. Van der Veen, A. L.: *Z. Krist.* **51**, 545 (1913).

TABLE 5d-14. TEMPERATURE DEPENDENCE OF SOME PIEZOELECTRIC STRAIN CONSTANTS
($\times 10^{-12}$ in coulomb/newton or meter/volt)

Substance	Formula	d_{ik}	123°K	153°K	193°K	243°K	258°K	273°K	293°K	307°K	321°K	343°K	390°K	423°K	473°K	Ref.
Ammonium dihydrogen phosphate	$NH_4H_2PO_4$	d_{36}	.....	−83	−69	−55	−51	−48	−46	.....	....	....	.....	...	...	6
Barium titanate.	$BaTiO_3$	d_{31}	.....	....	....	....	.....	.....	−37	−38	−39	−42	−170	0	0	4*
Barium titanate ceramics.	$BaTiO_3$	d_{31}	.....	....	....	−60	−65	−75	−85	−69	−64	−55	.....	...	...	2*
Heavy rochelle salt.	$KNaC_4H_2D_2O_6{\cdot}4D_2O$	d_{14}	.....	....	....	....	195	140	193	2,800	213	....	.....	...	...	3
Potassium dihydrogen phosphate.	KH_2PO_4	d_{36}	20,000	135	50	29	26	23	21	.....	....	....	.....	...	...	1
Rochelle salt.	$KNaC_4H_4O_6{\cdot}4H_2O$	d_{14}	.....	....	....	96	700	765	780	250	....	....	.....	...	...	7
					5.5	22	1,200	2,250	2,700	250	....	....	.....	...	...	8
						150	2,100	350	740	320	120	....	.....	...	...	2
Sodium bromate.	$NaBrO_3$	d_{14}	.....	....	....	....	.....	.....	2.7	2.8	3.0	3.2	3.7	4.1	5.1	5*
Sodium chlorate.	$NaClO_3$	d_{14}	.....	....	....	....	.....	.....	2.0	2.2	2.3	2.5	3.1	3.8	5.4	5*

References

1. Bantle, W., and C. Caflisch: *Helv. Phys. Acta* **16,** 235 (1943).
2. Brush Laboratories Company, Cleveland, Ohio: reports.
3. Cady, W.: "Piezoelectricity," McGraw-Hill Book Company, Inc., New York, 1946.
4. Caspari, M. E., and W. J. Merz: *Phys. Rev.* **80,** 1082 (1950).
5. Mason, W. P.: "Piezoelectric Crystals and Their Application to Ultrasonics," D. Van Nostrand Company, Inc., New York, 1950.
6. Matthias, B., W. Merz, and P. Scherrer: *Helv. Phys. Acta* **20,** 273 (1947).
7. Valasek, J.: *Science* **65,** 235 (1927).
8. Valasek, J.: *Phys. Rev.* **20,** 639 (1922).

TABLE 5d-15. TEMPERATURE COEFFICIENT OF SOME PIEZOELECTRIC STRAIN CONSTANTS AT ROOM TEMPERATURE

Substance	Formula	α_{11}	α_{14}	α_{25}	α_{36}	Ref.
Iodic acid	HIO_3		+3.5	−3.5	−0.9	3
Lithium ammonium tartrate monohydrate	$LiNH_4C_4H_4O_6 \cdot H_2O$		+39	−50	+31	3
Quartz	SiO_2	∼−10				2
		−2.15	12.9			1
Rochelle salt	$NaKC_4H_4O_6 \cdot 4H_2O$		See Table 5d-14	+49	+10.9	4
Sodium ammonium tartrate tetrahydrate	$NaNH_4C_4H_4O_6 \cdot 4H_2O$		+2.1	−19	+12.1	3
Strontium formate dihydrate	$Sr(HCOO)_2 \cdot 2H_2O$		−8	−3.8	−14.7	3

Temperature coefficient α is defined as $\alpha_{ik} = \frac{1}{d_{ik}} \frac{\partial d_{ik}}{\partial \theta}$ where θ is the temperature. α_{ik} is measured in degrees^{-1}. The listed numbers have to be multiplied by 10^{-4}.

References

1. Bechmann, R.: *Proc. Phys. Soc. (London)* **64B**, 323 (1951).
2. Cady, W.: "Piezoelectricity," McGraw-Hill Book Company, Inc., New York, 1946.
3. Mason, W. P.: "Piezoelectric Crystals and Their Application," D. Van Nostrand Company, Inc., New York, 1950.
4. Valasek, J.: *Science* **65**, 235 (1927).

TABLE 5d-16. TABLE OF PYROELECTRIC CONSTANTS

Substance	Formula	p	Ref.
1. Calamine	$2ZnO \cdot SiO_2 \cdot H_2O$	2.0	2, 4
2. Cane sugar	$C_{12}H_{22}O_{11}$	0.18	3
3. Diammonium tartrate	$(NH_4)_2C_4H_4O_6$	0.95	1, 3
4. Dipotassium tartrate hemihydrate	$K_2C_4H_4O_6 \cdot \frac{1}{2}H_2O$	2.0	1, 3
5. Lithium selenate monohydrate	$Li_2SeO_4 \cdot H_2O$	5.7	1, 3
6. Lithium sodium sulfate	$LiNaSO_4$	0.75	1, 3
7. Lithium sulfate monohydrate	$Li_2SO_4 \cdot H_2O$	7.7	1, 3
8. Lithium trisodium selenate hexahydrate	$LiNa_3(SeO_4)_2 \cdot 6H_2O$	1.8	1, 3
9. Potassium lithium sulfate	$KLiSO_4$	1.6	1, 3
10. Resorcinol	$C_6H_6O_2$	2.6	3
11. Rhamnose	$C_6H_{12}O_5 \cdot H_2O$	1.2	3
		0.17	
12. Scolecite	$CaAl_2Si_3O_{10} \cdot 3H_2O$	0.33	3
13. Strontium ditartrate tetrahydrate	$Sr(HC_4H_4O_6)_2 \cdot 4H_2O$	0.24	1
		2.7	4
14. Tartaric acid	$C_4H_6O_6$	2.5	3
15. Tourmaline	Variable	0.35–0.44	1

The pyroelectric constant is defined as $p = \left(\frac{\partial D}{\partial \theta}\right)_{E=0}$ where D is the electric displacement and θ the temperature. The units for p are coulomb/meter^2 degree (rationalized mks). The listed numbers have to be multiplied by 10^{-5}. They include both the true and the false pyroeffect.

References

1. Ackermann, W.: *Ann Physik* **46**, 197 (1915).
2. Curie and Curie: *Compt. rend.* **91**, 383 (1880).
3. Hayashi, F.: Dissertation, Göttingen, 1912.
4. Van der Veen, A.: Thesis, Delft, 1911.

TABLE 5d-17. TEMPERATURE DEPENDENCE OF SOME PYROELECTRIC CONSTANTS*
($\times 10^{-5}$ in coulomb/meter^2 degree)

Substance	Formula	23°K	88°K	198°K	253°K	274°K	293°K	352°K	372°K	408°K	488°K	578°K	648°K
Diammonium tartrate	$(NH_4)_2C_4H_4O_6$	0.05	0.10	0.39	0.80	0.86	0.95	1.14					
Lithium selenate monohydrate	$Li_2SeO_4 \cdot H_2O$	0.31	0.77	3.28	4.82	5.33	5.70	6.45					
Lithium sodium sulfate	$LiNaSO_4$	0.04	0.10	0.29	0.54	0.68	0.75	0.91					
Lithium sulfate monohydrate	$Li_2SO_4 \cdot H_2O$	0.40	1.27	4.07	6.15	6.82	7.75	9.0					
Lithium trisodium selenate hexahydrate	$LiNa_3(SeO_4)_2 \cdot 6H_2O$	0.12	0.31	0.98	1.53	1.69	1.80	2.12					
Potassium lithium sulfate	$KLiSO_4$	.....	0.23	0.83	1.36	1.50	1.61	1.78					
Dipotassium tartrate hemihydrate	$K_2C_4H_4O_6 \cdot \frac{1}{2}H_2O$	0.13	0.33	1.10	1.70	1.87	1.99	2.30					
Strontium ditartrate tetrahydrate	$Sr(HC_4H_4O_6)_2 \cdot 4H_2O$	0.013	0.04	0.15	0.21	0.23	0.24	0.27					
Tourmaline	Yellow-green	0.027	0.097	0.32	0.40	0.41	0.43	0.44	0.45	0.46	0.50	0.56	0.62
	Rose-red	0.027	0.10	0.33	0.41	0.42	0.44	0.47	0.48	0.49	0.51	0.58	0.65
	Blue-green	0.013	0.047	0.22	0.31	0.34	0.35	0.39	0.40	0.41	0.42	0.46	0.51

* W. Ackermann, *Ann. Physik* **46**, 197 (1915).

5d-6. Ferroelectric and Antiferroelectric Properties

TABLE 5d-18. FERROELECTRIC CRYSTALS

Substance	Formula	Structure at room temp.	Ferroelectric axis	Curie point, °K	Max spont. polarization, coulomb/meter²	Small-signal dielectric const at room temp.		
						ϵ_a/ϵ_v	ϵ_b/ϵ_v	ϵ_c/ϵ_v
Heavy rochelle salt......	$KNaC_4H_2D_2O_6{\cdot}4D_2O$	monoc.	*a*	308 upper, 251 lower	0.37×10^{-2} at 279°K	2,300 at θ up	9.4	9.8
Lithium ammonium tartrate monohydrate	$LiNH_4C_4H_4O_6{\cdot}H_2O$	orthorh.	*b*	106	0.21×10^{-2} at $T \ll \theta$	7.2	8.0	6.9
Lithium thallium tartrate monohydrate	$LiTlC_4H_4O_6{\cdot}H_2O$	orthorh.	*a*	10	0.14×10^{-2} at $T \ll \theta$			
Rochelle salt............	$KNaC_4H_4O_6{\cdot}4H_2O$	monocl.	*a*	297 upper, 255 lower	0.24×10^{-2} at 276°K	4,000 at θ up	10.0	9.6
Cesium dideuterium arsenate..................	CsD_2AsO_4	tetrag.	*c*	212				
Cesium dihydrogen arsenate..................	CsH_2AsO_4	tetrag.	*c*	143				
Potassium dideuterium arsenate............	KD_2AsO_4	tetrag.	*c*	162				
Potassium dideuterium phosphate	KD_2PO_4	tetrag.	*c*	213	4.8×10^{-2} at $T \ll \theta$	88	88	90
Potassium dihydrogen arsenate	KH_2AsO_4	tetrag.	*c*	97	5.0×10^{-2} at $T \ll \theta$	62	62	22
Potassium dihydrogen phosphate	KH_2PO_4	tetrag.	*c*	123	4.95×10^{-2} at $T \ll \theta$	42	42	21
Rubidium dideuterium arsenate............	RbD_2AsO_4	tetrag.	*c*	178				
Rubidium dideuterium phosphate............	RbD_2PO_4	tetrag.	*c*	218				
Rubidium dihydrogen arsenate............	RbH_2AsO_4	tetrag.	*c*	111				
Rubidium dihydrogen phosphate............	RbH_2PO_4	tetrag.	*c*	146	....	35	35	22
Barium titanate.........	$BaTiO_3$	tetrag.	*c*	393	26×10^{-2} at 296°K	~5,000	~5,000	~160
Cadmium niobate (ceramics)	$Cd_2Nb_2O_7$	cubic	...	185	1.8×10^{-2} at 100°K	......	~310	
Lead metaniobate (ceramics)...........	$Pb(NbO_3)_2$	orthorh.	...	843	....		~280	
Lead titanate (ceramics)..	$PbTiO_3$	tetrag.	*c*	763			~50	
Lithium niobate.........	$LiNbO_3$	trigonal	*c*					
Lithium tantalate........	$LiTaO_3$	trigonal	*c*	....	23×10^{-2} at 723°K			~40
Potassium niobate.......	$KNbO_3$	orthorh.	*c*	707	3.78×10^{-2} at 683°K	......	.....	~500
Potassium tantalate......	$KTaO_3$	cubic	*c*	13	....		.....	~500
Sodium niobate..........	$NaNbO_3$	orthorh.	*c*	<64	....	76	76	~670
Tungsten trioxyd........	WO_3	triclinic	...	983				
Guanidine aluminum sulfate hexahydrate	$C(NH_2)_3Al(SO_4)_2{\cdot}6H_2O$	trigonal	*c*	....	0.35×10^{-2} at 296°K	5	5	6
Guanidine chromium sulfate hexahydrate	$C(NH_2)_3Cr(SO_4)_2{\cdot}6H_2O$	trigonal	*c*	....	0.36×10^{-2} at 296°K	5	5	6
Guanidine gallium sulfate hexahydrate	$C(NH_2)_3Ga(SO_4)_2{\cdot}6H_2O$	trigonal	*c*	....	0.36×10^{-2} at 296°K	5	5	6
Guanidine vanadium sulfate hexahydrate	$C(NH_2)_3V(SO_4)_2{\cdot}6H_2O$	trigonal	*c*	....	0.36×10^{-2} at 296°K			

TABLE 5d-18. FERROELECTRIC CRYSTALS (*Continued*)

Substance	Formula	Structure at room temp.	Ferroelectric axis	Curie point, °K	Max spont. polarization, coulomb/meter²	Small-signal dielectric const at room temp.		
						ϵ_a/ϵ_v	ϵ_b/ϵ_v	ϵ_c/ϵ_v
Guanidine aluminum selenate hexahydrate	$C(NH_2)_3Al(SeO_4)_2 \cdot 6H_2O$	trigonal	*c*	....	0.45×10^{-2} at 296°K	5	5	6
Guanidine chromium selenate hexahydrate	$C(NH_2)_3Cr(SeO_4)_2 \cdot 6H_2O$	trigonal	*c*	....	0.47×10^{-2} at 296°K	5	5	6
Guanidine gallium selenate hexahydrate	$C(NH_2)_3Ga(SeO_4)_2 \cdot 6H_2O$	trigonal	*c*	....	0.47×10^{-2} at 296°K	5	5	6
Deutero guanidine aluminum sulfate hexadeuterate	$C(ND_2)_3Al(SO_4)_2 \cdot 6D_2O$	trigonal	*c*	....	0.35×10^{-2} at 296°K	5	5	6

TABLE 5d-19. ANTIFERROELECTRIC CRYSTALS

Substance	Formula	Structure at room temp.	Transition temp., °K	Small-signal dielectric const at room temp.		
				ϵ_a/ϵ_v	ϵ_b/ϵ_v	ϵ_c/ϵ_v
Ammonium dihydrogen arsenate	$NH_4H_2AsO_4$	tetrag.	216	75	75	12
Ammonium dihydrogen phosphate	$NH_4H_2PO_4$	tetrag.	148	56	56	15.5
Ammonium paraperiodate	$(NH_4)_2H_3IO_6$	trigonal	251	143	143	180
Deutero-ammonium dideuterium arsenate	$ND_4D_2AsO_4$	orthorh.	304			
Deutero-ammonium dideuterium phosphate	$NH_4D_2PO_4$	tetrag.	243	73	73	22.5
Deutero-ammonium paraperiodate	$(ND_4)_2D_3IO_6$	trigonal	266			
Lead hafnate (ceramics)	$PbHfO_3$	tetrag.	488		90	
Lead zirconate (ceramics)	$PbZrO_3$	orthorh.	506		80	
Silver paraperiodate (powder)	$Ag_2H_3IO_6$	trigonal	227		57	
Sodium niobate	$NaNbO_3$	orthorh.	911	76	76	670
Sodium tantalate	$NaTaO_3$	orthorh.				

5e. Properties of Semiconductors

R. L. SPROULL

Cornell University

5e-1. Energy Gap. The energy gap $\mathcal{E}_g$ is the minimum energy required to excite an electron from the normally filled (valence) band to the normally empty (conduction) band. The "thermal" $\mathcal{E}_g$ is determined from data on electron and hole concentrations (n and p, respectively) in thermal equilibrium at temperature T°K. Frequently both n and p per cubic centimeter are measured and the expression

$$np = 2.33 \times 10^{31} \left(\frac{m_n m_p}{m^2}\right)^{3/2} T^3 \exp\,(-\mathcal{E}_g/kT) \tag{5e-1}$$

is used to obtain $\mathcal{E}_g$. m_n and m_p are the effective masses of electrons and holes, m is the free electron mass, and k is the Boltzmann constant. If $\mathcal{E}_g$ varies linearly with T, the slope of log np vs. $1/T$ gives the value of $\mathcal{E}_g$ at $T = 0$°K. Many of the values of $\mathcal{E}_g$ tabulated in Table 5e-1 are obtained in less direct ways than by use of Eq. (5e-1).

The "optical" $\mathcal{E}_g$ is the minimum energy required to excite an electron from the valence band to the conduction band by an allowed optical transition. It is generally greater than the thermal $\mathcal{E}_g$. It is usually determined by measuring the optical absorption constant as a function of photon energy, but it can sometimes be inferred from photoconductivity or other measurements. In determination by optical absorption, the absorption constant should be at least 10^5 cm^{-1} in order to be sure the transition is allowed ("forbidden" transitions can produce absorption constants of the order of 10 to 10^4 cm^{-1} in imperfect crystals). There should be good theoretical arguments that the observed absorption is not caused by exciton production, or else the exciton binding energy should be computed and added to the optical absorption threshold energy. These requirements have rarely been met. The optical $\mathcal{E}_g$ values in Table 5e-1 are intended primarily as estimates, and the original literature should be consulted to determine their reliability.

5e-2. Mobility of Current Carriers. The mobility μ of a hole or electron is the drift velocity per unit electric field. It can be measured directly on materials with sufficiently long minority carrier lifetime τ. Table 5e-2 gives values from carrier injection, time-of-flight measurements of μ_n (electrons) and μ_p (holes).

The "Hall mobility" $\mu_n^{(H)}$ or $\mu_p^{(H)}$ can be measured on a much wider group of materials. The Hall effect is the transverse field E_y produced when a current of current density J_x is flowing in the x direction and a magnetic induction B is present in the z direction. If the specimen is long and thin enough so that the shunting effect of the electrodes can be neglected, the Hall constant is defined as

$$R = \frac{E_y}{B_z J_x} \tag{5e-2}$$

If the conductivity is exclusively by electrons,

$$R\sigma = \mu_n^{(H)} \tag{5e-3}$$

where σ is the electrical conductivity. Expressions similar to this and to the following equations can be obtained for conduction exclusively by holes if $\mu_p^{(H)}$, μ_p, and p are substituted for $\mu_n^{(H)}$, μ_n, and n, respectively.

TABLE 5e-1. ENERGY GAP $\mathcal{E}_g$

Material	Measurement	$\mathcal{E}_g$	Ref.*
C (graphite) (*P*)	*T*	~0	1
Ge	*T*	0.785–0.0003*T*	2
	T	0.75–0.0001*T*	3, 4, 5
	O	0.72–0.0001*T*	6, 7
P (black) (*P*)	*T*	0.4	8
Se (amorph)	*O*	~2	9, 10
Si	*T*	1.21–0.0004*T*	11
(*P*)	*O*	1.35–0.0004*T*	5, 12, 13
Sn (gray, α) (*P*)	*T*	0.08	9, 14, 15, 16
Te	*T*	0.33	17
	O	0.32 and 0.37	18
AlSb (*P*)	*T*	1.6	19, 20, 21
(*P*)	*O*	1.67–0.0004*T*	21, 22, 23
BaO	*O*	4.2	24
CdS	*T*	1.6	25, 26
	O	2.4	27, 28
CdSe	*O*	1.8	27, 28
CdTe	*O*	1.4	28
Cu_2O (*P*)	*T*	~1	29
GaAs	*O*	1.45	23
GaSb	*T*	0.80	30
	O	0.71	23, 30
InAs	*T*	~0.5	31
(*P*)	*O*	0.35	23
InP	*O*	1.25	32
InSb	*T*	0.23	33
	O	0.23–0.0002*T*	33, 34, 35, 36
Mg_2Ge (*P*)	*T*	0.55	37
Mg_2Si (*P*)	*T*	0.7	37

TABLE 5e-1. ENERGY GAP ε_g (*Continued*)

Material	Measurement	ε_g	Ref.*
Mg_2Sn	*T*	0.26	37, 38, 39
	O	0.24	38
PbS	*T*	0.37	40
	O	$0.3 + 0.0004T$	41, 42
PbSe	*O*	$0.14 + 0.0002T$	43
PbTe	*O*	$0.18 + 0.0002T$	44
SiC (*P*)	*T*	....	44, 45
TiO_2	*T*	3.7	46, 47
	O	....	46, 47
UO_2 (*P*)	*T*	0.2	48
ZnS	*O*	3.6	49, 50
ZnO	*O*	$3.37–0.0008T$	51

The tabulated values are in electron volts and should be multiplied by 1.60×10^{-19} to obtain values in mks units. The data are for single crystals unless (*P*) appears in the first column. Thermal values are designated *T* and are for 0°K unless the temperature dependence is given. Optical values are designated *O* and are for room temperature unless the temperature dependence is given. Optical values should be considered as only estimates.

* References are on p. 5-164.

TABLE 5e-2. DRIFT MOBILITIES μ_n AND μ_p

Material	Electrons		Holes		Ref.
	μ_n	T, °K	μ_p	T, °K	
Ge	3,900	300	1,900	300	1
	$3.5 \times 10^7 T^{-1.6}$	200–300	$9.1 \times 10^8 T^{-2.3}$	170–300	1
Si	1,200	300	500	300	2
	$4.4 \times 10^6 T^{-1.5}$	170–300	$2.4 \times 10^8 T^{-2.3}$	150–300	2

The tabulated values are in cm²/volt sec and should be multiplied by 10^{-4} to obtain mobilities in mks units (m²/volt sec). The data are for single crystals with a room-temperature conductivity less than 0.1 mho/cm.

References for Table 5e-2

1. Prince, M. B. *Phys. Rev.* **92,** 681 (1953).
2. Prince, M. B. *Phys. Rev.* **93,** 1204 (1954).

The Hall effect is sometimes described in terms of the "Hall angle" θ which is the angle through which the equipotential planes in a long rectangular specimen carrying a current are tilted when a magnetic induction B is applied normal to the direction of current flow. For conduction exclusively by electrons

$$\theta = \mu_n^{(H)}B \tag{5e-4}$$

For simple metals and "highly doped" (degenerate) semiconductors in which the energy of an electron or hole is a spherically symmetrical function of the momentum k

$$\mu_n = \mu_n^{(H)} \tag{5e-5}$$

The conductivity σ of a semiconductor containing only electron carriers and with n carriers per unit volume is

$$\sigma = ne\mu_n \tag{5e-6}$$

Combining (5e-3), (5e-5), and (5e-6) gives

$$R = \frac{1}{ne} \tag{5e-7}$$

For semiconductors in which the energy of an electron or hole is a spherically symmetrical and single-valued function of the momentum k and in which the temperature and purity are high enough so that thermal scattering predominates,

$$\mu_n^{(H)} = \frac{3\pi}{8}\mu_n \tag{5e-8}$$

and

$$R = \frac{3\pi}{8}\frac{1}{ne} \tag{5e-9}$$

Many reported values of mobility determined by Hall-effect experiments are the product of $8/3\pi$ and the observed Hall mobility. The values of $\mu^{(H)}$ reported in Table 5e-3 are simply the observed Hall mobilities, since in most solids the validity of Eq. (5e-8) has not yet been established.

The above equations are all written in mks units, in which μ and $\mu^{(H)}$ are in m²/volt sec and R is in m³/coulomb. It is convenient to have expressions in practical units: cm, volt, gauss, coulomb, and sec. In these units μ and $\mu^{(H)}$ are in cm²/volt sec and R is in cm³/coulomb. The expressions replacing Eqs. (5e-2) and (5e-4) are

$$R = \frac{10^8 E_y}{B_z J_x} \tag{5e-10}$$

and

$$\theta = 10^{-8}\mu_n^{(H)}B \tag{5e-11}$$

The diffusion constants D_n and D_p for electrons and holes can be calculated from the mobilities μ_n and μ_p by the Einstein relation:

$$D_n = \frac{kT}{e}\mu_n \tag{5e-12}$$

If $T = 300°K$, $D_n = 0.026\mu_n$. If μ_n is in cm²/volt sec, D_n from this equation is in cm²/sec; if μ_n is in mks units, D_n is in m²/sec.

5e-3. Representative Conductivity Values. In general the conductivity is

$$\sigma = e(n\mu_n + p\mu_p) \tag{5e-13}$$

For intrinsic conduction, $n = p$. In most practical cases either $n \gg p$ ("n type") or $p \gg n$ ("p type"). Since σ depends so sensitively upon the concentration and kind of intentionally added chemical elements ("impurities" or "doping agents"), only a few typical values can be given.

5e-4. Binding Energies of Carriers to Donors and Acceptors. Chemical additives or physical imperfections (vacancies, interstitials) create localized energy states which can provide free carriers or can trap free carriers. These are of two kinds: 1) "donors," or "hole traps," which can release (donate) an electron to the conduction or valence bands; 2) "acceptors," or "electron traps," which can remove (accept) an electron from the conduction or valence bands. The binding energy of an electron

TABLE 5e-3. HALL MOBILITIES $\mu_n^{(H)}$ AND $\mu_p^{(H)}$

Material	Electrons		Holes		Notes	Ref.*
	$\mu_n^{(H)}$	T, °K	$\mu_p^{(H)}$	T, °K		
C (graphite) (*P*)	$\sim 10^4$	300	$\sim 10^4$	300	...	1, 55
Ge	4,200	300	....	....	*a*	56
	$3.9 \times 10^7 T^{-1.6}$	150–300	....	....	*b*	56
	....	....	3,400	300	*b,c*	57
	....	....	$9.5 \times 10^7 T^{-1.8}$	150–300	*c,d*	57
P (black) (*P*)	....	....	400	300	...	8
Si	1,700	300	350	300	*e*	11
Sn (gray, α) (*P*)	$10^7 T^{-1.5}$	>250	....	....	*f*	14, 15, 16
Te	....	....	~600	300	...	58
AlSb	>100	300	>100	300	...	20, 21
BaO	~5	700	....	....	...	59
CdS	~250	290	....	....	...	26
CdTe	~300	....	>30	....	...	28
Cu_2O (*P*)	....	....	70	300	...	60
GaSb	~4,000	300	700	300	...	30, 61, 62
InAs	14,000	300	1,900	300	*g*	31
InSb	67,000	300	2,400	140	...	63
	325,000	78	10,000	78	*h*	64
Mg_2Ge	~170	300	....	....	...	37
Mg_2Si	~125	300	....	....	...	37
Mg_2Sn	3,500	100	2,900	100	*i*	37, 38
			200	273	...	37, 38
PbS	>400	290	>500	290	*j*	43, 66
PbSe	>1,000	290	>1,000	290	*j*	43, 66
PbTe	>1,500	290	>1,200	290	*j*	43, 66
TiO_2	~0.7	300	....	....	...	48
ZnO	~200	300	....	....	...	52

The tabulated values are in cm²/volt sec and should be multiplied by 10^{-4} to obtain $\mu_n^{(H)}$ and $\mu_p^{(H)}$ in mks units. The data are for single crystals unless (*P*) appears in the first column.

* References are on p. 5-164.

[a] For specimens with $\sigma < 1$ mho/cm at 300°K.

[b] For specimens with $\sigma < 0.2$ mho/cm at 300°K.

[c] At a magnetic induction of 3,000 gauss.

[d] For specimens with $\sigma < 0.1$ mho/cm at 300°K.

[e] For specimens with $\sigma < 0.03$ mho/cm at 300°K.

[f] $\mu_n^{(H)}/\mu_p^{(H)} = 1.3$.

[g] 10^{17} to 10^{19} carriers per cm³.

[h] 3 to 10×10^{14} carriers per cm³.

[i] $\mu_n^{(H)}/\mu_p^{(H)} = 1.2$.

[j] μ values are proportional to $T^{-\frac{5}{2}}$; $\mu_n^{(H)}/\mu_p^{(H)} = 2.5$.

TABLE 5e-4. REPRESENTATIVE VALUES OF THE CONDUCTIVITY σ

Material	No. of host crystal atoms per cm^3	No. of donors or acceptors per cm^3	Donor or acceptor	Conduction type	σ at 290–300°K	σ at another T		Ref.*
						σ	T, °K	
C (graphite)	1.15×10^{23}	Intrinsic	...	...	~200	~600	15	67†
					2.6×10^{4}	2.5×10^{5}	15	67‡
Ge	4.41×10^{22}	Intrinsic	...	...	0.022	....	.....	56
		8×10^{13}	As	n	0.05	0.45	78	56
		1.5×10^{15}	As	n	0.9	6	78	56
		9×10^{13}	Ga	p	0.03	0.5	78	57
		8×10^{14}	Ga	p	0.3	3	78	57
P (black) (P)	1.31×10^{22}	Intrinsic	...	...	....	3	400	8
Si	5.00×10^{22}	Intrinsic	...	...	1.57×10^{-5}	....	.....	68
		5×10^{14}	As	n	0.1	....	.....	68
		5×10^{15}	As	n	0.77	....	.....	68
		5×10^{16}	As	n	3.3	....	.....	68
		5×10^{14}	B	p	0.4	....	.....	68
		5×10^{15}	B	p	3.3	....	.....	68
		2×10^{16}	B	p	10	....	.....	68
Sn (gray, α)	2.92×10^{22}	Intrinsic	...	...	3,000	....	.....	15, 16
		2×10^{18}	Sb	n	5,000	4,000	78	15, 16
		6×10^{18}	Al	p	3,000	750	78	15, 16
Te	2.97×10^{22}	Intrinsic	...	...	2	....	.....	17
AlSb	3.45×10^{22}	...	...	...	....	3	1,000	21
		1.5×10^{15}	...	p	0.031	0.032	370	20
		1.5×10^{16}	...	p	0.30	0.28	370	20
		3.8×10^{18}	...	p	32	29	370	20
CdS	4.04×10^{22}	5×10^{18}	Ga	n	80	....	.....	26
GaSb	3.49×10^{22}	Intrinsic	...	...	0.01	2	500	83
InSb	2.97×10^{22}	Intrinsic	...	...	200	700	400	63
Mg_2Ge	4.63×10^{22}	Intrinsic	...	...	....	50	660	37
Mg_2Sn	3.86×10^{22}	Intrinsic	...	...	24	....	.....	37, 38
PbS	3.84×10^{22}	Intrinsic	...	...	0.3	....	.....	69
		3×10^{16}	Pb	n	....	16	77	69
		8×10^{16}	S	p	....	54	77	69
PbSe	3.44×10^{22}	Intrinsic	...	...	18 (est.)	....	.....	70
		2×10^{18}	Pb	n	400	20,000	77	70
		5×10^{18}	Se	p	900	16,000	77	70
PbTe	2.96×10^{22}	Intrinsic	...	...	1.8 (est.)	....	.....	70
		5×10^{17}	Pb	n	120	2,100	77	70
		3×10^{17}	Te	p	40	1,000	77	70
TiO_2	9.5×10^{22}	1.3×10^{19}	Ti	n	0.23	0.21	373	48†
		2.8×10^{19}	Ti	n	0.04	0.04	373	48‡
UO_2	2.46×10^{22}	3×10^{18}	O	p	0.01	0.04	373	49

The tabulated values are in mho/cm and should be multiplied by 100 to obtain σ in mks units (mho/m.). The number of atoms per cm^3 is included for convenience. n and p mean n-type and p-type conduction, respectively. The data are for single crystals unless (P) appears in the "material" column.

* References are on p. 5-164.

† Parallel to c axis.

‡ Perpendicular to c axis.

to a donor can be determined by measuring the fraction of the electrons that are released by the donor as a function of T (and similarly for acceptors).

At large donor (or acceptor) concentrations the interaction between donors (or acceptors) modifies the binding energy. This effect has not been studied for most of the substances listed in Table 5e-5. In the cases where it has been studied (some donors and acceptors in Si and Ge) the tabulated values are the limiting values at low concentrations.

TABLE 5e-5. BINDING ENERGIES OF CARRIERS TO DONORS OR ACCEPTORS

Host crystal	Donor	Binding energy	Acceptor	Binding energy	Ref.*
Ge	As	0.0127	Al	0.0102	71
	P	0.0120	B	0.0104	71
	Sb	0.0097	Ga	0.0108	71
			In	0.0112	71
			Au	0.15; 0.5	72
			Co	0.25	73
			Cu	0.04; 0.25	74, 75
			Ni	0.25	74
			Pt	0.04; 0.5	71, 75
			Zn	0.029	71, 75
	Li	0.01			76
	Fe	0.27	Fe	0.34	77
Si	As	0.049	Al	0.057	11, 78
	P	0.039	B	0.045	11, 78
	Sb	0.039	Ga	0.065	11, 78
			In	0.16	11, 78
			Au	0.39	11, 78
Sn (gray, α)	Sb	0.004	Mg	0.001	15, 79, 84
			Al	0.005	15, 79, 84
CdS	Cl, Ga, and vacancies	0.03			26, 80
CdTe	....	......	....	......	28
Cu_2O	....	......	Cu vacancy	0.3	60
PbS	Pb	0.03	S	0.001	69
UO_2	....	......	Oxygen	0.4	49
ZnS	....	......	....	......	81, 50
ZnO	Zn interstitial	0.02	....	......	82

The tabulated values are in electron volts and should be multiplied by 1.60×10^{-19} to obtain values in mks units. The values are for single crystals and for low concentrations of donors and acceptors. In the case of chemical additives (e.g., Fe, Cu) in germanium which are not from column III or column V of the periodic table, the energy levels introduced by the additive are measured from the conduction band if the additive is labeled "donor" and from the valence band if labeled "acceptor." The deep levels usually appear as trapping levels rather than as donors or acceptors.

* References are on p. 5-164.

References for Tables 5e-1 through 5e-5[1]

1. Kinchin, G. H.: *Proc. Roy. Soc.* (*London*), ser. A, **217**, 9 (1953).
2. Morin, F. J., and J. P. Maita: *Phys. Rev.* **94**, 1525 (1954).
3. Conwell, E. M.: *Proc. IRE* **40**, 1327 (1952).
4. Shockley, W.: "Electrons and Holes in Semiconductors," pp. 333ff., D. Van Nostrand Company, Inc., New York, 1953.
5. Bardeen, J., and W. Shockley: *Phys. Rev.* **80**, 72 (1950).
6. Haynes, J. R., and H. B. Briggs: *Phys. Rev.* **86**, 647 (1952).
7. Hall, Bardeen, and Blatt: *Phys. Rev.* **95**, 559 (1954).
8. Keyes, R. W.: *Phys. Rev.* **92**, 580 (1953).
9. Moss, T. S.: "Photoconductivity in the Elements," Butterworth & Co. (Publishers) Ltd., London, 1952.
10. Weimer, P. K., and A. D. Cope: *RCA Rev.* **12**, 314 (1951).
11. Morin, F. J., and J. P. Maita: *Phys. Rev.* **96**, 28 (1954). See also refs. 2, 3, and 4.
12. Becker, M., and H. Y. Fan: *Phys. Rev.* **76**, 1531 (1949).
13. Brattain, W. H., and H. B. Briggs: *Phys. Rev.* **75**, 1705 (1949).
14. Becker, J. H.: *Phys. Rev.* **98**, 1192 (1955).
15. Busch, G., and J. Wieland: *Helv. Phys. Acta.* **26**, 697 (1953).
16. Kendall, J. T.: *Phil. Mag.* **45**, 141 (1954).
17. Nussbaum, A.: *Phys. Rev.* **94**, 337 (1954).
18. Loferski, J. J.: *Phys. Rev.* **93**, 707 (1954).
19. Welker, H.: *Z. Naturforsch.* **8a**, 248 (1953).
20. Willardson, Beer, and Middleton: *J. Electrochem. Soc.* **101**, 354 (1954).
21. Blunt, Frederikse, Becker, and Hosler: *Phys. Rev.* **96**, 578 (1954).
22. Blunt, Frederikse, and Becker: *Phys. Rev.* **94**, 1431 (1954).
23. Briggs, Cummings, Hrostowski, and Tanenbaum: *Phys. Rev.* **93**, 912 (1954).
24. Sproull, R. L.: Cornell University.
25. Boer, K. W.: *Ann. Physik* **10**, 20 (1952).
26. Kroger, Vink, and van den Boomgaard, *Z. physik. Chem.* **203**, 1 (1954).
27. Frerichs, R.: Northwestern University.
28. Jenny, D. A., and R. H. Bube: *Phys. Rev.* **96**, 1190 (1954).
29. Anderson, J. S., and N. N. Greenwood: *Proc. Roy. Soc.* (*London*) **215**, 353 (1952).
30. Leifer, H. N., and W. C. Dunlap: *Phys. Rev.* **94**, 1431 (1954).
31. Folberth, Grimm, and Weiss: *Z. Naturforsch.* **8a**, 826 (1953).
32. Oswald, F.: *Z. Naturforsch.* **9a**, 181 (1954).
33. Breckenridge, Blunt, Hosler, Frederikse, Becker, and Oshinsky: *Phys. Rev.* **96**, 571 (1954).
34. Tanenbaum, M., and H. B. Briggs: *Phys. Rev.* **91**, 1561 (1953).
35. Hrostowski, Wheatley, and Flood: *Phys. Rev.* **95**, 1683 (1953).
36. Burstein, E.: *Phys. Rev.* **94**, 1431 (1954); *Phys. Rev.* **93**, 632 (1954).
37. Busch, G., and U. Winkler: *Helv. Phys. Acta* **26**, 395, 578 (1953).
38. Frederikse, H. P. R., and R. F Blunt, "Photoconductivity," John Wiley & Sons, Inc., New York, 1956.
39. Robertson, W. D., and H. H. Uhlig: *Trans. Am. Inst. Mining Met. Engrs.* **180**, 345 (1949).
40. Scanlon, W. W.: *Phys. Rev.* **92**, 1573 (1953).
41. Gibson, A. F.: *Proc. Phys. Soc.* (*London*), ser. B, **65**, 378 (1952).
42. Avery, D. G.: *Proc. Phys. Soc.* (*London*), ser. B, **67**, 2 (1954).
43. Putley, E. H.: *Proc. Phys. Soc.* (*London*), ser. B, **65**, 993 (1952).
44. Calculations by G. G. MacFarlane, R.R.E., Great Malvern, from thermal and optical data of refs. 41, 42, and 43.
45. Busch, G., and H. Labhart: *Helv. Phys. Acta* **19**, 463 (1946).
46. Kendall, J. T.: *J. Chem. Phys.* **21**, 821 (1953).
47. Cronemeyer, D. C.: *Phys. Rev.* **87**, 876 (1952).

[1] **Many of the values presented in the tables of Sec. 5e are subject to considerable doubt. Some of the references cited support the tabulated figures and some give contrary evidence. These references do, however, provide an entry into the original literature which should be consulted to determine the reliability of the tabulated figures.**

48. Breckenridge, R. G., and W. R. Hosler: *Phys. Rev.* **91**, 793 (1953).
49. Hartmann, W.: *Z. Physik* **102**, 709 (1936).
50. Bube, R. H.: *Phys. Rev.* **90**, 70 (1953).
51. Piper, W. W.: *J. Chem. Phys.* **20**, 1343 (1952).
52. Reboul, T. T.: University of Pennsylvania.
53. Prince, M. B.: *Phys. Rev.* **92**, 681 (1953).
54. Prince, M. B.: *Phys. Rev.* **93**, 1204 (1954).
55. Mrozowski, S.: *J. Chem. Phys.* **21**, 492 (1953).
56. Debye, P. P., and E. M. Conwell: *Phys. Rev.* **87**, 1131 (1952); *Phys. Rev.* **93**, 693 (1954).
57. P. P. Debye, Raytheon Mfg. Co., and E. M. Conwell, Sylvania Electric Products, Inc.
58. Fukuroi, F.: *Science Repts. Research Insts. Tôhoku Univ.* **A1**, 373 (1949).
59. Pell, E. M.: *Phys. Rev.* **87**, 457 (1952).
60. Brattain, W. H.: *Revs. Modern Phys.* **23**, 203 (1951).
61. Tanenbaum, Pearson, and Feldman: *Phys. Rev.* **93**, 912 (1954).
62. Detwiler, D. P.: *Phys. Rev.* **94**, 1431 (1954).
63. Tanenbaum, M., and J. P. Maita: *Phys. Rev.* **91**, 1009 (1953).
64. Hrostowski, Morin, Geballe, and Wheatley: *Phys. Rev.* **100**, 1672 (1955).
65. Putley, E. H.: *Proc. Phys. Soc. (London)*, ser. B, **65**, 388 (1952).
66. Petritz, Scanlon, and Lummis: *Phys. Rev.* **94**, 1430 (1954).
67. Primak, W., and L. H. Fuchs: *Phys. Rev.* **95**, 22 (1954).
68. Pearson, G. L., Bell Telephone Laboratories; Pearson, G. L., and J. Bardeen, *Phys. Rev.* **75**, 865 (1949).
69. Brebrick, R. F., and W. W. Scanlon: *Phys. Rev.* **96**, 598 (1954).
70. Putley, E. H., R.R.E., Great Malvern.
71. Geballe, T. H., and F. J. Morin: *Phys. Rev.* **95**, 1085 (1954).
72. Dunlap, W. C.: *Phys. Rev.* **91**, 1282 (1953).
73. Newman, R., and W. W. Tyler: *Phys. Rev.* **94**, 1419 (1954).
74. Burton, Hull, Morin, and Severiens: *J. Phys. Chem.* **57**, 853 (1953).
75. Dunlap, W. C.: *Phys. Rev.* **96**, 40 (1954).
76. Fuller, C. S., and J. A. Ditzenberger: *Phys. Rev.* **91**, 193 (1953).
77. Tyler, W. W., and H. H. Woodbury: *Phys. Rev.* **96**, 874 (1954).
78. Morin, Maita, Shulman, and Hannay: *Phys. Rev.* **96**, 833 (1954).
79. Busch, G., and E. Mooser: *Z. physik. Chem.* **198**, 23 (1951).
80. Bube, R. H.: *J. Chem. Phys.* 18 (1955).
81. Hoogenstaaten, W.: *J. Electrochem. Soc.*; Schon, M.: *Z. Naturforsch.* **6A**, 287 (1951); Garlick, G. F. J., and A. F. Gibson: *J. Opt. Soc. Am.* **39**, 935 (1949).
82. Hahn, E. E.: *J. Appl. Phys.* **22**, 855 (1951).
83. Blunt, Hosler, and Frederikse: *Phys. Rev.* **96**, 576 (1954).
84. Busch, G., and E. Mooser: *Helv. Phys. Acta.* **26**, 611 (1953).

General References

Principal

Shockley, W.: "Electrons and Holes in Semiconductors," D. Van Nostrand Company, Inc., New York, 1950.

Other

Hunter, Lloyd P., ed.: "Handbook of Semiconductor Electronics," McGraw-Hill Book Company, Inc., New York, 1956.
Mott, N. F., and R. W. Gurney: "Electronic Processes in Ionic Crystals," 2d ed., Oxford University Press, New York, 1948.
Seitz, F.: "The Modern Theory of Solids," McGraw-Hill Book Company, Inc., New York, 1940.
Wright, D. A.: "Semiconductors," John Wiley & Sons, Inc., New York, 1950.
"Abstracts of the Literature on Semiconducting and Luminescent Materials and Their Applications," John Wiley & Sons, Inc., New York, 1955.

5f. Properties of Nonmetallic Conductors

S. C. BROWN and W. P. ALLIS[1]

Massachusetts Institute of Technology

R. J. FRIAUF[2]

University of Kansas

CONDUCTION IN GASES[3]

5f-1. Ionization by Electrons. The rate of ionization by electrons in a gas is related to the "probability" of ionization P_i. The "probability" of ionization P_i by an electron is given in Sec. (7m-1). The ionization rate $\bar{\nu}_i$ is defined by

$$\frac{1}{n}\frac{dn}{dt} = \bar{\nu}_i = \int p_0 P_i f 4\pi v^3 \, dv \tag{5f-1}$$

where $p_0 = 273.16p/T$ is the "reduced" pressure in millimeters of Hg, and f is the normalized electron distribution function.

1. The first Townsend coefficient α_i, the number of ionizations per electron per centimeter path, is

$$\alpha_i = \frac{1}{n}\frac{dn}{dx} = \frac{\bar{\nu}_i}{v_d} = \frac{\bar{\nu}_i}{\mu E} \tag{5f-2}$$

α/p as a function of E/p is plotted in Figs. 5f-1, 2, 3, and 4. α_i can often can be represented by the function

$$\alpha_i = Ae^{-Bp/E} \tag{5f-3}$$

where A is a slowly increasing function of E/p.

2. The number of ionizations per electron per volt is

$$\eta = \frac{\alpha_i}{E} = \frac{\bar{\nu}_i}{\mu E^2} \qquad (\mu = \text{mobility}) \tag{5f-4}$$

This quantity is a function of E/p only.

5f-2. Deionization. 1. The attachment coefficient β is similar to α_i and measures the rate of attachment of electrons to neutral atoms.

$$\beta = -\frac{1}{n}\frac{dn}{dx} = \frac{\bar{\nu}_a}{\mu E} \tag{5f-5}$$

[1] Conduction in gases.
[2] Ionic conductivity in solid salts.
[3] Material taken from Sanborn C. Brown and W. P. Allis, Basic Data of Electrical Discharges, *Tech. Rept.* 83, Research Laboratory of Electronics, MIT, 1954.

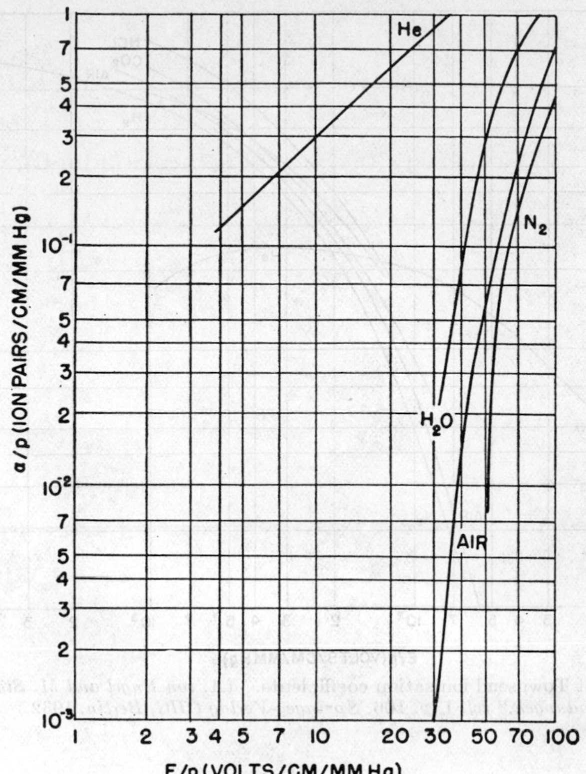

FIG. 5f-1. First Townsend ionization coefficients. (*A. von Engel and M. Steenbeck, "Elektrische Gasentladungen," vol. I, p.* 105, *Springer-Verlag OHG, Berlin,* 1932).

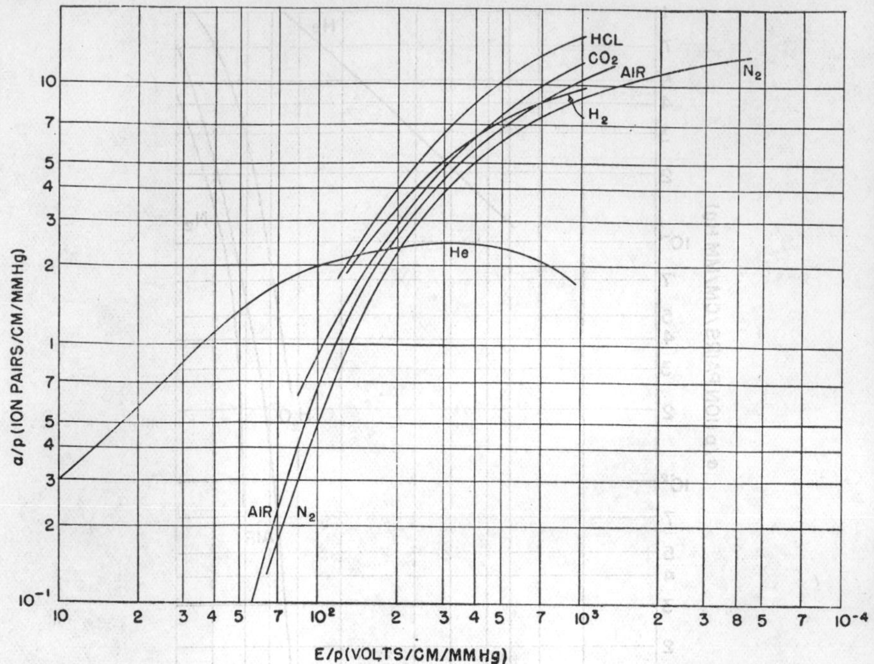

FIG. 5f-2. First Townsend ionization coefficients. (*A. von Engel and M. Steenbeck, "Elektrische Gasentladungen," vol.* I, *p.* 106, *Springer-Verlag OHG, Berlin,* 1932.)

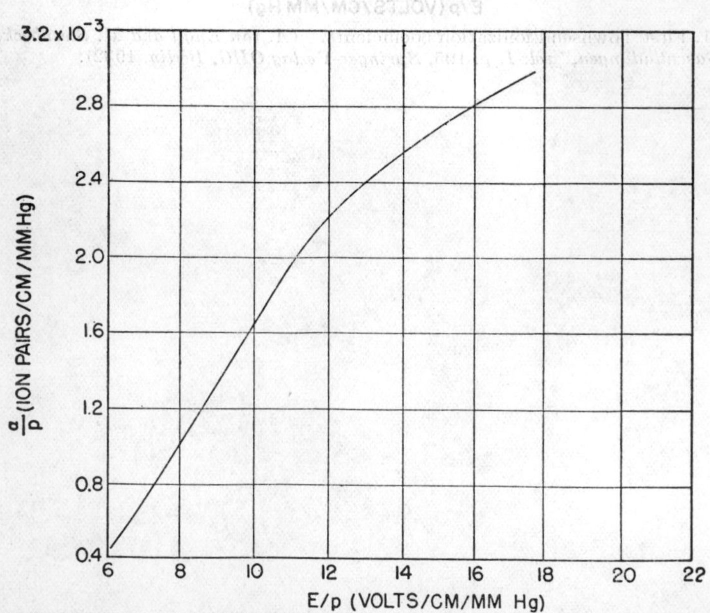

FIG. 5f-3. First Townsend coefficient in CO_2. (*D. R. Young, Laboratory for Insulation Research, M.I.T., Technical Report* 22, *August,* 1949.)

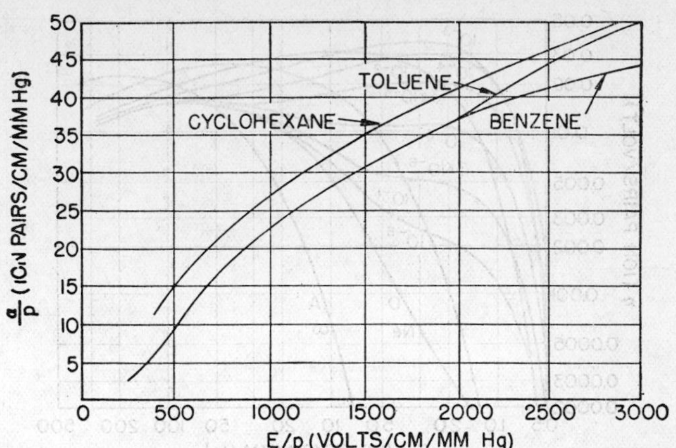

FIG. 5f-4. First Townsend coefficients for benzene, toluene, and cyclohexane. [*M. Valeriu-Petrescu, Bull. soc. roumaine phys.* **44**, 3 (1943).]

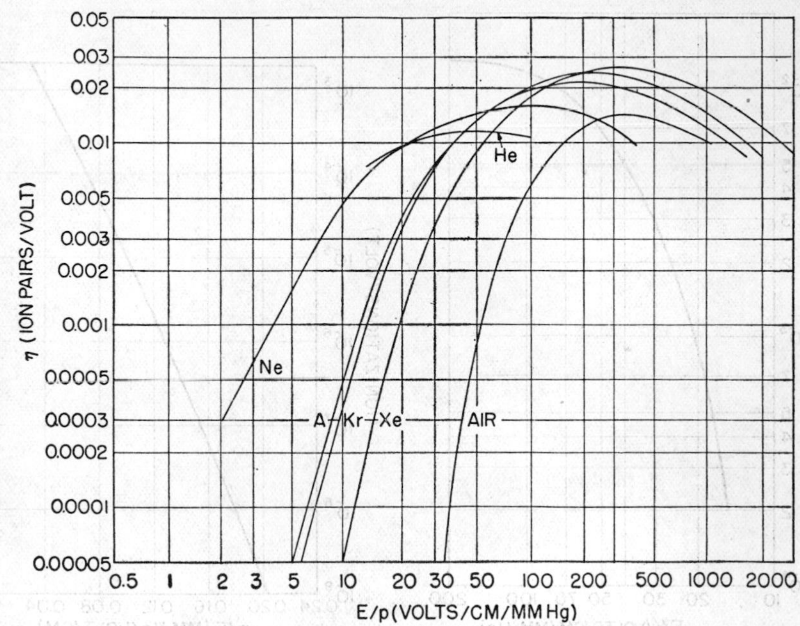

FIG. 5f-5. Ionizations per volt per mm Hg at 0°C for the rare gases. [*M. J. Druyvesteyn and F. M. Penning, Revs. Modern Phys.* **12**, 87 (1940).]

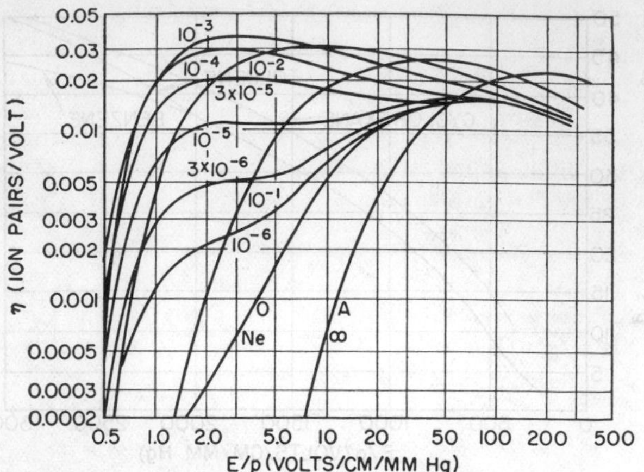

Fig. 5f-6. Ionizations per volt per mm Hg at 0°C for neon-argon mixtures. The numbers on each curve give the ratio of the argon pressure to the total pressure of the mixture. [*A. A. Kruithof and F. M. Penning*, *Physica* **4**, 450 (1937).]

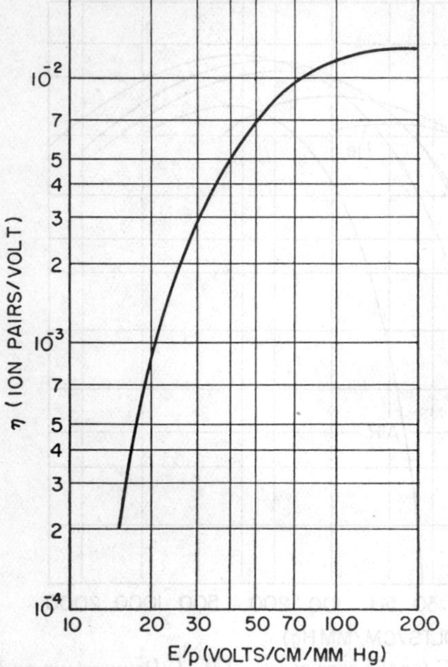

Fig. 5f-7. Ionizations per volt per mm Hg at 0°C in hydrogen. *L. J. Varnerin, Jr., and S. C. Brown, Phys. Rev.* **79**, 946 (1950).]

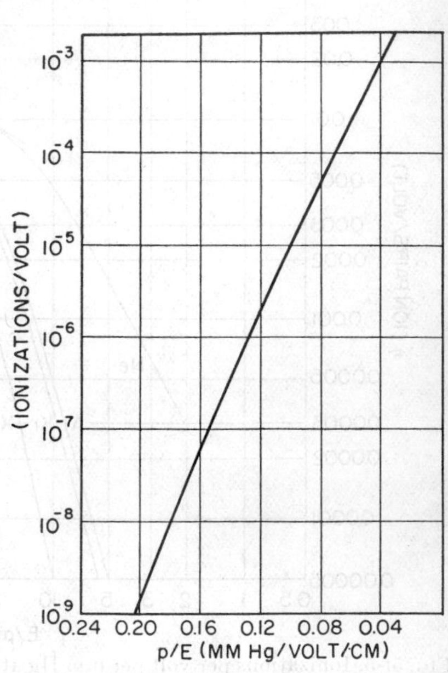

Fig. 5f-8. Variation of η with p/E for high pressure H_2. (*C. C. Leiby, Jr., Thesis, MIT, May*, 1954.)

The attachment efficiency h is the number of attachments per collision

$$h = \frac{\bar{\nu}_a}{\bar{\nu}_c} = \frac{\beta \mu E}{\bar{\nu}_c} \approx \frac{4}{3} \frac{mE}{e} \beta \mu^2 \tag{5f-6}$$

The last expression is generally used to compute h from experimental data but is correct only if P_c (collision probability) is independent of electron velocity.

2. The ion recombination coefficient α_r is defined by

$$\alpha_r = -\frac{1}{n^2}\frac{dn}{dt} \tag{5f-7}$$

Its dependence on pressure and temperature may be represented by

$$\frac{1}{\alpha_r} = a\frac{T^4}{p} + b\frac{p}{T} \tag{5f-8}$$

where the first term was proposed by Thomson, the second by Langevin.

TABLE 5f-1. RADIATIVE RECOMBINATION COEFFICIENTS

Element	α, cm³/sec	T, °K
H*........	10^{-11}	
A†........	2×10^{-10}	3100
Cs†........	3.4×10^{-10}	2000
Hg‡........	2.3×10^{-10}	2000

* Craggs and Hopwood, *Proc. Roy. Soc.* (*London*) **59,** 771 (1947).
† Kenty, *Phys. Rev.* **32,** 624 (1928).
‡ Mobler, *J. Research Natl. Bur. Standards* **19,** 447, 559 (1937).

TABLE 5f-2. DISSOCIATIVE RECOMBINATION

Gas	α, ions/cc/sec
He............	1.7×10^{-8}
Ne............	2.1×10^{-7}
A.............	3×10^{-7}
Kr............	6×10^{-7}
Xe............	2×10^{-6}
N_2............	1.4×10^{-6}
O_2............	2.8×10^{-7}

References for Table 5f-2.

1. M. A. Biondi and S. C. Brown, *Phys. Rev.* **76,** 1697 (1949).
2. B. Holt, J. M. Richardson, B. Howland, and B. T. McClure, *Phys. Rev.* **77,** 239 (1950).
3. R. A. Johnson, B. T. McClure, and R. B. Holt, *Phys. Rev.* **80,** 376 (1950).
4. A. Redfield and R. B. Holt, *Phys. Rev.* **82,** 874 (1951).
5. J. M. Richardson, *Phys. Rev.* **88,** 895 (1952).

TABLE 5f-3. THREE-BODY RECOMBINATION COEFFICIENTS FOR ELECTRONS*

Gas	α (at 0°C and 760 mm), cm³/sec	Est. saturation pressure, mm Hg
Helium..........	6.8×10^{-9}	2.8×10^{4}
Argon...........	6.8×10^{-11}	2.8×10^{-5}
Air.............	1.7×10^{-7}	10^{4}
Hydrogen........	1.6×10^{-7}	10^{4}

* H. S. W. Massey and E. H. S. Burhop, "Electronic and Ionic Impact Phenomena," p. 635, Oxford University Press, New York, 1952.

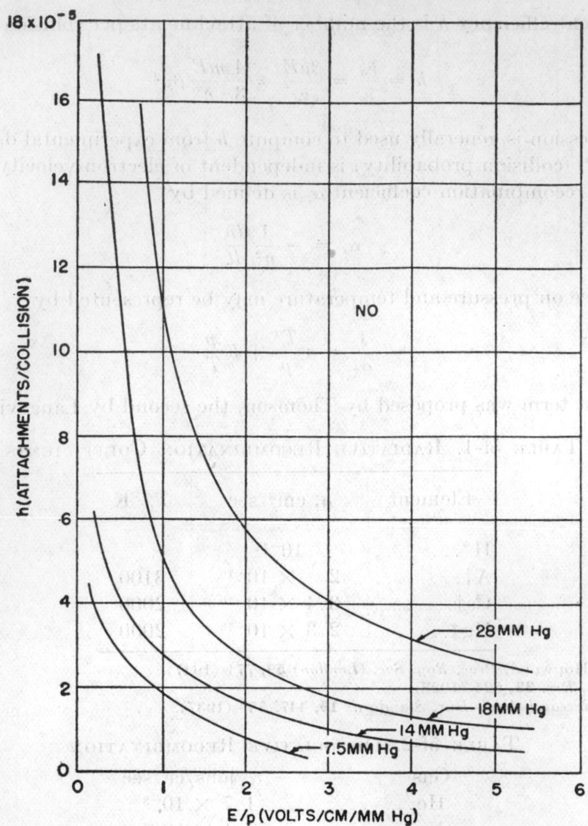

FIG. 5f-9. Efficiency of electron attachment in nitric oxide. [*N. E. Bradbury, J. Chem. Phys.* **2**, 827 (1934).]

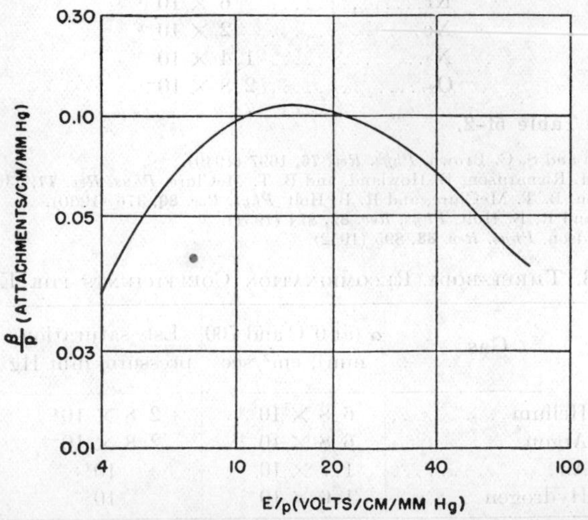

FIG. 5f-10. Attachment coefficients in O_2 per unit length in direction of drift. [*R. Geballe and M. A. Harrison, Phys. Rev.* **85**, 372 (1952).]

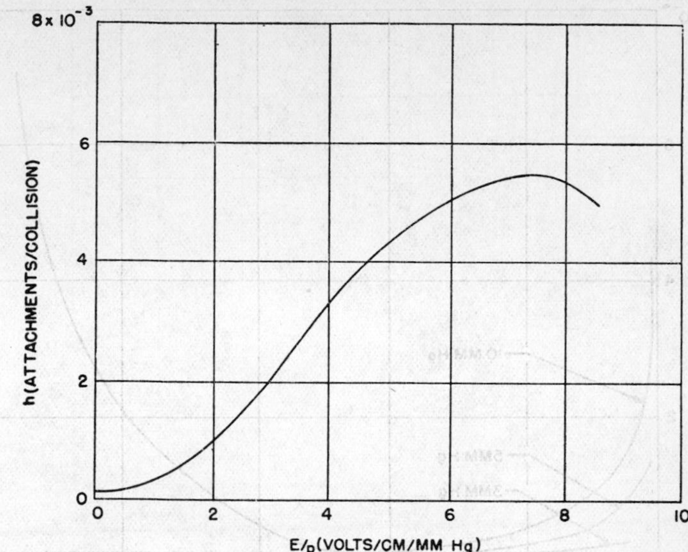

FIG. 5f-11. Efficiency of electron attachment in HCl in argon. [*N. E. Bradbury, J. Chem. Phys.* **2,** 827 (1934).]

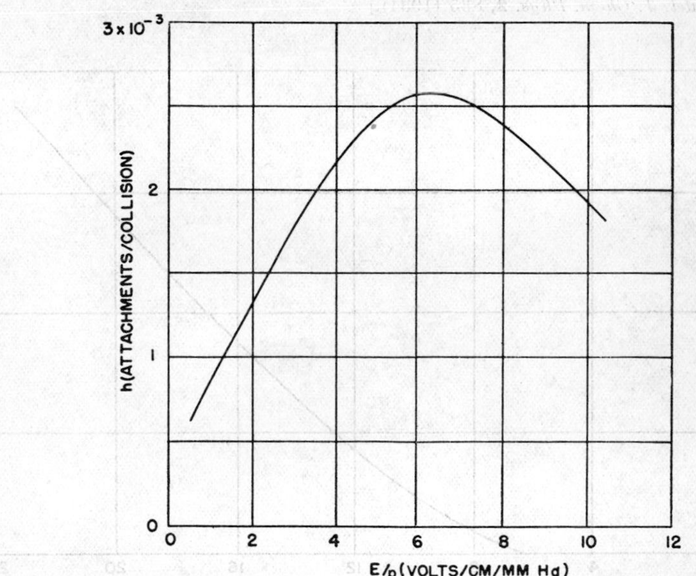

FIG. 5f-12. Efficiency of electron attachment in Cl_2 in argon. [*N. E. Bradbury, J. Chem. Phys.* **2,** 827 (1934).]

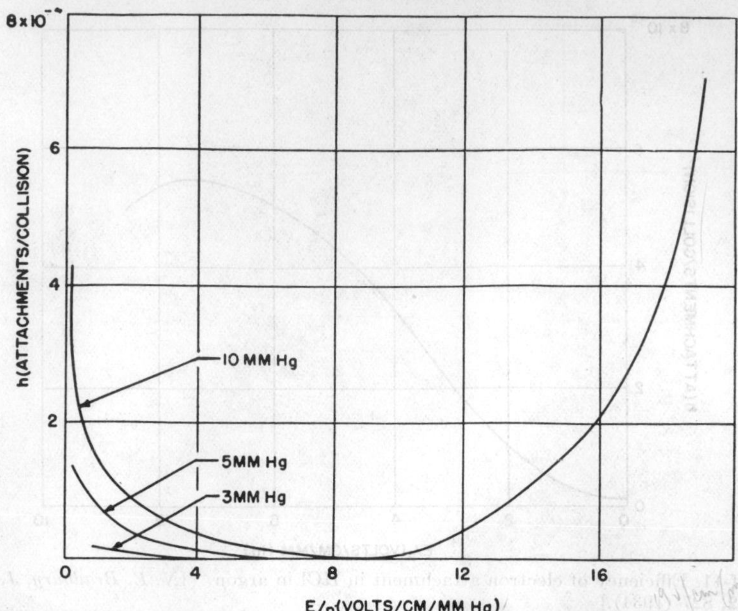

Fig. 5f-13. Efficiency of electron attachment in H_2O at different pressures. [*N. E. Bradbury and H. E. Tatel, J. Chem. Phys.* **2,** 835 (1934).]

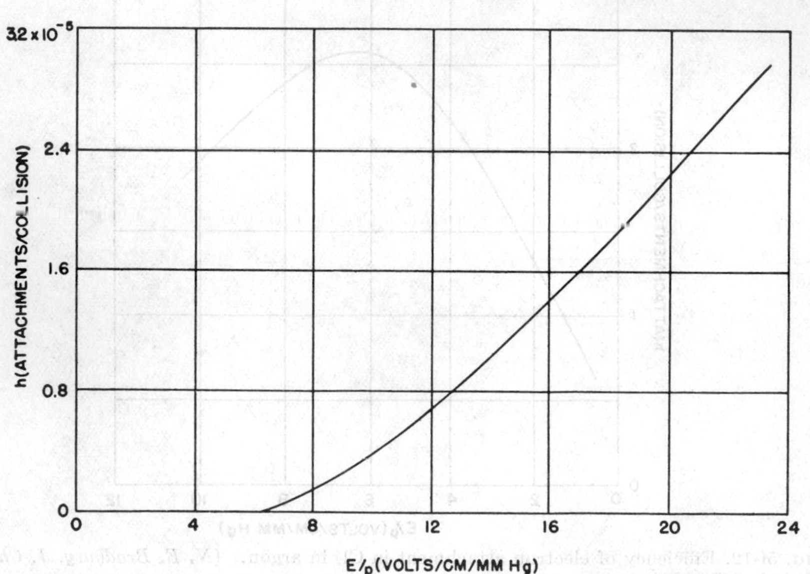

Fig. 5f-14. Efficiency of electron attachment in H_2S. [*N. E. Bradbury and H. E. Tatel, J. Chem. Phys.* **2,** 835 (1934).]

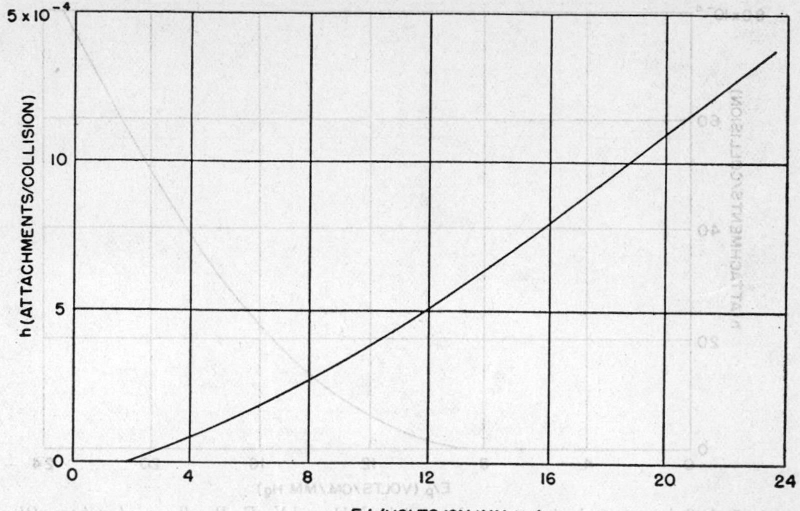

FIG. 5f-15. Efficiency of electron attachment in N_2O. [*N. E. Bradbury and H. E. Tatel, J. Chem. Phys.* **2,** 835 (1934).]

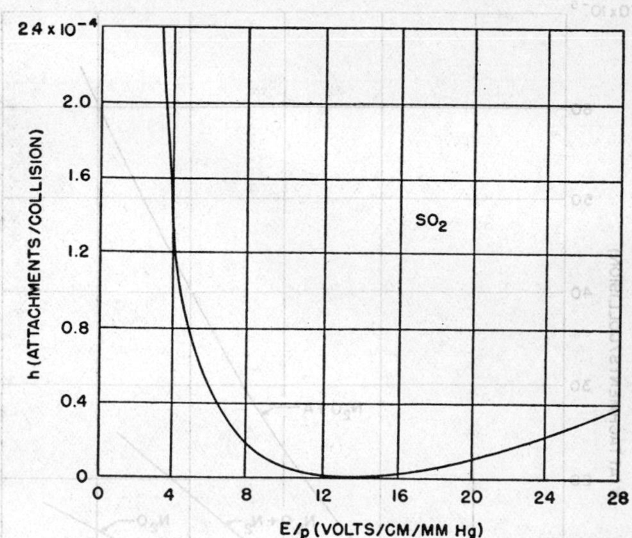

FIG. 5f-16. Efficiency of electron attachment in SO_2. [*N. E. Bradbury and H. E. Tatel, J. Chem. Phys.* **2,** 835 (1934).]

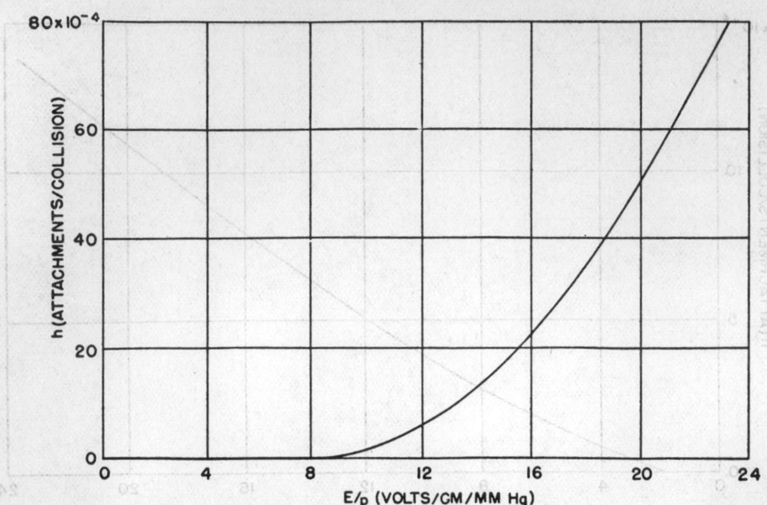

FIG. 5f-17. Efficiency of electron attachment in NH_3. [*N. E. Bradbury, J. Chem. Phys.* **2,** 827 (1934).]

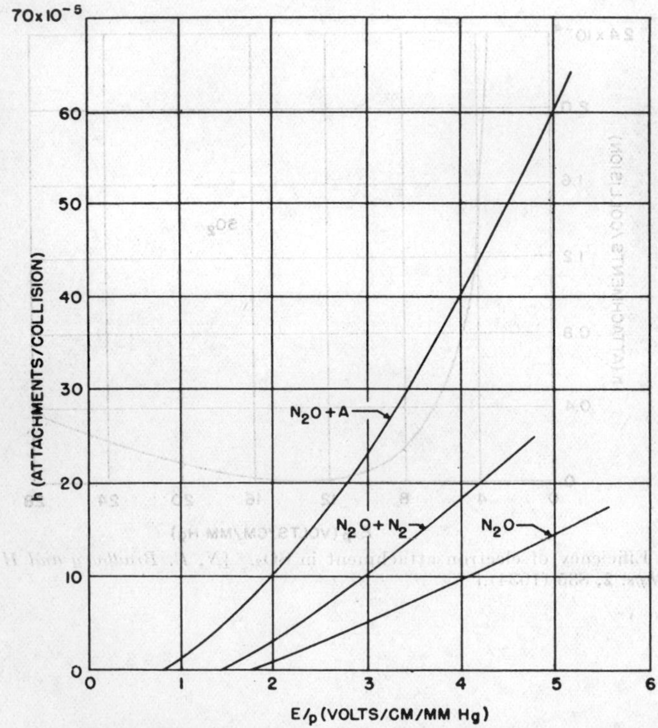

FIG. 5f-18. Efficiency of electron attachment in mixtures of N_2O in equal parts of N_2 or A. [*N. E. Bradbury and H. E. Tatel, J. Chem. Phys.* **2,** 835 (1934).]

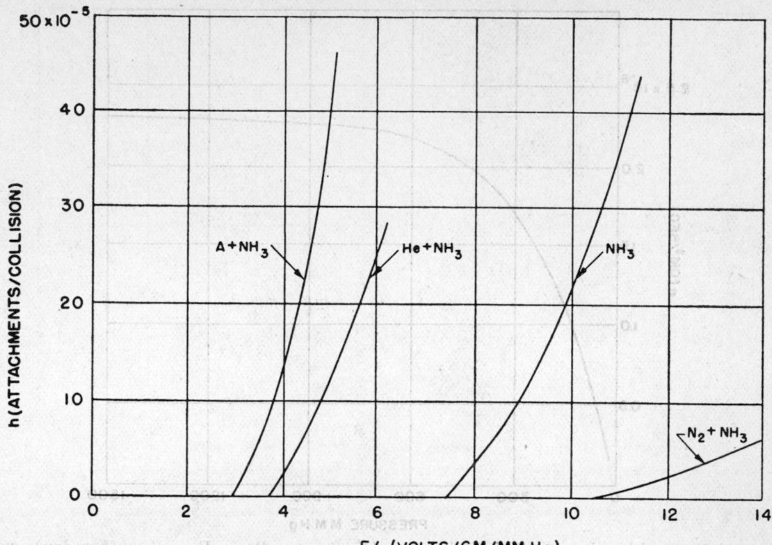

FIG. 5f-19. Efficiency of electron attachment in NH_3 and equal parts of He, A, or N_2. [*N. E. Bradbury, J. Chem. Phys.* **2**, 827 (1934).]

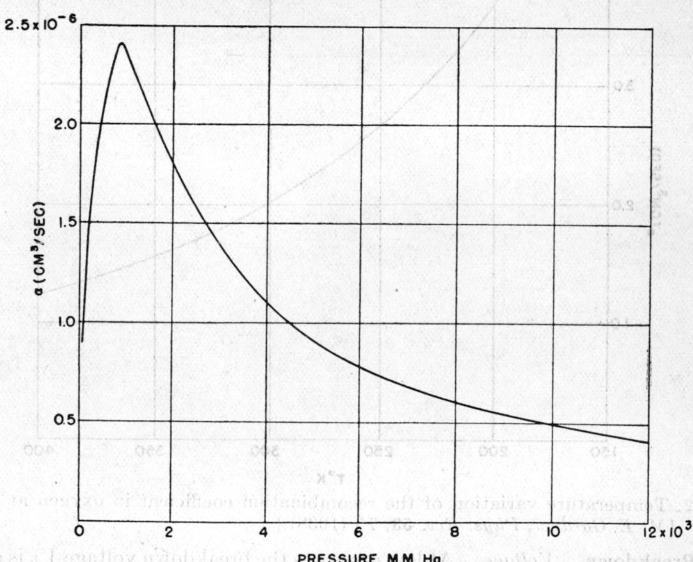

FIG. 5f-20. Recombination coefficient in air. [*J. Sayers, Proc. Roy. Soc.* (*London*), *ser.* A, **169**, 83 (1938).]

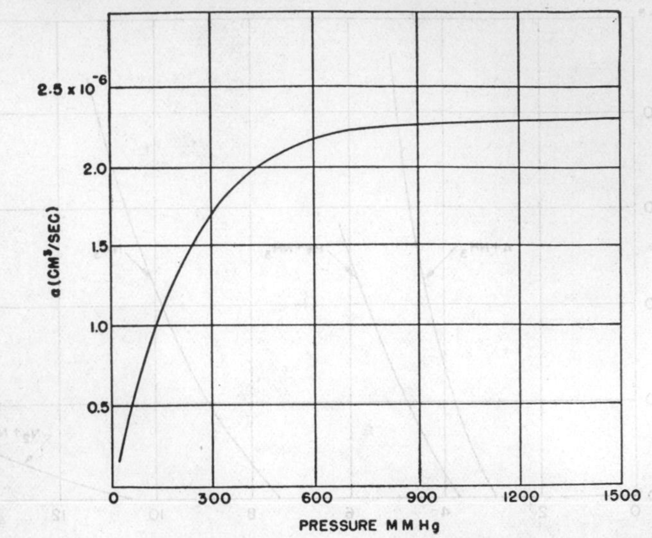

FIG. 5f-21. Recombination coefficient in air. [*J. Sayers, Proc. Roy. Soc. (London), ser.* A, **169,** 83 (1938).]

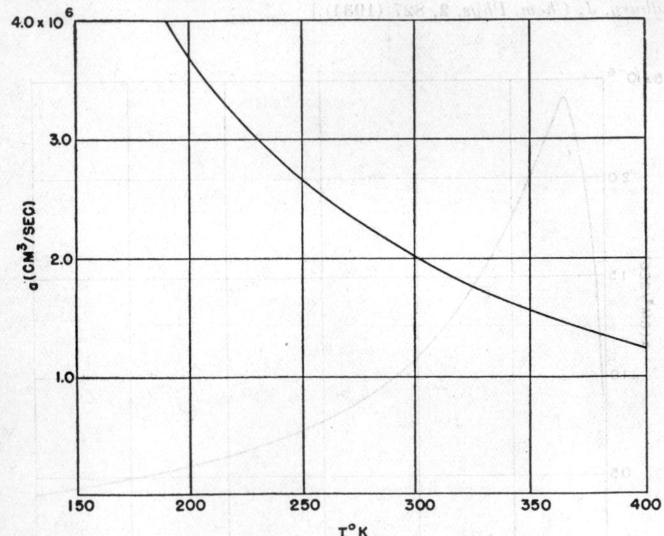

FIG. 5f-22. Temperature variation of the recombination coefficient in oxygen at constant pressure. [*M. E. Gardner, Phys. Rev.* **53,** 75 (1938).]

5f-3. Breakdown. *Voltage.* At low pressures the breakdown voltage V_B is given by

$$\eta V_B = \ln \left(1 - \frac{1}{\gamma}\right) \tag{5f-9}$$

where

$$\gamma = \gamma_i + \gamma_\phi \tag{5f-10}$$

is the secondary emission of the cathode attributable to ions and/or photons.

At high pressures the breakdown voltage by streamer formation (spark) is given by

$$N_c = e^{\alpha d} = 38\pi\epsilon_0 \frac{Dd}{\mu e} \tag{5f-11}$$

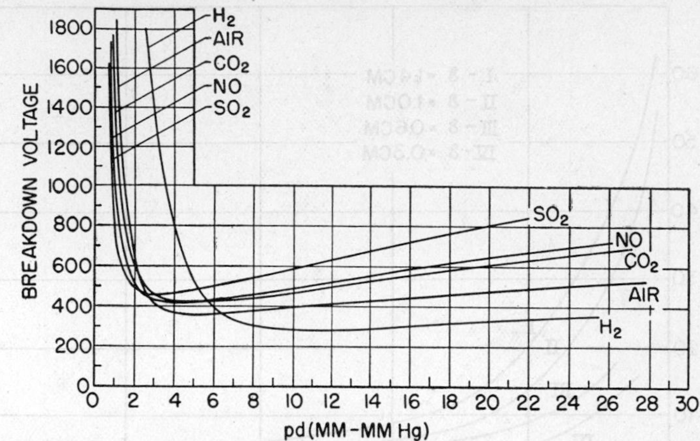

FIG. 5f-23. Paschen curves for various gases. (*M. Knoll, F. Ollendorff, and R. Rompe, "Gasentladungstabellen," p. 84, Springer-Verlag OHG, Berlin,* 1935.)

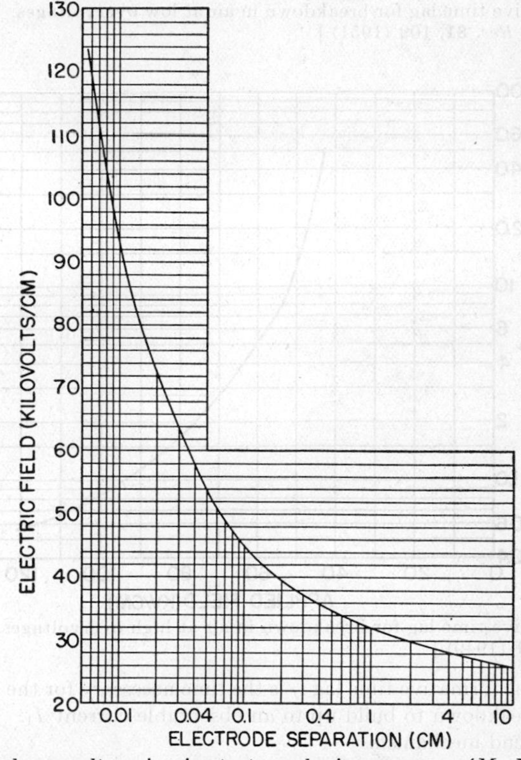

FIG. 5f-24. Breakdown voltage in air at atmospheric pressure. (*M. Knoll, F. Ollendorff and R. Rompe, "Gasentladungstabellen," p. 83, Springer-Verlag OHG, Berlin,* 1935.)

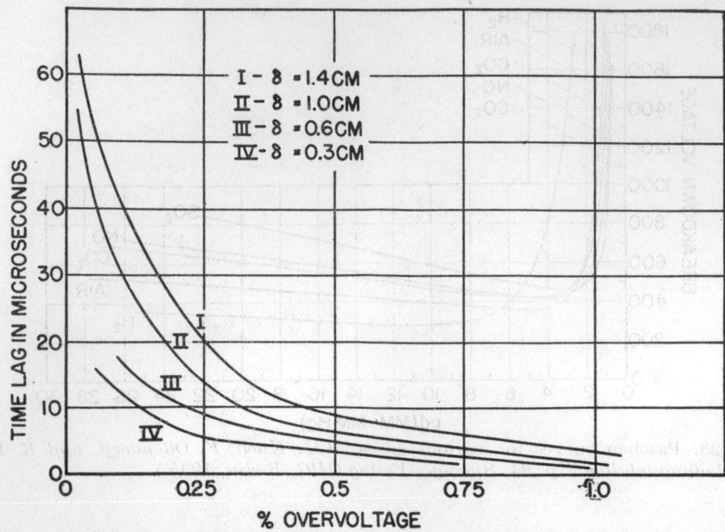

FIG. 5f-25. Formative time lag for breakdown in air at low overvoltages. [*L. H. Fisher and B. Bederson, Phys. Rev.* **81,** 109 (1951).]

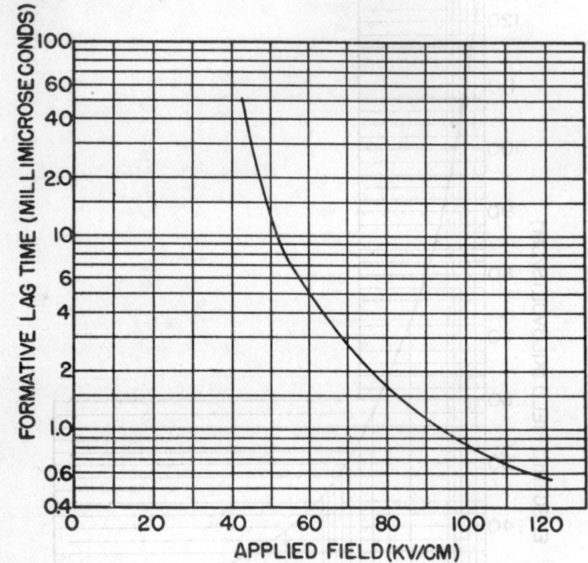

FIG. 5f-26. Formative time lag for breakdown in air at high overvoltages. [*R. C. Fletcher, Phys. Rev.* **76,** 1501 (1949).]

Time Lags. The formative time lag t_f is the time necessary for the initial current I_0 existing before breakdown to build up to an observable current I_1.

For the Townsend mechanism

$$t_f = t_i \frac{\log [(M - 1)I_1/I_0]}{\log M} \geq t_{\pm} \tag{5f-12}$$

where $t_{\pm}$ is the transit time for the slowest particle (ion or electron) and the multiplication factor M has the value $M = \gamma(e^{\eta V} - 1)$.

For the streamer mechanism

$$t_f = \frac{\log N_c}{\alpha \mu E} \leq t_- \tag{5f-13}$$

5f-4. Electron Energy Loss

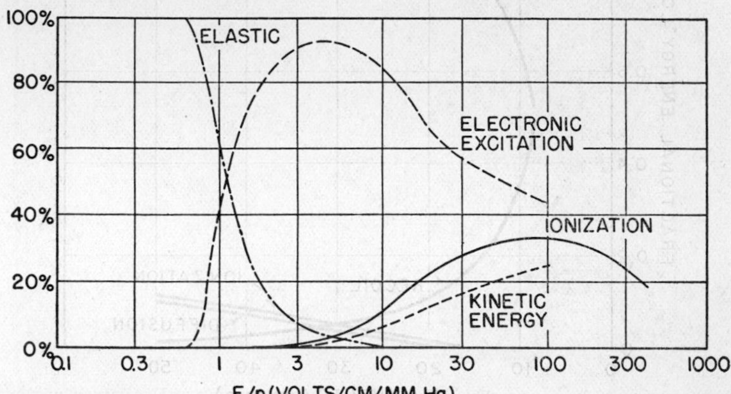

Fig. 5f-27. Distribution of electron energy losses in neon. [*F. M. Penning, Physica* **4,** 286 (1938).]

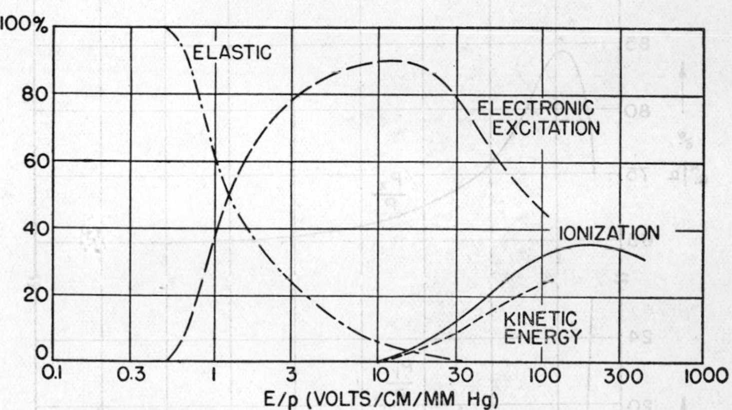

Fig. 5f-28. Distribution of electron energy losses in argon. [*F. M. Penning, Physica* **4,** 286 (1938).]

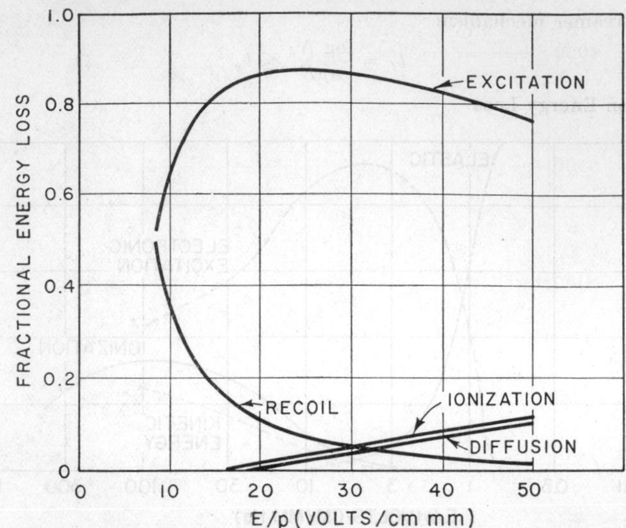

FIG. 5f-29. Fractional energy loss in H_2.

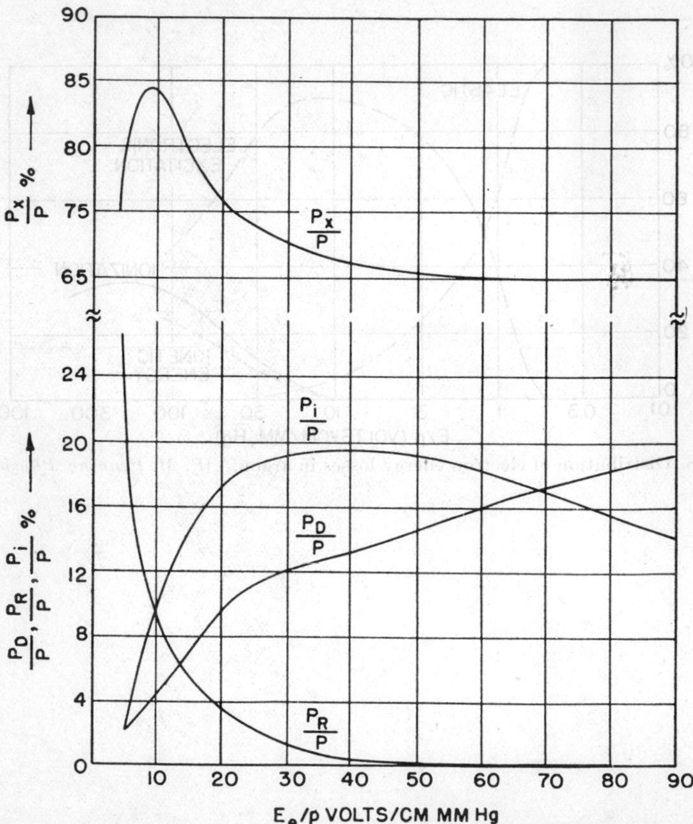

FIG. 5f-30. Various power losses of an electron in a microwave discharge in helium, in percentage of input power. [*F. H. Reder and S. C. Brown, Phys. Rev.* **95**, 885 (1954).]

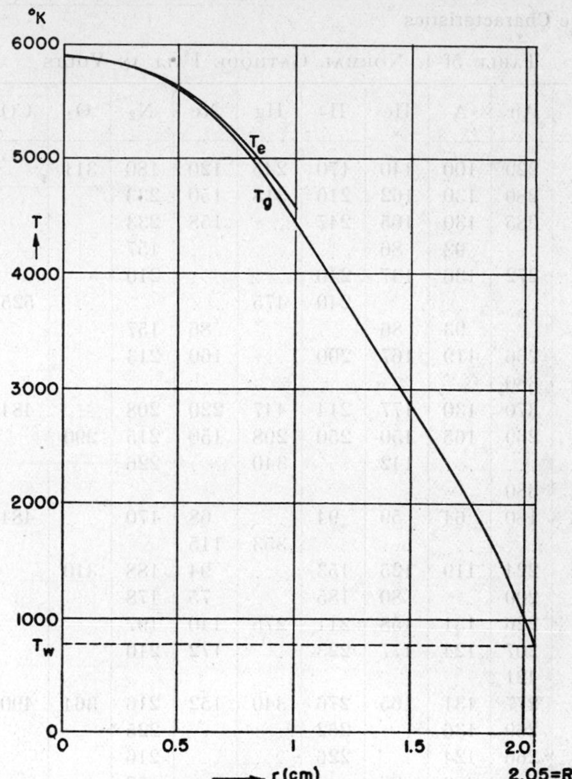

Fig. 5f-31. Electron temperature and gas temperature of a discharge as a function of tube radius. (*W. Elenbaas, "The High Pressure Mercury Vapour Discharge," p.* 40, *North Holland Publishing Company, Amsterdam,* 1951.)

5f-5. Discharge Characteristics

TABLE 5f-4. NORMAL CATHODE FALL IN VOLTS

Cathode	Air	A	He	H_2	Hg	Ne	N_2	O_2	CO	CO_2	Cl
Al	229	100	140	170	245	120	180	311			
Ag	280	130	162	216	318	150	233				
Au	285	130	165	247	...	158	233				
Ba	...	93	86	...	...	...	157				
Bi	272	136	137	240	...	...	210				
C	...	...	...	240	475	...	...	...	525		
Ca	...	93	86	...	...	86	157				
Cd	266	119	167	200	...	160	213				
Co	380										
Cu	370	130	177	214	447	220	208	...	484	460	
Fe	269	165	150	250	298	150	215	290			
Hg	...	...	142	...	340	...	226				
Ir	380										
K	180	64	59	94	...	68	170	...	484	460	
Mo	...	...	...	...	353	115					
Mg	224	119	125	153	...	94	188	310			
Na	200	...	80	185	...	75	178				
Ni	226	131	158	211	275	140	197				
Pb	207	124	177	223	...	172	210				
Pd	421										
Pt	277	131	165	276	340	152	216	364	490	475	275
Sb	269	136	...	252	...	...	225				
Sn	266	124	...	226	...	...	216				
Sr	...	93	86	...	...	...	157				
Th	...	...	...	...	...	125					
W	...	...	...	...	305	125					
Zn	277	119	143	184	...	...	216	354	480	410	

TABLE 5f-5. NORMAL CATHODE FALL THICKNESS
(d_np in cm-mm Hg at room temp.)

Cathode	Air	A	H_2	He	Hg	N_2	Ne	O_2
Al	0.25	0.29	0.72	1.32	0.33	0.31	0.64	0.24
C	....	....	0.9	....	0.69			
Cd	....	....	0.87					
Cu	0.23	....	0.8	....	0.6			
Fe	0.52	0.33	0.9	1.30	0.34	0.42	0.72	0.31
Mg	....	....	0.61	1.45	....	0.35	....	0.25
Hg	....	....	0.9					
Ni	....	....	0.9	....	0.4			
Pb	....	....	0.84					
Pt	....	....	1.0					
Zn	....	....	0.8					

TABLE 5f-6. NORMAL CATHODE CURRENT DENSITY IN A GLOW DISCHARGE
(μa/sq cm × mm sq of Hg at room temp.)

Cathode	Air	A	H_2	He	Hg	N_2	O_2	Ne
Al	330	...	90	...	4			
Au	570	...	110					
Cu	240	...	64	...	15			
Fe	...	160	72	2.2	8	400	...	6
Mg	...	20	...	3	...	...	...	5
Pt	...	150	90	5	...	380	550	18

TABLE 5f-7. SPUTTERED MASS IN MICROGRAMS PER AMPERE-SECOND FOR METALS IN HYDROGEN

Mg	Ta	Cr	Al	Cd	Mn	Mo	Co	W	Ni	Fe	Sn	C	Cu	Zn	Pb	Au	Ag
2.5	4.5	7.5	8	8.9	11	16	16	16	18	19	55	73	84	95	110	130	205

IONIC CONDUCTIVITY IN SOLID SALTS

5f-6. Conductivity for Pure Ionic Conductors. For many ionic salts it has been established by transport measurements that the conductivity observed at high temperatures is caused exclusively by the motion of ions. This motion is possible because of the existence in the crystal of a small number of ionic defects—vacancies where ions are missing from normally occupied positions and ions in interstitial positions in the structure. Two combinations of such defects have been observed. Schottky defects, occurring in the alkali halides, consist of equal numbers of positive and negative ion vacancies. Frenkel defects, occurring in the silver halides, consist of equal numbers of positive ion vacancies and interstitial positive ions.

It is usually observed that for a certain temperature range below the melting point the conductivity is characteristic of the pure substance. At a temperature several hundred degrees below the melting point, the actual temperature depending on the particular specimen, there is a sharp break in the dependence of conductivity on temperature, and at lower temperatures the magnitude of the observed conductivity varies considerably from specimen to specimen. This behavior is explained by supposing that at high temperatures the number of defects is determined by thermal equilibrium, whereas at lower temperatures the number of defects may depend on the amount of impurity present. Hence it is to be understood that, wherever two distinct temperature ranges are given for the same substance in Table 5f-8, the conductivity in the lower temperature range is probably related to the presence of impurities.

The conductivity can be determined by passage of direct current through the sample if sufficient precautions are taken, but more recently most measurements have been made either with current pulses of the order of 0.01 sec duration or alternating currents with a frequency in the neighborhood of 1,000 cps. In most cases a plot of log σ vs. $1/T$ is approximately a straight line, especially for the high-temperature range, indicating that the conductivity can be represented as

$$\sigma = \sigma_0 \exp(-W/kT) \tag{5f-14}$$

where k is the Boltzmann constant and T is the absolute temperature. W, the activation energy, and σ_0 are determined experimentally and are listed in Table 5f-8. The conductivity at the melting temperature has been calculated from Eq. (5f-14) if it is not given in the literature.

TABLE 5f-8. CONDUCTIVITY FOR PURE IONIC CONDUCTORS

Substance	T_m, °C	$\sigma(T_m)$	T, °C	σ_0	$W(eV)$	Ref.
LiF *	842	3 (−3)	....	3.0 (6)	1.99	H1
*	....	6 (−3)	....	4 (7)	2.20	L1
LiCl *	606	1.0(−2)	....	2.51 (6)	1.47	H1 (B5)
*	....	1.5(−2)	....	5 (7)	1.65	L1
		1.8(−3)	400–550	2.5 (5)	1.42	G2
			30–350	1.15	0.59	G2
LiBr *	550	1.8(−2)	....	1.41 (6)	1.29	H1
		1.4(−2)	350–500	4.2 (5)	1.22	G2
			30–300	3.3	0.56	G2
LiI *	452	5 (−2)	....	9.6 (5)	1.05	H1
		7 (−2)	250–350	1.8 (5)	0.92	G2
			30–150	1.4 (−1)	0.36	G2
NaF *	992	1.7(−3)	....	1.5 (6)	2.25	L1
		3 (−3)	330–980	1.3 (3)	1.42	P1
NaCl *	800	....	250–450	3.72 (8)/T	1.86	E1 (J6)
*	....	1.0(−4)	550–680	2.3 (9)/T	1.99	B1 (T1)
*	....	1.3(−3)	....	1 (6)	1.90	L1 (V1)
*	....	2.1(−4)	560–800	4.3 (4)	1.77	P1 (S2)
*	....		370–560	2.6–3.6	0.88	P1 (H5)
NaBr *	735	1.3(−3)	....	1 (6)	1.78	L1 (T1)
		7 (−3)	600–730	1.5 (6)	1.67	P1
			250–400	2 (−1)	0.80	P1
NaI *	661	4 (−3)	....	1.5 (5)	1.42	L1
		1.9(−3)	350–600	8.1 (3)	1.23	P1
			170–350	6 (−2)	0.60	P1
KF *	846	8 (−4)	....	3 (7)	2.35	L1
KCl *	768	2.0(−4)	....	2 (6)	2.06	L1 (T1)
*	....	1.9(−4)	600–725	5.5 (5)	1.96	W4
*	....	2.3(−4)	500–725	1–1.5 (6)	2.02	P3
*	....	....	250–450	1.3–20 (−1)	0.99	P3
		2 (−3)	220–560	1–50 (6)	1.99	B7
KBr *	728	2.0(−4)	....	1.5 (6)	1.97	L1 (T1)
*	....	1.5(−4)	500–725	1–1.3 (6)	1.97	P3
*	....	....	250–400	1–1,000(−2)	0.97	P3
			40–440	2–20	1.06	B7
KI *	680	1.5(−4)	....	3 (5)	1.77	L1
		1.1(−4)	450–675	3–5 (4)	1.62	P3
			220–400	9–30 (−2)	0.85	P3

TABLE 5f-8. CONDUCTIVITY FOR PURE IONIC CONDUCTORS (*Continued*)

Substance	T_m, °C	$\sigma(T_m)$	T, °C	σ_0	$W(eV)$	Ref.
RbCl *	717	5 (−5)	....	3 (6)	2.12	L1
RbBr *	681	3.5(−5)	....	1.8 (6)	2.03	L1
SrF_2	1190	1.6(−1)	450–1100	1.73 (4)	1.36	C1
$BaCl_2$	....	....	....	....	.....	(VI)
$BaBr_2$	847	1.4(−3)	390–750	1.0 (−1)	0.41	J2
Na_2CdCl_4	....	....	230–350	2.8 (3)	0.86	J2
K_2BaBr_4	....	....	430–600	7.1 (4)	1.33	J2
CuCl	426	5 (−1)	315–404	4.9 (8)	1.25	T7 (B5)
α-CuBr	491	3.58	470–491	6.57	0.040	T9
		4.2	470–488	2.1 (3)	0.42	G1
β-CuBr	tr. 470	(2.24)	391–470	1.12 (2)	0.25	T9
		(2.1)	421–470	1.2 (2)	0.26	G1
α-CuI	602	1.7	402–602	2.5 (2)	0.20	T18
AgCl	455	9 (−2)	....	3 (4)	0.80	K4
*	....	6 (−2)	....	1 (5)	0.90	L1
		1.1(−1)	250–450	1.5 (6)	1.03	T12
AgBr	422	4 (−1)	....	1.8 (5)	0.78	K4
*	....	1.0(−1)	....	6.3 (3)	0.66	L1
		5 (−1)	250–419	4.2 (6)	0.95	T12
		7.3(−1)	290–410	1.3 (7)	1.00	K5
			200–290	2.1 (5)	0.80	K5
		6.8(−1)	300–410	7.2 (6)	0.97	T2
			175–300	3.8 (5)	0.82	T2
α-AgI	555	2.5	145–555	5.5	0.052	T12
β-AgI	tr. 144.6	(4(−4))	125–144	3.9 (6)	0.83	T12
α-Ag_2HgI_4	....	....	50–93	4 (2)	0.37	K2
TlCl	428	5 (−3)	....	2.5 (3)	0.79	L1 (T12)
		3 (−3)	130–390	4.7 (2)	0.72	P3
TlBr	458	5 (−3)	....	1.7 (3)	0.80	L1 (T12)
		2 (−3)	150–400	2.2 (2)	0.73	P3
TlI	438	1.5(−3)	163–400	4.2 (1)	0.63	P3 (T12)
	tr. 163	(5 (−8))	90–163	2.5 (−3)	0.41	P3
$ZnCl_2$	....	....	....	....	.....	(B5)
$CdCl_2$	568	1.1(−1)	260–520	1.6 (5)	1.03	J2 (B5)

TABLE 5f-8. CONDUCTIVITY FOR PURE IONIC CONDUCTORS (*Continued*)

Substance	T_m, °C	$\sigma(T_m)$	T, °C	σ_0	$W(eV)$	Ref.
$HgCl_2$	....	....	....	....	.....	(H3)
$HgBr_2$	....	....	....	....	.....	(H3)
HgI_2	....	....	....	....	.....	(H3)
$SnCl_2$	....	....	....	....	.....	(K3)
$PbCl_2$	500	5 (−3)	....	1.4	0.47	G5
		5 (−3)	100–450	6.6	0.48	S3
$PbBr_2$	373	3 (−3)	200–300	5.7 (1)	0.55	S1
PbI_2	402	3 (−5)	275–375	1.2 (5)	1.29	S3
			150–275	9.8 (−4)	0.41	S3
*‖	....	1 (−5)	270–400	2.1 (4)	1.24	S4
*⊥	....	9 (−5)	180–370	4–8 (−2)	0.38	S4
La_2O_3	2315	....	1000–1300	3.8 (3)	1.94	C2 (F2)
			700–1000	5.0 (1)	1.46	C2
			500–700	3.5 (−5)	0.27	C2
CeO_2	1950	....	900–1300	3.0 (3)	1.45	C2 (F1)
			600–900	9.7 (1)	1.10	C2
			300–500	5.0 (−4)	0.26	C2
Pr_2O_3	....	....	....	....	.....	(F2)
Nd_2O_3	....	....	....	....	.....	(F2)
Sm_2O_3	....	....	....	....	.....	(F2)
GeO_2	1115	....	950–1080	5	1.41	J4
$MgAl_2O_4$†	2135	....	900–1060	2.3 (−1)	1.23	J3
$ZnAl_2O_4$†	....	....	1000–1140	2.1 (−2)	1.08	J3
Mg_2SiO_4†	....	....	940–1160	1.5 (−2)	0.83	J4
Mg_2GeO_4						
(rhomb.)‡	....	....	1070–1150	5–6	1.65	J4
(cub.)†	tr. 1065	....	1000–1040	2.0–2.5(−2)	0.97	J4
$BaMoO_4$†	....	....	800–1050	6 (−1)	1.10	J1
$CaWO_4$†	....	....	....	....	.....	(J1)
$SrWO_4$†	....	....	....	....	.....	(J1)
$BaWO_4$†	....	....	980–1120	1.4–1.8(2)	1.83	J1
			830–980	1.7–2.3(−2)	0.86	J1
$CdWO_4$†	....	....	760–1090	2–5 (3)	1.90	J1

Conductivity = $\sigma_0 \exp(-W/kT)$. Conductivities are expressed in ohm^{-1} cm^{-1}. T_m = melting temperature. Where no temperature interval is indicated, it is to be assumed that the data apply to a certain temperature interval near the melting temperature. * indicates that measurements were performed on single crystals. Numbers are written as 3(−3) = 3×10^{-3}. References are on p. 5-195. Additional references, enclosed in parentheses, refer only to the indicated substance, not to any particular data.

‖ Parallel to *c* axis.
⊥ Perpendicular to *c* axis.
† Conductivity is at least partly ionic.
‡ Conductivity is probably electronic.

5f-7. Density and Mobility of Defects for Pure Ionic Conductors. The conductivity of a crystal containing several types of defects is

$$\sigma = N \sum_j e_j x_j \mu_j \tag{5f-15}$$

where N is the number of molecules per unit volume of the perfect crystal and e_j is the magnitude of the charge, x_j the mole fraction, and μ_j the mobility of the jth type of defect. By measuring the conductivity of specimens containing known small amounts of impurities, it has been possible to evaluate separately the mole fractions and mobilities involved. In experiments of this type concerning the alkali halides it is usually observed that only the cations contribute appreciably to the conductivity; this observation is approximately in accord with the transport measurements except at the highest temperature (see Table 5f-10). For the other salts the type of defect is indicated in Table 5f-9.

TABLE 5f-9. DENSITY AND MOBILITY OF DEFECTS FOR PURE IONIC CONDUCTORS

Substance	T_m, °C	T, °C	x_0	$E(eV)$	μ_0	$U(eV)$	Notes	Ref.
LiF *	842	....	5.0(2)	2.68	6.1(−1)	0.65	*a*	H1
LiCl *	606	....	17.0(2)	2.12	3.15(−1)	0.41	*a*	H1
LiBr *	550	....	8.1(2)	1.80	4.5(−1)	0.39	*a*	H1
LiI *	452	....	5 (2)	1.34	6.5(−1)	0.38	*a*	H1
NaCl *	800	250–400	5.4	2.02	1.96(4)/T	0.85	*a*	E1
*	....	550–680	1.4(2)	2.42	4.6(3)/T	0.78	*a*	B1
*	....	160–250	....	....	6.3(5)/T	0.98	*a*	B1
KCl *	768	600–725	1.02(1)	2.08	3.1	0.78	*a*	W4, R6
AgCl	455	....	3.6(1)	1.08	1.2(−1)	0.26	*b*	K4
AgBr	422	....	2.9(1)	0.86	9.5(−1)	0.36	*b*	K4
		200–290	1.9(2)	1.19	1.5(2)/T	0.20	*c*	K5
					1.9(4)/T	0.48	*d*	K5
		175–350	5.3(2)	1.27	6.1(−2)	0.15	*c*	T2
					1.83	0.36	*d*	T2
SrF_2	1190	450–700	3.9(−2)	0.65	3.5(1)	1.04	*e*	C1

Mole fraction of defects $x = x_0 \exp(-E/2kT)$. Mobility $\mu = \mu_0 \exp(-U/kT)$ in cm² volt⁻¹ sec⁻¹. Numbers are written as 6.1(−1) = 6.1 × 10⁻¹. * indicates single crystal. References are on p. 5-195.

[a] μ(cation vacancy).

[b] Assuming μ(Ag vacancy) = μ(Ag interstitial).

[c] μ(Ag interstitial).

[d] μ(Ag vacancy).

[e] Assuming μ(F vacancy) = μ(F interstitial).

The temperature dependence of the mole fraction and mobility can be represented satisfactorily by equations similar to Eq. (5f-14) for the conductivity.

$$\begin{aligned} x &= x_0 \exp(-E/2kT) \\ \mu &= \mu_0 \exp(-U/kT) \end{aligned} \tag{5f-16}$$

E is the energy required to form a pair of defects and U is the height of the potential barrier a defect must overcome to move one interionic distance. Notice that when only one type of defect contributes to the conductivity, the activation energy in Eq. (5f-14) should be given by $W = \frac{1}{2}E + U$. Equations (5f-16) are the forms to be expected from the theory, except that μ_0 should vary as $1/T$. This variation is usually obscured by the exponential factor in μ.

5f-8. Transport Numbers. The transport number t_j of the jth type of defect is the fraction of the total current carried by that type of defect. By the performance of electrolysis experiments in which several disks of the material are present and the determination of the relative changes in weight of the various disks, the transport numbers in Table 5f-10 have been obtained. The amount of variance of different observers, e.g., for NaCl, indicates that the results of such experiments are not very reliable.

For a number of ionic crystals Faraday's law of electrolysis is not valid, and it has usually been assumed that the extent of the deviation from this law is a measure of the amount of electronic conductivity which is present. In Table 5f-11 transport numbers determined in this way when some electronic conductivity is present are given along with values of the conductivity. Occasionally this method of interpreting electrolysis experiments has led to incorrect conclusions, the most notable case being Ag_2S.

5f-9. Effect of Pressure on Conductivity. When the effect of high pressure is taken into consideration, Eqs. (5f-16) are modified to give

$$\begin{aligned} x &= x_0 \exp\left[-(E + P\,\Delta V)/2kT\right] \\ \mu &= \mu_0 \exp\left[-(U + P\,\Delta V_\mu)/kT\right] \end{aligned} \qquad (5f\text{-}17)$$

ΔV is related to the change in volume of the crystal when a pair of defects is formed, and ΔV_μ is related to the change in volume of the crystal which occurs when a defect moves from one position to another. If only one type of defect contributes appreciably to the conductivity, the conductivity should be given by an equation of the form of Eqs. (5f-17) with $\Delta V_\sigma = \frac{1}{2}\Delta V + \Delta V_\mu$. In Table 5f-12 values of the various free volumes are given for AgBr, and additional values of $\alpha_0 = -(d \log \sigma/dP)_{P=0}$ are given for AgBr and AgCl.

TABLE 5f-10. TRANSPORT NUMBERS FOR PURE IONIC CONDUCTORS
(The transport number $t = t_{cat} = 1 - t_{anion}$ is given)

Substance	T, °C	t_{cat}	Ref.
NaF	500	1.00	T11
	550	1.00	
	560	0.99	
	570	0.97	
	585	0.94	
	600	0.92	
	615	0.89	
	625	0.86	
KCl	435	0.96	T5
	500	0.94	
	550	0.92	
	600	0.88	
KBr	605	0.5	J10
	660	0.4	
KI	610	0.9	J10
BaF_2	500	0.00	T5
$BaCl_2$	400–700	0.00	T5
$BaBr_2$	350–450	0.00	T5
CuCl	315	1.00	T7
	366	1.00	
α-CuBr	470–491	1.00	T8
β-CuBr	391–445	1.00	
α-CuI	402–500	1.00	T21
AgCl	20	1.00	T13
	200–350	1.00	
AgBr	20	1.00	T13
	200–300	1.00	
	406	1.00	K5
α-AgI	150–400	1.00	T13
β-AgI	20	1.00	
α-Ag_2HgI_4	60	$t_{Ag} = 0.94$	K2
		$t_{Hg} = 0.06$	
PbF_2	200	0.00	T5
$PbCl_2$	200–450	0.00	T5
	90	10^{-10}	H4*
	270	10^{-5}	
	484	10^{-3}	
$PbBr_2$	250–365	0.00	T5

TABLE 5f-10. TRANSPORT NUMBERS FOR PURE IONIC CONDUCTORS (*Continued*)

Substance	T, °C	$t_{cat}(1)$†	$t_{cat}(2)$	$t_{cat}(3)$	$t_{cat}(4)$	Ref.
NaCl	400	1.00	....	1.00		
	500	0.98	....	0.95	....	(1) T19
	550	0.94	....	....	0.99	(2) J10
	557	....	0.75–1.00	....	....	(3) P2
	580	0.92	....	....	....	(4) J5
	600	0.90–0.95	....	0.64	0.92–0.96	
	605	....	0.55–0.59			
	610	....	0.52–0.75			
	620	0.88–0.93	....	0.77		
	658	....	0.36–0.38			
	710	....	0.12			
PbI_2	155	....	0.004			
	194	....	0.03	....	....	(1) T5
	228	....	0.12	....	....	(2) H4*
	255	0.39	0.30–0.35			
	270	0.45	0.40–0.50			
	290	0.67	0.55–0.65			
	338	....	0.79–0.85			
	376	....	0.93–1.00			

References are on p. 195.
* Calculated from diffusion data of Pb ions.
† Numbers in parenthesis refer to observer indicated in ref. column.

TABLE 5f-11. CONDUCTIVITY AND TRANSPORT NUMBERS FOR MIXED IONIC AND ELECTRONIC CONDUCTORS

(1) Total conductivity σ in ohm^{-1} cm^{-1}

Substance	T_m, °C	T, °C	σ_0	$W(eV)$	Ref.
CuCl	426	210–300	1.2 (6)	0.95	T7
		150–210	4.2 (4)	0.81	T7
		45–110	3.0	0.49	T7
γ-CuBr	tr. 391	250–380	5.9 (9)	1.36	T9
		140–230	2.0 (4)	0.80	T9
		240–380	8.1 (10)	1.51	G1
γ-CuI	tr. 402	360–400	3.0 (9)	1.30	T10 (M1)
		100–180	6.0 (−1)	0.047	T10 (V2)
α-Ag_2S	835	179–500*	6.4 (2)	−0.009	T15
		179–500†	1.73(2)	0.058	T15
		Above 179‡	3–7 (1)	0.14	W3, T16
β-Ag_2S	tr. 179	35–179*	9.0 (6)	0.60	R2
		110–179†	5.2 (8)	0.91	R2

TABLE 5f-11. CONDUCTIVITY AND TRANSPORT NUMBERS FOR MIXED IONIC AND ELECTRONIC CONDUCTORS (*Continued*)

(2) The transport number $t_{cat} = 1 - t_{electron}$ is given

Substance	T, °C	t_{cat}	Ref.
CuCl	18	0.00	T7
	40	0.02	
	154	0.04	
	197	0.12	
	218	0.29	
	225	0.39	
	232	0.50	
	244	0.78	
	254	0.90	
	294	0.96	
	300	0.98	
	315	1.00	
	366	1.00	
γ-CuBr	27	0.00	T8
	153	0.02	
	181	0.04	
	191	0.08	
	202	0.12	
	223	0.14	
	242	0.22	
	272	0.39	
	299	0.87	
	308	0.92	
	335	0.97	
	345	0.98	
	351	0.998	
	390	1.00	
γ-CuI	200	2.7×10^{-6}	N1
	200	0.00	T21
	255	0.01	
	300	0.25	
	325	0.50	
	350	0.75	
	375	0.98	
	390	0.997	
	400	1.00	
α-Ag_2S	200	10^{-2}–10^{-3}	J9, R5, T17, W2
β-Ag_2S	20†	0.99	T14
	60†	0.93	(H2)
	100†	0.90	
	150†	0.84	
	170†	0.81	
		t_{sulfur}	
α-Ag_2S	179	9 (−9)	B6
	571	6 (−5)	
	694	2.2(−5)	
	836	7 (−4)	

TABLE 5f-11. CONDUCTIVITY AND TRANSPORT NUMBERS FOR MIXED IONIC AND ELECTRONIC CONDUCTORS (*Continued*)

Substance	T, °C	t_{cat}			Ref. for t	σ	Ref. for σ
Cu_2Se	150–210		$\sim 10^{-4}$		R3		
α-Ag_2Se	190		$\sim 10^{-2}$–10^{-3}		T17	1.4(2)¶	T20
β-Ag_2Se	20		$<10^{-2}$		T5		
Cu_2Te	335–410		$\sim 10^{-4}$		R1		
α-Ag_2Te	190		$\sim 10^{-2}$–10^{-3}		T17		
β-Ag_2Te	20		$<10^{-2}$		T5		
		(1)	(2)	(3)			
Cu_2O	800	....	......	2(−4)	(1)G4		
	900	3.5(−4)	......	......	(2)D1	2.6–3.5	G3
	1000	5.2(−4)	4(−4)	5(−4)	(3)T5	4.5–7.4	G3
BaO	800	....	5(−4)	......	I1, (W1)	1(−5)	S5

References are on p. 5-195.
* In equilibrium with silver.
† In equilibrium with sulfur.
‡ Ionic part of conductivity only.
¶ In equilibrium with selenium.

References for Mixed Salts

In most cases values of the observed conductivity are the only data given. The number before the second substance indicates the maximum amount of the second substance in mole per cent.

LiF—5 MgF_2(H1); *LiCl*—100 KCl(B3), 5 $MgCl_2$(H1); *LiBr*—5 $MgBr_2$(H1); *LiI*—5 MgI_2(H1); *NaCl*—100 KCl(B4), 0.25 $CaCl_2$(B1), 100 AgCl(T6), 0.1 $CdCl_2$(E1); *NaBr*—100 AgBr(T6); *KF*—100 K_2SO_4(B2); *KCl*—100 LiCl(B3); 100 NaCl(B4), 5.3 KBr(T1), 1 $SrCl_2$(W4,K1), 100 AgCl(T6), 100 K_2CrO_4(B4); *KBr*—100 AgBr(T6); *SrF_2*—10 LaF_3 (C1).

CuBr—100 AgBr(R4); *CuI*—100 AgI(T21); *AgCl*—100 NaCl(T6), 100 KCl(T6), 100 AgBr(S1), 100 TlCl(S1), 10 $CdCl_2$(K4), 10 $PbCl_2$(K4), 100 $PbCl_2$(T22); *AgBr*—10 LiBr(T3), 10 NaBr(T3), 100 NaBr(T6), 100 KBr(T6), 10 $CaBr_2$(T2), 10 CuBr(T3), 100 CuBr(R4), 10 AgCl(T3), 100 AgCl(S1), 10 AgI(T3), 100 AgI(T12), 10 $ZnBr_2$(T2), 0.1 $CdBr_2$(K5), 10 $CdBr_2$(K4), 40 $CdBr_2$(T2), 10 $PbBr_2$(K4), 20 $PbBr_2$(T2), 100 $PbBr_2$(T22), 1 Ag_2S(T4), 1 CdS(T4), 1 PbS(T4); *AgI*—100 CuI(T21), 100 AgBr(T12), 100 PbI_2(T22); *TlCl*—100 AgCl(S1).

$SnCl_2$—100 $PbCl_2$(B3); *$PbCl_2$*—100 AgCl(T22), 100 $SnCl_2$(B3), 100 $PbBr_2$(S1); *$PbBr_2$*—100 AgBr(T22), 100 $PbCl_2$(S1); *PbI_2*—100 AgI(T22); *CeO_2*—30 La_2O_3(C2).

TABLE 5f-12. EFFECT OF PRESSURE ON CONDUCTIVITY
(1) Values of $\alpha_0 = -(d \log \sigma/dP)$ at $P = 0$

Substance	Temp., °C	Pressure, kg cm^{-2}	α_0, cm^2 kg^{-1}	Ref.
AgCl	300	0–300	2.5×10^{-4}	J8
	256–313	0–300	2.9	J7
AgBr	300	0–300	3.5	J8
	243–290	0–300	3.2	J7
	202	0–8,000	1.19	K5
	251	0–2,500	1.19	K5
	289	0–2,500	1.23	K5
	377	0–2,000	1.44	K5
	406	0–1,000	2.02	K5

(2) Values of free volume of formation and of mobility for AgBr, 202–289°C, 0–8,000 kg cm^{-2} (K5)

Quantity	ΔV, cm^3 mole^{-1}
Formation of Frenkel defects	16
Mobility of silver ion vacancy	7.4
Mobility of interstitial silver ion	2.6

References for Tables 5f-8 through 5f-12

1. "International Critical Tables," McGraw-Hill Book Company, Inc., New York, 1926.
2. Jost, W.: "Diffusion in Solids, Liquids, and Gases," Academic Press, Inc., New York, 1952.
3. Landolt-Börnstein: "Physikalisch-Chemische Tabellen," Springer-Verlag OHG, Berlin, 5th ed., Hauptwerk II, 1923; Ergänzungsband I, 1927; Ergänzungsband II, pt. 2, 1931; Ergänzungsband III, pt. 3, 1936.
4. Mott, N. F., and R. W. Gurney: "Electronic Processes in Ionic Crystals," 2d ed., Oxford University Press, New York, 1948.
5. Seitz, F.: "The Modern Theory of Solids," McGraw-Hill Book Company, Inc., New York, 1940.

B1. Bean, C.: Thesis, University of Illinois, 1952.
B2. Benrath, A., and K. Drekopf: *Z. physik. Chem.* **99**, 57 (1921).
B3. Benrath, A., and H. Tesche: *Z. physik. Chem.* **96**, 474 (1920).
B4. Benrath, A., and J. Wainoff: *Z. physik. Chem.* **77**, 257 (1911).
B5. Biltz, W., and W. Klemm: *Z. physik. Chem.* **110**, 318 (1924).
B6. Braune, H.: *Z. Elektrochem.* **31**, 576 (1925).
B7. Brennicke, C. G.: *J. Appl. Phys.* **11**, 202 (1940).
C1. Croatto, U., and M. Bruno: *Gazz. chim. ital.* **78**, 95 (1948).
C2. Croatto, U., and A. Mayer: *Gazz. chim. ital.* **73**, 199 (1943).
D1. Dünwald, H., and C. Wagner: *Z. physik. Chem.* **B22**, 215 (1933).
E1. Etzel, H. W., and R. J. Maurer: *J. Chem. Phys.* **18**, 1003 (1950).
F1. Foëx, M.: *Bull. Soc. Chim.* **11**, 6 (1944).
F2. Foëx, M.: *Compt. rend.* **220**, 359 (1945).
G1. Geiler, J.: Dissertation, Halle, 1928.
G2. Ginnings, D. C., and T. E. Phipps: *J. Am. Chem. Soc.* **52**, 1340 (1930).

G3. Gundermann, J., in ref. 2, p. 391.
G4. Gundermann, J., K. Hauffe, and C. Wagner: *Z. physik. Chem.* **B37**, 148, 155 (1937).
G5. Gyulai, Z.: *Z. Physik* **67**, 812 (1931).
H1. Haven, Y.: *Rec. trav. chim.* **69**, 1471 (1950).
H2. Hebb, M. H.: *J. Chem. Phys.* **20**, 185 (1952).
H3. Hevesy, G. V.: *Kgl. Danske Videnskab. Selskab, Mat.-fys. Medd.* **3** (13) (1921).
H4. Hevesy, G. V., and W. Seith: *Z. Physik* **56**, 790 (1929).
H5. Hochberg, B., and A. Walther: *Z. Physik* **64**, 392 (1930).
I1. Isensee, H.: *Z. physik. Chem.* **B35**, 309 (1937).
J1. Jander, W.: *Z. anorg. u. allgem. Chem.* **192**, 295 (1930).
J2. Jander, W.: *Z. anorg. u. allgem. Chem.* **199**, 306 (1931).
J3. Jander, W., and W. Stamm: *Z. anorg. u. allgem. Chem.* **199**, 165 (1931).
J4. Jander, W., and W. Stamm: *Z. anorg. u. allgem. Chem.* **207**, 289 (1932).
J5. Joffé, A., *Z. Physik* **62**, 730 (1930).
J6. Joffé, A., and E. Zechnowitzer: *Physica* **6**, 36 (1926).
J7. Jost, W., and S. Mennenöh: *Z. physik. Chem.* **196**, 188 (1950).
J8. Jost, W., and G. Nehlep: *Z. physik. Chem.* **B34**, 348 (1936).
J9. Jost, W., and H. Rüter: *Z. physik. Chem.* **B21**, 48 (1933).
J10. Jost, W., and H. Schweitzer: *Z. physik. Chem.* **B20**, 118 (1933).
K1. Kelting, H., and H. Witt: *Z. Physik* **126**, 697 (1949).
K2. Ketelaar, J. A. A.: *Z. physik. Chem.* **B26**, 327 (1934).
K3. Klemm, W., and W. Biltz: *Z. anorg. u. allgem. Chem.* **152**, 225 (1926).
K4. Koch, E., and C. Wagner: *Z. physik. Chem.* **B38**, 295 (1937).
K5. Kurnick, S.: *J. Chem. Phys.* **20**, 218 (1952).
L1. Lehfeldt, W.: *Z. Physik* **85**, 717 (1933).
M1. Maurer, R. J.: *J. Chem. Phys.* **13**, 321 (1945).
N1. Nagel, K., and C. Wagner: *Z. physik. Chem.* **B25**, 71 (1934).
P1. Phipps, T. E., W. D. Lansing, and T. G. Cooke: *J. Am. Chem. Soc.* **48**, 112 (1926).
P2. Phipps, T. E., and R. T. Leslie: *J. Am. Chem. Soc.* **50**, 2412 (1928).
P3. Phipps, T. E., and E. G. Partridge: *J. Am. Chem. Soc.* **51**, 1331 (1929).
R1. Reinhold, H , and H. Bräuninger: *Z. physik. Chem.* **B41**, 397 (1938).
R2. Reinhold, H., and H. Möhring: *Z. physik. Chem.* **B28**, 182 (1935).
R3. Reinhold, H., H. Möhring, and H. Seidel: *Z. physik. Chem.* **B38**, 221 (1937).
R4. Reinhold, H., and R. Schulz: *Z. physik. Chem.* **A164**, 241 (1933).
R5. Reinhold, H., and H. Seidel: *Z. Elektrochem.* **41**, 599 (1935).
R6. Ronge, G., and C. Wagner: *J. Chem. Phys.* **18**, 74 (1950).
S1. Sandoninni, C.: *Atti Accad. mazl. Lincei* **24** (5), 842 (1915).
S2. von Seelen, D.: *Z. Physik* **29**, 125 (1924).
S3. Seith, W.: *Z. Physik* **56**, 802 (1929); **57**, 869 (1929).
S4. Seith, W.: *Z. Elektrochem.* **39**, 538 (1933).
S5. Sproull, R. L., and W. W. Tyler: "Semi-conducting Materials," H. K. Henisch, ed., Butterworth & Co. (Publishers), Ltd., London, 1951.
T1. Tamman, G., and G. Veszi: *Z. anorg. u. allgem. Chem.* **150**, 355 (1926).
T2. Teltow, J.: *Ann. Physik* **5**, 63, 71 (1949).
T3. Teltow, J.: *Z. physik. Chem.* **195**, 197 (1950).
T4. Teltow, J.: *Z. physik. Chem.* **195**, 213 (1950).
T5. Tubandt, C.: "Handbuch exp. Physik," vol. XII, pt. 1, Akademische Verlagsgesellschaft M.B.H., Leipzig, 1932.
T6. Tubandt, C., and Abramowitsch: in ref. 3, 1927.
T7. Tubandt, C., and M. Baudouin: in ref. 3, 1931.
T8. Tubandt, C., and J. Geiler: in ref. 3, 1931.
T9. Tubandt, C., J. Geiler, and M. Baudouin: in ref. 3, 1931.
T10. Tubandt, C., and W. Jost: in ref. 3, 1927.
T11. Tubandt, C., and G. Leibold: in ref. 3, 1931.
T12. Tubandt, C., and E. Lorenz: *Z. physik. Chem.* **87**, 513, 543 (1914).
T13. Tubandt, C., and H. Reinhold: *Z. Elektrochem.* **29**, 313 (1923); **31**, 84 (1925).
T14. Tubandt, C., and H. Reinhold: *Z. anorg. u. allgem. Chem.* **160**, 222 (1927).

T15. Tubandt, C., and H. Reinhold: *Z. Elektrochem.* **37,** 589 (1931).
T16. Tubandt, C., and H. Reinhold: *Z. physik. Chem.*, Bodenstein Festband, 874 (1931).
T17. Tubandt, C., and H. Reinhold: *Z. physik. Chem.* **B24,** 22 (1934).
T18. Tubandt, C., H. Reinhold, and W. Jost: *Z. anorg. u. allgem. Chem.* **177,** 253 (1928).
T19. Tubandt, C., H. Reinhold, and G. Leibold: *Z. anorg. u. allgem. Chem.* **197,** 225 (1931).
T20. Tubandt, C., H. Reinhold, and A. Neumann: *Z. Elektrochem.* **39,** 227 (1933).
T21. Tubandt, C., and E. Rindtorff: in ref. 3, 1927.
T22. Tubandt, C., and Schaefer: in ref. 3, 1927.
V1. Vaillant, P.: *Compt. rend.* **182,** 1335 (1926).
V2. Vine, B. H., and R. J. Maurer: *Z. physik. Chem.* **198,** 147 (1951).
W1. Wagener, S.: *Proc. Phys. Soc.* (*London*) **61,** 521 (1948).
W2. Wagner, C.: *Z. physik. Chem.* **B21,** 25 (1933); **B23,** 469 (1933).
W3. Wagner, C.: *Z. physik. Chem.* **B21,** 42 (1933).
W4. Wagner, C., and P. Hantleman: *J. Chem. Phys.* **18,** 72 (1950).

5g. Properties of Metallic Conductors

STEPHEN J. ANGELLO

Westinghouse Electric Corporation

5g-1. Per Cent Conductivity, Definition. The per cent conductivity of a sample of copper is calculated by dividing the resistivity of the International Annealed Copper Standard at 20°C by the resistivity of the sample at 20°C. Either mass or volume resistivity may be used. If another metal resistivity is expressed relative to copper, mass or volume resistivity must be specified. This use of per cent conductivity is, however, not recommended.

5g-2. Resistance of Copper as a Function of Temperature. On the basis of very careful measurements[1] it has been found that the 20°C temperature coefficient of a sample of copper is given by multiplying the number expressing the per cent conductivity by 0.00393. For example, for 100 per cent conductivity

$$\alpha_{20} = 0.00393 = \frac{R_t - R_{20}}{R_{20}(t - 20)}$$

where t is the temperature in degrees centigrade. The relation above holds surely for per cent conductivities above 94 per cent and is quite good over a wider range.

5g-3. Effect of Frequency upon the Conductivity of Copper Conductors. *Low Frequency.* When alternating currents are carried by homogeneous conductors the current density is not uniformly distributed over the area of the conductor. A tendency for the current density to be higher near the conductor surface is due to magnetic flux within the conductor cross section (see Sec. 5b-15). Such current-density concentration reduces the effective area of a conductor cross section. The

[1] *Natl. Bur. Standards* (*U.S.*) *Circ.* 31, p. 11.

TABLE 5g-1. COPPER WIRE TABLES—SOLID COPPER WIRE,* MKS UNITS

Gage No.†	Diam, m at 20°C (× 10^{-3})	Cross section, m² at 20°C (× 10^{-6})	Ohms‡/m at 20°C (× 10^{-3})	M/ohm‡ at 20°C	Kg/m (× 10^{-3})
0000	11.68	107.2	0.1608	6,219	953.2
000	10.40	85.03	0.2028	4,932	755.9
00	9.266	67.43	0.2557	3,911	599.5
0	8.252	53.48	0.3224	3,102	475.4
1	7.348	42.41	0.4066	2,460	377.0
2	6.544	33.63	0.5127	1,951	299.0
3	5.827	26.67	0.6465	1,547	237.1
4	5.189	21.15	0.8152	1,227	188.0
5	4.621	16.77	1.028	972.9	149.1
6	4.115	13.30	1.296	771.5	118.2
7	3.665	10.55	1.634	611.8	93.78
8	3.264	8.366	2.061	485.2	74.37
9	2.906	6.634	2.599	384.8	58.98
10	2.588	5.261	3.277	305.1	46.77
11	2.305	4.172	4.132	242.0	37.09
12	2.053	3.309	5.211	191.9	29.42
13	1.828	2.624	6.571	152.2	23.33
14	1.628	2.081	8.285	120.7	18.50
15	1.450	1.650	10.45	95.71	14.67
16	1.291	1.309	13.17	75.90	11.63
17	1.150	1.038	16.61	60.20	9.226
18	1.024	0.8231	20.95	47.74	7.317
19	0.9116	0.6527	26.42	37.86	5.803
20	0.8118	0.5176	33.31	30.02	4.602
21	0.7230	0.4105	42.00	23.81	3.649
22	0.6438	0.3255	52.96	18.88	2.894
23	0.5733	0.2582	66.79	14.97	2.295
24	0.5106	0.2047	84.21	11.87	1.820
25	0.4547	0.1624	106.2	9.417	1.443
26	0.4049	0.1288	133.9	7.468	1.145
27	0.3606	0.1021	168.9	5.922	0.9078
28	0.3211	0.08098	212.9	4.697	0.7199
29	0.2859	0.06422	268.5	3.725	0.5709
30	0.2546	0.05093	338.6	2.954	0.4527
31	0.2268	0.04039	426.9	2.342	0.3590
32	0.2019	0.03203	538.3	1.858	0.2847
33	0.1798	0.02540	678.8	1.473	0.2258
34	0.1601	0.02014	856.0	1.168	0.1791
35	0.1426	0.01597	1,079	0.9265	0.1420
36	0.1270	0.01267	1,361	0.7347	0.1126
37	0.1131	0.01005	1,716	0.5827	0.08931
38	0.1007	0.007967	2,164	0.4621	0.07083
39	0.08969	0.006318	2,729	0.3664	0.05617
40	0.07987	0.005010	3,441	0.2906	0.04454

* Data obtained from *Natl. Bur. Standards* (*U.S.*) *Circ.* 31 for 100 per cent conductivity copper at 20°C (see Sec. 5g-1).

† American wire gage (Awg) or Brown and Sharpe gage (B&S).

‡ The tables in *Circ.* 31 are given in "international" electrical units. Since Jan. 1, 1948, "absolute" units are standard. To obtain absolute ohms the resistance values in the table must be multiplied by 1.000495 (see *Natl. Bur. Standards* (*U.S.*) *Circ.* 459).

TABLE 5g-2. COPPER WIRE TABLES—SOLID COPPER WIRE,* ENGLISH UNITS

Gage No.†	Diam, mils at 20°C	Cross section at 20°C		Ohms‡/1,000 ft at 20°C	Ft/ohm at 20°C	Lb/1,000 ft
		Cir mils	Sq in.			
0000	460.0	211,600	0.1662	0.04901	20,400	640.5
000	409.6	167,800	0.1318	0.06180	16,180	507.9
00	364.8	133,100	0.1045	0.07793	12,830	402.8
0	324.9	105,500	0.08289	0.09827	10,180	319.5
1	289.3	83,690	0.06573	0.1239	8,070	253.3
2	257.6	66,370	0.05213	0.1563	6,400	200.9
3	229.4	52,640	0.04134	0.1970	5,075	159.3
4	204.3	41,740	0.03278	0.2485	4,025	126.4
5	181.9	33,100	0.02600	0.3133	3,192	100.2
6	162.0	26,250	0.02062	0.3951	2,531	79.46
7	144.3	20,820	0.01635	0.4982	2,007	63.02
8	128.5	16,510	0.01297	0.6282	1,592	49.98
9	114.4	13,090	0.01028	0.7921	1,262	39.63
10	101.9	10,380	0.008155	0.9989	1,001	31.43
11	90.74	8,234	0.006467	1.260	794.0	24.92
12	80.81	6,530	0.005129	1.588	629.6	19.77
13	71.96	5,178	0.004067	2.003	499.3	15.68
14	64.08	4,107	0.003225	2.525	396.0	12.43
15	57.07	3,257	0.002558	3.184	314.0	9.858
16	50.82	2,583	0.002028	4.016	249.0	7.818
17	45.26	2,048	0.001609	5.064	197.5	6.200
18	40.30	1,624	0.001276	6.385	156.6	4.917
19	35.89	1,288	0.001012	8.051	124.2	3.899
20	31.96	1,022	0.0008023	10.15	98.50	3.092
21	28.46	810.1	0.0006363	12.80	78.11	2.452
22	25.35	642.4	0.0005046	16.14	61.95	1.945
23	22.57	509.5	0.0004002	20.36	49.13	1.542
24	20.10	404.0	0.0003173	25.67	38.96	1.223
25	17.90	320.4	0.0002517	32.37	30.90	0.9699
26	15.94	254.1	0.0001996	40.81	24.50	0.7692
27	14.20	201.5	0.0001583	51.47	19.43	0.6100
28	12.64	159.8	0.0001255	64.90	15.41	0.4837
29	11.26	126.7	0.00009953	81.83	12.22	0.3836
30	10.03	100.5	0.00007894	103.2	9.691	0.3042
31	8.928	79.70	0.00006260	130.1	7.685	0.2413
32	7.950	63.21	0.00004964	164.1	6.095	0.1913
33	7.080	50.13	0.00003937	206.9	4.833	0.1517
34	6.305	39.75	0.00003122	260.9	3.833	0.1203
35	5.615	31.52	0.00002476	329.0	3.040	0.09542
36	5.000	25.00	0.00001964	414.8	2.411	0.07568
37	4.453	19.83	0.00001557	523.1	1.912	0.06001
38	3.965	15.72	0.00001235	659.6	1.516	0.04759
39	3.531	12.47	0.000009793	831.8	1.202	0.03774
40	3.145	9.888	0.000007766	1,049	0.9534	0.02993

* Data obtained from *Natl. Bur. Standards (U.S.) Circ.* 31 for 100 per cent conductivity copper at 20°C (see Sec. 5g-1).

† American wire gage (Awg) or Brown and Sharpe (B&S).

‡ The tables in *Circ.* 31 are given in "international" electrical units. Since Jan. 1, 1948, "absolute" units are standard. To obtain absolute ohms the resistance values in the table must be multiplied by 1.000495 (see *Natl. Bur. Standards (U.S.) Circ.* 459).

consequence is a higher total resistance to a given rms alternating current vs. the total resistance to an equal direct current.

High Frequency. At very high frequencies the current in a conductor is nearly all concentrated at the surface to a depth called the "skin depth" which is given by

$$\delta = \sqrt{\frac{12.57}{2\pi}}\,\frac{1}{\sqrt{\pi}}\sqrt{\frac{\rho}{\mu\nu}} \qquad \text{meters}$$

where ρ = resistivity, ohm-m
ν = frequency, cps
μ = permeability, henrys/m

The effective area of a conductor carrying current of sufficiently high frequency for the skin depth to be small compared with the conductor thickness and small compared with radii of curvature is given by the conductor perimeter times the skin depth.

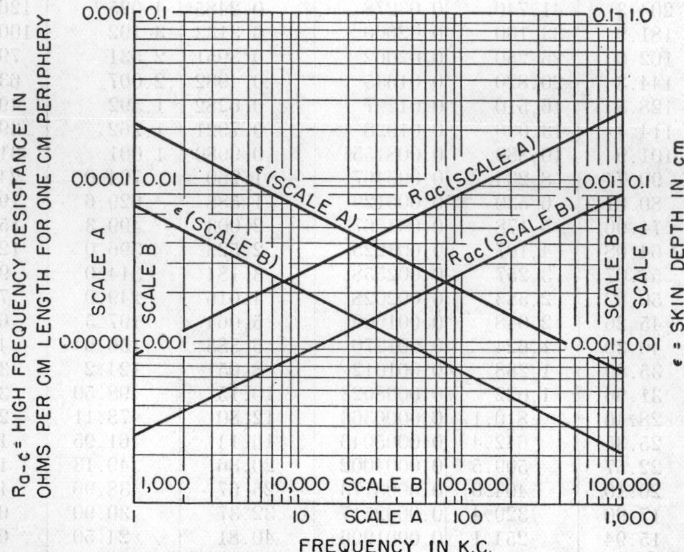

Fig. 5g-1. Skin depth and high-frequency resistance of copper. (*From F. E. Terman, "Radio Engineers' Handbook," p.* 35, *McGraw-Hill Book Company, Inc., New York,* 1943.)

Anomolous Skin Effect. At sufficiently low temperatures and high frequencies, the mean free path of the electrons in a good conductor becomes greater than the classically predicted skin depth, and the classical skin-effect equations break down.[1,2] Thus, the radio-frequency skin conductivity is practically independent of bulk conductivity (measured at direct current) when the mean free path of the electrons is sufficiently long. Data are given by Pippard[1] on Ag, Au, Cu, Sn, and Al. Chambers[3] gives additional data, and more recently Dingle[4] has given data for Na, Cu, Ag, Au, Pt, W, Al, Pb, and Sn.

5g-4. Other Wire Tables. *National Bureau of Standards Circular* 31 contains tables in additional to those for copper wire. These are for bare concentric-lay cables of standard annealed copper and hard-drawn aluminum wire.

[1] A. B. Pippard, *Proc. Roy. Soc.* (*London*), ser. A, **191,** 385–399 (1947).
[2] G. E. H. Reuter and E. H. Sondheimer, *Proc. Roy. Soc.* (*London*), ser. A, **195,** 336 (1948).
[3] R. G. Chambers, *Nature* **165,** 239–240 (1950).
[4] R. B. Dingle, *Physica* **19,** 348–364 (1953).

TABLE 5g-3. RATIO OF A-C RESISTANCE TO D-C RESISTANCE FOR A SOLID ROUND WIRE*

x†	$\frac{R_{a\text{-}c}}{R_{d\text{-}c}}$	x†	$\frac{R_{a\text{-}c}}{R_{d\text{-}c}}$	x†	$\frac{R_{a\text{-}c}}{R_{d\text{-}c}}$
0	1.0000	5.2	2.114	14.0	5.209
0.5	1.0003	5.4	2.184	14.5	5.386
0.6	1.0007	5.6	2.254	15.0	5.562
0.7	1.0012	5.8	2.324	16.0	5.915
0.8	1.0021	6.0	2.394	17.0	6.268
0.9	1.0034	6.2	2.463	18.0	6.621
1.0	1.005	6.4	2.533	19.0	6.974
1.1	1.008	6.6	2.603	20.0	7.328
1.2	1.011	6.8	2.673	21.0	7.681
1.3	1.015	7.0	2.743	22.0	8.034
1.4	1.020	7.2	2.813	23.0	8.387
1.5	1.026	7.4	2.884	24.0	8.741
1.6	1.033	7.6	2.954	25.0	9.094
1.7	1.042	7.8	3.024	26.0	9.447
1.8	1.052	8.0	3.094	28.0	10.15
1.9	1.064	8.2	3.165	30.0	10.86
2.0	1.078	8.4	3.235	32.0	11.57
2.2	1.111	8.6	3.306	34.0	12.27
2.4	1.152	8.8	3.376	36.0	12.98
2.6	1.201	9.0	3.446	38.0	13.69
2.8	1.256	9.2	3.517	40.0	14.40
3.0	1.318	9.4	3.587	42.0	15.10
3.2	1.385	9.6	3.658	44.0	15.81
3.4	1.456	9.8	3.728	46.0	16.52
3.6	1.529	10.0	3.799	48.0	17.22
3.8	1.603	10.5	3.975	50.0	17.93
4.0	1.678	11.0	4.151	60.0	21.47
4.2	1.752	11.5	4.327	70.0	25.00
4.4	1.826	12.0	4.504	80.0	28.54
4.6	1.899	12.5	4.680	90.0	32.07
4.8	1.971	13.0	4.856	100.0	35.61
5.0	2.043	13.5	5.033	∞	∞

* From *Natl. Bur. Standards (U.S.) Circ.* 74 and F. E. Terman, "Radio Engineers Handbook," p. 31, McGraw-Hill Book Company, Inc., New York, 1943.

†
$$x = \frac{\pi d}{\sqrt{6.285}} \sqrt{\frac{\mu \nu}{\rho}}$$

where ρ = resistivity, ohm-m; d = wire diameter, m; μ = permeability, henrys/m; ν = frequency, cps.

A resistance wire table covering nichrome, advance, and manganin is given on page 29 of F. E. Terman, "Radio Engineers' Handbook."[1]

5g-5. Electrical Properties of Pure Metals. Table 5g-5 gives a list of elements considered to be metals in a compilation by F. Seitz.[2] The resistivities given are bulk resistivities. Resistivities of thin films have been omitted because of the extreme

[1] McGraw-Hill Book Company, Inc., New York, 1943.

[2] F. Seitz, "The Modern Theory of Solids," p. 10, McGraw-Hill Book Company, Inc., New York, 1940.

TABLE 5g-4. ALLOWABLE CURRENT-CARRYING CAPACITIES OF INSULATED CONDUCTORS IN AMPERES*

(Single conductor in free air; based on room temperature of 30°C, 86°F)

Size Awg MCM	Rubber, type R,† type RW, type RU, type RUW (12-4); type z RH-RW‡; thermoplastic, type T, type TW	Rubber, type RH; type RH-RW‡; type RHW	Thermoplastic asbestos, type TA; Var-Cam type V; asbestos Var-Cam type AVB; MI cable	Asbestos Var-Cam, type AVA, type AVL	Impregnated asbestos, type AI (14-8), type AIA	Asbestos, type A (14-8), type AA	Slow-burning, type SB; weatherproof, type WP, type SBW
14	20	20	30	40	40	45	30
12	25	25	40	50	50	55	40
10	40	40	55	65	70	75	55
8	55	65	70	85	90	100	70
6	80	95	100	120	125	135	100
4	105	125	135	160	170	180	130
3	120	145	155	180	195	210	150
2	140	170	180	210	225	240	175
1	165	195	210	245	265	280	205
0	195	230	245	285	305	325	235
00	225	265	285	330	355	370	275
000	260	310	330	385	410	430	320
0000	300	360	385	445	475	510	370
250	340	405	425	495	530	...	410
300	375	445	480	555	590	...	460
350	420	505	530	610	655	...	510
400	455	545	575	665	710	...	555
500	515	620	660	765	815	...	630
600	575	690	740	855	910	...	710
700	630	755	815	940	1,005	...	780
750	655	785	845	980	1,045	...	810
800	680	815	880	1,020	1,085	...	845
900	730	870	940	.....	.....	...	905
1,000	780	935	1,000	1,165	1,240	...	965
1,250	890	1,065	1,130				
1,500	980	1,175	1,260	1,450	.....	...	1,215
1,750	1,070	1,280	1,370				
2,000	1,155	1,385	1,470	1,715	.....	...	1,405

TABLE 5g-4. ALLOWABLE CURRENT-CARRYING CAPACITIES OF INSULATED CONDUCTORS IN AMPERES* (*Continued*)

Size Awg MCM		Rubber, type R,† type RW, type RU, type RUW (12-4); type z RH-RW‡; thermoplastic, type T, type TW	Rubber type RH; type RH-RW‡, type RHW	Thermoplastic asbestos, type TA, Var-Cam, type V; Asbestos Var-Cam, type AVB; MI cable	Asbestos Var-Cam, type AVA, type AVL	Impregnated asbestos, type AI (14-8), type AIA	Asbestos, type A (14-8), type AA	Slow-burning, type SB; weatherproof, type WP, type SBW
Correction Factors for Room Temperatures over 30°C, 86°F								
°C	°F							
40	104	0.82	0.88	0.90	0.94	0.95		
45	113	0.71	0.82	0.85	0.90	0.92		
50	122	0.58	0.75	0.80	0.87	0.89		
55	131	0.41	0.67	0.74	0.83	0.86		
60	140	....	0.58	0.67	0.79	0.83	0.91	
70	158	....	0.35	0.52	0.71	0.76	0.87	
75	167	....	....	0.43	0.66	0.72	0.86	
80	176	....	....	0.30	0.61	0.69	0.84	
90	194	....	....	....	0.50	0.61	0.80	
100	212	....	....	....	....	0.51	0.77	
120	248	....	....	....	....	....	0.69	
140	284	....	....	....	....	....	0.59	

* Data from National Board of Fire Underwriters, Pamphlet 70, p. 289, National Electrical Code, November, 1953.

† Symbols in table:

Type Letter	*Insulation and Covering*
A	Asbestos without asbestos braid
AA	Asbestos with asbestos braid
AI	Impregnated asbestos without outer asbestos braid
AIA	Impregnated asbestos with outer asbestos braid
AVA	Impregnated asbestos and varnished cambric with outer asbestos braid
AVB	Impregnated asbestos and varnished cambric with flame-retardant cotton braid
AVL	Impregnated asbestos and varnished cambric with asbestos braid and lead sheath
MI	Magnesium oxide with copper covering
R	Code rubber with moisture-resistant, flame-retardant, nonmetallic covering
RH	Heat-resistant rubber with R covering
RHW	Moisture- and heat-resistant rubber with R covering
RU	90% unmilled grainless rubber with R covering
RUW	Same as RU
RW	Moisture-resistant rubber with R covering
SB	Three braids of impregnated fire-retardant cotton thread with outer cover finished smooth and hard
SBW	Two layers of impregnated cotton thread with outer fire-retardant coating
T	Flame-retardant thermoplastic compound with no covering
TA	Thermoplastic and asbestos with flame-retardant cotton braid
TW	Flame-retardant, moisture-resistant thermoplastic with no covering
V	Varnished cambric with nonmetallic covering or lead sheath
WP	At least three impregnated cotton braids or equivalent

‡ If type RH-RW rubber-insulated wire is used in wet locations, the allowable current-carrying capacities shall be that of column 2, Table 5g-4. If used in dry locations, the allowable current-carrying capacities shall be that of column 3.

TABLE 5g-5. ELECTRICAL PROPERTIES OF PURE METALS
(All measurements are at 20°C unless otherwise indicated)

Metal	$\rho \times 10^{-8}$ ohm-m	ρ/ρ_0 at 100,000 kg/cm²
Aluminum	2.828	0.770
Antimony	39.1*	0.605
Arsenic	35*	0.928
Barium	60	2.618
Beryllium	10.1	0.876
Bismuth	119.0†	0.474
Cadmium	7.54†	0.658
Calcium	4.59	4.399
Cesium	19.0	5.33
Chromium	2.6*	0.558
Cobalt	9.7	0.951
Copper	1.692	0.866
Gallium	53*	
Gold	2.44	0.816
Hafnium	32.1	
Indium	8.37*	0.493
Iridium	6.10*	0.886
Iron	8.85*	0.841
Lanthanum	57.6	0.842
Lead	19.8*	0.487
Lithium	8.55*	1.704
Magnesium	4.35*	0.767
Manganese		
Masurium		
Mercury (liq.)	95.783	0.555
Molybdenum	5.14*	0.892
Nickel	7.236	0.858
Niobium	21	0.894
Osmium	9.5	
Palladium	10.21*	0.847
Platinum	9.83*	0.861
Potassium	6.1*	0.596
Radium		
Rhenium	18.9	
Rhodium	5.11*	0.872
Rubidium	11.6*	2.95
Ruthenium	7.64	
Scandium		
Silver	1.468*	0.802
Sodium	4.3*	0.479
Strontium	24.8	1.810
Tantalum	15.5	0.882
Thallium	17.60*	0.265
Thorium	18	0.821
Tin	11.5	0.548
Titanium	55‡	0.916
Tungsten	5.51	0.895
Uranium	29*	0.724
Vanadium	58.8	0.878
Ytterbium		
Zinc	5.75*	0.679
Zirconium	41.0	0.9836¶

* 0°C.
† 18°C.
‡ 25°C.
¶ 80,000 kg/cm².

structure sensitivity of such data. The data on pressure effect upon resistivity are from P. W. Bridgman.[1] Resistivity values have been gathered from many sources in the literature.

TABLE 5g-6. SUPERCONDUCTING TRANSITION TEMPERATURE FOR METALS*

Metal	Nb	Pb	La	Ta	V	Hg	Sn	In	Tl	Th	U
Transition temp., °K	9.22	7.26	4.71	4.38	4.3	4.17	3.69	3.37	2.38	1.32	1.25

Metal	Al	Ga	Re	Zn	Os	Cd	Ti	Zr	Ru	Hf
Transition temp., °K	1.14	1.07	0.95	0.79	0.71	0.602	0.558	0.546	0.47	0.374

[1] Compiled from E. Justi, "Leitfähigkeit und Leitungsmechanismus fester Stoffe," Table 17, p. 188, Vandenhoech und Ruprecht, Göttingen, 1948; and T. S. Smith and J. G. Daunt, Some Properties of Superconductors below 10°K III Zr, Hf, Cd, and Ti, *Phys. Rev.* **88**, 1172–1176 (1952).

TABLE 5g-7. SUPERCONDUCTING TRANSITION TEMPERATURES FOR ALLOYS*
(In degrees Kelvin)

Nonsuperconductor	Pb	Sn	Tl	Au
Bi	8.8†	3.8†	(Bi_5Tl_3) 6.4	(Au_2Bi) 1.92
Sb	6.6†	(Sb_2Sn_3) 3.8	(Sb_2Tl) 5.2	
As	8.4†			
P	7.8†			
Cd	.....	3.6†	2.5†	
Zn	2.25†	(Cu_3Sn) 1.31		
Ag	7.2†	(Ag_3Sn) 1.36	2.67†	
Au	7.0†	....	1.92†	
Ca	7.0†			
Li	7.2†			

* Taken from E. Justi, "Leitfähigkeit und Leitungsmechanismus fester Stoffe," Table 17, p. 914, Vandenhoech und Ruprecht, Göttingen, 1948.
† Eutectic.

[1] P. W. Bridgman, The Resistance of 72 Elements, Alloys and Compounds to 100,000 kg/cm², *Proc. Am. Acad. Arts Sci.*, **81**, 165–251 (1952).

5h. Magnetic Properties of Materials

R. M. BOZORTH

Bell Telephone Laboratories, Inc.

5h-1. Symbols (Units in cgs system)

H	magnetic field strength, oersteds
B	magnetic induction, gauss
σ	magnetic moment/gram
σ_s	saturation magnetic moment/gram
σ_0	σ_s at 0°K
M	magnetic moment/cm³
M_s	saturation magnetic moment/cm³
M_0	M_s at 0°K
β	Bohr magneton
n_B	Bohr magneton number
θ	Curie point (°C or °K)
θ_N	Néel point (antiferromagnetic)
B_r	residual induction (gauss)
H_c	coercive force (oersteds)
μ_0	initial permeability (vacuum = 1)
μ_m	maximum permeability
μ_r	reversible permeability
K_1	magnetic crystal anisotropy constant (ergs/cm³)
λ	fractional increase in length (magnetostriction)
λ_s	λ at saturation
ω	fractional increase in volume (magnetostriction)
χ	magnetic moment/oersted for 1 g (σ/H)
χ_A	magnetic moment/oersted for g-atom

5h-2. Saturation Magnetization and Curie Points. When a magnetic field of increasing strength is applied to a ferromagnetic material the magnetic moment of the material increases toward a limit called the *saturation*, which is usually expressed as moment per unit weight σ, or as moment per unit volume (M, *intensity of magnetization*). The saturation can be determined as a function of temperature and extrapolated to 0°K, and one can calculate from this the magnetic moment per molecule (or per atom), and by dividing by the Bohr magneton (β, magnetic moment of the electron spin) one can obtain the *Bohr magneton number* n_B. The saturation decreases as the temperature increases and approaches zero in the neighborhood of the Curie point θ, the exact location of which is a matter of careful definition.

Data are given in Tables 5h-1 to 5h-9 and Figs. 5h-1 and 5h-2.

5h-3. Properties of Some High-permeability Materials. The induction B of a magnetic material is a function of the magnetic field H to which it is subjected. Some of the quantities derived from the B vs. H curves of materials are given in the follow-

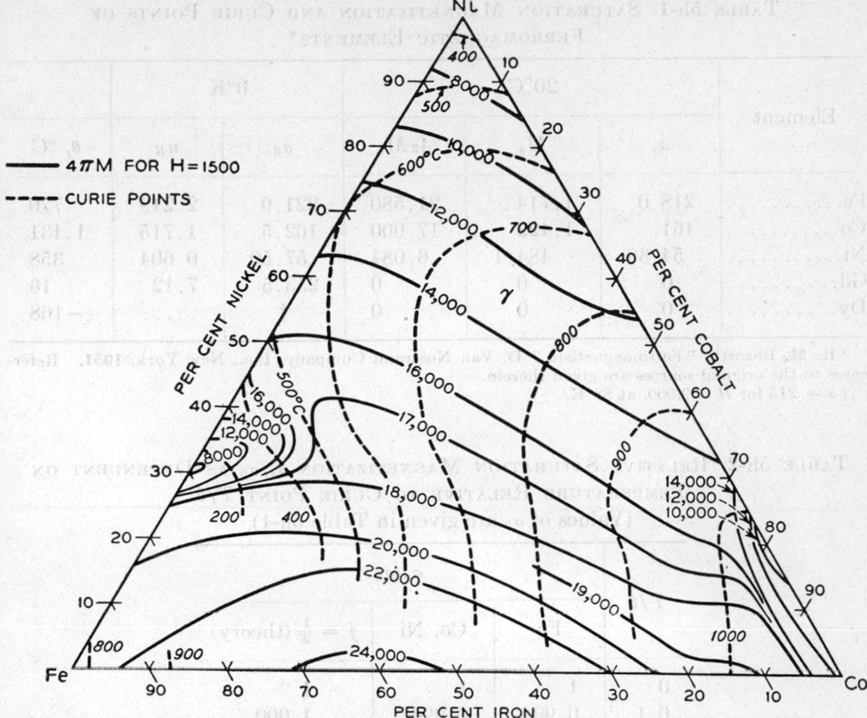

FIG. 5h-1. Approximate saturation ($4\pi M$ for $H = 1{,}500$) and Curie points of Fe-Co-Ni alloys. [*T. Kase, Science Repts. Tôhoku Imp. Univ.* **16**, 491 (1927).]

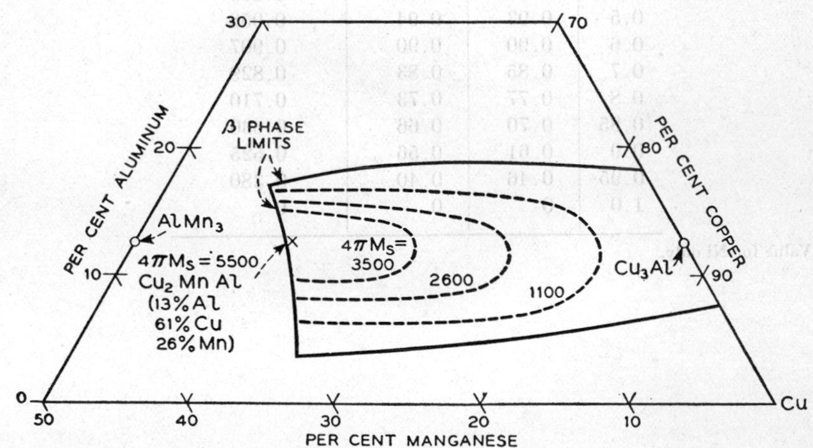

FIG. 5h-2. Saturation induction of Heusler Mn-Cu-Al alloys. (*O. Heusler, see R. M. Bozorth, "Ferromagnetism," D. Van Nostrand Company, Inc., New York,* 1951.)

TABLE 5h-1. SATURATION MAGNETIZATION AND CURIE POINTS OF FERROMAGNETIC ELEMENTS*

Element	20°C			0°K		
	σ_s	M_s	$4\pi M_s$	σ_0	n_B	θ, °C
Fe	218.0	1,714	21,580	221.9	2.219	770
Co	161	1,422	17,900	162.5	1.715	1,131
Ni	54.39	484.1	6,084	57.50	0.604	358
Gd	0	0	0	253.5	7.12	16
Dy	0	0	0	†	.....	−168

* R. M. Bozorth, "Ferromagnetism," D. Van Nostrand Company, Inc., New York, 1951. References to the original sources are given therein.

† σ = 215 for $H \approx$ 9,000, at 88°K.

TABLE 5h-2. RELATIVE SATURATION MAGNETIZATION σ_s/σ_0 AS DEPENDENT ON TEMPERATURE RELATIVE TO CURIE POINT T/θ
(Values of σ_0 are given in Table 5h-1)

T/θ	σ_s/σ_0		
	Fe	Co, Ni	$j = \frac{1}{2}$ (theory)
0	1	1	1
0.1	0.996	0.996*	1.000
0.2	0.99	0.99	1.000
0.3	0.975	0.98	0.997
0.4	0.95	0.96	0.983
0.5	0.93	0.94	0.958
0.6	0.90	0.90	0.907
0.7	0.85	0.83	0.829
0.8	0.77	0.73	0.710
0.85	0.70	0.66	0.630
0.9	0.61	0.56	0.525
0.95	0.46	0.40	0.380
1.0	0	0	0

* Value for Ni only.

TABLE 5h-3. SATURATION MAGNETIZATION AND CURIE POINTS OF ALLOYS OF IRON*

Addition	Atomic %	σ_s	n_B/atom	θ, °C
Co†	20	236	2.42	950
	33	238	2.52	970
	50	233	2.42	980
	75	203	2.14	870
	80	184	1.95	910
Ni‡	10	217	2.26	750
	20	209	2.22	720
	40	152	1.82	330
	60	136	1.45	560
	80	98	1.04	560
Al¶	7.1	207	2.05	756
	19.7	184	1.74	664
	24.9	134	1.29	441
	26.0	149	1.40	494
Si¶	8.3	204	2.00	720
	15.9	174	1.67	653
	23.5	141	1.32	587
V¶	5.9	204	2.09	815
	10.6	184	1.91	805
	18.6	149	1.58	783
Cr¶	17.7	166	1.70	678
	47.5	90	0.98	483
	67.8	35	0.53	268
Ru§	7.0	200	2.18	660
	12.5	105	1.17	
Rh§	10.0	209	2.32	
	25.0	192	2.39	714
	40.0	161	2.26	624
Pd§	5.5	203	2.19	754
	40.0	129	1.89	
	74.8	45	0.97	~250
Os§	8.1	158	1.97	
	12.5	50	0.69	
Sn¶	2.3	208	2.18	768
	6.0	197	2.16	768
Ir§	4.0	200	2.25	750
	15.0	120	1.67	
Pt§	8.1	191	2.36	
	12.4	177	2.43	
	24.8	104	2.23	164
	50.0	32	0.75	
	44.1	39	0.85	
Au¶	6.2	174	2.08	767
	10.5	154	2.02	768

* Additional data are given in the references.
† P. Weiss and R. Forrer, *Ann. phys.* **12** (10), 279 (1929).
‡ M. Peschard, *Compt. rend.* **180,** 1837 (1925); for change of saturation with ordering, see E. M. Grabbe and L. W. McKeehan, *Phys. Rev.* **57,** 728 (1940).
¶ M. Fallot, *Ann. phys.* **6** (11), 305 (1936).
§ M. Fallot, *Ann. phys.* **10** (11), 291 (1938).

TABLE 5h-4. SATURATION MAGNETIZATION AND CURIE POINTS OF ALLOYS OF COBALT*

Element	Atomic %	σ_s (20°C)	n_B/atom	θ, °C
Ni†	40	124	1.33	900
	70	90	0.97	680
Cr‡	5.6	134	1.42	
	10.6	100	1.07	
	16.7	59.5	0.64	
	22.1	19	0.24	
Mn¶	4.2	144	1.53	
	11.9	109	1.16	
	17.3	84	0.89	
	22.5	48	0.57	

* Additional data are given in the references.
† P. Weiss, R. Forrer, and F. Birch, *Compt. rend.* **189,** 789 (1929).
‡ T. Farcas, *Ann. phys.* **8** (11), 146 (1937).
¶ C. Sadron, *Ann. phys.* **17** (10), 371 (1932).

TABLE 5h-5. SATURATION MAGNETIZATION AND CURIE POINTS OF ALLOYS OF NICKEL*

Addition	Atomic %	σ_s	n_B/atom	θ, °C
Al	2.0	47.1	0.54	293
Au	3.4	46.6	0.58	321
Cr	1.7	49.8 (150°K)	0.53	298
	6.7	25.4 (150°K)	0.30	72
Mn	25 (ordered)	90	1.02	470
Mo	1.9	42.3	0.51	266
	4.2	23.1	0.37	120
Pd	12.1	....	0.60	330
	45.2	....	0.57	217
	91.3	....	....	−116
Pt	9.1	37.7	0.55	245
	25.0	16.4	0.44	86
	45.0	....	0.25	−71
Sb	7.5	12.6	0.24	23
Si	3.7	40.3	0.48	234
	6.8	23.7	0.36	117
	8.8	....	0.28	19
Sn	2.7	40.1	0.49	234
	9.0	9.9	0.30	225
Ta†	3.6	....	0.41	
	6.3	....	0.28	
Ti	4.8	34.5	0.43	207
	10.3	....	0.22	30
V	5.5	15.3	0.29	67
W	2.1	39.2	0.49	270
	3.9	19.9	0.34	150
Zn	4.1	45.3	0.52	300
	10.8	25.4	0.37	157

* V. Marian, *Ann. phys.* **7** (11), 459 (1937); additional data are given in the original.
† G. T. Rado and A. R. Kaufmann, *Phys. Rev.* **60,** 336 (1941).

TABLE 5h-6. SATURATION MAGNETIZATION AND CURIE POINTS OF SOME FERRITES[a]
($4\pi M_s$ at room temperature[b])

Ferrite	X-ray density	$4\pi M_s$	n_B/molecule	θ, °C
$MnFe_2O_4$	5.00	5,200	4.4–5.0	300
Fe_3O_4	5.24	6,000	4.0–4.1	585
$CoFe_2O_4$	5.29	5,000	3.7–3.9	520
$NiFe_2O_4$	5.38	3,400	2.2–2.4	585
$CuFe_2O_4$	5.35	1,700[c]	1.3–2.3[c]	455
$MgFe_2O_4$	5.42	1,400[c]	0.9–1.4[c]	440
$CdFe_2O_4$	....	0	0	0
$ZnFe_2O_4$[d]	....	0	0	60
$Li_{0.5}Fe_{2.5}O_4$	4.75	3,900	2.5–2.6	670
$BaFe_{12}O_{19}$[b]	5.3	4,800	20	450
$BaFe_{18}O_{22}$[b]	....	[e]	28	450

[a] E. W. Gorter, *Philips Research Repts.* **9,** 295, 403 (1954); J. Smit and H. P. J. Wijn, "Advances in Electronics and Electron Physics," vol. VI, p. 83, Academic Press, Inc., New York, 1954.
[b] Private communication from E. W. Gorter.
[c] Depends on heat-treatment.
[d] $ZnFe_2O_4$ magnetic when quenched, otherwise nonmagnetic; θ for rapid quench.
[e] $\sigma_s = 72$ at 20°C.

TABLE 5h-7. BOHR MAGNETON NUMBERS OF SOLID SOLUTIONS OF $ZnFe_2O_4$ WITH OTHER FERRITES*
(Averaged values.† Additional data in references)

Ferrite	n_B/molecule for following molecular % of $ZnFeO_4$		
	20	40	70
$MnFe_2O_4$	5.7	6.5	6.3
$FeFe_2O_4$	5.2	5.7	5.5
$CoFe_2O_4$	4.6	5.5	5.1
$NiFe_2O_4$	3.6	4.9	4.2
$MgFe_2O_4$	3.0	3.8	2.9
$Li_{0.5}Fe_{2.5}O_4$	3.7	4.4	1.8

* $Cu_{0.5}Zn_{0.5}Fe_2O_4$, $n_B = 4.7$ [E. W. Gorter, *Philips Research Repts.* **9,** 295, 403 (1954)]; $Mg_{0.5}Zn_{0.5}Fe_2O_4$, $n_B = 4.9$ [C. A. Clark and W. Sucksmith, *Proc. Roy. Soc.* (*London*), ser. A, **225,** 147 (1954)].
† C. Guillaud, *J. phys. radium* **12,** 239 (1951), E. W. Gorter, *Philips Research Repts.* **9,** 295, 403 (1954).

TABLE 5h-8. BOHR MAGNETON NUMBERS AND CURIE POINTS OF OTHER FERRITES AND SPINELS

Composition	n_B/molecule	θ, °C	Ref.
$CrFe_2O_4$	2.0	....	3
$FeCr_2O_4$	0.8	−185	5
$MnCr_2O_4$	1.23	−230	4
$MnFeCrO_4$	0.25	....	1
$MnFe_{0.5}Cr_{1.5}O_4$	0.77	−49	1
$MnCo_2O_4$	0.04	≈ −70	5
$Fe_{2.8}Al_{0.2}O_4$	3.4	....	10
$Mn_{1.5}FeTi_{0.5}O_4$	1.7	89	1
$CoCr_2O_4$	0.09	−175	4
$NiFe_{0.25}Al_{1.75}O_4$	0.07*	....	6
$NiCr_2O_4$	0.1	−195	4
$NiFe_{0.5}Al_{1.5}O_4$	0.16*	....	6
$NiFeAlO_4$	0.57*	171*	6
	0–0.6	198	1
$NiFe_{1.5}Al_{0.5}O_4$	0.5*	385*	6
$NiFe_{1.5}Sc_{0.5}O_4$	0.7	450	7
$NiFe_{1.5}Ga_{0.5}O_4$	2.9–3.2*	385*	6
$NiFeGaO_4$	2.8–3.0*	171*	6
$NiFe_{0.5}Ga_{1.5}O_4$	0.9	−100	6
$NiFe_{1.5}In_{0.5}O_4$	3.3*	325*	7
$NiFeInO_4$	2.5*	40*	7
$NiFe_{0.5}In_{1.5}O_4$	0.6*	−145*	7
$Ni_{1.5}FeTi_{0.5}O_4$	1.1–1.4	≈ 280	1
$NiZn_{0.5}FeTi_{0.5}O_4$	2.1	≈ 200	1
$CuCr_2O_4$	0.39	−140	4
$Cu_{0.5}Fe_{2.5}O_4$	4.1–4.5	390	2, 8
$MgFeAlO_4$	0.3	0	9
$Li_{0.5}Fe_{0.5}Cr_2O_4$	0.1	80	1
$MnCr_2S_4$	2.0	−170	5
$FeCr_2S_4$	1.5	−80	5
$CoCr_2S_4$	2.55	−35	5
$MFeO_3$†	small	200 to 500	11

* Slowly cooled from 1400°C.
† M = trivalent rare-earth metal.

References

1. Gorter, E. W.: *Philips Research Repts.* **9**, 295, 403 (1954).
2. Private communication from E. W. Gorter.
3. Private communication from M. A. Gilleo.
4. T. R. McGuire, private communication following *Phys. Rev.* **86**, 599 (1952).
5. Lotgering, F. K.: Thesis, Utrecht, 1956, and private communication.
6. Maxwell, L. R., and S. J. Pickart: *Phys. Rev.* **92**, 1120 (1953).
7. Maxwell, L. R., and S. J. Pickart: *Phys. Rev.* **96**, 1501 (1954).
8. Bertaut, F., and C. DeLorme: *Compt. rend.* **236**, 74 (1953).
9. Jones, G. O., and F. F. Roberts: *Proc. Phys. Soc.* (*London*), ser. B, **65**, 390 (1952).
10. Guillaud, C., and A. Michel: *J. phys. radium* **12**, 65 (1951).
11. Forestier, H., and G. Guiot-Guillain: *Compt. rend.* **230**, 1844 (1950).

TABLE 5h-9. SATURATION MAGNETIZATION AND CURIE POINTS OF SOME BINARY COMPOUNDS*

Substance	$4\pi M_s$ (20°C)	n_B/molecule	θ, °C
Fe_3Al	11,000	5.2	500
Fe_2B	15,100†	5.7	739
$FeBe_2$	....	....	520
$FeBe_5$	....	....	<0
Fe_3C	12,400	5.3	213
Fe_2Ce	....	....	116
Fe_4N	17,500	8.9	490
Fe_3P	....	....	420
Fe_7S_8	780	2.0‡	300
Co_2B	....	....	510
Co_2P	....	....	920
CoPt	7,200–0	....	<600
CoS_2¶	....	0.84	−163
CoZn	....	....	195
Co_4Zr	....	....	490
Ni_2Mg	....	....	235
Ni_3Mn	9,000	4.1	460
MnAs	8,400	3.4	45
MnB	1,850	....	260
MnBi	7,800	3.5	360
Mn_4N	2,300	0.97	470
MnP	....	1.2	25
$MnPt_3$	5,000		
Mn_2Sb	2,900	1.9	277
MnSb	8,900	3.5	314
Mn_4Sn	1,250	....	150
Mn_2Sn	....	2.7	*ca.* −10
CrO_2	....	2.1	
CrS	....	....	30
CrTe	3,100	2.4, 2.5†	66

* R. M. Bozorth, "Ferromagnetism," D. Van Nostrand Company, Inc., New York, 1951.
† Private communication from E. W. Gorter.
‡ F. K. Lotgering, thesis, Utrecht, and private communication.
¶ L. Néel and R. Benoit, *Compt. rend.* **237**, 444 (1953).

ing tables. The initial permeability μ_0 is the ratio B/H obtained by extrapolation to $H = 0$ and $B = 0$ (at zero frequency). The maximum permeability is the largest ratio B/H and occurs at intermediate values of B. When H is increased indefinitely $B - H$ (in cgs units) approaches the limit $4\pi M_s$, designated also B_s. The coercive force is that value of H necessary to bring B to zero after the material has been subjected to an indefinitely high field in the opposite direction. B vs. H curves for some common materials are in Fig. 5h-3.

The normal hysteresis loss is the energy dissipated as heat when the material is subjected to one or more cycles during which the induction is changed for one value

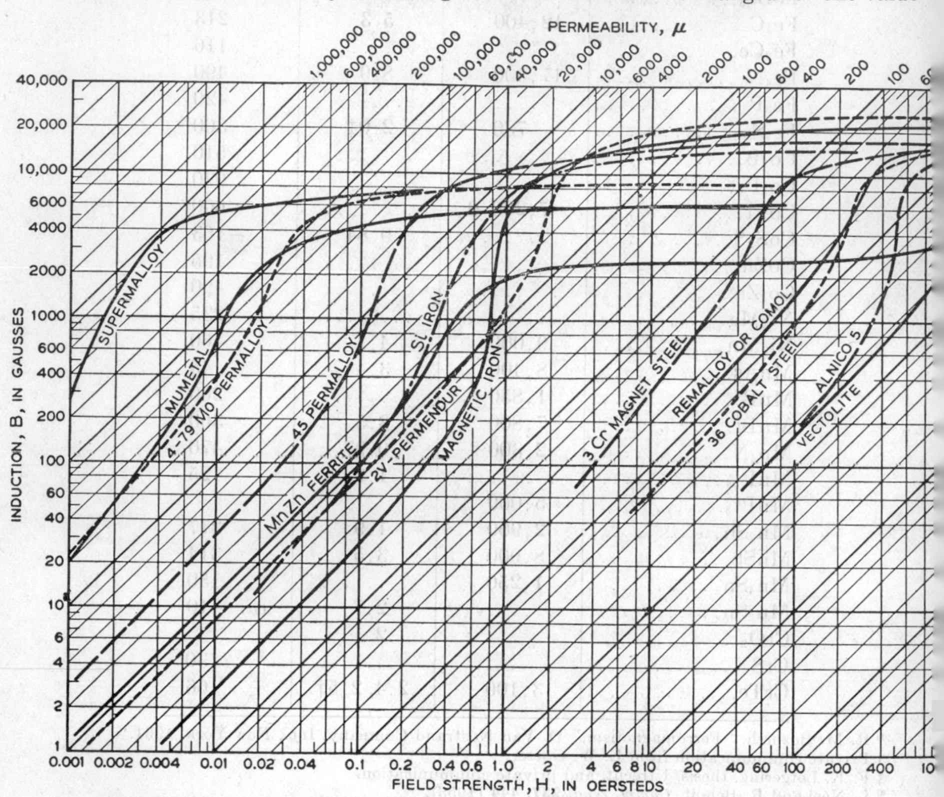

FIG. 5h-3. Representative magnetization curves of some commercial materials.[1]

B_m to $-B_m$; its magnitude for one cycle is $W_h = (1/4\pi)\oint B\,dH$ and is in ergs/cm³ when B and H are in gauss and oersteds, respectively. W_h is dependent on B_m and approaches a limiting value when B_m approaches $H + 4\pi M_s$. W_h is plotted against B_m for several materials in Fig. 5h-4. In low fields Rayleigh's laws apply;[1] $W_h = (4\pi/3)(d\mu/dH)H_m^3$, $d\mu/dH$ being the slope of the μ vs. H curve in low fields (near μ_0).

Data are given in Tables 5h-10 to 5h-12.

5h-4. Properties of Some Materials for Permanent Magnets. In the use of materials for permanent magnets, important quantities are the coercive force H_c, the residual induction B_r, and the energy product BH. The latter is the product of B and $-H$ for points on the demagnetization curve, the portion of the hysteresis loop

[1] R. M. Bozorth, "Ferromagnetism," D. Van Nostrand Company, Inc., New York, 1951.

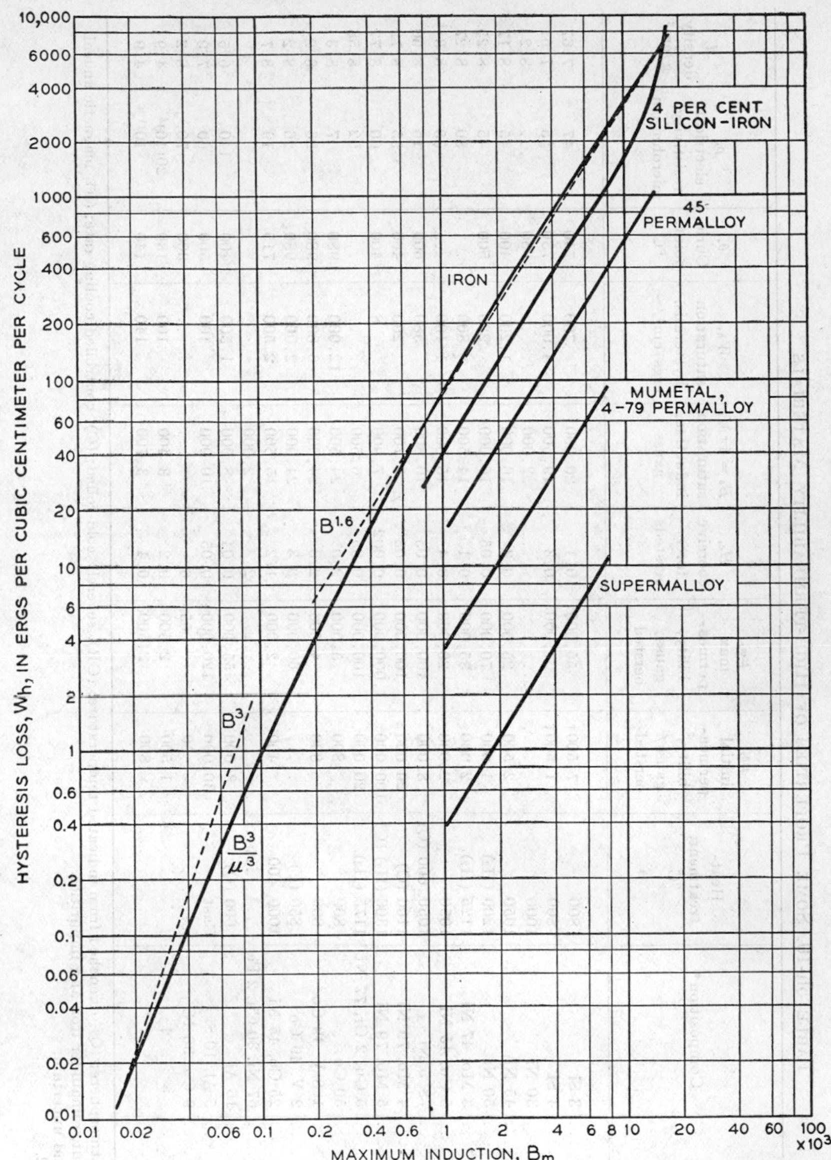

FIG. 5h-4. Variation of hysteresis loss with maximum induction in several materials.

TABLE 5h-10. SOME PROPERTIES OF HIGH-PERMEABILITY MATERIALS

Name	Composition*	Heat-treatment, °C	μ_0, initial permeability, gauss/oersted	μ_m, max permeability, gauss/oersted	H_c, coercive force, oersteds	$B_s = 4\pi M_s$ saturation induction, gauss	W_h, saturation hysteresis, ergs/cm³/~	θ, Curie point, °C	ρ, electrical resistivity, microhm-cm	d, density, g/cm³
Grain-oriented Fe-Si	3 Si	800	7,500†	55,000	0.1	20,000	700	740	47	7.67
Hot-rolled Fe-Si	4 Si	800	1,500†	7,000	0.3	19,500	4,000	730	55	7.61
Thermoperm	30 Ni	1000	....	....	.....	2,000	......	50	......	8.2
45 Permalloy	45 Ni	1050	2,500	25,000	0.3	16,000	1,200	400	45	8.17
Hipernik	50 Ni	1200 (H_2)	4,000	70,000	0.05	16,000	220	500	45	8.25
Monimax	3 Mo, 47 Ni	1125 (H_2)	2,000	35,000	0.1	14,500	800	...	80	8.27
Radio metal	5 Cu, 45 Ni	1050	2,000	20,000	0.4	15,600	1,100	...	55	8.3
78 Permalloy	78.5 Ni	1050, 600 (Q)	8,000	100,000	0.05	10,800	580	600	16	8.60
4-79 Permalloy	4 Mo, 79 Ni	1100 (C)	20,000	100,000	0.05	8,700	200	460	55	8.72
Supermalloy	5 Mo, 79 Ni	1300 (H_2) (C)	100,000	1,000,000	0.002	7,900	8	400	60	8.77
Mumetal	5 Cu, 2 Cr, 77 Ni	1175 (H_2)	20,000	100,000	0.05	6,500	......	...	62	8.58
Permendur	50 Co	800	800	5,000	2.0	24,500	12,000	980	7	8.3
Vanadium Permendur	1.8 V, 49 Co	800	800	4,500	2.0	24,000	6,000	980	26	8.2
Supermendur	2 V, 49 Co	850 (F)	....	60,000	0.3	24,000	2,000	980	26	8.2
45-25 Perminvar	25 Co, 45 Ni	1000, 400	400	2,000	1.2	15,500	2,500	715	19	8.7
Thermalloy	67 Ni, 30 Cu, 2 Fe	....	....	....	2	2,000				
Alperm	16 Al	600 (Q)	3,000	55,000	0.04	8,000	1,500	400	140	6.5
Sendust	5 Al, 10 Si	Cast	30,000	120,000	0.05	10,000	100	500	60	7.0
36 Isoperm	9 Cu, 36 Ni	....	60	65	6	......	......	300	70	8.2
Mn-Zn ferrite	‡	....	1,500	2,500	0.2	3,400	100	130	$20(10)^6$	4.9
Ni-Zn ferrite	‡	....	800	2,500	0.4	3,700	140	140	10^{11}	4.9

(H_2), annealed in hydrogen atmosphere; (Q), quenched from indicated temperature; (CR), severely cold-rolled; (C), controlled cooling rate; (F), magnetic anneal.

* Approximate weight per cent, remainder iron and impurities.

† For $B = 100$; μ_0 is lower and uncertain.

‡ See Tables 5h-11 and 5h-12.

TABLE 5h-11. FERROXCUBE-TYPE FERRITES*
(Commercial materials, representative values)

Designation	$MnFe_2O_4$, mole %	$ZnFe_2O_4$, mole %	B_s, gauss	θ,† °C	μ_0	d, g cm^{-3}	H_c, oersteds	ρ,† ohm-cm	Loss:‡ frequency for tan δ = 0.1, kc
III A	48	52¶	3,300	100	1,400	4.9	0.2	20	300
B	58	42	4,500	150	900	4.9	0.3	20–100	460
C2	62	38	4,700	150	1,100	4.9	0.4	80	420
D2	79	21	5,100	210	700	4.8	0.5	80	420
	$NiFe_2O_4$, mole %	$ZnFe_2O_4$, mole %							
IV A	36	64	3,600	125	650	4.9	0.4	10^5	1,800
B	50	50	4,200	250	230	4.55	0.7	10^5	7,000
C	64	36	4,100	350	90	4.2	2.1	10^5	16,000
D	80	20	3,600	400	45	4.1	4.2	10^5	29,000
E	100	0	2,300	500	17	4.0	11	10^5	60,000

* Compiled by F. G. Brockman, Philips Laboratories, and E. W. Gorter, Philips Research Laboratories.
† Minimum value.
‡ Loss angle δ. $\tan \delta = 1/Q = R/(\omega L)$. See Sec. 5h-5.
¶ All varieties of ferroxcube III include in the composition controlled amounts of ferrous ferrite. The amount varies with the grade but is in general a few mole per cent.

TABLE 5h-12. FERRAMIC-TYPE FERRITES[a]
(Commercial materials, representative values)

Designation	Composition, mole %: MgO	MnO	NiO	ZnO	Fe_2O_3	B for H = 25, gauss	θ, °C	μ_0 at 1 Mc/sec	μ_m	H_c, oersteds	$\mu_0 Q$ at 1 Mc/sec[b]
O-1	...	32	...	17	51	4,250	185	1,000	4,250	0.24	3,600[g]
Q	...	...	16	22	62	3,300	350	125	400	2.1	50,000
C	5	10	20	15	50	4,200	330	250	1,100	2.1	16,000
E	...	...	20	30	50	3,800	160	750	1,700	0.65	13,000
I	...	...	15	34	50	2,000	70	900	3,000	0.3	3,300
H	...	...	16	28[d]	51	3,400	150	850	4,300	0.18	3,500
H-1	20	...	4	22[e]	50	2,800	125	550	3,800	0.35	2,500
S-3[c]	32	27	...	...	41	2,000	265	45	1,800	0.6	
S-1[c]	34	23	...	...	42	1,780	265	40	515	1.5	
R-1[f]	58	6	...	...	36	1,600	...	50	350	2.5	1,700

[a] Compiled by C. L. Snyder and E. Albers-Schoenberg, General Ceramics Corp.
[b] Loss angle δ. $\tan \delta = 1/Q = R/(\omega L)$. See Sec. 5h-5.
[c] Square hysteresis loop, $Br/Bs = 0.90$.
[d] Contains also 5 mole per cent copper.
[e] Contains also 4 mole per cent copper.
[f] A little different in composition from ferramic A.
[g] $\mu_0 Q$ = 67,000 at 50 kc/sec.

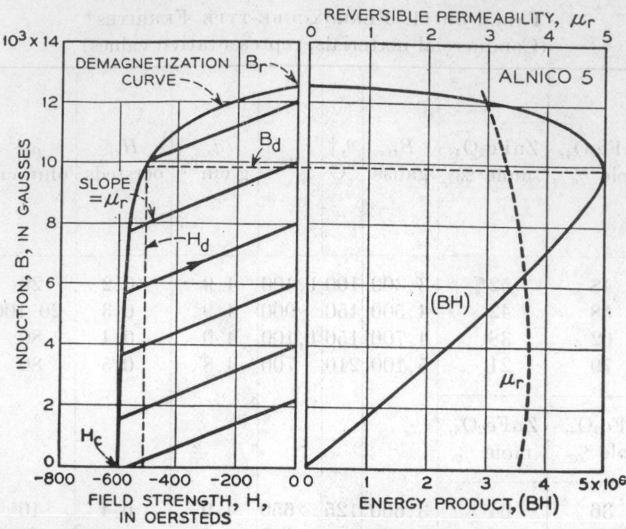

FIG. 5h-5. Demagnetization curve of Alnico 5, showing B_r, H_c, and optimum operating point B_d, H_d. Also energy-product curve and reversible permeability μ_r, as function of B.

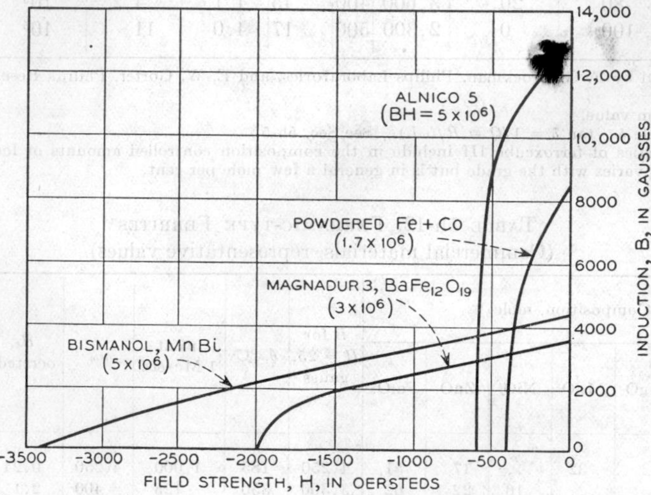

FIG. 5h-6. Demagnetization curves of some important materials for permanent magnets.

that lies in the second quadrant. The maximum energy product $(BH)_m$ is the largest value of BH for points on the demagnetization curve, and this is the best single criterion for a material for use in permanent magnets. The point B_d, H_d corresponding to $(BH)_m$ is the desirable point[1] for operation (see Fig. 5h-5).

Demagnetization curves for several important materials are given in Fig. 5h-6, and constants for the commonly used materials in Table 5h-13. [Note improved properties of fine-powder magnets recorded in Table 5h-13 (private communication from T. O. Paine)].

[1] R. M. Bozorth, "Ferromagnetism," D. Van Nostrand Company, Inc., New York, 1951; K. Hoselitz, "Ferromagnetic Properties of Metals and Alloys," Oxford University Press, New York, 1952.

TABLE 5h-13. CONSTANTS OF COMMONLY USED MATERIALS FOR PERMANENT MAGNETS

Name	Composition, % by weight, remainder iron	H_c, coercive force, oersteds	B_r, remanence, gauss	Optimum point B_d	Optimum point H_d	$(BH)_m \times 10^{-6}$, gauss-oersteds	μ_r, reversible permeability at H_d, B_d	Preparation	Heat-treatment	Mechanical properties	Density, g/cm³
Carbon steel	0.9 C, 1 Mn	50	10,000	6,200	32	0.2	...	Hot roll, machine, punch	Q 800	Hard, strong	7.8
Tungsten steel	0.7 C, 0.3 Mn, 5 W	70	10,300	6,800	45	0.3	30	Hot roll, machine, punch	Q 850	Hard, strong	8.1
36 Co steel	0.7 C, 36 Co, 4 Cr, 5 W	240	10,000	6,300	160	1.0	10	Hot roll, machine, punch	Q 930	Hard, strong	8.2
Alnico 2	12.5 Co, 17 Ni, 10 Al, 6 Cu	540	7,200	4,500	360	1.6	6	Cast and ground	AQ 1100	Hard, brittle	7.1
Alnico 5 (Ticonal)	24 Co, 14 Ni, 8 Al, 3 Cu	600	12,500	10,000	300	5.0	4	Cast and ground	AF 1300, B 600	Hard, brittle	7.3
Alnico 5 (DG)	24 Co, 14 Ni, 8 Al, 3 Cu	660	13,100	10,800	560	6.0	5	Cast and ground	AF 1300, B 600	Hard, brittle	7.3
Alnico 6	24 Co, 15 Ni, 8 Al, 3 Cu, 1.25 Ti	750	10,100	7,000	540	3.8	4	Cast and ground	AF 1300, B 600	Hard, brittle	7.4
Alnico 7	8.5 Al, 18 Ni, 24 Co, 5 Ti	1,050	7,000	3,700	670	2.5	4	Cast and ground	AF 1300, B 600	Hard, brittle	7.2
Alcomax II	22 Co, 11.5 Ni, 8 Al, 3 Cu	580	12,500	10,000	460	4.6	3	Cast and ground	AF 1300 B 600	Hard, brittle	7.3
Alcomax III	24 Co, 14 Ni, 8 Al, 3 Cu, 1 Nb	670	12,500	10,000	510	5.0	3.5	Cast and ground	AF 1300, B 600	Hard, brittle	7.3
Remalloy (Comol)	12 Co, 17 Mo	250	10,500	6,400	170	1.1	10	Hot roll, machine, punch	Q 1200, B 700	Hard, malleable	8.15
Vicalloy 2	52 Co, 14 V	510	10,000	8,000	430	3.5	5	Cold roll	D, B 600	Ductile	8.1
Cunife 1	20 Ni, 60 Cu	500	5,400	4,000	320	1.3	1.7	Draw, machine, punch	Q 1070, B 700, D,B 600	Ductile	8.6
Cunico	41 Co, 24 Ni, 35 Cu	660	3,400	2,000	400	0.8	3	Cold roll, machine, punch	Q 1080, B 625	Ductile	8.3
Vectolite	16 Co, 28 O(E)	900	1,600	1,000	500	0.5	...	Sinter	AF 1000	Hard, brittle	3.1
Ferroxdur 1, Indox 1, Magnadur 1	$BaFe_{12}O_{19}$	1,600	2,000	1,100	800	0.9	1.1	Sinter	....	Hard, brittle	4.8
Ferroxdur 2, Magnadur 2, Indox 5	$BaFe_{12}O_{19}$	1,600–2,000	3,700–3,100	2,100–1,800	1,400–1,200	3–2	1.1	Sinter	PF	Hard, brittle	4.8
Fine-powder Fe + Co	30Co	1,000	9,000	....	....	5.0	...	Press	None	Weak	
Bismanol	MnBi	3,400	4,300	....	....	4.3	1.1	Sinter	PF		
Silmanal	84 Ag, 9 Mn, 4 Al	550	550	280	280	0.08	1.1	Draw	B 250	Ductile	9.0

Q, quenched from indicated temperature (°C) in oil or water; AQ, quenched in air; AF, cooled in a magnetic field; PF, pressed in magnetic field; B, baked; D, drawn (wire); E, raw-material composition.

5h-5. Losses at Low Inductions. Losses in magnetic materials in alternating fields at low inductions (<100 gauss, approximately) are usually described by the following equation:[1]

$$\frac{R}{\mu L f} = aB + c + ef$$

R is in ohms (series) and L in henrys, as measured on an a-c bridge, μ the permeability, f the frequency of alternating current in cps, B the maximum induction in gauss during the cycle, and a, c, and e the constants given in Table 5h-14. The constant a is generally ascribed to hysteresis, c to lag, and e to eddy currents.

The loss angle δ is related to these constants and Q as follows:

$$\tan \delta = \frac{1}{Q} = \frac{R}{\omega L} = \frac{R}{2\pi f L}$$

This is valid only at low frequencies, when eddy-current shielding is negligible.

TABLE 5h-14. MATERIAL CONSTANTS FOR LOSSES AT LOW INDUCTIONS
(a is hysteresis constant, c the "lag" constant, and e the eddy-current constant)

Material	Size	μ_0	$a \times 10^6$	$c \times 10^6$	$e \times 10^9$
Carbonyl iron	5 μ	13	5	60	1
Mo Permalloy	0.001-in. sheet	13,000	2	0	10
Mo Permalloy	120 mesh	125	1.6	30	19
Mo Permalloy	400 mesh	14	11	140	7
Mn Zn ferrite	....	1,500	1.6	4.8*	0.3
Ni Zn ferrite	....	200	7	......	0.2

* $f < 1$ Mc/sec, higher values at higher frequencies.

TABLE 5h-15. CHANGE OF CURIE POINT WITH PRESSURE*

Specimen	Change, °C/1,000 atm	Approx θ, °C
Fe	0 ± 0.2	770
Co	0 ± 1	1120
Ni	$+0.35 \pm 0.03$	360
Gd	-1.2 ± 0.2	16
Fe with 4% Si-Fe	-0.1 ± 0.2	733
Fe with 10% Si-Fe	$+0.2 \pm 0.3$	615
30% Ni-Fe	-5.8 ± 0.2	80
36% Ni-Fe	-3.6 ± 0.1	210
68% Ni-Fe	-0.1 ± 0.2	606
Monel	$+0.07 \pm 0.03$	50
Alumel (94% Ni)	$+0.03 \pm 0.04$	143
$Mn_{0.5}Zn_{0.5}Fe_2O_4$	$+0.9 \pm 0.05$	90
$La_{0.75}Sr_{0.25}MnO_3$	$+0.6 \pm 0.06$	80

* L. Patrick, *Phys. Rev.* **93,** 384 (1954).

5h-6. Change of Curie Point with Pressure. Using magnetic material as the core of a transformer, the change in magnetic induction B at a field strength of about 1 oersted has been measured under hydrostatic pressures up to 9,000 atm. From this the change in Curie point has been derived. See Table 5h-15.

[1] C. D. Owens, *Proc. IRE* **41,** 359 (1953).

TABLE 5h-16. MAGNETIC CRYSTAL ANISOTROPY CONSTANTS OF CUBIC CRYSTALS[a]

Material	$K_1 \times 10^{-3}$, *ergs/cm³*
Fe:	
−196°C	520
20°C	460
200°C	290
400°C	120
Ni	
−253°C	−750
−100°C	−300
20°C	−51
200°C	5
40% Ni-Fe[b]	10
75% Ni-Fe,[b] disordered	0
75% Ni-Fe,[b] ordered	−40
90% Ni-Fe[b]	−15
30% Co-Fe	102
50% Co-Fe	−70
70% Co-Fe	−430
65% Co-Ni	−260
20% Co-Ni	−4
25% Co, 50% Ni, 25% Fe	4
3% Si-Fe	350
7% Si-Fe	180
24% Cu-Ni	5
Fe_3O_4	−135
Fe_3O_4[c]	−110[d]
Fe_3O_4, −150°C[c]	+25[d]
$Co_{0.8}Fe_{2.2}O_4$[e]	3,400
$Co_{1.1}Fe_{1.9}O_4$[e]	1,800
$Co_{0.3}Zn_{0.2}Fe_{2.2}O_4$[e]	1,500
$Mn_{0.45}Zn_{0.55}Fe_2O_4$[f]	−4
$Mn_{1.0}Fe_{1.9}O_4$, 20°C[g]	−33
$Mn_{1.0}Fe_{1.9}O_4$, −195°C[g]	−240
$Ni_{0.76}Fe_{2.16}O_4$, 20°C[h]	−39, −43[d]
$Ni_{0.76}F_{2.16}O_4$, −195°C[h]	−42, −74[d]

[a] Unless specified, values are for room temperature. See R. M. Bozorth, "Ferromagnetism," D. Van Nostrand Company, Inc., New York, 1951, except as noted. Additional data are given in the original reports.

[b] R. M. Bozorth and J. G. Walker, *Phys. Rev.* **89**, 624 (1953).

[c] L. R. Bickford, *Phys. Rev.* **78**, 449 (1950).

[d] Using microwave technique.

[e] R. M. Bozorth, E. F. Tilden, and A. J. Williams, *Phys. Rev.* **99**, 1788 (1955). Also other ferrites.

[f] J. K. Galt, et al., *Phys. Rev.* **81**, 470 (1951).

[g] Private communication from S. Geschwind and J. F. Dillon.

[h] Bozorth, Cetlin, Galt, Yager, and Merritt, *Phys. Rev.* **99**, 1898 (1955).

5h-7. Magnetic Crystal Anisotropy. For cubic crystals, anisotropy energy per unit volume is

$$E = K_1(\alpha_1^2\alpha_2^2 + \alpha_2^2\alpha_3^2 + \alpha_3^2\alpha_1^2) + K_2\alpha_1^2\alpha_2^2\alpha_3^2$$

where the α's are the direction cosines of saturation magnetization with respect to the crystal axes. Usually the K_2 term is negligible.

In uniaxial crystals (e.g., hexagonal) the energy is

$$E = K_1 \sin^2 \theta + K_2 \sin^4 \theta$$

Table 5h-17. Anisotropy Constants of Uniaxial Crystals

Material	Temperature, °C	$K_1 \times 10^{-6}$	$K_2 \times 10^{-6}$
Co	−176*	7.9	1.0
	20*	5.3	1.0
	20†	4.3	1.2
	220*	0.8	0.65
	39*	−2.1	0.4
$BaFe_{12}O_{19}$	20	3.2¶	0‡
	−190	3.5¶	0‡
$BaFe_{18}O_{27}$	20¶	3.0	
	−190¶	3.5	
		$K_1 + K_2$	
MnBi§	20	12×10^6	
	−190	0	
Mn_2Sb§	20	2,500	
	−190	−13,000	

* W. Sucksmith and J. E. Thompson, *Proc. Roy. Soc.* (*London*), ser. A, **225**, 362 (1954).
† R. M. Bozorth, *Phys. Rev.* **96**, 311 (1954).
‡ Private communication from E. W. Gorter.
¶ J. J. Went, G. W. Rathenau, E. W. Gorter, and G. W. van Osterhout, *Philips Tech. Rev.* **13**, 194 (1952).
§ C. Guillaud, Thesis, Strasbourg, 1943.

θ being the angle between the saturation magnetization and the axis. Higher-order terms may occur. See Tables 5h-16 and 5h-17.

5h-8. Saturation Magnetostriction. *Crystals.* When a cubic crystal is magnetized to saturation in a direction defined by the direction cosines $\alpha_1, \alpha_2, \alpha_3$, the fractional change in length measured in the direction $\beta_1, \beta_2, \beta_3$ is given to a first approximation by the relation

$$\left(\frac{\Delta l}{l}\right)_s = \lambda_s = \frac{3}{2}\lambda_{100}\left(\alpha_1^2\beta_1^2 + \alpha_2^2\beta_2^2 + \alpha_3^2\beta_3^2 - \frac{1}{3}\right) + 3\lambda_{111}(\alpha_1\alpha_2\beta_1\beta_2 + \alpha_2\alpha_3\beta_2\beta_3 + \alpha_3\alpha_1\beta_3\beta_1)$$

provided that in the initial condition, from which λ_s is measured, the domains are distributed equally among the easy directions of magnetization (6 $\langle 100 \rangle$ directions in Fe, 8 $\langle 111 \rangle$ directions in Ni). In any case, this equation gives the correct change in λ_s as the α's are varied. Higher-power terms are sometimes used. The constants λ_{100} and λ_{111} are given for some cubic materials in Table 5h-18.

The saturation magnetostriction of polycrystalline material with random crystal orientations and equally distributed domains can be calculated from these constants, and when the fractional change in length is measured parallel to the saturation magnetization (longitudinal magnetostriction) it is

$$\bar{\lambda}_s = \frac{2\lambda_{100} + 3\lambda_{111}}{5}$$

Observed values of the saturation magnetostriction are given in Table 5h-19.

TABLE 5h-18. MAGNETOSTRICTION CONSTANTS OF SOME CUBIC CRYSTALS*

Material	$\lambda_{100} \times 10^6$	$\lambda_{111} \times 10^6$
Fe	20	−20
40% Ni-Fe	−7	30
60% Ni-Fe	27	22
73% Ni-Fe (annealed)	19	7
73% Ni-Fe (quenched)	15	14
80% Ni-Fe	9	0
Ni	−46	−24
3% Si-Fe	27	−5
7% Si-Fe	−5	3
Fe_3O_4†	−20	80
Fe_3O_4, −150°C†	−23	55
$Ni_{0.8}Fe_{2.2}O_4$‡	−36	−4
$MnFe_2O_4$¶	−35	−1
$Co_{0.8}Fe_{2.2}O_4$¶	−590	120
$Co_{0.3}Zn_{0.2}Fe_{2.2}O_4$¶	−210	110
$Co_{0.3}Mn_{0.4}Fe_{2.0}O_4$¶	−200	65
$Mn_{0.6}Zn_{0.1}Fe_{2.1}O_4$¶	−14	14

* See above equations. R. M. Bozorth, "Ferromagnetism," D. Van Nostrand Company, Inc., New York, 1951.
† L. R. Bickford, J. Pappis, and J. L. Stull, *Phys. Rev.* **99**, 1210 (1955).
‡ R. M. Bozorth and J. G. Walker, *Phys. Rev.* **88**, 1209 (1952).
¶ R. M. Bozorth, E. F. Tilden, and A. J. Williams, *Phys. Rev.* **99**, 1788 (1955).

TABLE 5h-19. SATURATION MAGNETOSTRICTION OF SOME POLYCRYSTALLINE MATERIALS

Material* (wt. %)	$\lambda_s \times 10^6$	Material†	$\lambda_s \times 10^6$
100 Fe		$MnFe_2O_4$	−5
80 Fe, 20 Co	30	Fe_3O_4	+40
60 Fe, 40 Co	65	$CoFe_2O_4$	−110‡
40 Fe, 60 Co	70	$NiFe_2O_4$	−26
30 Fe, 70 Co	130¶	$CuFe_2O_4$	−10
20 Fe, 80 Co	30	$MgFe_2O_4$	−5
100 Co		$Li_{0.5}Fe_{2.5}O_4$	−1
80 Fe, 20 Ni	35	Ferroxcube III	$<\|1\|$
70 Fe, 30 Ni	0	Ferroxcube IV A	−4
60 Fe, 40 Ni	15	Ferroxcube IV E	≈ −22
40 Fe, 60 Ni	25	Ferroxdur I	≈ −25
20 Fe, 80 Ni	2		
10 Fe, 90 Ni	−25		
20 Co, 80 Ni	−10		
40 Co, 60 Ni	5		
60 Co, 40 Ni	−6		
80 Co, 20 Ni	−25		

* R. M. Bozorth, "Ferromagnetism," D. Van Nostrand Company, Inc., New York, 1951.
† C. M. Diethelm, *Tech. Mitt. PTT* **29**, 281 (1951); J. Smit and H. P. J. Wijn, "Advances in Electronics and Electron Physics," vol. VI, p. 83, Academic Press, Inc., New York, 1954.
‡ R. Vautier, *Compt. rend.* **235**, 417 (1952).
¶ Nesbitt, E. A., *J. Appl. Phys.* **21**, 879 (1950).

The saturation magnetostriction of hexagonal crystals is described[1] by the following 4-constant relation:

$$\begin{aligned}\lambda_s = {} & \lambda_A[(\alpha_1\beta_1 + \alpha_2\beta_2)^2 - (\alpha_1\beta_1 + \alpha_2\beta_2)\alpha_3\beta_3] \\ & + \lambda_B[(1 - \alpha_3^2)(1 - \beta_3^2) - (\alpha_1\beta_1 + \alpha^2\beta_2)^2] \\ & + \lambda_C[(1 - \alpha_3^2)\beta_3^2 - (\alpha_1\beta_1 + \alpha_2\beta_2)\alpha_3\beta_3] \\ & + 4\lambda_D(\alpha_1\beta_1 + \alpha_2\beta_2)\alpha_3\beta_3\end{aligned}$$

in which the direction cosines of M_s (α's) and λ_s (β's) are referred to rectangular axes so chosen that the 3 axis is the hexagonal crystal axis [001] and the 1 and 2 axes are, respectively, [100] and [1$\bar{2}$0] crystallographic axes.

The constants for cobalt[2] are

$$\lambda_A = -45 \times 10^{-6} \qquad \lambda_B = -95 \times 10^{-6}$$
$$\lambda_C = +110 \times 10^{-6} \qquad \lambda_D = -100 \times 10^{-6}$$
$$\bar{\lambda}_s = \frac{2\lambda_A}{5} + \frac{8\lambda_D}{15} = -70 \times 10^{-6} \text{ (calc)}$$

Polycrystalline Materials. Values of saturation magnetostriction λ_s of some alloys are given in Table 5h-19. The specimens do not necessarily have randomly oriented crystals and equally distributed domains. Further data and references to the original literature are found in Bozorth.[3] Magnetostriction in unsaturated material is shown in Fig. 5h-7 for Fe, Co, Ni, and 45 per cent Ni-Fe.

Volume Magnetostriction. In high fields the isotropic fractional change in volume ω usually depends linearly on the field strength H as shown in Table 5h-20. In low and intermediate field strengths when domain wall motion and domain rotation are taking place, there is some (anisotropic) change of volume; the only well-established observation of this kind is on cobalt[2] when it is saturated perpendicular to the hexagonal axis, and then is observed to be -26×10^{-6}.

TABLE 5h-20. FRACTIONAL CHANGE IN VOLUME WITH FIELD STRENGTH IN HIGH FIELDS*

(Temperature is 20°C unless otherwise noted)

Material	$\omega \times 10^9$/*oersted*
Fe	0.6
Co†	0.6
Ni	−0.6
Ni (340°C)	0.2
Fe_3O_4	−0.1
30% Ni-Fe	30
67% Ni-Cu	1.4

* As summarized by R. M. Bozorth, "Ferromagnetism," D. Van Nostrand Company, Inc., New York, 1951.

† R. M. Bozorth, *Phys. Rev.* **96**, 311 (1954).

5h-9. Antiferromagnetism. Antiferromagnetism is characterized by the tendency of the magnetic dipoles of near-neighboring atoms to be arranged antiparallel. The temperature at which the heat motions destroy the spatial arrangement is called the antiferromagnetic Curie point or the Néel point θ_N, and values for some materials are given in Table 5h-21. Here, the Néel points are based on specific heat and neutron diffraction as well as magnetic susceptibility measurements. Reference to original

[1] W. P. Mason, *Phys. Rev.* **96**, 302 (1954).

[2] R. M. Bozorth, *Phys. Rev.* **96**, 311 (1954).

[3] R. M. Bozorth, "Ferromagnetism," D. Van Nostrand Company, Inc., New York, 1951.

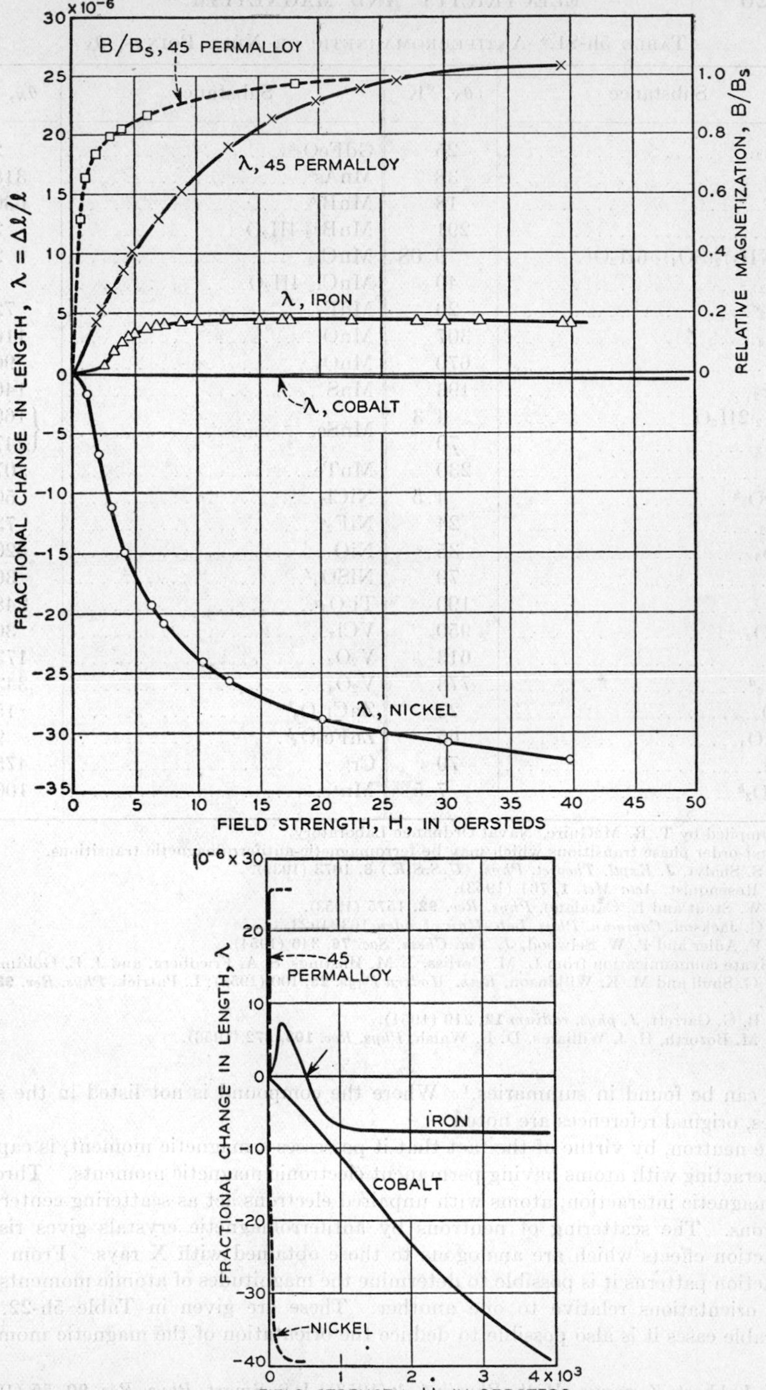

FIG. 5h-7. Longitudinal magnetostriction of some materials as dependent on field strength. (*Upper*) Weak fields; (*lower*) strong fields.

TABLE 5h-21.[a] ANTIFERROMAGNETIC OR NÉEL POINTS, θ_N

Substance	θ_N, °K	Substance	θ_N, °K
$CoCl_2$	25	$GdFeO_3$[k]	2.5
CoF_2	38	MnAs[b]	318
CoI_2[c]	18	MnBi[b]	630
CoO	291	$MnBr_2 \cdot 4H_2O$	2.2
$Co(NH_4)_2(SO_4)_2 \cdot 6H_2O$[j]	0.08	$MnCl_2$	2
$CrCl_2$	40	$MnCl_2 \cdot 4H_2O$	1.7
$CrCl_3$[c]	20	MnF_2	72
Cr_2O_3	307	MnO	116
CrSb	670	MnO_2	90
$CuBr_2$	193	MnS	140
$CuCl_2 \cdot 2H_2O$	4.3	MnSe	{160, 247}
$CuCl_2$	70		
CuO	230	MnTe	307
$ErFeO_3$[k]	4.5	$NiCl_2$	50
$FeCl_2$	24	NiF_2[e]	73
$FeCo_3$	35	NiO	520
FeF_2	79	$NiSO_4$[f]	30
FeO	190	Ti_2O_3[g]	248
αFe_2O_3	950	VCl_3	30
FeS	613	V_2O_3	173
$FeSb_2$[d]	773	V_2O_4	343
$FeSO_4$	23	$ZnCr_2O_4$[h]	15
Fe_2SiO_4	65	$ZnFe_2O_4$[h]	9
FeTe	70	Cr[i]	475
$GdVO_3$[k]	7.5	Mn[i]	100

[a] Compiled by T. R. McGuire, Naval Ordnance Laboratory.
[b] First-order phase transitions which may be ferromagnetic-antiferromagnetic transitions.
[c] S. S. Shalyt, *J. Exptl. Theoret. Phys.* (*U.S.S.R.*) **8,** 1073 (1939).
[d] T. Rosenquist, *Acta Met.* **1,** 761 (1953).
[e] J. W. Stout and E. Catalano, *Phys. Rev.* **92,** 1575 (1953).
[f] J. C. Jackson, *Commun. Phys. Lab. Univ. Leiden* 163, 1923.
[g] S. F. Adler and P. W. Selwood, *J. Am. Chem. Soc.* **76,** 346 (1954).
[h] Private communication from L. M. Corliss, J. M. Hastings, S. A. Friedberg, and J. E. Goldman.
[i] C. G. Shull and M. K. Wilkinson, *Revs. Modern Phys.* **25,** 100 (1953); L. Patrick, *Phys. Rev.* **93,** 370 (1954).
[j] C. B. G. Garrett, *J. phys. radium* **12,** 219 (1951).
[k] R. M. Bozorth, H. J. Williams, D. E. Walsh, *Phys. Rev.* **103,** 572 (1956).

work can be found in summaries.[1] Where the compound is not listed in the summaries, original references are noted.

The neutron, by virtue of the fact that it possesses a magnetic moment, is capable of interacting with atoms having permanent electronic magnetic moments. Through this magnetic interaction, atoms with unpaired electrons act as scattering centers for neutrons. The scattering of neutrons by antiferromagnetic crystals gives rise to diffraction effects which are analogous to those obtained with X rays. From such diffraction patterns it is possible to determine the magnitudes of atomic moments and their orientations relative to one another. These are given in Table 5h-22. In favorable cases it is also possible to deduce the orientation of the magnetic moments

[1] H. Labhart, *Z. angew. Math. Physik* **4,** 1 (1953); J. S. Smart, *Phys. Rev.* **90,** 55 (1953); A. B. Lidiard, *Repts. Prog. in Phys.* **17,** 240 (1954); T. Nagamiya, K. Yosida, R. Kubo, *Advances in Physics* **4,** 1 (1955).

TABLE 5h-22. ANTIFERROMAGNETIC MATERIALS STUDIED BY NEUTRON DIFFRACTION*

Substance	Structure type	Magnetic unit cell in terms of cryst. cell	Néel point from dif-fraction	Magnetic structure type (see Fig. 5h-8)	Direction of magnetic moments	Ref.
MnO......	NaCl (f.c. cubic)	$2a_0$	124°K	MnO	∥ cube edge	1
MnS.......	NaCl (f.c. cubic)	$2a_0$	....	MnO	∥ cube edge	1
MnSe......	NaCl (f.c. cubic)	$2a_0$	....	MnO	∥ cube edge	1
FeO.......	NaCl (f.c. cubic)	$2a_0$	....	MnO	⊥ ferro-magnetic (111) sheets	1
CoO.......	NaCl (f.c. cubic)	$2a_0$	....	MnO	∥ cube edge	1
NiO.......	NaCl (f.c. cubic)	$2a_0$	....	MnO	∥ cube edge	1
α-Fe_2O_3....	Cr_2O_3 (rhom-bohedral)	a_0	....	Fe_2O_3	∥ or ⊥ (111) sheets†	1, 2
Cr_2O_3......	Cr_2O_3 (rhom-bohedral)	a_0	....	Cr_2O_3	....	3
MnF_2......	SnO_2 (tetragonal)	a_0,c_0	75°K	MnF_2	∥ tetrag-onal axis	4
FeF_2.......	SnO_2 (tetragonal)	a_0,c_0	90°K	MnF_2	∥ tetrag-onal axis	4
CoF_2......	SnO_2 (tetragonal)	a_0,c_0	45°K	MnF_2	∥ tetrag-onal axis	4
NiF_2.......	SnO_2 (tetragonal)	a_0,c_0	83°K	MnF_2	10° from tetrag-onal axis	4
MnO_2.....	SnO_2 (tetragonal)	$2a_0,2c_0$	120°K	MnO_2	⊥ tetrag-onal axis¶	5
CrSb......	NiAs (hexagonal)	a_0,c_0		CrSb	∥ c axis	6
MnBi (>340–360°C)...	NiAs (hexagonal)	a_0,c_0	....	CrSb	∥ c axis	7
FeS_{1+x}.....	NiAs (hexagonal)	a_0,c_0	....	CrSb	⊥ c axis	8
CuO.......	Monoclinic (C_{2h}^6)	a_0,b_0,c_0	230°K	‡	....	9
Cr.........	b.c. cubic	....	≈475°K	....	....	10

TABLE 5h-22. ANTIFERROMAGNETIC MATERIALS STUDIED BY NEUTRON DIFFRACTION* (*Continued*)

Substance	Structure type	Magnetic unit cell in terms of cryst. cell	Néel point from diffraction	Magnetic structure type (see Fig. 5h-8)	Direction of magnetic moments	Ref.
α-Mn......	Cubic	a_0	≈100°K	Complex	....	10, 11
MnCu alloys (69–85% Mn)	f.c. (tetragonal)	a_0,c_0	380°K	MnCu§	∥ *c* axis	12
$ZnFe_2O_4$...	Spinel (cubic)	$2a_0$	≈9°K	Complex	....	13
$ZnCr_2O_4$...	Spinel (cubic)	$2a_0$	≈15°K	....	....	14
$LaMnO_3$...	Distorted perovskite (pseudo-cubic)	$a_0,2a_0$	140°K	$LaMnO_3$	∥ cell edge in (001) plane ⊥ *c* axis	15
$CaMnO_3$...	Distorted perovskite (pseudo-cubic)	$2a_0$	≈100°K	$CaMnO_3$	....	15
$LaFeO_3$**..	Distorted perovskite (pseudo-cubic)	$2a_0$	....	$CaMnO_3$	....	15
$LaCrO_3$....	Distorted perovskite (pseudo-cubic)	$2a_0$	....	$CaMnO_3$	....	15
$La_{\frac{1}{4}}Ca_{\frac{3}{4}}MnO_3$	Distorted perovskite (pseudo-cubic)	$2a_0,2a_0,a_0$	....	$La_{\frac{1}{4}}Ca_{\frac{3}{4}}MnO_3$	....	15
$La_{\frac{1}{2}}Ca_{\frac{1}{2}}MnO_3$	Distorted perovskite (pseudo-cubic)	$4a_0,4a_0,2a_0$	....	Complex	....	15

* Compiled by L. M. Corliss and J. M. Hastings, Brookhaven National Laboratory.
† Room temperature, ∥ (111) planes; low temperatures, ⊥ (111) planes.
‡ Alternate ($\bar{2}02$) planes coupled antiferromagnetically.
¶ *x,y* directions not determined.
§ Idealized for γ Mn.
** This compound and possibly all of the last 6 are orthorhomic [S. Geller and E. A. Wood, *Aeta Cryst.* **9**, 563 (1956)].

References

1. Shull, Strauser, and Wollan: *Phys. Rev.* **83**, 333 (1951).
2. Corliss, Hastings, and Goldman: *Phys. Rev.* **93**, 893 (1954).
3. Brockhouse, B. N.: *Can. J. Phys.* **21**, 961 (1953).
4. Erickson, R. A.: *Phys. Rev.* **90**, 779 (1953).
5. Erickson, R. A.: *Phys. Rev.* **85**, 365 (1952).
6. Snow, A. I.: *Phys. Rev.* **85**, 365 (1952).
7. Private communication from B. J. Roberts.

8. Sidhu, S. S.: Pittsburgh Diffraction Conference, 1954.
9. Brockhouse, B. N.: *Phys. Rev.* **94**, 781 (1954).
10. Shull, C. G., and M. K. Wilkinson: *Revs. Modern Phys.* **25**, 100 (1953).
11. Private communication from J. Kasper and B. J. Roberts.
12. Meneghetti, D., and S. S. Sidhu: *Argonne Natl. Lab. Rept.* ANL-5230 (1954).
13. Corliss, L. M., and J. M. Hastings: *Third Intern. Congr. Cryst.*, Paris, 1954.
14. Hastings, Corliss, and Goldman: Pittsburgh Diffraction Conference, 1954.
15. Wollan, E. O., and W. C. Koehler: *Oak Ridge Natl. Lab. Repts.* ORNL-1705, 1798 (1954).

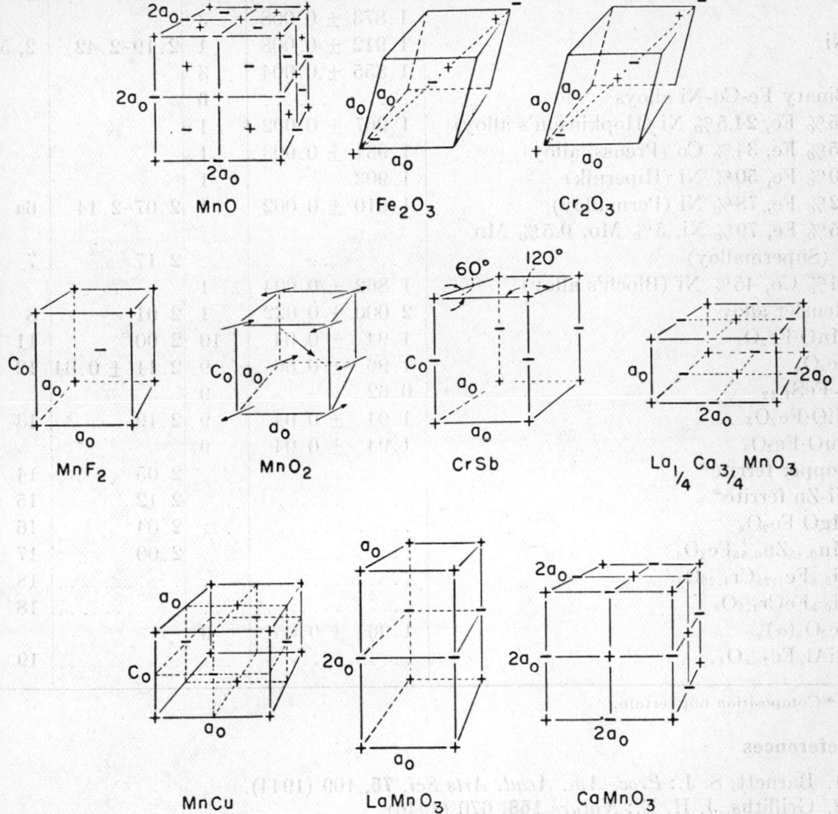

FIG. 5h-8. Orientations of magnetic moments in antiferromagnetic materials of various types. Here + and − signs indicate oppositely directed moments. The directions of the moments in any given material are given in Table 5h-22, column (6).

relative to the crystallographic axes. In the diagrams of Fig. 5h-8 plus and minus signs have been used whenever possible to denote oppositely directed magnetic moments. The orientation of the antiferromagnetically coupled system of moments relative to crystallographic axes is indicated in a separate column in Table 5h-22.

5h-10. Gyromagnetic Ratios and Spectroscopic Splitting Factors.[1] The gyromagnetic ratio g' is defined by the relation

$$g' = \frac{M}{J}\frac{2mc}{e}$$

[1] Compiled by J. K. Galt, Bell Telephone Laboratories.

TABLE 5h-23. SPECTROSCOPIC (LANDÉ) SPLITTING FACTORS g AND GYROMAGNETIC RATIOS g' OF VARIOUS SUBSTANCES
(Compiled July, 1953)

Substance	g'	Ref.	g	Ref.
Fe	1.934 ± 0.006	1	2.12	2
	1.946 ± 0.002	3	2.14	4
Co	1.855 ± 0.013	1	2.22	2
	1.873 ± 0.008	3		
Ni	1.912 ± 0.008	1	2.19–2.42	2, 5
	1.855 ± 0.004	3		
Binary Fe-Co-Ni alloys	....	6		
75% Fe, 24.5% Ni (Hopkinson's alloy)	1.967 ± 0.002	1		
65% Fe, 34% Co (Preuss' alloy)	1.931 ± 0.003	1		
50% Fe, 50% Ni (Hipernik)	1.903	1		
22% Fe, 78% Ni (Permalloy)	1.910 ± 0.002	1	2.07–2.14	6a
15% Fe, 79% Ni, 5% Mo, 0.5% Mn (Supermalloy)	....	...	2.17	7
54% Co, 45% Ni (Bloch's alloy)	1.862 ± 0.004	1		
Heusler alloy	2.000 ± 0.022	1	2.01	8
$MnO{\cdot}Fe_2O_3$	1.94 ± 0.04	10	2.00	11
Fe_3O_4	1.96 ± 0.06	9	2.11 ± 0.04	12
$\sim FeS_{1.12}$	0.62	9		
$NiO{\cdot}Fe_2O_3$	1.94 ± 0.04	9	2.19	13
$CuO{\cdot}Fe_2O_3$	1.94 ± 0.04	9		
Copper ferrite*	....	...	2.05	14
Ni-Zn ferrite*	....	...	2.12	15
$MgO{\cdot}Fe_2O_3$	....	...	2.04	16
$Mn_{0.45}Zn_{0.55}Fe_2O_4$	....	...	2.00	17
$Li_{0.5}Fe_{1.25}Cr_{1.25}O_4$	....	...	....	18
$Li_{0.5}FeCr_{1.5}O_4$	....	...	....	18
$Fe_2O_3(\alpha)$	1.96 ± 0.05	9		
$NiAl_xFe_{2-x}O_4$	....	...	....	19

* Composition not certain.

References

1. Barnett, S. J.: *Proc. Am. Acad. Arts Sci.* **75,** 109 (1944).
2. Griffiths, J. H. E.: *Nature* **158,** 670 (1946).
3. Scott, G. G.: *Phys. Rev.* **82,** 542 (1951); **87,** 697 (1952).
4. Kip, A. F., and R. D. Arnold: *Phys. Rev.* **75,** 1556 (1949).
5. Bloembergen, N.: *Phys. Rev.* **78,** 572 (1950).
6. Barnett, S. J., and G. S. Kenny: *Phys. Rev.* **87,** 723 (1953). A study of Ni-Fe, Ni-Co, and Co-Fe alloys. These results indicate that g' for these alloy systems varies linearly with composition as it changes from one pure element to the other.

6a. Kip, A. F., and R. D. Arnold: *Progr. Rept., MIT Research Lab. Electronics,* p. 31, Oct. 15, 1948.

7. Yager, W. A., and R. M. Bozorth: *Phys. Rev.* **72,** 80 (1947).
8. Yager, W. A., and F. R. Merritt, *Phys. Rev.* **75,** 318 (1949).
9. Ray Chaudhuri, D. P.: *Indian J. Phys.* **9,** 383 (1935).
10. Coeterier, F.: *Helv. Phys. Acta* **8,** 522 (1935).
11. Guillaud, Yager, Merritt, and Kittel: *Phys. Rev.* **79,** 181 (1950).
12. Bickford, L. R., Jr.: *Phys. Rev.* **78,** 449 (1950).
13. Yager, Galt, Merritt, and Wood: *Phys. Rev.* **80,** 744 (1950).

14. Okamura, T., and Y. Kojima: *Phys. Rev.* **86,** 1040 (1952).
15. Beljers, H. G.: *Physica* **14,** 629 (1949).
16. Okamura, T., and Y. Torizuka: *Nature* **167,** 986 (1951).
17. Galt, Yager, Remeika, and Merritt: *Phys. Rev.* **81,** 470 (1950).
18. van Wieringen, J. S.: *Phys. Rev.* **90,** 488 (1953). It is found that the g value of $Li_{0.5}Fe_{1.25}Cr_{1.25}O_4$ spinel is 2.0 at low temperatures. However, as the temperature increases it deviates from this value much in the form of a dispersion curve in the neighborhood of the point at which the magnetization in this spinel changes sign. Similar behavior was found for $Li_{0.5}FeCr_{1.5}O_4$.
19. Wangsness, R. K., and T. R. McGuire: *Phys. Rev.* **91** (1953). The g factor in this material increases from $g = 2.3$ at $x = 0$ to a peak, then passes through $g = 2$ at $x = 0.7$ and drops to 1.5 at higher values of x.

where m/e is the mass-to-charge ratio of the electron and c is the velocity of light. M/J is the ratio of the dipole moment to the angular momentum of the electrons which contribute to the spontaneous magnetization as measured in an Einstein-de Haas or a Barnett-effect experiment.

The spectroscopic splitting factor g for ferromagnetic materials is defined thus:

$$g = \frac{h\nu}{\beta H}$$

where ν is the Larmor precession frequency of the moment associated with a sample of the material in a field H as measured in a ferromagnetic-resonance experiment, h is Planck's constant, and β is the Bohr magneton. See Table 5h-23.

5h-11. Magneto-optical Rotation (Faraday Effect).[1] This subject is treated in two parts, separate attention being given to the Faraday effect in ferrites and related materials at microwave frequencies.

In most nonferromagnetic materials the rotation of the plane of polarization can be represented by the relation

$$\theta = KML + VHL$$

where θ = rotation, minutes of arc
M = intensity of magnetization of medium, cgs units
H = magnetic field, oersteds
L = path length, cm
V = Verdet's constant, minutes/(oersted-cm)
K = Kundt's constant, (minutes/cm)/(magnetic moment/cm³)

This equation is valid for most paramagnetic and diamagnetic materials if measurements are not taken in the region of an absorption line. If the susceptibility of the diamagnetic or paramagnetic substance does not depend upon field strength, then the rotation can be written in terms of a Verdet's constant alone. In ferromagnetic materials no simple relation is valid. Data are given in Table 5h-24.

The Faraday effect which occurs at microwave frequencies is described by the relation

$$\theta = \frac{\omega}{2c} \sqrt{\epsilon} \left(\sqrt{\mu + K} - \sqrt{\mu - K}\right) L$$

where θ = rotation, radians
ω = angular frequency, radians/sec
c = velocity of light
L = path length, cm
ϵ = dielectric constant

[1] Compiled by C. L. Hogan, Harvard University, and J. H. Rowen, Bell Telephone Laboratories.

Table 5h-24. Faraday Rotation in Various Materials

Thin Films of Iron[a] Wavelength 5,790 Å, $4\pi M_s \approx 21{,}000$ gauss

Magnetic field, oersteds	Path length, μ	Rotation × 10^{-4}, deg/cm
0	0.1	0
1,000	0.1	2
10,000	0.1	20
24,000	0.1	38
27,000	0.1	38
24,000	0.05	19

Diamagnetic Solids and Liquids

Substance	Wavelength, Å	$V \times 10^3$, min-oersted^{-1} cm^{-1}
H_2O, 25°C	2,496	0.1042[b]
	5,000	0.0184[c]
	10,000	0.00410[d]
	13,000	0.00264[d]
C_2H_5OH[d] 20°C	5,893	0.1112
CH_3OH[d], 20°C	5,893	0.0094
C_6H_6[d] 20°C	5,893	0.0297
CS_2[d], 20°C	5,893	0.04226
Quartz[d] ⊥ to axis	5,893	0.01664

Gases[e]

Substance	Wavelength, Å	$V \times 10^3$, min-oersted^{-1} cm^{-1}
O_2, 7.0°C, 100 kg/cm²	4,230	0.908
	5,550	0.604
	6,560	0.484
Air, 17.6°C, 100 kg/cm²	4,230	1.062
	5,550	0.618
	6,560	0.452
N_2, 100 kg/cm², 14°C	4,230	1.097
	5,550	0.620
	6,560	0.439
CO_2, 1 atm, 6.5°C	4,230	0.01723
	5,550	0.00975
	6,560	0.00691

Liquefied Gases[f]

Substance	Wavelength, Å	$V \times 10^3$, min-oersted^{-1} cm^{-1}
N_2, −195.5°C	5,893	4.15
O_2, −182.5°C	5,893	7.82
SO_2, −10°C	5,893	18
CS_2, +18°C	5,893	43
CH_3Cl, +18°C	5,893	12.9
CO_2, +26°C	5,893	2.07
N_2O, −92°C[g]	5,893	5.54

[a] H. König, *Optik* **3**, 101 (1948).
[b] S. Landau, *Physik. Z.* **9**, 417 (1918).
[c] L. H. Siertsema, *Arch. Néerl.* **6**, 826 (1901).
[d] L. R. Ingersoll, *Phys. Rev.* **23**, 489 (1906).
[e] Siertsema, Vers, *Konink. Ned. Akad. Wetenschap. Proc.* **2,** 31 (1894); **3,** 230 (1895); **4,** 317 (1896); **5,** 132 (1897).
[f] S. Chaudier, *Compt. rend.* **156,** 1008, 1529 (1913).
[g] Siertsema, *Commun. Phys. Lab. Univ. Leiden* 90, 91 (1904).

and μ and K are components of a permeability tensor which describes the behavior of materials under the combined influence of a static and an orthogonal r-f magnetic field. When $\omega \gg 4\pi M\gamma$ and $\omega \gg \gamma H$, the tensor components are given approximately by

$$\mu \approx 1 \qquad K \approx \frac{4\pi M\gamma}{\omega}$$

where $\gamma = ge/2mc \approx 1.76 \times 10^7$ radians/(sec-oersted). The rotation is then independent of frequency and field and is[1]

$$\theta = \frac{\sqrt{\epsilon}}{2C} 4\pi M\gamma$$

Table 5h-25 shows the Faraday rotation observed in a completely filled waveguide and in waveguides containing slender cylinders of ferrite along the waveguide axis. Measurements of completely filled waveguides are reliable only when the materials attenuate the wave appreciably because of the effects of internal reflections arising from the abrupt discontinuities at the ferrite-air interfaces. The data on the completely filled waveguide show the dependence of rotation upon magnetization as

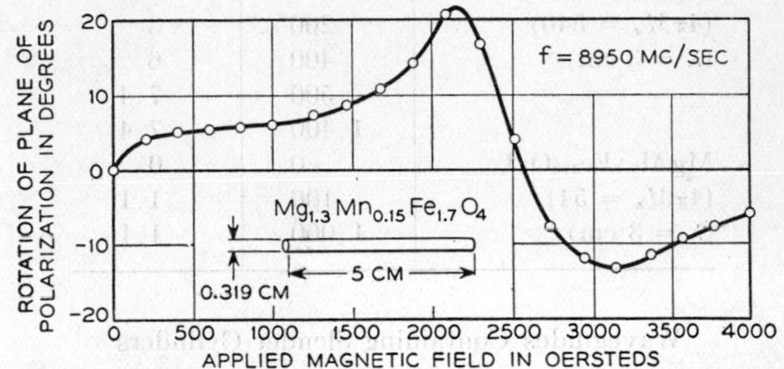

Fig. 5h-9. Faraday rotation in Mg-Mn-ferrite as a function of the magnetic field strength. Wavelength, 3 cm; path length, 5 cm.

evidenced by the fact that the rotation approaches a limit as the applied field saturates the sample.

The data on the slender samples give the rotation at a field just sufficient to saturate the sample. The losses observed under these conditions are also shown along with the figure of merit given by the rotation in degrees per decibel of loss.

The dependence of Faraday rotation on magnetizing field is given[2] in Fig. 5h-9 for a slender sample.

Table 5h-26 giving data on ionized gases and semiconductors is included here because the phenomenon involved is closely related to the Faraday rotation in ferrites and can be described by an equation similar to that on page 5-231 when the tensor permeability is replaced by a tensor dielectric constant.

5h-12. Hall Constants of Ferromagnetic Elements and Alloys.[3] In ferromagnetic materials the Hall potential difference E_H is given by the expression

$$E_H \frac{t}{I} = R_0 H + R_1 M = R_0(H + 4\pi\alpha M)$$

where t is the thickness of the sample measured parallel to the magnetic field H, and I is the electric current in the material. M is the macroscopic magnetization within the

[1] For further information, see C. L. Hogan, *Bell System Tech. J.* **31**, 1–30 (1952).
[2] Unpublished data by C. L. Hogan.
[3] Compiled by Emerson M. Pugh, Carnegie Institute of Technology.

TABLE 5h-25. FARADAY ROTATION IN FERRITE MATERIALS

Completely Filled Waveguide

(Note wavelength λ and saturated magnetization M_s)

Material	Applied H, oersteds	Rotation, deg/cm
$Mn_{0.5}Zn_{0.5}Fe_2O_4$*	0	0
($4\pi M_s$ = 1,500)	500	35
(λ = 3.33 cm)	1,000	80
	1,500	120
	2,000	123
	2,500	123
$MgFe_2O_4$†	0	0
($4\pi M_s$ = 900)	200	3
(λ = 3 cm)	600	9
	1,000	14.3
	1,400	14.3
$MgAl_{0.4}Fe_{1.6}O_4$†	0	0
($4\pi M_s$ = 540)	200	3
(λ = 3 cm)	400	6
	500	7.4
	1,400	7.4
$MgAl_{0.8}Fe_{1.2}O_4$†	0	0
($4\pi M_s$ = 54)	100	1.1
(λ = 3 cm)	1,000	1.1

Waveguides Containing Slender Cylinders

(Faraday rotation at 4,000 Mc.‡ Measurements on rods 1.35 cm diam, supported in polystyrene in 5 cm diam waveguide)

Composition	$4\pi M_s$, gauss	Rotation, deg/cm	Loss, db/cm	Fig. of merit, deg/db
$Ni_{0.6}Zn_{0.4}Mn_{0.2}Fe_{1.8}O_4$	3,840	17.5	0.9	19.5
$Mg_{1.5}Mn_{0.2}Fe_{1.5}O_4$	1,800	13.3	0.6	21.7
$Mg_{1.0}Mn_{0.1}Al_{0.2}Fe_{1.9}O_4$	1,600	10.5	0.026	410

(Faraday rotation at 11,200 Mc/sec.‡ Measurements on rods 0.355 cm diam, supported in polyfoam in 1.9 cm diam waveguide)

Composition	$4\pi M_s$, gauss	Rotation, deg/cm	Loss, db/cm	Fig. of merit, deg/db
$Ni_{0.4}Zn_{0.6}Mn_{0.02}Fe_{1.9}O_4$	3,850	9.4	0.013	730
$Ni_{0.7}Zn_{0.2}Mn_{0.1}Fe_{1.5}O_4$	2,800	5.6		2,150
$Mg_{0.1}Mn_{0.02}Al_{0.2}Fe_{1.7}O_4$	1,600	3.77	0.01+	370

TABLE 5h-25. FARADAY ROTATION IN FERRITE MATERIALS (*Continued*)

(Faraday rotation at 24,000 Mc, rods 1.0 mm diam ¶)

Composition §	$4\pi M_s$, gauss	Rotation, deg/cm
Ferroxcube 4A	3,360	13.8
4B	4,400	28.0
4C	4,365	20.0
4D	3,470	9.8
4E	2,315	5.8

* C. L. Hogan, *Bell System Tech. J.* **31,** 1–30 (1952).
† F. F. Roberts, *J. phys. radium* **12,** 305 (1951).
‡ Private communication from J. P. Schafer, Bell Telephone Laboratories.
¶ A.A.T.M. van Trier, Thesis, Delft, 1953.
§ See Table 5h-11.

TABLE 5h-26. FARADAY ROTATION IN OTHER MATERIALS

Free Electrons in Ionized Gases

Substance	Wavelength, cm	Magnetic field, oersteds	Pressure, mm Hg	Electron density* No./cm³	Rotation, deg/cm
Ne†	4	38.8	0.040	4.10×10^{11}	0.649
		51.8	0.030	5.31	1.28
A†	4	64.4	0.004	0.40	0.0653
		64.4	0.042	4.08	0.995
		75.0	0.040	5.21	1.74
N†	4	63.6	0.120	5.45	1.83
Ne + 1% A‡	5.45	500	1.0	....	0.394
		1,000	.....	....	2.36
		1,250	.....	....	7.08
		1,500	.....	....	12.6

Semiconductors

(The only data available are on high-purity germanium ¶ under the following conditions: temp., 77°K; *N* type; electron mobility at 77°K, 28,000 cm² volt⁻¹ sec⁻¹; carrier density, 10^{14} electrons/cm³; λ, 1.25 cm)

Magnetic field, oersteds	Rotation, deg/cm	Magnetic field, oersteds	Rotation, deg/cm
1,690	364	8,450	324
3,380	532	10,140	212
5,070	538	11,830	109
6,760	458	13,520	212

* Calculated.
† P. Keck and J. Zenneck, *Hochfreq. u. Elektroakus.* **40,** 153 (1932); Keck, *Ann. Physik* **15,** 903–925 (1932).
‡ L. Goldstein and M. Lampert, *Phys. Rev.* **82,** 956 (1951).
¶ H. Suhl and G. L. Pearson, *Phys. Rev.* **92,** 858 (1953).

material and R_0, R_1, and α are constants of the material when their temperatures are held constant. Table 5h-27 lists values of R_0 in ohm-cm/oersted and R_1 in ohm-cm per cgs unit of magnetization M. Negative signs indicate electronic-type conduction. $R_1 = 4\pi\alpha R_0$.

5h-13. Susceptibility.[1] The atomic susceptibilities of the elements at room temperature are shown in Fig. 5h-10.

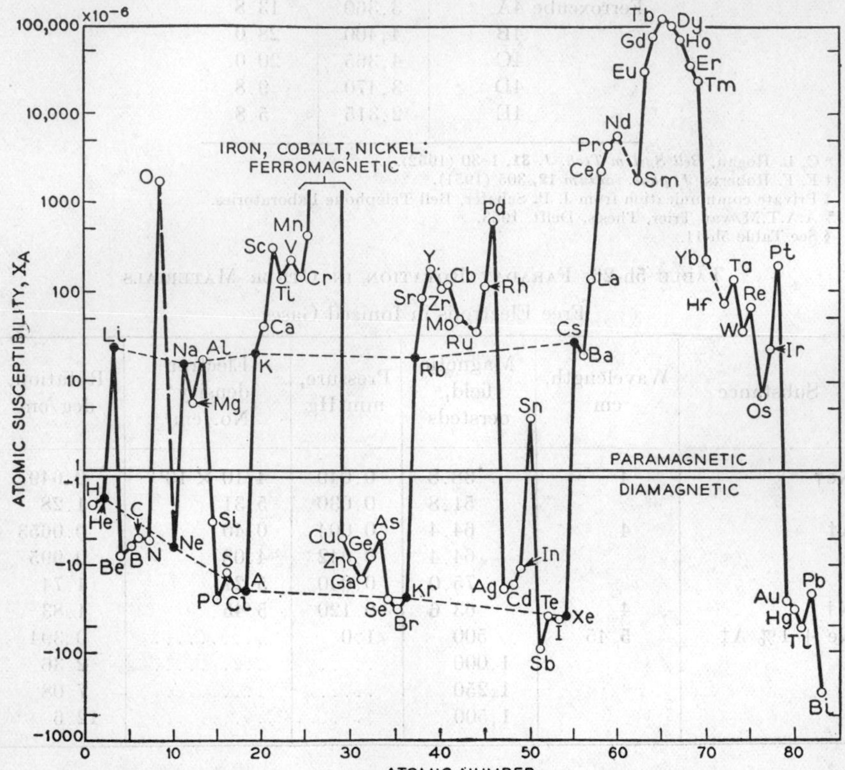

Fig. 5h-10. Atomic susceptibility of the elements at room temperature.

Data are given in Table 5h-28 for materials which follow a Curie-Weiss law over a substantial temperature range. The law is

$$\chi_{\text{mole}} = \frac{C}{T - \theta}$$

in which χ_{mole} is the molar susceptibility (cgs magnetic moment per mole per oersted), C the Curie-Weiss constant, T the temperature in °K, and θ a constant. In addition to C and θ, the corresponding number of effective Bohr magnetons per formula unit is given, obtained from the relation

$$n_{eff} = \left(3k\chi_{\text{mole}} \frac{T - \theta}{N\beta^2}\right)^{1/2} = 2.83\sqrt{C}$$

where β is the magnetic moment of the Bohr magneton (9.274×10^{-21} erg/gauss).

[1] Compiled by J. K. Galt, Bell Telephone Laboratories.

TABLE 5h-27. HALL CONSTANTS OF SOME MATERIALS

Elements

Element	Purity, atomic %	Temp., °K	$R_0 \times 10^{13}$	$R_1 \times 10^{13}$	α	Ref.
Fe	99.9	286	2.45	788	25.6	1
		293	....	698	......	2
		83	....	33.0		
		63.8	....	28.6		
		20.4	....	34.5		
		14.2	....	35.0		
Co	99.1	286	−13.3	23.4	−0.14	1
Ni	.....	283	−5.51	−879	12.7	2
		83	−3.51	−111	2.51	
		63.3	−3.27	−78.9	1.92	
		20.4	−3.01	−71.5	1.89	
		14.2	−3.06	−74.2	1.93	
Ni	99.6	282	−5.6	−655	9.3	3
		77	−4.8	−80	1.33	
		4	−5.5	−86	1.24	
	99.99	306	−5.7	−768	10.7	3
		77	−4.1	−69.8	1.36	
		20	−4.6	−67	1.16	
		14	−4.8	−70	1.16	
		4	−5.0	−68	1.08	
	99.99	290	−12.6	−463	2.93	4
		77	−3.6	−68	1.51	
		20	−5.0	−63	1.00	

Alloys with Nickel

Element and atomic %		Temp., °K	$R_0 \times 10^{13}$	$R_1 \times 10^{13}$	α	Ref.
Fe	10.5	290	−17	−448	2.1	4
		77	−4.5	−206	3.7	
		20	−4	−225	4.5	
	16	290	−17	−83	0.4	4
		77	−22	−193	0.7	
		20	−23.5	−240	0.8	
	25	289	−18.5	427	−1.81	5
	55	301	−18.7	11,000	−46.8	5
Co	10	290	−22.5	−1,210	4.3	4
		77	−11	−135	1.7	
		20	−12	−211	1.4	
	11	298	−11.3	−1,210	8.52	1
		280	−11.3	−1,040	7.32	
	20	290	−19	−320	1.34	4
		77	−20	−270	1.07	
		20	−21	−298	1.13	
	22	284	−15.6	−14	0.07	1

TABLE 5h-27. HALL CONSTANTS OF SOME MATERIALS (*Continued*)

Alloys with Nickel

Element and atomic %		Temp., °K	$R_0 \times 10^{13}$	$R_1 \times 10^{13}$	α	Ref.
Co	30	290	−13	75	−0.46	4
		77	−28	−284	0.81	
		20	−29	−404	1.11	
	38	294	−19.9	292	−1.17	1
		283	−19.9	250	−1.00	
	53	294	−19.6	411	−1.67	1
		279	−19.6	318	−1.29	
	70	298	−19.9	330	−1.32	1
		282	−19.9	268	−1.07	
	85	294	−16.4	179	−0.87	1
		282	−16.4	167	−0.81	
Cu	10	293	−10.8	−2,960	21.8	3
		77	−14.4	−1,230	6.8	
		14	−18.3	−1,130	4.9	
	20	301	−14.5	−6,615	36.3	3
		77	−19.8	−2,690	10.8	
		20	−23.2	−2,440	8.4	
		2	−23.4	−2,410	8.2	
	30*	293	−13	−10,000	61.2	3
		77	−19.5	−6,090	24.8	
		20	−21.2	−5,530	20.8	
		14	−21.2	−5,470	20.5	
	40*	293	−13	*n*	*n*	3
		77	−17.7	−4,810	21.6	
		20	−18.8	−4,300	18.2	
		4	−21.9	−4,290	15.6	
	50*	300	−14	*n*	*n*	3
		77	−14.8	1,730	9.3	
		20	−16.6	375	1.8	
	60	300	−13.5	*n*	*n*	3
		77	−14.3	*n*	*n*	
	65	292	−12.8	*n*	*n*	3
		77	−14.3	*n*	*n*	
		20	−11.7	*n*	*n*	
	80	300	−9.7	*n*	*n*	3
		20	−11.4	*n*	*n*	
	90	298	−7.4	*n*	*n*	3
		77	−8.3	*n*	*n*	
		14	−8.7	*n*	*n*	
Al	8	293	−10	−10,800	86	4
		77	−18	−5,400	24	
		20	−18	−4,700	21	
Si	3	293	−11	−5,000	36	4
		77	−10	−2,500	20	
		20	−7	−2,300	26	
Sn	3	293	−20	−4,500	18	4
		77	−9	−2,350	21	
		20	−8.5	−2,330	22	

TABLE 5h-27. HALL CONSTANTS OF SOME MATERIALS (*Continued*)

Alloys with Nickel

Element and atomic %		Temp., °K	$R_0 \times 10^{13}$	$R_1 \times 10^{13}$	α	Ref.
V	7	293	−48	−28,300	47	6
		77	−19.5	−32,300	132	
		20	−16	−30,000	149	
Mo	3	293	−15	−13,600	72	6
		77	−10.5	−10,600	81	
		20	−11.5	−10,500	73	
W	1.6	293	−11	−5,100	37	6
		77	−10.5	−2,700	21	
		20	−7	−2,640	30	
Mn	25[d]	309	+6.40	4,300	53	5
	25[p]	295	+4.53	13,850	243	5
		297	−2.21	8,870	−320	
	25[o]	304	−16.40	4,100	−20	5

Alloys with Iron

Element and atomic %		Temp., °K	$R_0 \times 10^{13}$	$R_1 \times 10^{13}$	α	Ref.
Si	1.30	300	....	6,230	....	7
		77	....	2,950		
	3.01	299	....	12,000	....	7
		77	....	6,620		
	3.91	298	....	20,200	....	7
		77	....	15,900		
	5.09	300	....	24,000	....	7
		77	....	20,000		

[o] ordered. [p] partial order. [d] disordered. [n] values are indeterminate, since the alloys are not ferromagnetic.

* Values for R_0 are obtained from the slope $\partial E_H/\partial B$ at high fields. For measurements near the Curie temperatures, $(\alpha - 1)\partial M/\partial B$ is large enough to cause errors in R_0. Corrections for this error have been made in the room-temperature measurements on the alloys marked. These room-temperature results may be in error by as much as 15%, since the values of $\partial M/\partial B$ are not well known. Values of R_1 are not affected by this correction.

References

1. Foner, Simon, and Emerson M. Pugh: *Phys. Rev.* **91**, 20 (1953).
2. Jan, J. P., and H. M. Gijsman: *Physica* **18**, 277 (1952).
3. Cohen, P.: Thesis, Carnegie Institute of Technology, 1955; see also E. Pugh, *Phys. Rev.* **97**, 647 (1955).
4. Smit, J., and J. Volger: *Phys. Rev.* **92**, 1576 (1953).
5. Private communication from S. Foner.
6. Private communication from J. Smit and J. Volger.
7. Kooi, C.: *Phys. Rev.* **95**, 843 (1954).

The chemical formulas as written are the simplest which include whole numbers only. In many cases, however, in order to make n_{eff} per formula unit correspond to the magnetic moment of an actual paramagnetic ion, the magnetic data and calculations refer to this formula multiplied by ½ or ⅓ or ¼. When this is the case, the multiplying factor is indicated immediately after the formula thus: $Dy_2O_3(\times\frac{1}{2})$. If n_{eff} does correspond to the moment of a single dipole, then under certain simplifying assumptions it is related to g and J by

$$n_{eff} = g\sqrt{J(J+1)}$$

where J is the quantum number appropriate to the orientable angular momentum of the molecule.

All data in Table 5h-28 for which references are not given are taken from H. Staude.[1] Paramagnetic properties of certain ferrites above their Curie temperatures have been discussed by Néel,[2] who gives references to experimental work in this field. Further references to other materials which do not obey the Curie-Weiss law are also to be found in Staude, and in Selwood.[3]

5h-14. Demagnetizing and Form Factors. When a rod is magnetized by an applied field H_a, its ends carry magnetic poles which themselves cause magnetic fields in all parts of the rod. Normally these fields are directed in the opposite direction to the applied field and are therefore called demagnetizing fields. The true field acting on a given section of the bar, e.g., its middle, is then the resultant of the applied field and the demagnetizing field ΔH:

$$H = H_a - \Delta H$$

The demagnetizing field is approximately proportional to the intensity of magnetization:

$$\Delta H = NM$$

In ellipsoids of revolution, in which the ratio of the long to the short axis is m, the demagnetizing factor N is as follows:
Prolate ellipsoid:

$$N = \frac{4\pi}{m^2 - 1}\left[\frac{m}{\sqrt{m^2 - 1}}\log_e\left(m + \sqrt{m^2 - 1}\right) - 1\right]$$

Oblate ellipsoid:

$$N = 2\pi\left[\frac{m^3}{(m^2 - 1)^{\frac{3}{2}}}\arcsin\frac{\sqrt{m^2 - 1}}{m} - \frac{1}{m^2 - 1}\right]$$

when the ellipsoid is magnetized in the direction of the long dimension. The sum of the demagnetizing factors for the three axial directions is 4π.

The demagnetizing factors of rods depend somewhat on their permeabilities. They have been determined empirically for materials of high permeability, and Table 5h-29 gives values of $N/4\pi$ for such rods, and for ellipsoids. The demagnetizing field is then

$$\Delta H = \frac{N}{4\pi}(B - H)$$

in oersteds, when B and H are in gauss and oersteds, respectively. Formulas for ellipsoids of any axial ratio, magnetized in any direction, have been given by Osborn[4] and by Stoner.[5]

In an analogous way the form of a body affects also its magnetostriction, causing it to be longer the smaller the dimensional ratio. As calculated by Becker,[6] in a prolate ellipsoid magnetized parallel to a long axis the fractional increase in length caused by the form is

$$\lambda_b = \frac{1}{2}M^2N\left(\frac{1}{3k} + \frac{a}{2G}\right)$$

[1] H. Staude, "Physikalisch-Chemisches Taschenbuch," vol. 2, p. 1624, Akademische Verlagsgesellschaft m.b.H., Leipzig, 1949.

[2] L. Néel, *Ann. phys.* **3** [12], 137 (1948).

[3] P. W. Selwood, "Magnetochemistry," Interscience Publishers, Inc., New York, 1956.

[4] J. A. Osborn, *Phys. Rev.* **67**, 351 (1945).

[5] E. C. Stoner, *Phil. Mag.* **36** [7], 803 (1945).

[6] R. Becker, *Z. Physik* **87**, 547 (1934).

TABLE 5h-28. MOLECULAR SUSCEPTIBILITIES, CURIE CONSTANTS, AND EFFECTIVE BOHR MAGNETON NUMBERS OF SOME PARAMAGNETIC MATERIALS
(θ is constant in Curie-Weiss law)

Substance	$\chi_{mole} \times 10^6$ (20°C)	Range of validity of Curie-Weiss law, °K	C	θ, °K	n_{eff} per formula unit
$B_2O_3 \cdot Fe_2O_3 \cdot 2MgO$[a]	....	....	8.66	−600	8.33
$B_2O_3 \cdot Fe_2O_3 \cdot 4CuO$[a]	....	....	10.5	−635	9.16
$B_2O_3 \cdot Fe_2O_3 \cdot 4CoO$[a]	....	....	19.8	−445	12.6
$B_2O_3 \cdot Fe_2O_3 \cdot 4NiO$[a]	....	....	16.9	−832	11.6
$CeCl_3$	2,520	>80	0.787	−23	2.51
CeF_3	2,240	>80	0.794	−62	2.52
$Ce(\beta)$[b]	2,430	>80	0.81	−50	2.55
$Ce(NO_3)_3 \cdot 5H_2O$	2,335	....	0.717	−17	2.39
Co	....	1500–1720	1.24	1400	3.15
$CoBr_2$	11,640	....	3.43	−6	5.24
$Co(CN)_2$	~3,870	....	1.21	−9	3.11
$CoCl_2$	....	>400	3.19	−48	5.05
	13,060	<400	3.56	18.5	5.33
$CoCr_2S_4$[c]	14,100	>500	6.36	−410	7.13
CoF_2	8,660	....	2.90	−44	4.81
CoI_2	10,860	>195	3.18	0	5.04
$Co(NO_3)_2 \cdot 6H_2O$[d]	9,050	>8	2.58	8	4.58
CoO[e]	5,235	>300	3.23	290	5.1
CoS_2	3,520	>155	0.49	155	1.97
$CoSO_4$	10,200	....	3.36	−34	5.18
$CoSO_4 \cdot 7H_2O$	9,780	....	2.94	−9	4.85
$CrCl_2$	7,330	>225	2.97	−116	4.88
$CrCl_3$	6,860	210–690	1.82	24	3.82
CrF_3	4,450	>65	1.90	−135	3.90
CrS[c]	1,610	>560	2.6	≈ −800	4.6
$Cr_{0.85}S$[c]	....	>400	2.52	≈ −650	4.49
$Cr_{0.675}S$[c]	1,640	>300	1.90	≈ −500	3.90
$Cr_2(SO_4)_3$[d]	10,500	>11	2.94	11	4.89
$Cr_2(SO_4)_3 \cdot 18H_2O$[d]	10,600	>19	2.88	19	4.85
$Cr(NO_3)_3 \cdot 9H_2O$[d]	5,320	>20	1.41	20	3.43
$CrK(SO_4)_2 \cdot 12H_2O$	6,320	....	1.84	0	3.84
$CuCl_2$	1,340	155–670	0.457	−52	1.92
$CuSO_4$	1,340	....	0.50	−79	2.00
$CuSO_4 \cdot 5H_2O$	1,570	....	0.46	−0.7	1.92
Dy	102,000	>150	14.6	150	10.8
$Dy_2O_3(\times \frac{1}{2})$	43,200	....	13.6	−24	10.5
$Dy_2(SO_4)_3 \cdot 8HO_2(\times \frac{1}{2})$	~45,000	....	13.74	−5	10.5
Er	44,500	>40	11.2	40	9.5
$Er_2O_3(\times \frac{1}{2})$	38,600	....	11.6	−8	9.65
$Er_2(SO_4)_3(\times \frac{1}{2})$	28,700	....	8.24	−2	8.12
$Er_2(SO_4)_3 \cdot 8H_2O(\times \frac{1}{2})$	36,500	....	11.18	−6	9.46
Eu	30,400	>145	8.45	15	8.2
$EuCl_2$	26,600	....	7.80	−1	7.90

TABLE 5h-28. MOLECULAR SUSCEPTIBILITIES, CURIE CONSTANTS, AND BOHR MAGNETON NUMBERS OF SOME PARAMAGNETIC MATERIALS (*Continued*)

Substance	$\chi_{mole} \times 10^6$ (20°C)	Range of validity of Curie-Weiss law, °K	C	θ, °K	n_{eff} per formula unit
Eu_2O_3 (×½)	5,550	....	3.26	−294	5.11
EuS	23,800	....	6.81	6	7.38
$EuSO_4$	25,800	....	7.64	−4	7.81
Fe	....	>1100	1.23	1093	3.14
$FeCl_2$	13,200	....	3.60	20.4	5.37
$FeCl_2 \cdot 4H_2O$	12,060	....	3.37	12	5.18
$FeCl_3$	13,900	....	3.93	10	5.6
$FeCr_2S_4$[c]	12,100	>300	6.63	−240	7.28
FeF_2	9,460	....	3.88	−117	5.57
$Fe_{0.876}S$[c]	....	>600	3.6	....	5.4
$Fe_{0.902}S$[c]	....	>600	3.8	....	5.5
$FeSO_4$	10,800	....	3.60	−39	5.35
$FeSO_4 \cdot 7H_2O$	11,930	....	3.52	−3	5.30
$Fe(NH_4)_2(SO_4)_2 \cdot 6H_2O$	13,100	....	3.78	2	5.49
$Fe_2(SO_4)_3$	12,100	....	4.3	−61	5.9
$Fe(NH_4)_2(SO_4)_2 \cdot 12H_2O$	14,900	>20	4.2	0	5.8
$Fe_4[Fe(CN)_6]_3 \cdot 14.5H_2O$[f] (×¼)	....	>77	3.92	14.7	5.6
Gd	....	>300	7.48	302	7.73
$GdCl_3$	24,700	....	7.51	−11	7.75
Gd_2O_3(×½)	24,500	....	7.61	−18	7.80
$Gd_2(SO_4)_3$(×½)	26,600	....	7.81	−0.4	7.90
$Gd_2(SO_4)_3 \cdot 8H_2O$(×½)	27,500	....	8.11	−2	8.06
Ho	68,200	>87	14.0	87	10.6
Ho_2O_3(×½)	44,800	....	13.7	−14	10.5
$Ho_2(SO_4)_3$(×½)	45,900	....	13.8	−8	10.5
$Ho_2(SO_4)_3 \cdot 8H_2O$(×½)	44,300	....	13.6	−7	10.43
$KFe[Fe(CN)_6] \cdot 1.9H_2O$[f]	....	>77	4.05	22	5.7
K_2MnO_4	1,270	....	0.383	−7	1.75
$MnBr_2$	14,000	70–180	4.26	−2	5.84
$MnCO_3$	~11,500	....	3.93	−40	5.61
$MnCl_2$	14,500	....	4.17	3	5.78
$MnCo_2O_4$[c]	8,600	>300	5.73	−380	6.77
$MnCr_2S_4$[c]	24,100	>300	7.50	−10	7.75
MnF_2	10,730	>90	~4.10	−92	5.7
MnF_3[g]	....	....	3.01	8	4.91
MnI_2	14,800	35–200	4.21	−4	5.80
MnO	5,040	>120	4.90	−680	6.26
Mn_2O_3(×½)	7,080	....	3.40	−188	5.21
MnO_2	~2,300	....	1.80	−480	3.78
$Mn(OH)_2$	~13,700	....	4.60	−56	6.06
$Mn_2P_2O_7$(×½)	14,400	195–770	4.58	−23	6.05
$MnSO_4$	13,960	....	4.34	−18	5.88
Nd	5,650	....	1.65	0	3.64

TABLE 5h-28. MOLECULAR SUSCEPTIBILITIES, CURIE CONSTANTS, AND BOHR MAGNETON NUMBERS OF SOME PARAMAGNETIC MATERIALS (*Continued*)

Substance	$\chi_{mole} \times 10^6$ (20°C)	Range of validity of Curie-Weiss law, °K	C	θ, °K	n_{eff} per formula unit
$NdCl_3$[h]	......	290–570	1.861	−57.4	3.87
NdF_3	5,020	>155	1.76	−56	3.75
$Nd_2O_3(\times\frac{1}{2})$	4,700	......	1.53	32	3.50
$Nd_2(SO_4)_3(\times\frac{1}{2})$	5,070	......	1.70	−42	3.69
$Nd_2(SO_4)_3 \cdot 8H_2O(\times\frac{1}{2})$	5,390	......	1.82	−44	3.81
Ni	......	>950	0.402	538	1.79
$NiCl_2$	6,250	>540	1.50	28	3.47
		<510	1.37	71	3.32
NiF_2	3,450	>75	1.34	−97	3.27
$Ni(NO_3)_2 \cdot 6H_2O$[d]	3,700	>21	1.01	21	2.86
O_2	3,380	>90	0.99 ± 0.02	0	2.80
Pr[b]	5,100	>77	1.58	−21	3.56
$PrCl_3$[h]	......	285–700	1.69	−29.4	3.69
$Pr_2O_3(\times\frac{1}{2})$	4,450	......	1.62	−71	3.60
$Pr_2(SO_4)_3(\times\frac{1}{2})$	~4,900	65–370	1.64	−44	3.62
$Pr_2(SO_4)_3 \cdot 8H_2O(\times\frac{1}{2})$	5,070	>140	1.63	−33	3.61
Sc	315 ± 10	......	0.395	−980	1.8
Tb(~85%)	115,000	......	10.0	205	~9.0
$Tb_2(SO_4)_3 \cdot 8H_2O(\times\frac{1}{2})$	37,500	......	11.86	−16	9.74
Tm	~25,600	......	7.19	10	7.6
$Tm_2(SO_4)_3(\times\frac{1}{2})$	20,800	......	6.33	−11.7	7.11
UCl_4[i]	......	......	......	−62	3.29
UBr_4[i]	......	......	......	−35	3.12
UBr_3[i]	......	......	......	25	3.29
UCl_3[i]	......	......	......	−29	3.03
UF_4[i]	......	......	1.36	−147	3.30
UI_3[i]	......	......	......	5	3.31
KUF_5[j]	......	......	1.30	−122	3.30
K_2UF_6[j]	......	>198	1.47	−108	3.45
$CaUF_6$[j]	......	......	1.31	−101	3.25
Na_3UF_7[j]	......	......	1.45	−290	3.40
UO_2	2,240	......	1.06	−185	2.92
$U_3O_8(\times\frac{1}{3})$	525	......	0.24	−170	1.39
$U(SO_4)_2$	3,060	......	1.32	−140	3.25
$Yb_2O_3(\times\frac{1}{2})$	6,700	......	2.43	−68	4.40
$Yb_2(SO_4)_3 \cdot 8H_2O(\times\frac{1}{2})$	~8,600	......	2.92	−42	4.83
$ZnCo_2O_4$[c]	1,960	>100	0.62	−20	2.2
$ZnCr_2S_4$[c]	11,800	>100	3.34	+10	5.17

[a] R. Benoit, *Compt. rend.* **231,** 1216 (1950).
[b] C. Henry La Blanchetais, *J. recherches* (*Paris*) (29), 103 (1954).
[c] Private communication from F. K. Lotgering.
[d] A. F. Johnson and H. Grayson-Smith, *Can. J. Research* **28A,** 229 (1950).
[e] N. Elliott, *J. Chem. Phys.* **22,** 1924 (1954).
[f] D. Davidson and L. A. Welo, *J. Phys. Chem.* **32,** 1191 (1928).
[g] W. Klemm and E. Krose, *Z. anorg. Chem.* **253,** 226 (1947).
[h] A. E. Sanchez, *Rev. acad. cienc. exact., fís. y nat. Madrid* **34,** 202 (1940).
[i] J. K. Dawson, *J. Chem. Soc.* (*London*), p. 429 (1951).
[j] N. Elliott, *Phys. Rev.* **76,** 431 (1949).

TABLE 5h-29. DEMAGNETIZING FACTORS, $N/4\pi$, FOR RODS AND ELLIPSOIDS MAGNETIZED PARALLEL TO LONG AXIS

Dimensional ratio (length/diam)	Rod	Prolate ellipsoid	Oblate ellipsoid
0	1.0	1.0	1.0
1	0.27	0.3333	0.3333
2	0.14	0.1735	0.2364
5	0.040	0.0558	0.1248
10	0.0172	0.0203	0.0696
20	0.00617	0.00675	0.0369
50	0.00129	0.00144	0.01472
100	0.00036	0.000430	0.00776
200	0.000090	0.000125	0.00390
500	0.000014	0.0000236	0.001567
1000	0.0000036	0.0000066	0.000784
2000	0.0000009	0.0000019	0.000392

TABLE 5h-30. MAGNETOSTRICTION FORM FACTORS
(See equation for λ_b)

m = length/diam	N	a
1	4.19	0.80
2	2.18	1.07
3	1.37	1.23
4	0.95	1.31
5	0.70	1.38
10	0.255	1.53
15	0.135	1.60
20	0.085	1.63
30	0.043	1.68

where M is the intensity of magnetization, N the demagnetizing factor, k the compression modulus, and G the shear modulus (respectively, 1.6 and 0.8×10^{12} dynes/cm² for iron), and a is $-(1/N)(\partial N/\partial A_{11})$, A_{11} being the principal component of the strain tensor. Values of a have been calculated by Becker and are given in Table 5h-30.

In a cubic crystal[1] magnetized parallel to a cube axis the increase in length caused by the form is

$$\lambda_f = \frac{FM^2}{3(c_{11} - c_{12})}$$

where c_{11} and c_{12} are the elastic constants,

$$F = \frac{3\pi}{2\epsilon^4}\left[(1 - \epsilon^2)(3 + 2\epsilon^2) - \frac{3}{\epsilon}(1 - \epsilon^2)^{\frac{1}{2}} \arcsin \epsilon \right]$$

and the three axes of the ellipsoid are related by

$$a = b = \frac{c}{(1 - \epsilon^2)^{\frac{1}{2}}}$$

[1] W. J. Carr and R. Smoluchowski, *Phys. Rev.* **83**, 1240 (1951).

5i. Electrical Power Practices

K. A. FEGLEY and C. N. WEYGANDT

University of Pennsylvania

5i-1. National Electrical Code. The purpose of the *National Electrical Code* is the safeguarding of persons and of buildings and their contents from electrical hazards arising from the use of electricity. It deals with the installation of electrical wiring and apparatus installed in and around public and private buildings and other premises. The provisions of the code constitute a minimum standard and while adherence to the code will result in a safe installation, it will not necessarily yield a well-designed or efficient system. Many governmental bodies exercising legal jurisdiction over electrical installations have adopted the code as their standard. In some localities local ordinances conflict with the code, so that adherence to the code does not always constitute a legal installation.

The National Electrical Code is revised periodically by the *National Fire Protection Association*,[1] an organization whose purpose is fire prevention. The revised code is submitted to the *American Standards Association* (see Sec. 5i-2) for approval. The code is also adopted by and published by the *National Board of Fire Underwriters*.[2]

National Board of Fire Underwriters.[1] Membership in this organization is limited to fire-insurance companies. It compiles fire-insurance and fire-loss data and establishes standards for fire-protection apparatus and apparatus that may cause fire damage if improperly designed.

Underwriters' Laboratories, Inc.[3] This organization sets standards that are consistent with the National Electrical Code for a large number of electrical products. Manufacturers may submit their products to Underwriters' Laboratories for test. Those products which comply with the standard are listed in the *List of Inspected Electrical Equipment*, a publication of Underwriters' Laboratories. Manufacturers may elect to participate in the *label service* furnished by the laboratories. In this case, a product that complies with the standards is checked through factory inspections and laboratory tests. The manufacturer may attach an Underwriters' Laboratories label to the approved product.

5i-2. Electrical-apparatus Standards. *NEMA Standards.* NEMA, the National Electrical Manufacturers Association, has established voluntary standards that are generally used in the electrical industry. They are designed to promote production economies and assist the users in the proper selection of motors and generators. They set standards of nomenclature, construction, dimensions, operating characteristics, rating, and testing.[4]

[1] National Fire Protection Association, 60 Batterymarch St., Boston, Mass.

[2] National Board of Fire Underwriters, 85 John St., New York; 222 West Adams St., Chicago; Merchants Exchange Building, San Francisco.

[3] Underwriters' Laboratories, Inc., 207 East Ohio St., Chicago; 161 Sixth Ave., New York; 500 Sansome St., San Francisco.

[4] NEMA standards may be obtained by writing to the National Electrical Manufacturers Association, 155 East 44th St., New York.

AIEE Standards. AIEE standards are established by the American Institute of Electrical Engineers and deal with standards of temperature rise, classification of insulating materials, rating methods, and test codes.[1]

ASA Standards. ASA standards are established by the American Standards Association which represents manufacturers, consumers, and others. An American standard implies a consensus of those substantially concerned with its scope. Although the existence of such a standard does not preclude the manufacture of machines that do not conform to ASA standards, most manufacturers adhere to them. ASA defines standards of nomenclature, composition, construction, tolerance, operating characteristics, rating, and testing.[2]

5i-3. A-C and D-C Motors and Generators. *Principles of Motor Operation.* In an electric motor, electrical energy is converted into mechanical energy. This electromechanical energy conversion is possible because a mechanical force is exerted on a current-carrying conductor lying in a magnetic field.

D-C Motors. A steady-magnetic field is obtained by applying a d-c voltage to the coil of wire wound about the stator-pole structure. The rotor-winding conductors

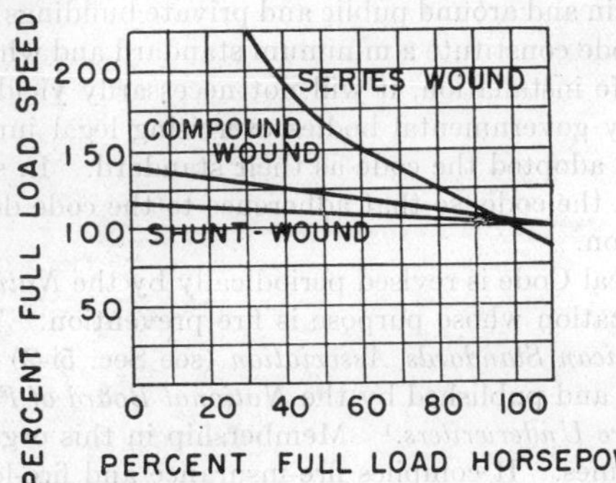

Fig. 5i-1. Per cent full-load horsepower typical characteristic curves for d-c motors.

are connected to copper segments that make up the commutator. Carbon or copper brushes make sliding contact with the commutator and supply the connection between the external electrical source and the rotor winding. The current-carrying rotor conductors lie in the magnetic field set up by the currents in the stator winding and a force is exerted that tends to turn the rotor.

SHUNT-WOUND, CONSTANT SPEED: The stator winding and the rotor winding are placed in parallel. The stator winding consists of a large number of turns of small-sized wire. The current required by the stator winding is small in comparison with the rated current of the rotor winding. This motor is designed to operate at an almost constant speed (Fig. 5i-1).

SHUNT-WOUND, ADJUSTABLE SPEED: This motor is similar to the shunt-wound, constant-speed motor, except that the current in the stator winding may be varied over a relatively wide range to obtain speed control. In fractional-horsepower motors speed control is obtained by varying the armature circuit resistance.

SERIES-WOUND, VARYING SPEED: The stator winding and the rotor winding are placed in series. The stator winding consists of a small number of turns of large-sized wire. Since the current in the stator winding increases with an increased motor load, the air-gap flux and motor speed vary with load (Fig. 5i-1).

[1] AIEE standards may be obtained from the American Institute of Electrical Engineers, 33 West 39th St., New York.

[2] For ASA standards, address requests to the American Standards Association, Inc., 70 East 45th St., New York.

COMPOUND-WOUND, CONSTANT SPEED: The compound-wound motor has two stator windings, one in parallel with the rotor winding and the second in series with the rotor winding. Usually the ampere-turns of the shunt winding greatly exceed those of the series winding, and hence the characteristics (Fig. 5i-1) of this motor are similar to those of the shunt-wound motor.

Polyphase A-C Induction Motor. A polyphase a-c voltage is applied to the stator windings. The current in the stator windings sets up a magnetic field in the air gap

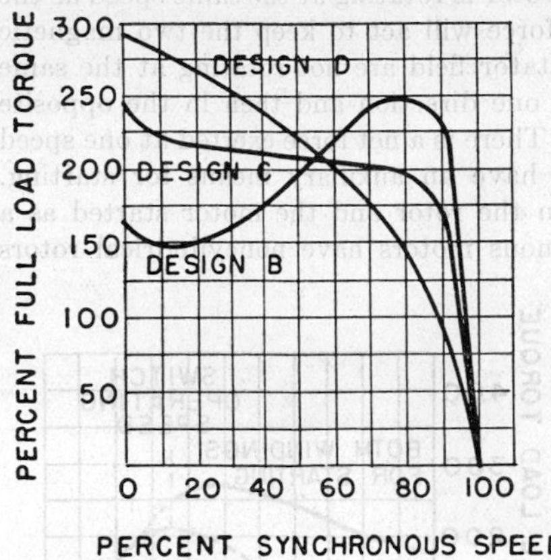

FIG. 5i-2. Typical characteristic curves for squirrel-cage induction motors.

FIG. 5i-3. Typical characteristic curves for the wound-rotor induction motor.

between the stator and rotor. The magnetic field in the air gap rotates around the air-gap periphery at a speed n_s given by the equation

$$n_s = \frac{120\nu}{p}$$

where n_s = synchronous speed
ν = frequency, cps, of the applied voltage
p = number of poles for which stator is wound

The rotor rotates at a lower speed than the revolving magnetic field in the air gap. The rotor conductors are linked, therefore, by a varying magnetic field and a voltage is induced in the rotor conductors. The rotor circuit is either short-circuited or closed through resistors. Since the rotor conductors carry a current and lie in the field of flux set up by the stator-winding currents, a force is exerted that tends to turn the rotor.

SQUIRREL-CAGE ROTOR: Uninsulated copper bars set in slots cut in the magnetic iron rotor laminations form the rotor winding. These bars are short-circuited by copper end rings. In some designs the rotor bars are cast and are not copper. NEMA has established many standards for induction-motor design. Figure 5i-2 shows torque-speed curves for the most used squirrel-cage motors, NEMA designs *B*, *C*, and *D*. The squirrel-cage induction motor operates at an almost constant speed. It generally has the lowest first cost and lowest maintenance costs of all motors.

WOUND ROTOR: The rotor winding is a distributed polyphase winding similar to the stator winding. The ends of the winding are connected to slip rings. Brushes make sliding contact with the slip rings and form the connection between the rotor winding and the external rotor resistance. Torque-speed curves for a typical wound-rotor induction motor are shown in Fig. 5i-3. As the resistance in the rotor circuit is increased, the full-load speed decreases, as does the speed at which maximum torque occurs. The speed control obtained by inserting rotor resistance is at the expense of reduced motor efficiency. Inserting additional resistance in the rotor circuit to start the motor reduces the starting current and makes it possible to obtain maximum torque at motor standstill (see curve R_4 of Fig. 5i-3).

Synchronous Motor. The synchronous motor has a polyphase a-c excited stator winding and a d-c excited rotor winding. A revolving magnetic field is set up in the air gap by the currents in the stator windings. A steady magnetic field is set up by the d-c current in the rotor winding. If the rotor is rotating at the same speed as the rotating field due to the stator currents, a force will act to keep the two magnetic fields lined up. If the rotor field and the stator field are not rotating at the same speed, the mechanical force will act first in one direction and then in the opposite direction, so that the net force will be zero. There is a net force exerted at one speed only, and so the synchronous motor must have an auxiliary means for starting. Usually a squirrel-cage winding is placed on the rotor and the motor started as a polyphase induction motor. Most synchronous motors have noncylindrical rotors

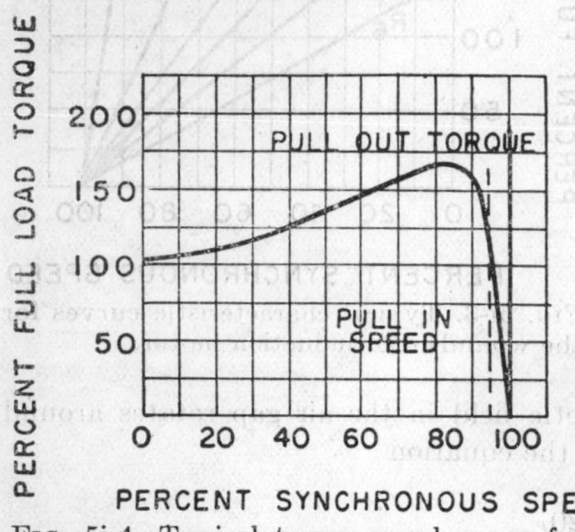

Fig. 5i-4. Typical torque-speed curve for a synchronous motor.

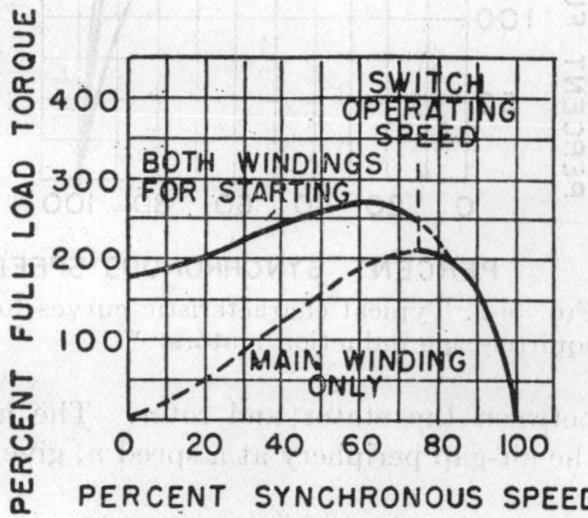

Fig. 5i-5. Typical torque curve for a split-phase motor.

and are called salient-pole machines. A typical torque-speed curve for a synchronous motor is shown in Fig. 5i-4. At speeds below synchronous speed, the torque developed is due to induction-motor action. At approximately 95 per cent of synchronous speed the motor will "pull in" to synchronism. After the motor is synchronized, it will continue to run at synchronous speed if the load torque does not exceed the "pull-out torque." Polyphase synchronous motors are not usually used in sizes below 20 hp. Their first cost is high, and for most constant-speed applications, the almost constant speed of the induction motor is satisfactory. For rating above 50 hp, there may be an economic advantage in using synchronous machines since their efficiency is higher than similarly rated induction motors, and they can be used for power-factor correction.

Single-phase A-C Induction Motor. If a single-phase voltage is applied to one phase winding on the stator of a polyphase motor, the motor will not start since there is no revolving field. If the motor is already running, however, single-phase excitation is sufficient to keep it running. For the single-phase motor, therefore, it is necessary to have some auxiliary means for starting the motor.

SPLIT-PHASE: An auxiliary stator winding is placed in electrical space quadrature with the main winding. This auxiliary winding has a different resistance to reactance ratio from the main winding, so that the currents in the two windings are not in phase. Since the windings are not in space phase and the currents in the windings are not in time phase, a component of the air-gap magnetic field will rotate even when the rotor is stationary, and starting torque is provided. To prevent overheating, the auxiliary winding is disconnected by a centrifugal switch or other means, after the motor is started. Figure 5i-5 shows a typical torque-speed curve for a split-phase motor.

CAPACITOR-START: As in the split-phase motor, an auxiliary winding is placed in quadrature with the main stator winding. A capacitor is placed in the external

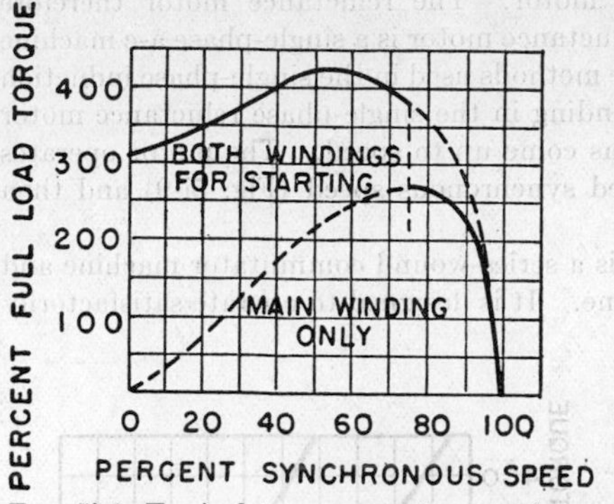

FIG. 5i-6. Typical torque-speed curve for a capacitor-start motor.

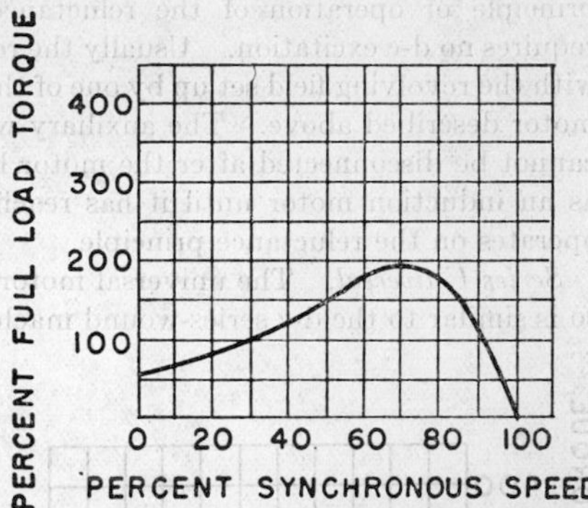

FIG. 5i-7. Typical torque-speed curve for a permanent-split-capacitor motor.

circuit of the auxiliary winding. The current in the auxiliary winding leads the applied voltage. The phase difference between the currents in the main and auxiliary windings can be made approximately 90 deg. The component of the magnetic field that rotates is larger than in the split-phase motor and hence the starting torque is larger. The auxiliary winding is disconnected after the motor has come up to speed.

PERMANENT-SPLIT-CAPACITOR: The auxiliary winding circuit is similar to the auxiliary winding circuit in the capacitor-start motor. The auxiliary winding is not, however, disconnected after the motor has come up to speed. A comparison of Figs. 5i-6 and 5i-7 shows that the permanent-split-capacitor motor has a lower starting torque and lower maximum torque than the capacitor-start motor.

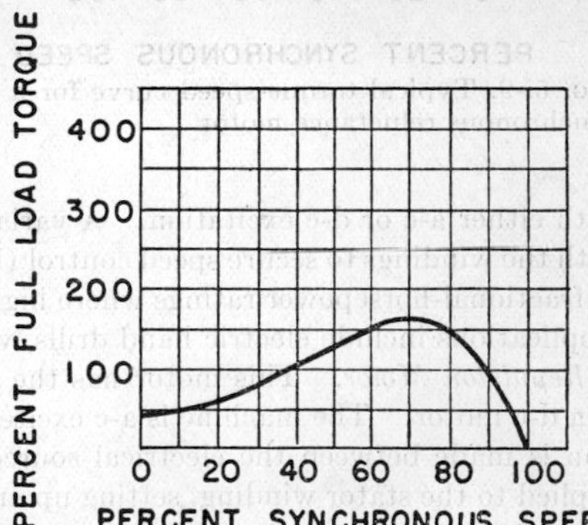

FIG. 5i-8. Typical torque-speed curve for a shaded-pole motor.

SHADED-POLE: A permanently short-circuited auxiliary winding is placed at an electrical angle of 30 to 60 deg from the main winding. This auxiliary winding is called a "shading coil" and is usually an uninsulated copper strap. The voltage induced in the "shading coil" produces a current that is not in phase with the current in the main winding, so that a revolving field, and hence a starting torque (Fig. 5i-8), is produced.

REPULSION-START: This motor operates on the repulsion-motor principle while accelerating. After it has approached normal speed, a centrifugal switch short-circuits the rotor commutator segments. This rotor circuit is then similar to a squirrel-cage rotor and the motor operates as an induction motor. The repulsion-start motor is used in applications where a high starting torque is needed. In recent years, the less expensive capacitor-start motor has largely replaced the repulsion-start motor.

Synchronous Reluctance Motor. If the d-c rotor winding of a salient-pole synchronous machine is disconnected from the d-c supply lines, the motor will continue to run if the load connected to the shaft of the machine is small. A mechanical force tends to bring the salient pole structure into line with the magnetic field. The magnetic field in the air gap is revolving and the pole structure follows. This is the principle of operation of the reluctance motor. The reluctance motor therefore requires no d-c excitation. Usually the reluctance motor is a single-phase a-c machine with the revolving field set up by one of the methods used in the single-phase induction motor described above. The auxiliary winding in the single-phase reluctance motor cannot be disconnected after the motor has come up to speed. The motor operates as an induction motor until it has reached synchronous speed (Fig. 5i-9) and then operates on the reluctance principle.

Series Universal. The universal motor is a series-wound commutator machine and so is similar to the d-c series-wound machine. It is designed to operate satisfactorily

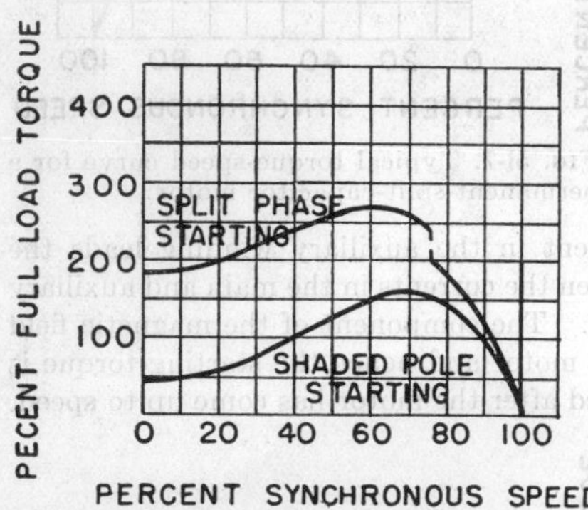

FIG. 5i-9. Typical torque-speed curve for a synchronous reluctance motor.

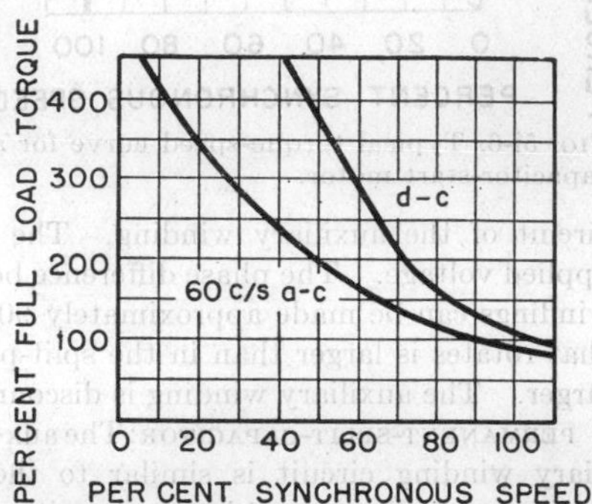

FIG. 5i-10. Typical torque-speed curve for a series universal motor.

with either a-c or d-c excitation. A variable resistance is frequently placed in series with the windings to secure speed control (Fig. 5i-10). Universal motors are employed in fractional-horsepower ratings where high speeds and/or variable speeds are needed. Applications include electric hand drills, vacuum cleaners, and food mixers.

Repulsion Motor. This motor has the commutator and distributed rotor winding of a d-c motor. The machine is a-c excited, however, and no direct electrical connection is made between the electrical source and the rotor circuit. An a-c voltage is applied to the stator winding, setting up an alternating field in the air gap. This field links the rotor winding and induces a voltage which causes a current in the rotor circuit. The brushes which make sliding contact with the commutator are short-circuited together. The operating characteristics of this motor are similar to those of the universal motor.

5i-4. Motor Selection. The following factors should be considered in selecting a motor:

1. Power supply available. The motor must be selected to match the power supply if the expense of purchasing a motor-generator set or other conversion equipment is to be avoided. Determine these characteristics of the power supply: (*a*) a-c or d-c, (*b*) voltage, (*c*) number of phases if it is an a-c supply, and (*d*) frequency if it is an a-c supply. Tables 5i-1 and 5i-2 indicate what power supply is required for motors.

2. Horsepower required. One of the following methods may be used to determine the horsepower required.

a. If the required torque is known, the horsepower required may be found by applying the equation

$$\text{hp} = \frac{\text{torque (ft-lb)} \times \text{speed of shaft (rpm)}}{5{,}250}$$

b. Connect a larger motor than the one needed to the machine to be driven. Use a wattmeter to determine the power input to the driving motor. The required horsepower is then

$$\text{hp} = \frac{\text{(wattmeter reading)} \times \text{(approx efficiency of driving motor)}}{746}$$

c. Ask the manufacturer of the machine to be driven what horsepower is required.

If the driven load imposes intermittent overloads on the driving motor, the motor must be able to handle these overloads.

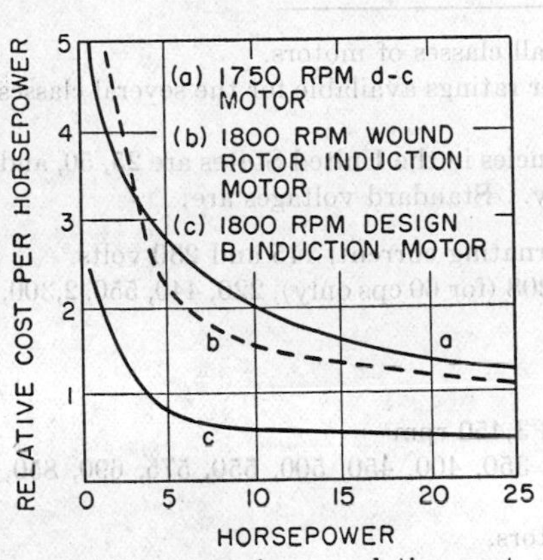

FIG. 5i-11. Approximate relative cost of several types of motors.

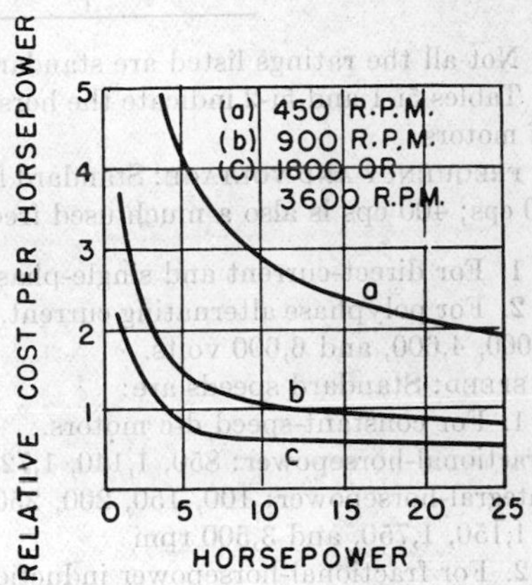

FIG. 5i-12. Approximate relative cost of design *B* induction motors at several speeds.

3. Torque requirements. The torque required to start and accelerate the load may exceed the torque needed to drive the load. This high starting torque is required for compressors, reciprocating pumps, and conveyors. In other applications, such as fans, centrifugal pumps, and many machine tools, the torque required at full load exceeds the starting torque. If the load torque fluctuates, the maximum torque the motor can develop must exceed the maximum load torque. Refer to Tables 5i-1 and 5i-2.

4. Speed requirements. Determine whether a constant-speed or adjustable-speed motor is needed. If an adjustable speed is required, what speed range is needed? If a constant speed, what is its value? Is it necessary to reverse the motor?

For a given horsepower, the size of the motor decreases as the speed is increased. The cost of the motor (Figs. 5i-11 and 5i-12) is largely dependent upon the size, and hence a saving usually results from using a high-speed motor. Above 3,600 rpm, however, the costs may increase with speed. A belt connection between the motor and load may permit the use of a high-speed motor to drive a load at low speed. A cost and space saving may be effected by using a motor with a built-in gearbox.

5. Selection of motor enclosure. The following motor enclosures are available: (*a*) open; (*b*) dripproof; (*c*) splashproof; (*d*) totally enclosed nonventilated; (*e*) totally enclosed, fan-cooled; (*f*) explosionproof; and (*g*) waterproof. The open motor has the lowest cost and is used where unusual surroundings do not require a more expensive enclosure.

6. Starting current. The large starting currents of some motors cause light flicker.

For this reason, many power companies set limits on the allowable starting current. See Table 5i-2 for the approximate starting current of integral-horsepower motors.

7. Capacity of power line. Refer to Table 5i-3 for the normal full-load motor current. Table 5i-4 gives the current-carrying capacity of conductors.

Standard Ratings. HORSEPOWER: The following horsepower ratings are standard:

0.001	$\frac{1}{20}$	1	15	100
0.0015	$\frac{1}{20}$	$1\frac{1}{2}$	20	125
0.002	$\frac{1}{8}$	2	25	150
0.003	$\frac{1}{6}$	3	30	200
0.005	$\frac{1}{4}$	5	40	
0.0075	$\frac{1}{3}$	$7\frac{1}{2}$	50	
0.01		10		

Not all the ratings listed are standard for all classes of motors.

Tables 5i-1 and 5i-2 indicate the horsepower ratings available for the several classes of motors.

FREQUENCY AND VOLTAGE: Standard frequencies in the United States are 25, 50, and 60 cps; 400 cps is also a much used frequency. Standard voltages are:

1. For direct-current and single-phase alternating current, 115 and 230 volts.

2. For polyphase alternating current, 110, 208 (for 60 cps only), 220, 440, 550, 2,300, 4,000, 4,600, and 6,600 volts.

SPEED: Standard speeds are:

1. For constant-speed d-c motors.

Fractional-horsepower: 850, 1,140, 1,725, and 3,450 rpm

Integral-horsepower: 100, 150, 200, 250, 300, 350, 400, 450, 500, 550, 575, 690, 850, 1,150, 1,750, and 3,500 rpm

2. For fractional-horsepower induction motors.

All motors except shaded-pole and permanent-split capacitor:

At 60 cps, 850, 1,140, 1,725, and 3,450 rpm
At 50 cps, 950, 1,425, and 2,850 rpm
At 25 cps, 1,425 rpm

Shaded-pole motor:

At 60 cps, 800, 1,050, 1,550, and 3,000 rpm
At 50 cps, 875, 1,300, and 2,500 rpm
At 25 cps, 1,300 rpm

Permanent-split capacitor motor:

At 60 cps, 825, 1,075, 1,625, and 3,250 rpm
At 50 cps, 900, 1,350, and 2,700 rpm
At 25 cps, 1,350 rpm

3. For integral-horsepower induction motors. (The speeds given below are rated synchronous speeds. The motors operate at a speed slightly below synchronous speed.)

Single-phase motors:

At 60 cps, 900, 1,200, 1,800, and 3,600 rpm
At 50 cps, 750, 1,000, 1,500, and 3,000 rpm
At 25 cps, 750 and 1,500 rpm

Polyphase motors:

At 60 cps, 450, 514, 600, 720, 900, 1,200, 1,800, and 3,600 rpm
At 50 cps, 750, 1,000, 1,500, and 3,000 rpm
At 25 cps, 500 and 750 rpm

The speeds listed do not apply to all horsepower ratings.

TABLE 5i-1. FRACTIONAL-HORSEPOWER MOTOR CHARACTERISTICS

Type of motor	Hp range	Speed data: Rated speed (for 60 cps a-c or d-c only)	Speed data: Speed characteristics	Speed control	Rated voltage	Torque (% of full load): Starting	Torque (% of full load): Max	Reversible	Radio interference	Approx price comparison, %	Application
A-C:											
Single phase:											
Shaded pole....	0.001–$\frac{1}{20}$	800, 1,050, 1,550, 3,000	Almost constant	None	115	30–50	Less than 175	No	No	...	Used for low-starting-torque loads. Typical applications include desk fans, phonograph turntables, and toys
Split phase.....	$\frac{1}{20}$–$\frac{1}{3}$	850, 1,140, 1,725, 3,450	Almost constant	None	115, 230	90–275	185–300	Yes, change connections	No	100	For applications with low- or medium-starting-torque loads, such as washing machines, light machine tools, oil burners, ironers, office appliances
Capacitor start..	$\frac{1}{6}$–$\frac{3}{4}$	850, 1,140, 1,725, 3,450	Almost constant	None	115, 230	250–425	225–500	Yes, change connections	No	125	A high-starting-torque motor, used for refrigerators, air conditioning, conveyors, compressors
Permanent-split capacitor	$\frac{1}{20}$–$\frac{3}{4}$	825, 1,075, 1,625, 3,250	Almost constant	None	115, 230	50–100	150–225	Yes, change connections	No	140	A medium-starting-torque motor. Used for fans blowers, tool grinders
Synchronous....	0.001–$\frac{1}{3}$	900, 1,200, 1,800, 3,600 and many speeds below 900	Absolutely constant	None	115	50–250	175–225	Yes, change connections	No	400	For applications where a constant speed is needed, such as timing devices, indicating instruments, testing equipment for speedometers, teleprinters, facsimile printers
Polyphase, squirrel cage	$\frac{1}{6}$–$\frac{3}{4}$	850, 1,140, 1,725, 3,450	Almost constant	None	110, 208, 220, 440	200–350	200–350	Yes, change connections	No	175	For practically all applications where a polyphase supply is available. Characteristics are similar to those of the capacitor-start motor
D-C, shunt wound...	$\frac{1}{20}$–$\frac{3}{4}$	850, 1,140, 1,725, 3,450	Almost constant	Field resistance	115, 230	Above 400%	....	Yes, change connections	Yes	200	For practically all applications where a d-c supply is available. May be used where an adjustable speed is required
			Varies with load	Armature resistance							
A-C or d-c, series universal	$\frac{1}{20}$–$\frac{3}{4}$	1,500–12,000	Varies with load	Resistance	115, 230	Above 400%	....	Yes, change connections	Yes	150	Used where a high-speed motor is required, such as vacuum cleaners, electric typewriters, electric drills. Speed may be adjusted, making it useful for sewing machines and food mixers

TABLE 5i-2. INTEGRAL-HORSEPOWER

Type of motor	Hp range	Rated speed	Speed characteristic	Full load speed, % of synchronous speed	Speed control	Rated voltage
A-C:						
Polyphase induction motors:						
NEMA design *A*	½-200	450, 514, 600, 720, 900, 1,200, 1,800, 3,600	Almost constant	95-97	None	208, 220, 440, 550, 2,300
NEMA design *B*	½-200	450, 514, 600, 720, 900, 1,200, 1,800, 3,600	Almost constant	95-97	None	208, 220, 440, 550, 2,300
NEMA design *C*	3-150	600, 720, 900, 1,200, 1,800, 3,600	Almost constant	95-97	None	208, 220, 440, 550, 2,300
NEMA design *D*	½-125	720, 900, 1,200, 1,800, 3,600	Almost constant	87-95	None	208, 220, 440, 550
Wound-rotor	½-200	450, 514, 600, 720, 900, 1,200, 1,800, 3,600	Adjustable	Adjustable	Rotor-circuit resistance	208, 220, 440, 550, 2,300
Polyphase synchronous	20-20,000	100-3,600	Absolutely constant	100	None	208, 220, 440, 550, 2,300
D-C:						
Shunt-wound	½-200	100-3,600	Adjustable	....	Shunt-field resistance or armature voltage	115, 230, 550
Compound wound	½-200	100-3,600	Adjustable	....	Shunt-field resistance or armature voltage	115, 230, 550
Series-wound	½-200	100-3,600	Adjustable, varies with load	....	Armature voltage	115, 230, 550

5i-5. Motor Control and Protection. *Starting D-C Motors.* Small d-c motors may be started by directly connecting them to the supply line. For motors rated 2 hp or above, resistance should be inserted in series with the armature winding to limit the current. As the motor accelerates, the armature-circuit starting resistance is shorted out in a series of steps. In order to prevent overspeeding of the motor, full line voltage should be applied to the shunt-field winding of shunt-wound and compound-wound motors during starting.

Starting A-C Motors. Fractional-horsepower motors, both single-phase and polyphase, are usually started by applying full line voltage to their terminals.

Polyphase Induction Motors. SQUIRREL-CAGE: Many polyphase induction motors are started with full line voltage. For many other applications, however, the large

MOTOR CHARACTERISTICS

Torque, % of full load: Starting	Torque, % of full load: Max	Starting current, % of full load current	Revers-ible	Radio inter-ference	Approx price compari-son, %	Application
105-275	200-300	500-100	Yes	No	100	Produces average starting torque and high max torque. The starting current is very high, however, so that this machine is becoming obsolete, being superseded by design *B* motors
105-275	200-300	500-550	Yes	No	100	Develops average starting torque and high max torque at relatively low starting current. Applications include fans, pumps, compressors, conveyors, machine tools. This is the most-used integral-horsepower motor
200-225	190-225	500-550	Yes	No	105	Develops high starting torque at low starting current. Used for hard-to-start loads such as conveyors, compressors, escalators, reciprocating pumps, and crushers
250-315	Same as starting torque	300-800	Yes	No	110	Has a high starting torque. Max torque occurs at rotor standstill. Used for high-inertia loads such as hoists, elevators, punch presses, and centrifuges.
100-300	200-300	150-1,000 depending on rotor-circuit resistance	Yes	Slight	225	Develops a high starting torque at low starting current when the external rotor resistance is properly adjusted. Speed can be adjusted by means of rotor-circuit resistance. Used for blowers, fans, pumps, conveyors, and crushers
20-200	140-200	300-1,000	Yes	Slight	350	Used on constant-speed applications and for power-factor correction. Polyphase synchronous motors are seldom used in sizes below 50 hp
High, should be limited to 200 by starting resistance	Should be limited to 200	Should be limited to 200 by starting resistance	Yes	Yes	275	Used for drives where the required starting torque is not high. A constant-speed or an adjustable-speed motor may be used. Applications include wood- and metalworking machines, elevators, blowers, centrifugal pumps, and conveyors
High, should be limited to 300 by starting resistance	Should be limited to 300	Should be limited to 200 by starting resistance	Yes	Yes	275	Used for machines requiring a high starting torque and fairly constant speed. Pulsating loads such as shears, bending rolls, plunger pumps, conveyors, and crushers frequently have compound-wound d-c motors as drives
Very high, should be limited to 350 by starting resistance	Should be limited to 350	Should be limited to 200 by starting resistance	Yes	Yes	275	Used as drives where very high starting torque is required and the load is always coupled to the motor. Applications include cranes, hoists, gates, bridges, railways, and streetcars

starting current required for a full-voltage start is prohibitive, and a starting compensator must be employed. This compensator may be (1) resistance inserted in series with each stator phase or (2) an autotransformer connected between the supply lines and the motor. The resistance usually has a lower first cost but it reduces the starting torque and line current in the same ratio while with the autotransformer the per cent decrease in line current at motor standstill is greater than the per cent decrease in starting torque. The autotransformer losses are smaller than the losses in the starting resistance.

WOUND-ROTOR: Starting compensators are sometimes used in the stator circuits of wound-rotor induction motors. In addition, the resistance in the rotor circuit is usually increased during starting. This increase in rotor-circuit resistance decreases

TABLE 5i-3. AVERAGE FULL-LOAD CURRENTS OF MOTORS
(From 1953 National Electrical Code; values of full-load current are approximate and typical only for motors running at usual speeds; low-speed motors may have larger full-load currents)

Motor rating, hp	Full-load current, amp							
	D-C motors		Single-phases motors		Three-phase induction motors, squirrel-cage and wound rotor			
	115 volts	230 volts	115 volts	230 volts	110 volts	220 volts	440 volts	550 volts
$\frac{1}{6}$	....	...	3.2	1.6				
$\frac{1}{4}$	...	...	4.6	2.3				
$\frac{1}{2}$	4.6	2.3	7.4	3.7	4	2	1	0.8
$\frac{3}{4}$	6.6	3.3	10.2	5.1	5.6	2.8	1.4	1.1
1	8.6	4.3	13	6.5	7	3.5	1.8	1.4
$1\frac{1}{2}$	12.6	6.3	18.4	9.2	10	5	2.5	2.0
2	16.4	8.2	24	12	13	6.5	3.3	2.6
3	24	12	34	17	....	9	4.5	4
5	40	20	56	28	....	15	7.5	6
$7\frac{1}{2}$	58	29	80	40	....	22	11	9
10	76	38	100	50	....	27	14	11
15	112	56	.....	....	....	40	20	16
20	148	74	.....	....	....	52	26	21
25	184	92	.....	....	....	64	32	26

the starting current, and if not too much resistance is added, it also increases the starting torque (see Fig. 5i-3).

Polyphase Synchronous Motors. Since synchronous motors require both a-c and d-c supplies, the starting procedure is more complex than for the induction motor. Automatic controls that permit "push-button" starting are usually employed.

Motor Controllers. A motor controller is any device used to start and stop a motor. It may also incorporate overload protection, short-circuit protection, and a device to regulate the motor speed.

Manual Starters. The manual starter for small motors may be nothing more than a snap-action switch. Starters for large induction motors may contain a resistance or autotransformer compensator. Those designed for large d-c motors will have a resistance that is inserted into the armature circuit.

Magnetic Starters. Magnetic starters perform the same function as manual starters but have the advantage of operating automatically after the operator pushes the "start" or "stop" button which can be remotely located.

Combination Starters. Manual and magnetic starters usually include overload protection. A combination starter has short-circuit protection in addition to overload protection. It may be either a magnetic or manual starter.

Motor and Motor-circuit Overload Protection. The National Electrical Code sets minimum standards for the protection of motors and motor circuits against overloads. This protection is achieved by the use of thermal cutouts, circuit breakers, or fuses.

The thermal cutout may consist of a heating coil surrounding a bimetallic strip

TABLE 5i-4. ALLOWABLE CURRENT-CARRYING CAPACITIES OF INSULATED CONDUCTORS*
(In amperes; based on room temperature of 30°C, 86°F)

Wire size, Awg	Type R, RW, RUW, T, TW		Type RH		Type TA, V, AVB		Type AVA, AVL		Type AI, AIA		Type A, AA	
	a	*b*	*a*	*b*	*a*	*b*	*a*	*b*	*a*	*b*	*a*	*b*
14	15	20	15	20	25	30	30	40	30	40	30	45
12	20	25	20	25	30	40	35	50	40	50	40	55
10	30	40	30	40	40	55	45	65	50	70	55	75
8	40	55	45	65	50	70	60	85	65	90	70	100
6	55	80	65	95	70	100	80	120	85	125	95	100
4	70	105	85	125	90	135	105	160	115	170	120	130
3	80	120	100	145	105	155	120	180	130	195	145	150
2	95	140	115	170	120	180	135	210	145	225	165	175
1	110	165	130	195	140	210	160	245	170	265	190	205
0	125	195	150	230	155	245	190	285	200	305	225	325
00	145	225	175	265	185	285	215	330	230	355	250	370
000	165	260	200	310	210	330	245	385	265	410	285	430
0000	195	300	230	360	235	385	275	445	310	475	340	510

Special Provisions	*Type Insulation*
General use	R, RW, RUW, T, TW, RH
Wet locations	RW, RUW, TW, AVL
Dry locations only (not general use)	V, AVA, AVB, A, AA, AI, AIA
Switchboard wiring only	TA

For aluminum conductors, the allowable current-carrying capacities shall be taken as 84 per cent of those given in the table for the respective sizes of copper conductors with the same kind of insulation.
Columns *a*. Not more than three conductors in raceway or cable.
Columns *b*. Single conductor in free air.
* See Table 5g-4 for additional data and explanation of insulation-type letters.

which bends on heating. The heater coil carries the line current. If the current is too large, the heat from the heater coil causes the bimetallic to bend and open the circuit. Another type of thermal cutout utilizes a fusible link.

Circuit breakers of the thermal-trip or magnetic-trip type may be used both for protection and as a switch.

Renewable or nonrenewable cartridge fuses, plug- or S-type fuses are much used for motor and motor-circuit protection. The plug fuse has an Edison base. The S-type fuse can be used in an ordinary plug-fuse socket with an adapter added. The holders for cartridge-type and S-type fuses prevent the insertion of fuses of the wrong rating.

For a motor with a continuous rating of more than 1 hp, an overcurrent device set to not more than 125 per cent of the motor full-load current should be used for protection. The conductors supplying this motor should have a current-carrying capacity of not less than 125 per cent of full-load motor current. Tables 5i-3 and 5i-4 give the full-load current of motors and the current-carrying capacity of conductors. Refer to the National Electrical Code for the rating of protective devices to be used with fractional-horsepower motors and motors with short-time ratings.

5i-6. Principles of Generator Operation. Electrical energy is supplied to a motor and mechanical energy withdrawn. In a generator mechanical energy is supplied and electrical energy withdrawn. This is the essential difference between motor and generator operation.

D-C Generator. The d-c generator is practically identical in construction to the d-c motor. The large majority of d-c generators are compound-wound (see Fig. 5i-13). Cumulative compounding, with the series field and shunt fields aiding, is usual. Shunt-wound generators are suitable for applications where the loading is constant and series-wound generators are used for booster sets and welding. There is less voltage drop with increased load with a separately excited, shunt-wound generator than with a self-excited, shunt-wound generator. The cumulative compound generator can be designed to have an almost constant terminal voltage for the normal range of load currents. The terminal voltage in all but the series generator can be controlled by varying the resistance in the shunt-field circuit.

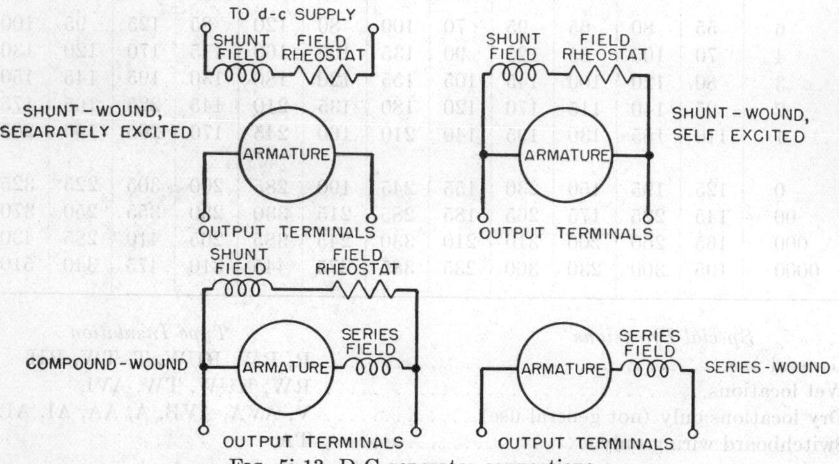

FIG. 5i-13. D-C generator connections.

A-C Generator. The polyphase a-c generator and the synchronous motor are essentially the same in construction. A cylindrical or salient-pole rotor carries a winding that is d-c excited. This pole structure sets up an air-gap field that induces an a-c voltage in the stator windings as the poles rotate. In the single-phase a-c generator, the stator has a single-phase winding instead of the three space-displaced windings of the three-phase generator. The frequency of the voltage induced in the stator windings for both single-phase and polyphase machines is

$$\nu = \frac{pn}{120}$$

where ν = frequency, cps
n = rotor speed, rpm
p = number of poles

5i-7. Transformers. *Principles of Operation.* A transformer is an electrical device, without continuously moving parts, which by electromagnetic induction transforms a-c electric energy from one circuit to another circuit at the same frequency, usually with changed values of voltage and current. Transformers usually have two or more insulated windings wrapped about a laminated-iron core. In some cases, however, the iron core is not present, and the coils are linked magnetically through an air path.

The winding connected to the energy source is called the *primary* winding and the winding from which the energy is withdrawn is called the *secondary* winding. *High-voltage winding* and *low-voltage winding* are terms used to designate the windings according to their voltage ratings.

Consider the operation of a two-winding transformer when an a-c voltage is applied to the primary winding and the secondary winding is open. Current in the primary winding causes a time-varying flux to be set up in the iron core of the transformer. This time-varying flux will induce a voltage in both the primary and secondary windings of the transformer. The magnitude of the voltage induced in the primary winding is approximately equal to the applied voltage, since the voltage drop due to the winding resistance is small. The induced primary voltage opposes the applied voltage and hence limits the current. The voltage induced in the secondary winding is the same per turn as that induced in the primary, so that the ratio of primary voltage to secondary voltage is the same as the ratio of the number of turns in the

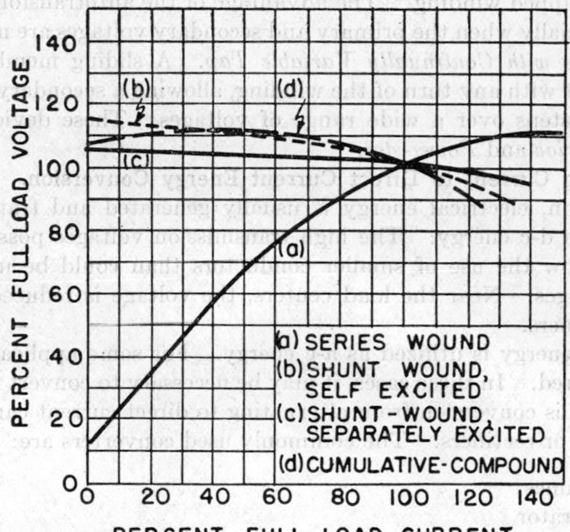

FIG. 5i-14. D-C generator characteristics.

transformer windings. When a load is connected to the secondary winding, a current will flow. The secondary current causes a magnetomotive force that opposes the magnetomotive force of the primary current. In order to have the same net magnetomotive force to set up the same flux in the core of the transformer that was present at no load, it is necessary for the primary current to increase over its no-load value. Except for the small no-load component of current, the ratio of the primary to secondary current is the same as the ratio of the number of secondary turns to the number of primary turns.

Small transformers have an efficiency of perhaps 90 per cent. Large power transformers have efficiencies of over 99 per cent. The losses are due to the resistance of the windings, hysteresis, and eddy currents in the iron core.

Transformer Cooling. The volt-ampere rating of a transformer is determined largely by the allowable temperature rise. Transformers with a rating of 1 kva or less are usually of the *dry type.* Larger transformers may be *oil-immersed* with plain or corrugated tank, a tank with radiators, or a tank with water-cooling coils immersed in the oil.

Instrument Transformers. Instrument transformers are classified as (1) *voltage* or *potential transformers* and (2) *current transformers.* Where a-c currents of more than 100 amp or a-c voltages of more than 500 volts are to be measured, instrument transformers and low-range instruments are usually employed.

Instrument transformers also serve to insulate a high-voltage primary winding from the low-voltage secondary, and thus protect personnel reading the instruments from the danger of high-voltage electric shock.

Two-winding Transformers. As the name implies, these transformers have only two windings. By suitable connection of three single-phase (two-winding) transformers, two three-phase circuits can be tied together.

Polyphase Transformers. A three-phase transformer usually has six insulated windings, three primaries and three secondaries all on the same core structure. It occupies less space and weighs less than three single-phase transformers that have the same total rating.

Autotransformers. A single-phase autotransformer has a single winding. The primary winding and the secondary winding are not electrically insulated but are both part of the same tapped winding. The advantage of the autotransformer is its small physical size, especially when the primary and secondary voltages are nearly the same.

Autotransformers with Continually Variable Tap. A sliding member is provided that makes contact with any turn of the winding, allowing a secondary voltage that is variable in small steps over a wide range of voltages. These devices carry trade names such as *Variac* and *Power-stat.*

5i-8. Alternating Current to Direct Current Energy Conversion. To reduce the cost of transmission, electrical energy is usually generated and transmitted as a-c energy rather than d-c energy. The high transmission voltages possible with alternating current allow the use of smaller conductors than could be used with lower transmission voltages. Near the load centers, the voltage is reduced to utilization levels by transformers.

Most electrical energy is utilized as a-c energy. For some applications, however, d-c energy is required. In these cases, it may be necessary to convert from a-c energy to d-c energy. This conversion from alternating to direct current can be made with rotating machines or rectifiers. The commonly used converters are:

A. Rotating machines
- 1. Motor generator
- 2. Rotary converter

B. Rectifiers
- 1. Electronic
  - *a.* Thermionic cathode, vacuum diode
  - *b.* Thermionic cathode, gas diode
  - *c.* Thermionic cathode, gas triode (thyratron)
  - *d.* Mercury-arc, with pool cathode (mercury-arc and ignitron)
  - *e.* Crystal diode
- 2. Metallic-plate
  - *a.* Selenium
  - *b.* Copper oxide
- 3. Mechanical

Rotating Machines. MOTOR GENERATOR: A d-c generator driven by a single-phase or polyphase induction motor or a synchronous motor provides one means of converting a-c energy to d-c energy. One feature of motor-generator sets that is important in some applications is the electrical isulation it gives between the a-c system and the d-c system. Other advantages are the small amount of a-c ripple voltage generated, the ease with which the d-c voltage can be varied, and the small voltage variation with a change in load current. The motor-generator set is, however, relatively expensive in first cost and relatively low in efficiency. It weighs more and requires more floor space than other devices of the same power rating.

TABLE 5i-5. TRANSFORMER CONNECTIONS
(This table illustrates only a few of many possible connections)

Type	Connection diagram	Phasor diagram of voltages	Application
Single-phase, two-winding, three-wire secondary	b, d, o, a, c	V_{ab}, V_{cd}, V_{co}, V_{od}	This single-phase transformer with center-tapped secondary is used in low-voltage distribution circuits. A secondary voltage of 120 volts to center tap is suitable for lighting circuits and 240 volts between outside lines for electric ranges, etc.
Autotransformer	b, d, a, c	V_{ab}, V_{cd}	Autotransformers may reduce transformer costs in applications where the primary-to-secondary turns ratio is near unity and electrical isulation of the primary and secondary is not required
Autotransformer with variable tap	b, d, a, c	V_{ab}, V'_{cd}, V_{cd}	For ratings of a few watts to several kilowatts, these conveniently provide a continuously variable a-c voltage
Delta-delta	a, a', c, b, c', b'	V_{ca}, V_{ab}, V_{bc}, $V_{c'a'}$, $V_{a'b'}$, $V_{b'c'}$	This three-phase connection can be used for three single-phase transformers or a three-phase transformer. It is especially suitable for heavy currents at low voltages and will operate with one winding open
Wye-wye	a, d, o, o', c, b, b'	V_{ca}, o, V_{bc}, V_{ab}, $V_{c'a'}$, o', $V_{b'c'}$, $V_{a'b'}$	Usually operated with one or both of the neutrals, *o* and *o'*, grounded. The voltage between lines is $\sqrt{3}$ times the line-to-line voltage
Delta-wye	a, c', a', o', c, b, b'	V_{ca}, V_{ab}, V_{bc}, $V_{c'a'}$, $V_{b'c'}$, $V_{a'b'}$	Commonly used with the neutral grounded at the generator end of transmission lines and in secondary distribution systems where there are both lighting and three-phase machine loads
Scott or T	a, o, a', o', c, b, b'	V_{ab}, V_{bo}, o, V_{oc}, $V_{o'a'}$, o', $V_{o'b'}$	For conversion from two-phase to three-phase or vice versa. Turn ratio from *ao* to *a'o'* $= 1/2\sqrt{3} \times$ turn ratio for *cb* to *o'b'*. Other connections allow conversion from three-phase to six- or twelve-phase

TABLE 5i-6. A-C TO D-C APPLICATION CHART

Device	Max current*	Max voltage*	Power range	Application
Rotating machines:				
Motor-generator set	ma to thousands of amp	A few volts to several thousand volts	A few watts to hundreds of kw	For most applications, other devices are more economical. Used where a-c and d-c systems must be completely isolated, where very little a-c ripple voltage can be tolerated or where good voltage regulation and control are needed
Rotary converter	ma to thousands of amp	A few volts to several thousand volts	A few watts to hundreds of kw	Most used in electric railways. In recent years it has been replaced in many applications by the mercury-arc rectifier. Has higher efficiency than motor generator
Rectifiers:				
Electronic				
Thermionic cathode, vacuum diode	ma to over 5.5 amp†	To over 200,000 volts	Usually only a few watts. Up to several kw	For voltages above 400 volts at currents up to several hundred ma. Where very high voltages are needed, X-ray and electrostatic precipitation
Thermionic cathode, gas diode	ma to over 50 amp†	To over 20,000 volts	A few watts to several kw	Battery chargers, radio transmitters and receivers, dielectric and induction heaters, etc. For moderate current and voltage requirements
Thermionic cathode, gas triode (thyratron)	ma to over 15 amp†	To over 10,000 volts	A few watts to several kw	Used where a variable d-c voltage is required, such as an electronically controlled d-c motor
Mercury arc with pool cathode (mercury arc and ignitron)	Up to thousands of amp	To over 20,000 volts	About 50 kw to over 3,000 kw	Electrochemical plants and electric railways. Not suitable for voltages below 200 volts. Voltage control is possible with ignitrons
Metallic plate				
Selenium Copper oxide	ma to above 10,000 amp	To over 75 kv	mw to 100 kw	Radio receivers, battery chargers, and small electronic devices. Not much used above 200 volts
Mechanical	Thousands of amp	To over 1,000 volts	Several hundred to several thousand kw	For applications requiring large amounts of d-c energy, such as electrochemical plants

* The maximum current and maximum voltage values given are mutually exclusive. A high-voltage tube is usually a low-current tube and vice versa.

† Maximum current for a single tube. In a rectifier utilizing several tubes, the rectifier current rating may be higher.

ROTARY CONVERTER: The rotary converter is an a-c motor and d-c generator with a single magnetic circuit. The machine has a d-c excited field winding on the stator and a distributed winding on the rotor. The rotor winding is connected to slip rings at one end of the rotor and to commutator bars at the other. Thus a-c voltage is applied to the same winding from which the d-c voltage is obtained. For this reason the ratio of the d-c voltage available to the a-c voltage applied is fixed. The rotary converter and its auxiliary equipment usually have a lower first cost and higher efficiency than a motor-generator set of similar rating.

Rectifiers. Both electronic and metallic-plate rectifiers have a nonlinear characteristic, allowing electron flow in one direction and blocking the flow of electrons in the opposite direction. The mechanical rectifier is a set of switches operated by a synchronous motor, opening and closing in such a manner that electrons can flow to a load circuit in one direction only.

THERMIONIC CATHODE, VACUUM DIODE: This tube has two elements, the cathode and the anode, enclosed in an evacuated shell. On heating, the cathode emits electrons which are attracted to the anode when the anode is at a higher potential than the cathode. Since the anode does not emit electrons in any quantity, the tube acts as a rectifier, allowing an electron flow in only one direction. Vacuum diodes have been designed that can withstand a negative anode voltage of over 200,000 volts. Tubes designed for high voltages have large spacing between the cathode and anode, which causes a high tube resistance and hence a large voltage drop across the tube at full load current. Tubes operating at lower voltages have smaller spacing and a correspondingly smaller tube resistance. Under normal operating conditions, the tube current is limited by a negative space charge caused by the electrons collecting around the cathode and producing a negative potential near the cathode that tends to drive emitted electrons back toward the cathode

THERMIONIC CATHODE, GAS DIODE: These tubes contain an inert gas or mercury which vaporizes when the cathode is heated. Upon application of a positive potential to the anode, the moving electrons will ionize the gas, leaving the heavy and slow-moving ions in the space between the tube electrodes. These positive ions neutralize the negative space charge that is present in vacuum diodes. With the space charge neutralized, the tube current is limited only by the emitting capacity of the cathode. The voltage drop between the tube electrodes is approximately the ionization potential of the gas. The gas diode has a higher efficiency than the vacuum diode and so is much used in low-voltage applications such as radio receivers. While gas diodes are available that will withstand voltages above 20,000 volts, most designs do not permit voltages above a few hundred volts. To prevent cathode disintegration in gas tubes, it is necessary to heat the cathode to normal operating temperature before applying anode voltage. The tube current should be limited to a safe value by placing resistance in the anode circuit.

THERMIONIC CATHODE, GAS TRIODE (THYRATRON): The thyratron has a grid placed between the anode and the cathode. By applying a negative voltage, with respect to the cathode, to the grid, tube conduction may be prevented. If the negative grid voltage is reduced toward zero sufficiently when the plate is at a positive voltage, the tube will conduct. Once the tube conducts, the grid cannot stop conduction. Increasing the negative voltage on the grid causes more positive ions to collect around the negative grid, preventing the negative voltage from becoming an effective barrier between the cathode and the anode. The cathode-to-anode electron flow can be stopped only by reducing the anode voltage to less than the gas-ionization voltage. Since the anode voltage goes to a negative value during every cycle of the a-c voltage, the grid regains control every cycle. By using the grid to control the period during each cycle that the tube may conduct, d-c output voltage control can be obtained in thyratron rectifiers.

MERCURY ARC, WITH POOL CATHODE (MERCURY ARC AND IGNITRON): Mercury-arc tubes have a pool of mercury for a cathode and source of electrons. Once the arc has been initiated, the supply of electrons is almost unlimited so that the current must be held to a safe value by the impedance in the tube circuit. Many of these tubes are water-cooled. Mercury-arc tubes may have several anodes and a single pool cathode. In this case it is necessary that the arc be maintained continuously after it has started. The arc is initiated by lifting a rod that completes an auxiliary circuit from the mercury pool. The ignitron has a single anode and an igniter rod that permits initiation

TABLE 5i-7. RECTIFIER CIRCUITS

Circuit name	Circuit diagram	Load voltage wave shape (for resistance load)	Application
Single-phase, half-wave	E_s Load	E_s One cycle	Used in low-power applications. The large a-c ripple voltage makes this circuit unsuitable for most applications unless a filter is added. Used mostly for vacuum and gas-diode rectifiers
Single-phase, full-wave, center tap	E_s Load	E_s One cycle	Much used in low-power-tube rectifiers. Used without filtering for battery chargers, etc. Used with filtering for radio receivers, radio transmitters, audio-amplifiers, etc.
Single-phase, full-wave, bridge	E_s Load	E_s One cycle	Most common for single-phase metallic rectifiers. It has the same field of application as the single-phase, full-wave, center-tap circuit
Three-phase, half-wave, star	E_s Load	E_s One cycle	This circuit is seldom used but is the simplest of several three-phase circuits. The output voltage is more nearly constant and the ripple frequency higher than in single-phase circuits

TABLE 5i-7. RECTIFIER CIRCUITS—(*Continued*)

Circuit name	Circuit diagram	Load voltage wave shape (for resistance load)	Application
Three phase, full-wave, bridge	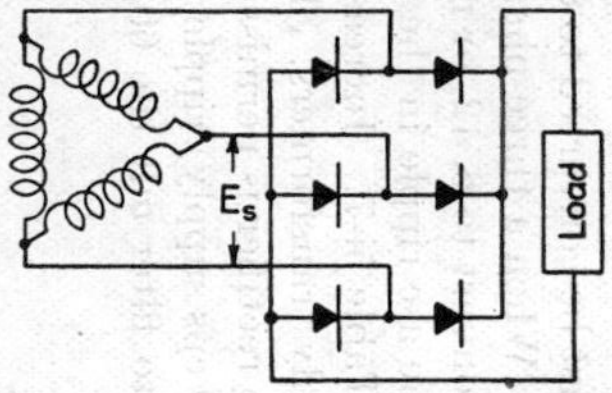	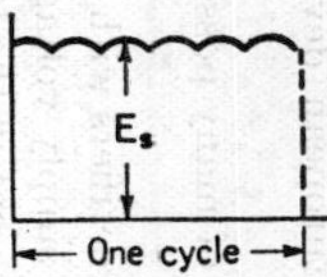	Used in high-power metallic-plate rectifiers. The almost constant output voltage (approximately 4% ripple voltage) makes this circuit suitable for many applications without filtering. The high ripple voltage frequency (360 cps ripple for 60 cps supply) makes filtering less expensive than for single-phase circuits
Six-phase, half-wave, star	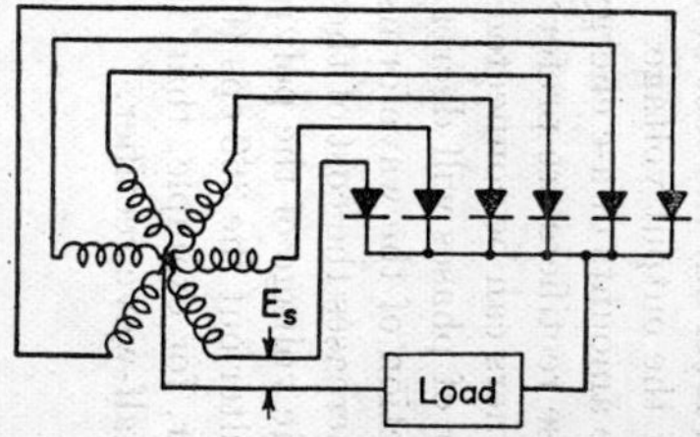	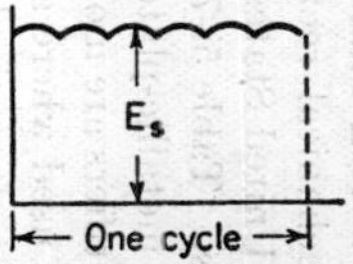	This seldom-used circuit illustrates one of many possible six-phase connections. Other six-phase circuits overcome some of the disadvantages of this star connection; 6, 12, and 24 phase connections are used only in high-power applications

of the arc each cycle. The rod is permanently dipped into the mercury pool and a pulse of current through this circuit initiates the arc. In rectifiers utilizing ignitrons, the output voltage can be controlled by varying the time when the arc is initiated with respect to the anode voltage. Mercury-arc tubes of the multianode and ignitron types are used only when large amounts of d-c energy are required.

SELENIUM: Each selenium rectifier cell consists of a metal disk to which a thin layer of selenium had been applied. The selenium is sprayed with an alloy coating. Current will flow freely through the cell from the metal disk to the alloy coating but with difficulty in the opposite direction. Selenium cells are stacked in series to obtain a rectifier with the desired voltage rating. Several stacks can be operated in parallel for increased current ratings. Large fins are sometimes attached to the disks to aid in cooling the stack, and forced-air cooling or oil-immersion cooling may be used. Selenium rectifiers are now used in ratings from a few milliwatts to many kilowatts.

COPPER OXIDE: The application of copper-oxide rectifiers is the same as that of selenium rectifiers. Copper-oxide cells are formed by coating cuprous oxide (Cu_2O) on a copper disk at a high temperature. The cell will pass current freely from oxide to copper but presents a high resistance to current flow in the opposite direction.

MECHANICAL RECTIFIERS: Mechanical rectifiers are used only where very large amounts of d-c power are required. A synchronous motor drives a set of switches that connect the d-c load circuit to each of the several a-c phases in such a way that the current flows to the load circuit in only one direction. The absence of a voltage drop across the closed switch makes this rectifier more efficient than the mercury-arc rectifier. The mechanical rectifier is a European development and is now being introduced in the United States.

Rectifier Circuits. Table 5i-7 lists a few of many possible circuits that are used for electron-tube and metallic-plate rectifiers.

Single-phase rectifiers are most used for rectifiers with an output rating of less than 1 kw and must be used where a polyphase supply voltage is not available. Because of the large amount of a-c ripple voltage present in the load voltage, it is often necessary to filter out the a-c component by the use of inductors and capacitors. In some applications gas-filled tubes are used to maintain an output voltage that is free of ripple. Many commercial power supplies (a-c to d-c converters) utilize single-phase rectifiers, filters, and voltage-regulating devices. The a-c ripple voltage can be held to any desired level but the cost of the power supply increases with a reduction of the a-c content of the output voltage.

Where large amounts of a-c energy must be converted to direct current by rectification, polyphase rectifiers are preferred. When a three-phase supply voltage is available, transformers can be connected to convert to 6, 12, or more phases. An increase in the number of phases will decrease the a-c ripple in the output voltage, as can be seen by inspection of the waveforms of Table 5i-7. Increasing the number of phases above three increases the cost of the supply transformers. For many applications the small a-c ripple voltage of the polyphase rectifier is permissible. If it is not, it is less expensive to filter out the 360 cps (for 60 cps supply) ripple voltage of the three-phase bridge rectifier, for example, than it is to filter out the 60 cps ripple voltage of the single-phase half-wave rectifier.

Bibliography

Electrical Engineering Handbooks

1. Knowlton, Archer E., ed.: "Standard Handbook for Electrical Engineers," 8th ed., McGraw-Hill Book Company, Inc., New York, 1949.
2. Pender, Harold, and W. A. DelMar, ed.: "Electrical Engineers Handbook," vol. I, Electric Power, 4th ed., John Wiley & Sons, Inc., New York, 1949.

National Electrical Code

3. Abbott, Arthur Laurie, and Charles L. Smith: "National Electrical Code Handbook," 8th ed., McGraw-Hill Book Company, Inc., New York, 1954.
4. National Board of Fire Underwriters: "National Electrical Code," N.B.F.U., New York.
5. Segall, B. Z.: "Electrical Code Diagrams," vols. I, II, McGraw-Hill Book Company, Inc., New York, 1954.

Motor and Generator Theory, Application, and Control

Books

6. Bottle, E. K.: "Fractional Horse-power Electric Motors: Guide to Types and Application," Charles Griffin & Co., Ltd., London, 1948.
7. Fitzgerald, A. E., and Charles Kingsley, Jr.: "Electric Machinery," McGraw-Hill Book Company, Inc., New York, 1952.
8. Harwood, Paisley Beach: "Control of Electric Motors," 3d ed., John Wiley & Sons, Inc., New York, 1952.
9. Heumann, Gerhart W.: "Magnetic Control of Industrial Motors," 2d ed., John Wiley & Sons, Inc., New York, 1954.
10. James, Henry Duvall, and Lewis Edwin Markle: "Controllers for Electric Motors," 2d ed., McGraw-Hill Book Company, Inc., New York, 1952.
11. Johnson, Theron Crawford, D. R. Shoults, and C. J. Rife: "Electric Motors in Industry," John Wiley & Sons, Inc., New York, 1942.
12. Jones, Richard W.: "Electric Control Systems," 3d ed., John Wiley & Sons, Inc., New York, 1953.
13. Liwschitz-Garik, Michael, and Clyde C. Whipple: "Electric Machinery," vols. I, II, D. Van Nostrand Company, Inc., Princeton, N. J., 1946.
14. Philpott, Stuart Fred: "Fractional Horse Power Motors," Chapman & Hall, Ltd., London, 1951.
15. Puchstein, Albert Frederick, Thomas Cox Lloyd, and A. G. Conrad: "Alternating-current Machines," 3d ed., John Wiley & Sons, Inc., New York, 1954.
16. Tarboux, Joseph Galluchat: "Alternating-current Machinery," International Textbook Company, Scranton, Pa., 1947.
17. Veinott, Cyril George: "Fractional Horsepower Electric Motors," 2d ed., McGraw-Hill Book Company, Inc., New York, 1948.

Articles

18. Butler, F.: Motor Control Devices, *Elec. Rev.* **144** (3734), 1029–1031 (June 17, 1949).
19. Carville, T. E. M.: Application of Small Motors, *Westinghouse Engr.* **9**, 52–57 (March, 1949).
20. Chandler, A. E.: Adjustable Speed D-C Motor Drives, *Elec. News and Engineering* **60** (8), 63–66 (Apr. 15, 1951).
21. Dyer, L. W.: New Controls for Industry, *Westinghouse Engr.* **9** (5), 159–160 (September, 1949).
22. Everett, R. R.: Special versus Standard Fractional Horsepower Motor, *Product Eng.* **21** (10), 111–114 (October, 1950).
23. Hough, W. R.: Standards as Applied to Motors, *Elec. Eng.* **67** (10), 69–71 (October, 1948).
24. Lebens, J. C.: Dual-element Fuses for Motor Protection, *Elec. Mfg.* **48** (3), 98–102 (September, 1951).
25. Lindsten, M. C.: Which Fractional-Horsepower Motor?, *Machine Design* **21** (6), 127–129 (June, 1949).
26. Matthias, L.: Thermal Overcurrent Relays for Motor Protection, *Electrical Mfg.* **48** (6), 114–118 (December, 1951).
27. Picking, J. W.: Development of Low-cost Electronic Drive in $\frac{3}{4}$ to 3 hp Ratings, *Elec. Mfg.* **48** (3), 124–127 (September, 1951).
28. Winston, J.: Choice of D-C Motors, *Product Eng.* **22** (7), 125–130 (July, 1951).

Rectifier Theory and Application

Books

29. Henisch, H.: "Metal Rectifiers," Oxford University Press, New York, 1949.
30. MIT Department of Electrical Engineering: "Applied Electronics," John Wiley & Sons, Inc., New York, 1943.
31. Terman, Frederick Emmons: "Radio Engineers' Handbook," McGraw-Hill Book Company, Inc., New York, 1943.
32. Westinghouse Electric Corp.: "Industrial Electronics Reference Book," John Wiley & Sons, Inc., New York, 1948.

Articles

33. Falls, W. H.: Selenium and Copper Oxide Rectifiers, *Gen. Elec. Rev.* **50** (2), 34–38 (February, 1947).
34. Jensen, O.: A Mechanical Rectifier, *Trans. Electrochem. Soc.* **90,** 93–103 (1946).
35. Thwaites, J. T.: Electronic Rectification, *Elec. News and Engineering* **57** (18), 115–117 (Sept. 15, 1948).
36. Wilcox, R. H.: Mechanical Rectifier . . . Efficient Source of D-C Power, *Mill & Factory* **49** (5), 86–88 (November, 1951).
37. Yarmack, J. E.: Selenium Rectifiers and Their Design, *Trans. Am. Inst. Elec. Engrs.* **61,** 488–495 (1942).

Transformer Theory and Application Books

38. Blume, Louis Frederick: "Transformer Engineering," 2d ed., John Wiley & Sons, Inc., New York, 1951.
39. Connelly, Frank Cecil: "Transformers," Pitman Publishing Corporation, New York, 1950.
40. Dunlap, Carl Harry, W. A. Diefert, and F. E. Austin: "Transformer Principles and Applications," American Technical Society, Chicago, 1947.
41. Gibbs, Jesse Berthold: "Transformer Principles and Practice," 2d ed., McGraw-Hill Book Company, Inc., New York, 1950.
42. MIT Department of Electrical Engineering: "Magnetic Circuits and Transformers," John Wiley & Sons, Inc., New York, 1943.

5j. Electrochemical Information

T. F. YOUNG

University of Chicago

Editor's note. The symbols used in electrochemistry do not always conform with those given in Sec. 5a which do follow the recommendations of the American Standards Association, ASA Z10.6-1948 and ASA Z10.5-1949. The user of electrochemical data may wish to refer to the electrochemical references. Therefore, some of the symbols used in this section are those most commonly found in the literature of this subject.

Conductance data and transference numbers were taken from Harned and Owen (1950), Kortum and Bockris (1951), and Robinson and Stokes (1955). Additional data may be found in these three books and in Conway (1952), Kohlrausch (1898), "International Critical Tables," and Landolt-Börnstein.

Diffusion coefficients were taken from Harned (1953), Robinson and Stokes (1955), and from recent scientific papers. Some more data may be found in these sources. Additional information may be derived from tables of polarographic data compiled by Koltoff and Lingane (1952) and by von Stackelberg (1950).

Standard electromotive forces of half cells were taken from Latimer (1952). Many additional data are available in his tables. Note especially the table on page 345 for alkaline solutions. Other values of E^{o} may be calculated from the free-energy data of Rossini et al. (1952).

Activity coefficients were selected from extensive tables in Harned and Owen (1950), Kortum and Bockris (1951), and Robinson and Stokes (1955). Additional data may be found in these sources and in Robinson and Stokes (1949) and in Conway (1952).

Dissociation constants are from Harned and Owen (1950) and Hood, Redlich, and Reilly (1954). Constants for many other equilibria may be found in Harned and Owen (1950), Redlich (1946), "International Critical Tables," Scudder (1914), and may be derived from thermodynamic data of Rossini et al. (1952) and of Latimer (1952).

The molal heat content (enthalpy) data were taken from Harned and Owen (1950).

Standard entropies of ions were taken from Latimer (1952) and from Powell and Latimer (1951). Additional values may be found in those sources and in Robinson and Stokes (1955) and in Kortum and Bockris (1951).

Electrochemical data of many other kinds have been tabulated by Robinson and Stokes (1955), Harned and Owen (1950), and Kortum and Bockris (1951). Information especially useful for the electrometric determination of pH has been assembled by Bates (1954). Polarographic data have been collected by Kolthoff and Lingane (1952) and by von Stackelberg (1950).

The large general tables of Landolt-Börnstein and the "International Critical Tables" also contain a wide variety of electrochemical information.

Notes on Abbreviations, Symbols, and Terminology Used in Table 5j-6 and in the Discussion Which Follows.

The letters (g), (l), (s), and (aq) denote *gas, liquid, solid,* and *aqueous solution,* respectively. These symbols are often omitted for substances which are in their most familiar states.

Pt. Many authors writing symbols for electrodes include the symbol "Pt" whenever no solid conducting element appears elsewhere in the formulation of the electrode. Its purpose is to remind the reader that some connection (not necessarily platinum) to the external portion of the circuit must be provided. The symbol is not essential and has been omitted in Table 5j-6.

Cathode and *Anode.* The words *cathode* and *anode* are not essential for a discussion of electrochemical cells. They are not used in the explanation which follows. Because some writers use the words frequently their meanings must be understood. At the cathode reduction occurs; at the anode oxidation occurs. In the external portion of the circuit electrons flow from anode to cathode, whereas the "positive current" is said to flow in the external conductor from cathode to anode. Within the cell the "positive current" flows from anode to cathode, thus completing the circuit. The current within the cell consists of both positive ions moving from anode to cathode and negative ions moving from cathode to anode. Note that in an electrochemical cell operating spontaneously the anode is the negative pole and the cathode is the positive pole. For a somewhat more detailed discussion of the words, see Daniels and Alberty (1955).

E denotes the electromotive force (emf) of a cell or half cell.

E^{o} denotes the standard emf defined below.

ΔF denotes the increase in Gibbs free energy for the reaction specified.

ΔF^{o} denotes the standard increase in free energy. It is related to E^{o} by an equation similar to Eq. (5j-1).

TABLE 5j-1. EQUIVALENT CONDUCTANCES AND CATION TRANSFERENCE NUMBERS OF ELECTROLYTES IN AQUEOUS SOLUTIONS AT 25°C
(Λ in cm² ohm⁻¹ equivalent⁻¹; N in equivalent liter⁻¹)

	N	0	0.001	0.01	0.02	0.05	0.1
HCl	Λ	426.16	421.36	412.00	407.24	399.09	391.32
	t_+	0.8209	......	0.8251	0.8266	0.8292	0.8314
LiCl	Λ	115.03	112.40	107.32	104.65	100.11	95.86
	t_+	0.3364		0.3289	0.3261	0.3211	0.3168
NaCl	Λ	126.45	123.74	118.51	115.76	111.06	106.74
	t_+	0.3963		0.3918	0.3902	0.3876	0.3854
KCl	Λ	149.86	146.95	141.27	138.34	133.37	128.96
	t_+	0.4906	......	0.4902	0.4901	0.4899	0.4898
NH_4Cl	Λ	149.7	......	141.28	138.33	133.29	128.75
	t_+	0.4909		0.4907	0.4906	0.4905	0.4907
KBr	Λ	151.9	......	143.43	140.48	135.68	131.39
	t_+	0.4849	......	0.4833	0.4832	0.4831	0.4833
NaI	Λ	126.94	124.25	119.24	116.70	112.79	108.78
KI	Λ	150.38	......	142.18	139.45	134.97	131.11
	t_+	0.4892	......	0.4884	0.4883	0.4882	0.4883
KNO_3	Λ	144.96	141.84	132.82	132.41	126.31	120.40
	t_+	0.5072		0.5084	0.5087	0.5093	0.5103
$KHCO_3$	Λ	118.00	115.34	110.08	107.22		
$NaO_2C_2H_3$	Λ	91.0	88.5	83.76	81.24	76.92	72.80
	t_+	0.5507	......	0.5537	0.5550	0.5573	0.5594
$NaO_2C(CH_3)_2CH_3$	Λ	82.70	80.31	75.76	73.39	69.32	65.27
NaOH	Λ	247.8	244.7	238.0			
$AgNO_3$	Λ	133.36	130.51	124.76	121.41	115.24	109.14
	t_+	0.4643		0.4648	0.4652	0.4664	0.4682
$\frac{1}{2}MgCl_2$	Λ	129.40	124.11	114.55	110.04	103.08	97.10
$\frac{1}{2}CaCl_2$	Λ	135.84	130.36	120.36	115.65	108.47	102.46
	t_+	0.4380		0.4264	0.4220	0.4140	0.4060
$\frac{1}{2}SrCl_2$	Λ	135.80	130.33	120.29	115.54	108.25	102.19
$\frac{1}{2}BaCl_2$	Λ	139.98	134.34	123.94	119.09	111.48	105.19
$\frac{1}{2}Na_2SO_4$	Λ	129.9	124.15	112.44	106.78	97.75	89.98
	t_+	0.386	......	0.3848	0.3836	0.3829	0.3828
$\frac{1}{2}CuSO_4$	Λ	133.6	115.26	83.12	72.20	59.05	50.58
$\frac{1}{2}ZnSO_4$	Λ	132.8	115.53	84.91	74.24	61.20	52.64
$\frac{1}{3}LaCl_3$	Λ	145.8	137.0	121.8	115.3	106.2	99.1
	t_+	0.477	......	0.4625	0.4576	0.4482	0.4375
$\frac{1}{3}K_3Fe(CN)_6$	Λ	174.5	163.1				
$\frac{1}{4}K_4Fe(CN)_6$	Λ	184.5	167.24	134.83	122.82	107.70	97.87

TABLE 5j-2. LIMITING EQUIVALENT CONDUCTANCES OF IONS IN WATER IN INFINITELY DILUTE SOLUTION

($cm^2\ ohm^{-1}\ equivalent^{-1}$)

Ion	°C	Λ_0	Ion	°C	Λ_0
H^+	15	300.6	OH^-	25	197.6
	25	349.8	Cl^-	15	61.42
	35	397.0		25	76.34
Li^+	25	38.69		35	92.21
Na^+	15	39.75	Br^-	15	63.3
	25	50.11		25	78.3
	35	61.53		35	94.2
K^+	15	59.66	I^-	25	76.8
	25	73.50	NO_3^-	25	71.4
	35	88.21	ClO_4^-	25	68.0
NH_4^+	25	73.4	HCO_3^-	25	44.5
Ag^+	25	61.92	$CH_3CO_2^-$	25	40.9
Tl^+	25	74.7	$ClCH_2CO_2^-$	25	39.8
$\frac{1}{2}$ Mg^{++}	25	53.06	$CH_3CH_2CO_2^-$	25	35.8
$\frac{1}{2}$ Ca^{++}	25	59.50	$CH_3(CH_2)_2CO_2^-$	25	32.6
$\frac{1}{2}$ Sr^{++}	25	59.46	$C_6H_5CO_2^-$	25	32.3
$\frac{1}{2}$ Ba^{++}	25	63.64	$HC_2O_4^-$	25	40.2
$\frac{1}{2}$ Cu^{++}	25	54	$\frac{1}{2}$ $C_2O_4^=$	25	74.2
$\frac{1}{2}$ Zn^{++}	25	53	$\frac{1}{2}$ $SO_4^=$	25	80
$\frac{1}{3}$ La^{3+}	25	69.5	$\frac{1}{3}$ $Fe(CN)_6^3$	25	101
$\frac{1}{3}$ $Co(NH_3)_6^{3+}$	25	102	$\frac{1}{4}$ $Fe(CN)_6^{4-}$	25	111

TABLE 5j-3. LIMITING EQUIVALENT CONDUCTANCES OF IONS IN METHANOL AND ETHANOL

($ohm^{-1}\ cm^2\ equivalent^{-1}$)

	Methanol		Ethanol	
	25°C	4°C	25°C	4°C
H^+	141.8	113.2	57.40	37.24
Li^+			15.00	9.62
K^+	53.6	39.35		
Cl^-	51.27	37.12	24.30	16.01
ClO_4^-	70.1	52.85	33.55	22.40
NO_3^-	60.5	45.2		

N denotes the number of Faradays (F) of electricity. N may have any positive value. For simplicity it is arbitrarily chosen as unity for all of Table 5j-6 and for each example of its use.

Significance of Table 5j-6 *and Conventions.* When current passes through a reversible electrolytic cell oxidation occurs at one electrode and reduction at the other. When the direction of the current is reversed the chemical reaction is reversed and oxidation and reduction exchange places. While no current is passing through the cell a reversible emf may be measured with a potentiometer. Electromotive

TABLE 5j-4. LIMITING VALUES OF DIFFERENTIAL DIFFUSION COEFFICIENTS IN H_2O AT 25° IN INFINITELY DILUTE SOLUTION

	$D \times 10^5$ cm² sec⁻¹		$D \times 10^5$ cm² sec⁻¹		$D \times 10^5$ cm² sec⁻¹
LiCl	1.368	$AgNO_3$	1.768	$SrCl_2$	1.336
NaCl	1.612	Li_2SO_4	1.041	$MgSO_4$	0.849
KCl	1.996	Na_2SO_4	1.230	$ZnSO_4$	0.849
RbCl	2.057	Cs_2SO_4	1.569	$LaCl_3$	1.294
KNO_3	1.931	$CaCl_2$	1.336	$K_4Fe(CN)_6$	1.473

TABLE 5j-5. DIFFERENTIAL DIFFUSION COEFFICIENTS OF POTASSIUM CHLORIDE AT 4°C AND 25°C

M mole liter⁻¹	$D \times 10^5$ at 4°C cm² sec⁻¹	$D \times 10^5$ at 25°C cm² sec⁻¹
0.000	(1.135)	(1.996)
0.0004	1.125	1.974
0.0016	1.115	1.957
0.01	1.091	1.915
0.04	1.063	1.870
0.25	1.036	1.836
1.00	.....	1.893
4.00	.....	2.207

forces of cells are important thermodynamic data since

$$\Delta F = -NFE \tag{5j-1}$$

It is conventional to associate ΔF with the reaction which occurs when N Faradays, i.e., *ca.* N 96,500 coulombs, of positive electricity is passed through the cell from left to right. It is conventional to write E as positive if this current flows spontaneously from left to right through the cell, i.e., if electrons are caused by the cell reaction to move in the external part of the circuit from left to right. According to this convention E of the cell is positive if the right-hand electrode is positive with respect to the left-hand electrode. If the cell is rewritten in the reverse order the algebraic sign of its emf is changed. [The negative sign in Eq. (5j-1) is a consequence of these two conventions.] Examples:

$$H_2,\ HCl\ (aq),\ Cl_2 \qquad E^o = 1.3595 \text{ volt at } 25°C \tag{5j-2}$$

$$Cl_2,\ HCl\ (aq),\ H_2 \qquad E^o = -1.3595 \text{ volt at } 25°C \tag{5j-3}$$

In these equations the symbol ^{o} (read "standard") indicates that all the cell reactants and products are in their standard states, i.e., each is at unit activity. Actually there are no criteria for the decision that the activity of any single ion (a_+ of H^+ or a_- of Cl^-, in this example) is unity. The emf of the cell is completely determined, however, by a product of ion activities; in this example by

$$a_+a_- = a_2 \tag{5j-4}$$

The activity a_2 of the solute, e.g., HCl, can be measured and is known for many electrolytes as functions of their concentration.

The emf of a cell may be regarded as the net result of two opposing half-cell reactions, one at each electrode. Each of these two half reactions may be thought of as having a tendency to liberate electrons or each may be considered to possess a tendency to consume electrons. The half reaction having the greater tendency to acquire electrons forces the other half reaction to surrender them, or according to the alternative point of view, the half reaction having the greater tendency to liberate electrons forces the other to accept them. These two points of view are designated below as plan *A* and plan *B*, respectively. Either plan is quite correct and general. Example: Consider the cell of Eq. (5j-2), H_2, HCl (aq), Cl_2. At the left-hand electrode the half reaction, for $N = 1$, may be considered to be either (*a*) or (*b*); thus

$$\begin{array}{ll} \text{Plan } A & \text{Plan } B \\ \tfrac{1}{2}\,H_2 \rightarrow H^+ + \ominus \quad (a) & \ominus + H^+ \rightarrow \tfrac{1}{2}\,H_2 \quad (b) \end{array} \qquad (5j\text{-}5a,\ 5b)$$

The opposing half-cell reaction (at the other electrode) is written

$$Cl^- \rightarrow \tfrac{1}{2}\,Cl_2 + \ominus \quad (c) \qquad \ominus + \tfrac{1}{2}\,Cl_2 \rightarrow Cl^- \quad (d) \qquad (5j\text{-}5c,\ 5d)$$

Since E^o of cell (2) is positive it is obvious that half reaction (*c*) has less tendency to proceed than half reaction (*a*), and that (*d*) has more tendency to proceed than (*b*). The difference in each case is 1.3595 volts.

Similarly the cell

$$Tl,\ TlCl\ (aq),\ Cl_2\ (g) \qquad E^o = 1.6958 \text{ volts} \qquad (5j\text{-}6)$$

involves two opposing half reactions which are

$$\begin{array}{ll} \text{Plan } A & \text{Plan } B \\ Tl \rightarrow Tl^+ + \ominus \quad (e) & \ominus + Tl^+ \rightarrow Tl \quad (f) \end{array} \qquad (5j\text{-}6e,\ 6f)$$

and

$$Cl^- \rightarrow \tfrac{1}{2}\,Cl_2 + \ominus \quad (c) \qquad \ominus + \tfrac{1}{2}\,Cl_2 \rightarrow Cl^- \quad (d) \qquad (5j\text{-}5c,\ 5d)$$

Since E^o of the cell is 1.6958 volts, the tendency of (*e*) is 1.6958 *greater* than that of (*c*) and the tendency of (*f*) is 1.6958 volts *less* than that of (*d*). To simplify the tabulation of relative half-cell emfs it has long been the custom to compare all reactions to (*a*) in plan *A* or to (*b*) in plan *B*. In the same sense that the altitude of sea level is arbitrarily set equal to zero the half-cell emfs of (*a*) and (*b*) are called zero and the emfs of all other half cells are listed relatively to (*a*) or to (*b*) depending upon the "plan" used by an author. Since the tendency of (*e*) is 1.6958 volts greater than that of (*c*) which, in turn, is 1.3595 volts less than that of (*a*), the appropriate entries for the table are, respectively,

$$\begin{array}{ll} \text{Plan } A & \text{Plan } B \\ Tl \rightarrow Tl^+ + \ominus \quad E^o = 0.3363 \text{ volt} & \ominus + Tl^+ \rightarrow Tl \quad E^o = -0.3363 \text{ volt} \end{array} \qquad (5j\text{-}6e,\ 6f)$$

Both plan *A* and plan *B* emfs are listed here because each plan corresponds rather closely to a set of conventions followed more or less closely by a large fraction of the scientists of the world. The conventions have not always been adopted in full. Some authors who use column (1) may omit either (2) or (3) [since (2) implies (3) and (3) implies (2)]. Similarly other authors use (6) and omit either (4) or (5). There is no objection to such conciseness if the material is addressed to an adequately informed audience. Unfortunately, some authors have mixed plan *A* and plan *B*. Some of them have done so consistently and logically, but confusion has nevertheless resulted when a reader of one book or table attempted to use another. To avoid confusion the Commission on Physicochemical Symbols and Terminology and the

TABLE 5j-6. STANDARD ELECTROMOTIVE FORCES OF HALF CELLS IN WATER AT 25°C
($E°$ in absolute volts relative to the standard hydrogen electrode)

Plan A			Plan B		
$E°$ (1)	Electrode (2)	Half-cell reaction (3)	Half-cell reaction (4)	Electrode (5)	$E°$ electrode potential (6)
3.045	Li, Li^+	$Li \rightarrow Li^+ + \ominus$	$\ominus + Li^+ \rightarrow Li$	Li^+, Li	−3.045
2.925	K, K^+	$K \rightarrow K^+ + \ominus$	$\ominus + K^+ \rightarrow K$	K^+, K	−2.925
2.925	Rb, Rb^+	$Rb \rightarrow Rb^+ + \ominus$	$\ominus + Rb^+ \rightarrow Rb$	Rb^+, Rb	−2.925
2.90	Ba, Ba^{++}	$\frac{1}{2}Ba \rightarrow \frac{1}{2}Ba^{++} + \ominus$	$\ominus + \frac{1}{2}Ba^{++} \rightarrow \frac{1}{2}Ba$	Ba^{++}, Ba	−2.90
2.89	Sr, Sr^{++}	$\frac{1}{2}Sr \rightarrow \frac{1}{2}Sr^{++} + \ominus$	$\ominus + \frac{1}{2}Sr^{++} \rightarrow \frac{1}{2}Sr$	Sr^{++}, Sr	−2.89
2.87	Ca, Ca^{++}	$\frac{1}{2}Ca \rightarrow \frac{1}{2}Ca^{++} + \ominus$	$\ominus + \frac{1}{2}Ca^{++} \rightarrow \frac{1}{2}Ca$	Ca^{++}, Ca	−2.87
2.714	Na, Na^+	$Na \rightarrow Na^+ + \ominus$	$\ominus + Na^+ \rightarrow Na$	Na^+, Na	−2.714
2.37	Mg, Mg^{++}	$\frac{1}{2}Mg \rightarrow \frac{1}{2}Mg^{++} + \ominus$	$\ominus + \frac{1}{2}Mg^{++} \rightarrow \frac{1}{2}Mg$	Mg^{++}, Mg	−2.37
2.32	Am, Am^{3+}	$\frac{1}{3}Am \rightarrow \frac{1}{3}Am^{3+} + \ominus$	$\ominus + \frac{1}{3}Am^{3+} \rightarrow \frac{1}{3}Am$	Am^{3+}, Am	−2.32
2.07	Pu, Pu^{3+}	$\frac{1}{3}Pu \rightarrow \frac{1}{3}Pu^{3+} + \ominus$	$\ominus + \frac{1}{3}Pu^{3+} \rightarrow \frac{1}{3}Pu$	Pu^{3+}, Pu	−2.07
1.90	Th, Th^{4+}	$\frac{1}{4}Th \rightarrow \frac{1}{4}Th^{4+} + \ominus$	$\ominus + \frac{1}{4}Th^{4+} \rightarrow \frac{1}{4}Th$	Th^{4+}, Th	−1.90
1.86	Np, Np^{3+}	$\frac{1}{3}Np \rightarrow \frac{1}{3}Np^{3+} + \ominus$	$\ominus + \frac{1}{3}Np^{3+} \rightarrow \frac{1}{3}Np$	Np^{3+}, Np	−1.86
1.85	Be, Be^{++}	$\frac{1}{2}Be \rightarrow \frac{1}{2}Be^{++} + \ominus$	$\ominus + \frac{1}{2}Be^{++} \rightarrow \frac{1}{2}Be$	Be^{++}, Be	−1.85
1.80	U, U^{3+}	$\frac{1}{3}U \rightarrow \frac{1}{3}U^{3+} + \ominus$	$\ominus + \frac{1}{3}U^{3+} \rightarrow \frac{1}{3}U$	U^{3+}, U	−1.80
1.66	Al, Al^{3+}	$\frac{1}{3}Al \rightarrow \frac{1}{3}Al^{3+} + \ominus$	$\ominus + \frac{1}{3}Al^{3+} \rightarrow \frac{1}{3}Al$	Al^{3+}, Al	−1.66
1.63	Ti, Ti^{++}	$\frac{1}{2}Ti \rightarrow \frac{1}{2}Ti^{++} + \ominus$	$\ominus + \frac{1}{2}Ti^{++} \rightarrow \frac{1}{2}Ti$	Ti^{++}, Ti	−1.63
0.763	Zn, Zn^{++}	$\frac{1}{2}Zn \rightarrow \frac{1}{2}Zn^{++} + \ominus$	$\ominus + \frac{1}{2}Zn^{++} \rightarrow \frac{1}{2}Zn$	Zn^{++}, Zn	−0.763
0.61	U^{3+}, U^{4+}	$U^{3+} \rightarrow U^{4+} + \ominus$	$\ominus + U^{4+} \rightarrow U^{3+}$	U^{4+}, U^{3+}	−0.61

0.440	Fe, Fe^{++}	$\frac{1}{2}Fe \rightarrow \frac{1}{2}Fe^{++} + \Theta$	$\Theta + \frac{1}{2}Fe^{++} \rightarrow \frac{1}{2}Fe$	Fe^{++}, Fe	−0.440
0.43	Eu^{++}, Eu^{3+}	$Eu^{++} \rightarrow Eu^{3+} + \Theta$	$\Theta + Eu^{3+} \rightarrow Eu^{++}$	Eu^{3+}, Eu^{++}	−0.43
0.403	Cd, Cd^{++}	$\frac{1}{2}Cd \rightarrow \frac{1}{2}Cd^{++} + \Theta$	$\Theta + \frac{1}{2}Cd \rightarrow \frac{1}{2}Cd$	Cd^{++}, Cd	−0.403
0.3363	Tl, Tl^{+}	$Tl \rightarrow Tl^{+} + \Theta$	$\Theta + Tl^{+} \rightarrow Tl$	Tl^{+}, Tl	−0.3363
0.250	Ni, Ni^{++}	$\frac{1}{2}Ni \rightarrow \frac{1}{2}Ni^{++} + \Theta$	$\Theta + \frac{1}{2}Ni^{++} \rightarrow \frac{1}{2}Ni$	Ni^{++}, Ni	−0.250
0.151	Ag, AgI, I^{-}	$Ag + I^{-} \rightarrow AgI + \Theta$	$\Theta + AgI \rightarrow Ag + I^{-}$	I^{-}, AgI, Ag	−0.151
0.136	Sn, Sn^{++}	$\frac{1}{2}Sn \rightarrow \frac{1}{2}Sn^{++} + \Theta$	$\Theta + \frac{1}{2}Sn^{++} \rightarrow \frac{1}{2}Sn$	Sn^{++}, Sn	−0.136
0.126	Pb, Pb^{++}	$\frac{1}{2}Pb \rightarrow \frac{1}{2}Pb^{++} + \Theta$	$\Theta + \frac{1}{2}Pb^{++} \rightarrow \frac{1}{2}Pb$	Pb^{++}, Pb	−0.126
±0.000	$H_2(g)$, H^{+}	$\frac{1}{2}H_2(g) \rightarrow H^{+} + \Theta$	$\Theta + H^{+} \rightarrow \frac{1}{2}H_2(g)$	H^{+}, $H_2(g)$	∓0.0000
−0.05	UO_2^{+}, UO_2^{++}	$UO_2^{+} \rightarrow UO_2^{++} + \Theta$	$\Theta + UO_2^{++} \rightarrow UO_2^{+}$	UO_2^{++}, UO_2^{+}	0.05
−0.095	Ag, AgBr, Br^{-}	$Ag + Br^{-} \rightarrow AgBr + \Theta$	$\Theta + AgBr \rightarrow Ag + Br^{-}$	Br^{-}, AgBr, Ag	0.095
−0.147	Np^{3+}, Np^{4+}	$Np^{3+} \rightarrow Np^{4+} + \Theta$	$\Theta + Np^{4+} \rightarrow Np^{3+}$	Np^{4+}, Np^{3+}	0.147
−0.15	Sn^{++}, Sn^{4+}	$\frac{1}{2}Sn^{++} \rightarrow \frac{1}{2}Sn^{4+} + \Theta$	$\Theta + \frac{1}{2}Sn^{4+} \rightarrow \frac{1}{2}Sn^{++}$	Sn^{4+}, Sn^{++}	0.15
−0.153	Cu^{+}, Cu^{++}	$Cu^{+} \rightarrow Cu^{++} + \Theta$	$\Theta + Cu^{++} \rightarrow Cu^{+}$	Cu^{++}, Cu^{+}	0.153
−0.2223	Ag, AgCl, Cl^{-}	$Ag + Cl^{-} \rightarrow AgCl + \Theta$	$\Theta + AgCl \rightarrow Ag + Cl^{-}$	Cl^{-}, AgCl, Ag	0.2223
−0.337	Cu, Cu^{++}	$\frac{1}{2}Cu \rightarrow \frac{1}{2}Cu^{++} + \Theta$	$\Theta + \frac{1}{2}Cu^{++} \rightarrow \frac{1}{2}Cu$	Cu^{++}, Cu	0.337
−0.52	$C_2H_6(g)$, $C_2H_4(g)$, H^{+}	$\frac{1}{2}C_2H_6(g) \rightarrow \frac{1}{2}C_2H_4(g) + H^{+} + \Theta$	$\Theta + H^{+} + \frac{1}{2}C_2H_4(g) \rightarrow \frac{1}{2}C_2H_6(g)$	H^{+}, $C_2H_4(g)$, $C_2H_6(g)$	0.52
−0.521	Cu, Cu^{+}	$Cu \rightarrow Cu^{+} + \Theta$	$\Theta + Cu^{+} \rightarrow Cu$	Cu^{+}, Cu	0.521
−0.5355	I_2, I^{-}	$I^{-} \rightarrow \frac{1}{2}I_2 + \Theta$	$\Theta + \frac{1}{2}I_2 \rightarrow I^{-}$	I^{-}, I_2	0.5355
−0.536	I_3^{-}, I^{-}	$\frac{3}{2}I^{-} \rightarrow \frac{1}{2}I_3^{-} + \Theta$	$\Theta + \frac{1}{2}I_3^{-} \rightarrow \frac{3}{2}I^{-}$	I^{-}, I_3^{-}	0.536
−0.62	U^{4+}, UO_2^{++}, H^{+}	$\frac{1}{2}U^{4+} + H_2O(l) \rightarrow \frac{1}{2}UO_2^{++} + 2H^{+} + \Theta$	$\Theta + 2H^{+} + \frac{1}{2}UO_2^{++} \rightarrow \frac{1}{2}U^{4+} + H_2O(l)$	H^{+}, UO_2^{++}, U^{4+}	0.62
−0.75	Np^{4+}, NpO_2^{+}, H^{+}	$Np^{4+} + 2H_2O(l) \rightarrow NpO_2^{+} + 4H^{+} + \Theta$	$\Theta + 4H^{+} + NpO_2^{+} \rightarrow Np^{4+} + 2H_2O(l)$	H^{+}, NpO_2^{+}, Np^{4+}	0.75
−0.771	Fe^{++}, Fe^{3+}	$Fe^{++} \rightarrow Fe^{3+} + \Theta$	$\Theta + Fe^{3+} \rightarrow Fe^{++}$	Fe^{3+}, Fe^{++}	0.771
−0.789	Hg(l), Hg_2^{++}	$Hg(l) \rightarrow \frac{1}{2}Hg_2^{++} + \Theta$	$\Theta + \frac{1}{2}Hg_2^{++} \rightarrow Hg(l)$	Hg_2^{++}, Hg(l)	0.789
−0.7991	Ag, Ag^{+}	$Ag \rightarrow Ag^{+} + \Theta$	$\Theta + Ag^{+} \rightarrow Ag$	Ag^{+}, Ag	0.7991
−0.920	Hg_2^{++}, Hg^{++}	$\frac{1}{2}Hg_2^{++} \rightarrow Hg^{++} + \Theta$	$\Theta + Hg^{++} \rightarrow \frac{1}{2}Hg_2^{++}$	Hg^{++}, Hg_2^{++}	0.920
−0.93	PuO_2^{+}, PuO_2^{++}	$PuO_2^{+} \rightarrow PuO_2^{++} + \Theta$	$\Theta + PuO_2^{++} \rightarrow PuO_2^{+}$	PuO_2^{++}, PuO_2^{+}	0.93

TABLE 5j-6. STANDARD ELECTROMOTIVE FORCES OF HALF CELLS IN WATER AT 25°C (*Continued*)

Plan A			Plan B		
E^o (1)	Electrode (2)	Half-cell reaction (3)	Half-cell reaction (4)	Electrode (5)	E^o electrode potential (6)
−0.97	Pu^{3+}, Pu^{4+}	$Pu^{3+} \rightarrow Pu^{4+} + \ominus$	$\ominus + Pu^{4+} \rightarrow Pu^{3+}$	Pu^{4+}, Pu^{3+}	0.97
−0.987	Pd, Pd^{++}	$\frac{1}{2}Pd \rightarrow \frac{1}{2}Pd^{++} + \ominus$	$\ominus + \frac{1}{2}Pd^{++} \rightarrow \frac{1}{2}Pd$	Pd^{++}, Pd	0.987
−1.0652	$Br_2(l)$, Br^-	$Br^- \rightarrow \frac{1}{2}Br_2(l) + \ominus$	$\ominus + \frac{1}{2}Br_2(l) \rightarrow Br^-$	Br^-, $Br_2(l)$	1.0652
−1.15	NpO_2^+, NpO_2^{++}	$NpO_2^+ \rightarrow NpO_2^{++} + \ominus$	$\ominus + NpO_2^{++} \rightarrow NpO_2^+$	NpO_2^{++}, NpO_2^+	1.15
−1.15	Pu^{4+}, PuO_2^+, H^+	$Pu^{4+} + 2H_2O(l) \rightarrow PuO_2^+ + 4H^+ + \ominus$	$\ominus + 4H^+ + PuO_2^+ \rightarrow 2H_2O(l) + Pu^{4+}$	H^+, PuO_2^+, Pu^{4+}	1.15
−1.229	$O_2(g)$, H^+	$\frac{1}{2}H_2O(l) \rightarrow \frac{1}{4}O_2(g) + H^+ + \ominus$	$\ominus + H^+ + \frac{1}{4}O_2(g) \rightarrow \frac{1}{2}H_2O(l)$	H^+, $O_2(g)$	1.229
−1.3595	$Cl_2(g)$, Cl^-	$Cl^- \rightarrow \frac{1}{2}Cl_2(g) + \ominus$	$\ominus + \frac{1}{2}Cl_2(g) \rightarrow Cl^-$	Cl^-, Cl_2	1.3595
−1.50	Au, Au^{3+}	$\frac{1}{3}Au \rightarrow \frac{1}{3}Au^{3+} + \ominus$	$\ominus + \frac{1}{3}Au^{3+} \rightarrow \frac{1}{3}Au$	Au^{3+}, Au	1.50
−1.6	Bk^{3+}, Bk^{4+}	$Bk^{3+} \rightarrow Bk^{4+} + \ominus$	$\ominus + Bk^{4+} \rightarrow Bk^{3+}$	Bk^{4+}, Bk^{3+}	1.6
−1.61	Ce^{3+}, Ce^{4+}	$Ce^{3+} \rightarrow Ce^{4+} + \ominus$	$\ominus + Ce^{4+} \rightarrow Ce^{3+}$	Ce^{4+}, Ce^{3+}	1.61
−1.64	AmO_2^+, AmO_2^{++}	$AmO_2^+ \rightarrow AmO_2^{++} + \ominus$	$\ominus + AmO_2^{++} \rightarrow AmO_2^+$	AmO_2^{++}, AmO_2^+	1.64
−1.68	Au, Au^+	$Au \rightarrow Au^+ + \ominus$	$\ominus + Au^+ \rightarrow Au$	Au^+, Au	1.68
−2.18	Am^{3+}, Am^{4+}	$Am^{3+} \rightarrow Am^{4+} + \ominus$	$\ominus + Am^{4+} \rightarrow Am^{3+}$	Am^{4+}, Am^{3+}	2.18
−3.06	$F_2(g)$, HF(aq), H^+	$HF(aq) \rightarrow \frac{1}{2}F_2(g) + H^+ + \ominus$	$\ominus + H^+ + \frac{1}{2}F_2(g) \rightarrow HF(aq)$	H^+, HF(aq), $F_2(g)$	3.06

Commission on Electrochemistry of the International Union of Pure and Applied Chemistry, meeting in Stockholm in 1953, voted to recommend that column (1) be associated henceforth with column (2) and that (6) be associated with (5). The associations with columns (3) and (4), respectively, are implicit. The commission also recommended that values in column (6) but not those in column (1) be referred to as "electrode potentials."

Incorrect Notions. Erroneous attempts have been made to associate the half-cell emf with the "difference in potential" between an electrode and the solution in which it is immersed. For a discussion of the logical difficulties involved, see Guggenheim (1930) and (1949).

The Use of Table 5j-6. To calculate E^o of any cell; e.g.,

$$\text{Tl, TlCl (aq), AgCl (s), Ag} \tag{5j-7}$$

according to plan A write the equation for the half-cell reaction and E^o of the left-hand electrode:

$$\text{Tl} \rightarrow \text{Tl}^+ + \ominus \qquad E^o = 0.3363 \text{ volt} \tag{5j-6e}$$

Subtract both the half-cell reaction and E^o of the right-hand electrode:

$$-[\text{Ag} + \text{Cl}^- \rightarrow \text{AgCl} + \ominus] \qquad -E^o = -(-0.2223 \text{ volt}) \tag{5j-7g}$$

The conventional cell reaction, i.e., the reaction accompanying the passage of positive electricity from left to right through the cell (and for $N = 1$), results. It may be represented by either of the two equivalent equations:

$$\left.\begin{array}{l}\text{Tl} + \text{AgCl} \rightarrow \text{Ag} + \text{Tl}^+ + \text{Cl}^- \\ \text{Tl} + \text{AgCl} \rightarrow \text{Ag} + \text{TlCl (aq)}\end{array}\right\} E^o = +0.5586 \text{ volt} \tag{5j-8}$$

Since E^o is positive ΔF^o is negative for the reaction indicated in Eq. (5j-8). Eq. (5j-8) is therefore the equation for the reaction actually taking place in the cell when all activities are unity. If the cell had been written Ag, AgCl, TlCl (aq), Tl, the indicated reaction would have been

$$\text{Ag} + \text{TlCl (aq)} \rightarrow \text{Tl} + \text{AgCl} \qquad E^o = -0.5586 \text{ volt} \tag{5j-9}$$

The conclusions concerning the actual reaction and the absolute values of ΔF^o and E^o would be unchanged.

The problem may be solved similarly by plan B. The essential notion of plan B is the comparison of tendencies to take up electrons: E^o of the cell is positive if the right-hand electrode has the greater tendency to acquire electrons. Using columns (4), (5), and (6) write the half-cell reaction and E^o for the *right*-hand electrode:

$$\ominus + \text{AgCl} \rightarrow \text{Ag} + \text{Cl}^- \qquad E^o = 0.2223 \text{ volt}$$

Subtract both the half-cell reaction and E^o of the left-hand electrode

$$-[\ominus + \text{Tl}^+ \rightarrow \text{Tl}] \qquad -E^o = -(-0.3363 \text{ volt})$$

$$\text{Tl} + \text{AgCl} \rightarrow \text{Ag} + \text{TlCl (aq)} \qquad E^o = 0.5586 \text{ volt} \tag{5j-8}$$

Again: E^o is plus and ΔF^o is negative for the reaction accompanying the passage of ("positive") electricity from left to right through the cell.[1]

A third procedure for the calculation of the emf of a cell can be used whenever a dual table such as Table 5j-6 is available. The cell emf may be regarded as the sum of

[1] Additional data are available in Latimer (1952). Note the special table (p. 345) for alkaline solutions. More emf values can be calculated by Eq. (5j-1) from the extensive free-energy tables of Rossini et al. (1952).

TABLE 5j-7. SELECTED MEAN-IONIC-ACTIVITY COEFFICIENTS $\gamma_\pm$ OF ELECTROLYTES IN AQUEOUS SOLUTIONS AT 25°C
(m in mole kg^{-1})

m	$HClO_4$	HNO_3	LiCl	NaCl	$NaClO_3$	$NaClO_4$	$NaBrO_3$	$NaNO_3$	KCl	KNO_3	RbCl	CsCl	$AgNO_3$	$TlClO_4$
0.1	0.803	0.791	0.790	0.778	0.772	0.775	0.758	0.762	0.770	0.739	0.764	0.756	0.734	0.730
0.2	0.778	0.754	0.757	0.735	0.720	0.729	0.696	0.703	0.718	0.663	0.709	0.694	0.657	0.652
0.5	0.769	0.720	0.739	0.681	0.645	0.668	0.605	0.617	0.649	0.545	0.634	0.606	0.536	0.527
1.0	0.823	0.724	0.774	0.657	0.589	0.629	0.528	0.548	0.604	0.443	0.583	0.544	0.429	
2.0	1.055	0.793	0.921	0.668	0.538	0.609	0.450	0.478	0.573	0.333	0.546	0.495	0.316	
4.0	2.08	.....	1.510	0.783	.....	0.626	.....	0.408	0.577	.....	0.538	0.473	0.210	

m	$MgCl_2$	$Mg(ClO_4)_2$	$CaBr_2$	$CaCl_2$	CaI_2	$SrCl_2$	BaI_2	$Sr(NO_3)_2$	$ZnCl_2$	$Zn(ClO_4)_2$	$UO_2(ClO_4)_2$	H_2SO_4	Na_2SO_4	Cs_2SO_4
0.1	0.529	0.590	0.532	0.518	0.560	0.511	0.542	0.478	0.515	0.581	0.626	0.2655	0.445	0.456
0.2	0.489	0.578	0.492	0.472	0.531	0.462	0.509	0.410	0.462	0.564	0.634	0.2090	0.365	0.382
0.5	0.481	0.647	0.491	0.448	0.561	0.430	0.523	0.329	0.394	0.629	0.790	0.1557	0.268	0.291
1.0	0.570	0.946	0.597	0.500	0.741	0.461	0.649	0.275	0.339	0.929	1.390	0.1316	0.204	0.235
2.0	1.053	2.65	1.121	0.792	1.640	0.670	1.221	0.232	0.289	2.74	5.91	0.1276		
4.0	5.54	34.1	6.28	2.934	.....	1.977	.....	.....	0.307	38.8	160.2	0.1700		

m	$CuSO_4$	$MgSO_4$	$ZnSO_4$	$CdSO_4$	UO_2SO_4	$AlCl_3$	$LaCl_3$	$EuCl_3$	$K_3Fe(CN)_6$	$K_4Fe(CN)_6$	$Al_2(SO_4)_3$	$Th(NO_3)_4$
0.1	(0.150)	(0.150)	(0.150)	(0.150)	(0.150)	0.337	0.314	0.318	0.268	0.139	0.0350	0.279
0.2	0.104	0.108	0.104	0.102	0.102	0.305	0.274	0.282	0.212	0.100	0.0225	0.225
0.5	0.062	0.068	0.063	0.061	0.0611	0.331	0.266	0.276	0.155	0.062	0.0143	0.189
1.0	0.043	0.049	0.043	0.041	0.0439	0.539	0.342	0.371	0.128	.....	0.0175	0.207
2.0	....	0.042	0.035	0.032	0.0367	.....	0.825	0.995	.....	.....	.....	0.326
4.0	....	....	....	....	0.0433	.....	.....	.....	.....	.....	.....	0.647

TABLE 5j-8. MEAN-ACTIVITY COEFFICIENTS $\gamma_\pm$ OF HCl IN AQUEOUS SOLUTION (m in mole kg^{-1})

m	0°	10°	20°	25°	40°	50°	60°
0.0001	0.9890	0.9890	0.9892	0.9891	0.9885	0.9879	0.9879
0.0002	0.9848	0.9846	0.9844	0.9842	0.9833	0.9831	0.9831
0.0005	0.9756	0.9756	0.9759	0.9752	0.9741	0.9738	0.9734
0.001	0.9668	0.9666	0.9661	0.9656	0.9643	0.9639	0.9632
0.002	0.9541	0.9544	0.9527	0.9521	0.9505	0.9500	0.9491
0.005	0.9303	0.9300	0.9294	0.9285	0.9265	0.9250	0.9235
0.01	0.9065	0.9055	0.9052	0.9048	0.9016	0.9000	0.8987
0.02	0.8774	0.8773	0.8768	0.8755	0.8715	0.8690	0.8666
0.05	0.8346	0.8338	0.8317	0.8304	0.8246	0.8211	0.8168
0.1	0.8027	0.8016	0.7985	0.7964	0.7891	0.7850	0.7813
0.2	0.7756	0.7740	0.7694	0.7667	0.7569	0.7508	0.7437
0.5	0.7761	0.7694	0.7616	0.7571	0.7432	0.7344	0.7237
1.0	0.8419	0.8295	0.8162	0.8090	0.7865	0.7697	0.7541
2.0	1.078	1.053	1.024	1.009	0.9602	0.9327	0.9072
4.0	2.006	1.911	1.812	1.762			

two tendencies supplementing each other instead of two opposing each other. The equation for the appropriate half reaction for the left-hand electrode is taken from plan A [column (3)] and the equation for the other half reaction from plan B [column 4]. The equation for the conventional cell reaction is the *sum* of these equations for the respective half reactions. The standard emf of the cell is the sum of the standard half-cell emfs [column (1) and column (6)]. This procedure can be instructive for beginning students but is not stressed here because the printing of lengthy tables in dual form is usually not feasible. Normally each author selects one plan or the other and uses that one exclusively.

General Discussion. Many electrochemists and many biologists prefer to use the "electrode potentials" of plan B. American physical chemists have usually preferred plan A. For his extensive treatise Prof. W. M. Latimer chose plan A. To use his tables those who prefer plan B should observe that the standard half-cell emfs tabulated by him are the negatives of the respective "electrode potentials" and that his equations may be written in the reverse direction to fit plan B rather than plan A. The user should also note that his equations are written for integral values of N but not always for $N = 1$.

It should be clearly understood that all of the standard emfs of Table 5j-6 are equilibrium values and are valid strictly only when no current is passing or when the current passing is so small that resulting changes in the cell are negligible. The reversal of such a current would not affect the magnitude and, of course, could not alter the algebraic sign of the emf of a cell or half cell. The choice of plan A or plan B is an arbitrary one and has nothing to do with the direction in which current is actually passed through a given cell.

TABLE 5j-9. DISSOCIATION CONSTANTS OF WATER AND OF ELECTROLYTES IN AQUEOUS SOLUTIONS
(Constants* are on the molality scale. *Italics* indicate maximum values)

Material	°C	0°	5°	10°	15°	20°	25°	30°	35°	40°	45°	50°
Water	$K \times 10^{14}$	0.1139	0.1846	0.2920	0.4505	0.6809	1.008	1.469	2.089	2.919	4.018	5.474
Formic acid	$K_A \times 10^4$	1.638	1.691	1.728	1.749	1.765	*1.772*	1.768	1.747	1.716	1.685	1.650
Acetic acid	$K_A \times 10^5$	1.657	1.700	1.729	1.745	1.753	*1.754*	1.750	1.728	1.703	1.670	1.633
Propionic acid	$K_A \times 10^5$	1.274	1.305	1.326	1.336	*1.338*	1.336	1.326	1.310	1.280	1.257	1.229
n-Butyric acid	$K_A \times 10^5$	1.563	1.574	*1.576*	1.569	1.542	1.515	1.484	1.439	1.395	1.347	1.302
Chloroacetic acid	$K_A \times 10^3$	1.528	.....	1.488	......	......	1.379	.....	.....	1.230		
Lactic acid	$K_A \times 10^4$	1.287	.....	......	......	......	*1.374*	.....	.....	.....	.....	1.270
Glycolic acid	$K_A \times 10^4$	1.334	.....	......	......	......	*1.475*	.....	.....	.....	.....	1.415
Sulfuric acid	$K_{2A} \times 10^2$	......	1.80	......	1.36	......	1.01	.....	0.75	.....	0.56	
Carbonic acid	$K_{1A} \times 10^7$	2.64	3.04	3.44	3.81	4.16	4.45	4.71	4.90	5.04	5.13	5.19
	$K_{2A} \times 10^{11}$	2.36	2.77	3.24	3.71	4.20	4.69	5.13	5.62	6.03	6.38	6.73
Phosphoric acid	$K_{1A} \times 10^3$	8.97	.....	......	......	......	7.52	.....	.....	.....	.....	5.50
	$K_{2A} \times 10^8$	4.85	5.24	5.57	5.89	6.12	6.34	6.46	6.53	6.58	*6.59*	6.55
Nitric acid	K_A	......	......	......	......	......	21					
Glycine	$K_A \times 10^3$	......	......	3.94	......	4.31	4.47	4.59	.....	4.81		
	$K_B \times 10^5$	......	......	4.68	5.12	5.57	6.04	6.52	6.98	7.43	7.87	
Alanine	$K_A \times 10^3$	......	......	......	......	4.47	4.57	4.66	4.71	4.74	4.76	
	$K_B \times 10^5$	......	......	......	......	6.90	7.47	8.08	8.61	9.10	9.60	

* Letter subscripts on K indicate dissociation as acid or base, respectively; number subscripts indicate first, second, or third dissociation.

TABLE 5j-10. RELATIVE APPARENT MOLAL HEAT CONTENT φL AND PARTIAL MOLAL HEAT CONTENT $\bar{L}_2$ OF SOLUTES IN DILUTE AQUEOUS SOLUTIONS AT 25°C
(cal mole^{-1})

m		0.0001	0.0004	0.0016	0.0064	0.0100	0.0400	0.0900
NaCl	φL	4.5	8.5	17.0	33	40	67	83
	$\bar{L}_2$	6.5	12.5	24.0	46	57	92	104
$NaIO_3$	φL	4.0	7.5	14.0	21	21	0	
	$\bar{L}_2$	5.8	11.0	19.8	24	20	−41	
KCl	φL	4.5	8.5	16.0	31	38	65	77
	$\bar{L}_2$	6.5	12.5	24.0	46	55	82	91
$KClO_4$	φL	4.3	8.0	13.0	16	14	−28	
	$\bar{L}_2$	6.2	11.3	16.6	13	4	−86	
Li_2SO_4	φL	24	47	91	177	218	377	488
	$\bar{L}_2$	35	69	135	260	317	508	620
Cs_2SO_4	φL	20	39	71	121	139	161	137
	$\bar{L}_2$	29	57	102	161	176	152	87
$SrCl_2$	φL	23	46	86	161	195	332	420
	$\bar{L}_2$	34	66	125	232	277	443	528
$SrBr_2$	φL	23	44	82	152	182	293	366
	$\bar{L}_2$	33	64	119	216	254	383	452
$Ba(NO_3)_2$	φL	19	36	59	72	66	−46	−223
	$\bar{L}_2$	27	51	75	68	37	−195	−528

TABLE 5j-11. STANDARD ENTROPIES OF MONATOMIC IONS IN AQUEOUS SOLUTIONS AT 25°C
(Referred* to $H_2 \rightarrow 2H^+ + 2\ominus$; $\Delta S^o = 0$; cal mole^{-1} deg^{-1})

Ion	$\bar{S}^o$	Ion	$\bar{S}^o$	Ion	$\bar{S}^o$
Cs^+	31.8	Ca^{++}	−13.2	Cr^{3+}	−73.5
Tl^+	30.4	Cd^{++}	−14.6	Al^{3+}	−74.9
Rb^+	29.7	Mn^{++}	−20	Ga^{3+}	−83
K^+	24.5	Cu^{++}	−23.6	U^{4+}	−78
Ag^+	17.67	Zn^{++}	−25.45	Pu^{4+}	−87
Na^+	14.4	Fe^{++}	−27.1	I^-	26.14
Li^+	3.4	Mg^{++}	−28.2	Br^-	19.25
Pb^{++}	5.1	U^{3+}	−36		
Ba^{++}	3.0	Pu^{3+}	−39	Cl^-	13.17
Hg^{++}	−5.4	Gd^{3+}	−43	F^-	−2.3
Sn^{++}	−5.9	In^{3+}	−62		
Sr^{++}	−9.4	Fe^{3+}	−70.1	$S^=$	−6.4

* This is not equivalent to the setting of S^o of H^+ equal to zero; cf. Klotz (1950).

TABLE 5j-12. STANDARD ENTROPIES OF POLYATOMIC IONS IN AQUEOUS SOLUTIONS AT 25°C
(Referred* to $H_2 \rightarrow 2H^+ + 2\Theta$; $\Delta S^o = 0$; cal mole^{-1} deg^{-1})

Ion	$\bar{S}^o$	Ion	$\bar{S}^o$	Ion	$\bar{S}^o$
OH^-	−2.5	HSO_4^-	30.3	PO_4^{3-}	−52
ClO^-	10.0			AsO_4^{3-}	−34.6
HCO_2^-	21.9	$H_2AsO_4^-$	28	HF_2^-	0.5
ClO_2^-	24.1	$H_2PO_4^-$	21.3	BF_4^-	40
NO_2^-	29.9	$HN_2O_4^-$	34	$SiF_6^=$	−12
NO_3^-	35.0	$BeO_2^=$	−27	$CuCl_2^-$	49.2
ClO_3^-	39.0	$CO_3^=$	−12.7	$AuCl_4^-$	61
BrO_3^-	38.5	$SO_3^=$	−7	$PdCl_4^=$	36
IO_3^-	28.0	$SO_4^=$	4.1	$PtCl_4^=$	42
ClO_4^-	43.2	$SeO_4^=$	5.7	$PtCl_6^=$	52.6
MnO_4^-	45.4	$N_2O_2^=$	6.6	I_3^-	41.5
HCO_3^-	22.7	$C_2O_4^=$	10.6	$Ag(CN)_2^-$	49
HSO_3^-	26	$Cr_2O_7^=$	51.1	$Ni(CN)_4^=$	33
SH^-	14.9	$HPO_4^=$	−8.6	$FeCl^{++}$	−22
		$HAsO_4^=$	0.9		

* This is not equivalent to the setting of S^o of H^+ equal to zero; cf. Klotz (1950).

References

1. Bates, R. G.: "Electrometric *p*H Determinations," John Wiley & Sons, Inc., New York, 1954.
2. Conway, B. E.: "Electrochemical Data," Elsevier Publishing Company, Amsterdam, 1952.
3. Daniels, F., and R. A. Alberty: "Physical Chemistry," John Wiley & Sons, Inc., New York, Chapman & Hall, Ltd., London, 1955.
4. Guggenheim, E. A.: *J. Phys. Chem.* **33**, 842 (1929).
5. Guggenheim, E. A.: "Thermodynamics," North Holland Publishing Co., Amsterdam, Interscience Publishers, Inc., New York, 1949.
6. Harned, H. S., in Electrochemical Constants, *Natl. Bur. Standards (U.S.) Circ.* 524, 1953.
7. Harned, H. S., and B. B. Owen: "The Physical Chemistry of Electrolytic Solutions," 2d ed., Reinhold Publishing Corporation, New York, 1950.
8. Hood, G. C., O. Redlich, and C. A. Reilly: *J. Chem. Phys.* **22**, 2067 (1954).
9. "International Critical Tables of Numerical Data, Physics, Chemistry and Technology," McGraw-Hill Book Company, Inc., New York, 1926–1933.
10. International Union of Pure and Applied Chemistry (Paris), Comptes rendus de la dix-septième conférence, Stockholm, 1953.
11. Klotz, I. M.: "Chemical Thermodynamics," Prentice-Hall, Inc., Englewood Cliffs, N. J., 1950.
12. Kohlrausch, F. W. G., and L. Holborn: "Das Leitvermögen der Elektrolyte," Teubnerverlagsgesellschaft, Leipzig, 1898.
13. Kolthoff, I. M., and J. J. Lingane: "Polarography," 2d ed., Interscience Publishers, Inc., New York, 1952.
14. Kortum, G., and J. O'M. Bockris: "Textbook of Electrochemistry," vol. II, Elsevier Publishing Company, Amsterdam, 1951.
15. Landolt-Börnstein: "Physikalisch-Chemische Tabellen," 5th ed., Springer-Verlag OHG, Berlin, 1927–1935.
16. Latimer, W. M.: "The Oxidation States of the Elements and Their Potentials in Aqueous Solutions," 2d ed., Prentice-Hall, Inc., Englewood Cliffs, N. J., 1952.
17. Powell, R. F., and W. M. Latimer: *J. Chem. Phys.* **19**, 1139–1141 (1951).

18. Redlich, O.: *Chem. Revs.* **39,** 333 (1946).
19. Robinson, R. A., and R. H. Stokes: *Trans. Faraday Soc.* **45,** 612 (1949).
20. Robinson, R. A., and R. H. Stokes: "Electrolyte Solutions," Butterworths Publications, Ltd., London, 1955.
21. Rossini, F. D., D. D. Wagman, W. H. Evans, S. Levine, and I. Jaffe: Selected Values of Chemical Thermodynamic Properties, *Natl. Bur. Standards (U.S.) Circ.* 500, 1952.
22. Scudder, H.: "The Electrical Conductivity and Ionization Constants of Organic Compounds," D. Van Nostrand Company, Inc., New York, 1914.
23. von Stackelberg, M.: "Polarographische Arbeitsmethoden," Walter De Gruyter & Co., Berlin, 1950.

5k. Electric and Magnetic Properties of the Earth and Stars

B. B. PHILLIPS[1]

U.S. Weather Bureau

R. G. VAN NOSTRAND[2]
Magnolia Petroleum Company

DAVID G. KNAPP[3]

U.S. Coast and Geodetic Survey

L. M. BRANSCOMB[4]

The National Bureau of Standards

ATMOSPHERIC ELECTRICITY

5k-1. Atmospheric Ionization. Cosmic radiation is the chief source of ionization in the lower stratosphere and throughout the troposphere except for the lowest 1 to 2 km over land (Table 5k-1). Within the air stratum adjacent to land surfaces, the predominant ionizer is radiation from radioactive matter in the earth and suspended in the atmosphere. The intense ionization of the ionosphere results from the ultraviolet and corpuscular radiation from the sun (Table 5k-2).

The mobility of small ions in pure dry air is given as 1.6 and 2.2 cm/sec/volt/cm for the positive and negative ions, respectively, by Loeb.[5] In the presence of air impurities, small ions are transformed into large ions whose mobilities are of the

[1] Atmospheric electricity.
[2] Terrestrial electricity.
[3] Terrestrial magnetism.
[4] Stellar and galactic magnetism.

[5] L. B. Loeb, "Kinetic Theory of Gases," 2d ed., McGraw-Hill Book Company, Inc., New York, 1934.

TABLE 5k-1. RATE OF FORMATION, DENSITY, AND MEAN LIFE OF SMALL IONS IN THE LOWER ATMOSPHERE

Altitude, km	Rate of formation [Fleming (1949)], ion pairs/cm³/sec		Density [Gish and Sherman, *Explorer II* (1936)], ion pairs/cm³	Mean life [Gish and Sherman, *Explorer II* (1936)], sec
	Madras, India, lat 3°N (mag)	Omaha, Nebr., lat 51°N (mag)		
Surface*				
Ocean........	...	2	600	300
Country.....	...	10	800	80
City.........	...	10	100	10
3	5	7	1,400	220
6	10	14	2,800	180
9	16	33	4,000	120
12	20	44	4,600	110
15	18	43	5,100	110
18	11	33	4,400	140
21	6	22	2,900	140
25	3	12		

* Author estimated values for middle latitudes.

TABLE 5k-2. CHARACTERISTICS OF THE DIFFERENT IONOSPHERIC REGIONS OF THE UPPER ATMOSPHERE*

Region	Level of max ionization, km	Particle density (per cm³)			Ion production rate per cm² vertical column I; recombination coefficient α, cm³/sec	$S = \frac{N_e \text{ in sunspot max}}{N_e \text{ in sunspot min}}$
		Electron max N_e		Neutral particle		
		Midday	Midnight			
D	60(?) (for ions; no max for electrons)	1.5×10^4	Absent	8×10^{15}	....	2.00
E	100	1.5×10^5	1×10^4	6×10^{12}	$I = 6 \times 10^8$; $\alpha = 1 \times 10^{-8}$	1.50
E_s	Thin strata within or slightly higher than the normal E	Higher than E ionization		6×10^{12}		
F_1	200	2.5×10^5	Absent	1×10^{11}	$I = 1.8 \times 10^9$; $\alpha = 4 \times 10^{-9}$	1.56
F_2	300	1.5×10^6	2.5×10^5	2×10^{10}	$I = 1.5 \times 10^9$; $\alpha = 8 \times 10^{-11}$ (day); $\alpha = 3 \times 10^{-10}$ (night)	4.00

*From Mitra, "The Upper Atmosphere," 2d ed., Asiatic Society, Calcutta, 1949; see pp. 290–291 for references to the theories of the origin of the various ionospheric regions.

order of 10^{-4} cm/sec/volt/cm, and to a lesser extent, intermediate ions of one-tenth to one-hundredth the mobility of the small ion. Small ions consist of not more than a few molecules, whereas large ions are molecular aggregates with a diameter of the order of 10^{-6} cm. The density of the large ion at the surface of the earth varies from a few hundred per cubic centimeter over the oceans to tens of thousands per cubic centimeter in polluted city air.

Table 5k-3. Representative Surface Mean Values of Air Conductivity, Electric Field, and Air-earth Current Density at Various Locations over the Earth

Place	Location	Total conductivity (esu) × 10^4	Positive/negative conductivity	Electric field, volts/m	Air-earth current density (esu) × 10^7	Ref.
Potsdam	52.4°N, 13.1°E	0.95	1.16	245	7.1	Swann (1947)
Davos	46.8°N, 9.8°E	2.68	1.13	64	5.2	Swann (1947)
Petermann	65.2°S, 295.8°E	4.16	1.62	176	22.6	Swann (1947)
Seeham	48.0°N, 346.9°E	2.64	1.02	84	6.9	Swann (1947)
College-Fairbanks	64.9°N, 212.2°E	3.10	1.29	104	.....	Sherman (1937)
Kew	51.5°N, 359.7°E	0.35*	....	363	3.1*	Scrase (1934)
Tucson	32.15°N, 110.5°E	4.29	1.10	55	7.1	Wait (1953)
Watheroo	30.3°S, 115.9°E	3.7	1.14	82	10. –	Wait and Torreson (1941)
Ocean:						
Carnegie (1915–1921)	....	3.0	1.14	124	10.3	Mauchly (1926)
Carnegie (1928–1929)	....	2.1	1.19	132	10.4	Torreson, Gish, Parkinson, and Wait (1946)

* Positive component only.

5k-2. Electric Field, Conductivity, and Air-earth Current. A 10 to 40 per cent diurnal variation is observed about the mean surface values of electric field, conductivity, and air-earth current. The largest variations occur over land according to local time and are of complex origin (Table 5k-3). Over the oceans the variation of electric field and conduction current depends upon universal time while the conductivity shows little daily variation. Surface oceanic observations and observations aloft (Tables 5k-4 and 5k-5) are considered to be representative of the average over the earth as a whole. In undisturbed weather the electric field is negative and the air-earth conduction current is directed toward the earth; i.e., positive ions move toward and negative ions away from the earth. The conductivity of the atomosphere is due chiefly to the small ion. The intermediate and large ions contribute little because of, respectively, meager concentration and low mobility. The total fair-weather air-earth current is about 1,800 amp. This current must have a counterpart which returns a positive excess of electricity to the upper atmosphere. The surviving hypothesis is that this positive current passes upward through thunderstorm cells (Table 5k-6 and see Fig. 5k-1 and Sec. 5k-4) to be distributed throughout the highly conductive upper atmosphere. The fair-weather air-earth current would neutralize 90 per cent of the bound charge on the earth's surface within 30 min in the absence of such a return current.

TABLE 5k-4. VARIATION OF POSITIVE CONDUCTIVITY WITH ALTITUDE IN THE LOWER ATMOSPHERE

Altitude, km	Mean value of positive conductivity (esu) × 10^4		
	Gish and Sherman, *Explorer II* (1936)	Gish and Wait (1950)	Callahan, Coroniti, Parziale, and Patten (1951)
1.5	1.9	2.2	2.4
3.0	3.1	2.8	4.0
6.0	10.5	8.8	9.7
9.0	18.9	17.8	18.8
12.0	35.2	29.2	
15.0	53.5		
18.0	75.5		
21.0	70.0		

TABLE 5k-5. VARIATION OF ELECTRIC FIELD WITH ALTITUDE IN THE LOWER ATMOSPHERE

Altitude, km	Electric field, volts/m		
	Schweidler, Germany (1929)	Wigand, Germany (1925)	Koenigsfeld,* Belgian Congo (1953)
Surface	130	136	20
0.5	50	.....	36
1.5	30	.....	64
2.5	...	27	58
3.0	20		27
4.4		18	10
6.0	10		10
6.5		8.8	8
9.0	5		8
12.0			6
15.0			6

* Altitudes based upon U.S. Standard Atmosphere pressure-height conversion.

TABLE 5k-6. ELECTRIC-FIELD INTENSITY INSIDE NATURAL CLOUDS (GUNN, 1948)

Average vertical field within stable nonprecipitating clouds	Small and <10 volts/cm
Average vertical field within stable precipitating clouds	<40 volts/cm
Average max vertical field observed within nine different thunderclouds	1,300 volts/cm
Max field observed (just prior to lightning strike to the observing aircraft)	3,400 volts/cm

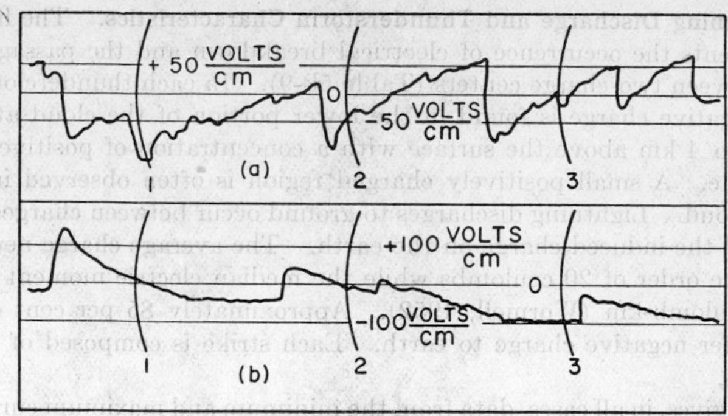

FIG. 5k-1. Characteristic surface electric field intensity variations observed near active thunderstorms. (*a*) Most common variation showing systematic induction of positive free charges on the earth's surface and their sudden destruction by lightning discharges; (*b*) less common type variation showing the induction of free charge of opposite polarity. (*Gunn*, 1954.)

5k-3. Precipitation Electricity

TABLE 5k-7. AVERAGE FREE ELECTRICAL CHARGE ON INDIVIDUAL PRECIPITATION PARTICLES
[(esu) × 10^3]

Observer	Altitude, ft	Sign of charge	Quiet rain	Shower rain	Electrical storm rain	Quiet snowfall	Squall snowfall
Gschwend (1920)......	Surface	+	0.24	1.75	8.11	0.09	5.64
		−	0.53	5.43	5.88	0.06	4.78
Banerji and Lele (1932)	Surface	+	....	6.4	6.9		
		−	....	6.7	7.3		
Chalmers and Pasquill (1938)	Surface	+	2.2	1.3	3.7*	....	10.5
		−	3.0	2.3	9.2*	....	5.7
Gunn and Devin (1953)	Surface	+	....	.....	22		
		−	....	.....	31		
Gunn (1947, 1950).....	5,000	+	....	.....	81		
		−	....	30	63		
	10,000	+	....	.....	148		
		−	....	34	112		
	15,000	+	....	17	123		
		−	....	36	76		
	20,000	+	....	63	52		
		−	....	.....	62		

* Actual lightning activity doubtful.

5k-4. Lightning Discharge and Thunderstorm Characteristics. The lightning discharge represents the occurrence of electrical breakdown and the passage of a spark discharge between two charge centers (Table 5k-9). In each thundercloud a concentration of negative charge is found in the lower portion of the cloud at an average height of 3 to 4 km above the surface with a concentration of positive charge at a higher altitude. A small positively charged region is often observed in the lowest limit of the cloud. Lightning discharges to ground occur between charged portions of the cloud and the induced charge on the earth. The average charge neutralized per strike is of the order of 20 coulombs while the median electric moment destroyed is about 110 coulomb-km (Wormell, 1952). Approximately 85 per cent of strokes to ground transfer negative charge to earth. Each strike is composed of one or more current peaks.

Table 5k-8 gives, in all cases, data from the minimum and maximum curves obtained from the published data on lightning discharges. Each quantity listed represents that value which was excelled by 90, 50, and 10 per cent of the strokes. The maximum observed value is given in the right-hand column.

Table 5k-8. Characteristics of Lightning Strokes*

Item		% of strokes with values in excess of those shown below			Max
		90%	50%	10%	
1. Current peaks measured in stroke path, kiloamp	Min	2.2	6.0	20.0	
	Max	5.0	8.6	27.5	160
2. Current amplitudes in steel towers, kiloamp	Min	1.0	8.8	28.4	
	Max	5.3	12.2	35.8	130
3. Stroke currents computed from item 2, kiloamp	Min	2.4	13.3	50.0	
	Max	10.3	40.0	101.0	220
4. Charges in current peaks, coulombs	Min				
	Max	0.04	0.23	1.03	5.6
5. Total stroke charges, coulombs	Min	2.3	10.4	86.0	
	Max	4.2	22.2	100.0	165
6. Total stroke duration, seconds	Min	. . . .	0.0006	0.2	
	Max	0.1	0.37	0.68	1.6
7. No. of current peaks per stroke	Min	1.0	1.8	4.0	
	Max	1.3	3.0	11.0	42

* J. H. Hagenguth, "Comp. of Meteorology," Malone, ed., American Meteorological Society, Boston, 1951.

Table 5k-9. Electrical Characteristics of Thunderstorms

Potential existing between centers of thunderstorm charge distributions prior to discharge	5×10^7 to 10^9 volts
Energy released per average lightning discharge	10^9 to 10^{10} joules
Rate of energy dissipation from the average thunderstorm	Approx 10^6 kw

References

1. Banerji, S. K., and S. R. Lele: *Nature* **130**, 998–999 (1932).
2. Callahan, R. C., S. C. Coroniti, A. J. Parziale, and R. Patten: *J. Geophys. Research* **56**, 545–551 (1951).
3. Chalmers, J. A., and F. Pasquill: *Proc. Phys. Soc.* (*London*) **50**, 1–15 (1938).

4. Fleming, J. A.: "Terrestrial Magnetism and Electricity," Dover Publications, New York, 1949.
5. Gish, O. H., and K. L. Sherman, *Natl. Geog. Soc., Contrib. Tech. Papers, Stratosphere Ser.*, no. 2, 94–116 (1936).
6. Gish, O. H., and G. R. Wait: *J. Geophys. Research* **55** (4), 473 (1950).
7. Gschwend, P.: *Jahrb. Radioakt. u. Elektronik* **17**, 62–79 (1920).
8. Gunn, R.: *Phys. Rev.* **71**, 181–186 (1947).
9. Gunn, R.: *J. Appl. Phys.* **19**, 481–484 (1948).
10. Gunn, R.: *J. Geophys. Research* **55**, 171–178 (1950).
11. Gunn, R.: *J. Meteorol.* **11** (2), 130–138 (1954).
12. Gunn, R., and C. Devin, Jr.: *J. Meteorol.* **10** (4), 279–284 (1953).
13. Koenigsfeld, L.: "Thunderstorm Electricity," Byers, ed., University of Chicago Press, 1953.
14. Mauchly, S. J.: *Research Dept. Terr. Mag. Carnegie Inst. Wash.* **5**, Publ. 175 (1926).
15. Schweidler, E.: "Einführung in die Geophysik," vol. 2, pp. 291–375, Springer-Verlag OHG, Berlin, 1929.
16. Scrase, F. J.: *London Meteorol. Off. Geophys. Mem.* **60** (1934).
17. Sherman, K. L.: *Terr. Mag. and Atmos. Elec.* **42**, 371–390 (1937).
18. Swann, W. F. G.: Encyclopaedia Britannica, 1947.
19. Torreson, O. W., O. H. Gish, W. C. Parkinson, and G. R. Wait: *Carnegie Inst. Wash. Publ.* 568 (1946).
20. Wait, G. R., and W. D. Parkinson: *Final Report AF Contract No.* AF 19(604)-251 (1953).
21. Wait, G. R., and O. W. Torreson: *Terrestrial Magnetism and Atm. Elec.* **46** (3), 319–342 (1941).
22. Wigand, A.: *Phys. Z.* **26**, 81 (1925).
23. Wormell, T. W.: *Rev. Modern Meteorol.* **8** (1952).

TERRESTRIAL ELECTRICITY

5k-5. Earth Currents. Electric currents in the earth consist of telluric currents, natural local currents, and currents derived from industrial sources. They are detected by observation of the potential difference between two electrodes embedded in the earth.

Telluric currents flow in fairly uniform sheets over large areas; their exact cause is still in doubt. Telluric currents change continually in magnitude and direction with component periods varying from less than a second to many days. Qualitatively, these variations are related to the corresponding variations in the geomagnetic field. The principal variation is daily and has a maximum amplitude of a few tens of millivolts per kilometer. Disturbances, such as those due to magnetic storms, display amplitudes as much as 30 times the normal in middle latitudes and 150 times normal in high latitudes. Extremely large earth currents flow during thunderstorms but are more random and more localized than normal telluric currents.

Steady local currents, of much larger magnitude than telluric currents, are produced by strong chemical reactions in the earth. For example, oxidation of that part of a sulfide deposit lying above the water table, in contrast to the inactive part lying below the water table, causes current to flow along the surface of the earth toward the zone of oxidation. Potential differences above 500 mv in 100 ft have been observed. The same type of differential chemical reaction in the corrosion of buried pipes causes the flow of currents which may be used to detect the centers of corrosion.

Artificial direct currents of large but variable magnitude are caused by the ground returns of electric railroads, etc. Alternating currents of comparatively low and unpredictable magnitude are associated with power lines; frequencies of 60 cps, and its odd harmonics, predominate.

For extensive discussions concerning the details of earth currents, and how they may be measured, the reader should consult the literature.[1]

5k-6. Resistivity of the Earth. The generalized representation of the resistivity of earth materials (Fig. 5k-2) can be useful only if one considers the many factors which cause so much variation in the resistivity reported for a given rock type. The principal mechanism of conduction in rocks is electrolytic and, therefore, the resistivity of a given rock is dependent upon the amount of water which the rock contains as well as the resistivity of that water. The amount of water contained in the rock is

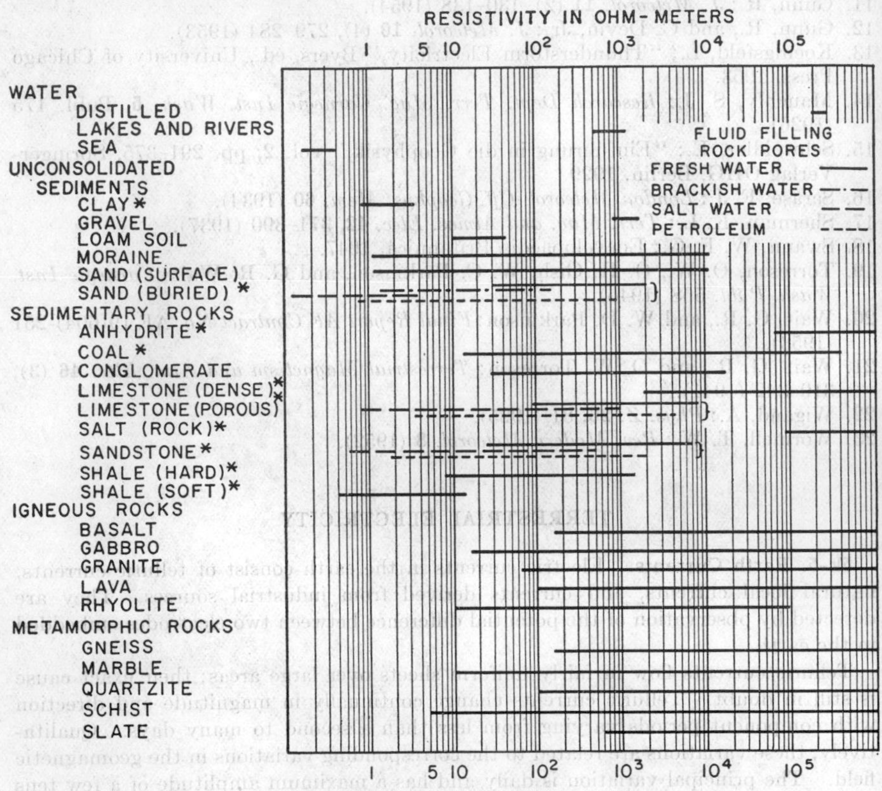

FIG. 5k-2. Resistivities of earth materials.

dependent upon two factors; the porosity of the rock, which is why the dense igneous rocks are usually more resistant than the sediments: and the availability of water to fill the pores, which explains why the near surface resistivities follow the meteorological conditions closely, rising in times of prolonged dry weather and decreasing after a soaking rain. The resistivity of the included water depends on the quantity of dissolved salts which have been gained either because the water has long been in contact with a rock normally thought to be insoluble or because the original rock minerals have been weathered into more soluble minerals. In drill holes, where the temperature increases with depth, it is important to note that the resistivity of a given rock decreases as the temperature increases. A further temperature effect lies in actual

[1] Sydney Chapman and Julius Bartels, "Geomagnetism," vol. 1, pp. 417–448, Oxford University Press, New York, 1940; "Terrestrial Magnetism and Electricity," pp. 270–307, McGraw-Hill Book Company, Inc., New York, 1939, pt. VIII of a series, "Physics of the Earth."

freezing of the enclosed water which causes the rock resistivity to increase almost infinitely. Earth materials are usually electrically anisotropic; the resistivity in a direction perpendicular to the bedding planes is appreciably greater than that in a direction parallel to the bedding planes.

In Fig. 5k-2, the values indicated with an asterisk are based on electrical resistivity logs made in drill holes.[1] Other data are largely based on laboratory and *in situ* measurements at the surface.[2] For a more detailed breakdown of rock types, etc., these references should be consulted. Either of the two textbooks gives an adequate description of how earth resistivities are measured in the field.

TERRESTRIAL MAGNETISM

5k-7. Scope and Nomenclature. Terrestrial magnetism, or *geomagnetism,* is concerned with the patterns and changes of the earth's magnetic field and with the physical entities that govern them.

The geomagnetic field vector **F** at any site is made up of the orthogonal components **X** (true north), **Y** (east), and **Z** (downward). The horizontal component of **F** (the resultant of **X** and **Y**) is **H**. The attitude of **F** is specified by its angle of *dip* or *inclination I* and by the *magnetic declination D*—the angle between **H** and true north. The angles I and D are given signs to conform, respectively, with **Z** and **Y**. These seven *magnetic elements* are connected by simple formulas, as are their small changes.

For evaluating the magnitudes F, H, X, Y, and Z, usage favors the *gamma* (γ), regarded interchangeably as a unit of induction or of magnetic intensity.[3] The methods of observation of the magnetic elements at different times and places are treated at length in the older literature. A few selected references are given.[4]

5k-8. Characteristics of the Main Field. For a general view of the geomagnetic field, Gauss devised the method of potential analysis in terms of spherical harmonics. The chief accuracy limitation arises from the scantiness of data for the polar and oceanic areas. The latest analysis[5] is one of the best available in this regard, but further strengthening may be expected as air-borne surveys encroach on the large remaining gaps.

All the analyses affirm that the field is in large part that of a centered dipole, a field pattern described by well-known functions and corresponding to the first-order terms of the harmonic expansion. The dipole axis (the earth's *magnetic axis*) is inclined about 11.5 deg to the axis of rotation; it reaches from a point in Smith Sound (longitude 69°W) to the antipodal point in the Antarctic. These points are called the *geomagnetic poles.* Geomagnetic latitude and the geomagnetic equator bear to them the same relation that the geographic latitude and equator bear to the geo-

[1] Hubert Guyod, "Electrical Well Logging Fundamentals," Well Instrument Development Company, Houston, Tex.

[2] J. J. Jakosky, "Exploration Geophysics," pp. 437–442, Trija Publishing Company, 1950; C. A. Heiland, "Geophysical Exploration," pp. 656–667, Prentice-Hall, Inc., New York, 1940; and "Handbook of Physical Constants," pp. 304–319, Geological Society of America, Special Paper 36, Jan. 31, 1942.

[3] As induction, 1 gauss = $10^5\gamma$, and 1 mks unit = $10^9\gamma$. As magnetic intensity, 1 oersted = $10^5\gamma$ and 1 mks unit = 100γ (unrationalized) or $4\pi \times 100\gamma$ (rationalized).

[4] G. Angenheister, Instrumente und Messmethoden, chap. 1 of Das Magnetfeld der Erde, in Wien-Harms, "Handbuch der Experimentalphysik," vol. 25, pt. 1, pp. 527–585, Leipzig, 1928; D. L. Hazard, Directions for Magnetic Measurements, U.S. Coast and Geodetic Survey Serial 166, 135 pp., Washington, D.C., 1930; E. Mascart, "Traité de magnétisme terrestre," 441 pp., Paris, 1900; H. E. McComb, Magnetic Observatory Manual, U.S. Coast and Geodetic Survey Special Publ. 283, 240 pp., Washington, 1952; E. O. Schonstedt and H. R. Irons, NOL Vector Airborne Magnetometer Type 2A, *Trans. Am. Geophys. Union* **36,** 25–41 (1955).

[5] H. Spencer Jones and P. J. Melotte, The Harmonic Analysis of the Earth's Magnetic Field for Epoch 1942, *Monthly Notices Roy. Astron. Soc., Geophys. Suppl.* **6,** 409–430 (1953).

graphic poles. The earth's *magnetic moment* is at present 8.1×10^{25} cgs electromagnetic units, and F ranges from about $30{,}000\gamma$ in the tropics to about $60{,}000\gamma$ in high latitudes.

However, when the actual field is compared with the centered-dipole field, there remain undoubted and serious disparities, which fall into two categories—regional and local. The *regional* departures, reflected in the higher-order terms of the analyses, are largely if not entirely capable of being described in terms of a distribution of additional dipoles embedded in a spherical boundary lying midway between the earth's center and its surface, all these dipoles being radially directed.[1] The *local* anomalies are on so small a scale geographically as to defy the practicable "resolving power" of the Gaussian treatment. They are ascribed to magnetic variegation of the relatively cool earth's crust, especially the deep-lying basement rocks. While their presence seriously impedes the determination of the regional patterns, the development of their fine structure constitutes an important phase of geophysical exploration for mineral wealth. The overlying sedimentary formations, being virtually nonmagnetic, serve to keep the observer at a distance from the chief sources of anomaly, and the intensity and scale of the surface magnetic patterns may reveal those localities where the basement rocks approach most closely to the surface.

Though the dipole approximation has its value, as in calculating the field at a distance from the earth, it is grossly inadequate for most purposes, owing to the disparities mentioned. To show the actual field, maps are overprinted with isopleths for the several magnetic elements, namely, *isogonic* lines for D, *isoclinic* lines for I, and *isodynamic* lines for the intensity elements. The isomagnetic patterns are governed to some extent by requirements arising from potential theory[2] but must be derived primarily from observed data. As commonly used to show the general patterns over large regions, the lines invariably have much or all of the local detail suppressed in their construction. Though placing some dependence on the proficiency of the cartographer, such treatment is a practical necessity, since widespread magnetic surveys cannot be conducted in the degree of detail that would be needed for full local development. Current world magnetic charts and the larger-scale series for the United States are listed in the references.

TABLE 5k-10. POSITIONS OF THE MAGNETIC DIP POLES AND OF THE F FOCI

	Northern		Southern	
	Lat	Long	Lat	Long
Dip pole.	74°N	101°W	68°S	144°E
Primary focus of F.	73°N	124°E	61°S	171°E

When such charts are studied as to the effects of the regional anomalies, it is found that: (1) the magnetic equator, or line of zero dip, does not coincide with the geomagnetic equator mentioned above but has segments lying both to the north and to the south of it; (2) the compass does not, in general, point to any pole—i.e., if azimuth lines are constructed from various localities in accordance with the values of D, such lines do not converge at a point; (3) the two magnetic dip poles, where H vanishes, do not coincide with the geomagnetic poles and are not directly opposite

[1] A. G. McNish, Physical Representations of the Geomagnetic Field, *Trans. Am. Geophys. Union* **21**, 287–291 (1940).

[2] S. Chapman, Notes on Isomagnetic Charts, *J. Geophys. Research* **45**, 433–450; **46**, 7–26, 163–172; **47**, 1–13, 115–146 (1940–1942).

one another; and (4) the foci of maximum F are even farther removed from the geomagnetic poles. When reference is made to the magnetic poles of the earth, this nearly always means the dip poles. The positions of the magnetic dip poles and of the F foci, as shown on current charts, are given in Table 5k-10.

5k-9. Secular Change. The magnetic elements are subject to gradual change from year to year. The changes for a stated interval such as a year may be depicted on a chart by means of *isoporic* lines. The patterns so formed depend on the element chosen, but in general their predominant aspect is one of regional foci of most rapid change of both signs, dispersed irregularly over the globe, and sometimes representing rates of change as great as 100γ per year at their centers. These foci have a life expectancy measured in decades, and during their lifetime they show a distinct but slow westward drift.[1]

Several investigators have sought to develop some worldwide systematic component of secular change. Thus Macht[2] fitted to the earth's field a combination of a paraxial and a transverse dipole, finding that the transverse one is displaced considerably from the axis and that it undergoes a translatory westward drift.

5k-10. Origin of the Field. The distribution of I suggests that the field is mainly of internal origin. A dipole field pattern might arise, for example, from a uniform distribution of magnetization lying parallel to a diameter, and completely filling the globe or any centrally enclosed sphere; or from a suitably disposed flow of internal electric current. The old notion that the earth was simply magnetized like a mass of magnetite failed to explain how the polarization could alter so as to account for the secular change, or how it might have arisen in the first place. And there is now ample evidence that the earth's interior is far too hot to have any permanent magnetization.

A suggestion that drew much attention in recent years held the development of magnetic moment to be a fundamental attribute of all massive rotating bodies, the magnitude being so small as to elude detection on a laboratory scale. This hypothesis says nothing of the substantial transverse component of the earth's magnetic moment, or of the secular change, and it has failed to meet certain tests involving measurements in deep mines.

The concepts now given most credence ascribe the observed field, with its regional anomalies and its secular change as well, to magnetohydrodynamic action assigned to a metallic, fluid sphere comprising the earth's core. Objections thought for a time to rule out self-exciting dynamo action in such a sphere have been met, and some progress has been made in exploring possible sources of the needed energy of maintenance, but no complete theory has as yet been formulated.[3]

5k-11. Transient Phenomena. Another segment of geomagnetism deals with small, rapid changes and has advanced chiefly through the operation of *magnetic observatories,* of which there are now about 90.

The action known as the *geomagnetic tide,* a complex system of motions in the ionosphere, involves changes in temperature and ionization in response to the variable access of solar energy, along with gravitational forces imposed by the sun and moon. The movement of conducting material across Z generates (probably in the E layer) electric currents that produce *daily variations* of all the elements, of the order of 10γ to 40γ in most latitudes. These fluctuations vary markedly from day to day in

[1] E. C. Bullard, C. Freedman, H. Gellman, and J. Nixon, The Westward Drift of the Earth's Magnetic Field, *Phil. Trans. Roy. Soc. (London)*, ser. A, **243**, 67–92 (1950).

[2] H. G. Macht, The Representation of the Main Geomagnetic Field and of Its Secular Variation by Means of Two Eccentric Dipoles, *Trans. Am. Geophys. Union* **32**, 555–562 (1951).

[3] W. M. Elsasser, Hydromagnetism: a Review, *Amer. J. Phys.* **23**, 590–608 (1955) and **24**, 85–110 (1956).

their amplitude and in their detailed configuration; but for ordinary ("quiet") days they present in long-term averages a clear-cut pattern depending on season and on the phase of the solar cycle. The study of such curves for various localities discloses the main features of the governing worldwide current system.

Several kinds of *irregularities* mark the traces recorded at magnetic observatories. A well-defined, rounded excursion of 50γ or so from an otherwise smooth course, completed in perhaps an hour, is termed a *magnetic bay*. With magnified scales it is found that fine-scale background activity of the order of 1γ is common, with characteristic frequencies predominating (depending on time of day). Near-sinusoidal trains of waves with a period of 20 to 30 sec may occur, suggesting some sort of resonance phenomenon.[1] Perturbations having a broad frequency spectrum are more often seen at the ordinary scale of recording. The incidence of these latter, as well as their severity, is loosely related to that of solar activity as reflected in the sunspot numbers. When a particularly severe solar disturbance is acting, the result may be what is termed a *magnetic storm*, lasting from several hours to a few days, with departures of possibly 500γ or more. Such disturbances are worldwide, and they may have a *sudden commencement* (SC), with a characteristic abrupt rise in H usually accompanied by an increase in activity, and followed by a progressive decrease in H in the first hour or so to abnormally low values.

Another recognized category of disturbance is the *crochet*, a sort of abbreviated magnetic bay, often associated with a solar flare (chromospheric eruption) and then called a *solar-flare effect* (SFE).[2]

Magnetic activity is reported in terms of the *K index*, a gauge of the deviations registered in successive 3-hr intervals from an assumed "normal" curve. Some progress has been made in working out techniques of forecasting magnetic activity. An important element is the 27-day recurrence tendency, a sort of quasi-periodicity that is probably connected with the longevity of the solar-disturbance centers in terms of solar rotation.

References

Chapman, S., and J. Bartels: "Geomagnetism," Oxford University Press, London, 1940. A two-volume comprehensive treatise.

Fleming, J. A., ed.: "Terrestrial Magnetism and Electricity," vol. 8 of "Physics of the Earth," McGraw-Hill Book Company, Inc., New York, 1939. A valuable compendium of monographs on various aspects of geomagnetism and related topics.

Ludy, A. K., and H. H. Howe: "Magnetism of the Earth," Serial 663 of U.S. Coast and Geodetic Survey, Government Printing Office, Washington, D.C., 1945. A nontechnical descriptive booklet that answers many questions on the topic.

U.S. Coast and Geodetic Survey: Isogonic Chart of the United States, 1955.0—Lines of Equal Magnetic Declination and Equal Annual Change, Chart 3077, scale 1:5,000,000, Washington, D.C., 1955. One of a series of magnetic charts for the various elements.

U.S. Navy Hydrographic Office: The Variation of the Compass for the Year 1955, Chart 1706, equatorial scale 1:39,000,000, Washington, D.C., 1955. One of a series of world magnetic charts for the various elements, including separate charts of the polar regions (prepared by the Coast and Geodetic Survey and published by the Hydrographic Office).

Vestine, E. H., L. Laporte, I. Lange, C. Cooper, and W. C. Hendrix: Description of the Earth's Main Magnetic Field and Its Secular Change 1905–1945, Carnegie Institution of Washington Publ. 578, Washington, 1947. Voluminous tables and charts covering many phases of the subject.

Vestine, E. H., I. Lange, L. Laporte, and W. E. Scott: The Geomagnetic Field, Its

[1] E. R. R. Holmberg, Rapid Periodic Fluctuations of the Geomagnetic Field, I, *Monthly Notices Roy. Astron. Soc., Geophys. Suppl.* **6**, 467–481 (1953).

[2] M. A. Ellison, Solar Flares and Their Terrestrial Effects, *Nature* **163**, 749–752 (1949).

Description and Analysis, Carnegie Institution of Washington Publ. 580, Washington, D.C., 1947. Details of the investigations governing the preceding item.

Vestine, E. H., and D. G. Knapp: Geomagnetism, in W. E. Forsythe, ed., "Smithsonian Physical Tables," 9th rev. ed., Smithsonian Institution Publ. 4169, Washington, D.C., 1954. A collection of 18 tables and 5 charts, giving summarized geomagnetic data for the United States and for the world. The longest table gives dated values of the seven magnetic elements for the observatories of the world.

STELLAR AND GALACTIC MAGNETISM

5k-12. Galactic Magnetism. Light from distant stars in our galaxy is appreciably polarized,[1] which has been interpreted as due to scattering from needle-shaped ferromagnetic dust particles oriented by a general magnetic field pervading the galaxy.[2] The lines of force are thought to follow, approximately, the spiral arms of the galaxy, and to deviate from mutual parallelism in the vicinity of the earth by about 10 deg due to the turbulence of the interstellar material. The fluctuations of these magnetic lines of force have been shown by Fermi, Chandrasekhar, and others to be a possible mechanism for the production of cosmic radiation.[3] The field intensity is estimated to be about 6×10^{-6} gauss.[4]

TABLE 5k-11. THE GENERAL MAGNETIC FIELD OF THE SUN

Investigator	Field intensity at north pole[a]	Year of measurements	Remarks
Hale, Langer[b]	−4 gauss	1912–1932	Reanalysis in 1935 of early data
Nicholson, Ellerman, and Hickox[c]	+3.6 ± 1.7	1933–1934	±45°
	−2.0 ± 2.8	1948–1949	Visual
von Kluber[d]	<1–2	1949–1950	±45°, photographic
Thiessen[e]	+1.5 ± 3.5	1947–1948	±45° photoelectric
	+1.5 ± 0.75	1949	
	+2.4 ± 0.5	1951	
Kiepenheuer[f]	<1 gauss	1951	Full disk, photoelectric
H. D. and H. W. Babcock[g]	+2–4 gauss at ±70°	1952	Photoelectric, recording full disk

[a] Polarity definition: magnetic vector toward observer is +. Note Thiessen used contrary definition.
[b] G. E. Hale, *Nature* **136**, 703 (1935).
[c] *Ann. Rept. Mt. Wilson Obs., C. I. W. Yearbook*, 1934, p. 138; 1949, p. 12.
[d] H. von Kluber, *Monthly Notices Roy. Astron. Soc.* **111**, 2 (1951); **114**, 242 (1954).
[e] G. Thiessen, *Z. Astrophys.* **26**, 16 (1949); **30**, 185 (1952); *Nature* **169**, 147 (1952); *Ann. astrophys.* **9**, 101 (1946).
[f] K. O. Kiepenheuer, *Astrophys. J.* **117**, 447 (1953).
[g] H. W. Babcock, *Astrophys. J.* **118**, 387 (1953); **119**, 687 (1954); H. W. Babcock and H. D. Babcock, *Publ. Astron. Soc. Pacific* **64**, 282 (1952).

5k-13. General Magnetic Field of the Sun. The Zeeman effect affords the only direct means for measuring the intensities of astronomical magnetic fields. It has been used to study the magnetic fields of variable stars and sunspots, and to search for a general dipole field of the sun. The techniques and results of the general solar field have been reviewed by H. W. Babcock and T. G. Cowling.[5] Table 5k-11 sum-

[1] W. A. Hiltner and J. Hall, *Astrophys. J.* **114**, 241 (1951).
[2] L. Spitzer and J. W. Tukey, *Astrophys. J.* **114**, 187 (1951).
[3] E. Fermi, *Astrophys. J.* **119**, 1 (1954).
[4] S. Chandrasekhar and E. Fermi, *Astrophys. J.* **118**, 113 (1953).
[5] H. W. Babcock and T. G. Cowling, *Monthly Notices Roy. Astron. Soc.* **113**, 357 (1953).

TABLE 5k-12. POLAR MAGNETIC FIELD STRENGTHS H_p OF 35 STARS*

Star	Mag.	Type	No. plates meas.	H_p, gauss, extremes	Probable error	Remarks
HD 2453......	6.7	Aop	1	−1,520	±300	
HD 4174......	7.5	M2ep	4	+3,500, −3,900	±600	$H\beta$ varies
HD 8441......	6.6	Aop	1	+1,300, −	±500	
HD 10783......	6.6	A3p	7	+5,000, −2,500		
HR 710......	5.8	A2p	11	−1,070, −2,970	±250	
HR 1105......	5.3	S	1	+1,470	±210	
36 Eri......	4.7	Aop	1	+1,360	±700	
μ Lep......	3.3	Aop	2	+620	±250	
WY Gem......	7	M3ep	1	+1,800	±500	
HD 42616......	6.9	Aop	3	+2,250, −2,770	±600	
HD 49976......	6.2	Aop	1	+3,400	±800	
HD 60414, 5..	5.1	M3ep	1	−2,200		
HD 71866......	6.7	Aop	1	−4,000	±400	
3 Hya......	5.6	A2p	7	+2,440, −1,600	±350	
49 Cnc......	5.6	A4p	5	+4,000, −600	±400	Sp. var.
45 Leo......	5.9	Ao	3	+1,000, −250	......	Sp. var.
17 Com A......	5.4	Aop	3	−1,600, −3,800	......	Sp. var.
α^2 C Vn......	2.9	Aop	21	+5,000, −4,000	......	Sp. var.
78 Vir......	4.9	A2p	13	−500, −3,350	±200	Sp. var.
HD 125248......	5.7	Aop	29	+7,000, −6,000	......	Sp. var.
μ Lib A......	5.4	A4p	2	−1,600, −3,900	±400	
HD 133029......	6.2	Aop	45	+4,300, +10,500	......	~1.5^d
β Cr B......	3.7	Fop	12	+2,670, −900	±150	
52 Her......	4.9	A2p	1	+2,780	±300	
HD 153882......	6.2	Aop	20	+4,500, −4,000	......	$P = 6^d.005$
HD 173650......	6.4	Aop	2	+1,600, −1,300	±350	
10 Aql......	5.9	A3p	2	+900, +460	±120	
21 Aql......	5.1	B8	4	+500, −1,900	±500	
HD 188041......	5.6	Fop	41	+1,240, +4,750	±150	$P = 226^d$
HD 192913......	6.7	Aop	1	−1,730		
73 Dra......	5.2	A2p	5	−1,200, −2,300	......	Sp. var.
γ Equ......	4.8	Fop	9	+760, +2,750	±110	
AG Peg......	7.6	Bep	5	−1,400, −4,000		
VV Cep......	5v	M2e	2	+2,000, −1,200	±300	
HD 224801......	6.2	Aop	1	+7,500	±1,400	

* Taken from Table I of H. W. Babcock and T. G. Cowling, *Monthly Notices Roy. Astron. Soc.* **113**, 357 (1953).

marizes the principal results. H. W. and H. D. Babcock now make daily records of the details of the solar field mapped over the whole disk, measured to a stated precision of 1 gauss. The longitudinal Zeeman effect due to a pure dipole field would be a maximum at ±45° solar latitude. The measurements of Thiessen and of von Kluber (see Table 5k-11) were made at this latitude. Thus the distorted general field of 2 to 4 gauss at latitudes > ±65° found by the Babcocks would presumably not have been detected by Thiessen or von Kluber. Kiepenheuer examined the full disk with negative results. The polarity of the field found by the Babcocks is opposite to the polarity of the earth and of the sunspots in cycle (No. 18) approaching a minimum in 1955. It is also opposite to the field found by Hale. It is possible that the solar field is not constant and that the sun may be thought of as a weak magnetic variable star.

5k-14. Sunspot Fields. Sunspots[1] vary greatly in both size and magnetic-field strength, although size and field are closely related. Sunspot areas are measured in units of one-millionth of a solar hemisphere and have been observed as large as 5,400 millionths (Feb. 6, 1946) and as small as one-millionth (specks). The corresponding magnetic-field strengths vary from about 3,700 to about 100 gauss. An individual spot has a dark central region (umbra) and a brighter filamentary region (penumbra) surrounding it. The field strength of the spot is found to vary radially according to the empirical formula of Broxon:[2] $H = H_m(1 - r^2/b^2)$, where H_m is the maximum field strength, and b is the outer radius of the penumbra. Sunspots are normally found in groups extended in the direction of solar rotation in two low-latitude zones on either side of the solar equator. Each group contains leader and follower spots of opposite magnetic polarity. The abundance of spots follows the 11-year sunspot cycle. Slightly in advance of sunspot minimum the new spots of the coming cycle appear near 30° latitude, gradually decreasing to about 8° during the cycle. In the present cycle (No. 18, beginning in 1944) the leading spots in the northern solar hemisphere are south poles, the following spots north. The polarity of the spots in the southern hemisphere is reversed. In the next sunspot cycle, all these polarities will be reversed: i.e., the leading northern hemisphere spots will be north poles, etc. Thus the "magnetic sunspot cycle" has a 22-year period.[3]

5k-15. Stellar Magnetic Fields. Many stars have strong magnetic fields easily detected with the Zeeman technique. Since only the integrated light from one hemisphere of the star can be measured, only those stars with general nonmultipolar fields which are oriented with the magnetic axis inclined toward the line of observation will show a strong Zeeman shift. To date observations are restricted to stars brighter than magnitude 7.6. Variable magnetic fields of 650 to 10,500 gauss maximum intensity have been measured in stars of a wide variety of spectral types. Among the most interesting are the spectrum variables, in which the magnetic oscillations are of greatest amplitude and are in fixed phase relationship with the spectral variations. The data of Table 5k-12 are taken from Babcock and Cowling's review, General Magnetic Fields in the Sun and Stars.[4] Theories of stellar magnetism are reviewed in Part II of their review.

[1] E. Pettit, "The Sun and Stellar Radiation," in J. A. Hynek, "Astrophysics, A Topical Symposium," McGraw-Hill Book Company, Inc., New York, 1951; W. Grotrian, *Z. angew. Phys.* **2,** 376 (1950).

[2] J. W. Broxon, *Phys. Rev.* **62,** 508 (1942).

[3] G. E. Hale and S. B. Nicholson, *Astrophys. J.* **62,** 270 (1925).

[4] H. W. Babcock and T. G. Cowling, *Monthly Notices Roy. Astron. Soc.* **113,** 357 (1953).

Section 6

OPTICS[1]

BRUCE H. BILLINGS, Editor
Baird-Atomic, Inc., and Harvard College Observatory

CONTENTS

6a. Fundamental Definitions, Standards, and Photometric Units 6-2
6b. Index of Refraction 6-11
6c. Absorption and Transmission 6-36
6d. Reflection 6-41
6e. Glass, Polarizing and Interference Filters 6-43
6f. Colorimetry 6-50
6g. Radiometry 6-64
6h. Wavelengths for Spectrographic Calibration 6-83
6i. Magneto- and Electro-optics 6-91
6j. Specific Rotation 6-98
6k. Optical Constants of Metals 6-102
6l. Fluorescence and Phosphorescence 6-111
6m. Radiation Detection 6-114
6n. Velocity of Light 6-119
6o. Radio Astronomy 6-120

[1] Subsections for which specific authors are not listed were compiled by the section editor. Source credits are indicated in the text.

6a. Fundamental Definitions, Standards, and Photometric Units[1]

6a-1. Fundamental Definitions

Absorption Factor. The ratio of the intensity loss by absorption to the total original intensity of radiation. If I_o represents the original intensity, I_r the intensity of reflected radiation, I_t the intensity of the transmitted radiation, the absorption factor is given by the expression

$$\frac{I_o - (I_r + I_t)}{I_o}$$

Also called *coefficient of absorption.*

Absorption, Lambert's Law. If I_o is the original intensity, I the intensity after passing through a thickness x of a material whose absorption coefficient is α,

$$I = I_o e^{-\alpha x}$$

The *extinction coefficient* κ is given by the relation $\kappa = (4\pi\kappa n)/\lambda$ where n is the index of refraction and λ the wavelength *in vacuo.* The *mass absorption* is given by k/d when d is the density. The transmission factor is given by I/I_o.

Absorption Spectrum. The spectrum obtained by the examination of light from a source, itself giving a continuous spectrum, after this light has passed through an absorbing medium in the gaseous state. The absorption spectrum will consist of dark lines or bands, being the reverse of the emission spectrum of the absorbing substance.

When the absorbing medium is in the solid or liquid state the spectrum of the transmitted light shows broad dark regions which are not resolvable into lines and have no sharp or distinct edges.

Absorptive Power or Absorptivity. For any body, this is measured by the fraction of the radiant energy falling upon the body which is absorbed or transformed into heat. This ratio varies with the character of the surface and the wavelength of the incident energy. It is the ratio of the radiation absorbed by any substance to that absorbed under the same conditions by a black body.

Achromatic. A term applied to lenses signifying their more or less complete correction for chromatic aberration.

Angular Aperture. The largest angular extent of wave surface which an objective can transmit.

Apochromat. A term applied to photographic and microscope objectives indicating the highest degree of color correction.

Astigmatism. An error of spherical lenses peculiar to the formation of images by oblique pencils. The image of a point when astigmatism is present will consist of two focal lines at right angles to each other and separated by a measurable distance

[1] Definitions, standards, and units presented in this section follow for the most part the wording used in the "Handbook of Chemistry and Physics," 36th ed., pp. 2480, 2787–2841, 2880–2881, Chemical Rubber Publishing Company, 1954–1955.

along the axis of the pencil. The error is not eliminated by reduction of aperture as is spherical aberration.

Balmer Series of Spectral Lines. The wavelengths of a series of lines in the spectrum of hydrogen are given in Angstroms by the equation

$$\lambda = 3{,}646 \frac{N^2}{N^2 - 4}$$

where N is an integer having values greater than 2.

Beer's Law (1852). If two solutions of the same salt are made in the same solvent, one of which is, say, twice the concentration of the other, the absorption due to a given thickness of the first solution should be equal to that of twice the thickness of the second.

Black Body. If, for all values of the wavelength of the incident radiant energy, all the energy is absorbed the body is called a black body.

Brewster's Law. The tangent of the polarizing angle for a substance is equal to the index of refraction. The polarizing angle is that angle of incidence for which the reflected polarized ray is at right angles to the refracted ray. If n is the index of refraction and θ the polarizing angle, $n = \tan\theta$.

Brightness. Measured by the flux emitted per unit emissive area as projected on a plane normal to the line of sight. The unit of brightness is that of a perfectly diffusing surface giving out one lumen per square centimeter of projected surface and is called the Lambert. The milli-Lambert (0.001 Lambert) is a more convenient unit. *Candle per square centimeter* is the brightness of a surface which has, in the direction considered, a luminous intensity of one candle per cm². The *international candle* is a unit of luminous intensity, based on a group of 45 carbon-filament lamps preserved at the National Bureau of Standards. The *new candle* is $\frac{1}{60}$ the intensity of one square centimeter of a black-body radiator at the solidification temperature of platinum (2042°K).

Chemiluminescence. Emission of light during a chemical reaction.

Christiansen Effect. When finely powdered substances, such as glass or quartz, are immersed in a liquid of the same index of refraction complete transparency can be obtained only for monochromatic light. If white light is employed, the transmitted color corresponds to the particular wavelength for which the two substances, solid and liquid, have exactly the same index of refraction. Because of differences in dispersion the indices of refraction will match for only a narrow band of the spectrum.

Chromatic Aberration. Because of the difference in the index of refraction for different wavelengths, light of various wavelengths from the same source cannot be focused at a point by a simple lens. This is called chromatic aberration.

Coma. An aberration of spherical lenses, occurring in the case of oblique incidence, when the bundle of rays forming the image is unsymmetrical. The image of a point is comet-shaped, hence the name.

Conjugate Foci. Under proper conditions light divergent from a point on or near the axis of a lens or spherical mirror is focused at another point. The point of convergence and the position of the source are interchangeable and are called conjugate foci.

Diffraction. If the light source were a point, the shadow of any object would have its maximum sharpness; a certain amount of illumination, however, would be found within the geometrical shadow because of the diffraction of the light at the edge of the object.

Diffraction Grating. If s is the distance between the rulings, d the angle of diffraction, then the wavelength where the angle of incidence is 90 deg is (for the nth order spectrum),

$$\lambda = \frac{s \sin d}{n}$$

Dispersion. The difference between the index of refraction of any substance for any two wavelengths is a measure of the dispersion for these wavelengths, called the coefficient of dispersion.

Dispersive Power. If n_1 and n_2 are the indices of refraction for wavelengths λ_1 and λ_2 and n the mean index or that for sodium light, the dispersive power for the specified wavelength is

$$\omega = \frac{n_2 - n_1}{n - 1}$$

Doppler Effect (Light). The apparent change in the wavelength of light produced by the motion in the line of sight of either the observer or the source of light.

If i is the angle of incidence, d the angle of diffraction, s the distance between the rulings, n the order of the spectrum, the wavelength is

$$\lambda = \frac{s}{n} (\sin i + \sin d)$$

Emissive Power, or Emissivity. This is measured by the energy radiated from unit area of a surface in unit time for unit difference of temperature between the surface in question and surrounding bodies. For the cgs system the emissive power is given in ergs per second per square centimeter with the radiating surface at 1°K and the surroundings at absolute zero. See Radiation Formula.

Faraday Effect. The rotation of the plane of polarization produced when plane-polarized light is passed through a substance in a magnetic field, the light traveling in a direction parallel to the lines of force. For a given substance, the rotation is proportional to the thickness traversed by the light and to the magnetic-field strength.

Fermat's Principle of Least Time. The path chosen by a ray joining two points is that which can be traveled over in the least possible time.

Fraunhofer's Lines. When sunlight is examined through a spectroscope it is found that the spectrum is traversed by an enormous number of dark lines parallel to the length of the slit. These dark lines are known as Fraunhofer's lines. Kirchhoff conceived the idea that the sun is surrounded by layers of vapors which act as filters of the white light arising from incandescent solids within and which abstract those rays which correspond in their periods of vibration to those of the components of the vapors. Thus reversed or dark lines are obtained because of the absorption by the vapor envelope, in place of the bright lines found in the emission spectrum.

Huygens' Theory of Light. This theory states that light is a disturbance traveling through some medium, such as the ether. Thus light is due to wave motion in ether.

Every vibrating point on the wavefront is regarded as the center of a new disturbance. These secondary disturbances, traveling with equal velocity, are enveloped by a surface identical in its properties with the surface from which the secondary disturbances start and this surface forms the new wavefront.

Illumination. On any surface, illumination is measured by the luminous flux incident on unit area. The units in use are: the *lux*, one lumen per square meter; the *phot*, one lumen per square centimeter and the lumen per square foot. Since at unit distance from a point source of unit intensity the illumination is unity, unit illumination may be defined as that produced by a unit source at unit distance, hence the *meter-candle* or *candle-meter* which is equal to the lux and the *foot-candle* equivalent to one lumen per square foot.

Index of Refraction. For any substance this is the ratio of the velocity of light in a vacuum to its velocity in the substance. It is also the ratio of the sine of the angle of incidence to the sine of the angle of refraction. In general, the index of refraction for any substance varies with the wavelength of the refracted light.

Intensity of Illumination. In candle-meters of a screen illuminated by a source of illuminating power P candles at a distance r meters, for normal incidence, intensity of illumination is

$$I = \frac{P}{r^2}$$

If two sources of illuminating power P_1 and P_2 produce equal illumination on a screen when at distances r_1 and r_2, respectively,

$$\frac{P_1}{r_1^2} = \frac{P_2}{r_2^2} \quad \text{or} \quad \frac{P_1}{P_2} = \frac{r_1^2}{r_2^2}$$

If I_o is the intensity of illumination when the screen is normal to the incident light and I the intensity when an angle θ

$$I = I_o \cos \theta$$

Intensity of Radiation. The radiant energy emitted in a specified direction per unit time, per unit area of surface, per unit solid angle.

Kirchhoff's Laws of Radiation. The relation between the powers of emission and the powers of absorption for rays of the same wavelength is constant for all bodies at the same temperature. First, a substance when excited by some means or other possesses a certain power of emission; it tends to emit definite rays, whose wavelengths depend upon the nature of the substance and upon the temperature. Second, the substance exerts a definite absorptive power, which is a maximum for the rays it tends to emit. Third, at a given temperature the ratio between the emissive and the absorptive power for a given wavelength is the same for all bodies and is equal to the emissive power of a perfectly black body.

Lambert's Law of Absorption. Each layer of equal thickness absorbs an equal fraction of the light which traverses it.

Lambert's Law of Illumination. The illumination of a surface on which the light falls normally from a point source is inversely proportional to the square of the distance of the surface from the source. If the normal to the surface makes an angle with the direction of the rays, the illumination is proportional to the cosine of that angle.

Lenses. For a single thin lens whose surfaces have radii of curvature r_1 and r_2 whose principal focus is F, the index of refraction n, and conjugate focal distances f_1 and f_2,

$$\frac{1}{F} = \frac{1}{f_1} + \frac{1}{f_2} = (n-1)\left(\frac{1}{r_1} + \frac{1}{r_2}\right)$$

For a thick lens, of thickness t,

$$F = \frac{nr_1r_2}{(n-1)[n(r_1+r_2) - t(n-1)]}$$

COMBINATIONS OF LENSES. If f_1 and f_2 are the focal lengths of two thin lenses separated by a distance d the focal length of the system,

$$F = \frac{f_1f_2}{f_1 + f_2 - d}$$

Luminous Flux. The total visible energy emitted by a source per unit time is called the total luminous flux from the source. The unit of flux, the *lumen*, is the flux emitted in unit solid angle (steradian) by a point source of one candle luminous intensity. A uniform point source of one candle intensity thus emits 4π lumens.

Luminous Intensity, or Candlepower. This is the property of a source of emitting luminous flux and may be measured by the luminous flux emitted per unit solid angle. The accepted unit of luminous intensity is the *international candle.* The *Hefner unit,* which is equivalent to 0.9 international candle, is the intensity of a lamp of specified design burning amyl acetate, called the Hefner lamp.

The mean horizontal candlepower is the average intensity measured in a horizontal plane passing through the source. The mean spherical candlepower is the average candlepower measured in all directions and is equal to the total luminous flux in lumens divided by 4π.

Magnifying Power. In an optical instrument this is the ratio of the angle subtended by the image of the object seen through the instrument to the angle subtended by the object when seen by the unaided eye. In the case of the microscope or simple magnifier the object as viewed by the unaided eye is supposed to be a distance of 25 cm (10 in.).

Minimum Deviation. The deviation or change of direction of light passing through a prism is a minimum when the angle of incidence is equal to the angle of emergence. If D is the angle of minimum deviation and A the angle of the prism, the index of refraction of the prism for the wavelength used is

$$n = \frac{\sin \frac{1}{2}(A + D)}{\sin \frac{1}{2}A}$$

Molecular Refraction. The molecular refraction of a substance may be computed by the following relation:

$$N = \frac{M(n^2 - 1)}{d(n^2 + 2)}$$

where N is the molecular refraction for a specified wavelength and temperature, M the molecular weight, d the density, and n the refractive index for the specified conditions.

Nodal Points. Two points on the axis of a lens such that a ray entering the lens in the direction of one, leaves as if from the other and parallel to the original direction.

Photographic Density. The density D of silver deposit on a photographic plate or film is defined by the relation

$$D = \log O$$

where O is the opacity. If I_o and I are the incident and transmitted intensities, respectively, the opacity is given by I_o/I. The transparency is the reciprocal of the opacity, or I/I_o.

Polarized Light. Light which exhibits different properties in different directions at right angles to the line of propagation is said to be polarized. Specific rotation is the power of liquids to rotate the plane of polarization. It is stated in terms of specific rotation or the rotation in degrees per decimeter per unit density.

Principal Focus. For a lens or spherical mirror this is the point of convergence of light coming from a source at an infinite distance.

Radiation. If I_o is the intensity of normal radiation and I the intensity at an angle Θ

$$I = I_o \cos \Theta$$

This is called Lambert's law. It does not apply in all cases.

Radiation Formula, Planck's. The emissive power of a black body at wavelength λ may be written

$$E_\lambda = \frac{c_1\lambda^{-5}}{e^{c_2/\lambda T} - 1}$$

where c_1 and c_2 are constants with numerical values 3.7403×10^8 microwatts per cm² per 0.01μ zone of spectrum and $14{,}384\mu$ deg, respectively, and T the absolute temperature.

Radius of Curvature from Spherometer Readings. If l is the mean length of the sides of the triangle formed by the points of the three legs, d the spherometer readings, the radius of curvature of the surface is

$$F = \frac{l^2}{6d} + \frac{d}{2}$$

Reflection Coefficient, or Reflectivity. This is the ratio of the light reflected from a surface to the total incident light. The coefficient may refer to diffuse or to specular reflection. In general it varies with the angle of incidence and with the wavelength of the light.

Reflection of Light by a Transparent Medium in Air (Fresnel's Formulas). If i is the angle of incidence, r the angle of refraction, n_1 the index of refraction for air (nearly equal to unity), n_2 the index of refraction for a medium, then the ratio of the reflected light to the incident light is

$$R = \frac{1}{2}\left(\frac{\sin^2(i - r)}{\sin^2(i + r)} + \frac{\tan^2(i - r)}{\tan^2(i + r)}\right)$$

If $i = 0$ (normal incidence), and $n_1 = l$ (approximate for air),

$$R = \left(\frac{n_2 - 1}{n_2 + 1}\right)^2$$

Refraction at a Spherical Surface. If u is the distance of a point source, v the distance of the point image or the intersection of the refracted ray with the axis, n_1 and n_2 the indices of refraction of the first and second medium, and r the radius of curvature of the separating surface,

$$\frac{n_2}{v} + \frac{n_1}{u} = \frac{n_2 - n_1}{r}$$

If the first medium is air the equation becomes

$$\frac{n}{v} + \frac{1}{u} = \frac{n - 1}{r}$$

Refractivity is given by $(n - 1)$ when n is the index of refraction; the *specific refractivity* is given by $(n - 1)/d$ where d is the density. *Molecular refractivity* is the product of specific refractivity by the molecular weight.

Resolving Power. For a telescope or microscope this is indicated by the minimum separation of two objects for which they appear distinct and separate when viewed through the instrument.

The *molecular* or *atomic rotatory power* is the product of the specific rotatory power by the molecular or atomic weight. Magnetic rotatory power is given by

$$\frac{\theta}{e} H \cos \alpha$$

where H is the intensity of the magnetic field, and α is the angle between the field and the direction of the light.

Snell's Law of Refraction. If i is the angle of incidence, r the angle of refraction, v the velocity of light in the first medium, v' the velocity in the second medium, the index of refraction n,

$$n = \frac{\sin i}{\sin r} = \frac{v}{v'}$$

Specific Rotation. If there are n grams of active substance in v cubic centimeters of solution and the light passes through l centimeters, r being the observed rotation in degrees, the specific rotation (for 1 cm),

$$[\alpha] = \frac{rv}{nl}$$

Spectral Series. These are spectral lines or groups of lines which occur in an orderly sequence.

Spherical Aberration. When large surfaces of spherical mirrors or lenses are used the light divergent from a point source is not exactly focused at a point. The phenomenon is known as spherical aberration. For axial pencils the error is known as axial spherical aberration; for oblique pencils, coma.

Spherical Mirrors. If R is the radius of curvature, F the principal focus, and f_1 and f_2 any two conjugate focal distances,

$$\frac{1}{f_1} + \frac{1}{f_2} = \frac{1}{F} = \frac{2}{R}$$

If the linear dimensions of the object and image be O and I, respectively, and u and v their distances from the mirror,

$$\frac{O}{I} = \frac{u}{v}$$

Total Reflection. When light passes from any medium to one in which the velocity is greater, refraction ceases and total reflection begins at a certain critical angle of incidence θ such that

$$\sin\theta = \frac{1}{n}$$

where n is the index of the first medium with respect to the second. If the second medium is air n has the ordinary value for the first medium. For any other second medium,

$$n = \frac{n_1}{n_2}$$

where n_1 and n_2 are the ordinary indices of refraction for the first and second medium, respectively.

Visibility. This is measured by the ratio of the luminous flux in lumens to the total radiant energy in ergs per second or in watts.

Watt of Maximum Visibility Radiation. 680 lumens.

Wien's Displacement Law. When the temperature of a radiating black body increases, the wavelength corresponding to maximum energy decreases in such a way that the product of the absolute temperature and wavelength is constant.

$$\lambda_{\max} T = w$$

Zeeman Effect. The splitting of a spectrum line into several symmetrically disposed components, which occurs when the source of light is placed in a strong magnetic field. The components are polarized, the directions of polarization and the appearance of the effect depending on the direction from which the source is viewed relative to the lines of force.

6a-2. Fundamental Standards. The *international candle* is a unit of luminous intensity. It is a specified fraction of the average horizontal candlepower of a group of 45 carbon-filament lamps preserved at the National Bureau of Standards. The *new candle* is $\frac{1}{60}$ of the intensity of one square centimeter of a black-body radiator at the solidification temperature of platinum (2042°K). The *primary standard wavelength* which defines the Angstrom unit is the red cadmium line in air, 760 mm pressure, 15°C, at 6,438.4696 A.

FLAME STANDARDS

(Value of various former standards in international candles)

	Candles
Standard pentane lamp, burning pentane	10.0
Standard Hefner lamp, burning amyl acetate	0.9
Standard Carcel lamp, burning colza oil	9.6

The *Carcel unit* is the horizontal intensity of the carcel lamp, burning 42 g of colza oil per hr. For a consumption between 38 and 46 g/hr the intensity may be considered proportional to the consumption.

The *Hefner unit* is the horizontal intensity of the Hefner lamp burning amyl acetate, with a flame 4 cm high. If the flame is l mm high, the intensity $I = 1 + 0.027(l - 40)$.

6a-3. Photometric Quantities, Units, and Standards.

Candle (or International Candle). The candle is the unit of luminous intensity. It is a specified fraction of the average horizontal candlepower of a group of 45 carbon-filament lamps preserved at the Bureau of Standards.

Candle (new unit). $\frac{1}{60}$ of the intensity of one square centimeter of a black-body radiator at the temperature of solidification of platinum (2042°K).

Lumen. The lumen is the unit of luminous flux. It is equal to the flux through a unit solid angle (steradian) from a uniform point source of one candle, or to the flux on a unit surface all points of which are at unit distance from a uniform point source of one candle.

Illumination. Illumination is the density of the luminous flux on a surface. It is the quotient of the flux by the area of the surface when the latter is uniformly illuminated.

Least Mechanical Equivalent of Light. One lumen at the wavelength of maximum visibility (0.556μ) equals 0.00161 watt (= 0.000385 g-cal/sec); one watt at the same wavelength equals 680 lumens.

Relative Visibility. The relative-visibility factor for a particular wavelength is the ratio of the visibility factor for that wavelength to the maximum visibility factor.

Values of the relative visibility are given as a part of the specification of the standard observer under Colorimetry.

Efficiency of a Source of Light. The efficiency of a source is the ratio of the total luminous flux to the total power consumed. In the case of an electric lamp it is expressed in lumens per watt.

Spherical Candlepower. The spherical candlepower of a lamp is the average candlepower of the lamp in all directions in space. It is equal to the total luminous flux of the lamp in lumens divided by 4π.

Lambert. The unit of brightness equal to $1/\pi$ candle per square centimeter.

Foot-Lambert. The unit of photometric brightness (luminance) equal to $1/\pi$ candle per square foot.

6a-4. Photometric Units

Bougie Decimale (intensity of source). 1.0 international candle (approximately).

Candle (International) (intensity of source). 0.104 Carcel unit (approximately);

1.0000 international lumen per steradian; 1 pentane candle (approximately); 1 English sperm candle (approximately); 1.11 Hefner unit (approximately).

Candle per square centimeter (surface brightness). 3.1416 Lamberts; 3141.6 milli-Lamberts.

Candle per square inch (surface brightness). 0.48695 Lambert; 486.95 milli-Lamberts.

Carcel unit (intensity of source). 9.6 international candle (approximately).

English sperm candle (intensity of source). 1.0 international candle (approximately).

Foot-candle (illumination of a surface). 1 lumen incident per square foot; 1.0764 milliphots; 10.764 lumens per square meter; 10.764 lux.

Hefner unit (intensity of source). 0.90 international candle (approximately).

Lambert (surface brightness). 0.3183 candle per square centimeter; 2.054 candles per square inch; 1 lumen emitted per square centimeter of a perfectly diffusing surface.

Lumen (flux of luminous energy). Is emitted by 0.07958 spherical candlepower. A source of one spherical candlepower emits 4π or 12.566 lumens.

Lumen per square centimeter per steradian (surface brightness). 3.1416 Lamberts.

Lumen per square foot (illumination of a surface). 1 foot-candle; 10.764 lumens per square meter.

Lumen per square foot per steradian (surface brightness). 3.3816 milli-Lamberts.

Lumen per square meter (surface illumination). 1×10^{-4} phot; 0.092902 foot-candle or lumen per square foot.

Lux (illumination of a surface). 1×10^{-4} phot; 0.1 milliphot; 0.092902 foot-candle; 1.000 lumen per square meter.

Meter-candle (illumination of a surface). 1.000 lumen per square meter.

Milli-Lambert (surface brightness). 0.929 lumen emitted per square foot (perfect diffusion).

Milliphot (illumination of a surface). 0.001 phot; 0.929 foot-candle.

Pentane candle (intensity of source). 1.0 international candle (approximately).

Phot (illumination of a surface). 1 lumen incident per square centimeter; 1,000 milliphots; 1.000×10^4 lumens per square meter; 1×10^4 lux.

Stilb (surface brightness). 1 candle per square centimeter.

6b. Index of Refraction

S. S. BALLARD
Scripps Institution of Oceanography

K. A. McCARTHY
Tufts University

W. BROUWER
Baird-Atomic, Inc.

The index of refraction, usually denoted by n, is defined as the ratio of the velocity of light in a vacuum to the velocity of light in the given material. Indices not otherwise indicated are for sodium light, $\lambda = 589.3$ mμ. Other wavelengths are indicated by the value in millimicrons or symbol in parentheses which follows the index. Wavelengths are indicated as follows: He, $\lambda = 587.6$ mμ; Li, $\lambda = 670.8$ mμ; Hg, $\lambda = 579.1$ mμ; A, $\lambda = 759.4$ mμ; C, $\lambda = 656.3$ mμ; D, $\lambda = 589.3$ mμ; F, $\lambda = 486.1$ mμ.

Temperatures are understood to be 20°C for liquids, or ordinary room temperatures in the case of solids. Other temperatures appear as superior figures with the index.

TABLE 6b-1. INDEX OF REFRACTION OF SELECTED UNIAXIAL MINERALS*

Mineral	Formula	Index of refraction	
		Ordinary ray	Extraordinary ray
Uniaxial Positive Minerals			
Ice	H_2O	1.309	1.313
Sellaite	MgF_2	1.378	1.390
Chrysocolla	$CuO \cdot SiO_2 \cdot 2H_2O$	1.460 ±	1.570 ±
Laubanite	$2CaO \cdot Al_2O_3 \cdot 5SiO_2 \cdot 6H_2O$	1.475	1.486
Chabazite	$(Ca, Na_2)O \cdot Al_2O_3 \cdot 4SiO_2 \cdot 6H_2O$	1.480 ±	1.482 ±
Douglasite	$2KCl \cdot FeCl_2 \cdot 2H_2O$	1.488	1.500
Hydronephelite	$2Na_2O \cdot 3Al_2O_3 \cdot 6SiO_2 \cdot 7H_2O$	1.490	1.502
Apophyllite	$K_2O \cdot 8CaO \cdot 16SiO_2 \cdot 16H_2O$	1.535 ±	1.537 ±
Quartz	SiO_2	1.544	1.553
Coquimbite	$Fe_2O_3 \cdot 3SO_3 \cdot 9H_2O$	1.550	1.556
Brucite	$MgO \cdot H_2O$	1.559	1.580
Alunite	$K_2O \cdot 3Al_2O_3 \cdot 4SO_3 \cdot 6H_2O$	1.572	1.592
Penninite	$5(Mg, Fe)O \cdot Al_2O_3 \cdot 3SiO_2 \cdot 4H_2O$	1.576	1.579
Cacoxenite	$2Fe_2O_3 \cdot P_2O_5 \cdot 12H_2O$	1.582	1.645
Eudialite	$6Na_2O \cdot 6(Ca, Fe)O \cdot 20(Si, Zr)O_2 \cdot NaCl$	1.606	1.611
Dioptase	$CuO \cdot SiO_2 \cdot H_2O$	1.654	1.707
Phenacite	$2BeO \cdot SiO_2$	1.654	1.670
Parisite	$2CeOF \cdot CaO \cdot 3CO_2$	1.676 ±	1.757
Willemite	$2ZnO \cdot SiO_2$	1.691	1.719
Vesuvianite	$2(Ca, Mn, Fe)O \cdot (Al, Fe)(OH, F)O \cdot 2SiO_2$	1.716 ±	1.721
Xenotime	$Y_2O_3 \cdot P_2O_5$	1.721	1.816
Connellite	$20CuO \cdot SO_3 \cdot 2CuCl_2 \cdot 20H_2O$	1.724	1.746
Benitoite	$BaO \cdot TiO_2 \cdot 3SiO_2$	1.757	1.804
Ganomalite	$6PbO \cdot 4(Ca, Mn)O \cdot 6SiO_2 \cdot H_2O$	1.910	1.945
Scheelite	$CaO \cdot WO_3$	1.918	1.934
Zircon	$ZrO_2 \cdot SiO_2$	1.923 ±	1.968 ±
Powellite	$CaO \cdot MoO_3$	1.974	1.978
Calomel	$HgCl$	1.973	2.650
Cassiterite	SnO_2	1.997	2.093
Zincite	ZnO	2.013	2.029
Phosgenite	$PbO \cdot PbCl_2 \cdot CO_2$	2.114	2.140
Penfieldite	$PbO \cdot PbCl_2$	2.130	2.210
Iodyrite	AgI	2.210	2.220
Tapiolite	$FeO \cdot (Ta, Nb)_2O_5$	2.270	2.420 (Li line)
Wurtzite	ZnS	2.356	2.378
Derbylite	$6FeO \cdot Sb_2O_3 \cdot 5TiO_2$	2.450	2.510 (Li line)
Greenockite	CdS	2.506	2.529
Rutile	TiO_2	2.616	2.903
Moissanite	CSi	2.654	2.697
Cinnabar	HgS	2.854	3.201

TABLE 6b-1. INDEX OF REFRACTION OF SELECTED UNIAXIAL MINERALS* (*Continued*)

Mineral	Formula	Index of refraction	
		Ordinary ray	Extraordinary ray
Uniaxial Negative Minerals			
Chiolite	$2NaF \cdot AlF_3$	1.349	1.342
Hanksite	$11Na_2O \cdot 9SO_3 \cdot 2CO_2 \cdot KCl$	1.481	1.461
Thaumasite	$3CaO \cdot CO_2 \cdot SiO_2 \cdot SO_3 \cdot 15H_2O$	1.507	1.468
Hydrotalcite	$6MgO \cdot Al_2O_3 \cdot CO_2 \cdot 15H_2O$	1.512	1.498
Cancrinite	$4Na_2O \cdot CaO \cdot 4Al_2O_3 \cdot 2CO_2 \cdot 9SiO_2 \cdot 3H_2O$	1.524	1.496
Milarite	$K_2O \cdot 4CaO \cdot 2Al_2O_3 \cdot 24SiO_2 \cdot H_2O$	1.532	1.529
Kaliophilite	$K_2O \cdot Al_2O_3 \cdot 2SiO_2$	1.537	1.533
Mellite	$Al_2O_3 \cdot C_{12}O_9 \cdot 18H_2O$	1.539	1.511
Marialite	"Ma" = $3Na_2O \cdot 3Al_2O_3 \cdot 18SiO_2 \cdot 2NaCl$	1.539	1.537
Nephelite	$Na_2O \cdot Al_2O_3 \cdot 2SiO_2$	1.542	1.538
Wernerite	Me_1Ma_1 ±	1.578	1.551
Beryl	$3BeO \cdot Al_2O_3 \cdot 6SiO_2$	1.581 ±	1.575 ±
Torbernite	$CuO \cdot 2UO_3 \cdot P_2O_5 \cdot 8H_2O$	1.592	1.582
Meionite	"Me" = $4CaO \cdot 3Al_2O_3 \cdot 6SiO_2$	1.597	1.560
Melilite	Contains Na_2O, CaO, Al_2O_3, SiO_2, etc.	1.634	1.629
Apatite	$9CaO \cdot 3P_2O_5 \cdot Ca(F, Cl)_2$	1.634	1.631
Calcite	$CaO \cdot CO_2$	1.658	1.486
Gehlenite	$2CaO \cdot Al_2O_3 \cdot SiO_2$	1.669	1.658
Tourmaline	Contains Na_2O, FeO, Al_2O_3, B_2O_3, SiO_2, etc.	1.669 ±	1.638 ±
Dolomite	$CaO \cdot MgO \cdot 2CO_2$	1.681	1.500
Magnesite	$MgO \cdot CO_2$	1.700	1.509
Pyrochroite	$MnO \cdot H_2O$	1.723	1.681
Corundum	Al_2O_3	1.768	1.760
Smithsonite	$ZnO \cdot CO_2$	1.818	1.618
Rhodochrosite	$MnO \cdot CO_2$	1.818	1.595
Jarosite	$K_2O \cdot 3Fe_2O_3 \cdot 4SO_3 \cdot 6H_2O$	1.820	1.715
Siderite	$FeO \cdot CO_2$	1.875	1.635
Pyromorphite	$9PbO \cdot 3P_2O_5 \cdot PbCl_2$	2.050	2.042
Barysilite	$3PbO \cdot 2SiO_2$	2.070	2.050
Mimetite	$9PbO \cdot 3As_2O_5 \cdot PbCl_2$	2.135	2.118
Matlockite	$PbO \cdot PbCl_2$	2.150	2.040
Stolzite	$PbO \cdot WO_3$	2.269	2.182
Geikielite	$(Mg, Fe)O \cdot TiO_2$	2.310	1.950
Vanadinite	$9PbO \cdot 3V_2O_5 \cdot PbCl_2$	2.354	2.299
Wulfenite	$PbO \cdot MoO_3$	2.402	2.304 (Li line)
Octahedrite	TiO_2	2.554	2.493
Massicotite	PbO	2.665	2.535 (Li line)
Proustite	$3Ag_2S \cdot As_2S_3$	2.979	2.711 (Li line)
Pryargyrite	$3Ag_2S \cdot Sb_2S_3$	3.084	2.881 (Li line)
Hematite	Fe_2O_3	3.220	2.940 (Li line)

* "Smithsonian Physical Tables," 1954, Table 546. Selected by Edgar T. Wherry from a private compilation of Esper S. Larsen, of the U.S. Geological Survey.

TABLE 6b-2. INDEX OF REFRACTION OF SELECTED BIAXIAL MINERALS*

Mineral	Formula	Index of refraction		
		n_α	n_β	n_γ
Biaxial Positive Minerals				
Stercorite	$NaO\cdot(NH_4)_2O\cdot P_2O_5\cdot 9H_2O$	1.439	1.441	1.469
Aluminite	$Al_2O_3\cdot SO_3\cdot 9H_2O$	1.459	1.464	1.470
Tridymite	SiO_2	1.469	1.470	1.473
Thenardite	$Na_2O\cdot SO_3$	1.464	1.474	1.485
Carnallite	$KCl\cdot MgCl_2\cdot 6H_2O$	1.466	1.475	1.494
Alunogen	$Al_2O_3\cdot 3SO_3\cdot 16H_2O$	1.474	1.476	1.483
Melanterite	$FeO\cdot SO_3\cdot 7H_2O$	1.471	1.478	1.486
Natrolite	$Na_2O\cdot Al_2O_3\cdot 3SiO_2\cdot 2H_2O$	1.480	1.482	1.493
Arcanite	$K_2O\cdot SO_3$	1.494	1.495	1.497
Struvite	$(NH_4)_2O\cdot 2MgO\cdot P_2O_5\cdot 12H_2O$	1.495	1.496	1.500
Heulandite	$CaO\cdot Al_2O_3\cdot 6SiO_2\cdot 3H_2O$	1.498	1.499	1.505
Thomsonite	$(Na_2, Ca)O\cdot Al_2O_3\cdot 2SiO_2\cdot 3H_2O$	1.497	1.503	1.525
Harmotome	$(K_2, Ba)O\cdot Al_2O_3\cdot 5SiO_2\cdot 5H_2O$	1.503	1.505	1.508
Petalite	$Li_2O\cdot Al_2O_3\cdot 8SiO_2$	1.504	1.510	1.516
Monetite	$2CaO\cdot P_2O_5\cdot H_2O$	1.515	1.518	1.525
Newberyite	$2MgO\cdot P_2O_5\cdot 7H_2O$	1.514	1.519	1.533
Gypsum	$CaO\cdot SO_3\cdot 2H_2O$	1.520	1.523	1.530
Mascagnite	$(NH_4)_2O\cdot SO_3$	1.521	1.523	1.533
Albite	"Ab" = $Na_2O\cdot Al_2O_3\cdot 6SiO_2$	1.525	1.529	1.536
Hydromagnesite	$4MgO\cdot 3CO_2\cdot 4H_2O$	1.527	1.530	1.540
Wavellite	$3Al_2O_3\cdot 2P_2O_5\cdot 12(H_2O, 2HF)$	1.525	1.534	1.552
Kieserite	$MgO\cdot SO_3\cdot H_2O$	1.523	1.535	1.586
Copiapite	$2Fe_2O_3\cdot 5SO_3\cdot 18H_2O$	1.530	1.550	1.592
Whewellite	$CaO\cdot C_2O_3\cdot H_2O$	1.491	1.555	1.650
Variscite	$Al_2O_3\cdot P_2O_5\cdot 4H_2O$	1.551	1.558	1.582
Labradorite	Ab_2An_3	1.559	1.563	1.568
Gibbsite	$Al_2O_3\cdot 3H_2O$	1.566	1.566	1.587
Wagnerite	$3MgO\cdot P_2O_5\cdot MgF_2$	1.569	1.570	1.582
Anhydrite	$CaO\cdot SO_3$	1.571	1.576	1.614
Colemanite	$2CaO\cdot 3B_2O_3\cdot 5H_2O$	1.586	1.592	1.614
Fremontite	$Na_2O\cdot Al_2O_3\cdot P_2O_5\cdot(H_2O, 2HF)$	1.594	1.603	1.615
Vivianite	$3FeO\cdot P_2O_5\cdot 8H_2O$	1.579	1.603	1.633
Pectolite	$Na_2O\cdot 4CaO\cdot 6SiO_2\cdot H_2O$	1.595	1.604	1.633
Calamine	$2ZnO\cdot SiO_2\cdot H_2O$	1.614	1.617	1.636
Chondrodite	$4MgO\cdot SiO_2\cdot Mg(F, OH)_2$	1.604	1.617	1.636
Turquoise	$CuO\cdot 3Al_2O_3\cdot 2P_2O_5\cdot 9H_2O$	1.610	1.620	1.650
Topaz	$2AlOF\cdot SiO_2$	1.619	1.620	1.627
Celestite	$SrO\cdot SO_3$	1.622	1.624	1.631
Prehnite	$2CaO\cdot Al_2O_3\cdot 3SiO_2\cdot H_2O$	1.616	1.626	1.649
Barite	$BaO\cdot SO_3$	1.636	1.637	1.648
Anthophyllite	$MgO\cdot SiO_2$	1.633	1.642	1.657
Sillimanite	$Al_2O_3\cdot SiO_2$	1.638	1.642	1.653
Forsterite	$2MgO\cdot SiO_2$	1.635	1.651	1.669

TABLE 6b-2. INDEX OF REFRACTION OF SELECTED BIAXIAL MINERALS* (*Continued*)

Mineral	Formula	Index of refraction		
		n_α	n_β	n_γ
Biaxial Positive Minerals				
Enstatite	$MgO \cdot SiO_2$	1.650	1.653	1.658
Euclase	$2BeO \cdot Al_2O_3 \cdot 2SiO_2 \cdot H_2O$	1.653	1.656	1.673
Triplite	$3MnO \cdot P_2O_5 \cdot MnF_2$	1.650	1.660	1.672
Spodumene	$Li_2O \cdot Al_2O_3 \cdot 4SiO_2$	1.660	1.666	1.676
Diopside	$CaO \cdot MgO \cdot 2SiO_2$	1.664	1.671	1.694
Olivine	$2(Mg, Fe)O \cdot SiO_2$	1.662	1.680	1.699
Triphylite	$Li_2O \cdot 2(Fe, Mn)O \cdot P_2O_5$	1.688	1.688	1.692
Zoisite	$4CaO \cdot 3Al_2O_3 \cdot 6SiO_2 \cdot H_2O$	1.700	1.702	1.706
Strengite	$Fe_2O_3 \cdot P_2O_5 \cdot 4H_2O$	1.708	1.708	1.745
Diaspore	$Al_2O_3 \cdot H_2O$	1.702	1.722	1.750
Staurolite	$2FeO \cdot 5Al_2O_3 \cdot 4SiO_2 \cdot H_2O$	1.736	1.741	1.746
Chrysoberyl	$BeO \cdot Al_2O_3$	1.747	1.748	1.757
Azurite	$3CuO \cdot 2CO_2 \cdot H_2O$	1.730	1.758	1.838
Scorodite	$Fe_2O_3 \cdot As_2O_5 \cdot 4H_2O$	1.765	1.774	1.797
Olivenite	$4CuO \cdot As_2O_5 \cdot H_2O$	1.772	1.810	1.863
Anglesite	$PbO \cdot SO_3$	1.877	1.882	1.894
Titanite	$CaO \cdot TiO_2 \cdot SiO_2$	1.900	1.907	2.034
Claudetite	As_2O_3	1.871	1.920	2.010
Sulfur	S	1.950	2.043	2.240
Cotunnite	$PbCl_2$	2.200	2.217	2.260
Huebnerite	$MnO \cdot WO_3$	2.170	2.220	2.320
Manganite	$Mn_2O_3 \cdot H_2O$	2.240	2.240	2.530 (Li)
Raspite	$PbO \cdot WO_3$	2.270	2.270	2.300
Mendipite	$2PbO \cdot PbCl_2$	2.240	2.270	2.310
Tantalite	$(Fe, Mn)O \cdot Ta_2O_5$	2.260	2.320	2.430 (Li)
Wolframite	$(Fe, Mn)O \cdot WO_3$	2.310	2.360	2.460 (Li)
Crocoite	$PbO \cdot CrO_3$	2.310	2.370	2.660 (Li)
Pseudobrookite	$2Fe_2O_3 \cdot 3TiO_2$	2.380	2.390	2.420 (Li)
Stibiotantalite	$Sb_2O_3 \cdot Ta_2O_5$	2.374	2.404	2.457
Montroydite	HgO	2.370	2.500	2.650 (Li)
Brookite	TiO_2	2.583	2.586	2.741
Massicot	PbO	2.510	2.610	2.710
Biaxial Negative Minerals				
Mirabilite	$Na_2O \cdot SO_3 \cdot 10H_2O$	1.394	1.396	1.398
Thomsenolite	$NaF \cdot CaF_2 \cdot AlF_3 \cdot H_2O$	1.407	1.414	1.415
Natron	$Na_2O \cdot CO_2 \cdot 10H_2O$	1.405	1.425	1.440
Kalinite	$K_2O \cdot Al_2O_3 \cdot 4SO_3 \cdot 24H_2O$	1.430	1.452	1.458
Epsomite	$MgO \cdot SO_3 \cdot 7H_2O$	1.433	1.455	1.461
Sassolite	$B_2O_3 \cdot H_2O$	1.340	1.456	1.459
Borax	$Na_2O \cdot 2B_2O_3 \cdot 10H_2O$	1.447	1.470	1.472

TABLE 6b-2. INDEX OF REFRACTION OF SELECTED BIAXIAL MINERALS* (*Continued*)

Mineral	Formula	Index of refraction		
		n_α	n_β	n_γ
Biaxial Negative Minerals				
Goslarite	$ZnO\cdot SO_3\cdot 7H_2O$	1.457	1.480	1.484
Pickeringite	$MgO\cdot Al_2O_3\cdot 4SO_3\cdot 22H_2O$	1.476	1.480	1.483
Bloedite	$Na_2O\cdot MgO\cdot 2SO_3\cdot 4H_2O$	1.483	1.487	1.486
Trona	$3Na_2O\cdot 4CO_2\cdot 5H_2O$	1.410	1.492	1.542
Thermonatrite	$Na_2O\cdot CO_2\cdot H_2O$	1.420	1.495	1.518
Stilbite	$(Ca, Na_2)O\cdot Al_2O_3\cdot 6SiO_2\cdot 5H_2O$	1.494	1.498	1.500
Niter	$K_2O\cdot N_2O_5$	1.334	1.505	1.506
Kainite	$MgO\cdot SO_3\cdot KCl\cdot 3H_2O$	1.494	1.505	1.516
Gaylussite	$Na_2O\cdot CaO\cdot 2CO_2\cdot 5H_2O$	1.444	1.516	1.523
Scolecite	$CaO\cdot Al_2O_3\cdot 3SiO_2\cdot 3H_2O$	1.512	1.519	1.519
Laumontite	$CaO\cdot Al_2O_3\cdot 4SiO_2\cdot H_2O$	1.513	1.524	1.525
Orthoclase	$K_2O\cdot Al_2O_3\cdot 6SiO_2$	1.518	1.524	1.526
Microcline	Same as preceding	1.522	1.526	1.530
Anorthoclase	$(Na, K)_2O\cdot Al_2O_3\cdot 6SiO_2$	1.523	1.529	1.531
Glauberite	$Na_2O\cdot CaO\cdot 2SO_3$	1.515	1.532	1.536
Cordierite	$4(Mg, Fe)O\cdot 4Al_2O_3\cdot 10SiO_2\cdot H_2O$	1.534	1.538	1.540
Chalcanthite	$CuO\cdot SO_3\cdot 5H_2O$	1.516	1.539	1.546
Oligoclase	Ab_4An	1.539	1.543	1.547
Beryllonite	$Na_2O\cdot 2BeO\cdot P_2O_5$	1.552	1.558	1.561
Kaolinite	$Al_2O_3\cdot 2SiO_2\cdot 2H_2O$	1.561	1.563	1.565
Biotite	$K_2O\cdot 4(Mg, Fe)O\cdot 2Al_2O_3\cdot 6SiO_2\cdot H_2O$	1.541	1.574	1.574
Autunite	$CaO\cdot 2UO_3\cdot P_2O_5\cdot 8H_2O$	1.553	1.575	1.577
Anorthite	"An" = $CaO\cdot Al_2O_3\cdot 2SiO_2$	1.576	1.584	1.588
Lanthanite	$La_2O_3\cdot 3CO_2\cdot 9H_2O$	1.520	1.587	1.613
Pyrophyllite	$Al_2O_3\cdot 4SiO_2\cdot H_2O$	1.552	1.588	1.600
Talc	$3MgO\cdot 4SiO_2\cdot H_2O$	1.539	1.589	1.589
Hopeite	$3ZnO\cdot P_2O_5\cdot 4H_2O$	1.572	1.590	1.590
Muscovite	$K_2O\cdot Al_2O_3\cdot 6SiO_2\cdot 2H_2O$	1.561	1.590	1.594
Amblygonite	$Al_2O_3\cdot P_2O_5\cdot 2LiF$	1.579	1.593	1.597
Lepidolite	$Al_2O_3\cdot 3SiO_2\cdot 2(K, Li)F$	1.560	1.598	1.605
Phlogopite	$K_2O\cdot 6MgO\cdot Al_2O_3\cdot 6SiO_2\cdot 2H_2O$	1.562	1.606	1.606
Tremolite	$CaO\cdot 3MgO\cdot 4SiO_2$	1.600	1.616	1.627
Actinolite	$CaO\cdot 3(Mg, Fe)O\cdot 4SiO_2$	1.614	1.630	1.641
Wollastonite	$CaO\cdot SiO_2$	1.620	1.632	1.634
Lazulite	$(Fe, Mg)O\cdot Al_2O_3\cdot P_2O_5\cdot H_2O$	1.612	1.634	1.643
Danburite	$CaO\cdot B_2O_3\cdot 2SiO_2$	1.632	1.634	1.636
Glaucophane	$Na_2O\cdot 2FeO\cdot Al_2O_3\cdot 6SiO_2$	1.621	1.638	1.638
Andalusite	$Al_2O_3\cdot SiO_2$	1.632	1.638	1.643
Hornblende	Contains Na_2O, MgO, FeO, SiO_2, etc.	1.634	1.647	1.652
Datolite	$2CaO\cdot 2SiO_2\cdot B_2O_3\cdot H_2O$	1.625	1.653	1.669
Erythrite	$3CoO\cdot As_2O_5\cdot 8H_2O$	1.626	1.661	1.699
Monticellite	$CaO\cdot MgO\cdot SiO_2$	1.651	1.662	1.668

TABLE 6b-2. INDEX OF REFRACTION OF SELECTED BIAXIAL MINERALS* (*Continued*)

Mineral	Formula	Index of refraction		
		n_α	n_β	n_γ
	Biaxial negative minerals			
Strontianite	$SrO \cdot CO_2$	1.520	1.667	1.667
Witherite	$BaO \cdot CO_2$	1.529	1.676	1.677
Aragonite	$CaO \cdot CO_2$	1.531	1.682	1.686
Axinite	$6(Ca, Mn)O \cdot 2Al_2O_3 \cdot B_2O_3 \cdot 8SiO_2 \cdot H_2O$	1.678	1.685	1.688
Dumortierite	$8Al_2O_3 \cdot B_2O_3 \cdot 6SiO_2 \cdot H_2O$	1.678	1.686	1.689
Cyanite	$Al_2O_3 \cdot SiO_2$	1.712	1.720	1.728
Epidote	$4CaO \cdot 3(Al, Fe)_2O_3 \cdot 6SiO_2 \cdot H_2O$	1.729	1.763	1.780
Atacamite	$3CuO \cdot CuCl_2 \cdot 3H_2O$	1.831	1.861	1.880
Fayalite	$2FeO \cdot SiO_2$	1.824	1.864	1.874
Caledonite	$2(Pb, Cu)O \cdot SO_3 \cdot H_2O$	1.818	1.866	1.909
Malachite	$2CuO \cdot CO_2 \cdot H_2O$	1.655	1.875	1.909
Lanarkite	$2PbO \cdot SO_3$	1.930	1.990	2.020
Leadhillite	$4PbO \cdot SO_3 \cdot 2CO_2 \cdot H_2O$	1.870	2.000	2.010
Cerusite	$PbO \cdot CO_2$	1.804	2.076	2.078
Laurionite	$PbCl_2 \cdot PbO \cdot H_2O$	2.077	2.116	2.158
Matlockite	$PbO \cdot PbCl_2$	2.040	2.150	2.150
Baddeleyite	ZrO_2	2.130	2.190	2.200
Lepidocrocite	$Fe_2O_3 \cdot H_2O$	1.930	2.210	2.510
Limonite	$2Fe_2O_3 \cdot 3H_2O$ in part	2.170	2.290	2.310
Goethite	$Fe_2O_3 \cdot H_2O$	2.210	2.350	2.350 (Li)
Valentinite	Sb_2O_3	2.180	2.350	2.350
Turgite	$2Fe_2O_3 \cdot H_2O$ in part	2.450	2.550	2.550 (Li)
Realgar	AsS	2.460	2.590	2.610 (Li)
Terlinguaite	Hg_2OCl	2.350	2.640	2.660 (Li)
Hutchinsonite	$(Tl, Ag)_2S \cdot PbS \cdot 2As_2S_3$	3.078	3.176	3.188
Stibnite	Sb_2S_3	3.194	4.303	4.460

* "Smithsonian Physical Tables," 1954, Table 548. The values are arranged in the order of increasing β index of refraction and are for the sodium D line except where noted. Selected by Edgar T. Wherry from private compilation of Esper S. Larsen, of the U.S. Geological Survey.

TABLE 6b-3. INDEX OF REFRACTION OF SOME LIQUIDS RELATIVE TO AIR*

Substance	Density	Temp., °C	Indices of refraction				
			0.397μ *H*	0.434μ *G'*	0.486μ *F*	0.589μ *D*	0.656μ *C*
Acetaldehyde, CH_3CHO	0.780	20	......	1.3394	1.3359	1.3316	1.3298
Acetone, CH_3COCH_3	0.791	20	......	1.3678	1.3639	1.3593	1.3573
Aniline, $C_6H_5{\cdot}NH_2$	1.022	20	......	1.6204	1.6041	1.5863	1.5793
Alcohol, methyl, $CH_3{\cdot}OH$	0.794	20	1.3399	1.3362	1.3331	1.3290	1.3277
Alcohol, ethyl, $C_2H_5{\cdot}OH$	0.808	0	......	1.3773	1.3739	1.3695	1.3677
Alcohol, ethyl	0.800	20	......	1.3700	1.3666	1.3618	1.3605
Alcohol, ethyl, *dn/dt*	.....	20	......	−0.0004	−0.0004	−0.0004	−0.0004
Alcohol, *n*-propyl, $C_3H_7{\cdot}OH$	0.804	20	......	1.3938	1.3901	1.3854	1.3834
Benzene, C_6H_6	0.880	20	......	1.5236	1.5132	1.5012	1.4965
Benzene, C_6H_6 *dn/dt*	.....	20	......	−0.0007	−0.0006	−0.0006	−0.0006
Bromnaphthalene, $C_{10}H_7Br$	1.487	20	1.7289	1.7041	1.6819	1.6582	1.6495
Carbon disulfide, CS_2	1.293	0	1.7175	1.6920	1.6688	1.6433	1.6336
Carbon disulfide	1.263	20	1.6994	1.6748	1.6523	1.6276	1.6182
Carbon tetrachloride, CCl_4	1.591	20	......	1.4729	1.4676	1.4607	1.4579
Chinolin, C_9H_7N	1.090	20	......	1.6679	1.6470	1.6245	1.6161
Chloral, $CCl_3{\cdot}CHO$	1.512	20	......	1.4679	1.4624	1.4557	1.4530
Chloroform, $CHCl_3$	1.489	20	1.463	1.458	1.4530	1.4467	1.4443
Decane, $C_{10}H_{22}$	0.728	14.9	......	1.4200	1.4160	1.4108	1.4088
Ether, ethyl, $C_2H_5{\cdot}O{\cdot}C_2H_5$	0.715	20	......	1.3607	1.3576	1.3538	1.3515
Ether, ethyl, *dn/dt*	.....	20	......	−0.0006	−0.0006	−0.0006	−0.0006
Ethyl nitrate, $C_2H_5{\cdot}O{\cdot}NO_2$	1.109	20	......	1.395	1.392	1.3853	1.3830
Formic acid, $H{\cdot}CO_2H$	1.219	20	......	1.3804	1.3764	1.3714	1.3693
Glycerine, $C_3H_8O_3$	1.260	20	......	1.4828	1.4784	1.4730	1.4706
Hexane, $CH_3(CH_2)_4CH_3$	0.660	20	......	1.3836	1.3799	1.3754	1.3734
Hexylene, $CH_3(CH_2)_3CH{\cdot}CH_2$	0.679	23.3	......	1.4059	1.4007	1.3945	1.3920
Methylene iodide, CH_2I_2	3.318	20	1.8027	....	1.7692	1.7417	1.7320
Methylene iodide *dn/dt*	.....	20	......	....	−0.0007	−0.0007	−0.0006
Naphthalene, $C_{10}H_8$	0.962	98.4	......	....	1.6031	1.5823	1.5746
Nicotine, $C_{10}H_{14}N_2$	1.012	22.4	......	1.5439	....	1.5239	1.5198
Octane, $CH_3(CH_2)_6CH_3$	0.707	15.1	......	1.4097	1.4046	1.4007	1.3987
Oil:							
Almond	0.92	0	......	....	1.4847	1.4782	1.4755
Anise seed	0.99	15.1	1.6084	....	1.5743	1.5572	1.5508
Anise	0.99	21.4	......	....	1.5647	1.5475	1.5410
Bitter almond	1.06	20	......	1.5775	1.5623	....	1.5391
Cassia	.....	10	1.7039	....	1.6389	1.6104	1.6007
Cassia	.....	22.5	1.6985	....	1.6314	1.6026	1.5930
Cinnamon	1.05	23.5	......	....	1.6508	1.6188	1.6077
Olive	0.92	0	......	....	1.4825	1.4763	1.4738
Rock	.....	0	......	....	1.4644	1.4573	1.4545
Turpentine	0.87	10.6	1.4939	....	1.4817	1.4744	1.4715
Turpentine	0.87	20.7	1.4913	....	1.4793	1.4721	1.4692
Pentane, $CH_3(CH_2)_3CH_3$	0.625	15.7	......	1.3645	1.3610	1.3581	1.3570
Phenol, C_6H_5OH	1.060	40.6	......	1.5684	1.5558	1.5425	1.5369
Phenol	1.021	82.7	......	....	1.5356	....	1.5174
Styrene, $C_6H_5CH{\cdot}CH_2$	0.910	16.6	......	1.5816	1.5659	1.5485	1.5419
Thymol, $C_{10}H_{14}O$	0.982	....	......	....	1.5386	....	1.5228
Toluene, $CH_3{\cdot}C_6H_5$	0.86	20	......	1.5170	1.5070	1.4955	1.4911
Water, H_2O	.....	20	1.3435	1.3404	1.3372	1.3330	1.3312
Water	.....	0	1.3444	1.3413	1.3380	1.3338	1.3319
Water	.....	40	1.3411	1.3380	1.3349	1.3307	1.3290
Water	.....	80	1.3332	1.3302	1.3270	1.3230	1.3313

* "Smithsonian Physical Tables," 1954, Table 551.

TABLE 6b-4. INDEX OF REFRACTION OF PLASTICS*

Optical Plastics

Name of monomer	Optical properties of polymer: Refractive index (N^{20})	Optical properties of polymer: Reciprocal dispersive power
p-Methoxy styrene	1.5967	28
β-Amino-ethyl methacrylate	1.537	52.5
Methyl α-bromoacrylate	1.5672	46.5
Vinyl benzoate	1.5775	30.7
Phenyl vinyl ketone	1.586	26.0
Vinyl carbazole	1.683	18.8
Lead methacrylate	1.645	28
2-Chlorocyclohexyl methacrylate	1.5179	56
1-Phenyl-cyclohexyl methacrylate	1.5645	40
Triethoxy-silicol methacrylate	1.436	53
p-Bromophenyl methacrylate	1.5964	33
2-3 Dibromopropyl methacrylate	1.5739	44
Diethyl-amino-ethyl methacrylate	1.5174	54
1-Methyl-cyclohexyl methacrylate	1.5111	54
n-Hexyl methacrylate	1.4813	57
2-6-Dichlorostyrene	1.6248	31.3
β-Bromo-ethyl methacrylate	1.5426	40
μ-Polychloroprene	1.5540	36
Methyl α-chloracrylate	1.5172	57
β-Naphthyl methacrylate	1.6298	24
Vinyl phenyl sulfide	1.6568	27.5
Methacryl methyl salicylate	1.5707	34
Methyl isopropenyl ketone	1.5200	54.5
Ethylene glycol mono-methacrylate	1.5119	56
N-Benzyl methacrylamide	1.5965	34.5
β-Phenyl-sulfone ethyl methacrylate	1.5682	39
N-Methyl methacrylamide	1.5398	47.5
N-Allyl methacrylamide	1.5476	47
Methacryl-phenyl salicylate	1.6006	36
N-β-Methoxyethyl methacrylamide	1.5246	53
N-β-Phenylethyl methacrylamide	1.5857	37
Cyclohexyl α-ethoxyacrylate	1.4969	58
1-3-Dichloropropyl-2-methacrylate	1.5270	56
2-Methyl-cyclohexyl methacrylate	1.5028	53
3-Methyl-cyclohexyl methacrylate	1.4947	55
3-3-5-Trimethyl-cyclohexyl methacrylate	1.485	54
N-Vinyl phthalimide	1.6200	24.1
Fluorenyl methacrylate	1.6319	23.1
α-Naphthyl-carbinyl methacrylate	1.63	25
p-p^3-Xylylenyl dimethacrylate	1.5559	37
Cyclohexanediol-1-4 dimethacrylate	1.5067	54.3
Ethylidene dimethacrylate	1.4831	52.9
p-Divinyl benzene	1.6150	28.1
Decamethylene glycol dimethacrylate	1.4990	56.3
Vinyl cyclohexene dioxide	1.5303	56.4
Methyl α-methylene butyrolactone	1.5118	53.9
α-Methylene butyrolactone	1.5412	56.4
4-Dioxolylmethyl methacrylate	1.5084	59.7
Methylene-α-valerolactone	1.5431	47.8
o-Methoxy-phenyl methacrylate	1.5705	33.4
Isopropyl methacrylate	1.4728	57.9
Trifluoroisopropyl methacrylate	1.4177	65.3
β-Ethoxy-ethyl methacrylate	1.4833	32.0
Name of polymer		
Condensation resin from di- (*p*-aminocyclohexyl) methane and sebacic acid	1.5199	52.0
Columbia resin 39	1.5001	58.8

Name of monomer	Optical properties of polymer: Refractive index (N^{20})	Optical properties of polymer: Reciprocal dispersive power
Allyl methacrylate	1.5196	49.0
Benzhydryl methacrylate	1.5933	31.0
Benzyl methacrylate	1.5680	36.5
n-Butyl methacrylate	1.483	49
Tert-butyl methacrylate	1.4638	51
o-Chlorobenzhydryl methacrylate	1.6040	30
α-(*o*-Chlorophenyl)-ethyl methacrylate	1.5624	37.5
Cyclohexyl-cyclohexyl methacrylate	1.5250	53
Cyclohexyl methacrylate	1.5064	56.9
p-Cyclohexyl-phenyl methacrylate	1.5575	39.0
α-β-Diphenyl-ethyl methacrylate	1.5816	30.5
Menthyl methacrylate	1.4890	54.5
Ethylene dimethacrylate	1.5063	53.4
Hexamethylene glycol dimethacrylate	1.5066	56
Methacrylic anhydride	1.5228	48.5
Methyl methacrylate	1.4913	57.8
m-Nitro-benzyl methacrylate	1.5845	27.4
2-Nitro-2-methyl-propyl methacrylate	1.4868	48
α-Phenyl-allyl methacrylate	1.5573	34.8
α-Phenyl-*n*-amyl methacrylate	1.5396	40
α-Phenyl-ethyl methacrylate	1.5487	37.5
β-Phenyl-ethyl methacrylate	1.5592	36.5
Tetrahydrofurfuryl methacrylate	1.5096	54
Vinyl methacrylate	1.5129	46
Styrene	1.5907	30.8
Vinyl formate	1.4757	55
Phenyl cellosolve methacrylate	1.5624	36.2
p-Methoxy-benzyl methacrylate	1.552	32.5
Ethylene chlorohydrin methacrylate	1.517	54
o-Chlorostyrene	1.6098	31
Pentachlorophenyl methacrylate	1.608	22.5
Phenyl methacrylate	1.5706	35.0
Vinyl naphthalene	1.6818	20.9
Vinyl thiophene	1.6376	29
Eugenol methacrylate	1.5714	33
m-Cresyl methacrylate	1.5683	36.8
o-Methyl-*p*-methoxy styrene	1.5868	30.3
o-Methoxy styrene	1.5932	29.7
o-Methyl styrene	1.5874	32
Ethyl sulfide dimethacrylate	1.547	44
Allyl cinnamate	1.57	30
Diacetin methacrylate	1.4855	50
Ethylene glycol benzoate methacrylate	1.555	36.8
Ethyl glycolate methacrylate	1.4903	55
p-Isopropyl styrene	1.554	35
Bornyl methacrylate	1.5059	54.6
Triethyl carbinyl methacrylate	1.4889	57
Butyl mercaptyl methacrylate	1.5390	41.8
o-Chlorobenzyl methacrylate	1.5823	37
α-Methallyl methacrylate	1.4917	49
β-Methallyl methacrylate	1.5110	47
α-Naphthyl methacrylate	1.6411	20.5
Ethyl acrylate	1.4685	58
Cinnamyl methacrylate	1.5951	26.5
Methyl acrylate	1.4793	59
Terpineyl methacrylate	1.514	50
Furfuryl methacrylate	1.5381	39.2

* H. C. Raine, Plastic Glasses, *Proc. London Conf. Opt. Instruments* **1950**, 243.

TABLE 6b-4. INDEX OF REFRACTION OF PLASTICS* (*Continued*)

Polystyrene

Spectral line	Wavelength, A	Refractive index at 15°C	35°C	55°C
A	7,679	1.581^2	1.578^5	1.575^8
C	6,563	1.587^0	1.584^3	1.581^6
D_1	5,896	1.592^3	1.589^7	1.586^9
F	4,861	1.606^2	1.603^4	1.600^6
g	4,358	1.617^6	1.614^8	1.612^0

Polycyclohexyl Methacrylate

Spectral line	Wavelength, A	Refractive index at 15°C	35°C	55°C
A	7,679	1.501^6	1.499^2	1.496^4
C	6,563	1.504^4	1.502^1	1.499^2
D_1	5,896	1.507^1	1.504^6	1.501^8
F	4,861	1.513^4	1.501^0	1.508^1
g	4,358	1.518^4	1.516^0	1.513^1

Polymethyl Methacrylate

Spectral line	Wavelength, A	Refractive index at 20°C
C	6,563	1.489^0
D	5,896	1.491^3
e	5,461	1.493^2
F	4,861	1.497^5
g	4,358	1.501^9

TABLE 6b-5. INDEX OF REFRACTION OF GASES AND VAPORS*

Wave-length μ	$(n-1)10^3$ Air	O	N	H	Wave-length μ	$(n-1)10^3$ Air	O	N	H
0.4861	0.2951	0.2734	0.3012	0.1406	0.4360	0.2971	0.2743	CO_2	0.1418
0.5461	0.2936	0.2717	0.2998	0.1397	0.5462	0.2937	0.2704	0.4506	0.1397
0.5790	0.2930	0.2710	......	0.1393	0.6709	0.2918	0.2683	0.4471	0.1385
0.6563	0.2919	0.2698	0.2982	0.1387	6.709	0.2881	0.2643	0.4804	0.1361
					8.678	0.2888	0.2650	0.4579	0.1361

The values are for 0°C and 760 mm Hg.

Substance	Kind of light	Indices of refraction	Substance	Kind of light	Indices of refraction
Acetone	*D*	1.001079–1.001100	Hydrogen	White	1.000138–1.000143
Ammonia	White	1.000381–1.000385	Hydrogen	*D*	1.000132
Ammonia	*D*	1.000373–1.000379	Hydrogen sulfide	*D*	1.000644
Argon	*D*	1.000281		*D*	1.000623
Benzene	*D*	1.001700–1.001823	Methane	White	1.000443
Bromine	*D*	1.001132	Methane	*D*	1.000444
Carbon dioxide	White	1.000449–1.000450	Methyl alcohol	*D*	1.000549–1.000623
Carbon dioxide	*D*	1.000448–1.000454	Methyl ether	*D*	1.000891
Carbon disulfide	White	1.001500	Nitric oxide	White	1.000303
	D	1.001478–1.001485	Nitric oxide	*D*	1.000297
Carbon monoxide	White	1.000340	Nitrogen	White	1.000295–1.000300
	White	1.000335	Nitrogen	*D*	1.000296–1.000298
Chlorine	White	1.000772	Nitrous oxide	White	1.000503–1.000507
Chlorine	*D*	1.000773	Nitrous oxide	*D*	1.000516
Chloroform	*D*	1.001436–1.001464	Oxygen	White	1.000272–1.000280
Cyanogen	White	1.000834	Oxygen	*D*	1.000271–1.000272
Cyanogen	*D*	1.000784–1.000825	Pentane	*D*	1.001711
Ethyl alcohol	*D*	1.000871–1.000885	Sulfur dioxide	White	1.000665
Ethyl ether	*D*	1.001521–1.001544	Sulfur dioxide	*D*	1.000686
Helium	*D*	1.000036	Water	White	1.000261
Hydrochloric acid	White	1.000449	Water	*D*	1.000249–1.000259
	D	1.000447			

* "Smithsonian Physical Tables," 1954, Table 554. A formula was given by Biot and Arago expressing the dependence of the index of refraction of a gas on pressure and temperature. More recent experiments confirm their conclusions. The formula is $n_t - 1 = \frac{n_0 - 1}{1 + at}\frac{p}{760}$, where n_t is the index of refraction for temperature t, n_0 for temperature zero, a the coefficient of expansion of the gas with temperature, and p the pressure of the gas in millimeters of mercury.

TABLE 6b-6. INDEX OF REFRACTION FOR SOLUTIONS OF SALTS AND ACIDS RELATIVE TO AIR*

Substance	Density	Temp., °C	Indices of refraction for spectrum lines C	D	F	$H\gamma$	H
Solutions in Water							
Ammonium chloride	1.067	27.05	1.37703	1.37936	1.38473	......	1.39336
Ammonium chloride	0.025	29.75	0.34850	0.35050	0.35515	....	0.36243
Calcium chloride	0.398	25.65	0.44000	0.44279	0.44938	....	0.46001
Calcium chloride	0.215	22.9	0.39411	0.39652	0.40206	....	0.41078
Calcium chloride	0.143	25.8	0.37152	0.37369	0.37876	....	0.38666
Hydrochloric acid	1.166	20.75	1.40817	1.41109	1.41774	....	1.42816
Nitric acid	0.359	18.75	0.39893	0.40181	0.40857	....	0.41961
Potash (caustic)	0.416	11.0	0.40052	0.40281	0.40808	....	0.41637
Potassium chloride	Normal solution		0.34087	0.34278	0.34719	1.35049	
Potassium chloride	Double normal		0.34982	0.35179	0.35645	0.35994	
Potassium chloride	Triple normal		0.35831	0.36029	0.36512	0.36890	
Soda (caustic)	1.376	21.6	1.41071	1.41334	1.41936	....	1.42872
Sodium chloride	0.189	18.07	0.37562	0.37789	0.38322	1.38746	
Sodium chloride	0.109	18.07	0.35751	0.35959	0.36442	0.36823	
Sodium chloride	0.035	18.07	0.34000	0.34191	0.34628	0.34969	
Sodium nitrate	1.358	22.8	1.38283	1.38535	1.39134	....	1.40121
Sulfuric acid	0.811	18.3	0.43444	0.43669	0.44168	....	0.44883
Sulfuric acid	0.632	18.3	0.42227	0.42466	0.42967	....	0.43694
Sulfuric acid	0.221	18.3	0.36793	0.37009	0.37468	....	0.38158
Sulfuric acid	0.028	18.3	0.33663	0.33862	0.34285	....	0.34938
Zinc chloride	1.359	26.6	1.39977	1.40222	1.40797	....	1.41738
Zinc chloride	0.209	26.4	0.37292	0.37515	0.38026	....	0.38845
Solutions in Ethyl Alcohol							
Ethyl alcohol	0.789	25.5	1.35971	1.35971	1.36395	....	1.37094
Ethyl alcohol	0.932	27.6	0.35372	0.35556	0.35986	....	0.36662
Fuchsin (nearly saturated)		16.0	0.3918	0.398	0.361	....	0.3759
Cyanin (saturated)	.....	16.0	0.3831	....	0.3705	....	0.3821

Note: Cyanin in chloroform also acts anomalously; for example, Sieben gives for a 4.5% solution $\mu_A = 1.4593$, $\mu_B = 1.4695$, μ_F (green) = 1.4514, μ_G (blue) = 1.4554. For a 9.9% solution he gives $\mu_A = 1.4902$, μ_F (green) = 1.4497, μ_G (blue) = 1.4597.

Solutions of Potassium Permanganate in Water

Wave-length, μ	Spec-trum line	Index for 1% sol	Index for 2% sol	Index for 3% sol	Index for 4% sol	Wave-length, μ	Spec-trum line	Index for 1% sol	Index for 2% sol	Index for 3% sol	Index for 4% sol
0.687	*B*	1.3328	1.3342	......	1.3382	0.516	...	1.3368	1.3385		
0.656	*C*	0.3335	0.3348	1.3365	0.3391	0.500	...	0.3374	0.3383	1.3386	1.3404
0.617	...	0.3343	0.3365	0.3381	0.3410	0.486	*F*	0.3377	......	......	0.3408
0.594	...	0.3354	0.3373	0.3393	0.3426	0.480	...	0.3381	0.3395	0.3398	0.3413
0.589	*D*	0.3353	0.3372	......	0.3426	0.464	...	0.3397	0.3402	0.3414	0.3423
0.568	...	0.3362	0.3387	0.3412	0.3445	0.447	...	0.3407	0.3421	0.3426	0.3439
0.553	...	0.3366	0.3395	0.3417	0.3438	0.434	...	0.3417	......	......	0.3452
0.527	*E*	0.3363	......	......	......	0.423	...	0.3431	0.3442	0.3457	0.3468
0.522	...	0.3362	0.3377	0.3388							

* "Smithsonian Physical Tables," 1954, Table 552.

TABLE 6b-7. INDEX OF REFRACTION OF SPECIAL OPTICAL MATERIALS*

Wave-length	Sodium chloride	Sylvine, KCl	Calcium flouride	Calcite	
				Ordinary ray	Extraordinary ray
0.185	1.893	1.837			
0.198	.....	.....	1.496	.....	1.578
0.340	.....	.....	.....	1.701	1.506
0.589	1.544	1.490	1.434	1.658	1.486
0.760	.....	.....	1.431	1.650	1.483
0.884	1.534	1.481	1.430		
1.179	1.530	1.478	1.428		
1.229	.....	.....	.....	1.639	1.479
2.324	.....	.....	.....	.....	1.474
2.357	1.526	1.475	1.421		
3.536	1.523	1.473	1.414		
5.893	1.516	1.469	1.387		
8.840	1.502	1.461	1.331		

λ, μ	Lithium fluoride	Mag-nesium oxide	Crystalline quartz		Rutile		Sapphire	
			Ordi-nary	Ex-traordi-nary	Ordi-nary	Ex-traordi-nary	Ordi-nary	Ex-traordi-nary
0.185	....	....	1.65751	1.68988				
0.193	1.4450							
0.198	....	....	1.65087	1.66394				
0.203	1.4390							
0.214	1.4319							
0.231	1.4244	....	1.61395	1.62555				
0.254	1.41792	1.8450						
0.265	....	1.8315						
0.280	1.41188	1.8171						
0.297	....	1.8046						
0.302	1.40818							
0.313	....	1.7945						
0.340	....	....	1.56747	1.57737				
0.3650	....	1.77186						
0.3654								
0.366	1.40121							
0.391	1.39937							
0.394	....	....	1.55846	1.56805				
0.405	....	1.76132						
0.434	....	....	1.55396	1.56339				
0.4358	....	....	....	....	2.853	3.216		

* Compiled from data of Martens, Paschen, and others.
Transmittance 10% for 1.0 mm thickness.

TABLE 6b-7. INDEX OF REFRACTION OF SPECIAL OPTICAL MATERIALS (*Continued*)

λ, μ	Lithium fluoride	Magnesium oxide	Crystalline quartz		Rutile		Sapphire	
			Ordinary	Extraordinary	Ordinary	Extraordinary	Ordinary	Extraordinary
0.436	....	1.75508						
0.447	....	1.75325						
0.471	....	1.74955						
0.4861	1.39480							
0.4916	....	....	....	....	2.723	3.047		
0.492	....	1.74678						
0.4960	....	....	....	....	2.715	3.040		
0.50	1.39430							
0.508	....	....	1.54822	1.55746				
0.535	....	....	....	....	.....	.....	1.7717	1.7634
0.5461	....	1.74119	....	....	2.652	2.958		
0.5770	....	....	....	....	2.623	2.922		
0.5791	....	....	....	....	2.621	2.919		
0.588	....	1.73787						
0.5893	....	1.73790	1.54424	1.55335	.....	.....	1.7681	1.7599
0.656	....	1.73364						
0.671	....	1.73304	....	....	.....	.....	1.7643	1.7563
0.6907	....	....	....	....	2.555	2.836		
0.707	....	1.73127						
0.7082	....	....	....	....	2.548	2.827		
0.768	....	....	1.53903	1.54794				
0.80	1.38896							
0.8325	....	....	1.53773	1.54661				
0.9914	....	....	1.53514	1.54392				
1.00	1.38711							
1.0140	....	1.72259	....	....	2.483	2.746		
1.12866	....	1.72059						
1.1592	....	....	1.53283	1.54152				
1.3070	....	....	1.53090	1.53951				
1.36728	....	1.71715						
1.3958	....	....	1.52977	1.53832				
1.4792	....	....	1.52865	1.53716				
1.50	1.38320							
1.5296	....	1.71496	....	....	2.451	2.709		
1.5414	....	....	1.52781	1.53630				
1.6815	....	....	1.52583	1.53422				
1.6932	....	1.71281						
1.7092	....	1.71258						
1.7614	....	....	1.52468	1.53301				
1.81307	....	1.71108						
1.9457	....	....	1.52184	1.53004				
1.97009	....	1.70885						
2.00	1.37875							

TABLE 6b-7. INDEX OF REFRACTION OF SPECIAL OPTICAL MATERIALS (*Continued*)

λ, μ	Lithium fluoride	Magnesium oxide	Crystalline quartz		Rutile		Sapphire	
			Ordinary	Extraordinary	Ordinary	Extraordinary	Ordinary	Extraordinary
2.0531	....	....	1.52005	1.52823				
2.24929	....	1.70470						
2.30	....	....	1.51561					
2.32542	....	1.70350						
2.50	1.37327							
2.60	....	....	1.50986					
3.00	1.36660	....	1.49953					
3.3033	....	1.68526						
3.50	1.35868	....	1.48451					
3.5078	....	1.68055						
4.00	1.34942	....	1.46617					
4.20	....	....	1.4569					
4.258	....	1.66039						
4.50	1.33875							
5.00	1.32661	....	1.417					
5.138	....	1.63138						
5.35	....	1.62404						
5.50	1.31287							
6.00	1.29745							
6.45	....	....	1.274					
6.91	1.260							
7.0	....	....	1.167					
7.53	1.239							
8.05	1.215							
8.60	1.190							
9.18	1.155							
9.79	1.109							

Table 6b-7. Index of Refraction of Special Optical Materials (*Continued*)

λ, μ	Sphalerite, ZnS	Spinel	Strontium titanate
0.3650	2.679		
0.3654	2.676		
0.3663	2.673		
0.3906	2.583		
0.4047	2.549		2.649
0.4077	2.540		
0.4358	2.490		2.569
0.4861	.....	1.736	2.488
0.4916	2.426		
0.5461	2.390		2.435
0.5780	2.375		
0.5893	.....	1.727	2.409
0.6563	.....	1.724	2.380
1.5296	2.284		

λ, μ	Arsenic trisulfide glass	Calcium fluoride	Germanium	Pyrite	Amorphous selenium	Silicon
0.19	....	1.50500				
0.20	....	1.49531				
0.26	....	1.46397				
0.30	....	1.45400				
0.40	....	1.44186				
0.50	....	1.43649				
0.579066	2.65822					
0.643847	2.59413					
0.819	....	1.43179	....	....	2.589	
1.00	....	1.42892				
1.01398	2.47230					
1.014	....	....	....	....	2.520	
1.12866	2.45897					
1.35703	2.44244					
1.39506	2.44050					
1.40	....	1.42677				
1.52952	2.43474					
1.6932	2.42965					
1.80	....	1.42489				
1.97009	2.42341					
2.00	....	1.42390	....	....	2.45	
2.32542	2.41848					
3.00	....	1.41793				
3.3033	2.41134					
3.4188	2.41068					
4.00	....	1.40971				
4.17	....	....	2.2	2.80	.....	1.5

TABLE 6b-7. INDEX OF REFRACTION OF SPECIAL OPTICAL MATERIALS (*Continued*)

λ, μ	Arsenic trisulfide glass	Calcium fluoride	Germanium	Pyrite	Amorphous selenium	Silicon
4.55	....	....	2.75	....	.....	1.5
5.00	....	1.39901	....	2.80		
5.344	2.39900					
6.238	2.39718					
6.25	....	....	3.0	3.0	.....	1.75
7.00	....	1.36932				
7.14	....	....	3.4			
7.30	....	....	....	....	.....	2.05
7.69	....	....	....	2.80		
8.00	....	1.34988				
8.33	....	....	3.65	....	.....	2.60
8.662	2.38734					
9.00	....	1.32685				
9.724	2.38029					
10.00	....	....	4	2.70	.....	2.9
11.035	2.37055					
12.5	....	....	4			
14.5	....	....	....	....	.....	3.1
15.4	....	....	....	1.90		

λ, μ	Cesium bromide	Cesium iodide	Potassium bromide	Silver chloride	Sodium chloride	Thallium bromide-iodide
0.19	....	......	....	....	1.85343	
0.20	....	......	....	....	1.79073	
0.206	....	......	1.9860			
0.210	....	......	1.9374			
0.214	....	......	1.9003			
0.22	....	......	....	....	1.71591	
0.225	....	......	1.8223			
0.24	....	......	1.7576	....	1.67197	
0.249	....	......	1.7330			
0.254	....	......	1.7198			
0.26	....	......	....	....	1.64294	
0.265	....	......	1.6950			
0.28	....	......	1.67125	....	1.62239	
0.289	....	......	1.65976	....	1.60714	
0.302	....	......	1.64603			
0.334	....	......	1.62093			
0.35	....	......	....	....	1.58232	
0.3610	....	1.8823				
0.365	....	1.8785				
0.366	....	......	1.60391			

TABLE 6b-7. INDEX OF REFRACTION OF SPECIAL OPTICAL MATERIALS (*Continued*)

λ, μ	Cesium bromide	Cesium iodide	Potassium bromide	Silver chloride	Sodium chloride	Thallium bromide-iodide
0.391	....	......	1.59444			
0.40	1.73519	......	....	....	1.56759	
0.4047	....	1.8475	1.58975			
0.4358	....	1.8303	1.58147			
0.4861	....	......	1.57179			
0.50	1.70896	......	....	2.09648	1.55175	
0.5086	....	......	1.56848			
0.5461	....	1.7951	1.56393			
0.5791	....	1.7888				
0.60	1.69583	......	....	2.06385	....	2.60591
0.6438	....	1.7793	1.55585			
0.70	1.68825	......	1.55276	2.04590	1.53881	2.53262
0.8521	....	1.7630				
1.0	1.67793	......	....	2.02239	1.53216	2.44789
1.0140	....	1.7569	1.54410			
1.6932	....	1.7470				
1.7012	....	......	1.53901			
2.0	1.67061	......	....	2.00615	1.52670	2.39673
3.0	1.66901	......	....	2.00239	1.52434	2.38760
3.418	....	1.7436				
3.419	....	......	1.53612			
5.0	1.66737	......	....	1.99745	1.51899	2.38173
9.724	....	1.7395	1.52689			
10.0	1.66251	......	....	1.98034	1.49482	2.37274
14.98	....	......	1.5128			
15.0	1.65468	......	....	1.95113	1.45145	2.36030
15.48	....	1.7341				
16.0	1.65272	......	....	1.94358	1.44001	2.35724
17.0	1.65062	......	....	1.93542	1.42753	2.35398
18.0	1.64838	......	....	1.92660	1.41393	2.35051
19.0	1.64600	......	....	1.91710	1.39914	2.34683
19.01	....	......	1.4970			
20.0	1.64348	......	....	1.90688	1.38307	2.34294
20.5	....	......	....	1.90149		
20.57	....	1.7268				
21.18	....	......	1.4866			
21.3	1.63997	......		....	1.352	
21.83	....	......	1.4830	....	1.318	
22.8	1.63561	......		....	1.299	
23.6	1.63313					
23.86	....	......	1.4713			
23.87	....	1.7212				
24.2	1.63121	......	....		1.278	
25.0	1.62856	......	....		1.254	2.32017
25.14	....	......	1.4631			

TABLE 6b-7. INDEX OF REFRACTION OF SPECIAL OPTICAL MATERIALS (*Continued*)

λ, μ	Cesium bromide	Cesium iodide	Potassium bromide	Silver chloride	Sodium chloride	Thallium bromide-iodide
25.8	1.62580	....	....	....	1.229	
26.6	1.62293	....	....	....	1.203	
26.63	....	1.7157				
27.3	1.62033	....	....	....	1.175	
29.82	....	1.7085				
30.0	1.60947	....	....	....	....	2.29154
33.0	1.59576	1.7004	....	....	....	2.27131
35.0	1.58558	....	....	....	....	2.25647
35.84	....	1.6921				
36.0	1.58016	....	....	....	....	2.24862
37.0	1.57450	....	....	....	....	2.24068
38.0	1.56860	....	....	....	....	2.23205
38.5	1.56556	....	....	....	....	2.22772
39.0	1.56245	....	....	....	....	2.22331
39.2	1.56119					
39.22	....	1.6810	....	....	....	2.21882
39.5	....	....	....	....	....	2.21882
44.05	....	1.6635				
45.04	....	1.6597				
47.06	....	1.6508				
48.08	....	1.6456				
49.16	....	1.6411				

References for Table 6b-7

1. *Lithium Fluoride.* Data at temperature of 20°C for wavelengths 0.193 to 0.231μ taken from Z. Gyulai, *Z. Physik* **46,** 84 (1927); at 20°C for 0.254 to 0.486μ taken from H. Harting, *Sitzber. deut. Akad. Wiss. Berlin* IV, 1948; at 23.6°C for 0.50 to 6.0μ from L. W. Tilton and E. K. Plyler, *J. Research Natl. Bur. Standards* **47,** 25 (1951); at 18°C for 6.91 to 9.79μ taken from H. W. Hohls, *Ann. Physik* **29,** 433 (1937).

2. *Magnesium Oxide.* Data at temperature of 23°C for wavelengths 0.25 to 0.707μ (except for datum at 0.3650μ) taken from J. Strong and R. T. Brice, *J. Opt. Soc. Am.* **25,** 207 (1935); at 23.3°C for 1.0140 to 5.35μ (plus datum at 0.3650μ) taken from R. E. Stephens and I. H. Malitson, *J. Research Natl. Bur. Standards* **49,** 252 (1952).

3. *Crystalline Quartz.* Data at temperature of 18°C for wavelengths 0.185 to 0.768μ taken from F. A. Martens, *Ann. Physik* **6,** 603 (1901) [similar data given by J. W. Gifford, *Proc. Phys. Soc.* (*London*) **70,** 329 (1902), and by H. Trommsdorff, *Physik. Z.* **2,** 576 (1901)]. See R. B. Sosman, "The Properties of Silica," Chemical Catalog Company, Inc., New York, 1927, for a collation of the above data. At 20°C for 0.8325 to 2.30μ taken from A. Carvallo, *Compt. rend.* **126,** 728 (1898). At 18°C for 2.60 to 7.0μ taken from H. Rubens, *Wied. Ann.* **54,** 488 (1895).

4. *Rutile.* Data for wavelengths 0.435 to 1.5296μ taken from J. R. DeVore, *J. Opt. Soc. Am.* **41,** 418 (1951). (No temperature given.)

5. *Sapphire.* Data for natural corundum at room temperature for wavelengths 0.535, 0.589, and 0.671μ taken from R. Brouns, *Centrabe Mineral* **673** (1909); data for wavelengths 0.4861 and 0.6563μ taken from "Synthetic Sapphire, Ruby, and Spinel," p. 23, The Linde Air Products Company, New York, 1946.

6. *Fused Silica.* Data at temperature of 18°C for wavelengths 0.185 to 0.5893μ taken from H. Trommsdorf, *Physik. Z.* **2**, 576 (1901) (except for datum at 0.23μ); at 18°C at wavelengths 0.231 and 0.768μ taken from J. W. Gifford, *Proc. Phys. Soc.* (*London*) **70,** 329 (1902); at 18°C for 0.886 to 2.595μ taken from A. Carvallo, *Compt. rend.* **126,** 728 (1898) (except for datum at 1.028μ); at 18°C for 1.028μ taken from C. Muller and A. Wetthauer, *Z. Physik* **85,** 559 (1938); at 24°C for 3.5078μ taken from W. S. Rodney and R. J. Spindler, *J. Opt. Soc. Am.* **44,** 678 (1954).
7. *Sphalerite.* Data for wavelengths 0.3650 to 1.5296μ taken from J. R. DeVore, *J. Opt. Soc. Am.* **41,** 417 (1951). (No temperature given.)
8. *Spinel.* Data taken from "Synthetic Sapphire, Ruby, and Spinel," p. 23, The Linde Air Products Company, New York, 1946.
9. *Strontium Titanate.* Data taken from private communication with W. B. Anderson, Titanium Pigment Corporation, July 9, 1954.
10. *Arsenic Trisulfide Glass.* Data at a temperature of 24°C for wavelengths 0.579066 to 11.035μ measured by the National Bureau of Standards and taken from literature from the American Optical Company and the Servo Corporation of America.
11. *Calcium Fluoride.* Data at a temperature of 20°C for wavelengths 0.19 to 9.00μ taken from F. Kohlrausch, "Praktische Physik," 18th ed., vol. 2, pp. 528–529, Mary S. Rosenberg, New York, 1947.
12. *Germanium.* Data for wavelengths 4.17 to 12.5μ taken from private communication from I. Simon, *J. Opt. Soc. Am.* **41,** 730 (1951).
13. *Pyrite.* Data from same source as data for germanium (see above).
14. *Amorphous Selenium.* Data for wavelengths 0.819 to 2.00μ taken from H. A. Gebbie and E. W. Saker, *Proc. Phys. Soc.* (*London*) **864,** 360 (1951).
15. *Silicon.* Data from same source as data for germanium (see above).
16. *Cesium Bromide.* Data at temperature of 27°C for wavelengths 0.40 to 39.2μ taken from W. S. Rodney and R. J. Spindler, *J. Research Natl. Bur. Standards* **51,** 126 (1953).
17. *Cesium Iodide.* Data at temperature of 24°C for wavelengths 0.3610 to 49.16μ taken from private communication from W. S. Rodney, National Bureau of Standards, August, 1954.
18. *Potassium Bromide.* Data at temperature of 48°C at wavelengths 0.206 and 0.210μ taken from Z. Gyulai, *Z. Physik* **46,** 80 (1927); at 20°C for wavelengths 0.214 to 0.391μ from H. Harting, *Sitzber. deut. Akad. Wiss. Berlin* no. IV, 1948; at 22°C for 0.40 to 0.70μ from R. J. Spindler and W. S. Rodney, *J. Research Natl. Bur. Standards* **49,** 258–260 (1952); at 22°C for 1.0140 to 25.14μ from private communication from Stephens, Plyler, Rodney, and Spindler, National Bureau of Standards, March, 1952.
19. *Silver Chloride.* Data at temperature of 23.9°C at wavelengths 0.50 to 20.5μ taken from L. W. Tilton, E. K. Plyler, and R. E. Stephens, *J. Opt. Soc. Am.* **40,** 543 (1950).
20. *Sodium Chloride.* Data at temperature of 20°C for wavelengths 0.19 to 21.0μ taken from F. Kohlrausch, "Praktische Physik," 18th edition, vol. 2, pp. 528–529, Mary S. Rosenberg, New York, 1947; at 18°C for 21.3 to 27.3μ from H. W. Hohls, *Ann. Physik* **29,** 433 (1937).
21. *Thallium Bromide-iodide.* Data at temperature of 27°C for wavelengths 0.60 to 39.5μ taken from L. W. Tilton, E. K. Plyler, and R. E. Stephens, *J. Research Natl. Bur. Standards* **43,** 86 (1949). These data are less (by approximately 5 per cent) than those reported by G. Hettner and G. Leisegang, *Optik* **3,** 305 (1948), but the percentage of thallium iodide differed in the samples studied by the two respective groups. The difficulties with the consistent preparation of this material have been analyzed by A. Smakula, J. Kalnajs, and V. Sils, *J. Opt. Soc. Am.* **43,** 698–701 (1953).

TABLE 6b-8. INDEX OF REFRACTION OF FUSED QUARTZ GLASS*

λ, μ	Index	λ, μ	Index	λ, μ	Index
0.185	1.57464	0.56	1.459561	1.50	1.444687
0.214	1.53386	0.57	1.459168	1.60	1.443492
0.275	1.49634	0.58	1.458794	1.70	1.442250
0.34	1.47877	0.59	1.458437	1.80	1.440954
0.35	1.47701	0.60	1.458096	1.90	1.439597
0.36	1.47540	0.61	1.457769	2.00	1.438174
0.37	1.47393	0.62	1.457456	2.10	1.436680
0.38	1.47258	0.63	1.457156	2.20	1.435111
0.39	1.47135	0.64	1.456868	2.30	1.433462
0.40	1.470208	0.65	1.456591	2.40	1.431730
0.41	1.469155	0.66	1.456324	2.50	1.429911
0.42	1.468179	0.67	1.456066	2.60	1.428001
0.43	1.467273	0.68	1.455818	2.70	1.425995
0.44	1.466429	0.69	1.455579	2.80	1.423891
0.45	1.465642	0.70	1.455347	2.90	1.421684
0.46	1.464908	0.80	1.453371	3.00	1.41937
0.47	1.464220	0.90	1.451808	3.10	1.41694
0.48	1.463573	1.00	1.450473	3.20	1.31440
0.49	1.462965	1.10	1.449261	3.30	1.41173
0.50	1.462394	1.20	1.448110	3.40	1.40893
0.51	1.461856	1.30	1.446980	3.50	1.40601
0.52	1.461346	1.40	1.445845		
0.53	1.460863				
0.54	1.460406				
0.55	1.459973				

Note. Biggest deviation from above values was 40 × 10^{-6} on a General Electric sample; other samples measured were from Heraeus and Corning.

* Most of the data in this table came from W. S. Rodney and R. J. Spindler, Index of Refraction of Fused Quartz Glass, *J. Research Natl. Bur. Standards* **53**, 185 (September, 1954).

TABLE 6b-9. REFRACTIVE INDICES OF OPTICAL GLASSES MADE AT NATIONAL BUREAU OF STANDARDS*

Name	Nominal n_D	V	A typical glass					Density
			n_D	$n_{G'}$	n_F	n_C	V	
BSC 511	1.5110	63.5	1.51100	1.52118	1.51666	1.50861	63.5	2.48
BSC 517	1.5170	64.5	1.51700	1.52709	1.52263	1.51461	64.5	2.51
BSC 536	1.5359	64.4	1.53598	1.54645	1.54182	1.53349	64.3	2.56
LC 513	1.5125	60.5	1.51250	1.52312	1.51845	1.50999	60.6	2.55
LC 523	1.5230	58.6	1.52300	1.53433	1.52928	1.52037	58.7	2.52
LC 529	1.5288	58.3	1.52882	1.54035	1.53520	1.52613	58.3	
BaC 541	1.5411	59.9	1.54110	1.55259	1.54746	1.53843	59.9	2.85
BaC 573	1.5725	57.4	1.57250	1.58518	1.57951	1.56958	57.6	3.21
BaC 574	1.5744	57.7	1.57440	1.58710	1.58143	1.57149	57.8	3.21
BaC 611	1.6109	57.2	1.61090	1.62451	1.61843	1.60777	57.3	3.48
BaC 611	1.6110	58.8	1.61100	1.62421	1.61832	1.60793	58.8	3.58
BaC 617	1.6170	55.0	1.61700	1.63135	1.62492	1.61372	55.1	3.66
BaC 620	1.6191	59.5	1.61919	1.63242	1.62652	1.61611	59.5	3.60
CF 529	1.5286	51.6	1.52860	1.54181	1.53587	1.52561	51.5	2.73
F 573	1.5725	42.5	1.57250	1.59056	1.58212	1.56862	42.4	3.28
F 580	1.5795	41.0	1.57950	1.59816	1.58966	1.57548	40.9	3.24
F 605	1.6050	38.0	1.60500	1.62604	1.61639	1.60046	38.0	3.49
F 617	1.6170	36.6	1.61700	1.63931	1.62906	1.61220	36.6	3.60
F 621	1.6210	36.2	1.62100	1.64369	1.63326	1.61612	36.2	3.64
F 649	1.6490	33.8	1.64900	1.67462	1.66278	1.64354	33.7	3.90
F 666	1.6660	32.4	1.66600	1.69335	1.68069	1.66021	32.5	4.03
F 673	1.6725	32.2	1.67250	1.70046	1.68752	1.66660	32.1	4.08
F 689	1.6890	30.9	1.68900	1.71867	1.70491	1.68275	31.1	4.24
F 720	1.7200	29.3	1.72000	1.75309	1.73769	1.71309	29.3	4.51
F 754	1.7543	27.7	1.75437	1.79132	1.77406	1.74671	27.6	4.79
BF 584	1.5838	46.0	1.58380	1.60024	1.59279	1.58015	46.2	3.21
BF 588	1.5880	53.4	1.58800	1.60210	1.59577	1.58479	53.5	3.33
BF 605	1.6053	43.6	1.60530	1.62350	1.61520	1.60130	43.5	3.47
			Rare-earth glasses					
714/531	1.714	53.1	1.7143	1.7315	1.7238	1.7103	53.1	
705/540	1.705	54.0	1.7049	1.7216	1.7142	1.7011	54.0	
682/553	1.682	55.3	1.6819	1.6976	1.6906	1.6782	55.3	
673/562	1.673	56.2	1.6733	1.6885	1.6817	1.6697	56.2	
656/582	1.656	58.2	1.6555	1.6698	1.6634	1.6522	58.2	
639/597	1.639	59.7	1.6395	1.6531	1.6470	1.6363	59.7	
610/620	1.610	62.0	1.6096	1.6220	1.6165	1.6067	62.0	

* Compiled by J. C. Baker, Harvard College Observatory.

Table 6b-10. Index of Refraction for Some New Glasses*

Origin	Type	μ	Indices of refraction				
			A'	C	D	F	G'
NBS.......	610/620	62.0	......	1.6067	1.6096	1.6165	1.6220
NBS.......	639/597	59.7	......	1.6363	1.6395	1.6470	1.6531
NBS.......	656/582	58.2		1.6522	1.6555	1.6634	1.6698
EK........	EK-110	56.2	1.68877	1.69313	1.69680	1.70554	1.71255
NBS.......	673/562	56.2		1.6697	1.6733	1.6817	1.6885
Hay.......	651/558	55.8	......	1.64757	1.65100	1.65924	1.66590
NBS.......	682/553	55.3		1.6782	1.6819	1.6906	1.6976
NBS.......	705/540	54.0		1.7011	1.7049	1.7142	1.7216
NBS.......	714/531	53.1		1.7103	1.7143	1.7238	1.7315
Hay.......	671/520	52.0	......	1.66724	1.67100	1.68018	1.68772
EK........	EK-210	51.2	1.72482	1.72979	1.73400	1.74413	1.75235
Corn'g.....	8313	47.8	......	1.69639	1.70065	1.71104	
EK........	EK-330	47.2	1.74499	1.75043	1.75510	1.76643	1.77571
EK........	EK-310	46.4	1.73491	1.74033	1.74500	1.75638	1.76577
EK........	EK-320	45.8	1.73432	1.73978	1.74450	1.75603	1.76557
EK........	EK-450	41.8	1.79180	1.79814	1.80370	1.81738	1.82880
EK........	EK-448	41.1	1.86714	1.87420	1.88040	1.89564	1.90827

Corn'g, Corning Glass Works.
EK, Eastman Kodak Company.
Hay, Hayward Scientific Glass Corp.
NBS, National Bureau of Standards.
* I. C. Gardner, New Types of Optical Glasses Available in the United States, *Proc. London Conf. Opt. Instruments*, p. 241, 1950.

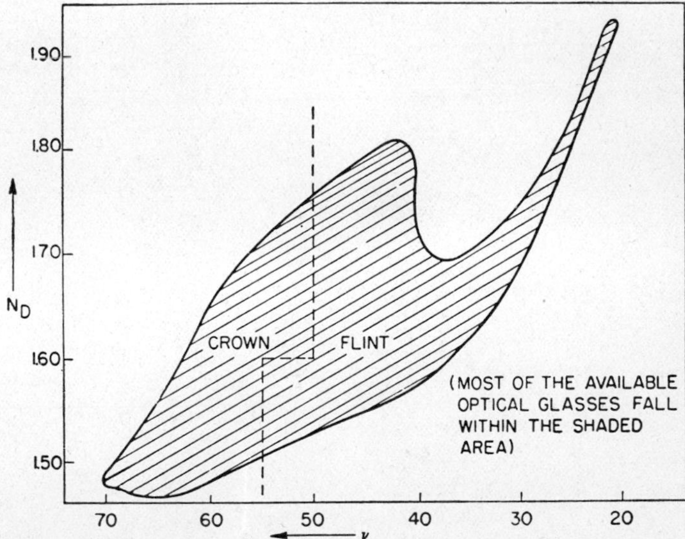

Fig. 6b-1. Relationship of N_D (index of refraction of the Fraunhofer D line) to ν (dispersion) for optical glasses.

Table 6b-11. Refractive Indices of Quartz at Various Temperatures [Measured by Rinne and Kolb (1910) and Recalculated as Absolute Indices]*

Solar line	Wave-length, mμ	−140°C	−45°C	23°C	115°C	212°C	305°C	410°C	550°C	580°C	650°C	765°C
					Extraordinary Index n_ϵ							
G' ($H\gamma$)	434.047	......	1.5633	1.5634	1.5629	1.5623	1.5615	1.5598	1.5551	1.5503	1.5521	1.5532
(d)	466.8	......	1.5609	1.5608	1.5603	1.5597	1.5588	1.5572	1.5526	1.5478	1.5492	1.5506
F	486.133	1.5594	1.5594	1.5593	1.5589	1.5581	1.5573	1.5558	1.5512	1.5464	1.5475	1.5490
(c)	495.75	......	1.5587	1.5587	1.5582	1.5576	1.5567	1.5552	1.5503	1.5456	1.5468	1.5481
b_2	517.27	......	1.5574	1.5574	1.5568	1.5562	1.5553	1.5538	1.5488	1.5442	1.5454	1.5469
D_2	588.997	1.5541	1.5539	1.5537	1.5532	1.5526	1.5515	1.5499	1.5451	1.5405	1.5417	1.5431
α	627.8	1.5526	1.5525	1.5522	1.5517	1.5510	1.5500	1.5486	1.5437	1.5389	1.5403	1.5416
C	656.278	......	1.5516	1.5513	1.5508	1.5502	1.5491	1.5475	1.5427	1.5380	1.5393	1.5406
B	687.2	1.5506	1.5506	1.5504	1.5499	1.5492	1.5481	1.5466	1.5419	1.5369	1.5383	1.5397
a	718.9	......	1.5499	1.5495	1.5490	1.5483	1.5472	1.5458	1.5408	1.5362	1.5375	1.5388
					Ordinary Index n_ω							
G' ($H\gamma$)	434.047	......	1.5539	1.5540	1.5536	1.5531	1.5523	1.5510	1.5469	1.5425	1.5439	1.5454
(d)	466.8	......	1.5515	1.5514	1.5511	1.5506	1.5498	1.5483	1.5442	1.5400	1.5414	1.5429
F	486.133	1.5504	1.5501	1.5500	1.5497	1.5491	1.5483	1.5469	1.5426	1.5385	1.5399	1.5414
(c)	495.75	......	1.5494	1.5494	1.5491	1.5485	1.5477	1.5465	1.5421	1.5379	1.5393	1.5406
b_2	517.27	......	1.5481	1.5481	1.5476	1.5472	1.5463	1.5452	1.5407	1.5363	1.5377	1.5392
D_2	588.997	1.5449	1.5448	1.5446	1.5441	1.5437	1.5428	1.5414	1.5370	1.5329	1.5341	1.5356
α	627.8	1.5434	1.5434	1.5431	1.5427	1.5422	1.5413	1.5401	1.5357	1.5314	1.5328	1.5340
C	656.278	......	1.5425	1.5423	1.5418	1.5414	1.5405	1.5390	1.5349	1.5304	1.5319	1.5331
B	687.2	1.5417	1.5416	1.5414	1.5410	1.5405	1.5395	1.5382	1.5337	1.5296	1.5309	1.5321
a	718.9	......	1.5408	1.5405	1.5401	1.5396	1.5386	1.5374	1.5327	1.5288	1.5301	1.5313

* R. B. Sosman, "The Properties of Silica," Chemical Catalog Company, Inc., New York.

Table 6b-12. Liquids Used for Determining Refractive Index by Transmission Method*

Liquid	N_D, 24°C
Trimethylene chloride	1.446
Cineole	1.456
Hexahydrophenol	1.466
Decahydronaphthalene	1.477
Isoamylphthalate	1.486
Tetrachloroethane	1.492
Pentachloroethane	1.501
Trimethylene bromide	1.513
Chlorobenzene	1.523
Ethylene bromide + chlorobenzene	1.533
o-Nitrotoluene	1.544
Xylidine	1.557
o-Toluidine	1.570
Aniline	1.584
Bromoform	1.595
Iodobenzene + bromobenzene	1.603
Iodobenzene + bromobenzene	1.613
Quinoline	1.622
α-Chloronaphthalene	1.633
α-Bromonaphthalene + α-chloronaphthalene	1.640–1.650
α-Bromonaphthalene + α-iodonaphthalene	1.660–1.690
Methylene iodide + iodobenzene	1.700–1.730
Methylene iodide	1.738
Methylene iodide saturated with sulfur	1.78
Yellow phosphorus, sulfur, and methylene iodide† (8:1:1 by weight)	2.06

* "Handbook of Chemistry and Physics," 36th ed., p. 2669, Chemical Rubber Publishing Company, 1954–1955.

† Can be diluted with methylene iodide to cover range 1.74–2.06. For precautions in use, cf. West, *Am. Mineral* **21,** 245–249 (1936).

6c. Absorption and Transmission

K. A. McCARTHY

Tufts University

S. S. BALLARD

Scripps Institution of Oceanography

6c-1. Definitions and Tables. Two important optical properties of a material are its *refractive index* n and its *absorption coefficient* α; both vary with wavelength. The absorption coefficient represents the fraction of radiant intensity lost by absorption per unit thickness of material, for very small thicknesses. Its value depends strongly on the purity of the sample and may vary widely for materials from different sources or prepared by different methods. Representative values are given in Table 6c-1 for several crystalline materials and for fused silica.

The *internal transmittance* T_i of a material is related to the absorption coefficient by

$$T_i = \frac{I}{I_0} = e^{-\alpha t}$$

where I_0 is the intensity of the radiation transmitted by the first surface of a plate of material of thickness t, and I is the intensity of the flux incident on the second surface. Values of I_0 and I measured in air outside the sample must be corrected for surface reflection loss before being used in computing absorption coefficient. It can be seen from the equation that the units of absorption coefficients are reciprocal length, and that the reciprocal of α is the absorption distance through which the intensity of radiation is reduced to $1/e$, or 36.8 per cent, of its original value.

Other optical constants commonly used include the extinction coefficient κ and the absorption constant k; these are related to absorption coefficient by

$$\kappa = \frac{k}{n} = \frac{\alpha\lambda}{4\pi n}$$

where λ is the wavelength of light.

TABLE 6c-1. ABSORPTION COEFFICIENTS OF VARIOUS SUBSTANCES (cm^{-1})

λ, μ	Calcium fluoride	Lithium fluoride	Magnesium oxide	Potassium bromide	Crystalline ordinary	Quartz extraordinary	Silica fused	Sodium chloride
2.4	.....	....	...	......	0.009	0.02	0.016	
2.5	.....	....	...	......	0.027	0.05	0.02	
3.0	.....	....	...	......	0.50	0.17	0.15	
3.5	.....	....	...	......	0.90	0.90	0.31	
4.0	.....	....	...	......	1.8	1.8	2.0	
4.5	.....	....	...	......	7.2	7.2	7.1	
5.0	.....	....	...	......	65	65	28	
5.5	.....	0.15						
6.0	.....	0.50						
6.5	.....	1.3						
7.0	0.04	2.4	2.0					
7.5	0.09	4.1						
8.0	0.19	7.0	6.0					
8.5	0.36							
9.0	0.62	13	15					
9.5	1.02							
10.0	1.7	31	50					
11.0	4.6	60						0.006
12.0	11.0	160	16					0.013
14.0		500	42					0.10
15.0		2,000						0.20
16.0				0.01				0.32
20.0	.....	....	....	0.072	....	....		3.3
24.0	.....	....	....	0.25	....	....		14
26.0	.....	....	....	......	....	....		21
28.0	.....	....	....	0.79	....	....		50
30.0	.....	....	....	......	....	....		100
32.0	.....	....	....	2				
38.0	.....	....	....	7				
40.0	.....	....	....	12				
45.0	.....	....	....	36				

References for Table 6c-1

1. *Calcium Fluoride.* Taken from graph computed from transmittance curve in S. S. Ballard, ed., "The Optical and Other Physical Properties of Infrared Optical Materials," p. 61, final report for ERDL Contract W-44-009 eng-473, 1949.
2. *Lithium Fluoride.* H. W. Hobbs, *Ann. Physik* **29**, 433 (1937).
3. *Magnesium Oxide.* E. Burstein, J. J. Oberly, and E. K. Plyler, *Proc. Ind. Acad. Sci.* **38**, 388 (1948).
4. *Potassium Bromide.* Z. Mentzel, *Z. Physik* **88**, 178 (1934).
5. *Crystalline Quartz.* See ref. 1 for ordinary ray; for extraordinary ray, D. G. Drummond, *Proc. Roy. Soc.* (*London*), ser. A, **153**, 328 (1935).
6. *Fused Silica.* See ref. 1.
7. *Sodium Chloride.* See ref. 1.

Table 6c-2. Extinction Coefficients in the Infrared*
(cm^{-1})

λ, μ	Germanium	Silicon	Pyrite
4.17	1.9	1.35	0
4.55	1.9	1.35	0
6.25	1.5	1.30	0
7.14	1.2	1.13	
7.69	....	....	0.42
8.33	0.73	0.52	
10.0	0	0.14	0.55
12.5	0	0.15	
15.4	....	....	0.67

* Private communication from I. Simon. For graphical presentation, see I. Simon, *J. Opt. Soc. Am.* **41,** 730 (1951).

6c-2. Notes on Absorption and Transmission of Optical Materials. Approximate spectral absorption characteristics of several optical materials are given on pages 116–124 of Office of Technical Services (U. S. Department of Commerce) publication No. 111053 of October, 1952: "Physical Properties of Optical Crystals with Special Reference to Infrared," by Alexander Smakula. He gives data for a so-called extinction coefficient, K_{10}, which is the common-logarithm analog of absorption coefficient: the reciprocal of K_{10} is the absorption distance through which the intensity of radiation is reduced to $\frac{1}{10}$, or 10 per cent, of its original value. Absorption coefficients, α, can be obtained by multiplying values of K_{10} by 2.303.

There are many materials of importance for which absorption coefficients are not available in the literature; however, the references listed below present transmittance data from which approximate values of absorption coefficients can be computed.

1. *Amorphous Selenium.* Transmission curves, for five thicknesses from 0.06 to 0.62 cm, to 25μ given. See H. A. Gebbie and C. E. Cannon, *J. Opt. Soc. Am.* **42,** 277L (1952).
2. *Arsenic Trisulfide Glass.* Transmission curves up to 13μ given. See R. Frerichs, *J. Opt. Soc. Am.* **43,** 1153 (1953).
3. *Barium Fluoride, Cadmium Fluoride, Lead Fluoride,* and *Strontium Fluoride.* See D. A. Jones, R. V. Jones, and R. W. H. Stevenson, *Proc. Phys. Soc.* (*London*), ser. B, **85,** 906 (1952). For cadmium fluoride, see also H. M. Haendler, C. M. Wheeler, and W. J. Bernard, *J. Opt. Soc. Am.* **43,** 215 (1953).
4. *Cesium Bromide.* A transmittance curve from 0.32 to 38μ is given for a 7-mm-thickness sample by E. K. Plyler and F. P. Phelps, *J. Opt. Soc. Am.* **41,** 209L (1951).
5. *Cesium Iodide.* A transmittance curve from 0.22 to 38μ is given for a 3-mm-thickness sample by E. K. Plyler and F. P. Phelps, *J. Opt. Soc. Am.* **42,** 432L (1952). This material probably transmits to a wavelength of 52μ.
6. *Rutile.* The transmission for a sample of thickness 1.86 mm from 2 to 8μ is given in S. S. Ballard, ed., "The Optical and Other Physical Properties of Infrared Optical Materials," p. 61, final report for ERDL Contract W-44-009 end-473, 1949.
7. *Sapphire.* The transmission for a sample of thickness 0.5 cm from 2 to 6μ is given in the same source as referred to for rutile.
8. *Silver Chloride.* The transmission for a sample of thickness 0.6 cm from 2 to 26μ is given in the same source as referred to for rutile.
9. *Spinel.* See G. Calingert, S. K. Heron, and R. Stair, *Trans. Soc. Automotive Engrs.* **31,** 448 (1936).

10. *Strontium Titanate.* Transmittance curves for the visible region for 1.0- and 1.1-mm samples are given in private communication with W. B. Anderson, Titanium Pigment Corporation, July 9, 1954.
11. *Thallium Bromide-iodide.* The transmission for a sample of thickness 0.4 cm to a wavelength of 38μ in the same source as referred to for rutile.

TABLE 6c-3

CONVERSION TABLE

OPTICAL DENSITY VS PERCENT TRANSMISSION

Density	Percent Transmission	Density	Percent Transmission	Density	Percent Transmission	Density	Percent Transmission	Density	Percent Transmission	Density	Percent Transmission	Density	Percent Transmission	Density	Percent Transmission
0.00	100.00	0.50	31.62	1.00	10.00	1.50	3.162	2.00	1.000	2.50	0.3162	3.00	0.1000	3.50	0.0316
0.01	97.72	0.51	30.90	1.01	9.772	1.51	3.090	2.01	0.9772	2.51	0.3090	3.01	0.0977	3.51	0.0309
0.02	95.50	0.52	30.20	1.02	9.550	1.52	3.020	2.02	0.9550	2.52	0.3020	3.02	0.0955	3.52	0.0302
0.03	93.33	0.53	29.51	1.03	9.333	1.53	2.951	2.03	0.9333	2.53	0.2951	3.03	0.0933	3.53	0.0295
0.04	91.20	0.54	28.84	1.04	9.120	1.54	2.884	2.04	0.9120	2.54	0.2884	3.04	0.0912	3.54	0.0288
0.05	89.13	0.55	28.18	1.05	8.913	1.55	2.818	2.05	0.8913	2.55	0.2818	3.05	0.0891	3.55	0.0289
0.06	87.10	0.56	27.54	1.06	8.710	1.56	2.754	2.06	0.8710	2.56	0.2754	3.06	0.0871	3.56	0.0275
0.07	85.11	0.57	26.92	1.07	8.511	1.57	2.692	2.07	0.8511	2.57	0.2692	3.07	0.0851	3.57	0.0269
0.08	83.18	0.58	26.30	1.08	8.318	1.58	2.630	2.08	0.8318	2.58	0.2630	3.08	0.0832	3.58	0.0263
0.09	81.28	0.59	25.70	1.09	8.128	1.59	2.570	2.09	0.8128	2.59	0.2570	3.09	0.0813	3.59	0.0257
0.10	79.43	0.60	25.12	1.10	7.943	1.60	2.512	2.10	0.7943	2.60	0.2512	3.10	0.0794	3.60	0.0251
0.11	77.62	0.61	24.55	1.11	7.762	1.61	2.455	2.11	0.7762	2.61	0.2455	3.11	0.0776	3.61	0.0245
0.12	75.86	0.62	23.99	1.12	7.586	1.62	2.399	2.12	0.7586	2.62	0.2399	3.12	0.0759	3.62	0.0239
0.13	74.13	0.63	23.44	1.13	7.413	1.63	2.344	2.13	0.7413	2.63	0.2344	3.13	0.0741	3.63	0.0234
0.14	72.44	0.64	22.91	1.14	7.244	1.64	2.291	2.14	0.7244	2.64	0.2291	3.14	0.0724	3.64	0.0229
0.15	70.79	0.65	22.39	1.15	7.079	1.65	2.239	2.15	0.7079	2.65	0.2239	3.15	0.0708	3.65	0.0223
0.16	69.18	0.66	21.88	1.16	6.918	1.66	2.188	2.16	0.6918	2.66	0.2188	3.16	0.0692	3.66	0.0218
0.17	67.61	0.67	21.38	1.17	6.761	1.67	2.138	2.17	0.6761	2.67	0.2138	3.17	0.0676	3.67	0.0214
0.18	66.07	0.68	20.89	1.18	6.607	1.68	2.089	2.18	0.6607	2.68	0.2089	3.18	0.0661	3.68	0.0218
0.19	64.57	0.69	20.42	1.19	6.457	1.69	2.042	2.19	0.6457	2.69	0.2042	3.19	0.0646	3.69	0.0204
0.20	63.10	0.70	19.95	1.20	6.310	1.70	1.995	2.20	0.6310	2.70	0.1995	3.20	0.06310	3.70	0.0199
0.21	61.66	0.71	19.50	1.21	6.166	1.71	1.950	2.21	0.6166	2.71	0.1950	3.21	0.0617	3.71	0.0195
0.22	60.26	0.72	19.05	1.22	6.026	1.72	1.905	2.22	0.6026	2.72	0.1905	3.22	0.0603	3.72	0.0190
0.23	58.88	0.73	18.62	1.23	5.888	1.73	1.862	2.23	0.5888	2.73	0.1862	3.23	0.0588	3.73	0.0186
0.24	57.54	0.74	18.20	1.24	5.754	1.74	1.820	2.24	0.5754	2.74	0.1820	3.24	0.0575	3.74	0.0182
0.25	56.23	0.75	17.78	1.25	5.623	1.75	1.778	2.25	0.5623	2.75	0.1778	3.25	0.0562	3.75	0.0178
0.26	54.95	0.76	17.38	1.26	5.495	1.76	1.738	2.26	0.5495	2.76	0.1738	3.26	0.0550	3.76	0.0174
0.27	53.70	0.77	16.98	1.27	5.370	1.77	1.698	2.27	0.5370	2.77	0.1698	3.27	0.0537	3.77	0.0169
0.28	52.48	0.78	16.60	1.28	5.248	1.78	1.660	2.28	0.5248	2.78	0.1660	3.28	0.0529	3.78	0.0166
0.29	51.29	0.79	16.22	1.29	5.129	1.79	1.622	2.29	0.5129	2.79	0.1622	3.29	0.0513	3.79	0.0162
0.30	50.12	0.80	15.85	1.30	5.012	1.80	1.585	2.30	0.5012	2.80	0.1585	3.30	0.0501	3.80	0.0158
0.31	48.98	0.81	15.49	1.31	4.898	1.81	1.549	2.31	0.4898	2.81	0.1549	3.31	0.0489	3.81	0.0155
0.32	47.86	0.82	15.14	1.32	4.786	1.82	1.514	2.32	0.4786	2.82	0.1514	3.32	0.0478	3.82	0.0152
0.33	46.77	0.83	14.79	1.33	4.677	1.83	1.479	2.33	0.4677	2.83	0.1479	3.33	0.0468	3.83	0.0148
0.34	45.71	0.84	14.45	1.34	4.571	1.84	1.445	2.34	0.4571	2.84	0.1445	3.34	0.0457	3.84	0.0145
0.35	44.67	0.85	14.13	1.35	4.467	1.85	1.413	2.35	0.4467	2.85	0.1413	3.35	0.0446	3.85	0.0141
0.36	43.65	0.86	13.80	1.36	4.365	1.86	1.380	2.36	0.4365	2.86	0.1380	3.36	0.0436	3.86	0.0138
0.37	42.66	0.87	13.49	1.37	4.266	1.87	1.349	2.37	0.4266	2.87	0.1349	3.37	0.04266	3.87	0.0135
0.38	41.69	0.88	13.18	1.38	4.169	1.88	1.318	2.38	0.4169	2.88	0.1318	3.38	0.0417	3.88	0.0132
0.39	40.74	0.89	12.88	1.39	4.074	1.89	1.288	2.39	0.4074	2.89	0.1288	3.39	0.0407	3.89	0.0129
0.40	39.81	0.90	12.59	1.40	3.981	1.90	1.259	2.40	0.3981	2.90	0.1259	3.40	0.0398	3.90	0.0126
0.41	38.90	0.91	12.30	1.41	3.890	1.91	1.230	2.41	0.3890	2.91	0.1230	3.41	0.0389	3.91	0.0123
0.42	38.02	0.92	12.02	1.42	3.802	1.92	1.202	2.42	0.3802	2.92	0.1202	3.42	0.0380	3.92	0.0120
0.43	37.15	0.93	11.75	1.43	3.715	1.93	1.175	2.43	0.3715	2.93	0.1175	3.43	0.0371	3.93	0.0117
0.44	36.31	0.94	11.48	1.44	3.631	1.94	1.148	2.44	0.3631	2.94	0.1148	3.44	0.0363	3.94	0.0114
0.45	35.48	0.95	11.22	1.45	3.548	1.95	1.122	2.45	0.3548	2.95	0.1122	3.45	0.0355	3.95	0.0112
0.46	34.67	0.96	10.96	1.46	3.467	1.96	1.096	2.46	0.3467	2.96	0.1096	3.46	0.0347	3.96	0.0109
0.47	33.88	0.97	10.72	1.47	3.388	1.97	1.072	2.47	0.3388	2.97	0.1072	3.47	0.0339	3.97	0.0107
0.48	33.11	0.98	10.47	1.48	3.311	1.98	1.047	2.48	0.3311	2.98	0.1047	3.48	0.0331	3.98	0.0105
0.49	32.36	0.99	10.23	1.49	3.236	1.99	1.023	2.49	0.3236	2.99	0.1023	3.49	0.0324	3.99	0.0102
0.50	31.62	1.00	10.00	1.50	3.162	2.00	1.000	2.50	0.3162	3.00	0.1000	3.50	0.0316	4.00	0.0100

6c-3. Additional Information on the Properties of Certain Optical Materials

1. *Lithium Fluoride.* Particularly useful as a prism material for the vacuum ultraviolet region transmitting to a minimum wavelength of almost 0.10μ, and in the infrared region to 5μ; however, since only selected pieces of the vacuum-grown material give such a low transmission in the ultraviolet, caution must be taken in choosing the particular sample. For an evaluation of lithium fluoride as a prism

material, see R. C. Gore, R. S. MacDonald, V. Z. Williams, and J. U. White, *J. Opt. Soc. Am.* **37**, 23 (1947). For an evaluation of the physical properties of lithium fluoride, see S. S. Ballard, L. S. Combes, and K. A. McCarthy, *J. Opt. Soc. Am.* **41,** 772 (1951).

2. *Magnesium Oxide.* Useful as a window material in equipment where both strength and high-temperature endurance are required. (The Young's modulus for magnesium oxide is approximately six times that of sodium chloride; its melting point is 2500 to 2800°C.) Specific information is contained in the literature of the Norton Company, Niagara Falls, Canada.
3. *Quartz.* Used both as a prism material and for other optical elements in spectrometers, particularly for measurements in the ultraviolet region; it is also an excellent window material. Its mechanical properties are quite remarkable, particularly when considered as a material for field use; quartz is very strong and extremely hard. A thorough summary of the mechanical, thermal, and optical properties is given by R. B. Sosman, "The Properties of Silica," Chemical Catalog Company, Inc., New York, 1927.
4. *Fused Silica.* Has uses similar to those of crystalline quartz. Information on its mechanical, thermal, and optical properties is given in Sosman (see quartz reference above); in Catalog Q-3, Fused Quartz Catalog, General Electric Company, Cleveland, Ohio, 1952; and in the literature of the Hanovia Chemical and Manufacturing Company, Newark, N.J. For a comparison of the refractive indices of samples of fused silica as produced by different manufacturers, see W. S. Rodney and R. J. Spindler, *J. Opt. Soc. Am.* **44,** 677–679 (1954).
5. *Rutile, Sapphire, and Spinel.* Of importance as window materials because of their unusual hardness and advantageous high-temperature mechanical properties. Most of the information on these three materials is contained in the literature of the Linde Air Products Company.
6. *Calcium Fluoride.* Used as a prism material in the vacuum ultraviolet region down to 120μ. For an evaluation of calcium fluoride as a prism material, see Gore et al. in lithium fluoride reference. For a comparison of its physical properties with those of barium fluoride, see S. S. Ballard, L. S. Combes, and K. A. McCarthy, *J. Opt. Soc. Am.* **42,** 684 (1952).
7. *Cesium Bromide, Cesium Iodide, and Thallium Bromide-iodide.* Cesium iodide transmits in the infrared to at least 50μ; cesium bromide and thallium bromide-iodide both transmit to about 40μ. A comparison of the physical properties of these three materials is given by S. S. Ballard, L. S. Combes, and K. A. McCarthy, *J. Opt. Soc. Am.* **42,** 65 (1952); **43,** 975 (1953). Certain properties to be noted are the toxicity of thallium bromide-iodide, which necessitates care in machining processes of this material; the high total reflection loss of thallium bromide-iodide; the solubility and corrosive effects on metals of cesium bromide; the extremely temperature-dependent solubility of cesium iodide.
8. *Potassium Bromide, Silver Chloride, and Sodium Chloride.* A comparison of the optical properties of potassium bromide and sodium chloride as prism materials is given by Gore et al. All three materials are quite soft; potassium chloride and sodium chloride are extremely water soluble. Silver chloride is particularly useful as a window material. However, it reacts with metals, and tools used on silver chloride should be carefully cleaned. Silver chloride windows must be coated to prevent darkening due to its sensitivity to ultraviolet light.

6d. Reflection[1]

TABLE 6d-1. INFRARED DIFFUSE PERCENTAGE REFLECTING FACTORS OF DRY PIGMENTS*

Wavelength, μ	Co_2O_3	CuO	Cr_2O_3	PbO	Fe_2O_3	Y_2O_3	$PbCrO_4$	Al_2O_3	ThO_2	ZnO	MgO	CaO	ZrO_2	$PbCO_3$	$MgCO_3$	White lead paint	Zn oxide paint
0.60†	3	...	27	52	26	74	70	84	86	82	86	85	86	88	85	76	68
0.95†	4	24	45	...	41	...	...	88	...	86	...	...	84	93	89	79	72
4.4	14	15	33	51	30	34	41	21	47	8	16	22	23	29	11		
8.8	13	...	5	26	4	11	5	20	7	3	2	4	5	10	4		
24.0	6	4	8	10	9	10	7	6	10	5	9	6	5	7	9		

A surface of plate glass, ground uniformly with the finest emery and then silvered, used at an angle of 75 deg, reflected 90 per cent at 4μ, approached 100 for longer waves, only 10 at 1μ, less than 5 in the visible red and approached 0 for shorter waves. Similar results were obtained with a plate of rock salt for transmitted energy when roughened merely by breathing on it. In both cases the finer the surface, the more suddenly it cuts off the short waves.

* "Smithsonian Physical Tables," 1954, Table 581.

† Nonmonochromatic means from Coblentz.

[1] Metallic reflections are discussed in Sec. 6k.

TABLE 6d-2. REFLECTION COEFFICIENTS FOR VISIBLE MONOCHROMATIC RADIATION*

Material	Wavelengths, μ			
	0.400	0.500	0.600	0.700
Carbon black in oil	0.003	0.003	0.003	0.003
Clay:				
Kaolin (treated)	0.82	0.81	0.82	0.82
Kaolin (untreated)	0.75	0.79	0.85	0.86
White Georgia	0.94	0.92	0.93	0.94
$MgCO_3$	.....	0.98	0.99	
Magnesium oxide	0.97	0.98	0.99	0.98
Paint:				
Lithopone	0.95	0.98	0.98	0.98
$MgCO_3$-vynal acetate lacquer	0.90	0.88	0.88	0.88
ZnO-milk	0.74	0.84	0.85	0.86
Paper:				
Blotting	0.64	0.72	0.79	0.79
Calendered	0.64	0.69	0.73	0.76
Crepe, green	0.23	0.49	0.19	0.48
Crepe, red	0.03	0.02	0.21	0.69
Crepe, yellow	0.17	0.44	0.75	0.79
Newsprint stock	0.38	0.61	0.63	0.78
Peach:				
Green	0.18	0.17	0.62	0.63
Ripe	0.10	0.10	0.41	0.42
Pear:				
Green	0.04	0.12	0.29	0.41
Ripe	0.08	0.19	0.46	0.53
Pigment:				
Chrome yellow	0.05	0.13	0.70	0.77
French ochre	0.06	0.14	0.50	0.56
Porcelain enamel:				
Blue	0.44	0.10	0.05	0.23
Orange	0.09	0.09	0.59	0.69
Red	0.05	0.03	0.08	0.62
White	0.77	0.73	0.72	0.70
Yellow	0.11	0.46	0.62	0.62
Talcum, Italian	0.94	0.89	0.88	0.88
Wheat flour	0.75	0.87	0.94	0.97

* J. L. Michaelson, in "Handbook of Chemistry and Physics," 36th ed., p. 2689, Chemical Rubber Publishing Company, 1954–1955.

TABLE 6d-3. REFLECTION COEFFICIENTS FOR INCANDESCENT LIGHT*

Material	Nature of surface	Coefficient	Authority
Aluminum, "Alzak"	Diffusing	0.77–0.81	3
"Alzak"	Specular	0.79–0.83	3
On glass	First surface	0.82–0.86	4
Polished	Specular	0.69	3
Black paper	Diffusing	0.05–0.06	4
Chromium	Specular	0.62	4
Copper	Specular	0.63	4
Gold	Specular	0.75	1
Magnesium oxide	Diffusing	0.98	5
Nickel	Specular	0.62–0.64	1, 3
Platinum	Specular	0.62	1
Porcelain enamel	Glossy	0.76–0.79	3
Porcelain enamel	Ground	0.81	3
Porcelain enamel	Matt	0.72–0.76	3
Silver	Polished	0.93	1
Silvered glass	Second surface	0.88–0.93	3
Snow	Diffusing	0.93	2
Steel	Specular	0.55	1
Stellite	Specular	0.58–0.65	4

1. Hagen and Rubens. 2. Nutting, Jones, and Elliot. 3. J. E. Bock. 4. Frank Benford. 5. J. L. Michaelson.

* "Handbook of Chemistry and Physics," 36th ed., p. 2689, Chemical Rubber Publishing Company, 1954–1955.

6e. Glass, Polarizing and Interference Filters

W. A. SHURCLIFF[1]

Polaroid Corporation

BRUCE H. BILLINGS[2]

Baird-Atomic, Inc.

6e-1. Colored Glasses. The transmission values of colored glasses are listed as functions of wavelength in the catalogues of various manufacturers. In the United States wide ranges of colored glass are available from the American Optical Company, Bausch and Lomb Company, Chicago Eye Shield Company, Corning Glass Works,

[1] Sheet polarizers.
[2] Interference filters.

and the Eastman Kodak Company. The German Jena glasses also extend over a wide range of transmission values.

6e-2. Sheet Polarizers. Sheet polarizers have several advantages over the nicol prism and other early types of linear polarizers. They accept a wide cone of light (half angle of 30 to 45 deg, for example). They are thin, light, and rugged, and are easily cut to any desired shape. Pieces many feet in length can be made. The cost is almost negligible compared with that of a nicol prism.

If a sheet polarizer is mounted perpendicular to a beam of 100 per cent linearly polarized radiation, and if the polarizer is slowly turned in its own plane, the transmittance k varies between a maximum value k_1 and a minimum value k_2 according to the following law:

$$k = (k_1 - k_2)(\cos^2 \theta) + k_2 \qquad \text{(6e-1)}$$

When such a polarizer is placed in a beam of unpolarized radiation, the transmittance is $\frac{1}{2}(k_1 + k_2)$. When two identical polarizers are mounted in the beam with their axes crossed, the transmittance is k_1k_2.

The principal transmittance values k_1 and k_2 vary with wavelength, the variation being different for different types of polarizers. Table 6e-1 presents data for several well-known types, produced by Polaroid Corporation, Cambridge, Massachusetts. H sheet, perhaps the most widely used sheet polarizer, is effective throughout the visual range; it is produced in three modifications having total luminous transmittance (for C.I.E. Illuminant C light) of 22 per cent (Type HN-22), 32 per cent (Type HN-32), and 38 per cent (HN-38). Type HN-22 provides the best extinction, Type HN-38 provides the highest transmittance, and Type HN-32 represents a compromise that is preferred in many applications. K sheet, also useful throughout the visual range, is particularly intended for applications involving very high temperature. Its transmittance is 35 to 40 per cent. HR sheet is effective in the infrared range from 0.7 to 2.2μ.

TABLE 6e-1. SPECTRAL PRINCIPAL TRANSMITTANCE OF SHEET POLARIZERS*

Wavelength, μ	HN-22 sheet		HN-32 sheet		HN-38 sheet		KN-36 sheet		HR sheet	
	k_1	k_2	k_1	k_2	k_1	k_2	k_1	k_2	k_1	k_2
0.375	.11	.000,005	.33	.001	.54	.02	.42	.002	.00	.00
0.40	.21	.000,01	.47	.003	.67	.04	.51	.001	.00	.00
0.45	.45	.000,003	.68	.000,5	.81	.02	.65	.000,3	.00	.00
0.50	.55	.000,002	.75	.000,05	.86	.005	.71	.000,05	.00	.00
0.55	.48	.000,002	.70	.000,02	.82	.000,7	.74	.000,04	.00	.00
0.60	.43	.000,002	.67	.000,02	.79	.000,3	.79	.000,03	.01	.00
0.65	.47	.000,002	.70	.000,02	.82	.000,3	.83	.000,08	.05	.00
0.7	.59	.000,003	.77	.000,03	.86	.000,7	.88	.02	.10	.00
1.0									.55	.05
1.5									.65	.00
2.0									.70	.00
2.5									.10	.02

* Data supplied by Polaroid Corporation, Cambridge, Massachusetts. For each type of polarizer, the transmittance values near the ends of the useful range depend on the type of supporting sheet or lamination used. Also some variation from lot to lot must be expected.

6e-3. Narrow-band Interference Filters.[1] The three types of narrow-band filters which are available commercially are:

1. The solid Fabry-Perot filter with a passband of 150 A and a peak transmission of 35 per cent.
2. The multilayer Fabry-Perot filter with bandwidth of 50 A and a peak transmission of 75 per cent.
3. The polarization interference filter with a passband of $\frac{1}{2}$ A or wider and a peak transmission of 2 to 7 per cent.

The construction of these filters is described and the principle of their operation is explained.

Fabry-Perot Filter. The solid Fabry-Perot filter was invented by Geffken and has recently been described by Struve.[2] The active elements in this filter are an evaporated layer of silver which is covered by a layer of dielectric and in turn followed by another evaporated layer of semitransparent silver.

At all wavelengths at which the dielectric layer has an optical thickness of an integral number of half waves the filter will have a passband. The number of half waves corresponding to a given passband is called the order of the passband. The transmission of the filter can be represented by the equation

$$T = \frac{t^2}{(1 - r)^2 + 4r \sin^2 \delta/2} \tag{6e-2}$$

where r is the reflectivity of the silver film, t the transmission of the film, and $\delta = (4\pi d/\lambda)n^2 - \sin^2 \theta + 2y$ where d is the thickness of the dielectric layer, n its index, λ the wavelength, y the phase shift experienced by the light at the metal dielectric boundary, and θ the angle of incidence.

By inspection of the equation it is apparent that maxima occur when $\delta/2 = m\pi$ where m is an integer.

There are five quantities which are of interest to the user of these filters.

1. The peak transmission
2. The transmission between peaks
3. The bandwidth
4. The separation between passbands
5. The angular field of view

Each of these quantities can be determined theoretically from Eq. (6e-2). The peak transmission is

$$T_{\max} = \frac{t^2}{(1 - r)^2} \tag{6e-3}$$

The minimum transmission is

$$T_{\min} = \frac{t^2}{(1 + r)^2} \tag{6e-4}$$

The bandwidth of this filter is defined as the distance between the two points at which the transmission is 50 per cent of peak transmission. The formula for the bandwidth can be written

$$W = \frac{2\lambda_{\max}}{m\pi - y_0} \sin^{-1} \left(\frac{1 - r}{2\sqrt{r}} \right) \tag{6e-5}$$

where $\lambda_{\max}$ is the wavelength of peak transmission, m is the order of the peak, and W is the band within the unit of λ.

[1] Bruce H. Billings, Narrow Band Optical Interference Filters, *Phot. Eng.* **2**, 2, 45–52 (1951).

[2] O. Struve, *Sky and Telescope*, January, 1951.

The equation for the bandwidth can be considerably simplified if the phase shift y_0 is neglected and the bandwidth is expressed in frequency units rather than in wavelength units. The formula then becomes

$$d\nu = \frac{K}{\pi nd} \sin^{-1} \frac{1 - r}{2\sqrt{r}} \qquad \text{(6e-6)}$$

where $d\nu$ is the bandwidth in cm^{-1}. $K = 10^8$ if nd is expressed in Angstroms.

The separation between passbands is given by the expression

$$\Delta\nu = \frac{K}{2nd} = \frac{K\Delta\lambda}{\lambda_{max}^2} \qquad \text{(6e-7)}$$

Although this separation is constant in frequency units, Eq. (6e-7) shows that in wavelength units successive passbands in a given filter are closer together in higher orders.

Another quantity which is of interest in discussing these filters is the ratio of peak transmission to minimum transmission. This is given by the expression

$$\frac{T_{max}}{T_{min}} = \frac{(1 + r)^2}{(1 - r)^2} \qquad \text{(6e-8)}$$

The angular field is defined as the angle through which the filter must be tilted to shift the wavelength of peak transmission a distance equal to the bandwidth. It can be calculated from the equation

$$\sin (\Delta\varphi) = n \frac{2W}{\lambda_{max}} \qquad \text{(6e-9)}$$

Most users of filters wish the bandwidth to be as narrow as possible, the peak transmission as high as possible, the ratio of peak transmission to minimum transmission as high as possible, and the separation between passbands to be as large as possible. There is a certain amount of incompatibility between these different desires. From Eq. (6e-6), to make the bandwidth narrow, two things can be done; one is to increase the reflectivity and the other is to increase the thickness of the dielectric layer. From Eq. (6e-8), however, it is apparent that the increase of thickness of the dielectric layer results in the passbands becoming much closer together. This particular technique is also rather difficult because thick dielectric layers cannot be made easily. After the thickness gets over four or five waves the layer usually begins to crack. An increase of reflectivity, on the other hand, not only gives the desired reduction in bandwidth but also improves the ratio of the peak transmission to the minimum transmission. Although it is possible to increase the reflectivity of the silver layer used in a standard Fabry-Perot filter, the increase is accompanied by an increase in absorption. This results in a reduction of the peak transmission as seen from Eq. (6e-3).

The solid Fabry-Perot filters made today are an attempt to meet an effective compromise in the different requirements. A typical filter has the following characteristics:

$$T_{max} = 35\% \qquad \lambda_{max} = 5{,}461 \text{ A}$$
$$T_{min} = 0.2\% \qquad W\ 5{,}461 = 150 \text{ A} \qquad \Delta\phi = 20°$$

These numbers represent just about the best that can be done with the simple metal dielectric filter.

Multilayer Filters. There are a series of techniques by which high reflectivities can be achieved which are lossless, i.e., which have no absorption. One of these techniques has yielded a filter which is already available commercially. This is the so-called multilayer Fabry-Perot filter.[1] Some of the first research on these filters was done by Dr. Aldus Fogelsanger of Evaporated Metal Films Corp., in Ithaca, N.Y. There is very little published material on these filters. In this device the metal layers are replaced by a series of dielectric layers. The boundary between two dielectric layers is reflecting with a reflecting power of perhaps 4 per cent in the case

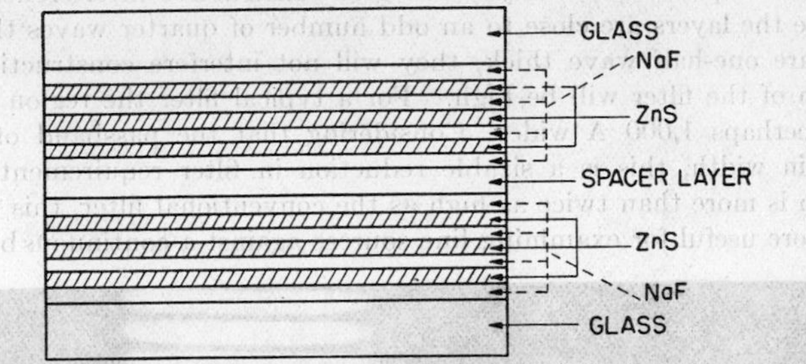

FIG. 6e-1. Schematic diagram of seven-layer solid Fabry-Perot filter.

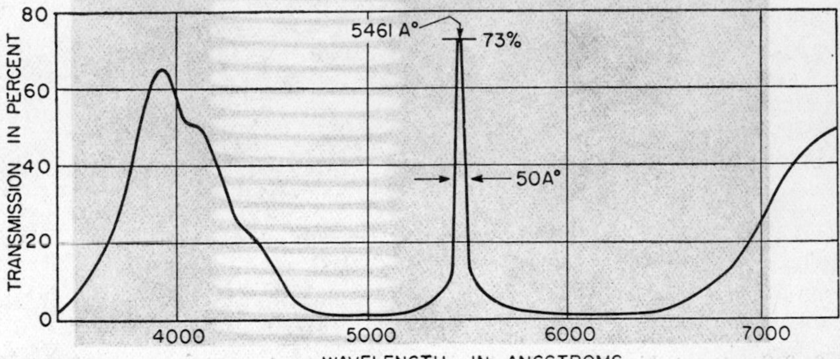

FIG. 6e-2. Transmission as a function of wavelength. (Off-peak transmission in this filter is approximately 0.03 per cent.)

of glass and air, or less for two dielectrics whose indices are close together. The value of the reflectivity is given by the standard Fresnel reflection law

$$r = \left(\frac{n_1 - n_2}{n_1 + n_2}\right)^2 \tag{6e-10}$$

By making several layers of alternate high- and low-index dielectric it is possible to reinforce the reflectivity of a single boundary and build it up by multiple reflection to any desired value. It is necessary only that the layers be of such thickness that the reflections from successive boundaries are in phase. When each layer is optically one-fourth of a wavelength in thickness, this reinforcement takes place. A complete filter is sketched in Fig. 6e-1. It might consist of seven alternate layers of high- and low-index dielectric of a thickness of a quarter wave apiece, followed by the dielectric spacer which is an integral number of half waves and which is followed by seven more quarter wavelength layers. The characteristics of such a filter are shown in Fig. 6e-2. For a seven-layer reflection filter the reflectivity can be built up to 95 per cent. From Eqs. (6e-3) to (6e-8) one would expect improvement over the metal filter and, in fact, the peak transmission of such a filter is as high as 80 per cent and the bandwidth as low as 30 A. The minimum transmission for a filter of this type

[1] H. D. Polster, *J. Opt. Soc. Am.* **39**, 1054A (1949).

is only 0.03 per cent. Thus, in the first three categories listed above, this filter is considerably superior to the standard silver-dielectric filter. It differs from the standard filter in another important respect. The region in which the transmission is extremely low is very much smaller than in the case of the standard metal filter. The reason for the narrow range of usefulness lies in the construction of the filter itself. The multiple-dielectric layer will give constructive interference only in the region where the layers are close to an odd number of quarter waves thick. Where the layers are one-half wave thick, they will not interfere constructively and the transmission of the filter will be high. For a typical filter the region of low transmission is perhaps 1,000 A wide. Considering that the passband of the filter is only 30 A in width, this is a sizable reduction in filter requirements. Since the transmission is more than twice as high as the conventional filter, this device is considerably more useful for examining line sources against a continuous background.

FIG. 6e-3. Spectrographic plate of the channel spectrum of a plate of ammonium dihydrogen-phosphate between crossed polarizers.

When the emission or absorption bands which are to be examined are less than 1 A or 2 deg in width, the advantage of the multilayer filter is decidedly noticeable.

Polarization Filters. Another useful filter is the polarization filter of Lyot[1] and Oehman.[2] Although the basic characteristics of this filter have changed very little since it was first invented, there has been a noticeable improvement in the manufacturing technique. Early units were made by individuals[3] as solutions to particular problems.

The basic filter consists of a series of birefringent plates which are separated by polarizers. A simple filter might have x-cut plates of quartz as the birefringent elements and these plates of quartz might be separated by parallel polarizing sheets. When a single birefringent plate is placed between parallel polarizers the transmission is given by the expression

$$I = \cos^2 \left[\frac{\pi d(n_e - n_o)}{\lambda} \right] \tag{6e-11}$$

where n_e is the extraordinary index and n_o the ordinary index of the material and d is the plate thickness. When light is shone through such a combination into a spectrograph the spectrum is seen to be crossed with a series of dark bands. Figure 6e-3 is

[1] B. Lyot, *Compt. rend.* **197,** 1593 (1933).

[2] Y. Oehman, *Nature* **141,** 291 (1938).

[3] E. Pettit, *Publs. Astron. Soc. Pacific* **53** (309), 305 (October, 1940); J. W. Evans, *Ciencia e invest.* (*Buenos Aires*) III (9), 365 (1947); *J. Opt. Soc. Am.* **39** (3), 229–242 (1949).

a spectrographic plate showing the transmission of a slab of quartz 4 cm thick. In the polarization filter this first plate is placed in series with another plate whose thickness is half as great. This other plate will have black bands which are spaced at twice the distance of the bands from the first plate. The black bands from the second plate can thus be made to fall on every other passband of the first plate. The resultant of the combination will be a series of transmission bands which are separated by twice their width. This process can be repeated by adding more plates until the final transmission is a series of bands whose separation is so many times their width that all the bands but one can be removed with a supplementary filter such as a dye filter or a Fabry-Perot interference filter.

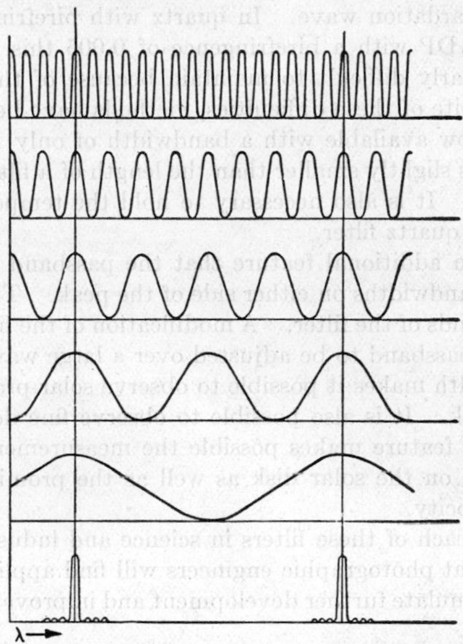

FIG. 6e-4. Transmission curves of filter plates of assembled filter.

In Fig. 6e-4 is the transmission curve of the individual members of such a filter and also the transmission curve of a complete assembly of plates. The bandwidth of such a filter will be determined by the thickest plate.

In the case of a 1 A passband filter at H alpha, the actual thicknesses involved can become quite large. For quartz and a simple filter the thickest plate will be 23.84 cm. This follows immediately from the formula

$$W = \frac{0.5\lambda_{\max}^2}{d(n_e - n_o)} \tag{6e-12}$$

Here W is the passband of the filter in Angstroms and λ is the position of the passband. This formula gives the interval between points where the relative transmission is 50 per cent. Most of the possible applications for narrow-band filters of this type require linear apertures of the order of 2 in. There are a few pieces of optical quartz in this country which are large enough to be used for making these thick plates.

Another possible material for a birefringent filter is calcite. Here the difference between the ordinary and extraordinary index of refraction is considerably larger than in the case of quartz and as a result a piece thick enough for a 1 A passband filter is very much thinner. From Eq. (6e-12) the actual thickness for a filter at H alpha can be calculated to be 0.9388 cm. However, even in calcite a 2-in.-diameter x-cut slab of this thickness, which will be of sufficient optical quality to make the last plate of a birefringent filter, is essentially unobtainable. Furthermore, the price of such material is quite high.

During the last few years a whole family of new crystals has been appearing. These crystals are being grown synthetically for the use of the electronic industry. One such crystal is ammonium dihydrogen phosphate (ADP), which is used in large Langevin plates for underwater signaling at supersonic frequencies.

ADP has been grown in sizes so that 2-in. disks of high optical quality can be obtained. It is also quite inexpensive. The material does, however, have several fairly serious disadvantages. It is water-soluble, slightly hygroscopic, soft, and brittle. For a birefringent filter it is necessary that the crystal plate be made plane parallel to $\frac{1}{20}$ of a retardation wave. In quartz with birefringence of 0.009 this is fairly stringent. In ADP with a birefringence of 0.005 this tolerance is positively drastic. It is particularly difficult to maintain because of the physical limitations of the material. In spite of these difficulties, methods have been devised for taming ADP and filters are now available with a bandwidth of only 1 A at H alpha. The length of these filters is slightly smaller than the length of a filter of equivalent bandwidth made in quartz. It is also necessary to hold the temperature more constant than in the equivalent quartz filter.

These filters have an additional feature that the passband can be shifted over a range of about three bandwidths on either side of the peak. This is done by rotating polarizers at opposite ends of the filter. A modification of the filter has been proposed which will enable the passband to be adjusted over a large wavelength interval.[1]

The narrow bandwidth makes it possible to observe solar prominences without the use of an occulting disk. It is also possible to observe fine detail on the surface of the sun. The tunable feature makes possible the measurement of radial velocities. Much of the structure on the solar disk as well as the prominences seems to have considerable radial velocity.

The exploitation of each of these filters in science and industry has not yet really begun. It is hoped that photographic engineers will find application for these filters as such activity will stimulate further development and improvements in these devices.

6f. Colorimetry

D. L. MacADAM

Eastman Kodak Company

6f-1. Luminosity. *Photopic Luminosity.* RELATIVE PHOTOPIC LUMINOSITY ($\bar{y}$): Adopted in 1931 by International Commission on Illumination (C.I.E.) (intended to represent normal eyes, for fields subtending about 2 deg, having about 1 foot-Lambert luminance).

ABSOLUTE PHOTOPIC LUMINOSITY (K_λ lumens per watt): 680 times photopic luminosities given in Table 6f-1.

[1] B. Billings, *J. Opt. Soc. Am.* **37**, 738 (1947).

TABLE 6f-1. PHOTOPIC AND SCOTOPIC LUMINOSITY DATA*

Wavelength, mμ	Photopic $\bar{y}$	Scotopic V'	Wavelength, mμ	Photopic $\bar{y}$	Scotopic V'
380	0.0000	0.00059	580	0.8700	0.1212
385	0.0001	0.00111	585	0.8163	0.0899
390	0.0001	0.00221	590	0.7570	0.0655
395	0.0002	0.00453	595	0.6949	0.0469
400	0.0004	0.00929	600	0.6310	0.03325
405	0.0006	0.01850	605	0.5668	0.02312
410	0.0012	0.03484	610	0.5030	0.01593
415	0.0022	0.0604	615	0.4412	0.01088
420	0.0040	0.0966	620	0.3810	0.00737
425	0.0073	0.1436	625	0.3210	0.00497
430	0.0116	0.1998	630	0.2650	0.003335
435	0.0168	0.2625	635	0.2170	0.002235
440	0.0230	0.3281	640	0.1750	0.001497
445	0.0298	0.3931	645	0.1382	0.001005
450	0.0380	0.4550	650	0.1070	0.000677
455	0.0480	0.5129	655	0.0816	0.000459
460	0.0600	0.5672	660	0.0610	0.0003129
465	0.0739	0.6205	665	0.0446	0.0002146
470	0.0910	0.6756	670	0.0320	0.0001480
475	0.1126	0.7337	675	0.0232	0.0001026
480	0.1390	0.7930	680	0.0170	0.0000716
485	0.1693	0.8509	685	0.0119	0.0000502
490	0.2080	0.9043	690	0.0082	0.00003533
495	0.2586	0.9491	695	0.0057	0.00002502
500	0.3230	0.9817	700	0.0041	0.00001780
505	0.4073	0.9984	705	0.0029	0.00001273
510	0.5030	0.9966	710	0.0021	0.00000914
515	0.6082	0.9750	715	0.0015	0.00000660
520	0.7100	0.9352	720	0.0010	0.00000478
525	0.7932	0.8796	725	0.0007	0.000003482
530	0.8620	0.8110	730	0.0005	0.000002546
535	0.9149	0.7332	735	0.0004	0.000001870
540	0.9540	0.6497	740	0.0003	0.000001379
545	0.9803	0.5644	745	0.0002	0.000001022
550	0.9950	0.4808	750	0.0001	0.000000760
555	1.0002	0.4015	755	0.0001	0.000000567
560	0.9950	0.3288	760	0.0001	0.000000425
565	0.9786	0.2639	765	0.0000	0.000000320
570	0.9520	0.2076	770	0.0000	0.000000241
575	0.9154	0.1602	775	0.0000	0.000000183
			780	......	0.000000139

*Optical Society of America, "The Science of Color," p. 309, Thomas Y. Crowell Company, New York, 1953.

LUMINOUS FLUX (lumens):

$$F = \sum_{\lambda=380}^{770} P_\lambda K_\lambda$$

for spectral distribution of radiant energy, P_λ (watts per 5-mμ-wavelength band).

LUMINOUS TRANSMITTANCE:

$$t = \frac{\sum_{\lambda=380}^{\lambda=770} \tau_\lambda P_\lambda K_\lambda}{\sum_{\lambda=380}^{\lambda=770} P_\lambda K_\lambda}$$

or

$$t = \frac{\sum_{\lambda=380}^{\lambda=770} \tau_\lambda P_\lambda \bar{y}}{\sum_{\lambda=380}^{\lambda=770} P_\lambda \bar{y}}$$

for material with spectral transmittance τ_λ irradiated with spectral distribution P_λ.

LUMINOUS REFLECTANCE r: Substitute spectral reflectance ρ_λ for τ_λ in either of above.

SELECTED ORDINATES P_i: At wavelengths given in Table 6f-2, these are such that

$$F = \frac{680}{30} \sum_{i=1}^{30} P_i$$

$$t = \frac{1}{30} \sum_{i=1}^{30} (\tau P)_i$$

$$r = \frac{1}{30} \sum_{i=1}^{30} (\rho P)_i$$

Revisions of photopic relative luminosity data, recommended in 1951 by the United States Technical Committee on Colorimetry of C.I.E.:

370mμ	380	390	400	410	420	430	440	450
0.0001	0.0004	0.0015	0.0045	0.0093	0.0175	0.0273	0.0379	0.0468

These revisions have not been adopted by C.I.E.

Scotopic Luminosity. RELATIVE VALUES V' (Table 6f-1): Adopted in 1951 by C.I.E. (intended to represent normal eyes of young subjects, age ≤ 30, when observing at angles of not less than 5 deg from foveal center, under conditions of complete dark adaptation).

INTERNATIONAL PHOTOMETRIC STANDARD: Black body at temperature (2042°K) of solidification of platinum, has intensity of 60 candles per square centimeter for both scotopic and photopic conditions.

TABLE 6f-2. WAVELENGTHS FOR SELECTED ORDINATES*

Ordinate No. i	Photopic luminosity	Scotopic luminosity	Ordinate No. i	Photopic luminosity	Scotopic luminosity
1	469.7	426.0	16	561.0	504.7
2	493.1	439.7	17	564.6	507.9
3	504.6	448.2	18	568.3	511.1
4	512.1	455.0	19	572.0	514.4
5	518.0	461.0	20	575.9	517.8
6	522.9	466.3	21	579.9	521.2
7	527.4	471.2	22	584.1	524.8
8	531.6	475.7	23	588.5	528.6
9	535.5	479.9	24	593.3	532.6
10	539.3	483.9	25	598.5	537.0
11	543.1	487.7	26	604.3	541.9
12	546.7	491.3	27	611.0	547.6
13	550.3	494.7	28	619.1	554.6
14	553.9	498.1	29	629.9	564.1
15	557.4	501.4	30	649.7	581.8

* "The Science of Color," pp. 273, 312.

ABSOLUTE SCOTOPIC LUMINOSITY K'_λ: 1,746 times scotopic luminosities given in Table 6f-1.

SCOTOPIC LUMENS, SCOTOPIC LUMINOUS TRANSMITTANCE, AND SCOTOPIC LUMINOUS REFLECTANCE: Substitute K_λ, V', or wavelengths for selected ordinates for scotopic luminosity (Table 6f-2) in formulas for corresponding photopic quantities.

6f-2. Colorimetry

Standard Color-mixture Data. C.I.E. standard observer for color measurement is determined by the specifications for the equal-energy spectrum, as given in Table 6f-3. The chromaticity coordinates (also known as trichromatic coefficients, or trilinear coordinates) listed are ratios such that $x + y + z = 1$. The tristimulus values are the amounts of three colors necessary to match equal energies of the indicated wavelengths. The value of $\bar{y}$ given in the table is the standard luminosity function or relative luminosity.

TRISTIMULUS VALUES:

$$X = 680 \sum_{\lambda=380}^{\lambda=770} P_\lambda \bar{x}$$

$$Y = 680 \sum_{\lambda=380}^{\lambda=770} P_\lambda \bar{y} = F \text{ (lumens)}$$

$$Z = 680 \sum_{\lambda=380}^{\lambda=770} P_\lambda \bar{z}$$

for spectral distribution of radiant energy P_λ (watts per 5 mμ wavelength band).

TABLE 6f-3. THE STANDARD OBSERVER

Wave-length, mμ	Chromaticity coordinates of the spectrum			Tristimulus values of the spectrum		
	x	y	z	$\bar{x}$	$\bar{y}$ (rel. lum.)	$\bar{z}$
380	0.1741	0.0050	0.8209	0.0014	0.0000	0.0065
385	0.1740	0.0050	0.8210	0.0022	0.0001	0.0105
390	0.1738	0.0049	0.8213	0.0042	0.0001	0.0201
395	0.1736	0.0049	0.8215	0.0076	0.0002	0.0362
400	0.1733	0.0048	0.8219	0.0143	0.0004	0.0679
405	0.1730	0.0048	0.8222	0.0232	0.0006	0.1102
410	0.1726	0.0048	0.8226	0.0435	0.0012	0.2074
415	0.1721	0.0048	0.8231	0.0776	0.0022	0.3713
420	0.1714	0.0051	0.8235	0.1344	0.0040	0.6456
425	0.1703	0.0058	0.8239	0.2148	0.0073	1.0391
430	0.1689	0.0069	0.8242	0.2839	0.0116	1.3856
435	0.1669	0.0086	0.8245	0.3285	0.0168	1.6230
440	0.1644	0.0109	0.8247	0.3483	0.0230	1.7471
445	0.1611	0.0138	0.8251	0.3481	0.0298	1.7826
450	0.1566	0.0177	0.8257	0.3362	0.0380	1.7721
455	0.1510	0.0227	0.8263	0.3187	0.0480	1.7441
460	0.1440	0.0297	0.8263	0.2908	0.0600	1.6692
465	0.1355	0.0399	0.8246	0.2511	0.0739	1.5281
470	0.1241	0.0578	0.8181	0.1954	0.0910	1.2876
475	0.1096	0.0868	0.8036	0.1421	0.1126	1.0419
480	0.0913	0.1327	0.7760	0.0956	0.1390	0.8130
485	0.0687	0.2007	0.7306	0.0580	0.1693	0.6162
490	0.0454	0.2950	0.6596	0.0320	0.2080	0.4652
495	0.0235	0.4127	0.5638	0.0147	0.2586	0.3533
500	0.0082	0.5384	0.4534	0.0049	0.3230	0.2720
505	0.0039	0.6548	0.3413	0.0024	0.4073	0.2123
510	0.0139	0.7502	0.2359	0.0093	0.5030	0.1582
515	0.0389	0.8120	0.1491	0.0291	0.6082	0.1117
520	0.0743	0.8338	0.0919	0.0633	0.7100	0.0782
525	0.1142	0.8262	0.0596	0.1096	0.7932	0.0573
530	0.1547	0.8059	0.0394	0.1655	0.8620	0.0422
535	0.1929	0.7816	0.0255	0.2257	0.9149	0.0298
540	0.2296	0.7543	0.0161	0.2904	0.9540	0.0203
545	0.2658	0.7243	0.0099	0.3597	0.9803	0.0134
550	0.3016	0.6923	0.0061	0.4334	0.9950	0.0087
555	0.3373	0.6589	0.0038	0.5121	1.0002	0.0057
560	0.3731	0.6245	0.0024	0.5945	0.9950	0.0039
565	0.4087	0.5896	0.0017	0.6784	0.9786	0.0027
570	0.4441	0.5547	0.0012	0.7621	0.9520	0.0021
575	0.4788	0.5202	0.0010	0.8425	0.9154	0.0018
580	0.5125	0.4866	0.0009	0.9163	0.8700	0.0017
585	0.5448	0.4544	0.0008	0.9786	0.8163	0.0014
590	0.5752	0.4242	0.0006	1.0263	0.7570	0.0011
595	0.6029	0.3965	0.0006	1.0567	0.6949	0.0010

* D. B. Judd, *J. Opt. Soc. Am.* **23**, 359 (1933).

TABLE 6f-3. THE STANDARD OBSERVER* (*Continued*)

Wave-length, mμ	Chromaticity coordinates of the spectrum			Tristimulus values of the spectrum		
	x	y	z	$\bar{x}$	$\bar{y}$ (rel. lum.)	$\bar{z}$
600	0.6270	0.3725	0.0005	1.0622	0.6310	0.0008
605	0.6482	0.3514	0.0004	1.0456	0.5668	0.0006
610	0.6658	0.3340	0.0002	1.0026	0.5030	0.0003
615	0.6801	0.3197	0.0002	0.9384	0.4412	0.0002
620	0.6915	0.3083	0.0002	0.8544	0.3810	0.0002
625	0.7006	0.2993	0.0001	0.7514	0.3210	0.0001
630	0.7079	0.2920	0.0001	0.6424	0.2650	0.0000
635	0.7140	0.2859	0.0001	0.5419	0.2170	0.0000
640	0.7190	0.2809	0.0001	0.4479	0.1750	0.0000
645	0.7230	0.2770	0.0000	0.3608	0.1382	0.0000
650	0.7260	0.2740	0.0000	0.2835	0.1070	0.0000
655	0.7283	0.2717	0.0000	0.2187	0.0816	0.0000
660	0.7300	0.2700	0.0000	0.1649	0.0610	0.0000
665	0.7311	0.2689	0.0000	0.1212	0.0446	0.0000
670	0.7320	0.2680	0.0000	0.0874	0.0320	0.0000
675	0.7327	0.2673	0.0000	0.0636	0.0232	0.0000
680	0.7334	0.2666	0.0000	0.0468	0.0170	0.0000
685	0.7340	0.2660	0.0000	0.0329	0.0119	0.0000
690	0.7344	0.2656	0.0000	0.0227	0.0082	0.0000
695	0.7346	0.2654	0.0000	0.0158	0.0057	0.0000
700	0.7347	0.2653	0.0000	0.0114	0.0041	0.0000
705	0.7347	0.2653	0.0000	0.0081	0.0029	0.0000
710	0.7347	0.2653	0.0000	0.0058	0.0021	0.0000
715	0.7347	0.2653	0.0000	0.0041	0.0015	0.0000
720	0.7347	0.2653	0.0000	0.0029	0.0010	0.0000
725	0.7347	0.2653	0.0000	0.0020	0.0007	0.0000
730	0.7347	0.2653	0.0000	0.0014	0.0005	0.0000
735	0.7347	0.2653	0.0000	0.0010	0.0004	0.0000
740	0.7347	0.2653	0.0000	0.0007	0.0003	0.0000
745	0.7347	0.2653	0.0000	0.0005	0.0002	0.0000
750	0.7347	0.2653	0.0000	0.0003	0.0001	0.0000
755	0.7347	0.2653	0.0000	0.0002	0.0001	0.0000
760	0.7347	0.2653	0.0000	0.0002	0.0001	0.0000
765	0.7347	0.2653	0.0000	0.0001	0.0000	0.0000
770	0.7347	0.2653	0.0000	0.0001	0.0000	0.0000
775	0.7347	0.2653	0.0000	0.0000	0.0000	0.0000
780	0.7347	0.2653	0.0000	0.0000	0.0000	0.0000
			Totals	21.3713	21.3714	21.3715

TABLE 6f-4. STANDARD ILLUMINANTS*

A. *Gas-filled tungsten* incandescent lamp of color temp. 2845°K.

B. Lamp as above in combination with a filter composed of a layer 1 cm thick of each of two separate solutions B_1 and B_2, contained in a double cell of colorless optical glass.

Solution B_1:		
Copper sulfate ($CuSO_4 \cdot 5H_2O$)	2.452	g
Mannite ($C_6H_8(OH)_6$)	2.452	g
Pyridine (C_5H_5N)	30.0	cc
Distilled water to make	1,000	cc
Solution B_2:		
Cobalt ammonium sulfate ($CoSO_4 \cdot (NH_4)_2SO_4 \cdot 6H_2O$)	21.71	g
Copper sulfate ($CuSO_4 \cdot 5H_2O$)	16.11	g
Sulfuric acid (density 1.835)	10.0	cc
Distilled water to make	1,000	cc

C. Lamp as in *A* in combination with a filter composed of a layer 1 cm thick of each of two separate solutions C_1 and C_2, contained in a double cell made of colorless optical glass.

Solution C_1:		
Copper sulfate ($CuSO_4 \cdot 5H_2O$)	3.412	g
Mannite ($C_6H_8(OH)_6$)	3.412	g
Pyridine (C_5H_5N)	30.0	cc
Distilled water to make	1,000	cc
Solution C_2:		
Cobalt ammonium sulfate ($CoSO_4 \cdot (NH_4)_2SO_4 \cdot 6H_2O$)	30.580	g
Copper sulfate ($CuSO_4 \cdot 5H_2O$)	22.520	g
Sulfuric acid (density 1.835)	10.0	cc
Distilled water to make	1,000	cc

* Recommendation of the International Commission on Illumination, 1931, as revised 1951.

For material with spectral transmittance τ_λ:

$$X = \frac{\sum_{\lambda=380}^{\lambda=770} \tau_\lambda P_\lambda \bar{x}}{\sum_{\lambda=380}^{\lambda=770} P_\lambda \bar{y}}$$

$$Y = \frac{\sum_{\lambda=380}^{\lambda=770} \tau_\lambda P_\lambda \bar{y}}{\sum_{\lambda=380}^{\lambda=770} P_\lambda \bar{y}} = t$$

$$Z = \frac{\sum_{\lambda=380}^{\lambda=770} \tau_\lambda P_\lambda \bar{z}}{\sum_{\lambda=380}^{\lambda=770} P_\lambda \bar{y}}$$

Relative values of P_λ are sufficient for determining tristimulus values X, Y, Z of material. For reflecting materials, substitute ρ_λ for τ_λ in above formulas.

TRISTIMULUS COMPUTATION DATA FOR STANDARD SOURCES: A (tungsten lamp at 2854° color temperature); B (artificial sunlight, about 4880° color temperature, Table 6f-4); and C (artificial daylight, about 6740° color temperature). For any standard source and any material with spectral transmittance τ_λ or spectral reflectance ρ_λ *tristimulus values* based on data in Table 6f-5 are:

$$X = 10^{-5} \sum_{\lambda=380}^{\lambda=770} \tau_\lambda(\bar{x}P) \quad \text{or} \quad 10^{-5} \sum_{\lambda=380}^{\lambda=770} \rho_\lambda(\bar{x}P)_\lambda$$

$$Y = 10^{-5} \sum_{\lambda=400}^{\lambda=760} \tau_\lambda(\bar{y}P)_\lambda \quad \text{or} \quad 10^{-5} \sum_{\lambda=400}^{\lambda=760} \rho_\lambda(\bar{y}P)_\lambda$$

$$Z = 10^{-5} \sum_{\lambda=380}^{\lambda=620} \tau_\lambda(\bar{z}P)_\lambda \quad \text{or} \quad 10^{-5} \sum_{\lambda=380}^{\lambda=620} \rho_\lambda(\bar{z}P)_\lambda$$

Luminous transmittance $t = Y$. *Luminous reflectance* $r = Y$.

TRUNCATED TRISTIMULUS COMPUTATION DATA: For use when τ_λ (or ρ_λ) are measured only in region 400 to 700 mμ. In place of the corresponding values shown in Table 6f-5, use the following values, and sum only from 400 to 700 mμ.

λ, mμ	Source A			Source B			Source C		
	$\bar{x}P$	$\bar{y}P$	$\bar{z}P$	$\bar{x}P$	$\bar{y}P$	$\bar{z}P$	$\bar{x}P$	$\bar{y}P$	$\bar{z}P$
400	40	1	198	113	2	532	166	2	791
410	48	2	223	154	6	741	240	9	1143
420	270	8	1297	834	24	4001	1269	37	6098
680	804	292	....	478	175	....	384	138	
690	0	0	....	0	0	....	0	0	
700	834	300	....	417	149	....	312	114	

Tristimulus computation data for black-body sources at 1000°K, 1500°K, 1900°K, 2360°K, 3000°K, 3500°K, 4800°K, 6000°K, 6500°K, 7000°K, 8000°K, 10,000°K, 24,000°K, and infinite temperature, for five phases of natural daylight and for three commercial sources of artificial daylight, are tabulated in "The Science of Color."[1]

SELECTED ORDINATES: τ_{Xi}, τ_{Yi}, τ_{Zi} at wavelengths given in Table 6f-6, and factors F_X, F_Y, F_Z are such that

$$X = F_X \sum_{i=1}^{i=30} \tau_{Xi}$$

$$Y = F_Y \sum_{i=1}^{i=30} \tau_{Yi}$$

$$Z = F_Z \sum_{i=1}^{i=30} \tau_{Zi}$$

For reflecting sample, substitute ρ_{Xi}, ρ_{Yi}, ρ_{Zi} for τ_{Xi}, τ_{Yi}, τ_{Zi}.

[1] Pp. 268–271, Thomas Y. Crowell Company, New York, 1953.

TABLE 6f-5. TRISTIMULUS COMPUTATION DATA FOR STANDARD SOURCES*

Wave-length, mμ	C.I.E. standard source *A* (Planck 2854°, c_2 = 1.438)			C.I.E. standard source *B*			C.I.E. standard source *C*		
	$\bar{x}P$	$\bar{y}P$	$\bar{z}P$	$\bar{x}P$	$\bar{y}P$	$\bar{z}P$	$\bar{x}P$	$\bar{y}P$	$\bar{z}P$
380	1	.....	6	3	.....	14	4	.....	20
390	5	.....	23	13	.....	60	19	.....	89
400	19	1	93	56	2	268	85	2	404
410	71	2	340	217	6	1,033	329	9	1,570
420	262	8	1,256	812	24	3,899	1,238	37	5,949
430	649	27	3,167	1,983	81	9,678	2,997	122	14,628
440	926	61	4,647	2,689	178	13,489	3,975	262	19,938
450	1,031	117	5,435	2,744	310	14,462	3,915	443	20,638
460	1,019	210	5,851	2,454	506	14,085	3,362	694	19,299
470	776	362	5,116	1,718	800	11,319	2,272	1,058	14,972
480	428	622	3,636	870	1,265	7,396	1,112	1,618	9,461
490	160	1,039	2,324	295	1,918	4,290	363	2,358	5,274
500	27	1,792	1,509	44	2,908	2,449	52	3,401	2,864
510	57	3,080	969	81	4,360	1,371	89	4,833	1,520
520	425	4,771	525	541	6,072	669	576	6,462	712
530	1,214	6,322	309	1,458	7,594	372	1,523	7,934	388
540	2,313	7,600	162	2,689	8,834	188	2,785	9,149	195
550	3,732	8,568	75	4,183	9,603	84	4,282	9,832	86
560	5,510	9,222	36	5,840	9,774	38	5,880	9,841	39
570	7,571	9,457	21	7,472	9,334	21	7,322	9,147	20
580	9,719	9,228	18	8,843	8,396	16	8,417	7,992	16
590	11,579	8,540	12	9,728	7,176	10	8,984	6,627	10
600	12,704	7,547	10	9,948	5,909	7	8,949	5,316	7
610	12,669	6,356	4	9,436	4,734	3	8,325	4,176	2
620	11,373	5,071	3	8,140	3,630	2	7,070	3,153	2
630	8,980	3,704	.....	6,200	2,558	.....	5,309	2,190	
640	6,558	2,562	.....	4,374	1,709	.....	3,693	1,443	
650	4,336	1,637	.....	2,815	1,062	.....	2,349	886	
660	2,628	972	.....	1,655	612	.....	1,361	504	
670	1,448	530	.....	876	321	.....	708	259	
680	804	292	.....	465	169	.....	369	134	
690	404	146	.....	220	80	.....	171	62	
700	209	75	.....	108	39	.....	82	29	
710	110	40	.....	53	19	.....	39	14	
720	57	19	.....	26	9	.....	19	6	
730	28	10	.....	12	4	.....	8	3	
740	14	6	.....	6	2	.....	4	2	
750	6	2	.....	2	1	.....	2	1	
760	4	2	.....	2	1	.....	1	1	
770	2	.....	.....	1	.....	.....	1		

* D. B. Judd, *J. Opt. Soc. Am.* **23**, 359 (1933).

TABLE 6f-6. SELECTED ORDINATES FOR STANDARD SOURCES*

Ordinate No. i	Source A			Source B			Source C		
	λ_{X_i}	λ_{Y_i}	λ_{Z_i}	λ_{X_i}	λ_{Y_i}	λ_{Z_i}	λ_{X_i}	λ_{Y_i}	λ_{Z_i}
1	444.0	487.8	416.4	428.1	472.3	414.8	424.4	465.9	414.1
2†	516.9	507.7	424.9	442.1	494.5	422.9	435.5	489.4	422.2
3	544.0	517.3	429.4	454.1	505.7	427.1	443.9	500.4	426.3
4	554.2	524.1	432.9	468.1	513.5	430.3	452.1	508.7	429.4
5†	561.4	529.8	436.0	527.8	519.6	433.0	461.2	515.1	432.0
6	567.1	534.8	438.7	543.3	524.8	435.4	474.0	520.6	434.3
7	572.0	539.4	441.3	551.9	529.4	437.7	531.2	525.4	436.5
8†	576.3	543.7	443.7	558.5	533.7	439.9	544.3	529.8	438.6
9	580.2	547.8	446.0	564.0	537.7	442.0	552.4	533.9	440.6
10	583.9	551.7	448.3	568.8	541.5	444.0	558.7	537.7	442.5
11†	587.2	555.4	450.5	573.1	545.1	446.0	564.1	541.4	444.4
12	590.5	559.1	452.6	577.1	548.7	448.0	568.9	544.9	446.3
13	593.5	562.7	454.7	580.9	552.1	450.0	573.2	548.4	448.2
14†	596.5	566.3	456.8	584.5	555.5	451.9	577.3	551.8	450.1
15	599.4	569.8	458.8	588.0	559.0	453.9	581.3	555.1	452.1
16	602.3	573.3	460.8	591.4	562.4	455.8	585.0	558.5	454.0
17†	605.2	576.9	462.9	594.7	565.8	457.8	588.7	561.9	455.9
18	608.0	580.5	464.9	598.1	569.3	459.8	592.4	565.3	457.9
19	610.9	584.1	467.0	601.4	572.9	461.8	596.0	568.9	459.9
20†	613.8	587.9	469.2	604.7	576.7	463.9	599.6	572.5	462.0
21	616.9	591.8	471.6	608.1	580.6	466.1	603.3	576.4	464.1
22	620.0	595.9	474.1	611.6	584.7	468.4	607.0	580.5	466.3
23†	623.3	600.1	476.8	615.3	589.1	470.8	610.9	584.8	468.7
24	626.9	604.7	479.9	619.1	593.9	473.6	615.0	589.6	471.4
25	630.8	609.7	483.4	623.3	599.1	476.6	619.4	594.8	474.3
26†	635.3	615.2	487.5	628.0	605.0	480.2	624.2	600.8	477.7
27	640.5	621.5	492.7	633.4	611.8	484.5	629.8	607.7	481.8
28	646.9	629.2	499.3	640.1	619.9	490.2	636.6	616.1	487.2
29†	655.9	639.7	508.4	649.2	630.9	498.6	645.9	627.3	495.2
30	673.5	659.0	526.7	666.3	650.7	515.2	663.0	647.4	511.2
Factors: F_X, F_Y, F_Z	0.03661	0.03333	0.01185	0.03303	0.03333	0.02842	0.03268	0.03333	0.03938

* MIT, "Handbook of Colorimetry," Technology Press, Cambridge, 1936.

† Abbreviated set for use with only slightly selective samples. In such cases, multiply factors by 3.

TABLE 6f-7. STANDARD COORDINATE SYSTEM

The tristimulus system of color specification is based on four chosen stimuli consisting of homogeneous radiant energy of wavelengths 700.0, 546.1, and 435.8 mμ and of standard illuminant B (see Table 6f-4).

To establish the system of specification, coordinates are assigned as follows:

Stimulus	x	y	z
700.0 mμ	0.73467	0.26533	0.00000
546.1 mμ	0.27376	0.71741	0.00883
435.8 mμ	0.16658	0.00886	0.82456
Standard source B	0.34842	0.35161	0.29997

Wavelengths for selected ordinates for black-body sources at intervals of 100° from 2000 to 4000°K and at 5000°K, 6000°K, 7000°K, 8000°K, 10,000°K, and infinite temperature, and for five phases of natural daylight and three commercial sources of artificial daylight, are given in "The Science of Color."[1]

Chromaticity Coordinates. Horizontal coordinate $x = X/(X + Y + Z)$. Vertical coordinate $y = Y/(X + Y + Z)$. (Ref. Table 6f-7)

	x	y
C.I.E. standard source A	0.4476	0.4075
C.I.E. standard source B	0.3485	0.3516
C.I.E. standard source C	0.3101	0.3163
Mean noon sunlight at Washington, D.C.	0.3442	0.3534
Overcast sky (typical)	0.3134	0.3275
Clear sky (typical zenith)	0.2631	0.2779

DOMINANT WAVELENGTH: Wavelength corresponding to intersection of spectrum locus with straight line drawn from point representing light source through point representing light reflected from (or transmitted by) sample.

COMPLEMENTARY WAVELENGTH: Wavelength corresponding to intersection of spectrum locus with straight line drawn from point representing light from sample, through point representing light source (used when dominant wavelength is not determinate).

PURITY: Ratio of distance from source point to sample point, compared with distance from source point to point on spectrum locus representing dominant wavelength (or, in case that dominant wavelength is not determinate, ratio of distance from source point to sample point compared with distance from source point to collinear point on line joining extremities of spectrum locus).

Color difference between two samples (x_1, y_1, r_1) and (x_2, y_2, r_2): (Table 6f-9)

$$\Delta S = \left[g_{11}\Delta x^2 + 2g_{12}\Delta x\, \Delta y + g_{22}\, \Delta y^2 + g_{33} \left(\frac{\Delta r}{\bar{r}}\right)^2 \right]^{\frac{1}{2}}$$

where $\Delta x = 100(x_2 - x_1)$, $\Delta y = 100(y_2 - y_1)$, $\Delta r = 100(r_2 - r_1)$, $\bar{r} = (r_1 + r_2)/2$. For sharp dividing line and samples subtending about 2 deg, $g_{33} \cong 1$. For less

[1] *Op. cit.*, pp. 278–291.

TABLE 6f-8. CHROMATICITY COORDINATES OF BLACK BODIES
(C_2 = 1.438 cm °K)

T, °K	x	y	T, °K	x	y
1000	0.6526	0.3446	3400	0.4109	0.3935
1500	0.5856	0.3932	3500	0.4053	0.3906
1600	0.5731	0.3993	3600	0.3997	0.3879
1700	0.5609	0.4043	3700	0.3945	0.3849
1800	0.5491	0.4083	3800	0.3896	0.3823
1900	0.5377	0.4112	3900	0.3847	0.3794
2000	0.5266	0.4133	4000	0.3804	0.3767
2100	0.5158	0.4146	4500	0.3607	0.3635
2200	0.5055	0.4152	5000	0.3450	0.3516
2300	0.4956	0.4152	5500	0.3324	0.3410
2400	0.4860	0.4147	6000	0.3220	0.3317
2500	0.4769	0.4137	6500	0.3135	0.3236
2600	0.4681	0.4123	7000	0.3063	0.3165
2700	0.4597	0.4106	7500	0.3003	0.3103
2800	0.4517	0.4086	8000	0.2952	0.3048
2900	0.4441	0.4064	8500	0.2907	0.2999
3000	0.4368	0.4041	9000	0.2869	0.2956
3100	0.4298	0.4015	9500	0.2836	0.2918
3200	0.4232	0.3989	10000	0.2806	0.2883
3300	0.4170	0.3962	20000	0.2565	0.2577
			∞	0.2399	0.2342

well-defined dividing line, g_{33} may be considerably less; e.g., for 5-deg separation between large samples $g_{33} \cong 0.005$. For extremely small samples, contrasted with color of their background, $g_{33} \cong 0.5$ and g_{11}, $2g_{12}$, g_{22} are about 1 per cent of the values given in Table 6f-9.

LOCALLY UNIFORM PORTION OF CHROMATICITY DIAGRAM (in neighborhood of x, y: Plot x values with length of scale unit: $U(g_{11})^{\frac{1}{2}}$; y values with length of scale unit: $U(g_{22})^{\frac{1}{2}}$; with angle $\cos^{-1} g_{12}/(g_{11}g_{22})^{\frac{1}{2}}$ between scales; where g_{11}, g_{12}, g_{22} are values at x, y, and U is arbitrary constant.

NEAREST CHROMATICITY C (selected from continuous series represented by smooth locus L) most nearly matching chromaticity C_1, near but not on L, is at intersection of L and straight line through C_1 with slope: $m' = -(g_{11} + g_{12}m)/(g_{12} + g_{22}m)$ where m is slope of L in neighborhood of C_1 and g_{11}, g_{12}, g_{22} are values at C_1.

Color-mixture Data. Amounts of R, G, B of any red, green, and blue primaries (at x_r, y_r; x_g, y_g; x_b, y_b) necessary to match color specified by tristimulus values X, Y, Z:

$$R = C_1[(1 - A_{bg})X - (A_{bg} + M_{bg})Y - A_{bg}Z]$$
$$G = C_2[(a_{rb} + m_{rb})X + (a_{rb} - 1)Y + a_{rb}Z]$$
$$B = C_3[(a_{rg} + m_{rg})X + (a_{rg} - 1)Y + a_{rg}Z]$$

where $x = M_{bg}y + A_{bg}$ is line through (x_b, y_b) and (x_g, y_g)
$y = m_{rb}x + a_{rb}$ is line through (x_b, y_b) and (x_r, y_r)
$y = m_{rg}x + a_{rg}$ is line through (x_r, y_r) and (x_g, y_g)
and C_1, C_2, C_3 are constants, evaluated by determining values of R, G, B; X, Y, Z for one color.

TABLE 6f-9. COEFFICIENTS FOR EVALUATION OF COLOR DIFFERENCE

y	$x = 0.1$	0.2	0.3	0.4	0.5	0.6	0.7
			g_{11}				
0.7	22	17	28*				
0.6	23	18	30	69*			
0.5	24	21	33	63	71*		
0.4	26	27	40	39	37	33*	
0.3	30	57	128	47	28	18	14*
0.2	73	160	182	62	38	24*	15*
0.15	112	270	170	67	42*	30*	
0.1	210*	380	158	70*	46*	35*	
0.05	420*	385	150*				
			$2g_{12}$				
0.7	15	5	−8*				
0.6	18	7	−9	−23*			
0.5	21	8	−11	−28	−33*		
0.4	28	8	−24	−38	−40	−40*	
0.3	44	5	−135	−65	−53	−49	−47*
0.2	65	−65	−260	−91	−67	−58*	−55*
0.15	71	−130	−260	−99	−74*	−63*	
0.1	60*	−235	−260	−120*	−80*	−68*	
0.05	0*	−360	−260*				
			g_{22}				
0.7	5	2	1*				
0.6	7	3	2	9*			
0.5	11	5	5	13	22*		
0.4	20	7	10	23	37	46*	
0.3	32	13	61	47	64	72	72*
0.2	55	28	102	68	82	90*	90*
0.15	90	36	118	80	91*	95*	
0.1	250*	63	140	100*	100*	100*	
0.05	450*	150	160*				

*** Entries marked with star in this and in Tables 6f-10 and 6f-11 are for chromaticities beyond domain of real colors, but are useful for interpolations. Approximate values for intermediate chromaticities may be determined by tabular interpolation. Contour diagrams permitting more accurate interpolation were published by MacAdam, *J. Opt. Soc. Am.* 33, 18–26 (1943).**

TABLE 6f-10. MAXIMUM POSSIBLE LUMINOUS EFFICIENCY (K_m)
(In lumens per watt of sources having indicated chromaticities)

y	$x = 0.1$	0.2	0.3	0.4	0.5	0.6	0.7
0.7	475	590	677*	(680 at $x = 0.337$, $y = 0.659$)			
0.6	425	548	620	670*			
0.5	375	500	553	590	610*		
0.4	310	430	480	505	500	480*	
0.3	245	350	380	385	370	320	226*
0.2	155	250	270	255	185		
0.1	80*	138	130				

* See footnote following Table 6f-9. A contour diagram permitting more accurate interpolation than Table 6f-10 was published in "The Science of Color,". p. 308, Thomas Y. Crowell Company, New York, 1953.

TABLE 6f-11. MAXIMUM POSSIBLE LUMINOUS REFLECTANCE
[For samples having indicated chromaticities when illuminated by standard source C (top) and A (bottom)]

y	$x = 0.1$	0.2	0.3	0.4	0.5	0.6	0.7
				r_C (or t_C), %			
0.7	31	51					
0.6	34	60	76	0*			
0.5	34	63	84	96	77*		
0.4	32	68	92	87	60	42*	
0.3	27	70	90	65	40	24	12*
0.2	17	39	48	35	14		
0.1	0*	17	15				
				r_A (or t_A), %			
0.7	21	38					
0.6	22	42	61	0*			
0.5	20	45	67	83	77*		
0.4	18	36	48	71	86	64*	
0.3	14	22	27	36	52	38	21*
0.2	7	12	15	17	19		
0.1	0*	5	4				

* See footnote following Table 6f-9. Contour diagrams permitting more accurate interpolation than Table 6f-11 were published in "The Science of Color,". pp. 310, 311, Thomas Y. Crowell Company, New York, 1953.

6g. Radiometry

M. M. REYNOLDS

Linde Air Products Co.

R. J. CORRUCCINI, M. M. FULK

NBS-AEC Cryogenic Engineering Laboratory

R. M. BURLEY

Baird-Atomic, Inc.

6g-1. Black-body Radiation. These tables contain various radiation functions derived from the Planck function

$$W(\lambda, T) = \frac{c_1}{\lambda^5(e^{c_2/\lambda T} - 1)}$$

where $W(\lambda, T)$ is defined as the power radiated per unit wavelength interval at wavelength λ by unit area of a black body at temperature T°K. c_2 was taken to be 1.438 cm °K. The constant c_1 does not enter into the functions here tabulated. The maximum value of $W(\lambda, T)$ is given by

$$W_{max}(T) = 1.290 \times 10^{-15}T^5 \qquad \text{watt cm}^{-2}\,\mu^{-1}$$

while the Stefan-Boltzmann function is given by

$$\int_0^\infty W\,d\lambda = 5.679 \times 10^{-12}T^4 \qquad \text{watt cm}^{-2}$$

6g-2. Optical Pyrometry (Narrow-band Radiation). When an optical pyrometer which has been calibrated to read the true temperature of a black-body source is sighted on a nonblack source, it reads values of "brightness temperature" $T_{b_r}(\lambda, T)$ lower than the true temperature T°K. Brightness temperature is related to true temperature through the following formula, which is derived from Planck's formula:

$$\ln \epsilon(\lambda, T) = \frac{c_2}{\lambda}\left(\frac{1}{T} - \frac{1}{T_{br}}\right)$$

where c_2 = 1.438 cm °K (international temperature scale of 1948)
$\epsilon(\lambda, T)$ = emissivity of the source at wavelength λ and temperature T

Commercial radiation pyrometers, although broad-band, do not utilize the complete spectrum of radiant energy. Hence there is no simple formula for precise calculation of the effect on temperature readings of varying emittance of the source. Table 6g-10 was calculated using the relation

$$T\ (°\text{K}) = \frac{T_{\text{apparent}}\ (°\text{K})}{\epsilon_t^{\frac{1}{4}}}$$

where ϵ_t is the total emissivity. It may be used to estimate approximate corrections in radiation pyrometry.

TABLE 6g-1. BLACK-BODY RADIATION FUNCTIONS

λT, cm-deg	$\frac{W(\lambda, T)}{W_{max}(T)}$	$\frac{\int_0^\lambda W\,d\lambda}{\int_0^\infty W\,d\lambda}$	λT, cm-deg	$\frac{W(\lambda, T)}{W_{max}(T)}$	$\frac{\int_0^\lambda W\,d\lambda}{\int_0^\infty W\,d\lambda}$
0.050	2.999×10^{-7}	1.316×10^{-9}	0.155	3.032×10^{-1}	1.610×10^{-2}
0.051	4.775×10^{-7}	2.184×10^{-9}	0.160	3.457×10^{-1}	1.979×10^{-2}
0.052	7.452×10^{-7}	3.552×10^{-9}	0.165	3.892×10^{-1}	2.396×10^{-2}
0.053	1.142×10^{-6}	5.665×10^{-9}	0.170	4.332×10^{-1}	2.862×10^{-2}
0.054	1.718×10^{-6}	8.871×10^{-9}	0.175	4.772×10^{-1}	3.379×10^{-2}
0.055	2.545×10^{-6}	1.366×10^{-8}	0.180	5.208×10^{-1}	3.946×10^{-2}
0.056	3.709×10^{-6}	2.068×10^{-8}	0.185	5.636×10^{-1}	4.561×10^{-2}
0.057	5.326×10^{-6}	3.084×10^{-8}	0.190	6.053×10^{-1}	5.225×10^{-2}
0.058	7.544×10^{-6}	4.532×10^{-8}	0.195	6.455×10^{-1}	5.935×10^{-2}
0.059	1.054×10^{-5}	6.568×10^{-8}	0.200	6.840×10^{-1}	6.690×10^{-2}
0.060	1.455×10^{-5}	9.395×10^{-8}	0.22	8.169×10^{-1}	1.011×10^{-1}
0.061	1.985×10^{-5}	1.327×10^{-7}	0.24	9.126×10^{-1}	1.405×10^{-1}
0.062	2.676×10^{-5}	1.853×10^{-7}	0.26	9.712×10^{-1}	1.834×10^{-1}
0.063	3.570×10^{-5}	2.558×10^{-7}	0.28	9.972×10^{-1}	2.282×10^{-1}
0.064	4.713×10^{-5}	3.493×10^{-7}	0.30	9.971×10^{-1}	2.736×10^{-1}
0.065	6.613×10^{-5}	4.721×10^{-7}	0.32	9.771×10^{-1}	3.185×10^{-1}
0.066	7.984×10^{-5}	6.319×10^{-7}	0.34	9.432×10^{-1}	3.621×10^{-1}
0.067	1.025×10^{-4}	8.380×10^{-7}	0.36	8.999×10^{-1}	4.040×10^{-1}
0.068	1.305×10^{-4}	1.101×10^{-6}	0.38	8.512×10^{-1}	4.438×10^{-1}
0.069	1.649×10^{-4}	1.435×10^{-6}	0.40	7.997×10^{-1}	4.813×10^{-1}
0.070	2.066×10^{-4}	1.856×10^{-6}	0.42	7.475×10^{-1}	5.164×10^{-1}
0.071	2.571×10^{-4}	2.380×10^{-6}	0.44	6.961×10^{-1}	5.492×10^{-1}
0.072	3.176×10^{-4}	3.030×10^{-6}	0.46	6.464×10^{-1}	5.796×10^{-1}
0.073	3.897×10^{-4}	3.831×10^{-6}	0.48	5.990×10^{-1}	6.079×10^{-1}
0.074	4.751×10^{-4}	4.810×10^{-6}	0.50	5.543×10^{-1}	6.341×10^{-1}
0.075	5.757×10^{-4}	5.999×10^{-6}	0.52	5.125×10^{-1}	6.583×10^{-1}
0.076	6.934×10^{-4}	7.436×10^{-6}	0.54	4.735×10^{-1}	6.807×10^{-1}
0.077	8.304×10^{-4}	9.162×10^{-6}	0.56	4.375×10^{-1}	7.013×10^{-1}
0.078	9.891×10^{-4}	1.122×10^{-5}	0.58	4.042×10^{-1}	7.204×10^{-1}
0.079	1.172×10^{-3}	1.367×10^{-5}	0.60	3.735×10^{-1}	7.381×10^{-1}
0.080	1.382×10^{-3}	1.657×10^{-5}	0.62	3.453×10^{-1}	7.544×10^{-1}
0.081	1.621×10^{-3}	1.997×10^{-5}	0.64	3.193×10^{-1}	7.694×10^{-1}
0.082	1.893×10^{-3}	2.395×10^{-5}	0.66	2.956×10^{-1}	7.834×10^{-1}
0.083	2.201×10^{-3}	2.859×10^{-5}	0.68	2.737×10^{-1}	7.963×10^{-1}
0.084	2.548×10^{-3}	3.398×10^{-5}	0.70	2.537×10^{-1}	8.083×10^{-1}
0.085	2.938×10^{-3}	4.020×10^{-5}	0.72	2.354×10^{-1}	8.194×10^{-1}
0.086	3.373×10^{-3}	4.735×10^{-5}	0.74	2.185×10^{-1}	8.297×10^{-1}
0.087	3.859×10^{-3}	5.555×10^{-5}	0.76	2.030×10^{-1}	8.392×10^{-1}
0.088	4.397×10^{-3}	6.491×10^{-5}	0.78	1.888×10^{-1}	8.481×10^{-1}
0.089	4.993×10^{-3}	7.556×10^{-5}	0.80	1.758×10^{-1}	8.564×10^{-1}
0.090	5.651×10^{-3}	8.763×10^{-5}	0.82	1.638×10^{-1}	8.641×10^{-1}
0.091	6.373×10^{-3}	1.013×10^{-4}	0.84	1.528×10^{-1}	8.713×10^{-1}
0.092	7.165×10^{-3}	1.166×10^{-4}	0.86	1.426×10^{-1}	8.780×10^{-1}
0.093	8.030×10^{-3}	1.339×10^{-4}	0.88	1.332×10^{-1}	8.843×10^{-1}
0.094	8.973×10^{-3}	1.532×10^{-4}	0.90	1.246×10^{-1}	8.901×10^{-1}
0.095	9.998×10^{-3}	1.747×10^{-4}	0.92	1.166×10^{-1}	8.956×10^{-1}
0.096	1.111×10^{-2}	1.986×10^{-4}	0.94	1.093×10^{-1}	9.007×10^{-1}
0.097	1.231×10^{-2}	2.252×10^{-4}	0.96	1.024×10^{-1}	9.055×10^{-1}
0.098	1.360×10^{-2}	2.546×10^{-4}	0.98	9.613×10^{-2}	9.100×10^{-1}
0.099	1.500×10^{-2}	2.870×10^{-4}	1.0	9.029×10^{-2}	9.143×10^{-1}
0.100	1.649×10^{-2}	3.228×10^{-4}	1.1	6.679×10^{-2}	9.319×10^{-1}
0.105	2.563×10^{-2}	5.591×10^{-4}	1.2	5.035×10^{-2}	9.451×10^{-1}
0.110	3.785×10^{-2}	9.162×10^{-4}	1.3	3.862×10^{-2}	9.551×10^{-1}
0.115	5.350×10^{-2}	1.431×10^{-3}	1.4	3.007×10^{-2}	9.629×10^{-1}
0.120	7.281×10^{-2}	2.145×10^{-3}	1.5	2.375×10^{-2}	9.690×10^{-1}
0.125	9.588×10^{-2}	3.099×10^{-3}	1.6	1.899×10^{-2}	9.738×10^{-1}
0.130	1.227×10^{-1}	4.336×10^{-3}	1.7	1.536×10^{-2}	9.777×10^{-1}
0.135	1.530×10^{-1}	5.897×10^{-3}	1.8	1.255×10^{-2}	9.808×10^{-1}
0.140	1.866×10^{-1}	7.822×10^{-3}	1.9	1.035×10^{-2}	9.834×10^{-1}
0.145	2.232×10^{-1}	1.015×10^{-2}	2.0	8.612×10^{-3}	9.856×10^{-1}
0.150	2.622×10^{-1}	1.290×10^{-2}			

TABLE 6g-2. TOTAL BLACK-BODY RADIATION

T, °K	$\int_0^\infty W\,d\lambda$, watt cm^{-2}	$W_{max}(T)$, watt cm^{-2} μ^{-1}	T, °K	$\int_0^\infty W\,d\lambda$, watt cm^{-2}	$W_{max}(T)$, watt cm^{-2} μ^{-1}
1	5.679×10^{-12}	1.290×10^{-15}	430	1.942×10^{-1}	1.896×10^{-2}
5	3.549×10^{-9}	4.030×10^{-12}	440	2.128×10^{-1}	2.127×10^{-2}
10	5.679×10^{-8}	1.290×10^{-10}	450	2.328×10^{-1}	2.380×10^{-2}
15	2.875×10^{-7}	9.794×10^{-10}	460	2.542×10^{-1}	2.656×10^{-2}
20	9.086×10^{-7}	4.127×10^{-9}	470	2.771×10^{-1}	2.958×10^{-2}
30	4.600×10^{-6}	3.134×10^{-8}	480	3.015×10^{-1}	3.286×10^{-2}
40	1.454×10^{-5}	1.321×10^{-7}	490	3.274×10^{-1}	3.643×10^{-2}
50	3.549×10^{-5}	4.030×10^{-7}	500	3.549×10^{-1}	4.030×10^{-2}
60	7.360×10^{-5}	1.003×10^{-6}	520	4.152×10^{-1}	4.904×10^{-2}
70	1.364×10^{-4}	2.168×10^{-6}	540	4.829×10^{-1}	5.922×10^{-2}
80	2.326×10^{-4}	4.226×10^{-6}	560	5.585×10^{-1}	7.103×10^{-2}
90	3.726×10^{-4}	7.616×10^{-6}	580	6.426×10^{-1}	8.465×10^{-2}
100	5.679×10^{-4}	1.290×10^{-5}	600	7.360×10^{-1}	1.003×10^{-1}
110	8.315×10^{-4}	2.077×10^{-5}	620	8.392×10^{-1}	1.182×10^{-1}
120	1.178×10^{-3}	3.209×10^{-5}	640	9.527×10^{-1}	1.385×10^{-1}
130	1.622×10^{-3}	4.789×10^{-5}	660	1.078	1.615×10^{-1}
140	2.181×10^{-3}	6.936×10^{-5}	680	1.215	1.875×10^{-1}
150	2.875×10^{-3}	9.794×10^{-5}	700	1.364	2.168×10^{-1}
160	3.722×10^{-3}	1.352×10^{-4}	720	1.527	2.496×10^{-1}
170	4.743×10^{-3}	1.831×10^{-4}	740	1.703	2.862×10^{-1}
180	5.961×10^{-3}	2.437×10^{-4}	760	1.895	3.270×10^{-1}
190	7.401×10^{-3}	3.194×10^{-4}	780	2.102	3.724×10^{-1}
200	9.086×10^{-3}	4.127×10^{-4}	800	2.326	4.226×10^{-1}
210	1.105×10^{-2}	5.267×10^{-4}	820	2.567	4.782×10^{-1}
220	1.331×10^{-2}	6.647×10^{-4}	840	2.827	5.394×10^{-1}
230	1.590×10^{-2}	8.301×10^{-4}	860	3.106	6.067×10^{-1}
240	1.885×10^{-2}	1.027×10^{-3}	880	3.406	6.806×10^{-1}
250	2.218×10^{-2}	1.260×10^{-3}	900	3.726	7.616×10^{-1}
260	2.595×10^{-2}	1.532×10^{-3}	920	4.069	8.500×10^{-1}
270	3.018×10^{-2}	1.851×10^{-3}	940	4.434	9.465×10^{-1}
280	3.491×10^{-2}	2.220×10^{-3}	960	4.824	1.052
290	4.017×10^{-2}	2.645×10^{-3}	980	5.239	1.166
300	4.600×10^{-2}	3.134×10^{-3}	1000	5.679	1.290
310	5.245×10^{-2}	3.692×10^{-3}	1020	6.147	1.424
320	5.955×10^{-2}	4.328×10^{-3}	1040	6.644	1.569
330	6.735×10^{-2}	5.047×10^{-3}	1060	7.170	1.726
340	7.589×10^{-2}	5.860×10^{-3}	1080	7.726	1.895
350	8.522×10^{-2}	6.774×10^{-3}	1100	8.315	2.077
360	9.538×10^{-2}	7.799×10^{-3}	1120	8.937	2.273
370	1.065×10^{-1}	8.944×10^{-3}	1140	9.591	2.483
380	1.184×10^{-1}	1.022×10^{-2}	1160	10.29	2.709
390	1.314×10^{-1}	1.164×10^{-2}	1180	11.01	2.951
400	1.454×10^{-1}	1.321×10^{-2}	1200	11.78	3.209
410	1.605×10^{-1}	1.494×10^{-2}	1220	12.58	3.486
420	1.768×10^{-1}	1.686×10^{-2}	1240	13.43	3.781

TABLE 6g-2. TOTAL BLACK-BODY RADIATION (*Continued*)

T, °K	$\int_0^\infty W\,d\lambda$, watt cm^{-2}	$W_{max}(T)$, watt cm^{-2} μ^{-1}	T, °K	$\int_0^\infty W\,d\lambda$, watt cm^{-2}	$W_{max}(T)$, watt cm^{-2} μ^{-1}
1260	14.32	4.096	1960	83.81	37.31
1280	15.25	4.431	1980	87.29	39.25
1300	16.22	4.789	2000	90.86	41.27
1320	17.25	5.169	2100	110.5	52.67
1340	18.32	5.572	2200	133.1	66.47
1360	19.43	6.001	2300	159.0	83.01
1380	20.59	6.455	2400	188.5	102.7
1400	21.81	6.936	2500	221.8	126.0
1420	23.09	7.446	2600	259.5	153.2
1440	24.42	7.986	2700	301.8	185.1
1460	25.80	8.556	2800	349.1	222.0
1480	27.24	9.158	2900	401.7	264.5
1500	28.75	9.794	3000	460.0	313.4
1520	30.31	10.46	3100	524.5	369.2
1540	31.94	11.17	3200	595.5	432.8
1560	33.63	11.92	3300	673.5	504.7
1580	35.39	12.70	3400	758.9	586.0
1600	37.22	13.52	3500	852.2	677.4
1620	39.12	14.39	3600	953.8	779.9
1640	41.08	15.30	3700	1065	894.4
1660	43.12	16.26	3800	1184	1022
1680	45.24	17.26	3900	1314	1164
1700	47.43	18.31	4000	1454	1321
1720	49.71	19.42	4500	2328	2380
1740	52.06	20.57	5000	3549	4030
1760	54.50	21.78	5500	5197	6491
1780	57.01	23.05	6000	7360	10030
1800	59.61	24.37	6500	10140	14960
1820	62.31	25.75	7000	13640	21680
1840	65.09	27.20	7500	17970	30610
1860	67.97	28.71	8000	23260	42260
1880	70.94	30.29	8500	29640	57230
1900	74.01	31.94	9000	37260	76160
1920	77.18	33.65	9500	46260	99800
1940	80.44	35.44	10000	56790	129000

TABLE 6g-3. TOTAL NORMAL EMISSIVITY

Material	Temp., °K	Emissivity (total normal) ϵ_n
Aluminum, annealed (electropolished)	1000†	0.07
	500	0.04
	300	0.03
	300	0.018 (76°K)*
	300	0.011 (4°K)
Aluminum oxide layer:		
0.25μ thick	311	0.06
0.50μ thick	311	0.11
1.0μ thick	311	0.30
2.0μ thick	311	0.65
3.0μ thick	311	0.70
4.0μ thick	311	0.70
7.0μ thick	311	0.75
Aluminum lacquer layer:		
0.5μ thick	311	0.05
1.0μ thick	311	0.08
1.5μ thick	311	0.15
2.0μ thick	311	0.30
3.0μ thick	311	0.38
4.0μ thick	311	0.41
5.0μ thick	311	0.45
8.0μ thick	311	0.57
Aluminum:		
Commercial plate	373	0.09
Commercial plate, polished	373	0.05
Commercial plate dipped in HNO_3	373	0.05
Commercial plate dipped in hot hydroxide	373	0.04
Al vaporized on 0.0005-in. Mylar plastic (both sides)	300	0.04 (76°K)*
Antimony	295	0.28
Bismuth	1000†	0.3
	373	0.06–0.19
Brass:		
Polished	373	0.03
Rolled plate	300	0.06
Shim stock 65/35	295	0.029 (76°K)*
	295	0.018 (4°K)
Oxidized	500	0.60
	373	0.60
Cadmium	300	0.02
Electroplate (mossy)	295	0.03 (76°K)*
Chromium	300–1000	0.08–0.26‡
Plated on copper	300	0.08 (76°K)*
Plated on iron	370	0.08
Cobalt	295	0.03

TABLE 6g-3. TOTAL NORMAL EMISSIVITY (*Continued*)

Material	Temp., °K	Emissivity (total normal) ϵ_n
Copper:		
Black oxidized	300	0.78
Scraped	300	0.07
Commercial polish	300	0.03
Electrolytic, careful polish	353	0.018
Electrolytic, careful polish	295	0.015 (76°K)*
Chromic acid dip	295	0.017 (76°K)*
Polished	295	0.019 (76°K)*
Liquid honed	295	0.088 (76°K)*
Electrolytic polish	295	0.006 (4°K)
Mechanical polish	295	0.015 (4°K)
Carefully prepared surface of pure Cu	295	0.008 (90°K)
Gold	300–1400†	0.02–0.03‡
0.0015-in. foil (on glass or Lucite plastic)	295	0.01 (76°K)*
0.0005-in. foil (on glass or Lucite plastic)	295	0.016 (76°K)*
0.000040-in. foil (on glass or Lucite plastic)	295	0.023 (76°K)*
0.000010-in. leaf (on glass or Lucite plastic)	295	0.063 (76°K)*
Au vaporized onto 2 sides of 0.0005-in. Mylar plastic	295	0.02 (76°K)*
Au plate 0.0002 in. on stainless steel (1% Ag in Au)	295	0.025 (76°K)*
Au plate 0.0001 in. on stainless steel (1% Ag in Au)	295	0.027 (76°K)*
Au plate 0.00005 in. on stainless steel (1% Ag in Au)	295	0.027 (76°K)*
Au plate 0.0002 in. on copper (1% Ag in Au)	295	0.025 (76°K)*
Iridium	295	0.04
Iron:		
Electrolytic	450–500	0.05–0.065‡
	533	0.07
	373	0.05
	295	0.05
	300	0.017 (90°K)
Oxidized	1500	0.89
	373	0.74
Cast iron, polished	311	0.21
Cast iron, oxidized	311	0.63
Cast iron, oxidized	533	0.66
Cast iron, oxidized	811	0.76
Iron sheet, rusted red	295	0.69
Galvanized iron	365	0.07
Steels:		
Stainless, polished	373	0.08
Stainless, type 302	300	0.048 (76°K)*
Stainless, oxidized	300–1000	0.79‡
Lead:		
Unoxidized, polished	400–500	0.057–0.075‡
Unoxidized, polished	373	0.05
0.004-in. foil	295	0.036 (76°K)*
	295	0.011 (4°K)

TABLE 6g-3. TOTAL NORMAL EMISSIVITY (*Continued*)

Material	Temp., °K	Emissivity (total normal) ϵ_n
Oxidized at 473°K	473	0.63
Gray oxidized	295	0.28
Red lead	373	0.93
Magnesium	295	0.07
	533	0.13 (295°K)
	811	0.18 (295°K)
	1000	0.21 (295°K)
Manganin, bright rolled	391	0.048
	295	0.076 (295°K)
	295	0.073 (90°K)
Mercury	273–373†	0.09–0.12‡
Molybdenum	2300	0.24
	1800	0.19
	1300	0.13
	373	0.07
	295	0.05
Nickel:		
Electrolytic	811	0.10
	533	0.07
	311	0.06
	295	0.04
Polished	395	0.045
Bright matte	395	0.041
0.004-in. foil	295	0.022 (76°K)*
Electroplated on iron and polished	298	0.045
Electroplated on pickled iron and unpolished	295	0.11
Electroplated on copper	300	0.03 (76°K)*
Oxidized	1500	0.85
Oxidized	500	0.37
Palladium	295	0.03
Platinum	1367	0.18
	811	0.10
	533	0.06
	373	0.05
	295	0.03
	290	0.016 (85°K)
Rhodium	295	0.05
Plated on stainless steel	295	0.078 (76°K)*
Silver	811	0.03
	373	0.025
	295	0.022
	273	0.02
	295	0.008 (76°K)*
Tantalum	2300	0.26
	1800	0.21
	295	0.05

TABLE 6g-3. TOTAL NORMAL EMISSIVITY (*Continued*)

Material	Temp., °K	Emissivity (total normal) ϵ_n
Tellurium	295	0.22
Tin	373	0.05
0.001-in. foil	295	0.013 (76°K)*
	295	0.012 (4°K)
1% indium	295	0.012 (4°K)
5% indium	295	0.017 (4°K)
Tinned iron sheet	297	0.064
Tungsten, filament	2300	0.28
	1800	0.23
	1300	0.15
	800	0.088
	500	0.053
	300	0.032
	300	0.019 (85°K)
Zinc	295	0.05
	295	0.026 (76°K)*
Solder, 50-50 solder on Cu	295	0.032 (76°K)*
Stellite	293	0.11
Monel metal:		
Polished	811	0.10 (295°K)
	1367	0.16 (295°K)
Smooth, not polished	366	0.16
Everdur, dull	366	0.11
Copper-nickel	373	0.059
Water	273–373	0.92–0.96‡
Ice:		
Smooth, H_2O	273	0.96
Rough crystals	273	0.985
Glass	293	0.94
Lacquer:		
White	373	0.925
Black matte	373	0.97
Oil paints, all colors	273–373	0.92–0.96‡
Enamel	295	0.90–0.95
Candlesoot	273–373	0.952
Plaster	273–373	0.91
Paper	373	0.92
Rubber, hard, glossy plate	297	0.945
Quartz (fused)	295	0.932

* ϵ_h determinations.
† Liquid phase.
‡ Linear interpolation fairly accurate.

TABLE 6g-4. NORMAL SPECTRAL EMISSIVITIES AT 295°K
(Wavelength in microns)

Material	0.50	0.60	0.80	1.0	2.0	3.0	4.0	5.0	7.0	9.0	10	12	14
Aluminum	....	....	....	0.26	0.18	0.12	0.08	0.07	0.04	0.03	0.02	0.02	
Antimony	....	0.47	0.46	0.45	0.40	0.35	0.32	0.31	0.29	0.28	0.28	....	0.28
Bismuth	....	....	....	....	0.32	0.28	....	0.23	....	0.19	....	....	0.17
Cadmium	....	....	....	0.30	0.13	0.07	0.04	0.04	0.02	0.02	0.02	0.01	0.01
Chromium	0.45	0.44	....	0.43	....	0.30	....	0.19	....	0.08			
Cobalt	....	....	....	0.32	0.28	0.23	0.19	0.15	0.07	0.04	0.03	0.03	0.03
Copper	0.56	0.28	....	0.10	....	0.03	....	0.02	....	0.02			
Copper, electrolytically deposited	0.47	0.17											
Copper, commercially pure	0.56	0.28	....	0.10	0.05	0.03	....	0.02	0.02	....	0.02	....	0.02
Gold	....	....	....	0.62	....	0.03	....	0.02	....	0.02	....	....	0.02
Gold, electrolytically deposited	0.53	0.16	....	0.04	0.03	0.03	0.03	0.03	0.02	0.02	0.02	....	0.02
Graphite	0.78	0.76	0.75	0.73	0.65	0.57	0.52	0.49	0.46	0.42	0.41	....	0.37
Iridium	....	....	....	0.22	0.13	0.09	0.06	0.06	0.05	0.04	0.04	0.04	
Iron	0.45	0.43	....	0.35	0.22	0.16	0.12	0.09	0.07	0.06	....	....	0.05
Lead	....	....	....	....	....	....	....	0.08	....	0.06	....	....	0.04
Magnesium	0.28	0.27	0.26	0.26	0.22	0.20	0.16	0.14	0.09	0.07			
Molybdenum	0.55	0.52	0.48	0.42	0.18	0.12	0.10	0.08	0.07	0.06	0.06	0.05	
Nickel	....	....	....	0.27	....	0.12	....	0.06	....	0.04			
Nickel, electrolytically deposited	0.39	0.35	....	0.28	0.17	0.12	0.09	0.06	0.06	0.05	....	....	0.03
Palladium	....	....	....	0.26	0.19	0.12	0.12	0.10	0.06	0.03	0.03	0.03	0.03
Platinum	....	0.45	....	0.27	0.19	0.11	0.08	0.06	0.05	....	0.04	0.04	0.04
Platinum, electrolytically deposited	0.42	0.36	....	0.27	0.20	0.11	0.09	0.06	0.05	....	....	....	0.04
Rhodium	0.24	0.23	0.19	0.16	0.09	0.08	0.08	0.07	0.06	0.05	0.05		
Silicon	0.66	0.68	0.71	0.72	0.72	....	0.72	....	0.72	....	0.72		
Silver	0.10	0.07	....	0.04	....	0.03	....	0.03	....	0.01	....	0.01	0.01
Silver, chemically deposited	0.09	....	....	0.03	0.02	0.02	....	....	....	....	0.014	....	0.01
Tantalum	0.62	0.55	0.36	0.22	0.10	0.08	0.07	0.07	0.06	0.06	....	0.05	
Tellurium	....	0.51	0.52	0.50	0.48	0.47	0.43	0.43	0.32	0.22			
Tin	....	....	....	0.46	0.39	0.32	0.28	0.24	0.19	0.16	0.16	0.15	
Tungsten	0.50	0.48	....	0.38	0.10	0.06	....	0.05	....	....	0.04	0.04	
Vanadium	0.43	0.41	....	0.39	0.31	0.26	0.21	0.18	0.12	0.08			
Zinc	....	....	....	0.20	0.08	0.04	0.03	0.03	0.02	0.02	0.02	0.01	0.01
Mach's magnalium (69 Al + 31 Mg)	0.17	0.17	....	0.16	....	0.13	....	0.11	....	0.10	....	....	0.08
Steel untempered	0.45	0.45	....	0.37	0.23	0.17	....	0.11	0.07	0.07	....	....	0.04
Stellite	0.36	....	....	0.31	0.25	0.21	0.18	0.15	....	0.12	....	0.11	
Brass, Trobridge	....	....	....	....	0.09	....	....	0.04	0.03	0.02			

Basic References

1. Hottel's table from McAdams, "Heat Transmission," 3d ed., McGraw-Hill Book Company, Inc., New York, 1954.
2. Smithells, "Metals Handbook," Interscience Publishers, Inc., New York, 1949.
3. T. S. Holden and J. J. Greenland, Report R. 6, "The Coefficient of Solar Absorptivity and Low Temperature Emissivity of Various Materials," A Review of Literature to 1951. Commonwealth Scientific and Industrial Research Organization, Division of Building Research, Victoria, Australia.
4. E. Schmidt and L. Furthmann, *Mitt. Kaiser-Wilhelm, Inst. Eisenforsch. Düsseldorf* **109**, 225 (1928). (Contains comprehensive bibliography.)
5. G. B. Wilkes, "Heat Insulation," John Wiley & Sons, Inc., New York, 1950.
6. R. B. Dingle, *Physica* **19**, 311–347 (pt. I, 1953); 348–364 (pt. II, 1953); 729–736 (pt. III, 1953); 1187–1199 (pt. IV, 1953).
7. M. M. Reynolds and M. M. Fulk, unpublished data, NBS, AEC, CEL.
8. "International Critical Tables."
9. M. Jakob, "Heat Transfer," vol. 1, John Wiley & Sons, Inc., New York, 1949.
10. G. Ribaud, Traité de pyrométrie optique, *Rev. opt.*, 1931.
11. Landolt-Börnstein tables.
12. "Temperature—Its Measurement and Control in Science and Industry," Reinhold Publishing Corporation, New York, 1941.

TABLE 6g-5. SPECTRAL EMISSIVITY OF MATERIALS, SURFACE UNOXIDIZED, FOR $\lambda = 0.65\mu$*

Element	Solid	Liquid	Element	Solid	Liquid
Beryllium	0.61	0.61	Thorium	0.36	0.40
Carbon	0.80–0.93		Titanium	0.63	0.65
Chromium	0.34	0.39	Tungsten	0.43	
Cobalt	0.36	0.37	Uranium	0.54	0.34
Columbium	0.37	0.40	Vanadium	0.35	0.32
Copper	0.10	0.15	Yttrium	0.35	0.35
Erbium	0.55	0.38	Zirconium	0.32	0.30
Gold	0.14	0.22	Steel	0.35	0.37
Iridium	0.30		Cast iron	0.37	0.40
Iron	0.35	0.37	Constantan	0.35	
Manganese	0.59	0.59	Monel	0.37	
Molybdenum	0.37	0.40	Chromel P (90 Ni, 10 Cr)	0.35	
Nickel	0.36	0.37	80 Ni, 20 Cr	0.35	
Palladium	0.33	0.37	60 Ni, 24 Fe, 16 Cr	0.36	
Platinum	0.30	0.38	Alumel (95 Ni; bal. Al, Mn, Si)	0.37	
Rhodium	0.24	0.30	90 Pt, 10 Rh	0.27	
Silver	0.07	0.07			
Tantalum	0.49				

* American Institute of Physics, "Temperature, Its Measurement and Control in Science and Industry," p. 1313, Reinhold Publishing Corporation, New York, 1941.

6g-3. Emissivity of Solids

ϵ_n = total normal emissivity (emission of radiant energy of all wavelengths normal to the specified surface divided by the corresponding emission from a black body)

ϵ_h = total hemispherical emissivity (emissivity for radiation into a hemisphere centered on the normal to the emitting surface)

a = total absorptivity (fraction of energy incident on a surface which is absorbed: quantities a_n and a_h analogous to ϵ_n and ϵ_h may be distinguished)

r = reflectivity (fraction of incident energy which is reflected)

T = temperature

For metals: $\frac{\epsilon_h}{\epsilon_n} = (1.05\text{–}1.33)$ (most metals $\cong$ 1.2)

For nonmetals: $\frac{\epsilon_h}{\epsilon_n} = (0.95\text{–}1.05)$ (most nonmetals $\cong$ 0.98)

Emissivities increase with surface roughness and, for metals, increase with work-hardening, addition of impurities, or formation of contaminating surface films such as oxides. An emissivity value followed by a temperature means absorptivity at that temperature for the black-body radiation of temperature in the °K column. Other values, not separately identified, were calculated from reflectivity data. At equilibrium (emitter and absorber at the same temperature) we have

$$(\epsilon = a = 1 - r)_T$$

The above relation would not strictly apply if the absorbing surface and the source of radiation were at different temperatures, because the distribution of energy with wavelength changes with the temperature of the radiating source, and the emissivities of materials vary with the wavelength of the radiation.

TABLE 6g-6. SPECTRAL EMISSIVITY OF OXIDES FOR $\lambda = 0.65\mu$*

Material	Range of observed values	Probable value for the oxide formed on smooth metal
Aluminum oxide	0.22–0.40	0.30
Beryllium oxide	0.07–0.37	0.35
Cerium oxide	0.58–0.80	
Chromium oxide	0.60–0.80	0.70
Cobalt oxide	....	0.75
Columbium oxide	0.55–0.71	0.70
Copper oxide	0.60–0.80	0.70
Iron oxide	0.63–0.98	0.70
Magnesium oxide	0.10–0.43	0.20
Nickel oxide	0.85–0.96	0.90
Thorium oxide	0.20–0.57	0.50
Tin oxide	0.32–0.60	
Titanium oxide		0.50
Uranium oxide		0.30
Vanadium oxide		0.70
Yttrium oxide		0.60
Zirconium oxide	0.18–0.43	0.40
Alumel (oxidized)	....	0.87
Cast iron (oxidized)	....	0.70
Chromel P (90 Ni, 10 Cr) (oxidized)	....	0.87
80 Ni, 20 Cr (oxidized)	....	0.90
60 Ni, 24 Fe, 16 Cr (oxidized)	....	0.83
55 Fe, 37.5 Cr, 7.5 Al (oxidized)	....	0.78
70 Fe, 23 Cr, 5 Al, 2 Co (oxidized)	....	0.75
Constantan (55 Cu, 45 Ni) (oxidized)	....	0.84
Carbon steel (oxidized)	....	0.80
Stainless steel (18-8) (oxidized)	....	0.85
Porcelain	0.25–0.50	

The emissivity of oxides and oxidized metals depends to a large extent upon the roughness of the surface. In general, higher values of emissivity are obtained on the rougher surfaces.

* American Institute of Physics, "Temperature, Its Measurement and Control in Science and Industry," p. 1313, Reinhold Publishing Corporation, New York, 1941.

TABLE 6g-7. TOTAL EMISSIVITY OF METALS, SURFACE UNOXIDIZED*

Material	25°C	100°C	500°C	1000°C	1500°C	2000°C
Aluminum	0.022	0.028	0.060			
Bismuth	0.048	0.061				
Carbon	0.081	0.081	0.079			
Chromium	.....	0.08				
Cobalt	.....	.....	0.13	0.23		
Columbium				(Liquid 0.15)	0.19	0.24
Copper		0.02				
Gold		0.02	0.03			
Iron		0.05				
Lead		0.05				
Mercury	0.10	0.12				
Molybdenum				0.13	0.19	0.24
Nickel	0.045	0.06	0.12	0.19		
Platinum	0.037	0.047	0.096	0.152	0.191	
Silver		0.02	0.035			
Tantalum					0.21	0.26
Tin	0.043	0.05				
Tungsten	0.024	0.032	0.071	0.15	0.23	0.28
Zinc	(0.05 at 300°C)					
Brass	0.035	0.035				
Cast iron	.....	0.21	.....	(Liquid 0.29)		
Steel	.....	0.08	.....	(Liquid 0.28)		

* American Institute of Physics, "Temperature, Its Measurement and Control in Science and Industry," p. 1314, Reinhold Publishing Corporation, New York, 1941.

TABLE 6g-8. RELATION BETWEEN BRIGHTNESS TEMPERATURE AND TRUE TEMPERATURE FOR VARIOUS VALUES OF SPECTRAL EMISSIVITY AT $\lambda = 0.65\mu$*

Brightness temp., °C	800	1000	1200	1400	1600	1800	2000
Emissivity ϵ (0.65μ)	True temp., °C						
0.05	982	1265	1567	1846	2236	2609	3011
0.10	934	1194	1467	1752	2054	2370	2704
0.15	909	1156	1413	1681	1958	2248	2549
0.20	891	1130	1377	1632	1895	2168	2451
0.30	867	1095	1329	1567	1813	2064	2320
0.40	850	1071	1296	1525	1757	1995	2236
0.50	837	1053	1272	1493	1717	1944	2174
0.60	827	1039	1252	1467	1685	1905	2125
0.70	819	1027	1236	1447	1659	1872	2087
0.80	812	1017	1222	1429	1636	1844	2054
0.90	805	1008	1210	1413	1617	1821	2025

* American Institute of Physics, "Temperature, Its Measurement and Control in Science and Industry," Reinhold Publishing Corporation, New York, 1941.

TABLE 6g-9. RELATION BETWEEN APPARENT AND TRUE TEMPERATURE FOR VARIOUS VALUES OF THE TOTAL EMISSIVITY*

Apparent temp., °C	100	200	400	600	800	1000	1200	1400	1600	1800
Total emissivity ϵ_t					True temp., °C					
0.05	422	686	1137	1567	1993	2317	2841	3264	3687	4110
0.10	316	536	913	1275	1632	1989	2345	2701	3057	3413
0.15	264	460	799	1126	1449	1771	2093	2415	2736	3058
0.20	231	410	725	1029	1330	1629	1929	2228	2527	2827
0.30	189	347	630	904	1175	1446	1717	1987	2258	2528
0.40	164	307	568	823	1075	1327	1579	1830	2082	2333
0.50	146	278	523	763	1002	1240	1478	1716	1954	2192
0.60	132	255	489	718	945	1173	1400	1628	1855	2082
0.70	121	238	461	680	900	1119	1337	1556	1775	1993
0.80	113	223	437	649	861	1073	1284	1496	1707	1919
0.90	106	211	417	623	828	1034	1239	1445	1650	1855

* American Institute of Physics, "Temperature, Its Measurement and Control in Science and Industry," Reinhold Publishing Corporation, New York, 1941.

TABLE 6g-10. EFFICIENCIES OF ILLUMINANTS*

Lamp	Rating, or specification	Eff.	Ab. eff.
Acetylene	1.0 liters/hr	0.67	0.0010
Arc, electric:			
Carbon, enclosed d-c	6.6 amp opal globe and reflector	5.9	0.0087
Carbon, open d-c	9.6 amp clear globe	11.8	0.0173
High intensity	150 amp bare arc	18.5	0.0272
Magnetite d-c	6.6 amp	21.6	0.0318
Gas burner, open flame	Bray high pressure	0.22	0.00032
Gas mantle, incandescent:			
High pressure	0.578 lumens/Btu/hr	2.0	0.0030
Low pressure	0.350 lumens/Btu/hr	1.2	0.0018
Incandescent electric carbon filament:			
First commercial	....	1.6	0.0023
Squirted cellulose	....	3.3	0.0048
Metalized	....	4.0	0.0059
Tungsten filaments:			
Vacuum	25 watt 120 volt (1,000 hr life)	10.6	0.0156
Gas-filled	40 watt 120 volt (1,000 hr life)	11.6	0.0171
Gas-filled	60 watt 120 volt (1,000 hr life)	13.9	0.0204
Gas-filled	100 watt 120 volt (750 hr life)	16.3	0.0239
Gas-filled	1,000 watt 120 volt (1,000 hr life)	21.6	0.0318
Gas-filled	5,000 watt 120 volt (75 hr life)	32.8	0.0482
Fluorescent lamps:			
General line	20 watt standard warm white (T12)	50.0	0.0735
General line	40 watt standard warm white (T12)	64.0	0.0940
General line	90 watt standard warm white (T17)	58.0	0.0850
Slimline	96T8 (120 ma) standard warm white	76.0	0.1115
Slimline	96T12 (425 ma) standard warm white	69.0	0.1015
General line	40 W daylight (T12)	54.0	0.0795
General line	40 W green (T12)	84.0	0.1235
General line	40 W blue (T12)	33.0	0.0485
General line	40 W red (T12)	3.6	0.0053
Mercury lamps	400 W (E1)	50.0	0.0735
	1,000 W (A6)	65.0	0.0955
Sodium	10,000 lumen	55.0	0.0808

The rating listed is the commercial rating of the lamp. The absolute efficiency is the equivalent power in light flux (0.556μ) per watt input. Efficiency is given in lumens per watt input.

* "Handbook of Chemistry and Physics," 36th ed., pp. 2480, 2481, Chemical Rubber Publishing Company, 1954–1955. Compiled by J. M. Smith and C. E. Weitz.

TABLE 6g-11. APPROXIMATE BRIGHTNESS OF VARIOUS LIGHT SOURCES*

Source		Lamberts†
Natural sources:		
Clear sky	Average brightness	2.5
Sun (as observed from earth's surface)	At meridian	519,000
Sun (as observed from earth's surface)	Near horizon	1,885
Moon (as observed from earth's surface)	Bright spot	0.8
Combustion sources:		
Candle flame (sperm)	Bright spot	3.1
Kerosene flame (flat wick)	Bright spot	3.8
Illuminating—gas flame	Fishtail burner	1.3
Welsbach mantle	Bright spot	20.0
Acetylene flame	Mees burner	34.0
Incandescent electric lamps:		
Carbon filament		165
Metalized carbon filament (Gem)		300
Tungsten filament	Vacuum lamp, 10 lumens per watt	650
Tungsten filament	Gas-filled lamp, 20 lumens per watt	3,800
Tungsten filament	750-watt projector lamp, 26 lumens per watt	7,500
Fluorescent lamps:		
20 watt T12 standard warm white		1.67
40 watt T12 standard warm white		2.10
96T12 standard warm white		2.052
Electric-arc lamps:		
Plain carbon arc	Positive crater 7 mm non-rotating	55,000
High-intensity carbon arc	Positive crater 8 mm non-rotating	125,000
High-intensity carbon arc	Positive crater 13.6 mm non-rotating	220,000
High-intensity carbon arc	Positive crater	314,000
Mercury lamps:		
Low-pressure mercury arc	50-in. a-c rectified tube	6.6
400 W (H1)		440
1,000 W (A6)	Water-cooled	94,000
Sodium lamps	10,000 lumens	18

* "Handbook of Chemistry and Physics," 36th ed., pp. 2481, 2482, Chemical Rubber Publishing Company, 1954–1955. Compiled by J. M. Smith and C. E. Weitz.

† To convert Lamberts to foot-Lamberts multiply by 929. To convert Lamberts to candles/cm² divide by π.

TABLE 6g-12. PROPERTIES OF TUNGSTEN*

Temp., °K	Normal brightness new candles/cm²	Spectral emissivity 0.65μ	Spectral emissivity 0.467μ	Color emis-sivity	Total emis-sivity	Bright-ness temp. 0.65μ	Color temp.
300	....	0.472	0.505	.....	0.032		
400	....	.....	.....	.....	0.042		
500	....	.....	.....	.....	0.053		
600	....	.....	.....	.....	0.064		
700	....	.....	.....	.....	0.076		
800	....	.....	.....	.....	0.088		
900	....	.....	.....	.....	0.101		
1000	0.0001	0.458	0.486	0.395	0.114	966	1007
1100	0.001	0.456	0.484	0.392	0.128	1059	1108
1200	0.006	0.454	0.482	0.390	0.143	1151	1210
1300	0.029	0.452	0.480	0.387	0.158	1242	1312
1400	0.11	0.450	0.478	0.385	0.175	1332	1414
1500	0.33	0.448	0.476	0.382	0.192	1422	1516
1600	0.92	0.446	0.475	0.380	0.207	1511	1619
1700	2.3	0.444	0.473	0.377	0.222	1599	1722
1800	5.1	0.442	0.472	0.374	0.236	1687	1825
1900	10.4	0.440	0.470	0.371	0.249	1774	1928
2000	20.0	0.438	0.469	0.368	0.260	1861	2032
2100	36	0.436	0.467	0.365	0.270	1946	2136
2200	61	0.434	0.466	0.362	0.279	2031	2241
2300	101	0.432	0.464	0.359	0.288	2115	2345
2400	157	0.430	0.463	0.356	0.296	2198	2451
2500	240	0.428	0.462	0.353	0.303	2280	2556
2600	350	0.426	0.460	0.349	0.311	2362	2662
2700	500	0.424	0.459	0.346	0.318	2443	2769
2800	690	0.422	0.458	0.343	0.323	2523	2876
2900	950	0.420	0.456	0.340	0.329	2602	2984
3000	1260	0.418	0.455	0.336	0.334	2681	3092
3100	1650	0.416	0.454	0.333	0.337	2759	3200
3200	2100	0.414	0.452	0.330	0.341	2837	3310
3300	2700	0.412	0.451	0.326	0.344	2913	3420
3400	3400	0.410	0.450	0.323	0.348	2989	3530
3500	4200	0.408	0.449	0.320	0.351	3063	3642
3600	5200	0.406	0.447	0.317	0.354	3137	3754

* "Handbook of Chemistry and Physics," 36th ed., p. 2691, Chemical Publishing Company, 1954–1955. Roeser and Wensel, National Bureau of Standards.

6g-4. Stellar Radiation. Brightness of stars as seen by any photoreceiver may be expressed as a stellar magnitude, related to the effective irradiance I in watts/cm² received from the star:

$$\text{Stellar magnitude } m = -2.5 \log_{10} \frac{I}{I_0}$$

The effective irradiance I from the star as seen by a photoreceiver is

$$I = \int_0^\infty J(\lambda)\sigma(\lambda)\, d\lambda$$

where $J\lambda$ = spectral distribution of radiation received from the star, in watts/cm² per wavelength increment $d\lambda$. $J(\lambda)$ for stars approximates black-body distribution for the assumed surface temperatures.

$\sigma(\lambda)$ = photoreceiver's spectral-response function normalized at the response peak. Spectral response of a number of photosensitive surfaces is shown in Figs. 6g-1 and 6g-2.

For visual magnitude

$$I_0 = \tfrac{1}{685} \times 10^{-(24.18/2.5)} = 3.1 \times 10^{-13} \text{ watts/cm}^2$$

(cf. definition of lumen, page 6-9; definition of stellar magnitude, "Smithsonian Tables," 8th ed., Table 798).

Star brightness as seen by photoreceivers other than the eye is also expressed as a stellar magnitude (e.g., bolometric magnitude, photographic magnitude). The magnitude scales are generally adjusted by setting I_0 so that a class A0 star (surface temperature 11,000°K) appears of the same magnitude to each photoreceiver. For stars at other temperatures the effective-irradiance integral can be evaluated to obtain an index, which when added to visual magnitude gives the star's magnitude as seen by other receivers. Early stellar photometry used the non-color-sensitized (blue-sensitive) photographic plate; the difference between photographic and visual magnitude was called color index. Difference between bolometric and visual magnitude was called heat index. Indices for the principal spectral classes of stars and for several photoreceivers are given in Table 6g-13.

TABLE 6g-13. COLOR INDICES OF VARIOUS STELLAR SPECTRAL CLASSES

Spectral class	Approx eff. surface temp., °K	Index			
		Photographic, visual	Bolometric, visual	S4 photosurface, visual	PbS, visual
B0........	20,000	−0.30	−1.4	−0.15	+0.2
A0........	11,000	0	0	0	0
F0........	7,500	+0.33	+0.6	+0.30	−0.4
gG0.......	5,000	+0.70	+0.4	+0.7	−1.0
gK0.......	4,200	+1.12	+0.1	+1.0	−1.5
gM0......	3,400	+1.70	−0.8	+1.1	−2.6

Effective temperature: Kuiper, *Astrophys. J.* **88**, 464 (1938).
S4 index: computed from manufacturers' data on 1P21 photomultiplier.
Bolometric index: Kuiper, *Astrophys. J.* **88**, 452 (1938).
Photographic index: "Smithsonian Tables," 8th ed.
PbS index: computed from manufacturers' data.

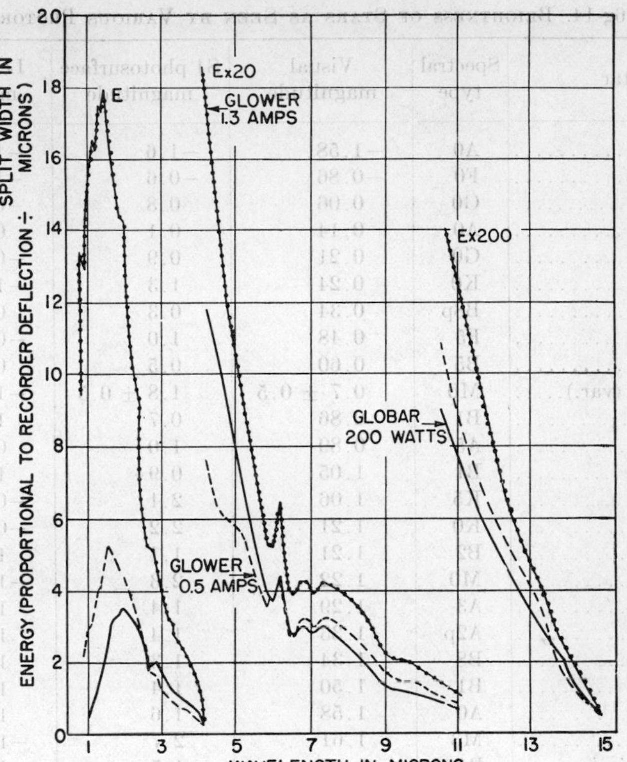

FIG. 6g-1. Characteristics of globar and glower sources.

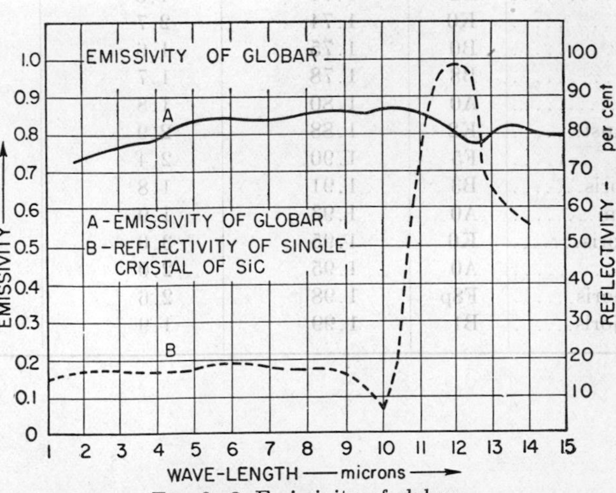

FIG. 6g-2. Emissivity of globar.

TABLE 6g-14. BRIGHTNESS OF STARS AS SEEN BY VARIOUS PHOTORECEIVERS

Star	Spectral type	Visual magnitude	S4 photosurface magnitude	Lead sulfide magnitude
Sirius	A0	−1.58	−1.6	−1.6
Canopus	F0	−0.86	−0.6	−1.3
α Centauri	G0	0.06	0.8	−0.9
Vega	A0	0.14	0.1	0.1
Capella	G0	0.21	0.9	−0.8
Arcturus	K0	0.24	1.3	−1.3
Rigel	B8p	0.34	0.3	0.3
Procyon	F5	0.48	1.0	−0.2
Achernar	B5	0.60	0.5	0.7
Betelgeuse (var.)	M0	0.7 ± 0.5	1.8 ± 0.5	−1.9 ± 0.5
β Centauri	B1	0.86	0.7	1.1
Altair	A5	0.89	1.0	0.7
α Crucis	B1	1.05	0.9	1.3
Aldebaran	K5	1.06	2.1	−0.8
Pollux	K0	1.21	2.2	−0.3
Spica	B2	1.21	1.1	1.4
Antares	M0	1.22	2.3	−1.4
Fomalhaut	A3	1.29	1.4	1.2
Deneb	A2p	1.33	1.4	1.2
Regulus	B8	1.34	1.3	1.4
β Crucis	B1	1.50	1.4	1.7
Castor	A0	1.58	1.6	1.6
γ Crucis	M3	1.61	2.7	−1.4
ε Canis Majoris	B1	1.63	1.5	1.8
ε Ursa Majoris	A0p	1.68	1.7	1.7
γ Orionis	B2	1.70	1.6	1.9
λ Scorpii	B2	1.71	1.6	1.9
ε Carniae	K0	1.74	2.7	0.2
ε Orionis	B0	1.75	1.6	2.0
β Tauri	B8	1.78	1.7	1.8
β Carniae	A0	1.80	1.8	1.8
α Triang. Aust.	K2	1.88	2.9	0.2
α Persei	F5	1.90	2.4	1.2
η Ursa Majoris	B3	1.91	1.8	2.1
γ Geminorum	A0	1.93	1.9	1.9
α Ursa Majoris	K0	1.95	3.0	0.5
ε Sagitarii	A0	1.95	2.0	2.0
δ Canis Majoris	F8p	1.98	2.6	1.1
β Canis Majoris	B1	1.99	1.9	2.2

6h. Wavelengths for Spectrographic Calibration[1]

TABLE 6h-1. WAVELENGTH STANDARDS FOR THE VACUUM ULTRAVIOLET*

Wavelength, A	Intensity	Spectrum	Estimated relative error (±mA)	Wavelength, A	Intensity	Spectrum	Estimated relative error (±mA)
1,942.273	20	Hg II	2	1,730.874	2	N I	3
1,930.902	10	C I	2	1,727.332[a]	4	Si I	3
1,900.284	5	Hg II	2	1,721.081	20	C II	3
1,880.969	5	Si I	2	1,720.158	18	C II	4
1,870.547	20	Hg II	4	1,707.397	4	Hg II	4
1,869.548	8	Hg II	2	1,704.558[a]	4	Si I	4
1,867.590	1	N II	3	1,702.805[a]	8	Si I	4
1,864.742	5	N II	2	1,702.733	8	Hg II	4
1,862.806	2	N II	5	1,700.522	3	Si I	4
1,861.750[a]	1	Si I	2	1,693.756	15	Si I	4
1,859.406	3	Ni I	2	1,676.913	5	Si I	4
1,857.956	8	Ni I	4	1,672.405	2	Hg II	3
1,853.260	3	Si I	4	1,658.117[c]	20	C I	1
1,850.665	5	Si I	5	1,657.899[c]	15	C I	4
1,849.497	50R[b]	Hg I	4	1,657.541	1	C I	5
1,849.380	5	Ni I	4	1,657.374[c]	10	C I	1
1,848.237	5	Si I	4	1,657.243	1	C I	5
1,846.014	8	N II	4	1,657.001[c]	30	C I	1
1,844.304	10	N II	4	1,656.923[c]	15	C I	1
1,842.066	1	N II	5	1,656.454	4	C I	4
1,839.995	4	Si I	4	1,656.259	15	C I	1
1,833.264	1	C	5	1,654.055	5	C I	3
1,831.973	5	N II	4	1,653.644	2	Hg II	3
1,830.458	4	N II	4	1,649.932	10	Hg II	4
1,820.336	20	Hg II	4	1,640.474	80[d]	He II	4
1,816.921	8	Si II	2	1,640.342	100[d]	He II	2
1,808.003	5	Si II	4	1,630.180	2	Si I	3
1,807.303	30	N II	5	1,629.931	4	Si I	4
1,803.888	2	Hg II	2	1,629.830	4	N II	4
1,796.897	15	Hg II	4	1,629.366	4	Si I	4
1,787.805[a]	10	Si I	2	1,613.251	4	He II	4
1,782.817	15	Na III	4	1,605.321	1	He II	3
1,775.677	1	Hg I	4	1,602.598	15	C I	3

[1] This section presents calibration standards in the ultraviolet and infrared wavelength regions. For corresponding data on visible wavelengths, see Sec. 7.

TABLE 6h-1. WAVELENGTH STANDARDS FOR THE VACUUM ULTRAVIOLET* (*Continued*)

Wavelength, A	Intensity	Spectrum	Estimated relative error (±*mA*)	Wavelength, A	Intensity	Spectrum	Estimated relative error (±*mA*)
1,774.941[a]	20	Si I	4	1,592.245	4	Si I	3
1,769.658[a]	1	Si I	4	1,589.607	2	Si I	3
1,753.113[a]	2	Si I	3	1,574.035	1	N II	3
1,749.771[a]	1	Si I	5	1,561.433	20	C I	2
1,745.246	30	N I	3	1,561.339	5	C I	4
1,743.322	10	N II	4	1,560.687[d]	15	C I	12
1,742.724	60	N I	3	1,560.301	2	C I	5
1,740.327	15	N II	3	1,504.474	5	Hg III	4
1,736.582	8	Si I	4	1,494.673	60	N I	4
1,732.142	15	Hg II	4	1,492.824	30	N I	4
1,492.624	80	N I	5	1,280.403[e]	5	C I	4
1,485.600	8	Si II	2	1,280.340[e]	15	C I	1
1,481.760	30	C I	3	1,280.140[e]	8	C I	1
1,470.082	5	C I	3	1,279.897[e]	10	C I	1
1,469.844	15	C I	4	1,279.230	8	C I	3
1,467.405	20	C I	3	1,277.727	20	C I	1
1,466.723	5	N I	4	1,277.551	50	C I	4
1,463.838	40	C	3	1,277.282	40	C I	1
1,463.346	40	C I	2	1,276.754	3	N II	1
1,459.034	20	C I	4	1,265.001	1	Si II	1
1,439.094	10	Si II	2	1,261.559[f]	15	C I	1
1,411.948	30	N I	3	1,261.430[f]	8	C I	4
1,393.322	1	Hg III	2	1,261.128[f]	8	C I	1
1,364.165	8	C I	4	1,261.000[f]	8	C I	1
1,361.267	8	Hg II	4	1,260.930[f]	8	C I	2
1,357.140	5	C I	2	1,260.738[f]	8	C I	1
1,355.598	2	O I	3	1,259.523	10	C I	3
1,354.292	8	C I	3	1,253.816	5	C I	1
1,350.074	4	Hg II	2	1,251.164	8	Si II	4
1,335.692	80	C II	5	1,250.586	4	Hg I	4
1,335.184	8	Hg	3	1,248.426	5	Si II	4
1,334.520	60	C II	5	1,246.738	1	Si II	3
1,331.737	20	Hg II	4	1,243.309	15	N I	4
1,329.590	40	C I	1	1,243.179	20	N I	1
1,329.108	40	C I	2	1,229.172	1	N I	1
1,328.836[d]	15	C I	10	1,228.790	10	N I	4
1,327.927	10	N I	2	1,228.410	5	N I	4
1,326.572	15	N I	4	1,225.372	10	N I	1
1,321.712	20	Hg II	3	1,225.028	15	N I	4
1,319.684	30	N I	4	1,215.662	100R[b]	H	5
1,319.003	20	N I	2	1,215.167	5	He II	5
1,316.287	1	N I	1	1,215.086	5	He II	4
1,311.365	20	C I	3	1,200.708[g]	30	N I	2

TABLE 6h-1. WAVELENGTH STANDARDS FOR THE VACUUM ULTRAVIOLET* (*Continued*)

Wavelength, A	Intensity	Spectrum	Estimated relative error ($\pm mA$)
1,310.952	25	N I	1
1,310.548	25	N I	3
1,309.278	3	Si II	5
1,307.928	10	Hg II	3
1,306.036	25	O I	3
1,304.872	30	O I	5
1,302.173	30	O I	1
1,288.430	5	C I	3
1,280.852[e]	10	C I	1
1,280.604[e]	8	C I	3
1,189.244	3	N I	3
1,188.972	5	N I	1
1,177.694	15	N I	3
1,176.626	3	N I	5
1,176.508	15	N I	1
1,170.276	1	N I	3
1,169.692	1	N I	1
1,168.537	20	N I	4
1,168.334	8	N I	4
1,167.450	25	N I	4
1,164.322	8	N I	3
1,163.884	12	N I	4
1,158.138	1	C I	5
1,158.030	8	C I	4
1,152.149	2	O I	5
1,134.988	25	N I	4
1,134.426	25	N I	4
1,134.176	20	N I	4
1,101.293	40	N I	5
1,100.362	30	N I	4
1,099.259	40	Hg II	3
1,099.153	25	N I	5
1,098.264	40	N I	5
1,098.103	40	N I	5
1,097.990	25	N I	4
1,097.245	50	N I	4
1,096.749	35	N I	4
1,096.322	35	N I	2
1,095.940	35	N I	3
1,085.707	50	N II	3
1,085.546	3	N II	5
1,085.442	3	N II	3
1,084.970	2	He II	4
1,200.226[g]	40	N I	1
1,199.718[g]	2	N I	4
1,199.551[g]	50	N I, C I	5
1,194.496	5	Si I	1
1,194.060	3	C I	3
1,193.674	3	C I	3
1,193.388[d]	3	C I	8
1,193.243	15	C I	2
1,193.013	15	C I	4
1,189.628	5	N I	4
1,069.984	30	N I	1
1,068.476	35	N I	4
1,067.607	35	N I	4
1,041.688	1	O I	4
1,040.941	15	O I	4
1,039.233	20	O I	4
1,037.627	0	O	3
1,037.020	0	C II	1
1,028.162	8	O I	3
1,027.433	20	O I	3
1,025.728	60	H	3
1,025.298	2[i]	He II	5
990.805[h]	2	O I	4
990,210[h]	8	O I	4
990,132[h]	1	O I	4
988,776[h]	15	O I	4
988,661[h,d]	2	O I	4
977,967	1	O I	4
964.626	1	N I	4
963.991	5	N I	4
953.658	15	N I	4
953.415	15	N I	3
952.522	4	N I	4
952.414	8	O I	4
952.304	8	N I	4
950.114	0	O I	4
949.742	25	H	4
910.279	0	N I	5
909.692	0	N I	5
906.722	1	N I	2
906.426	15	N I	4
906.202	10	N I	3
905.829	5	N I	4

TABLE 6h-1. WAVELENGTH STANDARDS FOR THE VACUUM ULTRAVIOLET* (*Continued*)

Wavelength, A	Intensity	Spectrum	Estimated relative error ($\pm mA$)	Wavelength, A	Intensity	Spectrum	Estimated relative error ($\pm mA$)
1,084.910	2	He II	5	893.079	0	Hg II	2
1,084.579	30	N II	3	888.363	0	N I	2
1,083.990	20	N II	4	888.019	0	N I	4
1,070.821	0	N I	5	875.092	5	N I	5

* *J. Opt. Soc. Am.* **45,** 10 (1955).

[a] Identification: A. Fowler, *Proc. Roy. Soc.* (*London*), ser. A, **123,** 422 (1929); J. C. Boyce and H. A. Robinson, *J. Opt. Soc. Am.* **26,** 133 (1936).

[b] Self-reversed resonance line.

[c] Resolved $2p^2\ ^3P - 3s^3P^0$ multiplet.

[d] Blended line.

[e] Completely resolved $2p^2\ ^3P - 4s\ ^3P^0$ multiplet.

[f] Completely resolved $2p^2\ ^3P - 3d\ ^3P^0$ multiplet.

[g] Resolved $2p^3\ ^4S^0 - 3s\ ^4P$ multiplet.

[h] $2p^4\ ^3P - 3s'\ ^3D^0$ multiplet.

[i] Diffuse line.

TABLE 6h-2. PROPOSED INTERNATIONAL WAVELENGTH STANDARDS IN THE VACUUM ULTRAVIOLET

Wave-length, A, this research	Spectrum	Wave-length, A, More and Rieke[a]	Wave-length, A, Boyce and Rieke[b]	Wave-length, A, Weber and Watson[c]	Wave-length, A, other observers	Wave-length, A, mean value
1,930.902	C I	.....	0.900	0.889	.....	1,930.897
1,745.246	N I	.....	0.246	0.255	.....	1,745.249
1,742.724	N I	.....	0.734	0.733	.....	1,742.730
1,740.327	N II	.....	.....	0.320	0.315[d]	1,740.321
1,658.117	C I	.....	0.126	0.127	.....	1,658.123
1,657.899	C I	0.909	.....	.....	0.891[e]	1,657.900
1,657.374	C I	.....	0.380	0.381	.....	1,657.378
1,657.001	C I	.....	0.005	.....	6.998[e]	1,657.001
1,656.259	C I	0.266	.....	.....	0.255[e]	1,656.260
1,560.301	C I	0.308	0.316	.....	.....	1,560.308
1,494.673	N I	0.672	0.669	0.668	.....	1,494.670
1,492.624	N I	.....	0.630	0.634	.....	1,492.630
1,481.760	C I	0.771	.....	.....	0.750[f]	1,481.760
1,335.692	C II	0.700	.....	.....	0.684[g]	1,335.692
1,329.590	C I	0.587	.....	.....	0.583[h]	1,329.587
1,329.108	C I	0.102	0.101	.....	.....	1,329.104
1,277.282	C I	.....	0.274	.....	0.280[h]	1,277.279
1,261.559	C I	.....	0.560	.....	0.565[h]	1,261.561
1,200.708	N I	0.719	0.706	0.693	.....	1,200.708
1,200.226	N I	0.217	0.220	0.215	.....	1,200.219
1,199.551	N I	0.552	0.547	0.557	.....	1,199.552
1,177.694	N I	0.701	.....	0.677	.....	1,177.691
1,176.508	N I	0.506	.....	0.498	.....	1,176.504
1,167.450	N I	0.442	.....	0.454	.....	1,167.449
1,134.988	N I	0.977	0.980	0.980	.....	1,134.981
1,134.426	N I	.....	0.419	0.416	.....	1,134.420
1,134.176	N I	.....	0.171	0.169	.....	1,134.172
1,085.546	N II	.....	0.546	0.546	.....	1,085.546
1,084.579	N II	0.584	0.579	0.582	.....	1,084.580
1,083.990	N II	.....	0.991	0.990	.....	1,083.990
990.805	C I	0.790	0.797	.....	.....	990.797
990.210	C I	0.198	0.213	.....	.....	990.207

[a] K. R. More and C. A. Rieke, *Phys. Rev.* **50**, 1054 (1936).
[b] J. C. Boyce and C. A. Rieke, *Phys. Rev.* **47**, 653 (1935).
[c] R. L. Weber and W. W. Watson, *J. Opt. Soc. Am.* **26**, 307 (1936).
[d] A. Fowler, *Proc. Roy. Soc.* (*London*), ser. A, **123**, 422 (1929).
[e] A. G. Shenstone, *Phys. Rev.* **72**, 411 (1947).
[f] E. Ekefors, *Z. Physik* **63**, 437 (1930).
[g] B. Edlén, *Z. Physik* **98**, 561 (1936); *Nature* **159**, 129 (1947).
[h] F. Paschen and G. Kruger, *Ann. phys.* **7**, 1 (1930).

TABLE 6h-3. INFRARED STANDARD WAVELENGTHS

Wave-length, μ	State	Description	Substance	Ref.
0.54607	Emission	AH-4 lamp	Mercury	9
0.57696	Emission	AH-4 lamp	Mercury	9
0.57907	Emission	AH-4 lamp	Mercury	9
1.01398	Emission	AH-4 lamp	Mercury	9
1.12866	Emission	AH-4 lamp	Mercury	9
1.140	Liquid	....	Benzene	6
1.35703	Emission	AH-4 lamp	Mercury	9
1.36728	Emission	AH-4 lamp	Mercury	9
1.39506	Emission	AH-4 lamp	Mercury	9
1.52452	Emission	AH-4 lamp	Mercury	9
1.6606	Liquid	0.5-mm cell	1,2,4-Trichlorobenzene	9
1.671	Liquid	....	Benzene	6
1.69202	Emission	AH-4 lamp	Mercury	9
1.69419	Emission	AH-4 lamp	Mercury	9
1.70727	Emission	AH-4 lamp	Mercury	9
1.71090	Emission	AH-4 lamp	Mercury	9
1.81307	Emission	AH-4 lamp	Mercury	9
1.97009	Emission	AH-4 lamp	Mercury	9
2.008	Gas	....	Carbon dioxide	
2.150	Liquid	....	Benzene	
2.1526	Liquid	0.5-mm cell	1,2,4-Trichlorobenzene	9
2.22	Liquid	....	Carbon disulfide	9
2.24929	Emission	AH-4 lamp	Mercury	9
2.3126	Liquid	0.5-mm cell	1,2,4-Trichlorobenzene	9
2.32542	Emission	AH-4 lamp	Mercury	9
2.37	Solid	25-μ film	Polystyrene	Wright
2.4030	Liquid	0.5-mm cell	1,2,4-Trichlorobenzene	9
2.4374	Liquid	0.5-mm cell	1,2,4-Trichlorobenzene	9
2.439	Gas	....	Carbon oxysulfide central min	8
2.464	Liquid	....	Benzene	5
2.4944	Liquid	0.5-mm cell	1,2,4-Trichlorobenzene	9
2.5434	Liquid	0.5-mm cell	1,2,4-Trichlorobenzene	9
2.688	Gas	....	Carbon dioxide	Barker and Wu
2.7144	Vapor	5.0-cm cell	Methanol	9
2.765	Gas	....	Carbon dioxide	Barker and Wu
2.79	Solid	....	Lithium fluoride	9
2.996	Gas	200-mm 5.0-cm cell	Ammonia-zero branch	2
3.2204	Solid	25-μ film	Polystyrene	9
3.230	Gas	....	Carbon oxysulfide central min	8
3.2432	Solid	25-μ film	Polystyrene	9
3.2666	Solid	25-μ film	Polystyrene	9
3.3033	Solid	25-μ film	Polystyrene	9
3.3101	Solid	25-μ film	Polystyrene	9

TABLE 6h-3. INFRARED STANDARD WAVELENGTHS (*Continued*)

Wave-length, μ	State	Description	Substance	Ref.
3.320	Gas	....	Methane-zero branch	7
3.3293	Gas	5.0-cm cell	Methane	9
3.4188	Solid	25-μ film	Polystyrene	9
3.426	Gas	....	Carbon oxysulfide central min	8
3.465	Gas	....	Hydrogen chloride central min	9
3.5078	Solid	25-μ film	Polystyrene	9
4.258	Gas	Atmospheric	Carbon dioxide	9
4.613	Vapor	....	Carbon disulfide central min	5
4.866	Vapor	5.0-cm cell	Methanol	9
4.875	Gas	....	Carbon oxysulfide central min	8
5.138	Solid	50-μ film	Polystyrene	9
5.284	Gas	....	Carbon oxysulfide central min	8
5.292	Gas	....	Ethylene central min	5
5.549	Solid	50-μ film	Polystyrene	9
5.847	Gas	....	Carbon oxysulfide central min	8
6.154	Gas	200-mm 5.0-cm cell	Ammonia-zero branch	2
6.238	Solid	50-μ film	Polystyrene	9
6.692	Solid	50-μ film	Polystyrene	9
6.753	Liquid		Benzene	S. Silverman
6.925	Gas	....	Ethylene-zero branch	5
7.268	Liquid	0.05-mm cell	Methylcyclohexane	9
7.681	Gas		Methane-zero branch	3
8.241	Gas	200-mm 5.0-cm cell	Ammonia	2
8.362	Gas	200-mm 5.0-cm cell	Ammonia	2
8.490	Gas	200-mm 5.0-cm cell	Ammonia	2
8.623	Gas	200-mm 5.0-cm cell	Ammonia	2
8.762	Gas	200-mm 5.0-cm cell	Ammonia	2
9.057	Gas	200-mm 5.0-cm cell	Ammonia	2
9.216	Gas	200-mm 5.0-cm cell	Ammonia	2
9.295	Gas	200-mm 5.0-cm cell	Ammonia	2
9.378	Gas	200-mm 5.0-cm cell	Ammonia	2
9.548	Gas	....	Carbon oxysulfide central min	8
9.608	Vapor	....	Methyl chloride	4
9.672	Vapor	5-cm cell	Methanol	9
9.673	Gas	....	Ammonia	Wright
9.724	Solid	50-μ film	Polystyrene	9
9.807	Vapor	....	Methyl chloride	4
9.85	Gas	....	Ammonia	Wright

TABLE 6h-3. INFRARED STANDARD WAVELENGTHS (*Continued*)

Wave-length, μ	State	Description	Substance	Ref.
10.073	Gas	200-mm 5.0-cm cell	Ammonia	2
10.53	Gas	....	Ethylene-zero branch	5
11.008	Gas	200-mm 5.0-cm cell	Ammonia	2
11.035	Solid	50-μ film	Polystyrene	9
11.26	Gas	200-mm 5.0-cm cell	Ammonia	*J. Opt. Soc. Am.*
11.475	Liquid	0.05-mm cell	Methylcyclohexane	9
11.793	Gas	200-mm 5.0-cm cell	Ammonia	2
11.862	Liquid	0.05-mm cell	Methylcyclohexane	9
12.075	Gas	200-mm 5.0-cm cell	Ammonia	2
12.381	Gas	200-mm 5.0-cm cell	Ammonia	2
12.732	Gas	....	Acetylene	1
12.809	Gas	....	Acetylene	1
12.885	Gas	....	Acetylene	1
12.961	Gas	....	Acetylene	1
12.99	Gas	....	Ammonia	Wright
13.69	Gas	....	Acetylene	1
13.883	Gas	Atmospheric	Carbon dioxide	9
14.29*	Solid	50-μ film	Polystyrene	9
14.42	Liquid	....	Toluene 1% in carbon disulfide	9
14.98	Gas	Atmospheric	Carbon dioxide	9
15.48	Liquid	0.05 mm (1:4 CS_2)	Unknown in technical grade of 1,2,4-trichlorobenzene	9
17.40*	Liquid	0.025-mm cell	1,2,4-Trichlorobenzene	9
18.16	Liquid	0.025-mm cell	1,2,4-Trichlorobenzene	9
20.56	Liquid	0.05-mm cell	1,2,4-Trichlorobenzene (sat. sol. in CS_2)	9
21.52	Liquid	0.05-mm cell	Toluene	9
21.80	Liquid	0.025-mm cell	1,2,4-Trichlorobenzene	9
22.76*	Liquid	0.025-mm cell	1,2,4-Trichlorobenzene	9
23.85	Vapor	Atmospheric	Water	9

* Broad bands.

References

1. Levin and Meyer: *J. Opt. Soc. Am.* **16,** 137 (1928); Meyer and Levin: *Phys. Rev.* **29**(2), 293 (1927).
2. Oetjen, Kao, and Randall: *Rev. Sci. Instr.* **13,** 515 (1942).
3. Cooley: *Astrophys. J.* **62,** 73 (1925).
4. Bennett and Meyer: *Phys. Rev.* **32,** 888 (1927).
5. McKinney, Leberknight, and Warner: *J. Am. Chem. Soc.* **59,** 481 (1937).
6. Liddel and Kaspar: *J. Research Natl. Bur. Standards* **11,** 599 (1933).
7. Nielsen and Nielsen: *Phys. Rev.* **48,** 864 (1935).
8. Bartunek and Baker: *Phys. Rev.* **48,** 516 (1935).
9. Plyler: *J. Research Natl. Bur. Standards* **45,** 463.

6i. Magneto- and Electro-optics

C. B. WEST
Polaroid Corporation

ROBERT O'B. CARPENTER
Baird-Atomic, Inc.

TABLE 6i-1. VERDET CONSTANTS*
Gases and Vapors, V_0 for λ578 as Reduced to 0°C and 760 mm Hg

Gas	$10^6 V_0$	Gas	$10^6 V_0$
He	+0.40	CO	11.0
Ne	1.0(4)	CO_2	9.39
A	9.3(6)	NO	−58
		N_2O	7.7(5)
H_2	6.2(9)	SO_2	30.5
N_2	6.4(6)		
Air	6.27	$(CN)_2$	22.5
O_2	5.69		
Cl_2	31.9	CH_4	17.4
		C_2H_2	33.0
HCl	21.5	C_2H_4	34.5
HBr	(32.0)	C_2H_6	23.5
H_2S	41.5	C_3H_8	34.0
H_2Se	61.0	n-C_4H_{10}	44.0
NH_3	19.0		
PH_3	(56.0)		
AsH_3	68.0		

* Selected except as noted from R. de Malleman, "Tables de Constantes Selectionnées, Pouvoir Rotatoire Magnetique (Effet Faraday)," Paris, Hermann & Cie, 1951.

6i-1. Magnetic Rotation (Faraday Effect). When a linear-polarized light ray of wavelength λ in vacuum traverses an inactive medium at temperature t of length l in the direction of an external magnetic field of strength H, the rotation α, associated with circular birefringence, which the ray very generally exhibits as a result of the field is expressed by

$$\alpha = VHl$$

where V is the Verdet constant of the medium. A possible natural rotatory power of the medium, α_0, may be provided for by the modified expression

$$\alpha = (\alpha_0 + VH)l$$

TABLE 6i-1. VERDET CONSTANTS* (*Continued*)
Inorganic and Metal-organic Liquids

Liquid	λ	t	$10^2 V$
Phosphorus	589	33	+13.3
Sulfur	589	114	8.1
Bromine	700	0	5.3
H_2O	589	20	1.309
D_2O	589	19.7	1.257
H_2O_2	578	10	1.14(8)
H_3PO_3	578	76	1.63(5)
H_3PO_4	578	97.4	1.35(4)
CS_2	589	20	4.255
S_2Cl_2	578	18	7.45
PCl_3	578	26	3.02
$AsCl_3$	589	.....	4.25
CCl_4	589–78	25.1	1.60
$SiCl_4$	578	20	2.04
$TiCl_4$	578	17	−1.65
$SnCl_4$	578	28	4.46
$SbCl_5$	578	18	7.45
PBr_3	578	20	6.05
$TiBr_4$[a]	578	46	−5.3
$Pb(C_2H_5)_4$	578	20	3.01
$Ni(CO)_4$[b]	578	17	7.35

[a] P. Fritsch, *Compt. rend.* **217**, 447 (1943).
[b] J. Verhaeghe, *Bull. Sci. acad. roy. Belg.* **18**, 532 (1932).

For para- and ferromagnetic media, especially as one proceeds to high field strengths and low temperatures, the foregoing relations may have only a limited range of validity; rather the rotation α may tend toward, or actually attain, a saturation value α_∞ as the external field is increased.

When the same light ray traverses an inactive absorbing medium in the magnetic field it may emerge elliptic-polarized with the major axis of the ellipse rotated through the analogous angle α and with ellipticity measured by the angle β of the same order of magnitude. Such ellipticity is associated with circular dichroism. The formal expressions for magnetic ellipticity are analogous to those for magnetic rotation; thus

$$\beta = RHl$$
$$\beta = (\beta_0 + RH)l$$

for media without or with measurable natural "ellipticity power" β_0, that is to say, natural circular dichroism. The material constants β_0 and R apparently were never given names.

The quantities α, α_0, V, and H are signed quantities whose signs are determined solely by conventions. The signs of α and V are conventionally positive when the rotation, as for water, takes place in the direction of the electric current which creates

TABLE 6i-1. VERDET CONSTANTS* (*Continued*)
Aqueous Solutions

Solute	Wt. %	λ	d	n	10^2V
At 25°, λ546 (Ref. 1)					
HOH	100	...	......	....	+1.547
NaOH	14.3	...	1.1157	....	1.743
HNO_3	62	...	1.3676	1.40269	1.161
$NaNO_3$	32.32	...	1.2407	1.37068	1.495
NH_4NO_3	34.85	...	1.1476	1.37913	1.483
$HClO_4$	60	...	1.5261	1.39828	1.253
NH_4ClO_4	15.22	...	1.0725	1.34506	1.508
H_2SO_4	92	...	1.8121	1.43163	1.250
Na_2SO_4	24.39	...	1.2349	1.36892	1.611
$(NH_4)_2SO_4$	33.58	...	1.1909	1.38559	1.634
H_3PO_4	100	...	1.866	1.45805	1.571
Na_3PO_4	17.92	...	1.0823	1.34997	1.588
$(NH_4)_3PO_4$	14.62	...	1.0921	1.36148	1.649
HCl	35.5	...	1.1735	1.42111	2.685
NH_4Cl	19.01	...	1.0519	1.36971	1.997
HBr	44.27	...	1.4294	1.43063	3.317
NH_4Br	46.21	...	1.2985	1.41186	2.843
HI	54.5	...	1.6553	1.48406	5.314
NH_4I	53.92	...	1.4838	1.45386	4.284
At 23° (Ref. 2)					
H_2O	100	600	0.997	1.3324	1.26
$K_3Fe(CN)_6$	31.4	600	1.187	1.3878	−2.33
$FeCl_3$	47.8	800	1.523	1.4941	−3.99
KI, HgI_2		600	2.445	(1.59)	8.41
Same		589			12.8 (Ref. 4)
Same		546			22 (Ref. 3)

References

1. Sivaramakrishnan, V.: (*a*) *Proc. Indian Acad. Sc.* **39,** 31 (1954); (*b*) *J. Indian Inst. Sc.* **36,** 193 (1954).
2. Ingersoll, L.: *J. Opt. Soc. Am.* **6,** 663 (1922).
3. Bubb, F.: *Proc. Eastern Photoelasticity Conf.* **13,** 17 (1941), U.S. Patent 2,341,422 (1944).
4. Cornu and Potier: *Compt. rend.* **102,** 385 (1886).

TABLE 6i-1. VERDET CONSTANTS* (*Continued*)
Organic Liquids for Refractive Index Determinations[1]

Liquid	λ	t	$n^{20}{}_D$	10^2V
Methanol	589	18.7	1.3289	+0.958
Acetone	589–78	20.0	1.3585	1.116
Ethyl acetate	589–78	20.0	1.3727	1.08
n-Heptane	589–78	15	1.3875	1.23
n-Butanol	589	20.0	1.3993	1.23
Ethylene glycol	589	15.1	1.4313	1.25
1,2-Dichloroethane	589	14.4	1.4448	1.65
Cyclohexanone	578	23.0	1.4500	1.33
Cyclohexanol	578	20.0	1.4663	1.43
p-Cymene	589	15.0	1.4900	2.30
Toluene	589–78	15.0	1.4950	2.71
Benzene	589–78	15.0	1.5005	3.00
Iodoethane	589–78	18.1	1.5130	2.95
Anisole	589	21.1	1.5170	3.02
1,3-Dibromopropane	589	19.6	1.5230	2.38
Chlorobenzene	589	15	1.5246	2.92
Iodomethane	589–78	19.5	1.5305	3.35
1,2-Dibromoethane	589	15.2	1.5380	2.66
o-Nitrotoluene	589	18	1.5465	2.16
Nitrobenzene	589	15	1.5523	2.17
Bromobenzene	589	15	1.5598	3.26
o-Toluidine	589	17.3	1.5720	3.79
Aniline	589	15	1.5859	4.18
Bromoform	589	17.9	1.5960	3.13
Iodobenzene	589	15	1.6095	4.06
Quinoline	589	16	1.6235	4.18
1, 1, 2, 2-Tetrabromoethane	578	18.0	1.6377	3.34
1-Bromonaphthalene	578	20	1.6578	5.19
Diiodomethane[2]	600	23	1.7400	4.76

[1] These are supplied by Eastman Kodak Company. See their List No. 39, 1954, of Organic Chemicals, from which the present n_D's are taken.
[2] L. Ingersoll, *J. Opt. Soc. Am.* **6,** 663 (1922).

the field *H*. Other material constants of interest in connection with magnetic rotation are density *d* and refractive index *n* (for isotropic) or ω (for uniaxial media). The magneto-optic anomaly γ is a dimensionless ratio of theoretical interest.

Verdet constants *V* are listed here in angular minutes cm^{-1} $gauss^{-1}$, the wavelengths in millimicrons or Angstrom units. Uncertain or approximate numerical values are enclosed in parentheses.

6i-2. The Pockels Effect. The alteration of the refractive properties of an optical medium by the application of a strong electric field is called the "electro-optic effect." In a liquid medium the effect is designated the "Kerr effect," in a piezoelectric crystalline medium, the "Pockels effect." The principal practical interest lies in the possibility of using this effect to produce a light-intensity modulator or "valve" by using an electroded liquid cell or crystal plate between polarizers in such a way as to produce electrically variable phase changes between two polarized interfering light beams.

In a crystal of low symmetry the optical dielectric property (the square of the

TABLE 6i-1. VERDET CONSTANTS* (*Continued*)
Solids at Room Temperature Except as Noted

Solid	n5,461	V5,461	γ5,461	n5,893	V5,893	γ5,893	Ref.
Oxide glasses:							
SiO_2	1.4601	0.01664	0.781	1.4585	0.01421	0.781	3*b*
Dense flint 18	1.8999	0.1180	0.78	1.8900	0.0969	0.78	3*b*
Dense flint 22	....	....	.....	1.920	0.1060	0.812	4
Oxide crystals:							
$NH_4Al(SO_4)_2{\cdot}12H_2O$	....	0.0151	0.552	1.4594	0.0128	0.543	3*c*
$KAl(SO_4)_2{\cdot}12H_2O$	....	0.0144	0.551	1.4564	0.0124	0.533	3*c*
$NH_4Fe(SO_4)_2{\cdot}12$ H_2O at 26°C	....	−0.00145		1.4848	−0.00058	.....	1
Same at −111°C	....	−0.0145	.....	....	−0.0111	.....	1
$NiSO_4{\cdot}6H_2O$ at 24°C	....	0.0256	.....	ω = 1.5109	0.0221	.....	5
Same at 1.36°K	....	0.419					2
$MgAl_2O_4$ (spinel)	....	....	.....	1.1718	0.021	.....	7
$CaCO_3$ (calcite)	....	....	.....	ω = 1.6585	0.019	.....	8
$NaClO_3$	....	0.0105	0.315	1.5151	0.0081	0.310	3*c*
SiO_2 (quartz)	ω = 1.5462	0.01952	0.785	1.5443	0.01664	0.789	3*b*
Al_2O_3 (corundum)	ω = 1.7712	0.0240	0.656	1.7685	0.0210	0.640	3*d*
Cubic halide crystals:							
NaCl	....	0.0410	0.901	1.5443	0.0345	0.890	3*c*
NaBr	....	0.0621	0.86	1.6412	....	.....	3*c*
KCl	....	0.0328	0.822	1.4904	0.0275	0.821	3*c*
KBr	1.5641	0.0500	0.795	1.5600	0.0425	0.785	3*c*
KI	1.6731	0.083	0.789	1.6664	0.070	0.782	3*c*
NH_4Cl	....	0.0430	0.727	1.6426	0.0362	0.719	3*c*
NH_4Br	....	0.0601	0.698	1.7108	0.0504	0.690	3*c*
CaF_2	....	....	.....	1.4338	0.00883	0.66	3*a*
Tetrahedral cubic crystals:							
C-C diamond	....	0.0278	0.28	2.4172	0.0233	0.28	3*a*
CuCl	....	0.20 ± .03	0.5	1.793	....	.....	6
ZnS	....	0.287	0.92	2.3683	0.226	0.91	3*a*

References

1. Kaufmann, H.: *Ann. Physik* **18**, 251 (1933). (Paramagnetic rotation.)
2. Levy and van den Handel: *Physica* **15**, 717 (1951). (Paramagnetic rotation.)
3. Ramaseshan, S.: *Proc. Indian Acad. Sci.* (*a*) **24**, 104 (1946); (*b*) **24**, 426 (1946); (*c*) **28**, 360 (1948); (*d*) **34**, 97 (1951); (*e*) *Current Science* **20**, 150 (1951).
4. Cole, H.: *J. Soc. Glass Technol.* **34**, 220 (1950).
5. O'Connor, Beck, and Underwood: *Phys. Rev.* **60**, 443 (1941).
6. Gassmann, G.: *Ann. Physik* **35**, 638 (1939). A volume of 23.9 cm^3/mole is assumed to derive this value of V.
7. DuBois: *Ann. Physik* **51**, 537 (1894).
8. Chauvin: *J. phys.* **9**, 5 (1890).

TABLE 6i-2. MAGNETIC ROTATORY POWER OF FILMS OF FERROMAGNETIC METALS MAGNETIZED TO SATURATION*

Metal	λ	α_∞/l, deg cm^{-1}
Ni	red	+89,000° ± 10%
Co	red	198,000 10%
Fe	red	209,000 10%
Fe[a]	578	382,500 ± 2%

* From W. Schutz, Wien-Harms Handbuch d. Experimental-physik 16, Part 1 (1936) 198, except as noted.

[a] H. König, *Naturwiss.* **33**, 71 (1946); *Optik* **3**, 101 (1948).

index of refraction) varies with the direction of vibration of the light wave and must be described by a symmetric second-rank tensor with six independent components. These six components can change with an applied electric field. There are a number of equivalent ways of introducing the electro-optic constants, but the most commonly accepted custom is to define the third-rank electro-optic tensor r_{ij} which relates the change in the *reciprocal* dielectric tensor to the applied field (a vector).

$$\Delta\left(\frac{1}{n^2}\right)_i = \left(\frac{1}{n^2}\right)_i - \left(\frac{1}{n_0{}^2}\right)_i = \sum_{j=1}^{3} r_{ij}E_j$$

where $i = 1, 2, 3, 4, 5, 6$
$j = 1, 2, 3$
0 = without field

This formulation is convenient because the index ellipsoid

$$\left(\frac{1}{n^2}\right)_1 x^2 + \left(\frac{1}{n^2}\right)_2 y^2 + \left(\frac{1}{n^2}\right)_3 z^2 + \left(\frac{1}{n^2}\right)_4 yz + \left(\frac{1}{n^2}\right)_5 zx + \left(\frac{1}{n^2}\right)_6 xy = 1$$

is commonly used in classical crystal optics to depict the optical behavior of a crystal.

The above formulation is only the linear term in an expansion in powers of the electric field. In the general case there are 18 linear electro-optic constants, but in a crystal of high symmetry many of these are not independent or may vanish. In a medium possessing a center of symmetry (thus many crystals and all liquids) all the linear terms and electro-optic constants must vanish. Twenty-one of the 32 crystal symmetry classes do not contain centers of symmetry, and of these, 20 may exhibit the linear Pockels effect. These are the same 20 classes which exhibit linear piezoelectricity, for the electro-optic tensor is of the same type as the piezoelectric tensor.

Some measured values of crystalline electro-optic constants are listed in the following table. The values given are for the crystal at constant stress. Because of the interaction of the piezoelectric and photoelastic effects, a different result is obtained if the crystal is clamped in a condition of constant strain.

The last column lists the potential difference in kilovolts required to develop a half wave of birefringent retardation in λ5,461 light.

TABLE 6i-3. POCKELS EFFECT

Measured electro-optic constants units of $10^{-8} \times$ (statvolts/cm)$^{-1}$

$$\Delta \left(\frac{1}{n^2}\right)_i = \sum_{j=1}^{3} r_{ij} E_j$$

Crystal	Symmetry class	Electro-optic coefficients	Half-wave voltage, kv at 5,461
Quartz[a,b]	D_3	$r_{41} = 1.4$; $r_{11} = 0.59$	
Rochelle salt[a]	D_2	$r_{41} = -6.0$; $r_{52} = -5.1$; $r_{63} = +0.95$	
Tourmaline[a]	C_{3v}	$r_{22} = 0.9$	
Sodium chlorate[a]	T	$r_{41} = 1.19$	200
Zinc sulfide[c,d]	T_d	$r_{41} = 5.0$	12.4
Zinc sulfide[g]	T_d	$r_{41} = 6.4$	9.3
Cuprous chloride[d]	T_d	$r_{41} = 18.4$	6.2
$NH_4H_2PO_4$[e]	V_d	$r_{63} = -25$; $r_{41} = 62$	9.6
KH_2PO_4[f]	V_d	$r_{63} = -32$; $r_{41} = 26$	7.5
KD_2PO_4[f]	V_d	$r_{63} = -70$	3.4
KH_2AsO_4	V_d	$r_{63} = -39$	6.2
RbH_2PO_4[f]	V_d	$r_{63} = -33$	7.3
$NH_4H_2AsO_4$[f]	V_d	$r_{63} = -19$	13

[a] F. Pockels, *Abhandl. Ges Wiss. Göttingen, Math. Physik. Kl.* **39**, 1 (1893).
[b] N. Gunther, *Ann. phys.* **13**, 783 (1932).
[c] C. Schramm, *Ann. phys.* **25**, 309 (1936).
[d] C. D. West, *J. Opt. Soc. Am.* **43**, 335 (1953).
[e] R. O'B. Carpenter, *J. Opt. Soc. Am.* **40**, 225 (1950).
[f] H. Jaffe, Brush Electronics Co., privately communicated.
[g] Kara, Mathieu, and Poulet, *J. phys. radium* **15**, 60–61 (1954).

6j. Specific Rotation

Table 6j-1. Specific Rotation*

Solids

Substance	Wave-length, μ	Rota-tion, deg/min	Substance	Wave-length, μ	Rota-tion, deg/min
Cinnabar (HgS)........	*D*	+32.5	Quartz...........	0.3726	+58.894
Lead hyposulfate.......	*D*	5.5		0.3609	63.628
Potassium hyposulfate..	*D*	8.4		0.3582	64.459
Quartz................	3.676	0.34		0.3466	69.454
	1.342	3.89		0.3441	70.587
	0.7604	12.668		0.3402	72.448
	0.7184	14.304		0.3360	74.571
	0.6867	15.746		0.3286	78.579
	0.6562	17.318		0.3247	80.459
	0.5895932	21.7010		0.3180	84.972
	0.5895	21.684		0.2747	121.052
	0.5892617	21.729		0.2571	143.266
	0.5889965	21.7492		0.2313	190.426
	0.5889	21.727		0.2265	201.824
	0.5460741	25.538		0.2194	220.731
	0.5269	27.543		0.21740	229.96
	0.4861	32.773		0.2143	235.972
	0.4307	42.604		0.1750	453.5
	0.4101	47.481		0.1525	776.0
	0.3968	51.193	Sodium bromate..	*D*	2.8
	0.3933	52.155	Sodium chlorate..	*D*	3.13
	0.3820	55.625			

Specific rotation or rotatory power is given in degrees per decimeter for liquids and solutions and in degrees per millimeter for solids; + signifies right-handed rotation, − left. Specific rotation varies with the wavelength of light used, with temperature and, in the case of solutions, with the concentration. When sodium light is used, indicated by *D* in the wavelength column, a value of $\lambda = 0.5893$ may be assumed.

Optical rotatory power for a large number of organic compounds will be found in the "International Critical Tables," vol. VII; for sugars, vol. II.

*Most of the data taken from "Handbook of Chemistry and Physics." 36th ed., pp. 2752, 2753, 2754, Cnemical Rubber Publishing Company, 1954–1955.

TABLE 6j-1. SPECIFIC ROTATION (*Continued*)
Liquid

Liquid	Temp., °C	Wave-length, μ	Specific rotation, deg/dm
Amyl alcohol	......	*D*	− 5.7
Camphor	204	*D*	+ 70.33
Cedar oil	15	*D*	− 30 to −40
Citron oil	15	*D*	+ 62
Ethyl malate $(C_2H_5)_2C_4H_4O_5$	11	*D*	− 10.3 to −12.4
Menthol	35.2	*D*	−49.7
Nicotine $C_{10}H_{14}N_2$	10–30	*D*	−162
	20	0.6563	−126
	20	0.5351	−207.5
	20	0.4861	−253.5
Turpentine $C_{10}H_6$	20	*D*	− 37
	20	0.6563	− 29.5
	20	0.5351	− 45
	20	0.4861	− 54.5

Specific rotation or rotatory power is given in degrees per decimeter for liquids and solutions and in degrees per millimeter for solids; + signifies right-handed rotation, − left. Specific rotation varies with the wavelength of light used, with temperature and, in the case of solutions, with the concentration. When sodium light is used, indicated by *D* in the wavelength column, a value of λ = 0.5893 may be assumed.

Optical rotatory power for a large number of organic compounds will be found in the "International Critical Tables," vol. VII; for sugars, vol. II.

* Most of the data taken from "Handbook of Chemistry and Physics," 36th ed., pp. 2752, 2753, 2754, Chemical Rubber Publishing Company, 1954–1955.

TABLE 6j-1. SPECIFIC ROTATION (*Continued*)

Solutions†

Substance	Solvent	Temp., °C	Wave-length, μ	Specific rotation, deg/dm	Correction for concentration or temp.
Albumen	Water	...	*D*	− 25 to −38	
Arabinose	Water	20	*D*	− 105.0	
Camphor	Alcohol	20	*D*	+ 54.4 − 0.135*d* for *d* = 45–91	
	Benzene	20	*D*	+ 56 − 0.166*d* for *d* = 47–90	
	Ether	...	*D*	+ 57	
Dextrose *d*-glucose $C_6H_{12}O_6$	Water	20	*D*	+ 52.5 + 0.025*d* for *d* = 1–18	
			0.5461	+ 62.03 + 0.04257*c* for *c* = 6–32	
Galactose	Water	...	*D*	+ 83.9 + 0.078*d* − 0.21*t* for *d* = 4–36 and *t* = 10–30°C	
l-Glucose (β)	Water	20	*D*	− 51.4	
Invert sugar $C_6H_{12}O_6$	Water	20	*D*	− 19.7 − 0.036*c* for *c* = 9–35 $\alpha_t = \alpha_{20} + 0.304(t - 20) + 0.00165 (t - 20)^2$ for *t* = 3–30°C	
		25	0.5461	− 21.5	
Lactose	Water	20	*D*	+ 52.4 + 0.072 (20° − *t*) for *c* = 5	
			0.5461	+ 61.9 + 0.085 (20° − *t*) for *c* = 5	
Levulose fruit sugar	Water	25	*D*	− 88.5 − 0.145*d* for *d* = 2.6–18.6	
		25	0.5461	− 105.30	
Maltose	Water	20	*D*	+ 138.48 − 0.01837*d* for *d* = 5–35	
		25	0.5461	+ 153.75	
Mannose	Water	20	*D*	+ 14.1	*c* = 10.2
Nicotine	Water	20	*D*	− 77 for *d* = 1–16	
	Benzene	20	*D*	− 164 for *d* = 8–100	
Potassium tartrate	Water	20	*D*	+ 27.14 + 0.0992*c* − 0.00094c^2 for *c* = 8–50	
Quinine sulfate	Water	17	*D*	− 214	
Santonin	Alcohol	20	*D*	− 161.0	*c* = 1.78
		20	*D*	+ 693	*c* = 4.05
	Chloroform	20	*D*	− 202.7 + 0.309*d* for *d* = 75–96.5	
	Alcohol	20	0.6867	+ 442	*c* = 4.05
			0.5269	+ 991	*c* = 4.05
			0.4861	+1,323	*c* = 4.05

† Corrections for values of the specific rotation for concentration are given in the last column. *c* indicates concentration in grams per 100 ml of solution; *d* indicates the concentration in grams per 100 g of solution.

Table 6j-1. Specific Rotation (*Continued*)
Solutions†

Substance	Solvent	Temp., °C	Wave-length, μ	Specific rotation, deg/dm	Correction for concentration or temp.
Sodium potassium tartrate (rochelle salt)	Water	20	*D*	+	29.75 − 0.0078*c*
Sucrose (cane sugar) $C_{12}H_{22}O_{11}$	Water	20	*D*	+	66.412 + 0.01267*d* − 0.000376d^2 for *d* = 0–50
					$\alpha_t = \alpha_{20}[1 - 0.00037(t - 20)]$ for *t* = 14–30°C

Table 6j-1. Specific Rotation (*Continued*)
Solutions†

Sucrose dissolved in water, 20°C

μ	Spec. rot.	μ	Spec. rot.	μ	Spec. rot.
670.8 (Li)	+50.51	510.6 (Cu)	+90.46	435.3 (Fe)	+128.5
643.8 (Cd)	55.04	508.6 (Cd)	91.16	433.7 (Fe)	129.8
636.2 (Zn)	56.51	481.1 (Zn)	103.07	431.5 (Fe)	130.7
589.3 (Na)	66.45	480.0 (Cd)	103.62	428.2 (Fe)	133.6
578.2 (Cu)	69.10	472.2 (Zn)	107.38	427.2 (Fe)	134.2
578.0 (Hg)	69.22	468.0 (Zn)	109.49	426.1 (Fe)	134.9
570.0 (Cu)	71.24	467.8 (Cd)	109.69	419.1 (Fe)	140.0
546.1 (Hg)	78.16	438.4 (Fe)	126.5	414.4 (Fe)	144.2
521.8 (Cu)	86.21	437.6 (Fe)	127.2	388.9 (Fe)	166.7
515.3 (Cu)	88.68	435.8 (Hg)	128.49	383.3 (Fe)	171.8
				382.6 (Fe)	173.1

Solutions†

Substance	Solvent	°C	μ	Spec. rot.	Correction
Tartaric acid (ord.).....	Water	20	*D*	+15.06 − 0.131*c*	
		20	0.6563	7.75	for *d* = 41
		20	*D*	8.86	for *d* = 41
		20	0.5351	9.65	for *d* = 41
		20	0.4861	9.37	for *d* = 41
Turpentine............	Alcohol	20	*D*	−37 − 0.00482*d* − 0.00013d^2 for *d* = 0–90	
	Benzene	20	*D*	−37 − 0.0265*d* for *d* = 0–91	
Xylose................	Water	20	*D*	+19.13	*d* = 2.7

† Corrections for values of the specific rotation for concentration are given in the last column. *c* indicates concentration in grams per 100 ml of solution; *d* indicates the concentration in grams per 100 g of solution.

6k. Optical Constants of Metals

GEORGE HASS

Engineer Research and Development Laboratories

Several constants have been used to describe the optical behavior of metals. In principle, at any wavelength, two such constants should be sufficient to give the complete behavior of the metal. One constant has to do with the velocity of light in the metal and the other with the absorption of light by the metal.

To determine these constants, it is necessary, in general, to make experimental measurements of the metal properties at the frequency required. The measurements cannot be made at direct current and extrapolated to light frequencies of the order of 10^{14} cps.

The constants tabulated in Tables 6k-1 to 6k-3 are the ones most commonly used. These are n = refractive index and k = absorption constant. The refractive index is defined as the ratio of the velocity of light in a vacuum to the velocity in the metal. This is the phase velocity, which in metals is frequently greater than c, the velocity of light in a vacuum. This is not a violation of the Einstein relativity law.

The absorption constant is defined by the equation

$$E = E_0 e^{-\frac{2\pi k t}{\lambda_0}}$$

where E_0 = amplitude of an electric wave measured at a point in an absorbing medium

E = amplitude measured at a distance t in the direction of propagation away from the first point

Both n and k can also be defined as the real and imaginary part of a complex index of refraction

$$N = n - ik$$

A variety of other constants have been used in treating metals and absorbing materials. First is the extinction coefficient κ which is equal to the absorption constant divided by the index of refraction. Second is the absorption coefficient α which is defined by the equation

$$I = I_0 e^{-\alpha t}$$

where I is the intensity of an electromagnetic disturbance and t is the distance traveled in the material.

When light is reflected from a metal surface, it experiences a phase-shift change which is a function of the angle of incidence of the light and its state of polarization. In connection with this phase shift, two other constants are commonly used to describe the optical behavior of a metal. These are the angle of principal incidence $\bar{\phi}$ and the principal azimuth $\bar{\psi}$.

At the angle of principal incidence there is a phase change of 90 deg between the components of polarized light vibrating in the plane of incidence and at right angles to the plane of incidence. Light vibrating in the principal azimuth reflected at the angle of principal incidence becomes circularly polarized.

These last two constants are tabulated particularly because these are the numbers which are measured directly in most of the techniques for determining the optical behavior of metals. Also, these numbers are used in some of the techniques for determining the thickness of dielectric films deposited on metal surfaces.

The index of refraction and the absorption constant are related to $\bar{\psi}$ and $\bar{\phi}$ by the equation

$$n = \frac{\sin \bar{\phi} \tan \bar{\phi}}{\left(1 + \frac{k}{n}\right)^2} \left(1 + \frac{1}{2} \cot^2 \bar{\phi}\right)$$

$$\frac{k}{n} = \tan 2\bar{\psi}(1 - \cot^2 \bar{\phi})$$

Since reflection methods are used in determining the constants, they are strongly dependent on the characteristics on the metallic surface. These characteristics vary considerably with the chemical and mechanical treatment. Accordingly, there has always been a certain degree of controversy on the subject of the optical constants of metals. Since the oldest measurements were made, there has been considerable development in the preparation of metallic surfaces by evaporation in a vacuum. They are frequently quite different from surfaces of bulk metals prepared by polishing. By no means all the metallic constants have been determined on such freshly prepared surfaces.

A great deal of work remains to be done in this area. The following tables include both old and new data. In a few places there is conflict. Rather than replace the old figures, it seemed appropriate to include all of them. It is recommended in conflicting cases that the new data be used.

Table 6k-1. Optical Constants of the Most Important Evaporated Mirror Coatings

Metal	λ, μ	n	k	R% computed	Ref.
Aluminum......	400	0.40	3.92	....	1
	435	0.40	4.16	91.6	2
	491	0.57	5.19	92.3	2
	546	0.76	5.49	90.8	2
	578	0.89	5.68	90.0	2
	644	1.12	6.26	89.6	2
	700	1.55	7.00	....	1
	750	1.80	7.12	....	1
	800	1.99	7.05	....	1
	850	2.08	7.15	....	1
	900	1.96	7.70	....	1
	950	1.75	8.50	....	1
Copper..........	450	0.87	2.20	....	1
	500	0.88	2.42	....	1
	550	0.756	2.462	66.7	3
	600	0.186	2.980	92.7	3
	650	0.142	3.570	95.9	3
	700	0.150	4.049	96.6	3
	750	0.157	4.463	96.9	3
	800	0.170	4.840	97.2	3
	850	0.182	5.222	97.3	3
	900	0.190	5.569	97.7	3
	950	0.197	5.900	97.8	3
	1,000	0.197	6.272	98.0	3
Gold.............	450	1.40	1.88	....	1
	500	0.84	1.84	....	1
	550	0.331	2.324	81.6	3
	600	0.200	2.897	91.9	3
	650	0.142	3.374	95.5	3
	700	0.131	3.842	96.7	3
	750	0.140	4.266	97.1	3
	800	0.149	4.654	97.4	3
	850	0.157	4.993	97.6	3
	900	0.166	5.335	97.8	3
	950	0.174	5.691	97.9	3
	1,000	0.179	6.044	98.1	3
Rhodium........	546	1.62	4.63	77.2	2
Silver...........	400	0.075	1.93	....	1
	450	0.055	2.42	....	1
	500	0.071	3.020	97.3	3
	550	0.069	3.429	97.9	3
	600	0.072	3.348	98.2	3
	650	0.080	4.257	98.4	3
	700	0.093	4.645	98.4	3
	750	0.103	5.005	98.4	3
	800	0.110	5.409	98.6	3
	850	0.121	5.757	98.6	3
	900	0.128	6.089	98.7	3
	950	0.130	6.476	98.8	3
	1,000	0.129	6.829	98.9	3

The true optical constants of metals can be determined only with compact evaporated films produced by fast evaporation under good vacuum conditions.

References

1. Schulz, L. G.: *J. Opt. Soc. Am.* **44,** 357 (1954). Schulz, L. G., and F. R. Tangherlini: *J. Opt. Soc. Am.* **44,** 362 (1954).
2. Hass, G.: *Optik* **1,** 2 (1946).
3. Weiss, K.: *Z. Naturforsch.* **3a,** 143 (1948).

TABLE 6k-2. OPTICAL CONSTANTS OF METALS

Metals	λ, μ	Φ		Ψ		Computed				Authority
		degrees	minutes	degrees	minutes	n	k/n	k	R	
Aluminum	0.589	...	...	...	...	1.44	.....	5.32	83	Drude
Antimony	0.589	...	...	...	...	3.04	.....	4.94	70	Drude
Bismuth (prism)	White	...	...	...	...	2.26	.....	.....	....	Kundt, 1889
Bronze	0.527	...	...	...	...	1.18	.....	.....	....	Jamin
	0.589	...	...	...	...	1.12	.....	.....	....	Jamin
Cadmium	0.589	...	...	...	...	1.13	.....	5.01	85	Drude
Chromium	0.579	...	...	...	...	2.97	.....	4.85	70	Wartenburg, 1910
Cobalt	0.231	64	31	29	39	1.10	1.30	1.43	32	Minor
	0.275	70	22	29	59	1.41	1.52	2.14	46	Minor
	0.500	77	5	31	53	1.93	1.93	3.72	66	Minor
	0.650	79	0	31	25	2.35	1.87	4.40	69	Ingersoll
	1.00	81	45	29	6	3.63	1.58	5.73	73	Ingersoll
	1.50	83	21	26	18	5.22	1.29	6.73	75	Ingersoll
	2.25	83	48	26	5	5.65	1.27	7.18	76	Ingersoll
Columbium	0.579	...	...	...	...	1.80	.....	2.11	41	Wartenburg, 1910
Copper	0.231	65	57	26	14	1.39	1.05	1.45	29	Minor
	0.347	65	6	28	16	1.19	1.23	1.47	32	Minor
	0.500	70	44	33	46	1.10	2.13	2.34	56	Minor
	0.650	74	16	41	30	0.44	7.4	3.26	86	Ingersoll
	0.870	78	40	42	30	0.35	11.0	3.85	91	Ingersoll
	1.75	84	4	42	30	0.83	11.4	9.46	96	Ingersoll
	2.25	85	13	42	30	1.03	11.4	11.7	97	Ingersoll
	4.00	87	20	42	30	1.87	11.4	21.3	....	Forst-Freed
	5.50	88	00	41	50	3.16	9.0	28.4	....	Forst-Freed
Gold	0.257	...	...	...	...	0.92	.....	1.14	28	Meier, 1903
Electrolytic	0.441	...	...	...	...	1.18	.....	1.85	42	Meier, 1903
	0.589	...	...	...	...	0.47	.....	2.83	82	Meier, 1903
	1.00	81	45	44	00	0.24	28.0	6.7	....	Forst-Freed
	2.00	85	30	43	56	0.47	26.7	12.5	....	Forst-Freed
	3.00	87	05	43	50	0.80	24.5	19.6	....	Forst-Freed
	5.00	88	15	43	25	1.81	18.1	33	....	Forst-Freed
Iodine	0.589	...	...	...	...	3.34	.....	0.57	30	Meier, 1903
Iridium	0.579	...	...	...	...	2.13	.....	4.87	75	Wartenburg, 1916
	1.00	82	10	29	15	3.85	1.60	6.2	....	Forst-Freed
	2.00	83	10	29	40	4.30	1.66	7.1	....	Forst-Freed
	3.00	81	40	30	40	3.33	1.79	6.0	....	Forst-Freed
	5.00	79	00	32	20	2.27	2.03	4.6	....	Forst-Freed
Iron	0.257	...	...	...	...	1.01	0.88	.....	16	Meier, 1903
	0.441	...	...	...	...	1.28	1.37	.....	28	Meier, 1903
	0.589	...	...	...	...	1.51	1.63	.....	33	Meier, 1903
Lead	0.589	...	...	...	...	2.01	.....	3.48	62	Drude
Magnesium	0.589	...	...	...	...	0.37	.....	4.42	93	Drude
Manganese	0.579	...	...	...	...	2.49	.....	3.89	64	Wartenburg, 1910
Mercury (liq.)	0.326	...	...	...	...	0.68	.....	2.26	66	Meier, 1903
	0.441	...	...	...	...	1.01	.....	3.42	74	Meier, 1903
	0.589	...	...	...	...	1.62	.....	4.41	75	Meier, 1903
	0.668	...	...	...	...	1.72	.....	4.70	77	Meier, 1903
Nickel	0.420	72	20	31	42	1.41	1.79	2.53	54	Tool
	0.589	76	1	31	41	1.79	1.86	3.33	62	Drude
	0.750	78	45	32	6	2.19	1.99	4.36	70	Ingersoll
	1.00	80	33	32	2	2.63	2.00	5.26	74	Ingersoll
	2.25	84	21	33	30	3.95	2.33	9.20	85	Ingersoll
	0.275	...	...	...	...	1.09	1.16	.....	24	Meier, 1903
	0.441	...	...	...	...	1.16	1.23	.....	25	Meier, 1903
	0.589	...	...	...	...	1.30	1.97	.....	43	Meier, 1903
Platinum	1.00	75	30	37	00	1.14	3.25	3.7	....	Forst-Freed
	2.00	74	30	39	50	0.70	5.06	3.5	....	Forst-Freed
	3.00	73	50	41	00	0.52	6.52	3.4	....	Forst-Freed
	5.00	72	00	42	10	0.34	9.01	3.1	....	Forst-Freed
Electrolytic	0.257	...	...	...	...	1.17	1.65	.....	37	Meier, 1903
	0.441	...	...	...	...	1.84	.....	3.16	58	Meier, 1903
	0.589	...	...	...	...	2.63	.....	3.54	59	Meier, 1903
	0.668	...	...	...	...	2.91	.....	3.66	59	Meier, 1903

TABLE 6k-2. OPTICAL CONSTANTS OF METALS (*Continued*)

Metals	λ, μ	Φ		Ψ		Computed				Authority
		degrees	minutes	degrees	minutes	*n*	*k/n*	*k*	*R*	
Potassium	0.665	65	27	43	56	0.066	26.8	....	93.8	Duncan, 1913
	0.589	62	58	43	42	0.068	22.1	....	92	Duncan, 1913
	0.472	57	9	43	0	0.070	14.3	....	86.9	Duncan, 1913
	0.546	...	...	...	...	1.09	1.16	....	24	Morgan, 1922
Rhodium	0.579	...	...	...	...	1.54	......	4.67	78	Wartenburg, 1910
Selenium	0.400	...	...	...	...	2.94	2.31	....	44	Wood
	0.490	...	...	...	...	3.12	1.49	....	35	Wood
	0.589	...	...	...	...	2.93	0.45	....	25	Wood
	0.760	...	...	...	...	2.60	0.06	....	20	Wood
Silicon, 95 %	Pure									
	0.579	75	38	...	...	3.87	0.116	....	35.7	Wartenburg, 1910
	0.589	...	...	...	...	4.18	0.09	....	38	Ingersoll
	1.25	...	...	...	...	3.67	0.08	....	33	Ingersoll
	2.25	...	...	...	...	3.53	0.08	....	31	Ingersoll
99.75 % pure	0.589	76	45	...	...	4.24	0.118	....	37.8	Littleton, 1912
Silver	0.226	62	41	22	16	1.41	0.75	1.11	18	Minor
	0.293	63	14	18	56	1.57	0.62	0.97	17	Minor
	0.316	52	28	15	38	1.13	0.38	0.43	4	Minor
	0.332	52	1	37	2	0.41	1.61	0.65	32	Minor
	0.395	66	36	43	6	0.16	12.32	1.91	87	Minor
	0.500	72	31	43	29	0.17	17.1	2.94	93	Minor
	0.589	75	35	43	47	0.18	20.6	3.64	95	Minor
	0.750	79	26	44	6	0.17	30.7	5.16	97	Ingersoll
	1.00	82	0	44	2	0.24	29.0	6.96	98	Ingersoll
	1.50	84	42	43	48	0.45	23.7	10.7	98	Ingersoll
	2.25	86	18	43	34	0.77	19.9	15.4	99	Ingersoll
	3.00	87	10	42	40	1.65	12.2	20.1	...	Forst-Freed
	4.50	88	20	41	10	4.49	7.42	33.3	....	Forst-Freed
Sodium	0.665	72	11	44	29	0.051	55.0	....	97.7	Duncan, 1913
	0.589	68	51	44	29	0.044	55.0	....	97.1	Duncan, 1913
	0.546	68	48	44	20	0.052	42.6	....	96.5	Duncan, 1913
	0.472	66	29	44	9	0.057	33.3	....	95.2	Duncan, 1913
	0.435	66	0	44	6	0.058	31.7	....	94.8	Duncan, 1913
(liq.)	0.589	...	...	...	...	0.004	.....	2.61	99	Drude
(solid)	0.546	...	...	...	...	0.047	47.3	....	96.9	Morgan, 1922
Sodium-potassium:										
17.3 % K	0.546	...	...	...	...	0.081	27.2	....	94.6	Morgan, 1922
45.0 % K	0.546	...	...	...	...	1.08	16.8	....	90.4	Morgan, 1922
66.0 % K	0.546	...	...	...	...	0.137	12.5	....	87.0	Morgan, 1922
74.2 % K	0.546	...	...	...	...	0.124	12.8	....	86.9	Morgan, 1922
84.3 % K	0.546	...	...	...	...	0.088	17.6	....	90.2	Morgan, 1922
Steel:										
0.44 % C	0.589	77	15	...	...	2.50	1.30	....	57.4	Littleton, 1912
1.28 % C	0.589	77	22	...	...	2.66	1.28	....	57.5	Littleton, 1912
3.5 % C	0.589	77	35	...	...	2.77	1.23	....	57.0	Littleton, 1912
	0.226	66	51	28	17	1.30	1.26	1.64	35	Minor
	0.257	68	35	28	45	1.38	1.35	1.86	40	Minor
	0.325	69	57	30	9	1.37	1.53	2.09	45	Minor
	0.500	75	47	29	2	2.09	1.50	3.14	57	Minor
	0.650	77	48	27	9	2.70	1.33	3.59	59	Ingersoll
	1.50	81	48	28	51	3.71	1.55	5.75	73	Ingersoll
	2.25	83	22	30	36	4.14	1.79	7.41	80	Ingersoll
Tantalum	0.579	...	...	...	...	2.05	.....	2.31	44	Wartenburg
Tellurium:										
axis horizontal	1.590	...	...	...	...	3.07	0.563	....	34	Van Dyke, 1922
axis vertical	0.590	...	...	...	...	2.68	0.632	....	30	Van Dyke, 1922
Tin	0.589	...	...	...	...	1.48	.....	5.25	82	Drude
Tungsten	0.579	76	0	...	...	2.76	0.98	....	48.6	Wartenburg
	0.589	78	31	...	...	3.46	0.94	....	54.5	Littleton, 1912
Vanadium	0.579	...	...	...	...	3.03	.....	3.51	58	Littleton, 1912
Zinc	0.257	...	...	...	...	0.55	.....	0.61	20	Meier, 1903
	0.441	...	...	...	...	0.93	.....	3.19	73	Meier, 1903
	0.589	...	...	...	...	1.93	.....	4.66	74	Meier, 1903
	0.668	...	...	...	...	2.62	.....	5.08	73	Meier, 1903

TABLE 6k-3. OPTICAL CONSTANTS OF CERTAIN OTHER METALS DETERMINED IN A VACUUM*

Metal	λ	$\bar{\phi}$	$2\bar{\psi}$	n	k/n	k	R
Beryllium........	5,780	74.5	42.2	2.64	0.86	2.27	43
	5,461	74.5	42.4	2.66	0.89	2.36	44
	4,916	74.4	43.1	2.64	0.85	2.25	42
	4,358	74.1	43.4	2.56	0.87	2.23	42
	4,046	73.8	44.1	2.48	0.89	2.20	42
Magnesium......	5,780	75.9	83.1	0.48	7.74	3.71	88
	5,461	75.3	81.6	0.57	6.14	3.47	85
	4,916	73.0	80.5	0.53	5.41	2.92	81
	4,358	71.6	80.1	0.52	5.09	2.65	76
	4,046	71.2	79.8	0.52	4.94	2.05	68
Calcium..........	5,780	69.4	83.7	0.29	7.94	2.31	83
	5,461	68.5	84.0	0.27	8.08	2.16	83
	4,916	66.9	83.1	0.29	6.64	1.92	78
	4,358	64.3	82.0	0.29	5.60	1.64	73
	4,046	63.6	80.6	0.34	4.53	1.56	68
Strontium........	5,780	68.6	76.3	0.61	3.50	2.13	66
	5,461	67.7	75.2	0.63	3.15	1.99	60
	4,916	64.5	74.4	0.58	2.78	1.61	55
	4,358	63.5	73.9	0.57	2.61	1.50	51
	4,046	61.1	73.0	0.55	2.32	1.28	46
Barium..........	5,780	64.5	65.7	0.88	1.73	1.52	40
	5,461	64.4	65.4	0.89	1.71	1.51	40
	4,916	61.9	63.7	0.86	1.48	1.26	32
	4,358	59.7	64.2	0.78	1.42	1.10	28
	4,046	59.1	63.4	0.82	1.23	1.07	26
Germanium.....	5,780	75.5	21.6	3.42	0.39	1.35	36
	5,461	75.2	23.4	3.47	0.40	1.40	37
	4,916	74.1	26.0	3.16	0.45	1.42	34
	4,358	73.8	31.8	2.93	0.57	1.67	34
	4,046	73.3	34.4	2.85	0.58	1.67	35
Lanthanum......	5,780	75.6	61.1	1.74	1.99	3.47	64
	5,461	75.7	60.8	1.79	1.91	3.43	63
	4,358	72.0	64.1	1.35	1.83	2.49	54
	4,046	71.5	64.4	1.34	1.74	2.33	51
Cerium..........	5,780	73.6	55.8	1.91	1.35	2.58	50
	5,461	72.4	56.7	1.74	1.38	2.39	47
	4,358	69.4	58.3	1.41	1.40	1.97	42
Manganese.......	5,780	76.4	51.3	2.59	1.18	3.04	53
	5,461	76.2	52.9	2.46	1.25	3.07	54
	4,358	74.1	53.8	2.08	1.26	2.62	50

* H. M. O'Bryan, *J. Opt. Soc. Am.* **26**, 122 (1936).

TABLE 6k-4. REFLECTANCE OF FRESHLY EVAPORATED FILMS OF ALUMINUM, SILVER, GOLD, COPPER, AND RHODIUM*
(From 0.22 to 10μ)

λ, μ	Al	Ag	Au	Cu	Rh
0.220	91.5	28.0	27.5	40.4	58.5
0.240	91.9	29.5	31.6	39.0	61.3
0.250	92.1	30.4	33.2	37.0	63.0
0.260	92.2	29.2	35.6	35.5	65.0
0.280	92.3	25.2	37.8	33.0	68.5
0.300	92.3	17.6	37.7	33.6	71.2
0.315	92.4	5.5	37.3	35.5	73.0
0.320	92.4	8.9	37.1	36.3	73.6
0.340	92.5	72.9	36.1	38.5	75.5
0.360	92.5	88.2	36.3	41.5	77.0
0.380	92.5	92.8	37.8	44.5	77.4
0.400	92.4	94.8	38.7	47.5	77.6
0.450	92.2	96.6	38.7	55.2	77.2
0.500	91.8	97.7	47.7	60.0	77.4
0.550	91.6	97.9	81.7	66.9	78.0
0.600	91.1	98.1	91.9	93.3	79.1
0.650	90.3	98.3	95.5	96.6	79.9
0.700	89.9	98.5	97.0	97.5	80.4
0.750	88.0	98.6	97.4	97.9	81.2
0.800	86.3	98.6	97.7	98.1	82.0
0.850	85.8	98.7	97.8	98.3	82.8
0.900	88.9	98.7	98.0	98.4	83.5
0.950	91.8	98.8	98.1	98.4	84.2
1.0	93.9	98.9	98.2	98.5	85.0
1.5	96.8	98.9	98.2	98.5	88.2
2.0	97.2	98.9	98.3	98.6	90.5
3.0	97.5	98.9	98.3	98.6	92.5
4.0	97.6	98.9	98.3	98.7	94.0
5.0	97.7	98.9	98.3	98.7	94.5
6.0	97.7	98.9	98.3	98.7	94.8
7.0	97.8	98.9	98.4	98.7	95.2
8.0	97.9	98.9	98.4	98.7	95.5
9.0	97.9	98.9	98.4	98.8	95.8
10.0	98.0	98.9	98.4	98.8	96.0

The reflectance of a good evaporated coating is always higher than that of a polished or electrolytically produced surface of the same material. One of the main conditions for preparing a high-quality reflection coating by evaporation in high vacuum is a high rate of deposition or fast evaporation of the metal.

* G. Hass, Engineer Research and Development Laboratories, Fort Belvoir.

Table 6k-5. Reflection of Light by Metals*

Wave-length	Anti-mony	Bronze (68 Cu, 32 Sn)	Copper, com-mercial	Gold, electro-lytic	Iron	Mag-nalium, Mach's	Mag-nesium	Mercury, backed glass
0.251	....	0.30	25.9	38.8	....	67.0		
0.288	....	....	24.3	34.0	....	70.6		
0.305	....	....	25.3	31.8	....	72.2		
0.326	....	....	24.9	28.6	....	75.5		
0.357	....	....	27.3	27.9	....	81.2		
0.385	....	0.53	28.6	27.1	....	83.9		
0.420	....	....	32.7	29.3	....	83.3		
0.450	....	....	37.0	33.1	....	83.4	....	72.8
0.500	....	0.63	43.7	47.0	0.55	83.3	0.72	70.9
0.550	....	....	47.7	74.0	....	82.7	....	71.2
0.600	0.53	0.64	71.8	84.4	0.57	83.0	0.73	69.9
0.650	....	....	80.0	88.9	....	82.7	....	71.5
0.700	....	....	83.1	92.3	0.59	83.3	....	72.8
0.800	....	....	88.6	94.9	....	84.3		
1.00	0.55	0.70	90.1	....	0.65	84.1	0.74	
2.0	0.60	0.80	95.5	96.8	0.78	86.7	0.77	
3.0	0.65	0.86	97.1	....	0.84	87.4	0.80	
4.0	0.68	0.88	97.3	96.9	0.89	88.7	0.83	
9.0	0.72	0.93	98.4	98.0	0.94	90.6	0.93	

Wave-length	Nickel, electro-lytic	Platinum, electro-lytic	Silver, chemi-cally de-posited	Silver-backed glass	Speculum metal	Steel	Tungsten
0.251	37.8	33.8	34.1	....	29.9	32.9	
0.288	42.7	38.8	21.2	....	37.7	35.0	
0.305	44.2	39.8	9.1	....	41.7	37.2	
0.326	45.2	41.4	14.6	....	....	40.3	
0.357	48.8	43.4	74.5	....	51.0	45.0	
0.385	49.6	45.4	81.4	....	53.1	47.8	
0.420	56.6	51.8	86.6	....	56.4	51.9	
0.450	59.4	54.7	90.5	85.7	60.0	54.4	
0.500	60.8	58.4	91.3	86.6	63.2	54.8	0.49
0.550	62.6	61.1	92.7	88.2	64.0	54.9	
0.600	64.9	64.2	92.6	88.1	64.3	55.4	0.51
0.650	66.6	66.5	94.7	89.1	65.4	56.4	
0.700	68.8	69.0	95.4	89.6	66.8	57.6	0.54
0.800	69.6	70.3	96.8	....	....	58.0	
1.00	72.0	72.9	97.0	....	70.5	63.1	0.62
2.0	83.5	80.6	97.8	....	80.4	76.7	0.85
3.0	88.7	88.8	98.1	....	86.2	83.0	0.90
4.0	91.1	91.5	98.5	....	88.5	87.8	0.93
9.0	95.6	95.4	98.7	....	92.2	92.9	0.95

The table gives the per cent of normally incident light which is reflected by the polished surface of various metals.

TABLE 6k-5. REFLECTION OF LIGHT BY METALS* (*Continued*)

Wavelength	Aluminum†	Cadmium†	Cobalt†	Graphite†	Iridium†	Molybdenum†	Palladium†	Rhodium†	Silicon†
0.5	...	...	...	22	...	46	...	76	34
0.6	...	...	...	24	...	48	...	77	32
0.8	...	...	...	25	...	52	...	81	29
1.0	71	72	67	27	78	58	72	84	28
2.0	82	87	72	35	87	82	81	91	28
4.0	92	96	81	48	94	90	88	92	28
7.0	96	98	93	54	95	93	94	94	28
10.0	98	98	97	59	96	94	97	95	28
12.0	98	99	97	...	96	95	97		

Wavelength	Tantalum	Tellurium	Tin	Vanadium	Zinc
0.5	38	...	...	57	...
0.6	45	49	...	58	...
0.8	64	48	...	60	...
1.0	78	50	54	61	80
2.0	90	52	61	69	92
4.0	93	57	72	79	97
7.0	94	68	81	88	98
10.0	...	...	84	...	98
12.0	95	...	85	...	99

Wavelength	Tungsten‡	Stellite‡
0.15	.....	0.32
0.20	.....	0.42
0.30	.....	0.50
0.50	0.50	0.64
0.75	0.52	0.67
1.00	0.576	0.689
2.00	0.900	0.747
3.00	0.943	0.792
4.00	0.948	0.825
5.00	0.953	0.848
9.00	.....	0.880

Wavelength, μ, 0.001 mm	Silver¶	Monel metal¶	Stellite¶	Zinc¶
0.45	88.0	56.5	63.5	54.0
0.50	90.0	57.8	65.8	55.0
0.55	91.5	59.0	68.3	56.0
0.60	92.7	60.2	70.1	57.5
0.65	93.5	61.8	71.0	60.0
0.70	94.1	63.7	71.8	61.0
0.75	94.7	65.6	72.4	61.5
0.80	95.1	67.2	73.0	61.5
0.90	96.0	70.0	73.5	55.5
0.95	96.3	71.1	...	51.0
1.00	96.5	72.3	74.0	49.0
1.05	96.7	73.0	...	53.5
1.10	96.9	73.6	...	62.5
1.20	97.2	74.8	74.5	74.7
1.40	97.4	77.0	75.0	85.8
1.50	97.6	78.2	75.3	88.4
1.75	97.8	81.2	76.0	92.0
2.00	97.9	83.8	76.8	94.0
2.50	98.0	87.0	78.6	95.3
3.00	98.0	88.7	80.0	95.5
3.50	98.0	89.5	81.4	95.8
4.00	98.0	91.0	82.8	96.2

* "Handbook of Chemistry and Physics," 36th ed., pp. 2684, 2685, 2686, Chemical Rubber Publishing Company, 1954–1955.

† Coblentz, 1906, 1911.

‡ Coblentz, Emerson, 1917.

¶ Coblentz, *Natl. Bur. Standards* (*U.S.*) *Bull.* 379 (1920).

6l. Fluorescence and Phosphorescence

TABLE 6l-1. SOME CHARACTERISTICS OF FLUORESCENT CHEMICALS*

Phosphor	Lamp color	Exciting range,† A	Sensitivity peak, A	Emitted range, A	Emitted peak, A
Calcium tungstate	Blue	2,200–3,000	2,720	3,100–7,000	4,400
Magnesium tungstate	Blue-white	2,200–3,200	2,850	3,600–7,200	4,800
Zinc silicate	Green	2,200–2,960	2,537	4,600–6,400	5,250
Calcium halophosphates	White	2,000–2,600	2,500	3,500–6,800	4,800, 5,800
Cadmium silicate	Yellow-pink	2,200–3,200	2,400	4,800–7,400	5,950
Cadmium borate	Pink	2,200–3,600	2,500	5,200–7,500	6,150
BL phosphor $BaSi_2O_5$ with Pb	Blue ultra	2,200–2,700	2,500	3,100–4,100	3,500
Calcium phosphate with Ce and Mn	Red	2,200–3,400	3,130	5,600–8,100 plus uv	6,500

* "Smithsonian Physical Tables," 1954, Table 96. Data furnished by H. C. Froelich, of Nela Park.
† 2,200 A was lower limit of measurements.

TABLE 6l-2. FLUORESCENCE OF ORGANIC SUBSTANCES IN SOLUTION*
(Excitation by white light)

Substance	Solvent	Wave-length, μ	Observer
Anthracene	Alcohol	0.400, 0.430, 0.436	Stark and Meyer, 1907
Eosine	Alcohol or water	0.589	Nichols and Merritt, 1907
Esculine	Alcohol	0.460	Nichols and Merritt, 1907
Fluorescein	Water (alkaline)	0.542	Nichols and Merritt, 1907
Naphthalin, red	Alcohol	0.632	Nichols and Merritt, 1907
Quinine sulfate	Water	0.437	Nichols and Merritt, 1907
Resorcin blue	Water	0.65	Nichols and Merritt, 1907
Rhodamin	Water	0.554	Nichols and Merritt, 1907

* "Handbook of Chemistry and Physics," 36th ed., p. 2736, Chemical Rubber Publishing Company, 1954–1955.

TABLE 6l-3. FLUORESCENCE OF GASES AND VAPORS*

Gas or vapor	Condition	Excitation	Color or wavelength of emitted light	Observer
Iodine.....	Vapor at ordinary temp.	Mercury arc $\lambda = 0.546\mu$	Strongest bands $\lambda = 0.5460\mu$, 0.5774μ 0.5730, 0.5796	Wood, 1911
Mercury...	Vapor at ordinary temp.	Spark between aluminum electrodes	Broad band $\lambda = 0.5900–0.3000$	Wood, 1909
Oxygen....	....	Mercury arc in quartz tube	Strongest lines $\lambda = 0.1849$, 0.1851 (ultraviolet)	Streubing, 1910
Potassium..	Vapor, 300–400°C	White light	Many strong lines from 0.6416–0.6768, strongest 0.6544 and 0.6584	Wood and Carter, 1908
Rubidium..	Vapor at 270°C	White light (elec. arc)	Strong red band $\lambda = 0.6900–0.6620$	Dunoyer, 1912
Sodium....	Vapor at 350°C	White light (elec. arc)	D, $\lambda = 0.5893$ (mean)	Dunoyer, 1912

* "Handbook of Chemistry and Physics," 36th ed., p. 2736, Chemical Rubber Publishing Company, 1954–1955.

TABLE 61-4. CHARACTERISTICS OF CATHODE-RAY-TUBE PHOSPHORS*

A summary of useful CRT screens, most of which have been coded by the Radio Manufacturer's Association

RMA No.	Representative phosphor or scotophor (P10)		Component cathodoluminescence emission bands, A (4,000 5,000 6,000 7,000)	Color of emission: During excit.	Color of emission: After excit.	Approx visible persistence	Current density for saturation	Approx avg crystal size, μ	Chief uses
P1	Rbhdl.-Zn_2SiO_4:Mn(0.3–1)			Green	Green	Short, ϵ^{-80t}	High	3	Oscilloscopes, radar
P2	Hex.-ZnS:Ag(0.02):Cu(0.01)			Green-blue	Green	Long, t^{-n}	Low	15	Oscilloscopes
P3	Rbhdl.-$Zn_3BeSi_5O_{19}$:Mn(1.4)			Green-yellow	Green-yellow	Short, ϵ^{-80t}	High	3	See P4 and P6
P4	Hex.-ZnS:Ag(0.015) mixed with hex.-1.3ZnS·CdS:Ag(0.01)	(a)		White	White	Short, t^{-n}	Low	8	Black and white television
P4	Hex.-ZnS:Ag(0.015) or P11 mixed with P3	(b)		White	Green-yellow	Short, $t^{-n} + \epsilon^{-80t}$	P11 low, P3 high	3	Black and white television
P4	Monocl.-$CaMg(SiO_3)_2$:Ti(1) + P3	(c)		White	White	Short, ϵ^{-80t}	High	3	Black and white television
P5	Tetr.-$CaWO_4$:[W]			Violet-blue	Violet-blue	Very short, ϵ^{-10^5t}	Med.	1	Oscilloscopes
P6	Hex.-ZnS:Ag(0.015) + hex.-7ZnS·3CdS:Ag(0.01) + hex.-3ZnS·7CdS:Ag(0.01)	(a)		White	White	Short, t^{-n}	Low	8	Color television
P6	Silicate:Ti(1) + P1 + P3*[Mn(2.5)]	(b)		White	White	Short, ϵ^{-80t}	High	3	Color television
P7	Hex.-ZnS:Ag(0.015) layer on top of hex.-9ZnS·CdS:Cu(0.0073)			Blue-white	Green-yellow	Long, t^{-n}	Low	14	Radar, oscilloscopes
P8	Canadian P7 (obsolete) (British M screen)			Blue-white	Green-yellow	Long, t^{-n}	Low	11	Radar, oscilloscopes
P9	Canadian $Ca_2P_2O_7$:Dм (obsolete) (British H screen)			White	White	Long, t^{-n}	Low	1	Radar, oscilloscopes
(P10)	Evaporated KCl (scotophor)			Magenta absorption		Long, t^{-n}	Low	1	Radar, oscilloscopes
P11	Cub.-ZnS:Ag(0.003–0.01)			Blue	Blue	Short, t^{-n}	Low	3–8	Oscilloscopes
P12	Tetr.-$(Zn:Mg)F_2$:Mn(1)			Orange	Orange	Med., ϵ^{-10t}	High	3	Radar, teleran
P13	Monocl.-$MgSiO_3$:Mn(1)			Red	Red	Med., $\epsilon^{-10^3t} \rightarrow \epsilon^{-10t}$	Med.	3	
P14	Hex.-ZnS:Ag(0.015) layer on top of hex.-4.5ZnS·CdS:Cu(0.008)			Purple-white	Yellow-orange	Med. long, t^{-n}	Low	14	Radar
P15	Hex.-ZnO:[Zn]			Blue-green	Blue-green	Very short, ϵ^{-10^6t}	Med.	3	Oscilloscopes
	Cub.-MgS:Sb(0.01)			Green-yellow	Green-yellow	Very short, ϵ^{-10^6t}	Med.	2	Oscilloscopes

* From H. W. Leverenz, "Luminescense of Solids," pp. 428–429, John Wiley & Sons, Inc., New York, 1950.

6m. Radiation Detection

Radiation detectors can be classed as either thermal detectors or quantum detectors. In the former the radiation is absorbed and transformed into heat in the detector, producing a temperature rise in the device. Some characteristic of the detector changes as a function of temperature, and this characteristic can be measured to determine the quantity of radiation striking the detector. In this type of receiver, then, the quantity actually measured is the temperature change. In the quantum detector, on the other hand, the incident photons change the detector characteristic directly.

There can be as many thermal detectors as there are material characteristics which change with temperature. Table 6m-1 lists some of the commercially available types.

TABLE 6m-1. THERMAL DETECTORS

Device	*Measured Characteristic*
Bolometer	Change of electrical resistance with temperature
Thermocouple	Peltier effect or change of contact potential at a junction as a function of temperature
Pneumatic detector	Change of gas pressure in an enclosed chamber as a function of temperature

Various kinds of quantum detectors are mentioned and described briefly in Table 6m-2.

TABLE 6m-2. QUANTUM DETECTORS

Device	*Measured Characteristic*
Photoelectric cell	The emission of an electron from a surface when struck by sufficiently energetic photons
Photoconductor cell	The resistance of the cell changes directly as a result of photon absorption
Photovoltaic cell	A voltage is generated directly as a result of the absorption of a photon
Photographic plate	A silver halide is reduced to silver by photon absorption

The important characteristics of radiation detectors are:

Spectral Response. This is a relative signal obtained from a detector at different wavelengths. In the case of thermal detectors, the response is generally independent of wavelength over a range from the ultraviolet to wavelengths which approach the dimensions of the detector. The responsivity of the detector is its output in volts or amperes as a function of light intensity or radiation intensity.

Noise. This is the random signal generated by a detector, independent of the signal from the radiation being measured. In the case of a thermal detector, this noise will include the basic statistical mechanical temperature fluctuation of whatever characteristic is being used to measure temperature. In the case of a bolometer this noise will be the Johnson or electronic thermal noise associated with the resistance. There can also be noise associated with the fluctuations in the radiation received by the detector from its environment and emitted by the detector to its environment. This photon fluctuation noise is usually smaller than other types of noises in detectors.

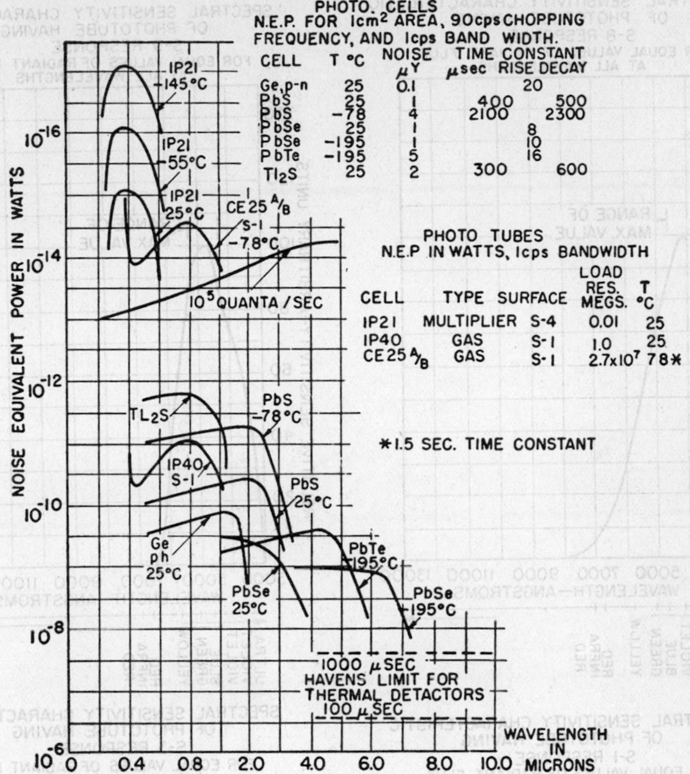

FIG. 6m-1. Characteristics of commercially available quantum detectors.

Quantum detectors that produce electrical signals also develop the same types of noises associated with thermal detectors. In addition, some of these detectors can develop "shot" noise which is associated with the random fluctuations in the emission of the electrons from a cathode surface. These noises are of the following kinds:

ELECTRONIC THERMAL AGITATION NOISE:

$$\text{rms voltage} = \sqrt{4kTR(f_2 - f_1)}$$

where k = Boltzmann constant = 1.374×10^{-23} joule/°K
T = absolute temperature, °K
R = electrical resistance, ohms
f_1, f_2 = frequency limits

SHOT NOISE:

$$\text{rms current} = \sqrt{2eI(f_2 - f_1)} \quad \text{amp}$$

where e = electronic charge, coulombs = 1.59×10^{-19}
I = direct current, amp

CURRENT NOISE: Noise arising from changes in state of the conducting holes and electrons in a semiconductor. Current noise voltage generally follows the relationship

$$\text{rms voltage} = \sqrt{CI^2 \log \frac{f_2}{f_1}}$$

where C = a constant for the geometry and semiconductor material.

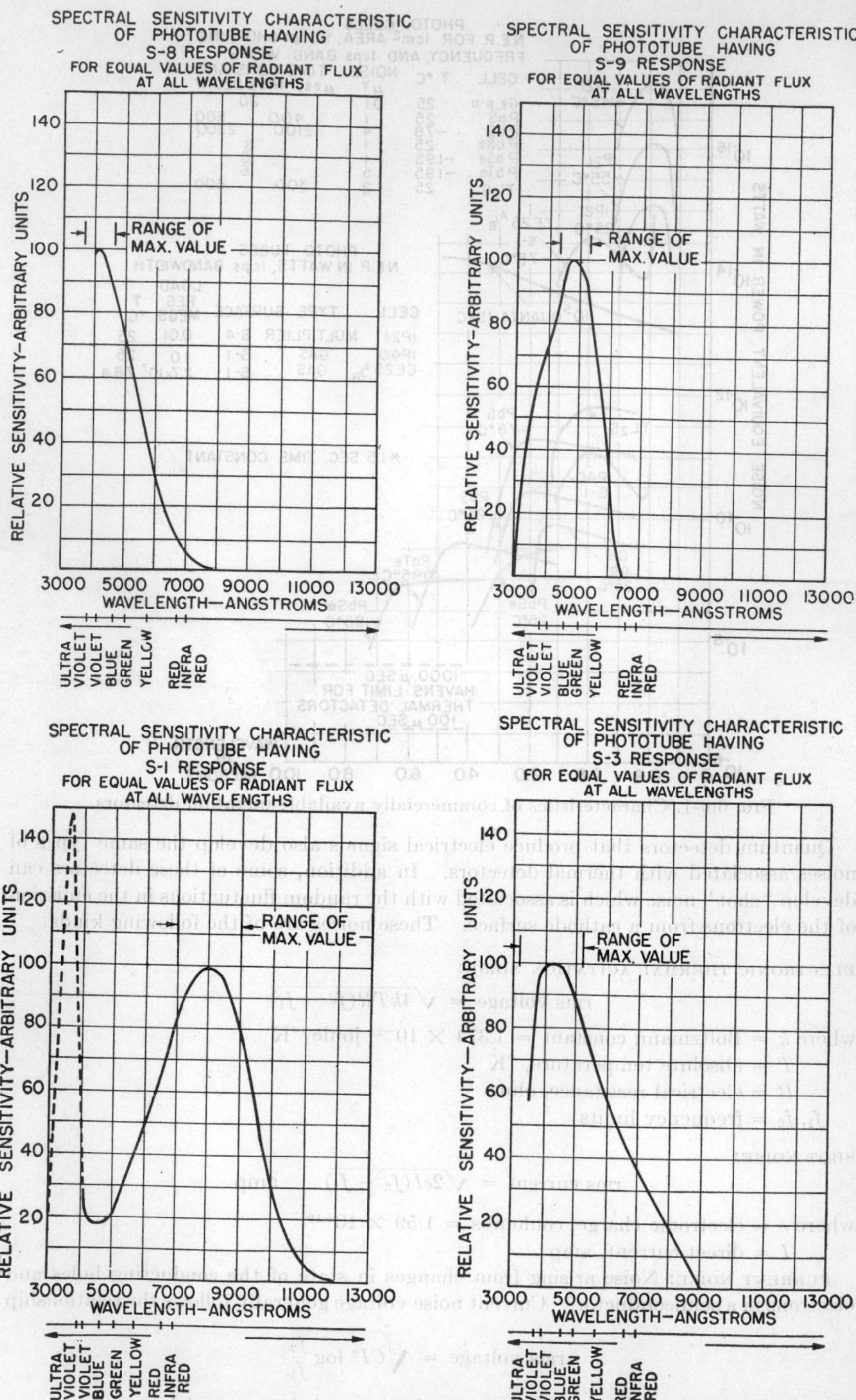

Fig. 6m-2. Spectral sensitivities of commercially available phototubes.

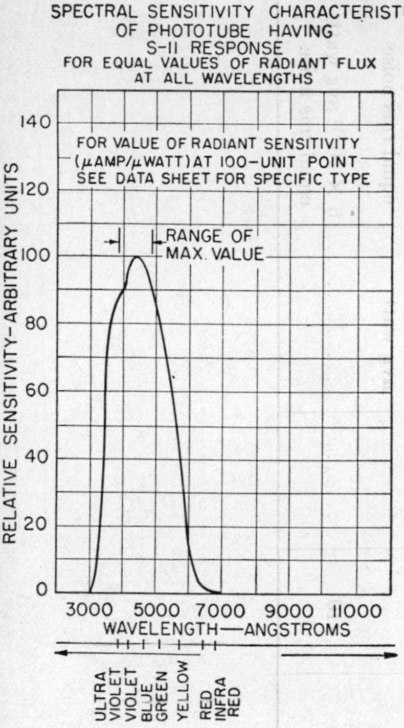

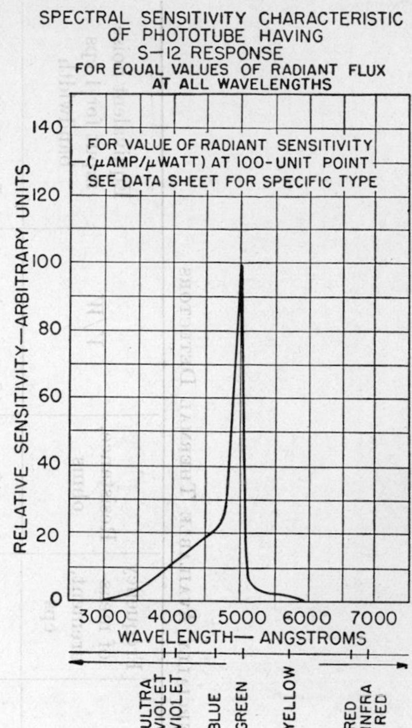

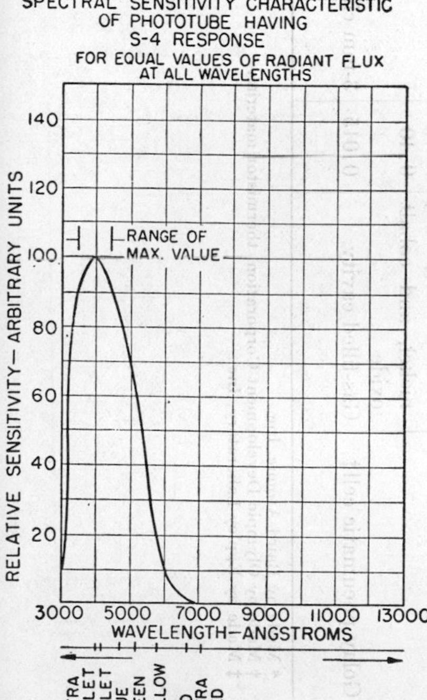

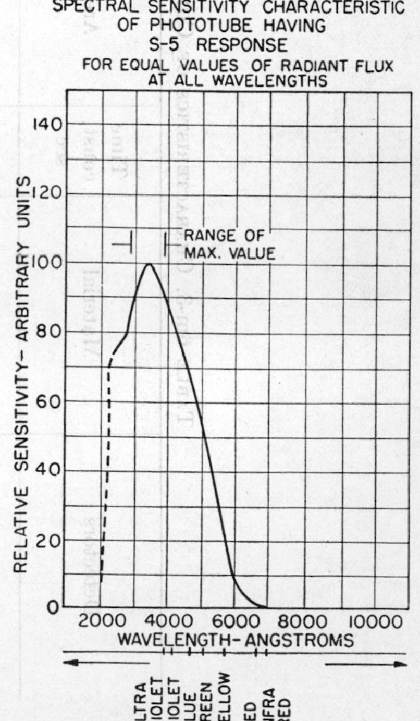

Fig. 6m-2. (*Continued*)

TABLE 6m-3. CHARACTERISTICS OF COMMERCIALLY AVAILABLE THERMAL DETECTORS

Detectors	Material	Time const, sec	Area	Frequency of measurement, cps	Resistance, ohms	V/W	Equivalent noise input for 1 cps bandwidth
Bolometer*	Platinum	0.016	6.5 × 0.25 mm	10	40	10 rms volt/avg watt	1.7 × 10^{-10} avg watt equal rms noise
Bolometer†	Mixture manganese, nickel, and cobalt oxide	0.20 0.40	2.5 × 0.2 mm	15	3 × 10^{6}	1,210 rms volt/avg watt	1.8 × 10^{-10} avg watt equal rms noise
Golay pneumatic cell‡	Gas-filled cavity	0.015	3-mm circle	10	....	....	6 × 10^{-11} avg watt equal rms noise

* Made by Baird-Atomic, Inc.
† Made by Olympic Development Corporation, thermistor material.
‡ Made by Eppley Laboratory, Inc.

Time Constant. The time required for the signal to complete all but $1/e$ of its steady-state change, following a step-function change in radiation, is called the *time constant.*

The Equivalent Noise Input (E.N.I.) or Noise Equivalent Power (N.E.P.). The E.N.I. or N.E.P. is the average watts required to give a signal equal to the rms noise from the detector. Table 6m-3 gives the characteristics of various commercially available thermal detectors. The chart and data presented in Fig. 6m-1 provide similar information for some of the quantum detectors. Figure 6m-2 provides spectral sensitivity characteristics of some commercially available phototubes.

6n. Velocity of Light

TABLE 6n-1*

No.	Date	Experimenter	Method		Velocity
1	1876	Cornu	Toothed wheel	L/T	299,990 ± 200
2	1880	Michelson	Rotating mirror	L/T	299,910 ± 50
3	1883	Newcomb	Rotating mirror	L/T	299,860 ± 30
4	1883	Michelson	Rotating mirror	L/T	299,853 ± 60
5	1902	Perrotin	Toothed wheel	L/T	299,901 ± 84
6	1906	Rosa and Dorsey	Maxwell's bridge	esu/emu	299,781 ± 10
7	1923	Mercier	Waves on wires	$\lambda\nu$	299,782 ± 15
8	1926	Michelson	Rotating mirror	L/T	299,796 ± 4
9	1928	Karolus and Mittelstaedt	Kerr cell	L/T	299,778 ± 10
10	1932	Michelson, Pease, and Pearson	Rotating mirror	L/T	299,774 ± 11
11	1940	Huettel	Kerr cell	L/T	299,768 ± 10
12	1941	Anderson	Kerr cell	L/T	299,776 ± 14
13	1950	Bergstrand	Electronic chopper	L/T	299,792.7 ± 0.25
14	1950	Essen	Microwave cavity	$\lambda\nu$	299,792.5 ± 3
15	1950	Houstoun	Vibrating crystal	L/T	299,775 ± 9
16	1950	Bol and Hansen	Microwave cavity	$\lambda\nu$	299,789.3 ± 0.4
17	1951	Aslakson	Shoran radar	L/T	299,794.2 ± 1.9
18	1952	Rank, Ruth, and Vander Sluis	Molecular spectra	$\lambda\nu$	299,776 ± 7
19	1952	Froome	Microwave interferometer	$\lambda\nu$	299,792.6 ± 0.7
20	1954	Florman	Radio interferometer	$\lambda\nu$	299,795 ± 3.1
21	1954	Plyler	Molecular spectra	$\lambda\nu$	299,792 ± 6

* *Scientific American.*

Principal attempts to measure the speed of light are summarized in the chart and Table 6n-1. Vertical lines on the chart represent the range of error in each measurement, with the most probable value indicated by the short cross mark. The column to the left of the list of velocities on Fig. 6n-1 refers to the theory underlying each method. L/T means that the experimenter essentially measured a distance and a

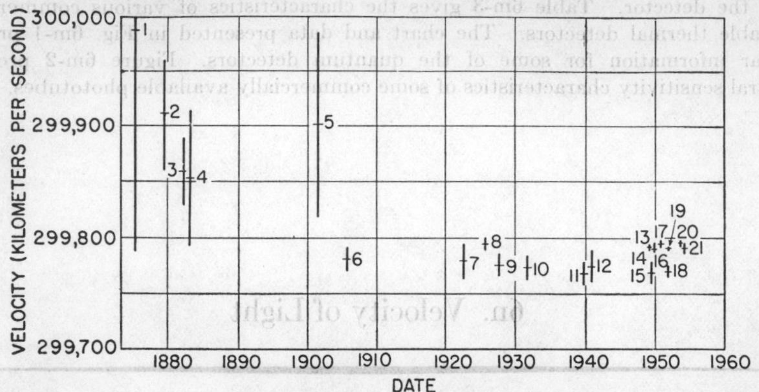

FIG. 6n-1. Determinations of the velocity of light. (*Scientific American.*)

time and found the velocity by dividing the two. esu/emu refers to the ratio of electrostatic to electromagnetic units. The expression $\lambda\nu$ indicates that the wavelength λ and the frequency ν of some electromagnetic radiation were each measured experimentally and that these values were multiplied together to give the waves' velocity.

6o. Radio Astronomy[1]

L. M. BRANSCOMB

National Bureau of Standards

6o-1. Radio-astronomical Measurements. Radio astronomy is an extension of photographic astronomy into the spectral range 15 to 30,000 Mc/sec to detect the radio noise which is part of the continuous spectrum of the radiation source. Large radio telescopes may have a beam width of the order of 1 deg, but modern radio interferometers can locate the positions of discrete sources of radio noise within angles smaller than 1 minute. To date, the only discrete spectral line observed is the hyperfine transition in the ground state of the hydrogen atom at a wavelength of 21 cm. In contrast with visual astronomy absolute intensities of the radio-frequency continuum are measured with relative ease. As a result the intensities P_ν

[1] The reader is advised to consult the current literature in this new and rapidly advancing field.

of radio noise signals from discrete sources are reported in either absolute units [watts/m²/sec)⁻¹] or in terms of the equivalent photographic magnitude or equivalent thermodynamic temperature of the source, if the angular size of discrete objects is known. The definition of *radio magnitude* given by Brown and Hazard[1] is

$$m_R = -53.4 - 2.5 \log P_\nu$$

where P_ν is the intensity in the units given above.

For a radio source of finite extent (spherical with angular diameter d minutes of arc), the *radio luminosity*[2] is

$$L_\nu = 1.2 \times 10^{41} P_\nu r^2 \qquad \text{ergs sec}^{-1}\ (\text{c/sec})^{-1}$$

where the distance to the source r is given in parsecs.[3] The *total volume emissivity* is

$$J_\nu = \frac{3.2 \times 10^{-4} P_\nu}{d^3 r} \qquad \text{ergs cm}^{-3}\ \text{sec}^{-1}\ (\text{c/sec})^{-1}$$

In these units the source emissivities vary from 1.4×10^{-30} for the galaxy[4] to at least 10^{-23} for the extragalactic sources of Taurus and Cassiopeia.[5]

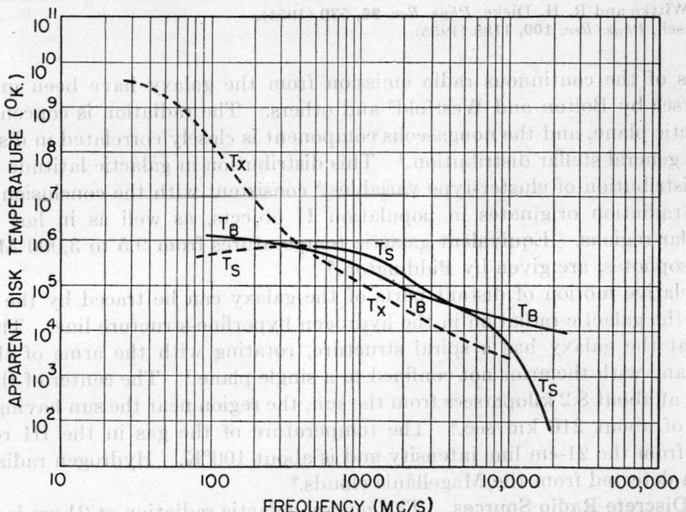

FIG. 6o-1. The spectra of the three components of solar radio-frequency radiation. That of T_B is constant (at least for several years) in form and level. That of T_S varies in level and the curve shown corresponds to a sunspot area of 5,000 millionths. That of T_X is highly variable in both form and level; the curve shown represents approximate, average, relative values for the various frequencies and for moderately disturbed conditions. [*Piddington and Minnett, Aust. J. Sci. Res.* **A4**, 131 (1951).]

6o-2. Solar Noise. Although solar noise power is often expressed in terms of the effective temperature of the source, the spectrum is not of black-body character. Figure 6o-1 shows the effective temperature of the sun as a function of the measured

[1] R. H. Brown and C. Hazard, *Phil. Mag.* **43,** 137 (1952).

[2] R. Minkowski and J. E. Greenstein, *Astrophys. J.* **119,** 238 (1954).

[3] Useful conversion factors from Aller, "Astrophysics," p. ix, The Ronald Press Company, New York, 1954. Parsec: 3.084×10^{18} cm/pc; 3.258 light-year/pc. Light-year: 9.463×10^{17} cm/light-year; log cm/light-year = 17.97603. Astronomical unit = 1.49674 × 10⁸ km.

[4] Westerhout and Oort, *Bull. Astron. Inst. Netherlands* **11,** 323 (1951).

[5] R. Minkowski and J. E. Greenstein, *Astrophys. J.* **119,** 238 (1954).

frequency.[1] Three components of the solar noise are distinguished by Piddington and Minnett: a basic steady component B from chromosphere and corona, a slowly varying component S associated with sunspot number, and rapid fluctuations of various kinds collectively termed X. The X component at low frequencies is closely related to violent solar activity and the correlated terrestrial atmospheric storms. About 80 per cent of solar flares are accompanied by radio noise at 200 Mc/sec.[2]

6o-3. Galactic Radio Noise. Galactic radiation is observed both in the continuous r-f spectrum and in the 21.10614-cm line of hydrogen. The frequency of this transition has recently been remeasured in the laboratory and is given in Table 6o-1. The

TABLE 6o-1. HYPERFINE SPLITTING OF ATOMIC HYDROGEN GROUND STATE (λ = 21.10614 cm)

ν_0, Mc/sec	Technique	Investigator
1,420.40580 ± 0.00005	Microwave absorption	Wittke and Dicke*
1,420.40573 ± 0.00005	Molecular beam	Kusch†

* J. P. Wittke and R. H. Dicke, *Phys. Rev.* **96,** 530 (1954).
† P. Kusch, *Phys. Rev.* **100,** 1188 (1955).

isophotes of the continuous radio emission from the galaxy have been mapped at 100 Mc/sec by Bolton and Westfold[3] and others. The radiation is concentrated in the galactic plane, and the nongaseous component is closely correlated in distribution with the general stellar distribution.[4] This distribution in galactic latitude is similar to the distribution of cluster-type variables,[5] consistent with the conclusion that the galactic radiation originates in population II objects, as well as in hot (ionized) interstellar regions. Equivalent galactic temperatures from 9.5 to 3,000 Mc/sec, as well as isophotes, are given by Piddington.[6]

The relative motion of distant parts of the galaxy can be traced by the Doppler shifts in the galactic radiation in the hydrogen hyperfine-structure line. The results show that the galaxy has a spiral structure, rotating with the arms of the spiral trailing, and with the arms not confined to a single plane.[7] The center of the galaxy is placed at about 8.2 kiloparsecs from the sun, the region near the sun having a linear velocity of about 216 km/sec.[8] The temperature of the gas in the HI regions is deduced from the 21-cm line intensity and is about 100°K. Hydrogen radiation has also been detected from the Magellanic clouds.[9]

6o-4. Discrete Radio Sources. The general galactic radiation at 21 cm is observed in emission. However, a source of strong hydrogen absorption (0.5 deg diameter) has been reported in a bright star cluster in Sagittarius.[10]

Discrete radio sources have been described by Baade and Minkowski[5] in four categories: remnants of supernovae; galactic nebulosities of a new type; peculiar

[1] J. H. Piddington and H. C. Minnett, *Australian J. Sci. Research*, ser. A, **4,** 131 (1951).
[2] R. Payne-Scott and A. G. Little, *Australian J. Sci. Research*, ser. A, **5,** 32 (1952); H. W. Dodson, E. R. Hedeman, and L. Owren, *Astrophys. J.* **118,** 169 (1953).
[3] J. G. Bolton and K. C. Westfold, *Australian J. Sci. Research*, ser. A, **3,** 19 (1950).
[4] R. H. Brown and C. Hazard, *Phil. Mag.* **44,** 939 (1953).
[5] W. Baade and R. Minkowski, *Astrophys. J.* **119,** 230 (1954).
[6] J. H. Piddington, *Monthly Notices Roy. Astron. Soc.* **111,** 45 (1951).
[7] H. C. Van de Hulst, *Observatory* **73,** 129 (1953); J. H. Oort, *Naturwiss.* **41,** 73 (1954); H. C. Van de Hulst, C. A. Muller, and J. H. Oort, *Bull. Astron. Inst. Netherlands* **12,** 117 (1954).
[8] *Ibid.*
[9] F. J. Ken, J. V. Hindman, and B. J. Robinson, *Australian J. Phys.* **7,** 297 (1954).
[10] J. P. Hagen and E. F. McClain, *Astrophys. J.* **120,** 368 (1954).

extragalactic nebulae; and normal extragalactic nebulae. The radio and photographic positions of the identified sources are given by Baade and Minkowski.[1] Among the peculiar extragalactic nebulae, one of the most interesting is the source in Cygnus A, where there is photographic evidence that the source is the remnant of two colliding galaxies.[2]

For detailed information on radio astronomy and related topics see:

Ryle, M.: *Repts. Progr. in Phys.* **13**, 214 (1950).

Lovell, A. C. B., and J. A. Clegg: "Radio Astronomy," Chapman & Hall, Ltd., London, 1952.

Van de Hulst, H. C.: "A Course in Radio Astronomy," Leiden Observatory, Leiden, 1951.

Aller, L.: "Astrophysics," The Ronald Press Company, New York, 1954.

Lovell, A. C. B., and colleagues: *Occasional Notes, Roy. Astron. Soc.* **16**, 29 (1954).

Kuiper, G. P.: "The Solar System," I. The Sun, University of Chicago Press, Chicago, 1953.

Bolton, J. G., F. G. Smith, R. Hanbury Brown, and B. Y. Mills: Discrete Source of Extra-terrestrial Radio Noise, Special Report 3, International Scientific Radio Union (URSI), Brussels, 1954.

[1] W. Baade and R. Minkowski, *Astrophys. J.* **119**, 206,230 (1954).

[2] *Ibid.*, p. 206.

Section 7

ATOMIC AND MOLECULAR PHYSICS*

G. H. DIEKE, Editor
The Johns Hopkins University

CONTENTS

7a. Atomic Constants . . . 7-2
7b. The Periodic System . . . 7-5
7c. The Electronic Structure of Atoms . . . 7-13
7d. Structure of Atomic Spectra . . . 7-16
7e. Energy-level Diagrams of Atoms . . . 7-26
7f. Persistent Lines of the Elements . . . 7-39
7g. Important Atomic Spectra . . . 7-42
7h. Data on Characteristic X-ray Spectra . . . 7-123
7i. Constants and Energy Levels of Diatomic Molecules . . . 7-136
7j. Constants of Polyatomic Molecules . . . 7-145
7k. Wave Mechanics . . . 7-162
7l. Zeeman Effect . . . 7-168
7m. Motions of Electrons and Ions in Gases . . . 7-174
7m-1 Collision Probabilities . . . 7-174
1.1 Elastic Collisions by Electrons . . . 7-175
1.2 Inelastic Collisions by Electrons . . . 7-177
1.3 Electron Attachment . . . 7-182
1.4 Elastic Collisions by Ions . . . 7-186
1.5 Charge Transfer . . . 7-189
7m-2 Surface Phenomena . . . 7-192
2.1 Secondary Emission . . . 7-192
2.2 Effective Secondary Emission . . . 7-199
2.3 Ion Conversions . . . 7-201
2.4 Secondary Emission by Electrons . . . 7-203
7m-3 Average Motion of Electrons and Ions . . . 7-203
3.1 Drift Velocity of Electrons . . . 7-205
3.2 Mean Energies of Electrons . . . 7-210
3.3 Drift Velocities of Ions . . . 7-212

* Where no contributor is specifically mentioned, the material of this section has been compiled by the editor. Dr. W. F. Meggers has reviewed some of the material and valuable corrections are due to him.

7a. Atomic Constants

Table 7a-1 gives the best values of the atomic constants with *probable errors* as of October, 1954, evaluated by J. A. Bearden, M. D. Earle, J. M. Minkowski, and J. S Thomsen of The Johns Hopkins University. While the least-squares method was used, the result is substantially equivalent to a direct solution based on the following experiments: the microwave measurement of the fine-structure constant α by Triebwasser, Dayhoff, and Lamb;[1] the determination of the magnetic moment of the proton in nuclear magnetons by Sommer, Thomas, and Hipple;[2] the measurement of the gyromagnetic ratio of the proton by Thomas, Driscoll, and Hipple;[3] a weighted mean of several recent velocity-of-light experiments; and the determination of the ratio of the proton magnetic moment to the anomalous moment of the electron by Koenig, Prodell, and Kusch.[4] Atomic masses were obtained from weighted means of recent values given in a review by Duckworth, Hogg, and Pennington.[5]

These values are in good agreement with most other recent experiments of high precision except for the X-ray determinations of h/e, where it seems possible there may be some unsuspected source of systematic error. For this reason, no X-ray data of any kind were used in the evaluation.

Wherever atomic weights are involved, the physical scale is used.

[1] Triebwasser, Dayhoff, and Lamb, *Phys. Rev.* **89**, 98 (1953).
[2] Sommer, Thomas, and Hipple, *Phys. Rev.* **82**, 697 (1951).
[3] Thomas, Driscoll, and Hipple, *J. Research Natl. Bur. Standards* **44**, 569 (1950).
[4] Koenig, Prodell, and Kusch, *Phys. Rev.* **88**, 191 (1952).
[5] Duckworth, Hogg, and Pennington, *Revs. Modern Phys.* **26**, 463 (1954).

TABLE 7a-1. GENERAL ATOMIC CONSTANTS

Symbol	Constant	Value
e	Electronic charge	$(4.8029 \pm 0.0001) \times 10^{-10}$ esu
e/m	Specific charge of electron	$(5.2731 \pm 0.0002) \times 10^{17}$ esu g^{-1}
N	Avogadro's number (molecules per mole)	$(6.0248 \pm 0.0003) \times 10^{23}$ (g-mole)$^{-1}$
n_0	Loschmidt's number (molecules per cm^3)	$(2.6871 \pm 0.0002) \times 10^{19}$ cm^{-3}
c	Velocity of light in vacuum	$(2.997923 \pm 0.000008) \times 10^{10}$ cm sec^{-1}
F	Faraday $F = Ne/c$	(9652.2 ± 0.2) emu (g-equivalent)$^{-1}$
h	Planck's constant	$(6.6253 \pm 0.0003) \times 10^{-27}$ erg sec
$\hbar$	$\hbar = h/2\pi$	$(1.05445 \pm 0.00005) \times 10^{-27}$ erg sec
h/e	....	$(1.37943 \pm 0.00003) \times 10^{-17}$ erg sec (esu)$^{-1}$
h/m	....	(7.27383 ± 0.00005) cm^2 sec^{-1}
μ_0	Bohr magneton $\mu_0 = he/4\pi mc$	$(0.92734 \pm 0.00003) \times 10^{-20}$ erg gauss^{-1}
μ_0/hc	Zeeman displacement per gauss	$(4.6689 \pm 0.0001)\ 10^{-5}$ cm^{-1} gauss^{-1}
μ_e	Magnetic moment of electron	$(0.92840 \pm 0.00003) \times 10^{-20}$ erg gauss^{-1}
μ_n	Nuclear magneton	$(5.0505 \pm 0.0002) \times 10^{-24}$ erg gauss^{-1}
μ_p	Magnetic moment of proton	$(1.41049 \pm 0.00004) \times 10^{-23}$ erg gauss^{-1}
R_H	Rydberg constant for hydrogen	(109677.58 ± 0.01) cm^{-1}
R_∞	Rydberg constant for infinite mass	(109737.31 ± 0.01) cm^{-1}
α	Fine-structure constant $2\pi e^2/hc$	$(7.29732 \pm 0.00003) \times 10^{-3}$
α^{-1}	....	137.0366 ± 0.0005
a_0	First Bohr radius $h^2/4\pi^2 me^2$	$(5.29175 \pm 0.00002) \times 10^{-9}$ cm
BI	Band-spectrum constant $BI = h/8\pi^2 c$	$(2.7990 \pm 0.0002) \times 10^{-39}$ g cm
c_1	First radiation constant $(8\pi hc)$	$(4.9919 \pm 0.0002) \times 10^{-15}$ erg cm
c_2	Second radiation constant hc/k	(1.43886 ± 0.00005) cm deg
	Stefan-Boltzmann constant $2\pi^5 k^4/15c^2h^3$	$(5.6685 \pm 0.0007) \times 10^{-5}$ erg cm^{-2} deg^{-4} sec^{-1}
k	Boltzmann constant	$(1.38041 \pm 0.00007) \times 10^{-16}$ erg deg^{-1}
k/hc	....	(0.69500 ± 0.00002) cm^{-1} deg^{-1}
$\lambda_{\max} T$	Wien-displacement-law constant	(0.289794 ± 0.000009) cm deg
R_0	Gas constant per mole $R_0 = Nk$	$(8.3167 \pm 0.0003) \times 10^7$ erg mole^{-1} deg^{-1}
V_0	Molar volume	$(2.24208 \pm 0.00003) \times 10^4$ cm^3 mole^{-1}
	Masses	
m	Mass of electron	$(9.1084 \pm 0.0004) \times 10^{-28}$ g
μ	Reduced mass of electron in hydrogen atom	$(9.1034 \pm 0.0004) \times 10^{-28}$ g
M_0	Mass of particle with atomic weight one $M_0 = N_0^{-1}$	$(1.65981 \pm 0.00007) \times 10^{-24}$ g
M/mN	Ratio proton to electron mass	$1{,}836.13 \pm 0.01$
r	Ratio of physical to chemical scale of atomic weights	1.000275
	Atomic Masses	
	H atom	1.008144 ± 0.000002
	D atom	2.014739 ± 0.000004
	T atom	3.01704
M	Proton	1.007595 ± 0.000002
d	Deuteron	2.014190 ± 0.000004
	Triton	3.01650
	Neutron	1.008982
Nm	Electron	$(5.48760 \pm 0.00004) \times 10^{-4}$
	Oxygen 16	16.00000

TABLE 7a-2. CONVERSION FACTORS OF ATOMIC UNITS

Electron volts	Energy, ergs	Frequency, sec^{-1}	Wave number, cm^{-1}	Wavelength, $A = 10^{-8}$ cm	Temp., °K	Mass, g	Atomic mass
$E = eVc^{-1}10^8$	E	$E = h\nu$	$E = hc\sigma$	$E = \frac{hc}{\lambda}$	$E = kT$	$E = Mc^2$	$E = \frac{M_0c^2}{N}$
1 volt	$ec^{-1} \times 10^8$ 1.60208×10^{-12}	$e(ch)^{-1} \times 10^8$ 2.41813×10^{14}	$eh^{-1}c^{-2} \times 10^8$ 8,066.0	hc^2e^{-1} 12,397.7	$e(ck)^{-1} \times 10^8$ 11,605.8	$ec^{-3} \times 10^8$ 1.78256×10^{-33}	$eNc^{-3} \times 10^8$ 1.07395×10^{-9}
$ce^{-1} \times 10^{-8}$ 6.24189×10^{11}	1 erg	h^{-1} 1.50937×10^{26}	$(hc)^{-1}$ 5.0347×10^{15}	$hc \times 10^8$ 1.98621×10^{-8}	k^{-1} 7.2442×10^{15}	c^{-2} 1.11265×10^{-21}	Nc^{-2} 6.7035×10^2
$hce^{-1}10^{-8}$ 4.13543×10^{-15}	h 6.6253×10^{-27}	1 sec^{-1}	c^{-1} 3.335643×10^{-11}	$c \times 10^8$ 2.997923×10^{18}	hk^{-1} 4.7995×10^{-11}	hc^{-2} 7.3716×10^{-48}	Nhc^{-2} 4.44125×10^{-24}
$hc^2e^{-1} \times 10^{-8}$ 1.23977×10^{-4}	hc 1.98621×10^{-16}	c 2.997923×10^{10}	1 cm^{-1}	10^8 10^8	hck^{-1} 1.43886	hc^{-1} 2.20996×10^{-37}	Nhc^{-1} 1.33145×10^{-13}
hc^2e^{-1} 12,397.7	$hc \times 10^8$ 1.98621×10^{-8}	$c \times 10^8$ 2.997923×10^{18}	10^8 10^8	1 A	$hck^{-1} \times 10^8$ 1.43886×10^8	$hc^{-1} \times 10^8$ 2.20996×10^{-29}	$Nhc^{-1} \times 10^8$ 1.33145×10^{-5}
$cke^{-1} \times 10^{-8}$ 8.6164×10^{-5}	k 1.38041×10^{-16}	kh^{-1} 2.08355×10^{10}	$k(hc)^{-1}$ 0.69500	$hck^{-1} \times 10^8$ 1.43886×10^8	1°K	kc^{-2} 1.53592×10^{-37}	Nkc^{-2} 9.2535×10^{-14}
$e^{-1}c^3 \times 10^{-8}$ 5.6099×10^{32}	c^2 8.98754×10^{20}	c^2h^{-1} 1.35655×10^{47}	ch^{-1} 4.5250×10^{36}	$c^{-1}h \times 10^8$ 2.20996×10^{-29}	c^2k^{-1} 6.5108×10^{36}	1 g	N 6.0248×10^{23}
$e^{-1}c^3N^{-1} \times 10^{-8}$ 9.3114×10^8	c^2N^{-1} 1.49176×10^{-3}	$c^2(hN)^{-1}$ 2.25162×10^{23}	$c(hN)^{-1}$ 7.51060×10^{12}	$c^{-1}hN \times 10^8$ 1.33145×10^{-5}	$c^2(kN)^{-1}$ 1.08067×10^{13}	N^{-1} 1.65980×10^{-24}	1 amu

Note that to convert to wavelength it is necessary to *divide* the conversion factor by the number of the other units and vice versa.
1 electron mass equivalent to 5.1097×10^5 volts, to 2.42629×10^{-2} A (Compton wavelength).

7b. The Periodic System

TABLE 7b-1. ALPHABETICAL LIST OF THE ELEMENTS

In later tables the elements are arranged according to increasing order number Z. This table gives in alphabetical order the names of the elements in English, French, and German, together with the chemical symbol, year of discovery, and order number of each. (A dash means that the name of the element in French or German is the same as in English.)

English	Name in Freneh	Name in German	Year of discovery	Symbol	Z
Actinium	—	—	1899	Ac	89
Alabamine*	....	....	....	(Ab)	(85)
Alumin(i)um	Aluminium	Aluminium	1827	Al	13
Americium	Américium	—	1945	Am	95
Antimony	Antimoine	Antimon	Old	Sb	51
Argentum*	....	....	....	Ag	47
Argon	—	—	1894	A	18
Arsenic	—	Arsen	Old	As	33
Astatine	—	—	1940	At	85
Barium	—	Baryum	1808	Ba	56
Berkelium	—	—	1950	Bk	97
Beryllium	Béryllium	—	1798	Be	4
Bismuth	—	Wismut	1753	Bi	83
Boron	Bore	Bor	1808	B	5
Bromine	Brome	Brom	1826	Br	35
Cadmium	—	—	1817	Cd	48
Calcium	—	—	1808	Ca	20
Californium	—	—	1950	Cf	98
Carbon	Carbone	Kohlenstoff	Old	C	6
Cassiopeium*	....	....	....	Lu	71
Celtium*	....	....	....	(Ct)	(72)
Cerium	Cérium	Cer	1803	Ce	58
Cesium	Césium	Caesium	1860	Cs	55
Chlorine	Chlore	Chlor	1774	Cl	17
Chromium	Chrome	Chrom	1797	Cr	24
Cobalt	—	—	1735	Co	27
Columbium*	....	....	....	(Cb)	41
Copper	Cuivre	Kupfer	Old	Cu	29
Curium	—	—	1944	Cm	96
Deuterium	—	—	1930	D	1
Dysprosium	—	—	1886	Dy	66
Einsteinium	—	—	1955	E	99
Emmanation*	....	....	....	Rn	86
Erbium	—	—	1843	Er	68

TABLE 7b-1. ALPHABETICAL LIST OF THE ELEMENTS (*Continued*)

English	Name in French	Name in German	Year of discovery	Symbol	Z
Europium	—	—	1896	Eu	63
Fermium	—	—	1955	Fm	100
Ferrum*	....	....	....	Fe	26
Fluorine	Fluor	Fluor	1771	F	9
Francium	—	—	1939	Fr	87
Gadolinium	—	—	1880	Gd	64
Gallium	—	—	1875	Ga	31
Germanium	—	—	1886	Ge	32
Gold	Or	—	Old	Au	79
Hafnium	—	—	1923	Hf	72
Helium	Hélium	—	1895	He	2
Holmium	—	—	1879	Ho	67
Hydrogen	Hydrogène	Wasserstoff	1766	H	1
Illinium*	....	....	....	(Il)	(61)
Indium	—	—	1863	In	49
Iodine	Iode	Jod	1811	I	53
Iridium	—	—	1803	Ir	77
Iron	Fer	Eisen	Old	Fe	26
Kalium*	....	....	....	K	19
Krypton	—	—	1898	Kr	36
Lanthanum	Lanthane	Lanthan	1839	La	57
Lead	Plomb	Blei	Old	Pb	82
Lithium	—	—	1817	Li	3
Lutetium	Lutétium	—	1907	Lu	71
Magnesium	Magnésium	—	1755	Mg	12
Manganese	Manganèse	Mangan	1774	Mn	25
Masurium*	....	....	....	(Ma)	(43)
Mendelevium	—	—	1955	Mv	101
Mercury	Mercure	Quecksilber	Old	Hg	80
Molybdenum	Molybdène	Molybdän	1778	Mo	42
Natrium*	....	....	....	Na	11
Nebulium*					
Neodymium	Néodyme	Neodym	1885	Nd	60
Neon	Néon	—	1898	Ne	10
Neptunium	—	—	1940	Np	93
Nickel	—	—	1751	Ni	28
Niobium	—	—	1801	Nb	41
Niton	....	....	....	Rn	86
Nitrogen	Nitrogène	Stickstoff	1772	N	7
Osmium	—	—	1803	Os	76
Oxygen	Oxygène	Sauerstoff	1774	O	8
Palladium	—	—	1803	Pd	46
Phosphorus	Phosphore	Phosphor	1669	P	15
Platinum	Platine	Platin	1735	Pt	78
Plumbum*	....	....	....	Pb	82
Plutonium	—	—	1940	Pu	94
Polonium	—	—	1898	Po	84
Potassium	—	Kalium	1807	K	19

TABLE 7b-1. ALPHABETICAL LIST OF THE ELEMENTS (*Continued*)

English	Name in French	Name in German	Year of discovery	Symbol	Z
Praseodymium	Praséodyme	Praseodym	1879	Pr	59
Prometheum	Prométheum	—	1947	Pm	61
Protactinium	—	—	1917	Pa	91
Radium	—	—	1898	Ra	88
Radon	—	—	1900	Rn	86
Rhenium	—	—	1925	Re	75
Rhodium	....	....	1803	Rh	45
Rubidium	—	—	1861	Rb	37
Ruthenium	Ruthenium	—	1844	Ru	44
Samarium	—	—	1879	Sm	62
Scandium	—	—	1879	Sc	21
Selenium	Sélénium	Selen	1817	Se	34
Silicon	Silicium	Silicium	1823	Si	14
Silver	Argent	Silber	Old	Ag	47
Sodium	—	Natrium	1807	Na	11
Stannum*	....	....	....	Sn	50
Stibium*	....	....	....	Sb	51
Strontium	—	—	1790	Sr	38
Sulfur	Soufre	Schwefel	Old	S	16
Tantalum	Tantale	Tantal	1802	Ta	73
Technetium	—	—	1937	Tc	43
Tellurium	Tellure	Tellur	1782	Te	52
Terbium	—	—	1843	Tb	65
Thallium	—	—	1861	Tl	81
Thorium	—	—	1828	Th	90
Thulium	—	—	1879	Tm	69
Tin	Etain	Zinn	Old	Sn	50
Titanium	Titane	Titan	1791	Ti	22
Tritium	—	—	....	T	1
Tungsten	Tungstène	Wolfram	1781	W	74
Uranium	—	Uran	1789	U	92
Vanadium	—	—	1830	V	23
Virginium*	....	....	....	(Vi)	(87)
Wolfram*	....	....	....	W	74
Xenon	Xénon	—	1898	Xe	54
Ytterbium	—	—	1878	Yb	70
Yttrium	—	—	1794	Y	39
Zinc	—	Zink	1746	Zn	30
Zirconium	—	Zircon	1789	Zr	40

* Alternate or obsolete names. An order number between parentheses means that the discovery of the element was an error and another element has taken its place. Element symbols between parentheses have been given up.

TABLE 7b-2. PERIODIC SYSTEM OF THE ELEMENTS

1 H $\underline{2}$																	2 He $\underline{1}$, 3
3 Li $\underline{2}$	4 Be $\underline{1}$, 3											5 B $\underline{2}$	6 C 1, $\underline{3}$	7 N 2, $\underline{4}$	8 O 1, $\underline{3}$, 5	9 F $\underline{2}$, 4	10 Ne $\underline{1}$, 3
11 Na $\underline{2}$	12 Mg $\underline{1}$, 3											13 Al $\underline{2}$	14 Si 1, $\underline{3}$	15 P 2, $\underline{4}$	16 S $\underline{3}$, 5	17 Cl $\underline{2}$, 4	18 A $\underline{1}$, 3
19 K $\underline{2}$	20 Ca $\underline{1}$, 3	21 Sc $\underline{2}$, 4	22 Ti 1, $\underline{3}$, 5	23 V 2, 4, $\underline{6}$	24 Cr 1, 3, 5, $\underline{7}$	25 Mn 2, 4, $\underline{6}$, 8	26 Fe 1, 3, $\underline{5}$, 7	27 Co 2, $\underline{4}$, 6	28 Ni 1, $\underline{3}$, 5	29 Cu $\underline{2}$, 4	30 Zn $\underline{1}$, 3	31 Ga $\underline{2}$, 4	32 Ge 1, $\underline{3}$	33 As 2, $\underline{4}$	34 Se $\underline{3}$, 5	35 Br $\underline{2}$, 4	36 Kr $\underline{1}$, 3
37 Rb $\underline{2}$	38 Sr $\underline{1}$, 3	39 Y $\underline{2}$, 4	40 Zr 1, $\underline{3}$, 5	41 Nb 2, 4, $\underline{6}$	42 Mo 1, 3, 5, $\underline{7}$	43 Tc 4, $\underline{6}$, 8	44 Ru 3, $\underline{5}$, 7	45 Rh 2, $\underline{4}$	46 Pd $\underline{1}$, 3, 5	47 Ag $\underline{2}$, 4	48 Cd $\underline{1}$, 3	49 In $\underline{2}$, 4	50 Sn 1, $\underline{3}$	51 Sb 2, $\underline{4}$	52 Te 1, $\underline{3}$, 5	53 I $\underline{2}$, 4	54 Xe $\underline{1}$, 3
55 Cs $\underline{2}$	56 Ba $\underline{1}$, 3	57 La $\underline{2}$, 4	* 72 Hf 1, $\underline{3}$, 5	73 Ta $\underline{4}$, 6	74 W $\underline{5}$, 7	75 Re 4, $\underline{6}$, 8	76 Os 3, $\underline{5}$, 7	77 Ir $\underline{4}$, 6	78 Pt 1, $\underline{3}$, 5	79 Au $\underline{2}$	80 Hg $\underline{1}$, 3	81 Tl $\underline{2}$	82 Pb 1, $\underline{3}$	83 Bi 2, $\underline{4}$	84 Po 3	85 At	86 Rn $\underline{1}$, 3
87 Fr $\underline{2}$	88 Ra $\underline{1}$, 3	89 Ac $\underline{2}$	†														

*Lanthanides (rare earths)	58 Ce	59 Pr $\underline{4}$	60 Nd $\underline{5}$	61 Pm	62 Sm $\underline{7}$, 9	63 Eu 6, $\underline{8}$, 10	64 Gd 7, $\underline{9}$, 11	65 Tb	66 Dy	67 Ho	68 Er	69 Tm $\underline{2}$	70 Yb $\underline{1}$, 3	71 Lu $\underline{2}$, 4
†Actinides	90 Th $\underline{3}$, 5	91 Pa	92 U $\underline{5}$, 7	93 Np	94 Pu	95 Am	96 Cm	97 Bk	98 Cf	99 E	100 Fm	101 Mv		

The numbers under the elements indicate the observed multiplicity in the first spectrum. The value for the ground state is underlined.

TABLE 7b-3. PROPERTIES OF ELEMENTS*

Z	Symbol	Element	Atomic wt.†	Valency	Atomic diam	Mass No. and (abundance)	Terrestrial abundance,¶ g/metric ton
(1)	(2)	(3)	(4)	(5)	(6)	(7)	(8)
1	H	Hydrogen	1.0080	1	3.0	1(99.985), 2(0.0146)	1,300
2	He	Helium	4.003	0	.....	4(100), 3(1.3 × 10⁻⁴)	0.003
3	Li	Lithium	6.940	1	3.13	7(92.48), 6(7.52)	65
4	Be	Beryllium	9.013	2	2.25	9(100),	6
5	B	Boron	10.82	3	.....	11(81.17), 10(18.83)	3
6	C	Carbon	12.011	±4, 2	1.54	12(98.9), 13(1.1)	320
7	N	Nitrogen	14.008	−3, 5, 2	1.06	14(99.635), 15(0.365),	46.3
8	O	Oxygen	16.0000	−2	.....	16(99.76), 18(0.204), 17(0.039)	466,000
9	F	Fluorine	19.00	−1	1.36	10(100)	900
10	Ne	Neon	20.183	0	3.20	20(90.92), 22(8.82), 21(0.257)	7×10^{-5}
11	Na	Sodium	22.991	1	3.83	23(100)	28,300
12	Mg	Magnesium	24.32	2	3.20	24(78.60), 26(11.29), 25(10.11)	20,900
13	Al	Aluminum	26.98	3	2.82	27(100)	81,300
14	Si	Silicon	28.09	4	2.34	28(92.28), 29(4.67), 30(3.05)	277,200
15	P	Phosphorus	30.975	5, ±3	2.16	31(100)	1,180
16	S	Sulfur	32.066	6, 4, −2	2.12	32(95.018), 34(4.215) 33(0.74), 36(0.016)	520
17	Cl	Chlorine	35.457	±1, 7, 5	1.94	35(75.4), 37(24.6)	314
18	A	Argon	39.944	0	3.82	40(99.60), 36(0.337), 38(0.060)	0.04
19	K	Potassium	39.100	1	4.76	39(93.1), 41(6.9), 40‡(0.012)	25,900
20	Ca	Calcium	40.08	2	3.93	40(96.96), 44(2.06), 42(0.64), 48(0.19), 43(0.15), 46(0.0033)	36,300
21	Sc	Scandium	44.96	3	3.20	45(100)	5
22	Ti	Titanium	47.90	4, 3	2.93	48(73.45), 46(7.95), 47(7.75), 49(5.51), 50 (5.34)	4,400
23	V	Vanadium	50.95	5, 4, 2	2.71	51(99.76), 50(0.24)	150
24	Cr	Chromium	52.01	6, 3, 2	2.57	52(83.76), 53(9.55), 50(4.31), 54(2.38)	200
25	Mn	Manganese	54.94	7, 4, 2, 6, 3	2.5	55(100)	1,000
26	Fe	Iron	55.85	3, 2	2.52	56(91.64), 54(5.81), 57(2.21), 58(0.34)	50,000
27	Co	Cobalt	58.94	3, 2	2.50	59(100)	23
28	Ni	Nickel	58.69	2, 3	2.49	58(67.76), 60(26.16), 62(3.66), 61(1.25), 64(1.16)	80
29	Cu	Copper	63.54	2, 1	2.551	63(69.09), 65(30.91)	70
30	Zn	Zinc	65.38	2	2.748	64(48.89), 66(27.81), 68(18.61), 67(4.07), 70(0.620)	132
31	Ga	Gallium	69.72	3	2.7	69(60.2), 71(39.8)	15
32	Ge	Germanium	72.60	4	2.788	74(36.74), 72(27.37), 70(20.55), 76(7.67), 73(7.61)	7
33	As	Arsenic	74.91	5, ±3	2.50	75(100)	5
34	Se	Selenium	78.96	6, 4, −2	2.32	80(49.82), 78(23.52), 82(9.19), 76(9.02), 77(7.58), 74(0.87)	0.09
35	Br	Bromine	79.916	±1, 5	2.26	79(50.5), 81(49.5)	1.62

TABLE 7b-3. PROPERTIES OF ELEMENTS* (*Continued*)

Z	Symbol	Element	Atomic wt.†	Valency	Atomic diam	Mass No. and (abundance)	Terrestrial abundance,¶ g/ton
(1)	(2)	(3)	(4)	(5)	(6)	(7)	(8)
36	Kr	Krypton	83.80	0	4.0	84(56.90), 86(17.37), 82(11.56), 83(11.55), 80(2.27), 78(0.354)	$9.8 \cdot 10^{-6}$
37	Rb	Rubidium	85.48	1	5.02	85(72.15), 87(27.85)	310
38	Sr	Strontium	87.63	2	4.29	88(82.56), 86(9.86), 87(7.02), 84(0.56)	300
39	Y	Yttrium	88.92	3	3.62	89(100)	28.1
40	Zr	Zirconium	91.22	4	3.19	90(51.46), 94(17.40), 92(17.11), 91(11.23), 96(2.80)	220
41	Nb	Niobium	92.91	5, 3	2.94	93(100)	24
42	Mo	Molybdenum	95.95	6, 3, 5	2.80	98(23.75), 96(16.5), 92(15.86), 95(15.7), 100(9.62), 97(9.45), 94(9.12)	15
43	Tc	Technetium	(99)	7			
44	Ru	Ruthenium	101.1	3, 4, 6, 8	2.67	102(31.34), 104(18.27), 101(16.98), 99(12.81), 100(12.70), 96(5.7), 98(2.22)	0.004
45	Rh	Rhodium	102.91	3, 4	2.7	103(100)	0.001
46	Pd	Palladium	106.7	2, 4	2.745	106(27.2), 109(26.8), 105(22.6), 110(13.5), 104(9.3), 102(0.8)	0.010
47	Ag	Silver	107.880	1	2.883	107(51.35), 109(48.65)	0.10
48	Cd	Cadmium	112.41	2	3.042	114(28.86), 112(24.07), 111(12.75), 110(12.39), 113(12.26), 116(7.58), 106(1.215), 108(0.875)	0.15
49	In	Indium	114.76	3	3.14	115(95.77), 113(4.23)	0.1
50	Sn	Tin	118.70	4, 2	3.164	120(33.03), 118(23.98), 116(14.07), 119(8.62), 117(7.54), 124(6.11), 122(4.78), 112(0.90), 114(0.61), 115(0.35)	40
51	Sb	Antimony	121.76	3, 5	3.228	121(57.25), 123(42.75)	1
52	Te	Tellurium	127.61	4, 6, −2	2.9	130(34.46), 128(31.72), 126(18.72), 125(7.01), 124(4.63), 122(2.49), 123(0.89), 120(0.091)	0.002
53	I	Iodine	126.91	−1, 5, 7	2.7	127(100)	0.3
54	Xe	Xenon	131.3	0	4.4	132(26.96), 129(26.44), 131(21.17), 134(10.44), 136(8.95), 130(4.07), 128(1.90), 124(0.094), 126(0.088)	$1.2 \cdot 10^{-6}$
55	Cs	Cesium	132.91	1	5.40	133(100)	7
56	Ba	Barium	137.36	2	4.48	138(71.66), 137(11.32), 136(7.81), 135(6.59), 134(2.42), 130(0.101), 132(0.097)	250
57	La	Lanthanum	138.92	3	3.741	139(99.91) 138(0.089)	18.3
58	Ce	Cerium	140.13	3, 4	3.64	140(88.48), 142(11.07), 138(0.250), 136(0.193)	46.1

TABLE 7b-3. PROPERTIES OF ELEMENTS* (*Continued*)

Z	Symbol	Element	Atomic wt.†	Valency	Atomic diam	Mass No. and (abundance)	Terrestrial abundance,¶ g/ton
(1)	(2)	(3)	(4)	(5)	(6)	(7)	(8)
59	Pr	Praesodymium	140.92	3	3.65	141(100)	5.53
60	Nd	Neodymium	144.27	3	3.63	142(27.13), 144(23.87), 146(17.18), 143(12.20), 145(8.30), 148(5.72), 150(5.60)	23.9
61	Pm	Promethium	(145)	3	.....	....	?
62	Sm	Samarium	150.43	3	.....	152(26.63), 154(22.53), 147(15.07), 149(13.84), 148(11.27), 150(7.47), 144(3.16)	6.47
63	Eu	Europium	152.0	3, 2	4.08	153(52.23), 151(47.77)	1.06
64	Gd	Gadolinium	156.9	3	3.59	158(24.78), 160(21.79), 156(20.59), 157(15.71), 155(14.78), 154(2.15), 152(0.20)	6.36
65	Tb	Terbium	158.93	3	3.54	159(100)	0.91
66	Dy	Dyprosium	162.46	3	3.54	164(28.18), 162(25.53), 163(24.97), 161(18.88), 160(2.294), 158(0.0902), 156(0.0524)	4.47
67	Ho	Holmium	164.94	3	3.52	165(100)	1.15
68	Er	Erbium	167.2	3	3.50	166(33.41), 168(27.07), 167(22.94), 170(14.88), 164(1.56), 162(0.1)	2.47
69	Tm	Thulium	168.94	3	3.48	169(100)	0.20
70	Yb	Ytterbium	173.04	3, 2	3.87	174(31.84), 172(21.82), 173(16.13), 171(14.26), 176(12.73), 170(3.03), 168(0.14)	2.66
71	Lu	Lutetium	174.99	3	3.47	175(97.5), 176(2.5)	0.75
72	Hf	Hafnium	178.6	4	3.17	180(35.11), 178(27.10), 177(18.47), 179(13.85), 176(5.30), 174(0.18)	4.5
73	Ta	Tantalum	180.95	5	2.94	181(100)	2.1
74	W	Wolfram	183.92	6	2.82	184(30.68), 186(29.17), 182(25.77), 183(14.24), 180(0.122)	69
75	Re	Rhenium	186.31	7, 4, −1	2.75	187(62.93), 185(37.07)	0.001
76	Os	Osmium	190.2	4, 6, 8	2.70	192(41.0), 190(26.4), 189(16.1), 188(13.3), 187(1.64), 186(1.59), 184(0.018)	0.005
77	Ir	Iridium	192.2	3, 4, 6	2.709	193(61.5), 191(38.5)	0.001
78	Pt	Platinum	195.23	4, 2	2.769	195(33.7), 194(32.8), 196(25.4), 198(7.23), 192(0.78), 190(0.012)	0.005
79	Au	Gold	197.0	3, 1	2.878	197(100)	0.005
80	Hg	Mercury	200.61	2, 1	3.10	202(29.80), 200(23.13), 199(16.84), 201(13.2), 198(10.02), 204(6.85), 196(0.15)	0.5
81	Tl	Thallium	204.39	1, 3	3.42	205(70.5), 203(29.5)	3
82	Pb	Lead	207.21	2, 4	3.49	208(52.3), 206(23.6) 207(22.6), 204(1.5), 202(<0.0004)	16

TABLE 7b-3. PROPERTIES OF ELEMENTS* (*Continued*)

Z (1)	Symbol (2)	Element (3)	Atomic wt.† (4)	Valency (5)	Atomic diam (6)	Mass No. and (abundance) (7)	Terrestrial abundance,¶ g/ton (8)
83	Bi	Bismuth	209.00	3, 5	3.64	209(100)	0.2
84	Po	Polonium	(210)	2, 4	.....	210‡	3×10^{-10}
85	At	Astatine	(210)	....	.....	206‡, 215‡	
86	Rn	Radon	(222)	0	.....	222‡	
87	Fr	Francium	(223)	1	.....	223‡	
88	Ra	Radium	226.05	2	.....	226,‡ 228‡, 224‡, 223‡	13×10^{-6}
89	Ac	Actinium	(227)	3	.....	227,‡ 228‡	3×10^{-10}
90	Th	Thorium	232.05	4	3.6	232‡(100)	11.5
91	Pa	Protactinium	(231)	5	.....	231‡	8×10^{-7}
92	U	Uranium	238.07	6, 5, 4, 3	3.0	238‡(99.28) 235‡(0.715) 234‡(0.0058)	4
93	Np	Neptunium	(237)	6, 5, 4, 3	.....	237,‡ 239‡	
94	Pu	Plutonium	(242)	6, 5, 4, 3	.....	238,‡ 239‡	
95	Am	Americium	(243)	3	.....	241‡	
96	Cm	Curium	(243)	3	.....	242‡	
97	Bk	Berkelium	(245)	4, 3	.....	243‡	
98	Cf	Californium	(246)	3	.....	244‡	
99	E	Einsteinium	.....	....	.....	253‡	
100	Fm	Fermium	.....	....	.....	256‡	
101	Mv	Mendelevium					

* Much of the material in this table was taken from Henry D. Hubbard and William F. Meggers "Key to Periodic Chart of the Atoms," 1950. Courtesy of W. M. Welch Manufacturing Company, Chicago.

† E. Wichers, *J. Am. Chem. Soc.* **76,** 2033 (1954).

‡ Radioactive isotope.

¶ For more recent values of abundances see H. E. Suess and H. C. Urey, *Revs. Modern Phys.* **28,** 53 (1956).

7c. The Electronic Structure of Atoms

Explanation of Table 7c-1. COLUMN (3): Electronic structure of the ground state. Rare-gas shells and similar closed shells are indicated by appropriate symbols and only the electrons outside them given explicitly. All structures are based on spectroscopic evidence except in a few cases (e.g., Fr, At) where there is no reasonable doubt about predictions.

The electron printed in boldface when removed produces the ground state of the ion. Where the other electrons are rearranged in the ion this is indicated in a footnote.

COLUMN (4): Ground state of atom.

COLUMN (5): First ionization potential of atom (in electron volts).[1]

COLUMN (6): Ground state of ion. For electron configuration of ion, see column (3).

COLUMN (7): Second ionization potential (ionization potential of singly ionized atom) in electron volts.

COLUMN (8): Resonance potentials (see below).

COLUMN (9): Resonance lines (see below).

RESONANCE POTENTIALS AND RESONANCE LINES: The resonance potential is the energy (in electron volts) required to raise an atom from the ground state to the lowest excited state. The resonance line is the spectrum line absorbed or emitted in this or the reverse transition. There is a clear and unambiguous situation with regard to resonance lines and potentials for atoms with simple structure such as the alkalies. For more complicated atoms the matter needs further amplification.

A line is not considered a resonance line if the excited state has the same parity as the ground state and thus the transition is forbidden as a dipole transition. If the line is allowed as a dipole transition but very weak, i.e., if it violates an approximate dipole-selection rule (usually the spin-selection rule $\Delta S = 0$), it is called subresonance line r. The resonance line R proper is the first line allowed by all the selection rules. Both R and r then are given in such cases. For the heavy elements r may be very strong.

The resonance potentials are in general those corresponding to the lines, with one exception. If there is a lower state than that of the first resonance line for which transitions to the ground state are forbidden by the J-selection rule (but allowed by the parity rule) this state is metastable. It may, however, often be excited by direct electron collisions, and the excitation potential for this state is given as first resonance potential followed by a letter m. There is no observed resonance line corresponding to this transition. An asterisk on the second resonance potential indicates that the corresponding line is that also marked with an asterisk.

A C preceding column (8) means that there are states of the same parity as the ground state between it and the first resonance state. These often belong to the electron configuration of the ground state. A C is *not* listed if these states are merely additional levels of the ground-state multiplet.

[1] For conversion from wave numbers into electron volts or vice versa, see Table 7a-2.

TABLE 7c-1. ELECTRONIC STRUCTURE OF ATOMS[a]

Z	El.	Ground state	Ground state	IP	Ion ground state	IP	Resonance potentials		Resonance lines	
(1)	(2)	(3)	(4)	(5)	(6)	(7)	(8)		(9)	
1	H	$1s$	^2S	13.595	...	......	10.15		1,215.67(^2P)	
2	He	$1s^2$	^1S	24.580	^2S	54.403	20.96*m*	21.13	591.43($^3P_1$)	584.35(^1P)
3	Li	[He]$2s$	^2S	5.390	^1S	75.619	1.84		6,707.85($^2P_{\frac{1}{2}}$)	
4	Be	—$2s^2$	^1S	9.320	^2S	18.206	2.71	5.25	4,548.3($^3P_1$)	2,348.61($^1P_1$)
5	B	—$2s^2$**2p**	$^2P_{\frac{1}{2}}$	8.296	^1S	25.149	3.57	4.94	3,470.6($^4P_{\frac{1}{2}}$)	2,497.72(^2S)
6	C	—$2s^2$**2p²**	$^3P_0$	11.264	$^2P_{\frac{1}{2}}$	24.376	*C*, 4.16	7.46	2,967.22(^5S)	1,656.998(^3P)
7	N	—$2s^2$**2p³**	^4S	14.54	$^3P_0$	29.605	*C*, 10.28		1,200.71(^4P)	
8	O	—$2s^2$**2p⁴**	$^3P_2$	13.614	^4S	35.146	*C*, 9.11	9.48	1,355.60(^5S)	1,302.17(^3S)
9	*F*	—$2s^2$**2p⁵**	$^2P_{\frac{3}{2}}$	17.418	$^3P_2$	34.98	12.69	12.98	976.50(^4P)	954.82(^2P)
10	Ne	—$2s^2$**2p⁶**	^1S	21.559	$^2P_{\frac{3}{2}}$	41.07	16.62*m*	16.84	743.71($^3P_1$)	735.89($^1P_1$)
11	Na	[Ne]$3s$	^2S	5.138	^1S	47.29	2.10		5,889.95($^2P_{\frac{3}{2}}$)	
12	Mg	—$3s^2$	^1S	7.644	^2S	15.03	2.71*m*	4.33	4,571.10($^3P_1$)	2,852.12($^1P_1$)
13	Al	—$3s^2$**3p**	$^2P_{\frac{1}{2}}$	5.984	^1S	18.823	3.13		3,961.52(^2S)	
14	Si	—$3s^2$**3p²**	$^3P_0$	8.149	$^2P_{\frac{1}{2}}$	16.34	*C*,	4.93		2,516.11($^3P_1$)
15	P	—$3s^2$**3p³**	^4S	10.55	$^3P_0$	19.65	*C*, 6.93		1,787.65(^4P)	1,774.94
16	S	—$3s^2$**3p⁴**	$^3P_2$	10.357	^4S	23.4	*C*, 6.50	6.83	1,900.27(^5S)	1,807 31(^3S)
17	Cl	—$3s^2$**3p⁵**	$^2P_{\frac{3}{2}}$	13.01	$^3P_2$	23.80	8.88	9.16	1,389.78($^4P_{\frac{5}{2}}$)	1,347.32($^2P_{\frac{3}{2}}$)
18	A	—$3s^2$**3p⁶**	^1S	15.755	$^2P_{\frac{3}{2}}$	27.62	11.55*m*	11.83	1,066.66($^3P_1$)	1,049.22($^1P_1$)
19	K	[A]$4s$	^2S	4.339	^1S	31.81	1.61		7,664.91($^2P_{\frac{3}{2}}$)	
20	Ca	—$4s^2$	^1S	6.111	^2S	11.87	1.88	2.92	6,572.78($^3P_1$)	4,226.73($^1P_1$)
21	Sc	—$3d$**4s²**	$^2D_{\frac{3}{2}}$	6.56	$^3D_1$	12.80	1.94*m*	1.98	6,378.82($^4F_{\frac{3}{2}}$)	6,305.67($^8D_5$)
22	Ti	—$3d^2$**4s²**	$^3F_2$	6.83	$^2F_{\frac{3}{2}}$	13.57	*C*, 1.96	2.39	6,296.65($^5G_2$)	5,173.74($^3D_1$)
23	V	—$3d^34s^2$	$^4F_{\frac{3}{2}}$	6.74[b]	$^5D_0$	14.65	*C*, 2.23	2.54	5,527.72($^6G_{\frac{1}{2}}$)	4,851.48($^4D_{\frac{1}{2}}$)
24	Cr	—$3d^5$**4s**	^7S	6.764	^6S	16.49	*C*, 2.90		4,289.72($^7P_2$)	
25	Mn	—$3d^5$**4s²**	^6S	7.432	^7S	15.64	*C*, 2.27	3.06	5,432.55($^8P_{\frac{5}{2}}$)	4,034.49($^6P_{\frac{3}{2}}$)
26	Fe	—$3d^6$**4s²**	$^5D_4$	7.90	$^6D_{\frac{9}{2}}$	16.18	*C*, 2.39	3.20	5,166.29($^7D_5$)	3,859.91($^5D_4$)
27	Co	—$3d^74s^2$	$^4F_{\frac{9}{2}}$	7.86[c]	$^3F_4$	17.05	*C*, 2.91	3.50	4,233.99($^6F_{\frac{11}{2}}$)	3,526.85($^4F_{\frac{9}{2}}$)
28	Ni	—$3d^84s^2$	$^3F_4$	7.633[d]	$^2D_{\frac{5}{2}}$	18.15	*C*, 3.18	3.64	3,884.58($^5D_4$)	3,670.43($^3P_2$)
29	Cu	—$3d^{10}$**4s**	^2S	7.724	^1S	20.29	*C*, 3.79		3,273.96($^2P_{\frac{1}{2}}$)	
30	Zn	—$3d^{10}$**4s²**	^1S	9.391	^2S	17.96	4.01*m*	5.77	3,075.90($^3P_1$)	2,138.56($^1P_1$)
31	Ga	—$3d^{10}4s^2$**4p**	$^2P_{\frac{1}{2}}$	6.00	^1S	20.51	3.06		4,032.98(^2S)	
32	Ge	—$3d^{10}4s^2$**4p²**	$^3P_0$	7.88	$^2P_{\frac{1}{2}}$	15.93	*C*, 4.64*m*		2,651.58($^3P_1$)	
33	As	—$3d^{10}4s^2$**4p³**	^4S	9.81	$^3P_0$	20.2	*C*, 6.26		1,972.62($^4P_{\frac{1}{2}}$)	
34	Se	—$3d^{10}4s^2$**4p⁴**	$^3P_2$	9.75	^4S	21.5	*C*, 5.95	6.30	2,074.79(^5S)	1,960.90($^3S_4$)
35	Br	—$3d^{10}4s^2$**4p⁵**	$^2P_{\frac{3}{2}}$	11.84	$^3P_2$	21.6	7.83	8.29	1,576.5($^4P_{\frac{5}{2}}$)	1,488.6($^2P_{\frac{3}{2}}$)
36	Kr	—$3d^{10}4s^2$**4p⁶**	^1S	13.996	$^2P_{\frac{3}{2}}$	24.56	9.91*m*	9.99*	1,235.82*($^3P_1$)	1,164.86(^1P)
37	Rb	[Kr]**5s**	^2S	4.176	^1S	27.5	1.56		7,947.64($^2P_{\frac{1}{2}}$)	
38	Sr	—**5s²**	^1S	5.692	^2S	11.027	1.78*m*	2.68*	6,892.58($^3P_1$)	4,607.33*(^1P)
39	Y	—**4d5**s^2	$^2D_{\frac{3}{2}}$	6.377	^1S	12.233	1.31		9,494.81($^2P_{\frac{1}{2}}$)	
40	Zr	—$4d^2$**5s²**	$^3F_2$	6.835	$^4F_{\frac{3}{2}}$	12.916	*C*, 1.83	2.71	6,762.38($^5G_2$)	4,575.52($^3G_3$)
41	Nb	—$4d^4$**5s**	$^6D_{\frac{1}{2}}$	6.881	$^5D_0$	13.895	*C*, 2.07*m*	2.97*	5,320.21($^6F_{\frac{1}{2}}$)	4,168.12*($^6F_{\frac{1}{2}}$
42	Mo	—$4d^5$**5s**	^7S	7.131	^6S	15.72	*C*, 3.18		3,902.96($^7P_{\frac{1}{2}}$)	
43	Tc	—$4d^5$**5s²**	^6S	7.23	^7S	14.87	2.09	2.88	5,924.57($^8P_{\frac{7}{2}}$)	4,297.06($^6P_{\frac{7}{2}}$)
44	Ru	—$4d^7$**5s**	$^5F_5$	7.365	$^4F_{\frac{9}{2}}$	16.597	*C*, 3.13	3.26*	3,964.90($^7D_5$)	3,799.35*($^5D_4$)
45	Rh	—$4d^8$**5s**	$^4F_{\frac{9}{2}}$	7.461	$^3F_4$	15.92	*C*, 3.36		3,692.36($^4D_{\frac{7}{2}}$)	
46	Pd	—**4d¹⁰**	^1S	8.33	$^2D_{\frac{5}{2}}$	19.42	*C*, 4.22*m*	5.01*	2,763.09($^3P_1$)	2,447.91*($^1P_1$)
47	Ag	—$4d^{10}$**5s**	^2S	7.574	^1S	21.48	3.66		3,382.89($^2P_{\frac{1}{2}}$)	
48	Cd	—$4d^{10}$**5s²**	^1S	8.991	^2S	16.904	3.73*m*	5.29	3,261.04($^3P_1$)	2,288.02($^1P_1$)
49	In	—$4d^{10}5s^2$**5p**	$^2P_{\frac{1}{2}}$	5.785	^1S	18.828	3.02		4,101.76(^2S)	
50	Sn	—$4d^{10}5s^2$**5p²**	$^3P_0$	7.332	$^2P_{\frac{1}{2}}$	14.63	*C*, 4.29*m*	4.33*	2,863.32*($^3P_1$)	
51	Sb	—$4d^{10}5s^2$**5p³**	^4S	8.639	$^3P_0$	19	*C*, 5.36		2,311.47($^4P_{\frac{1}{2}}$)	
52	Te	—$4d^{10}5s^2$**5p⁴**	$^3P_2$	9.01	^4S	21.5	*C*, 5.49	5.78	2,259.02($^5S_2$)	2,142.75($^3S_1$)
53	I	—$4d^{10}5s^2$**5p⁵**	$^2P_{\frac{3}{2}}$	10.44	$^3P_2$	19.0	6.77	7.66	2,062.1($^4P_{\frac{5}{2}}$)	1,617.7($^2P_{\frac{3}{2}}$)
54	Xe	—$4d^{10}5s^2$**5p⁶**	^1S	12.127	$^2P_{\frac{3}{2}}$	21.21	8.31*m*	8.44*	1,469.62*($^3P_1$)	1,295.56($^1P_1$)
55	Cs	[Xe]**6s**	^2S	3.893	^1S	25.1	1.38		8,943.46($^2P_{\frac{1}{2}}$)	8,521.10($^2P_{\frac{3}{2}}$)
56	Ba	—**6s²**	^1S	5.210	^2S	10.001	*C*, 1.52*m*	2.24*	7,911.36($^3P_1$)	5,535.53*(^1P)

TABLE 7c-1. ELECTRONIC STRUCTURE OF ATOMS[a] (*Continued*)

Z	El.	Ground state	Ground state	*IP*	Ion ground state	*IP*	Resonance potentials	Resonance lines	
(1)	(2)	(3)	(4)	(5)	(6)	(7)	(8)	(9)	
57	La	$—5d6s^2$	$^2D_{\frac{3}{2}}$	5.61[e]	$^3F_2$	11.43	*C*, 1.64 1.84*	7,539.24($^4F_{\frac{3}{2}}$)	6,753.05($^2D_{\frac{5}{2}}$)
58	Ce	$—4f5d6s^2$	$^3H_5$	[f]	$^4H_{\frac{7}{2}}$				
59	Pr	$—4f^36s^2$	$^4I_{\frac{9}{2}}$	......	$^5I_4$				
60	Nd	$—4f^46s^2$	$^5I_4$	6.3[g]	$^6I_{\frac{7}{2}}$				
61	Pm	$—4f^56s^2$	$^6H_{\frac{5}{2}}$						
62	Sm	$—4f^66s^2$	$^7S_0$	5.6	$^8F_{\frac{1}{2}}$	11.2	*C*, 1.71*m* 1.74*	7,141.13*($^9F_1$)	6,725.88($^9G_1$)
63	Eu	$—4f^76s^2$	^8S	5.67	^9S	11.24	*C*, 1.74 2.66*	7,106.48($^{10}P_{\frac{7}{2}}$)	4,661.88*($^8P_{\frac{5}{2}}$)
64	Gd	$—4f^75d6s^2$	$^9D_2$	6.16	$^{10}D_{\frac{5}{2}}$	12.+	....		4,225.85
65	Tb	$—4f^85d6s^2$							
66	Dy								
67	Ho								
68	Er								
69	Tm	$—4f^{13}6s^2$	$^2F_{\frac{7}{2}}$	......	$^3F_4$	......	....		5,675.83
70	Yb	$—4f^{14}6s^2$	^1S	6.22	^2S	12.10			3,987.99
71	Lu	$—4f^{14}5d6s^2$	$^2D_{\frac{3}{2}}$	6.15	^1S	14.7			
72	Hf	$—4f^{14}5d^26s^2$	$^3F_2$	5.5	$^2D_{\frac{3}{2}}$	14.9	*C*, 2.19		
73	Ta	$—4f^{14}5d^36s^2$	$^4F_{\frac{3}{2}}$	7.7	$^5F_1$	......	*C*, 2.90	4,280.47	
74	W	$—4f^{14}5d^46s^2$	$^5D_0$	7.98	$^6D_{\frac{1}{2}}$	......	*C*, 2.40*m*	4,982.16($^7F_1$)	4.008.75
75	Re	$—4f^{14}5d^56s^2$	^6S	7.87	^7S	......	*C*, 2.35 3.58	5,275.53($^8P_{\frac{5}{2}}$)	3,464.72($^6P_{\frac{5}{2}}$)
76	Os	$—4f^{14}5d^66s^2$	$^5D_4$	8.7	...	......	*C*, 2.80	4,420.67($^7D_4$)	
77	Ir	$—4f^{14}5d^76s^2$	$^4F_{\frac{9}{2}}$	9.2	....	......	*C*, 3.26	3,800.12($^6D_{\frac{9}{2}}$)	
78	Pt	$—4f^{14}5d^96s$	$^3D_3$	9.0	$^2D_{\frac{5}{2}}$	18.56	*C*, 3.74 4.04	3,315.05($^5D_4$)	3,064.71($^3P_2$)
79	Au	[h]6s	^2S	9.22	^1S	20.5	*C*, 4.63	2,675.95($^2P_{\frac{1}{2}}$)	2,427.95($^2P_{\frac{3}{2}}$)
80	Hg	$—6s^2$	^1S	10.434	^2S	18.751	4.67*m* 6.70	2,536.52($^3P_1$)	1,849.57($^1P_1$)
81	Tl	$—6s^26p$	$^2P_{\frac{1}{2}}$	6.106	^1S	20.42	3.29	3,775.72(^2S)	
82	Pb	$—6s^26p^2$	$^3P_0$	7.415	$^2P_{\frac{1}{2}}$	15.028	*C*, 4.33*m* 4.37	2,833.07*($^3P_1$)	
83	Bi	$—6s^26p^3$	^4S	7.287	$^3P_0$	19.3	*C*, 4.04	3,067.72($^4P_{\frac{1}{2}}$)	
84	Po	$—6s^26p^4$	$^3P_2$	8.43	...	......	....		2,449.99
85	At	$—6s^26p^5$	$^2P_{\frac{3}{2}}$*						
86	Rn	$—6s^26p^6$	^1S	10.745	...	......	6.77*m* 6.94*	1,786.07*($^3P_1$)	1,451.56($^1P_1$)
87	Fr	[Rn]7s	^2S*						
88	Ra	$—7s^2$	^1S	5.277	^2S	10.14	1.62*m* 2.57*	7,141.21	4,825.91*
89	Ac	$—6d7s^2$	$^2D_{\frac{3}{2}}$	......	^1S				
90	Th	$—6d^27s^2$	$^3F_2$	......	$^4F_{\frac{3}{2}}$				
91	Pa	$—6d^37s^2$*							
92	U	$—5f^36d7s^2$	$^5L_6$	4	$^4I_{\frac{9}{2}}$	......	....		5,915.40
93	Np								
94	Pu								
95	Am								
96	Cm								
97	Bk								
98	Cf								

[a] Data taken from current literature. Use has been made of Moore, "Atomic Energy Levels," vols. I and II, and "Smithsonian Physical Tables," 9th ed.

[b] Normal state of ion—$3d^4$.

[c] Normal state of ion—$3d^8$.

[d] Normal state of ion—$3d^9$.

[e] Normal state of ion—$5d^2$.

[f] Normal state of ion—$4f^26s$.

[g] Normal state of ion—$4f^56s$.

[h] Structure of closed shells [Xe]$4f^{14}5d^{10}$.

7d. Structure of Atomic Spectra

7d-1. General Structure of Spectra. There are three types of atomic spectra with many intergradations. The simplest type is the so-called *series spectrum*, in its simplest form due to one valence electron (example Na, but the spectra of He, Ca, Cu, etc., belong here in large part). These spectra are characterized by simple Rydberg series, each often containing many members, but the spectrum on the whole is not rich in lines. The structure is apparent and can easily be analyzed. The levels are single, double, or triple but very rarely of higher multiplicity.

The second type of spectrum is typified by the so-called *multiplet* structure which is based on the L, S coupling scheme. The most prominent lines usually can readily be recognized as transitions between two multiple levels, with multiplicities up to 11 actually being found. Recognition of this type of structure first became possible in the early 1920s with the advance of the quantum theory of atomic structure. Zeeman effects follow a simple pattern (see Sec. 7m) and are very helpful for the analysis. Typical examples are Fe and other elements of the iron group. The spectra of these are much richer in lines than the spectra of the first type. The analysis, while considerably more laborious than that of the series spectra, can usually be accomplished with a reasonable effort. Some regularities usually can be immediately recognized.

The third type, of which the spectra of the rare earths and of the actinides furnish typical examples, has no immediately discernible regularities. The spectra are extremely rich in lines, with no particular groups standing out. If one still can speak of multiplets, they have no regular structure and the Zeeman effects follow no simple rule; although very useful. They are much more difficult to interpret than the previous types. Only a very small fraction of this kind of spectrum has so far yielded to analysis.

Analysis of a spectrum means determining the energy levels which are responsible for the spectrum lines. Besides the magnitude of the energy level [now usually expressed in wave numbers (cm^{-1}) above the ground level of the atom] it is important to know the identity of the level, i.e., the set of quantum numbers that characterize it.

Each electron has in the first place a principal quantum number n and an azimuthal quantum number l. The latter is identical with the orbital angular momentum expressed in units $\hbar$. The value of the principal quantum number is expressed by an integer and that of the azimuthal quantum number by a letter symbol according to the following key:

l (or L)	0	1	2	3	4	5	6	7	8
	s	p	d	f	g	h	i	k	l
or	S	P	D	F	G	H	I	K	L

etc., in alphabetical sequence. Lower-case letters are used if the symbol refers to a single electron, capital letters when it refers to a configuration (resultant of several electrons). For the description of the optical spectra only the electrons outside a closed shell need to be specified. These are often, although somewhat loosely, called *valence* electrons.

Each electron, besides the quantum numbers n and l, has a spin which always has the value $s = \frac{1}{2}$ (again in units $\hbar$). Quantum numbers s and l form a resultant j (total angular momentum) which can have the two values $l + \frac{1}{2}$ and $l - \frac{1}{2}$ (except for $l = 0$; then $j = \frac{1}{2}$). Finally the orientation of the plane of the orbit may be specified by the projection m of j on a fixed axis. Usually the z axis, considered vertical, is taken as this fixed axis. The number m can have all values from $-j$ to $+j$ in integer steps. The four quantum numbers n, l, j, m, or an equivalent set, are sufficient for the characterization of the energy levels of a single electron. In this case, in the absence of external fields, the three angular momenta specified by l, j, and m are constants of the motion (in more precise quantum-mechanical terminology, they commute with each other and the Hamiltonian) and, therefore, have definite values.

If there are several valence electrons it might be thought appropriate to specify the values of n, l, j, m for each electron. This, however, is not particularly useful; because of the interaction between the electrons, the angular momenta of the individual electrons no longer are constants of the motion and, therefore, have no definite values. On the other hand, the total angular momentum J of a free atom is always a constant of the motion and has a definite value regardless of the internal forces in the atom. The same is true of M, the projection of J on a fixed axis (the z axis), which is constant even if the atom is in a constant electric or magnetic field parallel to the z axis. J and M, therefore, are appropriate quantum numbers for any state of the atom, but by themselves not enough to characterize it.

The other quantum numbers necessary for defining a level are usually arrived at by leaving out certain interactions between the various electrons. They have then a definite physical meaning and in most cases give the magnitude of certain angular momenta. If the omitted interactions are reinstated the quantum numbers lose their physical significance but still may be used to label the particular level. If the interaction is relatively small the quantum numbers still have approximately their original physical significance. The interactions within an atom are often called couplings, and in the treatment of atomic levels and states certain types of couplings can often be neglected with respect to others. This leads to different types of coupling schemes which differ by the particular interactions that are neglected in first approximation.

7d-2. Russell-Saunders Coupling. The most important coupling scheme and the only one suitable for an elementary discussion is the so-called Russell-Saunders coupling scheme, also called L, S coupling. The fundamental interactions within an atom are the electrostatic repulsion between the individual electrons, the magnetic interaction between spin and orbit, and the magnetic interaction between the individual spins. Interactions with the nuclear spin are ordinarily of much smaller magnitude and usually can be disregarded.

In the L, S coupling the magnetic spin-orbit interaction is disregarded in first approximation. Then the total orbital angular momentum L and the total spin S are completely independent of each other and both are constants of the motion. This is often expressed by saying that L and S are "good" quantum numbers. The characterization of the individual electrons by their values of n_i and l_i is retained. For two electrons the possible values of L and S are

$$|l_1 - l_2| \leq L \leq l_1 + l_2 \tag{7d-1}$$

$$s_1 - s_2 = 0 \leq S \leq s_1 + s_2 = 1 \qquad \text{as always, } s_i = \tfrac{1}{2} \tag{7d-2}$$

The case for more than two electrons can easily be derived by applying the above rules for quantum-vector addition repeatedly. By the same rule the total angular momentum J which is the vector resultant of L and S has the possible values

$$|L - S| \leq J \leq L + S \qquad \text{in integer steps} \tag{7d-3}$$

If $L \geq S$ this gives $2S + 1$ different J values for a given value of L and S (if $L < S$ this number is $2L + 1$). $2S + 1$ is called the *multiplicity* of the levels (even if $L < S$). It is an odd number if S is an integer and this is the case for an even number of electrons and the multiplicity is an even number for half integer values of S (odd number of electrons). As long as the spin-orbit interaction is disregarded all $2S + 1$ (or $2L + 1$, respectively) levels belonging to a fixed L and S have the same energy. If this interaction is not exactly zero the $2S + 1$ coinciding levels will split and we have a multiplet. In specific cases they are called singlets ($2S + 1 = 1$), doublets (2), triplets (3), quartets (4), quintets (5), sextets (6), etc.

Note that, for instance, a septet level is only sevenfold if $L \geq S$ or as $S = 3$ only for ${}^7F$ or higher levels. The S, P, D levels have one, three, and five components, respectively.

7d-3. L, S Notation. A particular level is now designated by the n and l values of the individual valence electrons, the resultant L of the whole configuration, the value of the multiplicity $2S + 1$ as an anterior superscript, and the value of J as a subscript.

One very important property of atomic-energy levels is called *parity*. A level is called even when the sum of the l values of all electrons outside a closed shell is even, odd if this sum is odd. It is obvious that, to determine this, it is only necessary to count the electrons with odd values of l—i.e., p and f electrons—as h ($l = 5$) or higher electrons virtually never occur. States can be called strictly even or odd only as long as there is a center of symmetry.

In many tabulations the odd levels are distinguished by a superscript ^{0}, e.g., ${}^3F^0_2$. Often the odd energy levels are printed in italics to distinguish them from the even ones.

An example is $3s3p3d4d\ {}^5F_4$ meaning $L = 3$, $S = 2$, $J = 4$. Equivalent electrons are electrons having the same n and l. Their number is indicated by an exponent instead of the repetition of the symbol, thus $3d^4$ instead of $3d3d3d3d$.

Limit of the Quantum Numbers. Once the number and type of valence electrons are specified the possible values of L, S, and J can easily be found.

The maximum value of L is for n electrons

$$L_{\max} = l_1 + l_2 + \cdot \cdot \cdot + l_n$$

the minimum value is the smallest number that can be obtained by combining the l_i as vectors. The same is true for the values of S and the resulting multiplicities. Table 7d-1 lists the possible multiplicities for up to 10 valence electrons.

TABLE 7d-1. POSSIBLE MULTIPLICITY WITH n ELECTRONS OUTSIDE A CLOSED SHELL

n											
1		2									
2	1		3								
3		2		4							
4	1		3		5						
5		2		4		6					
6	1		3		5		7				
7		2		4		6		8			
8	1		3		5		7		9		
9		2		4		6		8		10	
10	1		3		5		7		9		11

If the electrons are equivalent, use Table 7d-3, and add one for each nonequivalent electron added.

With L and S given, the possible J values are indicated by (7d-3). Table 7d-2 lists the J values for all multiplets likely to occur in all but the most complicated spectra.

Each multiplet state is $2J + 1$ fold degenerate. This degeneracy can be partly or

TABLE 7d-2. J VALUES FOR MULTIPLETS

Term	S =	0	1	2	3	4	5	$\frac{1}{2}$	$1\frac{1}{2}$	$2\frac{1}{2}$	$3\frac{1}{2}$	$4\frac{1}{2}$
		Multiplicity ($2S+1$)										
	L	1	3	5	7	9	11	2	4	6	8	10
S	0	0	1	2	3	4	5	$\frac{1}{2}$	$1\frac{1}{2}$	$2\frac{1}{2}$	$3\frac{1}{2}$	$4\frac{1}{2}$
P	1	...	0	1	2	3	4	$\frac{1}{2}$	$\frac{1}{2}$	$1\frac{1}{2}$	$2\frac{1}{2}$	$3\frac{1}{2}$
		1	1	2	3	4	5	$1\frac{1}{2}$	$1\frac{1}{2}$	$2\frac{1}{2}$	$3\frac{1}{2}$	$4\frac{1}{2}$
		...	2	3	4	5	6	...	$2\frac{1}{2}$	$3\frac{1}{2}$	$4\frac{1}{2}$	$5\frac{1}{2}$
D	2	...	...	0	1	2	3	...	$\frac{1}{2}$	$\frac{1}{2}$	$1\frac{1}{2}$	$2\frac{1}{2}$
		...	1	1	2	3	4	$1\frac{1}{2}$	$1\frac{1}{2}$	$1\frac{1}{2}$	$2\frac{1}{2}$	$3\frac{1}{2}$
		2	2	2	3	4	5	$2\frac{1}{2}$	$2\frac{1}{2}$	$2\frac{1}{2}$	$3\frac{1}{2}$	$4\frac{1}{2}$
		...	3	3	4	5	6	...	$3\frac{1}{2}$	$3\frac{1}{2}$	$4\frac{1}{2}$	$5\frac{1}{2}$
		...	...	4	5	6	7	...	...	$4\frac{1}{2}$	$5\frac{1}{2}$	$6\frac{1}{2}$
F	3	...	...	...	0	1	2	...	...	$\frac{1}{2}$	$\frac{1}{2}$	$1\frac{1}{2}$
		...	...	1	1	2	3	...	$1\frac{1}{2}$	$1\frac{1}{2}$	$1\frac{1}{2}$	$2\frac{1}{2}$
		...	2	2	2	3	4	$2\frac{1}{2}$	$2\frac{1}{2}$	$2\frac{1}{2}$	$2\frac{1}{2}$	$3\frac{1}{2}$
		3	3	3	3	4	5	$3\frac{1}{2}$	$3\frac{1}{2}$	$3\frac{1}{2}$	$3\frac{1}{2}$	$4\frac{1}{2}$
		...	4	4	4	5	6	...	$4\frac{1}{2}$	$4\frac{1}{2}$	$4\frac{1}{2}$	$5\frac{1}{2}$
		...	...	5	5	6	7	...	...	$5\frac{1}{2}$	$5\frac{1}{2}$	$6\frac{1}{2}$
		...	...	...	6	7	8	...	...	...	$6\frac{1}{2}$	$7\frac{1}{2}$
G	4	...	...	...	...	0	1	...	...	...	$\frac{1}{2}$	$\frac{1}{2}$
		...	...	...	1	1	2	...	...	$1\frac{1}{2}$	$1\frac{1}{2}$	$1\frac{1}{2}$
		...	...	2	2	2	3	...	$2\frac{1}{2}$	$2\frac{1}{2}$	$2\frac{1}{2}$	$2\frac{1}{2}$
		...	3	3	3	3	4	$3\frac{1}{2}$	$3\frac{1}{2}$	$3\frac{1}{2}$	$3\frac{1}{2}$	$3\frac{1}{2}$
		4	4	4	4	4	5	$4\frac{1}{2}$	$4\frac{1}{2}$	$4\frac{1}{2}$	$4\frac{1}{2}$	$4\frac{1}{2}$
		...	5	5	5	5	6	...	$5\frac{1}{2}$	$5\frac{1}{2}$	$5\frac{1}{2}$	$5\frac{1}{2}$
		...	...	6	6	6	7	...	...	$6\frac{1}{2}$	$6\frac{1}{2}$	$6\frac{1}{2}$
		...	...	...	7	7	8	...	...	...	$7\frac{1}{2}$	$7\frac{1}{2}$
		...	...	...	...	8	9	...	...	...	...	$8\frac{1}{2}$
H	5	...	...	...	...	...	0	...	...	...	...	$\frac{1}{2}$
		...	...	...	...	1	1	...	...	...	$1\frac{1}{2}$	$1\frac{1}{2}$
		...	...	...	2	2	2	...	...	$2\frac{1}{2}$	$2\frac{1}{2}$	$2\frac{1}{2}$
		...	...	3	3	3	3	...	$3\frac{1}{2}$	$3\frac{1}{2}$	$3\frac{1}{2}$	$3\frac{1}{2}$
		...	4	4	4	4	4	$4\frac{1}{2}$	$4\frac{1}{2}$	$4\frac{1}{2}$	$4\frac{1}{2}$	$4\frac{1}{2}$
		5	5	5	5	5	5	$5\frac{1}{2}$	$5\frac{1}{2}$	$5\frac{1}{2}$	$5\frac{1}{2}$	$5\frac{1}{2}$
		...	6	6	6	6	6	...	$6\frac{1}{2}$	$6\frac{1}{2}$	$6\frac{1}{2}$	$6\frac{1}{2}$
		...	...	7	7	7	7	...	...	$7\frac{1}{2}$	$7\frac{1}{2}$	$7\frac{1}{2}$
		...	...	...	8	8	8	...	...	...	$8\frac{1}{2}$	$8\frac{1}{2}$
		...	...	...	...	9	9	...	...	...	...	$9\frac{1}{2}$
		...	...				10					

TABLE 7d-2. J VALUES FOR MULTIPLETS (*Continued*)

Term	$S =$	0	1	2	3	4	5	$\frac{1}{2}$	$1\frac{1}{2}$	$2\frac{1}{2}$	$3\frac{1}{2}$	$4\frac{1}{2}$
	L	Multiplicity $(2S + 1)$										
		1	3	5	7	9	11	2	4	6	8	10
I	6	...	...	...	...	...	1	...	...	...	...	$1\frac{1}{2}$
		...	...	...	...	2	2	...	...	...	$2\frac{1}{2}$	$2\frac{1}{2}$
		...	...	...	3	3	3	...	...	$3\frac{1}{2}$	$3\frac{1}{2}$	$3\frac{1}{2}$
		...	...	4	4	4	4	...	$4\frac{1}{2}$	$4\frac{1}{2}$	$4\frac{1}{2}$	$4\frac{1}{2}$
		...	5	5	5	5	5	$5\frac{1}{2}$	$5\frac{1}{2}$	$5\frac{1}{2}$	$5\frac{1}{2}$	$5\frac{1}{2}$
		6	6	6	6	6	6	$6\frac{1}{2}$	$6\frac{1}{2}$	$6\frac{1}{2}$	$6\frac{1}{2}$	$6\frac{1}{2}$
		...	7	7	7	7	7	...	$7\frac{1}{2}$	$7\frac{1}{2}$	$7\frac{1}{2}$	$7\frac{1}{2}$
		...	...	8	8	8	8	...	...	$8\frac{1}{2}$	$8\frac{1}{2}$	$8\frac{1}{2}$
		...	...	...	9	9	9	...	...	...	$9\frac{1}{2}$	$9\frac{1}{2}$
		...	...	...	...	10	10	...	...	...	...	$10\frac{1}{2}$
		...	...	...	...	...	11	...	...	...	...	...
K	7	...	...	...	...	...	2	...	...	...	...	$2\frac{1}{2}$
		...	...	...	...	3	3	...	...	...	$3\frac{1}{2}$	$3\frac{1}{2}$
		...	...	...	4	4	4	...	...	$4\frac{1}{2}$	$4\frac{1}{2}$	$4\frac{1}{2}$
		...	...	5	5	5	5	...	$5\frac{1}{2}$	$5\frac{1}{2}$	$5\frac{1}{2}$	$5\frac{1}{2}$
		...	6	6	6	6	6	$6\frac{1}{2}$	$6\frac{1}{2}$	$6\frac{1}{2}$	$6\frac{1}{2}$	$6\frac{1}{2}$
		7	7	7	7	7	7	$7\frac{1}{2}$	$7\frac{1}{2}$	$7\frac{1}{2}$	$7\frac{1}{2}$	$7\frac{1}{2}$
		...	8	8	8	8	8	...	$8\frac{1}{2}$	$8\frac{1}{2}$	$8\frac{1}{2}$	$8\frac{1}{2}$
		...	...	9	9	9	9	...	...	$9\frac{1}{2}$	$9\frac{1}{2}$	$9\frac{1}{2}$
		...	...	...	10	10	10	...	...	...	$10\frac{1}{2}$	$10\frac{1}{2}$
		...	...	...	...	11	11	...	...	...	...	$11\frac{1}{2}$
		...	...	...	...	...	12	...	...	...	...	...
L	8	...	...	...	...	...	3	...	...	...	...	$3\frac{1}{2}$
		...	...	...	...	4	4	...	...	...	$4\frac{1}{2}$	$4\frac{1}{2}$
		...	...	...	5	5	5	...	...	$5\frac{1}{2}$	$5\frac{1}{2}$	$5\frac{1}{2}$
		...	...	6	6	6	6	...	$6\frac{1}{2}$	$6\frac{1}{2}$	$6\frac{1}{2}$	$6\frac{1}{2}$
		...	7	7	7	7	7	$7\frac{1}{2}$	$7\frac{1}{2}$	$7\frac{1}{2}$	$7\frac{1}{2}$	$7\frac{1}{2}$
		8	8	8	8	8	8	$8\frac{1}{2}$	$8\frac{1}{2}$	$8\frac{1}{2}$	$8\frac{1}{2}$	$8\frac{1}{2}$
		...	9	9	9	9	9	...	$9\frac{1}{2}$	$9\frac{1}{2}$	$9\frac{1}{2}$	$9\frac{1}{2}$
		...	...	10	10	10	10	...	...	$10\frac{1}{2}$	$10\frac{1}{2}$	$10\frac{1}{2}$
		...	...	...	11	11	11	...	...	...	$11\frac{1}{2}$	$11\frac{1}{2}$
		...	...	...	...	12	12	...	...	...	...	$12\frac{1}{2}$
		...	...	...	...	...	13	...	...	...	...	...

completely removed by an external field, which thus makes each level split into a maximum of $2J + 1$ components (see Zeeman effect in Sec. 7l).

7d-4. Equivalent Electrons. When equivalent electrons are involved the Pauli exclusion principle limits the number of possible states. Table 7d-3 gives a list of possible states for any number of equivalent electrons.

7d-5. Selection Rules. Not all transitions between levels are possible. Rules, derived from quantum mechanics and amply confirmed by experience, state which transitions are allowed and which are forbidden, these are called selection rules. In

TABLE 7d-3. ATOMIC LEVELS OF n EQUIVALENT ELECTRONS

s		^{2}S						
s^2	$^{1}\mathbf{S}$							
p or p^5		$^{2}\mathbf{P}$						
p^2 or p^4	^{1}SD		$^{3}\mathbf{P}$					
p^3		^{2}PD		$^{4}\mathbf{S}$				
d or d^9		$^{2}\mathbf{D}$						
d^2 or d^8	^{1}SDG		$^{3}P\mathbf{F}$					
d^3 or d^7		$^{2}PDFGH$ 2		$^{4}P\mathbf{F}$				
d^4 or d^6	$^{1}SDFGI$ 2 2 2		$^{3}PDFGH$ 2 2		$^{5}\mathbf{D}$			
d^5		$^{2}SPDFGHI$ 3 2 2		$^{4}PDFG$		$^{6}\mathbf{S}$		
f or f^{13}		$^{2}\mathbf{F}$						
f^2 or f^{12}	$^{1}SDGI$		$^{3}PF\mathbf{H}$					
f^3 or f^{11}		$^{2}PDFGHIKL$ 2 2 2 2		$^{4}SDFG\mathbf{I}$				
f^4 or f^{10}	$^{1}SDFGHIKLN$ 2 4 4 2 3 2		$^{3}PDFGHIKLM$ 3 2 4 3 4 2 2		$^{5}SDFG\mathbf{I}$			
f^5 or f^9		$^{2}PDFGHIKLMNO$ 4 5 7 6 7 5 5 3 2		$^{4}SPDFGHIKLM$ 2 3 4 4 3 3 2		$^{6}PF\mathbf{H}$		
f^6 or f^8	$^{1}SPDFGHIKLMNQ$ 4 6 4 8 4 7 3 4 2 2		$^{3}PDFGHIKLMNO$ 6 5 9 7 9 6 6 3 3		$^{5}SPDFGHIKL$ 3 2 3 2 2		$^{7}\mathbf{F}$	
f^7		$^{2}SPDFGHIKLMNOQ$ 2 5 7 10 10 9 9 7 5 4 2		$^{4}SPDFGHIKLMN$ 2 2 6 5 7 5 5 3 3		$^{6}PDFGHI$		$^{8}\mathbf{S}$

A number under a term symbol indicates the number of different levels of this type. The lowest level is normally that with the highest L of the highest multiplicity (Hund's rule). It is indicated in bold type.

applying selection rules one must realize that almost all of them are valid only as long as the assumptions necessary for their derivation remain valid. Therefore, some selection rules are much stricter than others. The principal selection rules for atoms are as follows:

Electric-dipole radiation. These are the most important and are based on the assumption that the radiation field around an atom can be considered with good approximation as the field of a vibrating electric dipole. In the optical region radiation that is *not* electric-dipole radiation is ordinarily at least 10^6 times weaker.

The chief selection rules for dipole radiation for L, S coupling are:

PARITY RULE: Only odd → even or even → odd transitions are allowed. This rule is based on the presence of a center of symmetry and is strictly valid as long as there are no external electric fields. For quadrupole radiation just the opposite rule applies.

To be allowed, a transition must satisfy the following conditions.

J RULE:

$$\Delta J = 0 \pm 1 \qquad (0 \to 0 \text{ is forbidden})$$

This rule is valid as long as J is a constant of motion, that is, in the absence of external fields. If there is a nuclear spin, the total quantum number F which includes the nuclear spin is strictly a constant of the motion and the J rule applies to F instead of J. The lines due to violations of the J rule because of nuclear spin are very weak, however. Strong external electric or magnetic fields, on the other hand, can produce prominent violations of the J rule.

TABLE 7d-4. PRESENT STATUS OF ANALYSIS OF ATOMIC SPECTRA*

Element \ Spectrum	I	II	III	IV	V	VI	VII	VIII	IX	X	XI	XII	XIII	XIV	XV	XVI	XVII	XVIII	XIX	XX	XXI	XXII	XXIII	XXIV
1 H	bA																							
2 He	aA	bA																						
3 Li	bA	bB	eD																					
4 Be	bA	aA	cC	eD																				
5 B	cB	bB	bB	dC	eE																			
6 C	bA	bA	bA	bA	eD	−E																		
7 N	bA	bA	bA	cB	dB	−D	−E																	
8 O	bA	bA	bA	bA	cA	cB	−C	−E																
9 F	cA	cB	cB	eA	−B	−A	−C	−E																
10 Ne	bA	bA	eC	cB	−B	−C																		
11 Na	bA	cB	eB	−C	−C	−B	−A	−A	−B															
12 Mg	bA	aA	cB	eB	eB	−B	−B	−A	−A	−C	−E													
13 Al	aA	aA	aA	eB	eB	eB	−B	−B	−B	−C	−D	−E												
14 Si	bA	bB	bB	bB	eC	−B	−A	−B	−B	−C	−C	−D												
15 P	cB	cB	cA	cA	bA	−C	−B	−B	−A	−B	−C	−C	−D											
16 S	bA	bB	bB	cC	cC	cB	−C	−B	−C	−D		−E												
17 Cl	bA	cA	cB	cB	dC	dC	eC	−C	−C	−C	−E													
18 A	bA	bB	dC	eC	−C	−C	−D	−B	−E	−E	−E			−E										
19 K	bA	cC	cC	eC	−C	−C	−C	−C	−C	−C	−E													
20 Ca	aA	aA	cC	eC	eC	−C	−C	−C	−C	−C	−C	−D	−E		−E									
21 Sc	aA	aA	cC	−E	−D	−C	−D	−C	−C	−D	−C	−D												
22 Ti	aA	aA	cC	cC	−D	−D	−C	−D	−D	−E	−D	−B	−D											
23 V	aA	aA	cC	cC	dD	−D	−D	−D	−D		−E	−C	−B	−D										
24 Cr	bA	cA	dB	cC	cC	eE	−D	−D	−D			−E	−C	−B	−D									
25 Mn	bA	dA	dB	eC	dC	−D	eC	−E	−D	−D			−E	−C	−C	−D								
26 Fe	bA	cA	−A	−E	eC	−C	−C	−C	−E	−D	−D		−E	−E	−D	−B	−D							
27 Co	bA	cB	−B	−E	−E	−C	−C	−D			−D			−E	−E	−D	−C	−D						
28 Ni	aA	bA	−B		−E	−E	−C	−C	−D			−E	−E		−E	−E		−D						
29 Cu	bA	cA	−A				−E												−E					
30 Zn	aA	bB	dD	−E																				
31 Ga	bB	bB	dD	dD																				
32 Ge	cB	cA	cC	cC	dD																			
33 As	cA	−C	cC	cC	dD	−D																		

34 Se	dB	−B	dC	−C	dD	dD	−B																	
35 Br	aA	eC	dD	dD	dD	−D	−E	−B	−D															
36 Kr	aA	cA	dB	−D					−D															
37 Rb	bA	cC	−C						−E	−B	−D	−E	−E	−E										
38 Sr	aA	bA		−D							−B	−D	−E	−E										
39 Y	aA	aA	dD		−B							−C	−D	−E	−E									
40 Zr	aA	aA	aB	cB		−B								−D										
41 Cb	dA	dA	dD	dB	−C	−D	−B																	
42 Mo	cB	dB	−D	−D	−C	−C	−D	−B								−E								
43 Tc	−B	−D																						
44 Ru	cB	cC																						
45 Rh	cB	cB	−C																					
46 Pd	aA	aA																−E		−E				
47 Ag	bA	bA	−B																−E		−E			
48 Cd	bA	bA	cA	−B																−E		−E		
49 In	bA	bA	cC	dD	−C																−E		−E	
50 Sn	cA	bA	cC	cC	dD	−C																−E		−E
51 Sb	dA	−C	cC	cC	dD	−E																	−E	
52 Te	dC	−D	−C	−D	dD	eD	−D																	
53 I	−C	−C	−E	−D				−E																
54 Xe	bA	−A	eA	−D																				
55 Cs	bA	dB	−D																					
56 Ba	aA	bA		−D																				
57 La	cA	bA	dA																					
58 Ce	−E	−B	−B	eB																				
59 Pr		−C																						
60 Nd	−C	−C																						
61 Pm																								
62 Sm	−B	−B																						
63 Eu	−A	−B	−D																					
64 Gd	−B	−B																						
65 Tb	−E	−E																						
66 Dy		−D																						
67 Ho																								
68 Er																								
69 Tm	−D	−C																						
70 Yb	−C	−B	−D																					
71 Lu	−C	−B	−D																					
72 Hf	cB	dA																						

TABLE 7d-4. PRESENT STATUS OF ANALYSIS OF ATOMIC SPECTRA* (*Continued*)

Element \ Spectrum	I	II	III	IV	V	VI	VII	VIII	IX	X	XI	XII	XIII	XIV	XV	XVI	XVII	XVIII	XIX	XX	XXI	XXII	XXIII	XXIV
73 Ta	–B	–B																						
74 W	cB	–C																						
75 Re	dB	–C																						
76 Os	eB																							
77 Ir	dB																							
78 Pt	bB	–A																						
79 Au	dA	dB																						
80 Hg	aA	bA	eC	–D																				
81 Tl	aA	cA	cC	eD																				
82 Pb	aA	cA	cB	dB	dB																			
83 Bi	cB	dC	cC	eC	eD	–B																		
84 Po																								
85 At																								
86 Rn	bA																							
87 Fr																								
88 Ra	–A	dA																						
89 Ac																								
90 Th	–D	–A	–B	–B																				
91 Pa																								
92 U	–B	–B																						
93 Np																								
94 Pu																								
95 Am																								
96 Cm																								
97 Bk																								
98 Cf																								
99																								
100																								

* Compiled by Meggers, *J. Opt. Soc. Am.* **41,** 143 (1951). The present state (1950) is indicated by letters A to E where A means a fairly complete analysis and E that only a few lines have been classified, with B, C, and D intermediate between the two extremes. The small letters preceding the capitals present the state of affairs in 1932.

S RULE:

$$\Delta S = 0$$

This rule applies only as long as S is a constant of the motion, i.e., as long as extreme L, S coupling applies. Spin-orbit interaction will cause deviations from the rule. These same interactions also cause the splitting of the multiplet components. Very narrow multiplets mean, therefore, that the S rule is good, wide multiplets that it is poor. The former happens chiefly for the light elements, the latter for the heavy elements. A magnetic field also can cause violations of the rule.

L RULE:

$$\Delta L = 0 \pm 1 \qquad (0 \rightarrow 0 \text{ excluded})$$

The validity of this rule is also dependent on how well L, S coupling is realized. For moderate multiplet widths, lines with larger changes in L than ± 1 are found but are progressively weaker as the change in L becomes larger. Strong electric fields can cause violations.

The L rule combined with the parity rule excludes $\Delta L = 0$ for one electron spectra.

M RULE:

$$\Delta M = 0 \pm 1$$

is valid to the same extent as the J rule but is also valid in a homogenous external electric or magnetic field. This rule is of importance only in the presence of external fields. For details, see Zeeman effect.

7d-6. Interval and Intensity Rules. The interval rule states that the separation between neighboring multiplet components in the same multiplet is proportional to the larger of the two J values.

Examples. ^3P; the J values are 0, 1, 2. The intervals (0, 1) and (1, 2) are in the ratio 1:2.

^8D, J values (Table 7d-2) $\frac{3}{2}, \frac{5}{2}, \frac{7}{2}, \frac{9}{2}, \frac{11}{2}$ ratio of the separations as 5:7:9:11.

In general we can say that the separation between multiplet components J and $J + 1$ is

$$E = a(J + 1)$$

where a is a constant for the same multiplet but varies from multiplet to multiplet. To calculate the value of a details of the orbits must be known. For a one-electron spectrum (doublets) the constant a is

$$a = \frac{2}{3} \alpha^2 R \frac{Z^4}{n^3 l(l + 1)}$$

where α is the fine-structure constant, R the Rydberg constant, and Z the nuclear charge. We see that the doublet separation diminishes with n as $1/n^3$ and with l as $1/l(l + 1)$. The expression is valid, however, only when the deviations from a Coulomb force field are small.

For elements on the left side of the periodic system, the constant a is positive, which means that the levels with the lower J values have the lower energy. Such multiplets are called *regular* multiplets. On the right side of the periodic system the situation is the opposite and we have inverted multiplets. In the middle the situation is often confused.

The interval rule holds only as long as L, S coupling is valid and is very sensitive for even small deviations from L, S coupling.

Multiplet Intensities. The relative intensities in a multiplet (or rather the line strengths) can easily be computed for L, S coupling. They are valid to the extent that L, S coupling is a good approximation

	Transition		*Line Strength*
$L \to L-1$	$J-1 \to J$	A	$\dfrac{(J+S-L)(J+S-L+1)(L+S-J)(L+S-J+1)}{4J}$
	$J \to J-1$	A	$\dfrac{(J+L-S-1)(J+L-S)(J+L+S+1)(J+L+S)}{4J}$
	$J \to J$	A	$\dfrac{(2J+1)(J+L+S+1)(J+L-S)(J+S-L+1)(L+S-J)}{4J(J+1)}$
$L \to L$	$\left.\begin{matrix} J \to J-1 \\ J-1 \to J \end{matrix}\right\}$	B	$\dfrac{(J+L+S+1)(J+L-S)(J+S-L)(L+S+1-J)}{4J}$
	$J \to J$	B	$\dfrac{(2J+1)[J(J+1)+L(L+1)-S(S+1)]^2}{4J(J+1)}$.

The arrows in the transitions may be reversed without affecting the line strength.

The constants A and B are constant in one multiplet but differ from multiplet to multiplet. Tables of the numerical values of the multiplet strength are found in Condon and Shortley (1935), pp. 241–243.[1] Similar formulas for quadrupole transitions are in Condon and Shortley (1935), p. 253.

Present status of analysis of atomic spectra. This is shown in Table 7d-4. This table shows the present status and the progress made since 1932. It should be kept in mind that even in most spectra marked A the analysis is not anywhere near complete.

7e. Energy-level Diagrams of Atoms

A number of energy-level diagrams are represented in Figs. 7e-1 through 7e-14. An attempt has been made to select typical cases which show characteristic features derived from optical spectra. The following comments may be helpful:

In almost all cases the energy levels have been arranged according to the Russell-Saunders scheme, also called L, S coupling (see Sec. 7d). This means that each level is characterized by the total orbital angular momentum L and the resultant spin S or rather the multiplicity $2S + 1$ [1 for singlets ($S = 0$), 2 for doublets ($S = \frac{1}{2}$), 3 for triplets ($S = 1$), etc.]. Each level characterized by L and S is broken up into $2S + 1$ or $2L + 1$ multiplet components, whichever is the smaller number, each component being characterized by its total angular momentum quantum number J. The possible values of J are shown in Table 7d-2.

The scale of the figures usually does not permit showing the individual multiplet components. However, the total width is indicated unless it is no greater than the thickness of the line.

Even levels are shown by entire lines or blocks, odd levels by broken ones. When an entire column has the same parity, as in the simple spectra, the odd parity is indicated by the term symbol at the bottom of the column in the usual way, e.g., $^3F^0$.

[1] Taken from White and Eliason, *Phys. Rev.* **44**, 753 (1933).

The horizontal line across the whole width of the diagram is at the first ionization potential. This is indicated by the term symbol for the ground state of the ion. In some cases higher ionization potentials are also indicated.

The electron configuration is given by symbols explained with each individual diagram.

Transitions which correspond to spectrum lines are left out in order to avoid confusion except for the important lowest transitions which often give rise to the strongest lines. The resonance line R is the lowest transition to the ground state allowed by the selection rules of L, S coupling, which are change of parity, no change in multiplicity ($\Delta S = 0$), and $\Delta J = 0 \pm 1$. The subresonance line r is a line from a lower level than that responsible for the resonance line; it obeys the same selection rules except $\Delta S = 0$. It is usually very weak for the lighter atoms but may be quite strong for the heavier elements (e.g., 2,537 of Hg).

There may be lines from even lower levels than the resonance line R or the subresonance line r but these would be forbidden lines violating either the parity rule or the ΔJ rule. Such lines are ordinarily much weaker (often of the order of 10^6 times) than the allowed lines and are found only under special conditions of observation. The spectra represented in the figures are given in Table 7e-1.

TABLE 7e-1. SPECTRA REPRESENTED BY FIGS. 7e-1 THROUGH 7e-14

Z	Element	Figure
2	He I	7e-1
6	C I	7e-2
7	N I	7e-3
8	O I	7e-4
11	Na I	7e-5
13	Al I	7e-6
17	Cl I	7e-7
18	A I	7e-8
20	Ca I	7e-9
25	Mn I	7e-10
26	Fe II	7e-11
	Fe I	7e-12
29	Cu I	7e-13
80	Hg I	7e-14

Further diagrams of simple spectra are found in Grotrian (1928).

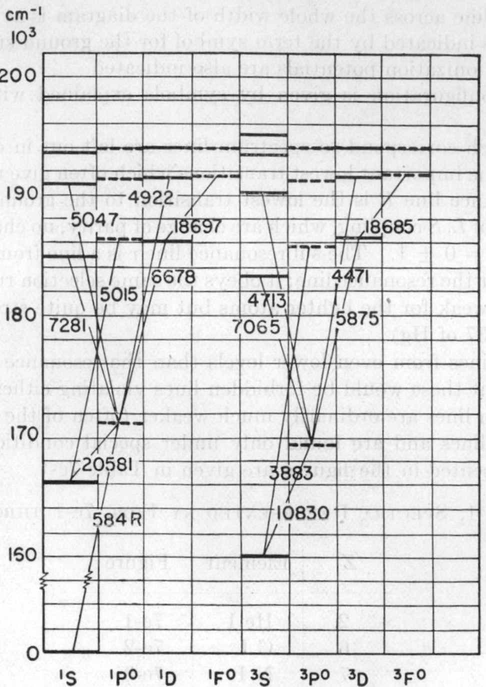

Fig. 7e-1. Energy-level diagram of He I—simplest atom with two valence electrons. The wavelengths of the principal lines are indicated.

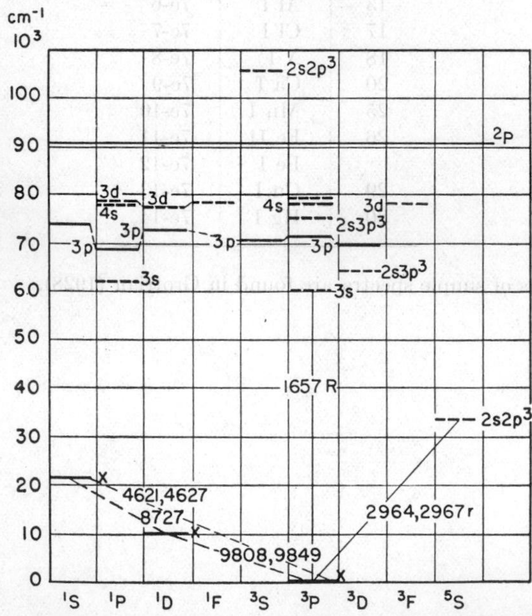

Fig. 7e-2. Energy-level diagram of C I—four valence electrons, lowest state $2s^22p^2$. Most excited states are $2s^22p \cdot nx$. The orbit nx of the last electron only is indicated in the figure except where one of the $2s$ electrons is excited, as, for instance, $2s2p^3$. The important forbidden lines are indicated.

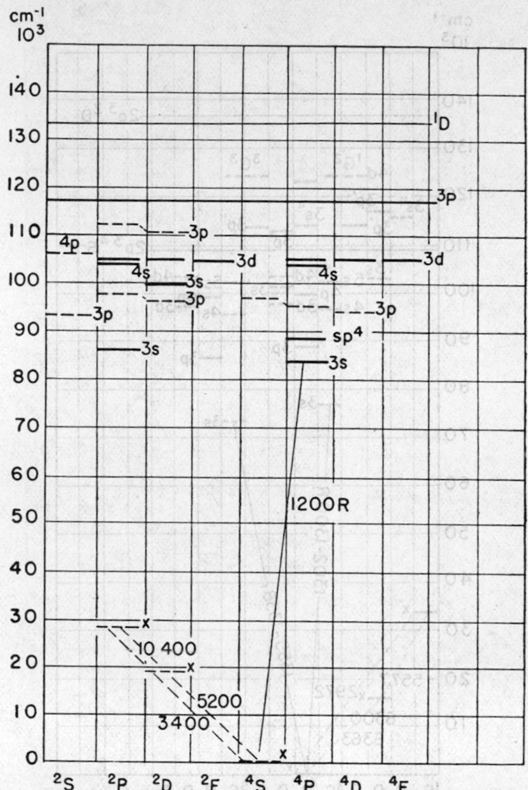

FIG. 7e-3. Energy-level diagram of N I—five valence electrons, normal state $2s^22p^3$. Excited states are $2s^22p^2 \cdot nx$, nx being indicated in the figure. When the $2s$ electron is excited the full configuration is given, e.g., $2s^22p^4$. The important forbidden lines are indicated.

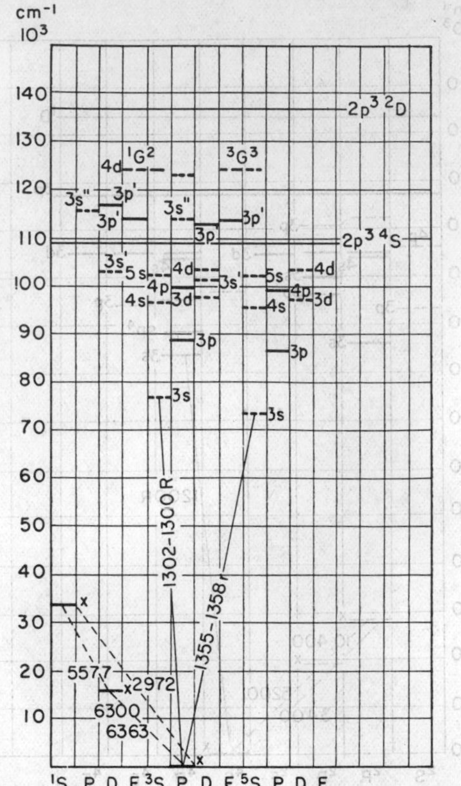

FIG. 7e-4. Energy-level diagram of O I—six valence electrons. Normal state is $2s^22p^4$ excited states are $2s^22p^3 \cdot nx$, nx being indicated in the figure. The important forbidden lines are indicated.

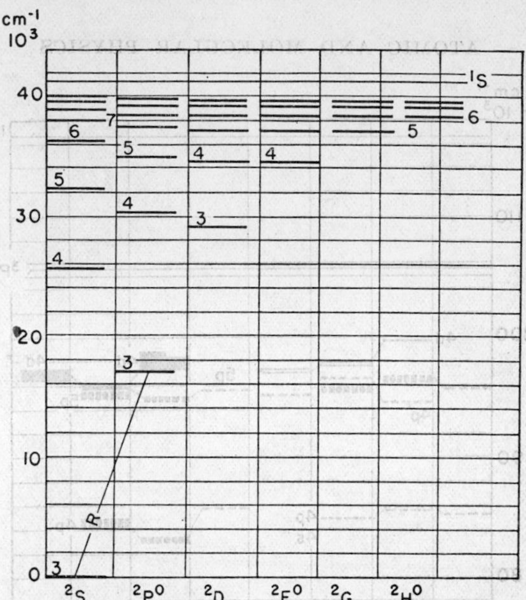

FIG. 7e-5. Energy-level diagram of Na I. Simple diagram typical for elements with one valence electron. The other alkalis have essentially the same scheme.

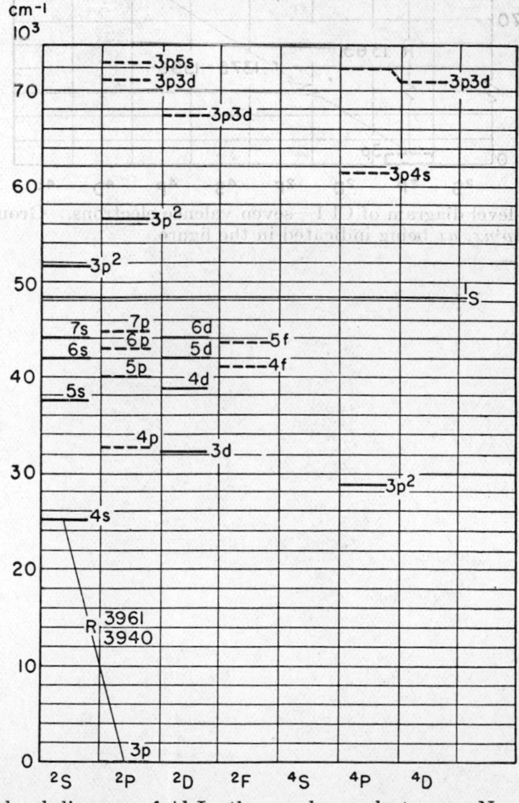

FIG. 7e-6. Energy-level diagram of Al I—three valence electrons. Normal state is $3s^23p$, excited states $3s^2 \cdot nx$ (nx is indicated) or $3s3pnx'$ (nx' is indicated with primed letters). The primed levels converge to a higher ionization limit.

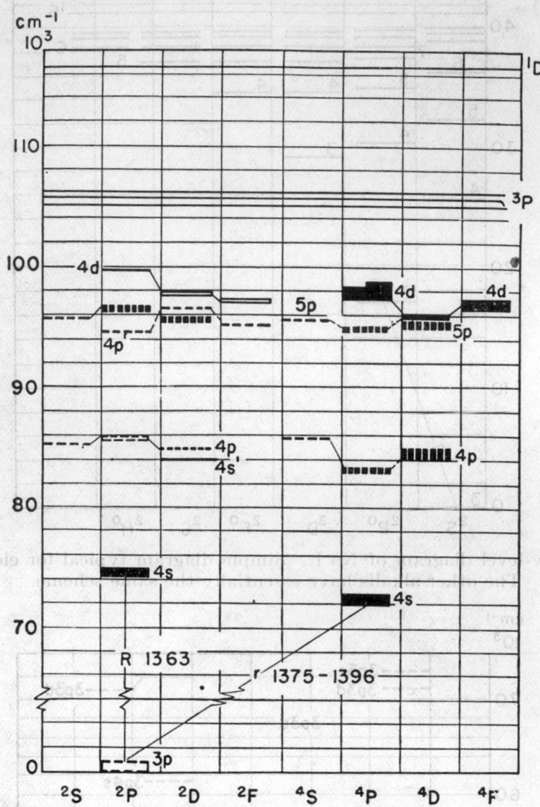

FIG. 7e-7. Energy-level diagram of Cl I—seven valence electrons. Ground state is $3s^23p^5$, excited states $3s^23p^4nx$, nx being indicated in the figure.

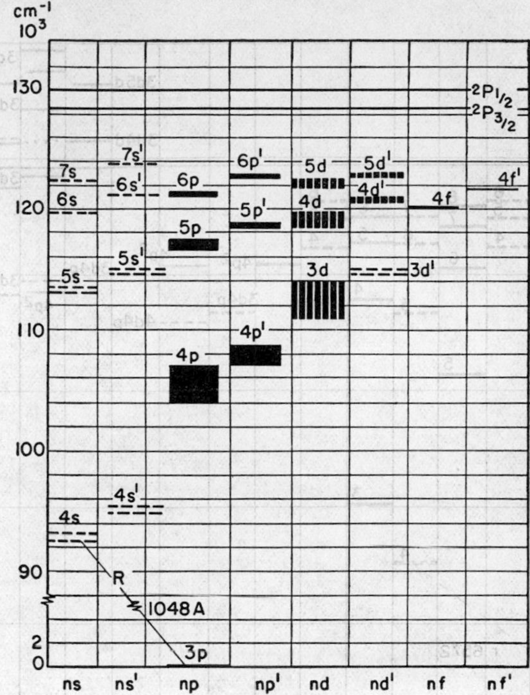

FIG. 7e-8. Energy-level diagram of A I—typical for the rare gases except helium. Levels $3s^23p^5 \cdot nx$ with nx indicated. L, S coupling is not appropriate here and therefore symbols like ^3P, etc., have no meaning. The primed levels converge to the higher ionization potential. See also Table 7g-3.

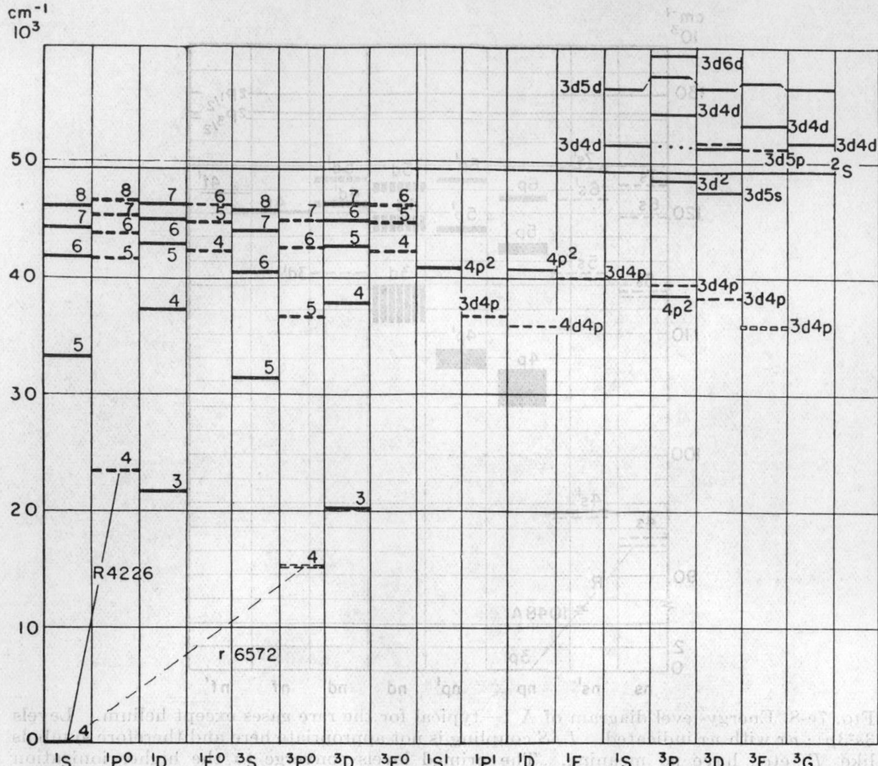

FIG. 7e-9. Energy-level diagram of Ca I. Characteristic for the elements in the second column of the periodic system. Ground state $4s^2$ and regular excited states $4s\ nx$ are indicated only by the value of n in the appropriate column. Levels with both electrons excited are given at the right.

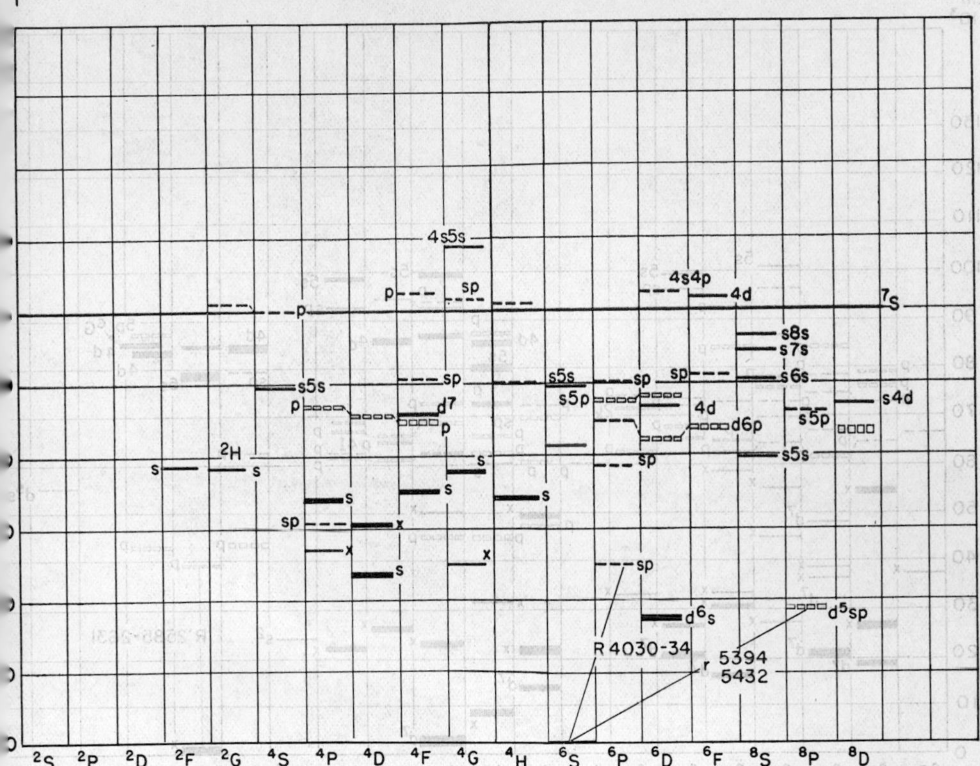

FIG. 7e-10. Energy-level diagram of Mn I. A typical element of the transition group. Seven valence electrons. Ground state $3d^54s^2$. This produces 16 multiplet levels of which only four (^6S, ^4P, ^4D, ^4G) are known. They are marked by an *x*. The other low states are $3d^64s$ (*s*), $3d^64p$ (*p*), $3d^54s4p$ (*sp*), $3d^54p^2$ (p^2), $3d^7$ (d^7). The symbol between parentheses indicates how the level is marked in the figure. If higher than $3d$, $4s$, $4p$ electrons are involved, the value of *n* is marked, e.g., $3d^54s5p$ (*s* 5*p*) or $3d^54s4d$ (*s* 4*d*). In general, the number of $3d$ electrons is left out in the figure (except for $3d^7$). Compare Mn I with Fe II, which has the same number of electrons (Fig. 7e-11).

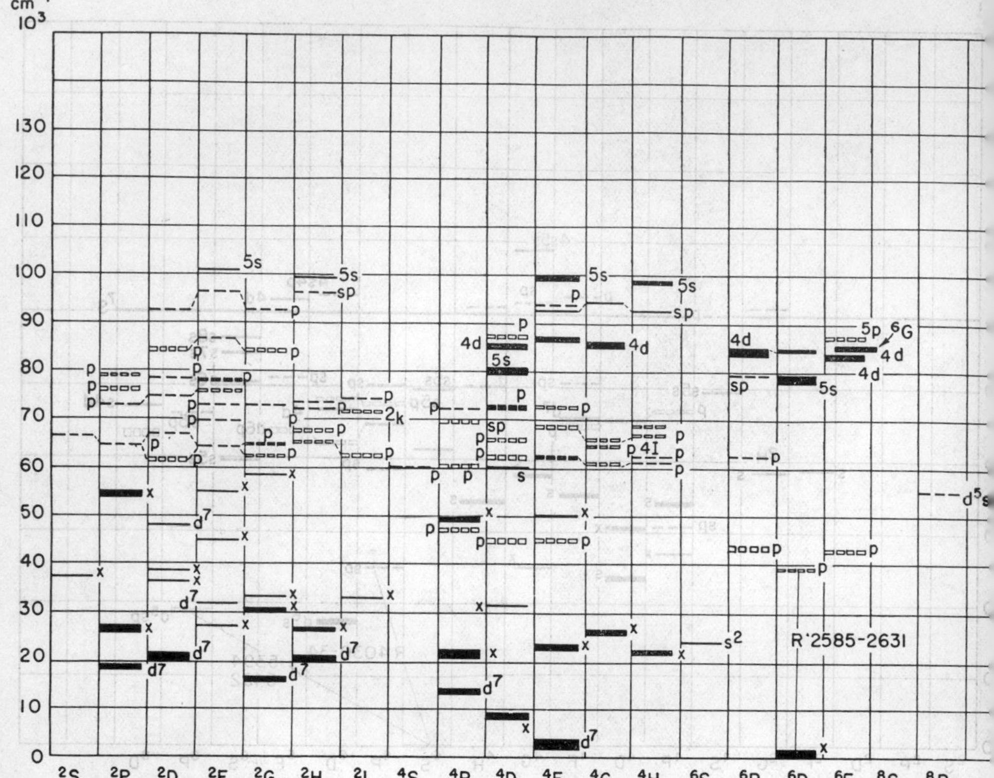

Fig. 7e-11. Energy-level diagram of Fe II. Fe II has the same number of electrons as Mn I and therefore the same type of levels. The relative position of the levels is, however, greatly changed by the increase in the nuclear charge. In general there is a tendency for levels containing $3d$ electrons to be lower than those with $4s$ or $4p$ electrons. The ground state is $3d^64s$. There are 24 multiplet levels of this configuration, of which 23 are known (marked with x). The excited levels are marked as for Mn I.

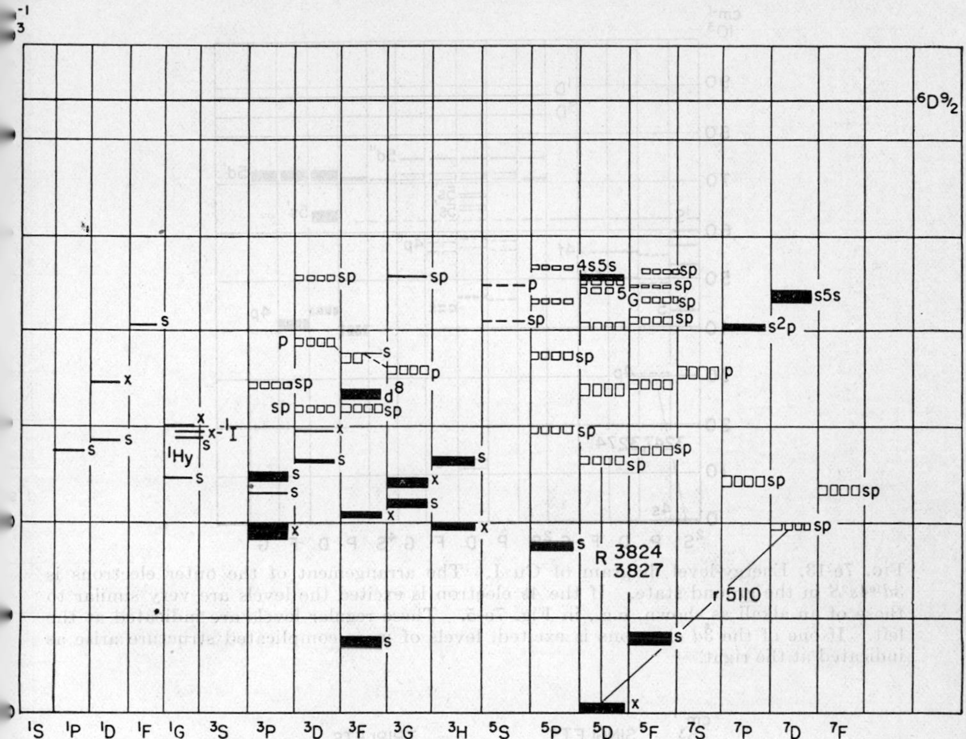

FIG. 7e-12. Energy-level diagram of Fe I. The spectrum of Fe I is one of the best studied and of particular importance because of the use of iron lines for wavelength standards and other applications (see Table 7g-6). Eight valence electrons, ground-state configuration $3d^64s^2$, which gives 16 multiplet levels, of which 9 are known (marked x in the figure). Other configurations leading to low-lying levels are $3d^74s$ (s), $3d^64s4p$ (sp), $3d^8$ (d^8), $3d^74p$ (p), $3d^54s^24p$ (s^2p). If n values higher than for $3d$, $4s$, $4p$ are involved, they are indicated as, e.g., $3d^64s5s$ ($s5s$).

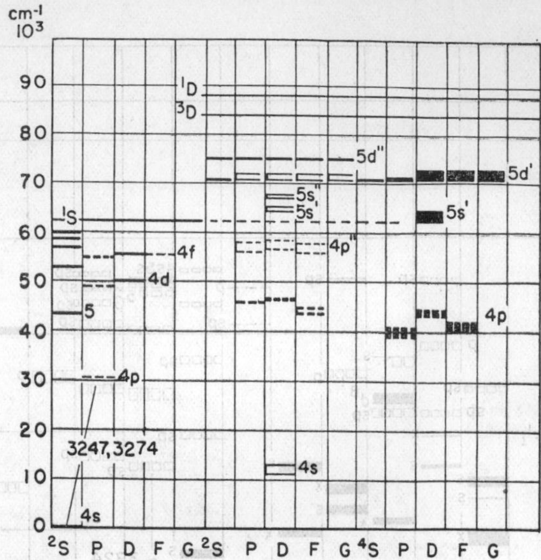

FIG. 7e-13. Energy-level diagram of Cu I. The arrangement of the outer electrons is $3d^{10}4s^2S$ in the ground state. If the $4s$ electron is excited the levels are very similar to those of an alkali as shown, e.g., in Fig. 7e-5. These regular levels are indicated at the left. If one of the $3d$ electrons is excited, levels of more complicated structure arise as indicated at the right.

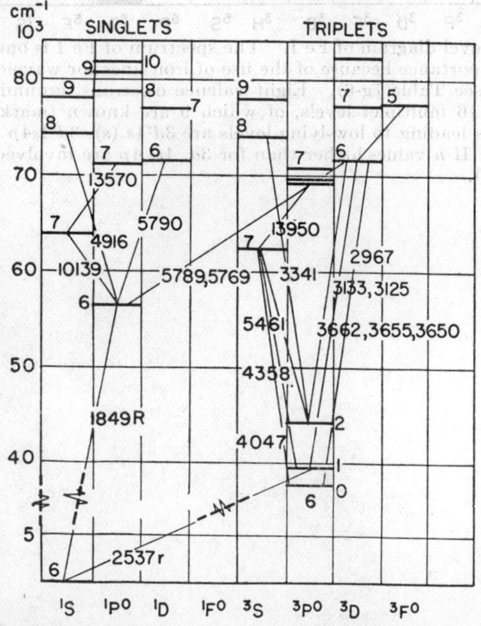

FIG. 7e-14. Energy-level diagram of Hg I. This is the diagram of a typical two-electron spectrum with singlets and triplets. Because of the wide use of the mercury spectrum in many applications the wavelengths of many transitions are indicated. Singlet triplet transitions are relatively strong. See also Table 7g-7 and Fig. 7g-6.

7f. Persistent Lines of the Elements

Table 7f-1 gives the strongest lines of each element and is useful for the spectroscopic identification of small traces of elements and spectrochemical analysis in general, when the elements in question occur in rather small concentrations. For the procedure of routine quantitative analysis with larger concentrations, see the special literature.

A selection of strong lines is given both from the spectrum of the neutral atom and from the spectrum of the singly ionized atom. The former are most prominent with mild excitation (d-c arc at atmospheric pressure, glow discharge in a gas at moderate pressure, microwave discharge). The lines of the ionized atoms appear with stronger excitation (condensed spark, discharge in a gas at very low pressure, etc.). The relative intensities even in the same spectrum may depend very pronouncedly on the discharge conditions so that what is indicated as the strongest line may be relatively weak at a particular condition. The two columns Strongest Line are taken from Meggers, "Smithsonian Physical Tables," 9th ed. (1954). Often they are identical with the resonance line given in Table 7c-1. In many cases the strongest line lies below 2,000 A, which region is less convenient because a vacuum spectrograph is needed. For the selection of other strong lines only those lying in the photographically accessible region from 2,000 to 10,000 A have been considered and preference given to the most convenient region from 3,000 to 8,000 A.

In general, wavelengths in Table 7f-1 and other tables of this section are wavelengths in standard air for $\lambda > 2,000$ A and in vacuum for $\lambda < 2,000$ A.

TABLE 7f-1. PERSISTENT LINES OF THE ELEMENTS

Z	Symbol	Neutral atoms				Singly ionized			
		Strongest line	Other strong lines			Strongest line	Other strong lines		
1	H	1,215.66	6,562.85	4,861.33					
2	He	584.33	5,875.62	3,888.65		303.78			
3	Li	6,707.85	6,103.64			199.26			
4	Be	2,348.61	3,321.34	....	....	3,130.42	3,131.07		
5	B	2,497.73	2,496.78	....	....	1,362.46	3,451.41		
6	C	1,657.01	2,478.57	....	....	1,335.71	4,267.27	2,836.71	
7	N	1,134.98	4,109.98	4,099.94	....	1,085.74	5,679.56	5,666.64	
8	O	1,302.19	7,771.93	7,774.14	7,775.43	834.47			
9	F	954.80	6,856.02	6,902.46		606.81			
10	Ne	735.89	5,852.49	6,402.25	5,400.56	460.73			
11	Na	5,889.95	3,302.32	5,895.92	....	372.07			
12	Mg	2,852.13	3,838.26	3,832.31	3,829.35	2,795.53	2,802.70		
13	Al	3,961.53	3,944.03	3,092.71	3,082.16	1,670.81	2,669.17	2,816.18	
14	Si	2,516.12	2,881.58	2,528.52	2,506.90	1,817.0			
15	P	1,774.94	2,535.65	2,553.28	....	1,542.32			
16	S	1,807.31	9,212.91	9,228.11	4,694.13	1,259.53			
17	Cl	1,347.2				1,071.05	4,794.54	4,810.06	4,819.46
18	A	1,048.22	8,115.31	7,067.22	6,965.43	919.78			
19	K	7,664.91	7,664.91	4,044.14	4,047.20	600.77			
20	Ca	4,226.73	4,454.78	4,434.96	4,425.44	3,933.67	3,968.47	3,179.33	3,158.87
21	Sc	5,671.80	3,911.81	3,907.48	4,023.69	3,613.84	3,630.74	3,642.78	
22	Ti	4,981.73	3,653.50			3,349.41	3,361.21	3,372.80	
23	V	4,379.24	3,185.40			3,093.11	3,102.30	3,110.71	3,118.38
24	Cr	4,254.35	4,274.80	5,208.44	5,206.04	2,835.63	2,843.25	2,849.84	2,855.68
25	Mn	4,030.76	4,033.07	4,034.49		2,576.10	2,593.73	2,605.69	
26	Fe	3,581.20	3,719.94	3,737.13	....	2,382.04	2,395.62	2,404.88	
27	Co	3,453.50	3,465.80	3,529.81	3,405.12	2,286.14	2,363.79		
28	Ni	3,414.76	3,492.96	3,524.54	....	2,216.47	2,287.08	2,270.21	2,264.46
29	Cu	3,247.54	3,273.96	5,218.20	5,153.24	2,135.98	2,192.26	2,247.00	
30	Zn	2,138.56	3,345.02	4,810.53	6,362.35	2,025.51	2,061.91		
31	Ga	4,172.06	4,032.98	2,943.64	2,874.24	1,414.44			
32	Ge	2,651.18	3,039.06	3,269.49	4,226.57	1,649.26			
33	As	1,890.43	2,288.12	2,349.84	9,626.70	1,266.36			
34	Se	1,960.91	2,039.85	4,730.78	4,739.03	1,192.29			
35	Br	1,488.4	....	....	....	1,015.42	4,704.86	4,785.50	4,816.71
36	Kr	1,235.82	5,870.92	5,570.29	....	917.43			
37	Rb	7,800.23	7,947.60	4,201.85	4,215.56	741.4			
38	Sr	4,607.33	4,832.08	4,872.49	4,962.26	4,077.71	4,215.52		
39	Y	5,466.47	4,674.85	4,643.70	....	3,710.29	3,600.73(?)	4,374.94	
40	Zr	4,687.80	3,601.19	3,547.68	3,519.61	3,391.98	3,438.23	3,496.21	
41	Nb	4,058.94	4,079.73	4,100.92	4,123.81	3,094.18	3,225.48		
42	Mo	3,798.25	3,864.11	3,902.96	....	2,816.15	2,848.23	2,871.51	2,890.99
43	Tc	3,636.10	4,297.06	4,262.26	....	2,543.24	2,610.00	3,237.02(?)	‡
44	Ru	3,498.94	3,436.74	3,596.18	....	2,402.72	2,945.67		
45	Rh	3,434.89	3,396.85	3,323.09	....	2,334.77			
46	Pd	3,404.58	3,421.24	3,634.70	....	2,296.53			
47	Ag	3,280.68	3,382.89	5,209.07	5,465.49	2,246.41	2,437.79		
48	Cd	2,288.02	6,438.47	3,610.51	....	2,144.38	2,265.02	2,437.79	2,246
49	In	4,511.32	4,101.77	3,256.09	3,039.36	1,586.4			
50	Sn	3,175.04	4,525.74	2,839.99	3,262.33	2,152.22			
51	Sb	2,068.38	2,175.89	2,528.54	3,232.50	1,606.98			
52	Te	2,142.75	2,385.76	2,383.25	....	1,161.52			
53	I	1,830.4	....	....	....	1,233.97	2,062.38	5,464.61	
54	Xe	1,469.62	4,671.23	4,624.28		1,100.42			

TABLE 7f-1. PERSISTENT LINES OF THE ELEMENTS (*Continued*)

Z	Symbol	Neutral atoms				Singly ionized			
		Strongest line	Other strong lines			Strongest line	Other strong lines		
55	Cs	8,521.10	8,943.50	4,555.36	4,593.18	926.75			
56	Ba	5,535.55	5,777.67	5,519.12	3,071.59	4,554.04	4,934.09		
57	La	6,249.93	5,930.65	5,455.15	....	3,949.10	4,077.34	4,123.23	
58	Ce	5,699.23	....	....	....	4,186.60	4,040.76	4,012.39	
59	Pr	4,951.36	....	....	....	4,179.42	4,062.82	4,408.84	
60	Nd	4,924.53	....	....	....	4,303.57	4,177.32	4,446.39	
61	Pm	....	....	....	....	3,892.16	3,910.26	3,998.96†	
62	Sm	4,296.75	....	....	....	3,568.27	4,424.34	4,434.32	4,433.88
63	Eu	4,594.02	4,627.12	....	....	4,205.05	4,129.74(?)		
64	Gd	4,225.85	....	....	....	3,422.47	3,646.20	4,262.10	
65	Tb	....	....	....	....	....	3,874.18(?)	3,561.74(?)	3,509.17
66	Dy	....	4,211.72(?)	4,045.98(?)	....	....	4,000.45(?)	4,077.97(?)	
67	Ho	....	3,891.02(?)	....	....	....	2,936.77		
68	Er	....	....	....	....	....	3,906.32(?)	3,692.65(?)	
69	Tm	5,675.83	....	....	....	3,848.02	3,761.33(?)	3,462.21(?)	
70	Yb	3,987.99	....	....	....	3,694.20	3,289.37		
71	Lu	4,518.57	....	....	....	2,615.43	2,911.39	2,894.84	
72	Hf	3,682.24	3,072.88	....	....	2,641.41	3,134.72	2,516.88	
73	Ta	2,647.47	3,311.16	3,318.84	....	2,685.17			
74	W	4,008.75	4,302.11	4,294.61	....	2,204.49	3,613.79		
75	Re	3,460.47	3,464.73	4,889.17	5,270.95	....	2,608.50	3,580.15	2,733.04
76	Os	2,909.06	3,058.66	4,420.47					
77	Ir	2,543.97	3,220.78	3,513.64					
78	Pt	2,659.44	3,064.71	2,830.30	2,997.97	1,777.09			
79	Au	2,427.95	2,675.95	....	....	1,740.47	2,802.19		
80	Hg	1,849.68	2,536.52	4,358.35	5,460.74	1,649.96			
81	Tl	5,350.46	3,775.72	3,519.24	3,229.75	1,908.64			
82	Pb	4,057.82	3,683.47	2,833.07	....	1,726.75	2,203.51	5,608.8	
83	Bi	3,067.72	2,897.98	4,722.55	....	1,902.41			
84	Po	2,449.99							
85	At								
86	Rn	1,786.07	7,450.00	7,055.42					
87	Fr								
88	Ra	4,825.91	....	....	....	3,814.42	4,682.28		
89	Ac								
90	Th	....	....	....	....	4,019.14	3,538.75(?)	4,281.42	
91	Pa	....	2,743	....	....	....	2,743.9	3,054.6	3,957.8¶
92	U	5,915.40	....	....	....	3,719.29	4,241.67	3,932.0	
93	Np	....	....	....	....	....	2,956.6	3,829.2	4,290.9¶
94	Pu	....	....	....	....	....	2,835.5	3,907.1	3,989.7¶
95	Am	....	....	....	....	....	2,832.3	3,926.2	4,188.2¶
96	Cm								
97	Bk								
98	Cf								
99	E								
100	Fm								

† Scribner, Bozman, Meggers, *J. Research Natl. Bur. Standards* **46**, 85 (1951) (*Pm*).
‡ Scribner, Bozman, Meggers, *J. Research Natl. Bur. Standards* **45**, 476 (1950).
¶ Fred, Tomkins, *J. Opt. Soc. Am.* **39**, 357 (1949).

7g. Important Atomic Spectra

H. M. CROSSWHITE AND G. H. DIEKE

Physics Department
The Johns Hopkins University

7g-1. General. The tables and figures of this section furnish data on spectra which are often used for reference. These are chiefly the spectra of the rare gases which can easily be obtained with simple discharge tubes (a neon advertising sign, for instance, is a good source for the neon spectrum); the iron spectrum which is the best source of standard lines for a spectrograph of moderate to high dispersion; and the mercury spectrum which, like that of helium, is particularly useful for spectrographs of low dispersion.

Data on other spectra of varying degrees of accuracy and completeness can be found in the MIT tables;[1] Kayser, "Handbuch der Spectroscopie," vols. 5–8; Paschen und Götze (1922); Fowler (1922); C. E. Moore, "Multiplet Tables" (1945); and Brode, "Chemical Spectroscopy" (1943).

An atlas of spectra is Gatterer and Junkes (1937 and 1945). For the solar spectrum, Minnaert, Mulders, and Houtgast (1940) is recommended.

The various tables of spectra and figures presented in this section are as follows:

Spectrum	Table	Figure
Helium	7g-1	
Neon Ne I	7g-2	7g-1
Argon A I	7g-3	7g-2
Krypton Kr I	7g-4	7g-3
Xenon Xe I	7g-5	7g-4
Iron Fe I	7g-6	7g-5
Mercury Hg I	7g-7	7g-6, 7

The wavelengths and intensities are listed as completely as space permits. Special attention has been paid to lines which can be used as standards for wavelength measurements of high accuracy.

The figures, which are direct photoelectric traces obtained at The Johns Hopkins University, will help to orient the reader in the particular spectra. The traces were made with a logarithmic amplifier and calibrated to compensate for variations in sensitivity of spectrograph and measuring devices. Furthermore, the intensity scale is the same for all spectra so that the values indicate relative brightnesses of the light sources. Intensities as read from the charts, however, are not meant for high accuracy.

In a number of spectra numerical intensity values are given on a logarithmic scale. Also the conditions under which the spectra were produced are shown in each case.

[1] See the references at the end of Sec. 7.

Without the knowledge of such conditions intensity tables have little meaning because the intensities vary greatly with the discharge conditions.

In both figures and tables (except for helium) the intensities are standardized to give the energy flux from 100 cm^2 of the light source per unit solid angle in ergs per second.

In Figs. 7g-1 through 7g-5, only whole numbers are given in the wavelength designations. Values accurate to several decimal places appear for many of these lines in Tables 7g-2 through 7g-7.

7g-2. Standard Wavelengths. Since 1927, the internationally accepted primary standard of wavelength has been the wavelength of the red cadmium line 6,438.4696 A when measured in air at standard conditions.[1] One Angstrom unit (A) is very closely equal to 10^{-10} m.

At the present time attempts are being made to replace the red cadmium line by a more suitable standard which combines higher accuracy and stability with better availability. It is very likely that this wavelength standard will also be the standard of length and thus replace the standard meter. Lines of the isotope 198 of mercury have been proposed[2] for this, but international adoption must wait until tests on the variability of the wavelengths with discharge conditions have been completed. It apparently is necessary to have the frequency of the exciting field fairly high (>100 Mc/sec). Lines of Kr^{84} are probably even better.

Accurate wavelength measurements are most conveniently made with the Fabry-Pérot interferometer or a similar device which permits direct comparison with the primary standard. For all practical purposes a number of secondary standards may be used instead of the primary standard without significant loss of accuracy. The advantages of doing so are that more easily handled light sources may be used and frequently the standard is more nearly equal in wavelength to the lines to be measured than the primary standard.

Secondary standards accepted by the International Astronomical Union are the wavelengths of suitable lines which have been measured with concordant results in at least three independent laboratories. The mean of such determinations is designated as a secondary international standard of wavelength and indicated by a letter *S* in subsequent wavelength tables. Whichever light sources are used to obtain wavelength standards it is very important that the conditions (pressure, discharge current, dimensions of light source, type of spectrograph used, etc.) be identical with those under which the standard wavelengths were determined.

Among the secondary standards, the wavelengths of some Hg^{198} lines are probably now as reliable as those of the primary standard. Neon and krypton wavelengths are almost as good, while the secondary iron standards are somewhat less reliable at the present time. A replacement of the iron arc by a more suitable light source will probably make many iron wavelengths available with greatly increased accuracy. More details will be found under the particular spectra.

If extreme wavelength accuracy is not required, as with grating measurements, many additional lines may be used as standards.

Helium I. The He I spectrum (Table 7g-1) consists of singlets and triplets. The latter appear as double lines except under the most favorable conditions. This is because the 2^3P_2 and 2^3P_1 levels almost coincide, whereas the 2^3P_0 level is about 1 cm^{-1} removed. The wavelengths are taken from the literature; some need revising. The intensities I_1 and I_2 are quantitative measurements at the following conditions: I_1, discharge with external electrodes; frequency 15 Mc/sec; pressure 7.5 mm; I_2, same, pressure 0.25 mm; I_0, estimates from the literature.

[1] For specifications of the lamp, see *Procès verbaux comité int. poids et mesures* **17** (2), 91 (1935).

[2] Meggers, *J. Opt. Soc. Am.* **38**, 7 (1948).

Table 7g-1. The Spectrum of Helium I and II

λ	Classification					I_0	I_1	I_2
	Singlets		Triplets		He II			
243.027	...	...	...	...	4 → 1			
256.317	...	...	...	...	3 → 1			
303.781	...	...	...	...	2 → 1			
522.208	1*S*	4*P*						
537.024	1*S*	3*P*						
534.331	1*S*	2*P*						
591.420	1*S*	...	...	2*p*				
1,084.975	...	...	...	...	5 → 2			
1,215.171	...	...	...	...	4 → 2			
1,640.474	...	...	...	...	3 → 2			
2,696.130	...	...	2*s*	9*p*		1		
2,723.175	...	...	2*s*	8*p*	....	1		
2,763.800	...	...	2*s*	7*p*		2		
2,829.063	...	...	2*s*	6*p*		4		
2,945.110	...	...	2*s*	5*p*		6		
3,187.744	...	...	2*s*	4*p*		8		
3,203.14	...	...	...	...	5 → 3			
3,354.550	2*S*	7*P*	...	...		2		
3,447.594	2*S*	6*P*	...	...		2		
3,587.252	...	...	2*p*	9*d*		2		
3,587.396	...	...	2*p*	9*d*	....	1		
3,599.304	...	...	2*p*	9*s*		1		
3,599.442	...	...	2*p*	9*s*		1		
3,613.641	2*S*	5*P*	...	...		3	19	260
3,634.235	...	...	2*p*	8*d*		2		
3,634.373	...	...	2*p*	8*d*		1		
3,651.971	...	...	2*p*	8*s*		1		
3,652.119	...	...	2*p*	8*s*		1		
3,705.003	...	...	2*p*	7*d*		3	28	260
3,705.140	...	...	2*p*	7*d*		1		
3,732.861	...	...	2*p*	7*s*		2		
3,732.993	...	...	2*p*	7*s*		1		
3,819.606	...	...	2*p*	6*d*		4	84	680
3,819.761	...	...	2*p*	6*d*		1		
3,867.477	...	...	2*p*	6*s*		2	23	160
3,867.631	...	...	2*p*	6*s*		1		
3,888.649	...	...	2*s*	3*p*		10	10,000	10,000
3,964.727	2*S*	4*P*	...	...		4	140	2,100
4,009.270	2*P*	7*D*	...	...		1	5	89
4,023.973	2*P*	7*S*	...	...		1		
4,026.189	...	...	2*p*	5*d*		5	370	1,450
4,026.362	...	...	2*p*	5*d*		1		
4,120.812	...	...	2*p*	5*s*		3	90	480
4,120.993	...	...	2*p*	5*s*		1		

TABLE 7g-1. THE SPECTRUM OF HELIUM I AND II (*Continued*)

λ	Classification					I_0	I_1	I_2
	Singlets		Triplets		He II			
4,143.759	2*P*	6*D*	...	...	....	2	19	210
4,168.965	2*P*	6*S*	...	...	....	1	3	36
4,387.928	2*P*	5*D*	...	...	....	3	83	590
4,437.549	2*P*	5*S*	...	...	....	1	17	290
4,471.477	...	...	2*p*	4*d*	....	6	2,300	2,220
4,471.688	...	...	2*p*	4*d*	....	1		
4,685.75	...	...	...	...	4 → 3			
4,713.143	...	...	2*p*	4*s*	....	3	350	370
4,713.373	...	...	2*p*	4*s*	....	1		
4,921.930	2*P*	4*D*	...	...	....	4	57	1,800
5,015.675	2*S*	3*P*	...	...	....	6	710	3,106
5,047.736	2*P*	4*S*	...	...	....	2	120	860
5,411.551	...	...	...	...	7 → 4			
5,875.662	...	...	2*p*	3*d*	....	10	18,200	7,100
5,875.867	...	...	2*p*	3*d*	....	1		
6,559.71	...	...	...	...	6 → 4			
6,678.150	2*P*	3*D*	...	...	....	6	2,400	1,850
7,065.188	...	...	2*p*	3*s*	....	5	7,100	1,450
7,065.719	...	...	2*p*	3*s*	....	1		
7,281.349	2*P*	3*S*	...	...	....	3*	1,450	
10,123.77	...	...	...	...	5 → 4			
10,829.081	...	...	2*s*	$2p_0$	....	500	105,000	6,950
10,830.250	...	...	2*s*	$2p_1$	....	1,500		
10,830.341	...	...	2*s*	$2p_2$	....	2,500		
12,784.79†	...	...	3*d*	5*f*	....	10†		
12,790.27	3*D*	5*F*	...	...	....	1		
17,003.11	...	...	3*p*	4*d*	....	20		
18,685.12	...	...	3*d*	4*f*	....	70		
18,697.00	3*D*	4*F*	...	...	....	10		
20,580.9	2*S*	2*P*	...	...	....	5,000		

* Change in the I_0 scale. From here on National Bureau of Standards values.
† Wavelengths and intensities from here on from Humphreys and Kostkowski, *J. Research Natl. Bur. Standards* **49,** 73 (1952).

The classification is indicated by capital letters for singlets, lower-case letters for triplets. A few of the He II lines are also listed. They have elaborate fine structures.

Neon I. The neon spectrum is moderately rich in lines and may serve, like the other rare-gas spectra, as an easily obtained comparison spectrum. Any neon-sign manufacturer can produce a satisfactory tube. The wavelengths of the strong lines have been measured with great accuracy and have been adopted as international secondary standards,[1] often replacing the primary standard for interferometric measurements.

Table 7g-2 lists the principal neon lines. The wavelengths are interferometric wavelengths when followed by a capital letter.

B, Burns, Adams, Longwell, *J. Opt. Soc. Am.* **40,** 339 (1950)
H, Humphreys, *J. Research Natl. Bur. Standards* **20,** 17(1938)

[1] *Trans. Intern. Astron. Union* **5,** 86 (1935).

TABLE 7g-2. THE SPECTRUM OF NEON I

Wavelength	Classification				I_0	log I_1	log I_2	log I_3
	System.		Paschen					
2,647.42	$3s_{12}$	$8p_1$	$1s_5$	$7p_{6,7}$	8			
2,675.24	$3s_{11}$	$7p'_{12}$	$1s_4$	$6p_4$	8			
2,675.64	$3s_{11}$	$7p'_{11}$	$1s_4$	$6p_5$	8			
2,872.663	$3s'_{00}$	$6p'_{00}$	$1s_2$	$5p_1$	5	.....	.....	2.73
2,913.168	$3s_{12}$	$5p'_{01}$	$1s_5$	$4p_2$	8	.....	.....	3.16
2,932.721	$3s'_{01}$	$6p_{00}$	$1s_2$	$5p_3$	7	.....	.....	3.30
2,947.297	$3s_{11}$	$5p_{12}$	$1s_4$	$4p_4$	8	.....	.....	3.2?
2,974.714	$3s_{12}$	$5p_{12}$	$1s_5$	$4p_6$	9	.....	.....	3.6?
2,980.642	$3s'_{00}$	$5p'_{01}$	$1s_3$	$4p_2$	5.5	.....	.....	2.7
2,980.922	$3s'_{00}$	$5p'_{11}$	$1s_3$	$4p_5$	6	.....	.....	2.80
2,982.663	$3s_{12}$	$5p_{23}$	$1s_5$	$4p_9$	9	.....	.....	3.52
2,992.420	$3s_{11}$	$5p_{00}$	$1s_4$	$4p_3$	8}	.....	.....	3.32
2,992.438	$3s_{12}$	$5p_{01}$	$1s_5$	$4p_{10}$	8}			
3,012.129	$3s_{11}$	$5p_{12}$	$1s_4$	$4p_6$	6	.....	.....	2.93
3,012.955	$3s_{11}$	$5p_{11}$	$1s_4$	$4p_7$	6	.....	.....	2.98
3,017.348	$3s_{11}$	$5p_{22}$	$1s_4$	$4p_8$	6	.....	.....	3.12
3,057.388	$3s'_{01}$	$5p'_{00}$	$1s_2$	$4p_1$	9	.....	.....	2.7
3,076.971	$3s'_{01}$	$5p'_{12}$	$1s_2$	$4p_4$	8	.....	.....	2.80
3,126.1986 *B*	$3s'_{01}$	$5p_{00}$	$1s_2$	$4p_3$	8	.....	.....	3.61
3,148.6107 *B*	$3s'_{01}$	$5p_{11}$	$1s_2$	$4p_7$	7	.....	.....	2.44
3,153.4107 *B*	$3s'_{01}$	$5p_{22}$	$1s_2$	$4p_8$	6	.....	.....	2.4?
3,167.5762 *B*	$3s'_{01}$	$5p_{01}$	$1s_2$	$4p_{10}$	6	.....	.....	2.21
3,369.8076 *B*	$3s_{12}$	$4p'_{12}$	$1s_5$	$3p_4$	10	.....	.....	3.90
3,369.9069 *B*	$3s_{12}$	$4p'_{01}$	$1s_5$	$3p_2$	15	.....	.....	4.36
3,375.6489 *B*	$3s_{12}$	$4p'_{11}$	$1s_5$	$3p_5$	6	.....	.....	2.98
3,417.9031 *B*	$3s_{11}$	$4p'_{12}$	$1s_4$	$3p_4$	10	.....	.....	4.62
3,418.0066 *H*	$3s_{11}$	$4p'_{01}$	$1s_4$	$3p_2$	6	.....	.....	4.14
3,423.9120 *B*	$3s_{11}$	$4p'_{11}$	$1s_4$	$3p_5$	6	.....	.....	3.57
3,447.7022 *B*	$3s_{12}$	$4p_{12}$	$1s_5$	$3p_6$	8	.....	.....	4.91
3,450.7641 *B*	$3s_{12}$	$4p_{11}$	$1s_5$	$3p_7$	6	.....	.....	4.18
3,454.1942 *B*	$3s_{11}$	$4p_{00}$	$1s_4$	$3p_3$	7	.....	.....	4.72
3,460.5235 *B*	$3s'_{00}$	$4p'_{01}$	$1s_3$	$3p_2$	7	.....	.....	4.37
3,464.3385 *B*	$3s_{12}$	$4p_{22}$	$1s_5$	$3p_8$	7	.....	.....	4.27
3,466.5781 *B*	$3s'_{00}$	$4p'_{11}$	$1s_3$	$3p_5$	8	.....	.....	4.64
3,472.5706 *B*	$3s_{12}$	$4p_{23}$	$1s_5$	$3p_9$	10	.....	.....	4.90
3,498.0632 *B*	$3s_{11}$	$4p_{12}$	$1s_4$	$3p_6$	7	.....	.....	4.45
3,501.2154 *B*	$3s_{11}$	$4p_{11}$	$1s_4$	$3p_7$	8	.....	.....	4.53
3,510.7207 *B*	$3s_{12}$	$4p_{01}$	$1s_5$	$3p_{10}$	6	.....	.....	3.85
3,515.1900 *B*	$3s_{11}$	$4p_{22}$	$1s_4$	$3p_8$	8	.....	.....	4.55
3,520.4714 *B*	$3s'_{01}$	$4p'_{00}$	$1s_2$	$3p_1$	20	.....	.....	5.32

TABLE 7g-2. THE SPECTRUM OF NEON I (*Continued*)

Wavelength	Classification				I_0	log I_1	log I_2	log I_3
	System.		Paschen					
3,562.9551 *B*	$3s_{11}$	$4p_{01}$	$1s_4$	$3p_{10}$	3			
3,593.5263 *B*	$3s'_{01}$	$4p'_{12}$	$1s_2$	$3p_4$	10	.....	.....	4.70
3,593.639 *B*	$3s'_{01}$	$4p'_{01}$	$1s_2$	$3p_2$	9	.....	.....	4.50
3,600.1694 *B*	$3s'_{01}$	$4p'_{11}$	$1s_2$	$3p_5$	7	.....	.....	4.17
3,609.1787 *B*	$3s'_{00}$	$4p_{01}$	$1s_3$	$3p_{10}$	6	.....	.....	3.26
3,633.6643 *B*	$3s'_{01}$	$4p_{00}$	$1s_2$	$3p_3$	7	.....	.....	4.28
3,682.2421 *B*	$3s'_{01}$	$4p_{12}$	$1s_2$	$3p_6$	7	.....	.....	4.21
3,685.7351 *B*	$3s'_{01}$	$4p_{11}$	$1s_2$	$3p_7$	7	.....	.....	4.08
3,701.2247 *B*	$3s'_{01}$	$4p_{22}$	$1s_2$	$3p_8$	7	.....	.....	4.06
3,754.2148 *B*	$3s'_{01}$	$4p_{01}$	$1s_2$	$3p_{10}$	6	.....	.....	3.42
4,270.2674 *B*	$3p_{01}$	$7d_{00}$	$2p_{10}$	$7d_6$	4	2.460		
4,275.5598 *B*	$3p_{01}$	$6d'_{22}$	$2p_{10}$	$6s_1''''$	5	2.70	2.61	
4,306.2625 *B*	$3p_{01}$	$8s_{12}$	$2p_{10}$	$6s_5$	5			
4,334.1267 *B*	$3p_{01}$	$7s'_{01}$	$2p_{10}$	$5s_2$	5			
4,363.524 *M*	$3p_{23}$	$9d_{34}$	$2p_9$	$9d'_4$	5			
4,381.220 *M*	$3p_{23}$	$10s_{12}$	$2p_9$	$8s_5$	3			
4,395.556 *M*	$3p_{22}$	$9d_{33}$	$2p_8$	$9d_4$	4			
4,422.5205 *B*	$3p_{01}$	$6d_{12}$	$2p_{10}$	$6d_3$	8	2.97	2.90	
4,424.8096 *B*	$3p_{01}$	$6d_{01}$	$2p_{10}$	$6d_5$	8	2.89	2.81	
4,425.400 *M*	$3p_{01}$	$6d_{00}$	$2p_{10}$	$6d_6$	7			
4,433.7239 *B*	$3p_{23}$	$8d_{34}$	$2p_9$	$8d'_4$	5	2.34	2.19	
4,460.175 *M*	$3p_{23}$	$9s_{12}$	$2p_9$	$7s_5$	6			
4,466.8120 *B*	$3p_{22}$	$8d_{33}$	$2p_8$	$8d_4$	5	2.02	1.81	
4,475.656 *M*	$3p_{11}$	$7d'_{12}$	$2p_7$	$7s_1''$	6			
4,483.199 *B*	$3p_{01}$	$7s_{11}$	$2p_{10}$	$5s_4$	7	2.098		
4.488.0926 *B*	$3p_{01}$	$7s_{12}$	$2p_{10}$	$5s_5$	8	2.811	2.673	
4,500.182 *M*	$3p'_{11}$	$8d'_{12}$	$2p_5$	$8s_1''$	4			
4,517.736 *M*	$3p'_{12}$	$8d'_{23}$	$2p_4$	$8s_1'''$	6			
4,525.764 *M*	$3p_{11}$	$8d_{22}$	$2p_7$	$8d_1''$	5			
4,536.312	$3p_{01}$	$5d'_{11}$	$2p_{10}$	$5s'_1$	7	2.694	2.699	
4,537.7545 *B*	$3p_{01}$	$5d'_{22}$	$2p_{10}$	$5s_1''''$	10	3.3	3.4	
4,538.2927 *B*	$3p_{23}$	$7d_{23}$	$2p_9$	$7d'_1$	8			
4,540.3801 *B*	$3p_{23}$	$7d_{34}$	$2p_9$	$7d'_4$	10	2.964	2.854	
4,552.598 *M*	$3p_{11}$	$9s_{11}$	$2p_7$	$7s_4$	3			
4,565.888 *M*	$3p_{12}$	$8d_{23}$	$2p_6$	$8d'_1$	4.5			
4,575.0620 *B*	$3p_{22}$	$7d_{33}$	$2p_8$	$7d_4$	8	2.714	2.569	
4,582.035 *M*	$3p_{22}$	$6d'_{23}$	$2p_8$	$6s_1'''$	7	2.4	2.3	
4,582.4521 *B*	$3p_{23}$	$8s_{12}$	$2p_9$	$6s_5$	7	2.4	2.3	
4,609.910 *M*	$3p'_{11}$	$7d'_{12}$	$2p_5$	$7s_1''$	7	2.19		
4,614.391 *M*	$3p_{22}$	$8s_{11}$	$2p_8$	$6s_4$	6	2.204		

TABLE 7g-2. THE SPECTRUM OF NEON I (*Continued*)

Wavelength	Classification				I_0	log I_1	log I_2	log I_3
	System.		Paschen					
4,617.837 *M*	$3p_{22}$	$8s_{12}$	$2p_8$	$6s_5$	5			
4,628.3113 *B*	$3p'_{12}$	$7d'_{23}$	$2p_4$	$7s_1'''$	7	2.49	2.39	
4,636.125 *M*	$3p_{11}$	$7d_{22}$	$2p_7$	$7d_1''$	5	2.0		
4,636.630	$3p_{11}$	$7d_{11}$	$2p_7$	$7d_2$	5	2.0		
4,645.4180 *B*	$3p_{11}$	$6d'_{12}$	$2p_7$	$6s_1''$	8	2.672	2.607	
4,649.904 *M*	$3p_{22}$	$7s'_{01}$	$2p_8$	$5s_2$	5			
4,656.3936 *B*	$3p_{01}$	$6s'_{01}$	$2p_{10}$	$4s_2$	8	2.916	2.828	2.799
4,661.1054 *B*	$3p_{01}$	$6s'_{00}$	$2p_{10}$	$4s_3$	7	2.634	2.559	
4,670.884 *M*	$3p'_{12}$	$8s'_{01}$	$2p_4$	$6s_2$	5			
4,678.218 *M*	$3p_{12}$	$7d_{23}$	$2p_6$	$7d_1'$	8	2.4	2.3	
4,679.135 *M*	$3p_{12}$	$7d_{12}$	$2p_6$	$7d_3$	7	2.2	2.1	
4,687.6724 *B*	$3p_{12}$	$6d'_{23}$	$2p_6$	$6s_1'''$	6	2.410	2.340	
4,702.526	$3p_{01}$	$5d_{11}$	$2p_{10}$	$5d_2$	7	2.472	2.427	
4,704.3949 *B*	$3p_{01}$	$5d_{12}$	$2p_{10}$	$5d_3$	15	3.701	3.729	3.437
4,708.8619 *B*	$3p_{01}$	$5d_{01}$	$2p_{10}$	$5d_5$	12	3.688	3.693	3.459
4,710.0669 *B*	$3p_{01}$	$5d_{00}$	$2p_{10}$	$5d_6$	10	3.33	3.33	3.34
4,712.0661 *B*	$3p_{23}$	$6d_{23}$	$2p_9$	$6d_1'$	10	2.96	2.90	2.55
4,715.3466 *B*	$3p_{23}$	$6d_{34}$	$2p_9$	$6d_4'$	15	3.57	3.50	3.17
4,725.145 *M*	$3p_{12}$	$8s_{12}$	$2p_6$	$6s_5$	5			
4,749.5754 *B*	$3p_{22}$	$6d_{22}$	$2p_8$	$6d_1'$	8	2.78	2.68	
4,752.7320 *B*	$3p_{22}$	$6d_{33}$	$2p_8$	$6d_4$	10	3.329	3.243	2.974
4,788.9270 *B*	$3p_{23}$	$7s_{12}$	$2p_9$	$5s_5$	12	3.16	3.05	
4,790.217 *B*	$3p'_{11}$	$6d_{22}$	$2p_5$	$6s_1''$	10	2.84	2.77	
4,800.100 *B*	$3p_{12}$	$7d_{23}$	$2p_4$	$7d_1'$	5			
4,810.0640 *B*	$3p'_{12}$	$6d'_{23}$	$2p_4$	$6s_1'''$	7	3.07	3.01	2.70
4,817.6386 *B*	$3p_{11}$	$6d_{22}$	$2p_7$	$6d_1''$	8	2.861	2.775	2.597
4,818.748	$3p_{11}$	$6d_{11}$	$2p_7$	$6d_2$	7	2.599	2.499	2.335
4,821.9236 *B*	$3p_{22}$	$7s_{11}$	$2p_8$	$5s_4$	8	2.864	2.646	2.693
4,823.174	$3p_{00}$	$6d'_{11}$	$2p_3$	$6s_1'$	6	2.3	2.2	
4,827.3444 *B*	$3p_{01}$	$6s_{11}$	$2p_{10}$	$4s_4$	10	2.9	2.8	
4,827.587 *B*	$3p_{22}$	$7s_{12}$	$2p_8$	$5s_5$	8			
4,837.3139 *B*	$3p_{01}$	$6s_{12}$	$2p_{10}$	$4s_5$	9	3.442	3.402	3.177
4,852.6571 *B*	$3p'_{01}$	$6d'_{22}$	$2p_2$	$6s_1''''$	6	2.731	2.632	
4,863.0800 *B*	$3p_{12}$	$6d_{23}$	$2p_6$	$6d_1'$	6	3.131	3.064	
4,865.5009 *B*	$3p_{12}$	$6d_{12}$	$2p_6$	$6d_3$	6			
4,866.477 *B*	$3p_{12}$	$6d_{33}$	$2p_6$	$6d_4$	5.5	2.61	2.53	
4,867.010	$3p'_{11}$	$7s'_{00}$	$2p_5$	$5s_3$	5	2.4	2.3	
4,884.9170 *B*	$3p'_{12}$	$7s'_{01}$	$2p_4$	$5s_2$	10	3.2	3.2	3.0
4,892.1007 *B*	$3p_{11}$	$7s_{11}$	$2p_7$	$5s_4$	9	2.58	2.38	
4,928.241 *B*	$3p'_{01}$	$7s'_{01}$	$2p_2$	$5s_2$	5			

TABLE 7g-2. THE SPECTRUM OF NEON I (*Continued*)

Wavelength	Classification System.		Classification Paschen		I_0	log I_1	log I_2	log I_3
4,939.0457 *B*	$3p_{12}$	$7s_{12}$	$2p_6$	$5s_4$	6	2.626	2.462	
4,944.9899 *B*	$3p_{12}$	$7s_{12}$	$2p_6$	$5s_5$	6	2.641	2.517	
4,957.0335 *B*	$3p_{11}$	$5d'_{12}$	$2p_7$	$5s''_1$	10	3.3	3.4	
4,957.123 *B*	$3p_{11}$	$5d'_{22}$	$2p_7$	$5s''''_1$	7			
4,973.538	$3p'_{11}$	$6d_{22}$	$2p_5$	$6d''_1$	6	2.496	2.406	2.89
4,994.913 *B*	$3p'_{12}$	$6d_{23}$	$2p_4$	$6d'_1$	7*ur*	2.451	2.365	
5,005.1587 *B*	$3p_{12}$	$5d'_{23}$	$2p_6$	$5s'''_1$	10	3.10	3.13	3.58
5,011.003 *M*	$3p_{00}$	$6d_{11}$	$2p_3$	$6d_2$	4	2.279	2.208	
5,022.864 *B*	$3p_{22}$	$6s'_{01}$	$2p_8$	$4s_2$	4	2.592	2.506	
5,031.3504 *B*	$3p_{23}$	$5d_{23}$	$2p_9$	$5d'_1$	9	3.634	3.665	3.374
5,035.989	$3p_{23}$	$5d_{12}$	$2p_9$	$5d_3$	5	2.818	2.823	
5,037.7512 *B*	$3p_{23}$	$5d_{34}$	$2p_9$	$5d'_4$	10	4.27	4.29	4.01
5,074.2007 *B*	$3p_{22}$	$5d_{22}$	$2p_8$	$5d'_1$	5	3.53	3.54	3.27
5,080.3852 *B*	$3p_{22}$	$5d_{33}$	$2p_8$	$5d_4$	8	4.038	4.061	3.803
5,104.7011 *B*	$3p_{11}$	$6s'_{00}$	$2p_7$	$4s_3$	5	2.798	2.745	
5,113.6724 *B*	$3p_{01}$	$4d'_{11}$	$2p_{10}$	$4s'_1$	7	3.475	3.654	3.326
5,116.5032 *B*	$3p_{01}$	$4d'_{12}$	$2p_{10}$	$4s''_1$	8	4.11	4.36	3.92
5,122.2565 *B*	$3p'_{11}$	$5d'_{12}$	$2p_5$	$5s''_1$	8	3.6	3.6	
5,144.9384 *B*	$3p'_{12}$	$5d'_{23}$	$2p_4$	$5s'''_1$	10	3.9	4.0	
5,150.077	$3p_{12}$	$6s'_{01}$	$2p_6$	$4s_2$	5	2.9	2.9	
5,151.9610 *B*	$3p_{11}$	$5d_{22}$	$2p_7$	$5d''_1$	7	3.595	3.597	3.352
5,154.4271 *B*	$3p_{11}$	$5d_{11}$	$2p_7$	$5d_2$	6	3.292	3.286	
5,156.6672 *B*	$3p_{11}$	$5d_{12}$	$2p_7$	$5d_3$	6	2.5	2.5	
5,158.9018 *B*	$3p_{00}$	$5d'_{11}$	$2p_3$	$5s'_1$	6	3.087	3.094	
5,188.6122 *B*	$3p_{23}$	$6s_{12}$	$2p_9$	$4s_5$	8	3.813	3.898	3.519
5,191.3223 *B*	$3p'_{01}$	$5d'_{11}$	$2p_2$	$5s'_1$	5			
5,193.1302 *B*	$3p'_{01}$	$5d'_{12}$	$2p_2$	$5s''_1$	8 }	3.6	3.6	
5,193.2227 *B*	$3p'_{01}$	$5d'_{22}$	$2p_2$	$5s''''_1$	8 }			
5,203.8962 *B*	$3p_{12}$	$5d_{23}$	$2p_6$	$5d'_1$	8	3.837	3.884	3.515
5,208.8648 *B*	$3p_{12}$	$5d_{12}$	$2p_6$	$5d_3$	7	3.584	3.585	
5,210.5672 *B*	$3p_{12}$	$5d_{33}$	$2p_6$	$5d_4$	6	.....	.....	2.860
5,214.3389 *B*	$3p_{12}$	$5d_{01}$	$2p_6$	$5d_5$	5	2.777	2.745	
5,222.3517 *B*	$3p_{22}$	$6s_{11}$	$2p_8$	$4s_4$	6	3.549	3.431	3.592
5,234.0271 *B*	$3p_{22}$	$6s_{12}$	$2p_8$	$4s_5$	6	3.161	3.125	
5,274.0393 *B*	$3p'_{11}$	$6s'_{01}$	$2p_5$	$4s_2$	5.5	2.767	2.649	
5,280.0853 *B*	$3p'_{11}$	$6s'_{00}$	$2p_5$	$4s_3$	6	2.962	2.899	2.660
5,298.1891 *B*	$3p'_{12}$	$6s'_{01}$	$2p_4$	$4s_2$	8	3.492	3.396	3.300
5,304.7580 *B*	$3p_{11}$	$6s_{11}$	$2p_7$	$4s_4$	7	3.255	3.154	3.088
5,326.3968 *B*	$3p_{01}$	$4d_{11}$	$2p_{10}$	$4d_2$	7	3.388	3.540	
5,330.7775 *B*	$3p_{01}$	$4d_{12}$	$2p_{10}$	$4d_3$	12	4.547	4.771	4.360

TABLE 7g-2. THE SPECTRUM OF NEON I (*Continued*)

Wavelength	Classification				I_0	log I_1	log I_2	log I_3
	System.		Paschen					
5,341.0938 *B*	$3p_{01}$	$4d_{01}$	$2p_{10}$	$4d_5$	20	4.537	4.732	
5,343.2834 *B*	$3p_{01}$	$4d_{00}$	$2p_{10}$	$4d_6$	12	4.3	4.5	3.936
5,349.2038 *B*	$3p'_{01}$	$6s'_{01}$	$2p_2$	$4s_2$	8	3.072	3.004	2.810
5,360.0121 *B*	$3p_{12}$	$6s_{11}$	$2p_6$	$4s_4$	8	3.392	3.297	3.129
5,372.3110 *B*	$3p_{12}$	$6s_{12}$	$2p_6$	$4s_5$	7	3.318	3.282	2.196
5,374.9774 *B*	$3p_{00}$	$5d_{11}$	$2p_3$	$5d_2$	6	3.002	2.984	
5,383.2503 *B*	$3p_{00}$	$5d_{01}$	$2p_3$	$5d_5$	4	2.487	2.525	
5,400.5616 *B*	$3s_{11}$	$3p'_{00}$	$1s_4$	$2p_1$	50	4.735	5.079	4.832
5,412.6490 *B*	$3p'_{01}$	$5d_{12}$	$2p_2$	$5d_3$	9	2.948	3.015	
5,418.5584 *B*	$3p'_{01}$	$5d_{01}$	$2p_2$	$5d_5$	8	2.88	2.85	
5,433.6513 *B*	$3p_{01}$	$5s'_{01}$	$2p_{10}$	$3s_2$	9	3.349	3.377	3.223
5,448.5091 *B*	$3p_{01}$	$5s'_{00}$	$2p_{10}$	$3s_3$	8	3.077	3.169	
5,494.4158 *B*	$3p'_{11}$	$6s_{11}$	$2p_5$	$4s_4$	6	2.843	2.745	
5,533.6788 *B*	$3p'_{12}$	$6s_{12}$	$2p_4$	$4s_5$	7	2.738	2.720	
5,538.6510 *B*	$3p_{00}$	$6s_{11}$	$2p_3$	$4s_4$	6	2.625	2.532	
5,562.7662 *B*	$3p_{22}$	$4d'_{23}$	$2p_8$	$4s_1'''$	10	3.9	4.1	3.7
5,652.5664 *B*	$3p_{11}$	$4d'_{11}$	$2p_7$	$4s_1'$	7	3.400	3.562	3.240
5,656.6588 *B*	$3p_{11}$	$4d'_{22}$	$2p_7$	$4s_1''''$	10	4.20	4.40	3.96
5,662.5489 *B*	$3p_{01}$	$5s_{11}$	$2p_{10}$	$3s_4$	7	3.438	3.665	
5,689.8163 *B*	$3p_{01}$	$5s_{12}$	$2p_{10}$	$3s_5$	8	4.179	4.305	3.949
5,719.2248 *B*	$3p_{12}$	$4d'_{23}$	$2p_6$	$4s_1'''$	10	3.9	4.1	3.7
5,748.2985 *B*	$3p_{23}$	$4d_{23}$	$2p_9$	$4d_1'$	10	4.4	4.6	4.1
5,760.5885 *B*	$3p_{23}$	$4d_{12}$	$2p_9$	$4d_3$	7	3.603	3.800	
5,764.4188 *B*	$3p_{23}$	$4d_{24}$	$2p_9$	$4d_4'$	15	5.080	5.312	4.868
5,804.4496 *B*	$3p_{22}$	$4d_{22}$	$2p_8$	$4d_1''$	10	4.374	4.585	4.121
5,811.4066 *B*	$3p_{22}$	$4d_{11}$	$2p_8$	$4d_2$	8	3.53	3.69	
5,820.1558 *B*	$3p_{22}$	$4d_{33}$	$2p_8$	$4d_4$	10	4.870	5.080	4.638
5,852.4878 *S*	$3s'_{01}$	$3p'_{00}$	$1s_2$	$2p_1$	50	5.904	6.268	6.442
5,868.4183 *B*	$3p'_{11}$	$4d'_{11}$	$2p_5$	$4s_1$	7	3.659	4.341	
5,872.8275 *B*	$3p'_{11}$	$4d'_{22}$	$2p_5$	$4s_1''''$	10	4.47	4.74	4.27
5,881.8950 *S*	$3s_{12}$	$3p'_{01}$	$1s_5$	$2p_2$	20	5.235	6.300	5.974
5,902.4623 *B*	$3p'_{12}$	$4d'_{23}$	$2p_4$	$4s_1'''$	6	4.82	5.05	4.626
5,902.7835 *B*	$3p'_{12}$	$4d'_{22}$	$2p_4$	$4s_1''''$	1.5			
5,906.4294 *B*	$3p_{11}$	$4d_{22}$	$2p_7$	$4d_1''$	6	4.448	4.671	4.185
5,913.6327 *B*	$3p_{11}$	$4d_{11}$	$2p_7$	$4d_2$	9	4.133	4.303	3.927
5,918.9068 *B*	$3p_{00}$	$4d'_{11}$	$2p_3$	$4s_1'$	9	4.09	4.28	3.860
5,944.8342 *S*	$3s_{12}$	$3p'_{12}$	$1s_5$	$2p_4$	10	5.365	6.380	6.104
5,961.6228 *B*	$3p'_{01}$	$4d'_{11}$	$2p_2$	$4s_1'$	7	3.903	4.198	3.717
5,965.4710 *B*	$3p'_{01}$	$4d'_{12}$	$2p_2$	$4s_1''$	10	4.54	4.75	4.25
5,974.6273 *B*	$3p_{12}$	$4d_{23}$	$2p_6$	$4d_1'$	10	4.7	5.6	

TABLE 7g-2. THE SPECTRUM OF NEON I (*Continued*)

Wavelength	Classification				I_0	log I_1	log I_2	log I_3
	System.		Paschen					
5,975.5340 *S*	$3s_{12}$	$3p'_{11}$	$1s_5$	$2p_5$	*12	5.14	6.05	
5,987.9074 *B*	$3p_{12}$	$4d_{12}$	$2p_6$	$4d_3$	8	4.373	4.601	4.058
5,991.6532 *B*	$3p_{12}$	$4d_{23}$	$2p_6$	$4d_4$	7	4.049	4.237	3.729
6,000.9275 *B*	$3p_{12}$	$4d_{01}$	$2p_6$	$4d_5$	6	3.725	3.925	
6,029.9971 *S*	$3s_{11}$	$3p'_{01}$	$1s_4$	$2p_2$	10	5.200	6.266	5.748
6,046.1348 *B*	$3p_{11}$	$5s'_{01}$	$2p_7$	$3s_2$	4	3.249	3.961	
6,064.5359 *B*	$3p_{11}$	$5s'_{00}$	$2p_7$	$3s_3$	4	3.613	3.995	
6,074.3377 *S*	$3s_{11}$	$3p_{00}$	$1s_4$	$2p_3$	10	5.411	6.490	6.093
6,096.1630 *S*	$3s_{11}$	$3p_{12}$	$1s_4$	$2p_4$	8	5.428	6.550	6.161
6,128.4498 *B*	$3s_{11}$	$3p'_{11}$	$1s_4$	$2p_5$	6	4.908	5.580	5.024
6,143.0623 *S*	$3s_{12}$	$3p_{12}$	$1s_5$	$2p_6$	10	5.48	6.63	6.198
6,163.5939 *S*	$3s'_{00}$	$3p'_{01}$	$1s_3$	$2p_2$	12	5.231	6.488	6.010
6,174.8829 *B*	$3p_{12}$	$4d_{23}$	$2p_4$	$4d_1$	5	3.9	4.3	
6,182.1460 *B*	$3p_{23}$	$5s_{12}$	$2p_9$	$3s_5$	7	3.610	4.737	4.334
6,189.0649 *B*	$3p_{12}$	$4d_{12}$	$2p_4$	$4d_3$	5	3.544	3.846	
6,193.0663 *B*	$3p_{12}$	$4d_{23}$	$2p_4$	$4d_4$	4	.....	3.498	
6,205.7775 *B*	$3p_{00}$	$4d_{11}$	$2p_3$	$4d_2$	6	3.785	4.043	
6,213.8758 *B*	$3p_{22}$	$5s_{11}$	$2p_8$	$3s_4$	7	4.376	4.473	
6,217.2813 *S*	$3s_{12}$	$3p_{11}$	$1s_5$	$2p_7$	15	5.359	6.436	5.962
6,246.7294 *B*	$3p_{22}$	$5s_{12}$	$2p_8$	$3s_5$	6	3.929	4.129	
6,266.4950 *S*	$3s'_{00}$	$3p'_{11}$	$1s_3$	$2p_5$	15	5.336	6.606	6.156
6,293.7447 *B*	$3p'_{00}$	$5s'_{01}$	$2p_5$	$3s_2$	6	3.683	3.900	
6,304.7892 *S*	$3s_{11}$	$3p_{12}$	$1s_4$	$2p_6$	6	5.422	6.391	6.009
6,313.6921 *B*	$3p'_{00}$	$5s'_{00}$	$2p_5$	$3s_3$	7	3.899	4.151	
6,328.1646 *B*	$3p'_{12}$	$5s'_{01}$	$2p_4$	$3s_2$	8	4.424	4.546	
6,334.4279 *S*	$3s_{12}$	$3p_{22}$	$1s_5$	$2p_8$	10	5.567	6.679	6.281
6,351.8618 *B*	$3p_{00}$	$5s'_{01}$	$2p_3$	$3s_2$	6			
6,382.9914 *S*	$3s_{11}$	$3p_{11}$	$1s_4$	$2p_7$	12	5.503	6.684	6.221
6,402.2460 *B*	$3s_{12}$	$3p_{23}$	$1s_5$	$2p_9$	20	5.93	6.83	6.389
6,421.7108 *B*	$3p'_{01}$	$5s_{12}$	$2p_2$	$3s_5$	6	3.701	3.893	
6,444.7118 *B*	$3p_{12}$	$5s_{12}$	$2p_6$	$3s_5$	7	4.094	4.191	3.823
6,506.5279 *S*	$3s_{11}$	$3p_{22}$	$1s_4$	$2p_8$	15	5.635	6.709	6.287
6,532.8824 *S*	$3s'_{00}$	$3p_{11}$	$1s_3$	$2p_7$	6	5.381	6.531	6.094
6,598.9529 *S*	$3s'_{01}$	$3p'_{01}$	$1s_2$	$2p_2$	15	5.736	6.691	6.213
6,652.0925 *B*	$3s'_{01}$	$3p_{00}$	$1s_2$	$2p_3$	7	4.279	4.681	4.203
6,666.8967 *B*	$3p_{00}$	$5s_{11}$	$2p_3$	$3s_4$	6			
6,678.2764 *S*	$3s'_{01}$	$3p'_{12}$	$1s_2$	$2p_4$	9	5.840	6.806	6.393
6,717.0428 *S*	$3s'_{01}$	$3p'_{11}$	$1s_2$	$2p_5$	2	5.765	6.712	6.286
6,929.4672 *B*	$3s'_{01}$	$3p_{12}$	$1s_2$	$2p_6$	10	5.965	6.783	6.421
7,024.0500 *B*	$3s'_{01}$	$3p_{11}$	$1s_2$	$2p_7$	9	5.436	6.068	5.568

TABLE 7g-2. THE SPECTRUM OF NEON I (*Continued*)

Wavelength	Classification: System.		Classification: Paschen		I_0	log I_1	log I_2	log I_3
7,032.4127 *S*	$3s_{12}$	$3p_{01}$	$1s_5$	$2p_{10}$	10	5.732	6.917	6.362
7,051.2937 *B*	$3p_{01}$	$3d'_{11}$	$2p_{10}$	$3s'_1$	5	4.286	. . . . .	4.281
7,059.1079 *B*	$3p_{01}$	$3d'_{12}$	$2p_{10}$	$3s''_1$	7.5	4.868	5.534	4.904
7,173.9380 *B*	$3s'_{01}$	$3p_{22}$	$1s_2$	$2p_8$	10	5.793	6.411	6.022
7,245.1665 *B*	$3s_{11}$	$3p_{01}$	$1s_4$	$2p_{10}$	10	5.751	6.756	6.289
7,438.8981 *B*	$3s'_{00}$	$3p_{01}$	$1s_3$	$2p_{10}$	8	5.510	6.424	
7,472.4383 *B*	$3p_{01}$	$3d_{11}$	$2p_{10}$	$3d_2$	4	4.432	5.021	4.441
7,488.8712 *B*	$3p_{01}$	$3d_{12}$	$2p_{10}$	$3d_3$	9	5.398	6.052	5.424
7,535.7739 *B*	$3p_{01}$	$3d_{01}$	$2p_{10}$	$3d_5$	8	5.352	5.978	5.387
7,544.0439 *B*	$3p_{01}$	$3d_{00}$	$2p_{10}$	$3d_6$	6	4.962	5.667	4.956
7,724.6281 *B*	$3p'_{00}$	$5s_{11}$	$2p_1$	$3s_4$	10			
7,839.0550 *B*	$3p_{23}$	$3d'_{23}$	$2p_9$	$3s'''_1$	30	3.303	3.939	3.19
7,927.1172 *B*	$3p_{22}$	$3d'_{11}$	$2p_8$	$3s'_1$	40	. . . .	. . . . .	3.48
7,936.9946 *B*	$3p_{22}$	$3d'_{12}$	$2p_8$	$3s''_1$	70	3.487	4.043	4.040
7,943.1805 *B*	$3p_{22}$	$3d'_{23}$	$2p_8$	$3s'''_1$	200	4.718	5.412	4.725
8,082.4576 *B*	$3s'_{01}$	$3p_{01}$	$1s_2$	$2p_{10}$	200	4.676	5.203	4.629
8,118.5495 *B*	$3p_{11}$	$3d'_{11}$	$2p_7$	$3s'_1$	100	4.452	5.030	4.419
8,128.9077 *B*	$3p_{11}$	$3d'_{12}$	$2p_7$	$3s'_1$	60	3.916	4.633	3.85
8,136.4061 *B*	$3p_{11}$	$3d'_{22}$	$2p_7$	$3s''''_1$	300	5.047	5.718	5.029
8,248.6812 *B*	$3p_{12}$	$3d'_{11}$	$2p_6$	$3s'_1$	30	3.467	4.038	3.34
8,259.3795 *B*	$3p_{12}$	$3d'_{12}$	$2p_6$	$3s'_1$	150	4.327	. . . . .	4.280
8,266.0788 *B*	$3p_{12}$	$3d'_{23}$	$2p_6$	$3s'''_1$	250	. . . .	5.387	4.691
8,267.1166 *B*	$3p_{12}$	$3d'_{22}$	$2p_6$	$3s''''_1$	80			
8,300.3248 *B*	$3p_{23}$	$3d_{23}$	$2p_9$	$3d'_1$	600	5.31	5.97	5.316
8,365.7464 *B*	$3p_{23}$	$3d_{12}$	$2p_9$	$3d_3$	150	4.439	. . .	4.415
8,377.6062 *B*	$3p_{23}$	$3d_{34}$	$2p_9$	$3d'_4$	800	. . . . .	. . . . .	5.957
8,417.1614 *B*	$3p_{22}$	$3d_{23}$	$2p_8$	$3d'_1$	100	4.2	4.9	
8,418.4265 *B*	$3p_{22}$	$3d_{22}$	$2p_8$	$3d'_1$	400	5.15	5.87	5.244
8,463.3569 *B*	$3p_{22}$	$3d_{11}$	$2p_8$	$3d_2$	150	4.433	5.039	4.452
8,484.4424 *B*	$3p_{22}$	$3d_{12}$	$2p_8$	$3d_3$	80	3.930	4.678	3.90
8,495.3591 *B*	$3p_{22}$	$3d_{33}$	$2p_8$	$3d_4$	500	5.703	6.324	5.764
8,544.6952 *B*	$3p_{22}$	$3d_{01}$	$2p_8$	$3d_5$	60	4.014	4.752	3.98
8,571.3535 *B*	$3p'_{11}$	$3d'_{11}$	$2p_5$	$3s'_1$	100	4.332	5.012	4.330
8,591.2583 *B*	$3p'_{11}$	$3d'_{22}$	$2p_5$	$3s''''_1$	400	5.436	6.057	5.450
8,634.6472 *B*	$3p_{11}$	$3d_{22}$	$2p_7$	$3d'_1$	600	5.3	6.0	5.386
8,647.0400 *B*	$3p_{12}$	$3d'_{12}$	$2p_4$	$3s''_1$	300	4.709	5.235	
8,654.3837 *B*	$3p'_{12}$	$3d'_{23}$	$2p_4$	$3s'''_1$	1,500	5.56	6.26	5.747
8,655.5206 *B*	$3p'_{12}$	$3d'_{22}$	$2p_4$	$3s''''_1$	400			
8,679.4898 *B*	$3p_{00}$	$3d'_{11}$	$2p_3$	$3s'_1$	500}	5.2	5.8	5.016
8,681.9216 *B*	$3p_{11}$	$3d_{11}$	$2p_7$	$3d_2$	500}			5.075

TABLE 7g-2. THE SPECTRUM OF NEON I (*Continued*)

Wavelength	Classification				I_0	log I_1	log I_2	log I_3
	System.		Paschen					
8,704.1132 *B*	$3p_{11}$	$3d_{12}$	$2p_7$	$3d_3$	200	4.243	4.992	4.201
8,771.6592 *B*	$3p'_{01}$	$3d'_{11}$	$2p_2$	$3s'_1$	400	4.845	5.467	4.888
8,780.6223 *B*	$3p_{12}$	$3d_{23}$	$2p_6$	$3d'_1$	1,200	.....	.....	5.642
8,783.7539 *B*	$3p'_{01}$	$3d'_{23}$	$2p_2$	$3s'''_1$	1,000	.....	.....	5.488
8,830.9078 *B*	$3p_{12}$	$3d_{11}$	$2p_6$	$3d_2$	50	3.606	4.258	3.61
8,853.8669 *B*	$3p_{12}$	$3d_{12}$	$2p_6$	$3d_3$	700	5.233	5.805	5.246
8,865.3057 *B*	$3p_{12}$	$3d_{33}$	$2p_6$	$3d_4$	100 }	5.0	5.6	5.0
8,865.7562 *B*	$3p_{01}$	$4s'_{01}$	$2p_{10}$	$2s_2$	500 }			
8,919.4987 *B*	$3p_{12}$	$3d_{01}$	$2p_6$	$3d_5$	300	4.623	5.290	4.624
8,988.58	$3p_{01}$	$4s'_{00}$	$2p_{10}$	$2s_3$	200	4.310	4.712	4.12
9,148.68	$3p'_{11}$	$3d_{22}$	$2p_5$	$3d''_1$	600	4.809	5.501	4.808
9,201.76	$3p'_{11}$	$3d_{11}$	$2p_5$	$3d_2$	600	4.786	5.381	4.826
9,220.05	$3p'_{12}$	$3d_{23}$	$2p_4$	$3d'_1$	400	4.54	5.23	4.624
9,221.59	$3p'_{12}$	$3d_{22}$	$2p_4$	$3d''_1$	200	4.0	4.7	
9,226.67	$3p'_{11}$	$3d_{12}$	$2p_5$	$3d_3$	200	4.040	4.785	4.01
9,275.53	$3p'_{12}$	$3d_{11}$	$2p_4$	$3d_2$	100	.....	4.466	3.83
9,300.85	$3p'_{12}$	$3d_{12}$	$2p_4$	$3d_3$	600	4.650	5.261	4.639
9,310.58	$3p'_{11}$	$3d_{00}$	$2p_5$	$3d_6$	150	4.213	4.966	3.60
9,313.98	$3p'_{12}$	$3d_{33}$	$2p_4$	$3d_4$	300	4.224	4.947	4.23
9,326.52	$3p_{00}$	$3d_{11}$	$2p_3$	$3d_2$	600	4.682	5.285	4.710
9,373.28	$3p'_{12}$	$3d_{01}$	$2p_4$	$3d_5$	200	4.008	4.712	3.96
9,425.38	$3p_{00}$	$3d_{01}$	$2p_3$	$3d_5$	500	4.472	5.225	4.47
9,459.21	$3p'_{01}$	$3d_{12}$	$2p_2$	$3d_3$	300	4.211	4.969	4.15
9,486.680 *M*	$3p_{01}$	$4s_{11}$	$2p_{10}$	$2s_4$	500	4.793	5.280	4.76
9,534.167 *M*	$3p'_{01}$	$3d_{01}$	$2p_2$	$3d_5$	500	4.555	5.319	4.567
9,547.40	$3p'_{01}$	$3d_{00}$	$2p_2$	$3d_6$	300	4.241	4.986	4.15
9,665.424 *M*	$3p_{01}$	$4s_{12}$	$2p_{10}$	$2s_5$	1,000	5.207	5.552	5.155

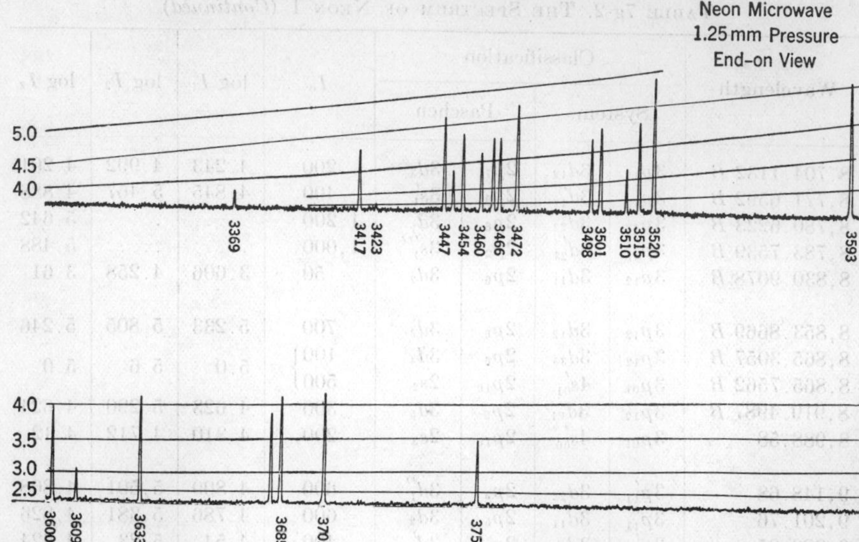

FIG. 7g-1. Photoelectric traces of the neon spectrum, microwave discharge at 1.25 mm. Wavelength range is 3,000–10,000 A.

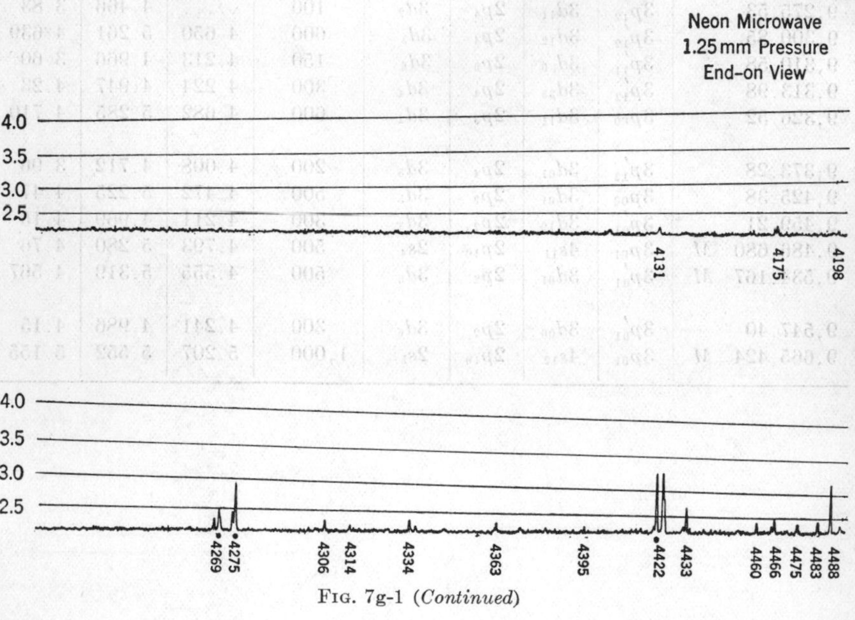

FIG. 7g-1 (*Continued*)

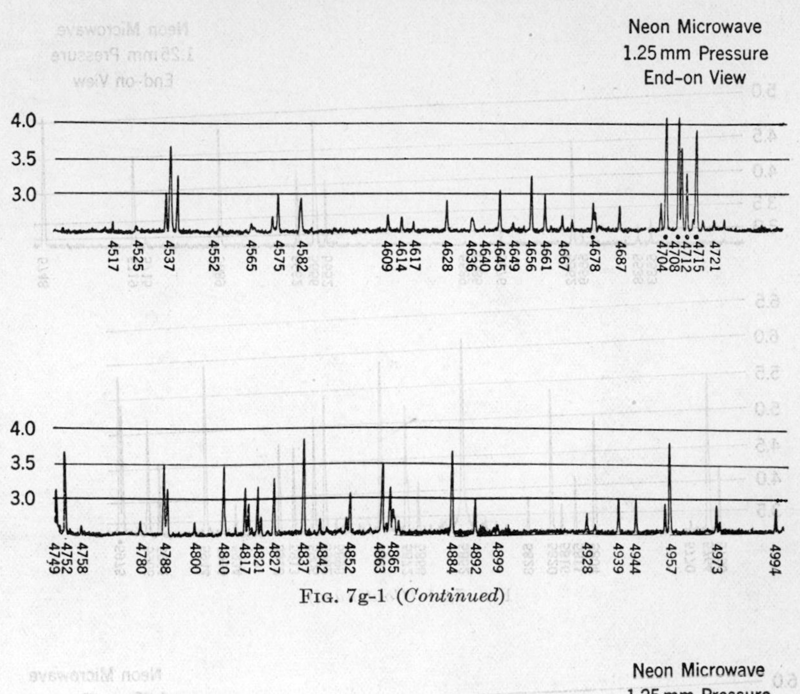

FIG. 7g-1 (*Continued*)

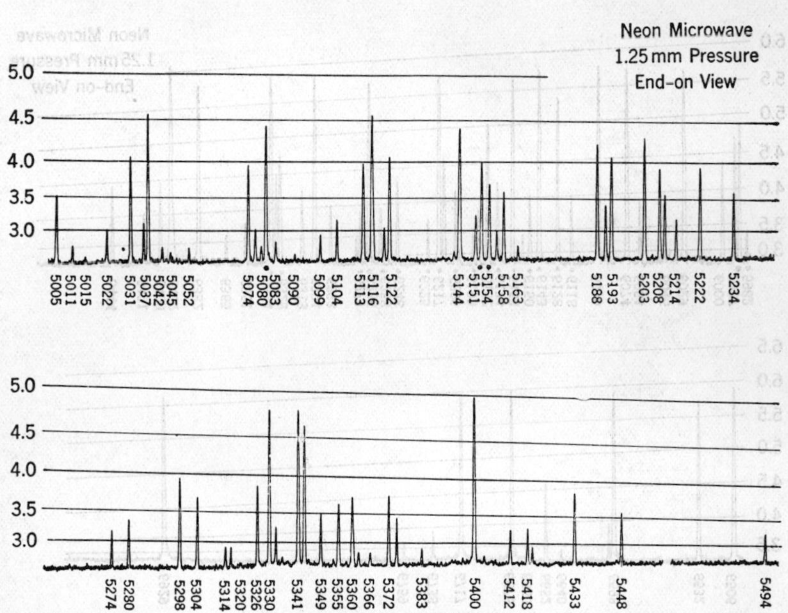

FIG. 7g-1 (*Continued*)

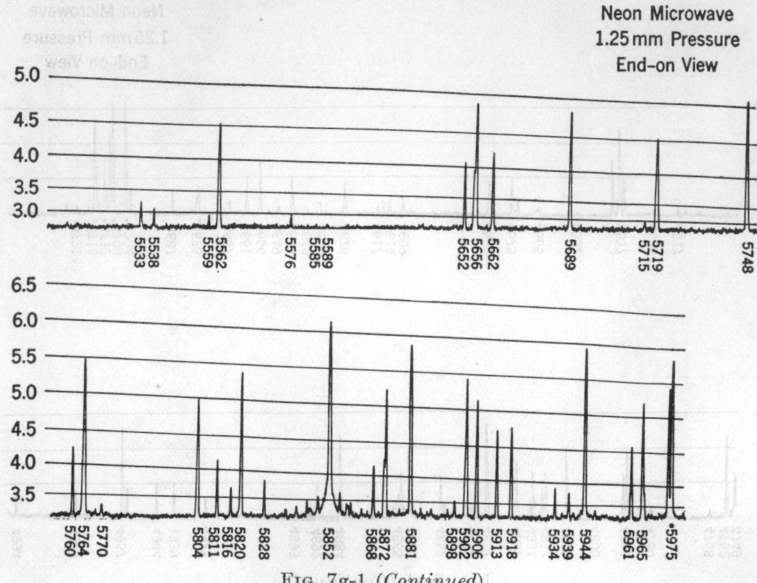

FIG. 7g-1 (*Continued*)

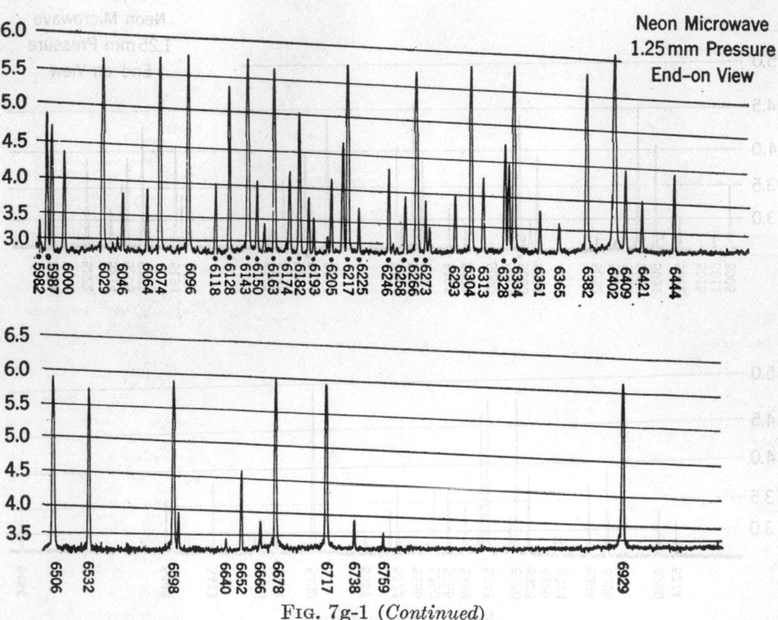

FIG. 7g-1 (*Continued*)

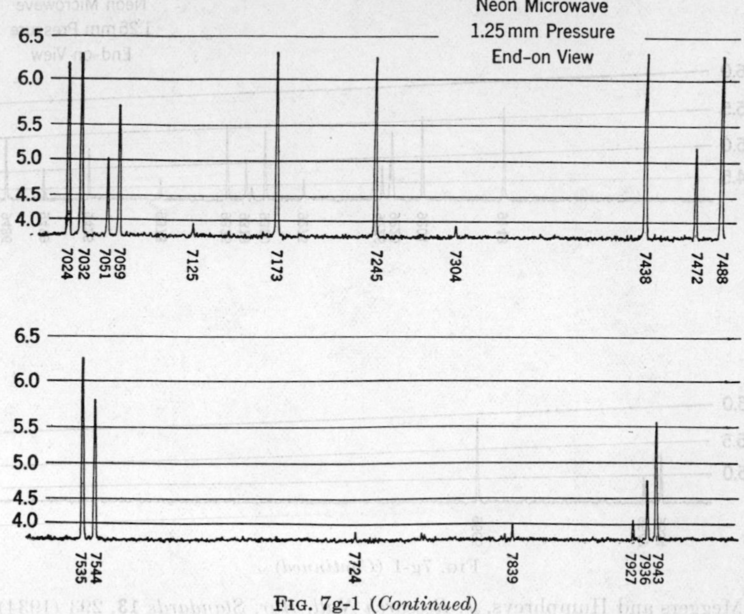

FIG. 7g-1 (*Continued*)

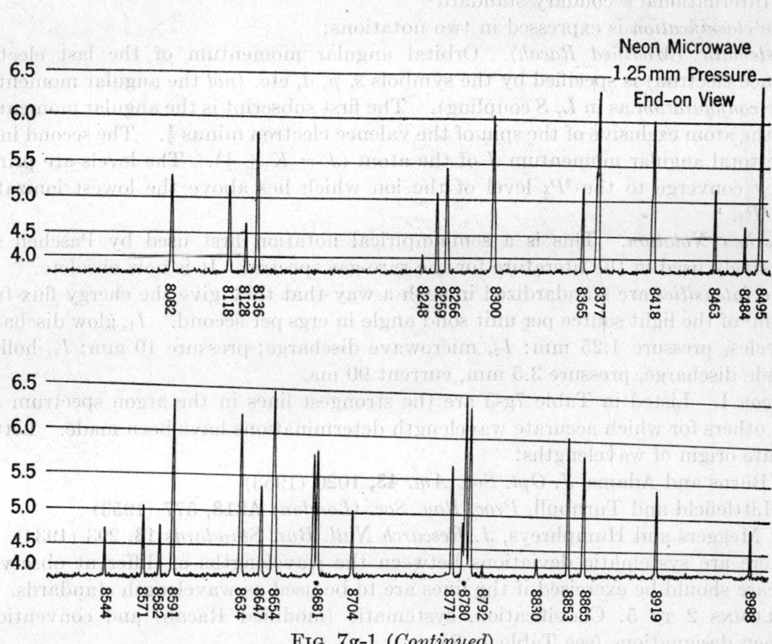

FIG. 7g-1 (*Continued*)

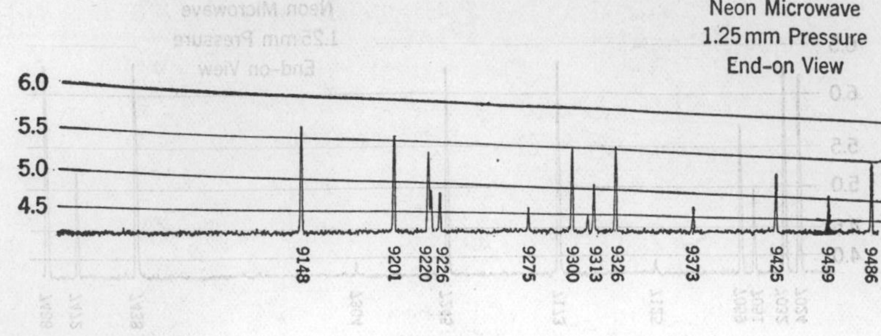

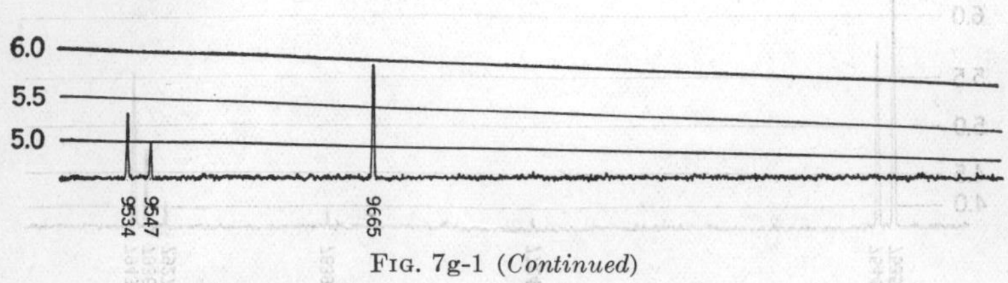

FIG. 7g-1 (*Continued*)

M, Meggers and Humphreys, *J. Research Natl. Bur. Standards* **13,** 293 (1934)

S, International secondary standard[1]

The *classification* is expressed in two notations:

Systematic (*Modified Racah*). Orbital angular momentum of the last electron (valence electron) is specified by the symbols *s*, *p*, *d*, etc. (*not* the angular momentum of the *configuration* as in *L*, *S* coupling). The first subscript is the angular momentum *K* of the atom exclusive of the spin of the valence electron minus $\frac{1}{2}$. The second index is the total angular momentum *J* of the atom ($J = K \pm \frac{1}{2}$). The levels are primed if they converge to the $^2P_{\frac{1}{2}}$ level of the ion which lies above the lowest ionization limit $^2P_{\frac{3}{2}}$.

Paschen Notation. This is a semiempirical notation first used by Paschen and extensively used in the literature for the rare-gas spectra. It is now obsolete.

The *intensities* are standardized in such a way that they give the energy flux from 100 cm² of the light source per unit solid angle in ergs per second. I_1, glow discharge, 60 cycles, pressure 1.25 mm; I_2, microwave discharge; pressure 10 mm; I_3, hollow-cathode discharge, pressure 3.5 mm, current 90 ma.

Argon I. Listed in Table 7g-3 are the strongest lines in the argon spectrum and some others for which accurate wavelength determinations have been made. Letters indicate origin of wavelengths:

B, Burns and Adams, *J. Opt. Soc. Am.* **43,** 1020 (1953)

L, Littlefield and Turnbull, *Proc. Roy. Soc.* (*London*) **A218,** 577 (1953)

M, Meggers and Humphreys, *J. Research Natl. Bur. Standards* **13,** 293 (1934)

There are systematic deviations between the wavelengths of different observers, and care should be exercised if the lines are to be used as wavelength standards.

COLUMNS 2 TO 5: Classification, systematic (modified Racah) and conventional Paschen designations (see Table 7g-2).

COLUMNS 6 AND 7: Intensities (logarithmic scale): I_1, intensity in 60-cycle a-c glow discharge; current 60 ma, argon pressure 3 mm; I_2, hollow-cathode discharge with iron electrodes, current 150 ma, argon pressure 1 mm.

[1] *Trans. Intern. Astron. Union* **5,** 86 (1935).

TABLE 7g-3. THE SPECTRUM OF ARGON I

λ	Classification				Intensities	
	System.		Paschen		log I_1	log I_2
3,319.3446 *B*	$4s_{12}$	$7p_{12}$	$1s_5$	$5p_6$		
3,373.4823 *B*	$4s_{11}$	$7p_{00}$	$1s_4$	$5p_5$		
3,554.3048 *L*	$4s_{12}$	$6p_{12}$	$1s_5$	$4p_6$		
3,567.6550 *L*	$4s_{12}$	$6p_{23}$	$1s_5$	$4p_9$		
3,572.2960 *B*	$4s'_{01}$	$7p_{00}$	$1s_2$	$5p_5$		
3,606.5207 *L*	$4s_{11}$	$6p_{00}$	$1s_4$	$4p_5$		
3,649.8310 *L*	$4s'_{01}$	$6p'_{00}$	$1s_2$	$4p_1$		
3,834.6775 *L*	$4s'_{01}$	$6p_{00}$	$1s_2$	$4p_5$	2.18	
3,894.6609 *L*	$4s'_{01}$	$6p_{01}$	$1s_2$	$4p_{10}$	1.75	
3,947.5046 *L*	$4s_{12}$	$5p'_{12}$	$1s_5$	$3p_3$	1.54	
3,948.9785 *L*	$4s_{12}$	$5p'_{01}$	$1s_5$	$3p_2$	3.09	2.65
4,044.4176 *L*	$4s_{11}$	$5p'_{12}$	$1s_4$	$3p_3$	3.16	
4,045.9645 *L*	$4s_{11}$	$5p'_{01}$	$1s_4$	$3p_2$	2.17	
4,054.5259 *L*	$4s_{11}$	$5p'_{11}$	$1s_4$	$3p_4$	1.92	
4,158.5906 *L*	$4s_{12}$	$5p_{12}$	$1s_5$	$3p_6$	3.80	3.56
4,164.1794 *L*	$4s_{12}$	$5p_{11}$	$1s_5$	$3p_7$	3.03	2.62
4,181.8833 *L*	$4s'_{00}$	$5p'_{01}$	$1s_3$	$3p_2$	3.13	2.56
4,190.7126 *L*	$4s_{12}$	$5p_{22}$	$1s_5$	$3p_8$	....	3.11
4,191.0292 *L*	$4s'_{00}$	$5p'_{11}$	$1s_3$	$3p_4$		
4,198.3174 *L*	$4s_{11}$	$5p_{00}$	$1s_4$	$3p_5$	3.53	
4,200.6745 *L*	$4s_{12}$	$5p_{23}$	$1s_5$	$3p_9$	3.83	
4,251.1848 *L*	$4s_{12}$	$5p_{01}$	$1s_5$	$3p_{10}$	2.73	
4,259.3615 *L*	$4s'_{01}$	$5p'_{00}$	$1s_2$	$3p_1$	3.40	
4,266.2865 *L*	$4s_{11}$	$5p_{12}$	$1s_4$	$3p_6$	3.29	3.11
4,272.1688 *L*	$4s_{11}$	$5p_{11}$	$1s_4$	$3p_7$	3.54	
4,300.1005 *L*	$4s_{11}$	$5p_{00}$	$1s_4$	$3p_5$	3.40	
4,333.5611 *L*	$4s'_{01}$	$5p'_{12}$	$1s_2$	$3p_3$	3.32	3.00
4,335.3374 *L*	$4s'_{01}$	$5p'_{01}$	$1s_2$	$3p_2$	2.95	2.52
4,345.1679 *L*	$4s'_{01}$	$5p'_{11}$	$1s_2$	$3p_4$	2.91	2.59
4,363.7944 *L*	$4s_{11}$	$5p_{01}$	$1s_4$	$3p_{10}$	1.89	2.30
4,510.7332 *L*	$4s'_{01}$	$5p_{00}$	$1s_2$	$3p_5$	3.13	2.92
4,522.3231 *L*	$4s'_{00}$	$5p_{01}$	$1s_3$	$3p_{10}$	2.62	2.19
4,596.0963 *L*	$4s'_{01}$	$5p_{11}$	$1s_2$	$3p_7$	2.65	2.20
4,628.4406 *L*	$4s'_{01}$	$5p_{22}$	$1s_2$	$3p_8$	2.42	
4,702.3160 *L*	$4s'_{01}$	$5p_{01}$	$1s_2$	$3p_{10}$	2.74	2.27
4,768.6750 *B*	$4p_{01}$	$6d'_{12}$	$2p_{10}$	$6s''_1$	1.63	
4,876.2610 *L*	$4p_{01}$	$7d_{12}$	$2p_{10}$	$7d_3$	1.80	
4,887.9478 *B*	$4p_{01}$	$7d_{01}$	$2p_{10}$	$7d_5$	1.77	
5,060.0793 *B*	$4p_{23}$	$8d_{34}$	$2p_9$	$8d_4$	1.65	
5,151.3943 *B*	$4p_{01}$	$6d_{00}$	$2p_{10}$	$6d_6$	2.00	

TABLE 7g-3. THE SPECTRUM OF ARGON I (*Continued*)

λ	Classification				Intensities	
	System.		Paschen		log I_1	log I_2
5,162.2847 *L*	$4p_{01}$	$6d_{01}$	$2p_{10}$	$6d_5$	2.47	
5,187.7467 *L*	$4p_{01}$	$5d'_{12}$	$2p_{10}$	$5s''_1$	2.53	2.01
5,221.2690 *L*	$4p_{23}$	$7d_{34}$	$2p_9$	$7d'_4$	2.17	
5,252.7857 *L*	$4p_{22}$	$7d_{33}$	$2p_8$	$7d_4$	1.85	
5,373.4951 *B*	$4p_{11}$	$7d_{22}$	$2p_7$	$7d''_1$	1.45	
5,410.4750 *B*	$4p_{12}$	$7d_{23}$	$2p_6$	$7d'_1$	2.49	
5,421.3492 *L*	$4p_{23}$	$8s_{12}$	$2p_9$	$5s_5$	2.00	
5,439.9903 *B*	$4p_{01}$	$7s_{11}$	$2p_{10}$	$4s_4$	1.67	
5,451.6506 *L*	$4p_{01}$	$7s_{12}$	$2p_{10}$	$4s_5$	2.42	2.00
5,457.4158 *B*	$4p_{22}$	$8s_{11}$	$2p_8$	$5s_4$	1.09	
5,467.1626 *B*	$4p_{22}$	$8s_{12}$	$2p_8$	$5s_5$	1.28	
5,473.455 *B*	$4p_{22}$	$7s'_{01}$	$2p_8$	$4s_2$	1.45	
5,495.8728 *L*	$4p_{23}$	$6d_{34}$	$2p_9$	$6d'_4$	2.72	2.39
5,506.1105 *L*	$4p_{22}$	$6d_{33}$	$2p_8$	$6d_4$	2.00	1.98
5,524.9576 *L*	$4p_{23}$	$5d'_{23}$	$2p_9$	$5s'''_1$	1.70	1.43
5,558.7015 *L*	$4p_{01}$	$5d_{12}$	$2p_{10}$	$5d_3$	2.84	2.48
5,572.5406 *L*	$4p_{22}$	$5d'_{23}$	$2p_8$	$5s'''_1$	2.35	2.09
5,588.7213 *B*	$4p_{22}$	$5d'_{22}$	$2p_8$	$5s''''_1$	1.55	
5,597.4783 *B*	$4p'_{12}$	$6d'_{23}$	$2p_3$	$6s'''_1$	1.58	
5,606.7328 *L*	$4p_{01}$	$5d_{01}$	$2p_{10}$	$5d_5$	2.84	2.56
5,650.7042 *L*	$4p_{01}$	$5d_{00}$	$2p_{10}$	$5d_6$	2.54	2.21
5,659.1278 *B*	$4p_{12}$	$8s_{12}$	$2p_6$	$5s_5$	1.61	
5,681.8976 *L*	$4p_{12}$	$6d_{23}$	$2p_6$	$6d'_1$	1.78	1.43
5,739.5191 *L*	$4p_{11}$	$5d'_{22}$	$2p_7$	$5s'''_1$	2.25	1.93
5,772.1143 *L*	$4p_{12}$	$5d'_{23}$	$2p_6$	$5s'''_1$	1.83	1.71
5,802.0802 *L*	$4p_{12}$	$6d_{01}$	$2p_6$	$6d_5$	1.69	
5,834.2640 *L*	$4p_{12}$	$5d'_{12}$	$2p_6$	$5s''_1$	2.01	1.75
5,860.3098 *L*	$4p_{01}$	$6s'_{01}$	$2p_{10}$	$3s_2$	2.19	2.05
5,882.6245 *L*	$4p_{01}$	$6s'_{00}$	$2p_{10}$	$3s_3$	2.41	1.98
5,888.5830 *L*	$4p_{23}$	$7s_{12}$	$2p_9$	$4s_5$	2.78	2.34
5,912.0848 *L*	$4p_{01}$	$4d'_{11}$	$2p_{10}$	$4s'_1$	2.82	2.62
5,928.8119 *L*	$4p_{22}$	$7s_{11}$	$2p_8$	$4s_4$	2.43	2.17
5,942.6676 *L*	$4p_{22}$	$7s_{12}$	$2p_8$	$4s_5$	1.96	1.84
5,987.3027 *B*	$4p_{23}$	$5d_{33}$	$2p_9$	$5d_4$	2.10	1.75
5,999.0004 *B*	$4p_{22}$	$5d_{22}$	$2p_8$	$5d''_1$	1.90	
6,005.7246 *B*	$4p'_{12}$	$8s_{11}$	$2p_3$	$5s_4$	1.33	
6,013.6790 *B*	$4p_{23}$	$5d_{12}$	$2p_9$	$5d_3$	1.75	
6,025.1515 *B*	$4p'_{12}$	$7s'_{01}$	$2p_3$	$4s_2$	1.97	
6,032.1273 *L*	$4p_{23}$	$5d_{34}$	$2p_9$	$5d'_4$	3.33	2.91
6,043.2232 *L*	$4p_{22}$	$5d_{33}$	$2p_8$	$5d_4$	2.88	2.46

TABLE 7g-3. THE SPECTRUM OF ARGON I (*Continued*)

λ	Classification				Intensities	
	System.		Paschen		log I_1	log I_2
6,052.7230 *L*	$4p_{01}$	$4d'_{22}$	$2p_{10}$	$4s_1''''$	2.28	1.84
6,059.3723 *L*	$4p_{01}$	$4d'_{12}$	$2p_{10}$	$4s_1''$	2.59	2.25
6,098.8046 *B*	$4p_{11}$	$7s_{11}$	$2p_7$	$4s_4$	2.10	2.05
6,105.6346 *L*	$4p'_{11}$	$5d'_{22}$	$2p_4$	$5s_1''''$	2.28	2.81
6,145.4406 *L*	$4p'_{12}$	$4d'_{23}$	$2p_3$	$5s_1'''$	2.25	1.93
6,155.2393 *B*	$4p_{12}$	$7s_{11}$	$2p_6$	$4s_4$	1.93	
	$4p'_{11}$	$5d'_{12}$	$2p_4$	$5s_1''$		
6,170.1734 *L*	$4p_{12}$	$7s_{12}$	$2p_6$	$4s_5$	2.25	
6,173.0949 *L*	$4p_{11}$	$5d_{22}$	$2p_7$	$5d_1''$	2.30	2.71
6,212.5015 *L*	$4p_{12}$	$5d_{23}$	$2p_6$	$5d_1'$	2.26	1.97
6,215.9423 *B*	$4p'_{12}$	$5d'_{12}$	$2p_3$	$5s_1''$	2.01	
6,296.8739 *L*	$4p'_{01}$	$5d'_{12}$	$2p_2$	$5s_1''$	2.18	
6,307.6561 *L*	$4p_{12}$	$5d_{12}$	$2p_6$	$5d_3$	2.36	2.09
6,364.8940 *L*	$4p_{11}$	$5d_{00}$	$2p_7$	$5d_6$	1.75	
6,369.5756 *L*	$4p_{12}$	$5d_{01}$	$2p_6$	$5d_5$	2.05	
6,384.7160 *L*	$4p_{01}$	$6s_{11}$	$2p_{10}$	$3s_4$	2.60	2.34
6,416.3064 *L*	$4p_{01}$	$6s_{12}$	$2p_{10}$	$3s_5$	3.36	2.87
6,431.5553 *L*	$4p_{22}$	$6s'_{01}$	$2p_8$	$3s_2$	1.60	
6,466.5498 *L*	$4p_{00}$	$5d_{11}$	$2p_5$	$5d_2$	1.64	
6,538.1118 *L*	$4p_{23}$	$4d'_{23}$	$2p_9$	$4s_1'''$	2.18	
6,604.8542 *B*	$4p_{22}$	$4d'_{23}$	$2p_8$	$4s_1'''$	2.43	
6,660.6784 *B*	$4p_{11}$	$6s'_{01}$	$2p_7$	$3s_3$	2 12	
6,664.0533 *B*	$4p_{22}$	$4d'_{12}$	$2p_8$	$4s_1''''$	2.16	
6,677.2812 *B*	$4s_{11}$	$4p'_{00}$	$1s_4$	$2p_1$	3.40	3.01
6,698.8752 *B*	$4p_{12}$	$6s'_{01}$	$2p_6$	$3s_2$	1.97	
6,719.2193 *B*	$4p_{00}$	$5d_{01}$	$2p_5$	$5d_5$	1.92	
6,752.8347 *B*	$4p_{01}$	$4d_{12}$	$2p_{10}$	$4d_3$	3.60	3.26
6,766.6134 *B*	$4p_{12}$	$4d'_{11}$	$2p_6$	$4s_1'$	2.27	
6,827.2529 *B*	$4p'_{12}$	$5d_{01}$	$2p_3$	$5d_5$	1.89	
6,871.2898 *B*	$4p_{01}$	$4d_{01}$	$2p_{10}$	$4d_5$	3.53	3.26
6,888.1704 *B*	$4p_{11}$	$4d'_{12}$	$2p_7$	$4s_1''$	2.45	
6,937.6658 *B*	$4p_{01}$	$4d_{00}$	$2p_{10}$	$4d_6$	3.15	2.86
6,965.4304 *B*	$4s_{12}$	$4p'_{01}$	$1s_5$	$2p_2$	5.06	4.75
7,030.2519 *B*	$4p_{23}$	$6s_{12}$	$2p_9$	$3s_5$	3.57	3.19
7,067.2175 *B*	$4s_{12}$	$4p'_{12}$	$1s_5$	$2p_3$	5.01	4.75
7,107.4777 *B*	$4p_{22}$	$6s_{12}$	$2p_8$	$3s_5$	2.79	
7,125.825 *B*	$4p'_{11}$	$6s'_{01}$	$2p_4$	$3s_2$	2.47	
7,147.0408 *B*	$4s_{12}$	$4p'_{11}$	$1s_5$	$2p_4$	4.42	3.83
7,206.9812 *B*	$4p'_{12}$	$6s'_{01}$	$2p_3$	$3s_2$	2.93	
7,272.9349 *B*	$4s_{11}$	$4p'_{01}$	$1s_4$	$2p_2$	4.71	4.23
7,311.724 *B*	$4p_{11}$	$6s_{11}$	$2p_7$	$3s_4$	2.89	

TABLE 7g-3. THE SPECTRUM OF ARGON I (*Continued*)

λ	Classification				Intensities	
	System.		Paschen		log I_1	log I_2
7,353.316	$4p_{22}$	$4d_{33}$	$2p_8$	$4d_4$	3.32	
7,372.1189 *B*	$4p_{23}$	$4d_{34}$	$2p_9$	$4d'_4$	3.76	3.44
7,383.9796 *B*	$4s_{11}$	$4p'_{12}$	$1s_4$	$2p_3$	5.02	5.03
7,412.334 *B*	$4p'_{11}$	$4d'_{22}$	$2p_4$	$4s''''_1$	2.55	
7,425.290 *B*	$4p'_{12}$	$4d'_{23}$	$2p_3$	$4s'''_1$	2.48	
7,471.1676 *B*	$4s_{11}$	$4p'_{11}$	$1s_4$	$2p_4$	2.86	
7,503.8685 *B*	$4s'_{01}$	$4p'_{00}$	$1s_2$	$2p_1$	5.35	5.28
7,514.6514 *B*	$4s_{11}$	$4p_{00}$	$1s_4$	$2p_5$	5.22	5.07
7,635.1056 *B*	$4s_{12}$	$4p_{12}$	$1s_5$	$2p_6$	5.53	5.36
7,723.7599 *B*	$4s_{12}$	$4p_{11}$	$1s_5$	$2p_7$	5.44	5.19
7,891.0777 *B*	$4p_{12}$	$4d_{12}$	$2p_6$	$4d_3$	3.60	
7,948.1755 *B*	$4s'_{00}$	$4p'_{11}$	$1s_3$	$2p_4$	5.13	5.13
8,006.1566 *B*	$4s_{11}$	$4p_{12}$	$1s_4$	$2p_6$	5.23	5.06
8,014.7853 *B*	$4s_{12}$	$4p_{22}$	$1s_5$	$2p_8$	5.30	5.29
8,103.6920 *B*	$4s_{11}$	$4p_{11}$	$1s_4$	$2p_7$	5.31	5.30
8,115.3108 *B*	$4s_{12}$	$4p_{23}$	$1s_5$	$2p_9$	5.58	5.59
8,264.5221 *B*	$4s'_{01}$	$4p'_{01}$	$1s_2$	$2p_2$	5.28	5.07
8,408.2094 *B*	$4s'_{01}$	$4p'_{12}$	$1s_2$	$2p_3$	5.36	5.35
8,424.6473 *B*	$4s_{11}$	$4p_{22}$	$1s_4$	$2p_8$	5.35	5.48
8,521.4428 *B*	$4s'_{01}$	$4p'_{11}$	$1s_2$	$2p_4$	5.18	5.09
8,605.7790 *B*	$4p'_{12}$	$4d_{12}$	$2p_3$	$4d_3$		
8,620.4602 *B*	$4p_{00}$	$4d_{01}$	$2p_5$	$4d_5$		
8,667.9438 *B*	$4s'_{00}$	$4p_{11}$	$1s_3$	$2p_7$	4.52	4.64
8,761.6907 *B*	$4p'_{01}$	$4d_{12}$	$2p_2$	$4d_3$		
8,799.082 *B*	$4p'_{12}$	$4d_{01}$	$2p_3$	$4d_5$		
9,122.9660 *B*	$4s_{12}$	$4p_{01}$	$1s_5$	$2p_{10}$	....	5.58
9,194.637 *B*	$4p_{01}$	$5s'_{00}$	$2p_{10}$	$2s_2$		
9,224.4955 *B*	$4s'_{01}$	$4p_{12}$	$1s_2$	$2p_6$	....	5.19
9,354.218 *M*	$4s'_{01}$	$4p_{11}$	$1s_2$	$2p_7$	....	4.18
9,657.7841 *M*	$4s_{11}$	$4p_{01}$	$1s_4$	$2p_{10}$	....	5.36
9,784.5010 *M*	$4s'_{01}$	$4p_{22}$	$1s_2$	$2p_8$	....	4.72
10,470.051 *M*	$4s'_{00}$	$4p_{01}$	$1s_3$	$2p_{10}$		

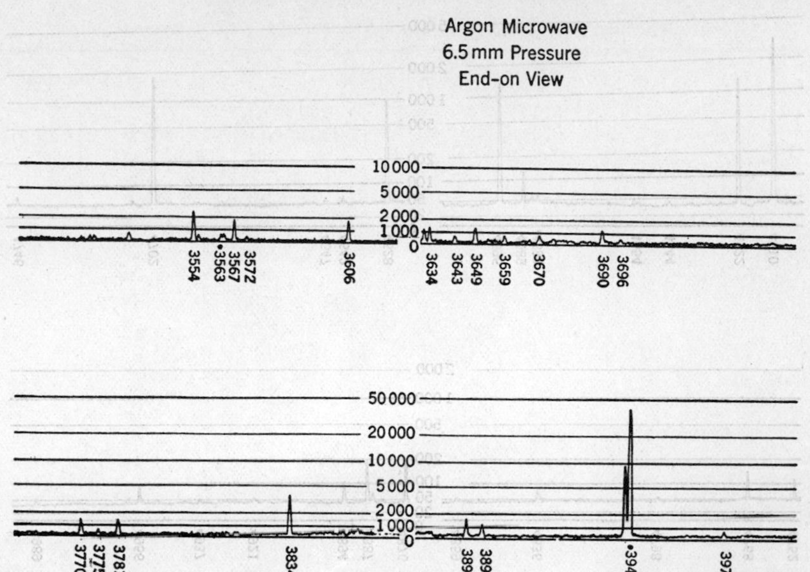

FIG. 7g-2. Photoelectric traces of the argon spectrum, microwave discharge at 6.5 mm pressure. Wavelength range is 3,500–10,000 A.

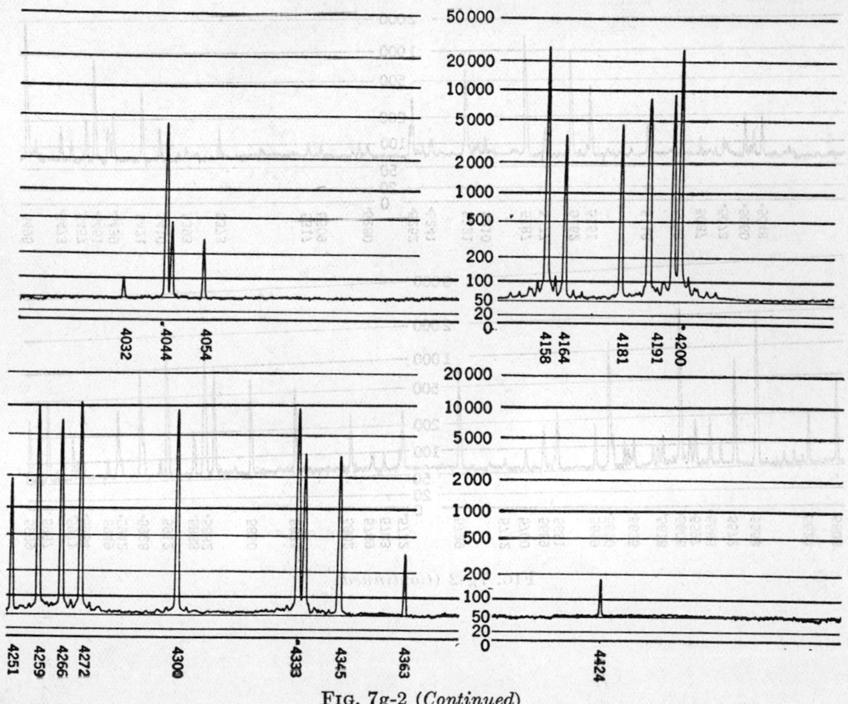

FIG. 7g-2 (*Continued*)

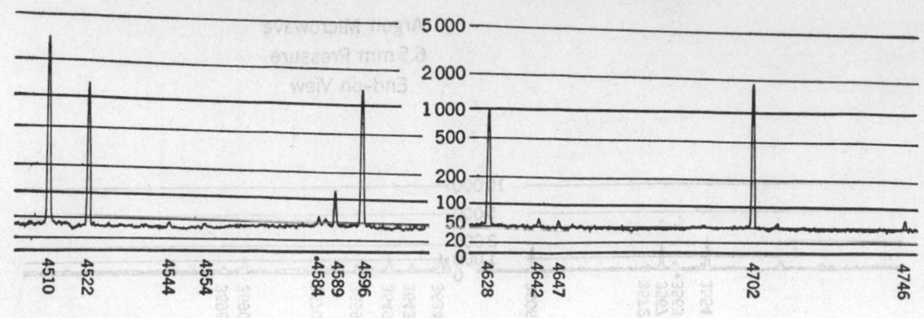

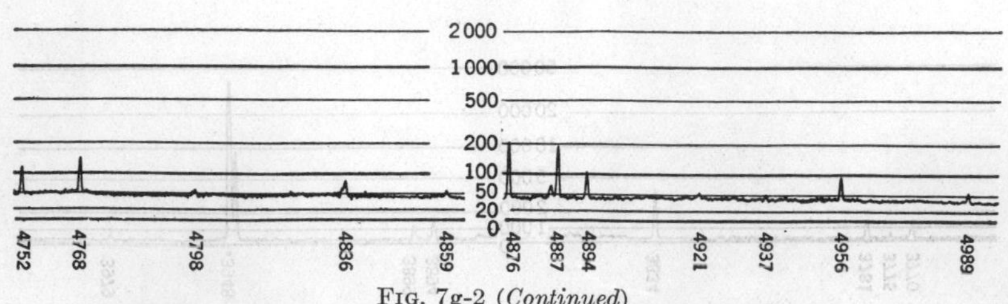

FIG. 7g-2 (*Continued*)

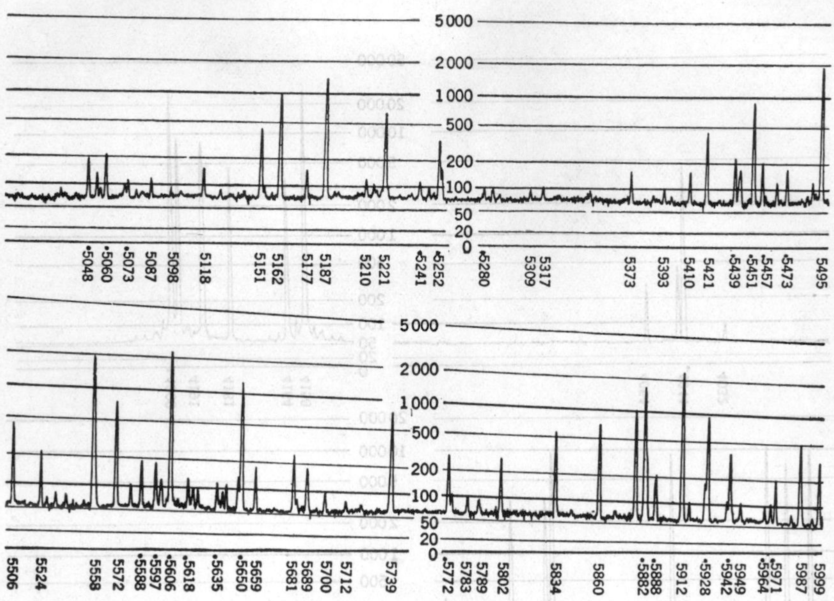

FIG. 7g-2 (*Continued*)

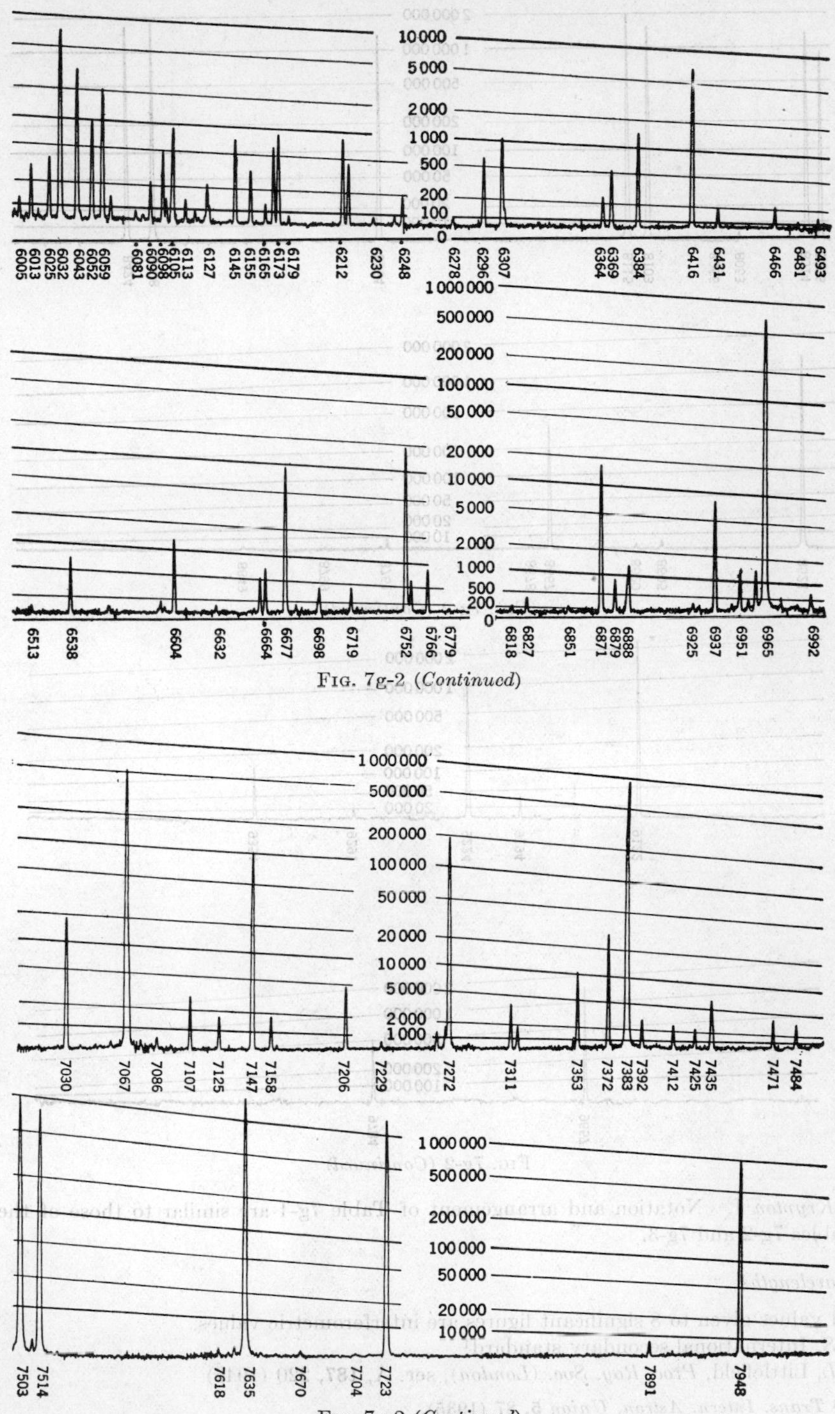

FIG. 7g-2 (*Continued*)

FIG. 7g-2 (*Continued*)

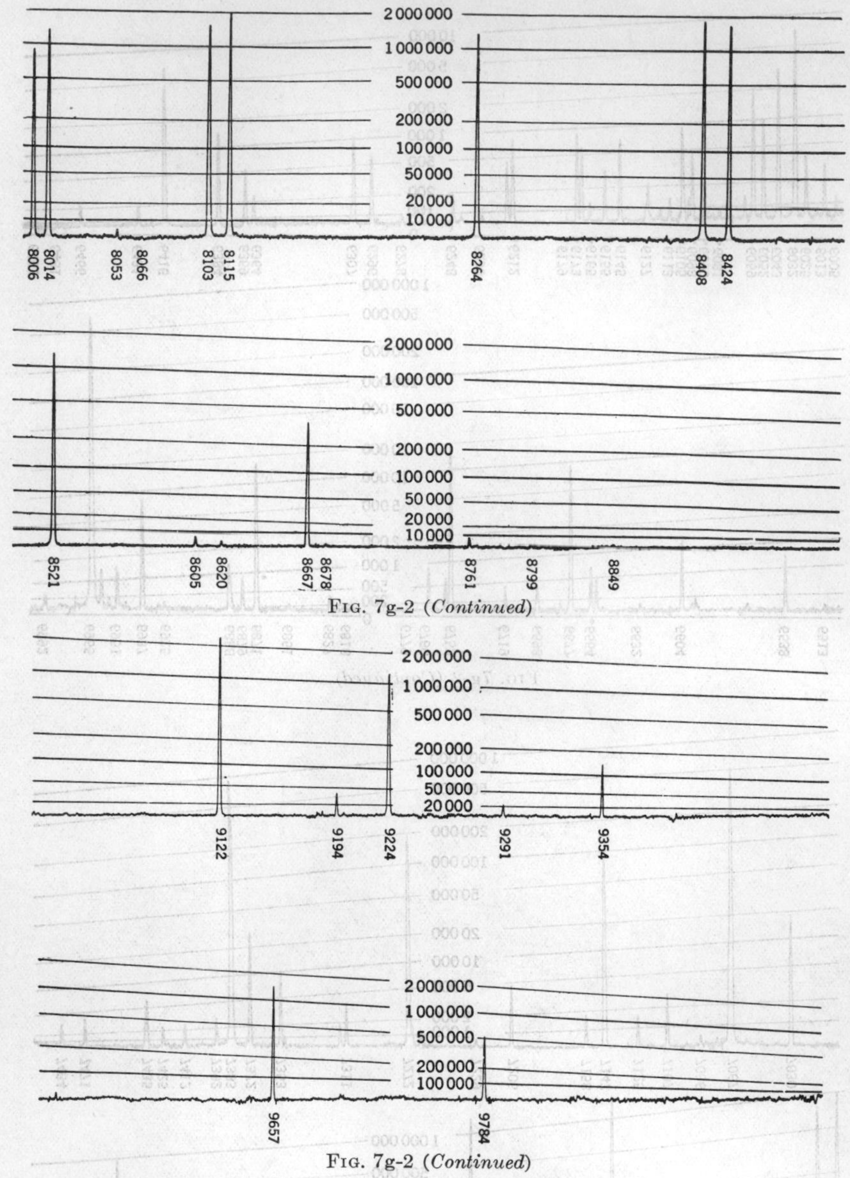

Fig. 7g-2 (*Continued*)

Fig. 7g-2 (*Continued*)

Krypton I. Notation and arrangement of Table 7g-4 are similar to those of the Tables 7g-2 and 7g-3.

Wavelengths

All values given to 8 significant figures are interferometric values.

S, International secondary standard[1]

L, Littlefield, *Proc. Roy. Soc.* (*London*), ser. A, **187**, 220 (1946)

[1] *Trans. Intern. Astron. Union* **5**, 87 (1935).

TABLE 7g-4. THE SPECTRUM OF KRYPTON I

λ	Classification		I_0	log I_1
4,273.9700 *S*	$5s_{12}$	$6p_{12}$	1,000	5.573
4,282.9683 *S*	$5s_{12}$	$6p_{11}$	100	4.540
4,286.4873 *S*	$5s'_{00}$	$6p'_{01}$	40	4.039
4,300.4877 *S*	$5s'_{00}$	$6p'_{11}$	50	3.812
4,318.5525 *S*	$5s_{12}$	$6p_{22}$	400	5.66
4,319.5797 *S*	$5s_{12}$	$6p_{23}$	1,000	
4,351.3607 *S*	$5s'_{01}$	$6p'_{00}$	100	3.938
4,362.6423 *S*	$5s_{12}$	$6p_{01}$	500	4.958
4,376.1220 *S*	$5s_{11}$	$6p_{00}$	800	5.208
4,399.9670 *S*	$5s'_{01}$	$6p'_{12}$	200	4.430
4,410.369	$5s'_{01}$	$6p'_{01}$	50	3.440
4,418.769	$5s'_{01}$	$5f_{22}$	50	3.391
4,425.1909	$5s'_{01}$	$6p'_{11}$	100	3.874
4,453.9179 *S*	$5s_{11}$	$6p_{12}$	600	5.027
4,463.6902 *S*	$5s_{11}$	$6p_{11}$	800	5.252
4,502.3547 *S*	$5s_{11}$	$6p_{22}$	600	5.117
4,550.298	$5s_{11}$	$6p_{01}$	40	3.210
4,812.607	$5s'_{00}$	$4f_{11}$	40	3.611
4,969.08	$5s'_{01}$	$4f_{12}$	20	3.560
5,490.94	$5p_{01}$	$7d_{12}$	50	3.903
5,500.71	$5p_{01}$	$7d_{01}$	50	3.924
5,520.52	$5p_{23}$	$8d_{34}$	40	3.757
5,562.2257 *S*	$5s_{12}$	$5p'_{12}$	500	5.338
5,570.2895 *S*	$5s_{12}$	$5p'_{01}$	2,000	5.937
5,580.3890 *L*	$5s'_{01}$	$6p_{00}$	80	4.399
5,649.5629 *S*	$5s'_{00}$	$6p_{01}$	100	4.518
5,672.4514 *L*	$5s_{12}$	$5p'_{11}$	50	3.993
5,707.5128 *L*	$5s'_{01}$	$6p_{12}$	40	3.800
5,824.50	$5p_{22}$	$7d_{33}$	40	4.032
5,827.07	$5p_{01}$	$8s_{12}$	20	3.833
5,832.8600 *L*	$5p_{23}$	$7d_{34}$	100	4.345
5,866.7514 *L*	$5s'_{01}$	$6p_{01}$	50	
5,870.9158 *S*	$5s_{11}$	$5p'_{12}$	3,000	6.040
5,879.9004 *L*	$5s_{11}$	$5p'_{01}$	50	4.696
5,993.8503 *S*	$5s_{11}$	$5p'_{11}$	60	4.618
6,012.1570 *L*	$5p_{01}$	$6d_{12}$	50	4.550
	$5p_{12}$	$9s_{12}$		
6,035.82	$5p_{11}$	$7d_{22}$	15	3.707
6,056.1274 *L*	$5p_{01}$	$6d_{01}$	60	4.617
6,075.24	$5p_{12}$	$7d_{23}$	20	3.780
6,082.8630 *L*	$5p_{01}$	$6d_{00}$	40	4.292

TABLE 7g-4. THE SPECTRUM OF KRYPTON I (*Continued*)

λ	Classification		I_0	log I_1
6,151.38	$5p_{12}$	$7d_{12}$	20	3.798
6,222.71	$5p_{22}$	$8s_{11}$	20	3.865
6,236.3520 *L*	$5p_{23}$	$8s_{12}$	30	4.140
6,346.66	$5p_{23}$	$6d_{23}$	20	3.795
6,373.58	$5p_{22}$	$6d_{22}$	30	4.027
6,421.0285 *L*	$5p_{22}$	$6d_{33}$	100	4.900
6,456.2910 *L*	$5p_{23}$	$6d_{34}$	200	5.103
6,576.42	$5p_{12}$	$8s_{12}$	20	3.799
6,652.24	$5p_{11}$	$6d_{22}$	40	4.351
6,699.23	$5p_{12}$	$6d_{23}$	60	4.474
6,740.10	$5p_{11}$	$6d_{12}$	20	3.75
6,813.10	$5p_{12}$	$6d_{12}$	50	4.466
6,846.40	$5p_{01}$	$7s_{11}$	20	3.83
6,869.63	$5p_{12}$	$6d_{01}$	20	4.025
6,904.68	$5p_{01}$	$7s_{12}$	100	5.029
7,224.109	$5p_{01}$	$5d_{12}$	100	5.090
7,287.262	$5p_{01}$	$6s'_{01}$	80	4.966
7,425.54	$5p_{22}$	$7s_{11}$	60	4.707
7,486.850	$5p_{01}$	$6s'_{00}$	100	5.119
	$5p_{23}$	$7s_{12}$		
7,493.58	$5p_{22}$	$5d_{11}$	20	4.692
7,494.15	$5p_{22}$	$7s_{12}$	30	
7,587.4135	$5s_{11}$	$5p_{00}$	1,000	6.357
7,601.5465	$5s_{12}$	$5p_{12}$	2,000	6.908
7,685.2472	$5s'_{01}$	$5p'_{00}$	1,000	6.369
7,694.5401	$5s_{12}$	$5p_{11}$	1,200	6.507
7,741.39	$5p_{23}$	$5d_{23}$	40	4.340
7,746.831	$5p_{01}$	$5d_{00}$	150	5.317
7,776.28	$5p_{22}$	$5d_{22}$	40	4.509
7,806.52	$5p_{11}$	$7s_{11}$	50	4.536
7,854.823	$5s'_{00}$	$5p'_{01}$	800	6.448
7,863.91	$5p_{23}$	$5d_{12}$	20	4.250
7,881.76	$5p_{11}$	$5d_{11}$	30	4.318
7,904.62	$5p_{12}$	$7s_{11}$	30	4.17
7,913.443	$5p_{01}$	$5d_{01}$	200	5.536
7,920.47	$5p_{23}$	$5d_{33}$	40	4.38
7,928.602	$5p_{22}$	$5d_{33}$	180	5.458
7,946.99	$5p_{22}$	$6s'_{01}$	20	4.05
7,982.42	$5p_{12}$	$7s_{12}$	100	4.826
8,059.5053	$5s'_{00}$	$5p'_{11}$	1,500	6.422
8,104.3660	$5s_{12}$	$5p_{22}$	4,000	6.813

TABLE 7g-4. THE SPECTRUM OF KRYPTON I (*Continued*)

λ	Classification		I_0	log I_1
8,112.9023	$5s_{12}$	$5p_{23}$	6,000	6.994
8,190.0570	$5s_{11}$	$5p_{12}$	3,000	6.682
8,218.40	$4d_{12}$	$6f_{22}$	80	3.99
8,263.2412	$5s'_{01}$	$5p'_{12}$	3,000	6.764
8,272.36	$5p_{12}$	$5d_{23}$	100	5.171
8,281.05	$5s'_{01}$	$5p'_{01}$	1,500	6.450
8,298.1091	$5s_{11}$	$5p_{11}$	5,000	6.857
8,412.45	$5p_{10}$	$5d_{12}$	100	4.746
8,498.21	$5p_{10}$	$6s'_{01}$	30	4.16
8,508.8736	$5s'_{01}$	$5p'_{11}$	3,000	6.537
8,537.93	$4d_{00}$	$5f_{11}$	40	4.17
8,560.89	$5p_{00}$	$7s_{11}$	50	4.22
8,569.02	$4d_{00}$	$6p'_{11}$	20	3.85
8,605.85	$4d_{33}$	$6f_{45}$	40	4.16
8,697.50	$5p_{22}$	$5d_{01}$	40	4.341
8,755.20	$4d_{01}$	$5f_{22}$	30	4.13
8,764.09	$5p_{23}$	$4d'_{23}$	150	5.149
8,776.7498	$5s_{11}$	$5p_{22}$	6,000	6.941
8,805.78	$4d_{01}$	$6p'_{11}$	20	3.78
8,928.6934	$5s_{12}$	$5p_{01}$	2,000	6.893
8,967.53	$5p_{23}$	$4d'_{22}$	10	3.95
8,977.99	$5p_{22}$	$4d'_{22}$	50	4.925
8,999.19	$5p_{11}$	$5d_{00}$	30	4.528
9,094.33	$4d_{22}$	$6f_3$	4*h*	3.94
9,111.69	$5p_{23}$	$4d'_{12}$	20	4.27
9,122.49	$5p_{22}$	$4d'_{12}$	20	4.32
9,243.54	....	....	30	4.783
9,270.96	$4d_{12}$	$5f_{12}$	10	4.38
9,326.03	$4d_{34}$	$5f_3$	10	4.17
9,352.23	$4d_{34}$	$5f_4$	100	5.122
9,362.03	$5p_{12}$	$5d_{01}$	100	5.181
9,450.88	$5p_{12}$	$4d'_{23}$	20	4.44
9,540.89	$5p_{11}$	$4d'_{22}$	30	4.72
9,687.83	$5p_{12}$	$4d'_{22}$	10	4.06
9,704.22	$5p_{11}$	$4d'_{12}$	50	5.00
9,714.85	$4d_{33}$	$5f_3$	15	2.26
9,743.11	$4d_{33}$	$5f_{44}$	50	4.990
9,751.74	$5s_{11}$	$5p_{01}$	2,000	6.545
9,856.24	$5p_{12}$	$4d'_{12}$	500	5.677
11,819.43	$5p_{01}$	$6s_{12}$	2,000	

TABLE 7g-4. THE SPECTRUM OF KRYPTON I (*Continued*)

λ	Classification		I_0	log I_1
12,204.39	$4d_{34}$	$4f_{45}$	700	
12,879.00	$4d_{33}$	$4f_{44}$	500	
13,177.38	$5p_{22}$	$6s_{11}$	850	
13,622.28	$5p_{22}$	$4d_{11}$	800	
13,634.22	$5p_{23}$	$6s_{12}$	1,700	
14,426.93	$5p_{11}$	$6s_{11}$	1,100	
14,734.46	$5p_{23}$	$4d_{23}$	900	
15,239.85	$5p_{22}$	$4d_{22}$	900	
15,335.29	$5p_{01}$	$4d_{12}$	850	
16,784.65	$5p_{12}$	$4d_{23}$	950	
16,890.40	$5p_{22}$	$4d_{33}$	1,000	
16,896.58	$5p_{01}$	$4d_{01}$	700	
16,935.71	$5p_{11}$	$4d_{22}$	800	
18,167.12	$5p_{23}$	$4d_{34}$	1,500	

Wavelengths not followed by a capital letter and all I_0 values are taken from the three following sources:

4,273 to 7,601 A: Meggers, deBruin, and Humphreys, *J. Research Natl. Bur. Standards* **7**, 643 (1931)

7,685 to 9,856 A: Meggers and Humphreys, *J. Research Natl. Bur. Standards* **10**, 443 (1933)

11,792 to 18,167 A: Humphreys and Kostkowski, *J. Research Natl. Bur. Standards* **49**, 73 (1952)

I_1, intensity in a microwave discharge at 1.6 mm pressure. This is approximately the vapor pressure of krypton at the temperature of liquid nitrogen (77°K). Immersing a discharge tube with krypton at a room-temperature pressure of more than 7 mm in liquid nitrogen will keep the pressure very steady at about 1.6 mm and therefore will produce very constant intensities.

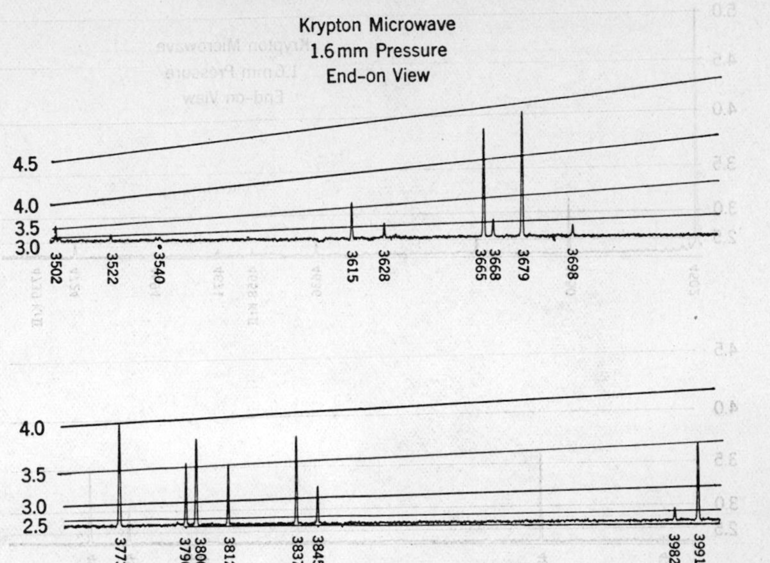

FIG. 7g-3. Photoelectric traces of the krypton spectrum, microwave discharge at 1.6 mm pressure. Wavelength range is 3,500–10,000 A.

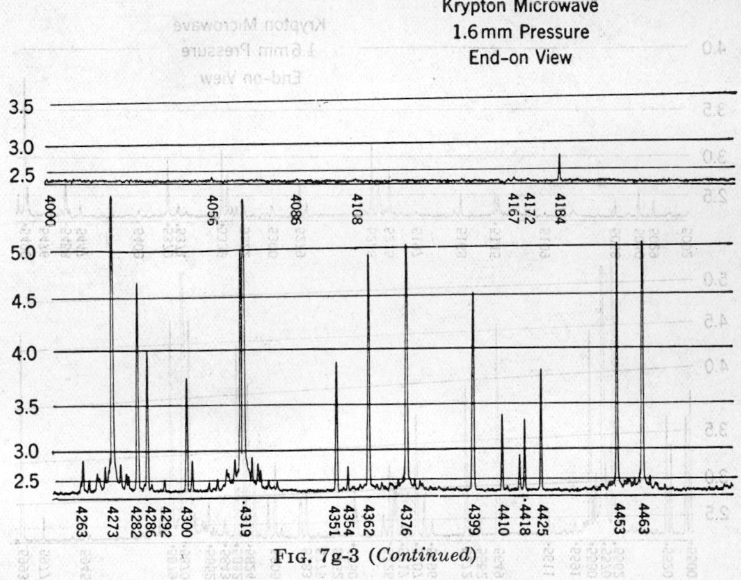

FIG. 7g-3 (*Continued*)

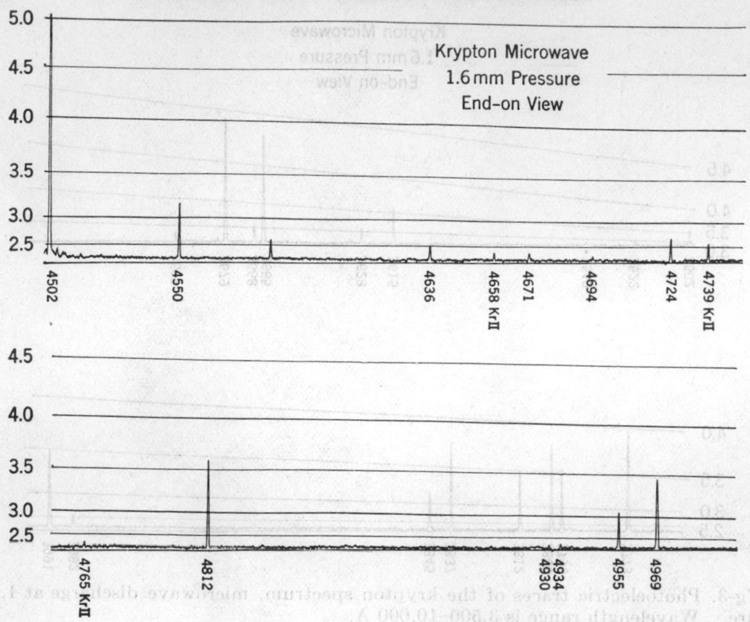

FIG. 7g-3 (*Continued*)

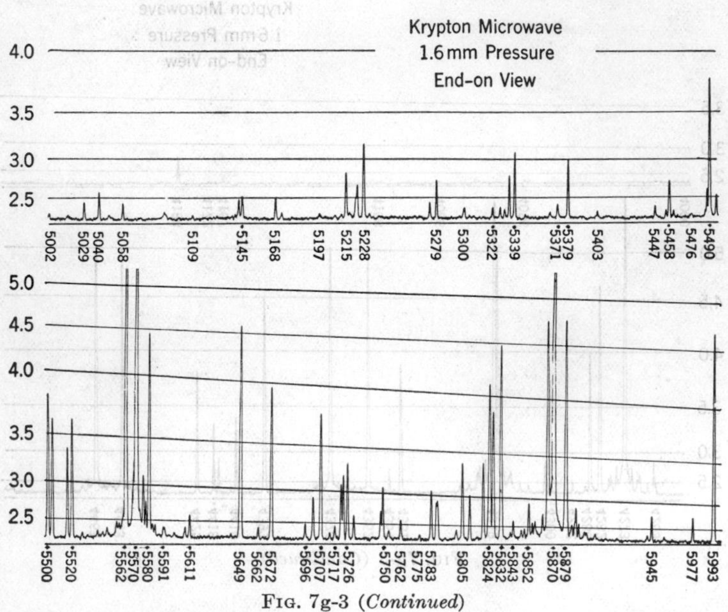

FIG. 7g-3 (*Continued*)

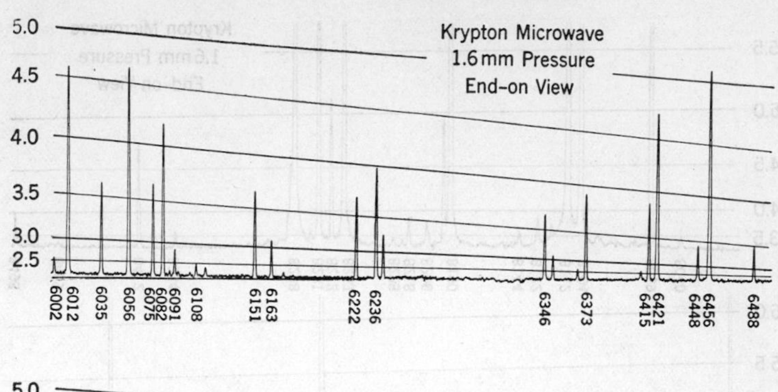

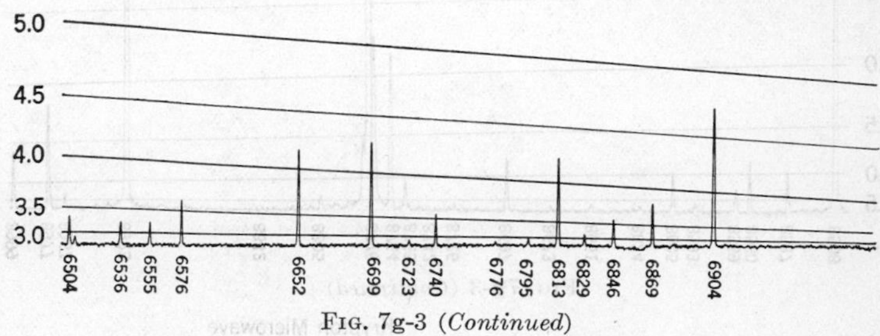

FIG. 7g-3 (*Continued*)

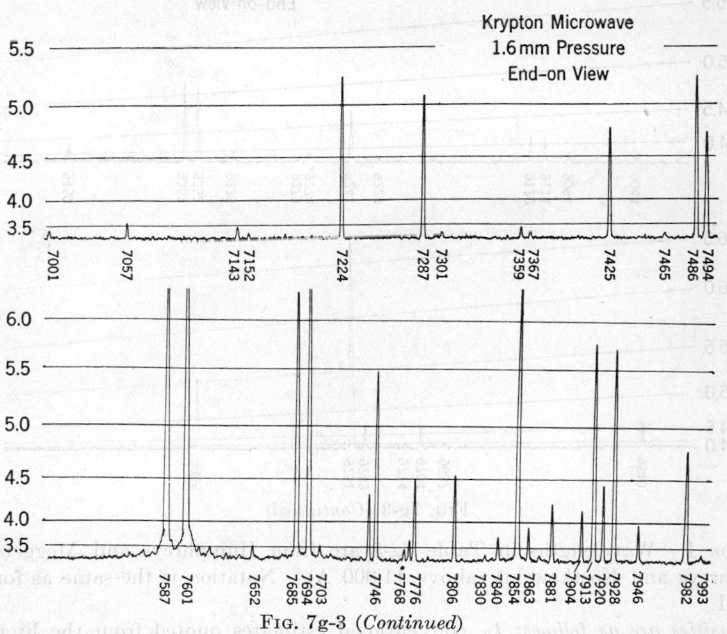

FIG. 7g-3 (*Continued*)

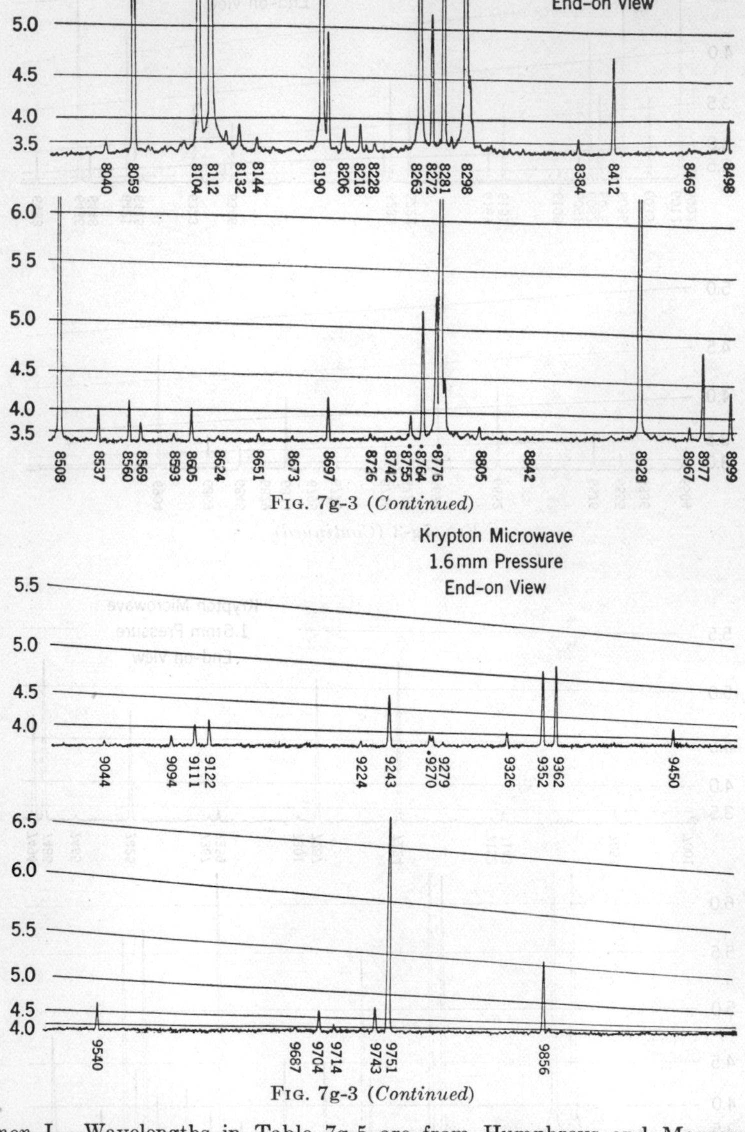

Fig. 7g-3 (*Continued*)

Fig. 7g-3 (*Continued*)

Xenon I. Wavelengths in Table 7g-5 are from Humphreys and Meggers[1] and Humphreys and Kostkowski[2] (above 11,000 A). Notation is the same as for Ne I and A I.

Intensities are as follows: I_0, conventional estimates quoted from the literature; I_1, microwave discharge, pressure of 0.002 mm; I_2, same, $p = 0.07$ mm; I_3, same, $p = 16$ mm; I_4, d-c glow discharge, $p = 4.1$ mm.[3]

For significance of the intensity scale, see Table 7g-2.

[1] C. V. Humphreys and W. F. Meggers, *J. Research Natl. Bur. Standards* **10,** 139 (1933).
[2] Humphreys and Kostkowski, *J. Research Natl. Bur. Standards* **49,** 73 (1952).
[3] The I_1 to I_4 intensities were measured by M. Thekaekara, S.J.

TABLE 7g-5. THE SPECTRUM OF XENON I

Wavelength	Classification		I_0	log I_1	log I_2	log I_3	log I_4
3,685.90	$6s_{12}$	$9p_{12}$	40				
3,693.49	$6s_{12}$	$9p_{23}$	40				
3,745.38	$6s_{11}$	$6f_{12}$	10				
3,796.30	$6s_{12}$	$5f_{23}$	40				
3,948.163	$6s_{11}$	$5f_{12}$	60	3.06	3.70	2.89	2.32
3,950.925	$6s_{12}$	$8p_{12}$	120	3.86	4.55	3.62	3.21
3,967.541	$6s_{12}$	$8p_{23}$	200	3.94	4.66	3.74	3.34
3,974.417	$6s_{12}$	$8p_{22}$	40	3.02	3.70	2.71	2.34
3,985.202	$6s_{12}$	$8p_{01}$	30	2.91	3.60	2.65	2.26
4,078.8207	$6s_{11}$	$8p_{00}$	100	4.06	4.32	3.40	2.76
4,109.7093	$6s_{11}$	$8p_{12}$	60	3.33	4.00	3.05	2.66
4,116.1151	$6s_{11}$	$8p_{11}$	80	3.56	4.17	3.23	2.71
4,135.1337	$6s_{11}$	$8p_{22}$	20	2.66	3.31		
4,193.5296	$6s_{12}$	$4f_{23}$	150	3.62	4.51	3.54	3.25
4,203.6945	$6s_{12}$	$4f_{12}$	50	2.91	4.01		
4,205.404	$6s_{12}$	$4f_{11}$	10	....	3.02		
4,372.287	$6s_{11}$	$4f_{22}$	20				
4,383.9092	$6s_{11}$	$4f_{12}$	100	3.08	4.13	3.12	2.83
4,385.7693	$6s_{11}$	$4f_{11}$	70	....	2.80	2.82	2.55
4,500.9772	$6s_{12}$	$6p'_{01}$	500	4.06	5.13	4.23	2.98
4,524.6805	$6s_{12}$	$6p'_{12}$	400	3.97	4.85	3.96	3.64
4,582.7474	$6s_{11}$	$6p'_{00}$	300	4.16	4.66	3.68	3.42
4,611.8896	$6s_{12}$	$7p_{11}$	100	2.86	3.86	2.84	2.61
4,624.2757	$6s_{12}$	$7p_{12}$	1,000	4.76	5.61	4.72	4.44
4,671.226	$6s_{12}$	$7p_{23}$	2,000	4.98	5.81	4.99	4.70
4,690.9711	$6s_{12}$	$6p'_{11}$	100	3.29	4.46	3.43	3.25
4,697.020	$6s_{12}$	$7p_{22}$	300	4.21	5.17	4.13	3.92
4,734.1524	$6s_{11}$	$6p'_{12}$	600	4.25	5.27	4.39	4.10
4,792.6192	$6s_{12}$	$7p_{01}$	150	3.48	4.32	3.29	3.12
4,807.019	$6s_{11}$	$7p_{00}$	500	4.52	5.31	4.35	4.12
4,829.709	$6s_{11}$	$7p_{11}$	400	4.27	5.19	4.21	3.97
4,843.294	$6s_{11}$	$7p_{12}$	300	4.50	5.06	4.07	3.84
4,916.508	$6s_{11}$	$6p'_{11}$	500	4.04	5.15	4.16	3.95
4,923.1522	$6s_{11}$	$7p_{22}$	500	4.30	5.22	4.21	3.99
5,028.2796	$6s_{11}$	$7p_{01}$	200	3.54	4.52	3.42	3.25
5,162.711	$6s'_{00}$	$7f_{11}$	10	2.86	3.30	3.12	
5,362.244	$6p_{01}$	$10d_{01}$	15 }	2.97	3.24	3.20	
5,364.626	$6p_{01}$	$10d_{12}$	30 }				
5,392.795	$6s'_{00}$	$6f_{11}$	100 }	3.31	3.86	3.35	2.46
5,394.738	$6p_{01}$	$7s'_{01}$	20 }				

TABLE 7g-5. THE SPECTRUM OF XENON I (*Continued*)

Wavelength	Classification		I_0	log I_1	log I_2	log I_3	log I_4
5,439.923	$6s'_{01}$	$7f_{12}$	30	3.65	3.49	3.21	2.03
5,460.037	$6p_{01}$	$11s_{12}$	15	3.23	3.12	2.81	
5,488.555	$6p_{22}$	$11d_{33}$	20*h*	2.85	3.22	3.56	
5,552.385	$6p_{01}$	$9d_{12}$	80	3.32	3.78	3.48	2.42
5,566.615	$6p_{01}$	$9d_{01}$	100	3.41	3.86	3.52	2.10
5,581.784	$6p_{01}$	$9d_{00}$	50	3.13	3.53	3.52	
5,618.878	$6p_{22}$	$10d_{33}$	80	3.21	3.60	3.61	2.21
5,688.373	$6s'_{01}$	$6f_{22}$	40	2.97	3.41	2.84	
5,695.750	$6s'_{01}$	$6f_{12}$	100 }	3.61	4.06	3.50	2.62
5,696.479	$6s'_{01}$	$6f_{11}$	80 }				
5,715.716	$6p_{01}$	$10s_{12}$	70 }	3.56	4.00	3.83	2.57
5,716.252	$6p_{23}$	$10d_{34}$	80 }				
5,807.311	$6p_{22}$	$9d_{23}$	15	2.39	2.93	2.67	
5,814.505	$6p_{22}$	$9d_{22}$	60	3.16	3.58	3.31	2.16
5,823.890	$6s'_{00}$	$5f_{11}$	300	3.96	4.65	4.08	3.23
5,824.800	$6p_{22}$	$9d_{33}$	150				
5,856.509	$6p_{01}$	$8d_{22}$	15	2.61	3.21	2.81	
5,875.018	$6p_{01}$	$8d_{12}$	100	4.03	5.41	3.77	2.98
5,894.988	$6p_{01}$	$8d_{01}$	100	3.92	4.44	3.85	3.02
5,904.462	$6p_{23}$	$9d_{23}$	20	3.15	3.42	3.16	
5,922.550	$6p_{23}$	$9d_{33}$	20	3.02	3.52	3.23	
5,931.241	$6p_{01}$	$8d_{00}$	80 }	3.83	4.32	4.05	2.95
5,934.172	$6p_{23}$	$9d_{34}$	100 }				
5,974.152	$6p_{12}$	$10d_{23}$	40	3.50	3.42	3.57	
5,989.18	$6p_{12}$	$10d_{12}$	20	2.90	3.19	3.17	
5,998.115	$6p_{22}$	$10s_{11}$	30	3.17	3.51	3.12	
6,007.909	$6p_{22}$	$10s_{12}$	15	2.87	3.20	2.79	
6,111.759	$6p_{11}$	$9d_{22}$	30 }	3.63	....	3.72	2.56
6,111.951	$6p_{23}$	$10s_{12}$	40 }				
6,152.069	$6p_{22}$	$8d_{23}$	20	....	3.46		
6,163.660	$6p_{22}$	$8d_{22}$	90 }	3.95	....	3.85	3.07
6,163.935	$6s'_{01}$	$5f_{22}$	80 }				
6,178.302	$6s'_{01}$	$5f_{12}$	150 }	3.99	....	3.95	3.28
6,179.665	$6s'_{01}$	$5f_{11}$	120 }				
6,182.420	$6p_{22}$	$8d_{33}$	300	4.19	....	4.19	3.42
6,189.10	$6p_{01}$	$9s_{11}$	20	2.89	3.43	3.16	
6,198.260	$6p_{01}$	$9s_{12}$	100 }	3.72	3.64	3.72	3.01
6,200.890	$6p_{12}$	$9d_{23}$	60 }				
6,206.297	$6p_{22}$	$8d_{01}$	20	3.18	....	3.27	
6,224.169	$6p_{12}$	$9d_{12}$	40	....	3.67	3.39	

TABLE 7g-5. THE SPECTRUM OF XENON I (*Continued*)

Wavelength	Classification		I_0	log I_1	log I_2	log I_3	log I_4
6,261.212	$6p_{23}$	$8d_{23}$	50	3.39	4.03	3.45	
6,265.301	$6s'_{00}$	$8p_{01}$	40	3.18	3.87	2.96	
6,286.011	$5d_{34}$	$8f_{45}$	100	3.34	3.82	3.84	
6,292.649	$6p_{23}$	$8d_{33}$	50	3.43	4.06	3.47	
6,318.062	$6p_{23}$	$8d_{34}$	500	4.34	4.93	4.42	3.66
6,430.155	$6p_{12}$	$10s_{12}$	20	....	3.44		
6,469.705	$6p_{01}$	$7d_{12}$	300	4.15	4.92	4.05	3.56
6,472.841	$6p_{01}$	$7d_{11}$	150	3.92	4.57	3.70	3.20
6,487.765	$6p_{01}$	$7d_{22}$	120	3.90	4.59	3.72	3.22
6,497.43	$5d_{34}$	$7f_{33}$	30*hl*				
6,498.718	$6p_{11}$	$8d_{22}$	100	3.90	4.44	3.89	3.09
6,504.18	$6s'_{01}$	$8p_{00}$	200*h*	3.82	4.37	4.16	3.05
6,521.508	$6p_{11}$	$8d_{12}$	40	3.30	3.88	3.25	
6,533.159	$6p_{22}$	$9s_{11}$	100		4.32	3.56	
6,543.360	$6p_{22}$	$9s_{12}$	40	3.78	3.95		
6,554.196	$5d_{12}$	$7f_{23}$	50*hl*	3.54	4.02	3.78	
6,595.561	$6p_{12}$	$8d_{23}$	100	4.08	4.61	4.05	3.20
6,632.464	$6p_{12}$	$8d_{12}$	50	3.76	4.32	3.73	
6,666.965	$6p_{23}$	$9s_{12}$	60 }	4.26	5.03	4.19	3.69
6,668.920	$6p_{01}$	$7d_{00}$	150 }				
6,678.972	$6s'_{01}$	$8p_{01}$	25	3.49	4.12		
6,681.036	$5d_{00}$	$6f_{11}$	20				
6,728.008	$6p_{01}$	$7d_{01}$	200	4.48	5.22	4.34	3.85
6,777.57	$5d_{01}$	$6f_{12}$	50 }	3.86	4.32	3.85	2.96
6,778.60	$5d_{01}$	$6f_{11}$	40 }				
6,827.315	$6s'_{00}$	$4f_{11}$	200	3.91	4.12	4.27	3.83
6,846.613	$6p_{22}$	$7d_{12}$	60	3.95	4.72	4.03	3.45
6,866.838	$6p_{22}$	$7d_{22}$	50	3.87	4.56		
6,872.107	$5d_{34}$	$6f_{45}$	100	4.19	4.84	4.52	3.58
6,882.155	$6p_{22}$	$7d_{33}$	300	4.77	5.41	4.68	4.14
6,925.53	$5d_{12}$	$6f_{23}$	100	3.97	4.51	3.88	3.25
6,976.182	$6p_{23}$	$7d_{23}$	100	4.07	4.93	3.99	3.52
7,119.598	$6p_{23}$	$7d_{34}$	500	4.91	5.62	4.92	4.43
7,257.94	$5d_{33}$	$6f_{44}$	60	4.07	4.73	4.07	3.39
7,262.54	$6p_{11}$	$7d_{12}$	20	4.02	4.70	3.83	3.26
7,266.49	$6p_{11}$	$7d_{11}$	25	....	4.60		
7,283.961	$6s'_{01}$	$4f_{22}$	40 }	4.61	5.33	4.50	4.00
7,285.301	$6p_{11}$	$7d_{22}$	60 }				
7,316.272	$6s'_{01}$	$4f_{12}$	70	4.09	5.07	4.35	3.83
7,321.452	$6s'_{01}$	$4f_{11}$	80	....	5.00		

TABLE 7g-5. THE SPECTRUM OF XENON I (*Continued*)

Wavelength	Classification		I_0	log I_1	log I_2	log I_3	log I_4
7,336.480	$6p_{22}$	$5d'_{23}$	50	4.57	5.02	3.97	3.56
7,355.58	$5d_{00}$	$5f_{11}$	40	3.80	5.63	3.79	3.26
7,386.002	$6p_{01}$	$8s_{12}$	100	4.26	5.16	4.27	3.85
7,393.793	$6p_{12}$	$7d_{23}$	150	4.49	5.30	4.46	3.96
7,400.41	$6p_{12}$	$7d_{12}$	30	4.05	4.80	3.89	3.46
7,451.00	$5d_{01}$	$5f_{22}$	25	3.69	4.46	. . . .	3.05
7,472.01	$5d_{01}$	$5f_{12}$	40	4.37	4.94	4.19	3.65
7,474.01	$5d_{01}$	$5f_{11}$	25				
7,492.23	$6p_{23}$	$5d'_{23}$	20	4.18	4.65	3.64	3.27
7,559.79	$5d_{34}$	$5f_{33}$	40	3.76	4.72	3.88	3.35
7,584.680	$5d_{34}$	$5f_{45}$	200	4.59	5.42	4.86	4.28
7,642.025	$6s'_{00}$	$6p'_{01}$	500 }	4.98	5.92	5.36	4.88
7,643.91	$5d_{12}$	$5f_{33}$	100 }				
7,664.56	$5d_{12}$	$5f_{12}$	30	4.26	4.83	4.00	3.47
7,740.31	$6p_{12}$	$7d_{01}$	40	3.87	4.59	3.67	3.17
7,783.66	$5d_{22}$	$6f_{33}$	50	3.90	4.55	3.84	3.17
7,802.651	$6p_{22}$	$8s_{11}$	100	4.31	5.19	4.33	3.89
7,881.320	$6p_{22}$	$8s_{12}$	100		4.73		3.45
7,887.395	$6s'_{01}$	$6p'_{00}$	300	5.20	5.66	4.90	4.45
7,937.41	$6p_{00}$	$7d_{11}$	40	3.75	4.42	3.50	3.05
7,967.341	$6s'_{00}$	$7p_{11}$	500	4.82	5.45	4.97	4.53
8,029.67	$5d_{33}$	$5f_{33}$	100	3.95	4.85	3.79	3.46
8,057.258	$5d_{33}$	$5f_{44}$	200	4.55	5.33	4.67	4.10
8,061.340	$6p_{23}$	$8s_{12}$	150	4.53	5.38	4.55	4.12
8,101.98	$5d_{23}$	$6f_{33}$	100	3.92	4.71	3.93	3.25
8,171.02	$5d_{01}$	$8p_{22}$	100	4.52	4.97	4.01	3.55
8,206.341	$6s'_{00}$	$6p'_{11}$	700	4.85	6.01	5.20	4.85
8,231.6348	$6s_{12}$	$6p_{12}$	10,000	5.66	7.16	6.87	6.37
8,266.519	$6s'_{01}$	$6p'_{01}$	500	4.75	5.93	5.20	4.72
8,280.1163	$6s_{11}$	$6p_{00}$	7,000	5.99	6.73	6.71	6.21
8,346.823	$6s'_{01}$	$6p'_{12}$	2,000	5.50	6.36	5.82	5.29
8,409.190	$6s_{12}$	$6p_{11}$	2,000	4.96	6.60	6.01	5.63
8,522.55	$6s'_{00}$	$7p_{00}$	30	3.69	4.72	3.69	3.28
8,530.10	$6p_{12}$	$8s_{11}$	30	3.79	4.74	3.83	3.39
8,576.01	$6s'_{01}$	$7p_{00}$	200	4.38	5.26	4.42	3.98
8,624.24	$6p_{12}$	$8s_{12}$	80	4.07	5.00	4.10	3.65
8,648.54	$6s'_{01}$	$7p_{11}$	250	4.65	5.56	4.77	4.32
8,692.20	$6s'_{01}$	$7p_{12}$	100 }	4.47	5.13	4.31	3.87
8,696.86	$5d_{22}$	$5f_{33}$	200 }		5.19	4.46	3.86
8,709.64	$5d_{22}$	$5f_{22}$	40	3.93	. . .	3.84	

TABLE 7g-5. THE SPECTRUM OF XENON I (*Continued*)

Wavelength	Classification		I_0	$\log I_1$	$\log I_2$	$\log I_3$	$\log I_4$
8,739.39	$6p_{01}$	$6d_{12}$	300	4.99	6.03	5.22	4.80
8,758.20	$6p_{22}$	$6d_{23}$	100	4.13	5.35	4.8	4.01
8,819.412	$6s_{12}$	$6p_{23}$	5,000	5.75	....	7.02	6.51
8,862.32	$6p_{01}$	$6d_{01}$	300	5.10	6.17	5.44	4.99
8,908.73	$6p_{01}$	$6d_{00}$	200	4.76	5.94	5.12	4.71
8,930.83	$6s'_{01}$	$6p'_{11}$	200	4.93	6.02	5.25	4.74
8,952.254	$6s_{11}$	$6p_{12}$	1,000	5.92	6.76	6.72	6.23
8,981.05	$6p_{23}$	$6d_{23}$	100	4.34	5.61	4.61	4.23
8,987.57	$6p_{22}$	$6d_{22}$	200	4.73	5.82	5.00	4.55
9,025.98	$6p_{11}$	$6d_{11}$	30	4.58	5.25	4.38	3.87
9,032.18	$5d_{00}$	$4f_{11}$	50	4.49	5.36	4.69	4.14
9,045.446	$6s_{12}$	$6p_{22}$	400	5.60	6.00	5.73	5.28
9,096.13	$5d_{23}$	$5f_{33}$	50	4.39	5.32	4.53	3.98
9,152.12	$5d_{01}$	$4f_{22}$	20	4.16	5.30		
9,162.654	$6s_{11}$	$6p_{11}$	500	5.97	6.93	6.94	6.39
9,167.52	$6p_{22}$	$6d_{33}$	100		6.22		
9,203.20	$5d_{01}$	$4f_{12}$	30	4.60	5.67	4.88	4.36
9,211.38	$5d_{01}$	$4f_{11}$	25	4.21	5.40	4.73	4.06
9,301.95	$5d_{34}$	$4f_{33}$	30	....	5.46	4.73	4.20
9,306.64	$6s'_{01}$	$7p_{01}$	40	4.74	5.59	4.75	4.33
9,374.76	$5d_{34}$	$4f_{45}$	100	4.86	5.66	5.61	5.08
9,412.01	$6p_{23}$	$6d_{33}$	60	4.66	5.10	5.05	4.56
9,445.34	$5d_{12}$	$4f_{23}$	80	4.81	5.86	5.31	4.77
9,497.07	$5d_{12}$	$4f_{12}$	40	4.40	5.50	4.71	4.19
9,513.379	$6p_{23}$	$6d_{34}$	200	5.48	6.30	5.91	5.41
9,585.14	$6p_{22}$	$6d_{01}$	20	3.95	....	4.27	3.77
9,685.32	$6p_{12}$	$6d_{23}$	150	5.04	6.04	5.40	4.88
9,700.99	$6p_{23}$	$6d_{12}$	20	4.14	6.00	4.31	3.82
9,718.16	$6p_{11}$	$6d_{22}$	100	5.04	6.95	5.31	4.80
9,799.699	$6s_{12}$	$6p_{01}$	2,000	5.79	6.78	7.00	6.49
9,923.192	$6s_{11}$	$6p_{22}$	3,000	6.19	....	7.03	6.51
10,023.72	$5d_{12}$	$4f_{33}$	50	4.49	....	4.85	4.39
10,107.34	$5d_{12}$	$4f_{44}$	80				
10,838.34	$6s_{11}$	$6p_{01}$	1,000				
11,742.26	$5d_{23}$	$4f_{34}$	90				
12,623.32	$6p_{01}$	$7s_{12}$	300				
13,656.48	$6p_{22}$	$7s_{11}$	150				
14,142.09	$6p_{22}$	$7s_{12}$	80				
14,732.38	$6p_{23}$	$7s_{12}$	200				
15,418.01	$6p_{11}$	$7s_{11}$	110				

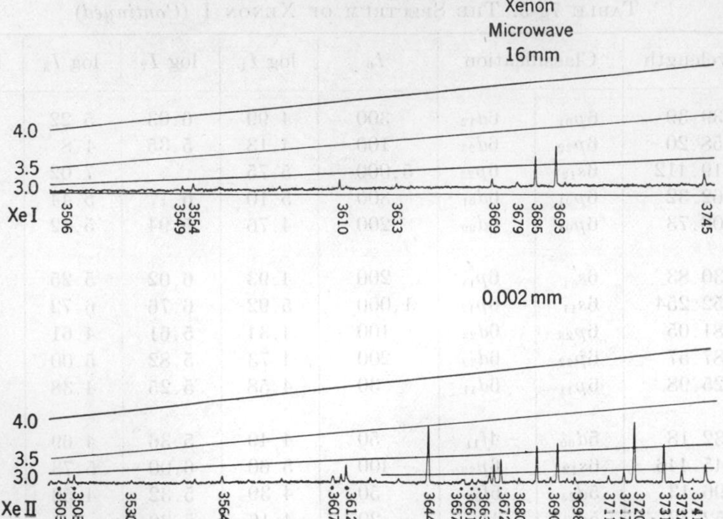

Fig. 7g-4. Photoelectric traces of the xenon spectrum, microwave discharges at 16 mm (upper traces) and 0.002 mm (lower traces). Wavelength range is 3,500-10,000 A. The 16-mm trace shows the Xe I spectrum with the lines broadened. The strongest lines in the 0.002-mm trace are those for Xe II.

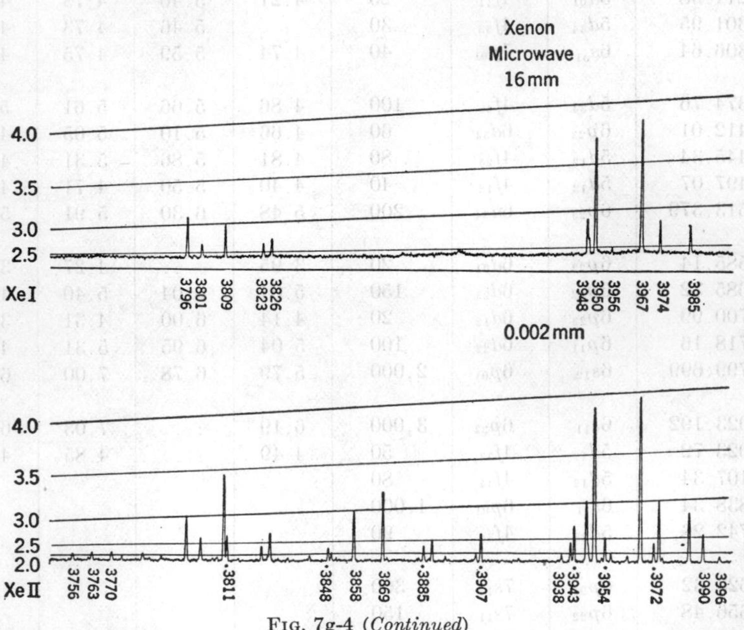

Fig. 7g-4 (*Continued*)

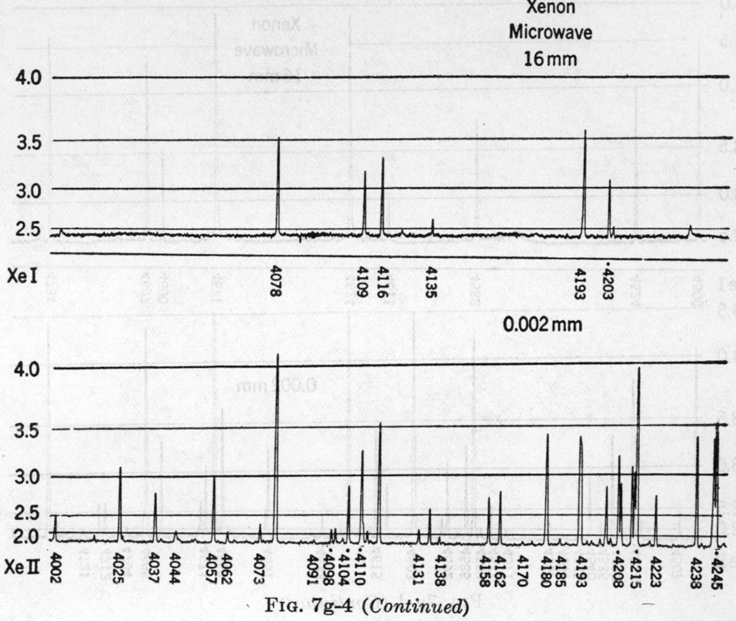

FIG. 7g-4 (*Continued*)

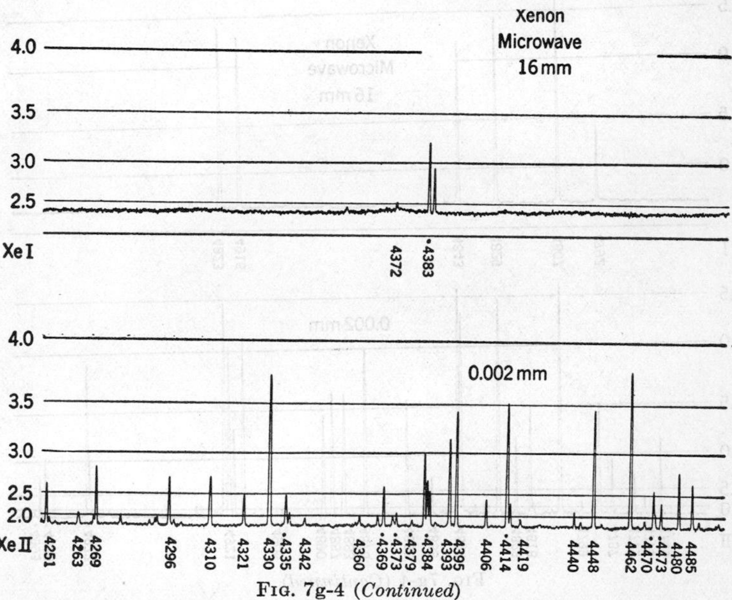

FIG. 7g-4 (*Continued*)

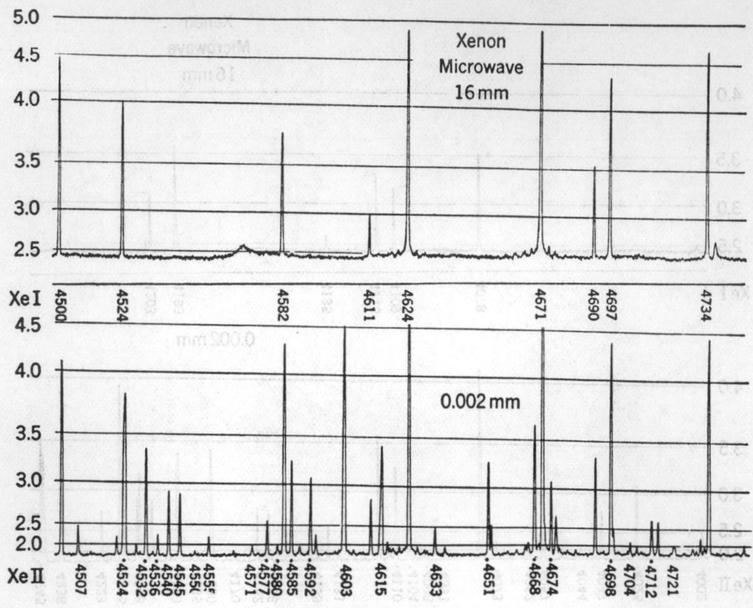

FIG. 7g-4 (*Continued*)

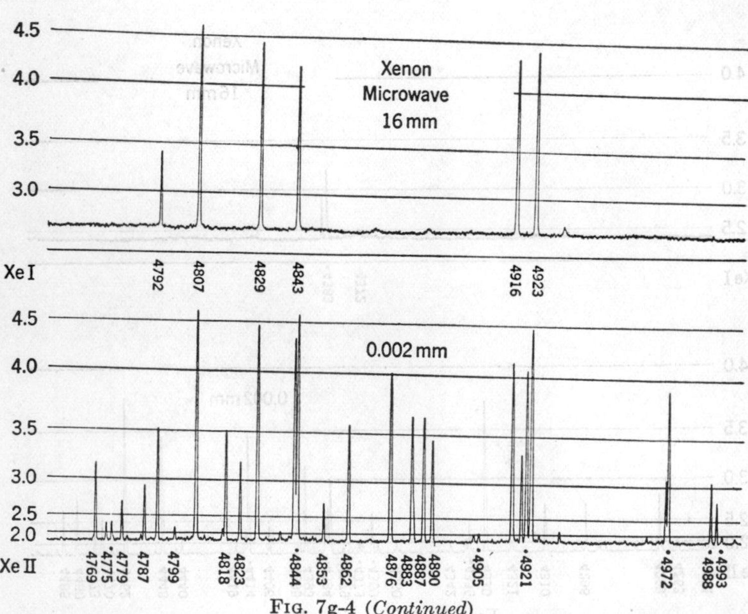

FIG. 7g-4 (*Continued*)

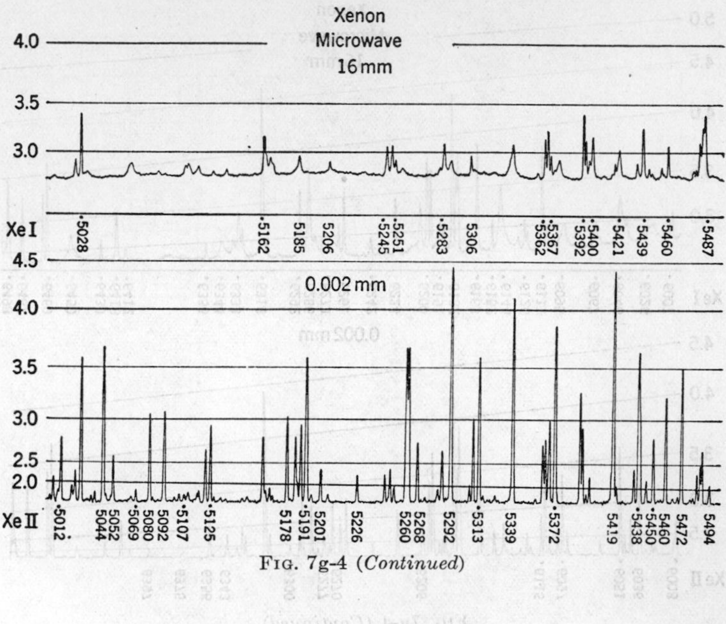

FIG. 7g-4 (*Continued*)

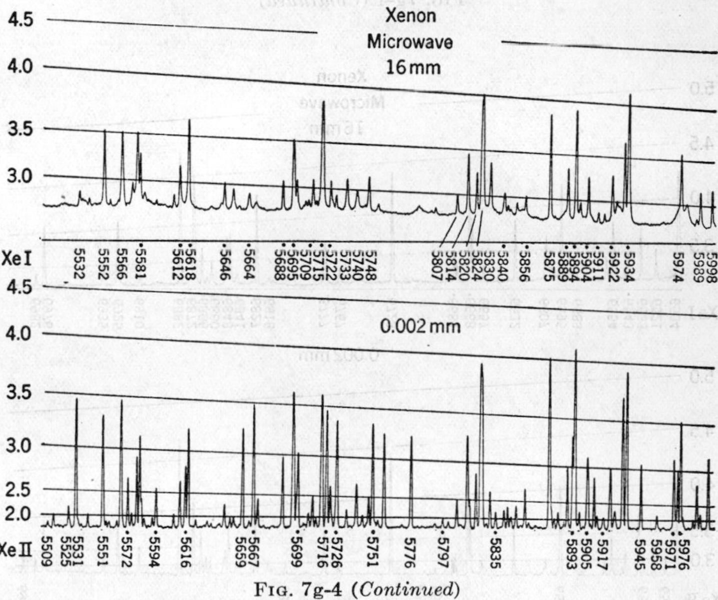

FIG. 7g-4 (*Continued*)

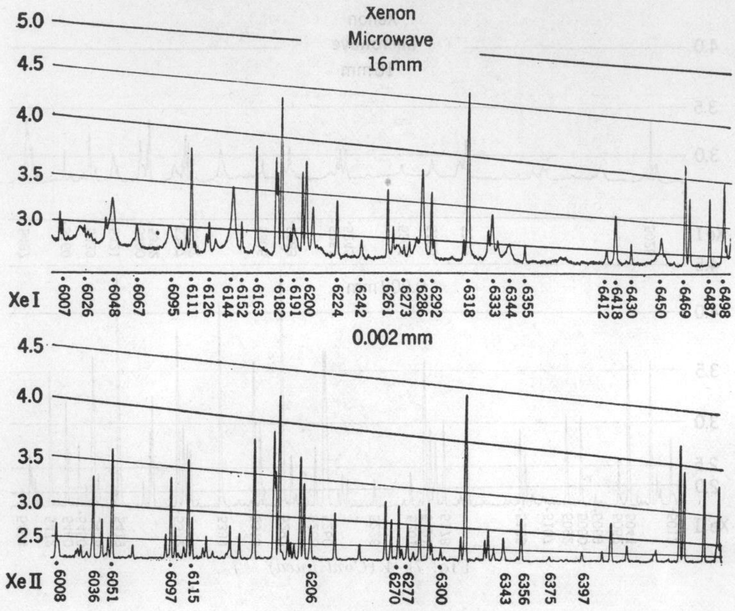

FIG. 7g-4 (*Continued*)

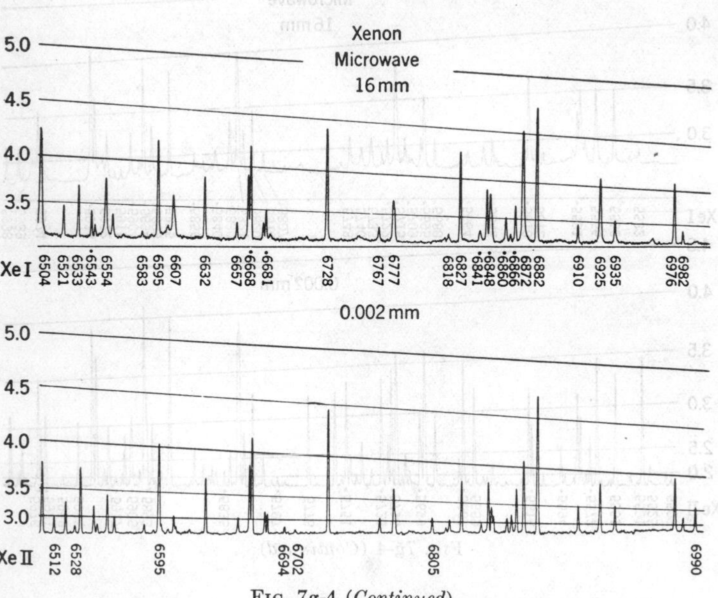

FIG. 7g-4 (*Continued*)

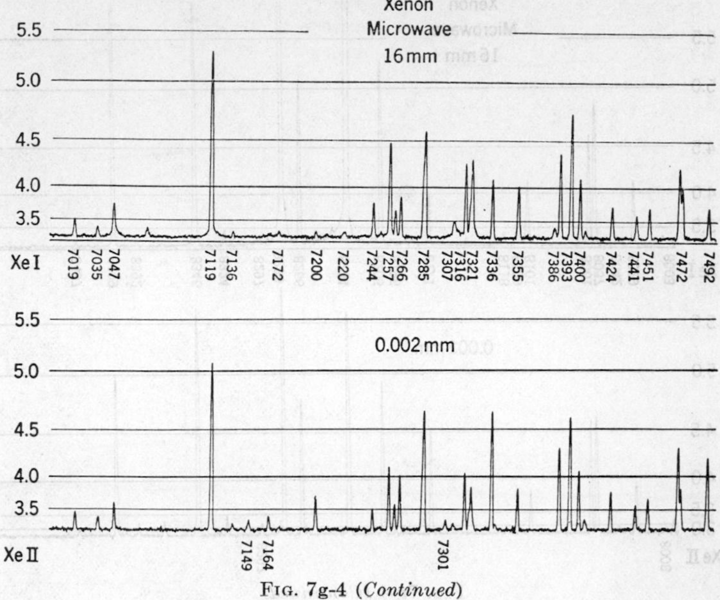

Fig. 7g-4 (*Continued*)

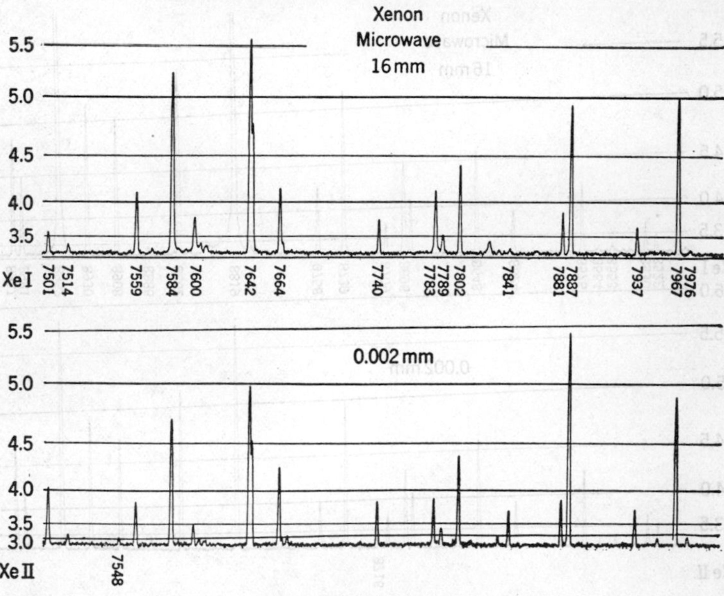

Fig. 7g-4 (*Continued*)

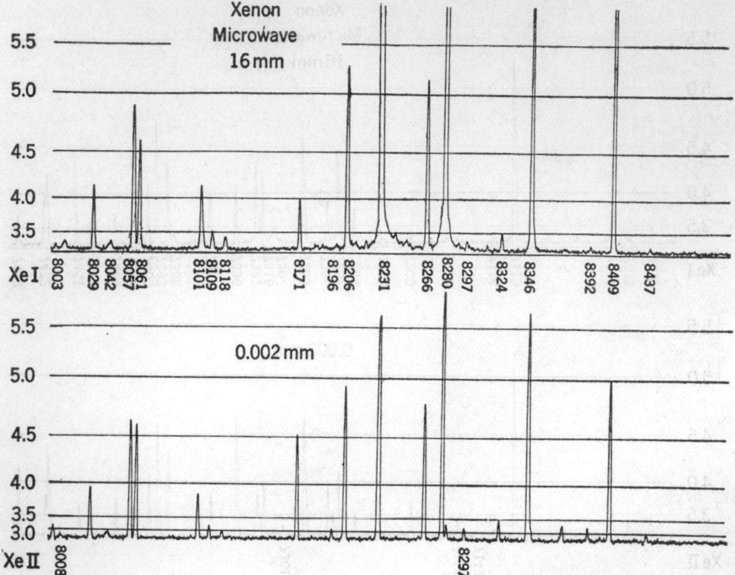

Fig. 7g-4 (*Continued*)

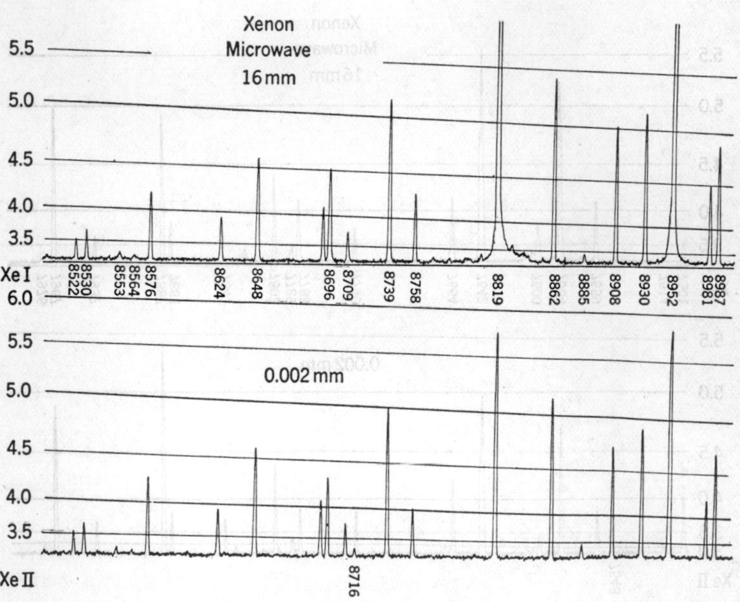

Fig. 7g-4 (*Continued*)

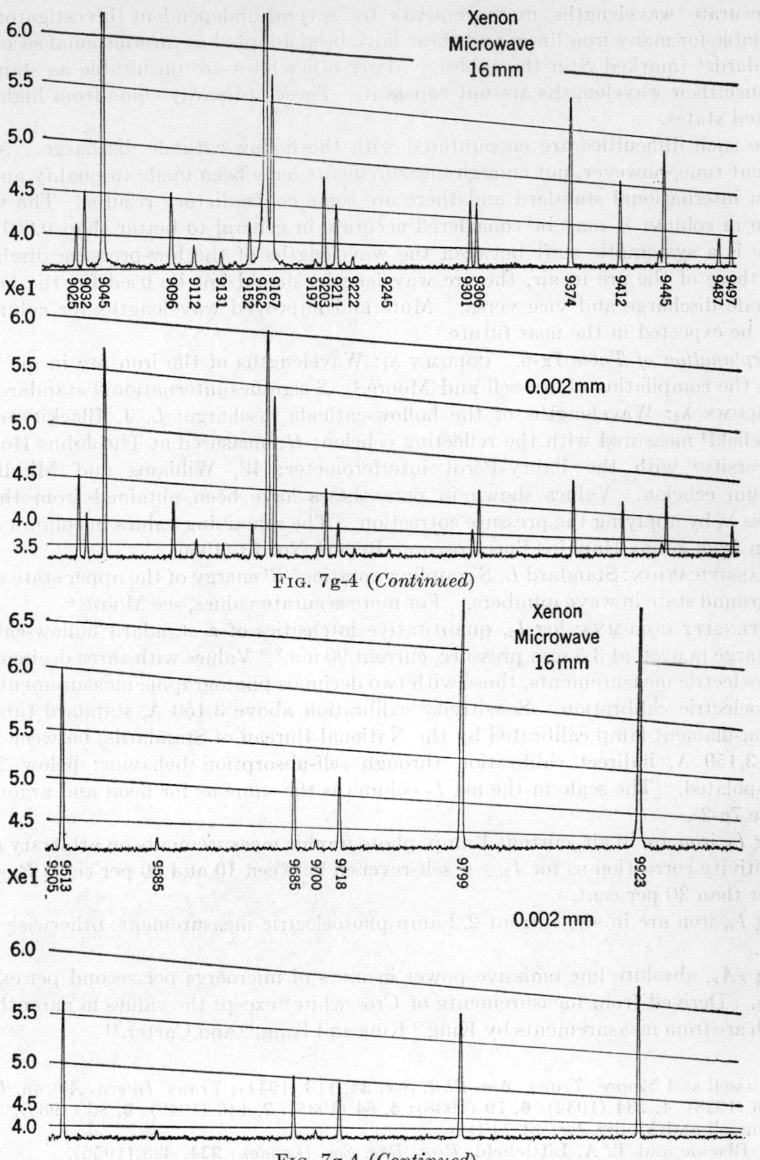

FIG. 7g-4 (*Continued*)

FIG. 7g-4 (*Continued*)

Iron I. The lines of the iron spectrum are extensively used as wavelength standards and may be used equally well as intensity standards. The traditional iron arc in air no longer satisfies the demands on accuracy and convenience because the lines are relatively broad, the wavelengths are not constant, and the arc cannot be made to burn steadily. A hollow-cathode discharge[1] with iron electrodes and neon at about 3 mm pressure is much superior. Microwave discharges[2] with volatile iron salts in a rare gas also give very sharp lines but are less suitable for providing intensity standards.

[1] Crosswhite, Dieke, and Legagneur, *J. Opt. Soc. Am.* **45,** 270 (1955).
[2] W. F. Meggers and F. O. Westfall, *J. Research Natl. Bur. Standards* **44**, 447 (1950).

Accurate wavelengths measurements by several independent investigators are available for many iron lines, and these have been adopted as international secondary standards[1] (marked *S* in the table). Many other lines are unsuitable as standards because their wavelengths are not constant. These ordinarily come from high-lying excited states.

No such difficulties are encountered with the hollow-cathode discharge. At the present time, however, not enough measurements have been made to qualify any line as an international standard and there are some contradictory results. The values given in column λ_2 may be considered accurate in general to better than 0.001. As there is a systematic shift between the wavelengths of the low-pressure discharges and those of the arc in air, the arc wavelengths should not be used for the hollow-cathode discharge and vice versa. More and improved wavelengths for column λ_2 may be expected in the near future.

Explanation of Table 7g-6. COLUMN λ_1: Wavelengths of the iron arc in air taken from the compilation of Russell and Moore.[2] *S* signifies international standard.

COLUMN λ_2: Wavelengths of the hollow-cathode discharge: *L*, J. Blackie and T. Littlefield[3] measured with the reflecting echelon; *H*, measured at The Johns Hopkins University[4] with the Fabry-Pérot interferometer; *W*, Williams and Middleton[5] vacuum echelon. Values shown in parentheses have been obtained from the arc values λ_1 by applying the pressure correction. The remaining values in column λ_2 are taken from Johns Hopkins Spectroscopic Report No. 13 (1956).

CLASSIFICATION: Standard *L*, *S* coupling notation[2] *E'* energy of the upper state above the ground state in wave numbers. For more accurate values, see Moore.[6]

INTENSITY COLUMNS: log I_2, quantitative intensities of a standard hollow-cathode discharge in neon at 3.5 mm pressure, current 90 ma.[7] Values with three decimals are photoelectric measurements, those with two decimals photographic measurement with photoelectric calibration. Sensitivity calibration above 3,150 A, standard tungsten ribbon-filament lamp calibrated by the National Bureau of Standards; between 2,700 and 3,150 A, indirect calibration through self-absorption behavior; below 2,700, extrapolated. The scale in the log I_2 column is the same as for neon and argon (see Table 7g-2).

log I_3, iron arc in air, current 1 amp, photographic measurements on arbitrary scale. Sensitivity correction as for I_2. *r*, self-reversal between 10 and 30 per cent; *R*, same, larger than 30 per cent.

log I_4, iron arc in air, current 2.2 amp photoelectric measurement; otherwise same as I_3.

log νA_ν, absolute line emissive power in units of microergs per second per excited atom. Derived from measurements of Crosswhite[8] except the values in parentheses, which are from measurements by King,[9] King and King,[10] and Carter.[11]

[1] Russell and Moore, *Trans. Am. Phil. Soc.* **34,** 113 (1944); *Trans. Intern. Astron. Union* **3,** 186 (1928); **4,** 234 (1932); **6,** 79 (1938); **5,** 84 (1935); **7,** 146 (1949); **6,** 80 (1938).

[2] Russell and Moore, *loc. cit.* (1944).

[3] J. Blackie and T. A. Littlefield, *Proc. Roy. Soc.* (*London*) **234,** 398 (1956).

[4] Stanley and G. H. Dieke, *J. Opt. Soc. Am.* **45,** 280 (1955).

[5] Williams and Middleton, *Proc. Roy. Soc.* (*London*) **172,** 159 (1939).

[6] Moore, "Atomic Energy Levels," vol. II, 1952.

[7] Unpublished measurements by Crosswhite.

[8] Dissertation, The Johns Hopkins University, and unpublished data.

[9] King, *Astrophys. J.* **95,** 78 (1942).

[10] King and King, *Astrophys. J.* **87,** 24 (1938).

[11] Carter, *Phys. Rev.* **76,** 962 (1949).

TABLE 7g-6. THE SPECTRUM OF IRON I

λ_1	λ_2	Classification		E'	log I_2	log I_3	log I_4	log νA_ν
2,408.045	....	a^5F_3	v^3D_2	49,243	4.44			
2,443.871	.872	a^5F_5	x^3G_5	47,835	4.36			
2,447.708 *S*	(.707)	a^5D_4	x^5F_3	40,842	3.85			
2,457.596	.5975 *L*	a^5F_5	v^5F_5	47,606	5.09			
2,462.645	.648	a^5D_4	x^5F_4	40,594	5.08			
2,465.148	.149	a^5F_4	v^5F_4	47,930	4.85			
2,468.878	.879	a^5F_5	w^5G_5	47,420	4.86			
2,472.343	....	a^5F_4	x^3G_4	47,812	4.87			
		a^5F_5	w^5G_6	47,363				
2,472.910	.895	a^5D_3	x^5F_3	40,842	5.13			
2,473.156	....	a^5D_4	y^7P_4	40,422	5.00			
2,474.813	.814	a^5F_3	v^5F_3	48,123	4.69			
2,479.775	.776	a^5D_2	x^5F_2	41,018	5.07			
2,483.270	.271	a^5D_4	x^5F_5	40,257	5.75			
2,483.531	....	a^5F_2	v^5F_2	48,239	4.54			
2,484.186	....	a^5D_1	x^5F_1	41,131	4.97			
2,486.372	....	a^5D_4	y^7P_3	40,207	4.90			
2,488.143	.143	a^5D_3	x^5F_4	40,594	5.59			
2,489.751	....	a^5D_0	x^5F_1	41,131	4.98			
2,490.642	.644	a^5D_2	x^5F_3	40,842	5.45			
2,491.155	.155	a^5D_1	x^5F_2	41,018	5.20			
2,496.532	.533	a^5F_4	w^5G^5	47,420	4.78			
2,501.130	.1326 *L*	a^5D_4	x^5D_3	39,970	5.03			
2,507.899	....	a^5F_3	w^5G_4	47,590	4.73			
2,510.833	.835	a^5D_3	x^5D_2	40,231	5.04			
2,512.361	....	a^5D_3	y^7P_3	40,207	4.63			
2,517.658	....	a^5F_2	w^5G_3	47,693	4.58			
2,518.100	.102	a^5D_2	x^5D_1	40,405	4.92			
2,522.848	.849	a^5D_4	x^5D_4	39,626	5.54			
2,524.290	.293	a^5D_1	x^5D_0	40,491	4.65			
2,527.433	.435	a^5D_3	x^5D_3	39,970	5.30			
2,529.134	.135	a^5D_2	x^5D_2	40,231	4.86			
2,535.604	.608	a^5D_0	x^5D_1	40,405	4.60			
2,540.971	.9719 *L*	a^5D_1	x^5D_2	40,231	4.85			
2,542.101	....	b^3F_2	r^3G_3	60,365	4.46			
2,543.920	....	b^3F_3	r^3G_4	60,172	4.40			
2,545.977	.9789 *L*	a^5D_2	x^5D_3	39,970	4.92			
2,549.612	.6140 *L*	a^5D_3	x^5D_4	39,626	4.87			
2,576.688	.6907 *L*	a^5F_5	x^5G_5	45,726	4.50			
2,584.536 *S*	.5364 *L*	a^5F_5	x^5G_6	45,608	5.17			
2,599.565	....	a^5F_4	x^5G_4	45,833	4.50			
2,605.656	.657	a^5F_5	y^3G_5	45,295	3.86			
2,606.826	.8270 *L*	a^5F_4	x^5G_5	45,726	4.56			
2,612.771	.772	a^5D_3	y^3D_2	38,678	3.2			
2,623.532	....	a^5F_3	x^5G_4	45,833	4.65			
2,635.808 *S*	.8096 *L*	a^5F_2	x^5G_3	45,914	4.48			
2,643.997	.998	a^5F_1	x^5G_2	45,965	4.32			
2,666.811	....	a^5F_5	v^5D_4	44,415	4.45			
2,679.062 *S*	.0622 *L*	a^5F_5	w^5F_5	44,244	4.79			
2,689.212 *S*	.2131 *L*	a^5F_4	v^5D_3	44,551	4.63			
2,699.107 *S*	(.105)	a^5F_4	v^5D_4	44,415	4.20			

TABLE 7g-6. THE SPECTRUM OF IRON I (*Continued*)

λ_1	λ_2	Classification		E'	log I_2	log I_3	log I_4	log νA_ν
2,706.581	.5829 *L*	a^5F_3	v^5D_2	44,664	4.59			
2,711.655	.6555 *L*	a^5F_4	w^5F_5	44,244	4.29			
2,719.027	....	a^5D_4	y^5P_3	36,767	5.44			
		(b^3F_3)	(t^3F_3)	(57,641)				
2,720.902	.902	a^5D_3	y^5P_2	37,158	5.08			
2,723.577 *S*	.5776 *L*	a^5D_2	y^5P_1	37,410	4.61			
2,733.581	.5810 *L*	a^5F_5	w^5D_4	43,500	4.96			
2,735.475 *S*	(.475)	a^5F_4	w^5D_3	43,923	4.71	4.70*R*		
2,737.310	.3099 *L*	a^5D_1	y^5P_1	37,410	4.74	4.70*R*		
2,742.256	.253	a^5F_3	w^5D_2	44,184	4.4	4.50*R*		
2,742.406	.4060 *L*	a^5D_2	y^5P_2	37,158	5.02	4.64*R*		
2,744.068	.068	a^5D_0	y^5P_1	37,410	4.33	4.66*R*		
2,750.140	.140	a^5D_3	y^5P_3	36,767	5.02	4.66*R*		
2,756.329	.325	a^5D_1	y^5P_2	37,158	4.36			
2,761.780	.781	a^5F_2	w^5D_2	44,184	4.14	4.32*R*		
2,762.027	.027	a^5F_3	w^5D_3	43,923	4.09	4.40*R*		
2,767.523 *S*	.516	a^5F_4	w^5D_4	43,500	4.39	4.44*R*		
2,772.083	.074	a^5F_5	z^5H_5	42,992	4.47	4.64*R*		
2,778.221 *S*	.2205 *L*	a^5F_5	y^5G_5	42,912	4.70	4.49*R*		
2,788.106	.108	a^5F_5	y^5G_6	42,784	5.60	4.65*R*		
2,797.775	.776	a^5F_4	z^5H_4	43,109	4.24	4.16*R*		
2,804.521 *S*	.521	a^5F_4	y^5G_4	43,023	4.65	4.48*R*		
2,806.984	.9845 *L*	a^5F_4	z^5H_5	42,992	5.02	4.56*R*		
2,813.288 *S*	.2867 *L*	a^5F_4	y^5G_5	42,912	5.37	4.62*R*		
2,823.276 *S*	.2763 *L*	a^5F_3	y^5G_3	43,138	4.56	4.50*R*		
2,825.557	.5559 *L*	a^5F_3	z^5H_4	43,109	4.81	4.52*R*		
2,825.687	.684	a^5D_4	z^3G_5	35,379	3.4	4.15*r*		
2,832.436 *S*	.4357 *L*	a^5F_3	y^5G_4	43,023	4.90	4.65*R*		
2,835.457	.455	a^5D_4	z^5G_4	35,257	3.29	4.06*R*		
2,838.120 *S*	.119	a^5F_2	y^5G_2	43,210	4.36	4.33*r*		
2,843.977	.976	a^5F_2	y^5G_3	43,138	4.96	4.61*R*		
2,851.798 *S*	.7973 *L*	a^5F_1	y^5G_2	43,210	4.80	4.60*R*		2.72
2,863.864	.863	a^5D_2	z^5G_3	35,612	3.23	4.10*r*		1.00
2,869.308 *S*	.307	a^5D_3	z^5G_4	35,259	3.76	4.41*R*		1.30
2,874.172	.173	a^5D_4	z^5G_5	34,782	3.92	4.48*R*		1.36
2,912.158 *S*	(.157)	a^5D_4	y^5F_3	34,329	4.08	4.55*R*	.....	(1.00)
2,929.008 *S*	(.007)	a^5D_3	y^5F_2	34,547	4.20	4.50*R*	.....	(1.12)
2,936.904	.904	a^5D_4	y^5F_4	34,040	5.02	4.55*R*	.....	(1.38)
2,941.343 *S*	(.342)	a^5D_2	y^5F_1	34,692	3.82	4.55*R*	.....	(1.06)
2,947.877	.876	a^5D_3	y^5F_3	34,329	4.95	4.54*R*	.....	(1.43)
2,953.940 *S*	(.939)	a^5D_2	y^5F_2	34,547	4.75	4.52*R*	.....	(1.42)
2,957.365 *S*	(.364)	a^5D_1	y^5F_1	34,692	4.45	4.55*R*	.....	(1.32)
2,965.255 *S*	(.254)	a^5D_0	y^5F_1	34,692	4.01	4.54*R*	.....	(1.20)
		(a^3G_5)	(v^3H_5)	(55,430)	.....	.....		
2,966.901	.898	a^5D_4	y^5F_5	33,695	5.48	4.47*R*	.....	(1.61)
2,970.106	....	a^5D_2	z^3P_1	34,363	4.80	4.52*R*	.....	(1.40)
		a^5D_1	y^5F_2	34,547				
2,973.134	.132	a^5D_2	y^5F_3	34,329	5.13	4.5*R*	.....	1.7
2,973.237	.235	a^5D_3	y^5F_4	34,040	4.7	4.5*R*	.....	1.3
2,981.446	.445	a^5D_3	z^3P_2	33,947	4.83	4.52*R*	.....	(1.11)
2,983.574	.570	a^5D_4	y^5D_3	33,507	5.11	4.55*R*	.....	(1.52)
2,986.456	.456	a^5D_1	z^3P_1	34,362	3.26	3.57	.....	(0.51)
2,987.292 *S*	(.291)	a^5F_4	x^5F_3	40,842	3.52	4.44*r*	.....	(2.22)

TABLE 7g-6. THE SPECTRUM OF IRON I (*Continued*)

λ_1	λ_2	Classification		E'	log I_2	log I_3	log I_4	log $\nu A\nu$
2,994.427	.427	a^5D_3	y^5D_2	33,802	5.1	4.56*R*	.....	(1.59)
2,994.507	.502	a^5D_0	z^3P_1	34,363	4.4	.....		1.0
2,999.512 *S*	(.511)	a^5F_5	x^5F_5	40,527	4.73	4.63*R*	.....	(2.49)
3,000.452	.451	a^3F_4	y^3G_5	45,295	4.11	3.98	.....	2.44
3,000.950	.947	a^5D_2	y^5D_1	34,017	4.94	4.53*R*	.....	(1.62)
3,003.031	.029	a^5F_3	x^5F_2	41,018	3.31	4.39*r*	.....	(2.24)
3,007.281	.282	a^5D_2	z^3P_2	33,947	4.36	4.5*R*	.....	(0.99)
3,008.139	.138	a^5D_1	y^5D_0	34,122	4.62	4.49*R*	.....	(1.50)
3,009.570	.568	a^5F_4	x^5F_4	40,594	4.27	4.61*R*	.....	(2.46)
3,016.186	.184	a^5F_2	x^5F_1	41,131	3.19	4.20*r*	.....	(2.15)
3,017.628	.627	a^5D_1	y^5D_1	34,017	3.80	4.51*R*	.....	(1.15)
3,018.983	.983	a^5F_3	x^5F_3	40,842	3.72	4.48*R*	.....	(2.44)
3,020.487	.490	a^5D_2	y^5D_2	33,802	4.7	4.5*R*	.....	(1.41)
3,020.640	.639	a^5D_4	y^5D_4	33,096	5.64	4.4*R*	.....	(1.66)
3,021.074	.073	a^5D_3	y^5D_3	33,507	5.24	4.46*R*	.....	(1.75)
3,024.033	.032	a^5D_1	z^3P_2	33,947	4.59	4.54*R*	.....	(1.15)
3,025.638	....	a^3H_6	w^3H_6	52,431	4.17	4.12*r*	.....	3.6
3,025.843	.843	a^5D_0	y^5D_1	34,017	4.69	4.54*R*	.....	(1.48)
3,026.462	.462	a^5F_2	x^5F_2	41,018	3.48	4.43*R*	.....	(2.38)
3,030.149	.148	a^3H_5	w^3H_5	52,613	3.92	4.04	.....	3.51
3,031.213	....	a^3H_4	w^3H_4	52,760	3.81	3.96	.....	3.45
3,031.638	.637	a^5F_1	x^5F_1	41,131	3.36	4.39*R*	.....	(2.31)
3,037.388 *S*	.387	a^5D_1	y^5D_2	33,802	4.89	4.56*R*	.....	(1.59)
3,040.428	.427	a^5F_4	x^5F_5	40,257	3.74	4.34*r*	.....	(2.14)
3,041.639	.637	a^3F_3	y^3G_4	45,428	3.9	3.8	.....	2.3
3,041.745	....	a^5F_3	x^5F_4	40,594	3.9	4.3*r*	.....	(2.30)
3,042.020	.020	a^5F_1	x^5F_2	41,018	3.12	4.16*r*	.....	(2.05)
3,042.666	.665	a^5F_2	x^5F_3	40,842	3.39	4.36*r*	.....	(2.28)
3,047.605 *S*	(.603)	a^5D_2	y^5D_3	33,507	5.02	4.56*R*	.....	(1.59)
3,057.446 *S*	.445	a^5F_5	x^5D_4	39,626	4.82	4.7*R*	.....	(2.63)
3,059.086 *S*	.087	a^5D_3	y^5D_4	33,096	5.06	4.5*R*	.....	(1.51)
3,067.244 *S*	.245	a^5F_4	x^5D_3	39,970	4.66	4.7*R*	.....	(2.64)
3,075.721 *S*	.721	a^5F_3	x^5D_2	40,231	4.09	4.7*R*	.....	(2.61)
3,083.742 *S*	.740	a^5F_2	x^5D_1	40,405	3.78	4.6*R*	.....	(2.50)
3,091.578 *S*	.577	a^5F_1	x^5D_0	40,491	3.41	4.5*r*	.....	(2.35)
3,099.897	.897	a^5F_1	x^5D_1	40,405	4.1	4.5*R*	.....	(2.48)
3,099.971	.967	a^5F_4	x^5D_4	39,626	4.1	4.6*R*	.....	(2.41)
3,100.304	.305	a^5F_2	x^5D_2	40,231	3.80	4.5*R*	.....	(2.51)
3,100.666	.666	a^5F_3	x^5D_3	39,970	4.01	4.6*R*	.....	(2.46)
3,116.633 *S*	.632	a^5F_1	x^5D_2	40,231	2.86	3.99	.....	(1.88)
3,125.653	....	a^5F_2	x^5D_3	39,970	3.49	4.18	.....	(1.98)
3,134.111 *S*	.109	a^5F_3	x^5D_4	39,626	3.05	3.97	.....	(1.79)
3,142.453	.456	z^7D_3	e^7S_3	51,570	2.84	3.25	.....	2.58
3,142.888	.890	a^3P_2	w^3P_2	50,187	2.90	3.23	.....	2.37
3,143.242	.242	a^5D_4	z^3F_3	31,805	2.88	3.05	.....	(−0.26)
3,143.990	....	z^5D_4	i^5D_4	57,698	3.14	3.19	.....	3.36
3,151.353	.353	a^3G_4	y^1H_5	53,722	3.39	3.45	3.880	3.08
3,153.200	.199	z^7D_3	f^5F_4	51,462	3.03	3.44	3.76	2.76
3,157.040 *S*	.037	z^7D_4	e^7G_5	51,229	3.24	3.66	3.974	2.96
3,157.88	.885	z^7D_2	e^7S_3	51,570	3.06	3.48	3.830	2.83

TABLE 7g-6. THE SPECTRUM OF IRON I (*Continued*)

λ_1	λ_2	Classification		E'	log I_2	log I_3	log I_4	log νA_ν
3,160.658 *S*	.659	z^7D_4	e^7F_4	51,192	3.33	3.73	4.06	3.02
3,161.949	.948	z^7D_5	e^7G_6	50,968	3.08	3.56	3.766	2.83
3,165.860	....	z^7D_3	e^7G_4	51,335	2.87	3.24	3.543	2.55
3,166.435	....	b^3F_4	t^3D_3	52,213	3.08	3.44	3.772	2.87
3,175.447 *S*	(.444)	z^7D_5	e^7F_5	51,192	3.44	3.77	4.072	3.07
3,178.015 *S*	(.012)	z^7D_5	f^7D_4	50,808	3.29	3.65	3.948	2.90
3,180.223	....	z^7D_3	e^7F_4	51,192	3.81	4.07	4.37*r*	3.36
3,180.756	.755	a^5D_2	z^3F_2	32,134	3.79	3.73	3.81*R*	(0.41)
3,182.970	.978	a^5P_2	v^3D_3	49,135	3.07	3.30	3.521	2.31
3,184.896 *S*	.895	a^5D_3	z^3F_3	31,805	4.29	4.15*R*	3.97*R*	(0.66)
3,188.567	....	z^7D_5	e^5G_5	50,704	3.06	3.31	3.81	2.54
3,188.819	....	z^7D_1	e^5G_2	51,370	3.48	3.58	3.95	2.93
3,191.659 *S*	.658	a^5D_4	z^3D_3	31,323	4.42	4.21*R*	4.00*R*	(0.58)
3,192.799	....	z^7D_1	e^7F_2	51,331	3.57	3.86	4.06	
		(b^3G_4)	(v^3H_5)	(55,430)				
3,193.228	....	a^5D_4	z^3F_4	31,307	4.86	4.44*R*	4.66*R*	(0.71)
3,196.930 *S*	(.927)	z^7D_4	e^7F_5	50,833	4.41	4.4*r*	4.67*r*	3.92
3,196.977	....	a^5D_3	z^3D_2	31,686	.....	4.1*r*	.....	(0.49)
3,199.530	....	z^7D_4	f^7D_4	50,808	4.03	4.08	3.53	3.30
		(a^5D_1)	(z^3F_2)	32,134	.....	.....	.....	(0.33)
3,200.475 *S*	(.472)	z^7D_2	e^7F_3	51,149	3.97	4.09	4.407	3.35
		z^7D_2	e^5S_2	51,149				
3,200.784	.784	a^5D_2	z^3D_1	31,937	3.10	3.22	.....	(−0.19)
3,205.400 *S*	(.397)	z^7D_1	e^7F_1	51,208	3.68	4.00	4.308	3.28
3,209.297	....	z^5F_2	g^5G_3	58,710	3.76	3.48	3.887	
		z^7F_6	g^7D_5	53,801				
3,210.230	....	z^7D_4	e^5G_5	50,704	3.56	3.64	4.05	2.84
3,210.830	....	z^7D_2	f^7D_1	51,048	3.65	3.89	4.25	3.13
3,211.487	....	z^7D_1	e^5S_2	51,149	3.0	3.34	.....	2.60
3,211.683	....	z^5F_5	g^5G_6	58,002	3.81	3.56	4.11	3.74
3,211.989	....	z^7D_5	e^7P_4	50,475	3.2	4.13	4.65*r*	3.29
3,214.044	....	z^5F_4	g^5G_5	58,271	4.38	4.07	4.78*r*	
		z^7D_3	f^7D_3	50,862				
		(z^7D_3)	(e^7P_2)	(50,861)				
3,214.396	.395	a^5D_2	z^3F_3	31,805	4.39	4.07	.....	(0.61)
3,215.940 *S*	(.937)	z^7D_2	f^7D_2	50,999	3.84	4.00	4.346	3.25
3,217.380 *S*	(.377)	z^7D_5	f^5D_4	50,423	3.75	3.87	4.162	3.04
3,219.581	....	z^7D_3	f^7D_4	50,808	3.93	4.12	4.41	3.35
3,219.806	....	z^7D_4	e^7P_3	50,611	3.87	3.95	4.33	
		(a^5D_1)	(z^3D_1)	(31,937)				
3,222.069 *S*	(.066)	z^7D_5	f^7D_5	50,378	4.53	4.52*r*	4.79*R*	3.89
3,225.789 *S*	(.786)	z^7D_5	e^7F_6	50,342	4.76	4.65*R*	4.89*R*	4.17
3,227.798	....	z^7D_4	f^5D_3	50,534	4.04	4.11	4.48	3.30
3,229.123	.121	a^5D_0	z^3D_1	31,937	3.70	3.62	.....	(0.22)
3,230.210	....	z^7D_2	e^7P_2	50,861	3.32	3.54	.....	2.78
3,230.963	....	z^7D_3	f^5D_2	50,699	3.66	3.83	4.156	3.04
3,233.053	....	b^3H_6	x^3I_7	57,028	3.87	3.52	4.060	3.58
3,233.967	....	z^7D_4	e^7P_4	50,475	3.76	3.82	4.149	2.99
3,234.614	.612	a^5D_3	z^3D_3	31,323	4.09	3.91	3.75	(0.44)
3,236.223 *S*	.222	a^5D_3	z^3F_4	31,307	4.55	4.18	3.98*r*	(0.64)
3,239.436 *S*	(.433)	z^7D_4	f^5D_4	50,423	4.12	4.10	4.427	3.27
3,244.190 *S*	(.187)	z^7D_4	f^7D_5	50,378	4.22	4.07	4.368	3.24

TABLE 7g-6. THE SPECTRUM OF IRON I (*Continued*)

λ_1	λ_2	Classification		E'	log I_2	log I_3	log I_4	log νA_ν
3,246.005	.004	a^5D_1	z^3D_2	31,686	4.02	.....	3.72	(0.48)
3,246.962	....	a^5P_2	x^3P_1	48,516	2.92	3.47	.....	2.37
3,248.206		z^7D_3	f^5D_3	50,534	3.1	3.75	3.964	2.93
3,254.363	.361	b^3H_5	x^3I_6	57,070	3.80	3.56	3.99	
3,257.594 *S*	.595	a^5P_3	v^5F_2	48,239	3.11	3.53	3.71	
3,265.046	.046	a^5D_2	z^3D_3	31,323	4.03	3.83	3.69	(0.36)
3,265.616	.617	a^5P_3	v^5P_2	48,163	3.78	4.03	4.293	
3,271.002 *S*	.999	a^5P_2	v^5P_1	48,290	3.74	4.05	4.279	
3,280.261	.262	b^3H_4	x^3I_5	57,104	3.78	3.46	3.89	
3,284.588 *S*	.587	a^5P_2	v^5P_2	48,163	2.81	3.40	3.552	
3,286.755 *S*	.7508 *W*	a^5P_3	v^5P_3	47,967	4.42	4.38	4.62*r*	
3,292.022	.020	a^3D_3	u^3F_4	56,593	3.70	3.49	3.861	
3,292.590	.589	a^5P_1	v^5P_1	48,290	3.41	3.76	4.008	
3,298.133 *S*	.130	a^5P_1	v^5F_2	48,239	3.27	3.51	3.687	
3,305.971	.973	a^5P_2	v^5P_3	47,967	4.09	4.25	4.44	
3,306.356	.352	a^5P_1	v^5P_2	48,163	4.20	4.29	4.48	
3,314.742	.742	a^3D_2	u^3F_3	56,783	3.67	3.41	3.80	
3,323.737	.738	b^3P_2	v^3P_2	52,916	.....	3.41	3.723	
3,328.867	.867	b^3H_5	u^3H_5	56,383	3.50	.....	3.666	
3,337.666	.666	a^3G_5	u^3G_4	51,668	3.25	.....	3.433	
3,340.566 *S*	.565	a^3P_2	x^3P_2	48,305	3.16	.....	3.305	
3,341.906	.906	a^3G_5	6_5	51,630	3.22			
3,342.216	.215	a^3P_2	v^5P_1	48,290	2.86	.....	3.53	
3,342.298	.292	b^3P_1	8_1	52,858	3.31			
3,347.927 *S*	.926	a^3P_2	v^5F_2	48,239	3.06	.....	3.331	
3,355.228	.226	b^3H_4	u^3H_4	56,423	3.43	.....	3.615	
3,369.549	.549	a^3G_4	u^3G_4	51,668	3.82	3.74	3.964	
3,370.786 *S*	.784	a^3G_5	u^3G_5	51,374	4.07	3.99	4.196	
3,378.676	.676	a^3G_5	v^3F_4	51,305	3.59	3.41	3.70	
3,379.017	.017	a^5P_3	w^3D_2	47,136	3.38	3.48	3.74	
3,380.111	.110	a^3G_3	u^3G_3	51,826	3.71	3.63	3.86	
3,383.981	.980	a^5P_3	x^3F_3	47,093	3.82	3.81	3.99	
3,389.748	.741	a^5P_1	1_2	47,420	3.05	.....	3.832	
3,392.304	.305	a^5P_2	x^3F_2	47,197	3.72	3.72		
3,392.652	.653	a^5P_3	w^3D_3	47,107	4.14	4.20	4.32	
3,394.583	.583	a^5P_2	u^5D_1	47,177	3.41	3.54	3.683	
3,396.978 *S*	.979	a^5F_3	y^5P_2	37,158	2.74	3.62	3.47	
3,399.336 *S*	.334	a^5P_2	w^3D_2	47,136	4.13	4.22	4.301	
3,401.521 *S*	.516	a^5F_4	y^5P_3	42,967	3.15	3.92	3.79*r*	
3,402.256	.255	b^3H_6	v^3H_6	55,490	3.67	3.51	3.770	
3,404.357	.351	a^5P_2	x^3F_3	47,093	4.06	4.11	4.270	
3,406.803	.803	a^5P_1	w^3D_1	47,272	3.75	3.86	3.95	
3,407.461 *S*	.4573 *W*	a^5P_3	x^3F_4	46,889	4.63	4.68	4.67*r*	
3,413.135 *S*	.1295 *W*	a^5P_2	w^3D_3	47,017	4.44	4.39	4.42*r*	
3,417.842	.843	a^5P_1	u^5D_1	47,177	4.62?	4.19	4.241	
3,418.507	.507	a^5P_1	u^5D_0	47,172	3.88	4.09	4.173	
3,422.656	.656	a^5P_1	w^3D_2	47,136	3.84	3.96	4.12	
3,424.284	.285	a^5P_3	u^5D_3	46,745	4.04	4.17	4.228	
3,426.383	.381	a^5P_3	y^3P_2	46,727	3.59	3.94	4.14	
3,426.637	....	a^5P_2	y^3P_1	46,902	3.73	3.85		

TABLE 7g-6. THE SPECTRUM OF IRON I (*Continued*)

λ_1	λ_2	Classification		E'	log I_2	log I_3	log I_4	log νA_ν
3,427.121 *S*	.119	a^5P_3	u^5D_4	46,721	4.57	4.63	4.61*r*	
3,428.192	.193	a^5P_2	u^5D_2	46,889	3.98	4.06	4.127	
3,440.610	.606	a^5D_4	z^5P_3	29,056	5.76	5.46*R*	4.6*R*	2.4
3,440.989	.989	a^5D_3	z^5P_2	29,469	5.39	5.22*R*	4.5*R*	2.0
3,443.878 *S*	(.878)	a^5D_2	z^5P_1	29,733	5.02	4.89*r*	4.32*R*	1.728
3,445.151 *S*	(.148)	a^5P_2	u^5D_3	46,745	4.28	4.32	4.34*r*	3.56
3,450.328	.328	a^5P_1	y^3P_1	46,902	3.75	3.93	3.922	3.20
3,451.915	.915	a^5P_1	u^5D_2	46,889	3.76	3.93	4.13	3.20
3,452.273	.274	a^5F_3	y^3F_4	36,686	3.69	4.14	4.13	(1.59)
3,465.863 *S*	.8592 *W*	a^5D_1	z^5P_1	29,733	5.13	5.02*r*	4.36*R*	1.898
3,475.450	.448	a^5D_2	z^5P_2	29,469	5.32	5.13*R*	4.48*R*	2.031
3,476.704 *S*	.7003 *W*	a^5D_0	z^5P_1	29,733	4.80	4.74*r*	4.32*R*	1.578
3,490.575 *S*	(.574)	a^5D_3	z^5P_3	29,056	5.38	5.06*R*	4.43*R*	1.971
3,497.110	....	a^5P_3	w^5P_3	46,137	3.58	3.99	4.152	3.18
3,497.843 *S*	.8384 *W*	a^5D_1	z^5P_2	29,469	4.82	4.62*r*	4.30*R*	1.537
3,513.820 *S*	.8158 *W*	a^5F_5	z^3G_5	35,379	4.55	4.48	4.48*R*	(2.16)
3,521.264 *S*	.2601 *W*	a^5F_4	z^3G_4	35,768	4.45	4.52	4.51	(2.24)
3,526.039	.040	a^5D_2	z^5P_3	29,056	4.65 }	4.6	4.7*R*	(0.83)
3,526.167	.163	a^5F_3	z^3G_3	36,079	4.15			(2.00)
3,533.201	.196	z^7F_1	e^7G_2	51,540	3.96	3.98	4.20	3.87
3,536.556	.554	z^7F_2	e^7G_3	51,461	4.15	4.15	4.425	4.04
3,541.083	.083	z^7F_4	e^7G_5	51,229	4.34	4.29	4.56*r*	4.14
3,542.076	.076	z^7F_3	e^7G_4	51,335	4.29	4.24	4.52*r*	4.10
3,554.122	.117	a^5F_3	z^5G_2	35,856	3.16	3.85	4.04	1.59
3,554.922	.927	z^7F_5	e^7G_6	50,968	4.29	4.53	4.79*r*	4.35
3,556.877	.877	z^7F_4	f^5F_5	51,103	4.22	4.10	4.326	3.93
3,558.518 *S*	(.516)	a^5F_2	z^3G_3	36,079	4.54	4.73	4.59*R*	(2.55)
3,565.381 *S*	.3778 *W*	a^5F_3	z^3G_4	35,768	4.98	5.22	4.80*R*	(2.99)
3,570.100	.0964 *H*	a^5F_4	z^3G_5	35,379	5.13	5.51*R* }	5.11*R*	(3.14)
3,570.243	....	z^7F_6	e^7G_7	50,652	4.91	.....		
3,571.995	.995	z^7F_5	e^7F_5	50,833	3.94	3.87	4.124	3.67
3,573.896	.886	b^3H_4	t^3G_3	54,600	3.81	3.79	4.00	4.12
3,581.195 *S*	.1926 *H*	a^5F_5	z^5G_6	34,844	5.56	5.73*R*	4.98*R*	3.6
3,582.201	.201	b^3H_6	12_5	54,014	4.05	.....	4.01	
3,584.663 *S*	(.659)	a^3G_5	y^3H_5	49,604	4.14	4.09	4.32	3.73
3,585.320 *S*	(.318)	a^5F_3	z^5G_3	35,612	4.60	4.72	5.02	(2.40)
3,585.708	....	a^5F_4	z^5G_4	35,257	4.35	4.47	4.74	(2.14)
3,586.114 *S*	(.109)	b^3H_6	t^3G_5	53,983	4.40	4.02	4.23	4.26
3,586.985	....	a^5F_2	z^5G_2	35,856	4.60	4.71	4.64*R*	(2.46)
3,589.107 *S*	(.105)	a^5F_5	z^5G_5	34,782	3.66	4.11	4.34	(1.42)
3,594.632	.631	z^7F_4	f^7D_4	50,808	3.91	3.91	4.068	3.71
3,603.205	.205	a^3G_5	v^3G_5	49,461	4.117	4.08	4.274	3.70
3,605.450	.454	a^3G_4	y^3H_4	49.727	4.386	4.22	4.56*r*	3.87
		(z^7F_6)	(f^7D_5)	50,378				
3,606.679	.679	a^3G_5	y^3H_6	49,434	4.38	4.52	4.65*r*	4.13
3,608.861 *S*	.8591 *H*	a^5F_1	z^5G_2	35,856	5.239	5.27*r*	4.78*R*	(3.02)
3,610.159	....	z^7F_6	e^7F_6	50,342	4.353	4.26	4.53*r*	3.99
3,617.788 *S*	....	c^3P_2	u^3D_3	51,969	4.137	4.01	4.26	3.97
3,618.769 *S*	.7672 *H*	a^5F_2	z^5G_3	35,612	5.364	5.35*r*	4.83*R*	(3.18)
3,621.463 *S*	(.460)	a^3G_4	y^3H_5	49,604	4.33	4.30	4.48*r*	3.94
3,622.001	.004	a^3G_3	v^3G_3	49,851	4.16	4.11	4.36	3.80

TABLE 7g-6. THE SPECTRUM OF IRON I (*Continued*)

λ_1	λ_2	Classification		E'	log I_2	log I_3	log I_4	log νA_ν
3,623.187	.186	a^3H_6	z^3H_6	46,982	4.141	3.88	4.013	3.59
3,631.464 S	.4625 H	a^5F_3	z^5G_4	35,257	5.441	5.38	4.85R	(3.01)
3,634.326	.325	z^7P_4	e^5G_3	51,219	3.53	.....	3.83	
3,638.296	.296	a^3G_3	y^3H_4	49,727	3.96	3.95	4.15	3.60
3,640.388	.388	a^3G_4	v^3G_5	49,461	4.253	4.21	4.390	3.83
3,645.822	.818	c^3P_0	u^3D_1	52,512	3.56	.....	3.83	
3,647.844 S	.8419 H	a^5F_4	z^5G_5	34,782	5.411	5.30r	4.80R	(2.91)
3,649.304	.301	a^5D_4	z^5F_3	27,395	3.58	4.00	.....	(0.13)
3,649.508 S	(.505)	a^3G_5	w^3F_4	49,109	4.397	4.23	3.44	
3,650.031	.026	z^7P_3	e^7S_3	51,570	3.54	4.05 }	3.0	3.95
3,650.280	.278	a^3H_5	z^3H_5	47,008	4.141	3.86 }		3.15
3,651.469 S	(.466)	a^3G_3	v^3G_4	49,628	4.361	4.21	3.471	3.85
3,659.516	.516	a^3H_4	z^3H_4	47,107	3.899	3.78	3.843	3.08
3,669.523 S	(.520)	a^3G_4	w^3F_3	49,243	4.101	3.95	4.19	3.54
3,676.314 S	(.311)	b^3F_4	x^3G_5	47,835	3.934	3.72	3.844	3.11
3,677.630 S	(.627)	a^3G_3	w^3F_2	49,433	4.15	4.16	4.38	3.77
3,679.915 S	.9128 H	a^5D_4	z^5F_4	27,167	5.071	4.88r	4.36R	1.449
3,682.226	....	a^1D_2	w^1D_2	55,754	4.175	3.97	4.260	4.45
3,683.054	....	a^5D_3	z^5F_2	27,560	3.945	3.89	4.10R	0.496
3,684.108	.109	a^3G_4	v^3D_3	49,135	4.156	4.04	4.210	3.61
3,685.998	.995	z^7P_4	e^7F_5	50,833	4.01	4.00	4.22	3.80
3,687.458 S	.4559 H	a^5F_5	y^5F_4	34,040	4.663	5.11r	4.63R	2.378
3,689.457	.457	z^7P_4	f^7D_4	50,808	3.876	3.97	4.196	3.77
		b^3P_1	w^3P_1	50,043				
3,694.005	.005	z^7P_2	e^7S_3	51,570	4.11	4.16	4.333	4.06
3,695.054 S	(.051)	b^3F_3	v^5F_4	47,930	4.014	3.80	3.998	3.20
3,697.426	.424	z^7P_3	e^5G_3	51,219	3.485	3.73	3.837	3.58
3,701.086	.085	z^7P_3	e^7F_4	51,192	4.10	4.11	4.330	3.96
3,703.556	.546	a^3G_3	w^3F_3	49,243	3.47	.....	3.93	
3,704.463 S	(.460)	a^3G_5	y^1G_4	48,703	3.971	4.12	4.00	3.64
3,705.567 S	.5657 H	a^5D_3	z^5F_3	27,395	5.249	4.04r	5.45R	1.698
3,707.048	.041	z^7P_3	e^7F_3	51,149	3.79	3.83	4.040	3.67
3,707.824	.822	a^5D_2	z^5F_1	27,666	4.17 }	4.56	4.65R	0.652
3,707.918	.918	a^5P_3	y^5S_2	44,512	4.42 }			
3,709.246	.246	a^5F_4	y^5F_3	34,329	4.758	5.00r	4.66R	2.540
3,716.442	.439	z^7P_4	e^7P_3	50,611	3.877	3.87	4.083	3.65
3,719.935 S	.9346 H	a^5D_4	z^5F_5	26,875	5.954	5.73R	4.76R	2.541
3,722.564 S	.5627 H	a^5D_2	z^5F_2	27,560	5.10	5.06r	4.45R	1.747
3,724.380 S	(.377)	a^3P_2	x^3D_3	45,221	4.04	3.99	4.162	3.03
3,727.621 S	.6174 W	a^5F_3	y^5F_2	34,547	4.69	4.97r	4.68R	2.543
3,730.386	.386	a^1G_4	u^3G_5	51,826	3.64	.....	3.804	
3,732.399 S	(.396)	a^5P_2	y^5S_2	44,512	4.29	4.22	4.43r	3.16
3,733.319 S	.3163 H	a^5D_1	z^5F_1	27,666	5.00	4.96r	4.46R	1.624
3,734.867 S	.8622 W	a^5F_5	y^5F_5	33,695	5.57	5.76R	5.03R	3.475
3,737.133 S	.1317 H	a^5D_3	z^5F_4	27,167	5.89	5.57R	4.79R	2.408
3,738.308 S	(.305)	b^3H_5	z^1I_6	53,094	4.31	3.86	4.19	3.97
3,743.364	.362	a^5F_2	y^5F_1	34,692	4.53	4.77	4.75R	2.392
3,745.561	.561	a^5D_2	z^5F_3	27,395	5.66	5.38R	4.7R	(2.20)
3,745.901	.900	a^5D_0	z^5F_1	27,666	5.09	4.96r	.....	(1.7)
3,748.264 S	(.262)	a^5D_1	z^5F_2	27,560	5.41	5.19R	4.61R	1.990
3,749.487 S	(.485)	a^5F_4	y^5F_4	34,040	5.43	5.57R	4.98R	3.310

TABLE 7g-6. THE SPECTRUM OF IRON I (*Continued*)

λ_1	λ_2	Classification		E'	log I_2	log I_3	log I_4	log νA_ν
3,753.610	.610	a^5P_3	w^5D_2	44,184	3.75	3.92	4.134	2.82
3,758.235 *S*	.2328 *H*	a^5F_3	y^5F_3	34,329	5.25	5.35*r*	4.90*R*	3.119
3,760.052 *S*	.0492 *H*	a^3H_6	z^3I_7	45,978	4.51	3.88	4.130	3.03
3,763.790 *S*	.7888 *H*	a^5F_2	y^5F_2	34,547	5.01	5.17*r*	4.81*R*	2.926
3,765.542 *S*	.5386 *H*	b^3H_6	y^3I_7	52,655	4.52	4.25	4.60*r*	4.31
3,767.194 *S*	.1911 *H*	a^5F_1	y^5F_1	34,692	4.75	5.03*r*	4.89*R*	2.785
3,785.950	....	a^3H_5	z^3I_6	46,027	4.36	3.86	4.04	3.00
3,786.678	.676	a^5F_1	z^3P_0	34,556	3.91	3.86	3.93*r*	(1.22)
3,787.883 *S*	.8799 *H*	a^5F_1	y^5F_2	34,547	4.450	4.76	4.63*R*	2.290
3,790.095 *S*	.0926 *H*	a^5F_2	z^3P_1	34,363	4.345	4.22	4.32*R*	(1.62)
3,794.340	....	a^3H_4	z^3I_5	46,136	4.226	3.74	3.936	2.90
3,795.004 *S*	(.002)	a^5F_2	y^5F_3	34,329	4.580	4.89	4.69*R*	2.384
3,797.517 *S*	(.514)	b^3H_6	w^3H_6	52,431	4.091	4.01	4.344	4.03
3,798.513 *S*	(.511)	a^5F_4	y^5F_5	33,695	4.421	4.66	4.61*R*	2.028
3,799.549 *S*	.5471 *H*	a^5F_3	y^5F_4	34,040	4.577	4.82	4.69*R*	2.306
3,805.345 *S*	.3425 *H*	b^3H_4	y^3I_5	52,889	4.304	4.18	4.440	4.27
3,806.697	....	b^3H_5	w^3H_5	52,613	3.945	3.98	4.24	4.03
		(b^3F_3)	(w^3D_2)	47,136				
3,807.534	.536	a^5P_1	w^5D_2	44,184	3.59	3.90	4.076	2.80
3,812.964	.9639 *H*	a^5F_3	z^3P_2	33,947	4.784	4.70	4.68*R*	(2.16)
3,814.526	....	a^5F_1	z^3P_1	34,363	3.74	3.80	3.90*R*	(1.02)
3,815.842 *S*	.8402 *H*	a^3F_4	y^3D_3	38,175	5.291	5.19*r*	4.98*R*	(3.36)
3,820.428	.4253 *H*	a^5F_5	y^5D_4	33,096	5.444	5.36*r*	4.98*R*	(3.13)
3,821.181	.175	b^3H_5	y^3I_6	52,514	4.21	.....	4.48	
3,824.444 *S*	.4440 *H*	a^5D_4	z^5D_3	26,140	5.357	5.04*r*	4.65*R*	1.634
3,825.884 *S*	.8809 *H*	a^5F_4	y^5D_3	33,507	5.240	5.42*r*	4.99*R*	(2.98)
3,827.825 *S*	.8228 *H*	a^3F_3	y^3D_2	38,678	5.001	5.06*r*	4.96*R*	(3.31)
3,834.225 *S*	.2219 *H*	a^5F_3	y^5D_2	33,802	4.973	5.11*r*	4.83*R*	(2.81)
3,839.259 *S*	(.256)	a^1G_4	x^1G_4	50,614	4.114	3.98	4.15	3.76
3,840.439 *S*	(.437)	a^5F_2	y^5D_1	34,017	4.697	5.02*r*	4.72*R*	(2.58)
3,841.051 *S*	.0481 *H*	a^3F_2	y^3D_1	38,996	4.942	4.98	4.86*R*	(3.19)
3,843.259 *S*	.2568 *H*	a^1G_4	z^1F_3	50,587	4.160			
3,846.803 *S*	.8004 *H*	a^3D_3	t^3D_3	52,213	3.938	3.95	4.22	3.94
3,849.969	.9591 *H*	a^5F_1	y^5D_0	34,122	4.326	4.80	4.65*R*	(2.34)
3,850.820 *S*	(.818)	a^5F_2	z^3P_2	33,947	4.083	4.25	4.34*R*	(1.63)
3,852.574	....	a^5P_3	w^5D_4	43,500	3.381	3.78	3.938	2.59
3,856.373 *S*	.3714 *H*	a^5D_3	z^5D_2	26,340	5.365	5.08*r*	4.25*R*	1.691
3,859.214	.211	a^3H_6	y^3G_5	45,295	4.17	.....	4.31	
3,859.913 *S*	.9123 *H*	a^5D_4	z^5D_4	25,900	5.978	5.52*R*	4.76*R*	2.244
3,865.526 *S*	(.524)	a^5F_1	y^5D_1	34,017	4.250	4.72	4.64*R*	(2.25)
3,867.219 *S*	.2157 *H*	c^3P_2	w^3P_2	50,817	3.801	3.82	4.004	3.62
3,872.504 *S*	.5006 *H*	a^5F_2	y^5D_2	33,802	4.366	4.77	4.63*R*	(2.24)
3,873.763 *S*	.7608 *H*	a^3H_5	y^3G_4	45,428	4.158	3.91	4.11	2.97
3,878.021 *S*	(.019)	a^5F_3	y^5D_3	33,501	4.36	4.79	4.66*R*	(2.24)
3,878.575 *S*	.5734 *H*	a^5D_2	z^5D_1	26,479	5.257	5.00*r*	4.68*R*	1.694
3,885.512	.508	a^3P_1	x^3D_2	45,282	3.57	.....	3.92	
3,886.284 *S*	.2829 *H*	a^5D_3	z^5D_3	26,140	5.619	5.11*r*	4.60*R*	1.865
3,887.051 *S*	(.049)	a^5F_4	y^5D_4	33,096	4.303	4.63	4.59*R*	(2.05)
3,888.517 *S*	.5135 *H*	a^3F_2	y^3D_2	38,678	4.459	4.57	4.78*R*	(2.70)
3,893.391	.390	b^3G_5	v^3G_5	49,461	3.71	3.80	4.04	3.42
3,895.658 *S*	.6563 *H*	a^5D_1	z^5D_0	26,550	4.907	4.81*r*	4.43*R*	1.266

TABLE 7g-6. THE SPECTRUM OF IRON I (*Continued*)

λ_1	λ_2	Classification		E'	log I_2	log I_3	log I_4	log νA_ν
3,897.896	.8899 *H*	a^3G_5	w^5G_6	47,363	2.54	4.09	4.35	(1.34)
3,898.012	.009	a^5F_1	y^5D_2	33,802	3.33			
3,899.709 *S*	.7077 *H*	a^5D_2	z^5D_2	26,340	5.112	4.99*r*	4.43*R*	1.402
3,902.948 *S*	.9454 *H*	a^3F_3	y^3D_3	38,175	4.624	4.72	4.78*R*	(2.87)
3,903.902	.898	b^3G_4	y^3H_4	49,727	3.20	3.60	3.794	3.25
3,906.482 *S*	.4795 *H*	a^5D_1	z^5D_1	26,479	4.371	4.40	4.28*R*	0.816
3,907.464	....	a^3G_3	x^3G_3	47,834	3.02			
3,907.937 *S*	(.934)	a^3G_3	w^5G_2	47,831	3.51	3.55	3.669	2.95
3,916.733	....	b^3H_6	6_5	51,630	3.732	3.56	3.79	3.47
3,917.185 *S*	(.183)	a^5F_2	y^5D_3	33,507	3.19	3.94	4.01	(1.23)
3,918.644	....	b^3G_3	v^3G_3	49,851	3.52	.....	3.87	
3,920.260 *S*	.2579 *H*	a^5D_0	z^5D_1	26,479	4.848	4.74*r*	4.34*R*	1.324
3,922.914 *S*	.9115 *H*	a^5D_3	z^5D_4	25,900	5.084	4.91*r*	4.42*R*	1.300
3,925.946	....	b^3P_0	x^3P_1	48,516	3.40	3.63	3.81	3.12
3,927.922 *S*	.9204 *H*	a^5D_1	z^5D_2	26,340	5.107	4.96	4.51*R*	1.391
3,930.299 *S*	.2967 *H*	a^5D_2	z^5D_3	26,140	5.161	5.00*r*	4.49*R*	1.389
3,935.815 *S*	.8125 *H*	b^3P_2	v^5F_2	48,239	3.41	3.62	3.764	3.07
3,940.882 *S*	(.880)	a^5F_3	y^5D_4	33,096	2.91	3.66	3.66	(0.80)
3,942.443 *S*	(.440)	b^3P_1	x^3P_2	48,305	3.14	3.54	3.688	3.00
3,948.779 *S*	(.776)	b^3H_5	u^3G_4	51,668	3.773	3.72	3.955	3.64
3,949.954	.9526 *H*	a^5P_3	x^5P_2	42,860	3.804	3.92	3.996	2.64
3,951.164	.1636 *H*	a^3D_1	y^1D_2	51,708	3.715	3.66	3.879	1.81
3,952.606	.6015 *H*	a^3G_5	z^3H_5	47,008	3.680	3.59	3.802	2.88
3,956.681 *S*	.6771 *H*	a^3G_5	z^3H_6	46,982	4.428	4.03	4.49	3.32
3,966.066 *S*	(.063)	a^3F_2	y^3D_3	38,175	3.41	3.85	4.04*r*	1.91
3,966.630	....	z^5D_4	f^5F_5	51,103	3.781	3.79	4.055	3.63
3,967.423 *S*	(.420)	b^3H_4	u^3G_3	51,826	3.07	3.59	3.836	3.53
3,969.261 *S*	.2570 *H*	a^3F_4	y^3F_3	37,163	4.796	4.81	4.85*R*	(2.77)
3,971.325	....	a^3G_5	x^3F_4	46,889	3.54	3.64	3.865	2.91
3,977.743	.7413 *H*	a^5P_2	x^5P_2	42,860	3.932	3.90	4.121	2.62
3,981.775	.7712 *H*	a^3G_4	z^3H_4	47.107	3.593	3.55	3.686	2.85
3,983.960	.9570 *H*	a^3G_4	x^3F_3	47.197	3.677	3.72	3.880	3.03
3,997.394	.3923 *H*	a^3G_4	z^3H_5	47,008	4.300	4.10	4.290	3.39
3,998.054	.052	a^3G_5	u^5D_4	46,721	3.613	3.78	3.981	3.03
4,005.246 *S*	.2419 *H*	a^3F_3	y^3F_2	37,521	4.591	4.64	4.76*R*	(2.66)
4,009.714	.7130 *H*	a^5P_1	x^5P_2	42,860	3.772	3.78	3.994	2.50
4,014.534 *S*	.5310 *H*	a^1H_5	y^1H_5	53,722	3.934	3.69	3.962	3.89
4,021.869	.8665 *H*	a^3G_3	z^3H_4	47,107	3.990	3.75	4.033	3.05
4,045.815 *S*	.8141 *H*	a^3F_4	y^3F_4	36,686	5.565	5.39*r*	5.08*R*	(3.34)
4,062.446	.4412 *H*	b^3P_1	y^3S_1	47,556	3.716	4.04	3.90	3.60
4,063.597	.5949 *H*	a^3F_3	y^3F_3	37,163	5.247	5.20*r*	4.96*R*	(3.19)
4,066.979 *S*	(.976)	b^3P_2	1_2	47,420	3.686	3.49	3.66	2.84
4,067.275 *S*	(.272)	b^3F_4	x^3D_3	45,221	3.37			
4,067.984	....	z^5D_4	e^7P_4	50,475	3.720	3.66	3.89	3.42
4,071.740	.7374 *H*	a^3F_2	y^3F_2	37,521	5.114	4.99*r*	4.98*R*	(3.14)
4,076.636	.6297 *H*	z^5D_4	f^5D_4	50,423	3.641	3.63	3.940	3.39
4,100.745	.7378 *H*	a^5F_5	z^3F_4	31,307	3.627	3.38	3.279	0.50
4,107.492 *S*	.4884 *H*	b^3P_2	u^5D_1	47,177	3.638	3.72	3.957	3.02
4,109.808	.8020 *H*	b^3P_1	w^3D_1	47,272	3.544	3.56	3.784	2.87
4,114.449 *S*	(.446)	b^3P_2	w^3D_2	47,136	3.25	3.37	3.478	2.66

TABLE 7g-6. THE SPECTRUM OF IRON I (*Continued*)

λ_1	λ_2	Classification		E'	log I_2	log I_3	log I_4	log $\nu A\nu$
4,118.549 *S*	.5450 *H*	a^1H_5	z^1I_6	53,094	4.225	3.93	4.30	4.04
4,120.211	.2065 *H*	b^3G_4	z^1H_5	48,383	3.302	3.30	3.393	2.76
4,121.806 *S*	(.803)	b^3P_2	x^3F_3	47,093	3.281	3.34	3.420	2.64
4,127.612 *S*	.6087 *H*	b^3P_0	w^3D_1	47,272	3.581	3.55	3.81	2.86
4,132.060 *S*	.0580 *H*	a^3F_2	y^3F_3	37,163	4.581	4.53	4.81*R*	(2.58)
4,132.903	.899	b^3P_1	w^3D_2	47,136	3.512	3.63	3.86	2.92
		(a^3F_2)	(y^5P_2)	37,158				
4,134.681 *S*	.6774 *H*	b^3P_2	w^3D_3	47,017	3.929	3.86	4.17	3.16
4,137.002	.9978 *H*	a^1P_1	y^1D_2	51,708	3.566	3.45	3.677	3.37
4,143.418	....	a^1G_4	y^1G_4	48,703	4.298	3.97	.....	3.50
4,143.871 *S*	.8684 *H*	a^3F_3	y^3F_4	36,686	4.862	4.70	4.86*R*	(2.68)
4,147.673 *S*	.6691 *H*	a^3F_4	z^3G_3	36,079	3.399	3.65	3.81	1.43
4,149.372	.3662 *H*	z^5F_5	e^7G_6	50,968	3.15	3.31	3.446	3.14
4,152.172	.1697 *H*	a^5F_3	z^3F_3	31,805	3.474	3.33	3.26	0.52
4,153.906	....	z^5F_3	f^5F_4	51,462	3.616	3.74	3.909	3.63
4,154.502	.499	b^3P_2	y^3P_1	46,902	3.749	3.53	4.15	2.80
4,156.803 *S*	(.800)	b^3P_2	u^5D_2	46,889	3.781	3.76	4.064	3.03
4,157.788	....	z^5F_2	f^5F_3	51,604	3.448	3.57	3.726	3.48
4,170.906 *S*	(.903)	c^3P_2	x^3P_2	48,305	3.300	3.40	3.575	2.88
4,172.126	....	a^3D_3	w^3P_2	50,187	3.323	3.37	3.57	3.09
4,172.749	.743	a^5F_3	z^3D_2	31,686	3.678	3.45	3.519	0.63
4,174.917	.911	a^5F_4	z^3D_3	31,323	3.783	3.48	3.452	0.60
4,175.640 *S*	(.637)	b^3P_1	u^5D_2	46,889	3.705	3.74	4.004	3.01
4,176.571	....	z^5F_4	f^5F_5	51,103	3.358	3.49	3.638	3.33
		(z^5F_3)	(e^7F_2)	51,331				
4,177.597	.5936 *H*	a^5F_4	z^3F_4	31,307	3.747	3.44	3.393	0.56
4,181.758	.7546 *H*	b^3P_2	u^5D_3	46,745	4.125	4.11	4.427	3.36
4,184.895 *S*	.8918 *H*	b^3P_2	y^3P_2	46,727	3.665	3.66	3.904	2.91
4,187.044	.041	z^7D_3	e^7D_2	43,634	4.110	4.12	4.48*r*	2.94
4,187.802	.798	z^7D_4	e^7D_3	43,435	4.146	4.12	4.49*r*	2.92
4,191.436	.4301 *H*	z^7D_2	e^7D_1	43,764	3.923	4.04	4.336	2.88
4,195.337	....	z^5F_5	e^5G_5	50,704	3.551	3.63	3.80	3.42
4,196.218	....	z^5F_3	e^5G_3	51,219	3.30	3.37	3.54	3.23
4,198.310	.3040 *H*	z^7D_5	e^7D_4	43,163	4.161	4.11	4.46*r*	2.87
4,199.098	.0952 *H*	a^1G_4	z^1H_5	55,526	4.620	4.23	4.64*r*	4.69
4,202.031 *S*	.0286 *H*	a^3F_4	z^3G_4	35,768	4.540	4.66	4.81*R*	(2.47)
4,203.987 *S*	(.984)	b^3P_1	y^3P_2	46,727	3.619	3.60	3.852	2.85
4,206.702	.6957 *H*	a^5D_3	z^7P_3	24,181	3.85?	3.35 }	3.30	(−0.71)
4,207.130	.127	b^3P_2	z^3S_1	46,601	3.03	3.26 }		
4,210.352	.347	z^7D_1	e^7D_1	43,764	3.87	3.86	4.124	2.70
4,213.650 *S*	(.647)	b^3P_1	y^3P_0	46,673	3.30	3.33	3.425	2.57
4,216.186 *S*	.1830 *H*	a^5D_4	z^7P_4	23,711	4.636	3.83	3.83*r*	(−0.16)
4,217.551	....	z^5F_1	e^5G_2	51,370	3.180	3.51	3.698	3.38
4,219.364 *S*	.3601 *H*	a^1H_5	y^3I_6	52,514	4.019	3.80	4.124	(3.92)
4,222.219	.2132 *H*	z^7D_3	e^7D_3	43,435	3.717	3.86	4.097	(2.63)
4,224.176	....	z^5F_4	e^7F_5	50,833	3.400	3.57	3.91	3.37
4,225.460	....	z^5F_2	e^5G_3	51,219	3.347	3.55	3.756	3.41
4,227.434	.4261 *H*	z^5F_5	e^5G_6	50,523	4.268	4.15	4.520	(3.86)
4,231.525	....	a^3D_3	v^3G_3	49,851	2.84	.....	.....	(3.55)
4,232.732	....	a^5D_1	z^7P_2	24,507	3.02	.....	.....	(−1.13)
4,233.608	.6023 *H*	z^7D_1	e^7D_2	43,634	4.021	4.06	4.42*r*	(2.95)
4,235.942	.9365 *H*	z^7D_4	e^7D_4	43,163	4.432	4.27	4.67*r*	(3.17)

TABLE 7g-6. THE SPECTRUM OF IRON I (*Continued*)

λ_1	λ_2	Classification		E'	log I_2	log I_3	log I_4	log νA_ν
4,238.816	.8091 *H*	z^5F_3	e^5G_4	50,980	3.661	3.81	3.982	(3.55)
4,239.847	....	a^3G_5	y^3G_5	45,295	2.67	.....		(−0.08)
4,245.258	.2568 *H*	b^3P_0	z^3S_1	46,661	3.191	3.43	3.570	2.67
4,247.432	.4250 *H*	z^5F_4	e^5G_5	50,704	3.749	3.75	4.008	(3.50)
4,248.228	....	c^3P_1	x^3P_2	48,305	2.969	3.18	3.267	(3.17)
4,250.125	....	z^7D_2	e^7D_3	43,435	4.278	4.22	4.59*r*	(3.01)
4,250.790 *S*	(.786)	a^3F_3	z^3G_3	36,079	4.508	4.59	4.76*R*	(2.45)
4,258.320	.3154 *H*	a^5D_2	z^7P_3	24,181	3.573	....	2.99	(−0.92)
4,260.479	.4737 *H*	z^7D_5	e^7D_5	42,816	4.894	4.62	4.95*r*	(3.41)
4,267.830 *S*	(.826)	c^3P_0	x^3P_1	48,516	3.14	3.33	3.417	2.82
4,271.159	....	z^7D_3	e^7D_4	43,163	4.40	4.25	4.67*r*	(3.12)
4,271.764 *S*	.7605 *H*	a^3F_4	z^3G_5	35,379	5.088	4.96*r*	4.95*R*	(2.88)
4,282.406 *S*	.4031 *H*	a^5P_3	z^5S_2	40,895	4.391	4.12	4.48*r*	(2.85)
4,285.445 *S*	(.441)	b^3H_6	y^3H_6	49,434	3.08	3.23	3.276	2.84
4,291.466	.4632 *H*	a^3F_3	z^5G_2	35,856	3.881	3.36	3.215	1.11
		a^5D_3	z^7P_4	23,711	.....	.....	.....	(−0.86)
4,294.128 *S*	.1245 *H*	a^3F_4	z^5G_4	35,257	4.148	4.35	4.65*R*	(2.07)
4,298.040 *S*	(.036)	a^1G_4	x^3G_5	47,835	3.313	3.23	3.255	2.62
4,299.242	.2343 *H*	z^7D_4	e^7D_5	42,816	4.394	4.23	4.66*r*	(2.82)
		(b^3H_5)	(y^3H_5)	49,604				
4,305.455 *S*	(.451)	c^3P_2	y^3S_1	47,556	3.20	3.29	3.344	2.65
4,307.906 *S*	.9019 *H*	a^3F_3	z^3G_4	35,768	5.129	4.91*r*	4.93*R*	(3.01)
4,309.380	.374	b^3G_5	z^3H_6	46,982	3.524	3.44	3.60	2.73
4,315.087 *S*	.0842 *H*	a^5P_2	z^5S_2	40,895	4.212	4.03	4.31	2.48
4,325.765 *S*	.7620 *H*	a^3F_2	z^3G_3	36,079	5.181	4.96*r*	4.95*R*	(3.06)
		(a^5D_4)	(z^7F_3)	23,111				
4,327.100	....	a^1D_2	y^1D_2	51,708	3.310	.....	3.38	
4,337.049 *S*	.0464 *H*	a^3F_3	z^5G_3	35,612	3.471	3.98	4.15*r*	(1.59)
4,347.239	....	a^5D_4	z^7F_4	22,997	2.53	.....		(−1.16)
4,352.737 *S*	.7342 *H*	a^5P_1	z^5S_2	40,895	3.9	3.82	3.998	2.27
4,367.581	.5779 *H*	b^3G_4	z^3H_5	47,008	3.400	3.32	.....	2.61
4,369.774 *S*	.7716 *H*	a^1G_4	z^1G_4	47,453	3.910	3.55	3.699	2.90
4,375.932 *S*	.9295 *H*	a^5D_4	z^7F_5	22,846	4.945	4.04	4.11*R*	(0.11)
4,383.547 *S*	.5454 *H*	a^3F_4	z^5G_5	34,782	5.472	4.99*r*	5.08*R*	(3.23)
4,388.412	....	z^5P_3	e^5P_3	51,837	3.200	3.36	3.441	3.30
4,390.954 *S*	(.950)	b^3G_3	z^3H_4	47,107	3.217	3.20	3.110	2.50
4,404.752 *S*	.7508 *H*	a^3F_3	z^5G_4	35,257	5.068	4.91	4.95*R*	(2.93)
4,408.419 *S*	(.415)	a^5P_2	x^5D_1	40,405	2.62	3.53	3.599	1.91
4,415.125 *S*	.1227 *H*	a^3F_2	z^5G_3	35,612	4.528	4.71	4.81*R*	(2.45)
4,422.570 *S*	.5680 *H*	b^3P_1	x^3D_1	45,552	3.483	3.53	3.669	2.61
4,427.312 *S*	.3098 *H*	a^5D_3	z^7F_4	23,193	4.823	3.99	4.08*R*	(0.09)
4,430.618 *S*	(.615)	a^5P_1	x^5D_0	40,491	2.67	3.57	3.66	(0.80)
4,433.223	....	z^5P_2	e^5P_1	52,020	3.12	3.25	3.328	3.22
4,442.343 *S*	(.340)	a^5P_2	x^5D_2	40,231	2.33	3.87	4.06	(2.25)
4,443.197 *S*	(.193)	b^3P_0	x^3D_1	45,552	3.509	3.57	3.72	(3.54)
4,445.48	....	a^5D_2	z^7F_2	23,193	2.39	.....	.....	(−1.43)
4,447.722 *S*	(.719)	a^5P_1	x^5D_1	40,405	3.017	3.78	3.958	(2.30)
4,450.320	....	c^3P_0	y^3S_1	47,556	3.39	.....	2.432	(3.92)

TABLE 7g-6. THE SPECTRUM OF IRON I (*Continued*)

λ_1	λ_2	Classification		E'	$\log I_2$	$\log I_3$	$\log I_4$	$\log \nu A_\nu$
4,454.383 *S*	(.379)	b^3P_2	x^3D_2	45,282	3.364	3.41	3.484	(2.84)
4,459.121 *S*	(.118)	a^5P_3	x^5D_3	39,970	3.24	3.89	4.072	(2.47)
4,461.654 *S*	.6528 *H*	a^5D_2	z^7F_3	23,111	4.576	3.94	3.88*R*	(−0.10)
4,466.554 *S*	.5506 *H*	b^3P_2	x^3D_3	45,221	4.057	3.93	4.164	(−0.57)
		(a^5D_1)	(z^7F_0)	23,270	.....	.....	.....	(−1.07)
4,469.381	.3747 *H*	z^5P_2	e^5P_3	51,837	3.391	3.47	3.614	3.41
4,476.021	.0173 *H*	b^3P_1	x^3D_2	45,282	3.895	3.85	4.086	(2.83)
4,482.171	.1689 *H*	a^5D_1	z^7F_2	23,193 }	4.4	3.9	4.0	
4,482.257	.253	a^5P_1	x^5D_2	40,231 }				(−0.36)
4,489.741 *S*	.7396 *H*	a^5D_0	z^7F_1	23,245	3.741	3.41	.....	(−0.77)
4,494.568 *S*	.5632 *H*	a^5P_2	x^5D_3	39,970	3.353	3.98	4.182	2.30
4,517.530 *S*	.526	c^3P_1	y^3P_1	46,902	2.40	.....	2.724	
4,528.619 *S*	.6137 *H*	a^5P_3	x^5D_4	39,626	3.747	4.17	4.46*r*	(2.74)
4,531.152 *S*	.149	a^3F_4	y^5F_4	34,040	3.050	.....	3.804	(1.41)
4,547.851 *S*	.847	a^1D_2	z^1F_3	50,587	3.409	.....	3.425	
4,592.655 *S*	.652	a^3F_3	y^5F_3	34,329	2.77	.....	3.500	
4,602.944 *S*	.942	a^3F_4	y^5F_5	33,695	3.123	.....	3.774	(1.48)
4,647.437 *S*	.4338 *H*	b^3G_5	y^3G_5	45,295	3.532	.....	3.473	
4,667.459 *S*	(.455)	z^5P_3	e^7P_4	50,475	3.231	.....	3.455	
4,678.852 *S*	(.848)	z^5P_3	f^5D_4	50,423	3.254	.....	3.556	
4,691.414 *S*	.410	b^3G_4	y^3G_4	45,428	3.345	.....	3.330	
4,707.281 *S*	.277	z^5D_3	e^5F_4	47,378	3.342	.....	3.525	
4,710.286 *S*	.282	b^3G_3	y^3G_3	45,563	3.26	.....	3.127	
4,733.596 *S*	.592	a^3F_4	y^5D_4	33,096	2.42	.....	3.025	
4,736.780	.777	z^5D_4	e^5F_5	47,006	3.517	.....	3.798	
4,741.533 *S*	.529	b^3P_2	w^5D_3	43,923	2.44	.....	2.87	
4,745.806 *S*	(.802)	z^5P_2	f^5D_3	50,534	2.605	.....	2.86	
		y^5D_4	f^5G_3	54.161				
4,772.817 *S*	(.814)	c^3P_2	x^3D_2	45,282	2.602	.....	2.84	
		a^3F_3	y^5D_3	33,507				
4,786.810 *S*	.807	c^3P_2	x^3D_3	45,221	2.888	.....	3.161	
4,789.654 *S*	.650	a^1D_2	z^1D_2	49,477	3.415	.....	3.301	
4,859.748 *S*	.744	z^7F_2	e^7D_1	43,764	3.654	.....	4.017	
4,871.323	.3174 *H*	z^7F_3	e^7D_2	43,634	4.096	.....	4.529	
4,872.144	.140	z^7F_1	e^7D_1	43,764	3.790	.....	4.207	
4,878.218 *S*	.214	z^7F_0	e^7D_1	43,764	3.527	.....	3.894	
4,890.762	.758	z^7F_2	e^7D_2	43,634	4.049	.....	4.352	
4,891.496	.4915 *H*	z^7F_4	e^7D_3	43,435	4.404	.....	4.64*r*	
4,903.317 *S*	.313	z^7F_1	e^7D_2	43,634	3.513	.....	3.852	
4,918.999 *S*	.996	z^7F_3	e^7D_3	43,435	4.178	.....	4.410	
4,920.509	.5020 *H*	z^7F_5	e^7D_4	43,163	4.681	.....	4.80*r*	
4,924.776 *S*	.772	a^3P_2	y^3D_2	38,678	2.75	.....	3.030	
4,938.820	.816	z^7F_2	e^7D_3	43,435	3.438	.....	3.74	
4,939.690 *S*	.687	a^5F_5	z^5F_4	27,167	3.024	.....	3.350	
4,957.302	.302	z^7F_4	e^7D_4	43,163	3.14	.....		
4,957.603	.5956 *H*	z^7F_6	e^7D_5	42,816	5.16	.....	5.0*R*	
4,966.096 *S*	.0937 *H*	z^5F_5	e^5F_5	47,005	3.400	.....	3.614	
4,982.507	.504	y^5D_4	f^5P_3	53,161	3.430	.....	3.714	

TABLE 7g-6. THE SPECTRUM OF IRON I (*Continued*)

λ_1	λ_2	Classification		E'	log I_2	log I_3	log I_4	log $\nu A \nu$
4,994.133 *S*	.129	a^5F_4	z^5F_3	27,395	3.191	.....	3.410	
5,001.871 *S*	.866	z^3F_4	e^3D_3	51,294	3.861	.....	3.895	
5,006.126	.125	z^7F_5	e^7D_5	42,816	4.051	.....	4.176	
5,012.071 *S*	.080	a^5F_5	z^5F_5	26,875	3.791	.....	3.887	(0.33)
5,014.950	.952	z^3F_3	e^3D_2	51,740	3.538	.....	3.682	
5,041.759 *S*	.756	a^3F_4	z^3F_3	31,806	4.241	.....	3.748	
5,049.825 *S*	.823	a^3P_2	y^3D_3	38,175	3.506	.....	3.979	
5,051.636 *S*	.636	a^5F_4	z^5F_4	27,167	3.523	.....	3.690	
5,079.226	.220	a^5P_2	y^5P_1	37,410	3.732	.....	3.557	
5,083.342 *S*	.341	a^5F_3	z^5F_3	26,875	3.278	.....	3.492	
5,110.414 *S*	.4127 *H*	a^5D_4	z^7D_4	19,562	4.238	.....	3.613	(−0.85)
		(a^1H_5)	(z^1H_5)	48,383				
5,123.723 *S*	.721	a^5F_1	z^5F_1	27,666	3.323	.....	3.415	
5,127.363 *S*	.361	a^5F_4	z^5F_5	26,875	3.002	.....	3.212	
5,133.692	.6893 *H*	y^5F_5	f^5G_6	53,169	3.577	.....	3.786	
5,150.843 *S*	.840	a^5F_2	z^5F_3	27,395	2.506	.....	3.322	
5,166.286	.2816 *H*	a^5D_4	z^7D_5	19,351	3.901	.....	3.190	(−1.21)
5,167.491 *S*	.4882 *H*	a^3F_4	z^3D_3	31,323	5.37	.....	4.71*R*	(1.67)
5,168.901 *S*	.8980 *H*	a^5D_3	z^7D_3	19,757	3.926	.....	3.48*r*	(−1.03)
5,171.599 *S*	.5959 *H*	a^3F_4	z^3F_4	31,307	4.651	.....	4.23*R*	(1.25)
5,191.460	.4539 *H*	z^7P_2	e^7D_1	43,764	3.701	.....	4.080	(2.64)
5,192.350	.3432 *H*	z^7P_3	e^7D_3	43,435	3.914	.....	3.250	(2.80)
5,194.943	.942	a^3F_3	z^3F_3	31,805	4.275	.....	3.88*r*	(0.96)
5,198.714 *S*	.713	a^5P_1	y^5P_2	37,158	2.39	.....	3.32	
5,202.339 *S*	.332	a^5P_3	y^5P_3	36,767	2.85	.....	3.725	(1.26)
5,204.582	.5822 *H*	a^5D_2	z^7D_2	19,913	3.464	.....	2.86	(−1.34)
5,216.278 *S*	.2737 *H*	a^3F_2	z^3F_2	32,134	4.171	.....	3.78	(0.97)
5,225.531	.531	a^5D_1	z^7D_1	20,020	2.90	.....	.....	(−1.78)
5,227.192 *S*	.1880 *H*	a^3F_3	z^3D_2	31,686	5.02	.....	4.93	
5,232.946	.9404 *H*	z^7P_4	e^7D_5	42,816	4.436	.....	4.61*r*	(2.95)
5,235.392 *S*	.387	b^3F_3	x^5D_3	39,970	2.73	.....	2.96	
		c^3F_4	u^3D_3	51,969				
5,236.204	....	c^3F_2	8_1	52,858	1.83			
5,242.495 *S*	.491	a^1I_6	z^1H_5	48,383	3.20	.....	3.326	
5,247.065	.061	a^5D_2	z^7D_3	19,757	2.89	.....	.....	(−2.00)
5,250.211	.216	a^5D_0	z^7D_1	20,020	2.44	.....	.....	(−1.93)
5,250.650 *S*	.647	a^5P_2	y^5P_3	36,767	2.78	.....	3.402	(1.02)
5,263.314	.3051 *H*	z^5D_2	e^5D_2	45,334	3.195	.....	3.60	
5,266.562	.5553 *H*	z^7P_3	e^7D_4	43,163	4.033	.....	4.281	(3.26)
5,269.541	.538	a^5F_5	z^5D_4	25,900	5.058	.....	4.68*r*	(1.45)
5,270.360 *S*	.357	a^3F_2	z^3D_1	31,937	4.914	.....	.....	(1.48)
5,281.796	.7899 *H*	z^7P_2	e^7D_3	43,435	3.477	.....	3.832	
5,283.628	.6208 *H*	z^5D_3	e^5D_3	45,061	3.811	.....	4.045	
5,302.307	.2994 *H*	z^5D_1	e^5D_2	45,335	3.423	.....	3.736	
5,307.365 *S*	.3607 *H*	a^3F_2	z^3F_3	31,805	3.337	.....	3.00	(0.12)
5,324.185	.1787 *H*	z^5D_4	e^5D_4	44,677	4.182	.....	4.393	(3.07)
5,328.042	.039	a^5F_4	z^5D_3	26,140	4.867	.....	4.70*R*	(1.29)

TABLE 7g-6. THE SPECTRUM OF IRON I (*Continued*)

λ_1	λ_2	Classification		E'	log I_2	log I_3	log I_4	log νA_ν
5,328.534 *S*	.530	a^3F_3	z^3D_3	31,323	4.507	.....	4.20*r*	(1.19)
5,332.903	.8990 *H*	a^3F_3	z^3F_4	31,307	3.951	.....	3.155	(0.25)
5,339.935	.9289 *H*	z^5D_2	e^5D_3	45,061	3.874	.....	3.846	
5,341.026 *S*	.0239 *H*	a^3F_2	z^3D_2	31,686	4.65	.....	4.00*r*	(1.11)
5,364.874	....	z^5G_2	e^5H_3	54,491	3.384	.....	3.64	
5,367.470	.4674 *H*	z^5G_3	e^5H_4	54,237	3.564	.....	3.79	
5,369.965	.9624 *H*	z^5G_4	e^5H_5	53,874	3.725	.....	3.91	
5,371.493 *S*	.4895 *H*	a^5F_3	z^5D_2	26,340	4.622	.....	4.61*R*	(1.10)
		(z^3G_4)	(e^3G_3)	54,379				
5,383.374	.3692 *H*	z^5G_5	e^5H_6	53,353	3.844	.....	4.11	
5,397.131 *S*	.1275 *H*	a^5F_4	z^5D_4	25,900	4.459	.....	4.43*R*	(0.81)
5,404.144	....	z^3G_4	e^3H_5	54,267	3.819	.....	4.08	
5,405.778 *S*	.7747 *H*	a^5F_2	z^5D_1	26,479	4.353	.....	4.49*R*	(0.86)
5,424.072	.0689 *H*	z^5G_6	e^5H_7	53,275	3.842	.....	4.08	
5,429.699 *S*	.6966 *H*	a^5F_3	z^5D_3	26,140	4.414	.....	4.48*R*	(0.89)
5,434.527 *S*	.5240 *H*	a^5F_1	z^5D_0	26,550	4.048	.....	4.28*R*	(0.72)
5,446.920 *S*	.9171 *H*	a^5F_2	z^5D_2	26,340	4.337	.....	4.42*R*	(0.82)
5,455.613 *S*	.6096 *H*	a^5F_1	z^5D_1	26,479	4.144	.....	4.42*R*	(0.72)
5,497.519 *S*	.5162 *H*	a^5F_1	z^5D_2	26,340	3.374	.....	3.60	
5,501.469 *S*	.4636 *H*	a^5F_3	z^5D_4	25,900	3.299	.....	3.46	
5,506.782 *S*	.7788 *H*	a^5F_2	z^5D_3	26,140	3.494	.....	3.68	
5,569.625 *S*	.6176 *H*	z^5F_2	e^5D_1	45,509	3.541	.....	3.807	
5,572.849 *S*	.8421 *H*	z^5F_3	e^5D_2	45,334	3.806	.....	4.06	
5,586.763 *S*	.7557 *H*	z^5F_4	e^5D_3	45,061	4.074	.....	4.43	
5,615.652 *S*	.6436 *H*	z^5F_5	e^5D_4	44,677	4.262	.....	4.375	
5,624.549 *S*	.5419 *H*	z^5F_2	e^5D_2	45,334	3.319	.....	3.574	
5,658.826 *S*	.8158 *H*	z^5F_3	e^5D_3	45,061	3.22	.....	3.597	
5,662.525 *S*	....	y^5F_5	g^5D_4	51,351	3.661	.....	3.241	
7,187.341	....	y^5D_4	e^5F_5	47,006	3.53			
7,445.776	....	y^5F_3	e^5F_3	47,756	3.48			
7,495.088	....	y^5F_4	e^5F_4	47,378	3.53			
7,511.045	....	y^5F_5	e^5F_2	47,006	3.66			
7,586.044	....	z^5G_5	e^3F_4	47,961	3.39			
7,780.586	....	z^3G_3	e^3F_2	48,928	3.28			
7,937.166	....	z^5G_5	e^5F_4	47,378	4.040			
7,998.972	....	z^5G_4	e^5F_3	47,756	3.26			
8,046.073	....	z^5G_3	e^3F_2	48,532	3.36			
8,220.406	....	z^5G_6	e^5F_5	47,006	3.69			
8,248.151	....	z^5G_4	e^5F_4	47,378	3.34			
8,327.063	....	a^5P_2	z^5P_1	29,773	3.61			
8,331.941	....	z^3G_5	e^5F_4	47,378	3.11			
8,387.781	....	a^5P_3	z^5P_2	29,469	3.79			
8,661.908	....	a^5P_1	z^5P_2	29,469	3.75			
8,688.633	....	a^5P_3	z^5P_3	29,056	4.161			
8,824.227	....	a^5P_2	z^5P_3	29,056	3.76			

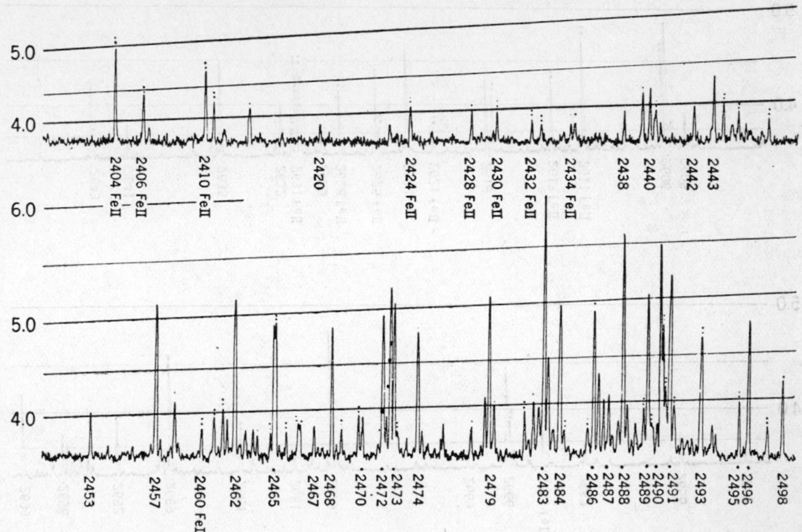

FIG. 7g-5. Photoelectric traces of the iron spectrum, hollow cathode discharge in neon. Wavelength range, 2,400–5,700 A. Single dots denote neon lines; two dots indicate Fe II lines.

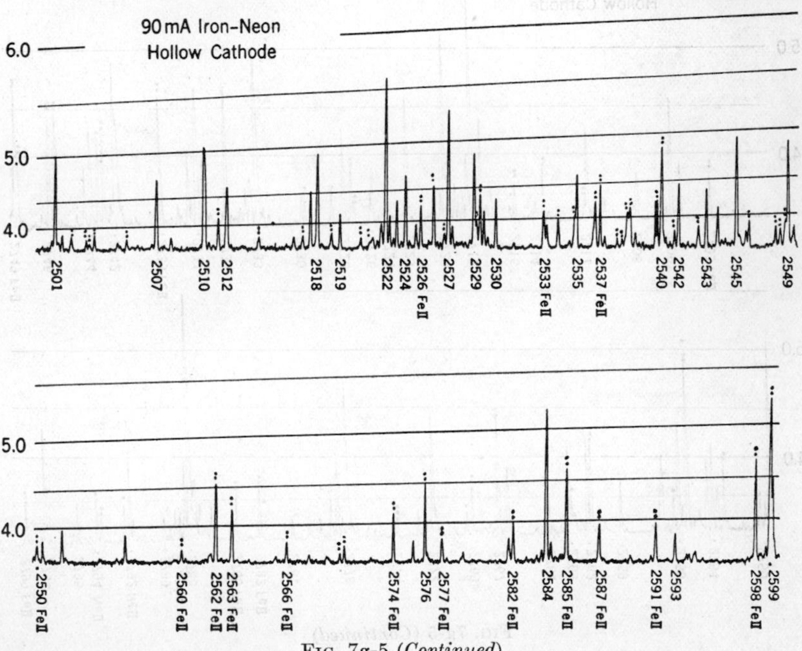

FIG. 7g-5 (*Continued*)

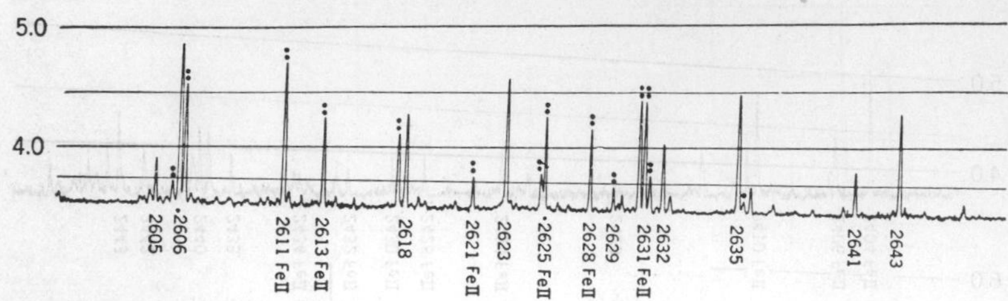

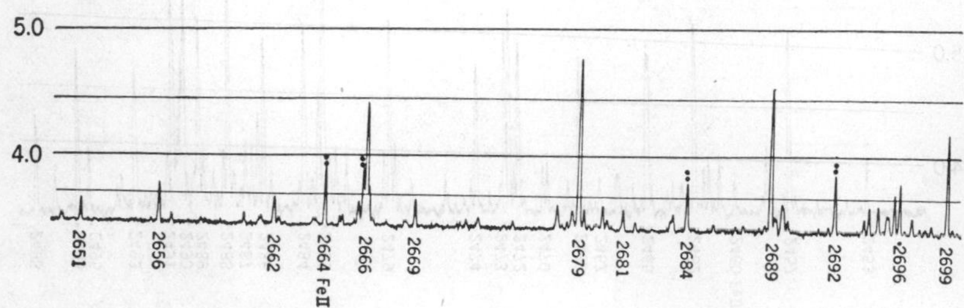

FIG. 7g-5 (*Continued*)

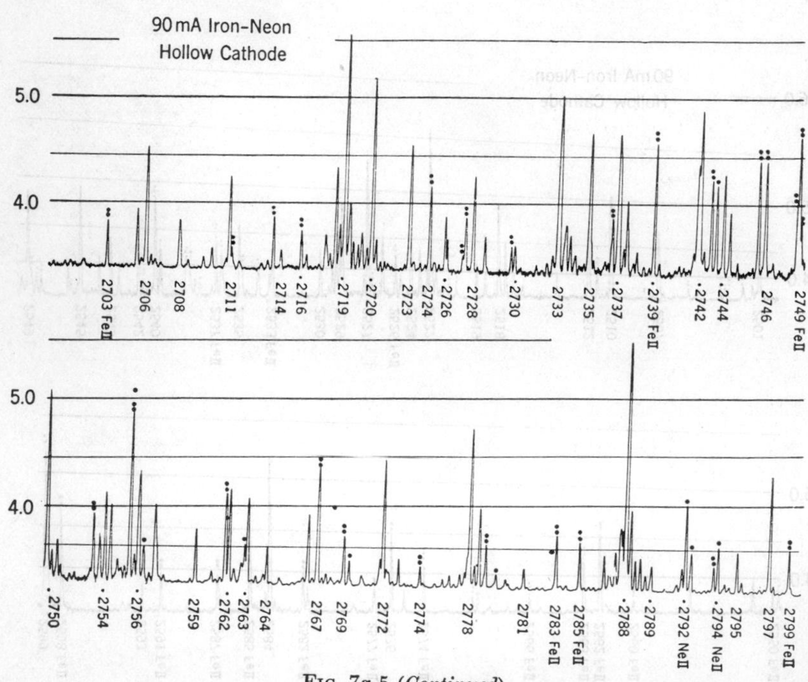

FIG. 7g-5 (*Continued*)

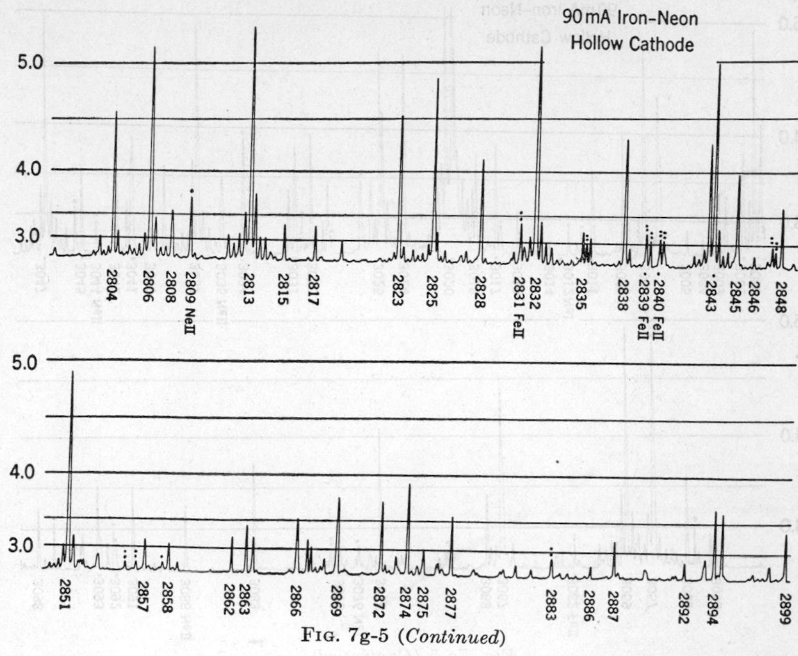

FIG. 7g-5 (*Continued*)

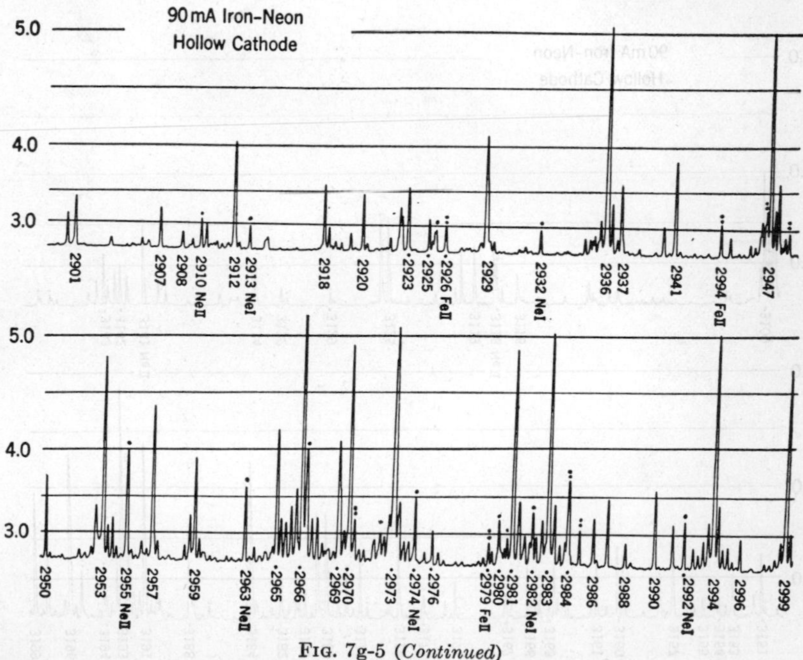

FIG. 7g-5 (*Continued*)

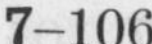

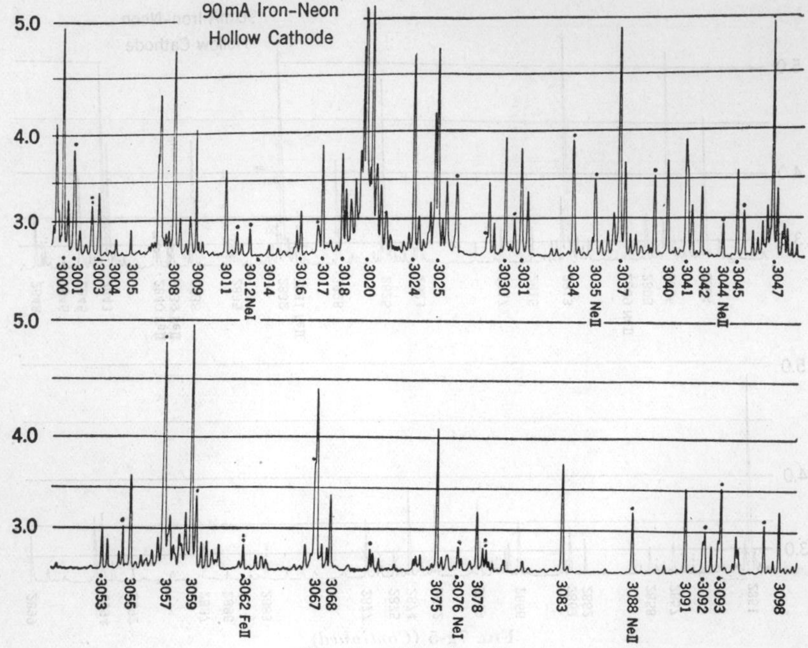

FIG. 7g-5 (*Continued*)

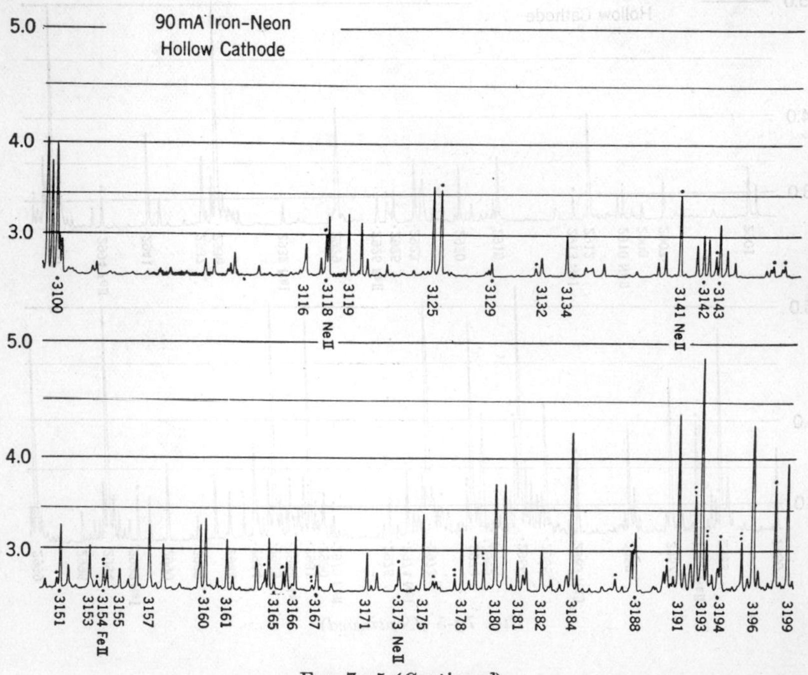

FIG. 7g-5 (*Continued*)

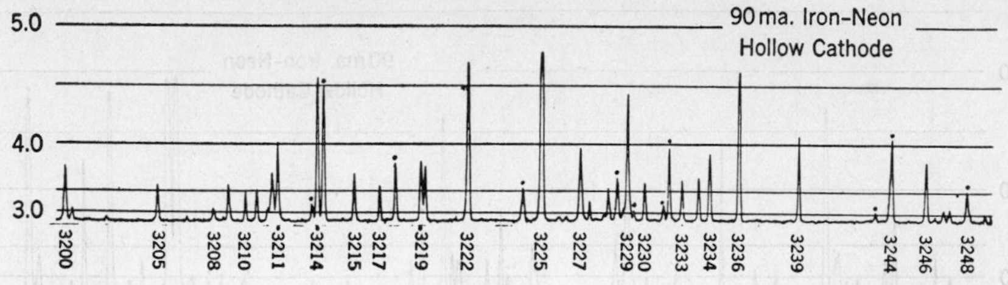

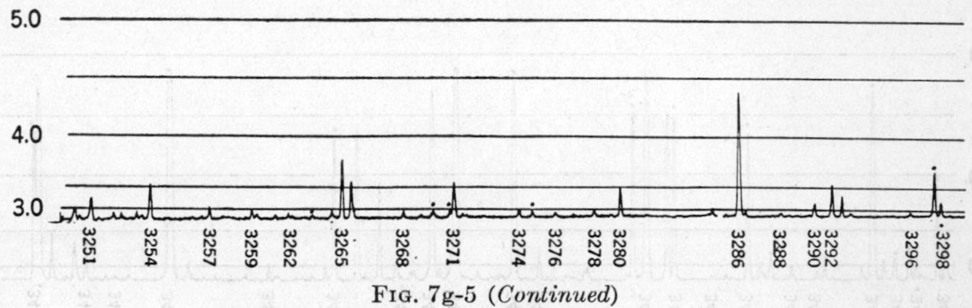

FIG. 7g-5 (*Continued*)

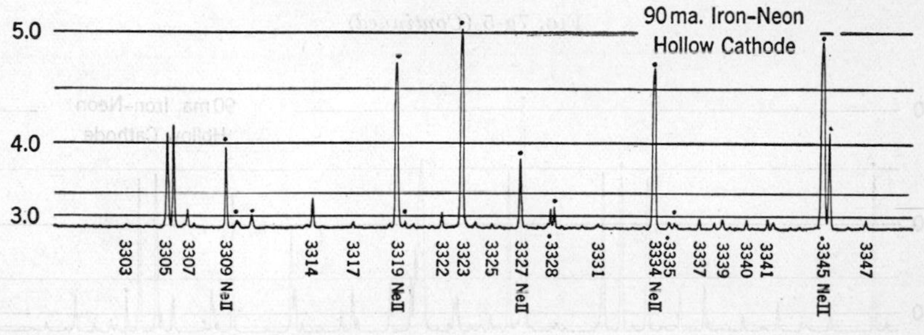

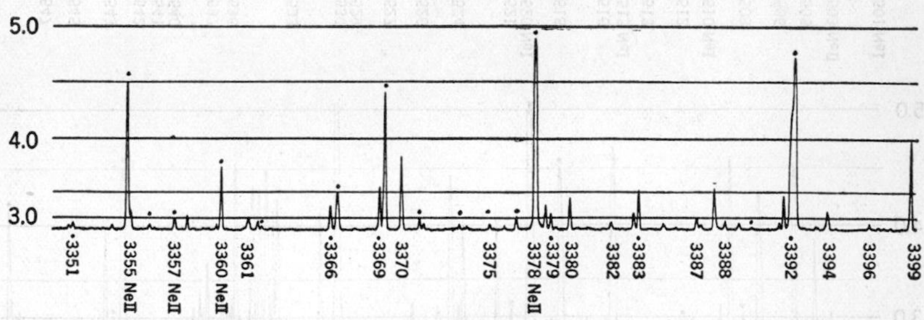

FIG. 7g-5 (*Continued*)

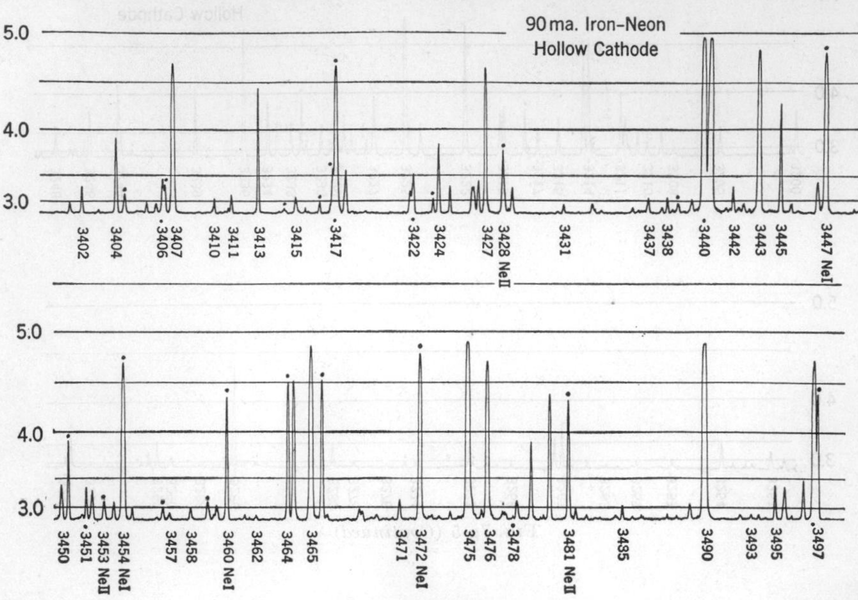

FIG. 7g-5 (*Continued*)

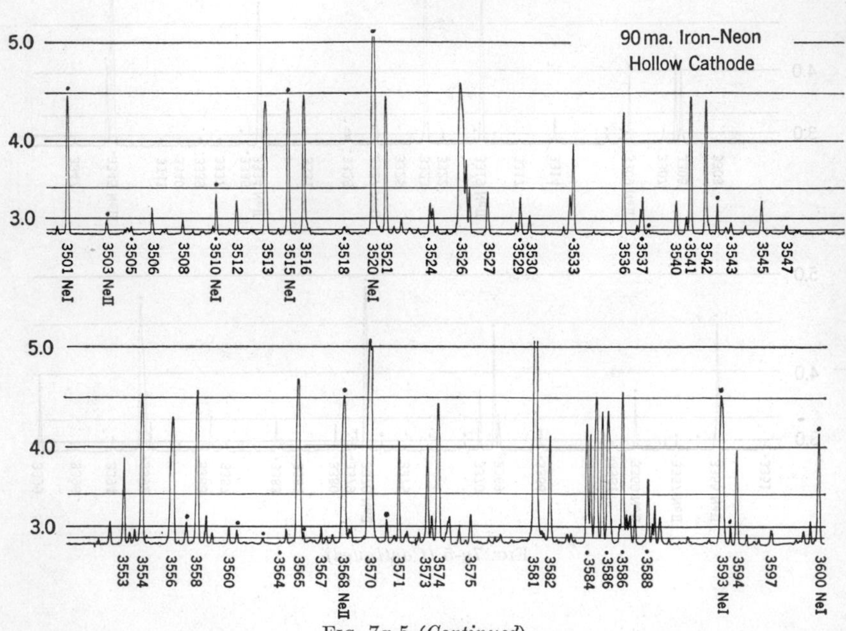

FIG. 7g-5 (*Continued*)

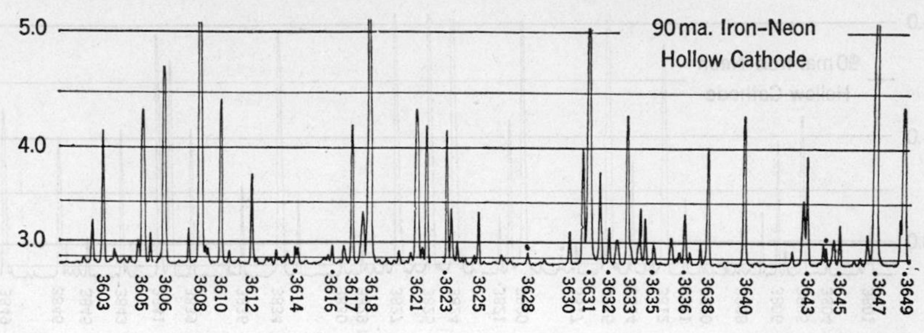

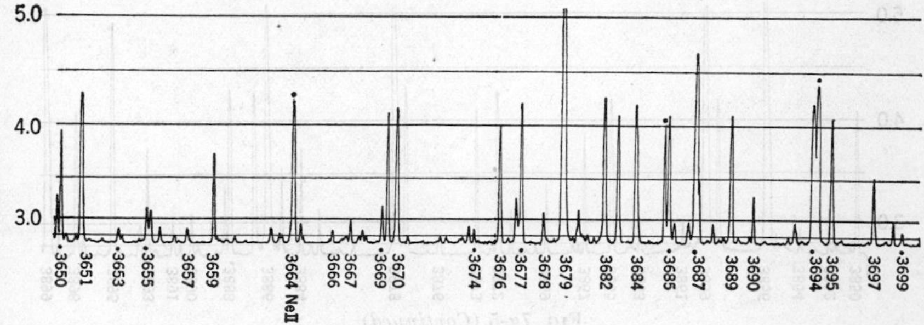

Fig. 7g-5 (*Continued*)

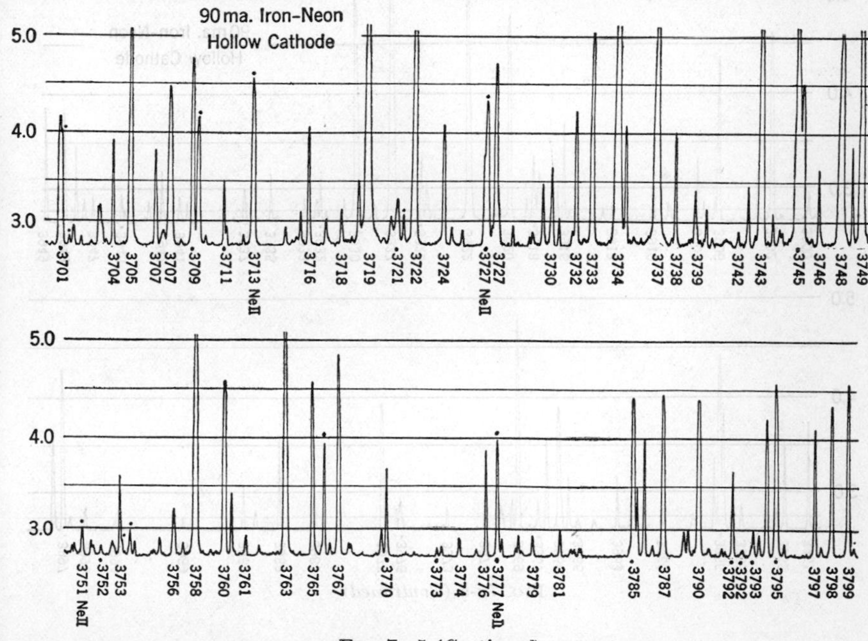

Fig. 7g-5 (*Continued*)

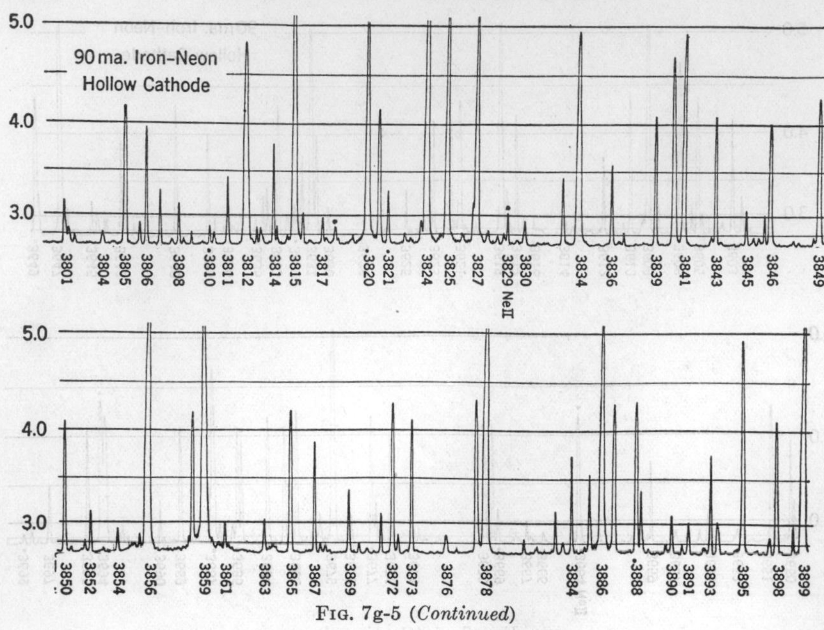

Fig. 7g-5 (*Continued*)

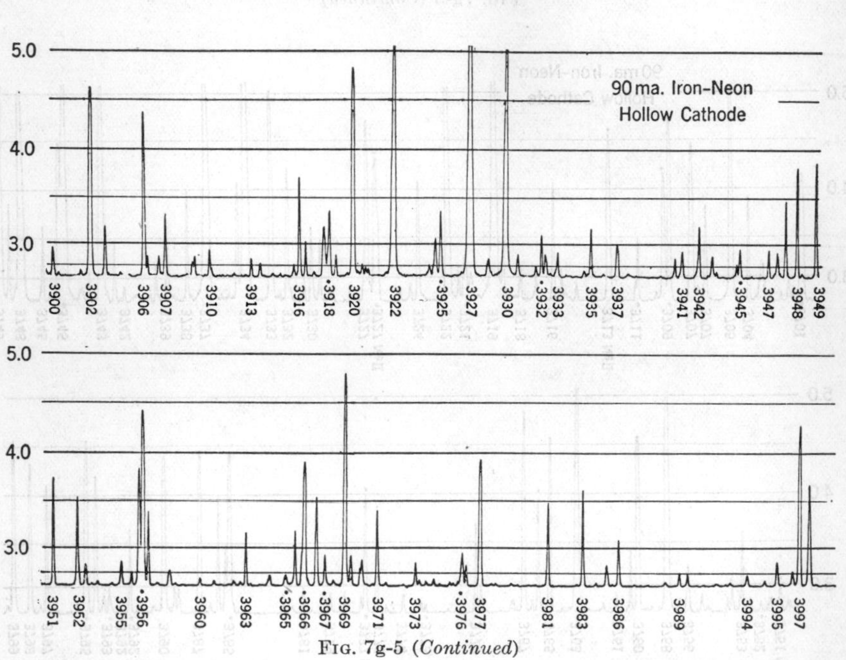

Fig. 7g-5 (*Continued*)

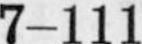

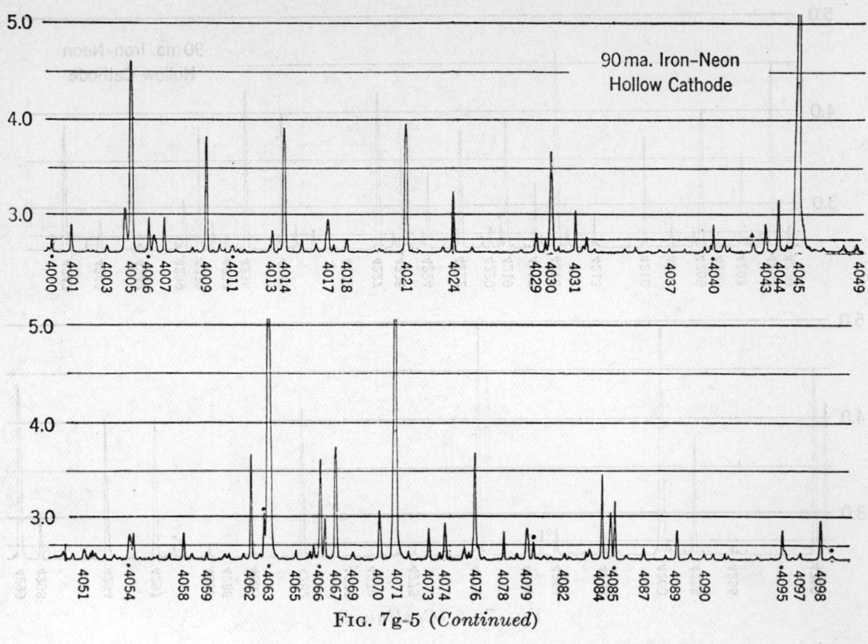

FIG. 7g-5 (*Continued*)

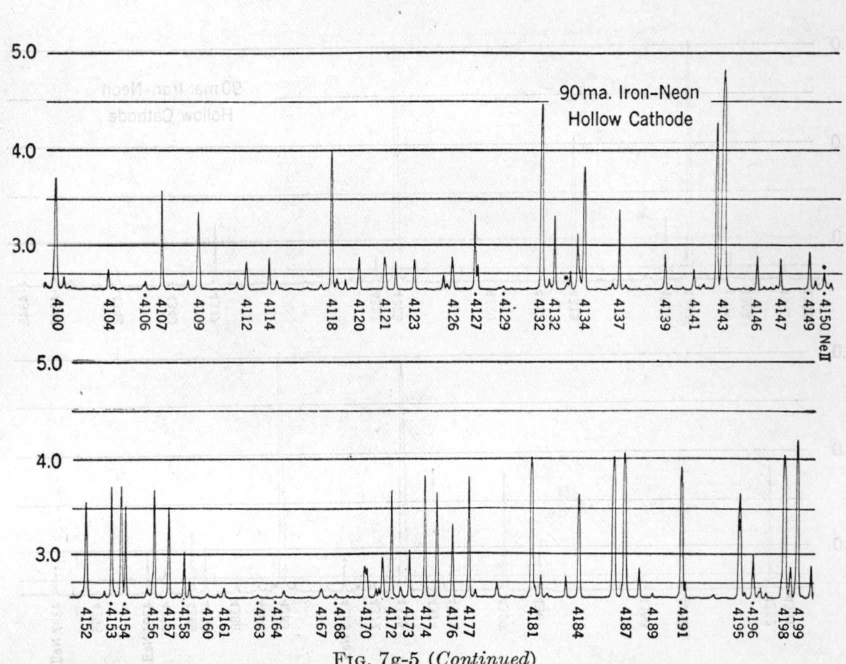

FIG. 7g-5 (*Continued*)

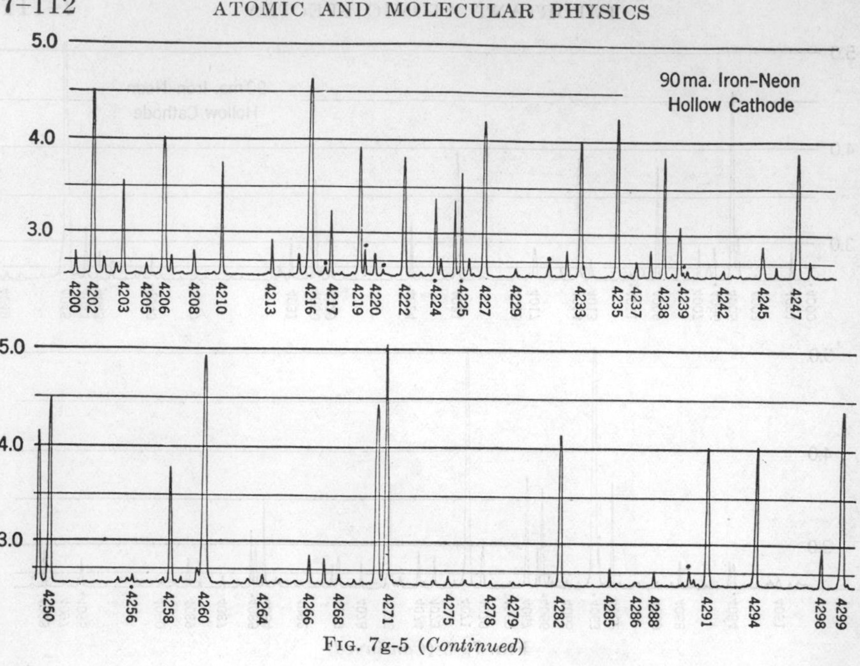

FIG. 7g-5 (*Continued*)

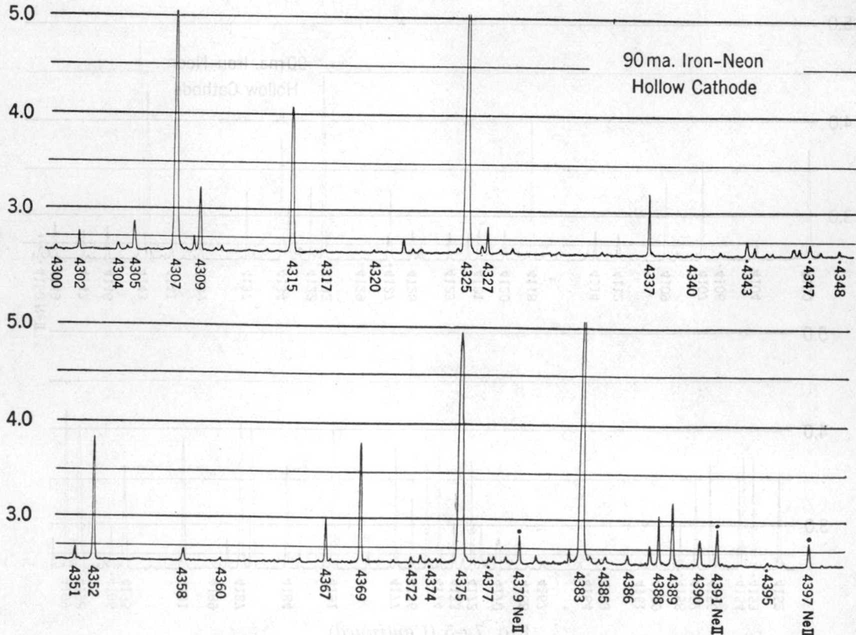

FIG. 7g-5 (*Continued*)

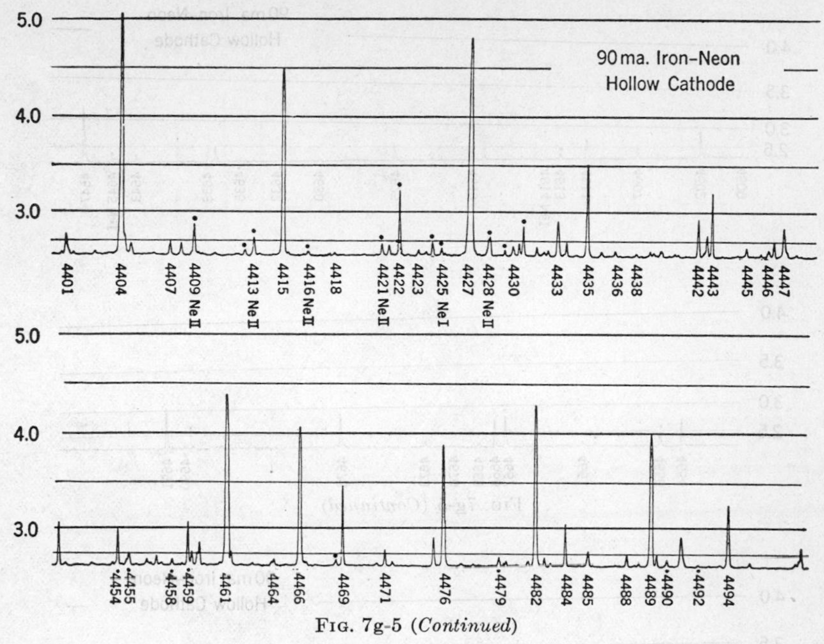

Fig. 7g-5 (*Continued*)

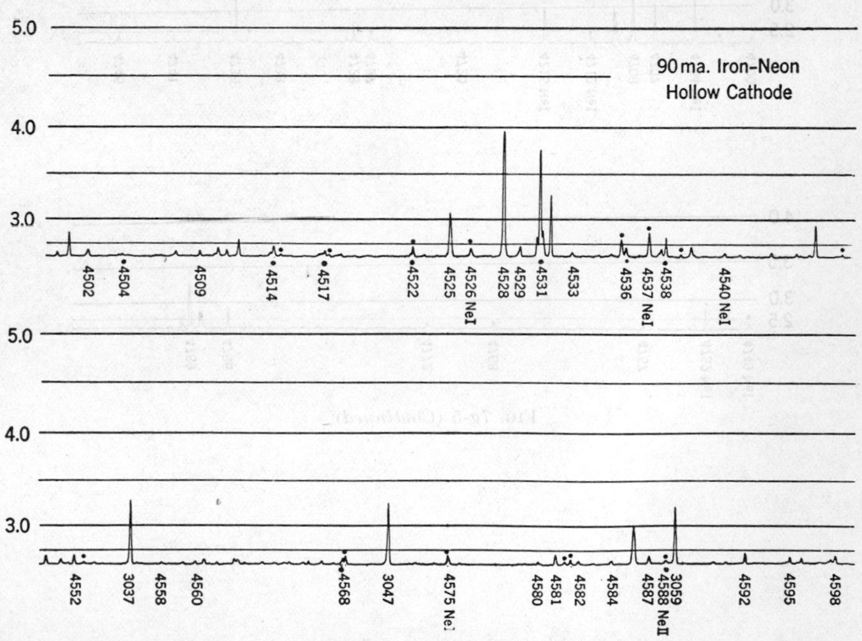

Fig. 7g-5 (*Continued*)

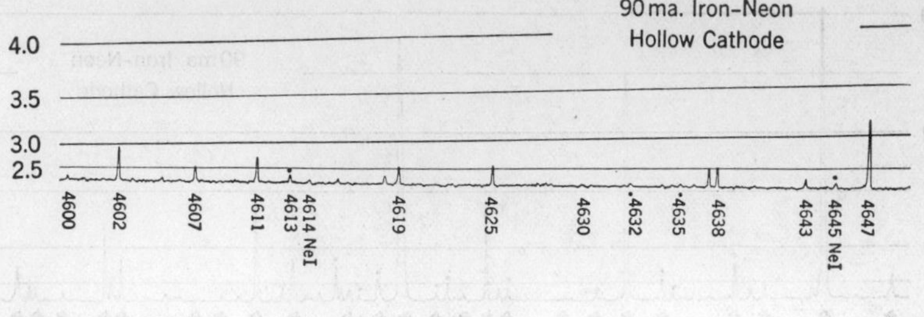

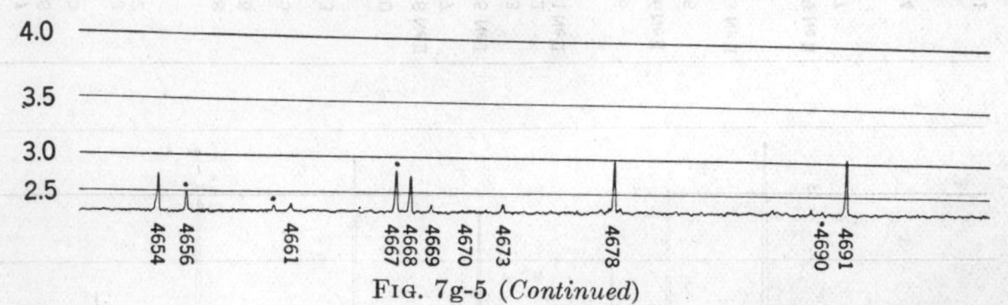

Fig. 7g-5 (*Continued*)

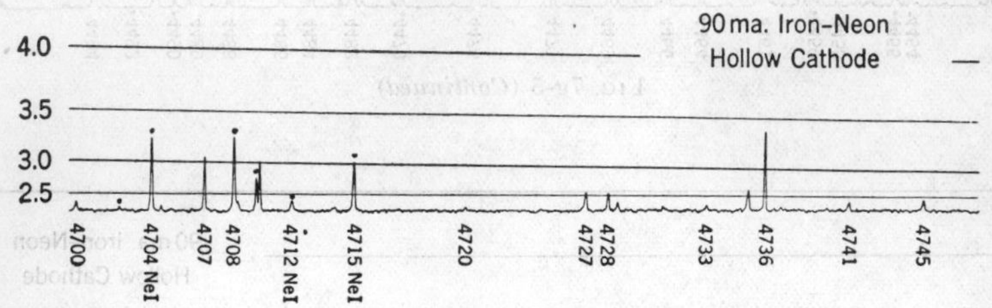

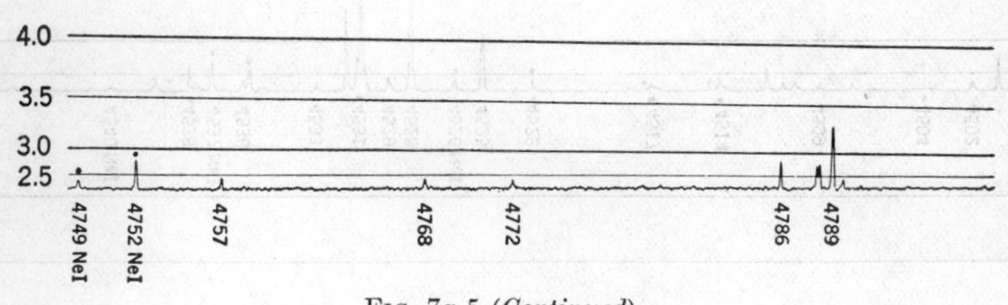

Fig. 7g-5 (*Continued*)

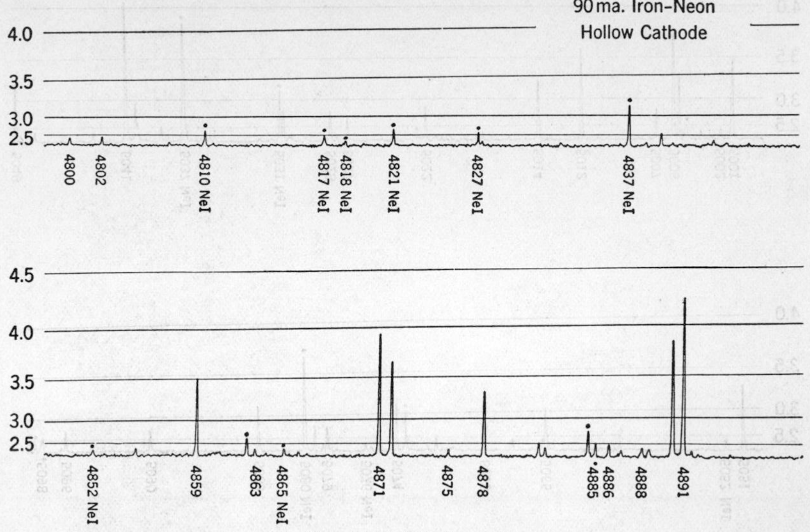

FIG. 7g-5 (*Continued*)

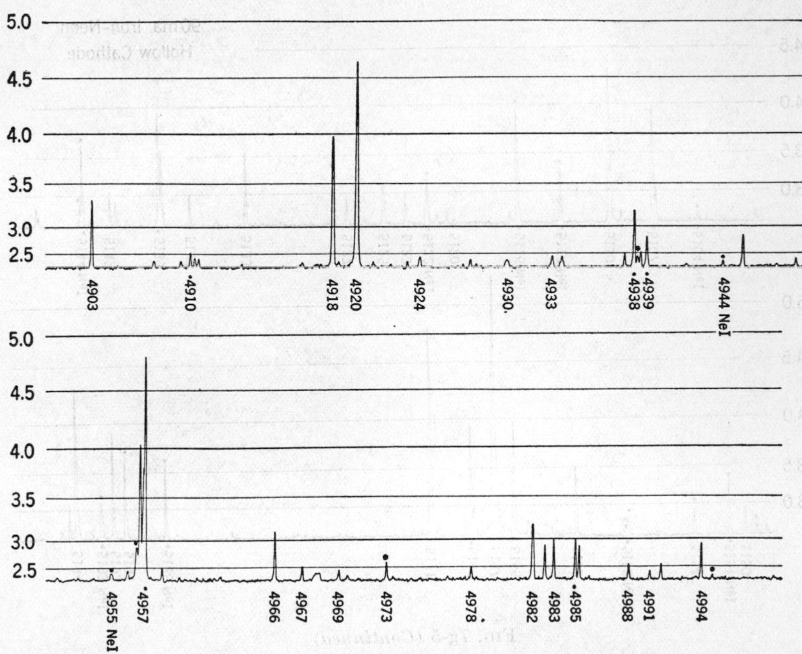

FIG. 7g-5 (*Continued*)

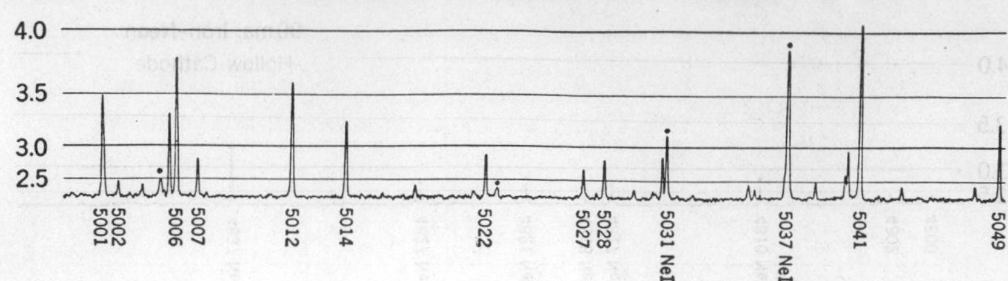

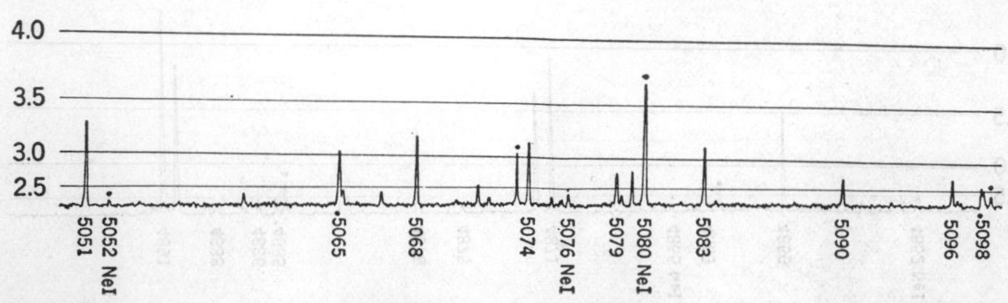

FIG. 7g-5 (*Continued*)

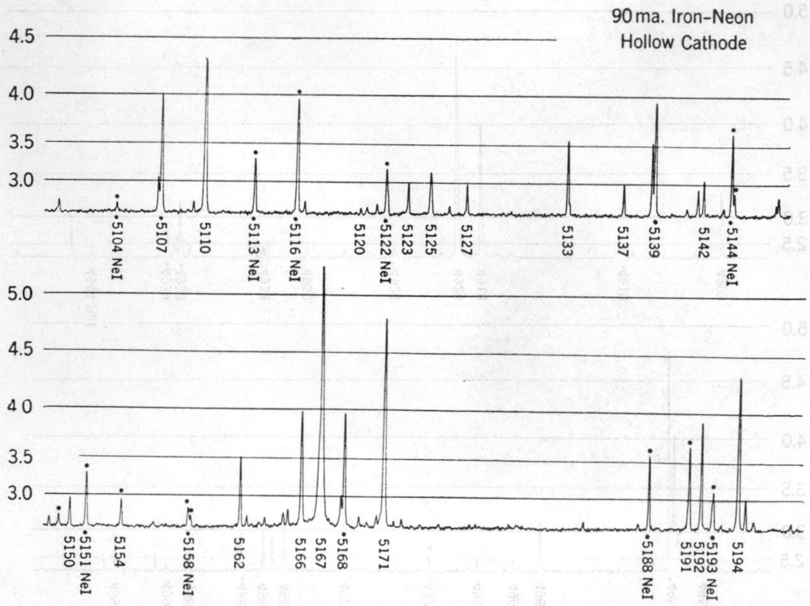

FIG. 7g-5 (*Continued*)

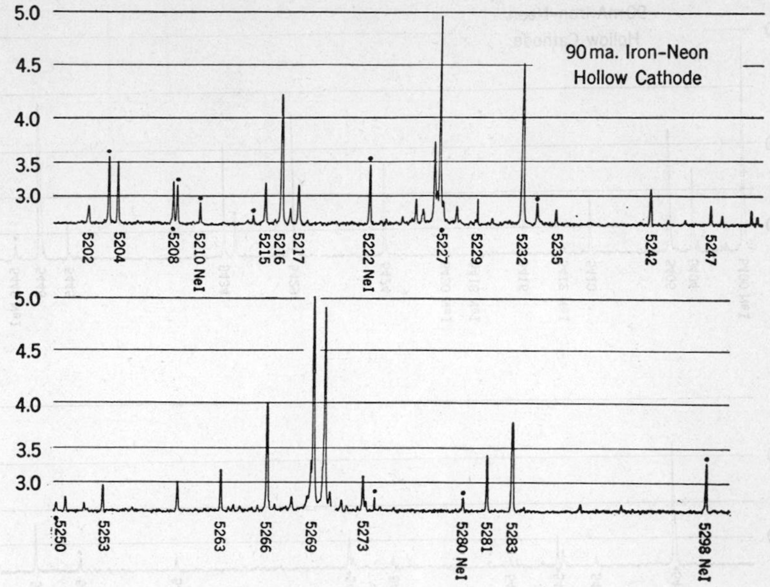

Fig. 7g-5 (*Continued*)

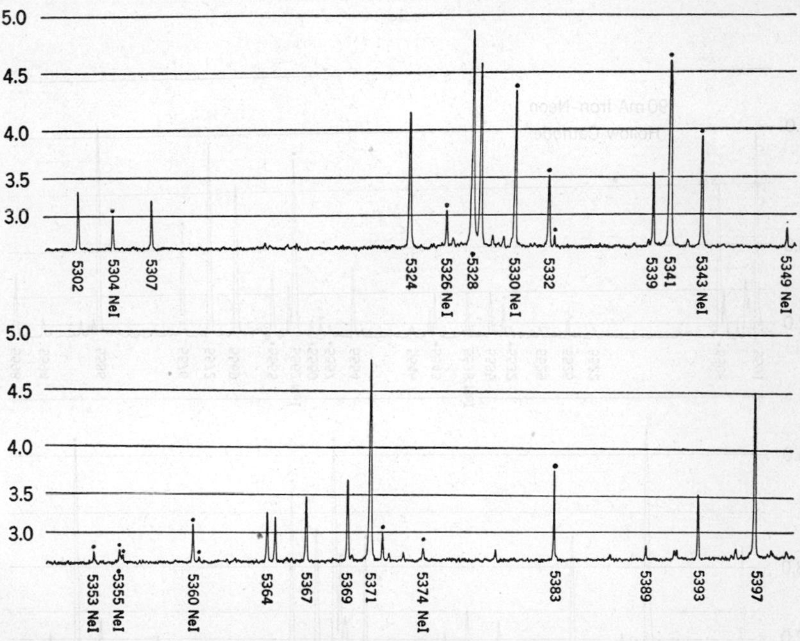

Fig. 7g-5 (*Continued*)

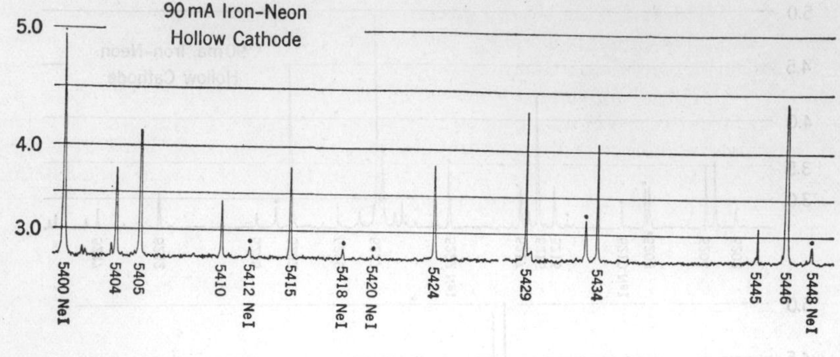

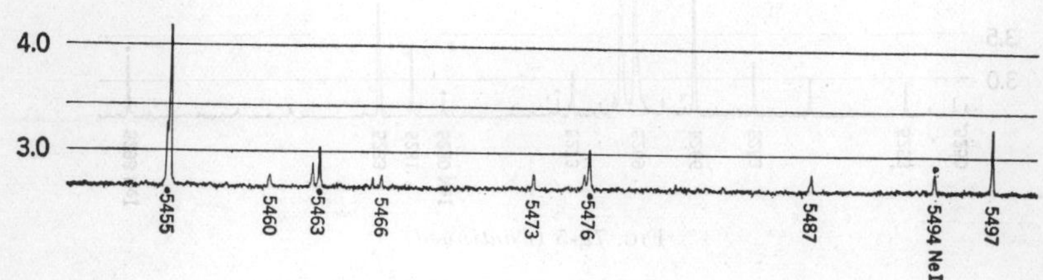

FIG. 7g-5 (*Continued*)

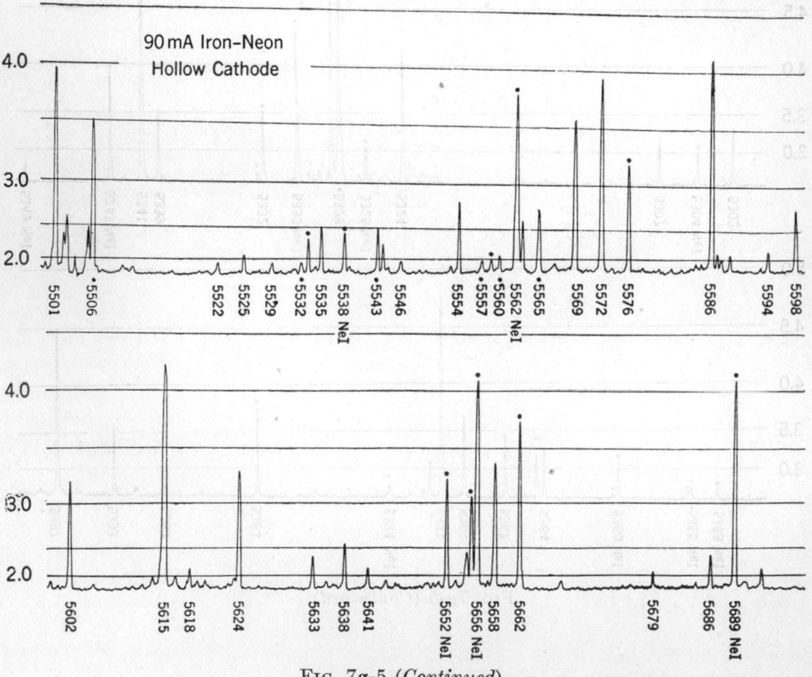

FIG. 7g-5 (*Continued*)

Mercury I. This spectrum is very useful because of the ease with which it can be obtained. Any low-pressure mercury tube gives sharp lines; for example, a commercial so-called bactericidal lamp is suitable. High-pressure lamps give broader lines and very-high-pressure lamps (commercial type H6) a continuous spectrum. The mercury spectrum is useful as a general reference spectrum. Under high dispersion most lines show elaborate isotopic and hyperfine structure because there are six isotopes with considerable abundance: 198 (10.1 per cent), 199 (17.0 per cent), 200 (23.3 per cent), 201 (13.2 per cent), 202 (29.6 per cent), 204 (6.7 per cent). The two odd ones have lines with hyperfine structure. The structure of the lines is sometimes useful for obtaining the resolving power of spectrographs (for details of structure, see Schüler and Burns and Adams[1]). An example is shown in Fig. 7g-6.

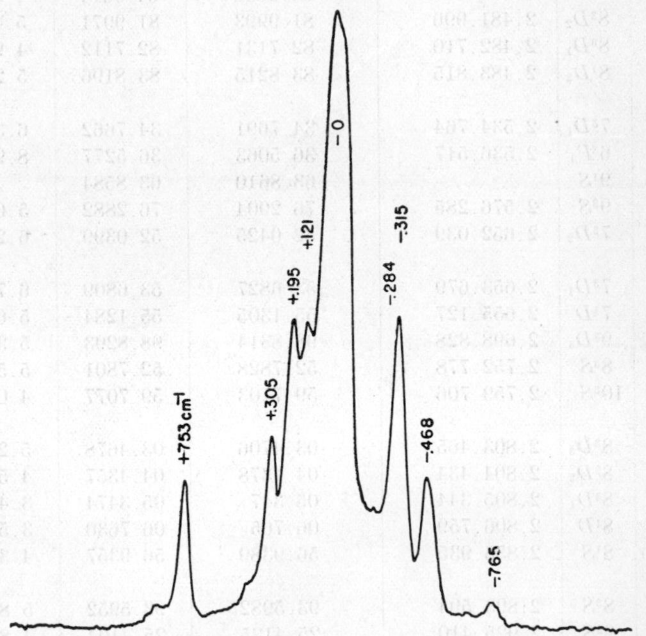

FIG. 7g-6. High-dispersion photoelectric trace of the 5,461-A line of ordinary mercury showing isotope and hyperfine structure. Resolving power was 400,000.

Pure Hg^{198} can be obtained by irradiation of gold with neutrons. Lamps with this isotope are now commercially available and the spectrum shows very sharp single lines. Meggers has proposed to adopt the wavelength of the green line (5,461) of Hg^{198} as a primary standard of length. International adoption of this proposal, however, awaits investigation of the variability of the wavelength with discharge conditions. In the meantime most of the strong lines of Hg^{198}, particulary those marked *S* in Table 7g-7, may be used as standards for interferometric wavelength measurements.

Hg^{202} is the most abundant isotope in natural mercury. Tubes with nearly pure Hg^{202} are also available and their wavelengths may also be used as standards.

Table 7g-7 gives the wavelengths of natural mercury, Hg^{198} and Hg^{202}. All valves listed between 2,300 and 6,900 A are recent interferometric wavelengths; those outside this interval are known with much less accuracy.

[1] Schüler and Keyston, *Z. Physik* **72**, 423 (1931); Schüler and Jones, *Z. Physik* **79**, 631 (1932); Burns and Adams, *J. Opt. Soc. Am.* **42**, 716 (1952).

TABLE 7g-7. THE SPECTRUM OF MERCURY I

Classification		λ (Hg nat.)	λ Hg^{198}	λ Hg^{202}	log I
6^1S	6^1P	1,402.72 O	....	....	(4)
6^1S	7^1P	1,849.52 O	....	....	(20)
6^1S	7^3P_2	2,296.97 O	....	....	
6^3P_0	10^3S	2,345.433 O	45.4400	45.4369	5.33
6^3P_0	8^3D_1	2,378.316 O	78.3246	78.3224	6.60
6^3P_1	10^3S	2,446.895	46.8998	46.8974	4.44
6^3P_0	9^3S	2,464.057	64.0636	64.0614	4.31
6^3P_1	8^3D_2	2,481.996	81.9993	81.9971	5.43
6^3P_1	8^3D_1	2,482.710	82.7131	82.7112	4.94
6^3P_1	8^1D_2	2,483.815	83.8215	83.8196	5.23
6^3P_0	7^3D_1	2,534.764	34.7691	34.7662	6.35
6^1S	6^3P_1	2,536.517	36.5063	36.5277	8.95
6^3P_1	9^1S	....	63.8610	63.8584	
6^3P_1	9^3S	2,576.285	76.2904	76.2882	5.00
6^3P_1	7^3D_2	2,652.039	52.0425	52.0399	6.20
6^3P_1	7^3D_1	2,653.679	53.6827	53.6809	6.75
6^3P_1	7^1D	2,655.127	55.1305	55.1284	5.63
6^3P_2	9^3D_3	2,698.828	98.8314	98.8293	5.35
6^3P_0	8^3S	2,752.778	52.7828	52.7801	5.58
6^3P_2	10^3S	2,759.706	59.7103	59.7077	4.0
6^3P_2	8^3D_3	2,803.465	03.4706	03.4678	5.25
6^3P_2	8^3D_2	2,804.434	04.4378	04.4357	4.56
6^3P_2	8^3D_1	2,805.344	05.347	05.3474	3.49
6^3P_2	8^1D	2,806.759	06.765	06.7630	3.52
6^3P_1	8^1S	2,856.935	56.9389	56.9357	4.30
6^3P_1	8^3S	2,893.594	93.5982	93.5952	5.88
6^3P_2	9^3S	2,925.410	25.4135	25.4104	4.82
6^3P_0	6^3D_1	2,967.280	67.2832	67.2819	6.52
6^3P_0	6^1D	2,967.543			
6^3P_2	7^3D_3	3,021.498	21.4996	21.4973	6.09
6^3P_2	7^3D_2	3,023.475	23.4764	23.4739	5.45
6^3P_2	7^3D_1	3,025.606	25.6080	25.6056	4.43
6^3P_2	7^1D	3,027.487	27.4896	27.4874	4.76
6^3P_1	6^3D_2	3,125.6681	25.6698	25.6675	6.62
6^3P_1	6^3D_1	3,131.5485	31.5513	31.5480	6.48
6^3P_1	6^1D	3,131.8391	31.8423	31.8394	6.56
6^3P_2	8^3S	3,341.4766	41.4814	41.4766	5.85
6^3P_2	6^3D_3	3,650.1533	50.1564*	50.1532	6.94
6^3P_2	6^3D_2	3,654.8363	54.8392	54.8361	6.51
6^3P_2	6^3D_1	3,662.879	62.8826	62.8801	5.70

TABLE 7g-7. THE SPECTRUM OF MERCURY I (*Continued*)

Classification		λ (Hg nat.)	λ Hg^{198}	λ Hg^{202}	log *I*
6^3P_2	6^1D	3,663.2793	63.2808	63.2778	6.35
6^1P	9^1D	3,704.1655	04.1698	04.1712	3.94
6^1P	8^1D	3,906.371	06.3715	06.3715	4.56
6^3P_0	7^3S	4,046.5630	46.5712*	46.5619	7.09
6^3P_1	7^1S	4,077.8314	77.8379	77.8284	6.00
6^1P	9^1S	4,108.054	08.0574	08.0572	
6^1P	7^3D_2	4,339.2232	39.2244	39.2251	4.74
6^1P	7^1D	4,347.4945	47.4958	47.4967	5.17
6^3P_1	7^3S	4,358.3277	58.3372*	58.3257	7.07
6^1P	8^1S	4,916.068	16.0681	16.0677	4.35
6^3P_2	7^3S	5,460.7348	60.7532 *S*	60.7355	6.76
6^1P_1	6^3D_2	5,769.5982	69.5985 *S*	69.6000	6.02
6^1P_1	6^3D_1	5,789.664	89.669	89.671	4.41
6^1P	6^1D_2	5,790.6630	90.6629 *S*	90.6648	5.97
7^3S	8^1P	....	6,072.7128	72.6260	
7^1S	9^1P	....	6,234.4020	34.3776	
7^1S	8^1P	....	6,716.4289	16.3253	
7^3S	8^3P_2	6,907.52 *O*	07.4612	07.4675	
7^3S	8^3P_1	7,082.01 *O*			
7^3S	8^3P_0	7,092.20 *O*			
6^1P	7^1S	10,139.75 *O*	....	....	6.20
7^3S	7^3P_2	11,287.04 *O*	....	....	5.98
7^1S	7^1P	13,570.70 *O*	....	....	5.36
7^3S	7^3P_1	13,673.09 *O*	....	....	5.53
7^3S	7^3P_0	13,950.75 *O*	....	....	5.26
		15,295.25 *O*	....	....	5.78
6^1D	5^1F	16,918.3 *O*			
7^3P_2	7^3D_3	16,920.97 *O*			
6^3D_1	5^4F_2	16,942.33 *O*	....	....	4.72
7^3P_2	7^1D	17,072.67 *O*			4.90
6^3D_2	5^3F_3	17,109.57 *O*			4.74
6^3D_3	5^3F_4	17,202.08 *O*			
7^3P_0	8^3S	22,499.29 *O*			
7^3P_1	8^3S	23,253.47 *O*	....	....	4.49
7^3P_2	8^3S	36,261 *O*			

Values obtained by Blank[1] for Hg^{198} are 3,650.1569, 4,046.5716, and 4,358.3376.

Intensities are rough photoelectric values obtained at The Johns Hopkins University with a low-pressure neon-mercury discharge. The scale is the same as for neon (Table 7g-2). Intensities may be considerably different for other discharge conditions.

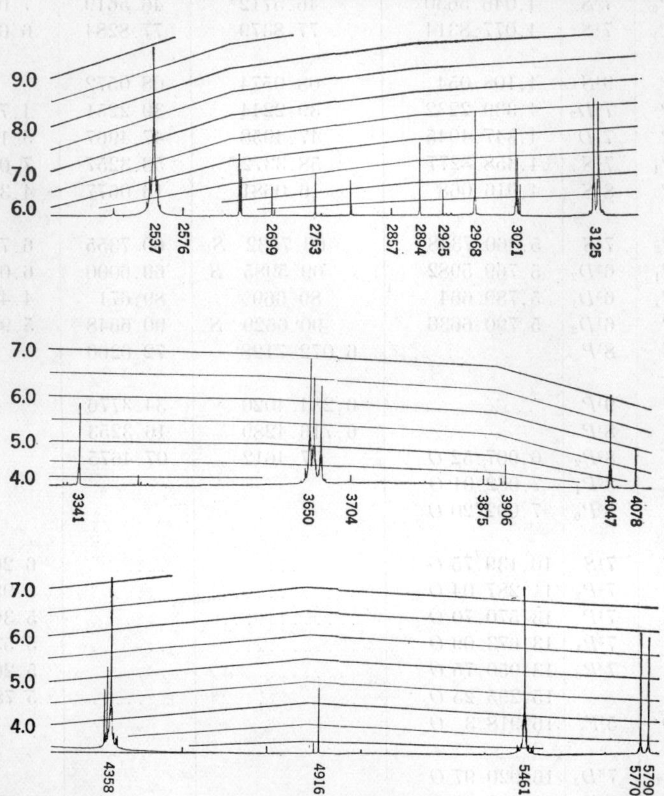

FIG. 7g-7. Photoelectric traces of the mercury spectrum, low-pressure mercury tube, 60-cps discharge. Wavelength range 2,400–5,800 A. In order to bring out the weaker lines, the sensitivity was increased so that the ghosts of the strong lines show.

Notes on Table 7g-7. All wavelengths are interferometric values by Burns,[2] except where otherwise noted.

Those marked *O* (natural mercury) are older values, sometimes of questionable accuracy. The values of Hg^{198} marked by * or *S* are averages, the latter proposed for international standards.

[1] Blank, *J. Opt. Soc. Am.* **40,** 345 (1950).

[2] Burns, Adams, and Longwell, *J. Opt. Soc. Am.* **40,** 339 (1950); Burns and Adams, *J. Opt. Soc. Am.* **42,** 56 (1952); **42,** 716 (1952).

7h. Data on Characteristic X-ray Spectra

X-ray wavelengths have been measured in two kinds of units. The older measurements are given in X units (XU) which are based on the effective lattice constant of rock salt being 2,814.00 XU. More recently X-ray wavelengths have been directly connected, through measurements with ruled gratings, to the wavelengths in the optical region and through them to the standard meter. It turned out that the XU which was originally intended as 10^{-11} cm was 0.202 per cent larger than this value. It has become customary to give X-ray wavelengths in Angstrom units (A) when the absolute scale is used (1 A = 10^{-8} cm). The two are related by

$$1{,}000 \text{ XU} = (1.00202 \pm 0.00003) \text{ A}$$

and wavelengths given in XU must be multiplied by 1.00202 and then divided by 1,000 in order to convert them into Angstrom units.

In the following tables the wavelengths are in general expressed in XU/1,000 and should be multiplied by the conversion factor, therefore, in order to convert them to absolute Angstroms.

The terminology of X-ray levels and lines is shown in Fig. 7h-1.

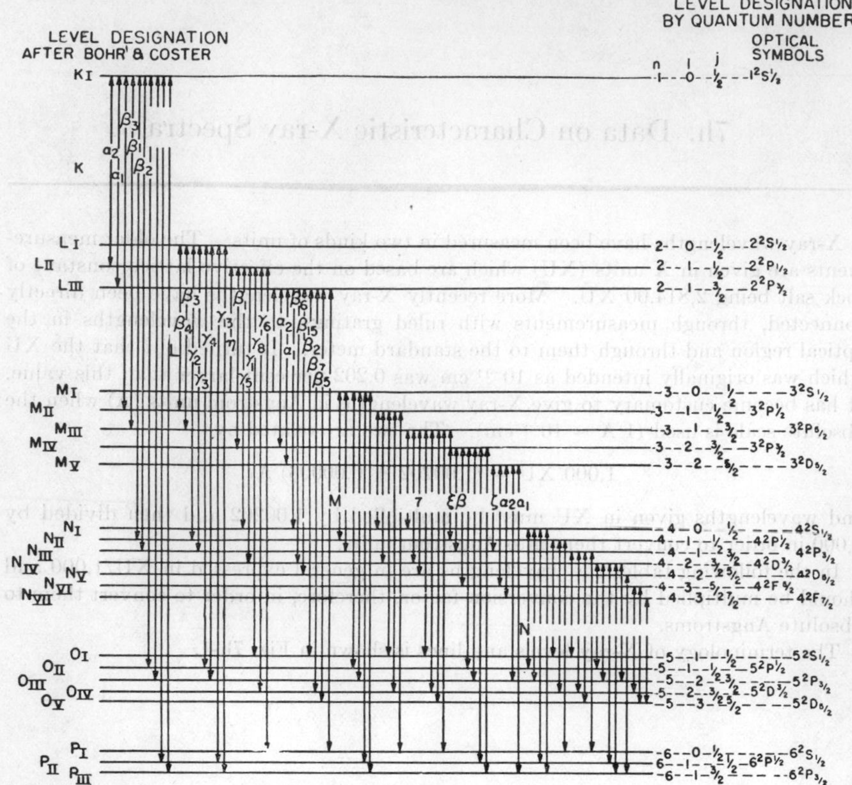

FIG. 7h-1. Energy-level diagrams of X-ray spectra.

TABLE 7h-1. WAVELENGTHS OF K SERIES LINES REPRESENTING TRANSITIONS IN THE ORDINARY X-RAY ENERGY-LEVEL DIAGRAM ALLOWED BY THE SELECTION PRINCIPLES*

Siegbahn	$K\alpha_2$	$K\alpha_1$	$K\beta$	$K\beta_1$	$K\beta_2$
Sommerfeld	$K\alpha'$	$K\alpha$	$K\beta_3$	$K\beta$	$K\gamma$
transition	K–L_{II}	K–L_{III}	K–M_{II}	K–M_{III}	K–$L_{II}N_{III}$
4 Be	115.7				
5 B	67.71				
6 C	44.54				
7 N	31.557				
8 O	23.567				
9 F	18.275				
11 Na	11.885		11.594		
12 Mg	9.869		9.539		
13 Al	8.3205		7.965		
14 Si	7.11106		6.7545		
15 P	6.1425		5.7921		
16 S	5.3637	5.3613	5.0211		
17 Cl	4.7212	4.7182	4.3942		
19 K	3.73707	3.73368	3.4468		
20 Ca	3.35495	3.35169	3.0834		
21 Sc	3.02840	3.02503	2.7739		
22 Ti	2.74681	2.74317	2.5090		
23 V	2.50213	2.49835	2.2797		
24 Cr	2.28891	2.28503	2.0806		
25 Mn	2.10149	2.09751	1.90620		
26 Fe	1.936012	1.932076	1.753013		
27 Co	1.78919	1.78529	1.61744		
28 Ni	1.65835	1.65450	1.47905		1.48561
29 Cu	1.541232	1.537395	1.38935		1.37824
30 Zn	1.43603	1.43217	1.29255		1.28107
31 Ga	1.34087	1.33715	1.20520		1.1938
32 Ge	1.25521	1.25130	1.12671		1.11459
33 As	1.17743	1.17344	1.05510		1.04281
34 Se	1.10652	1.10248	0.99013		0.97791
35 Br	1.04166	1.03759	0.93087		0.91853
36 Kr	0.9821	0.9781	0.8767		0.8643
37 Rb	0.92776	0.92364	0.82749	0.82696	0.81476
38 Sr	0.87761	0.87345	0.78183	0.78130	0.76921
39 Y	0.83132	0.82712	0.73972	0.73919	0.72713
40 Zr	0.78851	0.78430	0.70083	0.70028	0.68850
41 Nb	0.74889	0.74465	0.66496	0.66438	0.65280
42 Mo	0.712105	0.707831	0.631543	0.630978	0.619698
43 Tc	0.675	0.672	0.601		
44 Ru	0.64606	0.64174	0.57193	0.57131	0.56051
45 Rh	0.61637	0.61202	0.54509	0.54449	0.53396
46 Pd	0.58863	0.58427	0.52009	0.51947	0.50918
47 Ag	0.56267	0.55828	0.49665	0.49601	0.48603
48 Cd	0.53832	0.53390	0.47471	0.47408	0.46420
49 In	0.51548	0.51106	0.45423	0.45358	0.44408

TABLE 7h-1. WAVELENGTHS OF K SERIES LINES REPRESENTING TRANSITIONS IN THE ORDINARY X-RAY ENERGY-LEVEL DIAGRAM ALLOWED BY THE SELECTION PRINCIPLES* (*Continued*)

Siegbahn Sommerfeld transition	$K\alpha_2$ $K\alpha$ $K–L_{II}$	$K\alpha_1$ $K\alpha$ $K–L_{III}$	$K\beta$ $K\beta_3$ $K–M_{II}$	$K\beta_1$ $K\beta_1$ $K–M_{III}$	$K\beta_2$ $K\gamma$ $K–L_{II}N_{III}$
50 Sn	0.49402	0.48957	0.43495	0.43430	0.42499
51 Sb	0.47387	0.46931	0.41623		0.40710
52 Te	0.45491	0.45037	0.39926		0.39037
53 I	0.43703	0.43249	0.38292	0.38315	0.37471
54 Xe	0.417		0.360		
55 Cs	0.40411	0.39959	0.35436	0.35360	0.34516
56 Ba	0.38899	0.38443	0.34089	0.34022	0.33222
57 La	0.37466	0.37004	0.32809	0.32726	0.31966
58 Ce	0.36110	0.35647	0.31572	0.31501	0.30770
59 Pr	0.34805	0.34340	0.30439	0.30360	0.29625
60 Nd	0.33595	0.33125	0.29351	0.29275	0.28573
62 Sm	0.31302	0.30833	0.27325	0.27250	0.26575
63 Eu	0.30265	0.29790	0.26386	0.26307	0.25645
64 Gd	0.29261	0.28782	0.25471	0.25394	0.24762
65 Tb	0.28286	0.27820	0.24629	0.24551	0.23912
66 Dy	0.27375	0.26903	0.23787	0.23710	0.23128
67 Ho	0.26499	0.26030			
68 Er	0.25664	0.25197	0.22300	0.22215	0.21671
69 Tm	0.24861	0.24387	0.21558	0.21487	
70 Yb	0.24098	0.23628	0.20916	0.20834	0.20322
71 Lu	0.23358	0.2282	0.20252	0.20171	0.19649
72 Hf	0.22653	0.22173	0.19583	0.19515	0.19042
73 Ta	0.21973	0.21488	0.18991		0.18452
74 W	0.21337	0.20856	0.18475	0.18397	0.17906
76 Os	0.20131	0.19645	0.17361		0.16875
77 Ir	0.19550	0.19065	0.16850		0.16376
78 Pt	0.19004	0.18223	0.16370		0.15887
79 Au	0.18483	0.17996	0.15902		0.15426
81 Tl	0.17466	0.16980	0.15011		0.14539
82 Pb	0.17004	0.16516	0.14606		0.14125
83 Bi	0.16525	0.16041	0.14205		0.13621
92 U	0.13095	0.12640	0.11187		0.10842

* From "Smithsonian Physical Tables," and A. H. Compton, and S. K., Allison, "X-rays in Theory and Experiment," D. Van Nostrand Company, Inc., Princeton, N. J., 1935.

TABLE 7h-2. WAVELENGTHS OF THE MORE PROMINENT L GROUP LINES*

Siegbahn Sommerfeld transition	α_2 α' L_{III}–M_{IV}	α_1 α L_{III}–M_V	β_1 β L_{II}–M_V	l ϵ L_{III}–M_I	η η L_{II}–M_I
16 S	....		....	83.75	
20 Ca	36.27		....	40.90	
21 Sc	31.37		....	35.71	
22 Ti	27.37		....	31.33	
23 V	24.31		....	27.70	
24 Cr	21.53		21.19	23.84	23.28
25 Mn	19.40		19.04	22.34	
26 Fe	17.57		17.23	20.09	19.76
27 Co	15.93		15.63	18.25	17.86
28 Ni	14.53		14.25	16.66	16.28
29 Cu	13.306		13.027	15.26	14.87
30 Zn	12.229		11.960	13.97	13.61
31 Ga	11.27		11.01	12.89	12.56
32 Ge	10.415		10.153	11.922	11.587
33 As	9.652		9.395	11.048	10.711
34 Se	8.972		8.718	10.272	9.939
35 Br	8.358		8.109	9.564	9.235
37 Rb	7.3027				
38 Sr	6.8486		6.610	7.822	7.506
39 Y	6.4357		6.2039	....	7.0310
				β_2 γ L_{III}–N_V	γ_1 δ L_{II}–N_{IV}
40 Zr	6.057		5.8236	5.5742	5.3738
41 Nb	5.718	5.7120	5.4803	5.2260	5.0248
42 Mo	5.401	5.3950	5.1665	4.9100	
44 Ru	4.8437	4.8357	4.6110	4.3619	4.1728
45 Rh	4.5956	4.5878	4.3640	4.1221	3.9357
46 Pd	4.3666	4.3585	4.1373	3.9007	3.7164
47 Ag	4.1538	4.1456	3.9266	3.6938	3.5149
48 Cd	3.9564	3.9478	3.7301	3.5064	3.3280
49 In	3.7724	3.7637	3.5478	3.3312	3.1553
50 Sn	3.60151	3.59257	3.3779	3.16861	2.99494
51 Sb	3.4408	3.4318	3.2184	3.0166	2.8451
52 Te	3.2910	3.2820	3.0700	2.8761	2.7065
53 I	3.1509	3.1417	2.9309	2.7461	2.5775
55 Cs	2.8956	2.8861	2.6778	2.5064	2.3425
56 Ba	2.7790	2.7696	2.5622	2.3993	2.2366
57 La	2.6689	2.6597	2.4533	2.2980	2.1372
58 Ce	2.5651	2.5560	2.3510	2.2041	2.0443
59 Pr	2.4676	2.4577	2.2539	2.1148	1.9568
60 Nd	2.3756	2.3653	2.1622	2.0314	1.8738
62 Sm	2.2057	2.1950	1.9936	1.8781	1.7231
63 Eu	2.1273	2.1163	1.9163	1.8082	1.6543

TABLE 7h-2. WAVELENGTHS OF THE MORE PROMINENT L GROUP LINES* (*Continued*)

Siegbahn Sommerfeld transition	α_2 α' $L_{III}-M_{IV}$	α_1 α $L_{III}-M_V$	β_1 β $L_{II}-M_V$	l ϵ $L_{III}-M_I$	η η $L_{II}-M_I$
64 Gd	2.0526	2.0419	1.8425	1.7419	1.5886
65 Tb	1.9823	1.9715	1.7727	1.6790	1.5266
66 Dy	1.9156	1.9046	1.7066	1.6198	1.4697
67 Ho	1.8521	1.8410	1.6435	1.5637	1.4142
68 Er	1.79202	1.78068	1.58409	1.51094	1.3611
69 Tm	1.7339	1.7228	1.5268	1.4602	1.3127
70 Yb	1.67942	1.66844	1.4725	1.41261	1.26512
71 Lu	1.6270	1.61617	1.42067	1.36731	1.21974
72 Hf	1.57704	1.56607	1.3711	1.3235	1.1765
73 Ta	1.52978	1.51885	1.32423	1.28190	1.13558
74 W	1.48438	1.47336	1.27917	1.24203	1.09630
75 Re	1.4410	1.42997	1.23603	1.2041	1.0587
76 Os	1.39866	1.38859	1.19490	1.16884	1.02296
77 Ir	1.3598	1.34847	1.15540	1.13297	0.98876
78 Pt	1.32155	1.31033	1.11758	1.09974	0.95599
79 Au	1.28502	1.27377	1.08128	1.06801	0.92461
80 Hg	1.24951	1.23863	1.04652	1.03770	0.8946
81 Tl	1.21626	1.20493	1.01299	1.00822	0.86571
82 Pb	1.18408	1.17258	0.98083	0.98083	0.83801
83 Bi	1.15301	1.14150	0.95002	0.95324	0.81143
90 Th	0.96585	0.95405	0.76356	0.79192	0.65176
91 Pa	0.9427	0.9309	0.7407	0.7721	0.6325
92 U	0.92062	0.90874	0.71851	0.75307	0.61359

* From "Smithsonian Physical Tables."

TABLE 7h-3. WAVELENGTHS OF *M* SERIES LINES FROM 73 Ta TO 92 U*

Transition	73 Ta	74 W	75 Re	76 Os	77 Ir	78 Pt	79 Au	81 Tl	82 Pb	83 Bi	90 Th	92 U
$M_{II}O_{IV}$	.....	.....	.....	.....	.....	.....	.....	.....	.....	.....	2.613	2.440
$M_{I}N_{III}$	.....	5.163	.....	.....	.....	4.451	4.291	4.005	3.864	3.732	2.938	2.745
$M_{II}N_{IV}$	5.558	5.342	.....	4.944	4.770	4.590	4.424	4.110	3.964	3.829	3.006	2.813
$M_{III}O_{V}$	.....	.....	.....	.....	4.859	4.682	4.514	4.207	4.063	3.926	3.124	2.941
$M_{III}O_{I}$	.....	5.620	.....	.....	.....	.....	.....	.....	4.235	4.096	.....	3.114
$M_{II}N_{I}$	.....	.....	.....	.....	.....	.....	.....	.....	.....	.....	.....	3.322
γ'	.....	.....	.....	.....	.....	.....	.....	4.800	4.650	4.506	3.661	3.463
$M_{III}N_{V}$	6.299	6.076	5.875	5.670	5.490	5.309	5.135	4.815	4.665	4.522	3.672	3.473
$M_{III}N_{IV}$	6.340	6.121	5.919	5.712	5.529	5.346	5.175	4.855	4.705	4.560	3.710	3.514
$M_{IV}O_{II}$	7.083	6.794	.....	.....	.....	.....	.....	.....	.....	4.813	3.804	3.570
β'	6.984	6.718	.....	6.233	6.009	5.796	5.595	5.220	5.045	4.881	3.924	3.698
$M_{IV}N_{VI}$	7.008	6.743	6.491	6.254	6.025	5.8168	5.612	5.239	5.065	4.899	3.934	3.708
$M_{V}O_{III}$	.....	.....	.....	.....	.....	5.975	5.755					
α''	7.201	6.932	.....	6.440	6.215	5.997	5.794	5.416	5.239			
α'	7.219	6.948	.....	6.459	6.231	6.011	5.811	5.433	5.256	5.087	4.112	3.886
$M_{V}N_{VII}$	7.237	6.969	6.715	6.477	6.249	6.034	5.828	5.450	5.274	5.108	4.130	3.902
$M_{V}N_{VI}$	.....	.....	.....	.....	6.262	6.045	5.842	5.461	5.288	5.119	4.143	3.916
$M_{III}N_{I}$	7.596	7.346	.....	.....	6.653	6.442	6.241	5.870	5.694	5.526	4.554	4.322
$M_{IV}N_{III}$	.....	8.559	8.222	.....	7.629	7.356	7.086	.....	6.371	6.149	4.901	4.615
$M_{V}N_{III}$	9.297	8.943	8.612	8.293	8.002	7.722	7.451	6.960	6.726	6.508	5.229	4.937
$M_{IV}N_{II}$	9.311	8.977	8.646	8.344	8.048	7.774	7.507	7.017	6.788	6.571	5.329	5.040

* E. Lindberg, Dissertation, Uppsala, 1931. From "Smithsonian Physical Tables."

TABLE 7h-4. CRITICAL ABSORPTION WAVELENGTHS*

	K	L_{I}	L_{II}	L_{III}	M_{I}	M_{II}	M_{III}	M_{IV}	M_{V}	Longer wavelengths
1 H										
2 He	504.29									
3 Li										
4 Be	....	1,329.89								
5 B	64.3									
6 C	43.5									
7 N	31.1									
8 O	23.5									
9 F	18.0									
10 Ne	....	255.77	572.4	574.9						
11 Na										
12 Mg	9.4962	....	....	....	1,621.48					
13 Al	7.9356	....	181							
14 Si	6.7310	....	126							
15 P	5.7749	....	96.4							
16 S	5.0088	....	75.7							
17 Cl	4.3838	....	60.9							
18 A	3.8657	....	50.1		424.03	778.0	786.8			
19 K	3.4310									N_{I}
20 Ca	3.0643	....	35.63		....	......	....	....	....	2,028.20
21 Sc	2.7517									
22 Ti	2.4912	....	27.29							
23 V	2.2630									
24 Cr	2.0659									
25 Mn	1.8916									
26 Fe	1.7394									
27 Co	1.6040									
28 Ni	1.4839									
29 Cu	1.3774	....	12.9	13.15						N_{I}
30 Zn	1.2805	....	....	....	....	......	....	708.18	722.08	1,319.84

31 Ga	1.1902											
32 Ge	1.1164											
33 As	1.04263											
34 Se	0.97773											
35 Br	0.91809									N_{II}	N_{III}	
36 Kr	0.86372	....	....	....	....	....	....	....	....	845.42	855.63	
37 Rb	0.81410	5.9854	....	6.8413						O_I		
38 Sr	0.76837	5.5713	6.1621	6.3620	....	....	....	....	....	2,177.46		
39 Y	0.7255	5.2216	5.7373	5.9444								
40 Zr	0.68738	4.8574	5.3659	5.5610								
41 Nb	0.65158	4.5717	....	5.2121								
42 Mo	0.61848	4.2897	4.7120	4.9042								
43 Tc												
44 Ru	0.5584	....	4.1648	4.3577								
45 Rh	0.53303	3.61860	3.9340	4.1212						N_{IV}	N_V	
46 Pd	0.50795	3.4206	3.7512	3.9005	....	....	....	....	....	1,412.92	1,487.30	
47 Ag	0.48448	3.2474	3.5067	3.6908	....	....	....	30.82	31.14	N_V	N_{VI}	O_I
48 Cd	0.46313	3.0773	3.3192	3.4963	....	....	....	28.13		678.28	705.23	1,378.57
49 In	0.44298	2.9194	3.1395	3.3155								
50 Sn	0.42394	2.7696	2.9723	3.1493	....	....	....	24.28				
51 Sb	0.40609	2.6317	2.8219	2.9907								
52 Te	0.38926	2.5039	2.6793	2.8457				19.66		$O_{II,III}$		
53 I	0.37344	2.3839	2.5475	2.7139	....	....	....			1,022.13		
54 Xe	0.35777	2.2691	2.4241	2.5872								
55 Cs	0.34404	2.1605	2.3073	2.4678						P_I		
56 Ba	0.33070	2.0620	2.1993	2.3568	....	....	....	15.56	15.89	2,379.29		
57 La	0.31814	1.9689	2.0989	2.2537								
58 Ce	0.30626	1.8856	2.0067	2.1579								
59 Pr	0.2951	1.808	1.9197	2.0727								
60 Nd	0.28458	1.7317	1.8391	1.9907								
61 Pm												
62 Sm	0.2644	1.5954	1.6991	1.8408								
63 Eu	0.2548	1.5333	1.6228	1.7717								
64 Gd	0.2462	1.4740	1.5587	1.7062								
65 Tb	0.2376	1.4181	1.4981	1.6453								

* From "Smithsonian Physical Tables."

Table 7h-4. Critical Absorption Wavelengths (*Continued*)

	K	L_{I}	L_{II}	L_{III}	M_{I}	M_{II}	M_{III}	M_{IV}	M_{V}	Longer wavelengths		
66 Dy	0.2301	1.3648	1.4414	1.5870								
67 Ho	0.22264	1.3146	1.3869	1.5322								
68 Er	......	1.2660	1.3349	1.4796								
69 Tm	0.2085	1.2196	1.2849	1.4299								
70 Yb	0.2016	1.1764	1.2381	1.38264								
71 Lu	0.1951	1.1362	1.1945	1.3377								
72 Hf	0.1901	1.097	1.1515	1.2930								
73 Ta	0.1836	1.057	1.1102	1.2517								
74 W	0.17822	1.0205	1.0713	1.2116	4.365	4.800	5.427	6.487	6.702			
75 Re	0.1735	0.9873	1.0354	1.1755								
76 Os	0.16755	0.9558	0.9998	1.1390	4.037	4.412	5.027	5.975	6.194			
77 Ir	0.16209	0.9223	0.9654	1.1038	....	4.270	4.851	5.754	5.961			
78 Pt	0.15770	0.8914	0.9321	1.0710	3.603	3.738	4.676	5.544	5.746			
79 Au	0.15320	0.8622	0.9009	1.0382	3.742	4.085	4.508	5.330	5.529	O_{IV}	O_{V}	P_{I}
80 Hg	0.14893	0.8342	0.8708	1.0075	....	....	4.340	5.139	5.331	742.22	835.47	1,187.95
81 Tl	0.14441	0.8072	0.8419	0.9778	....	....	4.184	4.936	5.136			
82 Pb	0.14049	0.7812	0.8143	0.9492	....	....	4.034	4.747	4.945			
83 Bi	0.13678	0.7559	0.7878	0.9221	....	....	3.893	4.568	4.762			
84 Po												
85 At										$P_{II,III}$		
86 Rn	......	......	......	......	....	....	....	....	....	1,153.52		
87 Fr												
88 Ra	......	......	0.670	0.802								
89 Ac												
90 Th	0.11270	0.6039	0.6293	0.7600	2.388	2.571	3.062	3.550	3.722			
91 Pa												
92 U	0.10658	0.5680	0.5913	0.7208	2.228	2.385	2.877	2.327	3.491			

TABLE 7h-5. ENERGY LEVELS OF X-RAY SPECTRA*
[Units ν/R (R = 109,737.3 cm^{-1})]

	K	L_{I}	L_{II}	L_{III}	M_{I}	M_{II}	M_{III}	M_{IV}	M_{V}
2 He	**1.8**								
3 Li	**3.6**								
4 Be	**8.2**	0.7							
5 B	**14.2**								
6 C	**21.04**								
7 N	**29.4**	......	0.4						
8 O	**39.3**	......	0.7						
9 F	**50.6**	......	0.9						
10 Ne	**64.0**	3.56	1.59	1.58					
11 Na	**78.93**	4.678	2.263	2.248	....	0.048			
12 Mg	**96.0**	6.513	3.658	3.638	....	0.5			
13 Al	**114.8**	8.485	5.372	5.343	....	0.4			
14 Si	**135.4**	11.0	7.378	7.325	....	0.5			
15 P	**157.8**	13.6	9.68	9.60	....	0.5			
16 S	**181.9**	16.5	12.11	12.02	1.23	0.4			
17 Cl	**207.91**	19.8	14.9	14.8	1.4	0.5			
18 Ar	**235.7**	......	18.1	17.9	....	...	0.8		
19 K	**265.6**	27.7	21.7	21.5	2.40	1.2		0.26	
20 Ca	**297.4**	32.3	25.8	25.5	3.22	1.9		0.37	0.38

* From Landolt Börnstein, "Zahlenwerte und Funktionen," 6th ed., vol. I, Springer-Verlag OHG, Berlin, 1950. For literature references, see this volume.

Values given in heavy type represent the most reliable measurements.

TABLE 7h-5. ENERGY LEVELS OF X-RAY SPECTRA (*Continued*)

	K	L_{I}	L_{II}	L_{III}	M_{I}	M_{II}	M_{III}	M_{IV}	M_{V}	N_{I}	N_{II}	N_{III}	N_{IV}	N_{V}	Y_{I}	Y_{II}
21 Sc	**331.2**	37.2	30.3	30.0	4.27	2.7		0.81								
								0.77								
22 Ti	**365.8**	41.5	34.0	33.6	4.48	2.6		0.24								
								0.31								
23 Va	**402.7**	46.4	38.5	37.9	5.05	3.0		0.19								
								0.37								
24 Cr	**441.1**	51.4	43.0	42.3	5.40	3.1		0.05								
								0.15								
25 Mn	**481.9**	57.2	48.3	47.4	6.36	3.8		0.44								
								0.47								
26 Fe	**523.9**	62.5	53.2	52.2	6.95	4.1		0.31								
								0.37								
27 Co	**568.1**	......	58.8	57.7	7.73	4.7		0.42								
								0.49								
28 Ni	**614.1**	74.8	64.6	63.2	8.53	5.4		0.51								
								0.53								
29 Cu	661.44	80.8	70.18	**68.703**	9.06	5.54		0.28								
								0.30								
30 Zn	711.79	88.5	77.21	**75.50**	10.30	6.77		0.80	.....	0.7	0.5					
								0.75								
31 Ga	**765.6**	......	86.0	84.1	11.89	9.5		1.45								
								1.72								
32 Ge	**817.6**	......	91.6	89.3	12.9	8.8		1.82	.....	.....	0					
								1.92								
33 As	874.05	112.62	100.08	**97.48**	15.00	10.37		3.08		....	0.2					
34 Se	932.17	......	108.60	**105.62**	16.91	.....	11.82	5.07	4.00	....	0.32					
35 Br	**992.6**	......	117.8	114.3	19.48	13.60	13.21	5.27	5.13	....	0.5					
36 Kr	**1,055.05**	......	127.18	123.38	.....	15.62					0.71					
37 Rb	1,119.65	152.65	137.43	**133.04**	23.86	18.41	17.69	8.39	8.26	2.28	1.22					
38 Sr	1,186.27	163.33	147.90	**142.97**	26.44	20.71	19.92	10.06	9.91	2.89	1.55		....	....	0.58	
39 Y	1,254.90	174.72	158.72	**153.16**	29.03	23.00	22.10	11.72	11.56	3.31	1.87					
40 Zr	1,325.45	186.27	169.78	**163.56**	31.57	25.14	24.16	13.32	13.14	3.66	1.93		0.1	0	1.16	0.40
41 Nb	**1,398.5**	198.9	181.7	174.7	34.7	28.11	26.91	15.48	15.26	4.52	2.67		0.62		1.70	0.50
42 Mo	1.473.29	211.22	193.60	**185.87**	37.43	30.35	29.07	17.21	16.97	4.82	2.73		....	0.5	1.73	0.33
44 Ru	1.629.01	237.54	218.49	**209.00**	43.07	35.69	33.97	20.86	20.55	5.50	3.24		0.16		2.20	0.46
45 Rh	1,710.12	251.26	231.60	**221.11**	46.07	38.35	36.49	22.84	22.49	5.84	3.50		0.00		....	0.21
46 Pd	1.793.46	265.37	245.21	**233.65**	49.27	41.07	39.04	24.97	24.59	6.29	3.67		0.09		2.17	0.30
47 Ag	1.879.33	280.42	259.67	**246.94**	52.98	44.49	42.21	27.56	27.13	7.15	4.28		0.45	0.36	2.32	0.16
													0.39			

TABLE 7h-5. ENERGY LEVEL OF X-RAY SPECTRA (*Continued*)

	K	L_{I}	L_{II}	L_{III}	M_{I}	M_{II}	M_{III}	M_{IV}	M_{V}	N_{I}	N_{II}	N_{III}	N_{IV}	N_{V}	N_{VI}	N_{VII}	O_{I}	O_{II}	O_{III}	O_{IV}	O_{V}	P_{I}	P_{II}	P_{III}	$P_{IV,V}$
48 Cd	1,967.41	296.02	274.58	**260.61**	56.79	48.01	45.49	30.30	29.81	7.99	4.99		0.83	0.77	....	....	.....	0.28	0.18						
49 In	2,057.75	312.04	289.98	**274.67**	60.74	51.66	48.87	33.14	32.59	8.92	5.60		1.21	1.15	....	....	.....	0.01							
50 Sn	2,150.70	328.82	306.08	**289.34**	65.07	55.70	52.60	36.31	35.69	10.07	6.45		1.82	1.76	....	....	0	0.05							
51 Sb	2,245.84	346.07	322.67	**304.38**	69.55	59.83	56.42	39.59	38.88	11.28	7.27		2.45	2.36	....	....	.....	0.15							
52 Te	2,343.25	363.81	339.74	**319.79**	74.14	64.09	60.33	42.94	42.17	12.44	8.13		3.09	2.96	....	....	.....	0.19							
53 J	2,443.15	382.25	357.48	**335.78**	79.10	68.68	64.56	46.63	45.76	13.86	9.15		3.88	3.78	....	....	.....	0.38							
54 X	2,547.37	401.02	375.74	**352.18**	......	......	69.21	....	....	.....	10.13		.....	.....	....	....	.....	0.8							
55 Cs	2,650.3	421.34	394.64	**369.10**	89.55	78.90	73.91	54.40	53.37	16.90	13.14	12.33	5.71	5.52	....	....	1.6	0.97	0.84						
56 Ba	2,757.6	441.62	414.18	**386.45**	95.18	84.22	78.69	58.55	57.43	18.59	14.61	13.71	7.20	6.93	....	....	2.9	1.62	1.45						
57 La	2,867.5	461.4	434.7	**404.4**	101.0	88.5	82.5	63.1	61.8	20.6	15.0	14.9	8.3	7.8	0.4		3.0	0.9							
58 Ce	2,797.1	482.9	454.4	**421.9**	106.0	94.2	87.7	66.7	65.4	21.7	17.0	15.8	8.6	8.5	0.2		3.2	2.1							
59 Pr	3,093.1	503.6	474.8	**439.6**	111.5	98.6	91.7	70.4	68.8	22.8	17.6	16.3	9.1	8.7	....	....	3.1	1.6							
60 Nd	3,209.6	525.5	495.6	**457.8**	116.6	104.1	96.1	74.2	72.5	23.8	18.5	17.1	9.3	9.2	....	....	3.1	2.0							
62 Sm	3,451	570.3	538.9	**495.0**	127.2	113.8	104.9	81.7	79.8	25.7	20.0	18.6	10.0	9.8	....	....	3.0	1.9							
63 Eu	3,573	593.6	561.6	**514.4**	133.3	119.5	109.6	86.1	83.8	27.2	21.9	19.6	10.7	10.5	....	....	2.9								
64 Gd	3,700	617.5	585.0	**534.1**	139.1	124.7	114.2	90.3	87.7	28.6	22.3	20.4	11.4	11.0	....	....	4.2	2.5							
65 Tb	3,830	641.8	608.3	**553.9**	145.1	130.2	118.8	94.2	91.7	29.4	23.5	21.4	11.4	11.2	....	....	3.5	1.8							
66 Dy	3,961	666.8	632.5	**574.2**	150.0	136.0	123.7	98.6	95.8	31.1	25.2	22.3	12.5	11.6	0.8	....	3.1	2.3							
67 Ho	4,096	692.0	656.9	**594.7**	156.9	141.5	128.1	102.6	99.7	32.1	25.7	22.7	12.5	12.0	0.8	0.2	.....	1.5							
68 Er	4,233	718.5	682.8	**615.9**	163.6	147.7	133.6	107.3	104.1	33.2	27.3	23.8	13.9	12.6	0.9	0.3	4.0	2.8							
69 Tm	4,370.6	746.8	708.8	**637.3**	170.3	155.5	140.2	111.7	108.4	34.4	30.0	26.6	14.5	13.2	0.9	0.4									
70 Yb	4,516	772.9	735.5	**659.2**	176.9	160.6	144.2	116.5	112.9	36.2	29.4	25.8	15.0	14.2	0.9	0.6	5.5	1.9							
71 Cp	4 664	800.9	762.5	**681.2**	183.6	166.8	149.4	121.0	117.4	37.0	30.7	26.9	15.7	14.6	1.0	0.7	4.3	2.3							
72 Hf	4,813.59	829.74	790.73	**703.95**	191.29	173.99	154.99	126.17	122.17	39.39	31.98	27.76	16.22	15.49	2.39		4.52	2.58	2.03	0.24					
73 Ta	4,965.5	860.12	819.93	**727.51**	199.18	181.55	161.34	131.81	127.52	41.37	34.06	29.55	17.51	16.71	1.52		4.99	3.05	2.43	0.14					
74 W	5,120.3	890.64	849.75	**751.25**	207.17	189.20	167.58	137.36	132.76	43.38	35.70	30.79	18.57	17.58	1.99		5.19	2.96	2.20	0					
75 Re	5,279.02	922.43	880.64	**775.79**	215.77	197.24	174.15	143.39	138.53	45.88	37.92	32.57	19.99	19.02	2.8		5.96	3.16	2.37	0.11					
76 OS	5,440.88	955.04	912.17	**800.67**	224.50	205.60	180.90	149.50	144.29	48.19	40.09	34.39	21.32	20.09	3.41		6.18	4.16	3.21	0.02					
77 Ir	5,605.5	987.9	944.2	**825.6**	233.2	213.7	187.4	155.3	149.8	50.3	42.0	35.8	22.6	21.4	4.3	3.9	6.6	3.4							
78 Pt	5,773.8	1,021.92	977.41	**851.47**	242.60	222.46	194.73	162.01	156.01	53.06	44.51	37.82	24.24	22.84	5.15		7.29	4.51	3.51	0					
79 Au	5,945.4	1,056.94	1,011.33	**877.70**	252.11	231.77	201.78	168.54	162.26	55.85	47.13	40.13	25.87	24.47	6.3	5.7	7.79	5.1	3.8	0.08	0.04				
80 Hg	6,115.9	1,093.3	1,046.9	**905.0**	262.5	241.7	209.8	176.0	169.3	59.3	50.2	42.7	28.3	26.7	7.8	6.9	9.2	....		1.1	0.8				
81 Tl	6,299.6	1,130.48	1,082.68	**932.41**	272.99	251.82	217.96	183.22	176.12	62.47	53.42	45.18	30.15	28.63	8.7	8.4	9.3	7.47	5.75	1.25					
82 Pb	6,482.6	1,169.06	1,120.23	**960.88**	284.41	262.73	226.79	191.27	183.79	66.52	57.23	48.46	32.82	31.24	10.5	10.0	10.9	8.96	7.17	2.3					
83 Bi	6,668.23	1,207.60	1,157.71	**988.90**	295.10	272.88	234.69	198.53	190.62	69.64	59.98	50.67	34.74	32.90	12.33			0.26	7.54	2.54	2.34	....	1.0		
88 Ra	....	1,416.80	1,361.39	**1,137.54**	355.12	330.62	279.24	239.24	228.68	89.06	77.84	64.73	46.82	44.42	22.02		18.74	14.76	11.17	5.11	5.04	3.22	1.32		
90 Th	8,075.9	1,507.22	1,450.31	**1,200.48**	381.63	355.14	297.48	256.93	245.32	97.44	85.43	70.63	52.40	49.77	23.7	23.2	21.35	16.49	12.77	6.39		4.4	3.05		0.4
91 Pa	....	1,556.2	1.496.7	**1,232.5**	395.6	370.1	309.2	266.2	256.3	102.3	92.5	75.9	55.9	52.2	....	....	22.3	18.2		7.5					
92 U	8.515.0	1,602.44	1,542.73	**1,264.32**	408.66	381.66	316.90	274.42	261.51	106.00	93.69	76.79	57.43	54.36	28.5	27.6 / 27.98	23.94	18.86	13.59	7.12		5.32	2.04		0.27

7i. Constants and Energy Levels of Diatomic Molecules

7i-1. Constants of Diatomic Molecules

Explanation of Columns in Table 7i-1

1. Identification of molecule.
2. Mass numbers of the constituent atoms to which the data refer. If these are not specified, the naturally occurring isotope mixture is used.
3. Reduced mass μ in atomic units ($O^{16} = 16.0000$).
4. Designation of the normal state of the molecule.
5. $B = h/(8\pi^2 c\mu r_e^2)$ where r_e is the equilibrium distance.
6. α from $B_v = B - \alpha(v + \frac{1}{2})$; $-\alpha = Y_{11}$.
7. r_e equilibrium distance.
8. Vibrational frequency $\omega = Y_{10}$.
9. Anharmonic constant $-x = Y_{20}$, $E_v = \omega(v + \frac{1}{2}) - x(v + \frac{1}{2})^2$.
10. Dissociation energy D_0 in electron volts.

Uncertain quantities are enclosed in parentheses. Quantities listed within square brackets refer to the $v = 0$ state instead of the equilibrium state.

The data are derived mostly from molecular spectra (visible, infrared, or microwave); some are from X-ray or electron diffraction or thermochemical data. They have been chiefly taken from the compilation of Herzberg. For further details and literature references, see this compilation: G. Herzberg, "Spectra of Diatomic Molecules," D. Van Nostrand & Company, Inc., Princeton, N.J., 1950; also B. Rosen, "Données concernant les molécules diatomiques" (1951).

The constants in the expression for the potential energy,

$$V(r) = a_0(r - r_e)^2[1 + a_1(r - r_e)^2 + a_2(r - r_e)^2 + \cdot \cdot \cdot]$$

may be derived from the approximate expressions

$$\omega^2 = 4Ba_0 \qquad x = -\tfrac{3}{2}B(a_2 - \tfrac{5}{4}a_1^2)$$

$$\alpha = -\frac{6B^2}{\omega}(1 + a_1)$$

$$a_0 = \frac{\omega^2}{4B} \qquad a_1 = 1 - \frac{\alpha\omega}{6B^2} \qquad a_2 = -\frac{2x}{3B} + \frac{5}{4}a_1^2$$

TABLE 7i-1. CONSTANTS OF DIATOMIC MOLECULES*

	m_1	m_2	μ	Normal state	B	α	r_e	ω	x	D_0, electron volts
(1)	(2)		(3)	(4)	(5)	(6)	(7)	(8)	(9)	(10)
AgBr....	109	81	46.436	$^1\Sigma$?	....	....	....	247.42	0.6795	2 6
AgCl....	107	35	26.358	$^1\Sigma$?	....	....	....	343.6	1.163	3.1
AgH....	107	1	0.99880	$^1\Sigma^+$	6.543	0.203	1.617	1,760.0	34.05	2.5
AgI.....	107	127	58.0439	$^1\Sigma$?	....	....	....	206.18	0.4327	2.98_3
AgO.....	107	16	13.9340	$^2\Sigma^-$	....	....	....	493.2	4.10	(1.8)
AlBr....	27	79	20.1129	$^1\Sigma^+$	0.1591	8.53×10^{-4}	2.295	378.0	1.28	(2.47)
AlCl.....	27	35	15.2350	$^1\Sigma^+$	0.242	0.002	2.138	481.30	1.95	(3.1)
AlF.....	27	19	11.1521	$^1\Sigma^+$	....	....	....	814.5	8.1	(2.5)
AlH.....	27	1	0.971832	$^1\Sigma^+$	6.3962	0.188	1.6459_2	1,682.57	29.145	3.06
AlH⁺...	27	1	0.971831	$^2\Sigma^+$	6.763	0.398	1.601_6	1,610		
AlI.....	27	127	22.2578	$^1\Sigma^+$	....	....	....	316.1	1.0	(2.9)
AlO.....	27	16	10.0452	$^2\Sigma^+$	0.64148	0.00575	1.6176	978.2	7.12	3.75
As_2......	75	75	37.467	$^1\Sigma_g^+$	....	....	....	429.44	1.120	≤3.96
AsN.....	75	14	11.8015	$^1\Sigma^+$	....	....	....	1,068.0	5.36	(6.5)
AsO.....	75	16	13.1848	$^2\Pi$	....	....	....	967.4	5.3	≤5.0
AuCl....	197	35	29.7055	$^1\Sigma^+$?	....	....	....	382.8	1.30	3.5
AuH.....	197	1	1.002999	$^1\Sigma^+$	7.2401	0.2136	1.5237_3	2,305.01	43.12	3.1
B_2.......	11	11	5.50645	$^3\Sigma_g^-$	1.212	0.014	1.589	1,051.3	9.4	(3.6)
BaBr....	138	79	50.131	$^2\Sigma^+$	....	....	....	193.8	0.42	(2.8)
BaCl....	138	35	27.9022	$^2\Sigma$	....	....	....	279.3	0.89	(2.7)
BaF....	138	19	16.6953	$^2\Sigma$	....	....	....	468.9	1.79	(3.8)
BaH.....	138	1	1.000788	$^2\Sigma^+$	3.3823	0.0655	2.2318	1,172	16	≤1.82
BaI.....	138	127	65.979	$^2\Sigma$?	....	....	....			
BaO.....	138	16	14.3311	$^1\Sigma$	0.3126	0.0014	1.940	669.8	2.05	4.7
BaS.....	138	.....	26.004	....	....	....	....	....	......	(2.3)
BBr.....	11	79	9.6644	$^1\Sigma^+$	0.490	0.0035	1.887	684.31	3.52	(4.1)
BCl.....	11	35	8.37582	$^1\Sigma$	0.6838	0.00646	1.715_7	839.12	5.11	(4.2)
BeCl....	9	35	7.16766	$^2\Sigma^+$	(0.8)	....	(1.7)	846.58	5.11	(4.3)
BeF.....	9	19	6.11450	$^2\Sigma^+$	1.4877	0.01685	1.3614	1,265.6	9.12	(5.4)
BeH.....	9	1	0.906732	$^2\Sigma^+$	10.308	0.300	1.3431	2,058.6	35.5	(2.2)
BeH⁺....	9	1	0.906727	$^1\Sigma^+$	10.7996	0.2935	1.3121_6	2,221.7	39.79	(3.2)
BeO.....	9	16	5.76612	$^1\Sigma^+$	1.6510	0.0190	1.3308	1,487.323	11.8297	(3.7) (3.0)
BF......	11	19	6.97245	$^1\Sigma^+$	1.518	0.017	1.262	1,399.8	11.3	(4.3)
BH......	11	1	0.923585	$^1\Sigma^+$	12.018	0.412	1.2325	(2,366)	(49)	<3.51
BH⁺.....	11	1	0.923581	$^2\Sigma^+$	[12.374]	....	[1.2146]	2,435		
Bi_2......	209	209	104.528	$^1\Sigma_g^+$	....	....	....	172.71	0.3227	1.70
BiBr....	209	79	57.297	....	....	....	....	209.34	0.468	2.74
BiCl.....	209	35	29.9651	....	....	....	....	308.0	0.96	(3.0)
BiF.....	209	19	17.4209	....	....	....	....	510.7	2.05	(3.2)
BiH.....	209	1	1.00329	$^3\Sigma^-$?	5.137	0.148	1.809	1,698.9	31.6	(2.7)
BiI......	209	127	78.979	....	....	....	....	163.9	0.31	(2.7)
BiO.....	209	16	14.8625	....	....	....	....	702.1	5.20	(2.9)
BN......	11	14	6.16550	$^3\Pi$	1.666	0.025	1.281	1,514.6	12.3	(5.0)
BO......	11	16	6.52305	$^2\Sigma^+$	1.7803	0.01648	1.2049	1,885.44	11.769	(9.1)
Br_2......	79	81	39.958	$^1\Sigma_g^+$	0.08091	0.000275	2.283_6	323.2	1.07	1.971
BrCl....	79	35	24.567	$^1\Sigma^+$	....	....	....	....	......	2.26
BrF.....	79	19	15.3542	$^1\Sigma^+$	0.357165	0.005214	1.75555	671	3	2.19
BrO.....	79	16	13.3316	....	....	....	....	713	7	(2.2)
C_2......	12	12	6.00194	$^3\Pi_u$	1.6326	0.01683	1.3117	1,641.35	11.67	(3.6)
CaBr....	40	79	26.587	$^2\Sigma^+$	....	....	....	285.3	0.86	(2.9)
CaCl....	40	35	18.6804	$^2\Sigma^+$	[0.26]	....	[1.86]	369.8	1.31	≤2.76
CaF.....	40	19	12.88080	$^2\Sigma^+$	[0.322]	....	[2.02]	587.1	2.74	≤3.15
CaH.....	40	1	0.983332	$^2\Sigma$	4.2778	0.0963	2.0020	1,299	19.5	≤1.70
CaH⁺...	40	1	0.983332	$^1\Sigma$	[5.71]	....	[1.73]			
CaI.....	40	127	30.468	$^2\Sigma$?	....	....	....	242.0	0.64	(2.8)
CaO.....	40	16	10.4265	$^1\Sigma$	0.445	0.0033_5	1.822	732.1	4.81	5.9

* From G. Herzberg, "Spectra of Diatomic Molecules," 2d ed, D. Van Nostrand Company, Inc., Princeton, N. J., 1950.

TABLE 7i-1 CONSTANTS OF DIOMATIC MOLECULES (*Continued*)

	m_1	m_2	μ	Normal state	B	α	r_e	ω	x	D_0, electron volts
(1)	(2)		(3)	(4)	(5)	(6)	(7)	(8)	(9)	(10)
CaS	40	32	17.819	....	....	....	....	....	....	$\leq$5.2
CBr	12	.....	10.4367							
CCl	12	35	8.93694	$^2\Pi$	....	....	....	846	1.0	
Cd_2	112.4	112.4	56.221	....	....	....	....	....	....	0.087
CdBr	112.4	79	46.722	$^3\Sigma$	....	....	....	230.0	0.50	(3.3)
CdCl	112.4	35	26.6793	$^2\Sigma$	....	....	....	330.5	1.2	(2.8)
CdF	112.4	19	16.2568	$^2\Sigma$	....	....	....	(535)		
CdH	112.4	1	0.99917	$^2\Sigma^+$	5.437	0.218	1.762	1,430.7	46.3	0.678
CdH^+	112.4	1	0.99917	$^1\Sigma^+$	6.071	0.189	1.667	1,775.4	37.3	(2.0)
CdI	112.4	127	59.624	$^2\Sigma$	....	....	....	178.5	0.625	(1.6)
CdS	112.4	32	24.956	....	....	....	....	....	....	$\leq$3.9
CdSe	112.4	79	46.393	....	....	....	....	....	....	$\leq$3.2
CeO	140	16	14.3607	....	....	....	....	865.0	2.99	(7.7)
CH	12	1	0.930024	$^2\Pi$	14.457	0.534	1.1198	2,861.6	64.3	3.47
CH^+	12	1	0.930021	$^1\Sigma^+$	14.1767	0.4898	1.13083	....	....	3.6
Cl_2	35	35	17.48942	$^1\Sigma_g^+$	0.2438	0.0017	1.988	564.9	4.0	2.475
Cl_2^+	35	35	17.48928	$^2\Pi$?	0.2697	0.0018	1.891	645.3	2.90	(4.4)
ClF	35	19	12.31410	$^1\Sigma$	0.516509	0.004359	1.62813	793.2	9.9	2.616
ClO	35	16	11.026	....	....	....	....	(780)	....	1.9
CN	12	14	6.46427	$^2\Sigma^+$	1.8996	0.01735	1.1718	2,068.705	13.144	
CO	12	16	6.85841	$^1\Sigma^+$	1.9314	0.01748	1.1282	2,170.21	13.461	11.108
CO^+	12	16	6.85823	$^2\Sigma^+$	1.9772	0.01896	1.1151	2,214.24	15.164	(9.9)
CoCl	.....	.....	22.145	....	....	....	....	421.2	0.74	
CoH	.....	1	....	....	[7.151^0]	....	1.542°	(1,890)		
CP	12	31	8.65196	$^2\Sigma^+$	0.7986	0.00597	1.562	1,239.67	6.86	(6.9)
CrO	.....	16	12.2366	....	....	....	....	898.8	6.5	(3.8)
CS	12	32	8.72802	$^1\Sigma^+$	0.8205	0.00624	1.534	1,285.1	6.5	
Cs_2	133	133	66.473	$^1\Sigma_g^+$	....	....	....	41.99	0.080	0.45
CsBr	133	.....	49.921	$^1\Sigma^+$	....	....	[3.07]	(194)	2.0	$\geq$3.9
CsCl	133	.....	27.998	$^1\Sigma^+$	....	....	[3.06]			
CSe	12	.....	10.4202	$^1\Sigma$	....	....	....	1,036.0	4.8	(6.8)
CsF	133	19	16.6277	$^1\Sigma^+$	0.185	0.00185	2.34	(270)		
CsH	133	1	1.00054	$^1\Sigma^+$	2.709	0.057	2.494	890.7	12.6	(1.9)
CsI	133	127	64.935	$^1\Sigma$	....	....	[3.4]	142	(1.2)	3.3_7
CsRb	133	.....	52.0365	....	....	....	....	49.4		
Cu_2	.....	.....	31.779	$^1\Sigma_g^+$	....	....	....	160	5	(0.17)
CuBr	63	79	35.022	$^1\Sigma^+$	....	....	....	314.10	0.865	(2.5)
CuCl	63	35	22.4858	$^1\Sigma^+$	....	....	....	416.9	1.57	(3.0)
CuF	63	19	14.5979	$^1\Sigma^+$	0.3803	0.0046	1.743	622.6_5	3.95	(3.0)
CuH	63	1	0.992242	$^1\Sigma^+$	7.938	0.249	1.463	1,940.4	37.0	2.89
CuH^+	63	1	0.992242	$^2\Sigma$	[3.30]	....	[2.27]	(1,874)		
CuI	63	127	12.084	$^1\Sigma^+$	....	....	....	264.8	0.71	(3.0)
CuO	.....	16	12.7822	$^2\Sigma^+$?	....	....	....	628	3	
F_2	19	19	9.50227	$^1\Sigma_g^+$	....	....	[1.435]	892.1	....	2.75
FeCl	.....	35	21.5105	$^6\Sigma$	....	....	....	406.6	1.2	
FeH	.....	1	0.990261	....	[7.8155]	....	[1.4760]			
FeO	.....	16	12.4378	....	....	....	....	880	5	(4.8)
GaBr	69	81	37.232	$^1\Sigma^+$	....	....	....	263.0	0.81	(2.7)
GaCl	69	35	23.2069	$^1\Sigma^+$	....	....	....	365.0	1.1	(3.7)
GaI	69	127	44.682	$^1\Sigma^+$	....	....	....	216.4	0.5	2.88
GaO	69	16	13.0142	$^2\Sigma$	....	....	....	767.69	6.34	(2.9)
GdO	.....	16	14.520	....	....	....	....	841.0	3.70	(5.9)
GeBr	.....	.....	38.052	$^2\Pi$	....	....	....	296.6	0.9	(3.0)
GeCl	74	35	23.7466	$^2\Pi$	....	....	....	407.6	1.3_6	(4.0)
GeF	.....	19	15.0627	$^2\Pi$	....	....	....	665.2	2.7_9	(4.9)
GeO	74	16	13.1540	$^1\Sigma^+$	0.4704	0.0029	1.651	985.7	4.30	(6.9)
GeS	74	32	22.3266	$^1\Sigma$	....	....	....	575.8	1.80	(5.6)

TABLE 7i-1. CONSTANTS OF DIATOMIC MOLECULES (*Continued*)

	m_1	m_2	μ	Normal state	B	α	r_e	ω	x	D_0, electron volts
(1)	(2)		(3)	(4)	(5)	(6)	(7)	(8)	(9)	(10)
GeSe....	74	80	38.415	$^1\Sigma^+$	....	....	....	406.8	1.2	(4.1)
GeTe....	74	130	47.129	$^1\Sigma^+$	....	....	....	323.4	1.0	(3.2)
H_2......	1	1	0.504066	$^1\Sigma_g^+$	68.809	2.993	0.7416_6	4,395.24	117.99_5	4.476_3
H_2^+.....	1	1	0.503928	$^2\Sigma_g^+$	29.8	1.4	1.06	2,297	62	2.648_1
HBr.....	1	.....	0.99558	$^1\Sigma^+$	8.473	0.226	1.413_8	2,649.67	45.21	3.75_4
HBr^+....	1	.....	0.99558	$^2\Pi$	$[7.95_5]$	....	[1.459]	....	....	3.5_0
HCl.....	1	35	0.979889	$^1\Sigma^+$	10.5909	0.3019	1.27460	2,989.74	52.05	4.430
HCl^+....	1	35	0.979889	$^2\Pi$	9.9463	0.3183	1.3152_6	2,675.4	53.5	4.48
He_2.....	4	4	2.00193	$^1\Sigma_u^+$	7.664	0.131	1.0483	1,811.2	39.2	(2.6)
He_2^+....	4	4	2.00179	$^2\Sigma_u^+$	7.22	0.23	1.080	1,627.2	....	(3.1)
HF.....	1	9	0.957347	$^1\Sigma^+$	20.939	0.770_5	0.9171	4,138.52	90.069	6.40
Hg_2....	.....	.....	100.33	$^1\Sigma_g^+$	....	....	3.3	(36)	....	≤0.060
Hg_2^+....										
HgBr....	202	81	57.785	$^2\Sigma$?	....	....	....	186.25	0.975	0.7
HgCl....	202	35	29.7866	$^2\Sigma^+$	....	....	(2.23)	292.61	1.6025	1.0
HgF.....	202	19	17.3604	$^2\Sigma$?	....	....	....	490.8	4.05	(1.8)
HgH....	.....	1	1.00309	$^2\Sigma^+$	5.549	0.312	1.7404	1,387.09	83.01	0.376
HgH^+....	.....	1	1.00309	$^1\Sigma^+$	6.613	0.206	1.594_3	2,033.87	46.16	(2.3)
HgI.....	.....	127	77.751	$^2\Sigma$?	....	....	....	125.6	1.09	0.36
HgS.....	.....	32	27.655	....	....	....	....	....	....	≤2.8
HgSe....	.....	.....	56.674	....	....	....	....	....	....	≤2.7
HgTl....	.....	.....	101.27	....	....	....	....	26.9	0.69	(0.03)
HI.....	1	127	1.000187	$^1\Sigma^+$	6.551	0.183	1.604_1	2,309.53	39.73	3.056_4
HI^+.....	1	127	....	....	....	....	....	....	....	3.11
HS.....	1	32	0.977325	$^2\Pi$	[9.47]	....	[1.35]	....	....	<3.8
I_2.....	127	127	63.466_5	$^1\Sigma_g^+$	0.03736	0.000117	2.666_0	214.57	0.6127	1.5417
IBr.....	127	79	48.6670	$^1\Sigma^+$	....	....	....	268.4	0.78	1.817
ICl.....	127	35	27.4221	$^1\Sigma^+$	0.114162	0.000536	2.32070	384.18	1.465	2.152
InBr....	115	81	47.492	$^1\Sigma^+$	....	....	2.57	221.0	0.65	≤3.3
InCl....	115	35	26.8179	$^1\Sigma^+$	0.1170	0.0009	2.31_8	317.4	1.01	<4.54
InH....	115	1	0.999366	$^1\Sigma^+$	4.9959	0.14500	1.8376	1,474.7	24.7	≤2.48
InI.....	115	127	60.320_7	$^1\Sigma^+$	....	....	[2.86]	177.1	0.4	2.7
InO.....	115	16	14 0427	$^2\Sigma$?	....	....	....	703.09	3.71	(1.3)
IO.....	127	16	14.2090	....	....	....	....	687	5	(1.9)
K_2.....	39	39	19.488	$^1\Sigma_g$	0.05622	0.000219	3.923	92.64	0.354	0.514
KBr.....	39	.....	26.260	$^1\Sigma^+$	....	....	2.94	231	0.7	3.96
KCl.....	39	.....	18.599	$^1\Sigma^+$	....	....	2.79	280	0.9	4.42
KF.....	39	19	12.789_4	$^1\Sigma^+$	[0.2022]	....	$[2.55_3]$	(390)	....	≤5.9
KH.....	39	1	0.9827	$^1\Sigma^+$	3.407	0.0673	2.244	985.0	14.65	1.8_6
KI.....	39	127	29.896	$^1\Sigma^+$	....	....	3.23	212	0.7	3.33
LaO....	139	16	14.3479	$^2\Sigma$	....	....	....	811.6	2.23	(9)
Li_2.....	7	7	3.50908	$^1\Sigma_g^+$	0.6727_2	0.00704	2.672_5	351.43_5	2.592	1.03
LiBr.....	.....	.....	6.3872	....	....	....	....	....	....	4.5_3
LiCl.....	.....	.....	5.8056	....	....	....	....	....	....	5.1
LiCs.....	7	133	6.6663	$^1\Sigma^+$	....	....	....	(167)		
LiF.....	.....	19	5.0846	....	....	....	....	....	....	≤6.6
LiH.....	7	1	0.881506	$^1\Sigma^+$	7.5131	0.2132	1.5953_5	1,405.649	23.200	2.5
LiI.....	.....	127	6.582	$^1\Sigma^+$	....	....	....	450	1.5	3.5_8
LiK.....	.....	.....	5.895	$^1\Sigma^+$	....	....	....	(207)		
LiRb.....	.....	.....	6.421	$^1\Sigma$	....	....	....	(185)		
LuO.....	.....	16	14.6600	....	....	....	....	841.66	4.07	(5.3)
MgBr....	24	79	18.3998	$^2\Sigma$	....	....	....	373.8	1.34	≤3.35
MgCl....	24	35	14.23132	$^2\Sigma^+$	....	....	....	465.4	2.05	3.17
MgF....	24	19	10.60470	$^2\Sigma$	0.518	....	$[1.75_2]$	717.6	3.84	(4.2)
MgH....	24	1	0.967480	$^2\Sigma^+$	5.818_1	0.1668	1.7306	1,495.7	31.5	2.49
MgH^+...	24	1	0.967479	$^1\Sigma^+$	6.411	0.206	1.649	1,695.3	30.2	(2.1)
MgI.....	.....	127	20.415	$^2\Sigma$?	....	....	....	312		

TABLE 7i-1. CONSTANTS OF DIATOMIC MOLECULES (*Continued*)

	m_1	m_2	μ	Normal state	B	α	r_e	ω	x	D_0, electron volts
(1)	(2)		(3)	(4)	(5)	(6)	(7)	(8)	(9)	(10)
MgO	24	16	9.5989	$^1\Sigma$	0.5743	0.0050	1.749	785.1	5.1_8	(3.7)
MgS	...	...	13.834	...	...	...	...	525.2	2.93	(2.9)
MnBr	55	...	32.570	$^7\Sigma$	...	...	...	289.7	0.9	(2.9)
MnCl	55	35	21.3757	$^7\Sigma$?	...	...	...	384.9	1.4	(3.3)
MnF	55	19	14.1218	$^7\Sigma$?	...	...	...	618.8	3.01	(3.9)
MnH	55	1	0.989974	$^7\Sigma$	5.68548	0.16079	1.73075	[1,490.58]	...	(<2.4)
MnI	55	127	38.3560	$^7\Sigma$?	...	...	...	(240)	(1.5)	
MnO	55	16	12.3926	...	...	...	...	840.7	4.89	(4.4)
N_2	14	14	7.00377	$^1\Sigma_g^+$	2.010	0.0187	1.094	2,359.61	14.456	9.756
N_2^+	14	14	7.00363	$^2\Sigma_g^+$	1.932	0.020	1.116_2	2,207.19	16.136	8.724
Na_2	23	23	11.49822	$^1\Sigma_g^+$	0.15471	0.00079	3.078_6	159.23	0.726	0.73
NaBr	23	...	17.8588	$^1\Sigma^+$	...	...	(2.64)	315	1.15	3.85
NaCl	23	...	13.9508	$^1\Sigma^+$	...	...	(2.51)	380	1.0	3.58
NaCs	23	133	19.6052	$^1\Sigma^+$	...	...	...	(98)		
NaF	23	...	10.4054	...	...	...	...	...	...	≤5.3
NaH	23	1	0.96579	$^1\Sigma^+$	4.9012	0.1353	1.8873	1,172.2	19.72	(2.2)
NaI	23	127	19.4692	$^1\Sigma^+$	2.9	...	[2.90]	286	0.75	3.16
NaK	23	...	14.481	$^1\Sigma^+$	...	...	...	123.29	0.400	0.62
NaRb	23	...	18.122	$^1\Sigma^+$	...	...	...	106.64	0.455	(0.57)
NBr	14	...	11.919	...	...	...	...	693	5.0	(3.0)
NH	14	1	0.94045	$^3\Sigma^-$	16.65	0.64	1.038	(3,300)	...	(3.8)
NiCl	...	...	22.110	$^2\Pi$?	...	...	...	419.2	1.04	(7.3)
NiH	...	1	0.99111	$^2\Delta_{\frac{5}{2}}$	7.823	0.248	1.474_6	1,926.6	...	≤3.1
NiO	...	16	12.573	...	...	...	...	[615]		
NO	14	16	7.46881	$^2\Pi_{\frac{1}{2}}$	1.7046	0.0178	1.1508	1,904.03	13.97	6.487
NO^+	14	16	7.46869	...	...	...	...	...	...	10.6
NS	14	32	9.74115	$^2\Pi$	0.7736	0.00612	1.495	1,220.0	7.75	(5.9)
O_2	16	16	8.000000	$^3\Sigma_g^-$	1.44566_6	0.01579_1	1.20739_8	1,580.361	12.0730	5.080
O_2^+	16	16	7.99986	$^2\Pi_g$	1.6722	0.01984	1.1227	1,876.4	16.53	6.48
OH	16	1	0.94838	$^2\Pi$	18.871	0.714	0.9706	3,735.21	82.81	4.35
OH^+	16	1	0.94837	$^3\Sigma^-$	16.793	0.732	1.0289	[2,955]	...	4.4
P_2	31	31	15.49221	$^1\Sigma_g^+$	0.3032_7	0.00142	1.894_3	780.43	2.804	5.031
Pb_2	...	...	103.63	...	...	...	...	256.5	2.96	(0.7)
PbBr	...	79	57.161	$^2\Pi$?	...	...	...	207.5	0.50	2.97
PbCl	...	35	29.9281	$^2\Pi$?	...	...	...	303.8	0.88	3.1_2
PbF	...	19	17.4083	$^2\Pi$	...	...	...	507.2	2.30	3.4_7
PbH	...	1	1.00325	$^2\Pi$?	4.971	0.144	1.839	1,564.1	29.75	1.59
PbI	...	127	78.722	$^2\Pi$?	...	...	...	160.5	0.25	2.8_4
PbO	...	16	14.8534	$^1\Sigma^+$	0.3073	0.0019	1.922	721.8	3.70	(4.3)
PbS	208	32	27.7213	$^1\Sigma^+$	0.10605	0.000873	2.394_8	428.14	1.201	(4.7)
PbSe	...	...	57.189	$^1\Sigma^+$	...	...	...	277.6	0.51	(4.3)
PbTe	...	...	78.996	$^1\Sigma$	...	...	...	211.8	0.12	(3.5)
PH	31	1	0.976363	$^3\Sigma^-$	[8.412]	...	$[1.432_8]$	(2,380)		
PN	31	14	9.64651	$^1\Sigma^+$	0.7862_1	0.00557	1.4910	1,337.24	6.983	(6.3)
PO	31	16	10.55138	$^2\Pi$	0.7613	0.0055	1.448_8	$1,230.6_4$	6.52	(6.2)
PrO	141	16	14.369	...	...	...	...	818.9	1.20	
Rb_2	85	85	42.469	$^1\Sigma_g^+$	...	...	...	57.28	0.96	0.49
RbBr	...	...	41.313	...	...	...	...	...	...	3.9_3
RbCl	...	...	25.068	$^1\Sigma$	...	...	2.89	(253)	...	3.96
RbCs	...	133	52.036	$^1\Sigma^+$	...	...	...	49.41	...	5.4_5
RbF	...	19	15.5486							
RbH	...	1	0.99638	$^1\Sigma^+$	3.020	0.072	2.367	936.77	14.15	(1.9)
RbI	...	127	51.089	$^1\Sigma$	...	...	3.26	...	...	3.29
S_2	32	32	15.99126	$^3\Sigma_g^-$	0.2956	0.0016	1.889	725.68	2.852	4.4
Sb_2	...	...	60.897	$^1\Sigma_g^+$	...	...	...	269.85	0.59	(3.7)
SbBi	...	209	76.95_8	$^1\Sigma^+$	...	...	...	220.0	0.50	(3.0)
SbCl	...	35	27.174_4	...	...	...	...	369.0	0.92	(4.6)

TABLE 7i-1. CONSTANTS OF DIATOMIC MOLECULES (*Continued*)

	m_1	m_2	μ	Normal state	B	α	r_e	ω	x	D_0, electron volts
(1)	(2)		(3)	(4)	(5)	(6)	(7)	(8)	(9)	(10)
SbF	....	19	16.439_4	....	....	....	....	614.2	2.77	(4.2)
SbN	....	14	12.562_7	$^1\Sigma$	....	....	....	942.0	5.6	(4.8)
SbO	....	16	14.142_1	$^2\Pi$	....	....	....	817.2	5.30	(3.8)
ScO	45	16	11.8012	$^2\Sigma$	....	....	....	971.55	3.95	(7)
Se_2	80	80	39.971	$^1\Sigma_g^+$	0.0907	0.00027	2.15_7	391.77	1.06	3.55
SeO	....	16	13.304_7	....	....	....	....	907.1	4.61	(5.4)
Si_2	....	....	14.03_4	....	....	....	....	(750)		
SiBr	....	....	20.774	$^2\Pi$	....	....	....	425.4	1.5	(3.7)
SiCl	28	35	15.5474	$^2\Pi$	....	....	....	535.4	2.20	(4.0)
SiF	28	19	11.3187	$^2\Pi$	0.5795	....	1.603	856.7	4.7	
SiH	28	1	0.97308	$^2\Pi$	7.49_6	0.213	1.520	(2,080)		
SiN	28	14	9.33526	$^2\Sigma^+$	0.7310	0.00567	1.571_8	$1,151.68_0$	6.560_0	(4.5)
SiO	28	16	10.18013	$^1\Sigma^+$	0.7263	0.00494	1.510_1	1,242.03	6.047	(7.4)
SiO^+	28	16	10.18006	$^2\Sigma$	0.7320	0.0133	1.504_2	(851)		
SiS	28	32	14.92589	$^1\Sigma^+$	0.3036_3	0.0014_9	1.928_8	749.6_9	2.58	(6.6)
SiSe	28	....	20.664_6	$^1\Sigma$	....	....	....	580.0	1.78	(5.8)
SiTe	28	....	22.954_3	$^1\Sigma^+$	....	....	....	481.2	1.30	(5.5)
SnBr	....	....	47.774	$^2\Pi$	....	....	....	247.7	0.62	(3.0)
SnCl	....	35	27.0190	$^2\Pi$	....	....	....	352.5	1.06	(3.6)
SnF	....	19	16.3823	$^2\Pi_{\frac{1}{2}}$	....	....	....	582.9	2.69	(3.9)
SnH	....	1	0.99964	$^2\Pi$	5.293	....	1.785			
SnO	....	16	14.0999	$^1\Sigma^+$	0.3540	0.00450	1.837_9	822.4	3.73	(5.6)
SnS	....	....	25.253	$^1\Sigma^+$	(0.157)	....	(2.06)	487.68	1.34	3.0
SnSe	....	....	47.430	$^1\Sigma^+$	....	....	....	331.2	0.736	(4.6)
SnTe	....	....	61.514	$^1\Sigma$	....	....	....	259.5	0.50	(4.2)
SO	32	16	10.66472	$^3\Sigma^-$	0.7089_4	0.00562_2	1.4933	$1,123.7_3$	6.116	5.146
SrBr	....	79	41.532	$^2\Sigma^+$	....	....	....	216.5	0.51	(2.8)
SrCl	....	35	25.001_8	$^2\Sigma^+$	....	....	....	302.3	0.95	(3.0)
SrF	....	19	15.6183	$^2\Sigma^+$	....	....	....	500.1	2.21	(3.5)
SrH	....	1	0.99667	$^2\Sigma^+$	3.6751	0.0814	2.1455	1,206.2	17.0	≤ 1.68
SrI	....	127	51.849	$^2\Sigma$?	....	....	....	173.9	0.42	(2.2)
SrO	....	16	13.5302	$^1\Sigma$	0.3378	0.0020	1.921	653.5	4.0	(4.5)
SrS	....	....	23.482	....	....	....	....	....	....	≤ 2.7
Te_2	....	....	63.823	....	....	....	[2.59]	251	0.55	≤ 3.18
TeO	....	16	14.2169	....	....	....	....	796.0	3.50	3.453
TiCl	48	35	20.2278	....	....	....	....	456.4	6.3	(1.0)
TiO	48	16	11.9979	$^3\Pi$	0.5355	0.0031	1.620	1,008.4	4.61	(6.9)
TlBr	....	81	57.979	$^1\Sigma^+$	....	....	(2.68)	192.1	0.39	≤ 3.19
TlCl	....	35	29.869	$^1\Sigma^+$	....	....	2.55	287.47	1.24	3.75
TlF	....	19	17.3882	$^1\Sigma^+$	....	....	....	475.00	1.89	< 4.72
TlH	....	1	1.003184	$^1\Sigma^+$	4.806	0.154	1.870	1,390.7	22.7	≤ 2.18
TlI	....	127	78.312	$^1\Sigma^+$	....	....	(2.87)	150	0.6	≤ 2.64
VO	51	16	12.1768	$^2\Delta$?	0.3876	0.0024	1.890	1,012.7	4.9	(6.4)
YbCl	....	....	29.435	$^2\Sigma$?	....	....	....	293.6_1	1.23	(1.2)
YO	89	16	13.5606	$^2\Sigma$	....	....	....	852.5	2.45	(9)
ZnBr	....	....	35.970	$^2\Sigma$?	....	....	....	(220)		
ZnCl	....	35	22.790	$^2\Sigma$	....	....	....	390.5	1.55	(3.0)
ZnF	....	19	14.725	$^2\Sigma$	....	....	....	(630)	(3.5)	
ZnH	....	1	0.992826	$^2\Sigma^+$	6.6794	0.2500	1.5945	1,607.6	55.14	0.851
ZnH^+	....	1	0.992826	$^1\Sigma^+$	7.403	0.236	1.514_6	1,916	39	(2.5)
ZnI	64	127	42.528	$^2\Sigma$?	....	....	....	223.4	0.75	(2.0)
ZnS	....	....	21.520	....	....	....	....	....	....	4.4
ZnTe	....	....	43.243	....	....	....	....	....	....	2.2
ZrO	90	16	13.5836	$^3\Pi$	0.6187	0.0070	(1.416)	936.6	3.45	(7.8)

7i-2. Energy Levels and Potential Curves of Important Diatomic Molecules

The following molecules are represented:

C_2	Fig. 7i-1	N_2	Fig. 7i-4
CN	Fig. 7i-2	NO	Fig. 7i-5
CO	Fig. 7i-3	O_2	Fig. 7i-6

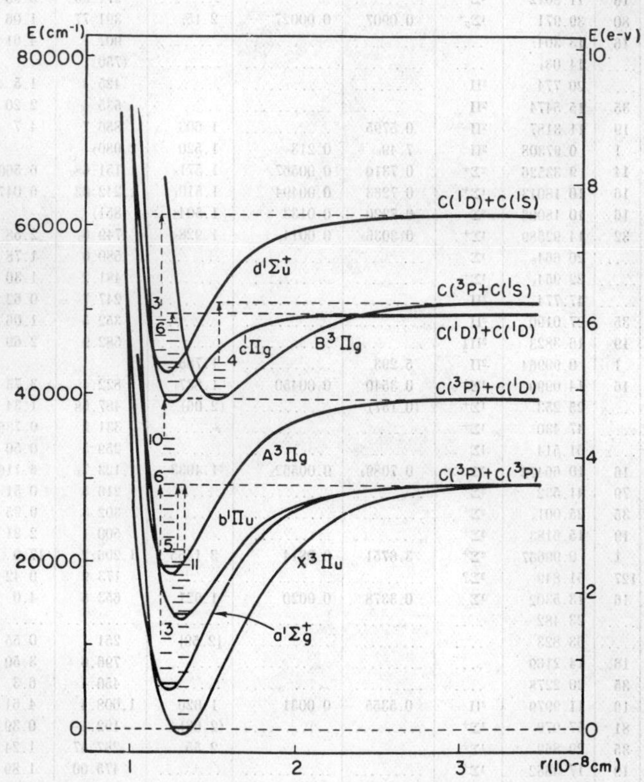

FIG. 7i-1. Potential curves of C_2. (G. Herzberg, "Spectra of Diatomic Molecules," 2d ed., D. Van Nostrand Company, Inc., Princeton, N.J., 1950.)

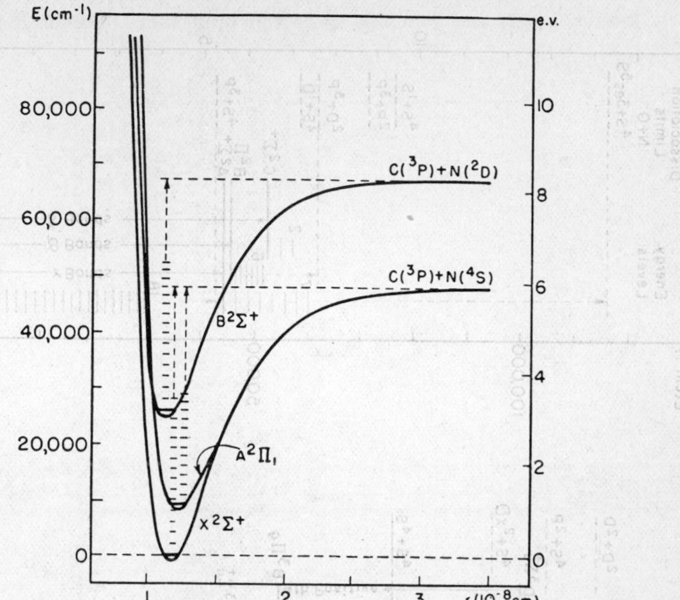

FIG. 7i-2. Potential curves of CN. (G. Herzberg, "Spectra of Diatomic Molecules," 2d ed., D. Van Nostrand Company, Inc., Princeton, N.J., 1950.)

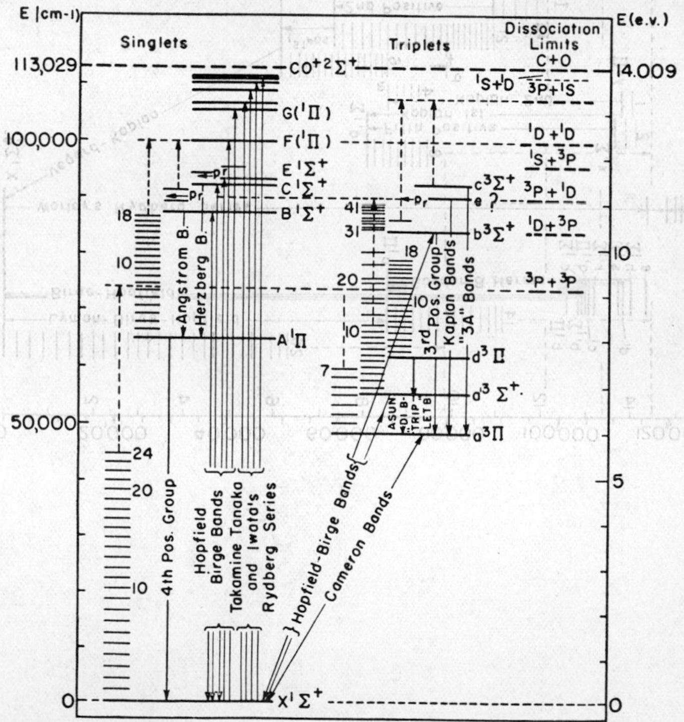

FIG. 7i-3. Energy levels of CO. (Herzberg, "Spectra of Diatomic Molecules," 2d ed., D. Van Nostrand Company, Inc., Princeton, N.J., 1950.)

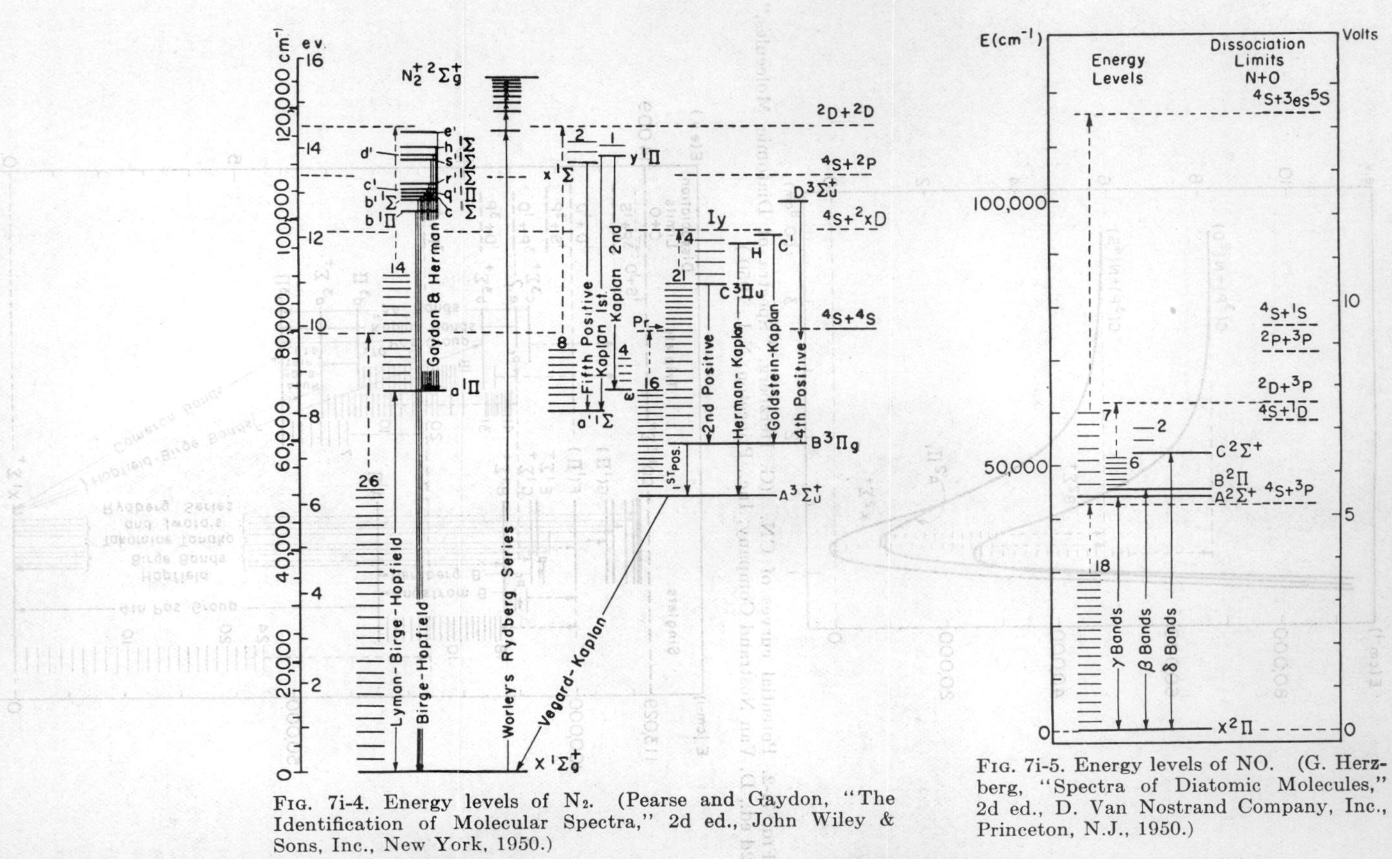

Fig. 7i-4. Energy levels of N_2. (Pearse and Gaydon, "The Identification of Molecular Spectra," 2d ed., John Wiley & Sons, Inc., New York, 1950.)

Fig. 7i-5. Energy levels of NO. (G. Herzberg, "Spectra of Diatomic Molecules," 2d ed., D. Van Nostrand Company, Inc., Princeton, N.J., 1950.)

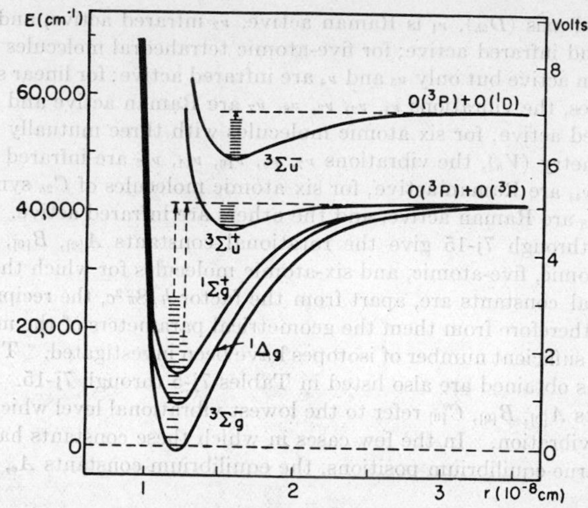

FIG. 7i-6. Potential curves of O_2. (G. Herzberg, "Spectra of Diatomic Molecules," 2d ed., D. Van Nostrand Company, Inc., Princeton, N.J., 1950.)

7j. Constants of Polyatomic Molecules

G. HERZBERG AND L. HERZBERG

Division of Physics

National Research Council of Canada

7j-1. Introduction. The following tables present some of the more important data on simple polyatomic molecules derived from infrared, Raman, and microwave spectra. Tables 7j-1 through 7j-4 give the fundamental vibrational frequencies (in cm^{-1}) of all triatomic and four-atomic molecules for which these quantities have been determined and for a few important five- and six-atomic molecules. The point groups to which the molecules belong are indicated in the last column. The numbering of the vibrations is in accordance with the practice followed by many authors in recent years[1] and now established by international agreement.[2]

For most molecules listed the fundamentals are active in both the infrared and the Raman spectrum. However, for molecules of high symmetry, certain vibrations cannot occur in the Raman spectrum, others not in the infrared spectrum, and a few in neither one: for triatomic linear symmetric molecules ($D_{\infty h}$), ν_1 is Raman active and ν_2 and ν_3 infrared active; for four-atomic linear symmetric molecules ($D_{\infty h}$), ν_1, ν_2, and ν_4 are Raman active and ν_3 and ν_5 infrared active; for four-atomic planar molecules

[1] G. Herzberg, "Molecular Spectra and Molecular Structure. II. Infrared and Raman Spectra of Polyatomic Molecules," D. Van Nostrand Company, Inc., Princeton, N.J., 1945.

[2] R. S. Mulliken, *JCP* **23**, 1997 (1955).

with a threefold axis (D_{3h}), ν_1 is Raman active, ν_2 infrared active, and ν_3 and ν_4 are both Raman and infrared active; for five-atomic tetrahedral molecules (T_d) all vibrations are Raman active but only ν_3 and ν_4 are infrared active; for linear symmetric six-atomic molecules, the vibrations ν_1, ν_2, ν_3, ν_6, ν_7 are Raman active and the remaining ones are infrared active, for six atomic molecules with three mutually perpendicular planes of symmetry (V_h), the vibrations ν_7, ν_9, ν_{10}, ν_{11}, ν_{12} are infrared active and all others, except ν_4, are Raman active, for six atomic molecules of C_{2h} symmetry, ν_1, ν_2, ν_3, ν_4, ν_5, and ν_8 are Raman active, and the others are infrared active.

Tables 7j-5 through 7j-15 give the rotational constants $A_{[0]}$, $B_{[0]}$, $C_{[0]}$ of all triatomic, four-atomic, five-atomic, and six-atomic molecules for which they are known. These rotational constants are, apart from the factor $h/8\pi^2c$, the reciprocal moments of inertia, and therefore from them the geometrical parameters of the molecule can be determined if a sufficient number of isotopes have been investigated. The geometrical parameters thus obtained are also listed in Tables 7j-5 through 7j-15.

The constants $A_{[0]}$, $B_{[0]}$, $C_{[0]}$ refer to the lowest vibrational level which still includes the zero-point vibration. In the few cases in which these constants have been determined for the true equilibrium positions, the equilibrium constants A_e, B_e, C_e are also listed.

Microwave spectra give the constants in Mc/sec while infrared and Raman spectra give them in cm^{-1}. Here all microwave values have been converted to cm^{-1} by dividing by $c = 2.997928 \times 10^{10}$ cm/sec.

In the alphabetical order used, D is counted as an H in order to have the deuterated molecules appear with the corresponding nondeuterated ones. Element symbols without mass numbers refer to the most abundant isotope.

Many of the data have been taken from the books by Herzberg[1] and by Gordy, Smith, and Trambarulo.[2] In addition, the literature up to the end of 1953 has been included. For detailed tables of microwave frequencies, reference should be made to Kisliuk and Townes.[3]

Most of the geometrical data are still based on DuMond and Cohen's 1951 set of atomic constants.[4] A few data that were recalculated are based on the 1953 set.[5] However, the difference amounts to less than 0.01 per cent (<0.0001 A).

[1] *Loc. cit.*

[2] W. Gordy, W. V. Smith, and R. F. Trambarulo, "Microwave Spectroscopy," John Wiley & Sons, Inc., New York, 1953.

[3] P. Kisliuk and G. H. Townes, *Natl. Bur. Standards* (*U.S.*) *Circ.* 518.

[4] J. W. M. DuMond and E. R Cohen, *Phys. Rev.* **82**, 555 (1951).

[5] J. W. M. DuMond and E. R. Cohen, *Revs. Modern Phys.* **25**, 691 (1953).

7j-2. Fundamental Vibrations

TABLE 7j-1. TRIATOMIC MOLECULES

Molecule	ν_1, cm^{-1}	ν_2, cm^{-1}	ν_3, cm^{-1}	Point group
$(BO_2)^-$	749*	....	(1,480)	$D_{\infty h}$
BrCN	580	368	2,187	$C_{\infty v}$
CF_2	1,162	665.0		
ClCN	714	396*	2,213	C_{2v}
Cl_2O	688	(330)	969	$C_{\infty v}$
ClO_2	943.2	445	1,110.5	C_{2v}
$(ClO_2)^-$	797	396	844	
CO_2	1,388.3; $2\nu_2$ = 1,285.5†	667.3	2,349.3	$D_{\infty h}$
$(CO_2)^+$	(1,265)	....	....	$D_{\infty h}$
CS_2	655	(397)	1,510	$D_{\infty h}$
FCN	(2,294)	....	(1,052)	$C_{\infty v}$
F_2O	928	461	828	C_{2v}
HCN	2,095.5	711.7	3,311.68	$C_{\infty v}$
DCN	1,928	568.9	2,629.3	$C_{\infty v}$
$(HF_2)^-$	(595)‡	1,248‡	1,510‡	$C_{\infty v}$(?)
$HgBr_2$	223	53	(307)	$D_{\infty h}$
HgBrI	195	....	....	$C_{\infty v}$
$HgCl_2$	363	75	423	$D_{\infty h}$
HgClBr	270	(40)	390	$C_{\infty v}$
HgClI	204	(50)	408	$C_{\infty v}$
HgI_2	156	46	(235)	$D_{\infty h}$
H_2O	3,657.05	1,595.0	3,775.79	C_{2v}
HDO	2,723.7	1,403	3,707.5	C_s
D_2O	2,666	1,178.7	2,787.3	C_{2v}
HOCl	3,626	1,242	739	C_s
DOCl	2,674	911	739	C_s
H_2S	2,610.8	1,183	2,626	C_{2v}
HDS	....	1,090	(2,684)	C_s
D_2S	1,892	855	1,900	C_{2v}
H_2Se	2,260	1,074	2,350	C_{2v}
HDSe	1,691	905	2,352	C_s
D_2Se	1,630	745	1,696	C_{2v}
ICN	470	321	2,158	$C_{\infty v}$
$(N_3)^-$	1,350*	630*	2,080*	$D_{\infty h}$
N_2O	1,285.0	588.78	2,223.75	$C_{\infty v}$
NO_2	1,306	755	1,621	C_{2v}
$(NO_2)^-$	1,325‡	831‡	1,360‡	C_{2v}
$(NO_2)^+$	1,400*			
NOCl	1,799	592	332	C_s
NOF	1,844.0	521	765.9	C_s
O_3	1,110	705	1,043	C_{2v}
$(OCN)^-$	870*	....	2,180*	$C_{\infty v}$
OCS	859.2	521.5	2,050.5	$C_{\infty v}$
$(SCN)^-$	2,066*	(398)*	750*	$C_{\infty v}$
$(SeCN)^-$	2,051.5*	575*	....	$C_{\infty v}$
SO_2	1,151.4	517.7	1,361.8	C_{2v}
$(UO_2)^{++}$	860‡	(210)‡	930‡	C_{2v}

Values in parentheses are uncertain or have been obtained indirectly.
* Observed in liquid only.
† Fermi resonance between ν_1 and $2\nu_2$.
‡ Observed in crystal only.

TABLE 7j-2. FOUR-ATOMIC MOLECULES

Molecule	ν_1, cm^{-1}	ν_2, cm^{-1}	ν_3, cm^{-1}	ν_4, cm^{-1}	ν_5, cm^{-1}	ν_6, cm^{-1}	Point group
$AsCl_3$	410	193	370	159	......	......	C_{3v}
AsF_3	707	341	644	274	......	......	C_{3v}
AsH_3	2,116.1	2,123	906	1,003	......	......	C_{3v}
AsD_3	1,523.1	1,529.3	660.0	714	......	......	C_{3v}
BBr_3	279	(372)	806	151	......	......	D_{3h}
BCl_3	471	460	956	243	......	......	D_{3h}
BF_3	888	691.3	1,445.9	480.4	......	......	D_{3h}
$BiCl_3$	288	130	242	96	......	......	C_{3v}
$(BrO_3)^-$	803*	428*	828*	350*	......	......	C_{3v}
CFClO	1,868	1,095	776	501	415	667	C_s
CF_2O	1,942	965; $2\nu_2 = 1,907$†	626	1,249	584	774	C_{2v}
C_2H_2	3,373.2	1,974.0	3,282.5	613.3	730.74	......	$D_{\infty h}$
C_2HD	3,334.8	1,851.2	2,584	518.8	683	......	$C_{\infty v}$
C_2D_2	2,701.8	1,764.9	2,439.1	511.4	538.7	......	$D_{\infty h}$
C_2I_2	2,113	191	718	307	(115)	......	$D_{\infty h}$
Cl_2CO	1,827	575	297	849	240	440	C_{2v}
Cl_2CS	1,121	496	287	(660)	(363)	(200)	C_{2v}
ClF_3	750	644	508	428	316	395	C_s
$(ClO_3)^-$	940*	617*	988*	479*	......	......	C_{3v}
C_2N_2	2,328.5	850.6	2,149	507.2	(240)	......	$D_{\infty h}$
$(CO_3)^=$	1,088*	1,438*	866*	714	......	......	D_{3h}
$(GeCl_3)^-$	320*	162*	253*	139*	......	......	C_{3v}
HC_2Cl	3,319	2,109	756	......	606	......	$C_{\infty v}$
DC_2Cl	2,610	1,979	742	......	476	......	$C_{\infty v}$
$(HCO_2)^-$	2,825*	1,584*	1,386*	1,352*	773*	1,069*	C_{2v}
H_2CO	2,780	1,743.6	1,503	2,874	1,280	1,167	C_{2v}
HDCO	2,845	2,121	1,723	1,398	1,041	1,074	C_s
D_2CO	2,055.8	1,700	1,105.7	2,159.7	990	938	C_{2v}
HN_3	3,335.6	2,140.4	1,269.0	1,152.5	657.9	738.8	C_s
HNCO	3,531	2,274	1,527	798	572	670	C_s
HNCS	3,536	1,963	995	(817)	469	600	C_s
HNO_2 (cis)	3,426	......	(1,292)	856	(598)	637	C_s
(trans)	3,590	1,696	1,260	794	598	543	C_s
DNO_2 (cis)	2,530	......	......	816	(591)	508	C_s
(trans)	2,650	1,690	1,018	739	591	416	C_s
H_2O_2	3,395*	1,421*	877	(490)	3,590	1,255	C_2
D_2O_2	2,510*	1,009*	878*	538*	2,482*	1,004*	C_2
H_2S_2	2,513*	882*	510*	......	2,577	886	C_2
$(IO_3)^-$	779*	390‡	826*	330*	......	......	C_{3v}
NF_3	1,032	647	905	493	......	......	C_{3v}
NH_3	3,336.7	949.8	3,444	1,627.5	......	......	C_{3v}
NH_2D	......	......	1,592	884	......	......	C_s
NHD_2	......	2,418	1,234	813	2,556	1,464	C_s
ND_3	2,420.4	748.8	2,555.6	1,191.2	......	......	C_{3v}
$(NO_3)^-$	1,048‡	1,380‡	714‡	834‡	......	......	D_{3h}
P_4	606	363	465	......	......	......	T_d

TABLE 7j-2. FOUR-ATOMIC MOLECULES (*Continued*)

Molecule	ν_1, cm⁻	ν_2, cm^{-1}	ν_3, cm^{-1}	ν_4, cm^{-1}	ν_5, cm^{-1}	ν_6, cm^{-1}	Point group
PBr_3	380	162	400	116	....	....	C_{3v}
PCl_3	510	257	480	190	....	....	C_{3v}
PF_3	892	487	860	344	....	....	C_{3v}
$PFBr_2$	817	421	....	....	393	....	C_s
$PFCl_2$	827	524	....	....	496	....	C_s
PF_2Cl	860	527	....	....	833	....	C_s
PFClBr	822	503	415	....	....	....	C_1
PH_3	2,322.9	992.0	2,327.7	1,122.4	....	....	C_{3v}
PH_2D	....	1,700	1,097	892	....	....	C_s
PHD_2	2,320	....	906	....	....	980	C_s
$SbCl_3$	360	165	320	134	....	....	C_{3v}
SbH_3	1,890.9	781.5	1,894.2	830.9	....	....	(?)C_{3v}
SbD_3	1,358.8	561.1	1,362.0	592.5	....	....	(?)C_{3v}
S_2Cl_2	448	438	206	53	537	245	C_2
$(SnCl_3)^-$	278*	....	220*	....	....	....	C_{3v}
SO_3	1,067	1,390	....	531	....	....	D_{3h}
S_2O_2	679	....	....	....	....	....	C_{2v}
$SOCl_2$	(1,229)	(488)	(443)	(343)	(282)	(192)	(?)C_s
SOF_2	(1,312)	(795)	(720)	(529)	(395)	(326)	C_s

Values in parentheses are uncertain or have been obtained indirectly.
* Observed in liquid only.
† Fermi resonance between ν_1 and $2\nu_2$.
‡ Observed in crystal only.

TABLE 7j-3. SOME FIVE-ATOMIC MOLECULES

Molecule	ν_1, cm^{-1}	ν_2, cm^{-1}	ν_3, cm^{-1}	ν_4, cm^{-1}	ν_5, cm^{-1}	ν_6, cm^{-1}	Point group
CH_4	2,916.5	1,533.6	3,018.7	1,306.2	......	......	T_d
CD_4	2,084.7	(1,054)	2,258.2	995.6	......	......	T_d
CF_4	904	435	1,283	632	......	......	T_d
CCl_4	459	221	{794 {756	310.0	......	......	T_d
CBr_4	267*	122*	671*	182*	......	......	T_d
SiH_4	2,187	978	2,183	910	......	......	T_d
SiF_4	800	268	1,031	391	......	......	T_d
$SiCl_4$	424*	150*	608*	221*	......	......	T_d
$SiBr_4$	249*	90*	487*	137*	......	......	T_d
GeH_4	....	819.3	2,113.6	930.9	......	......	T_d
GeF_4	(740)	(200)	800	260	......	......	T_d
$GeCl_4$	396*	134*	453*	172*	......	......	T_d
$GeBr_4$	(234)*	78*	328*	111*	......	......	T_d
CH_3F	2,964.5	1,475.3	1,048.2	2,983	1,468	1,198	C_{3v}
CH_3Cl	2,966.2	1,354.9	732.1	3,043	1,451	1,017	C_{3v}
CH_3Br	2,972	1,307	610	3,056	1,443	954	C_{3v}
CH_3I	2,969.8	1,251.5	532.8	3,061	1,439	882	C_{3v}
SiH_3Cl	2,195	1,090	(460)	2,150	952	770	C_{3v}
CHF_3	3,035	1,140	700	1,378	1,152.2	508	C_{3v}
$CHCl_3$	3,032	671	365	1,218	768	256	C_{3v}
$CHBr_3$	3,040	541	222	1,142	668	154	C_{3v}
CHI_3	(3,040)†	385†	145†	1,064†	581†	92†	C_{3v}
$SiHCl_3$	2,274	497	250*	810	600	179*	C_{3v}
$SiHBr_3$	2,232*	358*	169*	769*	473*	111*	C_{3v}
CF_3Cl	1,102	783	478*	1,210	560	356*	C_{3v}
CF_3Br	1,087	762	348	1,207	548	305*	C_{3v}
CF_3I	1,076	743	284	1,185	539	265*	C_{3v}

Values in parentheses are uncertain or have been obtained indirectly.
* Observed in liquid phase only.
† Observed in solution only.

TABLE 7j-4. SOME SIX-ATOMIC MOLECULES

Molecule	ν_1, cm^{-1}	ν_2, cm^{-1}	ν_3, cm^{-1}	ν_4, cm^{-1}	ν_5, cm^{-1}	ν_6, cm^{-1}	ν_7, cm^{-1}	ν_8, cm^{-1}	ν_9, cm^{-1}	ν_{10}, cm^{-1}	ν_{11}, cm^{-1}	ν_{12}, cm^{-1}	Point group
HC≡C—C≡CH	(3,293)	2,184	874	3,329	2,020	627	482	630	(231)	......	......	......	$D_{\infty h}$
C_2H_4	3,019.3	1,623.3	1,342.4	(1,027)	3,108	(1,236)	949.2	943	3,105.5	810.3	2,989.5	1,443.5	V_h
C_2D_4	2,251	1,515	981	(726)	2,305	(1,009)	720.0	780	2,345	(586)	2,200.2	1,077.9	V_h
C_2F_4	1,872	778	394	(210)	(1,100)	551	407	510	1,337	(245)	1,186	558	V_h
C_2Cl_4	1,571*	447*	237*	(135)	1,000*	347*	288*	512*	782	194*	913	318*	V_h
C_2Br_4	1,546*	266*	144*	......	886*	211*	......	463*	......	......	......	......	V_h
$H_2C{:}CF_2$	3,058.3	1,728.5	1,410	925.3	550	590	3,099.8	1,302	955	438	801	613	C_{2v}
$H_2C{:}CCl_2$	3,035*	1,616*	1,391*	601*	299*	686*	3,130*	1,088*	788*	375*	874*	458*	C_{2v}
cis $C_2H_2Cl_2$	3,077*	1,587*	1,179*	711*	173*	876*	406*	3,072*	1,294*	848*	571*	697*	C_{2v}
trans $C_2H_2Cl_2$	3,071*	1,576*	1,270*	844*	349*	895*	192*	758*	3,080*	1,200*	817*	265*	C_{2h}
$H_2C{:}CBr_2$	3,023*	1,593*	1,379*	467*	184*	668*	3,108*	1,065*	696*	322*	886*	405*	C_{2v}
cis $C_2H_2Br_2$	3,084*	1,584*	1,150*	580*	109*	......	372*	......	......	(673)	(460)	......	C_{2v}
trans $C_2H_2Br_2$	3,084*	1,578*	1,246*	748*	218*	......	......	......	......	......	(673)	......	C_{2h}
N_2O_4	1,360	813	283	......	1,724	500	680	......	1,749	380	1,265	752	V_h
N_2H_4	3,325	(3,160)	1,493	1,098	873	780	(725)	3,350	3,297	1,607	1,275	950	C_{2v}
CH_3CN	2,965.3	2,267.3	1,400.0	919.9	3,009.0	1,454.0	1,041.0	361.0	......	......	......	......	C_{3v}
CH_3NC	2,965.8	2,166.0	1,410.0	944.6	3,014.3	1,459.0	1,130.0	(270)	......	......	......	......	C_{3v}
CH_3OH	3,682	2,977	2,844	1,477	(1,430)	1,340	1,056	1,034	(2,977)	1,455	1,171	270	C_s
CH_3SH	2,946	2,869	2,607	1,475	1,335	1,070	803	704	2,999	1,430	955	(600)	C_s

Values in parentheses are uncertain or have been obtained indirectly.
* Observed in liquid only.

7j-3. Rotational Constants and Geometrical Parameters

TABLE 7j-5. TRIATOMIC LINEAR MOLECULES

Molecule	$B_{[0]}$, cm^{-1}	Point group	Geometrical parameters
$Br^{79}C^{12}N^{14}$	0.1374348	$C_{\infty v}$	$r_0(CBr) = 1.790$ A; $r_0(CN) = 1.159$ A
$Br^{79}C^{13}N^{14}$	0.1358729		
$Br^{79}C^{12}N^{15}$	0.1315857		
$Br^{81}C^{12}N^{14}$	0.1366539		
$Br^{81}C^{13}N^{14}$	0.1350802		
$Br^{81}C^{12}N^{15}$	0.1308165		
$Cl^{35}C^{12}N$	0.199164_8	$C_{\infty v}$	$r_0(CCl) = 1.629$ A; $r_0(CN) = 1.163$ A
$Cl^{35}C^{13}N$	0.198129_4		
$Cl^{36}C^{12}N$	0.19707		
$Cl^{37}C^{12}N$	0.195043_3		
$Cl^{37}C^{13}N$	0.193957_6		
$C^{12}O_2$	0.3902_0; $B_e = 0.3915_5$	$D_{\infty h}$	$r_0(CO) = 1.1621$ A; $r_e(CO) = 1.1601$ A
$C^{13}O_2$	0.39037	$D_{\infty h}$	$r_0(CO) = 1.1618$ A
$(CO_2)^+$	0.3806	$D_{\infty h}$	$r_0(CO) = 1.177$ A
CS_2	0.1092	$D_{\infty h}$	$r_0(CS) = 1.554$ A
$HC^{12}N$	1.47823; $B_e = 1.4849$	$C_{\infty v}$	$r_0(CH) = 1.064$ A; $r_e(CH) = 1.0657$ A; $r_0(CN) = 1.156$ A; $r_e(CN) = 1.1530$ A
$HC^{13}N$	1.43999		
$DC^{12}N$	1.20775; $B_e = 1.2118$		
$DC^{13}N$	1.18708		
$I^{127}C^{12}N$	0.1075935	$C_{\infty v}$	$r_0(CI) = 1.995$ A; $r_0(CN) = 1.159$ A
$I^{127}C^{13}N$	0.105974		
$N_2{}^{14}O$	0.4190113; $B_e = 0.42118_1$	$C_{\infty v}$	$r_0(NN) = 1.126$ A; $r_e(NN) = 1.126$ A; $r_0(NO) = 1.191$ A; $r_e(NO) = 1.186$ A
$N^{14}N^{15}O$	0.4189819		
$N^{15}N^{14}O$	0.404856_2; $B_e = 0.40693_5$		
$N_2{}^{15}O$	0.404859_2		
$O^{16}C^{12}S^{32}$	0.202857	$C_{\infty v}$	$r_0(CO) = 1.1637$ A; $r_0(CS) = 1.5584$ A
$O^{16}C^{13}S^{32}$	0.2022025		
$O^{16}C^{12}S^{33}$	0.2003016		
$O^{16}C^{12}S^{34}$	0.1978971		
$O^{16}C^{12}S^{35}$	0.1956134		
$O^{16}C^{12}S^{36}$	0.193456		
$O^{16}C^{13}S^{34}$	0.197194		
$O^{16}C^{14}S^{32}$	0.201581		
$O^{17}C^{12}S^{32}$	0.196258		
$O^{18}C^{12}S^{32}$	0.190292		
$O^{18}C^{12}S^{34}$	0.185458		
$O^{18}C^{13}S^{32}$	0.189829		

TABLE 7j-5. TRIATOMIC LINEAR MOLECULES (*Continued*)

Molecule	$B_{[0]}$, cm^{-1}	Point group	Geometrical parameters
$O^{16}C^{12}Se^{74}$	0.1366207	$C_{\infty v}$	$r_0(CO) = 1.1588$ A; $r_0(CSe) = 1.7090$ A
$O^{16}C^{12}Se^{76}$	0.1357092		
$O^{16}C^{12}Se^{77}$	0.1352700		
$O^{16}C^{12}Se^{78}$	0.1348418		
$O^{16}C^{12}Se^{79}$	0.1344213		
$O^{16}C^{12}Se^{80}$	0.1340151		
$O^{16}C^{12}Se^{82}$	0.1332256		
$O^{16}C^{13}Se^{78}$	0.1335960		
$O^{16}C^{13}Se^{80}$	0.1327598		
$S^{32}C^{12}Se^{76}$	0.068387	$C_{\infty v}$	
$S^{32}C^{12}Se^{77}$	0.068124		
$S^{32}C^{12}Se^{78}$	0.067757		
$S^{32}C^{12}Se^{80}$	0.067276		
$S^{32}C^{12}Se^{82}$	0.066773		
$Te^{122}C^{12}S^{32}$	0.05284053	$C_{\infty v}$	$r_0(TeC) = 1.904$ A; $r_0(CS) = 1.557$ A
$Te^{123}C^{12}S^{32}$	0.05273373		
$Te^{124}C^{12}S^{32}$	0.05262935		
$Te^{125}C^{12}S^{32}$	0.05252595		
$Te^{126}C^{12}S^{32}$	0.05242459		
$Te^{128}C^{12}S^{32}$	0.05222612		
$Te^{130}C^{12}S^{32}$	0.05203361		

TABLE 7j-6. TRIATOMIC, ASYMMETRIC TOP MOLECULES

Molecule	$A_{[0]}$(cm^{-1})	$B_{[0]}$(cm^{-1})	$C_{[0]}$(cm^{-1})	Point group	Geometrical parameters
ClO_2...	(1.740)	(0.3242)	(0.2733)	C_{2v}	
HCO...	....	1.495	1.401	C_s	$r_0(CH) = 1.08$ A (assumed) ∢HCO = 118°; $r_0(CO) = 1.19_3$ A
DCO...	....	1.282	1.172		
H_2O....	27.877; $A_e = 27.33$	14.512; $B_e = 14.57_5$	9.285; $C_e = 9.49_9$	C_{2v}	$r_0(OH) = 0.9568$ A; $∢_0(HOH) = 105°3'$; $r_e(OH) = 0.958_4$ A; $∢_e(HOH) = 104°27'$
HDO..	23.40	9.096	6.418	C_s	
D_2O....	15.38	7.25	4.835	C_{2v}	
H_2S....	10.373	8.991	4.732	C_{2v}	$r_0(SH) = 1.334$ A; ∢HSH = 92°16′
HDS...	9.683	4.843	3.140	C_s	
H_2Se...	7.7_7	3.8_3	....	C_{2v}	$r_0(HSe) = 1.6$ A
D_2Se...	3.8_3	1.92			
$NOCl^{35}$.	2.8448	0.1914	0.1793	C_s	
$NOCl^{37}$.	2.8538	0.1868	0.1753		
NOF...	3.175250	0.395070	0.350524	C_s	$r_0(NO) = 1.13$ A; $r_0(NF) = 1.52$ A; ∢ONF = 110°
O_3.....	3.55345	0.445276	0.394749	C_{2v}	$r_0(O'O) = 1.278$ A; ∢OO′O = 116°49′
SO_2....	2.02396	0.344161	0.293519	C_{2v}	$r_0(SO) = 1.433$ A; ∢OSO = 119°33′

TABLE 7j-7. FOUR-ATOMIC LINEAR MOLECULES

Molecule	$B_{[0]}$, cm^{-1}	Point group	Geometrical parameters
C_2H_2	1.17692; $B_e = 1.1838$	$D_{\infty h}$	r_0(CC) = 1.2080 A; r_e(CC) = 1.201_0 A; r_0(CH) = 1.0578 A; r_e(CH) = 1.0637 A
C_2HD	0.99141; $B_e = 0.996_7$	$C_{\infty v}$	
C_2D_2	0.84787; $B_e = 0.8507_5$	$D_{\infty h}$	
C_2N_2	0.1575_2	$D_{\infty h}$	r_0(C—C) = 1.380 A; r_0(C≡N) = 1.157 A (assumed)
$HC_2{}^{12}Cl^{35}$	0.189606	$C_{\infty v}$	r_0(CH) = 1.052 A; r_0(CC) = 1.211 A; r_0(CCl) = 1.632 A
$HC_2{}^{12}Cl^{37}$	0.185874		
$DC_2{}^{12}Cl^{35}$	0.173020		
$DC_2{}^{12}Cl^{37}$	0.169592		

TABLE 7j-8. FOUR-ATOMIC SYMMETRIC AND SPHERICAL TOP MOLECULES

Molecule	$A_{[0]}$ or $C_{[0]}$, cm^{-1}	$B_{[0]}$, cm^{-1}	Point group	Geometrical parameters
$AsCl_3{}^{35}$	....	0.071623	C_{3v}	r_0(AsCl) = 2.161 A; ∢(ClAsCl) = 98°25′
$AsCl_3{}^{37}$	....	0.068204		
AsF_3	....	0.1961011	C_{3v}	r_0(AsF) = 1.712 A; ∢(FAsF) = 102° (assumed)
AsH_3	....	3.723	C_{3v}	r_0(AsH) = 1.523 A; ∢(HAsH) = 91°34′
AsD_3	....	1.896		
BF_3	$A_{[0]} = (0.17_5)$	0.35_5	D_{3h}	r_0(BF) = 1.29_1 A
$N^{14}F_3$	....	0.356282	C_{3v}	r_0(NF) = 1.371 A; ∢(FNF) = 102°9′
$N^{15}F_3$	....	0.354556		
NH_3	A = (6.24)	9.941	C_{3v}	r_0(NH) = 1.014 A; ∢(HNH) = 106°47′
ND_3	A = (3.157)	5.138		
$PCl_3{}^{35}$	....	0.087297	C_{3v}	r_0(PCl) = 2.043 A; ∢(ClPCl) = 100°6′
$PCl_3{}^{37}$	....	0.082974		
PF_3	....	0.260847	C_{3v}	r_0(PF) = 1.535 A; ∢(FPF) = 100° (assumed)
PH_3	C = 3.87	4.446	C_{3v}	r_0(PH) = 1.424 A; ∢(HPH) = 93°50′
PH_2D	$\frac{A-C}{2} = 0.776956$	....	C_s	r_0(PH) = 1.4177 A; ∢(HPH) = 93°21′36″
PHD_2	$\frac{B-C}{2} = 0.284657$	....	C_s	r_0(PH) = 1.4116 A; ∢(HPH) = 93°15′24″
$Sb^{121}Cl_3$	....	0.05850	C_{3v}	r_0(SbCl) = 2.325; ∢(ClSbCl) = 99°30′
$Sb^{123}Cl_3$	....	0.05840		
SbH_3	$C_{[0]} = 2.80$	2.94	C_{3v}	r_0(SbH) = 1.71 A; ∢(HSbH) = 91°30′
SbD_3	....	1.49		

TABLE 7j-9. FOUR-ATOMIC ASYMMETRIC TOP MOLECULES

Molecule	$A_{[0]}$, cm^{-1}	$B_{[0]}$, cm^{-1}	$C_{[0]}$, cm^{-1}	Point group	Geometrical parameters
$CCl_2{}^{35}O$	0.264141	0.120086	0.0804639	C_s	
$CCl^{35}Cl^{37}O$	0.262440	0.112743	0.0787704		
CF_2O	$A \approx B = 0.3925$		0.19462	C_{2v}	
$Cl^{35}F_3$	0.458573	0.153830	0.115039	C_s	ClF_2F' $r_0(ClF) = 1.698$ A; $\sphericalangle(FClF) = 174°58'$ $r_0(ClF') = 1.598$ A; $\sphericalangle(F'ClF) = 87°29'$
$Cl^{37}F_3$	0.455421	0.153836	0.114840		
H_2CO	9.41003	1.2953_6	1.1342_5	C_{2v}	$r_0(CH) = 1.12$ A, $r_0(CO) = 1.21$ A; $\sphericalangle(HCH) = 118°$
$HN_3{}^{14}$	20.346	$\frac{1}{2}(B + C) = 0.397200$		C_s	$HN'N''N'''$ $r_0(N'H) = 1.021$ A; $\sphericalangle(N'N''N''') = (180°)$ (assumed) $r_0(N'N'') = 1.240$ A $r_0(N''N''') = 1.134$ A; $\sphericalangle(HN'N'') = 112°39'$
$HN^{14}N^{14}N^{15}$		$\frac{1}{2}(B + C) = 0.38440$			
$HN^{14}N^{15}N^{14}$		$\frac{1}{2}(B + C) = 0.39717$			
$HN^{15}N^{14}N^{14}$		$\frac{1}{2}(B + C) = 0.38521$			
$DN_3{}^{14}$		$\frac{1}{2}(B + C) = 0.37219$			
$HN^{14}CO$	30.57	$\frac{1}{2}(B + C) = 0.36662$		C_s	$r_0(HN) = 0.987$ A; $\sphericalangle(HNC) = 128°5'$ $r_0(NC) = 1.207$ A; $\sphericalangle(NCO) = (180°)$ (assumed) $r_0(CO) = 1.171$ A
$HN^{15}CO$		$\frac{1}{2}(B + C) = 0.35564$			
$DN^{14}CO$		$\frac{1}{2}(B + C) = 0.34015$			
$HN^{14}C^{12}S^{32}$		$0.19628 (K = 1)$ $\frac{1}{2}(B + C) = 0.19562 (K = 0)$	$0.19503 (K = 1)$	C_s	$r_0(NH) = (1.013$ A$)$; $\sphericalangle(HNC) = 130°15'$ $r_0(NC) = 1.2158$ A $r_0(CS) = 1.5609$ A
$HN^{14}C^{12}S^{33}$		$\frac{1}{2}(B + C) = 0.19325 (K = 0)$			
$HN^{14}C^{12}S^{34}$		$\frac{1}{2}(B + C) = 0.19102 (K = 0)$			
$HN^{14}C^{13}S^{32}$		$\frac{1}{2}(B + C) = 0.1950\ (K = 1)$			
$DN^{14}C^{12}S^{32}$		$\frac{1}{2}(B + C) = 0.18256 (K = 0)$		C_s	$r_0(ND) = 1.003$ A; $\sphericalangle(CND) = 132°16'$ $r_0(NC) = 1.2158$ A $r_0(CS) = 1.5609$ A
$DN^{14}C^{13}S^{32}$		$\frac{1}{2}(B + C) = 0.18212 (K = 1)$			
H_2O_2	10.056	(0.825) $\frac{1}{2}(B + C) \approx 0.82_5$		C_2	$r_0(OO) = 1.48$ A

TABLE 7j-10. FIVE-ATOMIC LINEAR MOLECULES

Molecule	$B_{[0]}$, cm^{-1}	Point group	Geometrical parameters
$HC^{12}C^{12}C^{12}N^{14}$	0.151740	$C_{\infty v}$	$r_0(CH) = 1.057$ A; $r_0(C{\equiv}C) = 1.203$ A; $r_0(C{-}C) = 1.382$ A; $r_0(CN) = 1.157$ A
$HC^{12}C^{12}C^{13}N^{14}$	0.151112		
$HC^{12}C^{13}C^{12}N^{14}$	0.151099		
$HC^{13}C^{12}C^{12}N^{14}$	0.147050		
$HC^{12}C^{12}C^{12}N^{15}$	0.147332		
$DC^{12}C^{12}C^{12}N^{14}$	0.140817		
$DC^{12}C^{12}C^{13}N^{14}$	0.140181		
$DC^{12}C^{13}C^{12}N^{14}$	0.140350		
$DC^{13}C^{12}C^{12}N^{14}$	0.137002		
$DC^{12}C^{12}C^{12}N^{15}$	0.136775		

TABLE 7j-11. FIVE-ATOMIC SYMMETRIC AND SPHERICAL TOP MOLECULES

Molecule	$A_{[0]}$ or $C_{[0]}$, cm^{-1}	$B_{[0]}$, cm^{-1}	Point group	Geometrical parameters
CF_3Br^{79}	....	0.069984	C_{3v}	r_0(CF) = 1.33 A; ∢(FCF) = 108° (assumed); r_0(CBr) = 1.908 A
CF_3Br^{81}	....	0.069331		
CF_3Cl^{35}	....	0.111262	C_{3v}	r_0(CF) = 1.328 A; ∢(FCF) = 108° (assumed); r_0(CCl) = 1.740 A
CF_3Cl^{37}	....	0.108458		
CF_3I	....	0.050809	C_{3v}	r_0(CF) = 1.33 A (assumed); ∢FCF = 108° (assumed); r_0(CI) = 2.134 A
CH_4	....	5.249	T_d	r_0(CH) = 1.0931 A
CH_3D	....	3.878	C_{3v}	r_0(CD) = r_0(CH) = 1.0936 A
CHD_3	....	3.278	C_{3v}	r_0(CH) = r_0(CD) = 1.0919 A
CD_4	....	2.64_7	T_d	r_0(CD) = 1.089 A
$CHBr_3^{79}$	....	0.041616	C_{3v}	r_0(CH) = 1.06_8 A; ∢(BrCBr) = 110°48′; r_0(CBr) = 1.930 A
$CHBr_3^{81}$	....	0.040605		
$CCDBr_3^{79}$	....	0.041344		
$CDBr_3^{81}$	....	0.040345		
$C^{12}H_3Br^{79}$	$A_{[0]} = 5.08_2$	0.319167	C_{3v}	r_0(CBr) = 1.9391 A; ∢(HCH) = 111°14′; r_0(CH) = 1.113
$C^{12}H_3Br^{81}$	$A_{[0]} = 5.08_2$	0.317953		
$C^{13}H_3Br^{79}$	....	0.304194		
$C^{13}H_3Br^{81}$	....	0.302971		
$C^{12}HD_2Br^{79}$	$2(B - C) = 0.010597$		C_s	
$C^{12}HD_2Br^{81}$	$2(B - C) = 0.010489$			
$C^{12}D_3Br^{79}$	....	0.257330	C_{3v}	r_0(CBr) = 1.9391 A; ∢(DCD) = 111°26′; r_0(CD) = 1.104 A
$C^{12}D_3Br^{81}$	....	0.256218		
$CHCl_3^{35}$	....	0.110141	C_{3v}	r_0(CH) = 1.073 A; ∢(ClCCl) = 110°24′; r_0(CCl) = 1.767 A
$CHCl_3^{37}$	....	0.104389		
$CDCl_3^{35}$	....	0.108414		
$C^{12}H_3Cl^{35}$	$A_{[0]} = 5.09_7$	0.443402	C_{3v}	r_0(CCl) = 1.7810 A; ∢(HCH) = 110°31′; r_0(CH) = 1.113 A
$C^{12}H_3Cl^{37}$	....	0.436574		
$C^{13}H_3Cl^{35}$	....	0.426835		
$C^{13}H_3Cl^{37}$	....	0.419957		
$C^{12}D_3Cl^{35}$	....	0.361647	C_{3v}	r_0(CCl) = 1.7810 A; ∢(DCD) = 110°43′; r_0(CD) = 1.104 A
$C^{12}D_3Cl^{37}$	....	0.355528		
$C^{12}H_3Cl^{36}$	....	0.439892	C_{2v}	
$C^{12}H_2DCl^{35}$	$\frac{1}{2}(B + C) = 0.41125$		C_s	
$C^{12}H_2DCl^{37}$	$\frac{1}{2}(B + C) = 0.40471$			
$C^{12}HD_2Cl^{35}$	$C_{[0]} = 0.37935$	0.38965		
$C^{12}HD_2Cl^{37}$	$\frac{1}{2}(B + C) = 0.37816$			
$C^{12}HF_3$	....	0.345196	C_{3v}	r_0(CH) = 1.098 A; ∢(FCF) = 108°48′; r_0(CF) = 1.332 A
$C^{12}DF_3$	....	0.330940		
$C^{13}HF_3$	....	0.347640		
$C^{12}H_3F$	$A_{[0]} = 5.10_0$	0.851785	C_{3v}	r_0(CH) = 1.10_9 A; ∢(HCN) = 110°0′; r_0(CF) = 1.385 A
$C^{13}H_3F$	....	0.829318		
$C^{12}D_3F$	....	0.682132		
$C^{12}H_3I$	$A_{[0]} = 5.07_7$	0.250215	C_{3v}	r_0(CH) = 1.106 A; ∢(HCH) = 111°10′; r_0(CI) = 2.1396 A
$C^{13}H_3I$	....	0.237465		
$C^{12}D_3I$	....	0.201482	C_{3v}	r_0(CI) = 2.1392 A; r_0(CD) = 1.104; ∢(DCD) = 111°37′
$C^{12}HD_2I$	$2(B - C) = 0.006519$		C_s	
$Ge^{70}F_3{}^{19}Cl^{35}$	....	0.072334	C_{3v}	r_0(GeF) = 1.688 A; ∢(FGeF) = 107°42′; r_0(GeCl) = 2.067 A
$Ge^{70}F_3{}^{19}Cl^{37}$	....	0.070320		
$Ge^{72}F_3{}^{19}Cl^{35}$	....	0.072301		
$Ge^{72}F_3{}^{19}Cl^{37}$	....	0.070283		
$Ge^{74}F_3{}^{19}Cl^{35}$	....	0.072270		
$Ge^{74}F_3{}^{19}Cl^{37}$	....	0.070248		
GeH_4	....	2.87	T_d	r_0(GeH) = 1.47_8 A
$Ge^{70}H_3Br^{79}$	....	0.081342	C_{3v}	r_0(GeH) = 1.55 A; ∢(HGeH) = 112°0′; r_0(GeBr) = 2.297 A
$Ge^{70}H_3Br^{81}$	....	0.080395		
$Ge^{72}H_3Br^{79}$	....	0.080269		
$Ge^{72}H_3Br^{81}$	....	0.079322		
$Ge^{74}H_3Br^{79}$	....	0.079251		
$Ge^{74}H_3Br^{81}$	....	0.078303		
$Ge^{76}H_3Br^{79}$	....	0.078282		
$Ge^{76}H_3Br^{81}$	....	0.077332		

TABLE 7j-11. FIVE-ATOMIC SYMMETRIC AND SPHERICAL TOP MOLECULES (*Continued*)

Molecule	$A_{[0]}$ or $C_{[0]}$, cm^{-1}	$B_{[0]}$, cm^{-1}	Point group	Geometrical parameters
$Ge^{70}HCl_3^{35}$	....	0.072475	C_{3v}	r_0(GeCl) = 2.1139 A; ∢(ClGeCl) = 108°17′; r_0(GeH) = 1.55 A
$Ge^{72}HCl_3^{35}$	....	0.0723586		
$Ge^{74}HCl_3^{35}$	....	0.0722445		
$Ge^{70}HCl_3^{37}$	....	0.0688389		
$Ge^{72}HCl_3^{37}$	....	0.0687284		
$Ge^{74}HCl_3^{37}$	....	0.0686207		
$Ge^{70}H_3Cl^{35}$	....	0.146828	C_{3v}	r_0(GeH) = 1.52 A; ∢(HGeH) = 111°4′; r_0(GeCl) = 2.147 A
$Ge^{74}H_3Cl^{35}$	$A_{[0]}$ = 2.603	0.144563		
$Ge^{74}H_3Cl^{37}$	....	0.139359		
$Ge^{76}H_3Cl^{37}$	....	0.13831		
MnO_3F	....	0.137732	C_{3v}	
$POCl_3^{35}$	....	0.067220	C_{3v}	r_0(PCl) = 1.99 A; ∢(ClPCl) = 103°36′; r_0(PO) = 1.45 A
$POCl_3^{37}$	....	0.064457		
$PO^{16}F_3$	....	0.1532485	C_{3v}	r_0(PF) = 1.52 A; ∢(FPF) = 102°30′; r_0(PO) = 1.45 A
$PO^{18}F_3$	....	0.146610		
$PS^{32}Cl_3^{35}$	....	0.046787	C_{3v}	r_0(PCl) = 2.02 A; ∢(ClPCl) = 100°30′; r_0(PS) = 1.85 A
$PS^{32}Cl_3^{37}$	....	0.045222		
$PS^{34}Cl_3^{35}$	....	0.045702		
$PS^{32}F_3$	....	0.0886500	C_{3v}	r_0(PF) = 1.53 A; ∢(FPF) = 100°18′; r_0(PS) = 1.87 A
$PS^{33}F_3$	....	0.087218		
$PS^{34}F_3$	....	0.086052		
$Re^{185}O_3Cl^{35}$	....	0.069856	C_{3v}	r_0(ReO) = 1.761 A; ∢(OReO) = 108°20′; r_0(ReCl) = 2.230 A
$Re^{185}O_3Cl^{37}$	....	0.067547		
$Re^{187}O_3Cl^{35}$	....	0.069834		
$Re^{187}O_3Cl^{37}$	....	0.067525		
SiF_3Br^{79}	....	0.051702	C_{3v}	r_0(SiF) = 1.560 A; ∢(FSiF) = 108°30′; r_0(SiBr) = 2.153 A
SiF_3Br^{81}	....	0.051173		
SiF_3Cl^{35}	....	0.082650	C_{3v}	r_0(SiF) = 1.560 A; ∢(FSiF) = 108°30′; r_0(SiCl) = 1.989 A
SiF_3Cl^{37}	....	0.080491		
SiH_4	....	(2.96)	T_d	r_0(SiH) = 1.4798 A
$SiHD_3$	....	1.7755	C_{3v}	
$Si^{28}H_3Br^{79}$	....	0.144159	C_{3v}	r_0(SiH) = 1.57 A; ∢(HSiH) = 111°20′; r_0(SiBr) = 2.209 A
$Si^{28}H_3Br^{81}$	....	0.143187		
$Si^{29}H_3Br^{79}$	....	0.141196		
$Si^{29}H_3Br^{81}$	....	0.140220		
$Si^{30}H_3Br^{79}$	....	0.138409		
$Si^{30}H_3Br^{81}$	....	0.137431		
$SiHCl^{35}$	....	0.0824732	C_{3v}	r_0(SiH) = 1.47 A; ∢(ClSiCl) = 109°22′; r_0(SiCl) = 2.021 A
$SiHCl^{37}$	....	0.0782564		
$Si^{28}H_3Cl^{35}$	....	0.22261	C_{3v}	r_0(SiCl) = 2.048 A; ∢(HSiH) = 110°57′; r_0(SiH) = 1.50 A
$Si^{30}H_3Cl^{35}$	....	0.21634		
$Si^{28}H_3Cl^{37}$	....	0.21723		
$Si^{28}D_3Cl^{35}$	....	0.19739		
$Si^{29}D_3Cl^{35}$	....	0.19715		
$Si^{30}D_3Cl^{35}$	....	0.19303		
$Si^{28}D_3Cl^{37}$	....	0.19256		
$Si^{28}HF_3$	....	0.240432	C_{3v}	r_0(SiF) = 1.565 A; ∢(FSiF) = 108°17′; r_0(SiH) = 1.455 A (assumed)
$Si^{29}HF_3$	....	0.240021		
$Si^{30}HF_3$	....	0.239622		
$Si^{28}H_3F$	....	0.477927	C_{3v}	r_0(SiH) = 1.503 A; ∢(HSiH) = (111°) (assumed); r_0(SiF) = 1.593 A
$Si^{29}H_3F$	....	0.473550		
$Si^{30}H_3F$	....	0.469411		
$Si^{28}D_3F$	....	0.408732		
$Si^{29}D_3F$	....	0.406150		
$Si^{30}D_3F$	....	0.403685		
SiH_3I	....	0.10726	C_{3v}	

TABLE 7j-12. FIVE-ATOMIC ASYMMETRIC TOP MOLECULES

Molecule	$A_{[0]}$, cm^{-1}	$B_{[0]}$, cm^{-1}	$C_{[0]}$, cm^{-1}	Point group	Geometrical parameters
CH_2Br_2	$\left[A - \frac{B+C}{2}\right] = 0.821$			C_{2v}	r_0(CBr) = 1.907 A; ∢(HCH) = 112° (elec. diffr.)
CH_2CO	....	0.343347	0.330757	C_{2v}	r_0(CH) = 1.075 A; ∢(HCH) = 122.0°; r_0(CO) = 1.16 A (assumed); r_0(CC) = 1.31_5 A
CHDCO	....	0.321790	0.306032	C_s	
CD_2CO	....	0.304237	0.285286	C_{2v}	
$CH_2Cl_2^{35}$	1.06746	0.11076	0.10224	C_{2v}	r_0(CCl) = 1.7724 A; ∢(ClCCl) = 111°47′; r_0(CH) = 1.068 A; ∢(HCH) = 112°0′
$CH_2Cl^{35}Cl^{37}$	1.063342	0.10779	0.099677	C_s	
$CH_2Cl_2^{37}$	1.0592	0.1048	0.09713	C_{2v}	
$CHDCl_2^{35}$	0.9072	0.1102	0.1010	C_s	
$CHDCl^{35}Cl^{37}$	0.90364	0.10732	0.09845	C_1	
$CD_2Cl_2^{35}$	0.78976	0.1095	0.09985	C_{2v}	
$CD_2Cl^{35}Cl^{37}$	0.78660	0.10666	0.09740	C_s	
CH_2ClBr	$\left[A - \frac{B+C}{2}\right] = 0.897_5$			C_s	r_0(CBr) = 1.911 A; r_0(CCl) = 1.766 A (assumed); ∢(HCH) = 112° (elec. diffr.)
CH_2F_2	1.6391	0.3537	0.3085	C_{2v}	r_0(CH) = 1.09 A; ∢(HCH) = 112°; r_0(CF) = 1.36 A; ∢(FCF) = 108°
HCO_2H	2.55_4	0.39991	0.34967	C_s(?)	
$S^{32}O_2F_2$	0.171444	0.169377	0.168690	C_{2v}	r_0(SO) = 1.370; ∢(OSO) = 129°38′; r_0(SF) = 1.570; ∢(FSF) = 92°47′
$S^{34}O_2F_2$	0.171444	0.169217	0.168533		

TABLE 7j-13. SIX-ATOMIC LINEAR MOLECULES

Molecule	$B_{[0]}$, cm^{-1}	Point group	Geometrical parameters
C_4H_2	1.14641	$D_{\infty h}$	r_0(C—C) = 1.37$_5$ A; assuming r_0(C≡C) = 1.207 A and r_0(CH) = 1.060 A

TABLE 7j-14. SIX-ATOMIC SYMMETRIC AND SPHERICAL TOP MOLECULES

Molecule	$B_{[0]}$, cm^{-1}	Point group	Geometrical parameters
$B^{10}H_3CO$	0.299538	C_{3v}	r_0(BH) = 1.194 A; r_0(BC) = 1.540 A; ∢(HBH) = 113°52′; r_0(CO) = 1.131 A
$B^{11}H_3CO$	0.288773		
$B^{10}D_3CO$	0.251185		
$B^{11}D_3CO$	0.244721		
CF_3CN^{14}	0.0982523	C_{3v}	r_0(CF) = 1.335 A; r_0(CN) = 1.158 A (assumed); ∢(FCF) = 108° (assumed); r_0(CC) = 1.464 A
CF_3CN^{15}	0.0952611		
$C^{12}H_3C^{12}N^{14}$	0.306840	C_{3v}(?)	r_0(CH) = 1.092 A; r_0(CC) = 1.460 A; ∢(HCH) = 109°8′; r_0(CN) = 1.158 A
$C^{12}H_3C^{12}N^{15}$	0.297599		
$C^{12}H_3C^{13}N^{14}$	0.306688		
$C^{13}H_3C^{12}N^{14}$	0.297977		
$C^{12}D_3C^{12}N^{14}$	0.262112		
$C^{12}D_3C^{13}N^{14}$	0.261798		
$CH_3Hg^{198}Br^{81}$	0.03754	C_{3v}	r_0(HgBr) = 2.406 A; r_0(CH) = 1.092 A (assumed); ∢(HCH) = 109°7′ (assumed); r_0(CHg) = 2.07 A
$CH_3Hg^{202}Br^{79}$	0.03803		
$CH_3Hg^{202}Br^{81}$	0.03743		
$CH_3Hg^{198}Cl^{35}$	0.069296	C_{3v}	r_0(CH) = 1.092 A (assumed); ∢(HCH) = 109°7′; r_0(CHg) = 2.059 A; r_0(HgCl) = 2.282 A
$CH_3Hg^{198}Cl^{37}$	0.066918		
$CH_3Hg^{199}Cl^{35}$	0.069286		
$CH_3Hg^{199}Cl^{37}$	0.066906		
$CH_3Hg^{200}Cl^{35}$	0.069275		
$CH_3Hg^{200}Cl^{37}$	0.066895		
$CH_3Hg^{202}Cl^{35}$	0.069255		
$CH_3Hg^{202}Cl^{37}$	0.066872		
$CH_3Hg^{204}Cl^{35}$	0.069234		
$CH_3Hg^{204}Cl^{37}$	0.066849		
CH_3NC^{12}	0.335328	C_{3v}(?)	r_0(CH) = 1.094 A; r_0(C—N) = 1.427 A; ∢(HCH) = 109°46′; r_0(N≡C) = 1.167 A
CH_3NC^{13}	0.323420		
CD_3NC^{12}	0.286266		
CD_3NC^{13}	0.276150		

TABLE 7j-15. SIX-ATOMIC ASYMMETRIC TOP MOLECULES

Molecule	$A_{[0]}$, cm^{-1}	$B_{[0]}$, cm^{-1}	$C_{[0]}$, cm^{-1}	Point group	Geometrical parameters
C_2H_4	4.867	(0.911$_6$)		V_h	r_0(CH) = 1.071 A; ∢(HCH) = 119°55′ r_0(C═C) = 1.353 A
C_2D_4	2.437	(0.652$_2$)			
CH_2CF_2	0.36698		0.17831	C_{2v}	r_0(CH) = (1.07 A); ∢(HCH) = (110°) r_0(CF) = (1.32 A); ∢(FCF) = (110°) r_0(CC) = (1.31 A)
CH_2CFCl^{35}	0.356300		0.115025	C_s	
CH_2CFCl^{37}	0.356290		0.112761		
CH_2CHBr^{79}		0.13885	0.12884	C_s	
CH_2CHBr^{81}		0.13804	0.12814		
CH_2CHCl^{35}		0.20116	0.18163	C_s	
CH_2CHCl^{37}		0.19693	0.17817		
CH_2CHI		0.10870	0.10230	C_s	
CH_3OH		(0.8032)		C_s	r_0(C—O) = 1.434 A; ∢(COH) = 105°56′ r_0(CH) = 1.093 A (assumed); ∢(HCH) = 109°30′ r_0(OH) = 0.937 A Distance of O atom from symmetry axis of CH_3 group: 0.079 A
$CH_3S^{32}H$		$\frac{1}{2}(B + C) = 0.42181$		C_s	r_0(CH) = 1.10 A (assumed) r_0(SH) = 1.34 A; ∢(HCH) = 109°28′ (assumed) r_0(CS) = 1.815 A; ∢(HSC) = 100° (assumed)
$CH_3S^{34}H$		$\frac{1}{2}(B + C) = 0.4150$			

7k. Wave Mechanics

7k-1. Fundamental Relations. A mechanical system is determined by its Hamiltonian $H(q_i p_i t)$ which is a function of the f coordinates q_i and their conjugate momenta p_i. The quantity f is the number of degrees of freedom. The Hamiltonian may or may not contain the time explicitly.

The wave equation

$$H\phi = -i\hbar \frac{\partial \phi}{\partial t} \tag{7k-1}$$

is obtained by considering H an operator in which $p_i \equiv -i\hbar(\partial/\partial q_i)$ ($\hbar = h/2\pi$). If $H(q_i, p_i)$ represents a conservative system (does not contain the time explicitly), one can write

$$\phi(q_i,t) = e^{-(2\pi i W/h)t}\psi(q_i) \tag{7k-2}$$

This changes (7k-1) into

$$H\psi(q_i) = W\psi(q_i) \tag{7k-3}$$

The task of wave mechanics is to find the solutions of Eqs. (7k-1) or (7k-3) with the following boundary conditions: ψ must be single-valued and it and its derivatives continuous everywhere. At infinity ψ must remain finite. The integral $\int|\psi|^2 d\tau$ over a finite part of the configuration space should not be infinite. If the integral $\int|\psi|^2 d\tau$ over the whole configuration space exists, the ψ can be normalized so that

$$\int|\psi|^2 d\tau = 1$$

7k-2. Special Solvable Systems. The wave equation can be solved in terms of known elementary functions in only relatively few cases. The following are some of the more important ones.

One-dimensional motion of particle in potential V

$$\frac{d^2\psi}{dx^2} + \frac{2m}{\hbar^2}(W - V)\psi = 0 \tag{7k-4}$$

1. Free particle $V = 0$

$$\frac{d^2\psi}{dx^2} + \frac{2mW}{\hbar^2}\psi = 0 \tag{7k-5}$$

$$\psi = Ae^{i(p_x/\hbar)} + Be^{-i(p_x/\hbar)} \qquad W = \frac{p_x^2}{2m}$$

all values of $E \geq 0$ allowed

2. Harmonic oscillator $V = 2\pi^2\omega^2 mx^2$

$$\frac{d^2}{dx^2} + \frac{2m}{\hbar^2}(E - 2\pi^2\omega^2 mx^2)\psi = 0 \tag{7k-6}$$

$$\psi(x) = 2^{-v/2}(v!)^{-\frac{1}{2}}\alpha^{\frac{1}{2}}\pi^{-\frac{1}{4}}e^{-\alpha^2x^2}H_v(x) \qquad \alpha^2 = \frac{4\pi^2 m\omega}{h}$$

where ω is classical vibration frequency and $H_v(x)$ Hermitian polynomial of order $\boldsymbol{v}$.

$$W_v = (v + \tfrac{1}{2})\omega h \qquad v = 0, 1, 2, \ldots$$

3. Morse potential $V(r) = D[1 - e^{-\beta(x-x_e)}]^2$

$$W_v = \beta h \sqrt{\frac{D}{2\pi^2 m}}\left(v+\frac{1}{2}\right) - \frac{\hbar^2\beta^2}{2m}\left(v+\frac{1}{2}\right)^2 \qquad (7k-7)$$

$$= \hbar\omega\left(v+\frac{1}{2}\right) - \frac{h^2\omega^2}{4D}\left(v+\frac{1}{2}\right)^2$$

with $\omega = (\beta/2\pi)\sqrt{2D/m}$ the classical frequency for small amplitudes. The wave functions are generalized Laguerre functions.[1]

4. Teller-Pöschl potential

$$V = \frac{\hbar^2\alpha^2}{2m}\left[\frac{\nu(\nu-1)}{\sinh^2\alpha(r-r_0)} - \frac{\mu(\mu+1)}{\cosh^2\alpha(r-r_0)}\right] \qquad \begin{array}{l}\mu > 1\\ \nu > 1\\ \alpha > 0\\ r_0 \le r \le \infty\end{array} \qquad (7k-8)$$

$$\psi_0 = K_0 \sinh^\nu \alpha(r-r_0)\cosh^{-\mu}\alpha(r-r_0)$$

$$\psi_v = K_v\psi_0 \sum_{k=0}^{v} a_{v,2k}\sinh^{2k}\alpha(r-r_0)$$

$$W_v = \frac{\hbar^2\alpha^2}{2m}(\mu-\nu-2v)^2 \qquad v = 0, 1, 2, \ldots$$

The Morse curve is a special case of the Teller-Pöschl potential for which $\nu \to \infty$, $\mu \to \infty$ with $\mu - \nu$ fixed, $r_0 \to -\infty$.

5. One-dimensional rotator

$$\frac{d^2\psi}{d\phi^2} + \frac{2IW}{\hbar^2}\psi = 0 \qquad I = \text{moment of inertia} \qquad (7k-9)$$

$$\psi(\phi) = A\cos m\phi + B\sin m\phi \qquad m = 0, 1, 2, 3$$

$$W = \frac{\hbar^2}{2I}m^2$$

6. Two-dimensional rotator (θ, ϕ)

$$\frac{1}{\sin\theta}\frac{\partial}{\partial\theta}\left(\sin\theta\frac{\partial\psi}{\partial\theta}\right) + \frac{1}{\sin^2\theta}\frac{\partial^2\psi}{\partial\phi^2} + \frac{2IW}{\hbar^2}\psi = 0 \qquad (7k-10)$$

$$\psi_{J,m} = P^m{}_J(\cos\theta)e^{\pm im\phi} \qquad J = 0, 1, 2, 3 \qquad |m| \le J$$

$$W_J = \frac{\hbar^2}{2I}J(J+1) \qquad \begin{array}{l}J\hbar = \text{total angular momentum}\\ m\hbar = \text{its projection on } z \text{ axis}\end{array} \qquad (7k-11)$$

Every state is $2J + 1$ fold degenerate

7. Symmetrical top

$$\frac{1}{\sin\theta}\frac{\partial}{\partial\theta}\left(\sin\theta\frac{\partial\psi}{\partial\theta}\right) + \frac{1}{\sin^2\theta}\left(\frac{\partial}{\partial\phi} - i\Lambda\cos\theta\right)^2\psi + \frac{A}{C}\frac{\partial^2\psi}{\partial\chi^2} + \frac{2AW}{\hbar^2}\psi = 0 \qquad (7k-12)$$

$\Lambda\hbar$ angular momentum about figure axis

$$\psi(\theta, \phi, \chi) = e^{\pm i(m\phi+\Lambda\chi)}U(u)$$

where $u = \cos\theta$, $m\hbar$ component of angular momentum along z axis, $\Lambda\hbar$ component of angular momentum along symmetry axis. $U(u)$ satisfies

[1] P. M. Morse, *Phys. Rev.* **34**, 57 (1929).

$$(1-u^2)\frac{d^2U}{du^2} - 2u(1-u^2)\frac{dU}{du} + [D(1-u^2) - (\Lambda^2+m^2) + 2\Lambda mu]U = 0$$

$$W = \frac{\hbar^2}{2}\left[\frac{J(J+1)-\Lambda^2}{A} + \frac{\Lambda^2}{C}\right] \quad \text{with } D = \frac{2AW}{\hbar^2} + \left(1-\frac{A}{C}\right)\Lambda^2$$

$$U_{\rho,\Lambda,m} = \sin^d\frac{\theta}{2}\cos^s\frac{\theta}{2}G_\rho\left(1+s+d, 1+d, \sin^2\frac{\theta}{2}\right)$$

α is equal to $|\Lambda|$ or $|m|$, whichever is larger; $s = |m+\Lambda|$; $d = |m-\Lambda|$; $\rho = J - \alpha$; G_ρ is the appropriate Jacobi polynomial.

8. One-center problem

$$V = -\frac{Ze^2}{r} \tag{7k-13}$$

Spherical coordinates $= r, \theta, \phi$

$\mu = mM/(m+M)$ = reduced mass; m = mass of electron; M = mass of nucleus. For $W < 0$

$$\psi(r,\theta,\phi) = R(r)\Theta(\theta)\frac{1}{\sqrt{2\pi}}e^{im\phi}$$

$$\Theta(\theta) = \frac{(2l+1)(l-m)!}{2(l+m)!}\sin^m\theta P_l{}^m(\cos\theta) \quad \text{(normalized)}$$

$P_l{}^m$ are the associate Legendre polynomials (see 7k-3)

$$R_{n,l}(\rho) = \frac{4(n-l-1)!Z^3}{(n+l)!^3n^4a_1{}^3}\rho^l e^{-\rho/2}L_{n+l}^{2l+1}(\rho) \quad \text{(normalized)}$$

where L_{n+l}^{2l+1} is an associate Laguerre polynomial (see 7k-3)

$a_1 = \dfrac{\hbar^2}{\mu e^2}$ = radius of the first Bohr orbit

$$W_n = -\frac{\mu e^4}{2\hbar^2}\frac{Z^2}{n^2}$$

For $W > 0$ all energies are allowed; wave functions, see Bethe (1933).

7k-3. Often-used Wave Functions

1. Hermite polynomials

$$\psi_v(x) = \rho^{-(\alpha^2/2)x^2}H(\alpha x)$$

$$\begin{aligned} H_0(x) &= 1 \\ H_1(x) &= 2x \\ H_2(x) &= 4x^2 - 2 \\ H_3(x) &= 8x^3 - 12x \\ H_4(x) &= 16x^4 - 48x^2 + 12 \\ H_5(x) &= 32x^5 - 160x^3 + 120x \end{aligned}$$

Normalization factor

$$N_v = \left(\frac{\alpha}{2^v v!}\right)^{\frac{1}{2}}\pi^{-\frac{1}{4}}$$

2. Legendre polynomials and associate Legendre polynomials

$$P_l{}^m(\cos\theta) = \sin^m\theta\frac{d^m}{(d\cos\theta)^m}P_l(\cos\theta)$$

where $P_l(z) = P_l(\cos\theta)$ are the Legendre polynomials defined by

$$P_l(z) = \frac{d^l(z^2-1)^l}{dz^l} \qquad z = \cos\theta$$

Legendre polynomials

$$\begin{aligned}
P_0(z) &= 1 \\
P_1(z) &= z && = \cos\theta \\
P_2(z) &= \tfrac{1}{2}(3z^2 - 1) && = \tfrac{1}{4}(3\cos 2\theta + 1) \\
P_3(z) &= \tfrac{1}{2}(5z^3 - 3z) && = \tfrac{1}{8}(5\cos 3\theta + 3\cos\theta) \\
P_4(z) &= \tfrac{1}{8}(35z^4 - 30z^2 + 3) && = \tfrac{1}{64}(35\cos 4\theta + 20\cos 2\theta + 9) \\
P_5(z) &= \tfrac{1}{8}(63z^5 - 70z^3 + 15z) && = \tfrac{1}{128}(63\cos 5\theta + 35\cos 3\theta + 30\cos\theta) \\
P_6(z) &= \tfrac{1}{16}(231z^6 - 315z^4 + 105z^2 - 5) && = \tfrac{1}{512}(231\cos 6\theta + 126\cos 4\theta \\
&&& \qquad + 105\cos 2\theta + 50)
\end{aligned}$$

Associate Legendre polynomials

$$\begin{aligned}
P_1{}^1(z) &= (1 - z^2)^{\frac{1}{2}} && = \sin\theta \\
P_2{}^1(z) &= 3(1 - z^2)^{\frac{1}{2}}z && = \tfrac{3}{2}\sin 2\theta \\
P_2{}^2(z) &= 3(1 - z^2) && = \tfrac{3}{2}(1 - \cos 2\theta) \\
P_3{}^1(z) &= \tfrac{3}{2}(1 - z^2)^{\frac{1}{2}}(5z^2 - 1) && = \tfrac{3}{8}(\sin\theta + 5\sin 3\theta) \\
P_3{}^2(z) &= 15(1 - z^2)z && = \tfrac{15}{4}(\cos\theta - 3\cos 3\theta) \\
P_3{}^3(z) &= 15(1 - z^2)^{\frac{3}{2}} && = \tfrac{15}{4}(3\sin\theta - \sin 3\theta) \\
P_4{}^1(z) &= \tfrac{5}{2}(1 - z^2)^{\frac{1}{2}}(7z^3 - 3z) && = \tfrac{5}{16}(2\sin 2\theta + 7\sin 4\theta) \\
P_4{}^2(z) &= \tfrac{15}{2}(1 - z^2)(7z^2 - 1) && = \tfrac{15}{16}(3 + 4\cos 2\theta - 7\cos 4\theta) \\
P_4{}^3(z) &= 105(1 - z^2)^{\frac{3}{2}}z && = \tfrac{105}{8}(2\sin 2\theta - \sin 4\theta) \\
P_4{}^4(z) &= 105(1 - z^2)^2 && = \tfrac{105}{8}(3 - 4\cos 2\theta + \cos 4\theta)
\end{aligned}$$

3. Radial wave functions of the one-center problem

$$\begin{aligned}
R_{10} &= 2e^{-r} \\
R_{20} &= \frac{1}{\sqrt{2}}\, e^{-\frac{1}{2}r}\left(1 - \frac{1}{2}\, r\right) \\
R_{21} &= \frac{1}{2\sqrt{6}}\, e^{-\frac{1}{2}r} r \\
R_{30} &= \frac{2}{3\sqrt{3}}\, e^{-\frac{1}{3}r}\left(1 - \frac{2}{3}\, r + \frac{2}{27}\, r^2\right) \\
R_{31} &= \frac{8}{27\sqrt{6}}\, e^{-\frac{1}{3}r} r \left(1 - \frac{1}{6}\, r\right) \\
R_{32} &= \frac{4}{81\sqrt{30}}\, e^{-\frac{1}{3}r} r^2 \\
R_{40} &= \frac{1}{4}\, e^{-\frac{1}{4}r}\left(1 - \frac{3}{4}\, r + \frac{1}{8}\, r^2 - \frac{1}{192}\, r^3\right) \\
R_{41} &= \frac{1}{16}\sqrt{\frac{5}{3}}\, e^{-\frac{1}{4}r} r \left(1 - \frac{1}{4}\, r + \frac{1}{80}\, r^2\right) \\
R_{42} &= \frac{1}{64\sqrt{5}}\, e^{-\frac{1}{4}r} r^2 \left(1 - \frac{1}{12}\, r\right) \\
R_{43} &= \frac{1}{768\sqrt{35}}\, e^{-\frac{1}{4}r} r^3
\end{aligned}$$

7k-4. Approximation Methods. *Perturbation Method for Non-time-dependent Cases.* Required, the solution of the wave equation

$$H\psi = W\psi \tag{7k-14}$$

If

$$H = H^0 + S$$

and $\psi_n{}^0$ and $W_n{}^0$ are the known solutions and eigen values of the "unperturbed" wave equation

$$H^0\psi^0 = W^0\psi^0 \tag{7k-15}$$

then often good approximations to the solution of (7k-14) can be found by the perturbation method. For this method to be applicable it is necessary that the influence of S is not large so that the solutions of (7k-14) are relatively close to those of (7k-15). For an exact meaning of this condition see later on. The procedure is simpler if the unperturbed states are not degenerate.

Nondegenerate States. Develop the solution of ψ_n of (7k-14) in terms of the $\psi_n{}^0$

$$\psi_n = \psi_n{}^0 + \sum_i a_{in}\psi_i{}^0 + \sum_i b_{in}\psi_i{}^0 + \cdots \tag{7k-16}$$

All a_{in} are small of first order, the b_{nn} are small of order two, etc. The energy becomes

$$W_n = W_n{}^0 + \epsilon_n{}^{(1)} + \epsilon_n{}^{(2)} + \cdots \tag{7k-17}$$

One finds, if the perturbation matrix elements S_{ij} are defined by

$$S_{ij} = \int \overline{\psi}_i S \psi_j d\tau \tag{7k-18}$$

that

$$\epsilon_n{}^{(1)} = S_{nn}$$

$$a_{in} = \frac{S_{in}}{W_i - W_n} \qquad \text{for } i \neq n, \qquad a_{nn} = 0$$

Σ' means summation over all values of i except $i = n$.

$$\epsilon_n{}^{(2)} = \sum_j{}' \frac{S_{nj}S_{jn}}{W_n - W_j}$$

$$b_{in} = \sum_j{}' \frac{S_{ij}S_{jn}}{(W_n - W_i)(W_n - W_j)} - \frac{S_{in}S_{nn}}{(W_n - W_i)^2}$$

b_{nn} is obtained from normalization. $-b_{nn} = \frac{1}{2}\sum_i |a_{in}|^2$. Higher-order approximations become increasingly complex.

Degenerate Case. Consider an f-fold degenerate state with energy W and wave functions $\psi_1{}^0$ to $\psi_f{}^0$ so that

$$H^0\psi_n{}^0 = W\psi_n{}^0 \qquad n = 1, 2, \cdots f \tag{7k-19}$$

Any linear combination

$$\psi_n = \sum_{i=1}^{f} A_{in}\psi_i^0$$

is again a solution (7k-19). A perturbation will in general require a definite linear combination as zero approximation. The coefficients A_{in} which are of order of magnitude one are found as solutions of the set of linear equations

$$\begin{array}{lllll}
(S_{11} - \epsilon_n)A_{1n} & + S_{12}A_{2n} & + \cdots + S_{1f}A_{fn} & & = 0 \\
S_{21}A_{1n} & + (S_{22} - \epsilon_n)A_{2n} & + \cdots + S_{2f}S_{fn} & & = 0 \\
\cdots & \cdots & \cdots & & \cdots \\
S_{f1}A_{1n} & + S_{f2}A_{2n} & + \cdots + (S_{ff} - \epsilon_n)A_{fn} & & = 0
\end{array}$$

These are solvable only if the secular determinant is zero

$$\begin{vmatrix}
S_{11} - \epsilon_n & S_{12} & \cdots & S_{1f} \\
S_{21} & S_{22} - \epsilon_n & & S_{2f} \\
\cdots & \cdots & \cdots & \cdots \\
S_{f1} & S_{f2} & \cdots & S_{ff} - \epsilon_n
\end{vmatrix} = 0$$

There are f solutions of the secular determinant for ϵ_n. All may be different. In that case the degeneracy is completely removed and the zero-order approximation is completely determined as all A_{ij} values are fixed, except for a common factor.

If there are two or more identical roots ϵ_n part of the degeneracy remains and some of the A_{ij} are arbitrary.

For cases where the degeneracy is removed only in a higher order, consult the literature.

Second and Higher Orders. With the wave functions $\psi_n{}^0$ as zero-order approximations, the second- and higher-order approximations can be carried out exactly as for the nondegenerate case.

Semidegenerate Case. If

$$|S_{ij}| \ll |W_i - W_j| \tag{7k-20}$$

the method for the nondegenerate states can be employed. If this condition is not fullfilled for some states for which, however, $W_i \neq W_j$, these states can be dealt with by a method very similar to that for the degenerate states. States for which (7k-20) is not fullfilled, whether they are degenerate or not, are called close states; their interaction can be taken care of provided their number f is finite.

The positions of the unperturbed levels are $\delta_1, \delta_2, \ldots \delta_f$ where the δ_i are counted from some fixed arbitrary energy. All δ_i may be different or some or all may be equal.

The procedure is now exactly the same as for an f-fold degenerate state except that the coefficients A_{mn} and the energies are given by the equations.

$$\begin{aligned}
&(S_{11} + \delta_1 - \epsilon_n)A_{1n} + S_{12}A_{2n} + \cdots + S_{1f}A_{fn} = 0\\
&S_{21}A_{1n} + (S_{22} + \delta_2 - \epsilon_n)A_{2n} + \cdots + S_{2f}A_{fn} = 0\\
&\cdots\cdots\cdots\cdots\cdots\cdots\cdots\cdots\cdots\cdots\\
&S_{f1}A_{1n} + A_{f2}A_{2n} + \cdots + (S_{ff} + \delta_f - \epsilon_n)A_{fn} = 0
\end{aligned}$$

with the secular determinant

$$\begin{vmatrix}
S_{12} + \delta_1 - \epsilon_n & S_{12} & \cdots & S_{1f}\\
S_{21} & S_{22} + \delta_2 - \epsilon_n & \cdots & S_{2f}\\
\cdots & \cdots & \cdots & \cdots\\
S_{f1} & S_{f2} & \cdots & S_{ff} + \delta_f - \epsilon_n
\end{vmatrix} = 0$$

Everything from here on is analogous to the procedure in the degenerate case.

Variation Method. It can be shown that, if χ is a normalized arbitrary function of the coordinates and W_0 the lowest energy value of a system, we have

$$W_0 \leq \int \bar{\chi} H \chi d\tau \tag{7k-21}$$

The equality sign applies when $\chi = \psi$ is the correct wave function of the lowest state.

The variational method consists of the systematic variation of a function with several adjustable parameters chosen so (often by intuition) as to be very similar to the wave function. The variation of the integral (7k-21) is observed when the constants are varied. The function which gives the smallest value for the integral is the best approximation to the wave function obtainable with the chosen function type, and the minimum value of the integral the best value for the energy. The accuracy of the energy value depends on how closely the trial function can approximate the real wave function.

If there are several different symmetry types the variational method can be used to calculate the lowest state of each symmetry type.

Upper values of other excited states can be obtained if the trial function is orthogonal to that of all lower states.

7l. Zeeman Effect

When atoms and molecules are placed in a magnetic field their spectrum lines usually are split into several components with characteristic polarization. As a rule the amount of the splitting is proportional to the field strength H (linear Zeeman effect). The following cases are of importance.

7l-1. Free Atoms, No Nuclear Spin. If J is the total angular momentum, the level is $2J + 1$ fold degenerate. In a magnetic field of strength H the level splits into $2J + 1$ components. The energy changes compared with the field free energy are given by

$$\epsilon = g\beta MH \qquad -J \leq M \leq +J \tag{7l-1}$$

$$\beta = \frac{\hbar}{2mc} \qquad \text{(Bohr magneton)}$$

The splitting factor for Russell-Saunders coupling is given by Landé's formula

$$g = 1 + \frac{J(J+1) + S(S+1) - L(L+1)}{2J(J+1)} \tag{7l-2}$$

Numerical values of g are given in Table 7m-1.[1]

In the literature the case for which $g = 1$ is usually called the normal Zeeman effect and other cases are called the anomalous Zeeman effects. Normal Zeeman effects occur chiefly for singlets ($S = 0$).

Equation (7l-2) holds only as long as L,S coupling is a good approximation. Equation (7l-1) holds with g values not necessarily given by (7l-2) as long as the magnetic splitting is small compared with the distance to a neighboring level.

Selection and Polarization Rules for Electric-dipole Transition

Transition	Polarization: Observation perpendicular to H	Polarization: Observation parallel to H
$\Delta M = \pm 1$	Linear, $\perp H$	$\Delta M = +1$ right circular $\Delta M = -1$ left circular (opposite if g' and g'' have opposite sign)
$\Delta M = 0$	Linear, $\parallel H$	Absent

For $g' = g'' = 1$, the normal triplet is obtained, as all lines with the same change in M coincide.

[1] A table of g values arranged in order of increasing numerical values is found in Charlotte E. Moore, "Atomic Energy Levels," vol. I, tables 3 and 4, 1949; Kiess and W. F. Meggers, *J. Research Natl. Bur. Standards* **1**, 641 (1928). For tables of g values for jj coupling, see J. C. Green et al., *Phys. Rev.* **52**, 736 (1937); **54**, 876 (1938); **58**, 1094 (1940); **59**, 72 (1941); **64**, 151 (1943).

For quadrupole transitions, see Condon and Shortley,[1] and Rubinowicz and Blaton.[2]

The intensities are given by

Transition		Intensity	
$J \to J$	$M \to M$	AM^2	
	$\left.\begin{matrix} M \to M+1 \\ M+1 \to M \end{matrix}\right\}$	$\frac{1}{2}A[J(J+1) - M(M+1)]$	(71-3*a*)
$J \to J+1$	$M \to M$	$B[(J+1)^2 - M^2]$	
	$M \to M+1$	$\frac{1}{2}B(J+M+1)(J+M+2)$	(71-3*b*)
	$M \to M-1$	$\frac{1}{2}B(J-M+1)(J-M+2)$	
$J \to J-1$	$M \to M$	$C[J^2 - M^2]$	
	$M \to M+1$	$\frac{1}{2}C(J-M)(J-M-1)$	(71-3*c*)
	$M \to M-1$	$\frac{1}{2}C(J+M)(J+M-1)$	

These formulas hold as long as Eq. (71-1) holds but are independent of the particular coupling scheme, i.e., independent of the g values. They hold equally well for diatomic molecules. A, B, and C are proportionality constants which are different for each line.

The formulas represent the intensity distribution in a Zeeman pattern as long as the temperature is so high that kT is large compared with the magnetic splitting. They are proportional to the transition probabilities for all temperatures.

When the magnetic splitting is not small compared with the distance to neighboring levels, the splitting is not symmetric. The line has asymmetries in both position of the components and their intensities (incipient Paschen back effect). When the distance between multiplet components is small compared with the magnetic splitting, the pattern is simple again and essentially that for the normal Zeeman ($S = 0$) effect (complete Paschen back effect).

71-2. Zeeman Effects in Other Cases. If there is *hyperfine structure* because the nuclear spin is different from zero, the number of components is given by $2F + 1$ when $F\hbar$ is the total angular momentum including nuclear spin $I\hbar$. The splitting factor is

$$g_n = g\frac{F(F+1) + J(J+1) - I(I+1)}{2F(F+1)}$$

where g is the splitting factor without consideration of the nuclear spin. This situation prevails only as long as the magnetic splitting is small compared with the hyperfine structure. At the other extreme (hyperfine structure small compared with magnetic splitting) the influence of the nuclear spin may be neglected.

Diatomic Molecules. The splitting and intensities are given by Eqs. (71-1) and (71-3). The splitting factor depends on the coupling within the molecule. A simple case is when influence of the spin can be neglected and the orbital angular momentum L is coupled to the internuclear axis (Hund's case b). If Λ is the component of L along the internuclear axis we have for the splitting factor

$$g = \frac{\Lambda^2}{J(J+1)}$$

This expression shows that appreciable splittings can be expected only for small values of J. Noticeable splittings for larger J values are found when the angular momentum L is decoupled from the internuclear axis.

[1] E. U. Condon and G. H. Shortley, "The Theory of Atomic Spectra," Cambridge University Press, New York, 1935 (reprinted 1953).

[2] A. Rubinowicz, *Z. Physik* **53,** 267 (1929); **61,** 338 (1930); A. Rubinowicz and J. Blaton, *Ergeb. exak. Naturwiss.* **11,** 176 (1932).

TABLE 71-1. VALUES OF g FOR L-S COUPLING
(Odd multiplicites)

Spin.		0	1	2	3	4	5
Multiplicity.		1	3	5	7	9	11
Level	J						
S		$g = 2$ for all multiplicities					
P	0		%				
	1	1.000	1.500	2.500			
	2	.....	1.500	1.833	2.333		
	3	.....		1.667	1.917	2.250	
	4	.....		.....	1.750	1.950	2.200
	5	.....	.....	.....	....	1.800	1.967
	6	.....	.....	.....	....	....	1.833
D	0			%			
	1		0.500	1.500	3.000		
	2	1.000	1.167	1.500	2.000	2.667	
	3	.....	1.333	1.500	1.750	2.083	2.500
	4	.....	.....	1.500	1.650	1.850	2.100
	5	.....	.....	.....	1.600	1.733	1.900
	6	.....	.....	.....	....	1.667	1.786
	7	.....	.....	.....	....	....	1.714
F	0				%		
	1	.....	.....	0.000	1.500	3.500	
	2	.....	0.667	1.000	1.500	2.167	3.000
	3	1.000	1.083	1.250	1.500	1.833	2.250
	4	.....	1.250	1.350	1.500	1.700	1.950
	5	.....	.....	1.400	1.500	1.633	1.800
	6	.....	.....	.....	1.500	1.595	1.714
	7	.....	.....	.....	....	1.571	1.661
	8	.....	.....	.....	....	....	1.625
G	0					%	
	1	.....	.....	.....	−0.500	1.500	4.000
	2	.....	.....	0.333	0.833	1.500	2.333
	3	.....	0.750	0.917	1.167	1.500	1.917
	4	1.000	1.050	1.150	1.300	1.500	1.750
	5	.....	1.200	1.267	1.367	1.500	1.667
	6	.....	.....	1.333	1.405	1.500	1.619
	7	.....	.....	.....	1.429	1.500	1.589
	8	.....	.....	.....	....	1.500	1.569
	9	.....	.....	.....	....	....	1.556
H	0						%
	1	.....	.....	.....	....	−1.000	1.500
	2	.....	.....	.....	0.000	0.667	1.500
	3	.....	.....	0.500	0.750	1.083	1.500
	4	.....	0.800	0.900	1.050	1.250	1.500
	5	1.000	1.033	1.100	1.200	1.333	1.500
	6	.....	1.167	1.214	1.286	1.381	1.500
	7	.....	.....	1.286	1.339	1.411	1.500
	8	.....	.....	.....	1.375	1.431	1.500
	9	.....	.....	.....	....	1.444	1.500
	10	.....	.....	.....	....	....	1.500

TABLE 71-1. VALUES OF g FOR L-S COUPLING (*Continued*)
(Odd multiplicities)

Spin		0	1	2	3	4	5
Multiplicity		1	3	5	7	9	11
Level	J						
S		$g = 2$ for all multiplicities					
I	1	.....	.....	.....	.....	.....	−1.500
	2	.....	.....	.....	.....	−0.333	0.500
	3	.....	.....	.....	0.250	0.583	1.000
	4	.....	.....	0.600	0.750	0.950	1.200
	5	.....	0.833	0.900	1.00	1.133	1.300
	6	1.000	1.024	1.071	1.143	1.238	1.357
	7	.....	1.143	1.179	1.232	1.304	1.393
	8	.....	.....	1.250	1.292	1.347	1.417
	9	.....	.....	.....	1.333	1.378	1.433
	10	.....	.....	.....	.....	1.400	1.445
	11	.....	.....	.....	.....	.....	1.455
K	2	.....	.....	.....	.....	.....	−0.667
	3	.....	.....	.....	.....	0.000	0.417
	4	.....	.....	.....	0.400	0.600	0.850
	5	.....	.....	0.667	0.767	0.900	1.067
	6	.....	0.857	0.905	0.976	1.071	1.191
	7	1.000	1.018	1.054	1.107	1.179	1.268
	8	.....	1.125	1.153	1.194	1.250	1.319
	9	.....	.....	1.222	1.256	1.300	1.356
	10	.....	.....	.....	1.300	1.336	1.382
	11	.....	.....	.....	.....	1.364	1.402

Atoms or Ions in Crystals. In this case the $2J + 1$ fold degeneracy is entirely or partly removed by the Stark effect due to the crystal field. If the electron orbits are protected, sharp levels may result, particularly at low temperatures. Sharp absorption or fluorescence lines in crystals have been observed for salts of elements where d and f shells are being filled. Such lines may show characteristic Zeeman effects. In general the level splits into two components if the number of electrons is odd (Kramers degeneracy). For an even number of electrons there is no degeneracy and therefore no linear Zeeman effect unless the symmetry of the crystal field is high. If the average orbital angular momentum is zero, the degeneracy is $2S + 1$ and is due to the resultant electron spin S.

This magnetic splitting of electronic levels in crystals is directly observed for the ground state in paramagnetic resonance experiments (often modified by the nuclear spin). It is also directly observed for the ground and excited states in optical-absorption spectra in a magnetic field when there are sharp lines. This splitting is directly connected with the magnitude of the magnetic susceptibility and paramagnetic rotation as well as with cooling by adiabatic demagnetization.

TABLE 7l-2. VALUES OF g FOR L-S COUPLING
(Even multiplicities)

Spin		$\frac{1}{2}$	$\frac{3}{2}$	$\frac{5}{2}$	$\frac{7}{2}$	$\frac{9}{11}$
Multiplicity		2	4	6	8	10
Level	J					
S		$g = 2$ for all multiplicities				
P	$\frac{1}{2}$	0.667	2.667			
	$1\frac{1}{2}$	1.333	1.733	2.400		
	$2\frac{1}{2}$	.....	1.600	1.886	2.86	
	$3\frac{1}{2}$	.....	.....	1.714	1.937	2.222
	$4\frac{1}{2}$	.....	.....	....	1.778	1.960
	$5\frac{1}{2}$	.....	.....	....	....	1.818
D	$\frac{1}{2}$	.....	0.000	3.333		
	$1\frac{1}{2}$	0.800	1.200	1.867	2.800	
	$2\frac{1}{2}$	1.200	1.371	1.657	2.057	2.572
	$3\frac{1}{2}$	.....	1.429	1.587	1.809	2.095
	$4\frac{1}{2}$	.....	.....	1.556	1.697	1.879
	$5\frac{1}{2}$	.....	.....	....	1.636	1.762
	$6\frac{1}{2}$	.....	.....	....	....	1.692
F	$\frac{1}{2}$	.....	.....	−0.667	4.000	
	$1\frac{1}{2}$	.....	0.400	1.067	2.000	3.200
	$2\frac{1}{2}$	0.857	1.029	1.314	1.714	2.229
	$3\frac{1}{2}$	1.143	1.238	1.397	1.619	1.905
	$4\frac{1}{2}$	.....	1.333	1.434	1.576	1.758
	$5\frac{1}{2}$	.....	.....	1.455	1.552	1.678
	$6\frac{1}{2}$	.....	.....	....	1.538	1.631
	$7\frac{1}{2}$	.....	.....	....	....	1.600
G	$\frac{1}{2}$	.....	.....	....	−1.333	4.667
	$1\frac{1}{2}$	.....	.....	0.000	0.933	2.133
	$2\frac{1}{2}$	.....	0.571	0.857	1.257	1.772
	$3\frac{1}{2}$	0.889	0.984	1.143	1.365	1.651
	$4\frac{1}{2}$	1.111	1.172	1.273	1.414	1.596
	$5\frac{1}{2}$	.....	1.273	1.343	1.441	1.566
	$6\frac{1}{2}$	.....	.....	1.385	1.456	1.549
	$7\frac{1}{2}$	.....	.....	....	1.467	1.537
	$8\frac{1}{2}$	.....	.....	....	....	1.529
H	$\frac{1}{2}$	.....	.....	....	....	−2.000
	$1\frac{1}{2}$	.....	.....	....	−0.400	0.800
	$2\frac{1}{2}$	.....	.....	0.286	0.686	1.200
	$3\frac{1}{2}$	.....	0.667	0.825	1.048	1.333
	$4\frac{1}{2}$	0.909	0.970	1.071	1.212	1.394
	$5\frac{1}{2}$	1.091	1.133	1.203	1.301	1.427
	$6\frac{1}{2}$	.....	1.231	1.282	1.354	1.446
	$7\frac{1}{2}$	.....	.....	1.333	1.388	1.459
	$8\frac{1}{2}$	.....	.....	....	1.412	1.467
	$9\frac{1}{2}$	.....	.....	....	....	1.474

TABLE 71-2. VALUES OF g FOR L-S COUPLING (*Continued*)
(Even multiplicities)

Spin		$\frac{1}{2}$	$\frac{3}{2}$	$\frac{5}{2}$	$\frac{7}{2}$	$\frac{9}{11}$
Multiplicity		2	4	6	8	10
Level	J					
I	$\frac{1}{2}$					
	$1\frac{1}{2}$	.....	.....	....	......	−0.800
	$2\frac{1}{2}$	.....	.....	....	0.000	0.514
	$3\frac{1}{2}$	.....	.....	0.444	0.667	0.952
	$4\frac{1}{2}$	.....	0.727	0.828	0.970	1.152
	$5\frac{1}{2}$	0.923	0.965	1.035	1.133	1.259
	$6\frac{1}{2}$	1.077	1.108	1.159	1.231	1.323
	$7\frac{1}{2}$		1.200	1.239	1.294	1.365
	$8\frac{1}{2}$			1.294	1.337	1.393
	$9\frac{1}{2}$				1.368	1.414
	$10\frac{1}{2}$	.....	.....	....		1.429
K	$2\frac{1}{2}$	.....	.....	....	....	−0.286
	$3\frac{1}{2}$	.....	.....	.....	0.222	0.508
	$4\frac{1}{2}$	.....	.....	0.545	0.687	0.869
	$5\frac{1}{2}$	.....	0.769	0.839	0.937	1.063
	$6\frac{1}{2}$	0.922	0.964	1.015	1.087	1.179
	$7\frac{1}{2}$	1.067	1.090	1.129	1.184	1.255
	$8\frac{1}{2}$	.....	1.176	1.207	1.251	1.307
	$9\frac{1}{2}$	.....	.....	1.263	1.298	1.343
	$10\frac{1}{2}$	.....	.....	.....	1.333	1.371
	$11\frac{1}{2}$	.....	.....	....	....	1.391

7m. Motions of Electrons and Ions in Gases

S. C. BROWN AND W. P. ALLIS

Massachusetts Institute of Technology

7m-1. Collision Probabilities. The probability of collision P_c is defined as the fraction of particles scattered out of a collimated beam per centimeter path per millimeter pressure at 0°C. Similarly the "probability" of any event occurring on collision, such as excitation P_x or ionization P_i, is the fraction of particles suffering that event per centimeter path and millimeter pressures. The probability P is related to the cross section q by

$$P = \frac{Lq}{760} \qquad \text{cm}^{-1}\ (\text{mm Hg})^{-1}$$

where L is Loschmidt's number, or

$$P = 3.5357q$$

where q is in square Angstrom units. The mean free path l is given by

$$l = \frac{1}{p_0} P \qquad \text{cm}$$

and the mean free time τ by

$$\frac{1}{\tau} = \frac{v}{l} = 5.93107 \times 10^7 u^{\frac{1}{2}} p_0 P \qquad \text{sec}^{-1}$$

Here $u = mv^2/2e$ is the energy in electron volts, and $p_0 = 273.16p/T$ is the "reduced" pressure in millimeters of mercury. p_0 does not express a pressure, but a concentration

$$\frac{N}{V} = 3.5357 \times 10^{16} p_0 \qquad \text{molecules/cm}^3$$

Cross sections are sometimes given in units of $\pi a_0^2 = 0.87981$ A^2, and energies in Hartree units, $k^2 = V/13.605$.

If $q(\theta)$ is the differential cross section for elastic scattering into unit solid angle at an angle θ to the incident direction,

$$q_c = \int q(\theta) 2\pi \sin\theta \, d\theta$$

A more important quantity is the cross section for momentum transfer.

$$q_m = \int q(\theta)(1 - \cos\theta) 2\pi \sin\theta \, d\theta$$

In general, $q_m \leq q_c$; experimental values of P_c should be "corrected" to P_m in all gas-discharge applications.

7m-1.1 Elastic Collisions by Electrons

Figs. 7m-1 to 7m-7

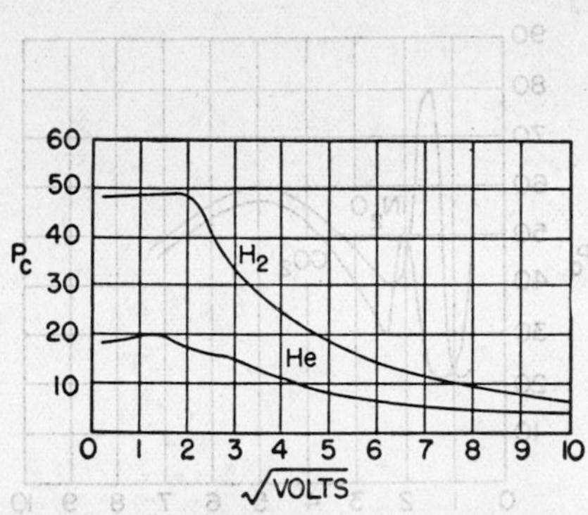

FIG. 7m-1. "Probability" of collision in H_2, He. [R. B. Brode, *Revs. Modern Phys.* **5**, 257 (1933); A. V. Phelps, O. T. Fundingsland, S. C. Brown, *Phys. Rev.* **84**, 559 (1951).]

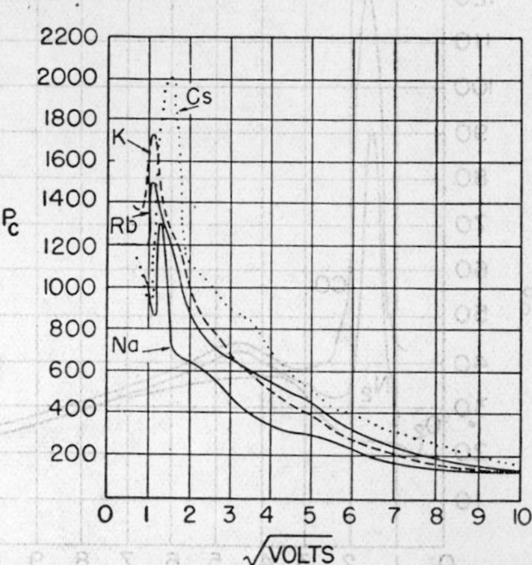

FIG. 7m-2. "Probability" of collision in the alkali metals. [R. B. Brode, *Revs. Modern Phys.* **5**, 257 (1933).]

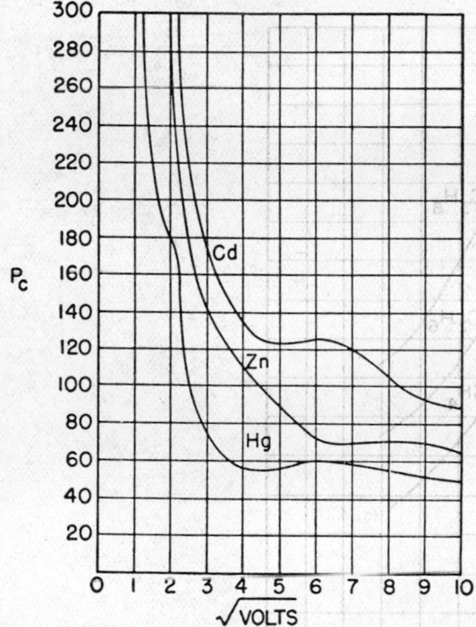

FIG. 7m-3. "Probability" of collision in Hg, Zn, Cd. [R. B. Brode, *Revs. Modern Phys.* **5**, 257 (1933).]

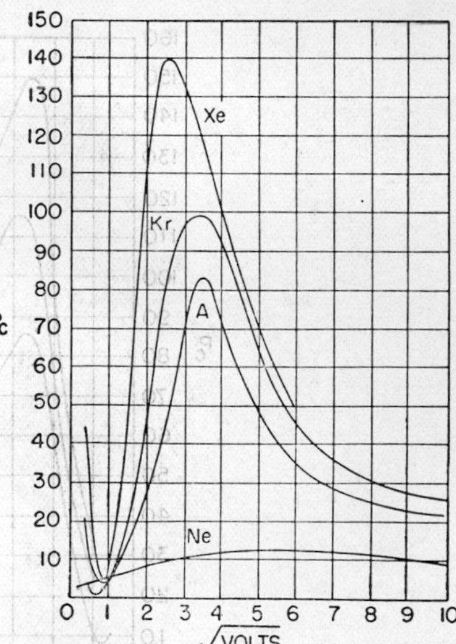

FIG. 7m-4. "Probability" of collision in Ne, A, Kr, Xe. [R. B. Brode, *Revs. Modern Phys.* **5**, 257 (1933).]

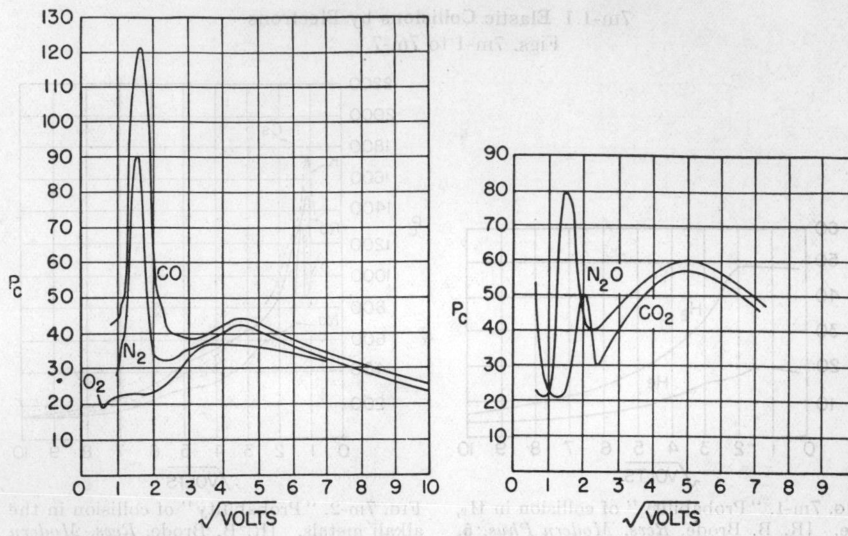

FIG. 7m-5. "Probability" of collision in O_2, N_2, CO. [R. B. Brode, *Revs. Modern Phys.* **5**, 257 (1933).]

FIG. 7m-6. "Probability" of collision in CO_2, N_2O. [R. B. Brode, *Revs. Modern Phys.* **5**, 257 (1933).]

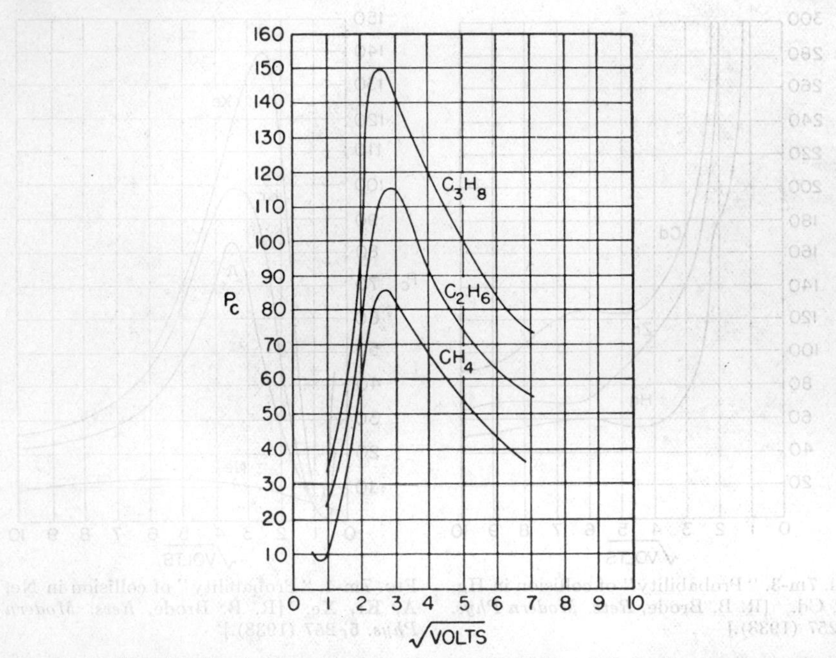

FIG. 7m-7. "Probability" of collision in CH_4, C_2H_6, C_3H_8. [R. B. Brode, *Revs. Modern Phys.* **5**, 257 (1933).]

7m-1.2 Inelastic Collisions by Electrons

Figs. 7m-8 to 7m-18

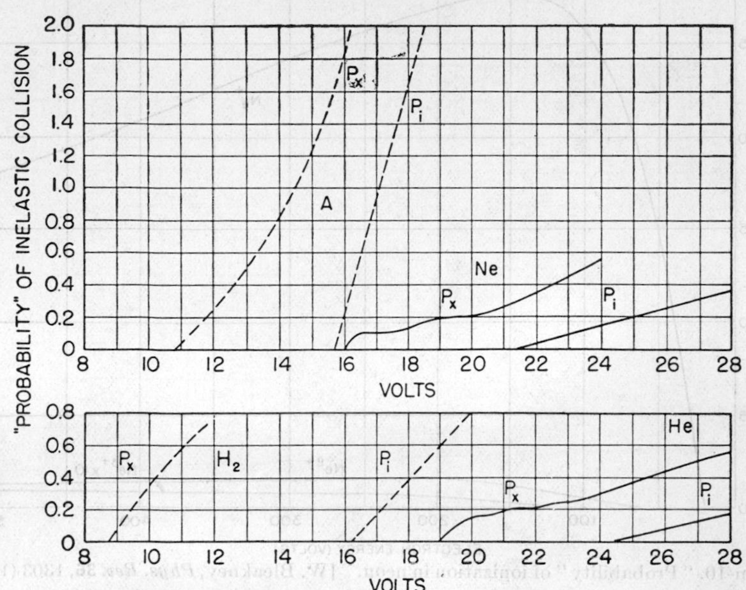

Fig. 7m-8. "Probability" of excitation and ionization in He, H_2, Ne, A. [M. J. Druyvesteyn, and F. M. Penning, *Revs. Modern Phys.* **12**, 87 (1940).]

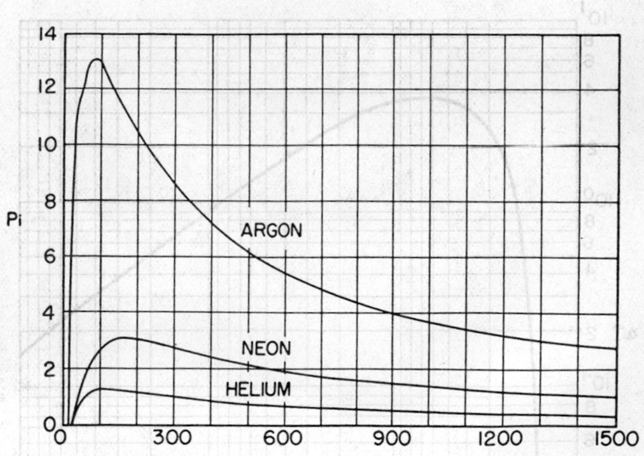

Fig. 7m-9. "Probability" of ionization in He, Ne, A. [P. T. Smith, *Phys. Rev.* **36,** 1293 (1930).]

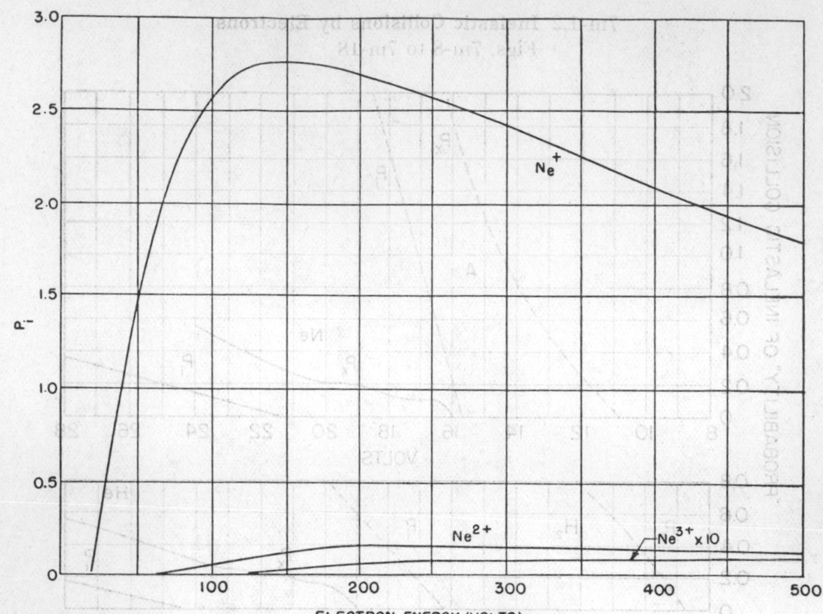

FIG. 7m-10. "Probability" of ionization in neon. [W. Bleakney, *Phys. Rev.* **36**, 1303 (1930).]

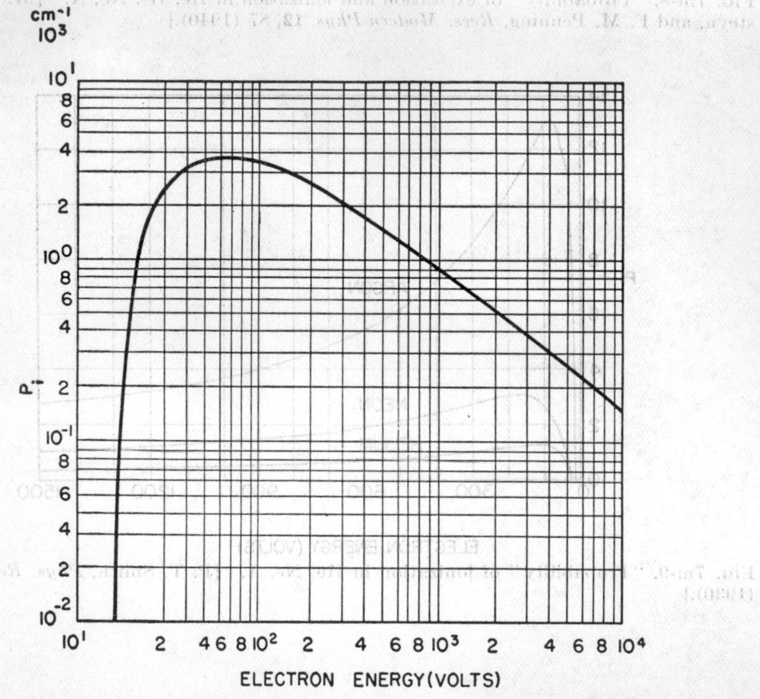

FIG. 7m-11. "Probability" of ionization in hydrogen. (M. Knoll, F. Ollendorff, and R. Rompe, "Gastentladungstabellen," p. 66, J. Springer Verlag, Berlin, 1935.)

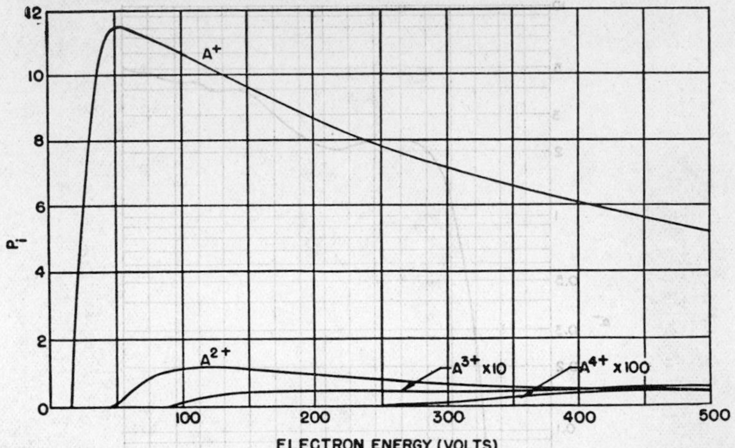

FIG. 7m-12. "Probability" of ionization in argon. [W. Bleakney, *Phys. Rev.* **36,** 1303 (1930).]

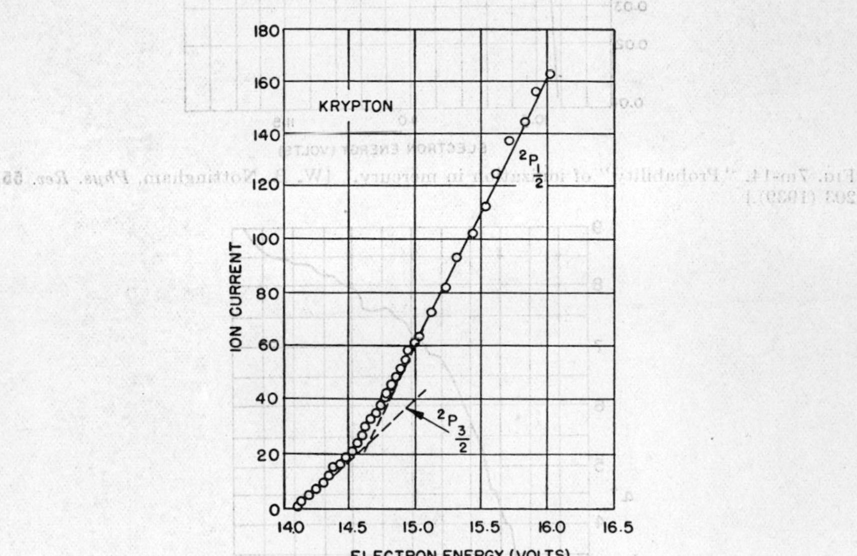

FIG. 7m-13. Relative ionization probability for ionization to the $^2P_{1/2}$ state in krypton. [R. E. Fox, W. M. Hickam, and T. Kjeldaas, *Phys. Rev.* **89,** 555 (1953).]

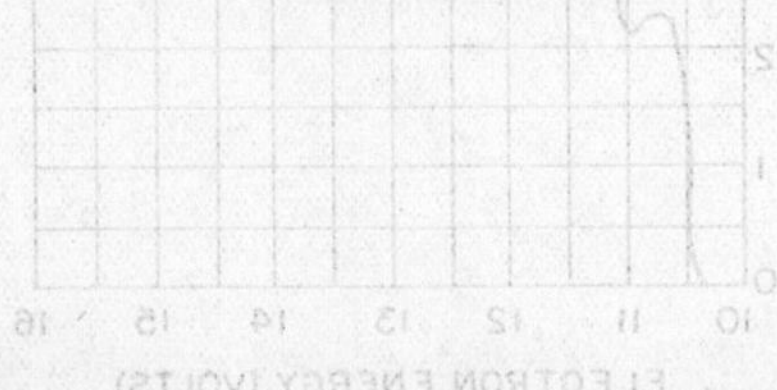

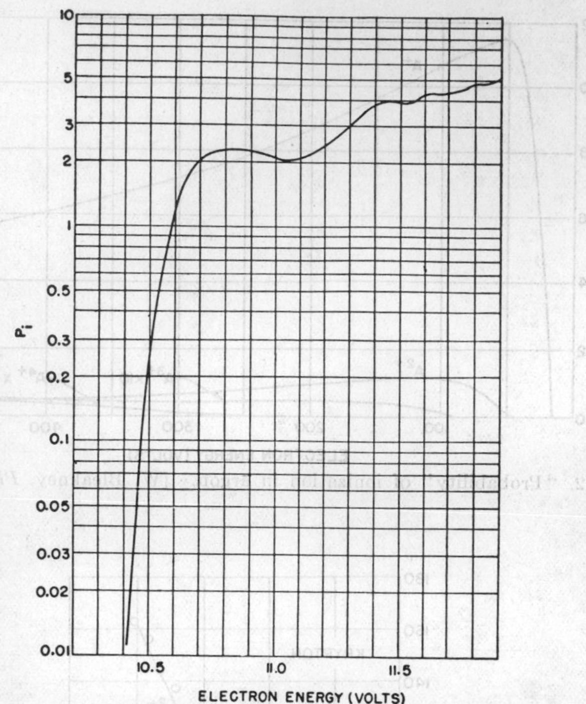

FIG. 7m-14. "Probability" of ionization in mercury. [W. B. Nottingham, *Phys. Rev.* **55**, 203 (1939).]

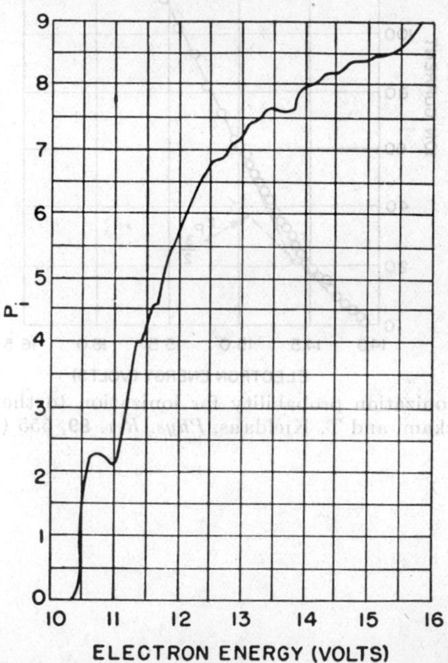

FIG. 7m-15. "Probability" of ionization in mercury. [W. B. Nottingham, *Phys. Rev.* **55**, 203 (1939).]

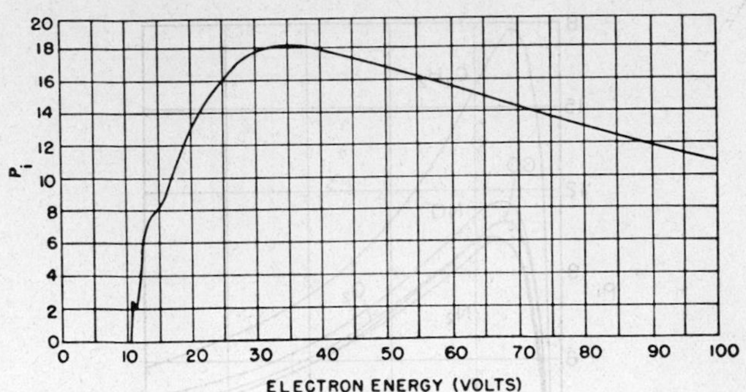

FIG. 7m-16. "Probability" of ionization in mercury. [W. B. Nottingham, *Phys. Rev.* **55,** 203 (1939).]

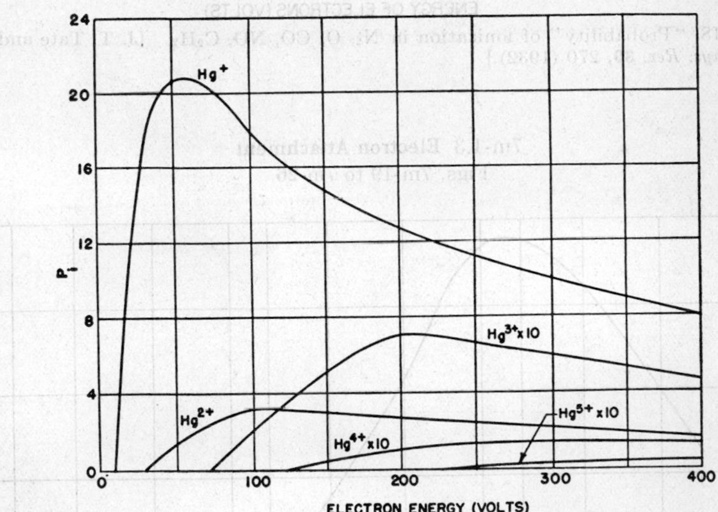

FIG. 7m-17. "Probability" of ionization in mercury. [W. Bleakney, *Phys. Rev.* **35,** 139 (1930).]

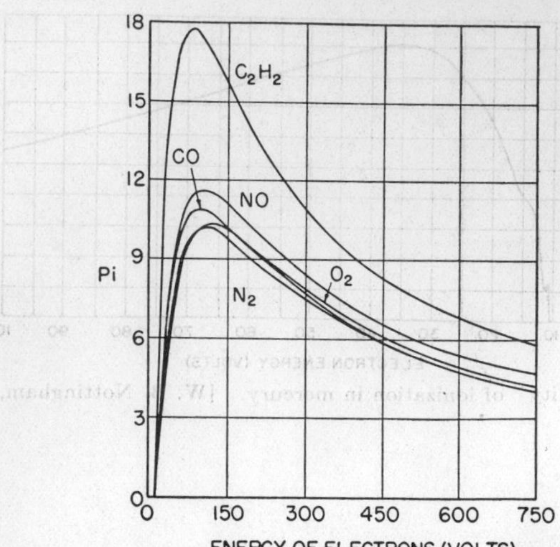

FIG. 7m-18. "Probability" of ionization in N_2, O, CO, NO, C_2H_2. [J. T. Tate and P.T. Smith, *Phys. Rev.* **39**, 270 (1932).]

7m-1.3 **Electron Attachment**

Figs. 7m-19 to 7m-26

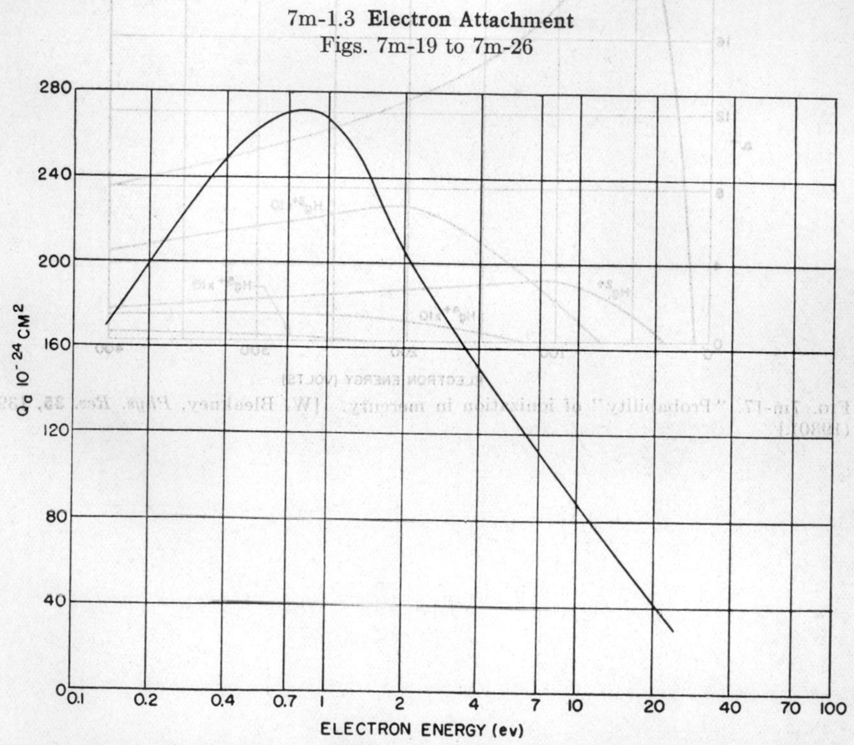

FIG. 7m-19. Cross sections for radiative attachment of electrons by neutral hydrogen atoms. (H. S. W. Massey and E. H. S. Burhop, "Electronic and Ionic Impact Phenomena," p. 335, Clarendon Press, Oxford, 1952.)

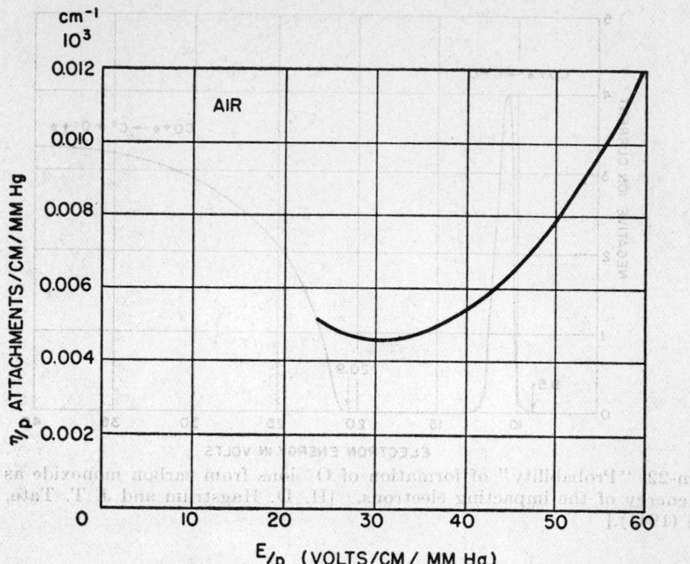

FIG. 7m-20. Electron attachment coefficient for air [M. A. Harrison and R. Geballe, *Phys. Rev.* **91,** 1 (1953).]

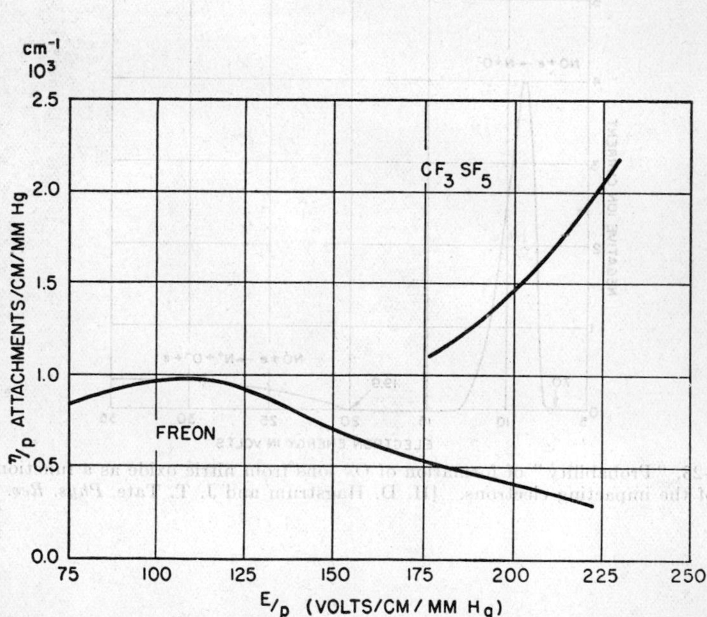

FIG. 7m-21. Electron attachment coefficients for freon-12 and CF_3SF_5 [M. A. Harrison and R. Geballe, *Phys. Rev.* **91,** 1 (1953).]

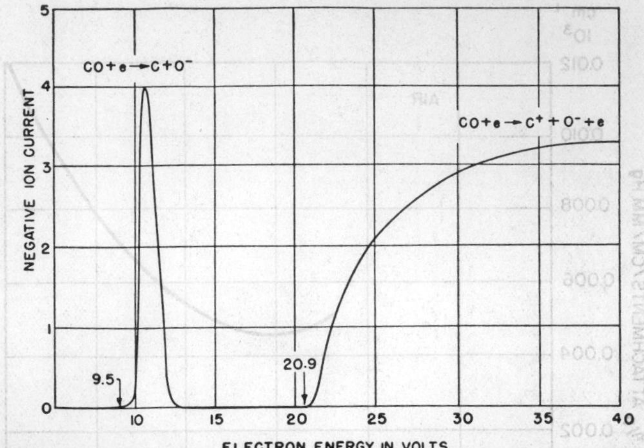

FIG. 7m-22. "Probability" of formation of O^- ions from carbon monoxide as a function of the energy of the impacting electrons. [H. D. Hagstrum and J. T. Tate, *Phys. Rev.* **59**, 354 (1941).]

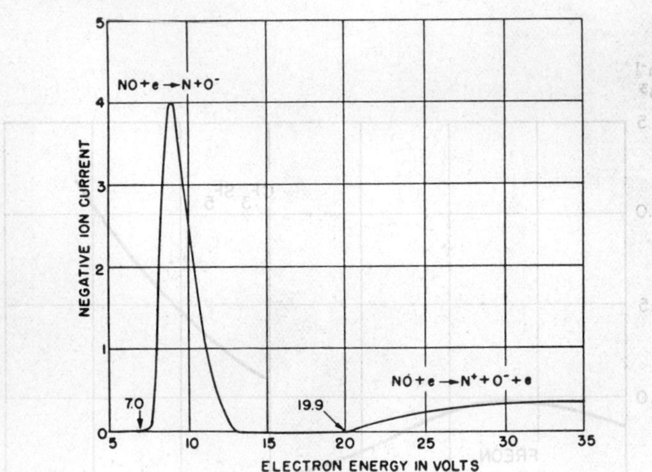

FIG. 7m-23. "Probability" of formation of O^- ions from nitric oxide as a function of the energy of the impacting electrons. [H. D. Hagstrum and J. T. Tate, *Phys. Rev.* **59**, 354 (1941).]

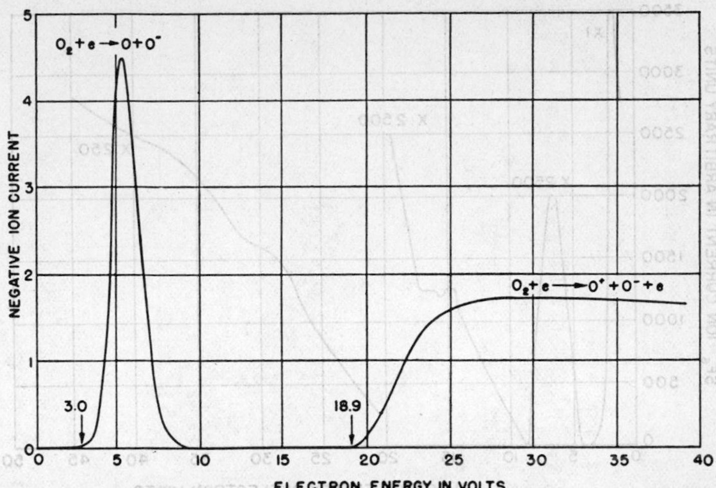

FIG. 7m-24. "Probability" of formation of O^- ions from oxygen. [H. D. Hagstrum and J. T. Tate, *Phys. Rev.* **59**, 354 (1941).]

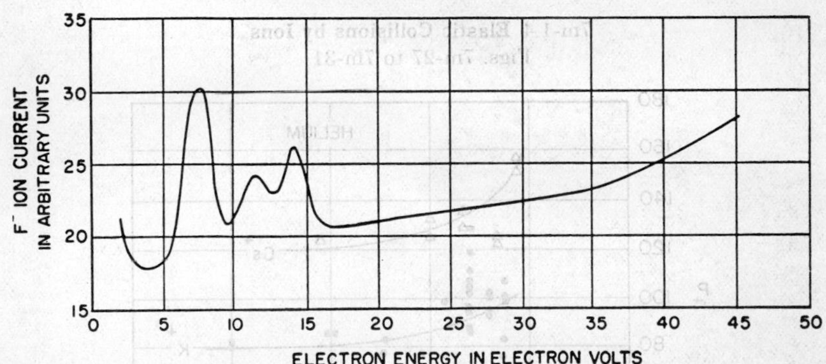

FIG. 7m-25. F^- ion current as a function of electron energy. [A. J. Ahearn and N. B. Hannay, *J. Chem. Phys.* **21**, 119 (1953).]

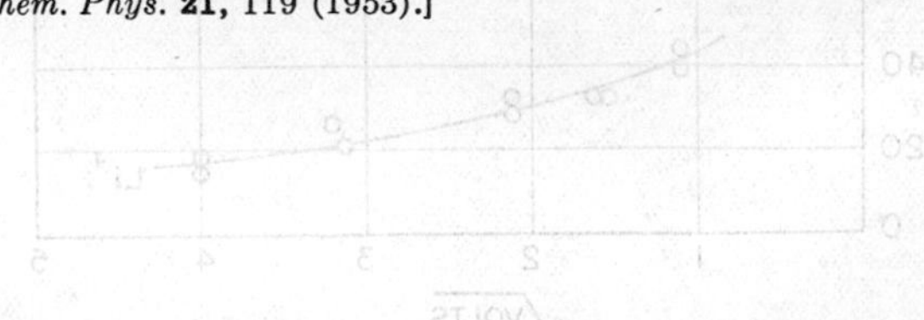

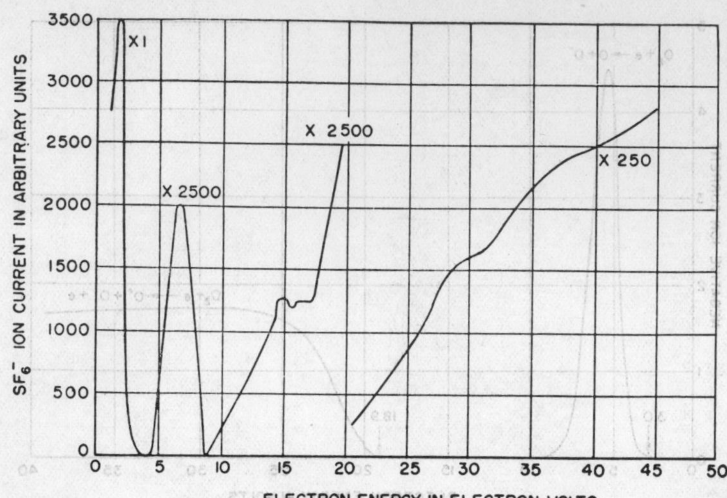

FIG. 7m-26. SF_6^- ion current as a function of electron energy. [A. J. Ahearn and N. B. Hannay, *J. Chem. Phys.* **21**, 119 (1953).]

7m-1.4 Elastic Collisions by Ions

Figs. 7m-27 to 7m-31

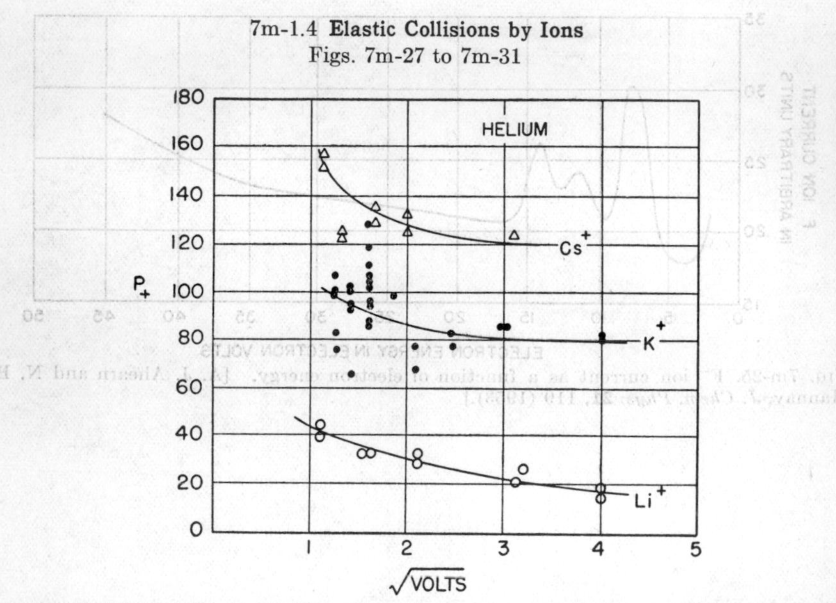

FIG. 7m-27. "Probability" of collision for positive ions of Li, K, Cs in helium. [C. Ramsauer and O. Beeck, *Ann. Physik* **87**, 1 (1928).]

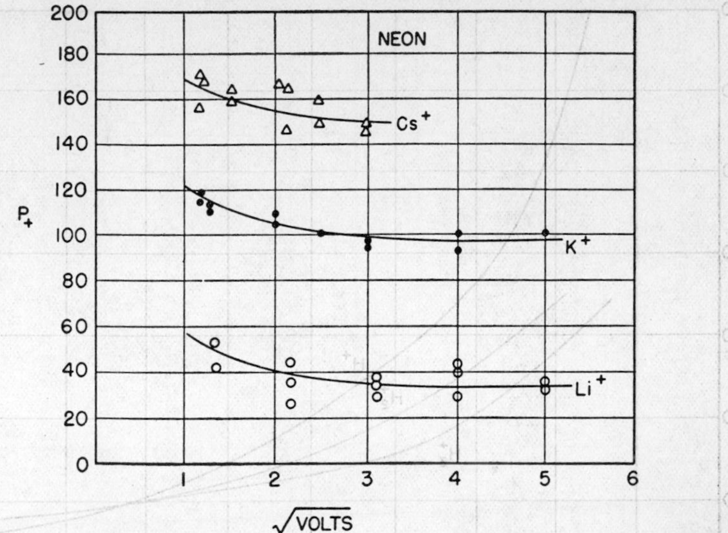

FIG. 7m-28. "Probability" of collision for positive ions of Li, K, Cs in neon. [C. Ramsauer and O. Beeck, *Ann. Physik* **87**, 1 (1928).]

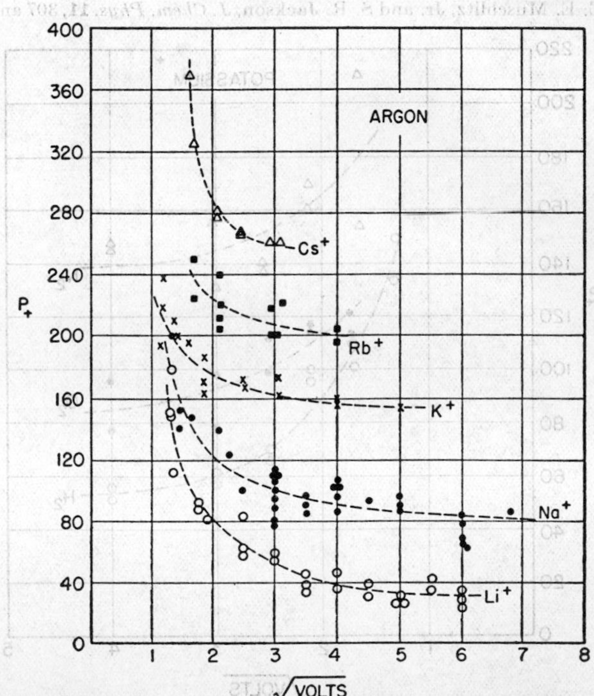

FIG. 7m-29. "Probability" of collision for positive ions of Li, Na, K, Rb, Cs in argon. [C. Ramsauer and O. Beeck, *Ann. Physik* **87**, 1 (1928).]

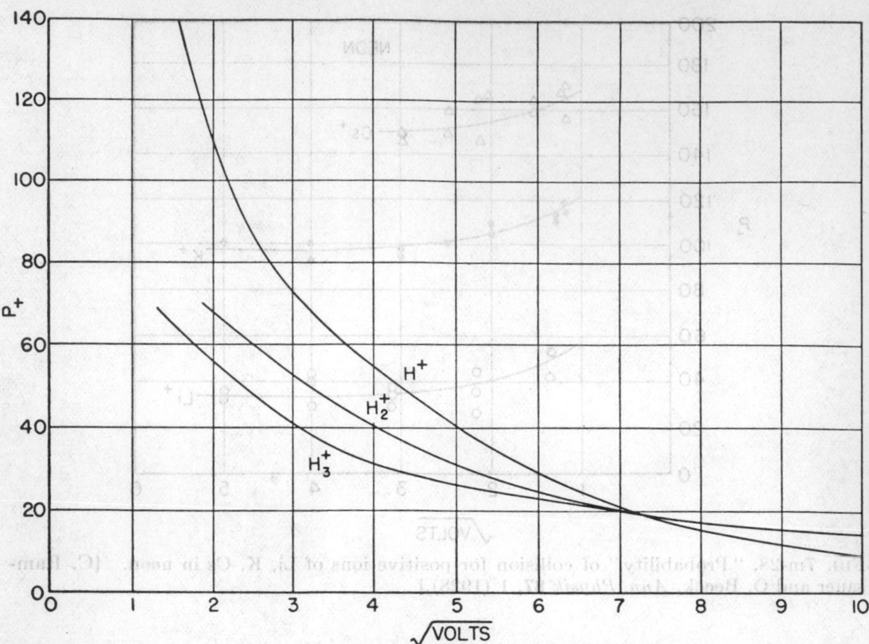

Fig. 7m-30. Elastic scattering of low-velocity hydrogen ions in hydrogen. [J. H. Simons, C. M. Fontana, E. E. Muschlitz, Jr. and S. R. Jackson, *J. Chem. Phys.* **11,** 307 and 316 (1943).]

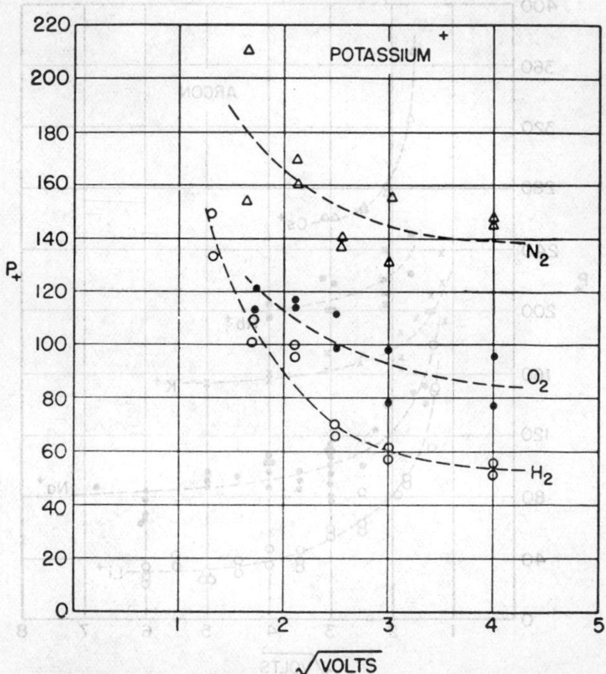

Fig. 7m-31. "Probability" of collision for positive ions of K in H_2, O_2, N_2. [C. Ramsauer and O. Beeck, *Ann. Physik* **87,** 1 (1928).]

7m-1.5 Charge Transfer

Figs. 7m-32 to 7m-37

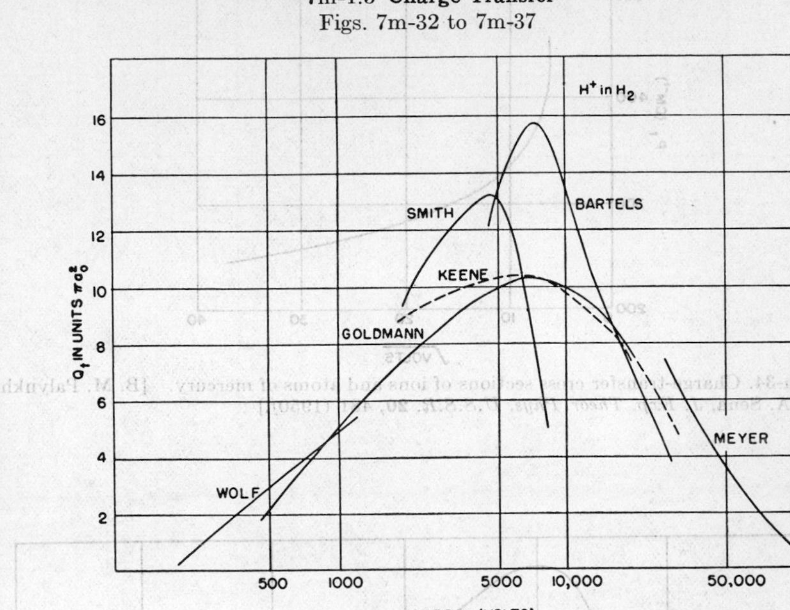

FIG. 7m-32. Charge-transfer cross section of H^+ in H_2. (H. S. W. Massey and E. H. S. Burhop, "Electronic and Ionic Impact Phenomena," p. 526, Clarendon Press, Oxford, 1952.)

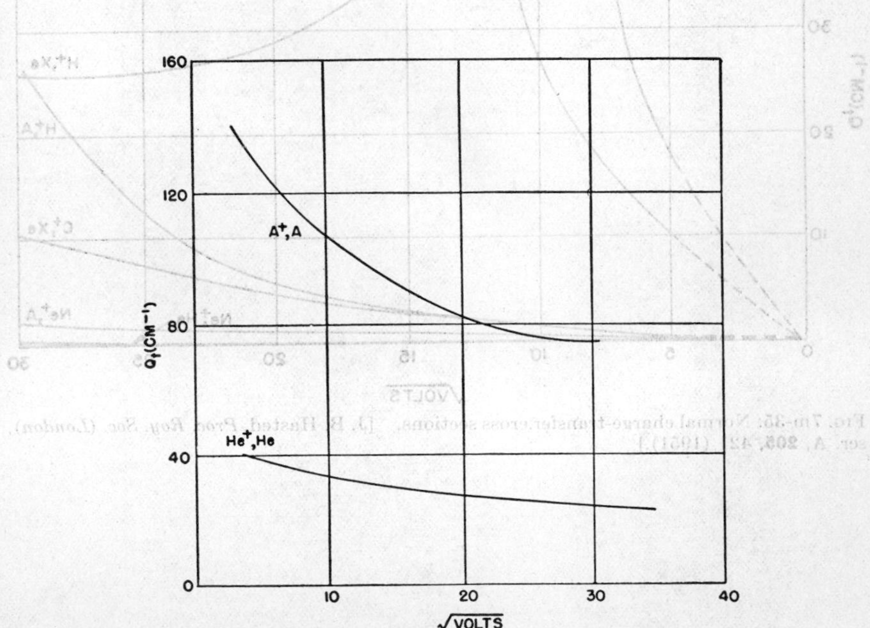

FIG. 7m-33. Charge-transfer cross sections of A^+ in A, He^+ in He as a function of energy. [J. B. Hasted, *Proc. Roy. Soc.* (*London*), ser. A **205**, 421 (1951).]

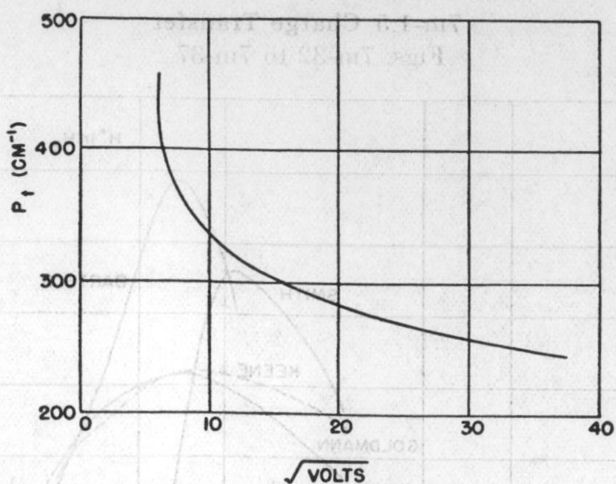

Fig. 7m-34. Charge-transfer cross sections of ions and atoms of mercury. [B. M. Palyukh and L. A. Sena, *J. Exp. Theor. Phys. U.S.S.R.* **20**, 481 (1950).]

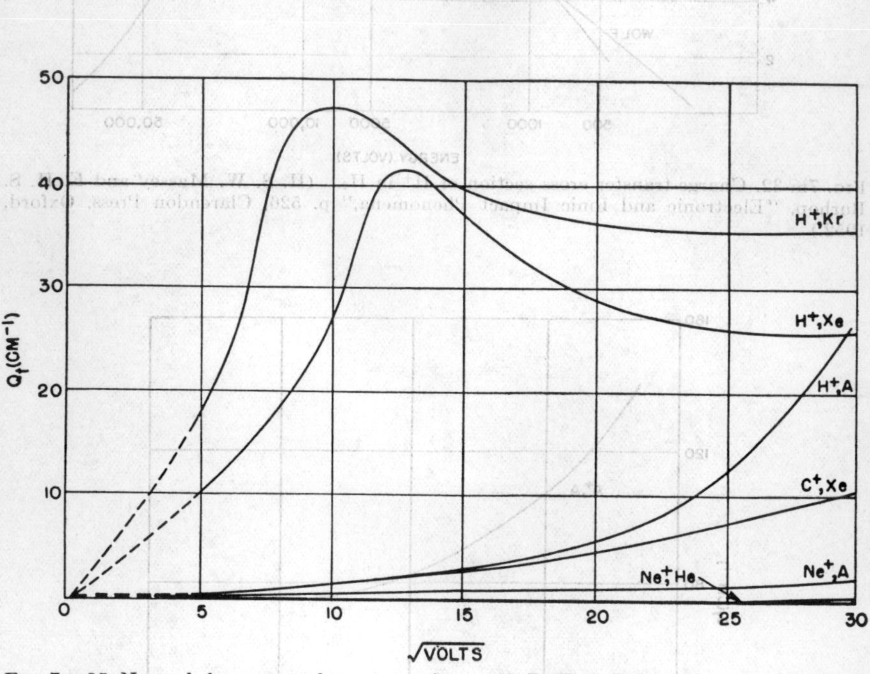

Fig. 7m-35. Normal charge-transfer cross sections. [J. B. Hasted, *Proc. Roy. Soc.* (*London*), ser. A, **205**, 421 (1951).]

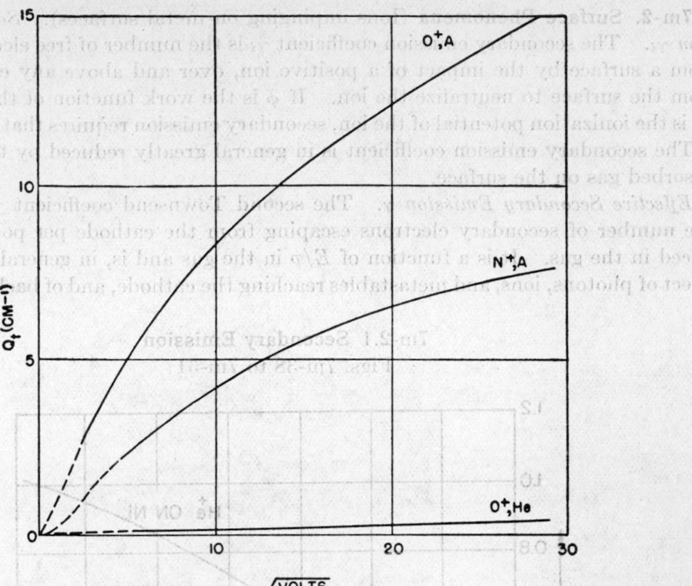

FIG. 7m-36. Abnormal charge-transfer cross sections with metastable ions present. [J. B. Hasted, *Proc. Roy. Soc.* (*London*), ser. A, **205,** 421 (1951).]

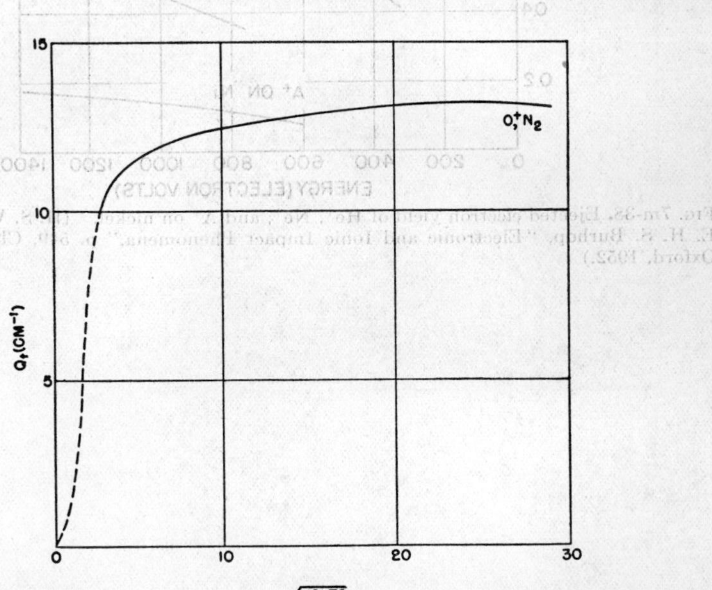

FIG. 7m-37. Charge-transfer cross section of O^+ in N_2 as a function of energy. Dashed line is extrapolated. [J. B. Hasted, *Proc. Roy. Soc.* (*London*), ser. A, **205,** 421 (1951).]

7m-2. Surface Phenomena (Ions impinging on metal surfaces). *Secondary Emission γ_i.* The secondary emission coefficient γ_i is the number of free electrons released from a surface by the impact of a positive ion, over and above any electrons taken from the surface to neutralize the ion. If ϕ is the work function of the surface, and V_i is the ionization potential of the ion, secondary emission requires that $V_i > 2\phi$.

The secondary emission coefficient is in general greatly reduced by the presence of adsorbed gas on the surface.

Effective Secondary Emission γ. The second Townsend coefficient γ is defined as the number of secondary electrons escaping from the cathode per positive ion produced in the gas. It is a function of E/p in the gas and is, in general, the resultant effect of photons, ions, and metastables reaching the cathode, and of back diffusion.

7m-2.1 Secondary Emission

Figs. 7m-38 to 7m-51

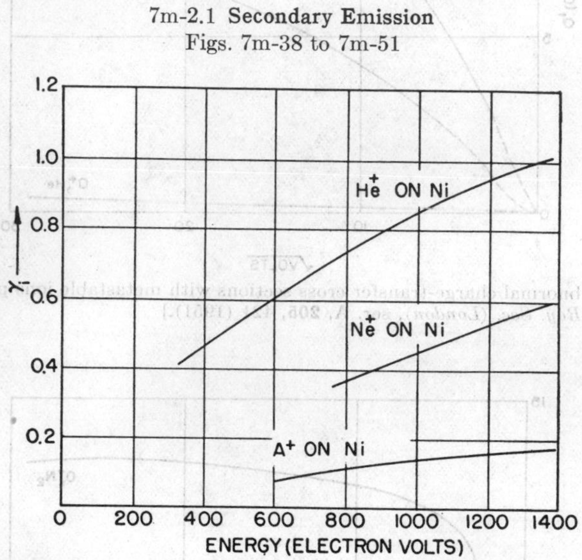

FIG. 7m-38. Ejected electron yield of He^+, Ne^+, and A^+ on nickel. (H. S. W. Massey and E. H. S. Burhop, "Electronic and Ionic Impact Phenomena," p. 549, Clarendon Press, Oxford, 1952.)

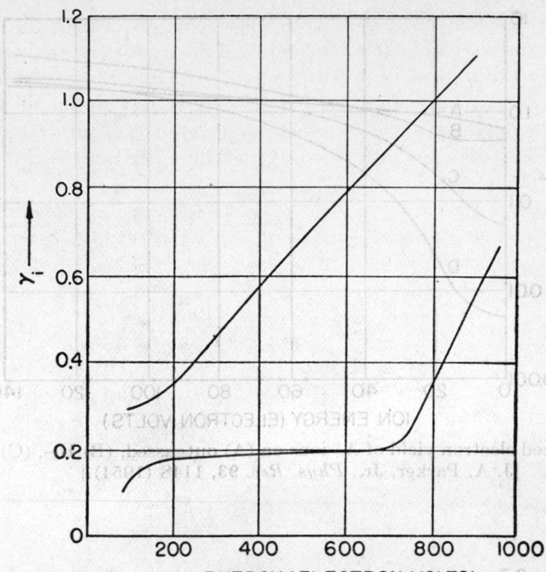

Fig. 7m-39. Ejected electron yield of He^+ on nickel outgassed (lower curve) and not outgassed (upper curve). (A. von Engel and M. Steenbeck, "Elektrische Gesentladungen," vol. I, p. 118, J. Springer Verlag, Berlin, 1932).

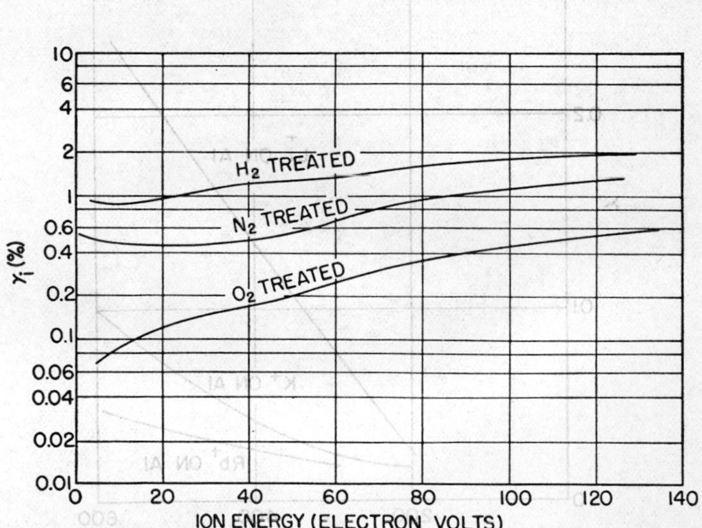

Fig. 7m-40. Ejected electron yield of A^+ ions on H_2-, N_2-, and O_2- treated platinum. [J. A. Parker, Jr., *Phys. Rev.* **93**, 1148 (1954).]

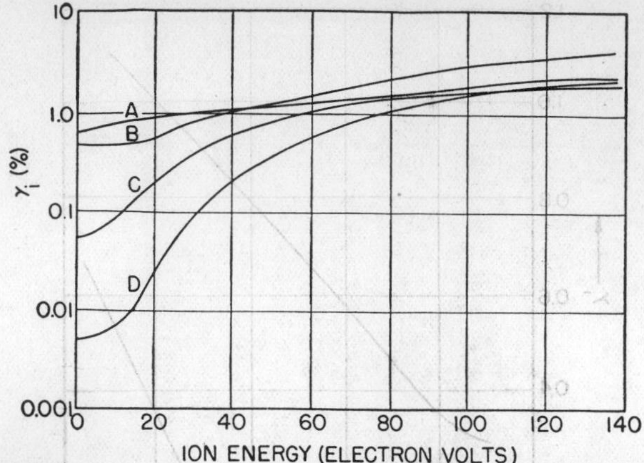

FIG. 7m-41. Ejected electron yield of A^+ ions on (A) outgassed, (B) H_2-, (C) N_2-, and (D) O_2-treated tantalum. [J. A. Parker, Jr., *Phys. Rev.* **93**, 1148 (1954).]

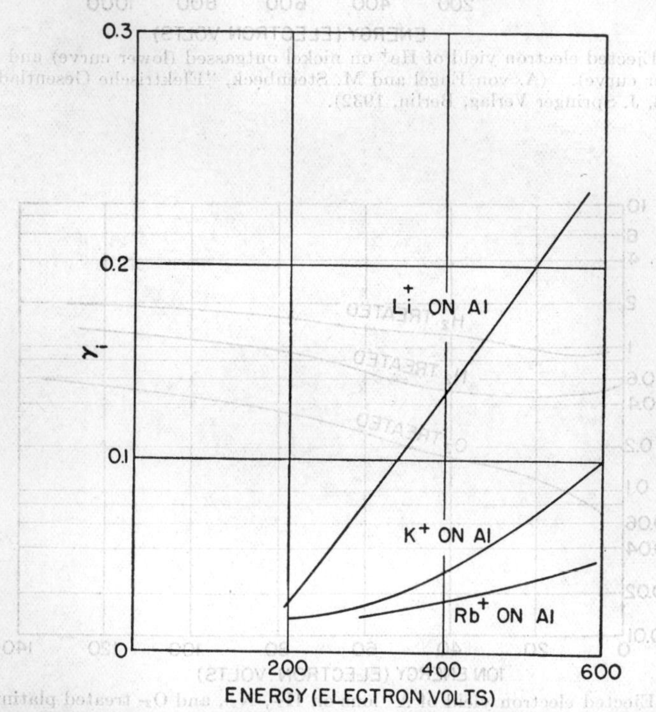

FIG. 7m-42. Ejected electron yield of Li^+, K^+, and Rb^+ on aluminum. (H. S. W. Massey and E. H. S. Burhop, "Electronic and Ionic Impact Phenomena," p. 549, Clarendon Press, Oxford, 1952).

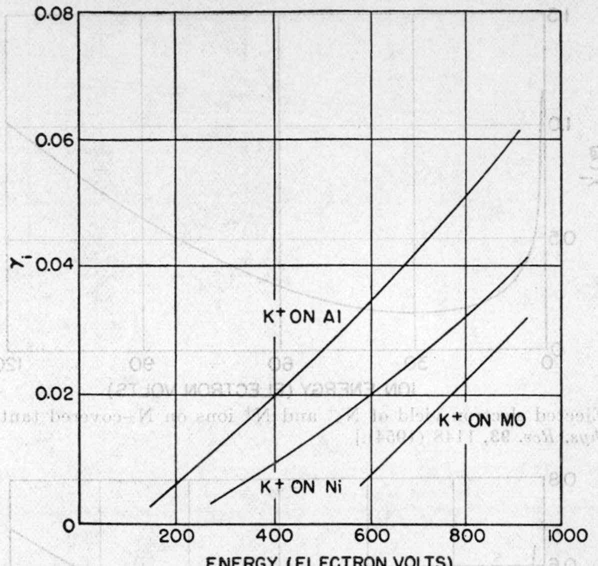

Fig. 7m-43. Ejected electron yield of K^+ on Al, Ni, and Mo. (H. S. W. Massey and E. H. S. Burhop, "Electronic and Ionic Impact Phenomena," p. 549, Clarendon Press, Oxford, 1952.)

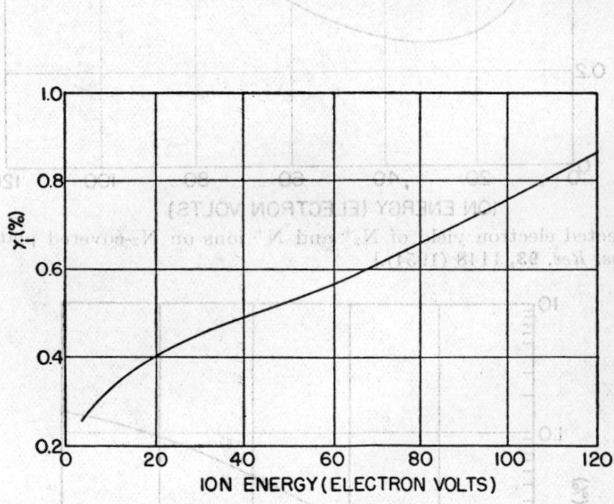

Fig. 7m-44. Ejected electron yield of H_2^+ and H^+ ions on H_2-covered platinum. [J. A. Parker, Jr., *Phys. Rev.* **93,** 1148 (1954).]

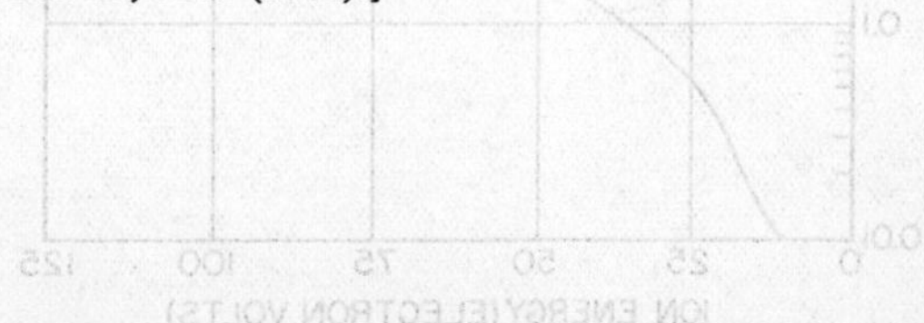

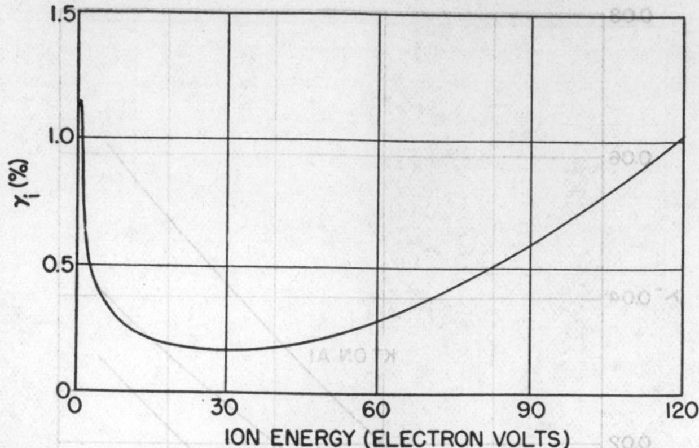

FIG. 7m-45. Ejected electron yield of N_2^+ and N^+ ions on N_2-covered tantalum. [J. A. Parker, Jr., *Phys. Rev.* **93,** 1148 (1954).]

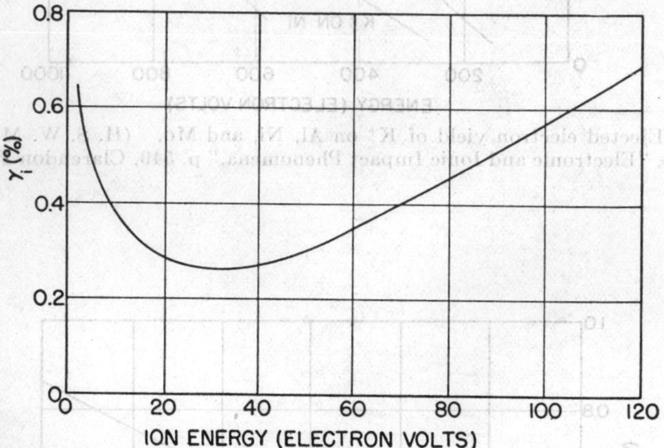

FIG. 7m-46. Ejected electron yield of N_2^+ and N^+ ions on N_2-covered platinum. [J. A. Parker, Jr., *Phys. Rev.* **93,** 1148 (1954).]

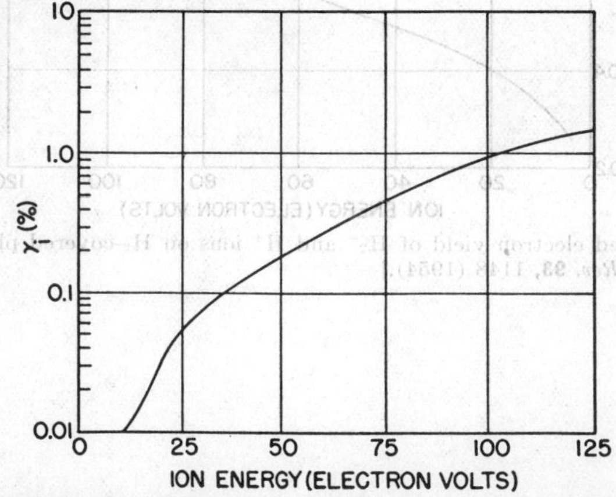

FIG. 7m-47. Ejected electron yield of O_2^+ and O^+ ions on O_2-covered tantalum. [J. A. Parker, Jr., *Phys. Rev.* **93,** 1148 (1954).]

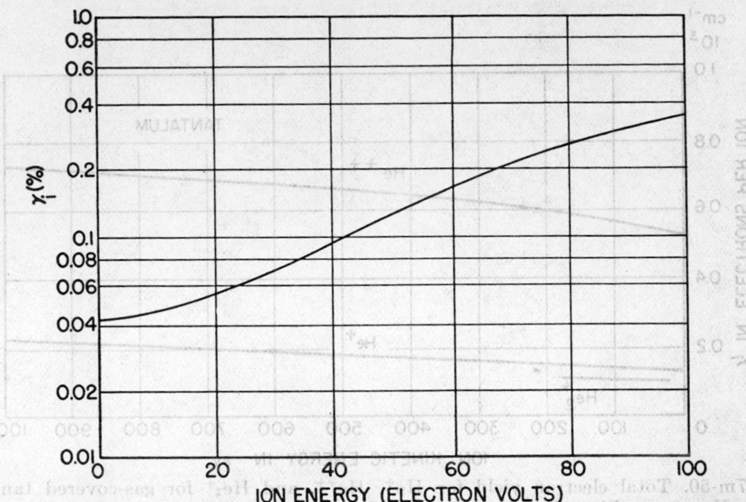

FIG. 7m-48. Ejected electron yield of O_2^+ and O^+ ions on O_2-covered platinum. [J. A. Parker, Jr., *Phys. Rev.* **93,** 1148 (1954).]

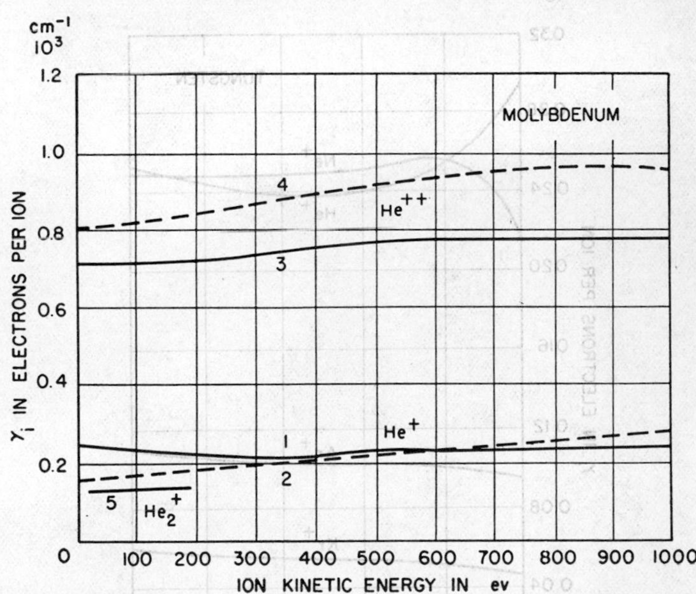

FIG. 7m-49. Total electron yield. Curves 1 and 3 are for atomically clean Mo, curves 2, 4, 5 for Mo covered with monolayer of gas. [H. D. Hagstrum, *Phys. Rev.* **89,** 244 (1953).]

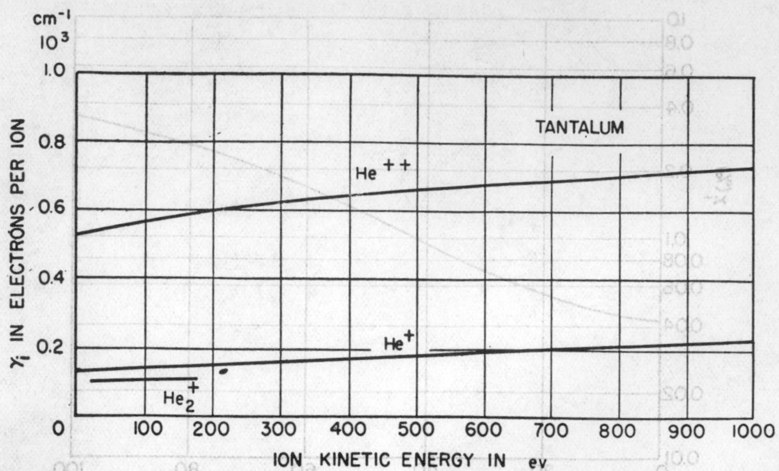

FIG. 7m-50. Total electron yield for He^+, He^{++}, and $He_2{}^+$ for gas-covered tantalum. [H. D. Hagstrum, *Phys. Rev.* **91**, 543 (1953).]

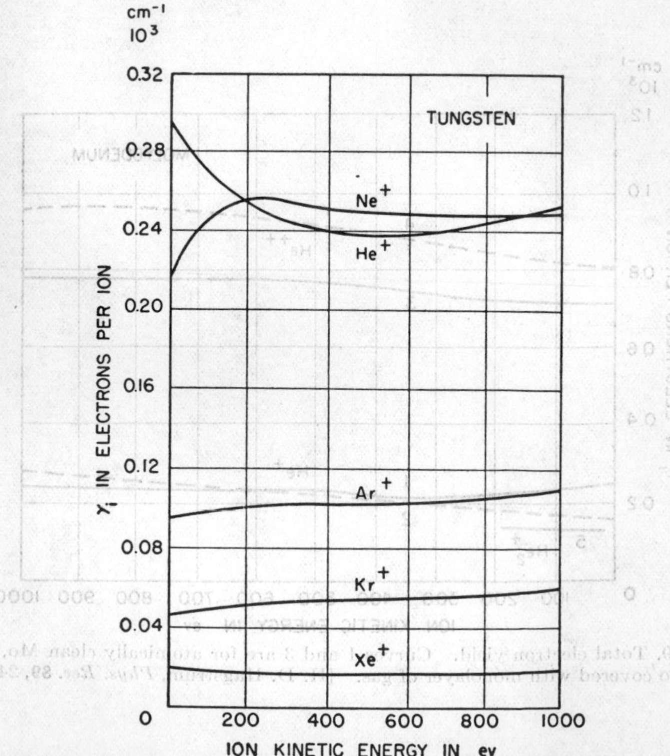

FIG. 7m-51. Total electron yield for singly charged ions on atomically clean tungsten. [H. D. Hagstrum, *Phys. Rev.* **96**, 325 (1954).]

7m-2.2 Effective Secondary Emission

Figs. 7m-52 to 7m-55

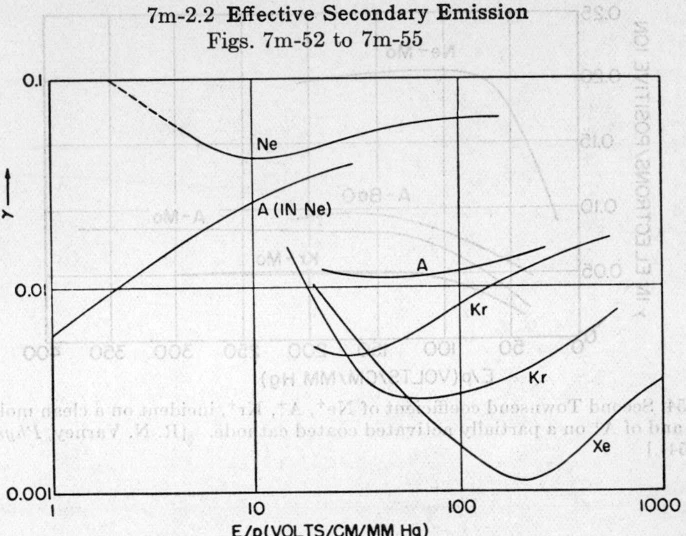

FIG. 7m-52. Second Townsend coefficient for copper in the rare gases. [M. J. Druyvesteyn and F. M. Penning, *Revs. Modern Phys.* **12**, 87 (1940).]

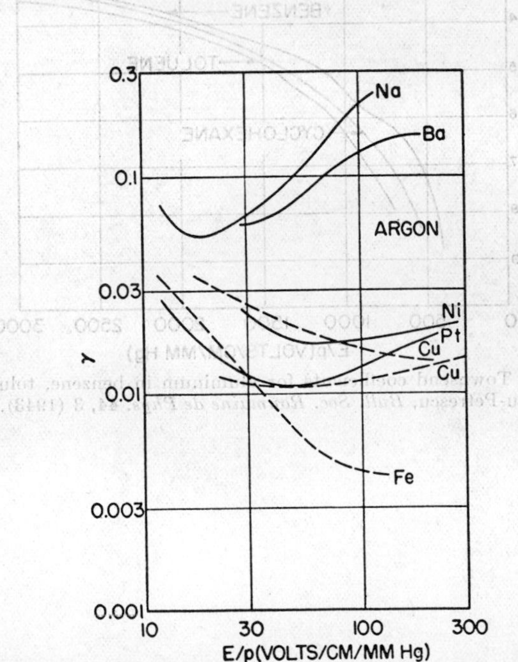

FIG. 7m-53. Second Townsend coefficient for argon with different cathode materials. [M. J. Druyvesteyn and F. M. Penning, *Revs. Modern Phys.* **12**, 87 (1940).]

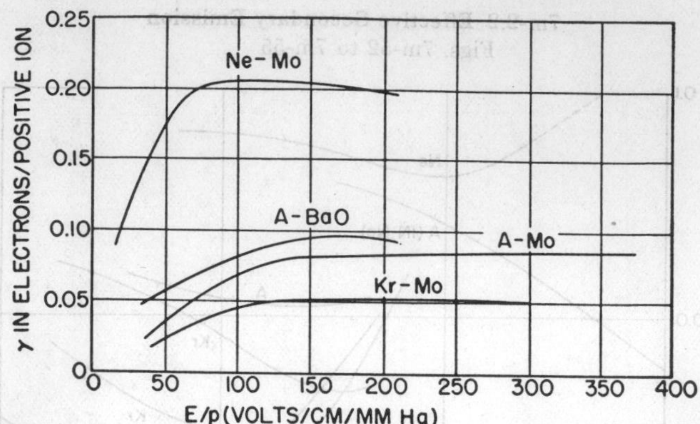

FIG. 7m-54. Second Townsend coefficient of Ne^+, A^+, Kr^+, incident on a clean molybdenum cathode, and of A^+ on a partially activated coated cathode. [R. N. Varney, *Phys. Rev.* **93**, 1156 (1954).]

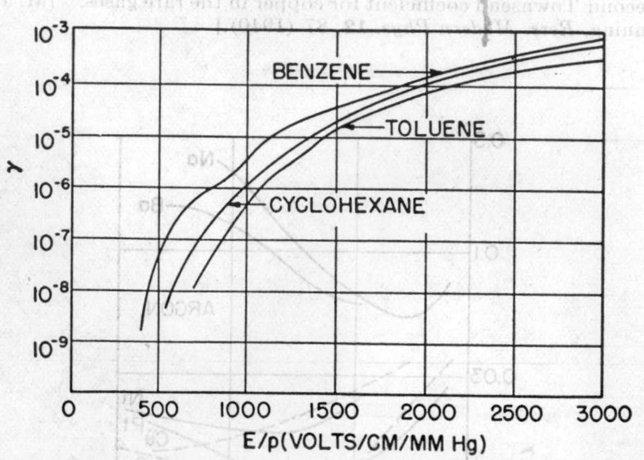

FIG. 7m-55. Second Townsend coefficients for aluminum in benzene, toluene, and cyclohexane. [M. Valeriu-Petrescu, *Bull. Soc. Roumaine de Phys.* **44**, 3 (1943).]

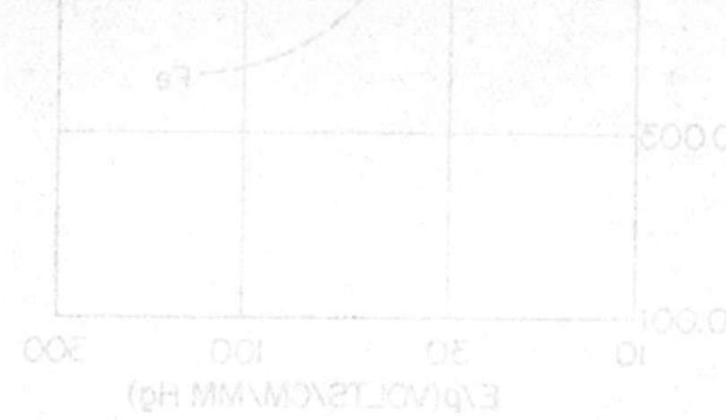

7m-2.3 Ion Conversions

Figs. 7m-56 to 7m-59

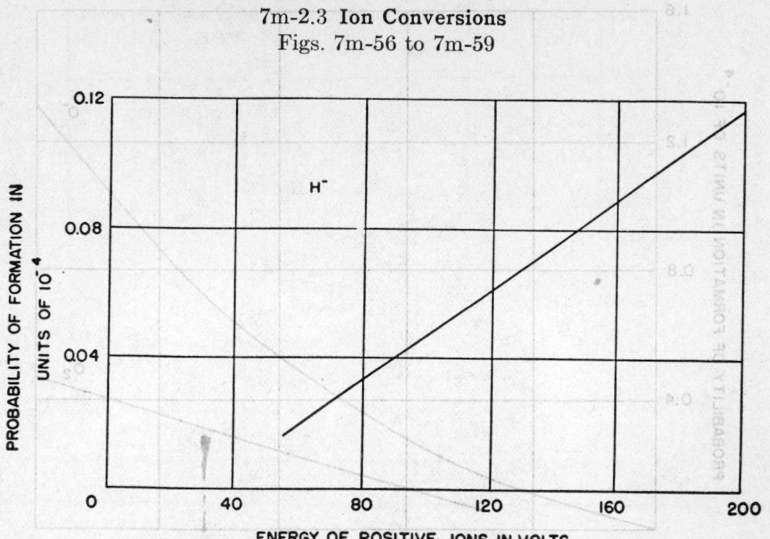

Fig. 7m-56. Probability of conversion of positive hydrogen ions into negative hydrogen ions on nickel. [F. L. Arnot, *Proc. Roy. Soc.* (*London*), ser. A, **158**, 137 (1937).]

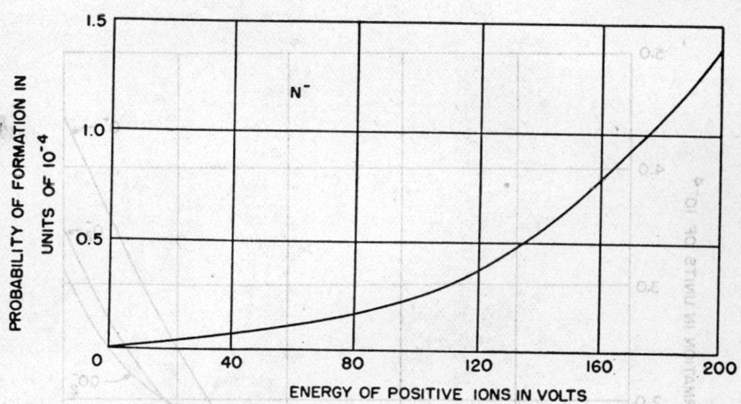

Fig. 7m-57. Probability of conversion of positive nitrogen ions into negative nitrogen ions on nickel. [F. L. Arnot, *Proc. Roy. Soc.* (*London*), ser. A, **158**, 137 (1937).]

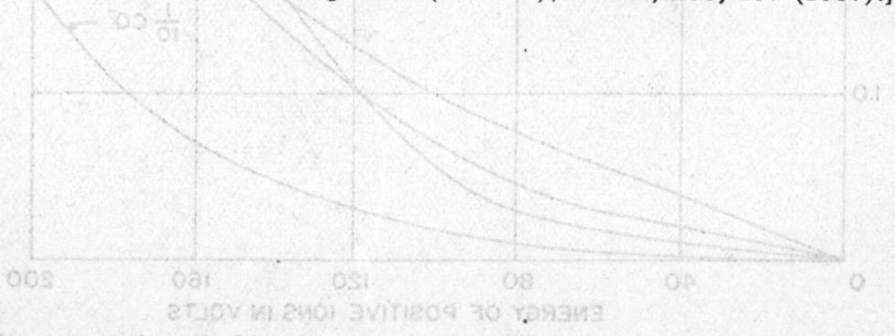

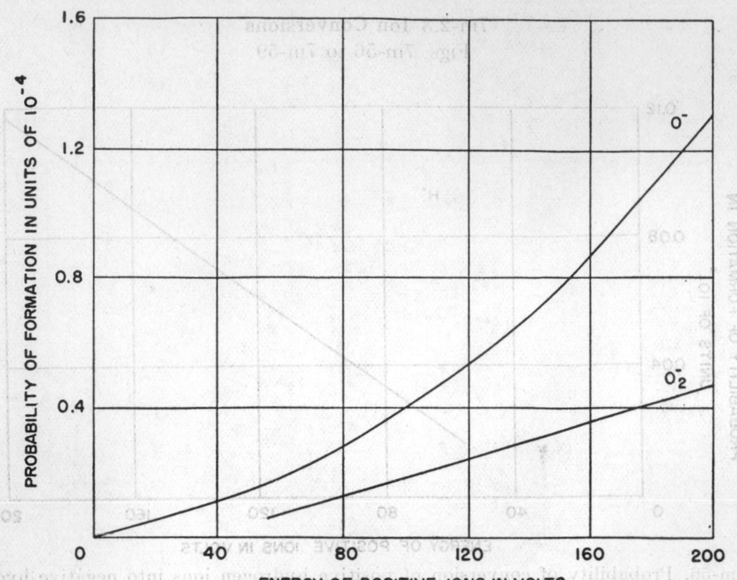

FIG. 7m-58. Probability of conversion of positive oxygen ions into negative oxygen ions on nickel. [F. L. Arnot, *Proc. Roy. Soc.* (*London*), ser. A, **158,** 137 (1937).]

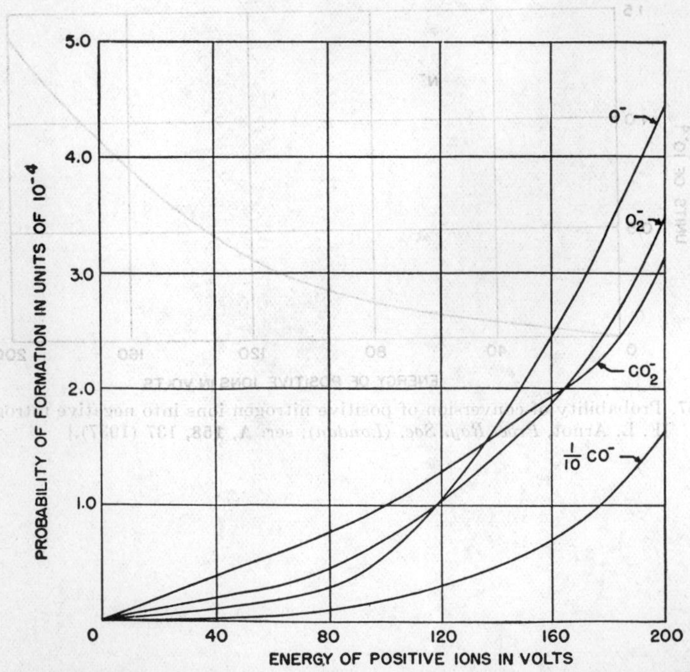

FIG. 7m-59. Probability of conversion of positive carbon dioxide ions into negative carbon dioxide ions on nickel. [F. L. Arnot, *Proc. Roy. Soc.* (*London*), ser. A, **158,** 137 (1937).]

7m-2.4 Seondary Emission by Electrons

Fig. 7m-60

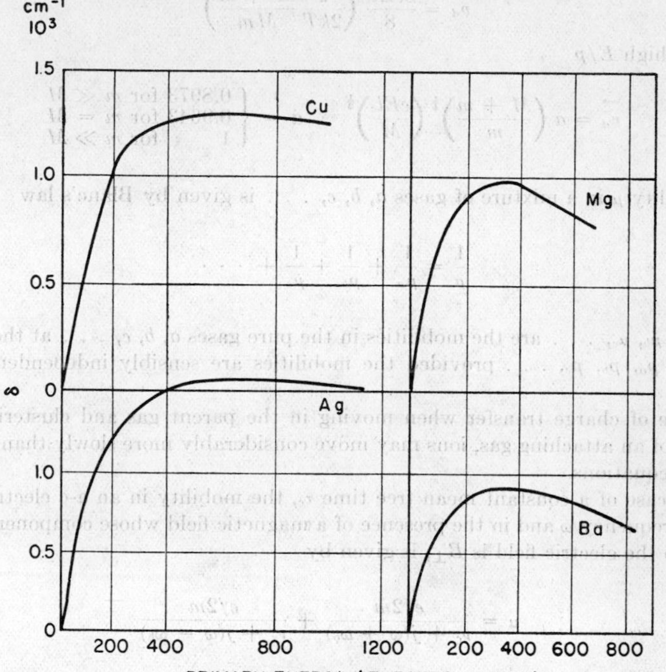

FIG. 7m-60. Ratio of the number of secondary electrons emitted from a surface to the number of primary electrons incident as a function of incident energy. (H. S. W. Massey and E. H. S. Burhop, "Electronic and Ionic Impact Phenomena," p. 306, Clarendon Press, Oxford, 1952.)

7m-3. Average Motions of Electrons and Ions. The drift velocity $\vec{v}_d$ of a charged particle of mass m and charge e in a gas of molecules of mass M, under an electric field $\vec{E}$, is given by

$$\vec{v}_d = e\vec{E}\,\frac{M+m}{Mm}\int l\,\frac{\partial f}{\partial v}\,\frac{4\pi}{3}\,v^2\,dv \tag{7m-1}$$

where $f(v)$ is the velocity-distribution function.

For particles with a constant mean free time τ_c this yields, for all E/p,

$$\vec{v}_d = \frac{M+m}{Mm}\,e\vec{E}\tau_c \tag{7m-2}$$

If collisions are caused by a polarization force

$$\tau_c = \frac{1.8096\epsilon_0}{en_g}\left(\frac{Mm/\alpha}{M+m}\right)^{\frac{1}{2}} \tag{7m-3}$$

where the polarizability $\alpha = (\epsilon - \epsilon_0)/n_g$.

For particles with a constant mean free path l_c (rigid spheres) there are two limiting forms:

1. Near thermal equilibrium

$$\vec{v}_d = \frac{3e\vec{E}l_c}{8}\left(\frac{\pi}{2kT}\frac{M+m}{Mm}\right)^{\frac{1}{2}} \tag{7m-4}$$

2. For high E/p

$$\vec{v}_d = a\left(\frac{M+m}{m}\right)^{\frac{1}{4}}\left(\frac{eEl_c}{M}\right)^{\frac{1}{2}} \qquad a = \begin{cases} 0.8973 & \text{for } m \ll M \\ 0.9643 & \text{for } m = M \\ 1 & \text{for } m \gg M \end{cases} \tag{7m-5}$$

The mobility μ in a mixture of gases $a, b, c, \ldots$ is given by Blanc's law

$$\frac{1}{\mu} = \frac{1}{\mu_a} + \frac{1}{\mu_b} + \frac{1}{\mu_c} + \cdots \tag{7m-6}$$

where $\mu_a, \mu_b, \mu_c, \ldots$ are the mobilities in the pure gases $a, b, c, \ldots$ at their partial pressures $p_a, p_b, p_c, \ldots$ provided the mobilities are sensibly independent of field strength.

Because of charge transfer when moving in the parent gas and clustering in the presence of an attaching gas, ions may move considerably more slowly than indicated by these equations.

In the case of a constant mean free time τ_c, the mobility in an a-c electric field of circular frequency ω and in the presence of a magnetic field whose component perpendicular to the electric field is $B_\perp$, is given by

$$\mu = \frac{e/2m}{\nu_c + j(\omega + \omega_b)} + \frac{e/2m}{\nu_c + j(\omega - \omega_b)} \tag{7m-7}$$

where $\omega_b = B_\perp e/m$ is the cyclotron frequency.

The complex conductivity of a plasma is given by

$$\sigma = n_+ e\mu_+ + ne\mu_- + j\omega\epsilon_0 \tag{7m-8}$$

For a completely ionized plasma

$$\sigma = \frac{1.1632m}{z \ln (q-1)}\left(\frac{4\pi\epsilon_0}{e}\right)^2\left(\frac{2kT}{\pi m}\right)^{\frac{3}{2}} = \frac{19{,}141}{z \ln (q-1)}\left(\frac{kT}{e}\right)^{\frac{3}{2}} \quad \text{mho/m} \tag{7m-9}$$

where $q = 12\pi n\lambda_D{}^3$, $\lambda_D{}^2 = \epsilon_0 kT/ne^2$ is the Debye length, and $n\lambda_D{}^2 = 3.134 \times 10^4 T$ m^{-1}. z is the charge on the ions.

If λ is the mean fraction of the energy difference which is transferred in a collision, the mean energy of an electron or ion is given by

$$\frac{1}{2}m\overline{v^2} = \frac{3}{2}kT + \frac{eE\tau_c v_d}{\lambda} \tag{7m-10}$$

For elastic collisions

$$\lambda = \frac{2Mm}{(M+m)^2}$$

For the mean free time case

$$\frac{v_d{}^2}{\overline{v^2}} = \frac{M+m}{2M}\lambda\left(1 - \frac{3kT}{m\overline{v^2}}\right) \tag{7m-11}$$

Mean energies are usually determined by the approximate relation

$$\frac{D}{\mu} = \frac{m(\overline{v^2} - v_d^2)}{3e} \tag{7m-12}$$

which is exact when the distribution function is Maxwellian.

The diffusion coefficient is given by

$$D = \int \frac{lv}{3} f 4\pi v^2 \, dv \tag{7m-13}$$

7m-3.1 Drift Velocity of Electrons

Figs. 7m-61 to 7m-72

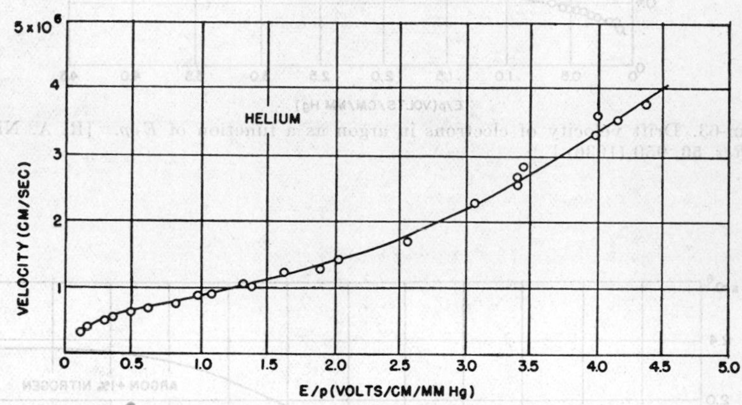

Fig. 7m-61. Drift velocity of electrons in helium as a function of E/p. [R. A. Nielsen, *Phys. Rev.* **50**, 950 (1936); J. A. Hornbeck, *Phys. Rev.* **83**, 374 (1951).]

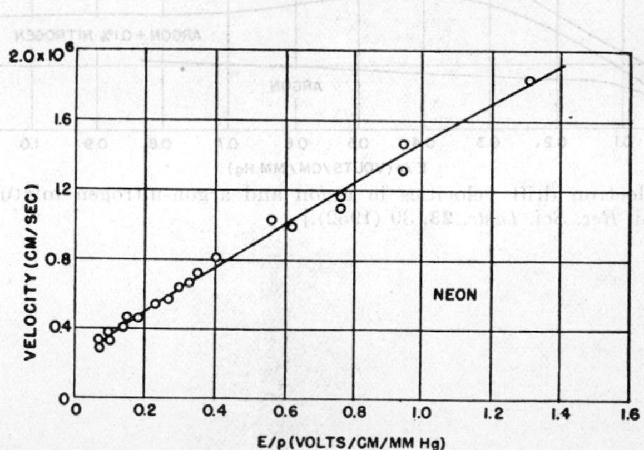

Fig. 7m-62. Drift velocity of electrons in neon as a function of E/p. [R. A. Nielsen, *Phys. Rev.* **50**, 950 (1936).]

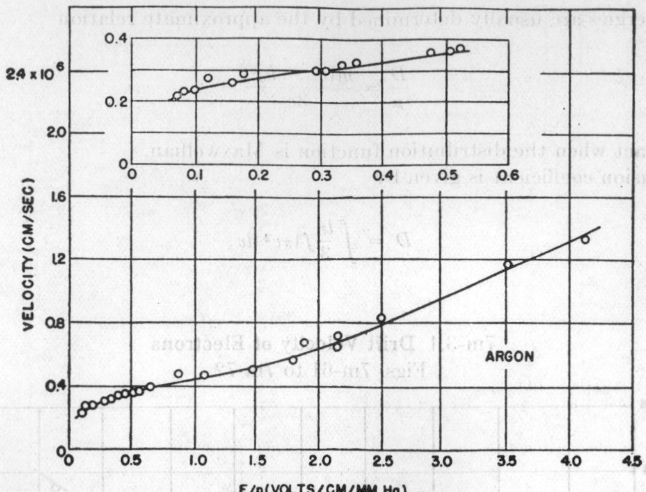

FIG. 7m-63. Drift velocity of electrons in argon as a function of E/p. [R. A. Nielsen, *Phys. Rev.* **50**, 950 (1936).]

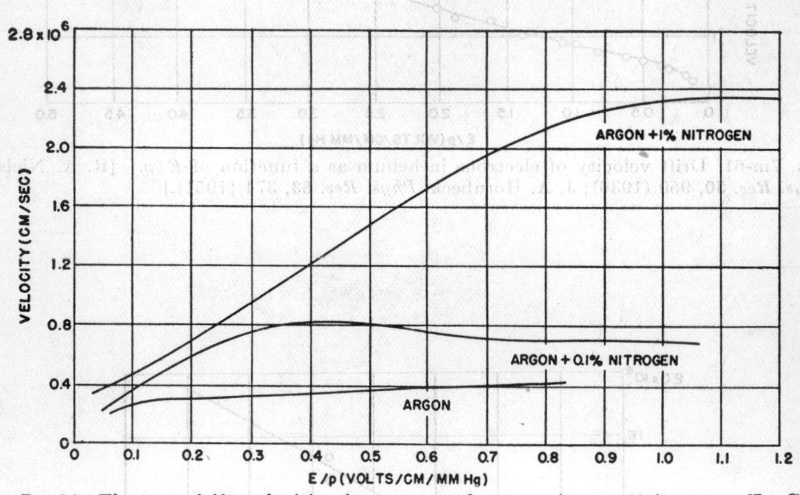

FIG. 7m-64. Electron drift velocities in argon and argon-nitrogen mixtures. [L. Colli and U. Facchini, *Rev. Sci. Instr.* **23**, 39 (1952).]

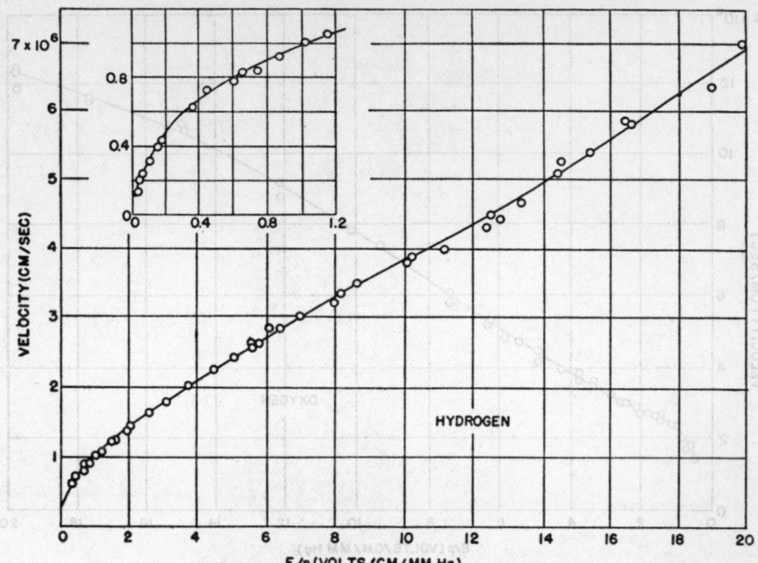

FIG. 7m-65. Drift velocity of electrons in hydrogen as a function of E/p. [N. E. Bradbury and R. A. Nielsen, *Phys. Rev.* **49**, 388 (1936).]

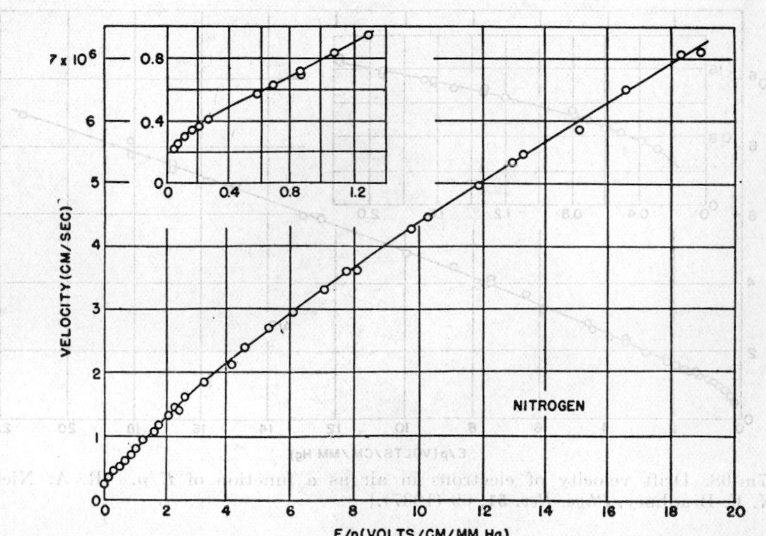

FIG. 7m-66. Drift velocity of electrons in nitrogen as a function of E/p. [R. A. Nielsen, *Phys. Rev.* **50**, 950 (1936).]

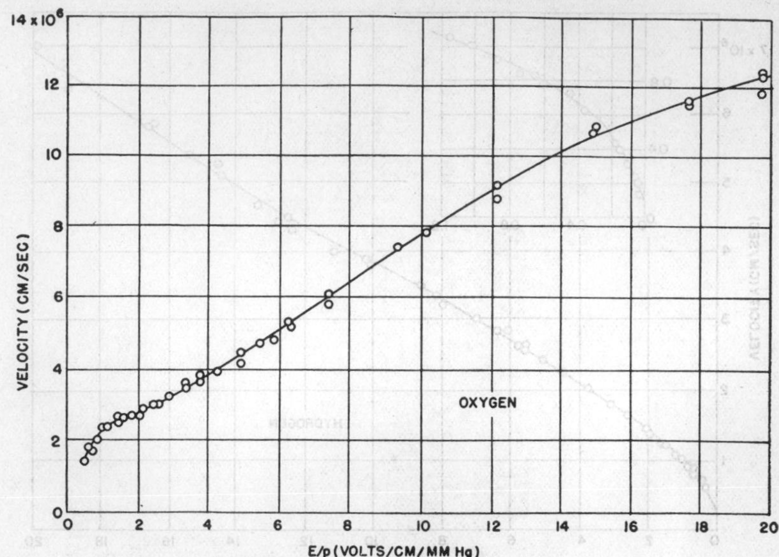

FIG. 7m-67. Drift velocity of electrons in oxygen as a function of E/p. [R. A. Nielsen and N. E. Bradbury, *Phys. Rev.* **51**, 69 (1937).]

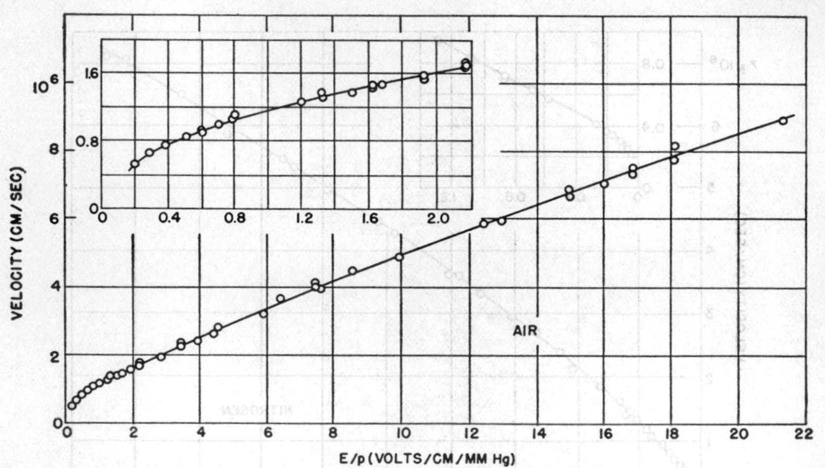

FIG. 7m-68. Drift velocity of electrons in air as a function of E/p. [R. A. Nielsen and N. E. Bradbury, *Phys. Rev.* **51**, 69 (1937).]

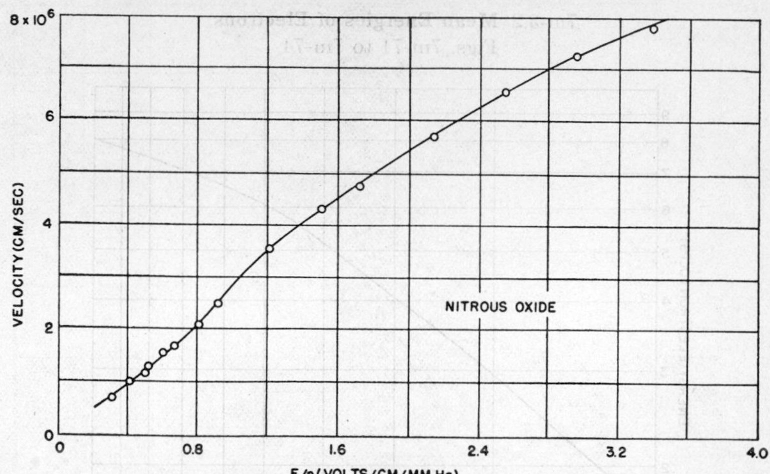

FIG. 7m-69. Drift velocity of electrons in nitrous oxide as a function of E/p. [R. A. Nielsen, N. E. Bradbury, *Phys. Rev.* **51**, 69 (1937).]

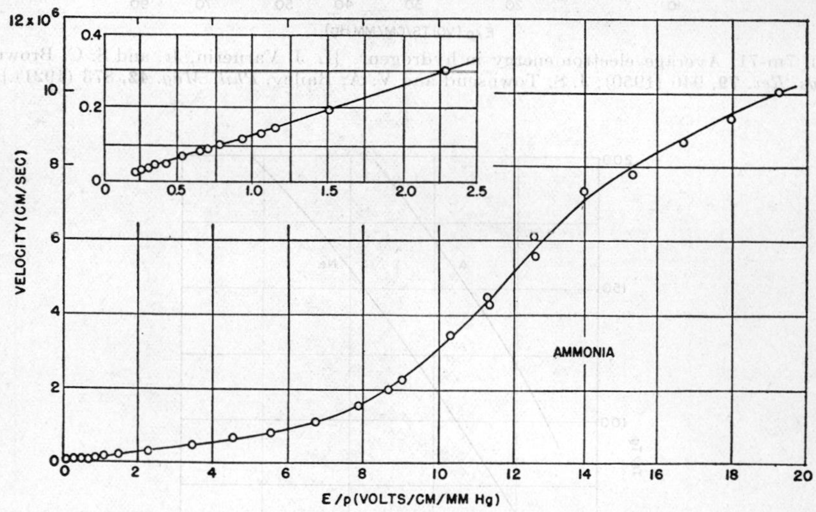

FIG. 7m-70. Drift velocity of electrons in ammonia as a function of E/p. [R. A. Nielsen and N. E. Bradbury, *Phys. Rev.* **51**, 69 (1937).]

7m-3.2 Mean Energies of Electrons

Figs. 7m-71 to 7m-74

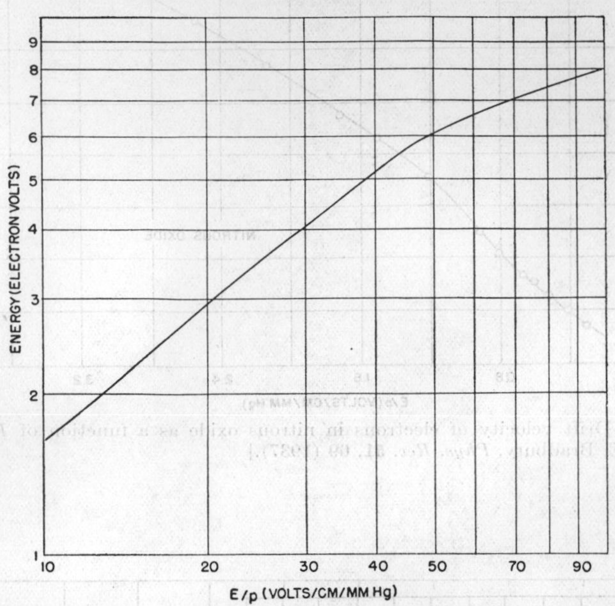

FIG. 7m-71. Average electron energy in hydrogen. [L. J. Varnerin, Jr. and S. C. Brown, *Phys. Rev.* **79,** 946 (1950); J. S. Townsend and V. A. Bailey, *Phil. Mag.* **42,** 873 (1921).]

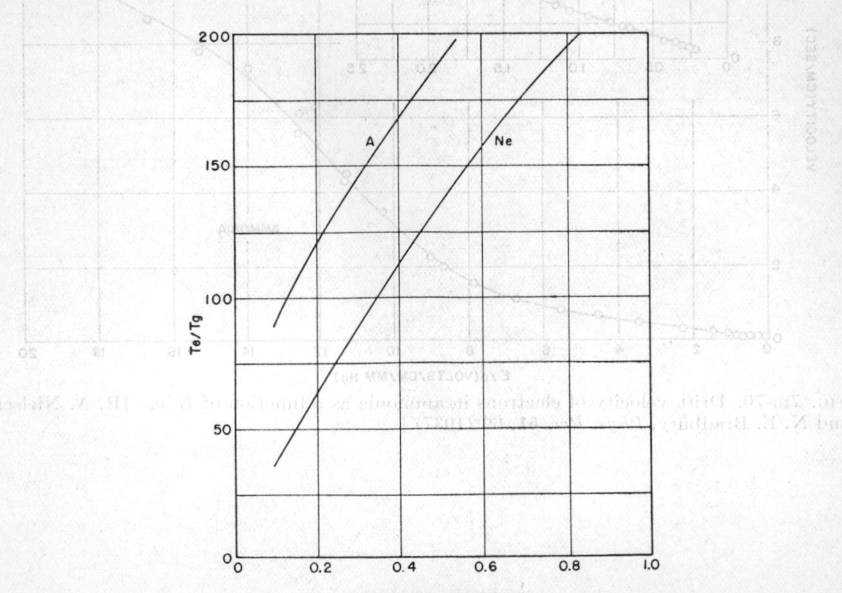

FIG. 7m-72. Ratio of electron to gas temperature. (R. H. Healey and J. W. Reed, "The Behavior of Slow Electrons in Gases," p. 78, Amalgamated Wireless, Ltd., Sydney, 1941.)

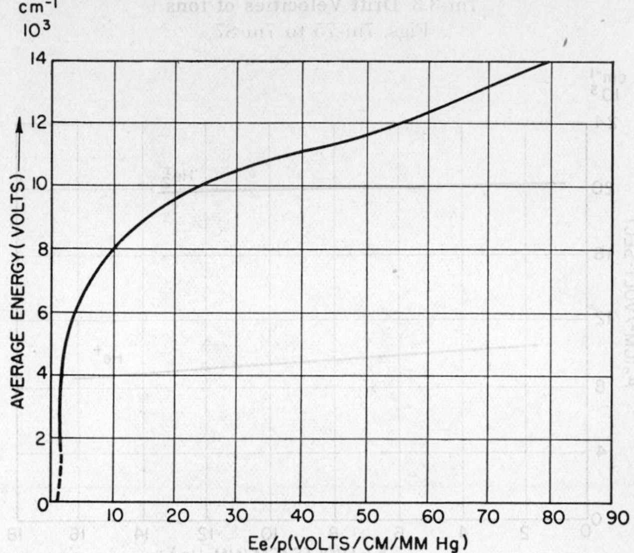

FIG. 7m-73. Average energy of electrons in helium. [F. H. Reder and S. C. Brown, *Phys. Rev.* **95,** 885 (1954).]

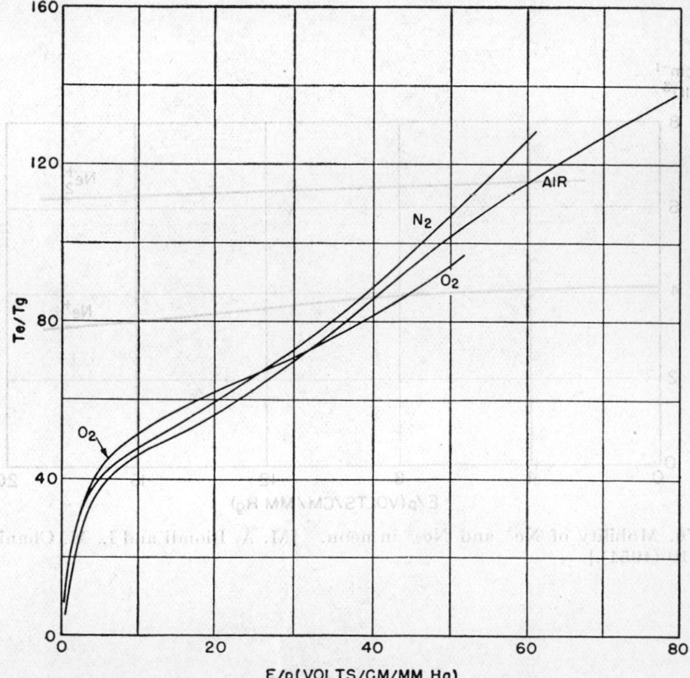

FIG. 7m-74. Ratio of electron to gas temperature. (R. H. Healey and J. W. Reed, "The Behavior of Slow Electrons in Gases," p. 79, Amalgamated Wireless, Ltd., Sydney, 1941.)

7m-3.3 Drift Velocities of Ions

Figs. 7m-75 to 7m-87

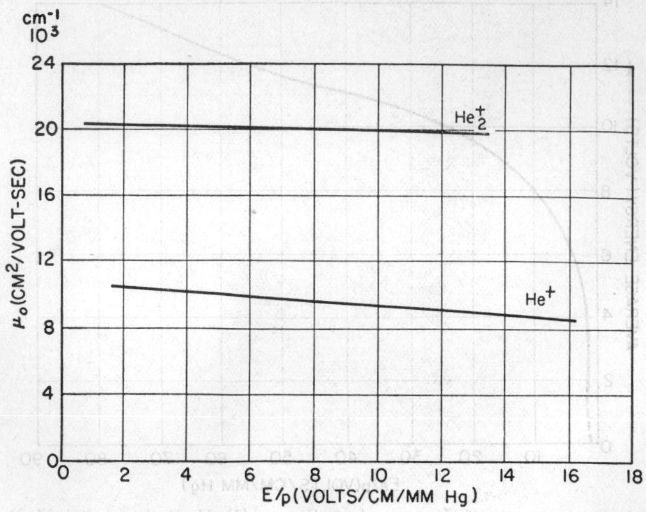

FIG. 7m-75. Mobility of He^+ and H_2^+ in helium. [M. A. Biondi and L. M. Chanin, *Phys. Rev.* **94**, 910 (1954).]

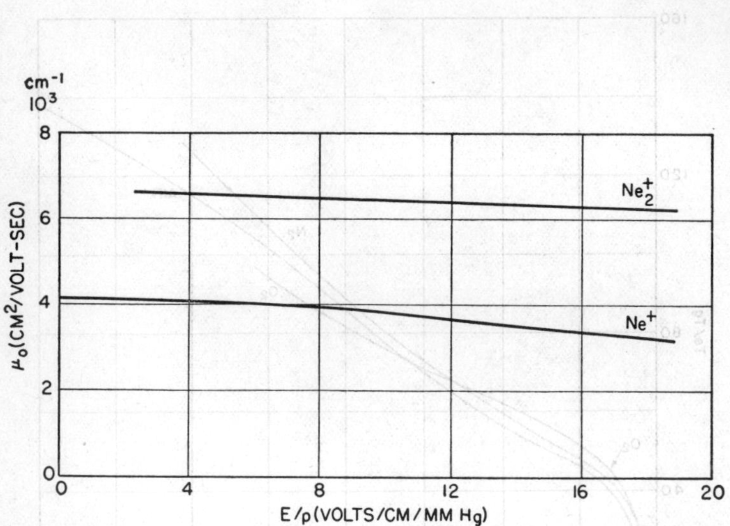

FIG. 7m-76. Mobility of Ne^+ and Ne_2^+ in neon. [M. A. Biondi and L. M. Chanin, *Phys. Rev.* **94**, 910 (1954).]

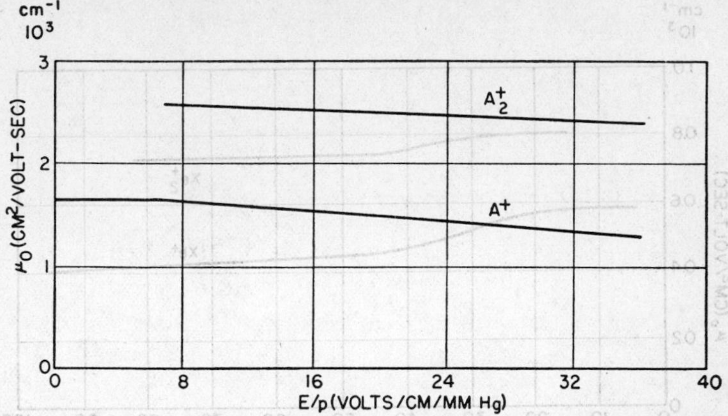

FIG. 7m-77. Mobility of A^+ and A_2^+ in argon. [M. A. Biondi and L. M. Chanin, *Phys. Rev.* **94,** 910 (1954).]

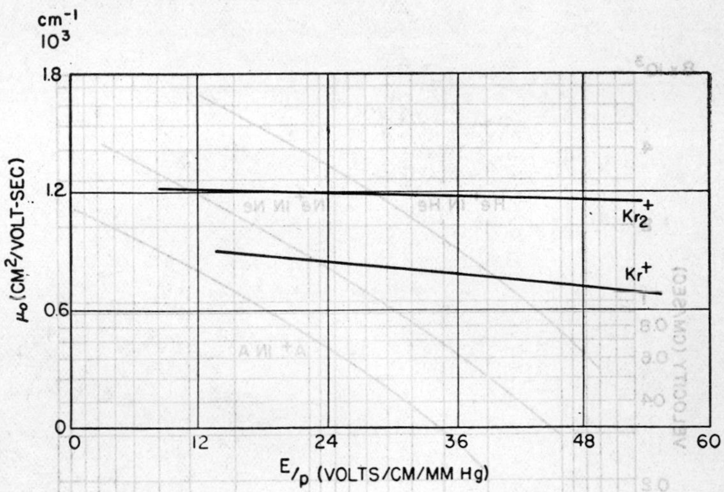

FIG. 7m-78. Mobility of Kr^+ and Kr_2^+ in krypton. [M. A. Biondi and L. M. Chanin, *Phys. Rev.* **94,** 910 (1954).]

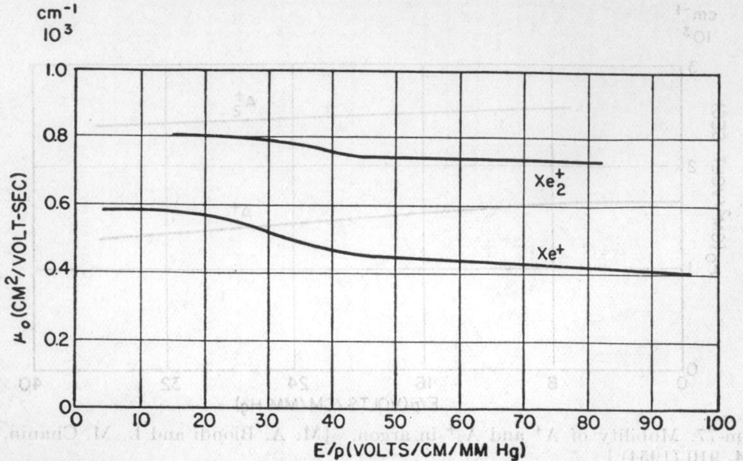

FIG. 7m-79. Mobility of Xe^+ and Xe_2^+ in xenon. [M. A. Biondi and L. M. Chanin, *Phys. Rev.* **94**, 910 (1954).]

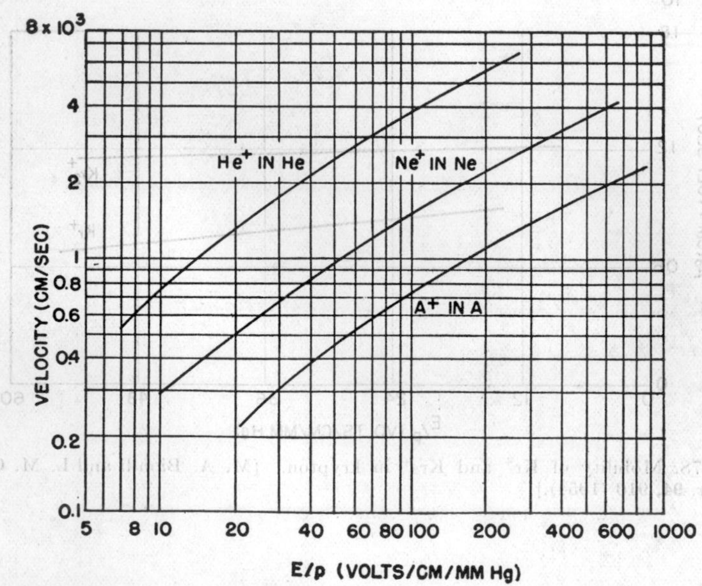

FIG. 7m-80. Drift velocity of atomic ions in helium, neon, and argon. [J. A. Hornbeck, *Phys. Rev.* **84**, 615 (1951).]

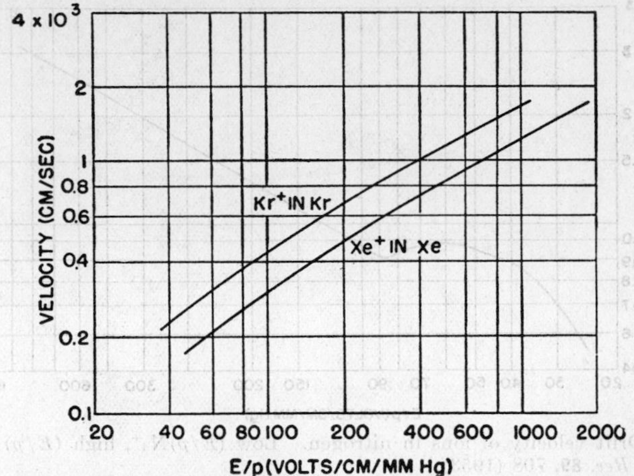

FIG. 7m-81. Drift velocity of atomic ions in krypton and xenon. [R. N. Varney, *Phys. Rev.* **88**, 362 (1952).]

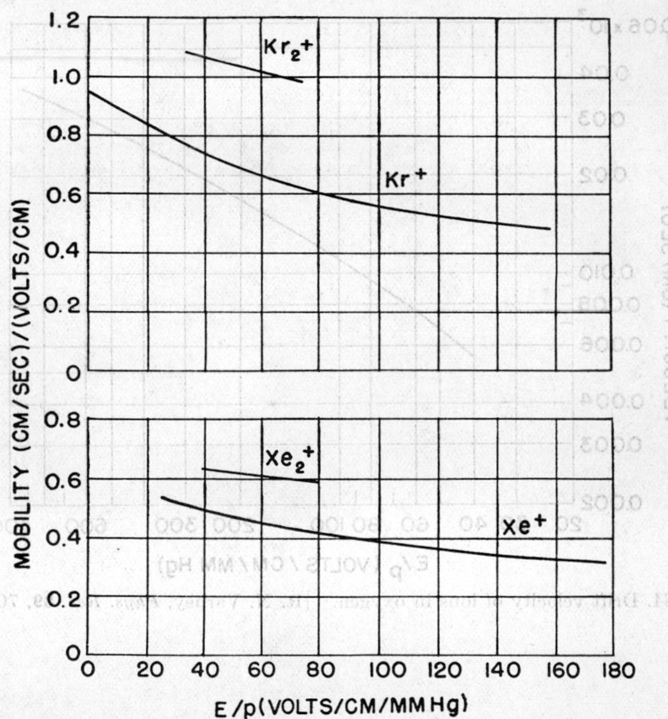

FIG. 7m-82. Mobility at standard gas density of atomic and molecular ions in krypton and xenon. [R. N. Varney, *Phys. Rev.* **88**, 362 (1952).]

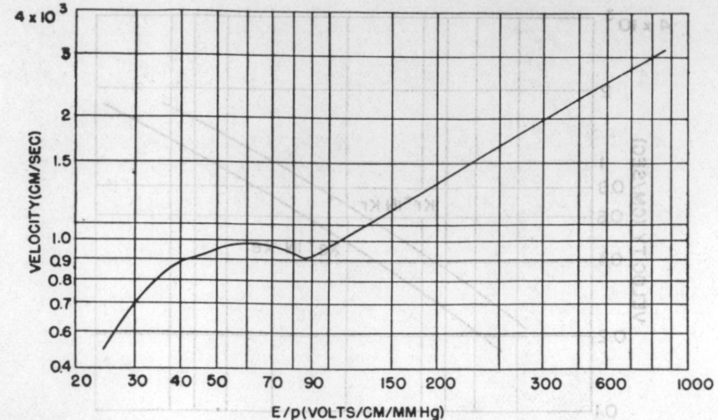

FIG. 7m-83. Drift velocity of ions in nitrogen. Low $(E/p)N_4^+$, high $(E/p)N_2^+$. [R. N Varney, *Phys. Rev.* **89**, 708 (1953).]

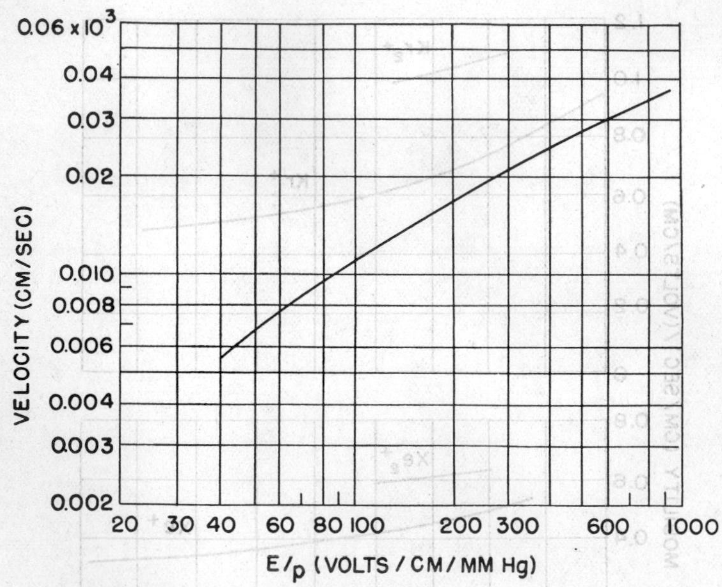

FIG. 7m-84. Drift velocity of ions in oxygen. [R. N. Varney, *Phys. Rev.* **89**, 708 (1953).]

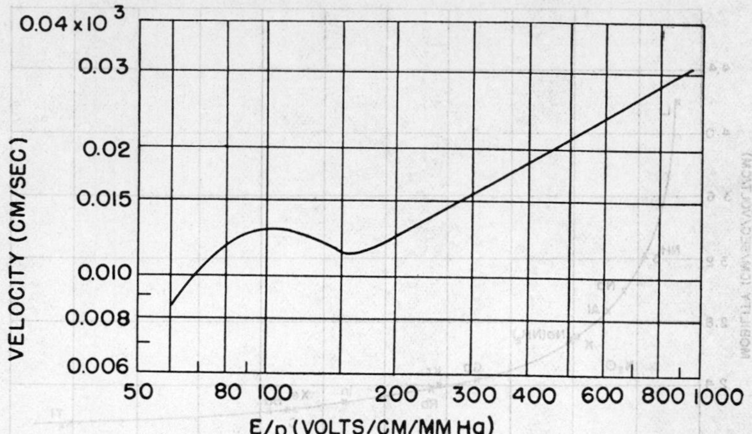

FIG. 7m-85. Drift velocity of ions in carbon monoxide. Low $(E/p)CO^+$, high (E/p), intermediate (E/p) may be CO_2^+. [R. N. Varney, *Phys. Rev.* **89**, 708 (1953).]

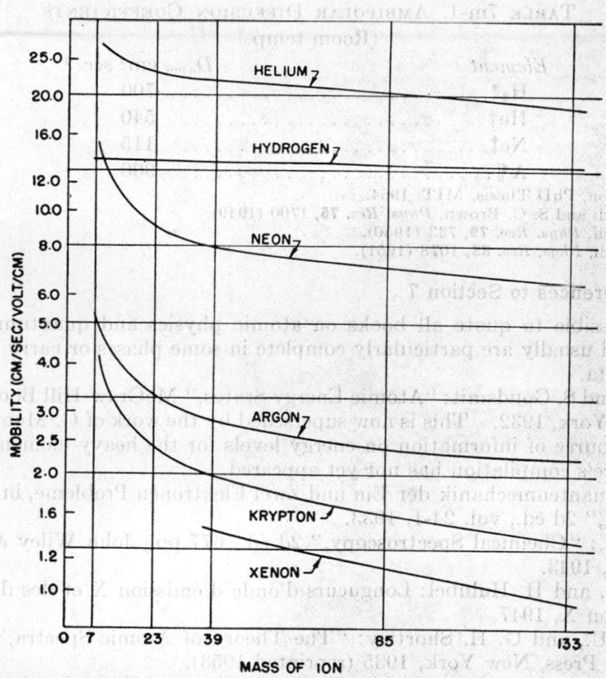

FIG. 7m-86. Mobility of alkali ions in gases at 1 atmospheric pressure. [C. F. Powell and L. Brata, *Proc. Roy. Soc.* (*London*), ser. A, **138**, 117 (1932).]

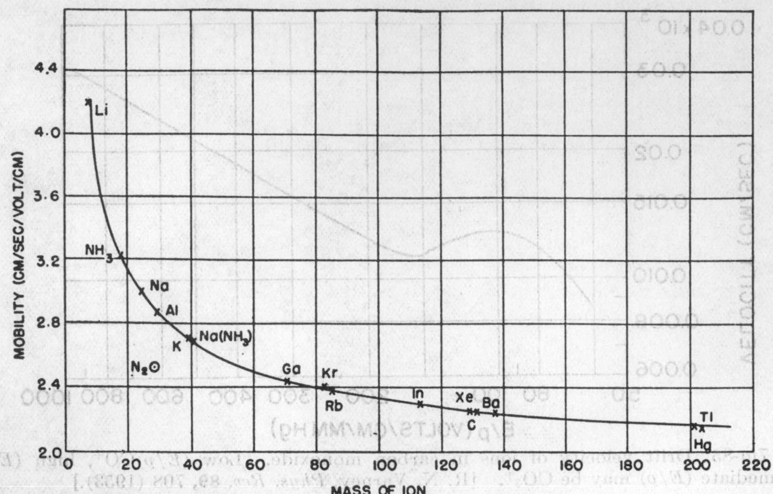

Fig. 7m-87. Mobility in nitrogen of various ions as a function of mass at 1 atmospheric pressure. [J. H. Mitchell, K. E. W. Ridler, *Proc. Roy. Soc.* (*London*), ser. A, **146**, 911 (1934).]

Table 7m-1. Ambipolar Diffusion Coefficients
(Room temp.)

Element	D_{apo}, cm² sec⁻¹
H_2*	700
He†	540
Ne‡	115
A¶	900

* K. B. Persson, PhD Thesis, MIT, 1954.
† M. A. Biondi and S. C. Brown, *Phys. Rev.* **75**, 1700 (1949).
‡ M. A. Biondi, *Phys. Rev.* **79**, 733 (1950).
¶ M. A. Biondi, *Phys. Rev.* **83**, 1078 (1951).

General References to Section 7

It is impossible to quote all books on atomic physics and quantum mechanics. Those quoted usually are particularly complete in some phases or carry considerable numerical data.

Bacher, R., and S. Goudsmit: "Atomic Energy States," McGraw-Hill Book Company, Inc., New York, 1932. This is now superseded by the work of C. Moore but is still the chief source of information on energy levels for the heavy elements for which Miss Moore's compilation has not yet appeared.

Bethe, H.: Quantenmechanik der Ein und Zwei Elektronen Probleme, in "Handbuch der Physik," 2d ed., vol. 24-1, 1933.

Brode, W. R.: "Chemical Spectroscopy," 2d ed., 677 pp., John Wiley & Sons, Inc., New York, 1943.

Canchois, Y., and H. Hulubel: Longueurs d'onde d'émission X et des discontinuités d'absorption X, 1947.

Condon, E. U., and G. H. Shortley: "The Theory of Atomic Spectra," Cambridge University Press, New York, 1935 (reprinted 1953).

Fowler, A.: "Report on Series in Line Spectra," Fleetway Press, London, 1922.

Gatterer, A., and J. Junkes: "Atlas der Restlinien von 30 chemischen Elementen Text and Atlas," Specolar Vaticana, 1937.

Gatterer, A., and J. Junkes: "Spektren der seltenen Erden," 2 vols., text and plates, Specolar Vaticana, 1945.

Gombás, P.: "Die statistische Theorie des Atoms und ihre Anwendungen Wien," 406 pp., Springer-Verlag OHG, Berlin, 1949.

Grotrian, W.: "Graphische Darstellung der Spektren von Atomen und Ionen mit ein, zwei und drei Valenzelektronen," vol. I, 245 pp.; vol. II, 268 pp., Springer-Verlag OHG, Berlin, 1928.

Herzberg, G.: "Spectra of Diatomic Molecules," 2d ed., D. Van Nostrand Company, Inc., Princeton, N.J., 1950.

Herzberg, G.: "Infrared and Raman Spectra," D. Van Nostrand Company, Inc., Princeton, N.J., 1945.

Kayser, H.: "Handbuch der Spektroscopie," 8 vols., S. Hirzel Verlag, Leipzig. Volumes I–VI (1912) are now out of date but are still the chief source for the earlier developments in spectroscopy. Vols. VII (1934) and VIII (1932) are more recent but also not quite up to modern standards. This handbook contains the most detailed compilation of spectroscopic data.

Landolt-Börnstein: "Zahlenwerte und Funktionen aus Physik, Chemie, Astronomie, Geophysik und Technik," 6th ed., A. Eucken, ed., Springer-Verlag OHG, Berlin, Göttingen, Heidelberg. This is probably the most complete and detailed collection of data in existence. For this section the following parts of vol. I: Atom und Molekularphysik, are of importance; (vol. I is published in 5 parts) I-1, Atome und Ionen, 441 pp., 1950; I-2, Molekeln I (Kerngerüst), 571 pp., 1951; I-3, Molekeln II (Elektronenhülle), 724 pp., 1951; I-4, Kristalle, 1007 pp., 1955.

Loeb, L. B.: "Basic Processes of Gaseous Electronics," 1,012 pp., University of California Press, 1955.

Minnaert, M., G. F. W. Mulders, and J. Houtgast: "Photometric Atlas of the Solar Spectrum," Amsterdam, 1940.

Moore, C. E.: A Multiplet Table of Astrophysical Interest, I. Table of Multiplets, II. Finding List, *Contribs. Princeton University Observatory*, no. 20, 1945.

Moore, C.: Atomic Energy Levels, *Natl. Bur. Standards (U.S.) Circ.* 467. Contains all available information on energy levels of atoms in all stages of ionization as derived from optical spectra and extensive references on the spectra themselves. So far two volumes have appeared. Two additional volumes are in preparation. vol. I, Elements 1 (H) to 23 (V), 1949; vol. II, Elements 24 (Cr) to 41 (Nb), 1952; vol. III, Elements 42 (Mo) to 57 (La) and 73 (Ta) to 89 (Ac), 1956; vol. IV, remaining elements (lanthanides and actinides).

Moore, C. E.: An Ultraviolet Multiplet Table, *Natl. Bur. Standards (U.S.) Circ.* 488. I, Elements (H) to 23 (V), 1950; II, Elements 24 (Cr) to 41 (Nb), 1952. List of the most important lines and multiplets for wavelengths shorter than 3,000 A.

Paschen, F., and R. Götze: "Seriengesetze der Linienspektren," 154 pp., Springer-Verlag OHG, Berlin, 1922. This and the similar book by Fowler, though now largely out of date, nevertheless contain material on the simpler spectra not found conveniently anywhere else.

Pearse, R. W. B., and A. G. Gaydon: "The Identification of Molecular Spectra," 2d ed., John Wiley & Sons, Inc., New York, 1950. A detailed compilation of molecular bands, chiefly those of diatomic molecules in the visible, ultraviolet, and photographic infrared.

Rosen, B., ed.: "Données spectroscopiques concernant les molecules diatomiques," 366 pp., Hermann & Cie, Paris, 1951.

Rosen, B.: "Atlas des longeurs d'onde caractéristiques des bandes d'émission et d'absorption des molécules diatomiques," 1952.

Wilson, E. B., Jr., J. C. Decius, and P. C. Cross: "Molecular Vibrations. The Theory of Infrared and Raman Vibrational Spectra," 388 pp., McGraw-Hill Book Company, Inc., New York, 1955.

Section 8

NUCLEAR PHYSICS

FRANZ N. D. KURIE, Editor

U.S. Navy Electronics Laboratory

CONTENTS

8a. Introduction and General Constants 8-2
8b. Systematics of Stable Nuclei 8-5
8c. Passage of Particles through Matter 8-23
8d. Decay-energy Systematics of the Heavy Elements 8-40
8e. Energy Levels of the Light Nuclei 8-56
8f. Gamma Rays 8-87
8g. Artificial Radioisotopes and Isomers 8-96
8h. Neutrons 8-129
8i. Particle Accelerators 8-172
8j. Fission-product Chains and Yields 8-202
8k. Nuclear Reactors 8-227
8l. Mesons and Hyperons 8-240
8m. Health Physics 8-250

8a. Introduction and General Constants

FRANZ N. D. KURIE

U.S. Navy Electronics Laboratory

8a-1. Definitions. Many of the terms of nuclear science are in common use in other branches of physics and will be found elsewhere in this handbook. The National Research Council has published a useful glossary of terms in this field.[1] It would be out of place, in this volume, to attempt to define all the unique terms used in nuclear science. There are, however, certain basic ones which are defined below.

Nucleon. A constituent of a nucleus, either a proton or a neutron.

Nuclide. A specific nucleus, characterized by having a definite number of neutrons and a definite number of protons.

Isotopes. A group of atoms whose nuclei have the same number of protons and are therefore chemically identical.

Isotones. A group of atoms whose nuclei have the same number of neutrons.

Isobars. A group of atoms whose nuclei have the same number of nucleons.

Nuclear Reaction (see Sec. 8a-2). The interaction between nuclides (including γ rays) to form a *compound nucleus* which separates into two or more different nuclides. In most cases there are only two products, one of which is quite light.

Energy Balance. The amount of energy released in each individual reaction. It is designated by Q and is positive when energy is produced, negative when it is absorbed.

Fission. A type of nuclear reaction in which the products (called *fragments*) are of comparable mass. It is usually accompanied by the emission of a number of neutrons and the release of energy.

Spallation Reactions. These are caused by particles of great energy and lead to the breakup of the compound nucleus into many parts.

8a-2. Nuclear Reactions. Nuclear science largely depends on the interactions of nuclides with each other. In order to simplify the discussion of these reactions symbolic representations are used. A nuclide is designated by the following symbol:

$$_Z(\text{Chemical symbol})^A$$

Z is the atomic number (number of protons) and A is the atomic weight (number of nucleons) of the isotope to which the nuclide belongs. This leads to symbols like $_{11}Na^{23}$ and $_{92}U^{235}$. Since the chemical symbol specifies Z it is usually omitted and one simply writes Na^{23} and U^{235}. It also is becoming common to see these written as Na-23 and U-235.

Certain nuclides and particles have acquired special names and symbols. These are given in Table 8a-1.

[1] "A Glossary of Terms in Nuclear Science and Technology," American Society of Mechanical Engineers, New York, 1954.

TABLE 8a-1. SPECIAL NUCLIDES* AND PARTICLES

Short symbol	Name	Standard symbol
p	Proton	H^1
n	Neutron	n^1
d	Deuteron	H^2
t	Triton	H^3
α	Alpha particle	He^4
γ	Gamma quantum	$h\nu$
β^-	Electron	
β^+	Positron	

* No notation for mesons is given here because they do not, as yet, figure in nuclear technology. The current nomenclature for mesons and related particles will be found in Sec. 8-l.

Nuclear reactions may be written like chemical reactions, thus:

$$Li^7 + H^1 \rightarrow 2\ He^4$$

This is cumbersome; so now one writes the same reaction more simply as

$$Li^7(p,\alpha)He^4$$

Other reactions may obviously be written

$$Na^{23}(d,p)Na^{24}$$
$$Cu^{65}(p,n)Zn^{65}$$
$$Br^{79}(d,2n)Kr^{79}$$

This symbolism may be extended to spallation reactions like

$$As^{75}(\alpha,18p23n)Cl^{38}$$

and fissions

$$U^{235}(n,Sr^{93})Xe^{143}$$

The probability of a nuclear reaction taking place is measured by the *cross section* σ for the reaction. The unit for nuclear cross sections is the *barn* ($= 10^{-24}$ cm²); occasionally small cross sections are expressed in millibarns ($= 10^{-3}$ barns $= 10^{-27}$ cm²).

8a-3. Unstable Nuclei. The products of many nuclear reactions are nuclei which are not found in nature. The number of neutrons and protons in these nuclides is out of stable balance. The nuclides proceed to adjust this by those nucleons which are in excess, changing, by a process known as *β decay*, to the type in which the nuclide is deficient. Thus, if the nuclide has more neutrons than its stable isobars, this is corrected by the neutrons changing to protons until it becomes stable. To conserve charge this $n \rightarrow p$ change is accompanied by the emission of a negative electron (*β^- particle*), often of high energy but never of constant energy. To conserve energy requires the emission of another neutral particle, a *neutrino* (symbol ν), the sum of whose energy with that of the β^- particle is constant. In other cases the number of protons may be excessive and one or more may change to neutrons. Accompanying each $p \rightarrow n$ change there may be a positron (*β^+ particle*) and an *antineutrino* emitted. Again the sum of the energies of positron and antineutrino is constant. Often an excess of protons is corrected by the nucleus capturing one of its orbital electrons. This process is called *K capture* and is accompanied by the emission of X rays or Auger electrons. β decay is frequently accompanied by γ radiation.

8a-4. Nuclear Constants. Only those general constants which are peculiar to nuclear science are given here. These are taken from a paper by DuMond and Cohen.[1] The symbols used, where not explained, are conventional.

[1] J. W. M. DuMond and E. R. Cohen, *Revs. Modern Phys.* **25**, 691 (1953).

Atomic mass of neutron

$$n = 1.008982 \pm 0.000003$$

Atomic mass of hydrogen

$$\mathrm{H} = 1.008142 \pm 0.000003$$

Atomic mass of deuterium

$$\mathrm{D} = 2.014735 \pm 0.000006$$

Electron rest mass

$$m = (9.1085 \pm 0.0006) \times 10^{-28}\ \mathrm{g}$$

Proton rest mass

$$m_p = (1.67243 \pm 0.00010) \times 10^{-24}$$

Neutron rest mass

$$m_n = (1.67474 \pm 0.00010) \times 10^{-24}$$

Ratio of proton mass to electron mass

$$= 1{,}836.13 \pm 0.04$$

Compton wavelength of the electron

$$\lambda_{ce} = h/mc = (24.2625 \pm 0.0006) \times 10^{-11}\ \mathrm{cm}$$

Compton wavelength of the proton

$$\lambda_{cp} = h/m_pc = (13.2139 \pm 0.0004) \times 10^{-14}\ \mathrm{cm}$$

Compton wavelength of the neutron

$$\lambda_{cn} = h/m_nc = (13.1958 \pm 0.0004) \times 10^{-14}\ \mathrm{cm}$$

Thomson cross section

$$\phi = (6.65196 \pm 0.0005) \times 10^{-25}\ \mathrm{cm}^2$$

Magnetic moment of the electron

$$\mu_e = (0.92838 \pm 0.00006) \times 10^{-20}\ \mathrm{erg\ gauss}^{-1}$$

Nuclear magneton

$$\mu_n = he/4\pi m_pc = (0.505038 \pm 0.000036) \times 10^{-23}\ \mathrm{erg\ gauss}^{-1}$$

Proton magnetic moment

$$\mu = 2.79277 \pm 0.00006\ \text{nuclear magnetons}$$

Mass energy conversion factors

$$1\ \mathrm{g} = (5.60999 \pm 0.00025) \times 10^{26}\ \text{Mev (million electronvolts)}$$
$$1\ \text{electron mass} = 0.510984 \pm 0.00016\ \text{Mev}$$
$$1\ \text{atomic mass unit} = 931.162 \pm 0.024\ \text{Mev}$$
$$1\ \text{proton mass} = 938.232 \pm 0.024\ \text{Mev}$$
$$1\ \text{neutron mass} = 939.526 \pm 0.024\ \text{Mev}$$

Quantum energy conversion factors

$$1\ \text{electron volt (ev)} = (1.60207 \pm 0.00007) \times 10^{-12}\ \text{erg}$$
$$1\ \text{million electron volts (Mev)} = (1.60207 \pm 0.00007) \times 10^{-6}\ \text{erg}$$
$$1\ \text{billion electron volts (Bev)} = (1.60207 \pm 0.00007) \times 10^{-3}\ \text{erg}$$

Velocity of a thermal ($\frac{1}{40}$ ev) neutron

$$v_{\frac{1}{40}} = 2{,}187.017 \pm 0.028\ \mathrm{m/sec}$$

8b. Systematics of Stable Nuclei

GEORGE L. TRIGG

Oregon State College

8b-1. Table of Nuclear Properties. Table 8b-1 lists the known properties of all stable nuclei, plus those whose half lives are long enough to be of geological significance. Unstable species are denoted by an asterisk following the mass number.

Nuclear spins are given in units of $\hbar(= h/2\pi)$, magnetic moments in units of the nuclear magneton, quadripole moments in units of the proton barn, and binding energies in Mev. Binding energies are given only when they have been determined directly from (γ,n) or (γ,p) thresholds or (d,n) or (d,p) Q values. Magnetic moments are quoted directly from the corresponding references and are therefore not uniformly corrected for diamagnetism. Cosmic abundances are numbers of atoms per 10^4 atoms of total silicon.

The number in parentheses following a listed value is the uncertainty of the last figure as given in the reference. The placing of an entire number in parentheses indicates that the quantity has not been measured; the value so designated is an estimate or a value suggested by theory.

For the radioactive elements, the mode of decay and half life are given in the Notes column; except for Nd^{144}, data are from ref. 46.

8b-2. Shell Structure. The existence of "shells" of nucleons is inferred from a single-particle model under the following assumptions:[1,2]

1. The single-particle levels of nucleons in a nucleus are those of a rounded-off square well, with strong spin-orbit coupling giving rise to inverted doublets; the doublet splitting increases with the orbital angular momentum quantum number l.

2. An even number of identical nucleons in any state with total angular momentum quantum number j couple to give total spin zero and no contribution to the magnetic moment; an odd number of identical nucleons in a state j couple to give total spin j (usually) and a magnetic moment equal to that of a single particle in that state.

3. For a given nucleus the pairing energy of nucleons in states of the same j increases with j.

It is recognized empirically that there exist differences in the behavior of neutrons and protons above N or $Z = 50$; one suggestion[2] is that this results from a lowering in energy of proton states corresponding classically to circular orbits, relative to the positions of the corresponding neutron states, due to Coulomb forces. On the other hand, the level order is presumably to be considered as resulting from the potential energy as seen by the "last" nucleon; and in view of the fact that, for N or Z above 50, $N = Z$ is not a valid approximation, there is no reason to expect that the potential energy of, say, the sixty-fifth neutron in a nucleus containing 65 neutrons should be the same as that of the sixty-fifth proton in a nucleus containing 65 protons.

[1] Mayer, *Phys. Rev.* **78**, 16 (1950).

[2] Klinkenberg, *Revs. Modern Phys.* **24**, 63 (1952).

TABLE 8b-1. PROPERTIES

Atomic No. Z	Name	Chem. symbol	Neutron No. N	Mass No. $A = N + Z$	Atomic mass M	Spin I	Parity	% abundance (ref. 46)	Cosmic abundance (ref. 4)
0	Neutron	n	1	1*	1.008986(3)	$\frac{1}{2}$	+	....	....
1	Hydrogen	H	0	1	1.008146(3)	$\frac{1}{2}$	+	99.9849–61	3.5×10^8
			1	2	2.014741(3)	1	+	0.0139–51	
2	Helium	He	1	3	3.016977(11)	$\frac{1}{2}$	(+)	$(1.3-1.7)\times10^{-4}$	3.5×10^7
			2	4	4.003879(9)	0	+	~100	
3	Lithium	Li	3	6	6.017021(22)	1	+	7.52	....
			4	7	7.018223(26)	$\frac{3}{2}$	(−)	92.48	....
4	Beryllium	Be	5	9	9.015043(30)	$\frac{3}{2}$	−	100	....
5	Boron	B	5	10	10.016110(10)	3	+	18.45–18.98	....
			6	11	11.012811(9)	$\frac{3}{2}$	(−)	81.02–81.55	....
6	Carbon	C	6	12	12.003842(4)	0	(+)	98.892	80,000
			7	13	13.007505(12)	$\frac{1}{2}$	−	1.108	
7	Nitrogen	N	7	14	14.007550(5)	1	+	99.635	160,000
			8	15	15.004902(9)	$\frac{1}{2}$	−	0.365	
8	Oxygen	O	8	16	16.00000000	0	+	99.759	220,000
			9	17	17.004533(7)	$\frac{5}{2}$	+	0.037	86
			10	18	18.004883(20)	0	+	0.204	450
9	Fluorine	F	10	19	19.004444(22)	$\frac{1}{2}$	+	100	90
10	Neon	Ne	10	20	19.998772(13)	(0)	(+)	90.92	42,000
			11	21	21.000504(22)	$\frac{3}{2}$	(+)	0.257	130
			12	22	21.998382(24)	(0)	(+)	8.82	4,300
11	Sodium	Na	12	23	23.001768(26)	$\frac{3}{2}$	+	100	462 ± 36
12	Magnesium	Mg	12	24	23.992628(26)	(0)	(+)	78.60	6,970 ± 240
			13	25	24.993745(27)	$\frac{5}{2}$	(+)	10.11	897 ± 97
			14	26	25.990802(29)	(0)	(+)	11.29	1,000 ± 100
13	Aluminum	Al	14	27	26.990109(23)	$\frac{5}{2}$	(+)	100	882 ± 81
14	Silicon	Si	14	28	27.985825(16)	(0)	(+)	92.27	9,228 ± 3
			15	29	28.985705(21)	$\frac{1}{2}$	(+)	4.68	467 ± 1
			16	30	29.983307(31)	(0)	(+)	3.05	305 ± 3
15	Phosphorus	P	16	31	30.983619(7)	$\frac{1}{2}$	(+)	100	130
16	Sulfur	S	16	32	31.982236(7)	0	+	95.018	3,300
			17	33	32.98213(5)	$\frac{3}{2}$	+	0.750	26
			18	34	33.97876(5)	0	+	4.215	150
			20	36	35.97893(7)	(0)	(+)	0.017	0.56
17	Chlorine	Cl	18	35	34.98004(5)	$\frac{3}{2}$	+	75.4	130
			20	37	36.97766(5)	$\frac{3}{2}$	(+)	24.6	42
18	Argon	A	18	36	35.97900(3)	(0)	(+)	0.337	450
			20	38	37.97491(4)	(0)	(+)	0.063	87
			22	40	39.97513(3)	(0)	(+)	99.600	....
19	Potassium	K	20	39	38.97606(3)	$\frac{3}{2}$	(+)	93.08(v)	64.7 ± 7.0
			21	40*	39.97654(8)	4	(−)	0.0119	0.0076(8)
			22	41	40.97490(4)	$\frac{3}{2}$	+	6.91	4.64(50)
20	Calcium	Ca	20	40	39.97545(9)	(0)	(+)	96.97	650(72)
			22	42	41.97216(4)	(0)	(+)	0.64	4.29(49)
			23	43	42.97251(6)	$\frac{7}{2}$	(−)	0.145	1.01(12)
			24	44	43.96924(6)	(0)	(+)	2.06	13.8(16)
			26	46	....	(0)	(+)	0.0033	0.022(4)
			28	48	47.96778(10)	(0)	(+)	0.0185	1.27(15)
21	Scandium	Sc	24	45	44.97010(5)	$\frac{7}{2}$	(−)	100	0.18
22	Titanium	Ti	24	46	45.96697(5)	(0)	(+)	7.95	2.07(72)
			25	47	46.96668(10)	$\frac{5}{2}$	(−)	7.75	2.02(70)
			26	48	47.96317(6)	(0)	(+)	73.45	19.1(66)
			27	49	48.96358(5)	$\frac{7}{2}$	(−)	5.51	1.43(50)
			28	50	49.96077(4)	(0)	(+)	5.34	1.39(48)

See page 8-16 for footnotes and pages 8-16 to 8-18 for References.

OF STABLE NUCLEI

Magnetic dipole moment μ	Electric quadrupole moment Q	Binding energy of last neutron E_n	Binding energy of last proton E_p	Ground-state configuration (ref. 38)	Ref. M	Ref. I	Ref. μ	Ref. Q	Ref. E_n	Ref. E_p	Notes
−1.91280(9)	....	2	2	$s_{\frac{1}{2}}$	15	7	7	...	...	...	β^-; 12.8 min
+2 79255(10)	....	2	2	$s_{\frac{1}{2}}$	18	7	38				
+0.957354(9)	+0.002738(14)	2.225(2)	2.225(2)	$(\frac{1}{2}, \frac{1}{2})_1$	40	7	7	55	15	15	
(−)2.127414(3)	....	6.255(6)	....	$s_{\frac{1}{2}}$	15	7	7	...	12		
....	....	....	....	....	40	7					
+0.82189(4)	....	5.35(20)	....	$(\frac{3}{2}, \frac{3}{2})_1$	15	7	...	...	37		
+3.25586(11)	+(0.02)(2)	7.244(7)	9.8(5)	$p_{\frac{3}{2}}$	15	7	7	7	37	37	
−1.1774(8)	(0.02)	1.664(2)	16.93(15)	$p_{\frac{3}{2}}$	15	38	38	38	21	29	
+1.8004(7)	+0.0740(50)	8.55(25)	....	$(\frac{3}{2}, \frac{3}{2})_3$	40	7	7	55	37		
+2.68858(28)	+0.0355(20)	11.460(11)	....	$p_{\frac{3}{2}}$	40	7	7	55	37		
....	....	....	....	....	18	7					
+0.70225(14)	....	4.957(6)	....	$p_{\frac{1}{2}}$	40	7	7	...	37		
+0.40365(3)	+0.02	10.7(2)	....	$(\frac{1}{2}, \frac{1}{2})_1$	40	7	7	7	37		
−0.28299(3)	....	10.838(11)	....	$p_{\frac{1}{2}}$	40	7	7	...	37		
....	....	16.3(4)	....	....	Standard	7	...	...	37		
−1.8935(2)	−0.005(+×2)	4.143(8)	....	$d_{\frac{5}{2}}$	32	38	38	20	37		
....	....	....	16.35(20)	....	40	46	...	...	...	37	
+2.62728(10)	....	....	....	?	40	7	35				
....	....	....	....	....	40	7					
....	....	6.754(7)	....	$(d_{\frac{5}{2}})^3{}_{\frac{3}{2}}$	32	7	...	...	37	...	*a*
....	....	10.362(11)	....	....	40	7	...	...	37		
+2.21711(25)	....	12.05(20)	....	$(d_{\frac{5}{2}})^3{}_{\frac{3}{2}}$	32	7	7	...	56		
(2)	....	16.55(25)	....	....	32	7	...	...	56		
−0.8552(2)	....	7.322(7)	11.5(10)	$d_{\frac{5}{2}}$	32	46	38	...	56	56	
....	....	11.15(20)	14.0(10)	....	32	7	...	...	56	56	
+3.6408(4)	+0.149(2)	12.75(20)	8.6(5)	$d_{\frac{5}{2}}$	40	7	7	55	56	56	
....	....	16.9(2)	11.31(20)	....	40	7	...	...	56	56	
−0.55492(4)	....	8.471(10)	....	$s_{\frac{1}{2}}$	40	55	55	...	56	56	
....	....	10.613(13)	....	....	40	7	...	...	56	56	
+1.13165(20)	....	12.35(20)	7.15(4)	$s_{\frac{1}{2}}$	41	7	7	...	56	19*a*	
....	....	....	9.04(8)	....	18	7	...	...	...	56	
+0.64292(14)	−0.064(10)	8.647(11)	....	$d_{\frac{3}{2}}$	18	7	55	53	56		
....	....	10.85(20)	....	....	18	7	...	...	56		
....	....	....	....	....	3	7					
+0.82191(22)	−0.07894(2)	....	....	$d_{\frac{3}{2}}$	18	7	7	38			
+0.68414(24)	−0.06213(2)	9.95(20)	....	$d_{\frac{3}{2}}$	18	7	7	38	56		
....	....	....	....	....	18	7					
....	....	....	....	....	18	7					
....	....	....	....	....	45	7					
+0.390873(13)	....	13.2(2)	....	$d_{\frac{3}{2}}$	18	7	47	...	56		
−1.2982(4)	....	7.801(10)	....	$(\frac{3}{2}, \frac{7}{2})_4$	34	7	23	...	56	...	β^-, EC; 1.2 × 10^9 years
+0.21453(3)	....	....	....	$d_{\frac{3}{2}}$	18	7	47				
....	....	15.9(4)	....	....	45	7	...	...	56		
....	....	....	....	....	18	7					
−1.3152(2)	....	7.93(2)	....	$f_{\frac{7}{2}}$	18	55	55	...	56		
....	....	....	....	....	18	7					
....	....	....	....	....	....	7					
....	....	....	....	....	18	7					
+4.75633(>12)	....	....	....	$f_{\frac{7}{2}}$	18	7	19				
....	....	13.3(2)	....	....	24	7	...	...	11		
−0.78706(10)	....	8.74(10)	....	$(f_{\frac{7}{2}})^5{}_{\frac{5}{2}}$	24	55	55	...	11	...	*b*
....	....	11.05(40)	....	....	24	7	...	...	11		
−1.1022(2)	....	8.15(5)	....	$f_{\frac{7}{2}}$	24	55	55	...	11		
....	....	....	....	....	24	7					

TABLE 8b-1. PROPERTIES

Atomic No. Z	Name	Chem. symbol	Neutron No. N	Mass No. $A = N + Z$	Atomic mass M	Spin I	Parity	% abundance (ref. 46)	Cosmic abundance (ref. 4)
23	Vanadium	V	27	50	49.96330(12)	6	(+)	0.24	0.006
			28	51	50.96052(5)	$\frac{7}{2}$	(−)	99.76	2.5
24	Chromium	Cr	26	50	49.96210(7)	(0)	(+)	4.31	4.3
			28	52	51.95707(9)	(0)	(+)	83.76	80
			29	53	52.95772(8)	$\frac{3}{2}$	(−)	9.55	9.0
			30	54	53.9563 (2)	(0)	(+)	2.38	2.2
25	Manganese	Mn	30	55	54.95581(10)	$\frac{5}{2}$	(−)	100	77
26	Iron	Fe	28	54	53.95704(5)	(0)	(+)	5.84	1,100
			30	56	55.95274(9)	(0)	(+)	91.68	17,000
			31	57	56.95359(10)	($\frac{3}{2}$)	(−)	2.17	400
			32	58	57.9520(4)	(0)	(+)	0.31	60
27	Cobalt	Co	32	59	58.95157(10)	$\frac{7}{2}$	(−)	100	99
28	Nickel	Ni	30	58	57.95349(9)	(0)	(+)	67.76	910
			32	60	59.94925(13)	(0)	(+)	26.16	350
			33	61	60.94907(23)	($\frac{3}{2}$)	(−)	1.25	17
			34	62	61.94681(9)	(0)	(+)	3.66	49
			36	64	63.94755(7)	(0)	(+)	1.16	16
29	Copper	Cu	34	63	62.94926(6)	$\frac{3}{2}$	−	69.1	3.2
			36	65	64.94835(6)	$\frac{3}{2}$	−	30.9	1.4
30	Zinc	Zn	34	64	63.94955(2)	(0)	(+)	48.89	0.78
			36	66	65.94722(6)	(0)	(+)	27.81	0.44
			37	67	66.94815(6)	$\frac{5}{2}$	−	4.11	0.065
			38	68	67.94686(7)	(0)	(+)	18.56	0.30
			40	70	69.94779(6)	(0)	(+)	0.62	0.0099
31	Gallium	Ga	38	69	68.94778(6)	$\frac{3}{2}$	−	60.2	0.39
			40	71	70.94752(9)	$\frac{3}{2}$	−	39.8	0.26
32	Germanium	Ge	38	70	69.94637(7)	(0)	(+)	20.55	0.51
			40	72	71.94462(7)	(0)	(+)	27.37	0.68
32	Germanium	Ge	41	73	72.94669(4)	$\frac{9}{2}$	+	7.67	0.19
			42	74	73.94466(6)	(0)	(+)	36.74	0.92
			44	76	75.94559(5)	(0)	(+)	7.67	0.19
33	Arsenic	As	42	75	74.94570(5)	$\frac{3}{2}$	−	100	4.8
34	Selenium	Se	40	74	73.94620(8)	0	(+)	0.87	0.0022
			42	76	75.94357(5)	(0)	(+)	9.02	0.023
			43	77	76.94459(5)	$\frac{1}{2}$	−	7.58	0.019
			44	78	77.94232(5)	0	(+)	23.52	0.059
			46	80	79.94205(5)	(0)	(+)	49.82	0.12
			48	82	81.94285(6)	(0)	(+)	9.19	0.023
35	Bromine	Br	44	79	78.94365(6)	$\frac{3}{2}$	−	50.52	0.21
			46	81	80.94232(6)	$\frac{3}{2}$	−	49.48	0.21
36	Krypton	Kr	42	78	77.94519(18)	(0)	(+)	0.354	~0.87 (total for Kr)
			44	80	79.94246(11)	(0)	(+)	2.27	
			46	82	81.93961(11)	(0)	(+)	11.56	
			47	83	82.94059(7)	$\frac{9}{2}$	+	11.55	
			48	84	83.93836(9)	(0)	(+)	56.90	
			50	86	85.93820(8)	(0)	(+)	17.37	
37	Rubidium	Rb	48	85	84.93920(8)	$\frac{5}{2}$	−	72.15	0.052
			50	87*	86.93709(17)	$\frac{3}{2}$	−	27.85	0.019
38	Strontium	Sr	46	84	83.94011(15)	(0)	(+)	0.56	0.0023
			48	86	85.93684(11)	(0)	(+)	9.86	0.040
			49	87	86.93677(8)	$\frac{9}{2}$	+	7.02	0.029
			50	88	87.93408(11)	(0)	(+)	82.56	0.34
39	Yttrium	Y	50	89	88.93421(11)	$\frac{1}{2}$	−	100	0.10

See page 8-16 for footnotes and pages 8-16 to 8-18 for References.

OF STABLE NUCLEI (*Continued*)

Magnetic dipole moment μ	Electric quadrupole moment Q	Binding energy of last neutron E_n	Binding energy of last proton E_p	Ground-state configuration (ref. 38)	Ref. M	Ref. I	Ref. μ	Ref. Q	Ref. E_n	Ref. E_p	Notes
+3.3412(3)	...	...	...	$(\frac{7}{2}, \frac{7}{2})_6$	27	55	28	...	...	...	*c*
+5.1478(5)	+0.3(2)	11.15(20)	...	$f_{\frac{7}{2}}$	24	7	38	44	17		
...	...	13.4(2)	...	...	24	7	...	...	11		
...	...	11.80(25)	...	...	24	7	...	...	17		
−0.47351(60)	...	7.75(20)	...	$p_{\frac{3}{2}}$	24	55	55	...	17		
...	...	...	...	...	24	7					
+3.4681(4)	+0.5	10.15(20)	...	$(f_{\frac{7}{2}})^5{}_{\frac{5}{2}}$	24	7	7	42	11		
...	...	13.8(2)	...	...	24	7	...	...	11		
...	...	11.15(25)	...	...	45	7	...	...	17		
+0.05	...	7.75(20)	...	$p_{\frac{3}{2}}$	24′	7	55	...	17		
...	...	...	...	...	24	7					
+4.6484(16)	+0.5(2)	10.25(20)	...	$f_{\frac{7}{2}}$	45	7	7	44	17		
...	...	11.7(2)	...	...	45	7	...	...	11		
...	...	...	...	...	45	7					
...	...	...	...	$p_{\frac{3}{2}}$	24	...	...	...	...	...	*d*
...	...	...	...	...	24	7					
...	...	...	...	...	24	7					
+2.22617(36)	−0.157	10.85(20)	...	$p_{\frac{3}{2}}$	24	7	7	55	17		
+2.3845(4)	−0.145	9.75(20)	...	$p_{\frac{3}{2}}$	24	7	7	55	17		
...	...	11.65(20)	...	...	24	7	...	...	17		
...	...	11.15(20)	...	...	24	7	...	...	17		
+0.87378(13)	...	7.00(20)	...	$f_{\frac{5}{2}}$	24	7	55	...	17		
...	...	10.15(20)	...	...	24	7	...	...	17		
...	...	9.2(2)	...	...	24	7	...	...	11		
+2.167(11)	+0.2318(23)	10.10(20)	...	$p_{\frac{3}{2}}$	52	7	7	7	17		
+2.5614(10)	+0.1461(15)	9.05(20)	...	$p_{\frac{3}{2}}$	52	7	7	7	17		
...	...	...	...	...	52	7					
...	...	...	...	...	52	7					
−0.87675(12)	−0.2(11)	...	...	$g_{\frac{9}{2}}$	52	55	55	38			
...	...	...	...	...	52	7					
...	...	...	...	...	52	7					
+1.4347(3)	+0.3(2)	10.2(2)	...	$p_{\frac{9}{2}}$	52	7	55	38	11		
...	...	...	...	...	52	7					
...	...	...	...	...	52	7					
+0.53326(5)	...	7.5(3)	...	$p_{\frac{1}{2}}$	52	7	55	...	10		
...	...	...	...	...	52	7					
...	...	...	...	...	52	7					
...	...	9.8(5)	...	...	52	7	...	...	11		
+2.10576(37)	+0.26(8)	10.60(20)	...	$p_{\frac{3}{2}}$	52	7	7	7	17		
+2.2696(5)	+0.21(7)	9.95(20)	...	$p_{\frac{3}{2}}$	52	7	7	7	17		
...	...	...	...	...	45	7					
...	...	...	...	...	45	7					
...	...	...	...	...	45	7					
−0.9704	+0.15	...	...	$g_{\frac{9}{2}}$	52	7	7	7			
...	...	...	...	...	45, 52	7					
...	...	...	...	...	45	7					
+1.3532(4)	...	...	...	$f_{\frac{5}{2}}$	52	7	7				
+2.7501(5)	...	10.0	...	$p_{\frac{3}{2}}$	52	7	7	...	11	...	β^-; 6×10^{10} years
...	...	...	...	...	52	7					
...	...	9.50(20)	...	...	52	7	...	...	17		
−1.0892(15)	...	8.40(20)	...	$g_{\frac{9}{2}}$	52	7	55	...	17		
...	...	11.15(20)	...	...	52	7	...	...	17		
−0.14	...	...	...	$p_{\frac{1}{2}}$	52	7	7				

TABLE 8b-1. PROPERTIES

Atomic No. Z	Name	Chem. symbol	Neutron No. N	Mass No. $A = N + Z$	Atomic mass M	Spin I	Parity	% abundance (ref. 46)	Cosmic abundance (ref. 4)
40	Zirconium	Zr	50	90	89.93311(25)	(0)	(+)	51.46	0.77
			51	91	90.9343(4)	$\frac{5}{2}$	+	11.23	0.17
			52	92	91.9339(4)	(0)	(+)	17.11	0.26
			54	94	93.9365(5)	(0)	(+)	17.40	0.26
			56	96	95.9394(5)	(0)	(+)	2.80	0.042
41	Columbium or Niobium	Cb or Nb	52	93	92.93540(9)	$\frac{9}{2}$	+	100	0.009
42	Molybdenum	Mo	50	92	91.9352(4)	(0)	(+)	15.86	0.030
			52	94	93.9353(4)	(0)	(+)	9.12	0.017
			53	95	94.946(8)	$\frac{5}{2}$	+	15.70	0.030
			54	96	95.9358(4)	(0)	(+)	16.50	0.031
			55	97	96.945(9)	$\frac{5}{2}$	+	9.45	0.018
			56	98	97.93610(40)	(0)	(+)	23.75	0.045
			58	100	99.93860(40)	(0)	(+)	9.62	0.018
44	Ruthenium	Ru	52	96	95.9388(4)	(0)	(+)	5.7	0.0053
			54	98	97.943(11)	(0)	(+)	2.2	0.0021
			55	99	98.944(11)	$\frac{5}{2}$	(+)	12.8	0.012
			56	100	99.942(11)	(0)	(+)	12.7	0.012
			57	101	100.946(11)	$\frac{5}{2}$	+	17.0	0.016
			58	102	101.941(11)	(0)	(+)	31.3	0.029
			60	104	....	(0)	(+)	18.3	0.017
45	Rhodium	Rh	58	103	102.941(11)	$\frac{1}{2}$	−	100	0.035
46	Palladium	Pd	56	102	101.93750(9)	(0)	(+)	0.8	0.00026
			58	104	103.93655(11)	(0)	(+)	9.3	0.0030
			59	105	104.93840(15)	$\frac{5}{2}$	+	22.6	0.0072
			60	106	105.93680(10)	(0)	(+)	27.2	0.0087
			62	108	107.93801(11)	(0)	(+)	26.8	0.0086
			64	110	109.93965(13)	(0)	(+)	13.5	0.0043
47	Silver	Ag	60	107	106.9387(2)	$\frac{1}{2}$	−	51.35	0.014
			62	109	108.9394(5)	$\frac{1}{2}$	−	48.65	0.013
48	Cadmium	Cd	58	106	105.93984(14)	(0)	(+)	1.215	0.00032
			60	108	107.93860(11)	(0)	(+)	0.875	0.00023
			62	110	109.93856(13)	(0)	(+)	12.39	0.0032
			63	111	110.93978(10)	$\frac{1}{2}$	+	12.75	0.0033
			64	112	111.93885(17)	(0)	(+)	24.07	0.0063
			65	113	112.94061(11)	$\frac{1}{2}$	+	12.26	0.0032
			66	114	113.93997(9)	(0)	(+)	28.86	0.0075
			68	116	115.94202(12)	(0)	(+)	7.58	0.0020
49	Indium	In	64	113	112.94045(12)	$\frac{9}{2}$	+	4.23	0.00042
			66	115*	114.94040(11)	$\frac{9}{2}$	+	95.77	0.0096
50	Tin	Sn	62	112	111.9407(5)	(0)	(+)	0.95	0.0056
			64	114	113.9394(6)	(0)	(+)	0.65	0.0038
			65	115	114.94014(25)	$\frac{1}{2}$	+	0.34	0.0022
			66	116	115.93927(11)	(0)	(+)	14.24	0.087
			67	117	116.94052(10)	$\frac{1}{2}$	+	7.57	0.047
			68	118	117.93978(16)	(0)	(+)	24.01	0.149
			69	119	118.94122(12)	$\frac{1}{2}$	+	8.58	0.053
			70	120	119.94059(14)	(0)	(+)	32.97	0.19
			72	122	121.94249(15)	(0)	(+)	4.71	0.030
			74	124	123.94490(11)	(0)	(+)	5.98	0.038
51	Antimony	Sb	70	121	120.9426(2)	$\frac{5}{2}$	+	57.25	0.0097
			72	123	122.9430(3)	$\frac{7}{2}$	+	42.75	0.0073
52	Tellurium	Te	68	120	119.94288(16)	(0)	(+)	0.089	....

See page 8-16 for footnotes and pages 8-16 to 8-18 for References.

OF STABLE NUCLEI (*Continued*)

Magnetic dipole moment μ	Electric quadrupole moment Q	Binding energy of last neutron E_n	Binding energy of last proton E_p	Ground-state configu-ration (ref. 38)	Ref. M	Ref. I	Ref. μ	Ref. Q	Ref. E_n	Ref. E_p	Notes
....	....	12.0(2)	....	....	52	7	...	...	11		
....	....	7.2(4)	....	$d_{\frac{5}{2}}$	45	7	...	...	11		
....	....	8.73(10)	....	....	45	7	...	...	11		
....	....	....	....	....	45	7					
....	....	....	....	....	45	7					
+6.1659	....	8.70(20)	....	$g_{\frac{9}{2}}$	52	7	7	...	17		
....	....	13.28(15)	....	....	45	7	...	...	11		
....	....	....	....	....	45	7					
−0.9140(2)	....	....	....	$d_{\frac{5}{2}}$	2	38	38				
....	....	....	....	....	45	7					
−0.9332(1)	....	7.1(3)	....	$d_{\frac{5}{2}}$	2	38	38	...	11		
....	....	....	....	....	14	7					
....	....	....	....	....	6	7					
....	....	....	....	....	45	7					
....	....	....	....	....	2	7					
....	....	....	....	$d_{\frac{5}{2}}$	2	46					
....	....	....	....	....	2	7					
....	....	....	....	$d_{\frac{5}{2}}$	2	46	...	...	...	...	*e*
....	....	....	....	....	2	7					
....	....	....	....	....	....	7					
(−)0.11	....	9.35(20)	8(1)	$p_{\frac{1}{2}}$	2	38	38	...	17	5	
....	....	....	....	....	31	7					
....	....	....	....	....	31	7					
−0.57(5)	....	7.2(3)	....	$d_{\frac{5}{2}}$	31	46	39	...	10	...	*e*
....	....	....	....	....	31	7					
....	....	....	....	....	31	7					
....	....	....	....	....	31	7					
−0.113042(13)	....	....	....	$p_{\frac{1}{2}}$	31	7	48				
−0.129955(13)	....	9.3(5)	6.1	$p_{\frac{1}{2}}$	31	7	48	...	11	13	
....	....	....	....	....	31	7					
....	....	....	....	....	31	7					
....	....	....	....	....	31	7					
−0.59492(8)	....	....	....	$s_{\frac{1}{2}}$	31	7	7				
....	....	....	....	....	31	7					
−0.62238(8)	....	6.44(15)	....	$s_{\frac{1}{2}}$	31	7	7	...	11		
....	....	....	....	....	31	7					
....	....	....	....	....	31	7					
+5.486(3)	+1.144	....	....	$g_{\frac{9}{2}}$	31	7	7	7			
+5.50945(11)	+1.161	9.5(5)	....	$g_{\frac{9}{2}}$	31	7	26	7	11	...	β^-; 6 × 10^{14} years
....	....	....	....	....	31	7					
....	....	....	....	....	31	7					
−0.91779(10)	....	....	....	$s_{\frac{1}{2}}$	31	7	7				
....	....	....	....	....	31	7					
−0.99982(10)	....	....	....	$s_{\frac{1}{2}}$	31	7	7				
....	....	9.10(20)	....	....	31	7	...	...	17		
−1.04600(10)	....	6.60(20)	....	$s_{\frac{1}{2}}$	31	7	7	...	17		
....	....	....	....	....	31	7					
....	....	....	....	....	31	7					
....	....	8.50(15)	....	....	31	7	...	...	11		
+3.360	−1.3(2)	9.25(20)	....	$d_{\frac{5}{2}}$	31	7	38	43	11		
+2.547	−1.7(2)	9.3	....	$g_{\frac{7}{2}}$	31	7	7	43	9		
....	....	....	....	....	31	7					

TABLE 8b-1. PROPERTIES

Atomic No. Z	Name	Chem. symbol	Neutron No. N	Mass No. $A = N + Z$	Atomic mass M	Spin I	Parity	% abundance (ref. 46)	Cosmic abundance (ref. 4)
52	Tellurium	Te	70	122	121.94193(8)	(0)	(+)	2.46	....
			71	123	122.94368(39)	$\frac{1}{2}$	+	0.87	....
			72	124	123.94278(11)	(0)	(+)	4.61	....
			73	125	124.94460(31)	$\frac{1}{2}$	+	6.99	....
			74	126	125.94420(7)	(0)	(+)	18.71	....
			76	128	127.94649(13)	(0)	(+)	31.79	....
			78	130	129.94853(10)	(0)	(+)	34.49	....
53	Iodine	I	74	127	126.94528(13)	$\frac{5}{2}$	+	100	0.018
54	Xenon	Xe	70	124	123.94578(7)	(0)	(+)	0.096	
			72	126	125.94476(14)	(0)	(+)	0.090	
			74	128	127.94446(9)	(0)	(+)	1.919	
			75	129	128.94601(15)	$\frac{1}{2}$	+	26.44	
			76	130	129.94501(10)	(0)	(+)	4.08	~0.015
			77	131	130.94673(42)	$\frac{3}{2}$	+	21.18	
			78	132	131.94615(10)	(0)	(+)	26.89	
			80	134	133.94803(12)	(0)	(+)	10.44	
			82	136	135.95046(11)	(0)	(+)	8.87	
55	Cesium	Cs	78	133	....	$\frac{7}{2}$	+	100	0.001
56	Barium	Ba	74	130	....	(0)	(+)	0.101	3.9×10^{-5}
			76	132	....	(0)	(+)	0.097	3.8×10^{-5}
			78	134	....	(0)	(+)	2.42	0.00094
			79	135	....	$\frac{3}{2}$	(+)	6.59	0.0026
			80	136	135.9488(10)	(0)	(+)	7.81	0.0030
			81	137	136.9502(10)	$\frac{3}{2}$	+	11.32	0.0044
			82	138	137.9498(5)	(0)	(+)	71.66	0.028
57	Lanthanum	La	81	138*	....	....	...	0.089	1.9×10^{-5}
			82	139	138.953(8)	$\frac{7}{2}$	(+)	99.911	0.021
58	Cerium	Ce	78	136	....	(0)	(+)	0.193	4.4×10^{-5}
			80	138	....	(0)	(+)	0.250	5.8×10^{-5}
			82	140	139.9488(10)	(0)	(+)	88.48	0.020
			84	142	141.9528(4)	(0)	(+)	11.07	0.0025
59	Praseodymium	Pr	82	141	140.9509(4)	$\frac{5}{2}$	+	100	0.0096
60	Neodymium	Nd	82	142	....	(0)	(+)	27.13	0.0090
			83	143	....	$\frac{7}{2}$	(−)	12.20	0.0040
			84	144*	143.9562(3)	(0)	(+)	23.87	0.0079
			85	145	144.962(4)	$\frac{7}{2}$	(−)	8.30	0.0027
			86	146	145.962(4)	(0)	(+)	17.18	0.0057
			88	148	147.9642(6)	(0)	(+)	5.72	0.0019
			90	150	149.9676(3)	(0)	(+)	5.60	0.0018
62	Samarium	Sm	82	144	143.9567(9)	(0)	(+)	3.16	0.00038
			85	147*	....	$\frac{7}{2}$	(−)	15.07	0.0018
			86	148	147.9616(7)	(0)	(+)	11.27	0.0014
			87	149	....	$\frac{7}{2}$	(−)	13.84	0.0017
			88	150	149.9632(10)	(0)	(+)	7.47	0.0009
			90	152	151.9677(5)	(0)	(+)	26.63	0.0032
			92	154	153.9712(5)	(0)	(+)	22.53	0.0027
63	Europium	Eu	88	151	....	$\frac{5}{2}$	(+)	47.77	0.0013
			90	153	....	$\frac{5}{2}$	+	52.23	0.0015
64	Gadolinium	Gd	88	152	....	(0)	(+)	0.20	3.4×10^{-5}
			90	154	153.9694(4)	(0)	(+)	2.15	0.00037
			91	155	154.971(6)	($\frac{7}{2}$)	(−)	14.73	0.0025

See page 8-16 for footnotes and pages 8-16 to 8-18 for References.

OF STABLE NUCLEI (*Continued*)

Magnetic dipole moment μ	Electric quadrupole moment Q	Binding energy of last neutron E_n	Binding energy of last proton E_p	Ground-state configuration (ref. 38)	Ref. M	Ref. I	Ref. μ	Ref. Q	Ref. E_n	Ref. E_p	Notes
					31	7					
−0.73188(4)				$s_{\frac{1}{2}}$	31	55	55				
					31	7					
−0.88235(4)		6.8(3)		$s_{\frac{1}{2}}$	31	7	55	...	10		
					31	7					
					31	7					
					31	7					
+2.8090(4)	−0.59(20)	9.10(20)		$d_{\frac{5}{2}}$	31	7	7	7	11		
					31	7					
					31	7					
					31	7					
−0.77255(2)				$s_{\frac{1}{2}}$	31	7	51				
					31	7					
+0.68680(2)				$d_{\frac{3}{2}}$	31	7	51				
					31	7					
					31	7					
					31	7					
+2.5771(9)		9.05(20)		$g_{\frac{7}{2}}$		7	7	...	17		
						7					
						7					
						7					
+0.8346(25)				$d_{\frac{3}{2}}$		7	7				
					16	7					
+0.9351(27)		7.1(3)		$d_{\frac{3}{2}}$	16	7	7	...	10		
					54	7					
				$(\frac{7}{2}, \frac{3}{2})$		...	...	...	...	...	β^-, EC; ~1 × 10^{11} years
+2.7760(28)	+0.9(1)	8.80(20)		$g_{\frac{7}{2}}$	2	7	7	44	17		
						7					
						7					
		9.05(20)			54	7	...	...	17		
		7.15(20)			54	7	...	...	17		
+3.8(4)	−0.054	9.8(3)		$d_{\frac{5}{2}}$	54	7	55	55	11		
						7					
−1.0(2)				$f_{\frac{7}{2}}$		38	38				
					16	7	...	...	...	...	α; 1.5 × 10^{15} years (ref. 49)
−0.65(9)				$f_{\frac{7}{2}}$	2	38	38				
					2	7					
					54	7					
		7.4(2)			54	7	...	...	11		
					54	7					
−0.68(10)				$f_{\frac{7}{2}}$		36	36*a*	...	...	...	α; 1.5 × 10^{11} years
					54	7					
−0.55(10)						36	36*a*				
					54	7					
					54	7					
					54	7					
+3.6	+1.2			$d_{\frac{5}{2}}$		7	38	7			
+1.6	+2.5			$d_{\frac{5}{2}}$		7	38	7			
						7					
					54	7					
				$f_{\frac{7}{2}}$	2	...	...	...	...	...	*d*

TABLE 8b-1. PROPERTIES

Atomic No. Z	Name	Chem. symbol	Neutron No. N	Mass No. $A = N + Z$	Atomic mass M	Spin I	Parity	% abundance (ref. 46)	Cosmic abundance (ref. 4)
64	Gadolinium	Gd	92	156	155.9715(4)	(0)	(+)	20.47	0.0035
			93	157	156.973(6)	($\frac{7}{2}$)	(−)	15.68	0.0027
			94	158	157.9736(8)	(0)	(+)	24.87	0.0042
			96	160	159.9785(12)	(0)	(+)	21.90	0.0037
65	Terbium	Tb	94	159	....	$\frac{3}{2}$	(+)	100	0.0052
66	Dysprosium	Dy	90	156	....	(0)	(+)	0.0524	1.0×10^{-5}
			92	158	....	(0)	(+)	0.0902	2.0×10^{-5}
			94	160	159.9752(14)	(0)	(+)	2.294	0.00046
			95	161	....	($\frac{7}{2}$)	(−)	18.88	0.0038
			96	162	161.9779(11)	(0)	(+)	25.53	0.0051
			97	163	....	($\frac{7}{2}$)	(−)	24.97	0.0050
			98	164	163.9814(14)	(0)	(+)	28.18	0.0056
67	Holmium	Ho	98	165	164.9822(8)	$\frac{7}{2}$	+	100	0.0057
68	Erbium	Er	94	162	....	(0)	(+)	0.136	1.6×10^{-5}
			96	164	163.9827(12)	(0)	(+)	1.56	0.00024
			98	166	....	(0)	(+)	33.41	0.0053
			99	167	....	$\frac{7}{2}$	(−)	22.94	0.0039
			100	168	167.9849(4)	(0)	(+)	27.07	0.0043
			102	170	(169.9907)	(0)	(+)	14.88	0.0023
69	Thulium	Tm	100	169	....	$\frac{1}{2}$	(+)	100	0.0029
70	Ytterbium	Yb	98	168	....	(0)	(+)	0.140	9.0×10^{-6}
			100	170	....	(0)	(+)	3.03	0.00063
			101	171	....	$\frac{1}{2}$	(−)	14.31	0.0021
			102	172	....	(0)	(+)	21.82	0.0032
			103	173	....	$\frac{5}{2}$	(−)	16.13	0.0026
			104	174	....	(0)	(+)	31.84	0.0044
			106	176	....	(0)	(+)	12.73	0.0020
71	Lutecium	Lu	104	175	....	$\frac{7}{2}$	(+)	97.40	0.0047
			105	176*	....	......	...	2.60	0.00012
72	Hafnium	Hf	102	174	....	(0)	(+)	0.18	1.3×10^{-5}
			104	176	175.9957(7)	(0)	(+)	5.15	0.00037
			105	177	....	$\frac{1}{2}, \frac{3}{2}$	(−)	18.39	0.0013
			106	178	177.9988(9)	(0)	(+)	27.08	0.0019
			107	179	....	$\frac{1}{2}-, \frac{3}{2}$	...	13.78	0.00097
			108	180	180.0031(8)	(0)	(+)	35.44	0.0025
73	Tantalum	Ta	108	181	181.0031(13)	$\frac{7}{2}$	+	100	0.0031
74	Wolfram	W	106	180	....	(0)	(+)	0.135	0.00021
			108	182	182.0041(7)	(0)	(+)	26.4	0.044
			109	183	183.0066(7)	$\frac{1}{2}$	(−)	14.4	0.024
			110	184	184.0074(7)	(0)	(+)	30.6	0.052
			112	186	....	(0)	(+)	28.4	0.050
75	Rhenium	Re	110	185	....	$\frac{5}{2}$	+	37.07	0.0015
			112	187*	....	$\frac{5}{2}$	+	62.93	0.0026
76	Osmium	Os	108	184	....	(0)	(+)	0.018	6.3×10^{-6}
			110	186	....	(0)	(+)	1.59	0.00056
			111	187	....	($\frac{1}{2}$)	(−)	1.64	0.00057
			112	188	188.0157(5)	(0)	(+)	13.3	0.0047
			113	189	189.04(2)	$\frac{3}{2}$	(−)	16.1	0.0056
			114	190	190.0174(6)	(0)	(+)	26.4	0.0092
			116	192	192.0225(6)	(0)	(+)	41.0	0.014
77	Iridium	Ir	114	191	191.038(10)	$\frac{3}{2}$	+	38.5	0.0054
			116	193	193.039(10)	$\frac{3}{2}$	+	61.5	0.0086

See page 8-16 for footnotes and pages 8-16 to 8-18 for References.

OF STABLE NUCLEI (*Continued*)

Magnetic dipole moment μ	Electric quadrupole moment Q	Binding energy of last neutron E_n	Binding energy of last proton E_p	Ground-state configuration (ref. 38)	Ref. M	Ref. I	Ref. μ	Ref. Q	Ref. E_n	Ref. E_p	Notes
...	...	...	...	...	54	7					
...	...	...	...	$f_{\frac{7}{2}}$	2	...	...	...	...	...	*d*
...	...	...	...	...	54	7					
...	...	...	...	...	54	7					
...	...	...	...	$d_{\frac{3}{2}}$	...	7					
...	...	...	...	...	...	7					
...	...	...	...	...	...	7					
...	...	...	...	...	54	7					
...	...	...	...	$f_{\frac{7}{2}}$	...	44					
...	...	...	...	...	54	7					
...	...	...	...	$f_{\frac{7}{2}}$	...	44					
...	...	...	...	...	54	7					
...	...	...	...	$g_{\frac{7}{2}}$	54	7					
...	...	...	...	...	...	7					
...	...	...	...	...	54	7					
...	...	...	...	...	...	7					
...	...	...	...	$f_{\frac{7}{2}}$	...	38					
...	...	...	...	...	54	7					
...	...	...	...	...	54	7					
...	...	...	...	$s_{\frac{1}{2}}$	...	7					
...	...	...	...	...	...	7					
...	...	...	...	...	...	7					
+0.45	...	...	...	$p_{\frac{1}{2}}$	...	7	7				
...	...	...	...	...	...	7					
−0.65	+3.9(4)	...	...	$f_{\frac{5}{2}}$	...	7	7	7			
...	...	...	...	...	...	7					
...	...	...	...	...	...	7					
+2.6	+5.9	...	...	$g_{\frac{7}{2}}$	...	7	7	7			
+3.8	+7(1)	...	...	$(\frac{11}{2}, \frac{13}{2})$	...	...	7	7	...	...	β^-; 7.5 × 10^{10} years
...	...	...	...	...		7					
...	...	...	...	...	54	7					
...	...	...	...	$p_{\frac{1}{2}}$	...	7					
...	...	...	...	...	...	7					
...	...	...	...	$p_{\frac{1}{2}}$	54	7					
...	...	...	...	...	54	7					
+1.9	+5.9	7.55(20)	...	$g_{\frac{7}{2}}$	16	7	33	33	17		
...	...	...	...	...		7					
...	...	...	...	...	54	7					
...	...	...	...	$p_{\frac{1}{2}}$	54	7					
...	...	...	...	...	54	7					
...	...	...	...	...	...	7					
+3.1714(6)	(+2.8)		...	$d_{\frac{5}{2}}$	...	7	38	7			
+3.2039(6)	+2.6	7.30(30)	...	$d_{\frac{5}{2}}$	...	7	38	7	17	..	β^-; 4 × 10^{12} years
...	...	...	...	...	...	7					
...	...	...	...	...	...	7					
...	...	...	...	$p_{\frac{1}{2}}$	...	...	...	...	...	...	*d*
...	...	...	...	...	54	7					
+0.70(9)	+2.0(8)	...	...	$p_{\frac{1}{2}}$	2	30	30	30			
...	...	...	...	...	54	7					
...	...	...	...	...	54	7					
+0.17(3)	+1.2(7)	...	...	$d_{\frac{3}{2}}$	1	38	30	30			
+0.18(3)	+1.0(5)	7.80(20)	...	$d_{\frac{3}{2}}$	1	38	30	30	17		

TABLE 8b-1. PROPERTIES

Atomic No. Z	Name	Chem. symbol	Neutron No. N	Mass No. $A = N + Z$	Atomic mass M	Spin I	Parity	% abundance (ref. 46)	Cosmic abundance (ref. 4)
78	Platinum	Pt	112	190	....	(0)	(+)	0.012	....
			114	192	....	(0)	(+)	0.78	0.00068
			116	194	194.0241(6)	(0)	(+)	32.8	0.029
			117	195	195.0265(6)	$\frac{1}{2}$	−	33.7	0.029
			118	196	196.0267(6)	(0)	(+)	25.4	0.022
			120	198	198.0327(6)	(0)	(+)	7.23	0.0063
79	Gold	Au	118	197	197.039(6)	$\frac{3}{2}$	+	100	0.0082
80	Mercury	Hg	116	196	....	(0)	(+)	0.146	....
			118	198	....	(0)	(+)	10.02	....
			119	199	....	$\frac{1}{2}$	−	16.84	....
			120	200	....	(0)	(+)	23.13	....
			121	201	....	$\frac{3}{2}$	(−)	13.22	....
			122	202	....	(0)	(+)	29.80	....
			124	204	....	(0)	(+)	6.85	....
81	Thallium	Tl	122	203	203.059(9)	$\frac{1}{2}$	+	29.50	....
			124	205	205.059(9)	$\frac{1}{2}$	(+)	70.50	....
82	Lead	Pb	122	204	204.0363(10)	(0)	(+)	1.48	0.0041
			124	206	206.0388(10)	(0)	(+)	23.6	0.064
			125	207	207.0405(10)	$\frac{1}{2}$	−	22.6	0.061
			126	208	208.0416(10)	(0)	(+)	52.3	0.14
83	Bismuth	Bi	126	209	209.0446(10)	$\frac{9}{2}$	(−)	100	0.0021
90	Thorium	Th	142	232*	232.1093(10)	(0)	(+)	100	0.012
92	Uranium	U	142	234*	234.1130(10)	(0)	(+)	0.0058	....
			143	235*	235.1156(10)	$\frac{5}{2}$	(+)	0.715	1.8×10^{-5}
			146	238*	238.1242(10)	(0)	(+)	99.28	0.0026

a. Ground-state configuration assigned by GLT by analogy with $Z = 11$.
b. Ground state configuration assigned by GLT by analogy with $Z = 25$.
c. Energetically unstable with respect to both β^- and β^+ (ref. 27); neither so far observed.
d. Probable spin and parity assignments by GLT based on shell-model predictions of ground-state configurations.
e. Ground-state configurations assigned by GLT.

References for Table 8b-1

1. Mattauch and Fluegge: "Nuclear Physics Tables," Interscience Publishers, Inc., New York, 1946.
2. Bethe: "Elementary Nuclear Theory," John Wiley & Sons, Inc., New York, 1947.
3. Low and Townes: *Phys. Rev.* **75**, 529 (1949).
4. Brown: *Revs. Modern Phys.* **21**, 625 (1949).
5. Curtis, Hornbostel, Lee, and Salant: *Phys. Rev.* **77**, 290 (1950).
6. Duckworth, Preston, and Woodcock: *Phys. Rev.* **79**, 188 (1950).
7. Mack: *Revs. Modern Phys.* **22**, 64 (1950).
8. Haslam, Katz, Moody, and Skarsgard: *Phys. Rev.* **80**, 318 (1950).
9. Johns, Katz, Douglas, and Haslam: *Phys. Rev.* **80**, 1062 (1950).
10. Sher, Halpern, and Stephens: *Phys. Rev.* **81**, 154 (1951).
11. Harvey: *Phys. Rev.* **81**, 353 (1951).
12. Strait, Van Patter, Buechner, and Sperduto: *Phys. Rev.* **81**, 747 (1951).
13. Katz, Johns, Baker, Haslam, and Douglas: *Phys. Rev.* **82**, 271 (1951).
14. Duckworth and Preston: *Phys. Rev.* **82**, 468 (1951).
15. Li, Whaling, Fowler, and Lauritsen: *Phys. Rev.* **83**, 512 (1951).

OF STABLE NUCLEI (*Continued*)

Magnetic dipole moment μ	Electric quadrupole moment Q	Binding energy of last neutron E_n	Binding energy of last proton E_p	Ground-state configuration (ref. 38)	Ref. M	Ref. I	Ref. μ	Ref. Q	Ref. E_n	Ref. E_p	Notes
...	...	...	...	...	...	7					
...	...	...	...	...	...	7					
...	...	9.50(20)	...	...	54	7	...	...	17		
+0.60592(8)	...	6.10(20)	...	$p_{\frac{1}{2}}$	54	7	7	...	17		
...	...	8.20(20)	...	...	54	7	...	...	17		
...	...	...	...	...	54	7					
+0.13(1)	...	7.90(20)	...	$d_{\frac{3}{2}}$	1	7	55	...	17		
...	...	...	...	...	...	7					
...	...	...	...	...	...	7					
+0.50413(3)	...	...	...	$p_{\frac{1}{2}}$	...	7	7				
...	...	...	...	...	...	7					
−0.5990(1)	+0.6	6.6(2)	...	$p_{\frac{3}{2}}$	...	7	7	50	11		
...	...	...	...	...	...	7					
...	...	...	...	...	...	7					
+1.61166(14)	...	8.80(20)	...	$s_{\frac{1}{2}}$	1	7	7	...	17		
+1.62750(14)	...	7.55(20)	...	$s_{\frac{1}{2}}$	1	7	7	...	17		
...	...	...	...	...	54	7					
...	...	8.25(10)	...	...	54	7	...	...	11		
+0.58750(7)	...	6.95(10)	...	$p_{\frac{1}{2}}$	54	7	...	...	11		
...	...	7.44(10)	...	...	54	7	...	...	11		
+4.082(1)	−0.4	7.40(20)	...	$h_{\frac{9}{2}}$	54	7	38	7	17		
...	...	6.0(1.5)	...	...	25	7	...	...	11	...	α; 1.4×10^{10} years
...	...	...	...	...	25	7	...	...	...	...	α; 2.5×10^{5} years
...	...	...	...	$d_{\frac{5}{2}}$	22	7	...	...	...	...	α; 7.1×10^{8} years
...	...	5.8(1.5)	...	...	25	7	...	...	11	...	α; 4.5×10^{9} years

16. Duckworth, Kegley, Olson, and Stanford: *Phys. Rev.* **83,** 1114 (1951).
17. Sher, Halpern, and Mann: *Phys. Rev.* **84,** 387 (1951).
18. Collins, Nier, and Johnson: *Phys. Rev.* **84,** 717 (1951).
19. Hunton: *Can. J. Phys.* **29,** 463 (1951).
19*a*. Mandeville, Swann, Chatterjee, and Van Patter: *Phys. Rev.* **85,** 193 (1952).
20. Geschwind, Gunther-Mohr, and Silvey: *Phys. Rev.* **85,** 474 (1952).
21. Noyes, Van Hoomissen, Miller, and Waldman: *Phys. Rev.* **85,** 727 (1952).
22. Stanford, Duckworth, Hogg, and Geiger: *Phys. Rev.* **85,** 1039 (1952).
23. Eisinger, Bederson, and Feld: *Phys. Rev.* **86,** 73 (1952).
24. Collins, Nier, and Johnson: *Phys. Rev.* **86,** 408 (1952).
25. Stanford, Duckworth, Hogg, and Geiger: *Phys. Rev.* **86,** 617 (1952).
26. Ting, Biard, and Williams: *Phys. Rev.* **86,** 618 (1952).
27. Johnson: *Phys. Rev.*, **87,** 166 (1952).
28. Walchli and Morgan: *Phys. Rev.* **87,** 541 (1952).
29. Tucker and Gregg: *Phys. Rev.* **87,** 907 (1952).
30. Murakawa and Suwa: *Phys. Rev.* **87,** 1048 (1952).
31. Halsted: *Phys. Rev.* **88,** 666 (1952).
32. Li: *Phys. Rev.* **88,** 1038 (1952).
33. Brown and Tomboulian: *Phys. Rev.* **88,** 1158 (1952).
34. Johnson: *Phys. Rev.* **88,** 1213 (1952).
35. Kanda: *J. Phys. Soc. Japan* **7,** 296 (1952).
36. Bogle and Scovil: *Proc. Phys. Soc.* (*London*) **A65,** 368 (1952).

36*a*. Elliott and Stevens: *Proc. Phys. Soc.* (*London*) **A65,** 370 (1952).
37. Ajzenberg and Lauritsen: *Revs. Modern Phys.* **42,** 321 (1952).
38. Klinkenberg: *Revs. Modern Phys.* **24,** 63 (1952).
39. Steudel: *Z. Physik* **132,** 429 (1952).
40. Ogata and Matsuda: *Phys. Rev.* **89,** 27 (1953).
41. Ogata and Matsuda: *Phys. Rev.* **89,** 333 (1953).
42. Javan, Silvey, Townes, and Grosse: *Phys. Rev.* **91,** 222 (1953).
43. Sprague and Tomboulian: *Phys. Rev.* **91,** 476 (1953).
44. Murakawa and Kamei: *Phys. Rev.* **92,** 254 (1953).
45. Hogg and Duckworth: *Can. J. Phys.* **31,** 942 (1953).
46. Hollander, Perlman, and Seaborg: *Revs. Modern Phys.* **25,** 469 (1953).
47. Brun, Oeser, Staub, and Telschow: *Phys. Rev.* **93,** 172 (1954).
48. Sogo and Jeffries: *Phys. Rev.* **93,** 174 (1954).
49. Waldron, Schultz, and Kohman: *Phys. Rev.* **93,** 254 (1954).
50. Dehmelt, Robinson, and Gordy: *Phys. Rev.* **93,** 480 (1954).
51. Brun, Oeser, Staub, and Telschow: *Phys. Rev.* **93,** 904 (1954).
52. Collins, Nier, and Johnson: *Phys. Rev.* **94,** 398 (1954).
53. Bird and Townes: *Phys. Rev.* **94,** 1203 (1954).
54. Hogg and Duckworth: *Can. J. Phys.* **32,** 65 (1954).
55. Pake: *Ann. Rev. Nuclear Sci.* **4** (1954).
56. Endt and Kluyver: *Revs. Modern Phys.* **26,** 95 (1954).

Assumption (2), if rigidly adhered to, leads to an *extreme single-particle model,* in which the properties of odd or odd-odd nuclei are to be deduced from the effects of the odd particle(s) alone. This model meets with a high degree of success in accounting for nuclear spins and parities but fails in a few cases, notably N or $Z = 11$ or 25, or $Z = 9$; its success is less marked, but still noteworthy, for more complex properties such as magnetic and quadrupole moments. Somewhat more general is the *odd-group* model, which allows for interactions among an odd number of identical particles outside a closed shell but retains the features of the single-particle model as regards an even number of identical particles outside a shell. This model can account for the spins of systems with N or $Z = 11$ or 25. A still more general model may be called the *open-shell* model; this permits interactions among all particles outside closed shells. A generalization in a different direction allows for a deformation of the "core" of nucleons in closed shells, either as a simple distortion[1] or as the excitation of "surface waves," the core being treated as a liquid drop.[2]

Both the single-particle and odd-group models treat odd-odd nuclei by ascribing to each group separately the properties it could be expected to have if the other group were even, and then combining the results. If the total angular momentum of one group is j_1, that of the other j_2, then the spin I of the nucleus lies between the bounds

$$|j_1 - j_2| \leq I \leq j_1 + j_2.$$

Some semiempirical rules have been set forth to reduce the indicated range of choice. One general set[3] is: given the j's and corresponding l's of the odd groups,

$$I = |j_1 - j_2| \quad \text{for } j_1 + j_2 + l_1 + l_2 = 2K;$$
$$I > |j_1 - j_2| \quad \text{for } j_1 + j_2 + l_1 + l_2 = 2K + 1.$$

Another[4] applies to systems in which one odd group consists of a single particle outside a closed shell while the other is one particle short of forming a closed shell; then the rule is $I = j_1 + j_2 - 1$. Both have some theoretical justification; in the only

[1] Rainwater, *Phys. Rev.* **79,** 432 (1950).
[2] Foldy and Milford, *Phys. Rev.* **80,** 751 (1950).
[3] Nordheim, *Phys. Rev.* **78,** 294 (1950).
[4] Kurath, *Phys. Rev.* **91,** 1430 (1953).

TABLE 8b-2. LEVEL ORDER

Proton levels			Total identical nucleons	Neutron levels		
Level	No. of protons: In level	No. of protons: In shell (in subshell)		No. of neutrons: In shell (in subshell)	No. of neutrons: In level	Level
$1s_{\frac{1}{2}}$	2	2	2	2	2	$1s_{\frac{1}{2}}$
$2p_{\frac{3}{2}}$	4				4	$2p_{\frac{3}{2}}$
$2p_{\frac{1}{2}}$	2	6	8	6	2	$2p_{\frac{1}{2}}$
$3d_{\frac{5}{2}}$	6	(6)	(14)	(6)	6	$3d_{\frac{5}{2}}$
$2s_{\frac{1}{2}}$	2	(2)	(16)	(2)	2	$2s_{\frac{1}{2}}$
$3d_{\frac{3}{2}}$	4	12	20	12	4	$3d_{\frac{3}{2}}$
$4f_{\frac{7}{2}}$	8	8	28	8	8	$4f_{\frac{7}{2}}$
$3p_{\frac{3}{2}}$	4				4	$3p_{\frac{3}{2}}$
$4f_{\frac{5}{2}}$	6	(10)	(38)	(10)	6	$4f_{\frac{5}{2}}$
$3p_{\frac{1}{2}}$	2	(2)	(40)	(2)	2	$3p_{\frac{1}{2}}$
$5g_{\frac{9}{2}}$	10	22	50	22	10	$5g_{\frac{9}{2}}$
$5g_{\frac{7}{2}}$	8	(8)	(58)		6	$4d_{\frac{5}{2}}$
$4d_{\frac{5}{2}}$	6				8	$5g_{\frac{7}{2}}$
$6h_{\frac{11}{2}}$	12				12	$6h_{\frac{11}{2}}$
$4d_{\frac{3}{2}}$	4	(22)	(80)	(30)	4	$4d_{\frac{3}{2}}$
$3s_{\frac{1}{2}}$	2	32	82	32	2	$3s_{\frac{1}{2}}$
$6h_{\frac{9}{2}}$	10				8	$5f_{\frac{7}{2}}$
$5f_{\frac{7}{2}}$	8				10	$6h_{\frac{9}{2}}$
$5f_{\frac{5}{2}}$	6				6	$5f_{\frac{5}{2}}$
$7i_{\frac{13}{2}}$	14				4	$4p_{\frac{3}{2}}$
$4p_{\frac{3}{2}}$	4				14	$7i_{\frac{13}{2}}$
$4p_{\frac{1}{2}}$	2	44	126	4	2	$4p_{\frac{1}{2}}$
$7i_{\frac{11}{2}}$	12				10	$6g_{\frac{9}{2}}$
					12	$7i_{\frac{11}{2}}$
					6	$5d_{\frac{5}{2}}$
					8	$6g_{\frac{7}{2}}$
					4	$5d_{\frac{3}{2}}$

case in which they conflict and a measurement has been made ($_{19}K^{40}$), the agreement is with the second rule.

8b-3. Semiempirical Mass Formulas. Wigner[1] deduces for the binding energy of a nucleus the expression

$$E_B = \tfrac{1}{2}A(A-1)L' - \Xi L + BA + \left(\frac{20B}{9}\right)(T_\zeta{}^2 + \tfrac{1}{2}\delta_A)A^{-1} + CZ(Z-1)A^{-\frac{1}{3}},$$

where

$$T_\zeta = \tfrac{1}{2}(N - Z)$$

$$\delta_A = 1 - \tfrac{1}{2}[(-1)^N + (-1)^Z],$$

$$\Xi = 2A - \left(\frac{A^2}{8}\right) - \tfrac{1}{2}T_\zeta(T_\zeta + 4) - \tfrac{3}{4}\delta_A;$$

[1] Wigner, "University of Pennsylvania Bicentennial Conference," University of Pennsylvania Press, Philadelphia, 1949.

B and C are constants, related by

$$BC^2 = (3\pi^2)^{\frac{1}{3}} \left(\frac{9\hbar e^2}{Mc}\right)^2;$$

and L and L' are functions of A. The first two terms are potential energy, the next two kinetic energy, and the last the Coulomb energy. C can be evaluated from mirror nuclei, and has the value 0.635 mmμ. L and L' can be calculated as follows: the difference between binding energies of two isobars depends only on L and known or calculable quantities; thus L can be determined (for a given A), and then from the original equation L' is determined.[1]

Carrying out the analogy between nuclear matter and liquid droplets gives the equation[2]

$$M(Z, N) = NM_n + ZM_p - \alpha A + \beta(N - Z)^2A^{-1} + \gamma A^{\frac{2}{3}} + \epsilon Z^2A^{-\frac{1}{3}}$$

The first two terms represent the masses of the constituents, the third term a "volume" energy, the fourth a symmetry energy, the fifth a surface energy, and the last the Coulomb energy. The last term is sometimes written as $\epsilon Z(Z - 1)A^{-\frac{1}{3}}$, with resulting changes in results to be given below. The most stable nucleus for a given value of A has atomic number

$$Z_A = \tfrac{1}{2}A(4\beta + M_n - M_p)(4\beta + \epsilon A^{\frac{2}{3}})^{-1},$$

and mass

$$M(A, Z_A) = (M_n - \alpha + \beta)A + \gamma A^{\frac{2}{3}} - \tfrac{1}{2}(4\beta + M_n - M_p)Z_A.$$

The Coulomb constant ϵ is evaluated from mirror nuclei, β from a fit of the curve of Z_A vs. A with known stable elements, and α and γ by fitting the masses of two stable elements.

Bohr and Wheeler[3] evaluate Z_A vs. A empirically, and write

$$M(Z_A, A) = A(1 + f_A),$$

$$M(Z, A) = M(Z_A, A) + \tfrac{1}{2}B_A(Z - Z_A)^2 + \begin{cases} 0, & A \text{ odd;} \\ -\tfrac{1}{2}\delta_A, & A \text{ even, } Z \text{ even;} \\ +\tfrac{1}{2}\delta_A, & A \text{ even, } Z \text{ odd;} \end{cases}$$

f_A is the average value of the packing fraction around mass number A;

$$B_A = [M_p - M_n + (6Z_Ae^2)(5r_0A^{\frac{1}{3}})^{-1}][\tfrac{1}{2}A - Z_A]^{-1} + (6e^2)(5r_0A^{\frac{1}{3}})^{-1};$$

and δ_A is a pairing energy, evaluated empirically. Their values for δ_A range from 2.8 Mev at $A = 50$ to 1.0 Mev at $A = 240$.

The Bethe-Bacher formula can be put in this form:[4] using the above expressions for Z_A and $M(A, Z_A)$,

$$M(Z, A) = M(Z_A, A) + (4\beta + M_n - M_p)\frac{(Z - Z_A)^2}{2Z_A}.$$

Both references also add the pairing-energy term; they use $\delta_A = 0.072A^{-\frac{3}{4}}$ amu without theoretical justification.

[1] For further details and values of L and L' see Collins, Nier, and Johnson, *Phys. Rev.* **86**, 408 (1952); and Halsted, *Phys. Rev.* **88,** 666 (1952).

[2] Bethe and Bacher, *Revs. Modern Phys.* **8,** 82 (1937).

[3] Bohr and Wheeler, *Phys. Rev.* **56,** 426 (1939).

[4] Fermi, "Nuclear Physics," University of Chicago Press, Chicago, 1950; and Metropolis and Reitwiesner, "Table of Atomic Masses," unpublished, 1950.

No account has been taken here of shell-structure effects. Wapstra[1] suggests an additional term in the liquid-drop formula of the form

$$E_i = A_i f\left(\frac{Z - Z_i}{W_i}\right)$$

for the ith proton shell, and an analogous term for neutrons; $f(x)$ is an unknown function such that $f(0) = 1, f(-x) = f(x)$. Taking for simplicity $f(x) = (1 + x^2)^{-1}$, he gets good results with $W_i = 3.5$ for all i, $A_{Z=50} = A_{N=50} = 6.25$ Mev, $A_{N=82} = 6.00$ Mev.

Stern[2] adds to the liquid-drop formula, for $A \geq 208$, a term

$$0.01270 - 0.02340 \exp\left[-18(A - 208)/208\right];$$

no theoretical explanation is offered, but agreement with experimental data is improved.

Coryell[3] suggests that solutions for Z_A, B_A, and δ_A should be sought only locally, i.e., between shells, and that good results follow from locally linear dependence of Z_A on A.

Kohman[4] maintains that the pairing-energy term should have the form $\frac{1}{2}\pi_A(-1)^{Z+1} + \frac{1}{2}\nu_A(-1)^{N+1}$. With $\pi_A + \nu_A = \delta_A$, $\pi_A - \nu_A = \epsilon_A$, then empirically $\delta_A \cong 1.3$ Mev, $\epsilon_A = 0.1$ Mev. See also Suess.[5]

Some attempts have been made to evaluate the coefficients in the liquid-drop formula on theoretical grounds, or to deduce the form of the equation[6] or to take account of other factors such as compressibility of nuclear matter.[7] However, in general the added complexity appears not to be compensated for by a significant increase in accuracy. It is of some interest to note that the expression deduced by Allard has some points of similarity to both the Wigner formula and the liquid-drop formula.

8b-4. Stability Rules. *General Considerations.* Assuming only (1) attractive pairing forces between nucleons and (2) saturation of nuclear forces, Sengupta[8] shows that, if an odd-A nuclide is β^--unstable, so are all its isobars of smaller Z; if an odd-A nuclide is β^+- or electron-capture-unstable, so are all its isobars of larger Z.

Let a given nuclide[9] be specified by the number of four groups m, the number of ungrouped neutrons n $(= N - 2m)$, and the number of unpaired protons p $(= Z - 2m, = 0 \text{ or } 1)$. Define (by interpolation, if necessary) $E_n(m, n, p)$ and $E_p(n, m, p)$ as the energy gained by adding an even neutron or proton, respectively, to nuclide (m, n, p), $E_n'(m, n, p)$ and $E_p'(m, n, p)$ as the energy gained by adding odd particles, and $E_c(m, n, p)$ as the Coulomb energy of nuclide (m, n, p). Let n_1, n_2, n_3, and n_4 be the solutions of

$$\begin{aligned} E_c(m + 1, n_1 - 4, 0) - E_c(m, n_1 - 1, 1) + m_ec^2 &= E_p(m, n_1 - 2, 1) - E_n'(m, n_1 - 2, 1), \\ E_c(m, n_2 - 1, 1) - E_c(m, n_2, 0) + m_ec^2 &= E_p'(m, n_2 - 1, 0) - E_n'(m, n_2 - 1, 0), \\ E_c(m + 1, n_3 - 4, 0) - E_c(m, n_3 - 1, 1) + m_ec^2 &= E_p(m, n_3 - 2, 1) - E_n(m, n_3 - 2, 1), \\ E_c(m, n_4 - 1, 1) - E_c(m, n_4, 0) + m_ec^2 &= E_p'(m, n_4 - 1, 0) - E_n(m, n_4 - 1, 0). \end{aligned}$$

[1] *Physica* **18**, 83 (1952).
[2] *Revs. Modern Phys.* **21**, 316 (1949).
[3] *Ann. Rev. Nuclear Sci.* **3**, 305 (1953).
[4] *Phys. Rev.* **85**, 530 (1952); also Suess, *Phys. Rev.* **81**, 1071 (1951).
[5] *Phys. Rev.* **81**, 1071 (1951).
[6] For example, Gombas, *Ann. Physik* **10**, 253 (1952); Allard, *J. phys. radium* **8** (ser. 8), 65 (1947); Hammack, PhD thesis, Washington University, 1951.
[7] Feenberg, *Revs. Modern Phys.* **19**, 239 (1947).
[8] *Phys. Rev.* **89**, 1296 (1953).
[9] Fuchs, *Proc. Cambridge Phil. Soc.* **35**, 242 (1939).

Then stable isobars of nuclide (m, n, p) can exist only for $n_1 < n < n_4$, stable nuclides of type $(m, 2k, 1)$ only for $n_2 < 2k + 1 < n_3$. Neglecting spin effects, $n_3 - n_2 \cong 2$; spin effects generally tend to increase this somewhat. Also $n_4 - n_3 = n_2 - n_1$. Rough estimates give

$$n_4 - n_1 \cong 3 - 7,$$
$$n_4 - n_3 = n_2 - n_1 \cong 0.5 - 2.5.$$

The difference between n_4 and n_1 should increase with increasing m; the actual decrease beyond $m \cong 30$ cannot be explained on these assumptions.

Shell structure is not taken into account in these estimates (or in others below). Its effect may be described[1] as a tendency to narrow the limits of stability when a "magic" number lies between them, to widen them when such a number lies outside but near them. Another description would be to say that the lines of stability tend to lie along the "magic" number lines.

Specific Models. McMillan[2] finds that, if nucleons form a degenerate Fermi gas, with *n-n*, *p-p*, and *n-p* forces equal apart from Coulomb interaction, the curve of greatest stability has the form

$$Z_A = \tfrac{1}{2}A[1 + (9K)(8\mu)^{-1}A^{\frac{2}{3}}]^{-1}$$

where μ is the maximum kinetic energy and K a constant whose value depends on the proton density distribution (cf. relation obtained by Bethe and Bacher from liquid-drop model, above).

The liquid-drop model gives for the energy available for β decay of nuclide (A, Z)[3]

$$E_\beta = B_A\{|Z - Z_A| - \tfrac{1}{2}\} + \begin{cases} 0, A \text{ odd}, \\ +\delta_A, A \text{ even}, Z \text{ odd}, \\ -\delta_A, A \text{ even}, Z \text{ even}. \end{cases}$$

From this[4] the upper limit of β stability is $Z''_A = Z_A + S_A$, the lower limit $Z'_A = Z_A - S_A$, where $S_A = (\delta_A/B_A) + \frac{1}{2}$. Below $A \cong 30$, $B_A > 2\delta_A$ and $S_A < 1$, and there may be no even-even nuclide between Z'_A and Z''_A; in this case an odd-odd one may be stable.

The energy of an α particle emitted by nuclide (A, Z) is[5]

$$Q_\alpha = \Delta_4(Af_A) - f_{\text{He}} - \tfrac{1}{2}B_A(2 - \Delta_4 Z_A)^2 - B_A(2 - \Delta_4 Z_A)(Z - Z_A),$$

where $\Delta_n F(A) = F(A) - F(A - n)$. If Z_A and Af_A are approximately linear in A, then

$$Q_\alpha \cong \Delta_4(Af_A) - f_{\text{He}} - \tfrac{1}{2}B_A(2 - \Delta_4 Z_A)^2 - B_A\Delta_1 Z_A(2 - \Delta_4 Z_A)(A - A_Z),$$

with A_Z the most stable A for given Z; the main term is $\Delta_4(Af_A)$. Nuclide (A, Z) is α-unstable for $Q_\alpha > 0$.

For liquid-drop model with shell-effect correction, Wapstra[6] deduces for the line of maximum stability ("center of the valley of stability")

$$Z_c = Z_A - \frac{M_n - M_{\text{H}}}{4c} - \frac{A_i}{4c}\phi_i(Z_c),$$

[1] Aten, *Science* **110**, 260 (1949).
[2] *Phys. Rev.* **92**, 210 (1953).
[3] Bohr and Wheeler, *loc. cit.*
[4] Kohman, *Phys. Rev.* **73**, 16 (1948).
[5] Kohman, *Phys. Rev.* **76**, 448 (1949).
[6] *Physica* **18**, 83 (1952).

and for the limits of stability

$$Z_l = Z_A - \frac{M_n - M_H}{4c} \pm \frac{1 + \delta_A}{2c} + \frac{A_i}{4c} \phi_i(Z_l \mp 1),$$

with

$$c = \tfrac{1}{4}\epsilon A^{-\frac{2}{3}}(A - 2Z_A)^{-1} \qquad \phi_i(Z) = f\left(\frac{Z - Z_i - 1}{2W_i}\right) - f\left(\frac{Z - Z_i + 1}{2W_i}\right).$$

8c. Passage of Particles through Matter

WALTER JOHN[1]

University of Illinois

8c-1. Introduction. This article presents some of the commonly used formulas and data concerning the passage of particles through matter. Because of space limitations, much useful material has been omitted. For general discussion of these topics and extensive bibliographies to the literature, the reader is referred to H. Bethe and J. Ashkin, Part II, "Experimental Nuclear Physics," E. Segrè, ed., John Wiley & Sons, Inc., New York, 1953, and to S. K. Allison and S. D. Warshaw, *Revs. Modern Phys.* **25**, 779 (1953).

8c-2. Range-Energy Relations for Heavy Charged Particles. Heavy charged particles lose energy principally by inelastic collisions with the electrons of the atoms in the stopping material. The average energy loss per centimeter of path length is called the *stopping power*. The stopping power is given by

$$-\frac{dE}{dx} = \frac{4\pi e^4 z^2 NZ}{mv^2}\left[\ln\frac{2mv^2}{I} - \ln(1 - \beta^2) - \beta^2\right]$$

where z = charge number of the incident particle
N = number of atoms/cm³ of the stopping material
Z = atomic number of the stopping material
m = electron mass
v = velocity of the incident particle
$\beta = v/c$, where c = the velocity of light

I is the average excitation potential of the atom. I is approximately $10Z$ ev.[2]

The range of a particle is obtained from the stopping power by integration. The range of a particle of charge ze, mass M, and kinetic energy E may be obtained from the range of a proton of energy $(M_p/M)E$, where M_p is the proton mass, by the following relation:

$$R_{Z,M}(E) = \frac{M}{M_p Z^2} R_p\left(\frac{M}{M_p} E\right)$$

The tables for energy loss are derived from considerations of collision losses only.

[1] The author is indebted to Prof. Emilio Segrè for valuable guidance in the preparation of this article.

[2] For experimental values of I, see R. Mather and E. Segrè, *Phys. Rev.* **81**, 191 (1951).

TABLE 8c-1. RATE OF ENERGY LOSS AND RANGE OF PROTONS IN COPPER, $I = 309.91$ EV*

E, Mev	$-\frac{dE}{dx}$, Mev g^{-1} cm^2	R, g cm^{-2}
4	......	4.666×10^{-2}
5	47.05	6.803
6	41.27	9.078
8	33.42	1.4499×10^{-1}
10	28.29	2.1031
12	24.65	2.8626
14	21.92	3.7248
16	19.79	4.6865
18	18.08	5.7452
20	16.67	6.8985
22	15.49	8.1444
24	14.48	9.4811
26	13.61	1.0907×10^0
28	12.85	1.2420
30	12.19	1.4019
35	10.82	1.8384
40	9.757	2.3259
45	8.913	2.8628
50	8.223	3.4474
55	7.647	4.0785
60	7.160	4.7547
65	6.741	5.4749
70	6.377	6.2380
75	6.057	7.0430
80	5.774	7.8888
85	5.523	8.7746
90	5.296	9.6994
95	5.093	1.0662×10
100	4.908	1.1663
110	4.585	1.3773
120	4.312	1.6023
130	4.079	1.8409
140	3.877	2.0925
150	3.701	2.3566
160	3.545	2.6328
170	3.407	2.9206
180	3.284	3.2197
190	3.172	3.5296
200	3.072	3.8500
225	2.858	4.6948
250	2.686	5.5979
275	2.545	6.5548
300	2.426	7.5615
325	2.326	8.6143
350	2.240	9.7099
375	2.166	1.0845×10^2

TABLE 8c-1. RATE OF ENERGY LOSS AND RANGE OF PROTONS IN COPPER, $I = 309.91$ EV* (*Continued*)

E, Mev	$-\frac{dE}{dx}$, Mev g^{-1} cm^2	R, g cm^{-2}
400	2.101	1.2018
425	2.045	1.3224
450	1.994	1.4463
475	1.948	1.5731
500	1.909	1.7028
550	1.840	1.9698
600	1.784	2.2459
650	1.737	2.5300
700	1.698	2.8212
750	1.665	3.1186
800	1.638	3.4215
850	1.613	3.7294
900	1.592	4.0414
950	1.575	4.3572
1,000	1.558	4.6764
1,100	1.533	5.3235
1,200	1.514	5.9800
1,300	1.499	6.6439
1,400	1.488	7.3134
1,500	1.480	7.9874
1,600	1.473	8.6647
1,700	1.469	9.3445
1,800	1.466	1.0026 $\times 10^3$
1,900	1.464	1.0709
2,000	1.463	1.1393
2,250	1.464	1.3102
2,500	1.467	1.4808
2,750	1.473	1.6508
3,000	1.481	1.8201
3,250	1.489	1.9885
3,500	1.497	2.1560
3,750	1.506	2.3226
4,000	1.515	2.4881
4,250	1.524	2.6526
4,500	1.533	2.8163
4,570	1.542	2.9789
5,000	1.551	3.1407
5,500	1.568	3.4613
6,000	1.584	3.7786
6,500	1.600	4.0926
7,000	1.616	4.4036
7,500	1.630	4.7116
8,000	1.644	5.0170
8,500	1.658	5.3198
9,000	1.671	5.6202
9,500	1.683	5.9182
10,000	1.695	6.2142

* W. Aron, UCRL-1325.

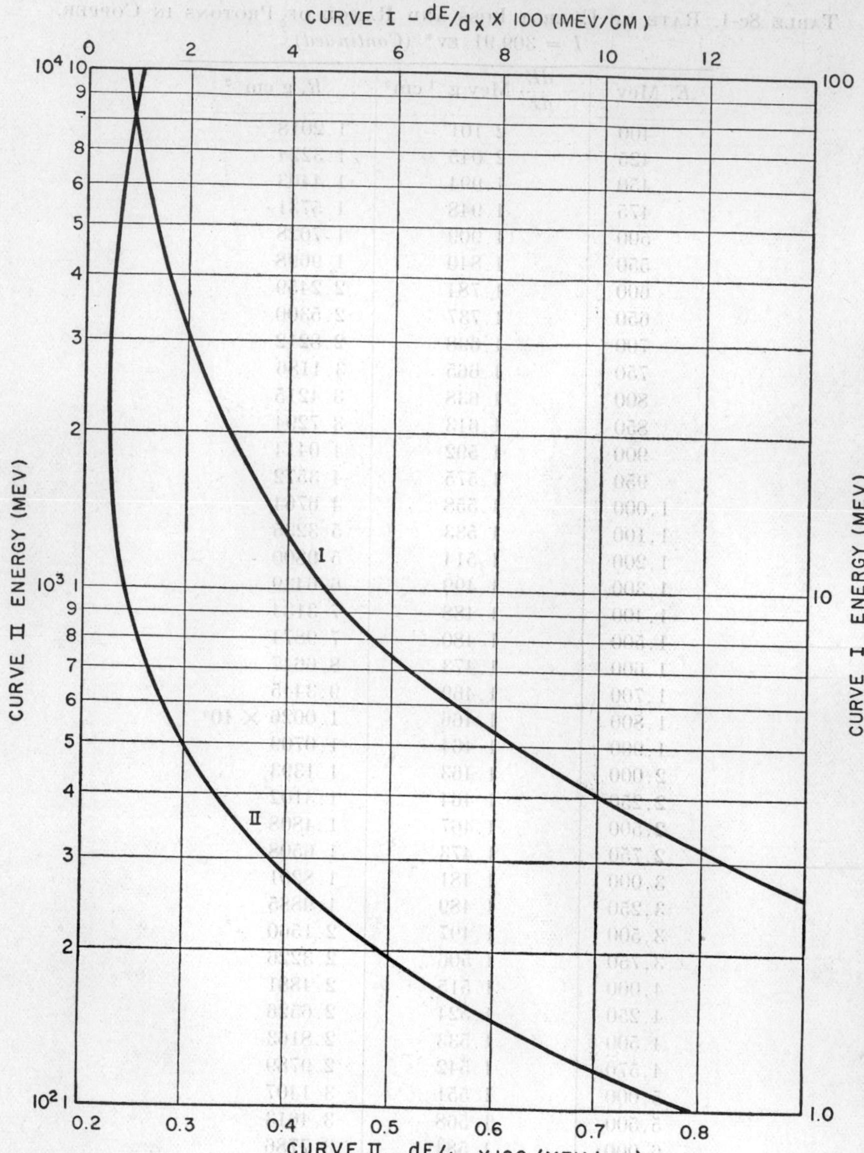

Fig. 8c-1. Rate of energy loss of protons in air. (*Aron, Hoffman, and Williams, AECU* 663.)

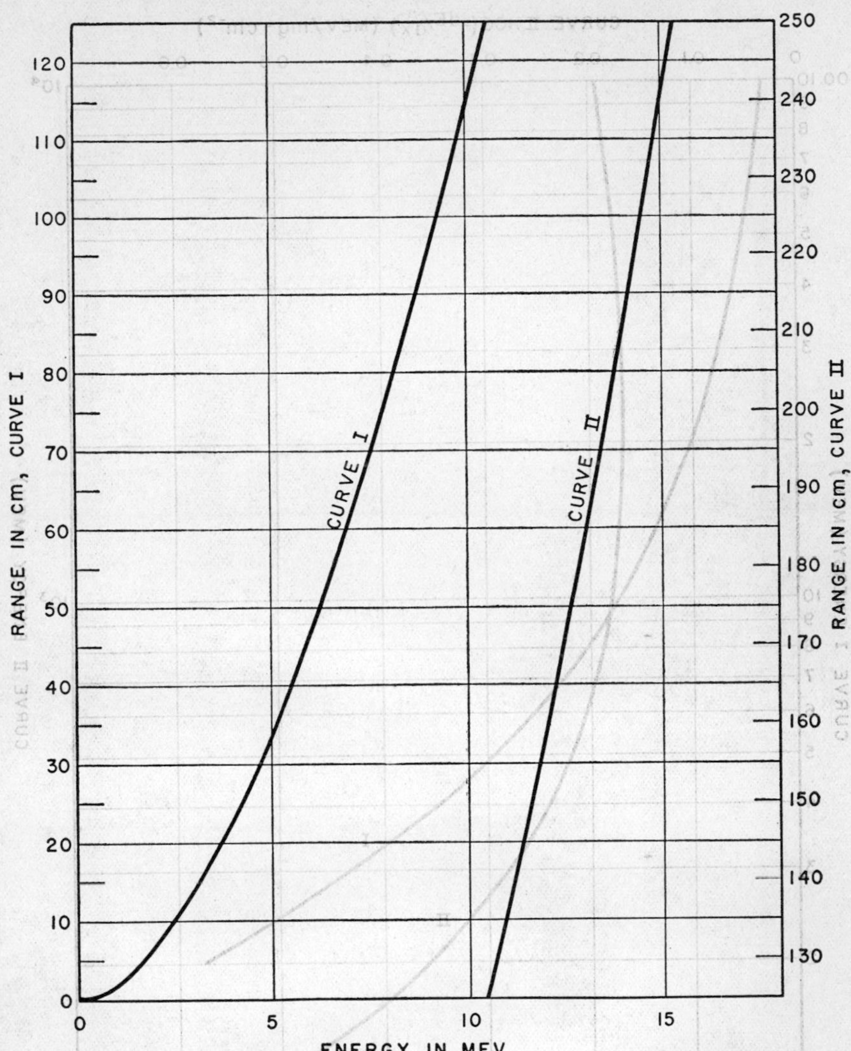

Fig. 8c-2. Range-energy relation for protons in air. (*Aron, Hoffman, and Williams, AECU 663.*)

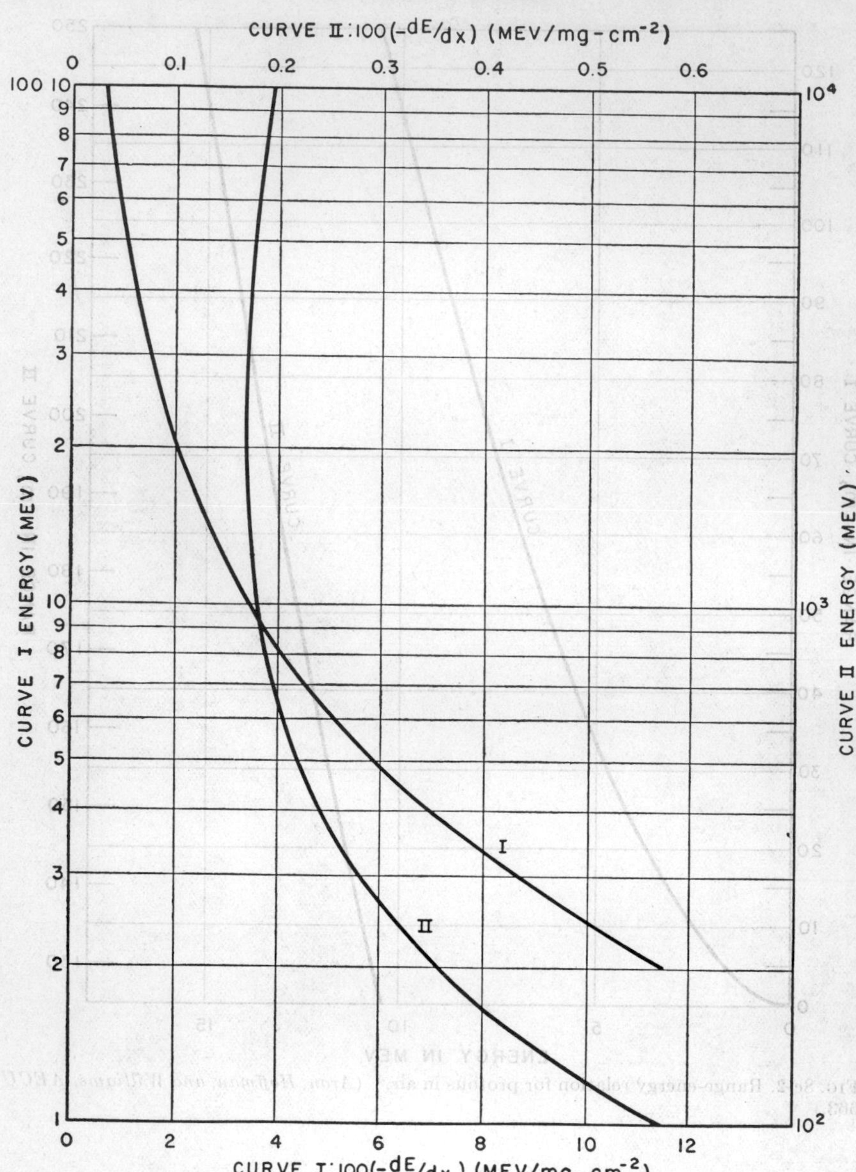

FIG. 8c-3. Rate of energy loss for protons in aluminum. (*Aron, Hoffman, and Williams, AECU* 663.)

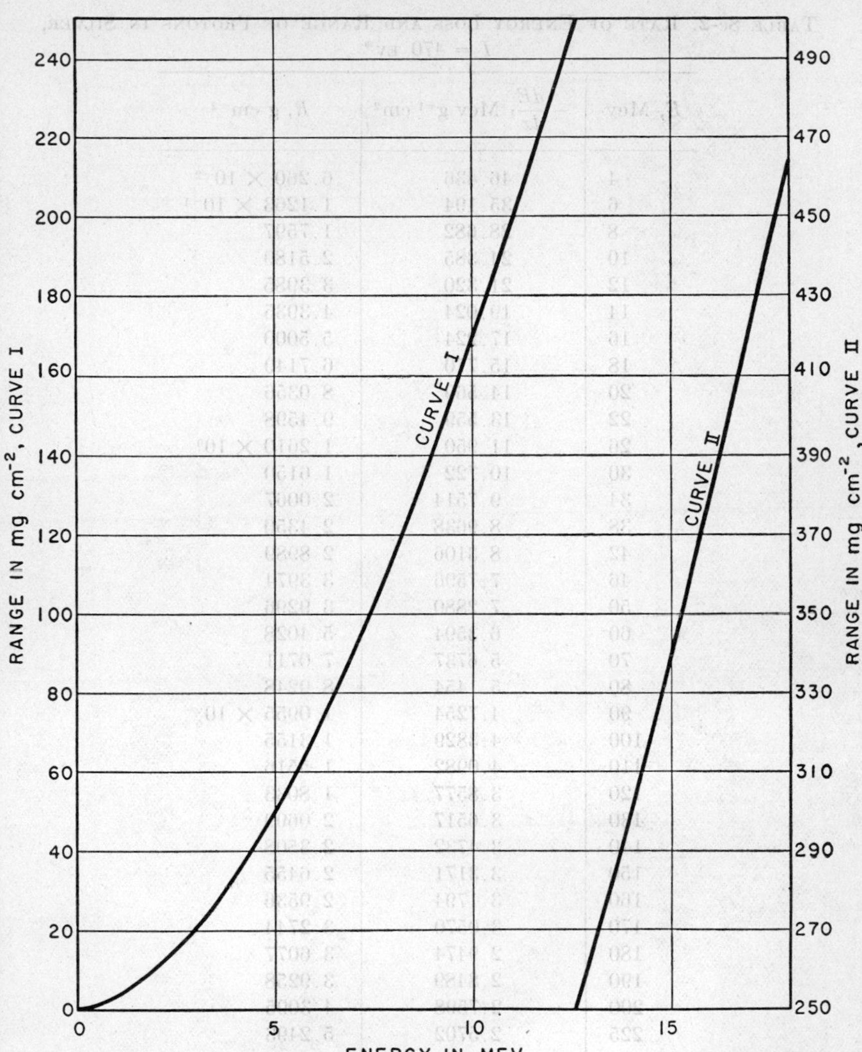

FIG. 8c-4. Range-energy relation for protons in aluminum (0 to 18 Mev). (*Aron, Hoffman, and Williams, AECU* 663.)

TABLE 8c-2. RATE OF ENERGY LOSS AND RANGE OF PROTONS IN SILVER, I = 470 EV*

E, Mev	$-\frac{dE}{dx}$, Mev g^{-1} cm^2	R, g cm^{-2}
4	46.436	6.260 × 10^{-2}
6	35.194	1.1263 × 10^{-1}
8	28.682	1.7597
10	24.385	2.5189
12	21.320	3.3985
14	19.024	4.3935
16	17.224	5.5000
18	15.770	6.7149
20	14.569	8.0356
22	13.559	9.4598
26	11.950	1.2610 × 10^0
30	10.722	1.6150
34	9.7514	2.0067
38	8.9638	2.4350
42	8.3106	2.8989
46	7.7596	3.3974
50	7.2880	3.9296
60	6.3594	5.4028
70	5.6737	7.0711
80	5.1454	8.9248
90	4.7254	1.0955 × 10
100	4.3829	1.3155
110	4.0982	1.5516
120	3.8577	1.8033
130	3.6517	2.0699
140	3.4732	2.3508
150	3.3171	2.6455
160	3.1794	2.9536
170	3.0570	3.2744
180	2.9474	3.6077
190	2.8489	3.9258
200	2.7598	4.3095
225	2.5702	5.2493
250	2.4173	6.2532
275	2.2915	7.3161
300	2.1864	8.4337
325	2.0972	9.6017
350	2.0208	1.0817 × 10^2
375	1.9547	1.2075
400	1.8970	1.3374
425	1.8462	1.4710
450	1.8014	1.6081
475	1.7614	1.7485
500	1.7257	1.8919
600	1.6148	2.4921
700	1.5388	3.1274

TABLE 8c-2. RATE OF ENERGY LOSS AND RANGE OF PROTONS IN SILVER, $I = 470$ EV* (*Continued*)

E, Mev	$-\frac{dE}{dx}$, Mev g^{-1} cm^2	R, g cm^{-2}
800	1.4847	3.7895
900	1.4452	4.4727
1,000	1.4158	5.1721
1,200	1.3769	6.6063
1,400	1.3548	8.0718
1,600	1.3426	9.5554
1,800	1.3368	1.1049×10^3
2,000	1.3351	1.2546
2,500	1.3413	1.6285
3,000	1.3548	1.9995
3,500	1.3712	2.3664
4,000	1.3887	2.7287
4,500	1.4063	3.0865
5,000	1.4235	3.4399
6,000	1.4563	4.1343
7,000	1.4864	4.8139
8,000	1.5141	5.4804
9,000	1.5395	6.1353
10,000	1.5630	6.7799

* W. Aron, UCRL-1325.

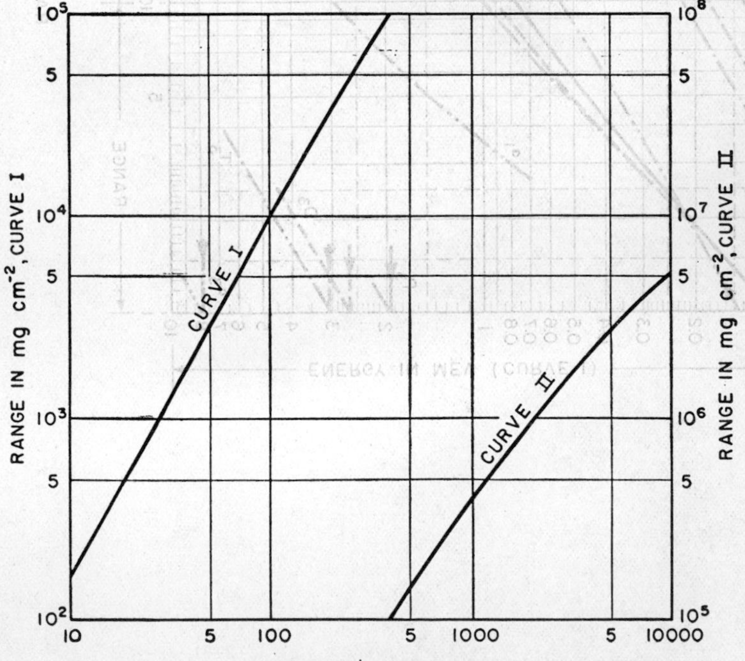

FIG. 8c-5. Range-energy relation for protons in aluminum (10 to 10,000 Mev). (*Aron, Hoffman, and Williams, AECU* 663.)

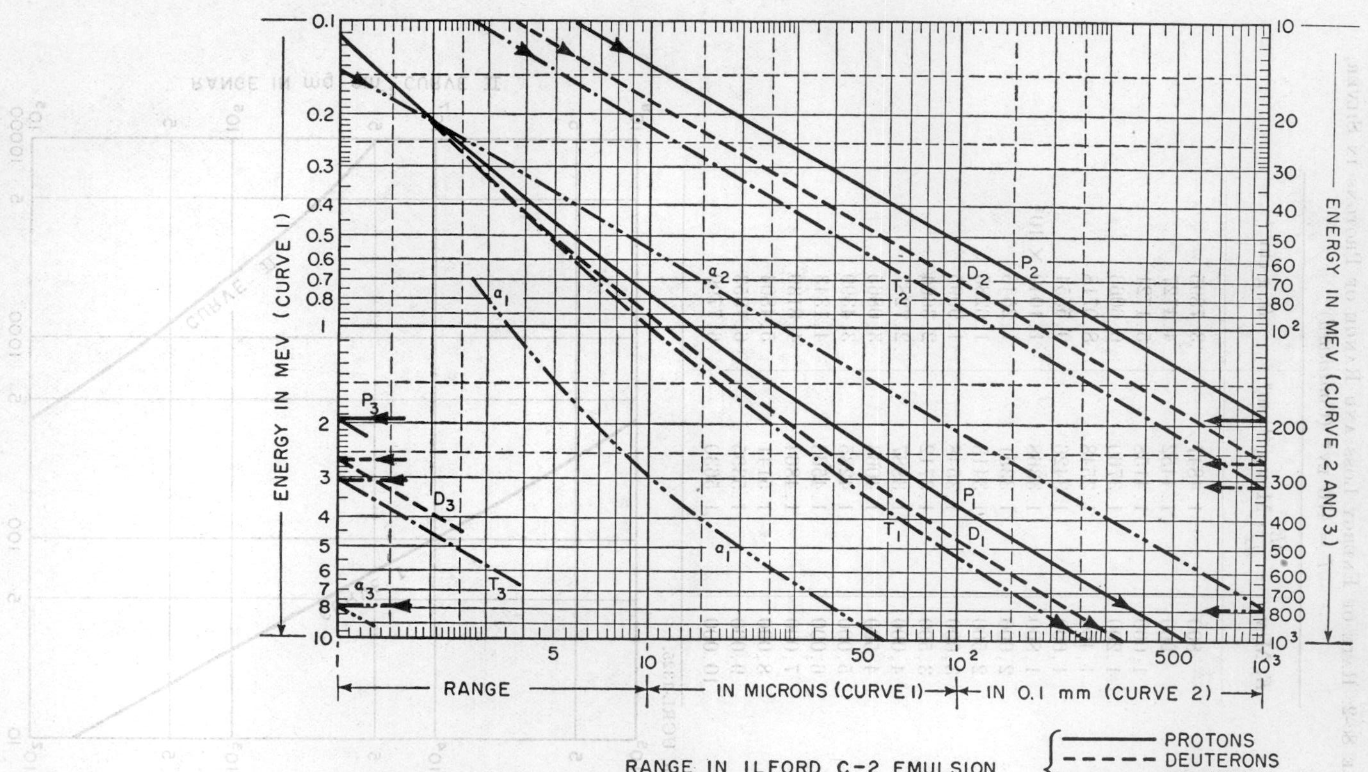

FIG. 8c-6. Range-energy relation for protons, deuterons, tritons, and alpha particles in Ilford C-2 emulsion. [*Vigneron, J. Phys. Radium* **14,** 145 (1953).]

TABLE 8c-3. RATE OF ENERGY LOSS AND RANGE OF PROTONS IN LEAD, $I = 810.79$ EV*

E, Mev	$-\frac{dE}{dx}$, Mev g^{-1} cm^2	R, g cm^{-2}
1	71.435	7.90×10^{-3}
2	51.304	2.505×10^{-2}
3	41.418	4.98
4	34.923	8.1668
6	26.940	1.4752×10^{-1}
8	22.176	2.2981
10	19.082	3.2755
12	16.808	4.3949
14	15.073	5.6537
16	13.700	7.0474
18	12.585	8.5722
20	11.659	1.0225×10^{0}
22	10.877	1.2002
24	10.206	1.3901
26	9.6238	1.5921
28	9.1136	1.8057
30	8.6622	2.0309
35	7.7317	2.6431
40	7.0065	3.3234
45	6.4252	4.0696
50	5.9480	4.8791
55	5.5483	5.7502
60	5.2081	6.6809
65	4.9148	7.6697
70	4.6592	8.7151
75	4.4343	9.8156
80	4.2348	1.0970×10
85	4.0566	1.2177
90	3.8963	1.3435
95	3.7514	1.4743
100	3.6198	1.6100
110	3.3894	1.8957
120	3.1944	2.1998
130	3.0271	2.5216
140	2.8820	2.8603
150	2.7549	3.2153
160	2.6427	3.5861
170	2.5428	3.9719
180	2.4534	4.3724
190	2.3729	4.7870
200	2.3001	5.2151
225	2.1450	6.3419
250	2.0197	7.5440
275	1.9166	8.8155
300	1.8304	1.0151×10^{2}
325	1.7572	1.1546
350	1.6945	1.2995
375	1.6402	1.4495

* W. Aron, UCRL-1325.

TABLE 8c-3. RATE OF ENERGY LOSS AND RANGE OF PROTONS IN LEAD, $I = 810.79$ EV (*Continued*)

E, Mev	$-\frac{dE}{dx}$, Mev g^{-1} cm^2	R, g cm^{-2}
400	1.5928	1.6042
425	1.5511	1.7633
450	1.5143	1.9265
475	1.4815	2.0934
500	1.4522	2.2639
550	1.4022	2.6145
600	1.3613	2.9766
650	1.3274	3.3487
700	1.2992	3.7295
750	1.2753	4.1180
800	1.2551	4.5133
850	1.2379	4.9145
900	1.2231	5.3209
950	1.2104	5.7319
1,000	1.1994	6.1469
1,100	1.1818	6.9871
1,200	1.1686	7.8383
1,300	1.1588	8.6978
1,400	1.1516	9.5635
1,500	1.1464	1.0434 $\times 10^3$
1,600	1.1428	1.1308
1,700	1.1405	1.2184
1,800	1.1392	1.3061
1,900	1.1387	1.3939
2,000	1.1390	1.4817
2,250	1.1417	1.7010
2,500	1.1467	1.9195
2,750	1.1531	2.1369
3,000	1.1604	2.3531
3,250	1.1681	2.5678
3,500	1.1762	2.7811
3,750	1.1844	2.9929
4,000	1.1927	3.2033
4,250	1.2009	3.4122
4,500	1.2091	3.6196
4,750	1.2171	3.8257
5,000	1.2251	4.0305
5,500	1.2405	4.4360
6,000	1.2553	4.8367
6,500	1.2694	5.2328
7,000	1.2830	5.6245
7,500	1.2959	6.0123
8,000	1.3083	6.3963
8,500	1.3202	6.7767
9,000	1.3315	7.1538
9,500	1.3425	7.5278
10,000	1.3529	7.8988

TABLE 8c-4. RATE OF ENERGY LOSS OF PROTONS IN BERYLLIUM, MICA, ALUMINUM, COPPER, AND GOLD FOR PROTON ENERGIES FROM 25 TO 2,000 KEV*

Proton energy, kev	dE/dx, kev $\times$ cm²/mg				
	Be	Mica (muscovite)	Al	Cu	Au
25	546				
50	617	. . .	422	185	61
75	640	. . .	439	212	77
100	615	. . .	416	221	87
150	521	. . .	366	225	90
200	468	. . .	334	222	91
250	433	. . .	314	212	90
300	405	. . .	293	202	86
350	381	312	279	190	84
400	360	286	268	183	81
450	342	266	258	175	79
500	325	250	250	169	76
550	311	236	241	162	74
600	298	224	233	156	72
650	284	214	224	151	70
700	272	204	217	146	68
750	266	196	210	141	66
800	251	189	202	138	64
850	241	182	196	133	62
900	232	176	190	129	60
950	223	171	183	127	58
1,000	215	165	177	124	56
1,050	206	160	171	120	54
1,100	198	154	165	117	52
1,150	192	150	159	113	51
1,200	188	146	154	110	49
1,250	182	143	148	108	48
1,300	178	139	143	105	47
1,350	175	136	139	102	46
1,400	171	133	135	100	45
1,500	164	127	127	96	44
1,600	158	122	123	91	42
1,700	152	117	120	88	42
1,800	148	112	117	83	42
1,900	144	108	115	79	42
2,000	139	102	112	75	42

* Allison and Warshaw, *Revs. Modern Phys.* **25**, 779 (1953).

8c-3. Straggling of Heavy Particles. $(\Delta R)_E{}^2$ denotes the mean-square fluctuation in the range of particles of energy E, i.e.,

$$(\Delta R)_E{}^2 = [(R^2)_{av} - (R_{av})^2]_E$$

The probability of finding a particle with range between R and $R + dR$ is

$$p(R)\,dR = \frac{1}{\alpha\sqrt{\pi}} \exp\left[-\frac{(R - R_{av})^2}{\alpha^2}\right] dR$$

where $\alpha^2 = 2(\Delta R)_E{}^2$. More accurate theory shows deviations from the Gaussian distribution function given here. $(\Delta R)_E{}^2$ may be calculated from

$$(\Delta R)_E{}^2 = 4\pi z^2 e^4 NZ \int_0^E \left(\frac{dE'}{dR'}\right)^{-3} \frac{1 - \beta^2/2}{1 - \beta^2}\,dE'$$

Here ze denotes the charge of the incident particle; N and Z the number of atoms per cm^3 and their atomic number, respectively, of the stopping material; and β is the ratio of the velocity of the incident particle to the velocity of light.

In Figs. 8c-7 and 8c-8 the per cent range straggling, $100(2\sigma/R)$, where $\sigma = (\Delta R)_E{}^2$, is plotted as a function of particle energy for protons, deuterons, and alpha particles in copper. The straggling of protons in other elements relative to that in copper is estimated in Table 8c-5.

TABLE 8c-5. PROTON STRAGGLING IN BE, AL, AG, AND PB RELATIVE TO COPPER

Element	*Ratio of* $(2\sigma/R)$ *Relative to That in Cu*
Be	0.90
Al	0.95
Ag	1.02
Pb	1.06

8c-4. Range of Fission Fragments. The ratio of the range of a fission fragment to the range of an alpha particle of the same initial velocity v is approximately

$$\frac{R_F}{R_\alpha} = 7\left(\frac{A_1}{Z_1^{\frac{2}{3}}}\right)\left(\frac{e^2}{\hbar v}\right)^2$$

where A_1 and Z_1 are the mass number and atomic number, respectively, of the fission fragment.

8c-5. Coulomb Scattering. The differential cross section for Coulomb scattering of a charged particle by a nucleus into the solid angle $2\pi \sin\theta\,d\theta$ is

$$\begin{aligned} d\Phi(\theta) &= \frac{2\pi e^4 z^2 Z^2}{16E^2 \sin^4(\theta/2)} \sin\theta\,d\theta \\ &= \frac{0.8139 z^2 Z^2}{E_{\text{Mev}}{}^2} \frac{\sin\theta\,d\theta}{\sin^4\theta/2} 10^{-26}\ \text{cm}^2 \end{aligned}$$

where θ is the angle of scattering from the incident direction, and ze and Ze are the charges of the incident particle and the scattering nucleus, respectively. The above formula assumes that the mass of the incident particle is small compared with the mass of the nucleus.

8c-6. Energy Loss per Ion Pair. The energy loss of a charged particle per ion pair formed in the material traversed is nearly independent of the energy and type of particle.

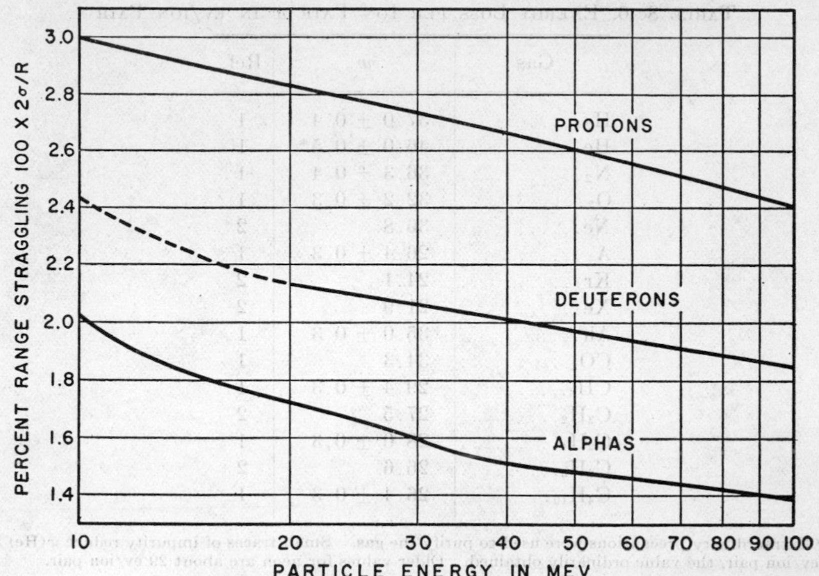

FIG. 8c-7. Range straggling of protons, deuterons, and alpha particles in copper. Particle energies from 10 to 100 Mev. (*Millburn and Schecter, UCRL-2234 rev.*)

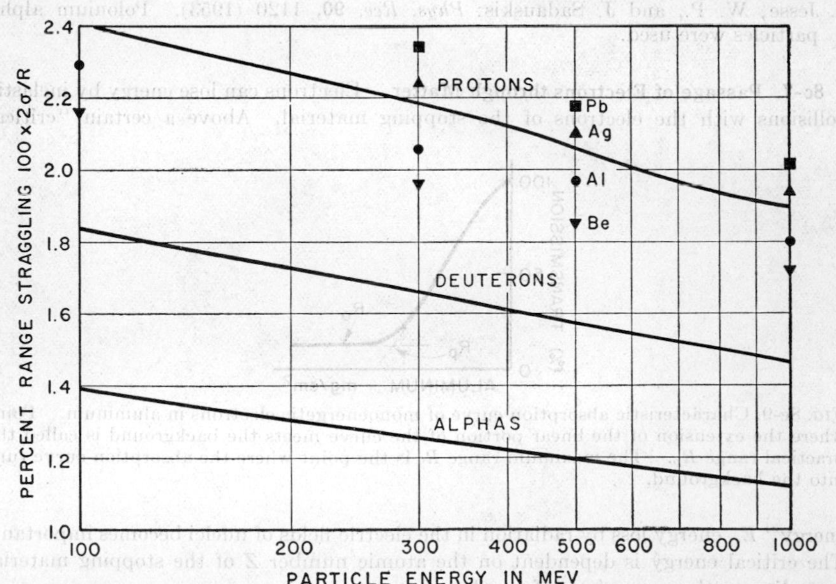

FIG. 8c-8. Range straggling of protons, deuterons, and alpha particles in copper. Particle energies from 100 to 1,000 Mev. (*Millburn and Schecter, UCRL-2234 rev.*)

TABLE 8c-6. ENERGY LOSS PER ION PAIR w IN EV/ION PAIR

Gas	w	Ref.
H_2	37.0 ± 0.4	1
He	46.0 ± 0.5*	1
N_2	36.3 ± 0.4	1
O_2	32.2 ± 0.3	1
Ne	36.8	2
A	26.4 ± 0.3	1
Kr	24.1	2
Xe	21.9	2
Air	35.0 ± 0.3	1
CO_2	34.3	1
CH_4	29.4 ± 0.3	1
C_2H_2	27.5	2
C_2H_4	28.0 ± 0.3	1
C_2H_6	26.6	2
C_4H_{10}	26.4 ± 0.3	1

* Extraordinary precautions were used to purify the gas. Small traces of impurity reduce w(He) to 30 ev/ion pair, the value ordinarily obtained. Older values for neon are about 29 ev/ion pair.

References

1. Bortner, T. E., and G. S. Hurst: *Phys. Rev.* **93,** 1236 (1954). Pu^{239} alpha particles were used. This reference also gives some results with mixtures of gases.
2. Jesse, W. P., and J. Sadauskis: *Phys. Rev.* **90,** 1120 (1953). Polonium alpha particles were used.

8c-7. Passage of Electrons through Matter. Electrons can lose energy by inelastic collisions with the electrons of the stopping material. Above a certain "critical

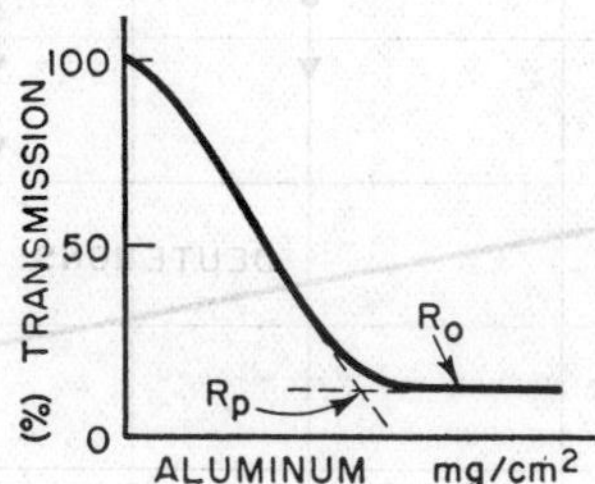

FIG. 8c-9. Characteristic absorption curve of monoenergetic electrons in aluminum. Point where the extension of the linear portion of the curve meets the background is called the practical range R_p. The maximum range R_0 is the point where the absorption curve runs into the background.

energy" E_c, energy loss by radiation in the electric fields of nuclei becomes important. The critical energy is dependent on the atomic number Z of the stopping material according to the approximate formula

$$E_c \cong \frac{800 \text{ Mev}}{Z}$$

More accurate values of E_c are given in Table 8c-7.

TABLE 8c-7. CRITICAL ENERGY E_c AND RADIATION LENGTH X_0 FOR VARIOUS SUBSTANCES*

Substance	E_c, Mev	X_0, g/cm²
Hydrogen	340	58
Helium	220	85
Carbon	103	42.5
Nitrogen	87	38
Oxygen	77	34.2
Aluminum	47	23.9
Argon	34.5	19.4
Iron	24	13.8
Copper	21.5	12.8
Lead	6.9	5.8
Air	83	36.5
Water	93	35.9

* The data in this table have been taken from E. Segrè, ed., "Experimental Nuclear Physics," p. 266, John Wiley & Sons, Inc., New York, 1953.

An important length is associated with the traversal of matter by electrons above E_c; this is the distance in which an electron's energy is reduced to $1/e$ of its original value and is called the "radiation length" X_0. Values of this quantity are also given in Table 8c-7.

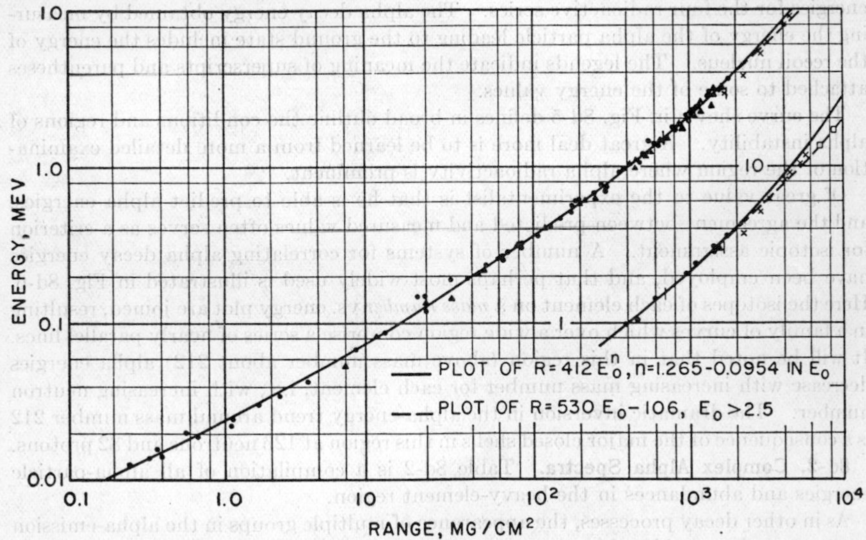

FIG. 8c-10. Range-energy curve for monoenergetic electrons in aluminum. Practical range is used. [*L. Katz and A. S. Penfold, Revs. Modern Phys.* **24**, 28 (1952).]

The range-energy relation for electrons is not strongly dependent on the atomic number of the stopping material. Only that for aluminum is given. Monoenergetic electrons are absorbed as indicated in Fig. 8c-9, which serves to define the "practical range" R_p and the "maximum range" R_0. The practical range, in aluminum, is given by

$$R_p = 412E_0{}^n \text{ mg/cm}^2 \qquad n = 1.265 - 0.0954 \ln E_0$$

for $0.01 \leq E_0 \leq 2.5$ Mev, and by

$$R_p = 530E_0 - 106 \text{ mg/cm}^2$$

for 2.5 Mev $\leq E_0 \leq 20$ Mev. A graph of these relations is given in Fig. 8c-10.

The formulas given above for monoenergetic electrons may be used for continuous beta-ray spectra where R_p and E_0 refer to the maximum beta-ray range and energy, respectively.[1]

8d. Decay-energy Systematics of the Heavy Elements[2]

I. PERLMAN AND FRANK ASARO

University of California

8d-1. Summary of Decay Energies. Figures 8d-1 to 8d-4 summarize total decay energies for the four radioactive series. The alpha decay energy obtained by measuring the energy of the alpha particle leading to the ground state includes the energy of the recoil nucleus. The legends indicate the meaning of superscripts and parentheses attached to some of the energy values.

The curve shown in Fig. 8d-5 defines in broad outline the conditions and regions of alpha instability. A great deal more is to be learned from a more detailed examination of the region where alpha radioactivity is prominent.

Of great value to the experimentalist is that he is able to predict alpha energies, and the agreement between predicted and measured values often serves as a criterion for isotopic assignment. A number of systems for correlating alpha decay energies have been employed, and that perhaps most widely used is illustrated in Fig. 8d-6. Here the isotopes of each element on a *mass number* vs. energy plot are joined, resulting in a family of curves which over a wide region comprise a series of nearly parallel lines. It will be noted that in this region (above mass number about 212) alpha energies decrease with increasing mass number for each element, i.e., with increasing neutron number. The dramatic inversion in the alpha-energy trend around mass number 212 is a consequence of the major closed shells in this region at 126 neutrons and 82 protons.

8d-2. Complex Alpha Spectra. Table 8d-2 is a compilation of all alpha-particle energies and abundances in the heavy-element region.

As in other decay processes, the appearance of multiple groups in the alpha-emission process may be considered as the result of competition in populating available energy levels. Alpha-decay lifetimes are influenced by a number of factors; among these is

[1] For a discussion of the methods of determining the range from an absorption curve, see L. Katz and A. S. Penfold, *Revs. Modern Phys.* **24**, 28 (1952).

[2] The data used in this compilation were originally drawn from many primary sources. Figures 8d-1 to 8d-4 are from R. A. Glass, S. G. Thompson, and G. T. Seaborg, Nuclear Thermodynamics of the Heaviest Elements, *J. Inorganic and Nuclear Chem.* **1**, 3 (1955). Figures 8d-5 to 8d-11 and Table 8d-2 are from Perlman and Asaro, Alpha Radioactivity, *Ann. Rev. Nuclear Sci.* **IV** (1954).

TABLE 8d-1. CLASSICAL AND MODERN DESIGNATIONS OF THE HEAVY RADIONUCLIDES*

Name	Classical designation	Modern designation
Uranium I	U I	U^{238}
Uranium X_1	U X_1	Th^{234}
Uranium Z, uranium X_2	U Z, U X_2	Pa^{234}
Uranium II	U II	U^{234}
Ionium	Io	Th^{230}
Radium	Ra	Ra^{226}
Radon	Rn	Em^{222}
Radium A	Ra A	Po^{218}
Radium B	Ra B	Pb^{214}
Radium C	Ra C	Bi^{214}
Radium C'	Ra C'	Po^{214}
Radium C''	Ra C''	Tl^{210}
Radium D (radiolead)	Ra D	Pb^{210}
Radium E	Ra E	Bi^{210}
Radium F (polonium)	Ra F	Po^{210}
Radium G	Ra G	Pb^{210}
Thorium	Th	Th^{232}
Mesothorium$_1$	MsTh$_1$	Ra^{228}
Mesothorium$_2$	MsTh$_2$	Ac^{228}
Radiothorium	RdTh	Th^{228}
Thorium X	Th X	Ra^{224}
Thoron	Tn	Em^{220}
Thorium A	Th A	Po^{216}
Thorium B	Th B	Pb^{212}
Thorium C	Th C	Bi^{212}
Thorium C'	Th C'	Po^{212}
Thorium C''	Th C''	Tl^{208}
Thorium D	Th D	Pb^{208}
Actinouranium	Ac U	U^{235}
Uranium Y	U Y	Th^{231}
Protoactinium	Pa	Pa^{231}
Actinium	Ac	Ac^{227}
Radioactinium	RdAc	Th^{227}
Actinium K	Ac K	Fa^{223}
Actinium X	Ac X	Ra^{223}
Actinon	An	Em^{219}
Actinium A	Ac A	Po^{215}
Actinium B	Ac B	Pb^{211}
Actinium C	Ac C	Bi^{211}
Actinium C'	Ac C'	Po^{211}
Actinium C''	Ac C''	Tl^{207}
Actinium D	Ac D	Pb^{207}

* By F. N. D. Kurie.

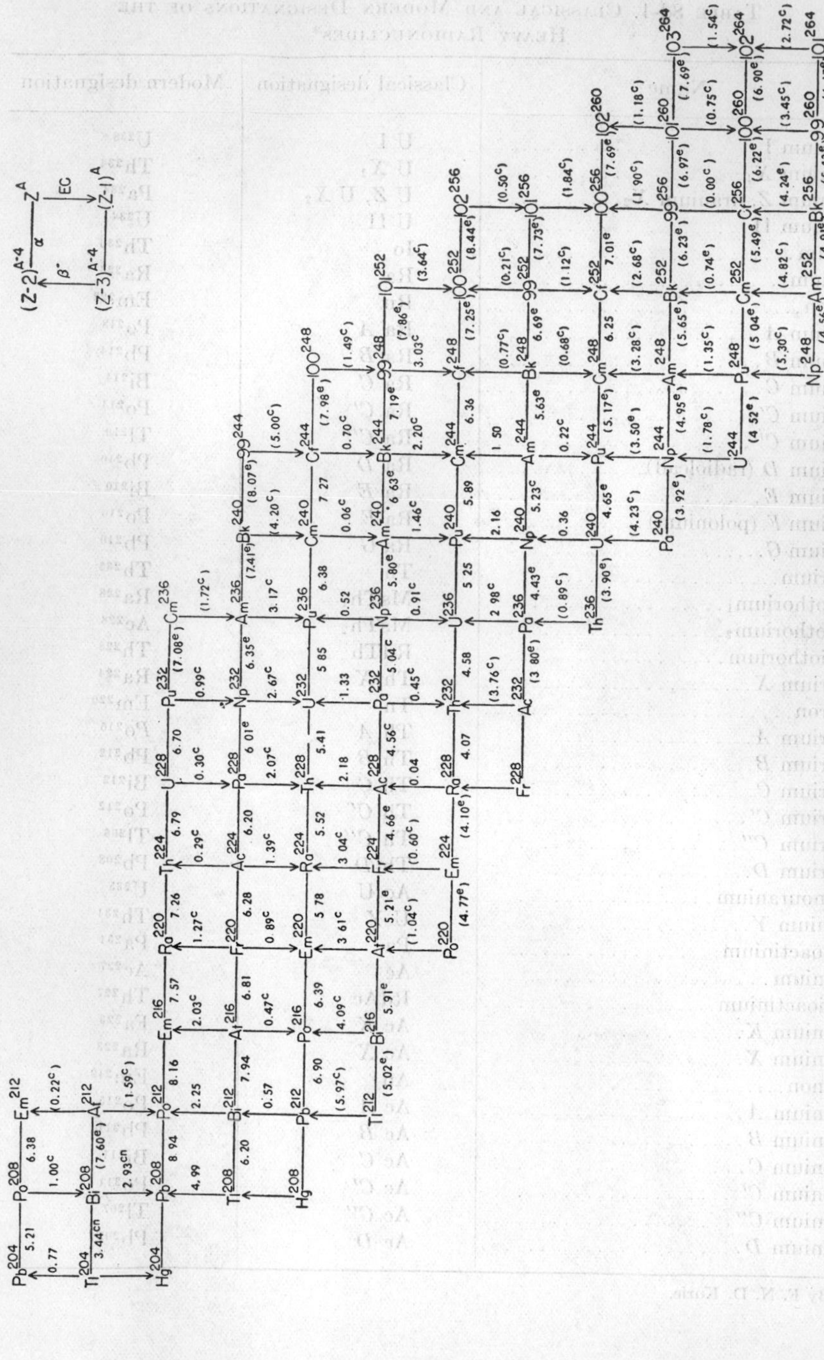

FIG. 8d-1. Closed decay-energy cycles for the 4*n* series; *c*, calculated; *e*, estimated; ( ) uncertain.

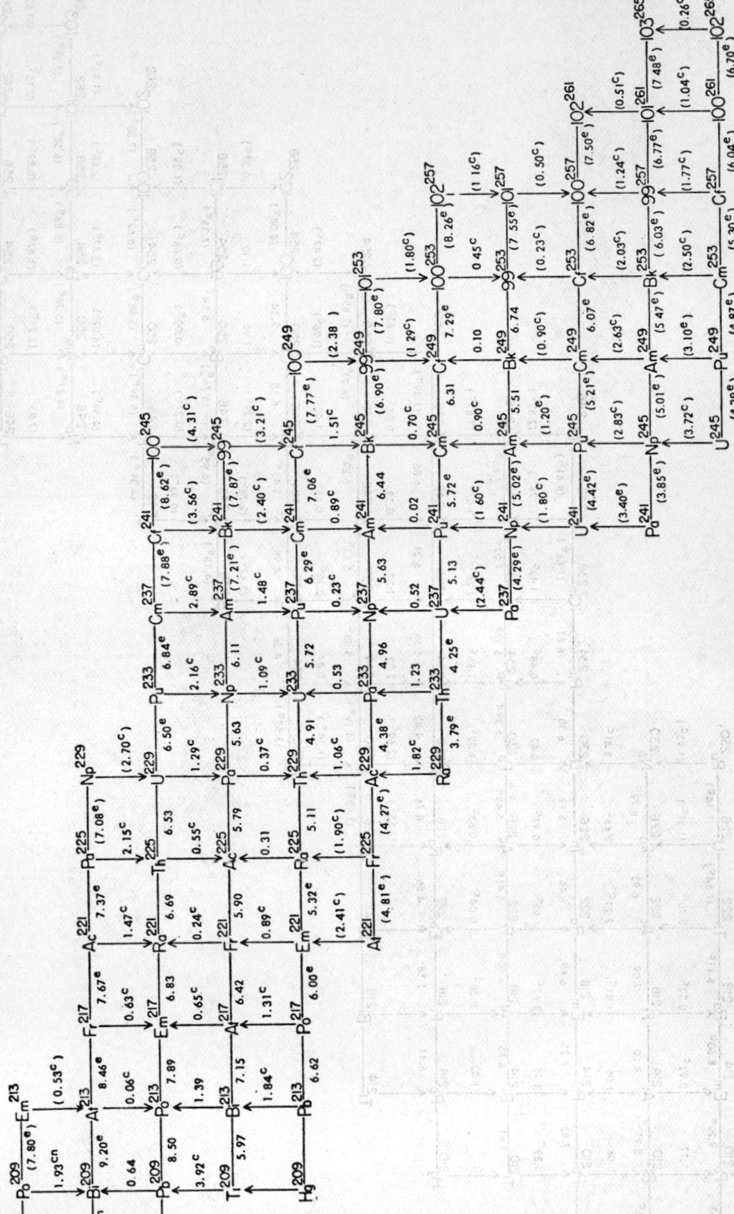

FIG. 8d-2. Closed decay-energy cycles for the 4*n* + 1 series: *c*, calculated; *e*, estimated; ( ), uncertain.

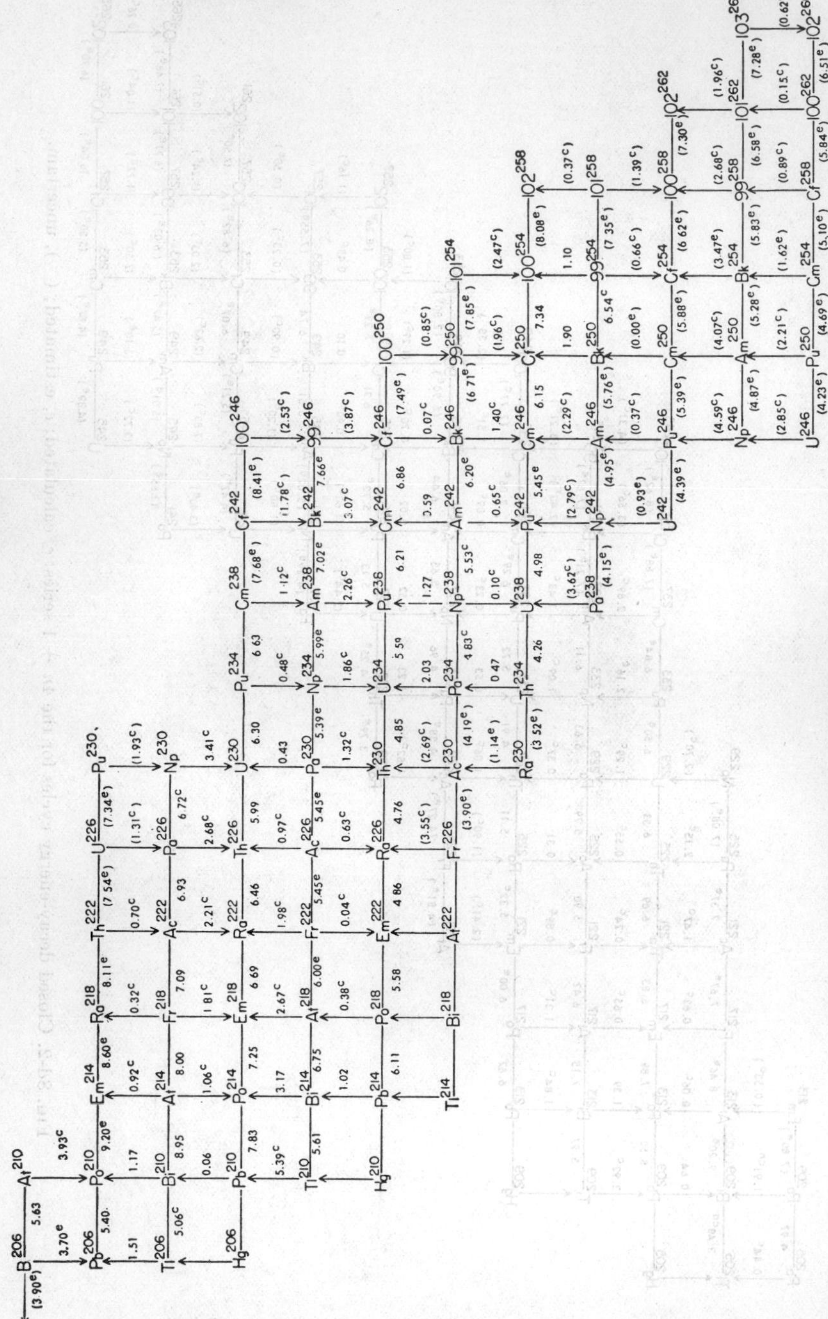

FIG. 8d-3. Closed decay-energy cycles for the $4n + 2$ series: *c*, calculated; *e*, estimated; ( ), uncertain.

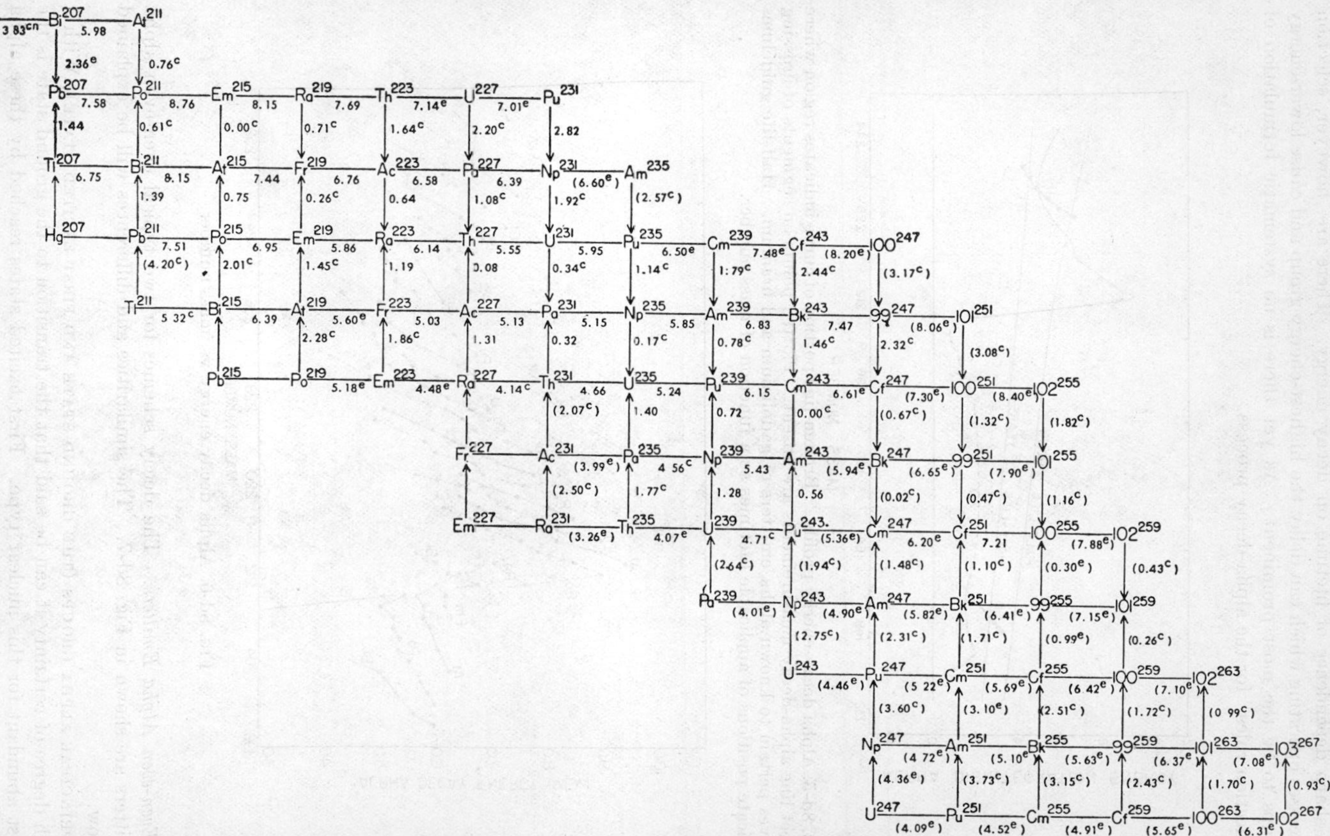

FIG. 8d-4. Closed decay-energy cycles for the $4n + 3$ series: *c*, calculated; *e*, estimated; ( ), uncertain.

the sharp dependence of lifetime on decay energy. There are, however, selection processes operating which can delay the highest-energy group and cause lower-energy groups to be the most prominent. As yet there is no systematic formulation of "selection rules" for the alpha-decay process.

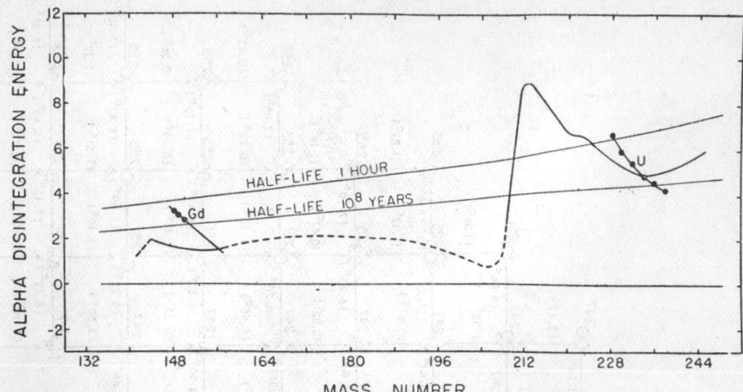

FIG. 8d-5. Alpha decay-energy profile. Broken-line portion of curve indicates region where direct line alpha-decay measurements are absent. Plotted points on segments of crossing curves pertain to known alpha emitters of gadolinium and uranium. Half-life guidelines indicate positions of applicable lifetimes as a function of mass number.

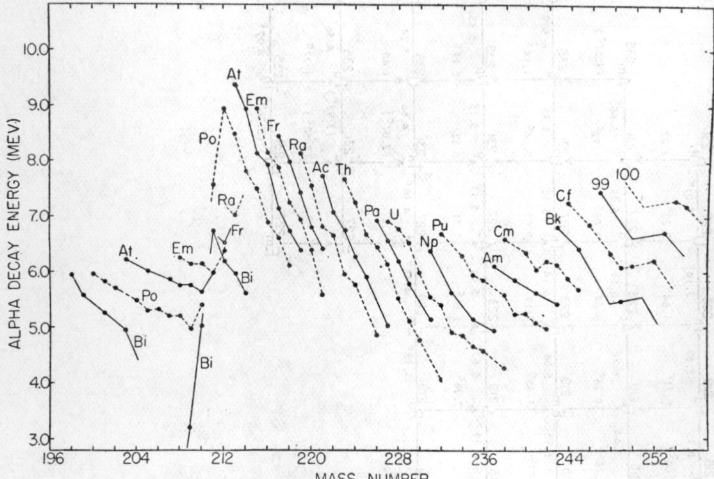

FIG. 8d-6. Alpha decay energy vs. mass number.

Even-even Alpha Emitters. The decay schemes for two typical even-even alpha emitters are shown in Fig. 8d-7. The similarities and differences will be explained below.

PRINCIPAL ALPHA GROUPS (THE GROUND STATE AND FIRST EXCITED STATE): With a high degree of certainty it can be said that the transition to the ground state is the most abundant for this nuclear type. First excited states reached by these alpha groups all have spin 2 and even parity (see Fig. 8d-7) and we shall call each the *first even-spin state* or simply the *first even state.* The alpha population to this state is close to theoretical expectations.

A summary of the energy spacings between the ground state and *first even state* as a function of neutron number and proton number is shown in Fig. 8d-8. The points divide into families according to atomic number and appear to reach maxima for nuclei with 126 neutrons.

RARE ALPHA GROUPS (HIGHER EVEN STATES AND FIRST ODD STATE): Many of the alpha emitters which have lent themselves to detailed analysis have proved to have one or more additional groups of lower energy and in low intensity.

In each case which could be examined in the necessary detail, there was found a rare alpha group going to a state which decays by an E2 transition only to the 2+ state. These states are those designated as 4+ in Fig. 8d-7 and will be known as the *second even states*. From the nature of the gamma-ray transition, the second state could be 0+, 2+, or 4+; the 4+ assignment is made largely from agreement with energy-level spacings predicted by the Bohr-Mottelson theory of rotational states.

In a few cases, very rare gamma rays have been seen (the alpha groups would be below the limits for detection) and are assigned to transitions between the third and

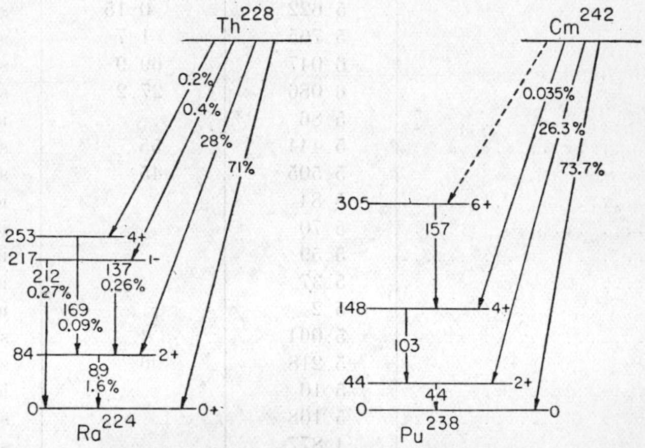

FIG. 8d-7. Decay schemes of Th^{228} and Cm^{242}.

second even states. In the case of Pu^{238} decay, the gamma ray was shown to be in coincidence with that between the 4+ and 2+ states. Since the energy of the state defined by the gamma ray corresponds closely with expectations if it were the *third even state* (6+) of the Bohr-Mottelson rotational band, it has been so designated (see Cm^{242} spectrum, Fig. 8d-7).

In a number of cases, a state believed to be 1− has entered among the low-lying even states. The spectrum for Th^{228} which is typical of this type is shown in Fig. 8d-7. In contrast to the second even state, this state always decays both to the first even state and to the ground state. The conversion coefficients of both conform with E1 transitions as do α-γ angular correlations made on Th^{226}, Th^{228}, Th^{230}, and U^{230}. The 1− state has probably been identified in the decay of Ra^{222}, Ra^{224}, Ra^{226}, U^{232}, and Cm^{242} as well as for the four cases just mentioned. From the fragmentary evidence at hand it seems possible that the state has a minimum energy at 136 neutrons and rises at both lower and higher neutron numbers.

With respect to the degree of population of the 1− state in the alpha-decay process, the data are too few to arrive at any generalizations. In the cases studied, the process seems to be competitive with that leading to the 4+ state for comparable energies.

Odd-nucleon Alpha Emitters. The alpha spectra of nuclei having odd nucleons are in general considerably more complex than those of even-even nuclei and conse-

TABLE 8d-2. ALPHA-PARTICLE ENERGIES AND ABUNDANCES

Alpha emitter	Alpha-particle energy, Mev	Relative abundances, %	Type of measurement
$Bi^{<198}$ (1.7 min)	6.2		ion ch
Bi^{198}	5.83		ion ch
Bi^{199}	5.47		ion ch
Bi^{201}	5.15		ion ch
Bi^{203}	4.85	....	range
Bi^{209}	~3.15		range
Bi^{210} (~10^6 year)	4.93		ion ch
Bi^{211}	6.272	16	spect
	6.618	84	spect
Bi^{212}	5.481	0.016	spect
	5.603	1.1	spect
	5.622	0.15	spect
	5.765	1.7	spect
	6.047	69.9	spect
	6.086	27.2	spect
Bi^{213}	5.86	....	ion ch
Bi^{214}	5.444	55	spect
	5.505	45	spect
Po^{200}	5.84	....	ion ch
Po^{201}	5.70	....	ion ch
Po^{202}	5.59	....	ion ch
Po^{204}	5.37	....	ion ch
Po^{205}	5.2	....	ion ch
Po^{206}	5.064	4	spect
	5.218	96	spect
Po^{207}	5.10	....	ion ch
Po^{208}	5.108	....	spect
Po^{209}	4.877		spect
Po^{210}	4.5	Weak	α-γ coinc
	5.299	100	spect
Po^{211} (0.52 sec)	6.56	0.53	spect
	6.88	0.50	spect
	7.434	99	range
Po^{211} ?(25 sec)	7.14	....	ion ch
Po^{212}	8.776		spect
Po^{213}	8.336		ion ch
Po^{214}	7.680		spect
Po^{215}	7.365		range
Po^{216}	6.774		spect
Po^{217}	6.5		ion ch
Po^{218}	5.998		spect
$At^{<202}$	6.50		ion ch
$At^{<203}$	6.35		ion ch
At^{203}	6.10		ion ch
At^{205}	5.90		ion ch
At^{207}	5.75		ion ch
At^{203} (1.7 hr)	5.65		ion ch

TABLE 8d-2. ALPHA-PARTICLE ENERGIES AND ABUNDANCES (*Continued*)

Alpha emitter	Alpha-particle energy, Mev	Relative abundances, %	Type of measurement
At^{209}	5.65	....	ion ch
At^{210}	5.355	37	spect
	5.437	31	spect
	5.519	32	spect
At^{211}	5.862	....	spect
At^{213}	9.2	....	range
At^{214}	8.78	....	ion ch
At^{215}	8.00	....	ion ch
At^{216}	7.79	....	ion ch
At^{217}	7.02	....	ion ch
At^{218}	6.63	....	range
At^{219}	6.27	....	ion ch
Em^{208}	6.138	....	spect
Em^{209}	6.02	....	ion ch
Em^{210}	6.036	....	spect
Em^{211}	5.605	~1.5	spect
	5.778	67	spect
	5.847	33	spect
Em^{212}	6.262	....	spect
Em^{215}	8.6	....	ion ch
Em^{216}	8.01	....	ion ch
Em^{217}	7.74	....	ion ch
Em^{218}	6.53	Weak	α-γ coinc
	7.127	100	spect
Em^{219}	6.214	4	spect
	6.434	12	spect
	6.559	15	spect
	6.824	69	spect
Em^{220}	5.747	~0.3	spect
	6.282	100	spect
Em^{222}	5.486	....	spect
Fr^{212}	6.339	24	spect
	6.387	39	spect
	6.409	37	spect
Fr^{217}	8.3	....	range
Fr^{218}	7.85	....	ion ch
Fr^{219}	7.30	....	ion ch
Fr^{220}	6.69	....	ion ch
Fr^{221}	6.05	~25	ion ch
	6.30	~75	ion ch
Ra^{213}	6.90	....	ion ch
Ra^{219}	8.0	....	ion ch
Ra^{220}	7.43	....	ion ch
Ra^{221}	6.71	....	ion ch
Ra^{222}	6.23	Weak	α-γ coinc
	6.554	100	spect

TABLE 8d-2. ALPHA-PARTICLE ENERGIES AND ABUNDANCES (*Continued*)

Alpha emitter	Alpha-particle energy, Mev	Relative abundances, %	Type of measurement
Ra^{223}	5.419	3	spect
	5.487	2	spect
	5.528	9	spect
	5.596	24	spect
	5.704	53	spect
	5.730	9	spect
	5.860	Weak	spect
Ra^{224}	5.445	5.2	spect
	5.681	95	spect
Ra^{226}	4.592	5.7	spect
	4.777	94	spect
Ac^{221}	7.6	....	range
Ac^{222}	6.96	....	ion ch
Ac^{223}	6.64	....	ion ch
Ac^{224}	6.17	....	ion ch
Ac^{225}	5.80	....	ion ch
Ac^{227}	4.942	....	spect
Th^{223}	7.55	....	ion ch
Th^{224}	7.13	....	ion ch
Th^{225}	6.57	....	ion ch
Th^{226}	6.037	0.6	spect
	6.100	1.8	spect
	6.228	21	spect
	6.336	77	spect
Th^{227}	5.651	~2	spect
	5.704	15	spect
	5.728	~1	spect
	5.749	17	spect
	5.796	2	spect
	5.860	4	spect
	5.922	~2	spect
	5.952	13	spect
	5.972	21	spect
	6.001	5	spect
	6.030	19	spect
Th^{228}	5.173	0.2	spect
	5.208	0.4	spect
	5.338	28	spect
	5.421	71	spect
Th^{229}	4.85	~70	ion ch
	4.94	~20	ion ch
	5.02	~10	ion ch
Th^{230}	4.437	0.07	spect
	4.471	0.2	spect
	4.613	23.4	spect
	4.682	76.3	spect

TABLE 8d-2. ALPHA-PARTICLE ENERGIES AND ABUNDANCES (*Continued*)

Alpha emitter	Alpha-particle energy, Mev	Relative abundances, %	Type of measurement
Th^{232}	(3.93)	24	γ energy
	3.994	76	ion ch
Pa^{226}	6.81	....	ion ch
Pa^{227}	6.46	....	ion ch
Pa^{228}	5.85	25	ion ch
	6.09	75	ion ch
Pa^{229}	5.69	....	ion ch
Pa^{231}	4.660	1–3	spect
	4.720	11	spect
	4.838	3	spect
	4.938	25	spect
	4.998	23	spect
	5.015	23	spect
	5.042	11	spect
U^{227}	6.8	....	ion ch
U^{228}	6.67	....	ion ch
U^{229}	6.42	....	ion ch
U^{230}	5.662	0.8	spect
	5.819	31	spect
	5.888	68	spect
U^{231}	5.45	....	ion ch
U^{232}	5.132	0.3	spect
	5.261	32	spect
	5.318	68	spect
U^{233}	4.731	2	spect
	4.780	15	spect
	4.823	83	ion ch
U^{234}	4.59	~0.3	α-γ coinc
	4.714	26	spect
	4.763	74	ion ch
U^{235}	4.20	4	ion ch
	4.40	83	ion ch
	4.47?	~3	ion ch
	4.58	10	ion ch
U^{236}	(4.45)	27	γ energy
	4.499	73	ion ch
U^{238}	(4.135)	23	γ energy
	4.182	77	ion ch
Np^{231}	6.28	....	ion ch
Np^{233}	5.53	....	ion ch
Np^{235}	5.06	....	ion ch
Np^{237}	4.77	....	ion ch
Pu^{232}	6.58	....	ion ch
Pu^{234}	(6.14)	14	γ energy
	6.19	86	ion ch
Pu^{235}	5.85	....	ion ch

TABLE 8d-2. ALPHA-PARTICLE ENERGIES AND ABUNDANCES (*Continued*)

Alpha emitter	Alpha-particle energy, Mev	Relative abundances, %	Type of measurement
Pu^{236}	(5.71)	20	γ energy
	5.75	80	ion ch
Pu^{238}	5.352	0.1	spect
	5.452	28	spect
	5.495	72	spect
Pu^{239}	5.099	11	spect
	5.137	20	spect
	5.150	69	spect
Pu^{240}	5.014	0.1	spect
	5.118	24	spect
	5.162	76	spect
Pu^{241}	4.848	25	spect
	4.893	75	spect
Pu^{242}	4.854	20	spect
	4.898	80	spect
Am^{237}	6.01	....	ion ch
Am^{239}	5.75	....	ion ch
Am^{241}	5.379	1.4	spect
	5.433	13.6	spect
	5.476	84	spect
	5.503	0.2	spect
	5.535	0.3	spect
Am^{243}	5.171	~3	spect
	5.225	13	spect
	5.267	84	spect
Cm^{238}	6.50	....	ion ch
Cm^{240}	6.25	....	ion ch
Cm^{241}	5.95	....	ion ch
Cm^{242}	5.697	0.035	spect
	6.066	26.3	spect
	6.110	73.7	spect
Cm^{243}	5.634	3	spect
	5.732	13	spect
	5.777	78	spect
	5.985	6	spect
Cm^{244}	5.755	25	spect
	5.798	75	spect
Cm^{245}	5.6	....	ion ch
Bk^{243}	6.20	17	ion ch
	6.55	53	ion ch
	6.72	30	ion ch
Bk^{245}	5.90	34	ion ch
	6.15	48	ion ch
	6.33	18	ion ch
Bk^{249}	5.4	....	ion ch
Cf^{244}	7.15	....	ion ch

TABLE 8d-2. ALPHA-PARTICLE ENERGIES AND ABUNDANCES (*Continued*)

Alpha emitter	Alpha-particle energy, Mev	Relative abundances, %	Type of measurement
Cf^{246}	6.711	22	spect
	6.753	78	spect
Cf^{248}	6.26	....	ion ch
Cf^{249}	5.82	90	ion ch
	6.00	10	ion ch
Cf^{250}	6.04	....	ion ch
Cf^{252}	6.13	....	ion ch
99^{247}	7.3	....	ion ch
99^{253}	6.62	....	ion ch
100^{254}	7.20	....	ion ch
100^{255}	7.1	....	ion ch

ion ch = ion chamber.
spect = spectrometer.
α-γ coinc = α-γ coincidence.

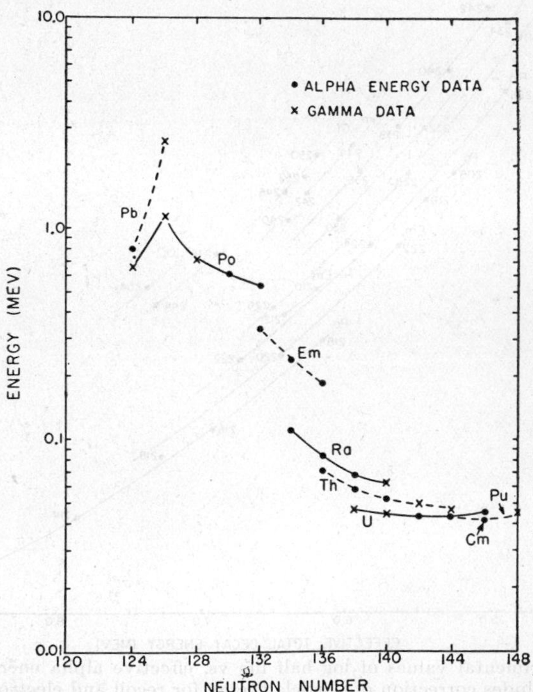

FIG. 8d-8. First excited-state energies of even-even nuclei in the heavy-element region.

quently have not been worked out with the same degree of certainty. Some typical decay schemes are shown in Fig. 8d-9. It will be noted that in each of the cases except that of U^{233} the most abundant alpha group does not lead to the ground state in sharp contrast with spectra of even-even nuclei. It is seen, however, that there is an alpha group in high abundance for each which lies at the bottom of a series of

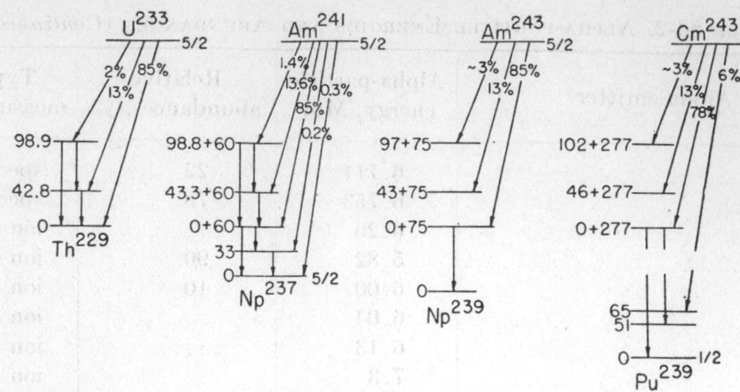

Fig. 8d-9. Decay schemes of some odd-nucleon alpha emitters.

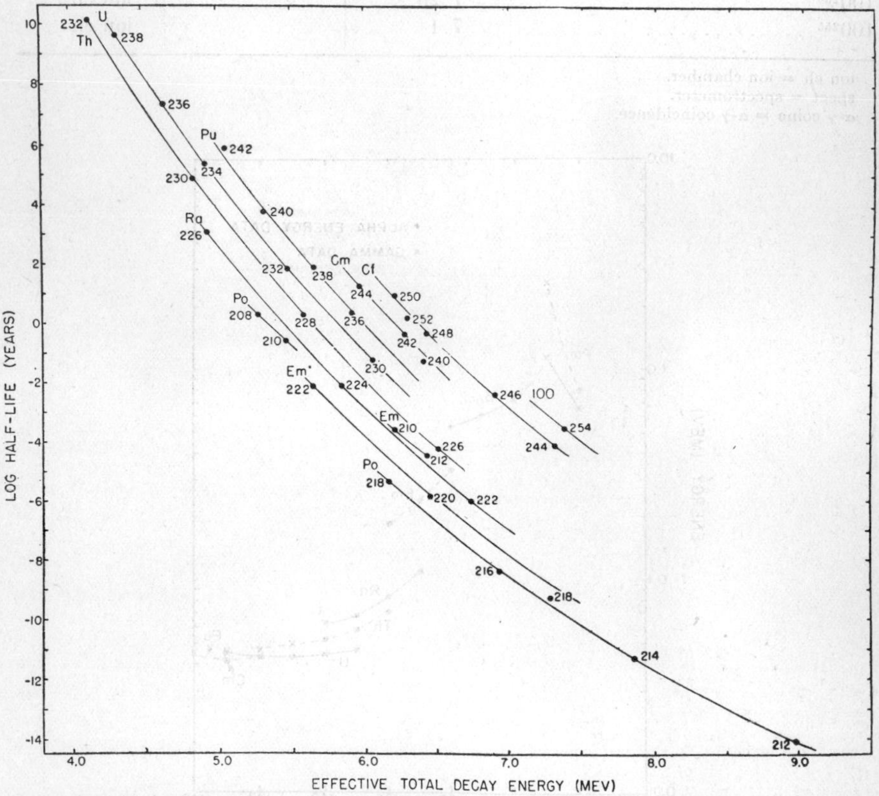

Fig. 8d-10. Experimental values of log half life vs. effective alpha energy. ("Effective alpha energy" includes correction of particle energy for recoil and electron screening.)

states which looks much like a rotational band of the even-even type. These are designated in Fig. 8d-9 by the terms "zero plus the energy above the ground states" (in Am^{241}, for example, by "zero plus 60"). Other alpha spectra (such as that for Th^{227}) are much more complex than those shown in Fig. 8d-9.

8d-3. Alpha-decay Lifetimes and Theory. It is possible to correlate alpha-decay lifetimes empirically and to arrive at systems which can be used to predict half lives.

Even-even Alpha Emitters—Ground-state Transitions. Figure 8d-10 shows a plot of the half life vs. energy relationship as a family of curves. The curves are defined by the experimental half lives and are in this respect empirical. If, however, we were to calculate half lives by using the measured alpha energy for each point and assuming a function for the nuclear radius, $1.52 \times 10^{-13} A^{\frac{1}{3}}$, the resulting curves would lie close to those of Fig. 8d-10.

In summary it can be said that the basic one-body theory of alpha decay applied to the ground-state transitions of even-even alpha emitters gives a remarkably consistent picture. When reasonable and consistent assumptions for the values of the nuclear radii are used, the theory explains observed half lives which differ by a factor

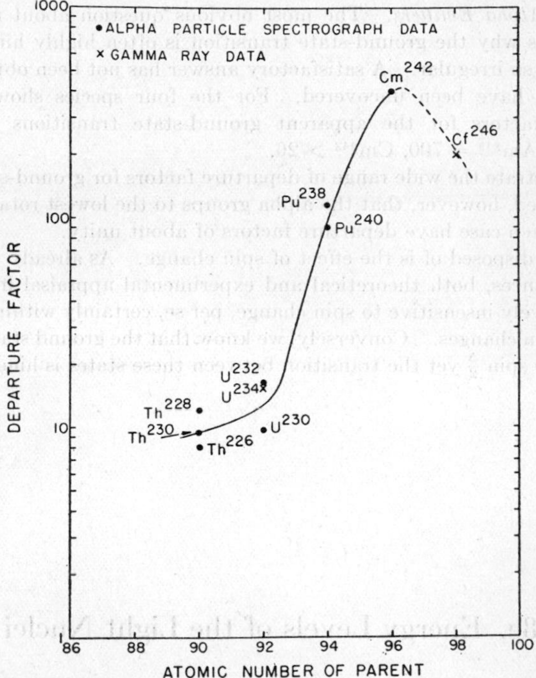

Fig. 8d-11. Departure factors for alpha groups to the second even-spin state of even-even nuclides.

of 10^{24}. It should be pointed out that different formulations of the theory will give somewhat different "best values" for the radius parameter, but each is internally consistent. It will be noted that some points (e.g., Po^{210}, Po^{208}, Em^{210}, Em^{212}) lie off their respective curves. These are the alpha emitters with 126 neutrons or fewer which have abnormally long lifetimes.

Even-even Alpha Emitters—Transitions to Excited States. For any particular case, one can calculate the partial half life to any excited state under the assumption that the only factor influencing the relative decay rates is the energy function. It is found that the populations of the 2+ states are not far from the calculated values. There are small but significant departures which do demand explanation by an extension of alpha-decay theory.

The examination of transitions to the 4+ states gives a totally different and unique picture. These 4+ states are populated much more sparsely than would be expected on the basis of alpha energy alone. The ratio of measured half life to calculated half life varies considerably and in a more or less regular way with atomic number, as shown in Fig. 8d-11. It is seen that for Cm^{242} the second even state is hindered in its population by a factor of 400, while for thorium isotopes this factor is of the order of 10. An explanation for the depressed population of these states and the trend observed has been developed in terms of the interaction of the emitted alpha-particle wave with the nuclear quadrupole moment.

Other low-lying states in even-even nuclei have been identified but detailed information is lacking. There is the third even state (6+?) which is a member of the well-defined rotational band. Also, in a limited region there appear 1− states which are populated roughly to the same extent as the 4+ states in the same region. It is not clear what type of nuclear configuration would give rise to such states.

Odd-nucleon Alpha Emitters. The most obvious question about this category of alpha emitters is why the ground-state transition is often highly hindered and why the hindrance is so irregular. A satisfactory answer has not been obtained, although promising leads have been uncovered. For the four species shown in Fig. 8d-9 the departure factors for the apparent ground-state transitions are $U^{233} = 1.4$, $Am^{241} = 1{,}000$, $Am^{243} = 700$, $Cm^{243} > 26$.

These demonstrate the wide range of departure factors for ground-state transitions. It should be noted, however, that the alpha groups to the lowest rotational state of a given band in each case have departure factors of about unity.

A point to be disposed of is the effect of spin change. As already pointed out in a number of instances, both theoretical and experimental appraisal indicate that the lifetime is relatively insensitive to spin change, per se, certainly within the framework of reasonable spin changes. Conversely, we know that the ground states of Am^{241} and Np^{237} both have spin $\frac{5}{2}$ yet the transition between these states is hindered 1,000-fold.

8e. Energy Levels of the Light Nuclei

T. LAURITSEN

California Institute of Technology

F. AJZENBERG-SELOVE

Boston University

In the following table are exhibited the excitation energies and principal properties of the known energy levels of the light nuclei from mass number 5 to 20, inclusive. The following information is tabulated in the columns indicated.

Column 1. Excitation energy E_x of the level, in Mev above the ground state. Parentheses enclosing this number indicate that the existence of the level is not clearly established.

Column 2. Total angular momentum J (in units of $h/2\pi$), parity Π, and isotopic (or "isobaric") spin T. Parentheses indicate that the quantity enclosed is uncertain. Where the experimental results serve only to limit the choice of J to one of several values, all possibilities are indicated.

Column 3. Width Γ or lifetime τ of the state, the former representing the full width, in center-of-mass coordinates, at half-maximum intensity, the latter either the half life $\tau_{\frac{1}{2}}$ or the mean life τ_m, as specified.

Column 4. Observed mode of decay, including γ radiation to a lower state of the same nucleus, or particle emission. When the level in question has been identified as an intermediate state in a nuclear reaction, it is assumed that the bombarding particle must also occur as a product, and it is so listed whether observed or not. Modes of decay whose occurrence is not clearly established are indicated in parentheses.

Supplementing the tables are diagrams in which the known levels for each isobaric set are plotted to scale. In these diagrams the level positions are indicated by horizontal lines, located at distances above the ground state proportional to the excitation energies. Where space permits, the excitation energies, in Mev, and the values of J, Π, and T (where known) are indicated. Uncertain values are again enclosed in parentheses, and levels whose existence is uncertain are represented by dashed lines. Levels which are known to be particularly broad are crosshatched. Crosshatching along the right-hand edge of the diagram indicates energy regions which have been incompletely explored. Binding energies of various particles are shown at the side of the diagrams.

The level diagrams are grouped in isobaric sets to exhibit the correspondence of levels comprising isotopic spin multiplets. The relative positions of the ground states in each set have been adjusted to the extent that the first-order electrostatic-energy differences and the intrinsic (neutron − hydrogen atom) mass differences have been removed, the former calculated from the uniform model according to the expression

$$E_e = 0.60 \frac{Z(Z-1)}{A^{\frac{1}{3}}} \qquad \text{Mev}$$

Levels for which the correspondence seems well established are connected by dashed lines.

The atomic masses used in computing binding energies and ground-state energy differences are given in the table in the form of the "mass excess" $M - A$ in Mev. The following values were assumed for the lighter particles:

$$\begin{aligned} n^1 &= 8.3638 \pm 0.0029 \text{ Mev} \\ H^1 &= 7.5815 \pm 0.0027 \text{ Mev} \\ H^2 &= 13.7203 \pm 0.006 \text{ Mev} \\ H^3 &= 15.8271 \pm 0.010 \text{ Mev} \\ He^3 &= 15.8086 \pm 0.010 \text{ Mev} \\ He^4 &= 3.6066 \pm 0.014 \text{ Mev} \end{aligned}$$

References to original work have been omitted in the present compilation; such references may be found in F. Azenberg and T. Lauritsen, Energy Levels of Light Nuclei, V, *Revs. Modern Phys.* **27**, 77 (1955). Similar information on heavier nuclides is available in P. M. Endt and J. C. Kluyver, Energy Levels of Light Nuclei ($Z = 11$ to $Z = 20$), *Revs. Modern Phys.* **26**, 95 (1954). An extensive theoretical discussion is given in D. R. Inglis, Energy Levels and Structure of Light Nuclei, *Revs. Modern Phys.* **25**, 390 (1953).

TABLE 8e-1. ENERGY LEVELS OF THE LIGHT NUCLEI

E_x	$J, \Pi; T$	Width or lifetime	Decay
		He^5: mass excess = 12.92 ± 0.08 Mev	
0	$\frac{3}{2}-; \frac{1}{2}$	$\Gamma = 680 \pm 200$ kev	*n*
(2.6)	$\frac{1}{2}-; \frac{1}{2}$	($\Gamma \sim 5$ Mev)	*n*
16.69	$\frac{3}{2}+; \frac{1}{2}$	$\Gamma \cong 100$ kev	*d, n*

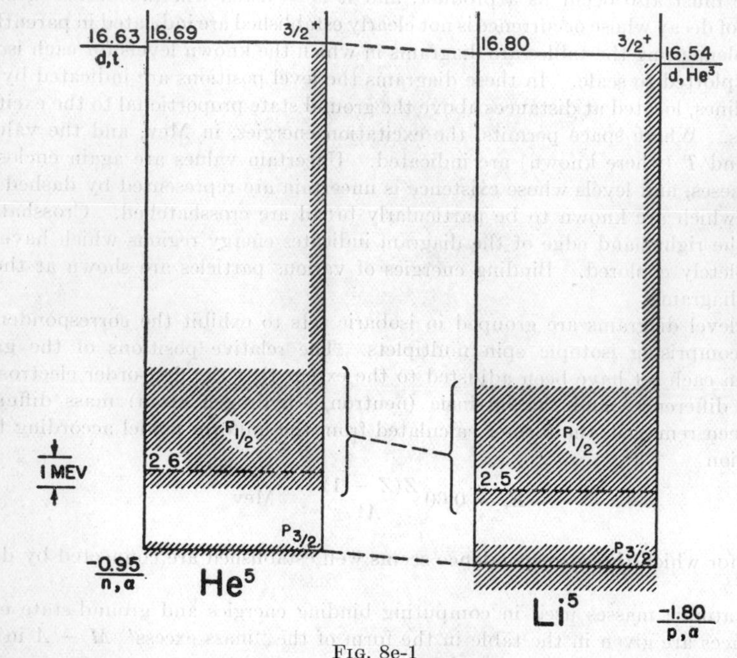

FIG. 8e-1

E_x	$J, \Pi; T$	Width or lifetime	Decay
		Li^5: mass excess = 12.99 ± 0.15 Mev	
0	$\frac{3}{2}^-; \frac{1}{2}$	$\Gamma = 1.5 \pm 0.5$ Mev	*p*
(2.5)	$\frac{1}{2}^-; \frac{1}{2}$	($\Gamma \sim 5$ Mev)	*p*
16.80	$\frac{3}{2}^+; \frac{1}{2}$	$\Gamma \cong 330$ kev	*d, p, γ*
		He^6: mass excess = 19.40 ± 0.036 Mev	
0	(0^+); 1	$\tau_{\frac{1}{2}} = 0.799 \pm 0.034$ sec	β^-
1.71	(2^+); 1	. . . .	(γ)
3.35	1		

TABLE 8e-1. ENERGY LEVELS OF THE LIGHT NUCLEI (*Continued*)

E_x	J, Π; T	Width or lifetime	Decay
		Li^6: mass excess = 15.850 ± 0.021 Mev	
0	1^+; 0	....	Stable
2.19	3^+; 0	Γ = 22 kev	*d*
3.57	(0^+; 1)	....	γ
4.52	2^+; 0	Γ ~ 600 kev	*d*
5.31	(1)	Γ ≲ 100 kev	
~5.4	1^+; 0	Γ ~ 1 Mev	*d*
6.63	(1)	Γ ≲ 100 kev	
7.40	(0)	Γ ~ 1 Mev	
8.37	(1)	Γ ≲ 100 kev	

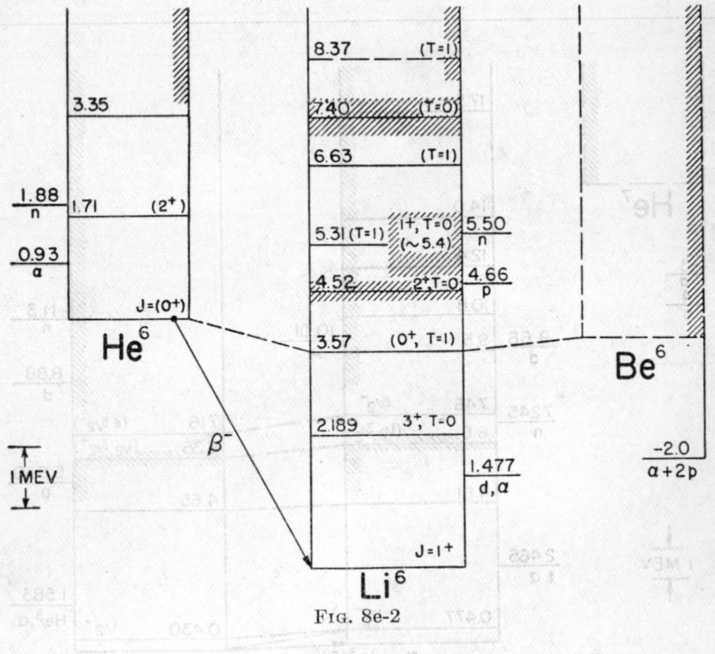

FIG. 8e-2

Be^6: mass excess = 20.8 ± 1 Mev

Not reported: ground state presumably $J = 0^+$; $T = 1$; unstable to decay into $He^4 + 2p$

He^7: mass excess = 31.5 ± 2 Mev

Not reported: if assumed mass excess is correct, the ground state ($T = \frac{3}{2}$) is unstable to decay into $He^6 + n$ and $He^4 + 3n$

TABLE 8e-1. ENERGY LEVELS OF THE LIGHT NUCLEI (*Continued*)

E_x	$J, \Pi; T$	Width or lifetime	Decay
Li^7: mass excess = 16.969 ± 0.024 Mev			
0	$\frac{3}{2}-; \frac{1}{2}$	....	Stable
0.477	$\frac{1}{2}-; \frac{1}{2}$	$\tau_m = 0.75 \pm 0.25 \times 10^{-13}$ sec	γ
4.61	$\frac{1}{2}$	....	$t, (\gamma)$
(5.5)	$\frac{1}{2}$	....	(γ, t)
6.6	$(\frac{1}{2}+, \frac{3}{2}+); \frac{1}{2}$	Broad	(γ, t)
7.46	$\frac{5}{2}-; \frac{1}{2}$	$\Gamma = 150$ kev	n, t
9.6	$\frac{1}{2}$	....	$\gamma, n, (t)$
10.8	$\frac{1}{2}$	....	γ, n
12.4	$\frac{1}{2}$	....	γ, n
14.0	....	....	γ, n
17.5	....	....	γ, n

FIG. 8e-3

E_x	$J, \Pi; T$	Width or lifetime	Decay
Be^7: mass excess = 17.832 ± 0.024 Mev			
0	$\leq\frac{5}{2}-; \frac{1}{2}$	$\tau_{\frac{1}{2}} = 53.4 \pm 0.3$ days	Orbital electron capture
0.430	$\frac{1}{2}-; \frac{1}{2}$	$(\tau_{\frac{1}{2}} = 1.4 \times 10^{-13}$ sec)	γ
4.65	$\frac{1}{2}$		
6.35	$(\frac{1}{2}+, \frac{3}{2}+); \frac{1}{2}$	$\Gamma \sim 1$ Mev	p, He^3, γ
7.16	$(\leq\frac{5}{2}-); \frac{1}{2}$	$\Gamma = 430$ kev	p, He^3, γ

TABLE 8e-1. ENERGY LEVELS OF THE LIGHT NUCLEI (*Continued*)

E_x	J, Π; T	Width or lifetime	Decay
		Li^8: mass excess = 23.296 ± 0.028 Mev	
0	(2^+); 1	$\tau_{\frac{1}{2}} = 0.844 \pm 0.005$ sec	β^-
0.97	$(\leq 3^+)$; 1	....	(γ)
2.28	3^+; 1	$\Gamma = 37$ kev	n
3.3	(1^+); 1	$\Gamma \sim 1$ Mev	n
		Be^8: mass excess = 7.309 ± 0.027 Mev	
0	0^+; 0	$\tau_{\frac{1}{2}} < 4 \times 10^{-15}$ sec	α
2.90	2^+; 0	$\Gamma = 1.2 \pm 0.3$ Mev	α
(4.2)	(2^+); 0	....	(α)
(5.4)	(2^+); 0	....	(α)
7.55	(0^+); 0	$\Gamma = 1.2 \pm 0.4$ Mev	α
10.8	(4^+); 0	$\Gamma = 1.2 \pm 0.4$ Mev	α
14.7	0	....	(α)
16.06	......	$\Gamma = 470$ kev	(α)
16.72	$(2^+; 1)$	$\Gamma = 150$ kev	(α)
17.63	1^+; (1)	$\Gamma = 10.7 \pm 0.5$ kev	p, γ
(17.8)	......	$\Gamma = 80$ kev	(α)
18.14	(1^+)	$\Gamma = 150$ kev	p, γ
(18.9)	......	....	p, n
19.0	......	....	p, γ
19.2	$(3^+; 1)$	$\Gamma \sim 180$ kev	p, n
19.9	(2^+)	$\Gamma \sim 1$ Mev	p, α
21.5	......	$\Gamma \sim 350$ kev	p, n
22.5	......	$\Gamma \sim 450$ kev	d, n, α, p
23.85	......	....	d, n

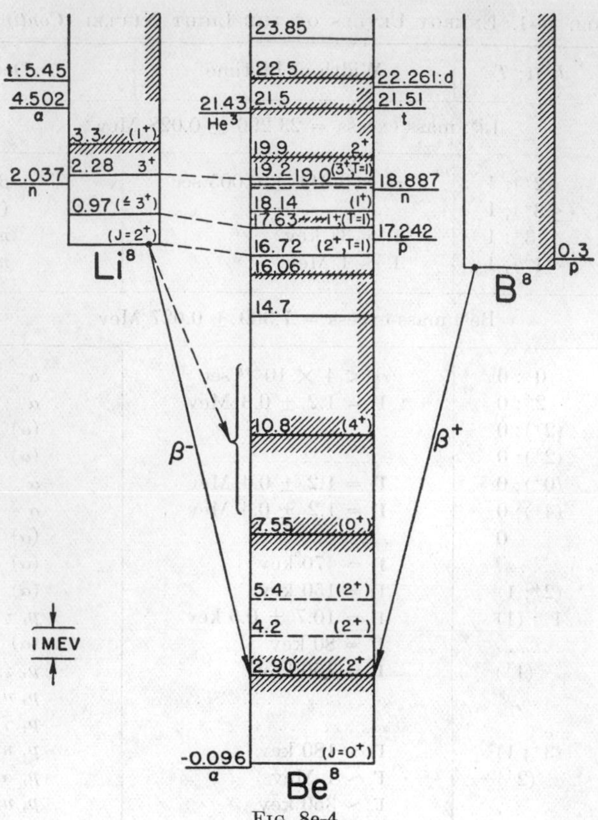

Fig. 8e-4

Table 8e-1. Energy Levels of the Light Nuclei (*Continued*)

B^8: mass excess = 25.1 ± 0.3 Mev

No excited states are reported. The ground state ($T = 1$) decays by positron emission ($\tau_{\frac{1}{2}} = 0.46 \pm 0.03$ sec) mainly to the 2.90-Mev state of Be^8. From analogy with Li^8, probably $J = 2^+$

Li^9: mass excess = 28.1 ± 1 Mev

No excited states are reported. The ground state ($T = 1$) decays by electron emission ($\tau_{\frac{1}{2}} = 0.169 \pm 0.003$ sec) to neutron-unstable states of Be^9

TABLE 8e-1. ENERGY LEVELS OF THE LIGHT NUCLEI (*Continued*)

E_x	$J, \Pi; T$	Width or lifetime	Decay
Be^9: mass excess = 14.007 ± 0.028 Mev			
0	$\frac{3}{2}-; \frac{1}{2}$	....	Stable
(1.8)	$\frac{1}{2}$		
2.43	$(>\frac{1}{2}^-); \frac{1}{2}$	$\Gamma < 3$ kev	*n*
(3.1)	$\frac{1}{2}$	$(\Gamma < 100$ kev)	
4.8	$\frac{1}{2}$	$\Gamma = 1.0 \pm 0.5$ Mev	(*n*)
6.8	$\frac{1}{2}$	....	(*n*, α)
7.9	$\frac{1}{2}$	....	(*n*, α)
11.3	$\frac{1}{2}$	....	(*n*, α)
17.27	....	$\Gamma = 200$ kev	*d*, *n*, *p*
17.47	....	$\Gamma = 47$ kev	*d*, *n*, *p*
(18.3)	....	$(\Gamma = 300$ kev)	(*d*, *n*)
(19.9)			
(21.7)			

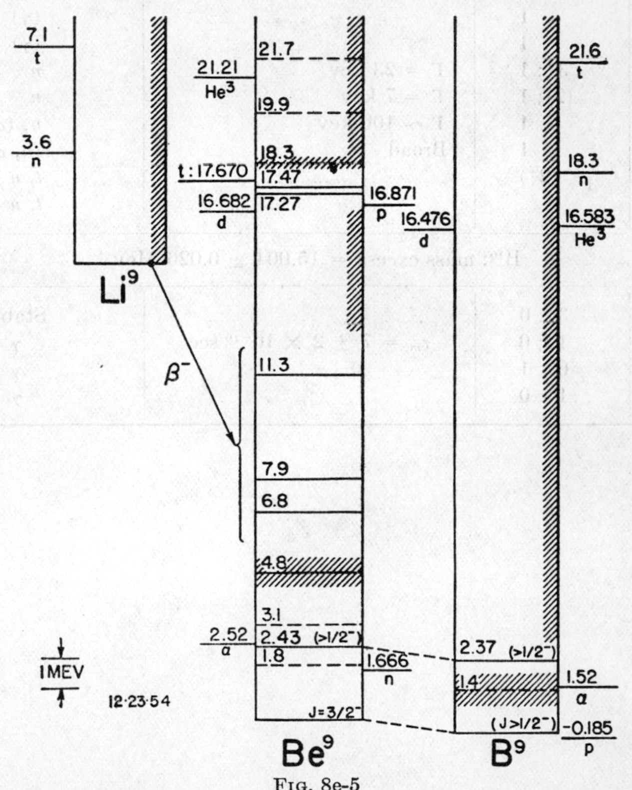

FIG. 8e-5

TABLE 8e-1. ENERGY LEVELS OF THE LIGHT NUCLEI (*Continued*)

E_x	$J, \Pi; T$	Width or lifetime	Decay
		B^9: mass excess = 15.076 ± 0.029 Mev	
0	$(>\frac{1}{2}^-); \frac{1}{2}$	$\Gamma < 2$ kev	(*p*)
(1.4)	$\frac{1}{2}$	$\Gamma \sim 1$ Mev	
2.37	$(>\frac{1}{2}^-); \frac{1}{2}$	$\Gamma < 100$ kev	
		C^9: mass excess = 32.2 ± 2 Mev	

Not reported: if assumed mass defect is correct, the ground state ($T = \frac{3}{2}$) is stable to nucleon decay

E_x	$J, \Pi; T$	Width or lifetime	Decay
		Be^{10}: mass excess = 15.560 ± 0.026 Mev	
0	$(0^+); 1$	$\tau_{\frac{1}{2}} = 2.7 \pm 0.4 \times 10^6$ years	β^-
3.37	$2^+; 1$	....	γ
5.96	1	....	(γ)
6.18	1	....	(γ)
6.26	1	....	(γ)
7.37	$3^+; 1$	$\Gamma = 23$ kev	n
7.54	$(2); 1$	$\Gamma = 7$ kev	n
9.27	1	$\Gamma \sim 100$ kev	$n, (\alpha)$
(9.4)	1	Broad	(n, α)
17.82	(2^+)	....	t, n
18.43	.....	....	t, n
		B^{10}: mass excess = 15.004 ± 0.026 Mev	
0	$3^+; 0$	....	Stable
0.72	$1^+; 0$	$\tau_m = 7 \pm 2 \times 10^{-10}$ sec	γ
1.74	$0^+; 1$	....	γ
2.15	$1^+; 0$	....	γ

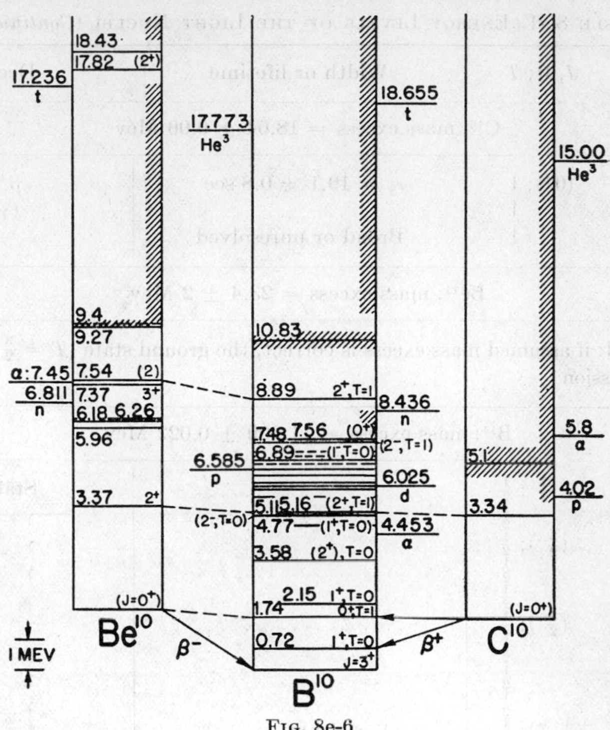

FIG. 8e-6

TABLE 8e-1. ENERGY LEVELS OF THE LIGHT NUCLEI (*Continued*)

E_x	$J, \Pi; T$	Width or lifetime	Decay
3.58	(2+); 0	....	γ
4.77	(1+; 0)	$\Gamma < 10$ kev	α, γ
5.11	(2−; 0)	$\Gamma < 10$ kev	(α)
5.16	(2+; 1)	$\Gamma < 10$ kev	α, γ
5.58	......	$\Gamma < 100$ kev	
5.93	......	$\Gamma < 10$ kev	(γ)
6.06	......	$\Gamma < 10$ kev	
6.16	......	$\Gamma < 20$ kev	
6.40	......	$\Gamma < 100$ kev	
6.58	......	$\Gamma \sim 30$ kev	
(6.77)	......	($\Gamma < 100$ kev)	
6.89	(1−; 0)	$\Gamma = 125$ kev	p, d, α, γ
(7.01)	......	....	(p, d)
(7.19)	......	....	(p, γ, d, α)
7.48	(2−; 1)	$\Gamma = 79 \pm 3$ kev	p, d, α, γ
7.56	(0+)	$\Gamma = 3.6$ kev	p, γ
8.89	2+; 1	$\Gamma = 36 \pm 2$ kev	p, n, α, γ
10.83	......	$\Gamma \sim 0.5$ Mev	$p, n, (\gamma)$

TABLE 8e-1. ENERGY LEVELS OF THE LIGHT NUCLEI (*Continued*)

E_x	$J, \Pi; T$	Width or lifetime	Decay
		C^{10}: mass excess = 18.64 ± 0.06 Mev	
0	(0^+); 1	$\tau_{\frac{1}{2}} = 19.1 \pm 0.8$ sec	β^+
3.34	1	....	(γ)
5.1	1	Broad or unresolved	
		Be^{11}: mass excess = 23.4 ± 2 Mev	
Not reported: if assumed mass excess is correct, the ground state ($T = \frac{3}{2}$) is stable to Nucleon emission			
		B^{11}: mass excess = 11.909 ± 0.022 Mev	
0	$\frac{3}{2}^-; \frac{1}{2}$	....	Stable
2.14	$\frac{1}{2}$	....	γ
4.46	$(\frac{5}{2}^-); \frac{1}{2}$	....	γ
5.03	$\frac{1}{2}$	....	γ
6.76	$\frac{1}{2}$	....	γ
6.81	$(\frac{3}{2}^-); \frac{1}{2}$	....	γ
7.30	$\frac{1}{2}$	....	γ
7.99	$\frac{1}{2}$	....	γ
8.57	$\frac{1}{2}$	....	γ
8.92	$(\frac{3}{2}, \frac{5}{2}); \frac{1}{2}$	$\Gamma < 1$ kev	γ
9.19	$(\frac{5}{2}^-); \frac{1}{2}$	$\Gamma \sim 2.5$ kev	γ
9.28	$(\frac{5}{2}^+); \frac{1}{2}$	$\Gamma = 4.5$ kev	γ
9.86	$(\leq\frac{5}{2}); \frac{1}{2}$	$\Gamma = 125 \pm 10$ kev	α
10.23	$(\leq\frac{7}{2}); \frac{1}{2}$	$\Gamma \sim 155$ kev	α
10.32	$\frac{1}{2}$	$\Gamma = 54 \pm 17$ kev	

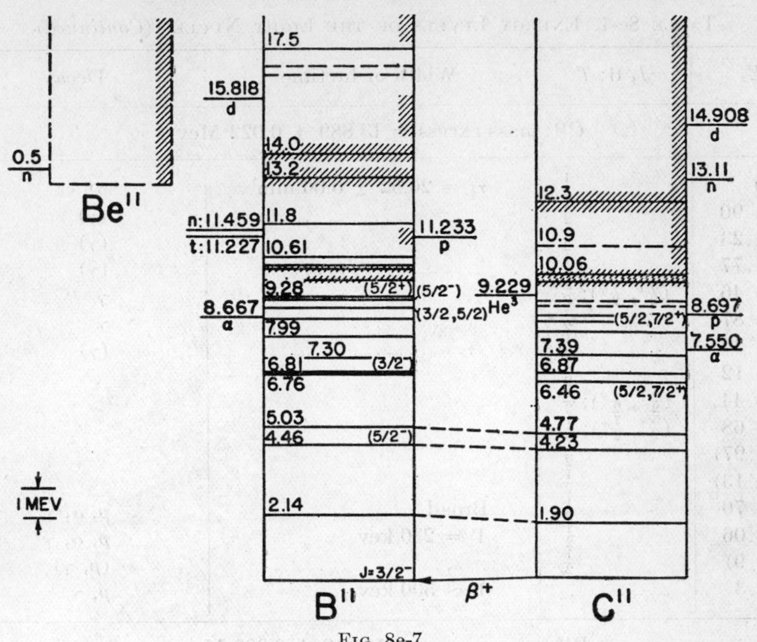

FIG. 8e-7

TABLE 8e-1. ENERGY LEVELS OF THE LIGHT NUCLEI (*Continued*)

E_x	J, Π; T	Width or lifetime	Decay
10.61	$\frac{1}{2}$	....	α
11.8	$\frac{1}{2}$	....	(n)
13.2	....	(Γ = 360 kev)	n, α
14.0	....	Broad	n
(16.6)	....	(Broad)	(d, p)
(16.9)	....	(Broad)	(d, p)
17.5	....	(Broad)	d, p

TABLE 8e-1. ENERGY LEVELS OF THE LIGHT NUCLEI (*Continued*)

E_x	J, Π; T	Width or lifetime	Decay
C^{11}: mass excess = 13.889 ± 0.022 Mev			
0	$\frac{1}{2}$	$\tau_{\frac{1}{2}}$ = 20.52 ± 0.06 min	β^+
1.90	$\frac{1}{2}$	....	(γ)
4.23	$\frac{1}{2}$	....	(γ)
4.77	$\frac{1}{2}$	....	(γ)
6.46	($\frac{5}{2}^+$, $\frac{7}{2}^+$); $\frac{1}{2}$	....	γ
6.87	$\frac{1}{2}$	....	γ
7.39	$\frac{1}{2}$	....	(γ)
8.12	$\frac{1}{2}$		
8.44	($\frac{5}{2}^+$, $\frac{7}{2}^+$); $\frac{1}{2}$		
8.68	($\frac{5}{2}^+$, $\frac{7}{2}^+$); $\frac{1}{2}$		
(8.97)	$\frac{1}{2}$		
(9.13)	$\frac{1}{2}$		
9.70	$\frac{1}{2}$	Broad	p, α, γ
10.06	$\frac{1}{2}$	Γ = 230 kev	p, α, γ
(10.9)	$\frac{1}{2}$	....	(p, γ)
12.3	......	Γ ~ 500 kev	p, γ
B^{12}: mass excess = 16.912 ± 0.020 Mev			
0	(1^+); 1	$\tau_{\frac{1}{2}}$ = 0.023 ± 0.002 sec	β^-
0.95	($\leq 3^+$); 1	....	γ
1.67	(1^-, 2^-); 1	....	γ
2.62	1	....	(γ)
2.72	1	....	(γ)
3.38	($\leq 3^+$); 1		
3.76	2^+; 1	Γ = 37 kev	n
4.53	3^-; 1	Γ = 120 kev	n
4.99	1; 1	Γ = 60 kev	n
5.61	2; 1	Γ = 110 kev	n
5.73	3; 1	Γ = 55 kev	n
C^{12}: mass excess = 3.542 ± 0.015 Mev			
0	0^+; 0	....	Stable
4.43	2^+; 0	$\tau_m < 3 \times 10^{-13}$ sec	γ
7.65	(0^+); 0	Γ < 25 kev	γ, (π, α)
9.61	0	Γ > 10 kev	(α)

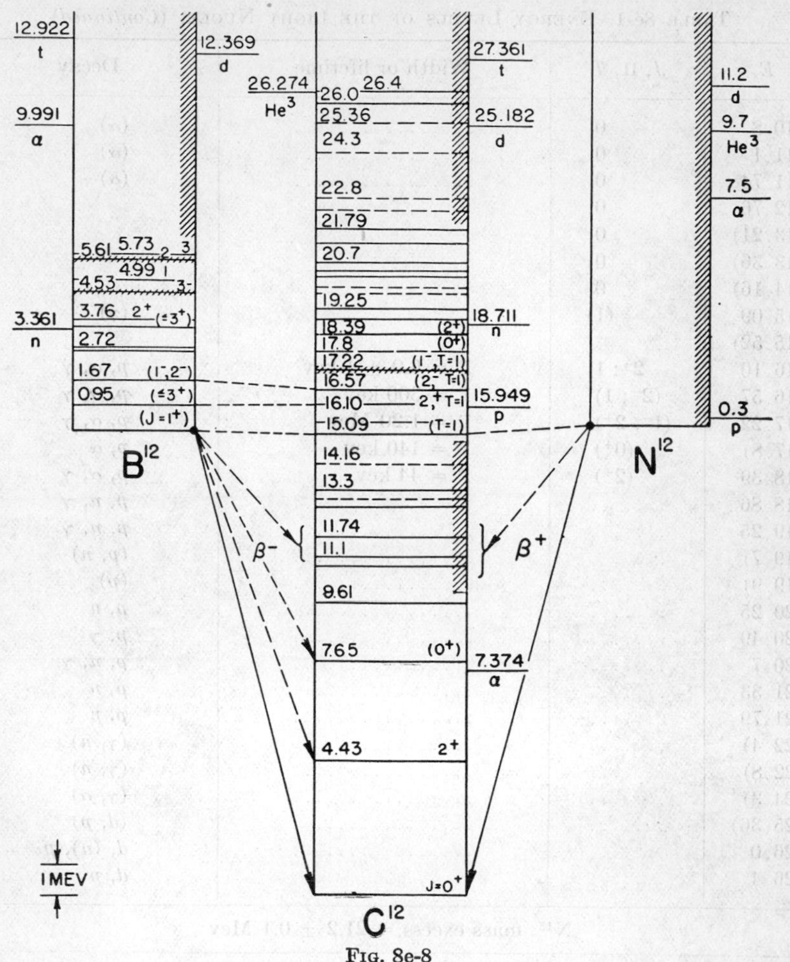
12.922
t
9.991
α
3.361
n
12.369
d
5.61 5.73 2 3
4.99 1
4.53 3-
3.76 2+ (≤3+)
2.72
1.67 (1-,2-)
0.95 (≤3+)
(J=1+)
B12
26.274
He3
26.0 26.4
25.36
24.3
22.8
21.79
20.7
19.25
18.39 (2+)
17.8 (0+)
17.22 (1-, T=1)
16.57 (2-, T=1)
16.10 2+, T=1
15.09 (T=1)
14.16
13.3
11.74
11.1
9.61
7.65 (0+)
4.43 2+
J=0+
C12
27.361
t
25.182
d
18.711
n
15.949
p
7.374
α
β-
β+
N12
11.2
d
9.7
He3
7.5
α
0.3
p
1 MEV

FIG. 8e-8

TABLE 8e-1. ENERGY LEVELS OF THE LIGHT NUCLEI (*Continued*)

E_x	$J, \Pi; T$	Width or lifetime	Decay
10.8	0	....	(α)
11.1	0	....	(α)
11.74	0	....	(α)
12.76	0		
(13.21)	0		
(13.36)	0		
(14.16)	0		
15.09	(1)	....	(γ)
(15.52)			
16.10	$2^+; 1$	$\Gamma = 6.0 \pm 1$ kev	p, α, γ
16.57	$(2^-; 1)$	$\Gamma = 300$ kev	p, α, γ
17.22	$(1^-, 2^+)$	$\Gamma = 1.20$ Mev	p, α, γ
(17.8)	(0^+)	$\Gamma = 140$ kev	p, α
18.39	(2^+)	$\Gamma = 44$ kev	p, α, γ
18.86	....	....	p, n, γ
19.25	....	....	p, n, γ
(19.7)	....	....	(p, n)
(19.9)	....	....	(p)
20.25	....	....	p, n
20.49	....	....	p, γ
20.7	....	....	p, n, γ
21.33	....	....	p, n
21.79	....	....	p, n
(22.4)	....	....	(γ, n)
(22.8)	....	....	(γ, n)
(24.3)	....	....	(γ, α)
(25.36)	....	....	(d, p)
26.0	....	....	$d, (n), p$
26.4	....	....	d, p

N^{12}: mass excess = 21.2 ± 0.1 Mev

No excited states are reported. The ground state ($T = 1$) decays by positron emission ($\tau_{\frac{1}{2}} = 0.0125 \pm 0.001$ sec) to the ground state and to α-unstable states of C^{12}. From analogy with B^{12}, probably $J = 1^+$

B^{13}: mass excess = 19 ± 2 Mev

Not reported: if the assumed mass excess is correct, the ground state ($T = \frac{3}{2}$) is stable with respect to nucleon emission

C^{13}: mass excess = 6.958 ± 0.013 Mev

0	$\frac{1}{2}^-; \frac{1}{2}$	....	Stable
3.09	$\frac{1}{2}^+; \frac{1}{2}$	$\tau_m < 3 \times 10^{-13}$ sec	γ
3.68	$\frac{3}{2}^-; \frac{1}{2}$	....	γ
3.86	$\frac{5}{2}^+; \frac{1}{2}$	....	γ
6.87	$\frac{3}{2}^+, \frac{5}{2}^+; \frac{1}{2}$	$\Gamma < 10$ kev	n

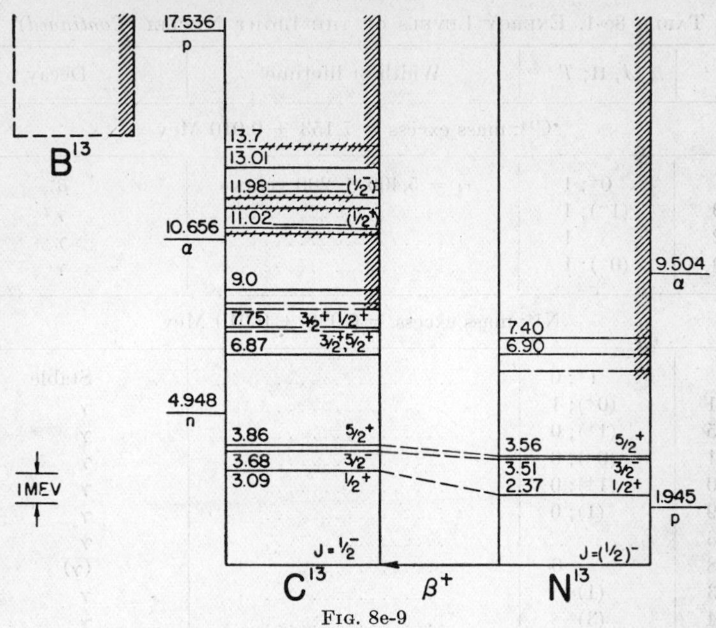

FIG. 8e-9

TABLE 8e-1. ENERGY LEVELS OF THE LIGHT NUCLEI (*Continued*)

E_x	$J, \Pi; T$	Width or lifetime	Decay
(7.67)	$(\frac{3}{2}^+; \frac{1}{2})$	....	(*n*)
7.75	$\frac{1}{2}^+; \frac{1}{2}$	....	*n*
(8.35)	$\frac{1}{2}$		
(8.55)	$\frac{1}{2}$		
9.0	$\frac{1}{2}$	....	*n*
10.8	$\frac{1}{2}$	$\Gamma \sim 100$ kev	*n*
11.02	$\frac{1}{2}$	....	α, *n*
11.08	$(\frac{1}{2}^+); \frac{1}{2}$	....	α, *n*
11.64	....	$\Gamma \sim 200$ kev	*n*
11.98	$(\frac{1}{2}^-)$	$\Gamma \sim 150$ kev	α, *n*
12.21	....	....	α, *n*
12.46	....	....	α, *n*
13.01	....	....	α, *n*
(13.7)	....	....	α, *n*
	N^{13}: mass excess = 9.179 ± 0.013 Mev		
0	$(\frac{1}{2})^-; \frac{1}{2}$	$\tau_{\frac{1}{2}} = 10.05 \pm 0.03$ min	β^+
2.37	$\frac{1}{2}^+; \frac{1}{2}$	$\Gamma = 35 \pm 1$ kev	*p*, γ
3.51	$\frac{3}{2}^-; \frac{1}{2}$	$\Gamma = 67 \pm 7$ kev	*p*, γ
3.56	$\frac{5}{2}^+; \frac{1}{2}$	$\Gamma = 61$ kev	*p*
(6.4)	$\frac{1}{2}$	....	(*p*)
6.90	$\frac{1}{2}$	....	*p*
7.40	$\frac{1}{2}$	....	*p*

TABLE 8e-1. ENERGY LEVELS OF THE LIGHT NUCLEI (*Continued*)

E_x	$J, \Pi; T$	Width or lifetime	Decay
		C^{14}: mass excess = 7.153 ± 0.010 Mev	
0	0^+; 1	$\tau_{\frac{1}{2}}$ = 5,400 ± 200 years	β^-
6.09	(1^-); 1	....	γ
6.72	1	....	γ
6.89	(0^-); 1	....	γ
		N^{14}: mass excess = 6.998 ± 0.010 Mev	
0	1^+; 0	....	Stable
2.31	(0^+); 1	....	γ
3.95	(1^+); 0	....	γ
4.91	(0^-); 0	....	γ
5.10	(1^+); 0	....	γ
5.69	(1); 0	....	γ
5.83	....	....	γ
5.98	0	....	(γ)
6.23	(1)	....	γ
6.44	(3)	....	γ
7.02	....	....	γ
7.40	....	....	γ
7.72	....	....	(p, γ)

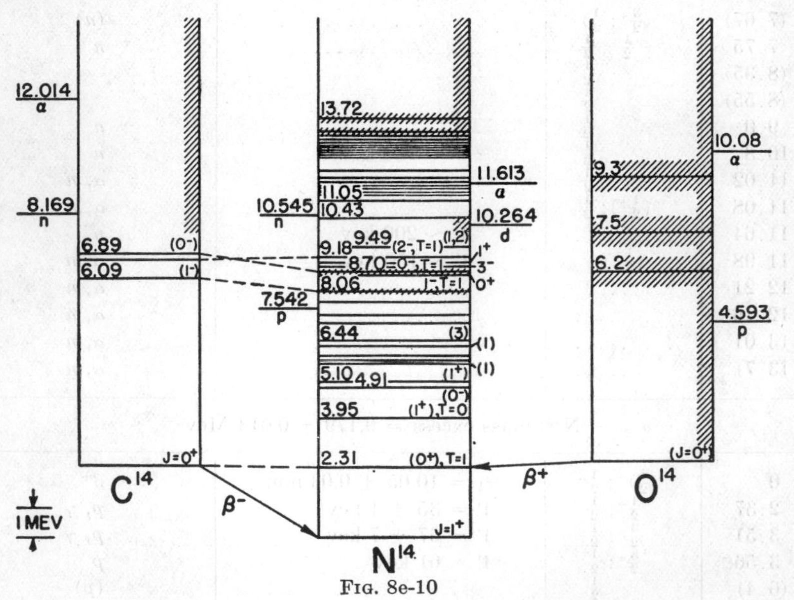

FIG. 8e-10

TABLE 8e-1. ENERGY LEVELS OF THE LIGHT NUCLEI (*Continued*)

E_x	J, Π; T	Width or lifetime	Decay
8.06	1^-; 1	Γ = 30.2 kev	p, γ
8.62	0^+	Γ = 5.6 ± 2 kev	p, γ
8.70	0^-; 1	Γ = 470 kev	p, γ
8.90	3^-	Γ = 19 kev	p, γ
8.98	1^+	Γ = 6.5 kev	p, γ
9.18	(2^-; 1)	Γ = 2.0 ± 0.2 kev	p, γ
9.49	(1, 2)	Γ = 42 ± 3 kev	p, γ
10.43	....	....	p, γ
11.05	....	Γ = 90 kev	d, n, p
11.23	....	Γ = 26 kev	d, p
11.26	....	Γ = 19 kev	p, n
11.26	....	Γ = 170 kev	d, n, p
11.35	....	Γ = 140 kev	n
11.41	....	Γ = 28 kev	d, n, p
11.49	....	Γ = 4.7 kev	d, p, n
11.65	....	Γ = 17 kev	d, n
11.75	....	Γ = 120 kev	d, n, p
12.0	....	Γ ≅ 90 kev	d, n, p
12.29	....	Γ ~ 200 kev	α, n, p, d
12.42	4^-	Γ = 43 ± 4 kev	α, n, p, d
12.50	....	Γ = 36 ± 5 kev	α, n, p, d
12.61	....	Γ = 50 ± 5 kev	α, p
12.69	3^-	Γ = 14 ± 4 kev	γ, n, p, d
12.79	4^+	Γ = 14 ± 4 kev	α, n, p, d
12.82	4^-	Γ = 5 ± 2 kev	α, p, d
12.92	4^+	Γ = 21 ± 4 kev	α, p, d
13.16	....	Sharp	α, n, p
13.24	....	Broad	α, n, p
13.72	....	Broad	α, n, p

O^{14}: mass excess = 12.168 ± 0.015 Mev

E_x	J, Π; T	Width or lifetime	Decay
0	(0^+); 1	$\tau_{\frac{1}{2}}$ = 72.1 ± 0.4 sec	β^+
6.2	1	Broad and/or unresolved	
7.5	1		
9.3	1		

C^{15}: mass excess = 13.17 ± 0.06 Mev

No excited states are reported. The ground state ($T = \frac{3}{2}$) decays by electron emission ($\tau_{\frac{1}{2}}$ = 2.4 ± 0.3 sec) to the ground state and to one or both of the 5.3-Mev states of N^{15}

TABLE 8e-1. ENERGY LEVELS OF THE LIGHT NUCLEI (*Continued*)

E_x	$J, \Pi; T$	Width or lifetime	Decay
		N^{15}: mass excess = 4.528 ± 0.011 Mev	
0	$\frac{1}{2}-; \frac{1}{2}$	....	Stable
5.28	$(\frac{1}{2}, \frac{3}{2}); \frac{1}{2}$	....	γ
5.31			γ
6.33	$(\frac{3}{2}-, \frac{5}{2}-); \frac{1}{2}$	....	γ
7.16	$(\frac{1}{2}+, \frac{3}{2}+); \frac{1}{2}$	....	γ
7.31			γ
7.58	....	....	(γ)
8.32	$(\frac{1}{2}+, \frac{3}{2}+); \frac{1}{2}$	....	γ
8.57			(γ)
9.06	$(\frac{1}{2}+, \frac{3}{2}+); \frac{1}{2}$	....	(γ)
9.17			γ
9.83	$\frac{1}{2}$	....	(γ)
10.07	$\frac{1}{2}$	....	γ
10.46			
10.54	....	....	p, γ
10.70	$\frac{3}{2}-$	....	p, γ
10.81	$\frac{3}{2}-$	....	p, γ
11.24	$>\frac{1}{2}$	$\Gamma = 3.3$ kev	n
11.29	$\frac{1}{2}-$	$\Gamma = 7$ kev	p, n, γ
11.43	$\frac{1}{2}+$	$\Gamma = 40$ kev	p, n, α, γ
11.57	$\frac{1}{2}+; (\frac{3}{2})$	$\Gamma = 445$ kev	$p, (n), \gamma$
11.77	$\frac{3}{2}+$	$\Gamma = 40$ kev	n, p, α
11.88	$(\frac{5}{2}+)$	$\Gamma = 17$ kev	n, p, α
11.94	$>\frac{1}{2}$	$\Gamma \leq 3.0$ kev	n, α
11.96	$(\frac{1}{2}-)$	$\Gamma = 13$ kev	n, p
12.09	$(\frac{3}{2}, \frac{5}{2})$	$\Gamma = 19$ kev	n, p, α
12.14	$(\frac{3}{2}-)$	$\Gamma = 50$ kev	n, p, α
12.32	$(\frac{5}{2}-)$	$\Gamma = 21$ kev	n, p
12.49	$\frac{5}{2}$	$\Gamma = 35$ kev	p, n, α
12.91	....	$\Gamma \sim 50$ kev	n, α, p
13.19	....	....	n, α
13.38*	....	....	n, α, p

* Numerous levels are reported to exist in the range E_x = 13.4 to 19.0 Mev, but their locations are not well established.

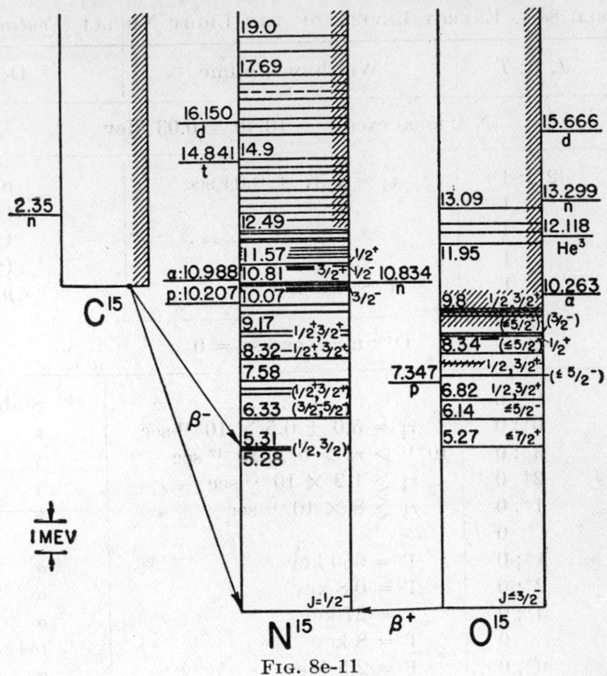

Fig. 8e-11

Table 8e-1. Energy Levels of the Light Nuclei (*Continued*)

E_x	J, Π; T	Width or lifetime	Decay
O^{15}: mass excess = 7.233 ± 0.012 Mev			
0	$\frac{1}{2}-, \frac{3}{2}-; \frac{1}{2}$	$\tau_{\frac{1}{2}}$ = 119.1 ± 1 sec	β^+
5.27	$(\leq\frac{7}{2}+); \frac{1}{2}$	....	γ
6.14	$(\leq\frac{5}{2}-); \frac{1}{2}$	....	γ
6.82	$\frac{1}{2}+, \frac{3}{2}+; \frac{1}{2}$	....	γ
7.61	$(\leq\frac{5}{2}-); \frac{1}{2}$	Γ < 2 kev	p, γ
8.0	$\frac{1}{2}+, \frac{3}{2}+; \frac{1}{2}$	Γ = 93 ± 30 kev	p, γ
8.34	$(\leq\frac{5}{2}-); \frac{1}{2}$	Γ = 4.5 ± 1 kev	p, γ
8.79	$\frac{1}{2}+; \frac{1}{2}$	Γ = 47 ± 20 kev	p, γ
8.98	$(\frac{3}{2}-); \frac{1}{2}$	Γ = 10 ± 3 kev	p, γ
9.04	$(\leq\frac{5}{2}-); \frac{1}{2}$	Γ = 6.5 ± 1.5 kev	p, γ
9.55	$\frac{1}{2}$	Γ = 13 ± 4 kev	p, γ
9.67	$\frac{1}{2}$	Γ = 10 ± 3 kev	p, γ
9.8	$\frac{1}{2}+, \frac{3}{2}+; \frac{1}{2}$	Γ = 1.20 ± 0.05 Mev	p, γ
11.95	$\frac{1}{2}$	Broad	p, α
12.3	$\frac{1}{2}$	Broad	p, α
12.6	$\frac{1}{2}$	Broad	p, α
13.09	$\frac{1}{2}$	Broad	p, α

Table 8e-1. Energy Levels of the Light Nuclei (*Continued*)

E_x	$J, \Pi; T$	Width or lifetime	Decay
N^{16}: mass excess = 10.40 ± 0.03 Mev			
0	$(2^-); 1$	$\tau_{\frac{1}{2}} = 7.37 \pm 0.04$ sec	β^-
0.113	1	. . . .	(γ)
0.300	1	. . . .	(γ)
0.391	1	. . . .	(γ)
12.35	1	$\Gamma \sim 400$ kev	p
O^{16}: mass excess = 0			
0	$0^+; 0$	. . . .	Stable
6.06	$0^+; 0$	$\tau_{\frac{1}{2}} = 5.0 \pm 0.5 \times 10^{-11}$ sec	π
6.14	$3^-; 0$	$10^{-11} > \tau_{\frac{1}{2}} > 5 \times 10^{-12}$ sec	γ
6.91	$2^+; 0$	$\tau_{\frac{1}{2}} \lesssim 1.2 \times 10^{-14}$ sec	γ
7.12	$1^-; 0$	$\tau_{\frac{1}{2}} \lesssim 8 \times 10^{-15}$ sec	γ
(8.6)	0		
9.58	$1^-; 0$	$\Gamma = 650$ kev	α
9.84	$2^+; 0$	$\Gamma = 0.8$ kev	α
10.36	$4^+; 0$	$\Gamma = 27$ kev	α
(11.10)	0	$\Gamma = 8$ kev	(α)
11.25	$0^+; 0$	$\Gamma = 2.5$ Mev	α
11.51	$2^+; 0$	$\Gamma = 80$ kev	α
11.62	$3^-; 0$	$\Gamma = 1.2$ Mev	α
12.43	$(0^+, 1^-); 0$	$\Gamma = 88$ kev	p, α
12.51	2^-	$\Gamma = 0.8$ kev	p, α
12.95	2^-	$\Gamma = 2.1$ kev	p, α
13.09	$1^-; (1)$	$\Gamma \sim 140$ kev	p, α, γ

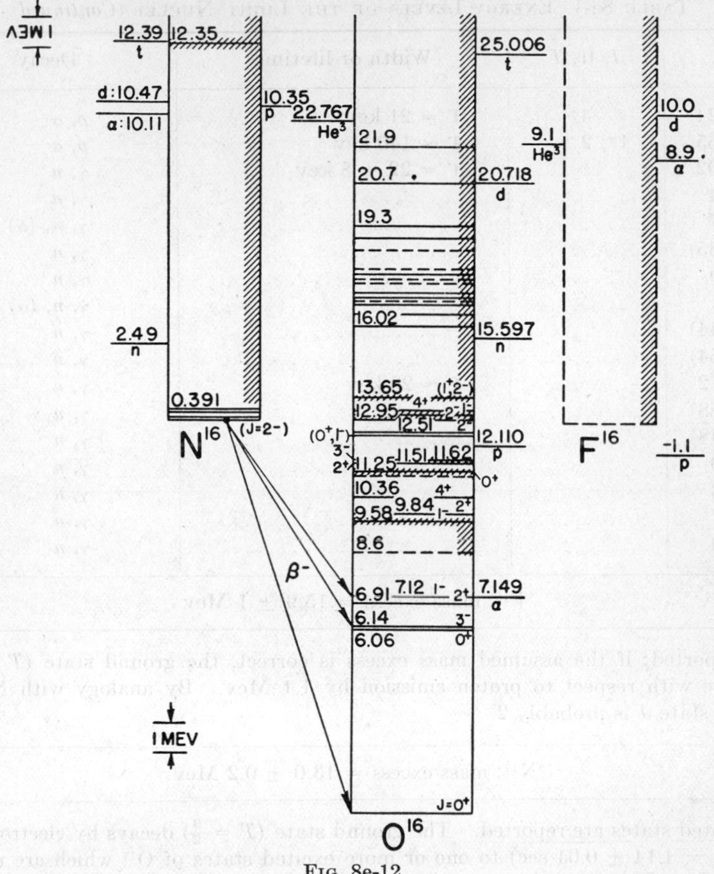
1 MEV
12.39
t
12.35
d:10.47
α:10.11
10.35
p
2.49
n
0.391
(J=2−)
N16
β−
1 MEV
25.006
t
22.767
He3
21.9
20.7
20.718
d
19.3
16.02
15.597
n
13.65
(1+,2−)
12.95
4+
2−
1−
12.51
2+
(0+,1−)
3−
2+
12.110
p
11.51
11.62
11.25
0+
10.36
4+
9.58
9.84
1−
2+
8.6
6.91
7.12
1−
2+
7.149
α
6.14
3−
6.06
0+
J=0+
O16
9.1
He3
10.0
d
8.9
α
F16
−1.1
p

Fig. 8e-12

TABLE 8e-1. ENERGY LEVELS OF THE LIGHT NUCLEI (*Continued*)

E_x	J, Π; T	Width or lifetime	Decay
13.24	4^+	Γ = 21 kev	p, α
13.65	1^+, 2^-	Γ ∼ 140 kev	p, α
16.02	....	Γ = 22 ± 8 kev	γ, n
16.4	....	....	γ, n
16.7	....	....	γ, n, (α)
(16.85)	....	....	γ, n
16.9	....	....	γ, n
17.1	....	....	γ, n, (α)
(17.44)	....	....	γ, n
(17.54)	....	....	γ, n
17.72	....	Γ ∼ 20 kev	γ, n
(17.88)	....	....	γ, n
(18.48)	....	....	γ, n
18.9	....	....	γ, n
19.3	....	....	γ, n
20.7	....	....	γ, n
21.9	....	....	γ, n

F^{16}: mass excess = 15.9 ± 1 Mev

Not reported: if the assumed mass excess is correct, the ground state (T = 1) is unstable with respect to proton emission by 1.1 Mev. By analogy with N^{16}, the ground state J is probably 2^-

N^{17}: mass excess = 13.0 ± 0.2 Mev

No excited states are reported. The ground state ($T = \frac{3}{2}$) decays by electron emission ($\tau_{\frac{1}{2}}$ = 4.14 ± 0.04 sec) to one or more excited states of O^{17} which are neutron unstable. Whether transitions occur to bound states of O^{17} is not known

O^{17}: mass excess = 4.221 ± 0.006 Mev

E_x	J, Π; T	Width or lifetime	Decay
0	$\frac{5}{2}^+$; $\frac{1}{2}$	....	Stable
0.87	$\frac{1}{2}^+$; $\frac{1}{2}$	$\tau_m = 2.5 \pm 1 \times 10^{-10}$ sec	γ
3.06	$\frac{1}{2}$	....	(γ)
3.85	$\frac{1}{2}$	....	(γ)
4.56	$\frac{3}{2}^-$; $\frac{1}{2}$	Γ = 42 kev	n
5.08	$\frac{3}{2}^+$; $\frac{1}{2}$	Γ = 95 kev	n
(5.23)	$\frac{1}{2}$	Γ = 8 ± 6 kev	
5.39	$\frac{3}{2}^-$; $\frac{1}{2}$	Γ = 33 kev	n
5.71	$\geq\frac{3}{2}$; $\frac{1}{2}$	Γ < 7 kev	n
5.87	$\geq\frac{3}{2}$; $\frac{1}{2}$	Γ < 10 kev	n
5.94	$\frac{1}{2}^-$; $\frac{1}{2}$	Γ = 28 kev	n
6.30	$\frac{1}{2}^+$; $\frac{1}{2}$	Γ = 110 kev	n
6.87	$\frac{1}{2}$		
(6.99)	$\frac{1}{2}$	Γ = 20 ± 11 kev	
7.16	$\frac{1}{2}$	Γ ∼ 3 kev	α

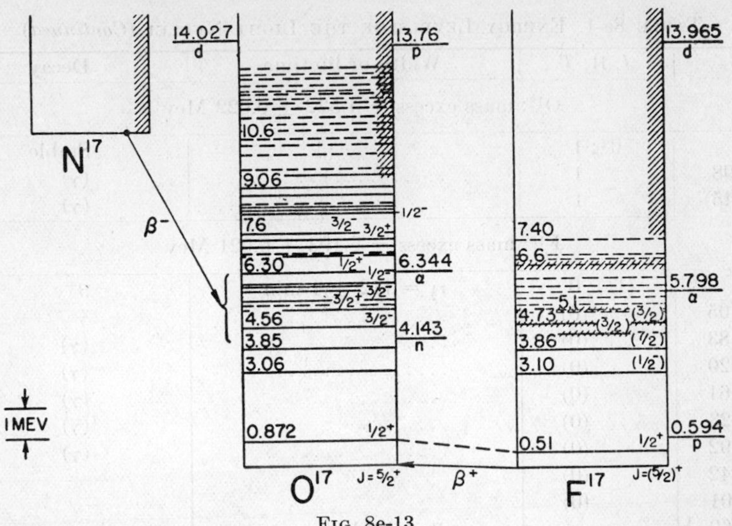

FIG. 8e-13

TABLE 8e-1. ENERGY LEVELS OF THE LIGHT NUCLEI (*Continued*)

E_x	$J, \Pi; T$	Width or lifetime	Decay
7.37	$\frac{3}{2}+; \frac{1}{2}$	$\Gamma = 210$ kev	α, n
7.6	$\frac{3}{2}-; \frac{1}{2}$	$\Gamma = 750$ kev	n
8.27	$\frac{1}{2}-; \frac{1}{2}$	$\Gamma = 260$ kev	α, n
8.38	$\frac{1}{2}$	....	α, n
8.46	$\frac{1}{2}$	....	α, n
(8.59)	$\frac{1}{2}$		
8.87	$\frac{1}{2}$	....	α, n
9.06	$\frac{1}{2}$	....	n
9.5	$\frac{1}{2}$	....	n
(9.7)	$\frac{1}{2}$	....	n
(10.2)	$\frac{1}{2}$	....	n
(10.5)	$\frac{1}{2}$	....	n
(10.6)*	$\frac{1}{2}$	....	n
		F^{17}: mass excess = 6.988 ± 0.005 Mev	
0	$(\frac{5}{2}+); \frac{1}{2}$	$\tau_{\frac{1}{2}} = 66.0 \pm 1$ sec	β^+
0.510	$\frac{1}{2}+; \frac{1}{2}$	....	γ
3.10	$(\frac{1}{2}-); \frac{1}{2}$	$\Gamma = 18.7$ kev	p
3.86	$(\frac{7}{2}-); \frac{1}{2}$	$\Gamma < 3.3$ kev	p, γ
4.35	$(\frac{3}{2}); \frac{1}{2}$	$\Gamma \sim 400$ kev	p
4.73	$(\frac{3}{2}); \frac{1}{2}$	$\Gamma = 300$ kev	p
(5.05)	$\frac{1}{2}$	$\Gamma < 25$ kev	(p)
5.1	$(\frac{1}{2}+); \frac{1}{2}$	$\Gamma = 190$ kev	p
(5.30)	$\frac{1}{2}$	$\Gamma < 25$ kev	(p)
(5.50)	$\frac{1}{2}$	$\Gamma < 25$ kev	p
(5.7)	$\frac{1}{2}$	$\Gamma < 25$ kev	p
(6.15)	$\frac{1}{2}$	$\Gamma < 25$ kev	p
6.6	$(\frac{1}{2}+); \frac{1}{2}$	$\Gamma = 140$ kev	p
(6.75)	$\frac{1}{2}$	$\Gamma < 25$ kev	p
(6.90)	$\frac{1}{2}$	$\Gamma < 25$ kev	p
(7.40)	$\frac{1}{2}$	$\Gamma < 25$ kev	p

* Twelve or more levels may exist in the range 10.6 to 12.8 Mev.

TABLE 8e-1. ENERGY LEVELS OF THE LIGHT NUCLEI (*Continued*)

E_x	$J, \Pi; T$	Width or lifetime	Decay
		O^{18}: mass excess = 4.522 ± 0.022 Mev	
0	0^+; 1	. . . .	Stable
1.98	1	. . . .	(γ)
(2.45)	1	. . . .	(γ)
		F^{18}: mass excess = 6.193 ± 0.021 Mev	
0	(1^+); 0	$\tau_{\frac{1}{2}}$ = 112 ± 1 min	β^+
1.05	(0)	. . . .	γ
1.83	(0)	. . . .	(γ)
2.20	(0)	. . . .	(γ)
2.61	(0)	. . . .	(γ)
3.23	(0)	. . . .	(γ)
3.92	(0)	. . . .	(γ)
4.42	(0)		
5.01	(0)		
5.60 }	(0)	Γ < 1.2 kev	α, γ
5.67 }		Γ < 0.8 kev	α, γ
6.69	. . . .	Γ = 27 ± 4 kev	α, p
6.85	. . . .	Γ = 93 ± 8 kev	α, p
(7.1)	. . . .	Γ ∼ 460 kev	(α, p)
(7.7)	. . . .	. . . .	(α, p)
8.0	. . . .	. . . .	α
8.5	. . . .	. . . .	α
9.0	. . . .	. . . .	d, p
9.5	. . . .	. . . .	d, p
9.8	. . . .	Broad	d, p
10.1	. . . .	Broad	d, p
10.5	. . . .	Broad	d, p
10.8*	. . . .	Broad	d, p

* Six additional levels are reported below 11.1 Mev.

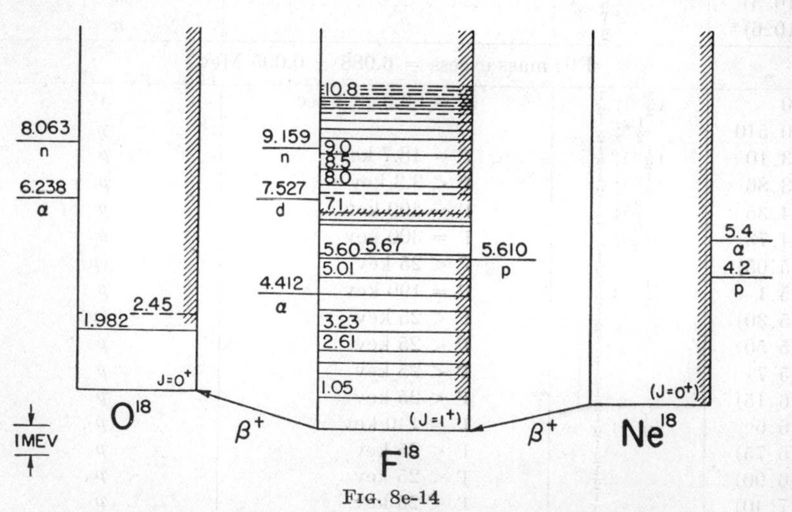

FIG. 8e-14

TABLE 8e-1. ENERGY LEVELS OF THE LIGHT NUCLEI (*Continued*)

E_x	J, Π; T	Width or lifetime	Decay
		Ne^{18}: mass excess = 10.4 ± 0.2 Mev	

No excited states are reported. The ground state ($T = 1$) decays by positron emission ($\tau_{\frac{1}{2}} = 1.6 \pm 0.2$ sec) to the ground state of F^{18}

E_x	J, Π; T	Width or lifetime	Decay
		O^{19}: mass excess = 8.930 ± 0.024 Mev	
0	$(\frac{5}{2}+)$; $\frac{3}{2}$	$\tau_{\frac{1}{2}} = 29$ sec	β^-
0.096	$\frac{3}{2}$	....	(γ)
1.470	$\frac{1}{2}+$; $\frac{3}{2}$	....	(γ)
		F^{19}: mass excess = 4.149 ± 0.014 Mev	
0	$\frac{1}{2}+$; $\frac{1}{2}$	....	Stable
0.110	$\frac{1}{2}-$; $\frac{1}{2}$	$\tau_m = 1.0 \pm 0.25 \times 10^{-9}$ sec	γ
0.197	$\frac{5}{2}+$; $\frac{1}{2}$	$\tau_m = 1.0 \pm 0.2 \times 10^{-7}$ sec	γ
(0.9)	$\frac{1}{2}$	....	(γ)
1.35	$\frac{1}{2}$	....	γ
1.57	$(\frac{3}{2}+)$; $\frac{1}{2}$	....	γ
(2.2)	$\frac{1}{2}$	....	(γ)
2.82	$\frac{1}{2}$	....	(γ)
3.94	$\frac{1}{2}$	....	(γ)
4.06	$\frac{1}{2}$		
4.41	$\frac{1}{2}$		
4.48	$\frac{1}{2}$		
4.59	$\frac{1}{2}$		
4.76	$\frac{1}{2}$		
(5.2)	$\frac{1}{2}$		
(5.5)	$\frac{1}{2}$		
8.56	$(\frac{3}{2})$	$\Gamma \sim 25$ kev	p, α
8.76	$(\frac{1}{2})$	$\Gamma \sim 45$ kev	p, α
10.47	....	$\Gamma = 38 \pm 2$ kev	p, n
10.54	....	....	p, n
10.59	....	$\Gamma = 33 \pm 5$ kev	p, n
10.84	$\frac{3}{2}$	$\Gamma = 57 \pm 2$ kev	p, n
10.96	$(\frac{1}{2})$	$\Gamma = 43 \pm 10$ kev	p, n
11.05	$\frac{3}{2}$	$\Gamma = 62 \pm 2$ kev	p, n
11.16	$(\frac{1}{2})$	$\Gamma = 43 \pm 2$ kev	p, n
11.27	....	....	p, n
11.37	....	$\Gamma = 80 \pm 20$ kev	p, n
11.51	....	....	p, n
12.0	....	....	p, n
12.8	....	....	p, n
13.3	....	....	p, n
13.8	....	....	p, n
14.3	....	....	p, n
15.3	....	....	γ, n

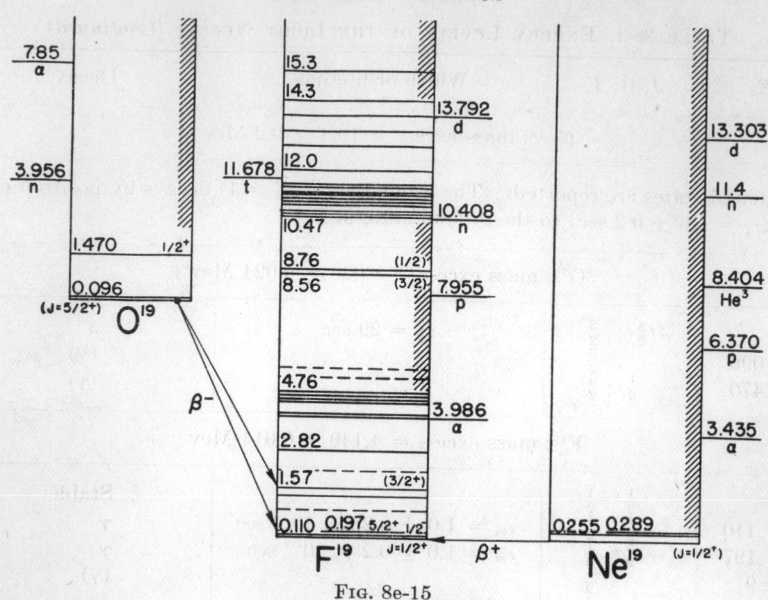
7.85
α
3.956
n
1.470
1/2+
0.096
(J=5/2+)
O19
β−
15.3
14.3
13.792
d
11.678
t
12.0
10.408
n
10.47
8.76
(1/2)+
8.56
(3/2)
7.955
p
4.76
3.986
α
2.82
1.57
(3/2+)
0.110
0.197
5/2+
1/2−
J=1/2+
F19
β+
0.255
0.289
Ne19
(J=1/2+)
13.303
d
11.4
n
8.404
He3
6.370
p
3.435
α

FIG. 8e-15

TABLE 8e-1. ENERGY LEVELS OF THE LIGHT NUCLEI (*Continued*)

E_x	J, Π; T	Width or lifetime	Decay
		Ne^{19}: mass excess = 7.405 ± 0.014 Mev	
0	$(\frac{1}{2}^+)$; $\frac{1}{2}$	....	β^+
0.255	$\frac{1}{2}$	....	(γ)
0.289	$\frac{1}{2}$	....	(γ)

O^{20}: mass excess = 13.3 ± 2 Mev

Not reported: if the assumed mass excess is correct, the ground state ($T = 2$) is stable with respect to nucleon emission

E_x	J, Π; T	Width or lifetime	Decay
		F^{20}: mass excess = 5.913 ± 0.016 Mev	
0	(1^+); 1	$\tau_{\frac{1}{2}} = 11.4 \pm 1$ sec	β^-
0.65	1	....	(γ)
0.83	1	....	(γ)
0.99	1	....	(γ)
1.06	1	....	(γ)
1.31	1	....	(γ)
1.97	1	....	(γ)
2.05	1	....	(γ)
2.20	1	....	(γ)
(2.55)	1	....	(γ)
2.87	1	....	(γ)
2.97	1	....	(γ)
3.49	1	....	(γ)
3.53	1	....	(γ)
3.59	1	....	(γ)
3.68	1	....	(γ)
3.96	1	....	(γ)
4.08	1	....	(γ)
4.28	1	....	(γ)
4.31	1	....	(γ)
(5.06)	1	....	(γ)
6.63	1	Γ = 3 kev	n
6.65	1	Γ = 5 kev	n
6.70	1	Γ = 15 kev	n
6.86	1	Γ = 28 kev	n, γ
6.92	1	Γ ~ 200 kev	n
7.00	1	Γ = 24 kev	n
7.08	1	Γ = 33 kev	n
7.17	1	Γ = 28 kev	n, γ
7.34	1	....	n
7.39	1	....	n
7.44	1	....	n
7.50	1	....	n
7.78	1	....	n

TABLE 8e-1. ENERGY LEVELS OF THE LIGHT NUCLEI (*Continued*)

E_x	J, Π; T	Width or lifetime	Decay
8.18	1	....	n
8.54	1	....	n
(10.7)	....	....	(n, α)
(11.2)	....	....	(n, α)
Ne^{20}: mass excess = −1.139 ± 0.019 Mev			
0	(0^+); 0	....	Stable
1.63	2^+; 0	....	γ
(2.2)	0	....	(γ)
4.36	0	....	(γ)
5.4	0		
6.74	0^+; 0	$\Gamma = 19$ kev	α
7.18	3^-; 0	$\Gamma = 8$ kev	α
7.22	0^+; 0	$\Gamma = 4$ kev	α
7.45	2^+; 0	$\Gamma = 8$ kev	α
7.85	2^+; 0	$\Gamma = 3$ kev	α
9.3	(1^-); 0	....	(γ, α)
10.0	(1^-)	....	(γ, α)
11.69	......	....	γ
11.87	......	....	γ
13.08	......	$\Gamma = 0.95$ kev	p, α
13.19	1^+	$\Gamma = 2.8$ kev	p, α
13.33	......	$\Gamma = 2.1$ kev	p, α
13.44	(2^-)	$\Gamma = 35$ kev	p, α
13.51	1^+	$\Gamma = 7.1$ kev	p, α, γ
13.55	......	$\Gamma = 35$ kev	p, α
13.61	......	$\Gamma \sim 10$ kev	p, α
13.66	......	$\Gamma \sim 7.9$ kev	p, α
13.67	0^+	$\Gamma = 28$ kev	p, α
13.70	2^-	$\Gamma = 5.0$ kev	p, α
13.73	......	$\Gamma = 4.5$ kev	p, α
13.76	1^+	$\Gamma = 7.6$ kev	p, α
13.91	......	$\Gamma < 1.2$ kev	p, α, γ
13.93	......	$\Gamma \sim 60$ kev	p, α
13.95	......	$\Gamma = 3.5$ kev	p, α
13.99	......	$\Gamma \sim 130$ kev	p, α
14.04	......	$\Gamma = 70$ kev	p, α
14.10	(3^+)	$\Gamma = 18.2$ kev	p, α
14.13	......	$\Gamma = 3.8$ kev	p, γ
14.16	2^-	$\Gamma = 4.3$ kev	p, α
14.17	(2^+)	$\Gamma = 35$ kev	p, α
14.18	2^-	$\Gamma = 14.2$ kev	p, α
14.23	1^+	$\Gamma = 14.9$ kev	p, γ
14.41	......	$\Gamma \sim 5$ kev	p
14.47	......	$\Gamma = 29$ kev	p, α
14.50	0^+	$\Gamma = 135$ kev	p, α

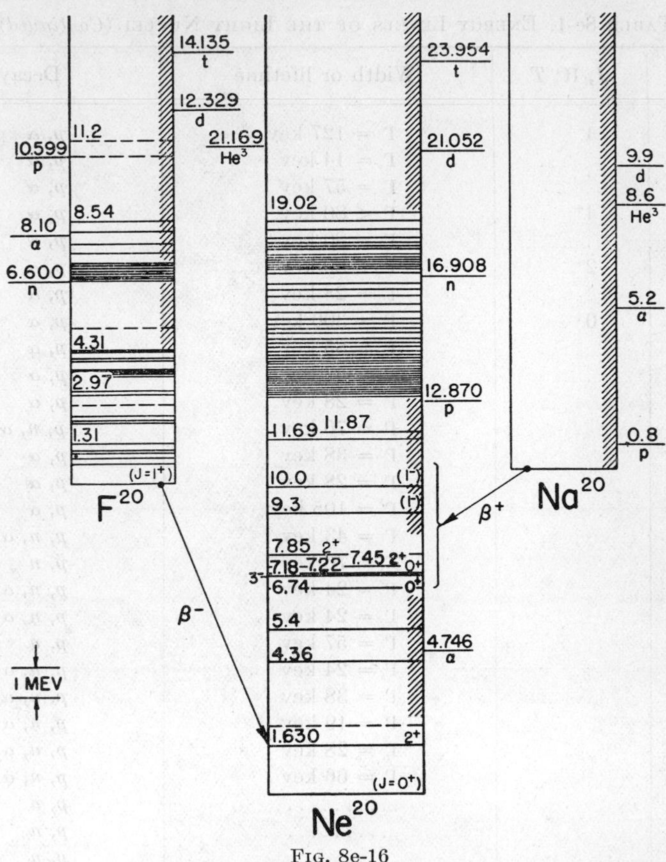
14.135
t
12.329
d
11.2
10.599
p
8.54
8.10
α
6.600
n
4.31
2.97
1.31
(J=1+)
F20
β-
I MEV
23.954
t
21.169
He3
21.052
d
19.02
16.908
n
12.870
p
11.69
11.87
10.0
(1-)
9.3
(1-)
7.85
2+
7.18-7.22
7.45
2+
0+
3-
6.74
0+
5.4
4.746
α
4.36
1.630
2+
(J=0+)
Ne20
9.9
d
8.6
He3
5.2
α
0.8
p
Na20
β+

Fig. 8e-16

TABLE 8e-1. ENERGY LEVELS OF THE LIGHT NUCLEI (*Continued*)

E_x	J, Π; T	Width or lifetime	Decay
14.64	1^-	Γ = 127 kev	p, α
14.71	......	Γ = 14 kev	p, α
14.80	......	Γ = 57 kev	p, α
14.89	4^+	Γ < 80 kev	p, α
15.07	......	Γ = 80 kev	p, α
15.08	2^+	Γ < 80 kev	p, α
15.25	......	Γ = 28 kev	p, α
15.34	0^+	Γ ~ 300 kev	p, α
15.37	......	Γ = 85 kev	p, α
15.53	......	Γ = 57 kev	p, α
15.74	......	Γ = 28 kev	p, α
15.90	......	Γ = 76 kev	p, n, α
16.19	......	Γ = 38 kev	p, α
16.59	......	Γ = 28 kev	p, α
16.67	......	Γ = 105 kev	p, α
16.95	......	Γ = 43 kev	p, n, α
17.11	......	Γ = 76 kev	p, n
17.14	......	Γ = 24 kev	p, n, α
17.21	......	Γ = 24 kev	p, n, α
17.26	......	Γ = 57 kev	p, n
17.35	......	Γ = 24 kev	p, n, α
17.41	......	Γ = 38 kev	p, n, α
17.61	......	Γ = 19 kev	p, n, α
17.69	......	Γ = 28 kev	p, n, α
17.81	......	Γ = 66 kev	p, n, α
18.01	......	....	p, n
18.36	......	....	p, n
18.65	......	....	p, n
19.02	......	....	p, n

Na^{20}: mass excess = 14.2 ± 0.5 Mev

No excited states are reported. The ground state (T = 1) decays by positron emission ($\tau_{\frac{1}{2}}$ = 0.38 ± 0.01 sec) to α-unstable states of Ne^{20}

8f. Gamma Rays

J. M. CORK

University of Michigan

8f-1. Absorption of Gamma Rays. A beam of gamma rays on passing through matter is reduced in intensity exponentially. If I_0 is the intensity of the incident radiation the intensity I after passing through a finite layer of material, whose thickness is x, is given by

$$I = I_0 e^{-\mu x}$$

where μ is the total absorption coefficient of the material. It is a function of the energy of the gamma rays and may be thought of as being the sum of a number of partial coefficients representing various processes of absorption.

It is customary to represent the probability of an absorption process by a cross section σ which is proportional to the absorption coefficient.

The total cross section may be regarded as the sum of the cross sections for each of the various processes by which the intensity of the beam of gamma rays is reduced. These processes are

1. Photoelectric effect
2. Compton scattering
3. Pair production
4. Nuclear photodisintegration
5. Elastic scattering

8f-2. The Photoelectric Effect. A photon of sufficiently high energy may give up its entire energy to an orbital electron. In this event the kinetic energy of the electron W_e is the difference between the gamma energy W_γ and the work function P of the electron, so that

$$W_e = W_\gamma - P$$

Absorption due to the photoelectric effect is greater the more tightly the electron is bound; hence it is more important for a K electron of the heavy elements. For these elements and radiation of low energy the photoelectric effect accounts for most of the absorption.

For energies up to 0.5 Mev, in light elements, Heitler has developed an expression for the cross section σ_K for the two K electrons which may be expressed as

$$\sigma_K = \frac{CZ^5}{W_\gamma^{\frac{7}{2}}} \qquad \text{cm}^2$$

where C is a calculable constant, approximately 10^{-33}, Z is the atomic number, and W_γ is the gamma energy in Mev. More detailed developments capable of being extended to the heavy elements and for higher energies have been made.

For very high energies, when $W_\gamma \gg 0.51$ Mev, the cross section is mainly given by

$$\sigma_K = \frac{1.41(10)^{-33}Z^5}{W_\gamma} \qquad \text{cm}^2$$

Values for the cross sections for K electrons in representative elements Be, Al, Cu, Ag, and Pb are shown graphically in Fig. 8f-1.

To obtain the contribution to the absorption coefficient due to the photoelectric effect it is necessary to consider not only the K, but also the L and M electrons.

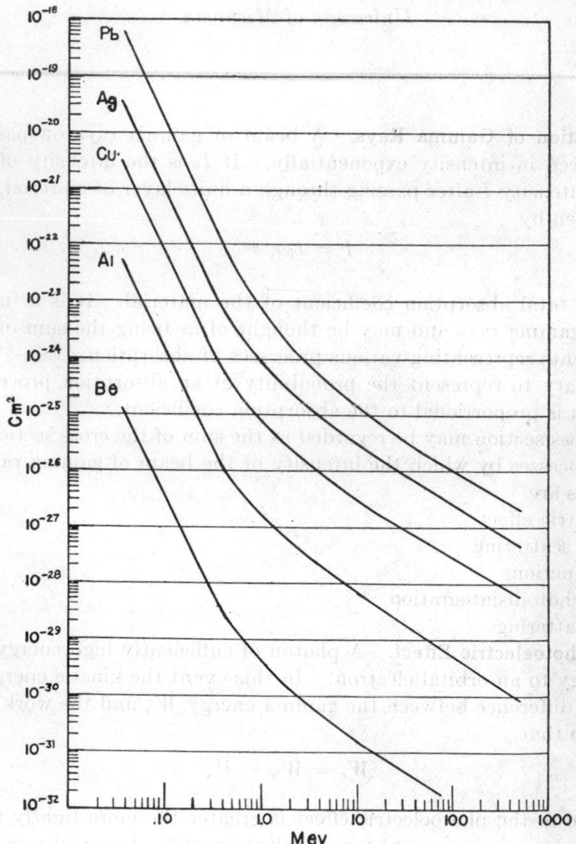

Fig. 8f-1. Photoelectric K electron cross sections as a function of gamma energy, in various elements.

Latyshev has reported that in heavy elements the total additional cross section due to all L electrons is about one-fifth that of the K electrons. In addition, the contribution due to all M electrons is estimated at one-twentieth that of the K electrons, so that the total photoelectric cross section per atom σ_p is about five-fourths of σ_K. For lighter elements the effect of the outer electronic shells is less, and $\sigma_p \cong (\frac{9}{8})\sigma_K$.

8f-3. The Compton Effect. A photon of energy W_γ, incident upon a loosely bound electron, may suffer an inelastic collision. The electron will recoil with some of the energy W_e leaving the scattered photon with a lower energy $(W_\gamma - W_e)$.

The kinetic energy of the electron W_e recoiling at an angle ϕ is equal in Mev to

$$W_e = \frac{1.02 W_\gamma \cos^2 \phi}{(W_\gamma + 0.51)^2 - W_\gamma^2 \cos^2 \phi}$$

The photon is scattered at an angle θ, which is related to ϕ by the relation

$$\tan \phi = \frac{0.51 \cot \theta/2}{W_\gamma + 0.51}$$

Compton scattering is particularly important in the lighter elements for energies up to a few Mev. The cross section σ_C for this scattering process per electron was first formulated by Klein and Nishina with the result which is shown graphically in Fig. 8f-2. Many experiments made at intermediate energies in elements of low

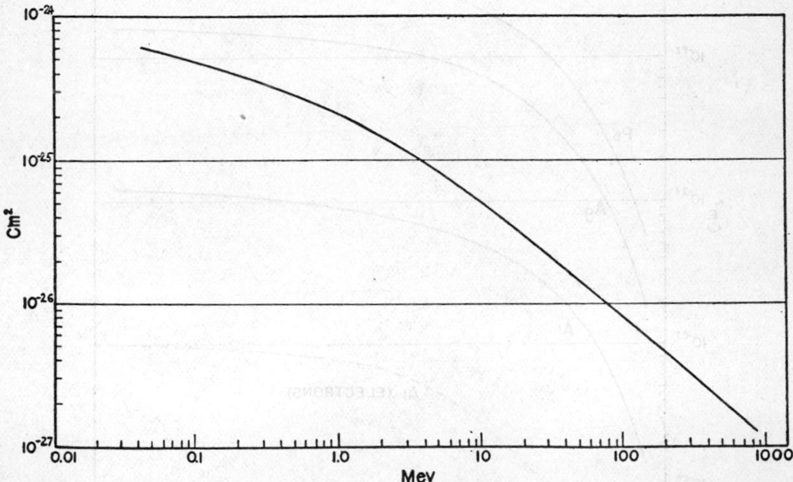

FIG. 8f-2. Cross section per electron for Compton scattering as a function of gamma energy.

atomic number, where corrections for the photoelectric effect and pair production are small, have confirmed the validity of this relationship.

8f-4. Pair Production. Following the discovery of the positron by Anderson several theoretical papers appeared dealing with the annihilation of a photon in the field of a nucleus. The energy of the photon W_γ in excess of that needed for the creation of the electron pair ($2m_0c^2 = 1.02$ Mev) appears as the kinetic energy of the two particles.

The differential cross section for the production of a pair of positive and negative electrons by a gamma ray has been computed by Bethe and Heitler. For intermediate energies, with no screening, this cross section is

$$\sigma_{pp} = 5.793 Z^2 (3.11 \log 3.92 W_\gamma - 8.07) 10^{-28} \text{ cm}^2$$

For the three elements Al, Ag, and Pb the cross sections are shown graphically in Fig. 8f-3.

At very high energies the screening cannot be neglected, and in this case the total cross section has been expressed as

$$\sigma_{pp} = 5.793 Z^2 (3.11 \log 183 Z^{-\frac{1}{3}} - 0.074) 10^{-28} \text{ cm}^2$$

This value for a particular Z is independent of the energy of the photon. Hence it can give only the upper asymptotes for the curves shown in Fig. 8f-3.

It is possible for a photon to produce pairs in the field of an electron. For an element such as aluminum with its 13 electrons the distribution with energy is shown in the lower dashed curve of Fig. 8f-3. It is apparent that the electronic effect is small compared with that due to the nucleus.

8f-5. Nuclear Photodisintegration. For photon energies, above the binding energy of the neutron, interactions may occur in which the neutron is ejected from the nucleus at the expense of the energy of the photon. The effect was first observed by

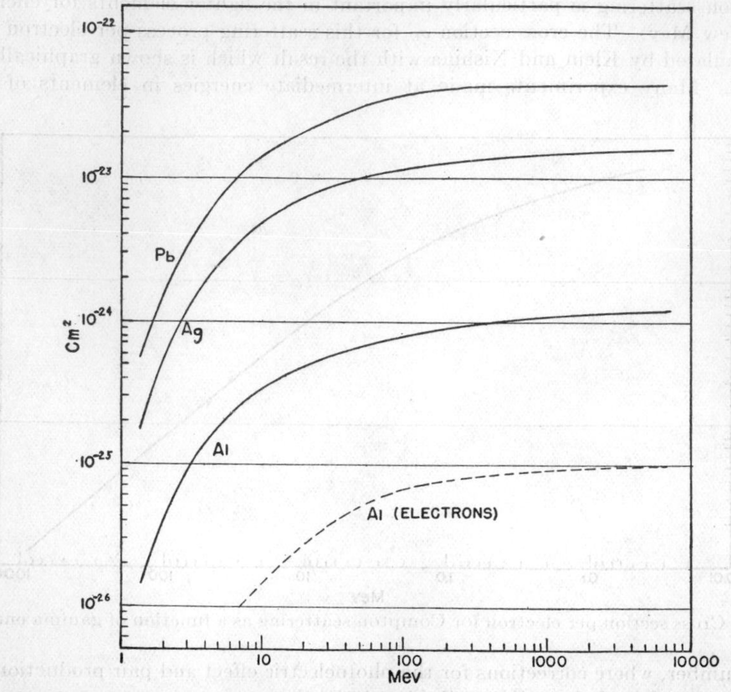

Fig. 8f-3. Cross section for pair production in Al, Ag, and Pb as a function of gamma energy. The dashed curve shows the contribution due to the electrons alone in Al.

Chadwick and Goldhaber in deuterium, which has a low threshold of only 2.224 Mev. For heavier elements energies of 10 Mev are required, and many observations of the effect have been made. The cross section for the effect is small, even at energies well above the binding energy of the neutron. It increases to a maximum at energies two to four times the binding energy of the neutron and then decreases for increasingly higher energies. This decrease is due to the introduction of competing decay processes at the higher energies, such as $(\gamma,2n)$ and (γ,np) interactions.

Below 30 Mev the interaction is assumed to be by dipole absorption. In general, for elements heavier than Be the value of the cross section is peaked between 15 and 25 Mev with a resonance width from 5 to 6 Mev. Empirically, the maximum cross section occurs at an energy W_m given by

$$W_m \cong 37A^{-0.186} \quad \text{Mev}$$

where A is the atomic mass of the nucleus.

The results of Montalbetti et al.[1] for Al, Ag, and Pb are shown in Fig. 8f-4. The values of the maximum cross sections are not in very good agreement with theory, especially for Pb.

8f-6. Elastic Scattering. Some contributions to the loss in intensity of a photon beam traversing matter are effected by "elastic" scattering. In this process the direction of the incident photon is altered with no change in its energy. The phenomenon is sometimes referred to as the Delbrück effect because of an early suggestion

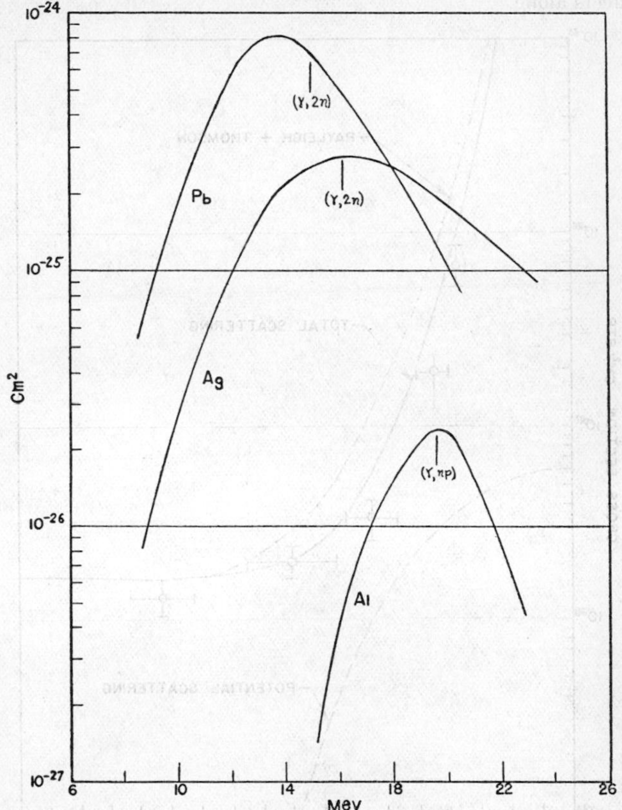

FIG. 8f-4. Cross section for nuclear photodisintegration in Al, Ag, and PB. (*Montalbetti, Katz, and Goldberg.*)

regarding the possibility of the scattering of a photon by a Coulomb field. It now appears that this may be accomplished by any of the following processes:

1. Thomson scattering by nucleus
2. Rayleigh scattering by bound electrons
3. Nuclear resonance scattering
4. Potential scattering by virtual pair production

The magnitude of each of these effects is small compared with that due to Compton scattering. Rayleigh scattering dominates at small angles and is due to the coherent scattering by the electrons. In the Thomson effect the nucleus vibrates under the action of the photon and reemits the same frequency. Nuclear resonance scattering

[1] Montalbetti, Katz, and Goldberg, *Phys. Rev.* **91**, 659 (1953).

occurs within the nucleus by the excitation to an excited virtual level by the absorption of the photon, followed by reemission. The probability of encountering this phenomenon is not large.

By observing only those scattered photons whose energies are unchanged, through the use of a pulse-height analyzer, experimental values have been obtained for the over-all effect as a function of angle. These experimental points[1] for lead, for a photon energy of 1.33 Mev, are shown graphically in Fig. 8f-5. The experimental values are smaller than those expected from calculations for the combined Rayleigh and Thomson effects alone.

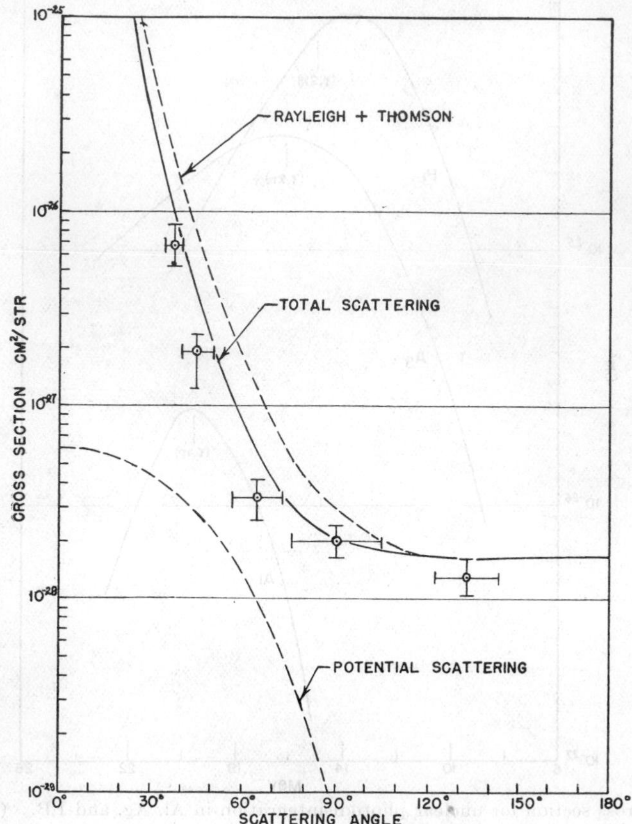

FIG. 8f-5. Cross section for the elastic scattering of photons.

A possible explanation of this discrepancy is to postulate the existence of some additional effect which is out of phase with the Rayleigh scattering. Such an effect might be the formation of a virtual electron pair which is annihilated with reemission of the incident energy at some angle other than the original. In combining computed values of this potential scattering with the Rayleigh and Thomson effects, the heavy curve of Fig. 8f-5 is obtained. The experimental points of Wilson show fair agreement with this curve.

8f-7. Total Absorption of Gamma Radiation. The total cross section for the loss of a gamma photon from the incident beam per atom of absorber is the sum of the individual cross sections, so that

[1] R. R. Wilson, *Phys. Rev.* **90**, 720 (1953).

$$\sigma_{\text{total}} = \underset{\text{(Photoelectric)}}{\sigma_p} + \underset{\text{(Compton)}}{\sigma_C} + \underset{\text{(Pair production)}}{\sigma_{pp}} + \underset{\text{(Photodisintegration)}}{\sigma_{pd}} + \underset{\text{(Elastic scattering)}}{\sigma_e}$$

At low energy, where the photoelectric effect predominates, σ varies approximately as Z^5 while at high energies, where pair production is the principal factor, it varies as Z^2. In general, the cross section at low energies is large and decreases to a minimum value as the energy increases. Beyond this minimum it rises steadily with increasing energy, because of pair production.

The calculated values for the absorption coefficient in Al, Cu, and Pb are shown graphically in Fig. 8f-6. It is apparent that minimum absorption occurs in these elements at 25, 10, and 3 Mev, respectively.

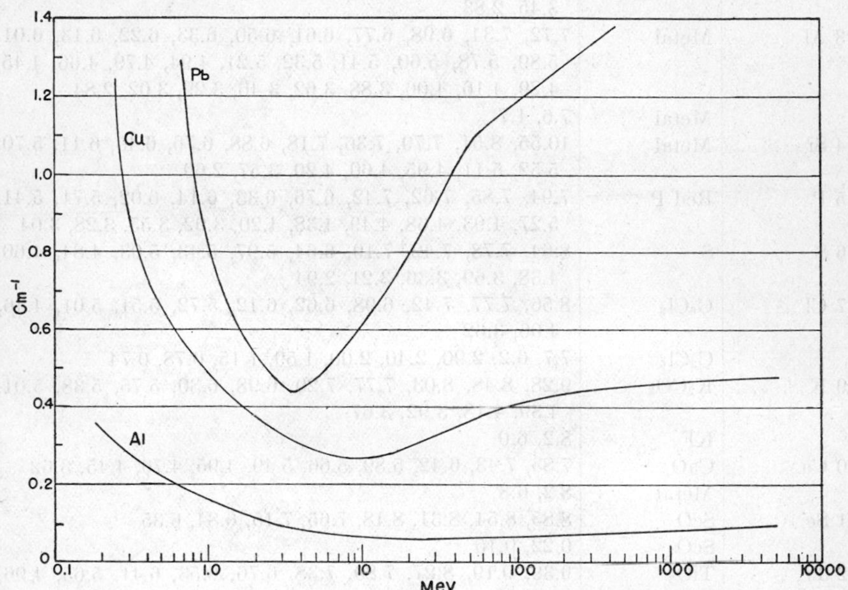

FIG. 8f-6. Total linear absorption coefficient as a function of gamma energy for Al, Cu, and Pb.

Many experiments on the over-all absorption coefficients of various elements for monoenergetic gamma rays have been made. The accuracy is dependent among other things on the use of an ideal geometry in which the absorber is remote from the receiver, a condition that is often overlooked. Conclusions from the experimental data have been varied. In some cases the experimental results appear to be in close agreement with theory, whereas in other reports considerable disagreement exists, especially for the heavy elements. For energies of 17.6, 88, and 280 Mev the experimental values have been reported to be less than the theoretical by about 10 per cent in lead and uranium, and by 3 per cent in tin. In aluminum and beryllium the experimental value is larger than the theoretical calculation. The deviation has been expressed[1] as a linear function of Z^2.

8f-8. Angular Correlation and Polarization of Gamma Rays. When an unstable nucleus emits in succession two radiations, there is the possibility that the directions of emission are not randomly distributed with respect to each other but that a certain anisotropy or correlation exists. Further a correlation may exist between the direction of propagation of one quantum and the polarization of a second emitted quantum.

[1] J. L. Lawson, *Phys. Rev.*, **75**, 433 (1949).

TABLE 8f-1. GAMMA RAYS ACCOMPANYING NEUTRON CAPTURE

Element	Source	Gamma energies, Mev
1 H........	H_2O	2.23
4 Be........	Be metal	3.41, 6.81
6 C........	Graphite	3.68, 4.95
7 N........	Be_3N_2	10.82, 9.16, 8.28, 7.36, 7.16, 6.32, 5.55, 5.29, 4.48
9 F........	C_2F_4	6.63
11 Na......	NaF	6.41, 5.61, 5.13, 3.96, 3.85, 3.60, 3.56
12 Mg......	Metal	9.26, 8.16, 7.37, 7.15, 6.75, 6.39, 5.73, 5.50, 5.05, 3.92, 3.45, 2.83
13 Al.......	Metal	7.72, 7.34, 6.98, 6.77, 6.61, 6.50, 6.33, 6.22, 6.13, 6.01, 5.89, 5.78, 5.60, 5.41, 5.32, 5.21, 4.94, 4.79, 4.66, 4.45, 4.29, 4.16, 4.06, 3.88, 3.62, 3.46, 3.29, 3.02, 2.84
	Metal	7.6, 1.7
14 Si.......	Metal	10.55, 8.51, 7.79, 7.36, 7.18, 6.88, 6.76, 6.40, 6.11, 5.70, 5.52, 5.11, 4.95, 4.60, 4.20, 3.57, 2.69
15 P........	Red P	7.94, 7.85, 7.62, 7.42, 6.76, 6.33, 6.14, 6.02, 5.71, 5.41, 5.27, 4.93, 4.68, 4.49, 4.38, 4.20, 3.92, 3.55, 3.28, 3.04
16 S........	S	8.64, 7.78, 7.42, 7.19, 6.64, 5.97, 5.43, 5.03, 4.84, 4.60, 4.38, 3.69, 3.36, 3.21, 2.94
17 Cl.......	C_6Cl_6	8.56, 7.77, 7.42, 6.98, 6.62, 6.12, 5.72, 5.51, 5.01, 4.46, 4.06, 3.62
	C_2Cl_6	7.7, 6.2, 2.90, 2.40, 2.00, 1.59, 1.15, 0.78, 0.74
19 K........	K_2CO_3	9.28, 8.48, 8.03, 7.77, 7.20, 6.98, 6.30, 5.75, 5.38, 5.01, 4.39, 4.18, 3.92, 3.67
	KF	8.2, 6.0
20 Ca......	CaO	7.83, 7.43, 6.42, 5.89, 5.66, 5.49, 4.95, 4.76, 4.45, 3.62
	Metal	8.2, 6.8
21 Sc	ScO	8.85, 8.54, 8.31, 8.18, 7.65, 7.15, 6.84, 6.35
	ScO	0.22, 0.15
22 Ti......	TiO_2	9.39, 9.19, 8.27, 7.80, 7.38, 6.76, 6.53, 6.41, 5.65, 4.96, 4.88, 4.67
	TiO_2	6.4, 3.97, 1.38, 1.00, 0.33
23 V.......	V_2O_5	7.31, 7.15, 6.87, 6.62, 6.51, 5.88, 5.74, 5.51, 5.21, 4.98, 4.85, 4.45, 4.15, 3.73, 3.59, 3.36
	Metal	7.4, 6.8, 5.7, 5.3
24 Cr......	Metal	9.72, 8.88, 8.50, 7.93, 7.67, 7.54, 7.36, 7.21, 7.10, 6.87, 6.64, 6.36, 6.26, 6.12, 6.00, 5.61, 5.26, 4.83, 3.72
	Metal	7.4, 6.8, 5.7, 5.3
25 Mn......	MnO_2	7.26, 7.15, 7.05, 6.78, 6.43, 6.11, 5.91, 5.77, 5.63, 5.53, 5.21, 5.04, 4.81, 4.72, 4.55, 4.24, 4.10, 3.82
	Metal	7.2, 5.0, 0.19, 0.09
26 Fe......	Metal	10.16, 9.30, 8.87, 8.35, 7.64, 6.02, 5.91, 4.97, 4.81, 4.44, 4.21, 3.86, 3.43
	Metal	8.5, 7.4, 6.0, 0.43
27 Co......	Metal	7.49, 7.20, 7.04, 6.97, 6.87, 6.69, 6.47, 6.25, 6.11, 5.97, 5.73, 5.65, 5.35, 5.18, 4.90, 4.59, 4.37, 4.18, 4.03, 3.69, 3.36
	Oxide	7.0, 5.9, 1.5, 1.1, 0.22

TABLE 8f-1. GAMMA RAYS ACCOMPANYING NEUTRON CAPTURE (*Continued*)

Element	Source	Gamma energies, Mev
28 Ni.......	Ni_2O_3	9.00, 8.53, 8.12, 7.82, 7.53, 7.22, 7.05, 6.84, 6.58, 6.34, 6.10, 5.99, 5.82, 5.70, 5.31
	Metal	9.0, 8.5, 7.5, 6.5
29 Cu......	Metal	7.91, 7.63, 7.30, 7.16, 7.01, 6.69, 6.41, 6.05, 5.75, 5.64, 5.43, 5.31, 5.18, 5.07
	Metal	7.5, 6.6, 0.15
30 Zn......	Metal	9.51, 9.12, 8.98, 8.58, 8.31, 7.88, 7.19, 6.94, 6.65, 6.49, 6.26, 6.03, 5.77, 5.48, 5.23, 4.84, 4.14
	Metal	7.5, 1.7
33 As.......	As_2O_3	7.30, 7.05, 6.85, 6.38, 6.05, 5.41, 5.17, 4.97, 4.77, 4.53
34 Se.......	SeO_2	10.48, 9.88, 9.17, 8.50, 8.09, 7.95, 7.73, 7.42, 7.19, 6.88, 6.59, 6.41, 6.23, 6.02, 5.80, 5.59, 5.21, 4.57
38 Sr.......	$SrCO_3$	9.22, 9.06, 8.38, 8.05, 7.53, 6.95, 6.87, 6.67, 6.27, 6.10, 5.82, 5.43
40 Zr.......	Metal	8.66, 7.71, 7.38, 6.30
41 Nb	Nb_2O_5	7.19, 6.85, 5.90
42 Mo......	MoC	9.15, 8.39, 7.79, 7.66, 7.54, 7.40, 6.92, 6.66, 6.39
45 Rh.......	Metal	0.16, 0.08
	Metal	6.79, 6.36, 6.20, 6.06, 5.91, 5.55
47 Ag......	Metal	0.19
	Metal	7.27, 7.06, 6.95, 6.67, 6.55, 6.27, 6.06
48 Cd.......	Metal	8.5, 0.56
	Metal	9.05, 8.48, 7.84, 7.73, 7.66, 6.82, 5.94
	Metal	(Cd^{113}) 0.070, 0.093, 0.535
49 In........	Metal	0.26, 0.16
	Metal	5.86, 5.73, 5.55, 5.34, 5.17, 4.97
50 Sn.......	Metal	8.0, 7.5
	Metal	9.35
51 Sb.......	Sb_2O_3	6.80, 6.50, 6.33, 6.11, 5.89, 5.61, 5.43
52 Te.......	Metal	0.61
56 Ba......	BaO	9.23, 7.79, 7.18, 6.68, 6.44, 6.06, 5.74, 4.98, 4.70, 4.10, 3.66
57 La.......	LaO	4.5
59 Pr.......	PrO_{11}	5.83, 5.67, 5.16, 4.79, 4.69
62 Sm......	Sm_2O_3	7.89, 7.24, 6.79, 6.54, 5.99
63 Eu......	$Sm_2{}^{149}O_3$	0.290, 0.329, 0.394, 0.433
64 Gd......	GdO	7.78, 7.36, 6.73, 6.41, 5.87, 5.61
	Metal	0.029, 0.038, 0.071, 0.077, 0.080, 0.130
66 Dy......	Dy_2O_3	0.074, 0.075, 0.079, 0.097, 0.135
73 Ta......	Metal	6.07, 5.78, 5.57, 5.38, 5.21, 5.05, 4.84
74 W.......	Metal	7.42, 6.73, 6.40, 6.18, 6.02, 5.77, 5.30, 5.25, 5.14, 4.94, 4.67
78 Pt.......	Metal	7.92, 7.26, 6.07, 5.24
79 Au......	Metal	6.49, 6.45, 6.31, 6.25, 6.15, 5.98, 5.70, 5.52, 5.20, 4.59
80 Hg......	HgF_2	6.45, 5.96, 5.65, 5.39, 5.07, 4.95, 4.83, 4.73, 4.66
	Metal Hg^{199}	0.282, 0.270
81 Tl.......	Tl_2O_3	6.54, 6.20, 5.90, 5.63, 5.25, 4.91, 4.72

With the development of scintillation counters, having greatly increased sensitivity, many examples of the effect have been found.

8f-9. Neutron Capture Gamma Rays. The binding energy per nucleon in the elements heavier than boron is of the order of 8 Mev. It must follow that the capture of a slow neutron in any isotope results in a highly excited state of the isotope greater in mass by unity. In the adjustment to the stable state of this isotope, gamma rays will be emitted.

Investigations confirmed the existence of these gamma rays and showed that the lifetime for many such emitters was less than 10^{-7} sec. It seems quite likely that this radiation consists of gamma rays with energies up to 10 Mev, because of transitions from a high-energy state whose lifetime is of the order of 10^{-14} sec, in cascade with low-energy gamma rays due to transitions from low-lying levels to the ground state. The latter states may have lifetimes of the order of 10^{-10} sec and the low-energy gammas are highly converted.

Extensive experimental studies have been made both at the Argonne National Laboratory and at the Canadian Chalk River Laboratory. Neutron beams from reactors irradiated the sources. In the investigations at Argonne the low-energy gamma energies have been evaluated by the use of magnetic beta spectrometers and multichannel scintillation crystal devices. The high-energy gamma rays have been studied at Chalk River by the use of magnetic electron-pair spectrometers. The difference in energies for the high-energy gamma rays should be in accord with the differences between the low-energy transitions. Many isotopes remain to be studied. The results to date are presented in Table 8f-1.

8g. Artificial Radioisotopes and Isomers

L. SLACK

George Washington University

8g-1. Introduction. Information on the radioactive isotopes from the neutron through the radioisotopes of bismuth is given in Table 8g-1. The values used were selected from the data in the files of the Nuclear Data Group of the National Research Council up to March 1, 1955, which were kindly made available to the author.

In a condensed table it is not possible to list all the work which has been done on each, or in fact most, of the isotopes. Accordingly one value for the energy of each of the various radiations is given. For references to the literature, as well as for other values, one should consult *National Bureau of Standards Circular* 499 and the subsequent publications of the Nuclear Data Group as listed in the References. The following classes of isotopes have been omitted: (1) the stable isotopes; (2) the isotopes having a nuclear charge Z greater than or equal to 84; (3) the isotopes emitting negative beta particles having no reported measurements of the energy of the betas; and (4) the isotopes for which the mass assignment is unknown or dubious.

8g-2. Explanation of Table 8g-1—Radioisotope Data. Column 1 lists the nucleus undergoing decay. The left subscript on the first isotope listed for a given element is the number of protons in the nucleus. The superscript is the mass number. The letter *m* following the mass number indicates that the decay data for the entry are for decay from a metastable or *isomeric* state. Decay from those states having half lives under a millisecond are listed under the parent radioactive nucleus. Metastable nuclei having half lives greater than a millisecond are listed under the nuclei themselves.

Column 2 lists the half life. Care has been exercised in the selection of values, but the values are not necessarily "best" values.

Column 3 gives the type of decay according to the following notation:

- β^- negative beta particle (negatron) emission
- β^+ positive beta particle (positron) emission
- ϵ electron capture (only when observed experimentally)
- α alpha-particle emission
- n neutron emission
- IT isomeric transition

Column 4 gives the energies of the component groups in beta transitions followed by information on the abundances of the groups according to the following notation:

For β^- transitions

- (+) relative number of β^- transitions in the group
- (%) number of β^- transitions in the group per 100 disintegrations

For β^+ transitions

- (+) relative number of β^+ transitions in the group
- (%) number of β^+ transitions in the group per 100 disintegrations
- (%*T*) number of transitions in the group ($\epsilon + \beta^+$) per 100 disintegrations
- [ ] ϵ/β^+, i.e., ratio of electron-capture transitions to β^+ transitions (total ϵ/β^+ if set off by a semicolon)

For some isotopes decaying by electron capture the disintegration energy has been measured and is denoted by E_{dis}. Conversion electron energies are not given. E_α and E_n are alpha and neutron energies, respectively.

Column 5 gives the energies of the gamma rays associated with the decay. Also given are data on the relative abundances of the gamma rays and the transitions, conversion coefficients, half lives of delayed radiations, and multipolarity in that order when these data are available. The following symbolism is used for gamma transitions:

- (+) relative number of gamma rays
- (%) number of transitions per 100 disintegrations
- [ ] number of conversion electrons per gamma ray = α
- [*K*] number of *K* conversion electrons per gamma ray = α_K
  number of *L* conversion electrons per gamma ray = α_L
- (τ =) half life of a delayed radiation
- M1, E2, etc. multipolarity of a transition when given in the literature
- w, vw, st, vst weak, very weak, strong, very strong (intensity)

The *L*-shell conversion coefficient α_L is given only when α_K has not been measured. *K/L* ratios are not given, nor are upper limits of half lives of delayed radiations when these are the only data given. For some isotopes only the energies of those transitions observed in more than one experiment are given. If the only value available for a transition is the conversion electron energy it is not, in general, listed. Selection of a particular value was based both on the method of measurement and on consistency with other data.

The References include general discussions of subjects pertinent to the study of radioisotopes.

TABLE 8g-1. RADIOISOTOPE DATA

Nuclide	Half life	Type of decay	Particle energy, Mev	Gamma-ray energy, Mev
$_0n^1$	13 min	β^-	0.78	
$_1H^3$	12.4 years	β^-	0.0180	
$_2He^6$	0.83 sec	β^-	3.50	
$_3Li^8$	0.9 sec	β^-, 2α	β_1^-13($\sim$90%); $\beta_2^-\beta_3^-$($\sim$10%), E_α (total) 3.2, 7–9	
Li^9	0.17 sec	β^-, n (delayed)	$\beta^- \sim 8$	
$_4Be^7$	53 days	ϵ	. . . .	0.479
Be^{10}	2.5 × 10^6 years	β^-	0.555	
$_5B^8$	0.7 sec	β^+, 2α	β^+: 13.7($\sim$85% T), <13, ($\sim$15% T); E_α cf. Li^8	
B^{12}	0.03 sec	β^-	13.43, $\sim$9.1($\sim$4%)	$\sim$4.5
$_6C^{10}$	19 sec	β^+	2.1(98% T)	0.72(100+), 1.03(2+)
C^{11}	20.4 min	β^+	0.968	
C^{14}	$\sim$5,600 years	β^-	0.155	No γ
C^{15}	2.4 sec	β^-	3.5, 8.8	5.3(intense)
$_7N^{12}$	0.013 sec	β^+, β^+, 3α	β^+ 16.6; E_α (total) $\sim$ 4 (τ_α = 0.013s)	
N^{13}	10.1 min	β^+	1.22	No γ between 0.14 and 0.7
N^{16}	7.4 sec	β^-	3.8($\sim$40%), 4.3($\sim$40%), 4.6($\sim$2%), 10.5($\sim$18%)	6.1(108+), 7.1(8+)
N^{17}	4.2 sec	β^-, n	β^-: 3.7; E_n = 0.92	
$_8O^{14}$	77 sec	β^+	1.83(100+), 4.14(3+)	2.30
O^{15}	2.0 min	β^+	1.683	No γ
O^{19}	29.4 sec	β^-	2.9(70%), 4.5(30%)	0.112(4+), 0.200(100+) (τ = 10^{-7}s), 1.366(67+)
$_9F^{17}$	70 sec	β^+	1.748	No γ
F^{18}	1.87 hr	β^+	0.649	No γ
F^{20}	12 sec	β^-	5.41	1.631
$_{10}Ne^{18}$	1.6 sec	β^+	3.2	

Ne^{19}	18.5 sec	β^+	2.16	No γ
Ne^{23}	40.2 sec	β^-	1.18(7%), 4.21(93%)	~2.8
$_{11}Na^{21}$	23 sec	β^+	2.50	No $\gamma > 0.5$
Na^{22}	2.6 years	β^+, ϵ	0.540(100+), 1.83(0.06+); ϵ(11%)	1.28
Na^{24}	15.0 hr	β^-	1.390, 4.17(0.003%)	1.368, 2.754
Na^{25}	62 sec	β^-	2.7(~45%), 3.7(~55%)	
$_{12}Mg^{23}$	11 sec	β^+	2.95	No γ
Mg^{27}	9.5 min	β^-	1.59(42%), 1.75(58%)	0.834, 1.015
Mg^{28}	21.4 hr	β^-	0.459	0.0319(96+)[K0.032]M1, 0.40(31+), 0.95(29+), 1.35(70+)
$_{13}Al^{24}$	2.1 sec	β^+	....	1.38, 2.7, 4.2, 5.4, 7.0
Al^{25}	7.6 sec	β^+	3.2	0.46, 2.03
Al^{26}	6.7 sec	β^+	3.2	
	Long	ϵ	....	1.83
Al^{28}	2.3 min	β^-	2.88, ~4.66(<0.8%)	1.78
Al^{29}	6.6 min	β^-	1.4(25%), 2.5(75%)	1.28(85+), 2.43(15+)
$_{14}Si^{27}$	4.0 sec	β^+	3.76	
Si^{31}	2.65 hr	β^-	1.47	1.26(0.07%)
Si^{32}	~700 years	β^-	~0.10	
$_{15}P^{28}$	0.28 sec	β^+	10.6	1.78, 2.67, 4.6, 4.89, 6.6, 7.1, 7.7
P^{29}	4.6 sec	β^+	~2.6(~3%), 3.95	1.28(1.5%), 2.43(2.5%)
P^{30}	2.5 min	β^+	3.3	No γ
P^{32}	14.3 days	β^-	1.71	No γ
P^{33}	24.4 days	β^-	0.25	No γ
P^{34}	12.4 sec	β^-	3.2(25%), 5.1(75%)	
$_{16}S^{31}$	2.4 sec	β^+	4.5	
S^{35}	87 days	β^-	0.167	
S^{37}	5.0 min	β^-	1.6(90%), 4.3(10%)	2.6
$_{17}Cl^{32}$	0.31 sec	β^+	9.4	2.25, 3.79, 4.33, 4.82
Cl^{33}	2.8 sec	β^+	4.43	2.85(~0.3%)
Cl^{34m}	32.4 min	β^+, IT	1.3, 2.6	0.145[0.16]M3, 2.13, 3.30

TABLE 8g-1. RADIOISOTOPE DATA (*Continued*)

Nuclide	Half life	Type of decay	Particle energy, Mev	Gamma-ray energy, Mev
Cl^{34}	1.5 sec	β^+	4.45	
Cl^{36}	4.4×10^5 years	β^-	0.714	
Cl^{38m}	1.5 sec	IT	....	0.66
Cl^{38}	37.3 min	β^-	1.11(31%), 2.77(16%), 4.81(53%)	1.6(43+), 2.15(57+)
Cl^{39}	56 min	β^-	1.65(93%), 2.96(7%)	0.35[0.5]
$_{18}A^{35}$	1.84 sec	β^+	4.4	
A^{37}	34 days	ϵ	$E_{dis} = 0.82$	
A^{39}	265 years	β^-	0.565	No $\gamma > 0.3$
A^{41}	1.8 hr	β^-	1.245(~100%)	1.3($\tau = 6.7 \times 10^{-9}$ sec)M2
$_{19}K^{38m}$	0.94 sec	β^+	4.57	
K^{38}	7.7 min	β^+	2.8	2.16
K^{40}	1.3×10^9 years	β^-, ϵ	1.32; ϵ: (91%)	1.46
K^{42}	12.5 hr	β^-	1.97(18%), 3.56(82%)	0.309(1.5+), 1.51(100+)
K^{43}	22 hr	β^-	0.24(5%), 0.46(5%), 0.83(83%), 1.22(5%), 1.84(2%)	0.219(1+), 0.369(67+), 0.393(6+), 0.627(100+)[$\sim 2 \times 10^{-4}$], 1.00(4+)
K^{44}	22 min	β^-	1.5, 4.9	1.13, 2.07, 2.48, others
$_{20}Ca^{39}$	0.9 sec	β^+	6.1	
Ca^{41}	1.1×10^5 years	ϵ		
Ca^{45}	164 days	β^-	0.254, none > 0.254	No γ
Ca^{47}	4.8 days	β^-	0.46(60%), 1.40(40%)	0.150, 0.234, 0.495, 0.80, 1.30
Ca^{49}	8.5 min	β^-	2.0	3.0
$_{21}Sc^{40}$	0.22 sec	β^+	9.0	3.75, no others
Sc^{41}	0.87 sec	β^+	4.94	
Sc^{43}	4.0 hr	β^+	0.39(4+), 0.82(17+), 1.20(79+)	0.25(1+), 0.369(16+), 0.627(4+), 0.84(w+)
Sc^{44m}	2.4 days	IT	....	0.271
Sc^{44}	4.0 hr	β^+, ϵ	1.46(98%)	1.16
Sc^{46m}	20 sec	IT	....	0.135 M3
Sc^{46}	84 days	β^-	0.36, 1.25(~0.1%)	0.885[1.9×10^{-4}], 1.119[0.88×10^{-4}]

Sc^{47}	3.44 days	β^-	0.28(28%), 0.49(72%)	~0.22
Sc^{48}	1.83 days	β^-	0.64	0.98(100+), 1.04(100+), 1.32(100+)
Sc^{49}	57 min	β^-	2.2	No γ
$_{22}Ti^{44}$	2.7 years	ϵ	....	0.16
Ti^{45}	3.07 hr	β^+	0.57(≤4%), 1.02(≥96%)	
Ti^{51}	5.8 min	β^-	1.9(80%), 2.2(20%)	0.32
$_{23}V^{46}$	0.4 sec	β^+	~6	
V^{47}	31.1 min	β^+	1.9	No γ
V^{48}	16.2 days	β^+, ϵ	0.69	0.99(100+), 1.32(100+), 2.29(1.7+)
V^{49}	600 days	ϵ	$E_{dis} = 0.617$, no β^+	0.128($\gamma/\epsilon \sim 10^{-4}$)
V^{52}	3.77 min	β^-	2.5	1.44
$_{24}Cr^{48}$	23 hr	ϵ	No β^+	0.116, 0.305
Cr^{49}	42 min	β^+	1.39(28%), 1.45(13%), 1.54(52%)	0.063(15+)[0.14]M1, 0.091(30+)[0.06]M2, 0.150(14+)[0.16]E2
Cr^{51}	27 days	ϵ	....	0.32(21%)[K0.0015]M1
Cr^{55}	3.5 min	β^-	~2.8	
$_{25}Mn^{50}$	0.3 sec	β^+	~6.3	
Mn^{51}	45 min	β^+	2.2	No γ
Mn^{52m}	21.3 min	β^+, IT	2.66(99.95%)	0.39(0.05%)E4
Mn^{52}	5.8 days	β^+, ϵ	0.582(32%)	0.73[3.0×10^{-4}], 0.94, [1.8×10^{-4}], 1.46, [7.2×10^{-5}]
Mn^{54}	320 days	ϵ	No β^+, no β^-	0.840
Mn^{56}	2.58 hr	β^-	0.65(20%), 1.04(30%), 2.81(50%)	0.822(12.5+), 1.8(19+), M1(98%)E2(2%), 2.13, (69+)M1(92%)E2(8%)
Mn^{57}	1.7 min	β^-	2.6	0.117(st+), 0.134(st+), 0.220(w+), 0.350(w+), 0.690(w+)
$_{26}Fe^{52}$	7.8 hr	β^+, ϵ	~0.64(40%)	No γ > 0.5
Fe^{53}	9 min	β^+	2.6(100+)	0.37(30+)
Fe^{55}	2.9 years	ϵ	$E_{dis} = 0.23$	No γ
Fe^{59}	45 days	β^-	0.271(46%), 0.462(54%), 1.56(0.3%)	0.191(2.8%)[7×10^{-3}]M1, 1.10(57%) [1.8×10^{-4}]M1, 1.29(43%)[1.4×10^{-4}]E2

TABLE 8g-1. RADIOISOTOPE DATA (*Continued*)

Nuclide	Half life	Type of decay	Particle energy, Mev	Gamma-ray energy, Mev
$_{27}Co^{55}$	18 hr	β^+	0.26(2.3+), 0.53(4.9+), 1.03(39.5+), 1.50(59.3+)	0.253(2+), 0.477(28+), 0.935(156+), 1.41(26+), 1.84(0.6+), 2.17(4+)
Co^{56}	77 days	β^+	0.44(4+), 1.50(96+)	0.85(100+), 1.24(55+), 1.75(24+), 2.30(12+), 2.60(14+), 3.25(24+)
Co^{57}	270 days	β^+	0.320	0.014(τ = 11 × 10^{-8} sec), 0.123(15+) [K0.011]M1, 0.138(1+)[K0.14]E2
Co^{58m}	9 hr	IT	....	0.025[large]M3
Co^{58}	72 days	β^+	0.472(15%)	0.805[2.9 × 10^{-4}]E2
Co^{60m}	10.5 min	β^-	1.56(0.28%)	0.059[K35]M3
Co^{60}	5.2 years	β^-	0.31, 1.48(0.15%)	1.1728[1.6 × 10^{-4}], 1.3325[1.2 × 10^{-4}]
Co^{61}	1.65 hr	β^-	1.00(45%), 1.42(55%)	~0.5
Co^{62}	14 min	β^-	2.8	1.0(40+), 1.17(100+), 1.7(10+), 2.0(15+)
$_{28}Ni^{56}$	6.4 days	ϵ	β^+: (<1%)	0.17(100+), 0.28(30+), 0.48(40+), 0.81(80+), 0.96(10+), 1.33(5+), 1.58(15+), 1.75(2+)
Ni^{57}	36 hr	β^+, ϵ	0.835(50%)	0.123, 1.38, 1.91
Ni^{59}	7.5 × 10^4 years	ϵ	E_{dis} = 1.07	
Ni^{63}	85 years	β^-	0.065, no β^+	
Ni^{65}	2.56 hr	β^-	0.60(29%), 1.01(14%), 2.10(57%)	0.37, 1.12, 1.49
$_{29}Cu^{60}$	23 min	β^+	2.00(69+), 3.00(18+), 3.92(6+)	0.85(15+), 1.33(80+), 1.76(52+), 2.13(5.7+), 2.64(5.5+), 3.13(3.7+), 3.52(2.0+), 4.0(1.1+)
Cu^{61}	3.3 hr	β^+, ϵ	0.550(4+), 1.21(96+)	0.076(0.01+), 0.284(4.5+), 0.655(25+)
Cu^{62}	10 min	β^+	2.92	
Cu^{64}	12.8 hr	β^+, β^-, ϵ	β^+: 0.657(62%T); β^-: 0.571	1.34[1.3 × 10^{-4}]
Cu^{66}	5.10 min	β^-	1.59(9%), 2.63(91%)	1.04[3 × 10^{-3}]
Cu^{67}	59 hr	β^-	0.395(45%), 0.484(35%), 0.577(20%)	0.092[0.5], 0.182[0.012]
Cu^{68}	32 sec	β^-	~3	

$_{30}Zn^{62}$	9.3 hr	β^+, ϵ	0.665(10%)	0.0413[K0.52]M1
Zn^{63}	38 min	β^+	0.47(1%), 1.40(7%), 2.36(85%)	0.960[1.8×10^{-4}], 1.89, 2.60
Zn^{65}	245 days	β^+	0.325(2%), ϵ_{gs}; (54.2%)	1.11(44.1%)[2.6×10^{-4}]E2
Zn^{69m}	14 hr	IT	....	0.435[0.06]M4
Zn^{69}	52 min	β^-	0.897(100%)	
Zn^{71}	3 hr	β^-	1.5	0.38, 0.49, 0.61
	2.2 min	β^-	2.4	0.12, 0.51, 0.90, 1.05
Zn^{72}	49 hr	β^-	0.3(95%), 1.6(5%)	
$_{31}Ga^{64}$	2.6 min	β^+	~5	0.97, 2.2, 3.8
Ga^{65m}	8 min	β^+	....	No γ
Ga^{65}	15 min	β^+	2.1(90%), 2.52(10%)	0.052[large], 0.092, 0.114
Ga^{66}	9.4 hr	β^+	0.40(1%), 0.90(4.5%), 1.38(2.7%), 4.15(56%); ϵ: (34%)	1.05(35%), 1.7(3.2%), 2.2(4.5%), 2.75(27.3%), 3.3(4.5%), 4.25(2.0%), 4.8(2%)
Ga^{67}	78 hr	ϵ	No β^+(<0.01%)	0.090(2.7+), 0.092(63.9+)[0.54]($\tau \sim 9 \mu$sec), 0.182(29.6+), 0.206(1.0+), 0.296(20.2+), 0.388(4.9+), 0.496(0.4+), 0.790(0.2+), 0.880(0.4+)
Ga^{68}	68 min	β^+	0.77(3%), 1.88(82%)	1.10(10%)
Ga^{70}	21.9 min	β^-	0.4(0.3%), 0.6(0.5%), 1.65	0.174, 1.036
Ga^{72}	14.1 hr	β^-	0.56(25%), 0.74(23%), 1.00(26%), 1.45(7%), 1.75(3%), 2.57(8%), 3.17(8%)	0.63(54+), 0.69(5+), ($\tau = 0.33$ μsec), 0.83(~100+), 1.05(15+), 1.47, 1.57, 1.81(10+), 2.18(35+), 2.491(6+), 2.508(10+)
Ga^{73}	5 hr	β^-	1.4	0.054, 0.135
$_{32}Ge^{67}$	20 min	β^+	3.4	0.17
Ge^{68}	250 days	ϵ		
Ge^{69}	40 hr	β^+, ϵ	0.220(2+), 0.610(10+), 1.215(88+); ϵ: (67%)	0.090, 0.388, 0.576(44+), 0.870(29+), 1.120(100+), 1.340, 1.610
Ge^{71}	11.4 days	ϵ	$E_{dis} = 0.237$	
Ge^{75m}	49 sec	IT	No β^-	0.139[2]

TABLE 8g-1. RADIOISOTOPE DATA (*Continued*)

Nuclide	Half life	Type of decay	Particle energy, Mev	Gamma-ray energy, Mev
Ge^{75}	82 min	β^-	0.614(15%), 1.137(85%)	0.067(2.2+), 0.138(<0.15+), 0.203(12+), 0.269(100+), 0.405(<0.03+), 0.427(2.5+), 0.48(2.3+), 0.628(1.8+)
Ge^{77m}	52 sec	β^-, IT	2.7	0.159(100+), 0.215(100+), 0.380
Ge^{77}	12 hr	β^-	0.710(23%), 1.379(35%), 2.196(42%)	0.042, 0.073, 0.213, 0.264, 0.300, 0.327, 0.368, 0.408, 0.418, 0.466, 0.564, 1.105, ~1.75
Ge^{78}	86 min	β^-	~0.9	
$_{33}As^{70}$	52 min	β^+, ϵ	2.7; [<0.2]	1.04, 1.7, 2.0
As^{71}	60 hr	β^+, ϵ	~0.30, 0.80; [~2]	0.0233, 0.175
As^{72}	26 hr	β^+, ϵ	0.27(2+), 0.67(5+), 1.84(12+), 2.50(62+), 3.34(19+); [~2]	0.702, 0.835, others up to ~3
As^{73}	76 days	ϵ	No β^+	0.0135[large](τ = 4.6 μsec), 0.054[4.7] (τ = 0.33 sec)
As^{74}	17.5 days	β^+, β^-, ϵ	β^+: 0.92(42+), 1.53(5+); β^-: 0.69(26+), 1.36(27+)	0.5963, 0.6352
As^{76}	26.5 hr	β^-	0.35(3%), 1.20(6%), 1.75(6%), 2.40(32%), 2.96(53%)	0.549(100+)E2, 0.643(22+), E2M1, 1.200(27+), 1.40(2+), 2.05(5+)
As^{77}	38.7 hr	β^-	0.679	0.088(0.3%), 0.155(~0.2%), 0.243(23%), 0.528(0.7%)
As^{78}	91 min	β^-	1.4(30%), 4.1(70%)	0.27
As^{79}	9 min	β^-	2.3	
$_{34}Se^{72}$	9.7 days	ϵ		
Se^{73}	7.1 hr	β^+	0.250(1.1+), 0.750(10.3+), 1.318 (87.4+), 1.680(1.2+); [0.59]	0.0671, 0.361, 0.860, 1.310
Se^{75}	127 days	ϵ	No β^+	0.067(0.5%), 0.077(14%), 0.098(6.5%)[8], 0.124(2%)[0.3], 0.138(21%)[0.12], 0.203 (0.04%), 0.268(70%)[0.09], 0.281(~5%), 0.307(0.03%), 0.405(14%)[0.0015]

Se^{77m}	17.5 sec	IT	....	0.162E3
Se^{79m}	3.9 min	IT	....	0.096E3
Se^{79}	6.5×10^4 years	β^-	0.16	
Se^{81m}	58 min	IT	....	$0.103[\sim\infty]$E3
Se^{81}	18 min	β^-	1.38	No γ
Se^{83m}	69 sec	β^-	3.4	
Se^{83}	26 min	β^-	1.5	0.176, 0.950
${}_{35}Br^{75}$	1.6 hr	β^+, ϵ	0.3(19+), 0.6(15+), 0.8(20+), 1.70(46+); $[\sim 4]$	$\sim$0.6
Br^{76}	17 hr	β^+	0.6(19+), 0.8(14+), 1.1(11+), 1.7(10+), 3.57(46+)	0.25, 0.33, 0.37, 0.42, 0.68, 0.75, 0.96, 1.21
Br^{77}	58 hr	β^+, ϵ	0.336(5%); [19]	0.160(0.64+), 0.237(20+), 0.284(0.22+), 0.298(0.25+), 0.520(100+), 0.641(8.6+), 0.813(25+). Cf. Se^{77m}
Br^{78}	6.4 min	β^+	2.3	0.046, 0.108
Br^{80m}	4.5 hr	IT	....	0.036[1.3]E1, 0.049[>50]M3
Br^{80}	18.5 min	β^+, β^-	$\beta^+ = 0.86(\sim 8\% T)$; $\beta^- = 1.42(\sim 15+)$, 2.04(85+)	0.62
Br^{82}	35.7 hr	β^-	0.465	0.535(368+), 0.602, 0.750(353+), 1.02(100+), 1.29(85+), 1.45(40+)
Br^{83}	2.3 hr	β^-	0.940	0.009, 0.032, 0.051. Cf. Kr^{83m}
Br^{84}	32 min	β^-	1.72(35%), 2.53(16%), 3.56(9%), 4.68(40%)	0.890, 1.89
Br^{85}	3 min	β^-	2.5	No γ
Br^{87}	55.6 sec	β^-, n	2.6(70%), 8.0(30%); delayed neutrons (2%)	$\sim$3(80+), 5.4(20+)
Br^{89}	4.5 sec	β^-, n	n: mean $E_n \approx 0.5$	
${}_{36}Kr^{77}$	1.1 hr	β^+, ϵ	1.7($\sim$30%)	
Kr^{79m}	55 sec	IT	....	0.127E3
Kr^{79}	34.5 hr	β^+, ϵ	0.595(10%)	0.044, 0.263[K0.016]
Kr^{81m}	10 sec	IT	....	0.19E3
Kr^{81}	2.1×10^5 years	ϵ		

TABLE 8g-1. RADIOISOTOPE DATA (*Continued*)

Nuclide	Half life	Type of decay	Particle energy, Mev	Gamma-ray energy, Mev
Kr^{83m}	1.88 hr	IT	....	0.009[~10]M1, 0.032[large]E3
Kr^{85m}	4.4 hr	β^-, IT	0.830(84%)	0.150[*K*0.040], 0.305[*K*0.41]M4
Kr^{85}	10.3 years	β^-	0.695	
Kr^{87}	78 min	β^-	1.27(25%), 3.63(75%)	0.45, 1.89, ~2.3
Kr^{88}	2.8 hr	β^-	0.52(68%), 0.9(12%), 2.7(20%)	0.028
Kr^{89}	3.1 min	β^-	2.0(35%), 4.0	
Kr^{90}	33 sec	β^-	3.2, others	
Kr^{91}	10 sec	β^-	~3.6, others	
$_{37}Rb^{81}$	4.7 hr	β^+, ϵ	0.990	0.95
Rb^{82m}	6.3 hr	β^+	0.175, 0.775	0.188, 0.248, 0.322, 0.389, 0.423, 0.464, 0.550, 0.610, 0.690, 0.768(vs+), 0.818, 1.020, 1.314, 1.464
Rb^{82}	1.25 min	β^+	3.15	
Rb^{83}	83 days	ϵ	....	~0.15, ~0.45, 0.8
Rb^{84m}	22 min	IT	....	0.239(100+), 0.463(70+), 0.890(6+)
Rb^{84}	34 days	β^+	0.37(3+), 0.82(58+), 0.839, 1.629(39+)	0.890
Rb^{86}	19.5 days	β^-	0.680(~12%), 1.770(~88%)	1.080
Rb^{87}	6.2 × 10^{10} years	β^-	0.275	No γ
Rb^{88}	17.8 min	β^-	2.04(15%), 3.29(19%), 5.13(66%)	0.90, 1.86, 2.8
Rb^{89}	15.4 min	β^-	4.5	
Rb^{90}	2.7 min	β^-	5.7, others	
Rb^{91}	100 sec	β^-	4.6, others	
	14 min	β^-	3.0, others	
$_{38}Sr^{82}$	26 days	β^+	3.15	
Sr^{83}	38 hr	β^+	1.15	0.040, 0.074, 0.101, 0.151, 0.165
Sr^{85m}	70 min	IT, ϵ	ϵ: (14%)	0.0075(84.7%)[large]E3, 0.150, 0.225(84.7%)M1, 0.233(1.3%)M4

Sr^{85}	65 days	ϵ	...	0.513(100%)[0.008](τ = 0.9 μsec)M2
Sr^{87}	2.8 hr	IT	...	0.388[K0.28]M4
Sr^{89}	53 days	β^-	1.463	
Sr^{90}	20 years	β^-	0.531	
Sr^{91}	9.7 hr	β^-	0.61(7%), 1.09(33%), 1.36(29%), 2.03(4%), 2.67(27%)	0.552(20.5+), 0.645(5.2+), 0.748(9.2+), 0.93(1.1+), 1.025(10.4+), 1.413(1.8+)
${}_{39}Y^{84}$	3.7 hr	β^+, ϵ	2.0	
Y^{86}	14.6 hr	β^+	1.19(~50%), 1.80(~50%)	1.4
Y^{87m}	14 hr	IT	...	0.384[0.24]M4
Y^{87}	80 hr	β^+, ϵ	~0.7	0.388, 0.483. Cf. Sr^{87}
Y^{88}	105 days	β^+, ϵ	0.83(0.19%)	0.908(~99%)[$K3.4 \times 10^{-4}$]E1, 1.853[$K1.7 \times 10^{-4}$], 2.76(~1%)
Y^{89}	14 sec	IT	...	0.913[0.01]M4
Y^{90}	64.6 hr	β^-	2.25	
Y^{91m}	50 min	IT	...	0.551[K0.046]M4
Y^{91}	57 days	β^-	0.33(0.35%), 1.55(~100%)	1.22(0.3%)
Y^{92}	3.5 hr	β^-	3.5	0.6
Y^{93}	10 hr	β^-	3.1	0.7
Y^{94}	17 min	β^-	5.4	1.4
${}_{40}Zr^{87}$	1.6 hr	β^+, ϵ	2.10	0.35, 0.65. Cf. Y^{87m}
Zr^{88}	85 days	ϵ	...	0.406
Zr^{89m}	4.3 min	β^+, IT	~0.85(1.5%), 2.43(~0.4%)	0.588(100+)[0.08]M4, 1.53(8+)
Zr^{89}	79 hr	β^+, ϵ	0.90	0.913
Zr^{93}	9.5×10^5 years	β^-	0.063	
Zr^{95}	65 days	β^-	0.364(54%), 0.396(43%), 0.88(3%)	0.235, 0.722, 0.754. Cf. Nb^{95m}
Zr^{97}	17 hr	β^-	1.91	0.75[0.015]. Cf. Nb^{97m}
${}_{41}Nb^{89}$	1.9 hr	β^+	2.9	
Nb^{90}	15 hr	β^+	1.2	0.14, 1.14, 2.23
Nb^{91m}	62 days	IT	...	0.104[~50]M4
Nb^{91}	~8 years	ϵ		
Nb^{92m}	13 hr	ϵ	No β	No γ

TABLE 8g-1. RADIOISOTOPE DATA (*Continued*)

Nuclide	Half life	Type of decay	Particle energy, Mev	Gamma-ray energy, Mev
Nb^{92}	10 days	ϵ	No β^+, no β^-	0.93(100+), 1.84(1+)
Nb^{93}	3.7 years	IT	....	0.027
Nb^{94m}	6.6 min	IT, β^-	1.3(~0.1%)	0.415(~99.9%)[$K > 100$]
Nb^{94}	2.7 × 10^4 years	β^-,IT	0.50	0.70(92+), 0.87(92+), 1.57(8+)
Nb^{95m}	90 hr	IT	....	0.231[very large]M4
Nb^{95}	35 days	β^-	0.16	0.771[0.0021]E2, M1
Nb^{96}	23 hr	β^-	0.370(8%), 0.750(92%)	0.216(7%)[<0.23], 0.238(10%)[<0.16], 0.451 (27%)[40], 0.560(61%)[16], 0.725(5%), 0.770 (100%)[12], 0.804(6%)[13], 1.078(52%)[5.6], 1.187(32%)[3.1]
Nb^{97m}	60 sec	IT	....	0.747[0.015]M4
Nb^{97}	74 min	β^-	1.267	0.665[~0.0015]
Nb^{99}	2.5 min	β^-	3.2	
$_{42}Mo^{90}$	5.7 hr	β^+	~1.4	~0.12, ~0.25, 1.1
Mo^{91m}	66 sec	β^+	2.6	
Mo^{91}	15.5 min	β^+	3.3	
Mo^{93m}	6.9 hr	IT	....	0.262[0.7]E4, 0.684[K0.0015]M1, 1.48[2.4 × 10^{-4}]E2M1
Mo^{93}	>2 years	ϵ		
Mo^{99}	68 hr	β^-	0.45(14%), 0.87(~1%),1.23(85%)	0.040[~5], 0.140, 0.181, 0.367(10+), 0.741(100+), 0.780(14+). Cf. Tc^{99m}
Mo^{101}	14.6 min	β^-	1.2(70%), 2.2(30%)	0.191, 0.96 M1 or E2
$_{43}Tc^{92}$	4.5 min	β^+, ϵ	3.5; [0.25]	1.5
Tc^{93m}	43.5 min	IT, ϵ	ϵ: (20%)	0.39(80%)[K0.31]M4, 2.7(20%)
Tc^{93}	2.7 hr	β^+, ϵ	0.64(13+)[0.67], 0.82(26+)[0.67]; ϵ: (93%)	1.35(200+), 1.50(100+), 2.0(15+)
Tc^{94}	52.5 min	β^+, ϵ	0.9(~1%), 2.41(73%)	0.874(21+), 1.85(2.5+), 2.73(0.3+), 3.27(0.3+)

Tc^{95m}	60 days	β^+, ϵ, IT	0.4(∼0.4%); ϵ: (96%)	0.039(3%)M4, 0.201(70+)[0.036], 0.570(40+)[0.0022], 0.810(30+)[0.0010], 1.017(3+)
Tc^{95}	20 hr	ϵ	No β^+	0.762, 0.932, 1.071
Tc^{96m}	51.5 min	IT	....	0.0344M3
Tc^{96}	4.3 days	ϵ	No β^+	0.312(25+), 0.771(123+), 0.806(91+), 0.842(100+), 1.19(10+)[2.7×10^{-4}]
Tc^{97m}	91 days	IT	....	0.095[large]M4
Tc^{97}	∼10^5 years			
Tc^{99m}	6.04 hr	IT	....	0.0018[large]E3, 0.140(98.6%), 0.142(1.4%)M4
Tc^{99}	2.2×10^5 years	β^-	0.293	
Tc^{100}	16 sec	β^-	2.8	
Tc^{101}	14.3 min	β^-	1.20	0.31, 0.556(w+), 0.734(w+)
Tc^{102}	5 sec	β^-	3.7	
$_{44}Ru^{95}$	1.6 hr	β^+, ϵ	1.1	
Ru^{97}	2.8 days	ϵ	....	0.220, 0.325, 0.565
Ru^{103}	40 days	β^-	0.217(99%), 0.70(∼1%)	0.404, 0.498(100+)[K0.0055], 0.608(7.5+)
Ru^{105}	4.4 hr	β^-	1.150	0.130, 0.726. Cf. Rh^{105m}
Ru^{106}	1 year	β^-	0.039	No γ
Ru^{107}	4 min	β^-	∼4	
$_{45}Rh^{98}$	9 min	β^+	4.0	
Rh^{99}	4.5 hr	β^+	0.74	0.286
Rh^{100}	20.8 hr	β^+, ϵ	0.15(0.06+), 0.54(3.6+), 1.26(13+), 2.07(39+), 2.62(45+); [0.062]	0.301(5.3+), 0.372(0.9+), 0.442(21.3+), 0.535(100+), 0.742(0.6+), 0.823(9.7+), 1.108(1.5+), 1.358(2.8+), 1.557(1.1+), 1.934(0.4+), 2.379(1.0+)
Rh^{101}	4.3 days	ϵ	....	0.144, 0.286
Rh^{102}	210 days	β^+, β^-, ϵ	β^+: 0.40(4+), 0.76(21+), 1.24(59+); β^-: 1.15(100+)	0.086, 0.124, 0.195, 0.353, 0.475
Rh^{103m}	57 min	IT	....	0.040[∼∞]E3

TABLE 8g-1. RADIOISOTOPE DATA (*Continued*)

Nuclide	Half life	Type of decay	Particle energy, Mev	Gamma-ray energy, Mev
Rh^{104m}	4.3 min	IT	. . . . . .	0.051[~25]E3, 0.077M3
Rh^{104}	44 sec	β^-	2.6	0.55, 1.2(w+)
Rh^{105m}	45 sec	IT	. . . . . .	0.130[1.8]E3
Rh^{105}	36.5 hr	β^-	0.21(~4%), 0.57(~96%)	0.32
Rh^{106}	30 sec	β^-	2.0(3%), 2.44(12%), 3.1(11%), 3.53(68%)	0.220, 0.409, 0.511(20.5%)[*K*0.0035]E2, 0.624 (10.4%)[*K*0.0021], 0.88(0.3%), 1.045(1.7%), 1.14(0.4%), 1.54(0.2%), 1.76(<0.1%), 2.28 (<0.1%), 2.42(<0.1%)
Rh^{107}	24 min	β^-	1.2	
${}_{46}Pd^{100}$	4 days	ϵ	. . . . . .	0.081, 1.8
Pd^{101}	9 hr	β^+, ϵ	2.3(10%); [~9]	No γ
Pd^{103}	17 days	ϵ	. . . . . .	0.040[*K*70]. Cf. Rh^{103m}
Pd^{107}	7 × 10^6 years	β^-	0.035	
Pd^{109m}	4.8 min	IT	. . . . . .	0.17[0.6]E3
Pd^{109}	13.6 hr	β^-	1.020	0.088. Cf. Ag^{109}
Pd^{111m}	5.5 hr	IT, β^-	(25%)	0.16, 1.77 and γ's in 22*m* Pd^{111}
Pd^{111}	22 min	β^-	2.15	0.38, 0.56, 0.65, 0.73
Pd^{112}	21 hr	β^-	0.28	0.018
${}_{47}Ag^{102}$	73 min	β^+, ϵ		
Ag^{103}	1.1 hr	β^+	1.3	0.554, 0.764
Ag^{104}	27 min	β^+	2.70	0.555
Ag^{105}	45 days	ϵ	No β^+	0.064, 0.154(w+), 0.180(w+), 0.281, 0.319, 0.331, 0.393(w+), 0.443
Ag^{106}	8.6 days	ϵ	No β^+	0.220, 0.409, 0.512[*K*0.003]E2, 0.620, 0.711, 0.815, 1.04, 1.24, 1.55
	24 min	β^+	1.5(29%), 1.94(71%)	0.511
Ag^{107m}	44 sec	IT	. . . . . .	0.093[*K*9.5]E3
Ag^{108}	2.3 min	β^-, β^+, ϵ	β^-: 1.15(0.8%), 1.15(97.3%); β^+: (0.14%)	0.43(100+), 0.60(79+), 0.62

Isotope	Half-life	Decay	Particle energies	Gamma energies
Ag^{109m}	40 sec	IT	....	0.0875[K9.5]E3
Ag^{110m}	270 days	β^-, IT	0.087(~58+), 0.530(35+)	0.116M4, 0.656(100+)[0.0025]M1 or E2, 0.676(w+), 0.706(w+), 0.759(w+), 0.814 (vw+), 0.885(81+), 0.935(31+), 1.389 (33+), 1.516(17+). Rel. intensities for equilibrium mixture of 270 days and 24 sec
Ag^{110}	24 sec	β^-	2.12, 2.24	0.66, 0.72(w+), 0.81(w+), 0.88(w+), 0.94
Ag^{111}	7.5 days	β^-	0.70(8%), 0.80(1%), 1.04(91%)	0.243(1%)($\tau = 9 \times 10^{-8}$ sec)[<0.08], 0.340(8%)[~0.015]
Ag^{112}	3.2 hr	β^-	~1(15%), 2.7(20%), 3.5(40%), 4.1(25%)	0.62, others
Ag^{113}	5.3 hr	β^-	2	0.298
Ag^{115}	21 min	β^-	~3	0.225(~9%). Cf. Cd^{115m}
${}_{48}Cd^{104}$	59 min	β^+	0.93	0.067, 0.084, 0.150
Cd^{105}	55 min	β^+	0.80, 1.69	0.025, 0.308, 0.320, 0.347, 0.433
Cd^{107}	6.7 hr	β^+, ϵ	0.32(0.32%)	0.094[16]E3. 0.846[~10^{-3}](0.4%) Cf. Ag^{107m}
Cd^{109}	470 days	ϵ	....	0.087[11.5](τ = 39.2 sec)E3
Cd^{111m}	48.7 min	IT	....	0.150(100+)[1.5]E3, 0.246(100+), ($\tau = 8 \times 10^{-8}$ sec)E2
Cd^{113m}	5 years	β^-	0.57	
Cd^{115m}	43 days	β^-	0.33(<1%), 0.65(~2%), 1.61(~98%)	0.46, 0.50, 0.96, 1.28
Cd^{115}	2.25 days	β^-	0.58(42%), 1.11(58%)	0.335, 0.363, 0.424, 0.525
Cd^{117m}	3.0 hr	β^-	1.0	0.267, 0.281, 0.331, 0.425, 0.84, 1.27, 1.55, 2.00
Cd^{117}	50 min	β^-	~1.8	0.281, 0.312(τ = 2.3 hr), 0.425
${}_{49}In^{107}$	33 min	β^+	~2	
In^{108}	50 min	β^+	2.31	0.285(<5%)[0.06]
In^{109}	4.3 hr	β^+	0.75	0.058(60+), 0.205(100+), 0.347(8+), 0.427(1.6+)
In^{110m}	4.9 hr	ϵ, IT	....	0.119(~0.3% IT)M4, 0.661 M1 or E2, 0.885, 0.935
In^{110}	66 min	β^+	2.25	0.656
In^{111}	2.8 days	ϵ	....	0.093(w+), 0.172(~100%)[0.12](~98.7% M1, 1.3% E2), 0.247(~100%), 0.330(w+)

TABLE 8g-1. RADIOISOTOPE DATA (*Continued*)

Nuclide	Half life	Type of decay	Particle energy, Mev	Gamma-ray energy, Mev
In^{112m}	21 min	IT	....	0.155[large]E3 or M3
	14 min	β^-, β^+, ϵ	β^-: 0.656(44%), β^+: 1.52(56% *T*)	
In^{113m}	1.73 hr	IT	....	0.393[0.55]M4
In^{114m}	50 days	IT	....	0.192[$K \sim 5$]E4
In^{114}	72 sec	β^-, β^+, ϵ	β^-: 1.98(96%), β^+: ~1.2 (~0.004%)	0.556(100+), 0.576, 0.722(80+)(96% M1, 4% E2), 1.271(4+), 1.300
In^{115m}	4.5 hr	β^-, IT	0.84(55%)	0.334[*K*0.64]M4
In^{115}	6×10^{14} years	β^-	0.83	
In^{116m}	54.1 min	β^-	0.60(21%), 0.87(28%), 1.00(51%)	0.137(3%), 0.406(25%), 1.085(54%) [8.4×10^{-4}], 1.274(75%)[5.7×10^{-4}], 1.487(21%), 2.090(25%)
In^{116}	13 sec	β^-	3.29	No γ
In^{117m}	1.9 hr	β^-, IT	1.61(16%), 1.77(39%)	0.161[*K*0.13]M1, 0.315[*K*1.3]M4
In^{117}	1.1 hr	β^-	0.740	0.161(86+)[*K*0.13]M1, 0.565(100+)[*K*0.005]. Cf. Sn^{117m}
In^{118}	<1 min	β^-	4.0	
	4.5 min	β^-	1.5	
In^{119}	18 min	β^-	2.7	
$_{50}Sn^{111}$	35 min	β^+, ϵ	1.51(29%)	
Sn^{113}	118 days	ϵ	....	0.393. Cf. In^{113m}
Sn^{117m}	14 days	IT	....	0.156M4, 0.159[*K*0.1]M1
Sn^{119m}	250 days	IT	....	0.024[7], 0.065
Sn^{121m}	>400 days	β^-	0.42	
Sn^{121}	27 hr	β^-	0.383	No γ
Sn^{123}	40 min	β^-	1.26	0.153
	136 days	β^-	1.42	No γ
Sn^{125}	9.5 min	β^-	~0.5, 1.17, 2.05	0.326, 1.37
	9.9 days	β^-	0.40(~5%), 2.37(95%)	1.67

$_{51}Sb^{116}$	15.5 min	β^+	2.40	0.90, 1.30, 2.20
	60 min	β^+	$\sim$1.45	0.41(15+), 0.95(130+), 1.31(150+)
Sb^{117}	2.8 hr	ϵ	No β^+	0.156[large]
Sb^{118}	3.5 min	β^+	3.1	
	5.1 hr	ϵ	....	0.260, 1.5
Sb^{119}	39 hr	ϵ	No β^+	No γ
Sb^{120}	16.4 min	β^+	1.70	No γ
Sb^{122m}	3.5 min	IT	....	0.059, 0.074
Sb^{122}	2.75 days	β^-, ϵ	β^-: 0.730(4.4%), 1.42(69%), 1.99(26.5%); ϵ: (3%)	0.563, 0.693E2M1, 1.256E2
Sb^{124m}	21 min	IT	....	0.0185[$\sim\infty$]
	1.3 min	IT	....	0.012[$\sim\infty$]
Sb^{124}	60 days	β^-	0.24(14%), 0.61(49%), 0.966(9%), 1.602(7%), 2.317(21%)	0.603(100+)[0.0034]E2, 0.642, 0.716, 0.99 (5.4+), 1.38(6.2+), 1.71(46+), 2.11(10+)
Sb^{125}	$\sim$2.7 years	β^-	0.128(33%), 0.299(49%), 0.616(18%)	0.035(86+), 0.110(18+), 0.175(6+), 0.255 (2+), 0.290(2+), 0.428(37+), 0.463(4+), 0.598(28+), 0.638(7+)
Sb^{126}	9 hr	β^-	1	0.4, 0.90
Sb^{127}	93 hr	β^-	1.50	
$_{52}Te^{117}$	2.5 hr	β^+	2.5	
Te^{118}	6 days	ϵ		
Te^{119}	4.5 days	ϵ	....	1.5
Te^{121m}	154 days	IT	....	0.082[$\sim\infty$]M4, 0.213[K0.09]M1
Te^{121}	17 days	ϵ	....	0.506(13%)[$\sim$0.018], 0.573(87%)[0.009]
Te^{123m}	104 days	IT	....	0.0885[$\sim\infty$]M4, 0.159[K0.19] ($\tau = 1.9 \times 10^{-10}$ sec)M1
Te^{125m}	58 days	IT	....	0.0354[K11.4]M1($\tau = 1.6 \times 10^{-9}$ sec), 0.110[K = 160]M4
Te^{127m}	113 days	IT	....	0.0887[very large]M4
Te^{127}	9.3 hr	β^-	0.7	
Te^{129m}	38 days	IT	....	0.106[very large]M4

TABLE 8g-1. RADIOISOTOPE DATA (*Continued*)

Nuclide	Half life	Type of decay	Particle energy, Mev	Gamma-ray energy, Mev
Te^{129}	72 min	β^-	1.8	
Te^{131m}	1.2 days	IT	....	0.183[0.6]M4
Te^{131}	25 min	β^-	1.35(45%), 2.0(55%)	0.16(1.5+), 0.7(1.0+)
Te^{132}	78 hr	β^-	0.22	0.23
Te^{133m}	63 min	IT	....	~0.4[large]
Te^{133}	2 min	β^-	1.3(~70%), 2.4(~30%)	0.6, 1.0
$_{53}I^{120}$	30 min	β^+	4.0	
I^{121}	1.4 hr	β^+	1.2	0.213
I^{122}	3.5 min	β^+	3.12	No γ
I^{123}	13 hr	ϵ	....	0.160M1
I^{124}	4.5 days	β^+, ϵ	ϵ(~70%); β^+: 0.67(5+), 1.50(44+), 2.2(51+)	0.602, 0.73, 1.72, 1.95
I^{125}	60 days	ϵ	....	0.0354
I^{126}	13.3 days	β^-, β^+, ϵ	β^-: 0.385(5.8%), 0.865(29%), 1.250 (9.3%); β^+: 0.460(0.28%), 1.110 (0.96%); ϵ: (~55%)	0.386(336+)[*K*0.017], 0.480(50.4+), 0.650 (330+), 0.750(36+), 0.860(8.4+), 1.42(5+)
I^{128}	25 min	β^-, ϵ	ϵ: (~6%); β^-: 1.59(7+), 2.02(93+)	0.455(100+), 0.98(2+)
I^{129}	1.7×10^7 years	β^-	0.150	0.038[*K*22]
I^{130}	12.5 hr	β^-	0.597(54%), 1.02(46%)	0.409(30+)[*K*0.016], 0.528(100+)[*K*0.0055], 0.660(90+)[*K*0.0032], 0.744(80+) [*K*0.00027], 1.15(40+)[$K2.5 \times 10^{-4}$]
I^{131}	8.05 days	β^-	0.255(~3%), 0.339(9%), 0.607(87%), 0.80(~1%)	0.08016(6.3+)[*K*1.7]($\tau = 5 \times 10^{-10}$ sec)M1, 0.163(~1%)M1, 0.28431(6.3+)[*K*0.047]E2, 0.36447(80.9+)[*K*0.018]E2, 0.638(9.3+) [*K*0.0037]E1, 0.724(2.8+)[*K*0.0028]. Cf. Xe^{131m}
I^{132}	2.4 hr	β^-	0.73(15%), 0.9(20%), 1.16(23%), 1.53(24%), 2.12(18%)	0.777(80+), 0.96(20+)

I^{133}	20.8 hr	β^-	0.40(∼9%), 1.25(∼91%), 1.5(∼1–2%)	0.232, 0.53(94+), 0.87(5+), 1.2
I^{134}	53 min	β^-	1.5, 2.5	0.86, 1.10, 1.78
I^{135}	6.7 hr	β^-	0.47(35%), 1.0(40%), 1.4(25%)	1.27, 1.8
I^{136}	1.5 min	β^-	3.7, 5.0, 6.3	1.38, 2.9
I^{137}	19 sec	β^-, delayed neutrons	E_n = 0.56(6%)	
$_{54}Xe^{121}$	40 min	β^+	....	0.096
Xe^{122}	19 hr	ϵ	....	0.182, 0.235
Xe^{123}	1.8 hr	β^+, ϵ	1.7	0.148
Xe^{125m}	55 sec	IT	....	0.110
Xe^{125}	18 hr	ϵ	No β^+	0.056, 0.187, 0.243
Xc^{127m}	75 sec	ϵ, IT	....	0.096E2, 0.125, 0.175E3
Xe^{127}	36.4 days	ϵ	....	0.057, 0.145, 0.170, 0.203, 0.365(w+)
Xe^{129m}	8.0 days	IT	....	0.040, 0.196[K11]M4
Xe^{131m}	12 days	IT	....	0.163[K29]M1. Cf. I^{131}
Xe^{133m}	2.3 days	IT	....	0.232[K4.4]M4
Xe^{133}	5.27 days	β^-	0.347	0.81($\tau = 6 \times 10^{-9}$ sec)[K1.8]M1
Xe^{135m}	15.3 min	IT	....	0.520M4
Xe^{135}	9.2 hr	β^-	0.548(∼5%), 0.910(∼95%)	0.247(100+)($\tau = 2.8 \times 10^{-10}$ sec), 0.37, 0.61(6+)
Xe^{137}	3.9 hr	β^-	∼4	
$_{55}Cs^{125}$	45 min	β^+, ϵ	2.05	0.112
Cs^{126}	1.6 min	β^+	3.8	0.385
Cs^{127}	6.3 hr	β^+	0.68, 1.06	0.125, 0.406, 0.440
Cs^{128}	3.8 min	β^+	1.1, 3.1; ϵ: (∼71%)	0.135(100+), 0.29, 0.455(30+), 0.97(w+)
Cs^{129}	31 hr	ϵ	No β^+	0.385, 0.560
Cs^{130}	30 min	β^-, β^+, ϵ	β^-: 0.442(1+), β^+: 1.97(27.6+)	No γ
Cs^{131}	10 days	ϵ	No β^+, no β^-	No γ
Cs^{132}	7.1 days	ϵ	....	0.69
Cs^{134m}	3.15 hr	β^-, IT	....	0.0105[∼200]M1, 0.1271[K2.6]E3, 0.1374M4

TABLE 8g-1. RADIOISOTOPE DATA (*Continued*)

Nuclide	Half life	Type of decay	Particle energy, Mev	Gamma-ray energy, Mev
Cs^{134}	2.3 years	β^-	0.79(21%), 0.253(6%), 0.640(54%), 0.676(19%)	0.561(11+)M1, 0.567(16+), 0.601(89+) [*K*0.0057]E2, 0.793(100+)[*K*0.0021]E2
Cs^{135}	2.1×10^6 years	β^-	0.210	
Cs^{136}	12.9 days	β^-	0.341(92.6%), 0.657(7.4%)	0.0672, 0.153, 0.162, 0.265, 0.335, 0.822, 1.041, 1.245
Cs^{137}	33 years	β^-	0.512(92%), 1.17(8%)	0.6616[0.095]M4. Cf. Ba^{137m}
Cs^{138}	33 min	β^-	3.40	0.463(33+), 0.98(43+), 1.44(100+)
$_{56}Ba^{126}$	96 min	ϵ	....	0.225(100+), 0.700(33+), 0.9(w+)
Ba^{128}	2.4 days	ϵ	ϵ: (100%)	
Ba^{129}	1.9 hr	β^+	1.6	
Ba^{131}	13 days	ϵ	No β^+	0.122, 0.196, 0.213, 0.241, 0.371, 0.497, 0.620
Ba^{133m}	38.9 hr	IT	....	0.012, 0.275[*K*3]
Ba^{133}	10 years	ϵ	....	0.057(1+), 0.082(22+), [3.5]M1, 0.300(31+), 0.357(69+)
Ba^{135m}	28.7 hr	IT	....	0.269[3.5]M4
Ba^{137m}	2.60 min	IT	....	0.6616[0.095]M4
Ba^{139}	85 min	β^-	0.82, 2.23, 2.38	0.163[*K*0.22]M1, 1.43
Ba^{140}	13 days	β^-	0.48(40%), 1.022(60%)	0.0296, 0.132, 0.162, 0.304, 0.537
Ba^{141}	18 min	β^-	2.8	
$_{57}La^{131}$	58 min	β^+	1.6	
La^{132}	4.5 hr	β^+	3.5	1.0
La^{133}	4.0 hr	β^+, ϵ	1.2(w+)	0.8
La^{134}	6.5 min	β^+, ϵ	2.7; [1.3]	No γ
La^{135}	19.5 hr	ϵ	....	0.49(2%), 0.66(0.3%)
La^{136}	9.5 min	β^+, ϵ	2.1; [~2]	
La^{138}	2×10^{11} years	ϵ	....	0.535(51%), 0.807(33%), 1.390(15%)
La^{140}	40.2 hr	β^-	0.83(12%), 1.10(26%), 1.34(45%), 1.67(10%), 2.15(7%)	0.110, 0.130, 0.240, 0.270, 0.3286(10+), 0.4867(10+), 0.8151(10+), 1.596(100+)

La^{141}	3.7 hr	β^-	0.9(~5%), 2.43(~95%)	~1.5(w+)
La^{142}	74 min	β^-	>2.5	0.63(90+), 0.87(10+)
$_{58}Ce^{133}$	6.3 hr	β^+, ϵ	1.3	1.8
Ce^{134}	72 hr	ϵ	....	No γ
Ce^{135}	22 hr	β^+, ϵ	0.8; [>100]	
Ce^{137}	36 hr	ϵ	No β^+	0.253
Ce^{139}	140 days	ϵ	No β^+	0.166, ~0.8
Ce^{141}	32.8 days	β^-	0.444(70%), 0.582(30%)	0.143[K0.46]M1
Ce^{143}	33 hr	β^-	0.37, 1.09(40+), 1.37(30+)	0.57, 0.283(70+)[K0.03], 0.649(15+)[K0.01], 0.705(15+)
Ce^{144}	290 days	β^-	0.170(~30%), 0.304(70%)	0.0337(15+), 0.041(12+), 0.0535(3+), 0.0807(59+)M2, 0.94(7+), 0.100(5+), 0.134(115+)M1
Ce^{145}	3 min	β^-	~2.0	
Ce^{146}	14 min	β^-	0.7	0.05(w+), 0.110(20+), 0.142(42+), 0.22 (50+), 0.25(w+), 0.27(12+), 0.32(100+)
$_{59}Pr^{135}$	22 min	β^+, ϵ	....	0.080, 0.220, 0.300
Pr^{136}	70 min	β^+, ϵ	....	0.170
Pr^{137}	1.3 hr	β^+	1.8	
Pr^{138}	2.0 hr	β^+, ϵ	1.4(14+); [7]	0.16(22+), 0.50(36+), 1.3(75+)
Pr^{139}	4.5 hr	β^+, ϵ	1.0(6+); [17]	1.0(4+)
Pr^{140}	3.5 min	β^+, ϵ	2.23; [0.65]	1.2(~2%)
Pr^{142}	19.2 hr	β^-	0.59(~7%), 2.166(~93%)	1.572
Pr^{143}	13.8 days	β^-	0.915	No γ
Pr^{144}	17.5 min	β^-	0.86(~5%), 2.3(~5%), 2.96(90%)	0.0603(w+), 0.695(91+), 1.48(36+), 2.18(100+)
Pr^{145}	6 hr	β^-	~1.7	
Pr^{146}	24.6 min	β^-	2.3(44+), 3.7(56+)	0.46(100+), 0.59(w+), 0.75(22+), 1.49(33+),
$_{60}Nd^{138}$	22 min	β^+	2.4	
Nd^{139}	5.5 hr	β^+, ϵ	3.1(11+); [9]	1.3(10+)

TABLE 8g-1. RADIOISOTOPE DATA (*Continued*)

Nuclide	Half life	Type of decay	Particle energy, Mev	Gamma-ray energy, Mev
Nd^{140}	3.3 days	ϵ	$E_{dis} \sim 0.1$	
Nd^{141}	2.4 hr	β^+, ϵ	0.7; [49]	1.05(w+)
Nd^{144}	$\sim 1.5 \times 10^{15}$ years	α	1.8	
Nd^{147}	11.6 days	β^-	0.35(~33%), 0.78(~67%)	0.0918(66%)[K0.8]M1, 0.522(32%)E2
Nd^{149}	1.7 hr	β^-	0.95, 1.1, 1.5	0.030, 0.096E2, 0.112, 0.114, 0.124, 0.188, 0.198, 0.226, 0.240, 0.266, 0.424, 0.538, 0.650
Nd^{151}	12 min	β^-	1.93	0.085, 0.110, 0.117, 0.421, 0.72, 1.14
$_{61}Pm^{141}$	20 min	β^+	~2.6	
Pm^{143}	320 days	β^-(?), ϵ	0.6(β or e^-)	0.17, 0.44, 0.65
Pm^{145}	24 years	ϵ	....	0.0678, 0.0727
Pm^{146}	~1 year	β^-	~0.7	
Pm^{147}	2.6 years	β^-	0.229	
Pm^{148}	5.3 days	β^-	~2.5	~0.8
	42 days	β^-	0.7(93%), 2.7(7%)	~1.0
Pm^{149}	50 hr	β^-	1.05	0.285M1, 1.3
Pm^{150}	2.7 hr	β^-	2.01(70%), 3.00(30%)	0.3, 1.4
Pm^{151}	28 hr	β^-	1.1	0.065E2, 0.066E2, 0.070E2, 0.100, 0.116, 0.144, 0.163, 0.168, 0.177, 0.208, 0.232, 0.240, 0.275, 0.340, 0.715
$_{62}Sm^{145}$	410 days	ϵ	....	0.061
Sm^{146}	5×10^7 years	α	2.55	
Sm^{151}	~70 years	β^-	0.076	0.019
Sm^{153}	47 hr	β^-	0.26(9%), 0.685(70%), 0.795(21%)	0.069[K3.8]M1E2, 0.103(100+)[K1.1] ($\tau = 3.4 \times 10^{-9}$ sec), 0.545(~4+)
Sm^{155}	24 min	β^-	1.8	0.105M1E2, 0.246M1
Sm^{156}	~10 hr	β^-	0.9	
$_{64}Eu^{144}$	18 min	β^+	2.4	
Eu^{145}	5 days	ϵ	....	?

Eu^{146}	38 hr	ϵ	....	?
Eu^{147}	24 days	ϵ, α	No β^+; α: 2.88($\sim 10^{-3}$%)	0.12, 0.21
Eu^{148}	54 days	ϵ	No β^+	0.58
Eu^{149}	120 days	ϵ	....	0.30, 0.57
Eu^{150}	13.7 hr	β^-	No β^+; β^-: 1.07	No γ
Eu^{152}	9.2 hr	β^-, ϵ	1.54(?), 1.88	0.1218, 0.123, 0.344, 0.820, 0.940
	13 years	β^-, ϵ	....	0.1218($\tau = 1.40 \times 10^{-9}$ sec), 0.2436, 0.344, 0.98
Eu^{154}	16 years	β^-	0.71	0.1234, 0.2477, 1.17
Eu^{155}	1.7 years	β^-	0.152, 0.252	0.0187, 0.0598, 0.0863, 0.1051
Eu^{156}	14 days	β^-	0.5(60%), 2.4(40%)	2.0
Eu^{157}	15.4 hr	β^-	$\sim$1.0(75%), $\sim$1.7(25%)	0.2, 0.6
Eu^{158}	60 min	β^-	$\sim$2.6	
$_{64}Gd^{148}$	>35 years	α	3.2	
Gd^{149}	9 days	ϵ, α	3.0($\sim$0.0007%)	
Gd^{151}	$\sim$150 days	ϵ	No β^+	0.265
Gd^{153}	236 days	β^+, ϵ	....	0.0694, 0.0973, 0.1031
Gd^{159}	18.0 hr	β^-	$\sim$0.9, $\sim$1.1	0.0575, 0.364
Gd^{161}	3.6 min	β^-	$\sim$1.6	0.060[K large], 0.102, 0.316, 0.360
$_{65}Tb^{149}$	4.1 hr	ϵ, α	No β^+; α: 3.95(>0.002%)	
Tb^{151}	19 hr	ϵ, α	3.4(>0.0004%)	
Tb^{152}	4.5 hr	ϵ		
Tb^{153}	5.1 days	....	No β^+	0.23(10+), 1.2(2+)
Tb^{154}	17.2 hr	β^+, ϵ	1.66, 2.75; [99]	?
Tb^{155}	190 days	ϵ	....	1.4
Tb^{156}	5.0 hr	β^+, ϵ	1.3(20%)	
Tb^{157}	4.7 days	ϵ	....	1.4
Tb^{160}	73 days	β^-	0.521, 0.860	0.0863($\tau = 1.8 \times 10^{-9}$ sec), 0.93, 0.196, 0.215, 0.298, 0.391, 0.759, 0.873, 0.960, 1.174, 1.265
Tb^{161}	6.8 days	β^-	0.50	0.049

TABLE 8g-1. RADIOISOTOPE DATA (*Continued*)

Nuclide	Half life	Type of decay	Particle energy, Mev	Gamma-ray energy, Mev
$_{66}Dy^{157}$	8.2 hr	ϵ	No β^+	0.325
Dy^{159}	140 days	ϵ		
Dy^{165m}	1.2 min	β^-, IT	0.84(calc.)	0.108[$K \sim 4$]E3, 0.16, 0.36, 0.515
Dy^{165}	2.32 hr	β^-	~0.3, 1.25	0.094[≤2.9]M1E2, 0.279, 0.361, 0.634, 0.71, 1.02
Dy^{166}	81 hr	β^-	0.22	<0.05
$_{67}Ho^{160}$	23 min	β^+, ϵ	~1.3(0.5%)	~1.2(100%)
Ho^{161}	2.5 hr	ϵ	No β^+	0.090, 0.17(w+)
Ho^{162}	5.0 hr	β^-, ϵ	No β^+; β^-: 0.8(15%)	0.19, 0.71, 0.95
Ho^{164}	36.7 min	β^-	~0.90, 0.99	0.037, 0.046, 0.073, 0.090
Ho^{166}	27.3 hr	β^-	0.23(~0.3%), 0.40(1%), 1.76(74%), 1.84(25%)	0.080(85+)[1.9]($\tau = 1.7 \times 10^{-9}$ sec)E2, 1.36(10+), 1.53(2+), 1.61(~1+)
Ho^{167}	96 min	β^-	1.0	0.35
$_{68}Er^{161}$	3.6 hr	ϵ	No β^+	0.065, 0.824, 1.120
Er^{163}	75 min	ϵ	No β^+	0.43, 1.10
Er^{165}	9.9 hr	ϵ	....	No γ
Er^{169}	9.4 days	β^-	0.33	0.185
Er^{171}	7.5 hr	β^-	0.67(22%), 1.05(72%), 1.49(6%)	0.113[1.3]($\tau = 2.5$ μsec), 0.118, 0.126, 0.176, 0.295, 0.308, 0.420, 0.805
$_{69}Tm^{165}$	24.5 hr	ϵ	No β^+	0.205, 0.808, 1.16, 1.38
Tm^{166}	7.7 hr	β^+, ϵ	2.1	1.7
Tm^{167}	9.6 days	ϵ	....	0.22, 0.95
Tm^{168}	87 days	ϵ	....	0.21, 0.85
Tm^{170}	127 days	β^-	0.884(24%), 0.968(76%)	0.0841[K1.6]($\tau = 1.57 \times 10^{-9}$ sec)E2
Tm^{171}	680 days	β^-	0.10	
$_{70}Yb^{166}$	58 hr	ϵ		
Yb^{167}	18.5 min	ϵ	....	0.118

Yb^{169}	31.8 days	ϵ	....	0.023, 0.064, 0.093, 0.109, 0.130, 0.177, 0.198, 0.307
Yb^{175}	4.2 days	β^-	0.13, 0.50	0.138, 0.259, 0.283, 0.396
Yb^{177}	1.8 hr	β^-	1.3	0.15(τ = 0.13 μsec)
$_{71}Lu^{170}$	1.7 days	ϵ	....	~2.5
Lu^{171}	8.5 days	ϵ	....	~1.2
Lu^{172}	6.7 days	ϵ	....	1.2
	4.0 hr	β^+	1.2	
Lu^{173}	~500 days	ϵ	....	0.22, 0.88
Lu^{174}	165 days	β^-, ϵ	0.6(~25%)	
Lu^{176m}	3.7 hr	β^-	1.1, 1.2	0.089[*K*1.2](τ = 1.4 × 10^{-9} sec)E2
Lu^{176}	2.4 × 10^{10} years	β^-	0.43	0.089(6+), 0.203(33+), 0.306(37+)
Lu^{177}	6.8 days	β^-	0.169(18%), 0.366(17%), 0.495(65%)	0.112[*K*0.81]E2, 0.206[*K*0.04]E1, 0.318(4.5%)
$_{72}Hf^{170}$	1.9 hr	β^+	2.4	
Hf^{172}	5 years	ϵ	....	0.28, 0.8
Hf^{173}	23.6 hr	ϵ	....	0.121(100+), 0.299(75+)
Hf^{175}	70 days	ϵ	....	0.089, 0.113, 0.228, 0.318, 0.342, 0.431
Hf^{179m}	19 sec	IT	....	0.161[large]M3, 0.217 M1
Hf^{180m}	5.5 hr	IT	....	0.0576 M3, 0.0933 E2, 0.2155 E2, 0.3330 E2, 0.4435 E2
Hf^{181}	46 days	β^-	0.406	0.132(τ = 19 μsec)E2, 0.136(τ = 0.002 μsec) E2(20%)M1(80%), 0.345(τ = 0.0104 μsec) E2(50%)M1(50%), 0.480(τ = 0.0104 μsec) E2(60%)M1(40%)
$_{73}Ta^{176}$	8.0 hr	ϵ	....	~1.2
Ta^{177}	2.2 days	ϵ	....	~1.4
Ta^{178}	9.4 min	β^+, ϵ	1.06(~6%)	~1.5(~3%)
	2.1 hr	β^+, ϵ	~1(~3%)	~1.4
Ta^{179}	~600 days	ϵ	....	0.7(w+)
Ta^{180}	8.15 hr	β^-, ϵ	No β^+; 0.605(~11%), 0.705(~10%)	0.093(τ = 1.39 × 10^{-9} sec), 0.102(w+)
Ta^{182m}	16.4 min	β^-, IT	0.6(~5%)	0.180[*K*0.8]E3

TABLE 8g-1. RADIOISOTOPE DATA (*Continued*)

Nuclide	Half life	Type of decay	Particle energy, Mev	Gamma-ray energy, Mev
Ta^{182}	111 days	β^-	0.510, 0.442, 0.178?	0.06571(9+)M1E2, 0.06774(100+)E1, 0.08467(6+)M1E2, 0.1009(46+)[K1.5]E2, 0.11366(9+)[K1.75]M1, 0.15241(43+)[K0.07]E1, 0.15637(14+)[K small], 0.17936(19+)[K0.41]M1E2, 0.19831(9+)[K0.24]E2, 0.22205(45+)[K0.06]E1, 0.22927(24+)[K0.16]E2, 0.26409(27+)[K0.11]E2, 1.122(120+)[K0.005]E2M1, 1.155(8+)[K0.004]M2, 1.189(56+)[K0.006]E3M2, 1.222(115+)[K0.003]E2, 1.231(58+)[K0.003]E2, eight others (<2+ each)
Ta^{183}	5 days	β^-	0.56	0.04097(10.3+)M1, 0.04648(61.4+)M1, 0.05259(41.7+)M1, 0.08292(2.5+), 0.08470(14.0+)M1, 0.09907(31.9+)E2, 0.10793(45.7+)M1, 0.10973(2.9+), 0.14412(6.4+)M1, 0.16053(4.4+)E2, 0.16136(18.2+)M1, 0.16233(9.8+)M1, 0.20987(5.4+)E2, 0.24426(10.0+)E2, 0.24605(35.6+)M1, 0.29171(5.4+)E2, 0.31303(8.8+)M1, 0.35404(12.0+)M1, nine others (<2+ each)
Ta^{184}	9.3 hr	β^-	1.4	
Ta^{185}	48 min	β^-	1.6	
$_{74}W^{176}$	80 min	β^+, ϵ	~2(~0.5%)	~1.3
W^{177}	2.2 hr	ϵ	....	~0.45, 1.2
W^{178}	22 days	ϵ	....	0.27
W^{179}	30 min	ϵ	....	No γ
	5.2 min	ϵ	....	No γ

W^{181}	140 days	ϵ	....	0.1365, 0.1525, 1.83(w+)
W^{183m}	5.5 sec	IT	....	0.081E3 or M3
W^{185m}	1.9 min	IT	....	0.075E3 or M3
W^{185}	73 days	β^-	0.428	0.134
W^{187}	23.9 hr	β^-	0.622(80%), 1.304(20%)	0.07200[$K \sim 2$]E1, 0.13425[$K \sim 2$] ($\tau = 0.55\ \mu$sec)M1, 0.4795, 0.552, 0.6189, 0.6861, 0.774E1
$_{75}Re^{182}$	14 hr	ϵ	....	0.92
Re^{183}	2.8 days	ϵ	....	1.75
	~120 days	ϵ	....	1.07
Re^{184}	50 days	ϵ or IT	....	0.159, 0.206, 0.244, 0.784, 0.89
Re^{186}	3.8 days	β^-, ϵ	~0.3(~0.4%), 0.926(19%), 1.063	0.123[K0.4], 0.137(19%)($\tau = 8 \times 10^{-10}$ sec)E2, 0.627(0.2%), 0.764(0.2%)
Re^{187}	$<10^{11}$ years	β^-	<0.008	
Re^{188m}	22 min	IT	....	0.0635, 0.105
	16.9 hr	β^-	2.07(others ?)	0.1553(~130+)[0.046]($\tau = 6.5 \times 10^{-10}$ sec), 0.4782(10+), 0.6331(15+), 0.674(1+), 0.828(5+), 0.931(6+), 1.132(1+), 1.608(2+)
$_{76}Os^{182}$	24 hr	ϵ	No β^+	
Os^{183}	12 hr	ϵ	....	0.34(18+), 1.6(10+)
Os^{185}	97 days	ϵ	....	0.163, 0.234, 0.645(85+), 0.879(15+)
Os^{191m}	14 hr	IT	....	0.0742M3
Os^{191}	15 days	β^-	0.143	0.0417E2, 0.1291[K2.1]M1E2. Cf. Ir^{191m}
Os^{193}	31 hr	β^-	0.6(w+), 0.82(w+), 0.96(w+), 1.03(w+), 1.10(>98+)	0.073($\tau = 0.006\ \mu$sec), 0.139, 0.251, 0.281, 0.321, 0.460, 0.558
$_{77}Ir^{187}$	12 hr	β^+, ϵ	2.2(0.2+)	1.3(75+)
Ir^{188}	42 hr	β^+, ϵ	2(0.3+)	0.156, 1.8(55+)
Ir^{190}	3.2 hr	β^+, ϵ	1.7	
	13 days	ϵ	....	0.17(45+), 0.55(42+)
Ir^{191m}	7 sec	IT	....	0.125[K1.25]

TABLE 8g-1. RADIOISOTOPE DATA (*Continued*)

Nuclide	Half life	Type of decay	Particle energy, Mev	Gamma-ray energy, Mev
Ir^{192m}	1.42 min	β^-, IT	β^-: (~0.1%)	0.0574[$L \sim 750$]E2 or M3
Ir^{192}	74.4 days	β^-, ϵ	0.24(16%), 0.54(40%), 0.67(44%)	0.13633(0.4+), 0.20131(1.0+), 0.20574 (7.5+), 0.29594(38.0+), 0.30845(37.0+), 0.31646(99.0+), 0.46798(30.0+), 0.4848 (1.1+), 0.5884(1.1+), 0.6045(1.4+), 0.6129(0.5+)
Ir^{194}	19 hr	β^-	0.48(w+), 2.18	0.3275(100+), 0.148(100+), 1.8(w+), 2.1(w+)
Ir^{195}	2.3 hr	β^-	1.2, 2.1	0.42, 0.66, 0.88
Ir^{197}	7 min	β^-	<1.6, 1.6	1.8
Ir^{198}	50 sec	β^-	3.6	0.78
$_{78}Pt^{188}$	10.3 days	ϵ		
Pt^{190}	~10^{12} years	α	3.3	
Pt^{191}	3.0 days	ϵ	....	0.826, 0.0964, 0.1296, 0.1723, 0.1784, 0.2197, 0.2684, 0.3509, 0.360, 0.409, 0.456, 0.539
Pt^{193m}	3.4 days	IT	....	0.1355M4
Pt^{195m}	~6 days	IT	....	0.0311[$L \geq 6$], 0.097[K7.4], 0.126, 0.1299[$\sim \infty$]M4
Pt^{197m}	88 min	IT	....	0.337M4
	18 hr	β^-	0.48(1.5%), 0.67(98.5%)	0.0774, 0.191(w+)
Pt^{199}	29 min	β^-	~1.2	0.07, 0.197, 0.246, 0.316, ~0.48, 0.54, 0.71, 0.78, 0.96
$_{79}Au^{191}$	~4 hr	ϵ	....	0.0480, 0.0910, 0.130, 0.1587
Au^{192}	4.8 hr	β^+, ϵ	1.9	0.2598(20+), 0.3168(40+)
Au^{193}	<1 hr	IT(?)	....	0.0319E2, 0.2579M4, 0.2906
	17.4 hr	ϵ	....	0.1124, 0.1735, 0.1862
Au^{194}	39 hr	ϵ	....	0.291[0.054], 0.328, 0.466, 1.48, 2.1

Au^{195m}	30 sec	IT	...	0.0569[~∞]E3, 0.2615M1E2, 0.318M4
Au^{195}	185 days	ε	...	0.0308(35+)M1, 0.0988(100+)M1, 0.126
Au^{196}	14 hr	ε or IT		
	5.6 days	β^-, ε	0.270(4.5%)	0.332E2(95%)M1(5%), 0.354E2, 0.426[L ~ 0.007]
Au^{197m}	7.4 sec	IT	...	0.130[$K \leq 2$]E3, 0.277[K ~ 0.29]M1, 0.407[~∞]M4
Au^{198}	2.70 days	β^-	0.283(0.98%), 0.959(99%), 1.371(0.025%)	0.41177[K0.0318]E2, 0.6765[0.022]E2(68%) M1(32%), 1.0889[K0.0045]E2
Au^{199}	3.16 hr	β^-	0.250(23%), 0.300(73%), 0.460(4%)	0.0498[L6], 0.1585($\tau = 2.4 \times 10^{-9}$ sec) [K0.19]E2, 0.2083[K0.54]. Cf. Hg^{199m}
Au^{200}	48 min	β^-	2.2(5+)	1.13(1+)
Au^{201}	26 min	β^-	1.5(20+)	0.55(1+)
Au^{203}	55 sec	β^-	1.9(10+)	0.69(1+)
$_{80}Hg^{191}$	57 min	ε	...	0.2526, 0.2741
Hg^{192}	8.4 hr	ε	...	0.0313, 0.1143M1, 0.1423, 0.1460M1, 0.1574, 0.275
Hg^{193m}	12 hr	ε, IT	ε: (84%)	0.032E3, 0.0392M1, 0.1012M4, 0.258M1, 0.291M4. Cf. Au^{193m}
Hg^{193}	4 hr	ε	...	0.0379M1E2, 0.1865M1
Hg^{194}	0.4 sec	ε	...	0.048, 0.134
Hg^{195m}	40 hr	ε, IT	ε: (95%)	0.0371[~∞]M1, 0.057E3, 0.1226M4, 0.262M1. Cf. Au^{195m}
Hg^{195}	9.5 hr	ε	...	0.0612M1E2, 0.1798M1
Hg^{197m}	23 hr	ε, IT	ε: (3%)	0.130E3, 0.134($\tau = 0.008$ μsec)E2, 0.165M4, 0.279M1
Hg^{197}	65 hr	ε	...	0.077[2.5]M1E2, 0.191[K0.9]M1
Hg^{199m}	44 min	IT	...	0.159($\tau = 2.4 \times 10^{-9}$ sec)[0.25]E2, 0.368[>11]M4
Hg^{203}	47 days	β^-	0.210	
Hg^{205}	5.6 min	β^-	1.7	0.203

TABLE 8g-1. RADIOISOTOPE DATA (*Continued*)

Nuclide	Half life	Type of decay	Particle energy, Mev	Gamma-ray energy, Mev
$_{81}Tl^{198m}$	1.8 hr	IT	....	0.0484[>10]E2, 0.261M4, 0.282M1E2
Tl^{198}	5.3 hr	ϵ	....	0.195, 0.284, 0.402, 0.411, 0.675
Tl^{199}	7.4 hr	ϵ	....	0.0500, 0.1584, 0.2081, 0.2472M1, 0.3336, 0.4546M1, 0.4913M1
Tl^{200}	27 hr	ϵ	....	0.252, 0.289, 0.368, 0.579, 0.629, 0.829
Tl^{201}	3 days	ϵ	....	0.03, 0.032, 0.135M1, 0.168M1
Tl^{202}	12 days	ϵ	....	0.4391E2
Tl^{204}	4.1 years	β^-, ϵ	0.765(98.3%)	No γ
Tl^{206}	4.19 min	β^-	1.51	No γ
Tl^{207}(AcC″)	4.79 min	β^-	1.44	0.870(∼5%)
Tl^{208}(ThC″)	3.1 min	β^-	1.25, 1.6, 1.792	0.233, 0.27735(5+), 0.5108(15+)E2(63%) M1(37%), 0.5830(40+)($\tau = 2.4 \times 10^{-10}$ sec)[K0.015]E2, 0.860E2, 2.6072[K0.0018]E3
Tl^{209}	2.2 min	β^-	1.99	0.12
Tl^{210}(RaC″)	1.32 min	β^-	1.8	
$_{82}Pb^{198}$	25 min	ϵ	....	0.0484, 0.2607, 0.2824. Cf. Tl^{198m}
Pb^{200}	180 hr	ϵ	....	0.139, 0.320
Pb^{201}	8.4 hr	ϵ	....	0.325(100+), 0.583(33+)
Pb^{202m}	3.5 hr	IT	....	0.128E4, 0.392, 0.421(95+)[K0.035]E2, 0.461 (<15+)[K>0.06]M1, 0.658(36+) [K0.005]E1, 0.788(54+)[K1.08]E5, 0.963(106+)[0.0055]E2
Pb^{203}	52 hr	ϵ	....	0.153(<0.4+), 0.279(82.3+)[K0.15]M1E2, 0.400(3.8+)[K0.12]M1E2, 0.678(0.7+) [K0.009]E2
Pb^{204m}	68 min	IT	....	0.374(135+)(τ = 0.26 μsec)[K0.04]E2, 0.913(100+)[K0.05]E5

Pb^{206m}	145 μsec	IT	....	0.203E3, 0.314, 0.343, 0.516, 0.537, 0.657, 0.803E2, 0.880
Pb^{207m}	0.82 sec	IT	....	0.54E2, 1.063M4
Pb^{209}	3.3 hr	β^-	0.64	No γ
Pb^{210}(RaD)	22 years	β^-	0.023	0.0467[12]
Pb^{211}(AcB)	36.1 min	β^-	~0.5(~20%), 1.39(~80%)	0.065, 0.083, 0.404, 0.425, 0.487, 0.764, 0.829
Pb^{212}(ThB)	10.6 hr	β^-	0.331(88%), 0.569(12%)	0.115(2+), 0.164, 0.176(1+), 0.23860(90+)
Pb^{214}	26.8 min	β^-	0.59(56%), 0.65(44%)	0.05323M1, 0.2419M1, 0.25885, 0.2952M1, 0.3520M1
$_{83}Bi^{198}$	7 min	ε, α	5.83(0.2%)	
Bi^{199}	25 min	ε, α	5.47(0.8%)	
Bi^{200}	35 min	ε	No α	
Bi^{201}	62 min	ε, α	5.15(0.03%)	
Bi^{202}	95 min	ε	No β^+, no α	
Bi^{203}	12 hr	ε, α	4.85(~10^{-5}%)	
Bi^{204}	12 hr	ε	....	0.374, 0.905. Cf. Pb^{204m}
Bi^{205}	14.5 days	ε	....	0.2844, 0.704, 0.912, 0.989, 1.045, 1.074, 1.190, 1.615, 1.766, 1.864
Bi^{206}	6.4 days	ε	No β^+	28 γ's from 0.1072 to 1.7917
Bi^{207}	~50 years	ε	....	0.565(100+)[*K*0.018]E2, 1.063(74+) [*K*0.113]M4, 1.46, 2.05, 2.20, 2.23, 2.49
Bi^{210m}(RaE)	5.00 days	β^-, α	β^-: 1.17(>99%); α: (~5 × 10^{-5}%)	No γ
Bi^{210}	2.6 × 10^6 years	α	4.94	
Bi^{211}(AcC)	2.16 min	β^-, α	β^-: (0.32%); α: 6.272(16+), 6.618(84+)	0.354[*K*0.18]
Bi^{212}	60.5 min	β^-, α	β^-: (66.3%), 2.256, others α: five α's in Bi^{212}, 5.601–6.113; four α's in 3 μsec Po^{212}, 8.776–10.538	7 γ's in β^- branch: 0.719–2.20 16 γ's in α branch: 0.03985–0.719

References

Nuclear Data

Hollander, J. M., I. Perlman, and G. T. Seaborg: Table of Isotopes, *Revs. Modern Phys.* **25,** 469 (1953).

Way, K., et al.: Nuclear Data, *Natl. Bur. Standards (U.S.) Circ.* 499 and supplements; New Nuclear Data, *Nuclear Science Abstracts* **6,** 24B (1952); **7,** 24B (1953); **8,** 24B (1954); **9,** 24B (1955).

Beta Decay

Cook, C. S.: The Capture of Orbital Electrons by Nuclei, *Am. J. Phys.* **19,** 37 (1951).

Cook, C. S., and G. E. Owen: The Allowed Beta Spectrum, *Am. J. Phys.* **18,** 453 (1950).

Konopinski, E. J.: Beta Decay, *Revs. Modern Phys.* **15,** 209 (1943).

Konopinski, E. J., and L. M. Langer: Experimental Clarification of the Theory of Beta Decay, *Ann. Rev. Nuclear Sci.* **2** (1953).

Wu, C. S.: Investigation of the Shapes of Beta Ray Spectra, *Revs. Modern Phys.* **22,** 386 (1950).

Wu, C. S.: Beta Disintegration, Allowed and Forbidden Decay, *Physica* **XVIII,** 989 (1952).

Shell Structure

Feenberg, E.: "The Shell Theory of the Nucleus," Princeton University Press, Princeton, N.J., 1955.

Haxel, O., J. H. D. Jensen, and H. E. Suess: On the Magic Numbers in Nuclear Structure, *Phys. Rev.* **75,** 1766 (1949).

Mayer, M. G.: On Closed Shells in Nuclei, *Phys. Rev.* **75,** 1969 (1949); Nuclear Configurations in the Spin Orbit Coupling Model, *Phys. Rev.* **78,** 16 (1950).

Mayer, M. G., and J. H. D. Jensen: "Elementary Theory of Nuclear Shell Structure," John Wiley & Sons, Inc., New York, 1955.

Isomerism

Goldhaber, M., and R. D. Hill: Nuclear Isomerism and Shell Structure, *Revs. Modern Phys.* **24,** 179 (1952).

Goldhaber, M., and A. W. Sunyar: Classification of Nuclear Isomers, *Phys. Rev.* **83,** 906 (1951).

Segrè, E., and A. C. Helmholtz: Nuclear Isomerism, *Revs. Modern Phys.* **21,** 271 (1949).

Detection and Measurements

Bell, R. E.: Nuclear Particle Detection, *Ann. Rev. Nuclear Sci.* **4** (1954).

Cavanagh, P. E.: Spectroscopy of Beta and Gamma Rays, "Progress in Nuclear Physics," vol. 1, Academic Press, Inc., New York, 1950.

Curtiss, L. F.: Measurements of Radioactivity, *Natl. Bur. Standards (U.S.) Circ.* 476 (1949).

Hayward, R. W.: Beta Ray Spectroscopy, "Advances in Electronics," vol. V, Academic Press, Inc., New York, 1953.

Marshall, J.: Nuclear Particle Detection, *Ann. Rev. Nuclear Sci.* **4** (1953).

Persico, E., and C. Geoffrion: Beta Ray Spectroscopes, *Rev. Sci. Instr.* **21,** 945 (1950).

Swank, R. K.: Nuclear Particle Detection, *Ann. Rev. Nuclear Sci.* **4** (1954).

General Theory

Blatt, J. M., and V. F. Weisskopf: "Theoretical Nuclear Physics," John Wiley & Sons, Inc., New York, 1952.

Gamow, G., and C. L. Critchfield: "Theory of Atomic Nucleus and Nuclear Energy Sources," Oxford University Press, New York, 1949.

Siegbahn, K.: "Beta and Gamma Ray Spectroscopy," North Holland Publishing Co., Amsterdam, 1955.

8h. Neutrons

D. J. HUGHES
Brookhaven National Laboratory

J. A. HARVEY
Oak Ridge National Laboratory

Primarily because of their lack of charge and their availability in high intensity, neutrons have been used to study interactions with matter over a 10^{13}-fold energy range (10^{-4} to 10^9 ev). The complexity of these interactions is such that they cannot all be presented in tabular or graphical form in reasonable space. Here only the interactions that have been fairly well established and are of general use are included, most of these corresponding to the low-energy region.

8h-1. Neutron Properties[1]

Spin, $\hbar/2$

Statistics, Fermi-Dirac

Radioactive decay, half life = 12.8 ± 2.5 min; mass difference $m_n - m_H = 782 \pm 1$ kev

Magnetic moment $\mu_n = -1.913148 \pm 0.000066$ nuclear magnetons

Neutron mass, 1.008982 ± 0.000003 atomic mass units (physical scale), $(1.67474 \pm 0.00010) \times 10^{-24}$ g, 939.526 ± 0.024 Mev

Compton wavelength of the neutron

$$\lambda_{cn} = \frac{h}{m_n c} = (1.31958 \pm 0.00004) \times 10^{-13} \text{ cm}$$

$$\bar{\lambda}_{cn} = \frac{\lambda_{cn}}{2\pi} = (2.10017 \pm 0.00007) \times 10^{-14} \text{ cm}$$

Nonrelativistic conversion formulas $[E = kT,\ \lambda = h/(2mE)^{\frac{1}{2}}]$

$$T \text{ (degrees K)} = 1.16057 \times 10^4 E = 6.06607 \times 10^{-5} v^2 = \frac{9.49334 \times 10^{-4}}{\lambda^2}$$

$$E \text{ (ev)} = 8.6164 \times 10^{-5} T = 5.22680 \times 10^{-9} v^2 = \frac{8.17989 \times 10^{-18}}{\lambda^2}$$

$$v \text{ (m/sec)} = 1.28394 \times 10^2 T^{\frac{1}{2}} = 1.38319 \times 10^4 E^{\frac{1}{2}} = \frac{3.95599 \times 10^{-5}}{\lambda}$$

$$\lambda \text{ (cm)} = \frac{3.08112 \times 10^{-7}}{T^{\frac{1}{2}}} = \frac{2.86005 \times 10^{-9}}{E^{\frac{1}{2}}} = \frac{3.95599 \times 10^{-5}}{v}$$

For neutron with $v = 2{,}200$ m/sec

$$T = 293.60 \pm 0.02°\text{K}$$
$$\lambda = (1.79818 \pm 0.00006) \times 10^{-8} \text{ cm}$$
$$E = 0.0252977 \pm 0.0000006 \text{ ev}$$

[1] Based on results of J. W. M. DuMond and E. R. Cohen, *Revs. Modern Phys.* **25**, 691 (1953).

8h-2. Neutron Binding Energies. The compound nucleus formed by addition of a neutron to a target nucleus has an excitation energy equal to the neutron's binding energy B_n (of the "last" neutron in the compound nucleus) plus its kinetic energy. As a result, B_n is important in determining the excitation energy involved in neutron reactions. The binding energy of the last neutron in the nuclide indicated is tabulated in Table 8h-1, which is based on a compilation of neutron binding energies by N. Feather.[1]

8h-3. Types of Neutron Cross Sections. The various interactions of neutrons with matter are specified quantitatively in terms of *cross sections*, which give the probabilities of these interactions in a given neutron flux nv,

$$\text{Interactions per second} = nvN\sigma_i$$

where N is the number of atoms present and σ_i is the cross section for the interaction of type i. Cross sections have the dimensions of area, the usual unit being the *barn* ($= 10^{-24}$ cm^2), with millibarns, microbarns, etc., also being used.

Partial cross sections refer to specific processes, as neutron capture, scattering, etc., and the sum of all the possible processes is the *total cross section* σ_T. The total cross section determines the diminution of a neutron beam as it traverses a sample; the ratio of the beam intensity after traversal to the incident intensity, or the transmission T, is given by

$$T = e^{-n\sigma_T x}$$

where x is the sample thickness and n the number of atoms per cm^3. The *differential scattering cross section* $d\sigma_s/d\omega$ gives the probability that a neutron will be scattered in a given direction, and the integral of $d\sigma_s/d\omega$ over 4π solid angle is the *scattering cross section* σ_s. The *transport cross section* σ_{tr} is related to the scattering cross section by

$$\sigma_{tr} = \sigma_s(1 - \overline{\cos\theta})$$

where θ is the angle of scattering in the laboratory coordinate system. The *activation cross section* refers to the production of a specific radioactive isotope, usually as a result of the (n,γ) reaction (neutron capture).

8h-4. Fast-neutron Cross Sections. The classification "fast neutrons" refers to a rather vague energy region, about 10 kev to 10 Mev. In this region, individual neutron resonances cannot be resolved in most heavy elements, and a cross section varying smoothly with energy is observed as a result. For the great majority of the fast-neutron cross-section work, total cross sections alone have been measured, although reactions and scattering have also been studied. As individual resonance parameters are not determined, except for the lightest elements, the data are not amenable to tabular presentation and the curves presenting the known results fill a large volume, "Neutron Cross Sections." Several illustrative curves only for total cross sections are reproduced here. Figure 8h-1 for H is smooth because there are no resonances in the energy region shown. The curve for C (Fig. 8h-2) is smooth in the low-energy region for the same reason, exhibits resonances in the 1- to 10-Mev region, and is smooth at higher energy because of failure to resolve resonances. Iron (Fig. 8h-3) is similar to carbon, but the characteristic features are moved to lower energies, and in U (Fig. 8h-4) the levels are so close that they are unresolved for the entire energy range shown. For those few resonances in the light elements for which reso-

[1] *Advances in Phys.* **2,** 141 (1953). Additional pertinent information was derived from the nuclear data tables published in *Nuclear Science Abstracts* (through June, 1954); J. M. Hollander, I. Perlman, and G. T. Seaborg, *Revs. Modern Phys.* **25,** 469 (1953); F. Ajzenberg and T. Lauritsen, *Revs. Modern Phys.* **24,** 321 (1952); P. M. Endt and J. C. Kluyver, *Revs. Modern Phys.* **26,** 95 (1954); J. R. Huizenga and L. B. Magnusson, ANL-5158 (November, 1953); N. S. Wall, *Phys. Rev.* **96,** 664 (1954).

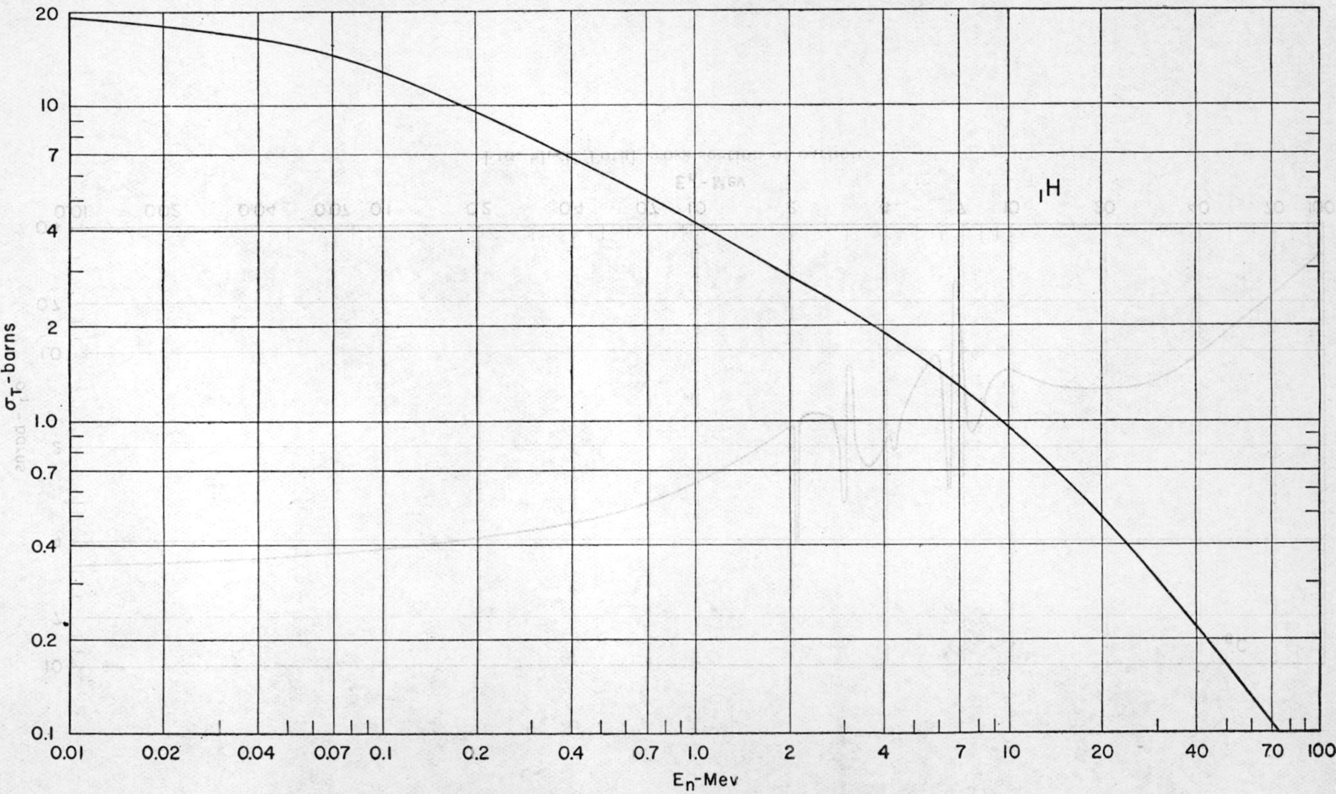

FIG. 8h-1. Total cross section of hydrogen.

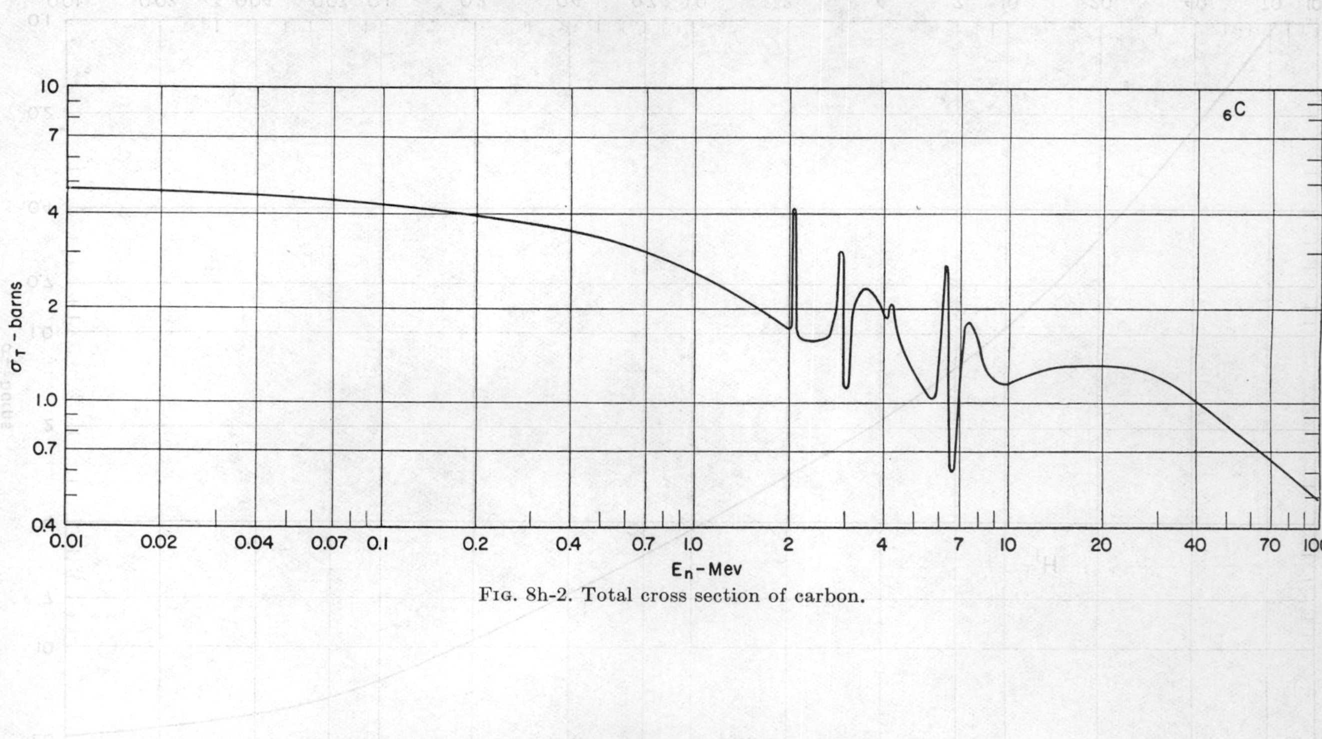

FIG. 8h-2. Total cross section of carbon.

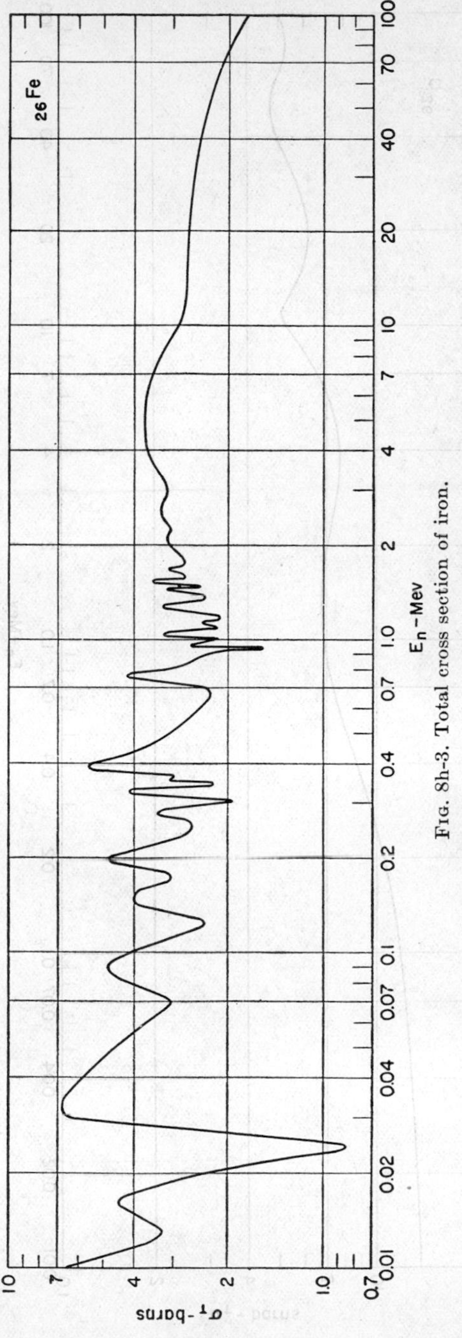

FIG. 8h-3. Total cross section of iron.

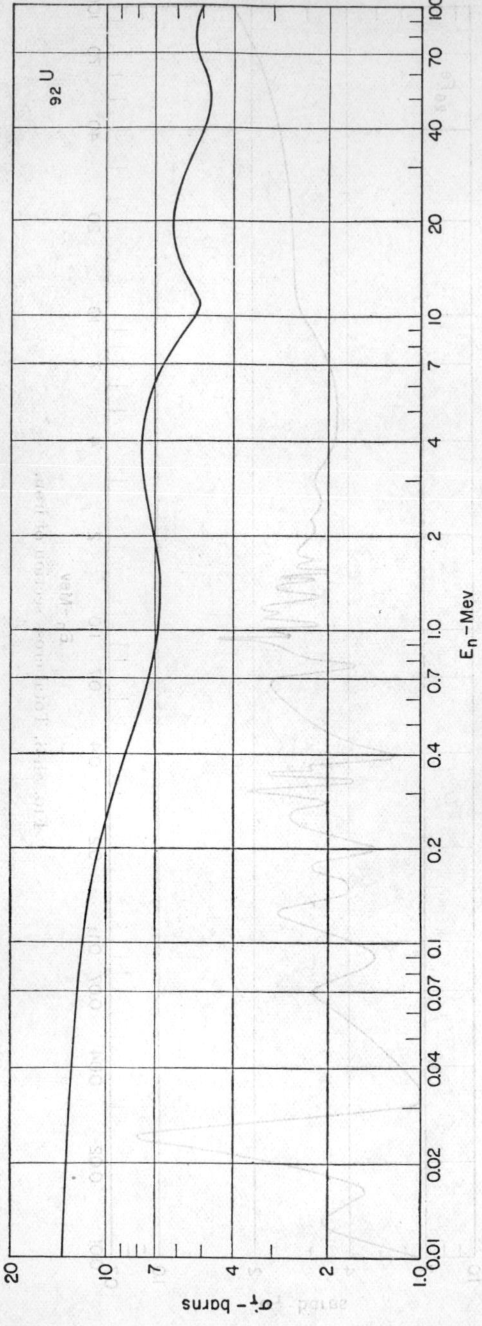

FIG. 8h-4. Total cross section of uranium.

TABLE 8h-1. TABLE OF NEUTRON BINDING ENERGIES

Z	Element	A	N	B_n, Mev
1	H	2	1	2.226 ± 0.003
		3	2	6.256 ± 0.007
2	He	4	2	20.58 ± 0.02
		6	4	1.90 ± 0.08
3	Li	6	3	5.35 ± 0.20
		7	4	7.254 ± 0.003
		8	5	2.034 ± 0.003
4	Be	8	4	18.884 ± 0.010
		9	5	1.667 ± 0.002
		10	6	6.816 ± 0.006
5	B	9	4	18.4 ± 0.3
		10	5	8.44 ± 0.02
		11	6	11.453 ± 0.005
		12	7	3.364 ± 0.006
6	C	11	5	13.38 ± 0.10
		12	6	18.77 ± 0.06
		13	7	4.946 ± 0.002
		14	8	8.169 ± 0.004
		15	9	2.2 ± 0.5
7	N	13	6	20.45 ± 0.10
		14	7	10.55 ± 0.01
		15	8	10.832 ± 0.008
		16	9	2.6 ± 0.2
		17	10	5.6 ± 0.4
8	O	15	7	13.23 ± 0.10
		16	8	15.6 ± 0.2
		17	9	4.143 ± 0.006
		18	10	8.06 ± 0.02
		19	11	3.961 ± 0.008
9	F	18	9	9.13 ± 0.05
		19	10	10.3 ± 0.3
		20	11	6.599 ± 0.008
10	Ne	20	10	16.86 ± 0.04
		21	11	6.755 ± 0.008
		22	12	10.363 ± 0.011
		23	13	5.190 ± 0.008
11	Na	23	12	12.25 ± 0.05
		24	13	6.953 ± 0.007
		25	14	9.2 ± 0.3
12	Mg	24	12	16.59 ± 0.02
		25	13	7.334 ± 0.007
		26	14	11.106 ± 0.010
		27	15	6.440 ± 0.008
13	Al	25	12	17.0 ± 0.4
		26	13	11.5 ± 0.2
		27	14	12.99 ± 0.06
		28	15	7.724 ± 0.006

TABLE 8h-1. TABLE OF NEUTRON BINDING ENERGIES (*Continued*)

Z	Element	A	N	B_n, Mev
14	Si	28	14	16.84 ± 0.11
		29	15	8.468 ± 0.008
		30	16	10.601 ± 0.011
		31	17	6.590 ± 0.007
15	P	30	15	11.25 ± 0.25
		31	16	12.1 ± 0.2
		32	17	7.930 ± 0.008
		33	18	10.09 ± 0.02
		34	19	6.0 ± 0.3
16	S	32	16	14.71 ± 0.12
		33	17	8.65 ± 0.01
		34	18	10.9 ± 0.2
		35	19	7.0 ± 0.3
		36	20	9.2 ± 0.3
		37	21	5.7 ± 0.3
17	Cl	34	17	10.8 ± 0.4
		35	18	12.8 ± 0.3
		36	19	8.56 ± 0.03
		37	20	9.95 ± 0.20
		38	21	6.3 ± 0.3
		39	22	8.4 ± 0.3
18	A	36	18	14.7 ± 0.2
		37	19	8.82 ± 0.03
		38	20	11.8 ± 0.3
		39	21	6.9 ± 0.3
		40	22	9.99 ± 0.10
		41	23	6.07 ± 0.08
19	K	39	20	13.2 ± 0.2
		40	21	7.795 ± 0.008
		41	22	10.20 ± 0.10
		42	23	7.34 ± 0.02
20	Ca	40	20	15.4 ± 0.2
		41	21	8.366 ± 0.010
		42	22	11.37 ± 0.12
		49	29	5.0 ± 0.3
21	Sc	46	25	8.85 ± 0.08
		47	26	10.5 ± 0.2
		48	27	7.98 ± 0.10
		49	28	10.29 ± 0.10
22	Ti	46	24	13.3 ± 0.2
		47	25	8.70 ± 0.05
		48	26	11.36 ± 0.05
		49	27	8.10 ± 0.05
		50	28	10.85 ± 0.05
		51	29	6.34 ± 0.07

TABLE 8h-1. TABLE OF NEUTRON BINDING ENERGIES (*Continued*)

Z	Element	A	N	B_n, Mev
23	V	49	26	11.51 ± 0.10
		50	27	9.07 ± 0.10
		51	28	11.05 ± 0.20
		52	29	7.305 ± 0.007
24	Cr	50	26	13.4 ± 0.2
		51	27	9.1 ± 0.3
		52	28	11.80 ± 0.25
		53	29	7.929 ± 0.008
		54	30	9.716 ± 0.008
		55	31	5.9 ± 0.3
25	Mn	52	27	10.5 ± 0.4
		53	28	12.0 ± 0.2
		54	29	8.94 ± 0.10
		55	30	10.1 ± 0.2
		56	31	7.261 ± 0.006
26	Fe	53	27	10.5 ± 0.3
		54	28	13.8 ± 0.2
		55	29	9.298 ± 0.007
		56	30	11.12 ± 0.10
		57	31	7.639 ± 0.004
		58	32	10.16 ± 0.04
		59	33	6.4 ± 0.3
27	Co	58	31	9.0 ± 0.3
		59	32	10.25 ± 0.20
		60	33	7.486 ± 0.006
		61	34	9.96 ± 0.05
28	Ni	58	30	11.7 ± 0.2
		59	31	8.997 ± 0.005
		60	32	11.40 ± 0.10
		61	33	8.532 ± 0.008
		63	35	6.7 ± 0.2
		64	36	9.66 ± 0.03
		65	37	6.02 ± 0.10
29	Cu	61	32	10.6 ± 0.2
		63	34	10.65 ± 0.10
		64	35	7.914 ± 0.004
		65	36	9.80 ± 0.05
		66	37	7.1 ± 0.2
		67	38	9.1 ± 0.3
30	Zn	63	33	9.0 ± 0.2
		64	34	11.80 ± 0.10
		65	35	7.876 ± 0.007
		66	36	11.15 ± 0.20
		67	37	7.0 ± 0.2
		68	38	10.15 ± 0.20
		69	39	6.3 ± 0.3
		70	40	9.2 ± 0.2

TABLE 8h-1. TABLE OF NEUTRON BINDING ENERGIES (*Continued*)

Z	Element	A	N	B_n, Mev
31	Ga	67	36	11.2 ± 0.3
		68	37	8.3 ± 0.3
		69	38	10.1 ± 0.2
		71	40	9.05 ± 0.20
32	Ge	75	43	6.5 ± 0.3
33	As	75	42	10.2 ± 0.2
		76	43	7.30 ± 0.04
34	Se	77	43	7.416 ± 0.009
		78	44	10.483 ± 0.014
		79	45	7.0 ± 0.3
		80	46	9.35 ± 0.20
		81	47	6.8 ± 0.3
		82	48	9.8 ± 0.5
35	Br	77	42	10.66 ± 0.05
		78	43	8.40 ± 0.10
		79	44	10.65 ± 0.20
		80	45	7.3 ± 0.3
		81	46	10.1 ± 0.2
36	Kr	80	44	11.3 ± 0.4
		85	49	5.95 ± 0.05
		87	51	5.53 ± 0.05
		88	52	6.8 ± 0.3
37	Rb	87	50	9.96 ± 0.05
		88	51	6.0 ± 0.2
		89	52	7.4 ± 0.3
38	Sr	85	47	7.5 ± 0.3
		86	48	9.5 ± 0.2
		87	49	8.43 ± 0.01
		88	50	11.07 ± 0.06
		89	51	6.55 ± 0.10
		90	52	7.6 ± 0.2
		91	53	5.7 ± 0.2
39	Y	87	48	10.5 ± 0.5
		88	49	9.4 ± 0.2
		89	50	11.7 ± 0.2
		90	51	6.70 ± 0.10
		91	52	7.80 ± 0.10
		92	53	6.60 ± 0.10
		93	54	6.8 ± 0.4
40	Zr	88	48	<12.3
		89	49	>9.3
		90	50	11.8 ± 0.2
		91	51	7.16 ± 0.05
		92	52	8.66 ± 0.04
		93	53	6.65 ± 0.05
		95	55	6.42 ± 0.05
		97	57	3.7 ± 0.4

TABLE 8h-1. TABLE OF NEUTRON BINDING ENERGIES (*Continued*)

Z	Element	A	N	B_n, Mev
41	Nb	91	50	10.0 ± 0.6
		92	51	8.5 ± 0.5
		93	52	8.7 ± 0.2
		94	53	7.19 ± 0.03
		95	54	9.2 ± 0.4
		96	55	6.9 ± 0.2
		97	56	8.1 ± 0.3
42	Mo	92	50	13.28 ± 0.15
		93	51	7.90 ± 0.05
		94	52	9.9 ± 0.5
		95	53	8.0 ± 0.3
		96	54	9.15 ± 0.05
		97	55	6.9 ± 0.2
		98	56	8.29 ± 0.10
43	Tc	93	50	>10.2
		94	51	8.7 ± 0.5
		95	52	9.5 ± 0.4
		100	57	7.1 ± 0.4
44	Ru	99	55	7.1 ± 0.2
		100	56	9.5 ± 0.2
		103	59	6.5 ± 0.3
45	Rh	100	55	8.0 ± 0.3
		103	58	9.4 ± 0.2
		104	59	6.792 ± 0.014
		105	60	9.1 ± 0.3
46	Pd	105	59	7.1 ± 0.2
		108	62	9.4 ± 0.2
47	Ag	108	61	7.27 ± 0.02
		109	62	9.07 ± 0.10
		113	66	8.6 ± 0.4
48	Cd	108	60	10.20 ± 0.10
		113	65	6.40 ± 0.10
		114	66	9.046 ± 0.008
		115	67	5.6 ± 0.2
49	In	113	64	9.2 ± 0.3
		115	66	9.1 ± 0.2
		116	67	6.6 ± 0.2
		118	69	<9.8
		119	70	>5.4
50	Sn	115	65	7.7 ± 0.3
		116	66	8.9 ± 0.3
		118	68	9.3 ± 0.2
		119	69	6.6 ± 0.2
		121	71	6.15 ± 0.07
		124	74	8.50 ± 0.15
		125	75	5.75 ± 0.07

TABLE 8h-1. TABLE OF NEUTRON BINDING ENERGIES (*Continued*)

Z	Element	A	N	B_n, Mev
51	Sb	121	70	9.25 ± 0.10
		122	71	6.80 ± 0.04
		124	73	6.6 ± 0.2
		125	74	8.62 ± 0.10
52	Te	122	70	>9.3
		125	73	6.48 ± 0.07
		126	74	7.2 ± 0.2
53	I	127	74	9.10 ± 0.20
		128	75	6.58 ± 0.05
55	Cs	133	78	9.05 ± 0.20
		134	79	6.73 ± 0.10
		137	82	7.1 ± 0.3
		138	83	4.9 ± 0.4
56	Ba	137	81	6.8 ± 0.2
		138	82	8.55 ± 0.25
		139	83	5.2 ± 0.3
		141	85	<5.2
57	La	139	82	8.8 ± 0.2
		140	83	5.10 ± 0.10
		141	84	6.93 ± 0.15
58	Ce	140	82	9.05 ± 0.20
		141	83	5.50 ± 0.15
		142	84	7.15 ± 0.20
		143	85	5.09 ± 0.07
59	Pr	140	81	7.8 ± 0.3
		141	82	9.40 ± 0.15
60	Nd	143	83	5.02 ± 0.08
62	Sm	155	93	5.58 ± 0.30
73	Ta	181	108	7.55 ± 0.20
		182	109	6.03 ± 0.15
74	W	183	109	6.25 ± 0.30
		186	112	7.15 ± 0.30
75	Re	187	112	7.3 ± 0.3
76	Os	187	111	6.6 ± 0.3
77	Ir	193	116	7.8 ± 0.2
		195	118	6.5 ± 0.3
78	Pt	194	116	9.5 ± 0.2
		195	117	6.12 ± 0.08
		196	118	8.2 ± 0.2
		197	119	<6.5
79	Au	197	118	8.0 ± 0.1
		198	119	6.35 ± 0.15
80	Hg	201	121	6.3 ± 0.2
81	Tl	203	122	8.80 ± 0.20
		204	123	6.52 ± 0.15
		205	124	7.60 ± 0.20
		206	125	6.16 ± 0.15

TABLE 8h-1. TABLE OF NEUTRON BINDING ENERGIES (*Continued*)

Z	Element	A	N	B_n, Mev
81	Tl	207	126	6.79 ± 0.03
		208	127	3.83 ± 0.03
		209	128	4.84 ± 0.11
		210	129	3.88 ± 0.13
82	Pb	205	123	6.40 ± 0.18
		206	124	8.10 ± 0.10
		207	125	6.73 ± 0.01
		208	126	7.38 ± 0.01
		209	127	3.87 ± 0.05
		210	128	5.24 ± 0.06
		211	129	3.78 ± 0.04
		212	130	5.17 ± 0.03
83	Bi	209	126	7.44 ± 0.05
		210	127	4.67 ± 0.06
		211	128	5.10 ± 0.04
		212	129	4.38 ± 0.02
		213	130	5.07 ± 0.12
		214	131	4.24 ± 0.12
84	Po	209	125	6.65 ± 0.18
		210	126	7.66 ± 0.10
		211	127	4.55 ± 0.03
		212	128	6.01 ± 0.03
		213	129	4.31 ± 0.05
		214	130	5.91 ± 0.06
		215	131	4.10 ± 0.04
		216	132	5.78 ± 0.03
85	At	215	130	5.90 ± 0.06
		216	131	4.59 ± 0.06
		217	132	5.86 ± 0.12
		218	133	4.64 ± 0.14
86	Em	216	130	6.66 ± 0.08
		217	131	4.58 ± 0.07
		218	132	6.55 ± 0.07
		219	133	4.40 ± 0.05
		220	134	6.33 ± 0.03
87	Fr	219	132	6.46 ± 0.08
		220	133	5.22 ± 0.07
		221	134	6.25 ± 0.12
88	Ra	220	132	7.19 ± 0.11
		221	133	5.32 ± 0.08
		222	134	6.75 ± 0.08
		223	135	5.17 ± 0.10
		224	136	6.43 ± 0.10
		225	137	5.07 ± 0.13
		226	138	6.33 ± 0.14
		227	139	4.56 ± 0.16
		228	140	6.10 ± 0.11

TABLE 8h-1. TABLE OF NEUTRON BINDING ENERGIES (*Continued*)

Z	Element	A	N	B_n, Mev
89	Ac	223	134	6.79 ± 0.10
		224	135	5.70 ± 0.09
		225	136	6.62 ± 0.13
		226	137	5.43 ± 0.15
		227	138	6.58 ± 0.13
		228	139	4.84 ± 0.10
90	Th	224	134	7.62 ± 0.11
		225	135	5.89 ± 0.08
		226	136	7.03 ± 0.09
		227	137	5.44 ± 0.10
		228	138	7.05 ± 0.10
		229	139	5.48 ± 0.13
		230	140	6.68 ± 0.14
		231	141	5.18 ± 0.16
		232	142	6.20 ± 0.04
		233	143	5.16 ± 0.11
		234	144	6.01 ± 0.14
91	Pa	227	136	7.14 ± 0.11
		228	137	6.08 ± 0.09
		229	138	7.03 ± 0.13
		232	141	5.28 ± 0.10
		233	142	6.95 ± 0.15
		234	143	5.38 ± 0.14
		235	144	5.90 ± 0.15
92	U	228	136	7.73 ± 0.13
		229	137	6.15 ± 0.09
		230	138	7.61 ± 0.09
		231	139	5.83 ± 0.12
		232	140	7.20 ± 0.12
	U	233	141	5.97 ± 0.14
		234	142	6.74 ± 0.14
		235	143	5.37 ± 0.15
		236	144	6.29 ± 0.04
		237	145	5.45 ± 0.12
		238	146	6.03 ± 0.13
		239	147	4.87 ± 0.13
		240	148	5.77 ± 0.30
93	Np	236	143	5.61 ± 0.10
		237	144	6.91 ± 0.16
		238	145	5.19 ± 0.14
		239	146	6.41 ± 0.15
		240	147	4.83 ± 0.30
94	Pu	235	141	6.18 ± 0.14
		236	142	7.30 ± 0.14
		239	145	5.71 ± 0.15
		240	146	6.28 ± 0.05
		241	147	5.55 ± 0.12

TABLE 8h-1. TABLE OF NEUTRON BINDING ENERGIES (*Continued*)

Z	Element	A	N	B_n, Mev
94	Pu	242	148	6.06 ± 0.14
		243	149	5.15 ± 0.15
95	Am	242	147	5.41 ± 0.14
		243	148	6.44 ± 0.15
96	Cm	243	147	5.72 ± 0.15
		244	148	6.51 ± 0.07

nance-level parameters have been determined, the results are given in Sec. 8h-5, although they refer to the "fast-neutron" rather than the "resonance-neutron" energy region.

8h-5. Resonance Cross Sections. The neutron energy region in which individual resonances can be resolved varies from nuclide to nuclide, but for all but the lightest elements it is about 1 ev to 10 kev. In this energy region only $l = 0$ interactions are appreciable and the analysis of resonances is thereby simplified. The scattering and capture characteristics of the resonance level are given as functions of the neutron energy E by the Breit-Wigner single-level formulas for scattering and neutron capture:

$$\sigma_s(E) = 4\pi \lambda\!\!\!^{-}{}_0^2 g \left| \frac{\Gamma_n/2}{E - E_0 + i\Gamma/2} + \frac{R}{\lambda\!\!\!^{-}{}_0} \right|^2 + 4\pi(1-g)R^2$$

$$\sigma_\gamma(E) = \pi \lambda\!\!\!^{-}{}_0^2 g \left(\frac{E_0}{E}\right)^{\frac{1}{2}} \frac{\Gamma_n \Gamma_\gamma}{(E - E_0)^2 + (\Gamma/2)^2}$$

$$\Gamma = \Gamma_\gamma + \Gamma_n + \Gamma_p + \Gamma_\alpha + \cdots$$

$$g = \frac{1}{2}\left(\frac{2J+1}{2I+1}\right) \qquad J = I \pm \frac{1}{2} \text{ (for } l = 0 \text{ neutrons)}$$

Here Γ_γ, Γ_n, etc., the "resonance parameters," are the radiation, neutron, etc., widths of the nuclear energy level corresponding to the neutron resonance, and Γ is the total width, related to the lifetime of the state t_0 by $t_0 = \hbar/\Gamma$. The cross sections for the (n,p), (n,α), etc., reactions are the same as σ_γ, with p, α, etc., substituted for γ. The neutron width is the value at the resonance energy E_0 ($\lambda\!\!\!^{-}{}_0$ is the neutron wavelength/2π at resonance), I is the spin of the target nucleus, of radius R, and J is the spin of the compound nucleus. For incoming neutrons of angular momentum l greater than zero the factor g is unknown in general because of the various l's that can produce a given J. Because neutron widths are proportional to velocity, it is often convenient to list $\Gamma_n{}^0$, the neutron width reduced to its value at 1 ev,

$$\Gamma_n{}^0 = \frac{\Gamma_n}{E^{\frac{1}{2}}}$$

For an actual sample, the resonance has an observed width greater than Γ because of the temperature motion of the atoms. This motion produces a resonance spread that is gaussian with a width Δ given by

$$\Delta = 2\left(\frac{kTE_0 m}{M}\right)^{\frac{1}{2}}$$

where m/M is the mass ratio of neutron to nucleus and T is a temperature slightly greater than the actual sample temperature.[1]

[1] W. E. Lamb, Jr., *Phys. Rev.* **55**, 190 (1939).

In Tables 8h-2 (light elements) and 8h-3 (heavy elements) the parameters are listed for those resonances for which at least E_0 and Γ_n are known. Because the neutron width is much larger than the radiation width in light elements, the latter is very seldom known; partly as a result of this fact, however, the neutron angular momentum l and the level spin J can often be obtained. For many of the heavy elements Γ_n can be obtained if Γ_γ, which is usually much larger, is approximately known. As the dependence of Γ_n on Γ_γ is often weak in these cases it is usually sufficiently accurate to use an average Γ_γ for the particular nuclide in obtaining the Γ_n's of individual levels. The average Γ_γ indicated in the table is obtained either from the individual Γ_γ's of resonances of the nuclide itself or from neighboring nuclides. The error quoted for Γ_n includes the error resulting from the uncertainty in fixing this average Γ_γ. An additional error in Γ_n arises because J (hence g) is usually not known; this error, which is not included, is largest for $I = \frac{1}{2}$, negligible for high I, and zero for $I = 0 (g = 1)$. For the few cases where J's (hence g's) are known, they are included.

8h-6. Thermal Cross Sections. Thermal neutrons are those in equilibrium with a moderating material, such as graphite or water, usually at or near room temperature. The velocity distribution of the neutrons is then Maxwellian,

$$dn = \frac{4n}{J_0{}^3\sqrt{\pi}} v^2 e^{-(v/v_0)^2}\, dv$$

where dn is the density of neutrons in the velocity band dv, the flux being given by Jnv. The velocity v_0 is the most probable velocity and the energy corresponding to $v_0 = 2{,}200$ m/sec is 0.0253 ev, or a wavelength of 1.80 A (see Sec. 8h-1 for exact values).

The wavelength of thermal neutrons is convenient for observation of such optical phenomena as diffraction and refraction. In neutron optics it is necessary to consider the coherent and incoherent parts of the nuclear scattering cross section, the incoherent part arising from isotopic and spin-dependent scattering. For the two types of scattering, the coherent and incoherent components of the cross section are given by

Isotopic incoherence (for two isotopes, of abundances f_1 and f_2 and cross sections σ_1 and σ_2):

$$\sigma_{\text{coh}} = (f_1\sigma_1{}^{\frac{1}{2}} + f_2\sigma_2{}^{\frac{1}{2}})^2$$
$$\sigma_{\text{inc}} = f_1 f_2(\sigma_1{}^{\frac{1}{2}} - \sigma_2{}^{\frac{1}{2}})^2$$

Spin-dependent incoherence (for target nucleus of spin I, and cross sections σ_+ and σ_- for the $I + \frac{1}{2}$ and $I - \frac{1}{2}$ compound states):

$$\sigma_{\text{coh}} = \left(\frac{I+1}{2I+1}\sigma_+{}^{\frac{1}{2}} + \frac{I}{2I+1}\sigma_-{}^{\frac{1}{2}}\right)^2$$
$$\sigma_{\text{inc}} = \frac{I(2I+1)}{(2I+1)^2}(\sigma_+{}^{\frac{1}{2}} - \sigma_-{}^{\frac{1}{2}})^2$$

The coherent scattering cross section determines the index of refraction of a noncapturing medium for neutrons,

$$\mu^2 - 1 = \pm 2N\lambda\!\!\!^{-2}(\pi\sigma_{\text{coh}})^{\frac{1}{2}}$$

where N is the number of nuclei per cm³ and the minus sign corresponds to a positive amplitude (hard-sphere scattering). Presence of neutron capture (written σ_γ) modifies the index slightly and adds an imaginary component

$$\mu^2 - 1 = N\lambda\!\!\!^{-2}\left[\pm\left(4\pi\sigma_{\text{coh}} - \frac{\sigma_\gamma{}^2}{\lambda\!\!\!^{-2}}\right)^{\frac{1}{2}} + \frac{i\sigma_\gamma}{\lambda\!\!\!^{-}}\right]$$

TABLE 8h-2. RESONANCE PARAMETERS OF LIGHT NUCLEI

Isotope	I	E_0, kev	J	l	Γ_n, kev
$_2He^4$	0	1,150 ± 50	$\frac{3}{2}$	1	1,400 ± 200
$_3Li^6$	1	248 ± 4	$\frac{5}{2}$	1	Γ 90 ± 10
					Γ_n 60 ± 15
					Γ_α 30 ± 10
$_3Li^7$	$\frac{3}{2}$	258 ± 3	3	1	35 ± 5
$_4Be^9$	$\frac{3}{2}$	620 ± 10	3	1	25 ± 4
		810 ± 10	2	1,2	8 ± 3
$_5B^{11}$	$\frac{3}{2}$	430 ± 10	2	1	40 ± 5
		1,260 ± 20	3	2	140 ± 20
		1,780 ± 20	1	1,2	60 ± 20
		2,450 ± 20	2	1,2	120 ± 40
		2,580 ± 20	3	1,2	60 ± 20
$_6C^{12}$	0	2,080 ± 10	$\geq\frac{3}{2}$	$\geq$1	$\leq$11
		2,950 ± 20	$\frac{3}{2}$	2	60 ± 20
		3,650 ± 20	$\frac{1}{2}$	0	1,200 ± 400
$_7N^{14}$	1	430 ± 5	$\geq\frac{3}{2}$	$\geq$1	Γ_n <3
					Γ_p <0.01
		495 ± 5			Γ_p <10
					Γ_n <3
		639 ± 5	$\frac{1}{2}$	0	Γ_n 34 ± 4
					Γ_p 9 ± 3
		998 ± 5	$\frac{3}{2}$	0	Γ_n 45 ± 5
					Γ_p 0.8 ± 0.3
		1,120 ± 6	$\frac{5}{2}$	1, 2	Γ_n 19 ± 3
					Γ_p 0.20 ± 0.12
		1,188 ± 6	$\geq\frac{3}{2}$	$\geq$1	Γ_n <2
					Γ_p <0.1
		1,211 ± 7	$\frac{1}{2}$	1	Γ_n 12 ± 2
					Γ_p 0.4 ± 0.2
		1,350 ± 7	$\frac{5}{2}$	1, 2	Γ_n 21 ± 4
					Γ_p 1.0 ± 0.6
		1,401 ± 8	$\frac{3}{2}$	1	Γ_n 42 ± 10
					Γ_p 10 ± 3
					Γ_α 2 ± 1
		1,595 ± 8	$\frac{5}{2}$	1, 2	Γ_n 21 ± 3
					Γ_p 0.4 ± 0.2
					Γ_α 0.20 ± 0.15
		1,779 ± 10	$\frac{5}{2}$	1, 2	Γ_n 18 ± 4
					Γ_α 6 ± 2
					Γ_p 0.20 ± 0.15
$_8O^{16}$	0	435 ± 5	$\frac{3}{2}$	1	40 ± 4
		1,000 ± 10	$\frac{3}{2}$	2	100 ± 10
		1,320 ± 10	$\frac{3}{2}$	1	35 ± 4
		1,660 ± 10	$\geq\frac{3}{2}$	$\geq$1	<7
		1,840 ± 10	$\geq\frac{3}{2}$	$\geq$1	<10
		1,910 ± 20	$\frac{1}{2}$	1	30 ± 6
		2,370 ± 20	$\frac{1}{2}$	0	140 ± 50

Table 8h-2. Resonance Parameters of Light Nuclei (*Continued*)

Isotope	I	E_0, kev	J	l	Γ_n, kev
$_8O^{16}$		3,330 ± 30	$\frac{3}{2}$	2	220 ± 40
		3,800 ± 80	$\frac{3}{2}$	1	800 ± 200
		4,400 ± 40	$\frac{1}{2}$	1	280 ± 80
$_9F^{19}$	$\frac{1}{2}$	28 ± 1	≥1	≥1	<1.0
		50 ± 2	≥1	≥1	<2
		100 ± 2	1	1, 2	13 ± 3
		275 ± 10			25 ± 10
		340 ± 20			200 ± 100
		420 ± 10			25 ± 15
		510 ± 10			25 ± 15
		590 ± 10			25 ± 10
$_{11}Na^{23}$	$\frac{3}{2}$	2.9 ± 0.2	2	0	0.24 ± 0.12
		55 ± 3			<5
		204 ± 3	1	1	5 ± 2
		217 ± 3	0	1	14 ± 10
		243 ± 3	1, 2	1	7 ± 2
		297 ± 3	1	0	4.0 ± 1.0
		396 ± 4	0, 1	1	23 ± 3
		451 ± 4	1	1, 2	9 ± 3
		542 ± 5	1	0	39 ± 7
		602 ± 4	≥1		6 ± 4
		710 ± 7	≥5		72 ± 10
		784 ± 5	≥2		38 ± 6
		914 ± 5	≥3		36 ± 5
		988 ± 5	≥1		24 ± 10
$_{12}Mg^{24}$	0	85 ± 3	$\frac{1}{2}$	1	13 ± 3
		275 ± 8	$\frac{1}{2}$	1	80 ± 20
		430 ± 5	$\frac{3}{2}$	1	30 ± 10
$_{13}Al^{27}$	$\frac{5}{2}$	35 ± 2	3	0	1.2 ± 0.5
		90 ± 4	3	0	7 ± 2
$_{14}Si^{28}$	0	195 ± 6	$\frac{1}{2}$	0	60 ± 10
		570 ± 5	$\frac{3}{2}$	1	15 ± 5
$_{16}S^{32}$	0	111 ± 2	$\frac{1}{2}$	0	18 ± 3
		203 ± 2		≥1	<2
		274 ± 2		≥1	<3
		290 ± 2		≥1	<3
		375 ± 3	$\frac{1}{2}$	0	12 ± 2
		585 ± 3	$\frac{3}{2}$	1	1.4 ± 0.5
		700 ± 4	$\frac{1}{2}$	0	14 ± 3

TABLE 8h-3. RESONANCE PARAMETERS OF HEAVY NUCLEI

Isotope	I	E_0, ev	Γ_γ, mv*	Γ_n, mv	Γ_n^0, mv
$_{25}Mn^{55}$...	$\frac{5}{2}$	337 ± 6	....	(22 ± 4) × 10^3	1,200 ± 200
		1,080 ± 30	....	(16 ± 5) × 10^3	500 ± 200
		2,360 ± 100	....	(340 ± 30) × 10^3 (J = 3)	7,000 ± 600
$_{27}Co^{59}$....	$\frac{7}{2}$	132 ± 2	....	(4.9 ± 0.7) × 10^3	430 ± 60
$_{28}Ni^{62}$....	0	4,200 ± 1,000	....	(1,300 ± 400) × 10^3	(20 ± 6) × 10^3
$_{30}Zn^{64}$....	0	2,750 ± 100	....	(70 ± 10) × 10^3	1,300 ± 200
		4,600 ± 300	....	(60 ± 30) × 10^3	900 ± 400
$_{30}Zn^{67}$....	$\frac{5}{2}$	225 ± 3	....	(1.3 ± 0.2) × 10^3	87 ± 13
		455 ± 10	....	(13 ± 3) × 10^3	610 ± 140
		1,620 ± 70	....	(19 ± 9) × 10^3	500 ± 200
		2,300 ± 100	....	(29 ± 15) × 10^3	600 ± 300
$_{30}Zn^{68}$....	0	530 ± 11	....	(10 ± 2) × 10^3	440 ± 90
$_{42}Mo^{95}$...	$\frac{5}{2}$	45.6 ± 0.6	210 ± 60	174 ± 10	26.0 ± 1.6
		162 ± 4	....	13.6 ± 1.9	1.1 ± 0.2
		570 ± 30	....	120 ± 60	5 ± 3
		700 ± 40	....	740 ± 130	28 ± 5
$_{42}Mo^{96}$...	0	133 ± 2	26.0 ± 60	200 ± 15	17.3 ± 1.3
$_{42}Mo^{97}$...	$\frac{5}{2}$	....	260 ± 80		
		71.5 ± 1.2	330 ± 80	16.6 ± 1.8	2.0 ± 0.2
		292 ± 10	....	75 ± 15	4.4 ± 0.9
		406 ± 17	....	80 ± 40	4 ± 2
		580 ± 30	....	670 ± 130	28 ± 6
$_{42}Mo^{98}$...	0	....	260 ± 80		
		480 ± 20	....	740 ± 110	34 ± 5
$_{42}Mo^{100}$..	0	....	260 ± 80		
		367 ± 15	....	1,000 ± 120	52 ± 6
$_{44}Ru$†....	...	....	150 ± 50		
		9.8 ± 0.2	....	0.8 ± 0.3*	0.26 ± 0.09*
		15.2 ± 0.3	....	1.1 ± 0.4*	0.28 ± 0.09*
		24.1 ± 0.5	....	2.2 ± 0.8*	0.45 ± 0.15*
		40.9 ± 0.8	....	7 ± 3*	1.1 ± 0.5*
$_{45}Rh^{103}$...	$\frac{1}{2}$	1.260 ± 0.004	155 ± 5	0.76 ± 0.04	0.68 ± 0.04
$_{47}Ag^{107}$...	$\frac{1}{2}$	....	140 ± 30		
		16.60 ± 0.15	170 ± 30	4.8 ± 0.5	1.20 ± 0.12
		42.4 ± 0.6	....	9 ± 2	1.4 ± 0.3
		45.4 ± 0.6	....	1.2 ± 0.3	0.18 ± 0.04
		52.2 ± 0.6	120 ± 30	34 ± 4	4.8 ± 0.6
$_{47}Ag^{109}$...	$\frac{1}{2}$	5.120 ± 0.010	136 ± 6	(13.4 ± 0.6) (J = 1)	5.9 ± 0.3 (J = 1)
		30.9 ± 0.3	100 ± 30	11 ± 2	2.0 ± 0.4
		40.8 ± 0.6	....	8 ± 2	1.2 ± 0.4
		56.8 ± 0.9	....	20 ± 5	2.7 ± 0.7
		72.0 ± 1.2	....	43 ± 7	5.1 ± 0.8
		86.5 ± 1.5	....	6.0 ± 1.5	0.65 ± 0.16
$_{48}Cd^{113}$...	$\frac{1}{2}$	0.178 ± 0.002	113 ± 5	0.65 ± 0.02 (J = 1)	1.50 ± 0.05 (J = 1)
$_{49}In^{113}$...	$\frac{9}{2}$	1.80 ± 0.03	avg 80 ± 20	< 0.1	
		4.71 ± 0.03	....	0.104 ± 0.016	0.048 ± 0.007
		14.7 ± 0.1	60 ± 20	7.7 ± 1.0	2.0 ± 0.3
		21.7 ± 0.2	....	4.4 ± 0.9	0.95 ± 0.20
		25.2 ± 0.2	110 ± 40	9.7 ± 1.6	1.9 ± 0.3
		32.5 ± 0.4	....	8.5 ± 1.0	1.49 ± 0.18
		45.6 ± 0.6	....	4.7 ± 1.2	0.69 ± 0.018
$_{49}In^{115}$...	$\frac{9}{2}$	....	avg 77 ± 15		
		1.458 ± 0.003	72 ± 2	3.36 ± 0.10	2.78 ± 0.08
		3.86 ± 0.02	81 ± 4	0.318 ± 0.015	0.162 ± 0.008
		9.10 ± 0.09	80 ± 40	1.73 ± 0.17	0.57 ± 0.06

* 1 mv = 10^{-3} ev.

† The resonances have not been identified with a particular isotope, and as a result the neutron widths listed are actually $a\Gamma_n$ and $a\Gamma_n^0$, where a is the abundance of the isotope.

TABLE 8h-3. RESONANCE PARAMETERS OF HEAVY NUCLEI (*Continued*)

Isotope	I	E_0, ev	Γ_γ, mv*	Γ_n, mv	$\Gamma_n{}^0$, mv
		12.1 ± 0.1	140 ± 60	0.106 ± 0.013	0.031 ± 0.004
		23.0 ± 0.2	....	1.0 ± 0.2	0.21 ± 0.04
		39.9 ± 0.5	140 ± 50	3.5 ± 0.4	0.55 ± 0.06
		46.3 ± 0.5	....	0.43 ± 0.09	0.063 ± 0.013
		48.6 ± 0.7	....	0.65 ± 0.08	0.093 ± 0.012
		63.2 ± 1.0	....	1.1 ± 0.3	0.014 ± 0.04
$_{50}Sn^{112}$...	0	....	avg 110 ± 30		
		96.5 ± 2.0	....	85 ± 10	8.7 ± 1.0
		280 ± 9	....	36 ± 17	2.2 ± 1.0
$_{50}Sn^{114}$...	0	....	avg 110 ± 20		
		280 ± 9	....	450 ± 90	27 ± 5
$_{50}Sn^{115}$...	½	....	avg 110 ± 30		
		290 ± 10	....	260 ± 130	3.0 ± 1.5
$_{50}Sn^{116}$...	0	....	avg 110 ± 30		
		112 ± 2	....	58 ± 6	5.5 ± 0.6
		149 ± 4	....	4.5 ± 1.4	0.37 ± 0.11
$_{50}Sn^{117}$...	½	....	avg 110 ± 30		
		39.4 ± 0.5	106 ± 25	5.4 ± 0.5	0.86 ± 0.09
		122 ± 3	....	15 ± 3	1.4 ± 0.3
		125 ± 3	....	2.8 ± 0.8	0.25 ± 0.08
		197 ± 6	....	35 ± 9	2.5 ± 0.6
		259 ± 8	....	12 ± 4	0.8 ± 0.3
$_{50}Sn^{118}$...	0	....	avg 110 ± 33		
		46.3 ± 0.6	....	0.7 ± 0.2	0.11 ± 0.03
		368 ± 14	....	420 ± 30	22.0 ± 1.3
$_{50}Sn^{119}$...	½	....	avg 110 ± 30		
		1.41 ± 3	....	30 ± 12	2.5 ± 1.0
		222 ± 7	....	24 ± 6	1.6 ± 0.4
		460 ± 20	....	200 ± 70	9 ± 3
$_{50}Sn^{120}$...	0	....	avg 101 ± 30		
		425 ± 18	....	44 ± 18	2.1 ± 0.8
$_{50}Sn^{124}$...	0	....	avg 110 ± 30		
		62.5 ± 0.9	....	12 ± 2	1.5 ± 0.3
$_{52}Te^{123}$...	½	2.334 ± 0.008	104 ± 9	10.4 ± 0.5 (J = 1)	6.8 ± 0.4 (J = 1)
$_{53}I^{127}$.....	5/2	20.5 ± 0.3	avg 100 ± 30	1.6 ± 0.5	0.34 ± 0.10
		31.4 ± 0.5	....	21 ± 7	3.8 ± 1.2
		37.7 ± 0.7	....	40 ± 13	7 ± 2
		46 ± 1	....	22 ± 10	3.3 ± 1.5
$_{53}I^{127}$	5/2	66 ± 2	....	3 ± 2	0.3 ± 0.2
		78 ± 2	....	30 ± 20	3 ± 2
		91 ± 3	....	30 ± 20	3 ± 2
$_{54}Xe^{135}$...	3/2	0.082 ± 0.002	86 ± 11	24 ± 4	83 ± 12
$_{55}Cs^{133}$...	7/2	....	avg 110 ± 30		
		5.90 ± 0.04	115 ± 20	5.2 ± 0.7	2.1 ± 0.3
		22.6 ± 0.3	120 ± 40	6.6 ± 1.4	1.4 ± 0.2
		47.8 ± 0.6	140 ± 60	19 ± 3	2.8 ± 0.4
		83.1 ± 1.5	....	9 ± 3	1.0 ± 0.3
		94.8 ± 1.8	....	19 ± 6	2.0 ± 0.6
		128 ± 2	....	112 ± 19	9.9 ± 1.7
		143 ± 3	....	9 ± 4	0.8 ± 0.4
		149 ± 4	....	45 ± 20	3.7 ± 1.6
		182 ± 5	....	3.4 ± 1.1	0.25 ± 0.08
		204 ± 6	....	57 ± 22	4.0 ± 1.5
		224 ± 6	....	49 ± 22	3.3 ± 1.5
		240 ± 7	....	480 ± 90	31 ± 6
$_{62}Sm^{149}$...	7/2	0.096 ± 0.001	65 ± 2	0.56 ± 0.04	1.81 ± 0.13

* 1 mv = 10^{-3} ev.

TABLE 8h-3. RESONANCE PARAMETERS OF HEAVY NUCLEI (*Continued*)

Isotope	I	E_0, ev	Γ_γ, mv*	Γ_n, mv	Γ_n^0, mv
$_{63}Eu^{151}$...	$\frac{5}{2}$	....	avg 85 ± 15		
		0.0006 ± 0.0010	67 ± 5	....	0.10 ± 0.02
		0.327 ± 0.003	70 ± 10	0.088 ± 0.010	0.15 ± 0.02
		0.461 ± 0.002	93 ± 3	0.80 ± 0.04	1.11 ± 0.06
		1.055 ± 0.005	94 ± 4	0.27 ± 0.04	0.25 ± 0.04
		2.73 ± 0.05	....	0.08 ± 0.04	0.05 ± 0.02
		3.35 ± 0.02	....	3.4 ± 0.4	1.8 ± 0.2
$_{63}Eu^{151,3}$..	$\frac{5}{2}$	....	avg 90 ± 20		
		4.83 ± 0.04	....	0.048 ± 0.0008	0.022 ± 0.004
		5.47 ± 0.05	....	0.133 ± 0.018	0.057 ± 0.008
		6.03 ± 0.08	....	0.35 ± 0.05	0.14 ± 0.02
		6.25 ± 0.08	....	0.41 ± 0.07	0.16 ± 0.03
		7.24 ± 0.10	....	2.4 ± 0.5	0.89 ± 0.18
		7.47 ± 0.10	....	2.4 ± 0.5	0.88 ± 0.18
$_{64}Gd^{157}$...	$\frac{7}{2}$	0.030 ± 0.003	100 ± 30	0.65 ± 0.10	3.7 ± 0.5
		2.58 ± 0.05	70 ± 10		
$_{65}Tb^{159}$...	$\frac{3}{2}$	3.35 ± 0.02	avg 90 ± 30	0.43 ± 0.05	0.24 ± 0.03
		4.99 ± 0.05	....	0.055 ± 0.008	0.025 ± 0.004
		11.14 ± 0.10	....	9.2 ± 1.8	2.8 ± 0.6
		14.4 ± 0.2	....	0.54 ± 0.11	0.14 ± 0.03
		21.4 ± 0.2	....	2.1 ± 0.2	0.46 ± 0.05
		24.7 ± 0.3	....	5.8 ± 0.7	1.17 ± 0.14
		27.8 ± 0.3	....	0.90 ± 0.12	0.17 ± 0.02
		34.1 ± 0.3	....	3.3 ± 0.7	0.57 ± 0.11
		44.2 ± 0.6	....	5.6 ± 0.8	0.84 ± 0.13
		46.6 ± 0.6	....	15 ± 3	2.2 ± 0.4
		51.1 ± 0.7	....	3.7 ± 0.7	0.52 ± 0.10
		54.9 ± 0.7	....	1.6 ± 0.6	0.21 ± 0.08
		58.7 ± 0.8	....	4.6 ± 1.1	0.60 ± 0.14
		66.1 ± 1.1	....	15 ± 4	1.9 ± 0.5
		74.6 ± 1.3	....	20 ± 5	2.3 ± 0.6
		78.2 ± 1.4	....	15 ± 4	1.7 ± 0.4
$_{67}Ho^{165}$...	$\frac{7}{2}$	3.92 ± 0.03	avg 90 ± 20	2.5 ± 0.5	1.3 ± 0.2
		12.8 ± 0.1	....	13.1 ± 1.8	3.4 ± 0.5
		18.2 ± 0.2	180 ± 90	0.92 ± 0.17	0.22 ± 0.04
		21.3 ± 0.2	....	0.73 ± 0.12	0.16 ± 0.03
		35.9 ± 0.4	60 ± 20	7.5 ± 1.1	1.20 ± 0.18
		37.9 ± 0.5	....	0.36 ± 0.07	0.059 ± 0.012
		40.3 ± 0.5	60 ± 30	21 ± 3	3.3 ± 0.5
		48.5 ± 0.7	60 ± 30	25 ± 4	3.6 ± 0.5
		52.2 ± 0.7	....	51 ± 6	7.0 ± 0.8
		55.3 ± 0.8	....	7 ± 3	0.9 ± 0.4
		66.3 ± 1.1	....	38 ± 6	4.6 ± 0.7
		70.0 ± 1.2	....	1.1 ± 0.4	0.13 ± 0.04
		73.1 ± 1.3	140 ± 60	35 ± 6	4.1 ± 0.7
		83.4 ± 1.5	....	1.2 ± 0.6	0.13 ± 0.06
		87.2 ± 1.6	260 ± 130	96 ± 10	10.3 ± 1.1
		96 ± 2	....	125 ± 15	12.7 ± 1.5
		104 ± 2	....	65 ± 13	6.4 ± 1.3
$_{69}Tm^{169}$...	$\frac{3}{2}$	3.92 ± 0.03	avg 70 ± 20	12 ± 4	6 ± 2
		14.4 ± 0.1	75 ± 20	5.7 ± 0.8	1.5 ± 0.2
		17.6 ± 0.2	63 ± 16	3.2 ± 0.4	0.76 ± 0.10
		29.1 ± 0.3	....	0.37 ± 0.13	0.07 ± 0.02

* 1 mv = 10^{-3} ev.

TABLE 8h-3. RESONANCE PARAMETERS OF HEAVY NUCLEI (*Continued*)

Isotope	I	E_0, ev	$\Gamma\gamma$, mv*	Γ_n, mv	$\Gamma_n{}^0$, mv
$_{69}$TM^{169}..	$\frac{3}{2}$	35.2 ± 0.4	110 ± 40	13 ± 2	2.2 ± 0.4
		38.1 ± 0.5	....	0.61 ± 0.12	0.10 ± 0.02
		45.6 ± 0.6	....	6.4 ± 1.3	1.0 ± 0.2
		51.6 ± 0.7	....	7.7 ± 1.6	1.1 ± 0.2
		59.8 ± 0.8	....	25 ± 5	3.1 ± 0.6
		66.8 ± 1.1	....	100 ± 15	12 ± 4
		84.4 ± 1.5	....	11 ± 3	1.2 ± 0.4
		96 ± 2	....	74 ± 11	7.6 ± 1.5
		104 ± 2	....	2.7 ± 1.5	0.26 ± 0.14
		118 ± 2	....	41 ± 12	3.8 ± 1.1
$_{70}$Yb^{168}...	0	0.597 ± 0.003	70 ± 10	3.3 ± 0.5	4.3 ± 0.7
$_{71}$Ln^{176}...	≥7	....	avg 70 ± 20		
		0.142 ± 0.001	63 ± 5	0.093 ± 0.009	0.25 ± 0.03
		1.57 ± 0.01	....	0.6 ± 0.2	0.5 ± 0.2
$_{71}$Lu†....	.....	....	avg 70 ± 20		
		2.62 ± 0.02	....	0.16 ± 0.07*	0.10 ± 0.04*
		4.39 ± 0.03	....	0.012 ± 0.006*	0.006 ± 0.003*
		4.78 ± 0.03	....	0.28 ± 0.03*	0.128 ± 0.014*
		5.22 ± 0.04	....	1.2 ± 0.02*	0.52 ± 0.09*
		6.17 ± 0.05	....	0.062 ± 0.012*	0.025 ± 0.005*
		9.8 ± 0.1	....	0.044 ± 0.012*	0.014 ± 0.004*
		11.3 ± 0.1	40 ± 20	3.2 ± 0.5*	0.95 ± 0.15*
		14.1 ± 0.1	....	18 ± 3*	4.8 ± 0.7*
		15.5 ± 0.2	....	1.4 ± 0.15*	0.35 ± 0.04*
		20.0 ± 0.2	....	0.08 ± 0.02*	0.018 ± 0.005*
		20.7 ± 0.2	160 ± 50	2.3 ± 0.3*	0.51 ± 0.07*
		22.0 ± 0.2	....	0.07 ± 0.2*	0.015 ± 0.004*
		23.7 ± 0.2	70 ± 20	4.9 ± 0.7*	1.01 ± 0.14*
		24.8 ± 0.3	....	0.17 ± 0.06*	0.034 ± 0.012*
		27.3 ± 0.3	....	0.27 ± 0.08*	0.052 ± 0.016*
		28.2 ± 0.3	....	1.4 ± 0.3*	0.26 ± 0.05*
		30.4 ± 0.3	....	9.2 ± 0.7*	1.7 ± 0.3*
		31.2 ± 0.3	....	2.3 ± 0.6*	0.41 ± 0.10*
		37.1 ± 0.4	90 ± 30	6.4 ± 0.9*	1.05 ± 0.14*
		41.5 ± 0.5	80 ± 30	24 ± 3*	3.7 ± 0.4*
$_{72}$Hf^{176}..	0	....	60 ± 20		
		30 ± 0.4	....	49 ± 6	8.9 ± 1.2
$_{72}$Hf^{177}...	$\frac{1}{2}$, $\frac{3}{2}$	....	avg 56 ± 15		
		1.08 ± 0.02	43 ± 10	1.8 ± 0.5	1.7 ± 0.5
		2.36 ± 0.02	63 ± 8	5.2 ± 0.9	3.4 ± 0.6
		5.9 ± 0.1	....	5.1 ± 1.5	2.1 ± 0.6
		6.6 ± 0.1	44 ± 20	11 ± 3	4.3 ± 1.3
		8.8 ± 0.1	....	8 ± 3	2.7 ± 1.1
		13.7 ± 0.2	....	0.67 ± 0.08	0.18 ± 0.02
		14.1 ± 0.2	....	2.2 ± 0.3	0.59 ± 0.08
		22.2 ± 0.2	....	2.7 ± 0.3	0.57 ± 0.06
		23.5 ± 0.2	....	1.6 ± 0.4	0.33 ± 0.07
		25.9 ± 0.3	....	0.41 ± 0.08	0.08 ± 0.02
		27.2 ± 0.3	....	1.80 ± 0.18	0.35 ± 0.04
		33.2 ± 0.4	....	1.2 ± 0.2	0.21 ± 0.04
		37.2 ± 0.5	....	23 ± 5	3.8 ± 0.8
		43.6 ± 0.6	....	4.3 ± 0.5	0.65 ± 0.08
		45.7 ± 0.6	....	4.6 ± 0.6	0.68 ± 0.10
		46.8 ± 0.6	....	4.9 ± 0.8	0.72 ± 0.12

* 1 mv = 10^{-3} ev.

† The resonances have not been identified with a particular isotope, and as a result the neutron widths are actually $a\Gamma_n$ and $a\Gamma_n{}^0$, where a is the abundance of the isotope.

TABLE 8h-3. RESONANCE PARAMETERS OF HEAVY NUCLEI (*Continued*)

Isotope	I	E_0, ev	$\Gamma\gamma$, mv*	Γ_n, mv	Γ_n^0, mv
		49.4 ± 0.7	....	55 ± 5	7.8 ± 0.6
		55.6 ± 0.7	....	18 ± 4	2.4 ± 0.5
		57.2 ± 0.8	....	13 ± 3	1.7 ± 0.3
		60.3 ± 1.0	....	2.8 ± 0.8	0.36 ± 0.11
		64.4 ± 1.0	....	66 ± 8	8.2 ± 0.4
		67.7 ± 1.1	....	36 ± 4	4.4 ± 0.5
		72.3 ± 1.2	....	14 ± 4	1.6 ± 0.4
		77.1 ± 1.3	....	16 ± 3	1.8 ± 0.3
$_{72}Hf^{178}$...	0	....	60 ± 20		
		7.80 ± 0.10	....	49 ± 3	17.5 ± 1.0
$_{72}Hf^{179}$...	½, $\frac{3}{2}$	5.7 ± 0.1	avg 60 ± 20	4.2 ± 1.3	1.8 ± 0.6
		17.8 ± 0.2	....	2.0 ± 0.2	0.47 ± 0.05
		24.0 ± 0.2	....	5.3 ± 1.4	1.1 ± 0.3
		27.0 ± 0.3	....	1.25 ± 0.19	0.24 ± 0.04
		31.5 ± 0.4	....	6.0 ± 1.2	1.1 ± 0.2
		36.8 ± 0.5	....	17 ± 5	2.8 ± 0.8
		40.6 ± 0.5	....	20 ± 4	3.1 ± 0.6
$_{72}Hf^{179}$...	½, $\frac{3}{2}$	42.8 ± 0.6	....	11.9 ± 1.7	1.8 ± 0.2
		44.7 ± 0.6	....	0.41 ± 0.12	0.06 ± 0.02
		48.1 ± 0.7	....	0.8 ± 0.2	0.12 ± 0.03
		51.1 ± 0.7	....	0.9 ± 0.2	0.13 ± 0.03
		51.7 ± 0.7	....	0.51 ± 0.10	0.07 ± 0.02
		52.4 ± 0.7	....	0.53 ± 0.10	0.07 ± 0.02
		53.5 ± 0.7	....	0.56 ± 0.12	0.08 ± 0.02
		55.4 ± 0.8	....	3.7 ± 0.5	0.50 ± 0.07
		61.2 ± 1.0	....	0.63 ± 0.16	0.08 ± 0.02
		63.0 ± 1.0	....	0.73 ± 0.15	0.09 ± 0.02
$_{72}Hf^{180}$...	0	....	60 ± 20		
		73.9 ± 1.2	....	50 ± 6	5.8 ± 0.7
$_{73}Ta^{180}$...	...	0.433 ± 0.004	30 ± 5	0.12 ± 0.02	0.18 ± 0.03
$_{73}Ta^{181}$...	$\frac{7}{2}$	....	49 ± 10		
		4.28 ± 0.02	49 ± 6	4.3 ± 0.7	2.1 ± 0.3
		10.38 ± 0.10	49 ± 11	4.5 ± 0.5	1.40 ± 0.17
		13.95 ± 0.12	50 ± 10	1.1 ± 0.05	0.29 ± 0.02
		20.5 ± 0.2	51 ± 10	1.1 ± 0.06	0.24 ± 0.02
		22.8 ± 0.3	....	0.25 ± 0.02	0.052 ± 0.008
		24.1 ± 0.3	50 ± 15	7.0 ± 0.6	1.43 ± 0.13
		29.8 ± 0.3	....	0.26 ± 0.03	0.048 ± 0.005
		35.4 ± 0.4	....	15 ± 2	2.5 ± 0.3
		36.1 ± 0.4	....	17 ± 2	2.8 ± 0.3
		39.3 ± 0.5	40 ± 15	51 ± 5	8.1 ± 0.8
$_{74}W^{182}$...	0	4.15 ± 0.05	70 ± 20	1.1 ± 0.4	0.5 ± 0.3
$_{74}W^{183}$...	½	7.8 ± 0.2	60 ± 20	2.1 ± 1.0	0.8 ± 0.4
$_{74}W^{186}$...	0	19.2 ± 0.3	....	250 ± 100	60 ± 20
$_{75}Re^{185}$...	$\frac{5}{2}$	2.18 ± 0.04	90 ± 20	2.3 ± 0.4	1.6 ± 0.3
$_{75}Re^{187}$...	$\frac{5}{2}$	4.40 ± 0.09	90 ± 30	0.54 ± 0.11	0.26 ± 0.05
$_{75}Re^{185,7}$..	$\frac{5}{2}$	....	90 ± 30		
		5.92 ± 0.08	....	0.25 ± 0.15	0.10 ± 0.06
		7.18 ± 0.15	....	1.1 ± 0.5	0.4 ± 0.2
		11.3 ± 0.2	....	4 ± 2	1.3 ± 0.6
		13.1 ± 0.3	....	4 ± 2	1.0 ± 0.6
		17.7 ± 0.4	....	12 ± 7	2.7 ± 1.5
		21.1 ± 0.5	....	6 ± 4	1.3 ± 0.8
$_{77}Ir^{191}$....	½, $\frac{3}{2}$				
		0.654 ± 0.006	74 ± 3		
$_{77}Ir^{193}$....	$\frac{3}{2}$				
		1.303 ± 0.010	87 ± 3		

* 1 mv = 10^{-3} ev.

TABLE 8h-3. RESONANCE PARAMETERS OF HEAVY NUCLEI (*Continued*)

Isotope	I	E_0, ev	Γ_γ, mv*	Γ_n, mv	Γ_n^0, mv
$_{79}Au^{197}$...	$\frac{3}{2}$	....	125 ± 30		
		4.906 ± 0.010	124 ± 3	15.6 ± 0.4 (J = 2)	7.1 ± 0.2 (J = 2)
		58.1 ± 0.7	....	<10	
		61.5 ± 1.0	170 ± 80	110 ± 20	14 ± 3
		80.2 ± 1.5	....	15 ± 5	1.7 ± 0.5
$_{79}Au^{197}$ ..	$\frac{3}{2}$	110 ± 3	....	9 ± 4	0.9 ± 0.3
		153 ± 4	....	50 ± 30	4 ± 2
		168]± 5	....	100 ± 50	8 ± 4
		194 ± 6	....	50 ± 30	4 ± 2
$_{80}Hg^{198}$...	0	23.3 ± 0.2	145 ± 20	5.8 ± 0.5	1.20 ± 0.10
$_{80}Hg^{199}$...	$\frac{1}{2}$	34.0 ± 0.5	250 ± 70	78 ± 6	13.4 ± 1.0
$_{82}Pb^{208}$...	0	(352 ± 3) × 10^3	....	(8 ± 2) × 10^6 ($J = \frac{1}{2}, l = 1$)	
		(524 ± 5) × 10^3	....	(6 ± 2) × 10^6 ($J = \frac{3}{2}, l = 1$)	
		(718 ± 7) × 10^3	....	(6 ± 2) × 10^6 ($J = \frac{3}{2}, l = 1$)	
$_{83}Bi^{209}$...	$\frac{9}{2}$	810 ± 30	....	(5.3 ± 1.0) × 10^3	190 ± 40
		2,370 ± 100	....	(19 ± 4) × 10^3	390 ± 80
$_{90}Th^{232}$...	0	....	avg 30 ± 10		
		22.0 ± 0.2	30 ± 10	2.0 ± 0.4	0.43 ± 0.08
		23.7 ± 0.3	30 ± 10	3.7 ± 0.6	0.76 ± 0.13
		59.6 ± 0.6	....	4.5 ± 0.9	0.59 ± 0.12
		70.1 ± 0.8	....	40 ± 8	4.7 ± 0.9
		114 ± 2	....	10 ± 4	0.9 ± 0.3
		123 ± 2	....	27 ± 6	2.4 ± 0.6
		131 ± 3	....	11 ± 5	0.9 ± 0.4
		152 ± 3	....	15 ± 6	1.2 ± 0.5
		174 ± 3	....	70 ± 13	5.3 ± 1.0
		195 ± 5	....	30 ± 14	2.1 ± 1.0
		202 ± 5	....	19 ± 0	1.3 ± 0.7
		215 ± 5	....	2.3 ± 1.2	0.16 ± 0.08
		226 ± 6	....	41 ± 16	2.7 ± 1.1
		235 ± 6	....	1.3 ± 0.6	0.08 ± 0.04
		256 ± 7	....	51 ± 19	3.2 ± 1.2
		269 ± 7	....	22 ± 2	1.4 ± 0.7
		290 ± 8	....	57 ± 18	3.3 ± 1.0
		310 ± 9	....	105 ± 30	6.0 ± 1.6
$_{92}U^{234}$....	0	5.10 ± 0.05	19 ± 9	4.5 ± 0.8	2.0 ± 0.4
$_{92}U^{238}$....	0	....	avg 25 ± 5		
		6.70 ± 0.06	24 ± 2	1.52 ± 0.07	0.59 ± 0.03
		21.00 ± 0.2	25 ± 5	8.9 ± 0.4	1.94 ± 0.11
		36.9 ± 0.2	29 ± 9	32.5 ± 1.9	5.3 ± 0.3
		66.3 ± 0.5	2.7 ± 1.0	25 ± 2	3.1 ± 0.3
		81.3 ± 0.5	....	2.1 ± 0.4	0.23 ± 0.04
		103.5 ± 0.7	....	67 ± 9	6.6 ± 0.9
		117.5 ± 0.8	....	15 ± 2	1.4 ± 0.2
		117.5 ± 0.8	....	15 ± 2	1.4 ± 0.2
		146 ± 3	....	0.9 ± 0.9	0.07 ± 0.03
		166 ± 2	....	4 ± 2	0.31 ± 0.16
		192 ± 2	....	140 ± 20	10.1 ± 1.5
$_{93}Np^{237}$...	$\frac{5}{2}$	....	32 ± 6		
		0.489 ± 0.005	32 ± 3	0.032 ± 0.002	0.046 ± 0.003
		1.34 ± 0.02	....	0.030 ± 0.006	0.026 ± 0.005
		1.49 ± 0.02	....	0.16 ± 0.04	0.13 ± 0.03
$_{94}Pu^{240}$...	...	1.06 ± 0.02	42 ± 15	3.2 ± 1.4	3.1 ± 1.4

* 1 mv = 10^{-3} ev.

TABLE 8h-4. RESONANCE PARAMETERS OF FISSIONABLE NUCLEI

Isotope	I	E_0, ev	Γ_γ, mv	Γ_F, mv	Γ_n, mv	Γ_n^0, mv
$_{92}U^{233}$	...	1.76 ± 0.03	70 ± 30	380 ± 50	0.49 ± 0.03	0.37 ± 0.02
$_{92}U^{235}$	$\frac{7}{2}$	....	30 ± 6			
		0.29 ± 0.01	31 ± 10	110 ± 30	0.0040 ± 0.0006	0.007 ± 0.001
		1.12 ± 0.02	15 ± 15	130 ± 20	0.016 ± 0.003	0.015 ± 0.003
		2.04 ± 0.01	27 ± 10	20 ± 12	0.008 ± 0.002	0.005 ± 0.001
		2.86 ± 0.07	....	60 ± 40	0.004 ± 0.001	0.002 ± 0.001
		3.17 ± 0.02	30 ± 15	130 ± 40	0.024 ± 0.003	0.014 ± 0.002
		3.60 ± 0.02	40 ± 20	110 ± 20	0.050 ± 0.005	0.027 ± 0.003
		4.85 ± 0.05	....	20 ± 10	0.052 ± 0.004	0.024 ± 0.002
		5.4 ± 0.2 5.9 ± 0.2 }	....	....	0.04 ± 0.02	0.017 ± 0.009
		6.2 ± 0.2	....	....	0.04 ± 0.02	0.016 ± 0.008
		6.4 ± 0.1	30 ± 20	16 ± 6	0.34 ± 0.03	0.13 ± 0.01
		7.1 ± 0.1	30 ± 20	30 ± 20	0.13 ± 0.01	0.049 ± 0.005
		8.8 ± 0.1	34 ± 14	100 ± 30	1.08 ± 0.09	0.36 ± 0.03
		9.3 ± 0.2	....	....	0.14 ± 0.03	0.046 ± 0.009
		9.5 ± 0.2 9.8 ± 0.2 }	....	....	0.06 ± 0.03	0.02 ± 0.01
		10.2 ± 0.1	....	....	0.09 ± 0.02	0.027 ± 0.005
$_{94}Pu^{239}$	...	0.296 ± 0.004	41 ± 7	47 ± 7	0.12 ± 0.01	0.21 ± 0.02

TABLE 8h-5. THERMAL CROSS SECTIONS (ELEMENTS 1 TO 83)

Element	Isotope (%)	Reaction cross sections (2,200 m/sec)		Scattering cross sections		
		σ_{abs}	σ_{act}	σ_{coh} (sign)	$\sigma_{fa}\left(\frac{A+1}{A}\right)^2$	$\bar{\sigma}_s$
$_1$H......	......	330 ± 3 mbarn	......	1.79 ± 0.02 (−)	81.5 ± 0.4	38 ± 4 (gas)
	H^1(∼100)					
	H^2(0.015)	0.46 ± 0.1 mbarn	12.4 years, 0.57 ± 0.01 mbarn	5.4 ± 0.3 (+)	7.6 ± 0.1	7 ± 1
$_2$He......	......	......	......	1.1 ± 0.2 (+)	1.3 ± 0.2	0.8 ± 0.2
	He^3(0.00013)	*np* 5,400 ± 300	......	......	......	1.0 ± 0.7
	He^4(∼100)	0	0			
$_3$Li......	......	71.0 ± 1.0	......	0.40 ± 0.03 (−)	1.2 ± 0.3	1.4 ± 0.3
	Li^6(7.52)	(*nα* 945)	<0.1	6 ± 3 (+)		
	Li^7(92.48)	......	0.85 sec, 33 ± 5 mbarn	0.80 ± 0.05 (−)	1.4 ± 0.2	
$_4$Be......	Be^9(100)	10 ± 1 mbarn	2.7 × 10^6 years, 9 ± 3 mbarn	7.53 ± 0.07 (+)	7.54 ± 0.07	7 ± 1
$_5$B......	......	755 ± 4	......	......	4.4 ± 0.2	4 ± 1
	B^{10}(18.8)	(*nα* 4,010)	......	......	4.0 ± 0.5	
		np <0.2				
	B^{11}(81.2)	......	0.03 sec, <50 mbarn	......	4.4 ± 0.3	
$_6$C......	......	3.2 ± 0.2 mbarn	......	5.50 ± 0.04	5.51 ± 0.03	4.8 ± 0.2
	C^{12}(98.89)		3.3 ± 0.2 mbarn			
	C^{13}(1.11)	0.5 ± 0.2 mbarn	5,570 years, 1.0 ± 0.3 mbarn	4.5 ± 0.6 (+)	5.5 ± 1.0	
	C^{14}(5,570 years)	<200	2.4 sec, <1 μbarn			
$_7$N......	......	1.88 ± 0.05	......	11.0 ± 0.5 (+)	11.4 ± 0.5	10 ± 1
	N^{14}(99.63)	*np* 1.75 ± 0.05				
		nγ 0.10 ± 0.05				
	N^{15}(0.37)	......	7.4 sec, 24 ± 8 μbarn			
$_8$O......	......	<0.2 mbarn	......	4.2 ± 0.3 (+)	4.24 ± 0.02	4.2 ± 0.3
	O^{16}(99.59)					

	O^{17}(0.037)	....	5,570 years, C^{14} 0.5 ± 0.1			
	O^{18}(0.204)	....	29 sec, 0.21 ± 0.04 mbarn			
$_9$F......	F^{19}(100)	<10 mbarn	11 sec, 9 ± 2 mbarn	3.8 ± 0.3 (+)	4.0 ± 0.1	3.9 ± 0.2
$_{10}$Ne....	....	<2.8	....	....	2.9 ± 0.2	2.4 ± 0.3
	Ne^{20}(90.92)					
	Ne^{21}(0.26)					
	Ne^{22}(8.82)	....	40 sec, 36 ± 15 mbarn			
$_{11}$Na....	Na^{23}(100)	0.505 ± 0.010	15.0 hr, 0.56 ± 0.03	1.55 ± 0.05 (+)	3.4 ± 0.2	4.0 ± 0.5
$_{12}$Mg....	....	63 ± 4 mbarn	....	3.60 ± 0.10 (+)	3.70 ± 0.10	3.6 ± 0.4
	Mg^{24}(78.60)	33 ± 10 mbarn				
	Mg^{25}(10.11)	270 ± 90 mbarn				
	Mg^{26}(11.29)	60 ± 60 mbarn	9.5 min, 50 ± 10 mbarn			
$_{13}$Al.....	Al^{27}(100)	0.230 ± 0.005	2.27 min, 0.21 ± 0.04	1.5 ± 0.1 (+)	1.51 ± 0.03	1.4 ± 0.1
$_{14}$Si.....	....	0.13 ± 0.03	....	2.0 ± 0.2 (+)	2.4 ± 0.2	1.7 ± 0.3
	Si^{28}(92.27)	80 ± 30 mbarn				
	Si^{29}(4.68)	0.27 ± 0.09				
	Si^{30}(3.05)	0.4 ± 0.4	2.62 hr, 110 ± 10 mbarn			
$_{15}$P......	P^{31}(100)	0.19 ± 0.03	14.3 days, 0.23 ± 0.05	3.1 ± 0.16 (+)	3.6 ± 0.3	5 ± 1
$_{16}$S......	....	0.49 ± 0.02	....	1.20 ± 0.08 (+)	1.2 ± 0.2	1.1 ± 0.2
	S^{32}(95.018)					
	S^{33}(0.750)	....	25.1 days, P^{33} 2.3 ± 1.0 mbarn			
	S^{34}(4.215)	....	87 days, 0.26 ± 0.05			
	S^{36}(0.017)	....	5.0 min, 0.14 ± 0.04			
$_{17}$Cl.....	....	31.6 ± 1.0	....	12.1 ± 0.8 (+)	16 ± 3	
	Cl^{35}(75.4)	*np* 0.30 ± 0.10	3.08 × 10^5 years, 30 ± 20 87 days, S^{35} 0.17 ± 0.04 90 ± 30			
	Cl^{36}(3.08 × 10^5 years)	....				
	Cl^{37}(24.6)	....	37.5 min, 0.56 ± 0.12			
$_{18}$A.....	....	0.62 ± 0.04	....	0.5 ± 0.1 (+)	0.9 ± 0.2	1.5 ± 0.5
	A^{36}(0.37)	....	35 days, 6 ± 2			
	A^{38}(0.063)	....	265 years, 0.8 ± 0.2			
	A^{40}(99.600)	....	109 min, 0.53 ± 0.02			
	A^{41}(109 min)	....	>3.5 years, >0.06			

TABLE 8h-5. THERMAL CROSS SECTIONS (ELEMENTS 1 TO 83) (*Continued*)

Element	Isotope (%)	Reaction cross sections (2,200 m/sec)		Scattering cross sections		
		σ_{abs}	σ_{act}	σ_{coh} (sign)	$\sigma_{fa}\left(\frac{A+1}{A}\right)^2$	$\bar{\sigma}_s$
$_{19}$K	...	1.97 ± 0.06	...	1.5 ± 0.1 (+)	2.2 ± 0.1	1.5 ± 0.3
	K^{39}(93.08)	1.87 ± 0.15	1.3 × 10^9 years, 3 ± 2*			
	K^{40}(0.012)	70 ± 20				
		np <1				
	K^{41}(6.91)	1.19 ± 0.10	12.4 hr, 1.0 ± 0.2			
$_{20}$Ca	...	0.43 ± 0.02	...	3.0 ± 0.1 (+)	3.2 ± 0.3	
	Ca^{40}(96.97)	0.22 ± 0.04	...	3.0 ± 0.1 (+)	3.1 ± 0.3	
	Ca^{42}(0.64)	40 ± 3				
	Ca^{43}(0.145)					
	Ca^{44}(2.06)	...	152 days, 0.63 ± 0.12	0.40 ± 0.03 (+)		
	Ca^{46}(0.0033)	...	4.8 days, 0.25 ± 0.10			
	Ca^{48}(0.185)	...	8.5 min, 1.1 ± 0.1			
$_{21}$Sc	Sc^{45}(100)	24.0 ± 1.0	20 sec, 10 ± 4	17.5 ± 1.5 (+)	...	24 ± 2
			85 days, 12 ± 6			
			(20 sec + 85 days), 22 ± 2			
			(20 sec → 85 days)			
$_{22}$Ti	...	5.6 ± 0.4	...	1.4 ± 0.3 (−)	4.4 ± 0.2	4 ± 1
	Ti^{46}(7.95)	0.6 ± 0.2	...	...	3.3 ± 1.0	2 ± 2
	Ti^{47}(7.75)	1.6 ± 0.3	...	...	5.2 ± 1.0	4 ± 1
	Ti^{48}(73.45)	8.0 ± 0.6	...	...	9 ± 4	4 ± 2
	Ti^{49}(5.51)	1.8 ± 0.5	...	...	2.8 ± 1.0	1 ± 1
	Ti^{50}(5.34)	<0.2	5.8 min, 0.14 ± 0.03	...	3.3 ± 1.0	3 ± 1
$_{23}$V	...	5.1 ± 0.2	...	0.032 ± 0.008 (−)	5.1 ± 0.1	5 ± 1
	V^{50}(0.24)	250 ± 200				
	V^{51}(99.76)	...	3.76 min, 4.5 ± 0.9			

$_{24}$Cr...	...	2.9 ± 0.2	...	1.56 ± 0.03 (+)	4.1 ± 0.3	3.0 ± 0.5
	Cr^{50}(4.31)	16.3 ± 1.3	27.8 days, 11 ± 5			
	Cr^{52}(83.76)	0.73 ± 0.06				
	Cr^{53}(9.55)	17.5 ± 1.4				
	Cr^{54}(2.38)	<0.3	3.6 min 0.37 ± 0.04			
$_{25}$Mn...	Mn^{55}(100)	13.2 ± 0.4	2.58 hr, 13.4 ± 0.3	1.7 ± 0.1 (−)	2.0 ± 0.1	2.3 ± 0.3
$_{26}$Fe...	...	2.53 ± 0.06	...	11.37 ± 0.05	11.80 ± 0.04	11 ± 1
		$n\alpha$ <5 mbarn				
	Fe^{54}(5.84)	2.2 ± 0.2	2.96 years, 2.2 ± 0.5	2.20 ± 0.13 (+)	2.5 ± 0.3	
	Fe^{56}(91.68)	2.6 ± 0.2	...	12.8 ± 0.2 (+)	12.8 ± 0.2	
	Fe^{57}(2.17)	2.4 ± 0.2	...	0.64 ± 0.04 (+)	2.0 ± 0.5	
	Fe^{58}(0.31)	2.5 ± 2.0	46 days, 0.9 ± 0.2			
	...	$n\alpha$ <1.5 mbarn				
$_{27}$Co...	Co^{59}(100)	37.0 ± 1.5	10.4 min, 16 ± 3	1.00 ± 0.06 (+)	6 ± 1	7 ± 1
			5.28 years, 20 ± 3			
			(99.7% of 10.4 min → 5.28 years)			
	Co^{60m}(10.7 min)	...	1.75 hr, 100 ± 50			
	Co^{60}(5.3 years)	...	1.75 hr, 6 ± 2			
$_{28}$Ni...	...	4.6 ± 0.2	...	13.2 ± 0.2 (+)	18.04 ± 0.05	17.5 ± 1.0
	Ni^{58}(67.76)	4.2 ± 0.3	...	25.9 ± 0.3 (+)	24.4 ± 0.5	
	Ni^{60}(26.16)	2.5 ± 0.2	...	1.1 ± 0.1 (+)	1.0 ± 0.1	
	Ni^{61}(1.25)	1.9 ± 1.0				
	Ni^{62}(3.66)	15 ± 2	...	9.5 ± 0.4 (−)	9 ± 1	
	Ni^{64}(1.16)	...	2.57 hr, 2.6 ± 0.4			
	Ni^{65}(2.57 hr)		56 hr, 6 ± 3			
$_{29}$Cu...	...	3.69 ± 0.12	...	7.0 ± 0.4 (+)	8.0 ± 0.1	7.2 ± 0.7
	Cu^{63}(69.1)	4.3 ± 0.3	12.8 hr, 3.9 ± 0.8			
	Cu^{65}(30.9)	2.11 ± 0.17	5.14 min, 1.8 ± 0.4			
$_{30}$Zn...	...	1.06 ± 0.05	...	4.3 ± 0.3 (+)	4.1 ± 0.2	3.6 ± 0.4
	Zn^{64}(48.89)	...	250 days, 0.5 ± 0.1			
			12.8 hr, Cu^{64} <10^{-5}			
	Zn^{66}(27.81)	$n\alpha$ <0.02 mbarn				

* Pile neutrons.

TABLE 8h-5. THERMAL CROSS SECTIONS (ELEMENTS 1 TO 83) (*Continued*)

Element	Isotope (%)	Reaction cross sections (2,200 m/sec)		Scattering cross sections		
		σ_{abs}	σ_{act}	σ_{coh} (sign)	$\sigma_{fa}\left(\frac{A+1}{A}\right)^2$	$\bar{\sigma}_s$
$_{30}$Zn....	Zn^{67}(4.11)	$n\alpha$ 6 ± 4 μbarn				
	Zn^{68}(18.56)	$n\alpha$ <0.02 mbarn	13.8 hr, 0.10 ± 0.03			
			52 min, 1.0 ± 0.2			
	Zn^{70}(0.62)	....	2.2 min, 85 ± 20 mbarn			
$_{31}$Ga....	....	2.77 ± 0.12	....	....	7.5 ± 0.5	4 ± 1
	Ga^{69}(60.2)	2.0 ± 0.2	20.2 min, 1.4 ± 0.3			
	Ga^{71}(39.8)	4.9 ± 0.4	14.2 hr, 3.4 ± 0.7			
$_{32}$Ge....	....	2.35 ± 0.20	....	8.8 ± 0.5 (+)	9.0 ± 0.5	3 ± 1
	Ge^{70}(20.55)	3.3 ± 0.3	11.3 days, 3 ± 1			
	Ge^{72}(27.37)	0.94 ± 0.09				
	Ge^{73}(7.67)	13.7 ± 1.1				
	Ge^{74}(36.74)	0.60 ± 0.06	82 min, 0.45 ± 0.08			
	Ge^{76}(7.67)	0.35 ± 0.07	57 sec, 30 ± 20 mbarn			
			12 hr, 0.2 ± 0.1			
			(~50% 57 sec → 12 hr)			
$_{33}$As.....	As^{75}(100)	4.1 ± 0.2	27 hr, 4.2 ± 0.8	5.0 ± 0.3 (+)	8 ± 1	6 ± 1
$_{34}$Se.....	....	11.8 ± 0.4	....	10.0 ± 0.6 (+)	8 ± 1	11 ± 2
	Se^{74}(0.87)	48 ± 7	123 days, 26 ± 6			
	Se^{76}(9.02)	82 ± 7	18 sec, 7 ± 3			
	Se^{77}(7.58)	40 ± 4				
	Se^{78}(23.52)	0.4 ± 0.4				
	Se^{80}(49.82)	0.59 ± 0.06	57 min, 30 ± 10 mbarn			
			17 min, 0.5 ± 0.1			
	Se^{82}(9.19)	2.0 ± 1.4	67 sec, 50 ± 25 mbarn			
			25 min, 4 ± 2 mbarn (order of isomers unknown)			

$_{35}$Br		6.6 ± 0.5	...	5.7 ± 0.4 (+)	6.1 ± 0.2	6 ± 1
	Br^{79}(50.52)	10.4 ± 1.0	4.6 hr, 2.9 ± 0.5 18 min, 8.5 ± 1.4			
	Br^{81}(49.48)	2.6 ± 0.4	35.9 hr, 3.5 ± 0.5			
$_{36}$Kr		28 ± 5	...	...	...	7.2 ± 0.7
	Kr^{78}(0.35)	...	34.5 hr, 2.0 ± 0.5			
	Kr^{80}(2.27)	95 ± 15				
	Kr^{82}(11.56)	45 ± 15				
	Kr^{83}(11.55)	205 ± 10				
	Kr^{84}(56.90)	<2	4.4 hr, 0.10 ± 0.03 9.4 years, 60 ± 20 mbarn (23% 4.4 hr → 9.4 years)			
	Kr^{85}(9.4 years)	<15				
	Kr^{86}(17.37)	<2	77 min, 60 ± 20 mbarn			
	Kr^{87}(77 min)	...	2.8 hr <600			
$_{37}$Rb		0.70 ± 0.07	...	3.8 ± 0.3 (+)	5.5 ± 0.5	12 ± 2
	Rb^{85}(72.15)	...	19.5 days, 0.72 ± 0.15			
	Rb^{87}(27.85)	...	17.8 min, 0.12 ± 0.03			
	Rb^{88}(17.8 min)	...	15.4 min, <200			
$_{38}$Sr		1.16 ± 0.06	...	4.1 ± 0.3 (+)	10 ± 2	10 ± 1
	Sr^{84}(0.56)	<3	65 days, 1.0 ± 0.3			
	Sr^{86}(9.86)	...	2.80 hr, 1.3 ± 0.4			
	Sr^{87}(7.02)					
	Sr^{88}(82.56)	...	53 days, 5 ± 1 mb			
	Sr^{89}(53 days)	...	19.9 years, <90			
	Sr^{90}(19.9 years)	...	9.7 hr, 1.0 ± 0.6			
$_{39}$Y	Y^{89}(100)	1.38 ± 0.14	63 hr, 1.2 ± 0.3	...	...	3 ± 2
$_{40}$Zr	...	180 ± 4 mbarn	...	5.0 ± 0.3 (+)	6.3 ± 0.3	8 ± 1
	Zr^{90}(51.46)	0.10 ± 0.07				
	Zr^{91}(11.23)	1.52 ± 0.12				
	Zr^{92}(17.11)	0.25 ± 0.12				
	Zr^{94}(17.40)	0.08 ± 0.06	65 days, 0.10 ± 0.05			
	Zr^{96}(2.80)	0.1 ± 0.1	17.0 hr, 0.2 ± 0.1			

TABLE 8h-5. THERMAL CROSS SECTIONS (ELEMENTS 1 TO 83) (*Continued*)

Element	Isotope (%)	Reaction cross sections (2,200 m/sec)		Scattering cross sections		
		σ_{abs}	σ_{act}	σ_{coh} (sign)	$\sigma_{fa}\left(\frac{A+1}{A}\right)^2$	$\bar{\sigma}_s$
$_{41}$Nb....	Nb^{93}(100)	1.1 ± 0.1	6.6 min, 1.0 ± 0.5	6.0 ± 0.2 (+)	6.6 ± 0.3	5 ± 1
	Nb^{94}(2.2 × 10^4 years)	....	36 days, 15 ± 4			
$_{42}$Mo....	....	2.5 ± 0.2	....	5.6 ± 0.2 (+)	6.1 ± 0.2	7 ± 1
	Mo^{92}(15.86)	<0.3	6.9 hr, <6 mbarn			
	Mo^{94}(9.12)					
	Mo^{95}(15.70)	13.4 ± 1.3				
	Mo^{96}(16.50)	1.2 ± 0.6				
	Mo^{97}(9.45)	2.1 ± 0.7				
	Mo^{98}(23.75)	0.4 ± 0.4	67 hr, 0.13 ± 0.05			
	Mo^{100}(9.62)	0.5 ± 0.5	14.3 min, 0.20 ± 0.05			
$_{43}$Tc....	Tc^{99}(2.1 × 10^5 years)	100 ± 25				
$_{44}$Ru....	....	2.46 ± 0.12	....	....	6.6 ± 0.5	6 ± 1
	Ru^{96}(5.7)	....	2.8 days, 10 ± 4 mbarn			
	Ru^{98}(2.2)					
	Ru^{99}(12.8)					
	Ru^{100}(12.7)					
	Ru^{101}(17.0)					
	Ru^{102}(31.3)	....	41 days, 1.2 ± 0.3			
	Ru^{104}(18.3)	....	4.5 hr, 0.7 ± 0.2			
$_{45}$Rh....	Rh^{103}(100)	150 ± 7	4.5 min, 12 ± 2	4.5 ± 0.5 (+)	5.6 ± 1.0	5 ± 1
			44 sec, 140 ± 30			
$_{46}$Pd....	....	8.0 ± 1.5	....	5.0 ± 0.3 (+)	4.8 ± 0.3	3.6 ± 0.6
	Pd^{102}(0.8)	....	17.0 days, 4.8 ± 1.5			
	Pd^{104}(9.3)					

	Pd^{105}(22.6)					
	Pd^{106}(27.1)					
	Pd^{108}(26.7)	....	13.6 hr, 12 ± 3			
	Pd^{110}(13.5)	....	22 min, 0.3 ± 0.1			
$_{47}Ag$....	....	62 ± 2	....	4.6 ± 0.3 (+)	6.5 ± 0.5	6 ± 1
	Ag^{107}(51.35)	30 ± 2	2.3 min, 44 ± 9	8.7 ± 0.5 (+)	10 ± 2	
	Ag^{109}(48.65)	84 ± 7	270 days, 2.8 ± 0.5 24.2 sec, 110 ± 20	2.3 ± 0.2 (+)	6 ± 1	
$_{48}Cd$....	....	2,550 ± 100 (not $1/v$, × 1.3)	....	....	....	7 ± 1
	Cd^{106}(1.22)	....	6.7 hr, 1.0 ± 0.5			
	Cd^{108}(0.87)					
	Cd^{110}(12.39)	....	49 min, 0.2 ± 0.1			
	Cd^{111}(12.75)					
	Cd^{112}(24.07)	....	5.1 years, 30 ± 15 mbarn			
	Cd^{113}(12.26)	20,800 (not $1/v$, × 1.3)				
	Cd^{114}(28.86)	....	43 days, 0.14 ± 0.03 53 hr, 1.1 ± 0.3			
	Cd^{116}(7.58)	....	2.9 hr, 1.5 ± 0.3			
$_{49}In$....	....	190 ± 10	....	....	....	2.2 ± 0.5
	In^{113}(4.23)	....	49 days, 56 ± 12 72 sec, 2.0 ± 0.6			
	In^{115}(95.77)	....	54.1 min, 145 ± 15 13 sec, 52 ± 6			
$_{50}Sn$....	....	0.60 ± 0.10	....	4.6 ± 0.3 (+)	4.9 ± 0.5	4 ± 1
	Sn^{112}(0.95)	....	112 days, 1.3 ± 0.3			
	Sn^{114}(0.65)					
	Sn^{115}(0.34)					
	Sn^{116}(14.24)	....	14.5 days, 6 ± 2 mbarn			
	Sn^{117}(7.57)					

TABLE 8h-5. THERMAL CROSS SECTIONS (ELEMENTS 1 TO 83) (*Continued*)

Element	Isotope (%)	Reaction cross sections (2,200 m/sec)		Scattering cross sections		
		σ_{abs}	σ_{act}	σ_{coh} (sign)	$\sigma_{fa}\left(\frac{A+1}{A}\right)^2$	$\bar{\sigma}_s$
$_{50}$Sn....	Sn^{118}(24.01)	....	250 days, 10 ± 6 mbarn			
	Sn^{119}(8.58)					
	Sn^{120}(32.97)	....	>400 days, 1 ± 1 mbarn			
			27.5 hr, 0.14 ± 0.03			
	Sn^{122}(4.71)	....	40 min, 0.16 ± 0.04			
			130 days, 1.0 ± 0.5 mbarn (order of isomers unknown)			
	Sn^{124}(5.98)	....	10 min 0.2 ± 0.1			
			10 days 4 ± 2 mbarn			
	Sn^{124}(5.98)	....	10 days, 4 ± 2 mbarn (none of 10 min → 10 days)			
$_{51}$Sb.....	....	5.5 ± 1.0	....	3.7 ± 0.3 (+)	4.2 ± 0.3	4.3 ± 0.5
	Sb^{121}(57.25)	5.7 ± 0.5	2.8 days, 6.8 ± 1.5			
	Sb^{123}(42.75)	3.9 ± 0.3	21 min, 30 ± 15 mbarn			
			1.3 min, 30 ± 15 mbarn			
			60 days, 2.5 ± 0.5 (% of 21 min and 1.3 min → 60 days unknown)			
$_{52}$Te....	....	4.5 ± 0.2	....	4.0 ± 0.3 (+)	4.5 ± 0.3	5 ± 1
	Te^{120}(0.089)	70 ± 70				
	Te^{122}(2.46)	2.7 ± 0.9	110 days, 1.1 ± 0.5			
	Te^{123}(0.87)	390 ± 30				
	Te^{124}(4.61)	6.5 ± 1.2	58 days, 5 ± 3			
	Te^{125}(6.99)	1.50 ± 0.15				
	Te^{126}(18.71)	0.8 ± 0.2	110 days, 90 ± 20 mbarn			
			9.3 hr, 0.8 ± 0.2			
	Te^{128}(31.79)	0.3 ± 0.3	33 days, 15 ± 5 mbarn			
			72 min, 0.13 ± 0.03			

	Te^{130}(34.49)	0.5 ± 0.3	30 hr, <8 mbarn			
			25 min, 0.22 ± 0.05			
$_{53}$I......	I^{127}(100)	6.7 ± 0.6	25.0 min, 5.5 ± 0.5	3.4 ± 0.2 (+)	3.8 ± 0.4	3.6 ± 0.5
	I^{129}(1.7 × 10^7 years)	....	12.6 hr, 11 ± 4			
	I^{131}(8.1 days)	....	2.4 hr, 600 ± 300			
$_{54}$Xe....	....	35 ± 5	....	....	....	4.3 ± 0.4
	Xe^{124}(0.096)					
	Xe^{126}(0.090)					
	Xe^{128}(1.92)	<5				
	Xe^{129}(26.44)	45 ± 15				
	Xe^{130}(4.08)	<5				
	Xe^{131}(21.18)	120 ± 15				
	Xe^{132}(26.89)	<5	5.3 days, 0.2 ± 0.1			
	Xe^{134}(10.44)	<5	9.13 hr, 0.2 ± 0.1			
	Xe^{135}(9.13 hr)	2.7 ± 0.3 × 10^6 (not 1/v, × 1.2)				
	Xe^{136}(8.87)	<5	3.9 min, 0.15 ± 0.08			
$_{55}$Cs.....	Cs^{133}(100)	29.0 ± 1.5	3.2 hr, 17 ± 4 mbarn	3.0 ± 0.2 (+)	7 ± 1	20 ± 5
			2.3 years, 26 ± 5 (∼100% 3.2 hr → 2.3 years)			
	Cs^{135}(2.6 × 10^6 years)	....	13.7 days, 15 ± 8			
	Cs^{137}(33 years)	....	33 min, <2			
$_{56}$Ba....	....	1.17 ± 0.10	....	3.5 ± 0.2 (+)	6 ± 1	8 ± 1
	Ba^{130}(0.101)	....	12.0 days, 24 ± 8 mbarn			
	Ba^{132}(0.097)	....	10 years, 3 ± 2			
	Ba^{134}(2.42)	2 ± 2				
	Ba^{135}(6.59)	5.6 ± 0.9				
	Ba^{136}(7.81)	0.4 ± 0.4				
	Ba^{137}(11.32)	4.9 ± 0.4				
	Ba^{138}(71.66)	0.68 ± 0.10	85 min, 0.5 ± 0.1			
	Ba^{139}(85 min)	....	12.8 days, 4 ± 1			
$_{57}$La.....	....	8.9 ± 0.3	....	8.7 ± 0.3 (+)	9.3 ± 0.7	15 ± 5
	La^{138}(0.089)					

TABLE 8h-5. THERMAL CROSS SECTIONS (ELEMENTS 1 TO 83) (*Continued*)

Element	Isotope (%)	Reaction cross sections (2,200 m/sec)		Scattering cross sections		
		σ_{abs}	σ_{act}	σ_{coh} (sign)	$\sigma_{fa}\left(\frac{A+1}{A}\right)^2$	$\bar{\sigma}_s$
$_{57}$La. . . .	La^{139}(99.911)	. . . .	40 hr, 8.4 ± 1.7			
	La^{140}(40 hr)	. . . .	3.7 hr, 3.1 ± 1.0			
$_{58}$Ce.	. . . .	0.70 ± 0.08	. . . .	2.7 ± 0.2 (+)	2.8 ± 0.5	9 ± 6
	Ce^{136}(0.19)	25 ± 25				
	Ce^{138}(0.26)	9 ± 6	140 days, <0.4			
	Ce^{140}(88.48)	0.63 ± 0.06	32 days, 0.31 ± 0.10	2.8 ± 0.11 (+)	2.8 ± 0.5	
	Ce^{142}(11.07)	1.8 ± 0.3	34 hr, 1.0 ± 0.2	2.6 ± 0.2 (+)	2.6 ± 0.5	
$_{59}$Pr.	Pr^{141}(100)	11.2 ± 0.6	19.2 hr, 10 ± 3	2.4 ± 0.2 (+)	4.0 ± 1.0	
$_{60}$Nd. . . .	. . . .	46 ± 2	. . . .	6.5 ± 0.4 (+)	16 ± 3	
	Nd^{142}(27.13)	18 ± 2	. . . .	7.5 ± 0.6 (+)		
	Nd^{143}(12.20)	280 ± 20				
	Nd^{144}(23.87)	4.5 ± 0.5	. . . .	1.0 ± 0.2 (+)		
	Nd^{145}(8.30)	52 ± 4				
	Nd^{146}(17.18)	9.2 ± 0.8	11.3 days, 1.8 ± 0.6	9.5 ± 0.4 (+)		
	Nd^{148}(5.72)	3.2 ± 1.0	1.8 hr, 3.7 ± 1.2			
	Nd^{150}(5.60)	2.8 ± 1.5				
$_{61}$Pm. . . .	Pm^{147}(2.5 years)	. . . .	5.3 days, 60 ± 20			
$_{62}$Sm. . . .	. . . .	5,500 ± 200 (not 1/v, × 1.5)				
	Sm^{144}(3.16)	. . . .	400 days, <2			
	Sm^{147}(15.07)					
	Sm^{148}(11.27)					
	Sm^{149}(13.84)	50,000 ± 20,000*				
	Sm^{150}(7.47)					

	Sm^{151}(73 years)	7,000 ± 2,000*				
	Sm^{152}(26.63)	. . . .	47 hr, 140 ± 40	3 ± 1 (−)		
	Sm^{154}(22.53)	. . . .	24 min, 5.5 ± 1.1	8 ± 2 (+)		
$_{63}$Eu. . . .	. . . .	4,600 ± 400 (not $1/v$, × 0.95)	. . . .	. . . .	. . . .	8 ± 1
	Eu^{151}(47.77)	9,000 ± 3,000*	9.2 hr, 1,400 ± 300*			
	Eu^{152}(13 years)	5,500 ± 1,500*				
	Eu^{153}(52.23)	420 ± 100*				
	Eu^{154}(16 years)	1,500 ± 400*				
	Eu^{155}(1.7 years)	14,000 ± 4,000*				
$_{64}$Gd. . . .	. . . .	46,000 ± 2,000 (not $1/v$, × 0.85)				
	Gd^{152}(0.20)	. . . .	230 days, <125			
	Gd^{154}(2.15)					
	Gd^{155}(14.73)	70,000 ± 20,000*				
	Gd^{156}(20.47)					
	Gd^{157}(15.68)	160,000 ± 60,000*				
	Gd^{158}(24.87)	. . . .	18.0 hr, 4 ± 2			
	Gd^{160}(21.90)	. . . .	3.6 min, 0.8 ± 0.3			
$_{65}$Tb. .	Tb^{159}(100)	44 ± 4	73 days, >22			
$_{66}$Dy. . . .	. . . .	1,100 ± 150				
	Dy^{156}(0.052)					
	Dy^{158}(0.090)					
	Dy^{160}(2.298)					
	Dy^{161}(18.88)					
	Dy^{162}(25.53)					
	Dy^{163}(24.97)					
	Dy^{164}(28.18)	. . . .	1.3 min, 2,600 ± 300* 139 min, <1,000* (1.3 min → 139 min)			
	Dy^{165}(139 min)	. . . .	82 hr, 5,000 ± 2,000*			

* Pile neutrons.

TABLE 8h-5. THERMAL CROSS SECTIONS (ELEMENTS 1 TO 83) (*Continued*)

Element	Isotope (%)	Reaction cross sections (2,200 m/sec)		Scattering cross sections		
		σ_{abs}	σ_{act}	σ_{coh} (sign)	$\sigma_{fa}\left(\frac{A+1}{A}\right)^2$	$\bar{\sigma}_s$
$_{67}$Ho....	Ho^{165}(100)	64 ± 3	27.3 hr, 60 ± 12			
$_{68}$Er.....	....	166 ± 16	....	7.8 ± 0.4 (+)	....	15 ± 4
	Er^{162}(0.136)					
	Er^{164}(1.56)					
	Er^{166}(33.4)					
	Er^{167}(22.9)					
	Er^{168}(27.1)	....	9.4 days, 2.0 ± 0.4			
	Er^{170}(14.9)	....	(2.5 sec + 7.5 hr)9 ± 2			
$_{69}$Tm....	Tm^{169}(100)	118 ± 6	129 days, 130 ± 30			
$_{70}$Yb....	....	36 ± 4	....	....	....	12 ± 5
	Yb^{168}(0.140)	....	32 days, 11,000 ± 3,000*			
	Yb^{170}(3.03)					
	Yb^{171}(14.31)					
	Yb^{172}(21.82)					
	Yb^{173}(16.13)					
	Yb^{174}(31.84)	....	101 hr, 60 ± 40			
	Yb^{176}(12.73)	....	1.8 hr, 5.5 ± 1.0			
$_{71}$Lu.....	....	108 ± 5				
	Lu^{175}(97.40)	....	3.7 hr, 35 ± 15			
	Lu^{176}(2.60)	....	6.8 days, 4,000 ± 800			
$_{72}$Hf.....	....	105 ± 5	....	....	....	8 ± 2
	Hf^{174}(0.18)	1,500 ± 1,000				
	Hf^{176}(5.15)	15 ± 15				
	Hf^{177}(18.39)	380 ± 30				
	Hf^{178}(27.08)	75 ± 10				
	Hf^{179}(13.78)	65 ± 15				
	Hf^{180}(35.44)	13 ± 5	46 days, 10 ± 3			

$_{73}$Ta. . . .	Ta^{181}(100)	21.3 ± 1.0	16.4 min, 30 ± 10 mbarn 111 days, 19 ± 7 (~95% 16.4 min → 111 days)	6.1 ± 0.4 (+)	6 ± 1	5 ± 1
	Ta^{182}(111 days)	. . . .	5.5 days, 30,000 ± 15,000			
$_{74}$W.	. . . .	19.2 ± 1.0	. . . .	2.74 ± 0.05 (+)	5.7 ± 0.6	5 ± 1
	W^{180}(0.14)	60 ± 60	140 days, 10 ± 10			
	W^{182}(26.4)	19 ± 2				
	W^{183}(14.4)	11 ± 1				
	W^{184}(30.6)	2.0 ± 0.3	73 days, 2.1 ± 0.6			
	W^{186}(28.4)	34 ± 3	24 hr, 34 ± 7			
	W^{187}(24 hr)	. . . .	65 days, 90 ± 40			
$_{75}$Re. . . .	. . . .	84 ± 4				14 ± 4
	Re^{185}(37.07)	100 ± 8	92 hr, 100 ± 20			
	Re^{187}(62.93)	63 ± 5	18 hr, 75 ± 15			
$_{76}$Os. . . .	. . . .	14.7 ± 0.7	. . . .	. . . .	15 ± 2	11 ± 1
	Os^{184}(0.018)	. . . .	97 days, <200			
	Os^{186}(1.59)					
	Os^{187}(1.64)					
	Os^{188}(13.3)					
	Os^{189}(16.1)					
	Os^{190}(26.4)	. . . .	16.0 days, 8 ± 3			
	Os^{192}(41.0)	. . . .	31 hr, 1.6 ± 0.4			
	Os^{193}(31 hr)	. . . .	700 days, 60 ± 20			
$_{77}$Ir.	. . . .	430 ± 20				
	Ir^{191}(38.5)	. . . .	1.4 min, 260 ± 100 74 days, 700 ± 200 (1.4 min → 74 days)			
	Ir^{193}(61.5)	. . . .	19.0 hr, 130 ± 30			
$_{78}$Pt. . . .	. . . .	8.1 ± 0.4	. . . .	11.2 ± 0.7 (+)	12 ± 1	10 ± 1
	Pt^{190}(0.012)					
	Pt^{192}(0.78)	. . . .	4.3 days, 90 ± 40			

* Pile neutrons.

TABLE 8h-5. THERMAL CROSS SECTIONS (ELEMENTS 1 TO 83) (*Continued*)

Element	Isotope (%)	Reaction cross sections (2,200 m/sec)		Scattering cross sections		
		σ_{abs}	σ_{act}	σ_{coh} (sign)	$\sigma_{fa}\left(\frac{A+1}{A}\right)^2$	$\bar{\sigma}_s$
$_{78}$Pt. . . .	Pt^{194}(32.8)					
	Pt^{195}(33.7)					
	Pt^{196}(25.4)	. . . .	18 hr, 1.1 ± 0.3 due to Ir^{193}			
	Pt^{198}(7.2)	. . . .	31 min, 3.9 ± 0.8			
$_{79}$Au. . . .	Au^{197}(100)	98.0 ± 1.0	2.7 days, 96 ± 10	7.3 ± 0.1 (+)	. . . .	9.3 ± 1.0
	Au^{198}(2.7 days)	. . . .	3.2 days, 35,000 ± 10,000			
$_{80}$Hg. . . .	. . . .	380 ± 20 (not 1/v, × 0.95)	. . . .	22 ± 2 (+)	. . . .	20 ± 5
	Hg^{196}(0.146)	3,100 ± 1,000*				
	Hg^{198}(10.02)					
	Hg^{199}(16.84)	2,500 ± 800*				
	Hg^{200}(23.13)	<60*				
	Hg^{201}(13.22)	<60*				
	Hg^{202}(29.80)	<60*	47 days, 3.8 ± 0.8			
	Hg^{204}(6.85)	<60*	5.5 min, 0.43 ± 0.10			
$_{81}$Tl.	. . . .	3.3 ± 0.5	. . . .	9 ± 2 (+)	10.0 ± 0.5	14 ± 2
	Tl^{203}(29.50)	11.0 ± 0.9	2.7 years, 8 ± 3			
	Tl^{205}(70.50)	0.77 ± 0.08	4.2 min, 0.10 ± 0.03			
$_{82}$Pb. . . .	. . . .	0.17 ± 0.01	. . . .	11.5 ± 0.2 (+)	11.4 ± 0.1	11 ± 1
	Pb^{204}(1.48)	0.8 ± 0.6				
	Pb^{206}(23.6)	25 ± 5 mbarn				
	Pb^{207}(22.6)	0.70 ± 0.03				
	Pb^{208}(52.3)	<30 mbarn	3.2 hr, 0.6 ± 0.2 mbarn			
$_{83}$Bi.	Bi^{209}(100)	32 ± 2 mbarn	5.0 days, 19 ± 2 mbarn	9.35 ± 0.04 (+)	9.37 ± 0.03	9 ± 1

* Pile neutrons.

The various types of thermal cross sections are listed in Table 8h-5 for all but the heaviest elements, which (to the extent available) are in Table 8h-6. "Reaction cross sections" apply to all cross sections except scattering, and because the former are strongly velocity-dependent, they are quoted for 2,200 m/sec neutron velocity.

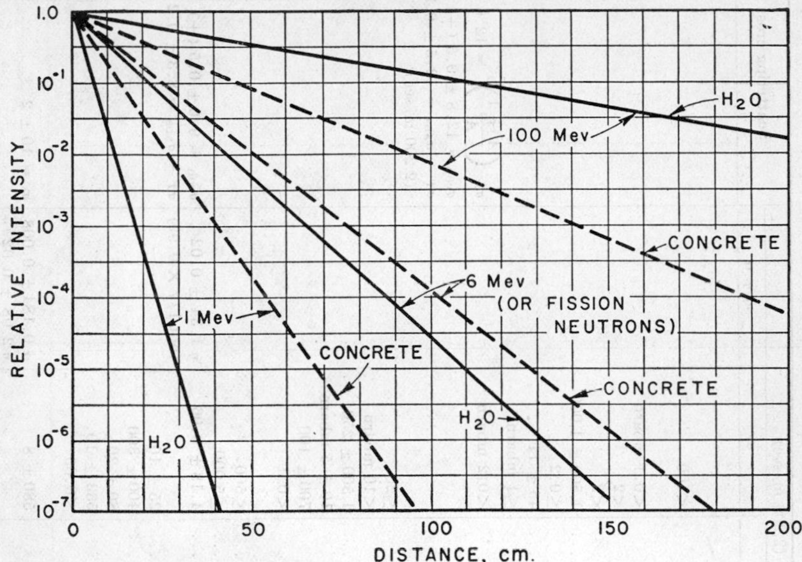

FIG. 8h-5. Attenuation of neutrons. This figure gives the attenuation of neutrons in concrete and water at energies 1, 6, and 100 Mev. The 6-Mev curves can be taken to apply to fission neutrons because this is their effective energy for shielding purposes even though much higher than the average energy of fission neutrons. The concrete is of density 2.3 composed of 4 parts limestone gravel, 2 parts sand, and 1 part Portland cement, and is in the cured state. Its composition is approximately 70 per cent oxygen, 15 per cent silicon, and 15 per cent calcium. The intensity unit refers to the decrease in relative *dose rate* for an incident beam of parallel neutrons, although the intensity unit can be considered as roughly equivalent to neutron flux as well. The equivalence of dose rate received from neutrons and neutron flux is a result of the fact that the dose rate received from fast neutrons does not vary rapidly with neutron energy in the region of a few Mev. The tolerance dose rate is a flux of about 38 neutrons per cm² per sec for a 40-hr week at 2.5 Mev and 26 at 10 Mev, for example. The curves take into account the build-up of neutrons of lower energy as the fast neutrons are moderated.

For those reaction cross sections differing greatly from $1/v$ (marked "not $1/v$") a factor is given that, multiplied by the quoted cross section, gives the value appropriate for a Maxwell distribution—for all others the factor is unity. The "bound-atom" cross section listed after σ_{coh} is obtained from the measured free-atom cross section by use of the reduced mass factor; the difference between it and σ_{coh} gives σ_{inc}. The average-scattering cross section (averaged over the Maxwell distribution) is listed as $\bar{\sigma}_s$.

TABLE 8h-6. THERMAL CROSS SECTIONS (ELEMENTS 86 TO 99)

Element	Isotope (%, $T_{\frac{1}{2}}$)	Reaction cross sections (2,200 m/sec)				Scattering cross sections
		σ_{abs}	σ_{act}	σ_F	ν, η, α	
^{86}Rn...	Rn^{220}(54 sec)	...	30 sec, <0.2*			
	Rn^{222}(3.83 days)	...	11.2 days, 0.72 ± 0.07*			
^{88}Ra....	Ra^{223}(11.2 days)	...	3.64 days, 130 ± 20*	<100		
	Ra^{224}(3.64 days)	...	14.8 days, 12 ± 0.5*			
	Ra^{226}(1,620 years)	...	41.2 min, 20 ± 3*	<0.1 mbarn		
	Ra^{228}(6.7 years)	...	<10 min, 36 ± 5*	<2		
^{89}Ac....	Ac^{227}(22 years)	510 ± 40	6.13 hr, 520 ± 50	<2		
^{90}Th....	Th^{227}(18.6 days)	...	...	1,500 ± 1,000		
	Th^{228}(1.90 years)	...	7.3 × 10³ yr, 123 ± 15	≤0.2		
	Th^{229}(7.3 × 10³ years)	...	...	45 ± 11		
	Th^{230}(8.0 × 10⁴ years)	27 ± 2	25.6 hr, 35 ± 10*	≤1 mbarn		
	Th^{232}(100)(1.39 × 10¹⁰ years)	7.0 ± 0.4	23.3 min, 7.7 ± 0.4	<0.2 mbarn		$\sigma_{fa}\left(\frac{A+1}{A}\right)^2 = 12.6 \pm 0.2$ $\sigma_{coh} = 12.8 \pm 0.5$ (+) $\sigma_T - \sigma_{abs} = 12.5 \pm 0.3$ (2,200 m/sec)
	Th^{233}(23.3 min)	...	24.1 days, 1,400 ± 200*	≤20		
	Th^{234}(24.1 days)	...	≤10 min, 1.8 ± 0.5*	<10 mbarn		
^{91}Pa....	Pa^{230}(17.3 days)	...	...	1,500 ± 250		
	Pa^{231}(3.4 × 10⁴ years)	...	1.31 days, 260 ± 50*	10 ± 5 mbarn		
	Pa^{232}(1.31 days)	...	27.4 days, 50 ± 30*	700 ± 100		
	Pa^{233}(27.4 days)	...	1.18 min, 40 ± 6	<0.1		
			6.7 hr, 20 ± 4			
	Pa^{234}(UX_2) (1.18 min)	...	...	≤500		
	(UZ) (6.7 hr)	...	...	≤5,000		
^{92}U.....	...	7.68 ± 0.07	...	4.18 ± 0.06	η 1.34 ± 0.02 (not 1/v × 0.99)	$\sigma_{coh} = 9.0 \pm 0.5$ (+) $\sigma_T - \sigma_{abs} = 8.3 \pm 0.2$ (2,200 m/sec)
	U^{230}(20.8 days)	...	...	25 ± 10		
	U^{231}(4.3 days)	...	...	400 ± 300		
	U^{232}(73 years)	...	1.62 × 10⁵ years, 300 ± 200*	80 ± 20		
	U^{233}(1.62 × 10⁵ years)	585 ± 10	2.52 × 10⁵ years, 52 ± 2	533 ± 10		
	U^{234}(0.0057) (2.52 × 10⁵ years)	92 ± 7	7.1 × 10⁸ years, 72 ± 10*	≤0.65		
	U^{235}(0.714) (7.1 × 10⁸ years)	687 ± 7	2.40 × 10⁷ years, 107 ± 5	580 ± 8	α 0.184 ± 0.008 η 2.08 ± 0.02 ν 2.46 ± 0.03	$\sigma_s = 10 \pm 2$

	U^{236}(2.40 × 10^7 years)	6 ± 2	6.7 days, 9 ± 2*			
	U^{238}(99.3) (4.50 × 10^9 years)	2.75 ± 0.04	23.5 min, 2.8 ± 0.2	<0.5 mbarn		
	U^{239}(23.5 min)	....	17 hr, 22 ± 5*	12 ± 8		
^{93}Np...	Np^{234}(4.4 days)	....	....	900 ± 300		
	Np^{236}(22 hr)	....	....	<10^5		
	Np^{237}(2.2 × 10^6 years)	170 ± 20	2.10 days, 170 ± 20	19 ± 3 mbarn		
	Np^{238}(2.10 days)	....	....	1,600 ± 100		
	Np^{239}(2.3 days)	....	7.3 min, 80 ± 20*	<3		
^{94}Pu....	Pu^{238}(89.6 years)	....	2.44 × 10^4 years, 430 ± 70*	18 ± 2		
	Pu^{239}(2.44 × 10^4 years)	1,065 ± 15	6.6 × 10^3 years, 315 ± 16	750 ± 15	α 0.42 ± 0.03 η 2.03 ± 0.03 ν 2.88 ± 0.04	$\bar{\sigma}_s$ = 9.6 ± 0.5
	Pu^{240}(6.6 × 10^3 years)		12.9 years, 510 ± 50*	<40*		
	Pu^{241}(12.9 years)	....	~5 × 10^5 years, 380 ± 50 ± 50*	1100 ± 100*		
	Pu^{242}(~5 × 10^5 years)	....	4.98 hr, 30 ± 10*			
	Pu^{243}(4.98 hr)	....	>10^3 years, 100 ± 50*			
	Pu^{245}(10h)	....	11.2 days, 260 ± 150*			
^{95}Am...	Am^{241}(470 years)	620 ± 30	15.8 hr, 700 ± 200* 500 years, <50* (20% 15.8 hr → 500 years)	3.2 ± 0.2		
	Am^{242}(15.8 hr)	....	....	2,500 ± 1,000		
	Am^{242}(500 years)	8,000 ± 1,000*	....	3,500 ± 1,000*		
	Am^{243}(8.8 × 10^3 years)	....	~25 min, 120 ± 30*	<25*		
^{96}Cm...	Cm^{240}(27 days)	....	....	20,000 ± 10,000		
	Cm^{242}(162.5 days)	....	20 ± 10*	<5*		
	Cm^{243}(35.1 years)	500 ± 300*	19.2 years, 250 ± 150*			
	Cm^{244}(19.2 years)	....	>500 years, 15 ± 10*			
	Cm^{245}(>500 years)	....	2,000 years, 200 ± 100*	1,800 ± 300		
	Cm^{246}(2,000 years)	....	15 ± 10*			
^{97}Bk....	Bk^{249}(290 days)	1,100 ± 300*	500 ± 200*			
^{98}Cf....	Cf^{249}	900 ± 400*	270 ± 100*	600 ± 400*		
	Cf^{250}(10 year)	....	1,500 ± 1000*			
	Cf^{252}(2.2 years)	....	30 ± 10*			
	Cf^{254}	....	<2*			
99......	99^{253}	....	160 ± 70			
	99^{254}	....	<15*			

* Pile neutrons.

8i. Particle Accelerators

E. H. KRAUSE

Aeronutronic Systems, Inc.

PARTICLE ACCELERATORS—DESCRIPTIONS

8i-1. Electrostatic Accelerators. The acceleration of protons with high voltage was first accomplished by J. D. Cockcroft and E. T. S. Walton in England in 1929. Using a voltage-multiplier device, they obtained protons of energy up to 0.38 Mev, and two years later with about half this energy they accomplished the first disintegration of the lithium nucleus. At about the same time, R. J. Van de Graaff developed his accelerator, the first apparatus constructed attaining 1.5 million volts.

Today, there are approximately forty small accelerators using voltage multipliers and over one hundred Van de Graaff machines in physics laboratories throughout the world. The Cockcroft-Walton types are mostly of about 1 Mev energy; the most numerous Van de Graaff accelerators are commercially manufactured machines of 2 to 3 Mev energy. There are about ten Van de Graaff machines larger than 5 Mev in the United States and Europe, the 8.5-Mev machine at MIT being the largest.

Regardless of the source of high voltage, all these machines accelerate particles through a long tube by the potential difference between a high-voltage terminal at one end and a grounded shield at the other. The high potential is either plus or minus depending on the type of particle to be accelerated. A source of ions, or electrons, injects the particles by some focusing method at the high-potential end and they are accelerated to the target by the grounded electrode at the opposite end. They gain energy from the electrostatic field as a fall from terminal potential to zero potential.

The tube, usually made of glass, porcelain, or similar material and evacuated, must be long enough to eliminate spark discharge between the ends. Most accelerator tubes contain alternate conducting sections (metal plates with holes in the center) so that the potential gradient can be distributed along the length by external resistors.

The simplest, but a limited, method of obtaining high potential is a standard transformer and diode-rectifier combination. Higher voltages can be obtained by the voltage-multiplier arrangement of Cockcroft and Walton (C-W) and by the electrostatic sphere and belt method of Van de Graaff (VdG). The Cockcroft-Walton voltage multiplier utilizes a bank of condensers and vacuum-tube or selenium rectifiers connected as a series of voltage doublers. By using an a-c source of 400 cps or higher, very compact high-voltage supplies can be built. This high-voltage system has the advantage of simplicity, with no moving parts. The transformer and C-W types of supplies are usually operated at atmosphere pressure in the open laboratory. Cockcroft-Walton type accelerators can supply fairly large ion currents at a constant energy and are very useful in work requiring particles of no more than 1 Mev energy.

In the Van de Graaff electrostatic machine (ref. 14), the terminal is charged by means of a fast-moving belt which, after having charges sprayed onto it at the ground end from a d-c source of about 20,000 volts, travels into the high-potential terminal where the charge is drawn off and transferred to the surface of the "sphere." Compared with about 1 million volts obtained from the voltage-multiplier arrangements, the Van de Graaff method can produce potentials of several million volts. The higher voltages are obtained by pressurizing the high-voltage system with an inert gas, breakdown potential being proportional to the pressure up to about 6 atm. Adding small percentages of carbon dioxide and/or freon increases breakdown potential, although gases like freon can cause severe corrosion problems resulting from the breakdown of the freon during discharge.

The continuous, high-intensity, monoenergetic beam from electrostatic accelerators is advantageous for many types of nuclear research as well as therapeutic and industrial applications. Also, the output energy can usually be adjusted up to the maximum of the machine. However, accelerators which produce their full energy by one single drop in potential are limited to a few Mev. Higher energies must be obtained from machines which impart repeated accelerations to the particle.

8i-2. Cyclotron. In this section the standard cyclotron and the synchro (or FM) cyclotron are discussed separately. In Table 8i-2 all types of cyclotrons are listed by location.

Standard Cyclotron. E. O. Lawrence and N. E. Edlefson reported the cyclotron principle in 1930, and in 1931 Lawrence, with M. S. Livingston, made the first experimental machine. This original cyclotron accelerated protons to an energy of 0.08 Mev. Most of the standard cyclotrons operational in 1954 (nearly 40 throughout the world) attain energies of the order of 10 Mev for protons.

Practically all cyclotrons are positive-ion accelerators. The ions are introduced at the center of a gap between two flat semicircular boxes or "dees." These evacuated chambers are positioned so that the entire circular area is between the poles of a constant-field magnet. The chambers are connected across the output of an r-f oscillator. Acceleration starts when the r-f potential attracts an ion across the gap into one of the chambers. Within the field-free chamber the principal force on the ion is the perpendicular magnetic field; so it drifts in a half-circle path. At the instant it emerges again into the gap the r-f field reverses, the ion is accelerated into the opposite "dee," and again it travels a semicircular path of a larger radius. The ions thus move in an increasing spiral gaining energy (velocity) at each turn until they reach a maximum at the outer periphery. Targets can be placed inside the "dees," or magnetic or electrostatic ejection devices can be used to bring the ion stream out of the chamber.

The "standard" cyclotron is based on the Larmor principle that the time for the ion to traverse each semicircular path is constant. This fact, which permits using a constant-frequency r-f oscillator, results from the basic relationship between the magnetic and centrifugal forces acting on a charged particle in a magnetic field:

$$Hev = \frac{mv^2}{r} \tag{8i-1}$$

where H is the field strength, e (in emu), v, and m are the charge, velocity, and mass of the particle, and r is the radius of the circular path in which it moves.

For any one path the radius is

$$r = \frac{mv}{He} \tag{8i-2}$$

and the time to traverse it is

$$T = \frac{\pi r}{v} \tag{8i-3}$$

Substituting from Eq. (8i-2) into Eq. (8i-3),

$$T = \frac{\pi m}{He} \tag{8i-4}$$

Since H, e, and m are constant, the orbit time T and the angular velocity are constant, provided v is small compared with the speed of light.

It is apparent from Eq. (8i-4) that the frequency of the r-f oscillator must be matched to the field and to the mass/charge ratio of the particle. Thus a cyclotron designed for protons requires an oscillator frequency of twice that for deuterons or alpha particles of the same energy. The design choice determines the energies obtainable from the basic particles. The kinetic energy on ejection is

$$E = \frac{1}{2} m \left(\frac{HeR}{m}\right)^2 = \frac{H^2R^2}{2} \frac{e^2}{m} \tag{8i-5}$$

where R is the radius of the outer orbit. If H and R are kept constant, E is proportional to e^2/m and protons and alpha particles acquire the same energy and deuterons one-half that amount. If oscillator frequency is kept constant, E is proportional to m and independent of e, so that deuterons and alpha particles acquire two and four times, respectively, the energy of protons. This can be shown from Eqs. (8i-4) and (8i-5):

Angular frequency is

$$\omega = \frac{He}{2\pi m}$$

Substituting in Eq. (8i-5),

$$E = 2\pi^2R^2\omega^2m$$

If ω is constant, maximum energy is proportional to m and independent of e.

The positive-particle output of most standard cyclotrons has two to five times the energy of that from high-voltage accelerators. The copious, practically continuous (pulses are two times oscillator frequency) high-intensity beam can produce large yields of neutrons or induced radioactivities. However, the beam contains a background of mixed radiations and the particles are of a wide range of energies. Magnetic separation methods are used to sort out reasonably homogeneous beams. External beams are only a small fraction of the internal intensity.

As the maximum energy obtained from the cyclotron is proportional to the square of the magnetic field and the square of the radius, a practical limit on all cyclotrons is the cost of the magnet. Another basic limitation results from the fact that the relative mass of an ion increases with velocity, causing a decrease in angular velocity so that it arrives late at the accelerating gap. This relativistic-effect limitation of the standard cyclotron, which occurs at 10 to 20 Mev, is overcome in the synchrocyclotron.

Synchrocyclotron (FM Cyclotron). A means of overcoming the relativistic limitation of the standard cyclotron was suggested independently in 1945 by two physicists—V. Veksler (ref. 24) in Russia and E. M. McMillan (ref. 39) in the United States. They pointed out that allowance for the increasing mass of the revolving particle and the resulting decrease in angular frequency could be made by introducing a steady increase in H, so that m/H remained constant, or by steadily decreasing the frequency of the r-f oscillator. This was tested by modifying the 37-in. cyclotron and then the 184-in. cyclotron, under construction at Berkeley, was redesigned to include modulation of the r-f oscillator. In November, 1946, synchrocyclotron operation was achieved with deuterons and alpha particles, and with protons in 1949.

The five large synchrocyclotrons in the United States (1954) produce proton energies ranging from 240 to 450 Mev. Plans are complete for rebuilding the 184-in. Berkeley machine to bring its output to 700 Mev.

In the synchrocyclotron the r-f oscillator is frequency-modulated by a rotating condenser so as to decrease the excitation frequency applied to the dees in synchronism with decreasing orbit frequency of the particle. The design requirement for the matching oscillator frequency to the mass/charge ratio of the particle and to the magnetic field strength was discussed under Standard Cyclotron. Because modulated r-f oscillators suitable for deuterons and alpha particles are incorrect for protons, the Berkeley and Chicago machines have dual-range r-f systems. The synchrocyclotron at Liverpool also has this flexibility.

Variation of frequency to correspond to the increase of mass automatically brings about synchronization of phase as a result of the relativistic effect; i.e., if a particle arrives at the gap late in phase by a few degrees it will receive less energy, there will be less increase in mass, and the orbit time will be shortened. The particle will then be advanced in phase on the next orbit. Thus the ions oscillate in phase about their equilibrium orbits which are of increasing radius and energy. Because of this phase synchronism, the rate at which the radio frequency is decreased is not critical.

The University of Chicago synchrocyclotron, for proton acceleration, decreases the frequency from 28.6 to 18.0 Mc in 2 μsec. In this time, the ions are carried from the source at the center to the outer radius of 76 in. where they have an energy of 450 Mev. They have traveled approximately 350 miles. Modulation frequency for FM cyclotrons is usually about 60 cps. The output, therefore, for a single-dee machine (one chamber is a "dummy dee") consists of 60 pulses per second (ref. 19).

Reference to the tables indicates the order of energy being obtained from the combination of a large machine and synchronous operation as compared with the standard cyclotron. The acceleration of particles to these energies has opened up new research fields, particularly in meson production, detection, and mass measurement, and the distribution of high-energy neutron scattering. Like the standard cyclotron, the synchrocyclotron has the characteristic of a copious beam of high energy, but of mixed radiations and energies, so that auxiliary means of sorting and focusing are necessary. Because of the cost limitation imposed by the physical size of the magnet, it is to be expected that future higher-energy positive-ion machines will be synchrotrons or linear accelerators.

8i-3. Betatron. The first machine to produce a usable beam of electrons which were accelerated by a changing magnetic field was designed and built by D. W. Kerst in 1940 (ref. 29). Prior to this, other investigators had pointed out the feasibility of using magnetic induction to accelerate electrons—R. Wideröe in Germany in 1928 and E. T. S. Walton in England in 1929. In 1936, a German patent was issued to M. Steinbeck for an equivalent device claimed to produce 1.8-Mev electrons in a small-intensity beam. The original betatron of 1940 produced X rays of 2.3 Mev. Today, the majority of about 20 medium-sized betatrons are in the 25-Mev region; there are two laboratory machines of 100 Mev and one of 340 Mev.

As compared with the cyclotron, the betatron accelerates the particle in a continuous circumferential electric field instead of a periodic field across a gap. The machine can be compared with a transformer—the electrons in an evacuated doughnut chamber constituting a secondary winding about the pole of a large magnet. An electron injected into the chamber with a preliminary high-voltage acceleration will move in a circular path as a result of the perpendicular magnetic field. The basic equation of centrifugal and electric forces applies:

$$Hev = \frac{mv^2}{r}$$

or, setting the electron's momentum, $mv = p$,

$$p = \frac{eHr}{c} \tag{8i-6}$$

If now the magnetic flux enclosed by the orbit ϕ is increased, a tangential electric field will be produced at the orbit $E_\phi = \phi/2\pi rc$, which will accelerate the electron. If the magnetic field is so arranged that p and H increase proportionately, the radius of the orbit will remain unchanged; the electron will continue to move in the equilibrium orbit ($r = r_0$), but with momentum constantly increasing as H is increased (ref. 30).

The proper rate of increase of the field to maintain a constant-radius orbit is found as follows:

The rate of increase of momentum of the electron is

$$\dot{p} = \frac{e\phi}{2\pi r_0 c}$$

which gives

$$p = \frac{e(\phi - \phi_1)}{2\pi r_0 c}$$

Using Eq. (8i-6) with $r = r_0$,

$$H = \frac{\phi - \phi_1}{2\pi r_0^2} \tag{8i-7}$$

Thus the average magnetic field enclosed by the orbit must be twice the field at the orbit in order to keep the radius constant.

Because this 2:1 relationship must be maintained, if for example, a change of 5,000 gauss is required to produce the desired increase of electron momentum in the orbit, a change of 10,000 gauss must take place in the central flux. This requires a large magnet, designed for the strong central field and the weaker field at the orbit. The magnet must also shape the field (rate of change with increasing radius) so as to accomplish radial and vertical focusing of the electrons into the desired orbit (refs. 6, 30).

Acceleration takes place in the first quarter cycle of the excitation to the magnet. At the peak of the quarter cycle of magnetic excitation, an auxiliary winding so disturbs the field that the electron stream is deviated from the orbit to the inner wall of the tube where it strikes a target for the production of X rays, or emerges as a beam of electrons.

In the 100-Mev betatron an electron makes 250,000 turns between injection and removal, traveling 900 miles. The particles gain 400 ev each turn. At ejection, their velocity is 99.99 per cent of the speed of light and their mass is 200 times rest mass.

The betatron is limited, as are all circular electron machines, to a maximum energy set by the radiation loss of the electron. The particle eventually loses what it gains during each turn. Radiation loss can be reduced by using a larger orbit and by imparting greater energy at each turn to reduce the number of orbits. This is done in the larger machines, but it appears that 500 Mev is about the limit that can be obtained with this principle.

8i-4. Electron Synchrotron. In 1946, F. K. Goward and D. E. Barnes in England converted a 4-Mev betatron to 8-Mev output by applying the principle of phase stability proposed by McMillan and by Veksler. In 1947, the betatron group at General Electric Company applied the synchrotron principle to a betatron and obtained energies of 70 Mev (ref. 35). In the 8 years since the 330-Mev synchrotron at Berkeley became operational in December, 1948, about 20 electron synchrotrons have been constructed of which 8 are of 300-Mev energy or higher.

Electron synchrotrons combine the induction action of the betatron with the principle of synchronously imparting periodic increments of energy from an electric field. In contrast to the synchrocyclotron, synchronism is achieved by increasing the magnetic field rather than decreasing the oscillator frequency so the orbit radius is constant. The accelerating chamber is either a circular or a racetrack path. The magnet is distributed along its circumference, and because the radius is constant, the magnet's radial width can be kept small. A resonant cavity containing a gap is fitted into one segment of the vacuum chamber and connected to a constant-frequency r-f oscillator.

Operation of most electron synchrotrons starts out like that of the betatron. Electrons are injected into the ring and an increasing field orbits them in a circle. At about 2-Mev energy betatron action stops because of saturation of the limited-sized core of small flux bars. At this point, r-f energy is applied to the cavity and the electrons receive a thrust at each revolution. The velocity is already 97.9 per cent of the velocity of light so that it is essentially constant. On each orbit, the electrons gain energy from the r-f field, therefore, by an increase in their mass. At 2 Mev the mass is 5 times the rest mass; at 330 Mev it is 625 times the rest mass.

One typical synchrotron has a field of 80 gauss when synchrotron action begins, increasing to 10,000 gauss, a factor of 125. An oscillator of 47 Mc and 3,000 volts maximum connected to one side of the gap imparts 2,000 ev to the particle each time it passes the gap in phase.

The synchrotron output, like that of the betatron and synchrocyclotron, is always in pulses at the frequency of the magnetic excitation. The electron synchrotron, like the betatron, is subject to the radiation loss of the revolving particle. However, because of the principle of phase stability the loss can be compensated to a higher-energy level. This compensation, together with the larger orbits obtainable with the distributed-type magnet, indicates that the practical limit is between 1 and 2 Bev. The Cornell and California Institute of Technology machines are designed for such an energy. There is considerable variation in design features among electron synchrotrons: As examples—at least one machine (at General Electric) is completely "ironless"; at Michigan the betatron phase of operation is eliminated by using a variable plus a fixed-frequency r-f system; and at Berkeley a linear-electron-accelerator injector will eventually replace the need for betatron starting.

8i-5. Proton Synchrotron. The proton synchrotron, like the synchrocyclotron and the electron synchrotron, is based on the synchronous principle described by McMillan and Veksler in 1945. The idea of a proton synchrotron was advanced by Oliphant as early as 1943. The first particles of 1,000-Mev (1-Bev) energy were obtained from the proton synchrotron ("Cosmotron") of the Brookhaven Laboratory in May, 1952. In July, 1953, the accelerator at Birmingham, England, was also in operation at this energy. In January, 1954, the Cosmotron output reached 2.9 Mev, and shortly after this the larger "Bevatron" was in operation at Berkeley. Protons of 6 Bev were obtained from the Bevatron in April, 1954. These three machines are the only operational proton synchrotrons. Three others, when completed, will have higher-energy outputs. The Australian National University at Canberra is building a synchrotron expected to exceed 10 Bev, and the European Council for Nuclear Research and the Brookhaven National Laboratories are each planning similar machines, to be completed about 1960, which should attain 30 Bev or higher.

The basic principle of the proton synchrotron is similar to the electron synchrotron in that an increasing magnetic field perpendicular to the doughnut vacuum chamber induces the particles to travel in a circular orbit and an accelerating cavity imparts increments of energy to the particle each trip around. However, protons do not approach the constant velocity approximating that of the velocity of light until they have attained an energy of 4 Bev as compared with 2 Mev for electrons. Therefore, the r-f energy applied to the cavity must increase in frequency as the proton velocity increases in order to maintain phase stability. The rate of increase of frequency and field must be accurately keyed so as to maintain a constant-radius circular orbit.

Injectors for proton synchrotrons, operational and projected, include electrostatic, linear, and cyclotron accelerators of energies from 0.5 to 50 Mev. High injection energy facilitates defining the beam, amplitudes of radial and vertical oscillation are reduced, and the frequency range required of the r-f oscillator is less.

In the cycle of operation, field strength and oscillator frequency simultaneously increase for about 1 sec, after which several seconds are required to reestablish the magnetic field. The output is therefore a series of pulses at 5- to 6-sec intervals. In the Cosmotron, for example, when the field reaches 300 gauss, an 80- to 100-μsec pulse of 3.6-Mev protons is injected into the chamber from a Van de Graaff machine, and after a delay of 150 μsec, the radio frequency is applied. Frequency rises from an initial value of 300 kc to a final of 4.18 Mc while the field is increasing to 14,000 gauss. The protons make about 3 million revolutions, acquiring 800 ev each turn, and reach the maximum of 2.9 Bev in 1 sec. Pulse frequency is 12 per minute, each pulse lasting for about 1 msec and containing 10^{10} to 10^{11} protons. The protons can be ejected from the chamber or directed against probe targets.

Recently developed "strong-focusing" methods make it possible to confine the synchrotron beam to a small cross section (ref. 44). The "alternating-gradient-synchrotron (AGS)" design passes the beam through successive magnetic fields of alternating transverse gradients (i.e., alternate positive and negative n values[1] in successive sectors). The resulting reduction in size of the required aperture, and hence of the guide magnet, makes it possible to go to higher energies without prohibitive magnet costs. The 30-Bev machines being planned for the Brookhaven National Laboratories and the European Council for Nuclear Research (CERN) will utilize this principle. The distributed magnet (in an underground tunnel) may be as large as 850 ft in diameter, although the aperture will be the order of 1 by 2 in.

The proton synchrotron has the same advantage over the cyclotron that the electron synchrotron has over the betatron—it does not require a solid-core magnet. Its distributed magnet is considerably more practical and economical to construct. In contrast with the electron synchrotron, the proton accelerator is free of the orbit-radiation problem since the proton rest mass is nearly 2,000 times that of the electron. At 6,000 Mev, the orbit radiation loss would just reach the negligible value the electron loses at 3 Mev.

Thus the proton synchrotron ranks highest of the high-energy accelerators. Today's machines make available protons of ten times the energy obtainable from the largest synchrocyclotron. The AGS accelerators planned for Brookhaven and CERN in 1960 will effect at least another tenfold increase in energy. Such high energies have previously been available only from cosmic rays. The availability of laboratory-controlled particles in the Bev energy range opens up increasing new fields of nuclear research.

8i-6. Linear Electron Accelerator. Linear electron accelerators originated at Stanford where W. W. Hansen in 1948 obtained energies of 6 Mev with a 10-ft model of his traveling-wave accelerator. The latest Stanford machine was operating at 630 Mev in 1954. In the United States and Great Britain there are about nine other laboratory machines in operation at various energies from 0.5 to 38 Mev. Partly because of the increasing interest in the therapeutic application, linear electron accelerators are now being made by two commercial companies in England.

The linear electron accelerator devised by Hansen is a wave guide of circular cross section divided into sections of increasing length by disks with holes in the center. When pulsed radio frequency of about 3,000 Mc is introduced into the guide, the wavelength of a given phase is determined by the distance between disks. Wavelength and phase velocity increase along the tube as frequency remains constant. Electrons are injected into the evacuated tube from a gun and receive acceleration from the forward phase of the axial component of the electromagnetic wave. They remain in phase with the traveling wave, increasing in velocity and, as they approach the velocity of light, increasing in mass.

Most electron accelerators are traveling-wave tubes. Both pulsed magnetrons and klystrons are used in various arrangements of power feed. The MK III Stanford tube, consisting of twenty-two 10-ft sections, is fed by twenty-two separate klystrons driven from a common source. An energy of 630 Mev has been obtained in a beam of 0.5 μa average current consisting of 0.3-μsec pulses at 60 pps. It is expected that 1 Bev will eventually be obtained from this machine.

Unlike the proton linear accelerator, the energy of the emergent beam is not rigorously built into the machine. Since the electrons approximate the velocity of light for most of the distance, particles slightly out of phase pick up less energy but remain at essentially the same velocity. The energy output can therefore be regulated to a considerable extent by varying the power fed to the accelerator. Conversely, there is the disadvantage that the beam consists of particles of a wider energy range. However, the well-collimated high-intensity output plus elimination of the exit problem present in the betatron and electron synchrotron make this accelerator very useful for nuclear research. It is also receiving increasing use in therapy applications. The linear electron accelerator is of course free of the radiation-loss limitation characteristic of the orbit-type accelerators.

[1] Here $n = -(r/H)(dH/dr)$, in obvious nomenclature.

8i-7. Linear Proton Accelerator. A linear accelerator for heavy positive ions, built by D. H. Sloan and E. O. Lawrence in 1931, was based on a principle suggested by R. Wideröe in Germany in 1929. The availability of high-power very-high-frequency oscillators permitted L. W. Alvarez at Berkeley in 1947 to build a similar accelerator for the lighter, faster-moving proton (ref. 51). The only other linear proton accelerator is at the University of Minnesota. The first section was operating at 10 Mev in February, 1954, and additional sections will bring the output to 68 Mev. In England, a 600-Mev linear proton accelerator is in the planning stage.

The Alvarez design of the proton accelerator utilizes a series of spaced cylinders mounted in a straight line within a larger tube. Alternate tubes are connected to opposite sides of an r-f source. The protons are accelerated across each gap, the lengths of the successive tubes being made so that the particle arrives at a gap when the r-f polarity and phase are correct. A proton acquires additional energy (velocity) each time it is so accelerated by the potential difference across a gap and drifts through successive tubes at a velocity which is constant within any one tube.

As the proton must go from one gap to the next in one period of the r-f field, the frequency and voltage of the standing wave put on the array determine the dimensions of the tubes, the number of tubes determines the final energy, and flexibility of output energy can be obtained only by constructing the array to permit combinations of demountable sections.

The r-f source at Berkeley is actually a series of 28 self-excited oscillators (202.5 Mc) operating into the one resonant cavity. At Minnesota, the three-sectioned accelerator is excited by three power amplifiers operating from a common crystal-controlled source. In both the Berkeley and Minnesota machines, r-f energy is pulsed and the output beam (Minnesota) consists of pulses of the order of 200 μsec at 50 pps. The protons are injected into the accelerator at 4 Mev by a Van de Graaff machine at Berkeley and at 0.5 Mev by a transformer-rectifier at Minnesota.

The long pulse of monoenergetic well-collimated protons obtainable from a linear accelerator is particularly useful in certain types of nuclear research, such as proton-proton scattering and inelastic scattering of protons for measuring energy levels, and for work on short-lived isotopes. Because the output beam of the linear proton accelerator is within a uniform band of energy and because the machine is inherently free from exit difficulties, it is expected that the large accelerator projected for the Atomic Energy Research Establishment at Harwell, England, will permit precise experiments hitherto impossible with synchrotron and cyclotron accelerators.

References

Reference Lists

1. Brookhaven National Laboratory: "Report on Particle Accelerators," May, 1948.
2. Cushman, B. E.. Bibliography of Particle Accelerators, July, 1948, to December, 1950, *U.S. Atomic Energy Commission Document*, UCRL-1238, March, 1951.
3. Thomas, E., et al.: Particle Accelerators—Bibliography and List of High Energy Machines, *Brookhaven Natl. Lab. Report*, BNL-L-101, July 1, 1948.

General

4. Chew, G. F., and B. J. Mayer: High Energy Accelerators at University of California Radiation Laboratory, *Am. J. Phys.* **18**, 125 (1950).
5. Glasstone, S.: The Acceleration of Charged Particles, "Source Book on Atomic Energy," chap. 9, pp. 213–244, D. Van Nostrand Company, Inc., Princeton, N.J., 1950.
6. Langmuir, R. V.: Electronuclear Machines, "Modern Physics for the Engineer," Louis Ridenour, ed., chap. 9, pp. 123–196, McGraw-Hill Book Company, Inc., New York, 1954.
7. High Energy Accelerators, *Ann. Rev. Nuclear Sci.*, pp. 157–206, 1952. (Authors and section references for specific accelerators are given below.)

Electrostatic Accelerator

8. Bergstralh, T. A., et al.: Portable 250-kv Accelerator, *Rev. Sci. Instr.* **24,** 417 (June, 1953).
9. Everhart, E., and P. Lorrain: Cockroft-Walton Voltage Multiplying Circuit, *Rev. Sci. Instr.* **24,** 221–226 (March, 1953).
10. Inglis, D. R., et al.: A Statitron for a Small Nuclear Laboratory, *Rev. Sci. Instr.* **20,** 834–835 (1949).
11. Jennings, B.: Electronics and the Electrostatic Generator, *Proc. Inst. Radio Engrs.* **38,** 1126–1138 (October, 1950).
12. Turner, C. M.: The Berkeley 4-Mev Electrostatic Generator, *Phys. Rev.* **73,** 534 (1948).
13. Van de Graaff, R. J., et al.: 5-Mev Electrostatic Generator, *Phys. Rev.* **70,** 797 (1946).
14. Van de Graaff, R. J., et al.: Electrostatic Generators for the Acceleration of Charged Particles, *Repts. Progr. in Phys.* **11,** 1 (1948).

Standard Cyclotron

15. Livingston, M. S.: The Cyclotron, *J. Appl. Phys.* **15,** 2, 128 (1944).
16. Livingston, M. S.: Standard Cyclotron, *Ann. Rev. Nuclear Sci.* **1,** 157 (1952).
17. Mann, W. B.: "The Cyclotron," 3d ed., John Wiley & Sons, Inc., New York, 1950.
18. Schmidt, F. H., et al.: University of Washington 60-inch Cyclotron, *Rev. Sci. Instr.* **25,** 499–510 (May, 1954).

Synchrocyclotron

19. Anderson, H. L., et al.: Synchrocyclotron for 450-Mev Protons, *Rev. Sci. Instr.* **23,** 707–728 (December, 1952).
20. Henrich, L. R., et al.: Operation of the 184-inch Cyclotron, *Rev. Sci. Instr.* **20,** 887–898 (1949).
21. Livingston, M. S.: Synchrocyclotron, *Ann. Rev. Nuclear Sci.* **1,** 163 (1952).
22. Oliphant, M. L.: Cyclosynchrotron, *Nature* **165,** 466 (1950).
23. Riddiford, L.: Air-cored Synchrocyclotron for 400-Mev Protons, *Proc. Phys. Soc. (London)* **64,** 218–274 (March, 1951).
24. Veksler, V.: *J. Phys. U.S.S.R.* **9,** 153 (1945).

Electron Cyclotron

25. Henderson, C., et al.: Design and Operation of 4–5 Mev Microtron, *Proc. Phys. Soc. (London)* **66,** 654–664 (August, 1953).
26. Henderson, W. J., and P. A. Redhead: The Electron Cyclotron, *Nucleonics* **5,** 60 (1949).
27. Redhead, P. A., et al.: The Electron Cyclotron, *Can. J. Research* **A28,** 673–691 (1950).

Betatron

28. Gregg, E. C.: Flux Forced, Field Biased Betatron, *Rev. Sci. Instr.* **22,** 176–182 (March, 1951).
29. Kerst, D. W.: Acceleration of Electrons by Magnetic Induction, *Phys. Rev.* **60,** 47–53 (1941).
30. Kerst, D. W., and R. Serber: Electron Orbits in the Induction Accelerator, *Phys. Rev.* **60,** 53–58 (1941).
31. Kerst, D. W., et al.: An 80-Mev Model of 300-Mev Betatron, *Rev. Sci. Instr.* **21,** 462–480 (1950).
32. Kerst, D. W., et al.: Operation of a 300-Mev Betatron, *Phys. Rev.* **78,** 297 (1950).
33. Skaggs, L. S., et al.: Development of the Betatron for Electron Therapy, *Radiology* **50,** 167–173 (1948).

Electron Synchrotron (see also Proton Synchrotron and Betatron)

34. Camac, Morton: Characteristics of the Synchrotron Beam, *Rev. Sci. Instr.* **24,** 290–297 (April, 1953).

35. Elder, F. R., et al.: A 70-Mev Synchrotron, *J. Appl. Phys.* **18,** 810 (1947).
36. Fry, D. W., et al.: Design and Operation of a 30 Mev Synchrotron, *Proc. Inst. Elec. Engrs.* **97,** 305–319 (1950).
37. Goward, F. K., et al.: Design of Electron Synchrotrons, *Proc. Inst. Elec. Engrs.* **97,** 320–334 (1950).
38. Livingston, M. S.: "Advances in Electronics," vol. 1, chap. 6, Academic Press, Inc., New York, 1948.
39. McMillan, E. M.: The Synchrotron—A Proposed High-energy Particle Accelerator, *Phys. Rev.* **68,** 143 (1945).
40. Thomas, J. E., et al.: Synchrotrons, *Ann. Rev. Nuclear Sci.* **1,** 175–198 (1952).

Proton Synchrotron

41. Blewett, M. H., et al.: The Cosmotron—A Review, *Rev. Sci. Instr.* **24,** 723–870 (September, 1953).
42. Blumenthal, I. S.: Operating Principles of Synchrotron Accelerators, *Am. J. Phys.* **21,** 164–170 (March, 1953).
43. Brobeck, W. M.: Design Study for a 10-Bev Magnetic Accelerator, *Rev. Sci. Instr.* **19,** 545–551 (1948).
44. Courant, E. D., M. S. Livingston, and Hartland Snyder: The Strong Focusing Synchrotron . . . , *Phys. Rev.* **88,** 1190 (December, 1952).
45. Hibbard, L. U.: The Birmingham Proton Synchrotron, *Phys. Rev.* **73,** 1258 (1948).
46. Livingston, M. S., et al.: Design Study for a 3-Bev Proton Accelerator, *Rev. Sci. Instr.* **21,** 7–22 (1950).
47. Livingston, M. S.: Proton Synchrotron, *Ann. Rev. Nuclear Sci.* **1,** 169–174 (1952).
48. Oliphant, M. L., et al.: The Acceleration of Charged Particles to Very High Energies, *Proc. Phys. Soc.* (*London*) **59,** 666 (1947).
49. White, M. G.: Design of the Brookhaven High Energy Proton Synchrotron, *Phys. Rev.* **75,** 1288 (1949).
50. The Proton Synchrotron at Birmingham University, *Engineer* **195,** 271 (Feb. 20, 1953); 305 (Feb. 27, 1953).

Linear Accelerators

51. Alvarez, L., et al.: The Berkeley Proton Linear Accelerator, *U.S. Atomic Energy Commission Document,* AECU-120 (UCRL-236), Nov. 30, 1948.
52. Bareford, C. F., and M. G. Kelliher: 15-Mev Linear Accelerator for Harwell, *Philips Tech. Rev.* **15,** 1–26 (July, 1953).
53. Becker, G. E., and D. A. Caswell: Operation of 6-Mev Linear Electron Accelerator, *Rev. Sci. Instr.* **22,** 402–405 (June, 1951).
54. Demos, P. T., et al.: MIT Linear Electron Accelerator, *J. Appl. Phys.* **23,** 53–65 (January, 1952).
55. Fry, D. W., and W. Walkinshaw: Linear Accelerators, *Repts. Progr. in Phys.* **12,** 102–132 (1949).
56. Fry, D. W.: The Linear Electron Accelerator, *DeIngenieur* **64** (14), 0.51 (1952); also *Philips Tech. Rev.* **14,** 2 (July, 1952).
57. Mullett, L. B.: Design Study for a 600-Mev Proton Linear Accelerator, *Atomic Energy Research Establishment Document* G/M 151, April, 1953.
58. Schultz, H. L., and W. G. Wadly: Yale Linear Electron Accelerator, *Rev. Sci. Instr.* **22,** 383–385 (June, 1951).
59. Slater, J. C.: The Design of Linear Accelerators, *Revs. Modern Phys.* **20,** 473 (1948).
60. Slater, J. C.: Linear Accelerators, *Ann. Rev. Nuclear Sci.* **1,** 199–206 (1952).

LOCATIONS AND PRINCIPAL CHARACTERISTICS OF OPERATIONAL MACHINES THROUGHOUT THE WORLD

The information in the following table was, for the most part, obtained from questionnaires returned to the editor by the operating laboratories. A few entries were obtained from publications and from data supplied by manufacturers. These cases are so indicated in the remarks column.

TABLE 8i-1. ELECTROSTATIC GENERATORS

Location	Type of machine	Type of particle	Energy, Mev	Ion source	Accelerating tube		Tank			Avg beam current	Date of first operation, remarks
					Length, ft	Axis	Diam, ft	Length, ft	Operating pressure, psi		
In the United States											
Argonne Cancer Research Hospital, Chicago..........	VdG	X ray	2.0	Fil	3	V	3	5	350	250 μa	1953, mfr data
Argonne National Laboratory	VdG	p,d	3.6	Oak Ridge (Moak) r-f, 100 Mc	18	H	7	25	120, N + freon	50 μa	1948, rebuilt 1953
	VdG	e	1.0	....	....	V	3.5	9	200, N	100 μa	1954
Bartol Research Foundation..	VdG	p	5.0	r-f, Bartol design	0.20	V	12.5	35	300	5 μa (p) resolved	1953
	VdG	d,p	1.75	r-f, Bartol design	5	V	4	12	200	40 μa resolved	1946
	C-W	d,p	0.10	r-f, Oak Ridge design	0.8	V	....	....	Atm	150 μa unresolved	1952
Bradley Container Corp., Maynard, Mass..........	VdG	e	2.0	Fil	3.7	V	2.9	6.4	350	250 μa	1955, mfr data
Brookhaven National Laboratory	VdG	p	4	PIG	12	H	8	24	130	~10[12] protons/pulse	1952, injector for Cosmotron
	VdG	e	2.0	Fil	3	H	3	6.5	350	....	1954, experimental injector
	VdG	p,d,α	3.5	Arc	8	H	8	18	140	10 to 50 μa (p,d)	1949
	VdG	e	2	Fil	3	H	3	4.5	350	200 μa	1950
California Institute of Technology	VdG	p,d,α	0.6	r-f	2.25	V	5	10	150	10 μa	1949
	VdG	p,d,α	1.8	Low-voltage arc	8	V	8	13	80	1 μa	1938
	VdG	p,d,α	2.8	r-f	9	V	8	22	150	4 μa	1949
University of California, Livermore....................	C-W	p,d	0.5	r-f	6.2	H	....	....	Atm	1 ma	1950
University of California, Los Alamos	VdG	p,d	2.7	Mod. Zinn	5.5	H	5.5	16.5	140	50 μa analyzed	1940 at University of Wisconsin, 1944 at Los Alamos
	VdG	Tritons, He[3]	2.7	Mod. Zinn	5.5	H	7.2	16	140	10 μa analyzed	1953
	VdG	p,d	6.5	r-f	20	V	13.5	40	100	30 μa	1951

	C-W	*p,d*	0–0.25	r-f	3.3	*H*	Separation column; outer region: 250 psi max. Four interpotential shells			10 μa	1952
	C-W	*p,d*	0.60	r-f	6.3	*V*	....	....	....	1 ma	1954 scheduled
Carnegie Institution, Washington	VdG	*p,d,α*	1.0	r-f, Oak Ridge type	14	*V*	....	....	Atm	30 μa	1933
	VdG	*p,d,α*	3.5	r-f, Oak Ridge type	24	*V*	38 ft max, pear-shape	55	50	5 μa	1939
University of Chicago	C-W	Pos. ions	0.45	Low-voltage arc	7.5	*H*	....	....	....	50 μa	1938
	VdG	Pos. ions	2.0	Cup	2.7	*V*	2.9	6.4	350	6 μa	1951
Columbia University	VdG	Pos. ions	5.5	r-f	12	*V*	8	23	250	25 μa	1955
Dow Chemical Co., Midland, Mich.	VdG	*p,e*	2.0	r-f	2.7	*H*	2.9	6.4	350	25 μa (*p*)	1954, mfr data
Duke University	VdG	*p,d,α*	4.0	r-f	12	*H*	8	24	175	40 μa (*p*) analyzed	1952
Evans Signal Laboratory	VdG	Pos. or *e*	2.0	Cup	2.7	*V*	2.9	6.4	350	6 μa	1954
University of Florida	VdG	*p,d*	1.0	Fil	4.3	*H*	4	8	100	1 μa	1951
Foster Wheeler Corp., Mountaintop, Pa.	VdG	X rays	2.0	Fil	3.7	*V*	2.9	6.4	350	250 μa	1954, mfr data
General Electric Co.:											
Hanford	VdG	Pos. or *e*	2.0	r-f	2.7	*H*	2.9	6.4	350	25 μa (*p*)	1954, mfr data
	VdG	*e*	2.0	Fil	3.7	*H*	2.9	5.4	350	100 μa (*e*)	1952, mfr data
Lockland	VdG	*e*	2.0	Fil	2.7	*V*	2.9	5.4	350	100 μa (*e*)	1950, mfr data
Iowa, Agriculture and Mechanics, Ames	C-W	*p,d*,He	0.3	Arc, r-f planned	5	*H*	....	....	Atm	3.5 ma, unresolved	1949
Iowa State College, Iowa City	VdG	*p,d*	4.0	Zinn	22	*H*	8.5	50	120	1.5 μa	1948
	C-W	*p,d*	0.5	r-f	12	*V*	....	....	Atm	300 μa	1937
Johns Hopkins University	VdC	*p,d*	1.4	r-f	6	*H*	6	13	60	10 μa, analyzed	1948
University of Kansas	VdG	*p,d*	2.25	Zinn, r-f in 1955	7	*H*	6	14	150	5 μa	1952
University of Kentucky	VdG	*p,d*	2.5	r-f	7.5	*V*	8	10	100, N + CO_2	50 μa	1949
	C-W	*d*	0.125	r-f	2.5	*H*	....	....	Atm	1 ma	1953
Los Angeles Tumor Institute	VdG	X ray	2.0	Fil	3	*V*	2.9	5.4	350	250 μa	1953, mfr data
Massachusetts General Hospital	VdG	X ray	2.0	Fil	2.7	*V*	2.9	5.4	350	250 μa	1949, mfr data
Massachusetts Institute of Technology	VdG	*p,d,α*	8.5	r-f	18	*V*	12	31	200–400	0.25 μa	1952
	VdG(2)	*e*	2.0	Fil	2.7	*H/V*	2.9	5.4	350	100 μa	1948
	VdG	*p,d*	4.0	r-f	9	*V*	5	16	150	5 μa	1948
	VdG	X ray	2.0	Fil	2.7	*V*	2.9	5.4	350	250 μa	1950
University of Minnesota	VdG	*p,d*	3.5	Arc	20	*V*	18	36	100	5 μa	1941
National Bureau of Standards	Rect. a-c	*e*	1.4	....	2, 25 ft each	*V*	....	....	....	15 ma	1940
	C-W	*p,d*	0.25	r-f	5	*V*	....	....	Atm	350 μa	1952

TABLE 8i-1. ELECTROSTATIC GENERATORS (*Continued*)

Location	Type of machine	Type of particle	Energy, Mev	Ion source	Accelerating tube		Tank			Avg beam current	Date of first operation, remarks
					Length, ft	Axis	Diam, ft	Length, ft	Operating pressure, psi		
Naval Radiological Defense Laboratory	VdG	Pos. ions	2.0	r-f	2.7	*V*	2.9	6.4	350	25 μa (*p*) 100 μa (*e*)	1954, mfr data
Naval Research Laboratory...	C-W	Pos. ions	0.25	Arc	3.3	*H*	....	....	Atm	350 μa	1950
	C-W	Pos. ions	0.50	Arc	4.5	*H*	....	....	....	600 μa	1952
	VdG	Pos. ions	5.5	r-f	14.5	*H*	9	30	150, N + CO_2 freon	5–10 μa	1953
	VdG	Pos. ions	2.0	r-f	5	*V*	2.9	6.4	350	15–20 μa	1949
	VdG	*e*	2.0	Fil	5	*V*	3	7	350	200 μa	1953
	VdG	Pos. or *e*	2.0	r-f and fil	5	*H*	3	8	350	50 μa (*p*) 200 μa (*e*)	1953
Naval Post. School..........	VdG	Pos. ions	2.0	r-f	2.7	*V*	2.9	6.4	350	25 μa (*p*) 100 μa (*e*)	1955, mfr data
Northwestern University.....	VdG	*p,d*,He	5.0	r-f	12	*V*	8	22	300	....	Plan for early 1955
University of Notre Dame....	VdG	*e*	3.0	....	16	*H*	8	40	150	200 μa	1941
	VdG	*e*	2.0	Fil	2.7	*H*	2.9	5.4	350	100 μa	1950
Oak Ridge National Laboratory	VdG	*p,d*,He	5.5	r-f	12	*V*	8	26	225, N + CO_2	10 μa	1950
	VdG	*p,d*	2.5	r-f	4.7	*V*	4.5	12	200, N + CO_2	50 μa	1951
	VdG	*e*, X ray	2.0	Fil	2.7	*H*	2.9	5.4	350	100 μa (*e*)	1952, mfr data
	C-W	*p,d,t*, He^3,He^4	0.4	r-f	3.2	*V*	....	....	....	~1 ma	1950
	C-W	Heavy ions	0.25	PIG	3.2	*V*	....	....	....	~400 μa	1952
Ohio State University........	VdG	*p*	1.3	Fil	10	*H*	5	20	150	1.5 μa	1949
University of Pennsylvania...	VdG	*p,d*	3.0	r-f	12	*V*	8	24	150	1–10 μa	1952
Rice Institute..............	C-W	*p,d*	0.2	Arc	2	*V*	....	....	Atm	0–50 μa	1936
	VdG	*p,d*	2.0	r-f	12	*H*	6	29	100	0–30 μa	1939
	VdG	*p,d*	6.0	r-f	14	*V*	8.5	23	240	0–50 μa	1953
Shell Development Corp., Houston..............	VdG	Pos. ions	2.0	r-f	2.7	*H*	2.9	6.4	350	50 μa	1955, mfr data
Stanford Research Institute..	VdG	Pos. ions	2.0	Cup	2.72	*V*	2.9	6.4	350	6 μa	1952
Swedish Hospital, Seattle.....	VdG	X ray	2.0	Fil	2.7	*V*	2.9	5.4	350	250 μa	1953, mfr data

Eugene Talmadge Hospital, Georgia	VdG	X ray	2.0	Fil	2.7	*V*	2.9	5.4	350	250 μa	1955, mfr data
University of Texas	VdG	*p,d*	4.0	r-f	10	*V*	7	20	300	5 μa	1953
	C-W	*d*	0.1	r-f	2	*V*	...	...	Atm	300 μa	1951
Upjohn Company, Kalamazoo	VdG	*e*	2.0	Fil	2.7	*V*	2.9	5.4	350	250 μa	1950, mfr data
University of Virginia	VdG	*p,d*	0.5	r-f	5	*V*	...	...	Atm	2 μa	1950
	VdG	*p,d*	1.0	r-f	3	*H*	4.6	5.3	200	75 μa	Scheduled for 1955
University of Washington	VdG	*e*	0.25	Fil	2	*H*	...	...	...	~0.1 μa	1938
Watertown Arsenal	VdG	*e*	2.0	Fil	4	*V*	2.9	6.4	350	250 μa	1955, mfr data
Wells Surveys, Inc., Tulsa	VdG	Pos. ions	0.5	Cup	1.1	*H*	2.9	4.8	350	...	1953, mfr data
Westinghouse Electric Corp., Pittsburgh	VdG	*p,d*	3.0	r-f	35	*V*	30 max, pear-shape	47	...	5–10 μa, analyzed	1938
	VdG	*e*	2.0	Fil	3.75	*V*	3	6	350	100 μa	1953
University of Wisconsin	VdG	*p,α*	4.5	Arc	13	*H*	5.5	20	100	2 μa	1940
Wright Air Development Center	VdG	Pos. or *e*	2.0	r-f	2.7	*H*	2.9	6.4	350	25 μa (*p*) 100 μa (*e*)	1953, mfr data
Outside the United States											
Australia:											
Australian National University,	C-W	*p,d*,trit.	1.2	h-f	10	*V*	No tank		Atm	1.0 ma	1952
sity, Canberra, A.C.T.	C-W	...	0.6	...	6	45°	...		...	...	1954
University of Melbourne,	VdG	*p,d*	1.0	h-f	10	*V*	...	...	Atm	30 μa	1947
Victoria	VdG	...	0.7	...	6.5	*V*	...	...	...	100 μa	1951
Belgium:											
University of Brussels, Brussels	C-W	*p,d*	0.7	h-v	4 m	...	...	...	...	200 μa	1950
École Royale Militaire, Brussels	C-W	...	1.4	...	...	...	...	...	...	...	Mfr data
Faculté Polytechnique de Mons, Mons	C-W	...	1.4	...	...	...	...	...	...	...	Mfr data
University of Liége, Liége	VdG	*p,d*	2.0	h-f	2.7	*V*	...	...	350	25 μa	1954, mfr data
University of Louvain, Heverleé-Louvain	VdG	*p,d*,He	1.67	h-f	2.3 m	*V*	1.5 m	3.7 m	5 kg/cm²	50 μa (*d*)	1951
Canada:											
National Research Council (Elect. Eng. Lab.), Ottawa	VdG	*e*	0.60	Hot cathode	16.5 in.	*H*	2.3	4.5	500	100 μa	1951
National Research Council, Chalk River	VdG	*p*	4.0	...	9	*V*	5.5	16	400		

TABLE 8i-1. ELECTROSTATIC GENERATORS (*Continued*)

Location	Type of machine	Type of particle	Energy, Mev	Ion source	Accelerating tube		Tank			Avg beam current	Date of first operation, remarks
					Length	Axis	Diam	Length	Operating pressure		
Denmark:											
Institute for Theoretical Physics, Copenhagen	VdG	*p*	5.0	h-f	4.2 m	*V*	2.5 m	7.0 m	12 atm	Few μa	1954
	VdG	....	2.5	Arc-cap.	2.6 m	*V*	2.4 m	4.5 m	....	....	1946
France:											
Commissariat à l'Energie Atomique, Box 2, Giff-sur-Yvette	VdG	*p,d*	5.0	PIG	3.75 m	*V*	1.6 m	6.4 m	10 atm	10 μa	1952
	VdG	$p \rightarrow n$	1.5	h-f, PIG	1.25 m	*V*	1.1 m	2.6 m	1 atm, freon	6 μa, 1 μsec pulse	Under construction, 1954
École Normale Superieure, Paris........	C-W	*d*	0.6	h-f	2.1 m	*V*	None			500 μa	1954
École Polytech, Paris......	VdG	*p,e*	2.0								
Institut Interuniversitaire des Sciences Nucleaires, Mons..............	C-W	*p,d*	1.4	h-v	5 m	*V*	....	......	....	250 μa	Planned for November, 1954
University of Strasbourg...	C-W	*p,d*,He	1.5	Oliphant	5 m	*V*	....	......	....	1 μa (*p*) 750 μa (*d*)	1948
Laboratoire de Synthese Atomique, Ivry	C-W	*d*	0.9	Oliphant and h-f	....	....	....	......	....	600 μa	1954
Germany:											
Max Planck Institute for Chemistry, Mainz	C-W	$d \rightarrow n$	1.4	Canal ray	4.2 m	*V*	None			700 μa	1949
	VdG	*e,p,d*	3.0	Penning, cold cathode	3.5 m	*V*	2.4 m	6.0 m	20 atm	....	Under construction, 1954
Physical Institute, Free University, Berlin-Dahlen...	VdG	*e*	1.0	....	2 m	*V*	None		Atm	....	Under construction, 1954
Max Planck Institute for Physics of the Stratosphere (H U Lab), Hechingen	VdG	*p,d*, other ions	1.5	Canal ray and h-f	5.5 m	*V*	....	......	....	1 μa	1949; pulse-operated machine under construction, 1954
Institut für Physik in Max Planck Institut Med. Forschung, Meidelberg...	VdG	*e,p,d,α*	1.0 (*e*)	Oliphant	3 m	*V*	None			....	1937
Institut für Strahlen und Kerphysik, Univ. Bonn...	VdG	*p,d*	1.5	....	....	....	....	......	....	....	Under construction, 1954

University of Danzig University of Freiburg University of Hamburg University of Rostock University of Tübingen } ..	Details not available										
Great Britain:											
Associated Electrical Industries, Ltd., Aldermaston..	VdG	*p,d*	3.8	....	9 ft	*V*	6.8 ft	15 ft	150 psi	....	1951
Department of Physics, University of Cambridge	VdG	H_1^+, H_2^+	2.8	Thonemann	9 ft	*V*	5.8 ft	18 ft	320 psi	50 μa	1948
	C-W	*p,d*	1.0	Oliphant, to be r-f	12 ft	*V*		None		80 μa	1937
	C-W	*p,α*	1.4	Thonemann	16 ft	*V*		None		200 μa	1939
Clarendon Laboratory, Oxford	C-W	H,*d*,He	1.1	h-f	12 ft	*V*	....	......	....	200 μa	1949
	C-W	....	0.5		6 ft	*V*	....	......	....	350 μa	1951
University of Edinburgh, Edinburgh, Scotland	C-W	*p,d*,He^+	1.0	Oliphant, to be magnetic	12 ft	*V*	....	......	....	25 μa (resolved)	1950
Medical Research Council, Hammersmith Hospital, London	VdG	*d,e*	2.0	PIG with magnetic separation	7.5 ft	*V*	4.5 ft	11 ft	10 atm N + CO_2	250 μa	1947
Atomic Energy Research Establishment, Harwell	VdG	*p,d,a*	2.7	....	9 ft	....	....	......	....	....	Listed in ref. 2
	VdG	*e*	2.3	....	8.3 ft	....	5 in.	......	350 psi	....	Listed in ref. 2
	C-W	*d*	1.0	....	....	....	2 m	3 m			
University of London......	VdG	*e*	2								
Royal Cancer Hospital.....	VdG	*e*	2.0	Hot wire	4.4 ft	Variable	2.5 ft	5.6 ft	340 psi	150 μa	1950
National Physics Lab., Sheffield Hospital, Westminister Hospital........	VdG	*e*	2.0	Similar to HVEC machine at Royal Cancer Hospital							
Italy:											
CISE Laboratory, Milan....	C-W	*d*	0.40	7 inkelstein	1 m	*V*	....	......	....	800 μa	1951
Instituto Superiore di Sanita, Rome..................	C-W	*p,d*	1.1	Oliphant	3 m	*V*	....	......	....	600 μa	1939
Mexico:											
National University of Mexico, Mexico 20, D F......	VdG	*p,d,e*	2.0	Arc	50 in.	*V*	2.9 ft	6.5 ft	380 psi	18 μa	1952
Netherlands:											
Physics Lab., Rijks University, Utrecht	C-W	*p,d*	0.70	PIG	8 ft	*V*	....	......	....	6 μa after magnetic analysis	1946
Norway:											
Physical Institute, University of Oslo, Blindern	VdG	*p*	3.5	h-f, Thoneman	3.6 m	*V*	2.4 m	7 m	up to 15 atm	3 μa after magnetic separation	1954
	VdG	*p*	0.5	h-f, Thoneman	1.2 m	*H*		None		5 μa	1937

TABLE 8i-1. ELECTROSTATIC GENERATORS (*Continued*)

Location	Type of machine	Type of particle	Energy, Mev	Ion source	Accelerating tube		Tank			Avg beam current	Date of first operation, remarks
					Length	Axis	Diam	Length	Operating pressure		
Norway:											
Norges Tehniske Hogskole, Trondheim	VdG	*p,d*	4.0	....	3.6 m	......	2.35 m	6.6 m	....	....	Listed in ref. 2
Municipal Hospital, Bergen	VdG	*e*	1.5	....	....	......	......	......	....	....	Listed in ref. 2
	VdG	*p*	1.5								
Russia:											
Physico-Technical Institute,	VdG	....	1								
Ukrainian SSR Academy	VdG	....	3	....	....	......	......	......	....	....	Listed in ref. 2
of Sciences, Kharkov	VdG	....	5								
Spain:											
Junta de Energic Nuclear,	VdG	*e,p*	2.0	....	....	......		HVEC		....	1954
Madrid	C-W	....	0.6	Magnetic	....	V	......	......	....	....	1954
Sweden:											
Forsvarets Forskningsanstalt, Stockholm	VdG	*e,p,d*	1.8 (*p,d*)	Arc, Zinn	2.25 m	V	1.8 m	4.1 m	9 atm	20 μa	1948
Fysiska Institutionen, Lund	VdG	*p,d*	4.0	h-f	4.0 m	V	2.0 m	7.0 m	15 atm	100 μa	Under construction, 1954
Chalmers University of Technology, Gothenburg	VdG	*p,d,e*	5.0	h-f, Thorneman	4.5 m	V	2.5 m	7.3 m	16 atm	10 μa	1954
Radiofysiska Institutionen, Kavolinska Sjukhuset, Stockholm	C-W	$e \rightarrow$ X ray	1.2	Tungsten wires	Conical anode surrounded by filaments	......	0.5–1.0 m	3.5 m	$<10^{-5}$ mm Hg	Approx 100 μa 1-μsec pulses	1949
Nobelinstitutet for Fyski, Stockholm	C-W	*p,d*	1.4	h-f, Thorneman	6.5 m	V	......	......	....	50 μa	1950
University of Uppsala, Uppsala	VdG	*e*	0.8	....	1.5 m	V	......	......	....	250 μa	1949
Switzerland:											
Physikalisches Institut der Universität, Basel	C-W	*p,d*	1.0	h-f	3 m	V	......	......	....	600 μa (*d*+)	1949
Physikalisches Institut der Universitat, Zurich	VdG	*p,d*	1.7	h-f	1.1 m	V	1.6 m	3.0 m	10 atm	30 μa	1953

TABLE 8i-2. CYCLOTRONS AND SYNCHROCYCLOTRONS

Location	Type of machine	Type of particle	Energy, Mev	Magnet			Beam characteristics, avg beam current (particle), pulse data, meson intensities, etc.	Date of first operation, remarks
				Pole diam, in.	Field, gauss	Weight, tons		
In the United States								
Argonne National Laboratory, Lemont, Ill.	Cyl	α	42	.....	....	.....	....	1951
		d	21	62	15,000	25	200 μa (d)	
		p	10.5					
Biochemical Research Foundation, Newark, Del.	Cyl	d	12	38	....	.....	....	Listed in ref. 2
Brookhaven National Laboratory	Cyl	p	3	18	14,000	6	1 ma deflected, 3 ma internal	1952
	Cyl	p	10	.....	....	.....	1 ma internal, 50 μa external (p,d)	1950
		d	20	60	15,000	264	100 μa internal, 20 μa external (α)	
		α	40					
University of California, Berkeley	Cyl	p	10	.....	....	.....	100 μa (p,d), 50 μa (α) external	1939
		d	20	60	15,000	202	C, N, and Ne ions at approx 7 Mev per nucleon	
		α	40	.....	....	.....	0.1 μa N ions, internal	
	Sync-cyl	p	350					
		d	190	184	15,500	4,000	Beam: 1 μa internal, 10^{-10} amp external (350-Mev protons) in 0.1–0.25-μsec pulses or 2×10^{-11} amp in 10-μsec pulses; 1.5×10^{-9} μa (190-Mev deuterons) external; 1×10^{-11} μa (400-Mev alphas) external Meson intensities: External, 1π meson/cm²/sec Mev energy internal at 60 Mev; internal, approx 100 times external	1946, to be rebuilt in 1955 to ~700 Mev (p)
		α	400					
University of California, Livermore	Cyl	p	3–15	90*	....	311	Max radius of orbit during accelerating, 35 in.	Under construction, 1954
		d	4–13					
University of California, Los Alamos	Cyl	d	16					
		p	8	42	18,000	65	500 μa internal, 100 μa external	Expected values, rebuilding 1954
		t	11					
		α	32					
University of California, Los Angeles	Sync-cyl	p	20.5	41	15,000	70	0.3 μa, 1,000 pps, 2×10^{12} particles/pulse	1948

* Cam-shape pole to provide sharp cutoff of field for deflected beam.

TABLE 8i-2. CYCLOTRONS AND SYNCHROCYCLOTRONS (*Continued*)

Location	Type of machine	Type of particle	Energy, Mev	Magnet: Pole diam, in.	Magnet: Field, gauss	Magnet: Weight, tons	Beam characteristics, avg beam current (particle), pulse data, meson intensities, etc.	Date of first operation, remarks
Carnegie Institute of Technology, Pittsburgh	Sync-cyl	*p*	450	140	20,500	1,487	Beam: 1.0 μa, 250 pps, 3×10^{10} particles/pulse Meson intensities: External, 500/cm²/sec 130 Mev π^- in focused beam 20 ft from target; internal, 20,000/cm²/sec, 185 Mev π^+	1951
Carnegie Institution of Washington	Cyl	*p,d,α*	16(*d*)	60	16,000	200	200 μa internal, 6 μa external (*d*)	1944
University of Chicago	Sync-cyl	*p*	450	.....	.....	.....	Beam: 1 to 2 μa, ~60 pps, 1 to 2×10^{11} particles/pulse	1951
		d	260	170	18,600	2,200	Meson intensities: Usable external meson beams available up to 250 Mev π^- and 150 Mev π^+. Intensity of collimated beams ranges from $\sim 2 \times 10^6$/min for 120 Mev π^- to ~5,000/min for 150 Mev π^+ measured with a 1.75-in.-diam counter	
		α	520					
Columbia University	Cyl	*α*	20					
		p	14	36	17,000	55	1 ma (*d*)	1938
		d	10					
	Sync-cyl	*p*	385	164	18,000	2,500	Beam: approx 1 μa, pulse rate variable 30 to 90 pps; usually 60 pps; approx 10^{11} particles/pulse Meson intensities: external, ~100/sec/cm² over 100 cm²; internal, ~104/sec/cm²	1950
General Electric Co.	Cyl	*d*	20	.....	.....	.....	.....	Under construction for NACA
		α	40	60				
Harvard University	Sync-cyl	*p*	100	95	16,000	800	Approx 0.3 μa; pulse rate, 170 pps; 10^{10} particles/pulse	1949
Hofstra College	Cyl	*p*	6	24	.....	.....	.....	Listed in ref. 2
University of Illinois	Cyl	*p*	6					
		d	12					
		α	24	43	14,000	.....	20 μa	1944
Indiana University	Cyl	*α*	23					
		d	11.5	45	14,400	87	150 μa (*d*) 30–40 μa (*α*)	1940

Massachusetts Institute of Technology	Cyl	p	7.5	42	17,000	90	0–25 μa (p)	1940
		d	15	.....	....	.....	0–100 μa (d)	
		α	30	.....	....	.....	0–2 μa (α)	
University of Michigan	Cyl	d	7.8	42	13,500	50	100 μa external; 1 μa scattering chamber	1935
Naval Research Laboratory	Electron, cyl	e	3.3	.....	1,670 (for 255-kev mode)	.....	10^{-9} to 10^{-6} amp avg, ~0.15-μsec pulse; 500 to 1,000 pps, 8-in.-diam vacuum chamber; extraction by magnetically shielded orifices; orbit separation facilitates extraction	1951
Oak Ridge National Laboratory	Cyl	p	1.5 or 5.0*	58	6,400	.....	2000 μa internal	1949
	Cyl	N^{3+}	29	63	15,500	.....	100 μa internal, 2 μa deflected	1952
	Cyl	p	26	86	8,800	410	1500 μa internal	1950
Ohio State University	Cyl	p,d,α	14(d)	47	14,500	80	....	1938
University of Pittsburgh	Cyl	d	16	47	16,000	100	150 μa internal, 70 μa external 1.5 μa of analyzed beam in scattering chamber 30 ft from exit	1947
Princeton University	Sync-cyl	p	18.5†	35	19,300	40	1 μa; pulse rate, 1,800 pps; pulse length, 5–10 μsec	1936, rebuilt 1947, 1951
Purdue University	Cyl	d	10	36.5	16,200	45	External beam, 20 μa (d), 8 μa (α)	1938
		α	20					
University of Rochester	Sync-cyl	p	240	130	17,000	1,000	Beam: 0.1 μa, 100 pps; anticipate that new shielding (1955) will permit increase (× 3) in beam current Meson intensities: (0.1-μa beam); at about 8 ft from target, approx 25,000 π^+ mesons of 50 ± 1 Mev $1\frac{1}{4}$-in.-diam circle. Half that yield for π^-	1948
Stanford University	Cyl	d	2.9	27	....	.....	....	Listed in ref. 2
University of Washington, Seattle	Cyl	α	43	.....	....	.....	Deflected beam, steady operating current, 50 μa (α), 200 μa (d) (p)	1951
		d	21.5	60	15,000	218		
		p	10.7					
Washington University, St. Louis	Cyl	d	10.2	.....	....	.....	Normal currents, external targets, 250 μa (d), 70 μa (p), 20 μa (α); have obtained 80 μa max with 15-Mev deuterons	1941
		p	5.1	45	14,300	92		
		α	20.4					
Yale University	Cyl	d	4	28	14,000	18	40 μa (d), 10 μa (α) external beam, not analyzed	1939
		α	8					
Outside the United States								
Argentina	Sync-cyl	.....	....	....	....	....	Similar to Amsterdam machine	Reported under construction, 1954

* Remodeling in 1954 for operation at either of two beam radii, 11 or 20 in.

† 18.5 Mev in external focused beam

TABLE 8i-2. CYCLOTRONS AND SYNCHROCYCLOTRONS (*Continued*)

Location	Type of machine	Type of particle	Energy, Mev	Magnet: Pole diam, in.	Magnet: Field, gauss	Magnet: Weight, tons	Beam characteristics, avg beam current (particle), pulse data, meson intensities, etc.	Date of first operation, remarks
Australia:								
Australian National University, Canberra, A.C.T.	Cyl	*p*	8	26 in.	15,000	25	1 μa	1954, injector for the 10-Bev synchrotron
University of Melbourne, Victoria	Cyl	*p* *d* α	5–10 4–5 8–10	40 in.	12,500	45	1 μa	1955
Belgium:								
University of Louvain, Heverlée-Louvain	Cyl	*d*	13	94 cm	18,000	68	90 μa	1953
Canada:								
McGill University, Montreal	Sync-cyl	*p*	100	82 in.	16,400	265	1 μa, 200 pps, 3 × 10^{10} particles/pulse	1949
University of Western Ontario, London, Ontario	Electron cyl	*e*	5	35 mm	1,000	....	0.5 μa, 500 pps, 2-μsec pulses, 10-cm tunable magnetron	1947
Denmark:								
Institute for Theoretical Physics, Copenhagen	Cyl	*d*	10	90 cm	18,000	40	200 μa	
France:								
Commissariat à l'Énergie Atomique, Box 2, Giff-sur-Yvette	Cyl	*n* *d* C,O	140	160 cm	15,000	270	....	1954
Germany:								
Institut für Physik im Max Planck Institut Med. Forschung, Heidelberg	Cyl	*d* *p* α	13	101 cm	17,000	80	80 μa	1944
Institut für Strahlen und Kernphysik, University of Bonn	Cyl	*d*	30	....	....	....	....	Under construction, 1954
Great Britain:								
Atomic Energy Research Establishment, Harwell	Sync-cyl	*p*	175	110 in.	....	....	....	Listed in ref. 2

Physics Dept., University of Birmingham	Cyl	*d* *p* *α*	20 10 40	61.5 in.	13,500	250	300 μa, internal, 4 μa, analyzed (*d*)	
Department of Physics, University of Cambridge	Cyl	*p,d,α*	8(*d*)	35.5 in.	16,000	62	30 μa	1938
Physics Dept., University College, London	Microton (elect cyl)	*e*	5	17 in.	1,070	0.50	0.2 μa, 50 pps, 3 × 10¹⁰ particles/pulse	1952
Medical Research Council, Hammersmith Hospital, London	....	*d* or *α*	15–20	50 in.	16,000	122	....	Estimated 1955
University of Liverpool	Sync-cyl	*p,d,α*	400	150 in.	....	....	....	Listed in ref. 2
	Cyl	*d*	9	36 in.				
Japan:								
Scientific Research Institute, Ltd., Bunkyo-ku, Tokyo	Cyl	*d*	3.7	63 cm	15,000	23	20 μa	1952
Netherlands:								
Institute voor Kernphysisch, Onderzoek, Amsterdam	Sync-cyl	*d*	27.5	71 in.	13,570	180 Fe, 30 Cu	30 μa	1949
Russia:								
Radium Institute, USSR Academy of Sciences, Leningrad	Cyl	*d*	1.8	14 in.	....	....	....	Listed in ref. 2
South Africa:								
National Physical Laboratory, Pretoria	Cyl	....	....	....	....	....	Description not available	Reported under construction, 1954
Sweden:								
Nobel Institute for Physics, Stockholm	Cyl	*p,d,α* Heavy ions	25(*d*) 50(*a*) 200 (oxygen ions)	225 cm	18,500 (max)	400 (Fe + Cu)	250 μa (internal)	1951
	Cyl	*p,d,α*	7(*d*)	80 cm	15,500	17	500 μa (internal)	1939
Gustaf Werner Institute for Nuclear Chemistry, University of Uppsala	Sync-cyl	*p*	192	230 cm	21,500	650	1.0 μa, 240 pps, 2 × 10¹⁰ particles/pulse	1951
Switzerland:								
European Council for Nuclear Research (CERN), Geneva	Sync-cyl	*p*	600	500 cm	10,000	3,000	50 pps	Projected for 1958
Eidgenossische Technische Hochschule, Zurich	Cyl	*p* *d*	8 14	100 cm	....	....	....	Listed in ref. 2

TABLE 8i-3. BETATRONS

Location	Max electron energy, Mev	Injection energy, kev	Resonant frequency, cps	Vacuum chamber cross-section dimensions	Weight of magnet (Fe + Cu)	Orbit radius	Beam: Electrons/pulse	Beam: r/min at 1 m inside $\frac{1}{8}$ in. of lead	Date of first operation, remarks
In the United States									
University of California, Los Alamos	24	60	180	1.75 × 3.5 in.	0.5	19 cm	10^8–10^9	200	March, 1950
Case Institute of Technology	25	40	180	1.62 × 2.75 in. (outside)	3	17.25 cm	....	10	September, 1949, flux-forced, field-biased type
University of Chicago	100	60	60	4 × 7 in. oval	140	33 in.	....	~2,000	April, 1950 (research operation)
General Electric Co., Schenectady	100	70	60	5 × 9 in.	125	33 in.	....	~4,000	August, 1943
	50	50	180	1.75 × 3.5 in.	9	11.5 in.	....	~1,000	May, 1947
	11.3	50	310	1.75 × 3.0 in.	1	5.25 in.	....	~75	July, 1945
University of Illinois	24	45	180	9.3 × 3.8 cm (rectangular)	3.5	20 cm	7 × 10^7 external, 6 × 10^9 circulating; pulse, $\frac{1}{2}$–300 μsec	70 r/min at 22 Mev in Al block 12 × 11.5 × 9.3 cm	September, 1941
	80	25	60	5.6 × 2 cm oval	4	26 cm	10^8	20 mr/min at 75 Mev in Al block 12 × 11.5 × 9.3 cm	September, 1948
	340	100	60	5.75 × 10 in. oval	350	48.61 in.	Pulse, 1–1,200 μsec; 6 pps	~15,000	February, 1950
National Bureau of Standards	50	40	180	2.5 in. high × 3.25 in. radial	12.5	11.5 in.	....	400	January, 1952
Naval Ordnance Laboratory	10	45	1,920	7.5 in. ID, 4.5 sq in. section	3	5.2 in.	1.65 × 10^9	75	November, 1948
Naval Research Laboratory	22	65	180	2 × 3 in. inside	5	18.5 cm	3 × 10^9, 0.1 μa avg	100	April, 1945
University of Pennsylvania	25	70	180	8 × 6 cm oval	5	19.1 cm	....	~100	December, 1948
Picatinny Arsenal, Dover, N.J	25	31 kw	180	2.5 × 5 in.	4	19 cm	....	~125	April, 1947
Rock Island Arsenal, Rock Island, Ill	22	60	180	2.1 × 2.8 in.	4.5	8.5 in.	....	100-in. polystyrene cylinder, 2-in. wall	March, 1945
Washington University Medical School	24	60	180	2.5 × 3.6 in.	6	19 cm	....	80	April, 1954

TABLE 8i-3. BETATRONS (*Continued*)

Location	Max electron energy, Mev	Injection energy, kev	Resonant frequency, cps	Vacuum chamber cross-section dimensions	Weight of Magnet (Fe + Cu)	Orbit radius	Beam: Electrons/pulse	Beam: r/min at 1 m inside $\frac{1}{8}$ in. of lead	Date of first operation, remarks
Outside the United States									
Canada:									
University of Saskatchewan, Saskatoon	26	60	180	Standard Allis-Chalmers model			....	200 r/min inside 4 cm of lucite	1948
Germany:									
Megavolt Versuchstanstalt, Wrist...	15	.....	...	....	....	....	....	....	Listed in ref. 2
Siemens-Reiniger-Werke, Erlanger..	6	4	550	4 × 2.5 cm	260 kg	8.3 cm	1.6×10^9	0.5	Types built for research since 1944; also building a 35-Mev machine in 1954
	15	45	50	7.6 × 3.2 cm	390 kg	10.5 cm	4.5×10^{10}	20	
Great Britain:									
Metropolitan Vickers, Ltd., Manchester	20 30	.....	...	....	....	....	....	....	Listed in ref. 2
Oxford University..................	16	.....	...	....	....	20 cm	....	....	Listed in ref. 2
Sweden:									
Institutionen for Fysikalisk Kemi, Stockholm......................	5	20–50	50	5 × 6 cm (elliptic)	300 kg	9.5 cm	5×10^7	0.6	1945
Switzerland:									
Physikalisches Institut der Universität, Zurich (Cantonal Hospital)...	31	45	50	9 × 5 cm (elliptic)	3.5 tons	24.5 cm	0.17×10^{11}	220	1951 (in hospital)

TABLE 8i-4. ELECTRON

Location	Energy max, Mev	Beam	Orbit radius, in.	Magnet	
				Type, weight, flux bars	Gap, in.
					In the
University of California, Berkeley	330	500 to 1,000 r/min 1 m from target. Internal beam, 10^8 electrons per pulse reach target	39.4	Three-leg, 136 tons, 214 in.^{2} $\times$ 78 in.	3.7 $\times$ 4.75
California Institute of Technology	500	7×10^{12} Mev/min after collimation through $\frac{5}{8}$-in.-diam hole 140 in. from target, approx 10^{11} electrons/pulse	138	Distributed, 155 tons, flux return both inside and outside of orbit	13.5 $\times$ 20
Cornell University......	420	Approx 10^{10} electrons/pulse (strong-focusing)	~140	Distributed, 20 tons, 26 ft diam, 13,000 gauss	3.25 $\times$ 5.5
General Electric Co. Research Lab.	70	1,500 r/min at 1 m inside $\frac{1}{8}$ in. lead 10^{10} electrons/pulse	23	Three-leg, 8 tons, 21.25 in.^{2} $\times$ 13.75	....
	300	700 r/min at 1 m inside $\frac{1}{8}$ in. lead 10^9 electrons/pulse	24	Air-core, 16,000 gauss, peak	
Iowa State............	70	800 r/min at 1 m inside $\frac{1}{8}$ in. of lead	11.5	Servo-controlled alternator*	....
Massachusetts Institute of Technology	350	10^8 electrons/burst; about 2,000 mesons per burst from an avg target	40	Distributed, 51 tons	2.9 $\times$ 3.5
University of Michigan..	350	10^9 equiv photons/min, 10^7 electrons/pulse	40	Three-leg, 16.5 tons, gap in middle leg, no flux bars	3.5 $\times$ 7
National Bureau of Standards	180	10,000 esu/cc/min, 2.8 esu/cc/pulse, at 1 m inside $\frac{1}{8}$ in. lead	33	Two-leg, 150 tons, cylindrical flux bar	....
Naval Research Laboratory	100	10^8 electrons/pulse, estimate	30	Air core, 400 lb Cu, 180 in.^{2} $\times$ 120 in.	1.62 wide
Purdue University......	290	Central beam Q: 10^9/min, 10^7/pulse through 1 $\times$ 0.62 in. at 1.5 m	40	Distributed, 51 tons, 240 in.^{2} $\times$ 27.5 in.	2.9 $\times$ 3.5

Location	Energy max, Mev	Beam	Orbit radius	Magnet	
				Type, weight, flux bars	Gap
					Outside the
Royal Cancer Hospital, London	30	X rays, 8–9 r/min at 1 m, unfiltered	10 cm	Central poles with 8 C-type return paths, 3 tons	....
Clarendon Lab., Oxford..	125	30 r/min, 0.01 r/pulse, at 1 m inside $\frac{1}{8}$ in. lead, 2×10^8 electrons/pulse	18.4 in.	Split C, 9.75 tons, 64 in.^{2} $\times$ 15 in.	2.25 in. high
University of Melbourne	21	1 r/min, 3.3×10^{-4} r/pulse, at 1 m inside 4 cm lucite, 2×10^9 electrons/pulse	10 cm	Three-leg, 0.5 ton	2.5 $\times$ 4 in.
Queens University, Kingston, Ontario	70	....	....	....	....
Lunds University, Sweden	35	2 r/min, 7×10^{-4} r/pulse at 1 m inside $\frac{1}{8}$ in. lead, 10^9–10^9 electrons/pulse	20 cm	20-leg, 1.3 tons, 3.5 cm^2 $\times$ 19.7 cm	6.8 $\times$ 7.5 cm
Addenbrookes Hospital..	30				
Atomic Energy Two Research Est.	25				
Glasgow University, Glasgow, Scotland	25	....	....	....	....
University of Johannesburg, S. Africa	13				

* See *J. Appl. Phys.* **18**, 811.

SYNCHROTRONS

Magnet		Vacuum chamber, material opening, in.	r-f system, type, freq. peak power, gap V (operating)	Injection, type, energy; at injection/end betatron phase	Date, first operation
Rep. freq., pps	Res. freq., cps				
United States					
6	32.1	Fused quartz, 2.63 × 5.38	Self-excited, class C, 47.7 Mc, 6 kw, 3.0 kv	Hot-cathode gun, 100 kv/2 Mev	December, 1948
1.0	.....	0.030 in. stainless steel, 9.5 × 38	MO-PA, 20.3 Mc (twice the revolution freq.), 0.6 kw, 6.0 kv	Pulse transformer, short accel. column, 1,000 kv/no betatron phase	July, 1952, designed for 1 Bev, rebuilding 1954–1955
30	30	Pyrex, 1.87 × 6	Self-excited, 47.5 Mc, 5.5 kw, 1.9 kv	VdG, 80 kv/2 Mev	1953 (300 Mev) rebuilt, 1954 (420 Mev), designed for 1 Bev
60	60	Porcelain, 2.25 × 4.5	163 Mc, 0.06 kw, 0.5 kv	Pulse transformer, 70 kv/2 Mev	October, 1946
12	300	Porcelain, 2 × 0.1	77.8 Mc, 20 kw, 10 kv	Pulse transformer, 80 kv/3.5 Mev	January, 1954
....	52	1.62 × 3.25	163 Mc	Pulsed filament, 60 kv/2 Mev	January, 1950
2 6 (later)	45	Slip-cast steatite, 1.8 × 6.0	Self-excited, class C, 46.5 Mc, 7 kw	Two-electrode, 80 kv/7 Mev	February, 1950
20	20	Ceramic, 2.25 × 6.75	Two stages: FM followed by FF. FM: 26.4–32 Mc, 4 kw; FF: 32 Mc, 5.4 kw; 2.0 kv	Electron gun with pulse transformer, 500 kv/no betatron phase	August, 1952
60	60	Pyrex, 4 × 7, elliptical	Cavity, 57 Mc, 1.5 kw, 1.5 kv	Lanthanum boride cathode, 60 kv/1.5 Mev	February, 1954 (180 Mev)
1	250	Pyrex, 1.12 diam	Cavity, class C, 1,250 Mc (20th harmonic of revolution freq.), 15 kv	35 kv/4 Mev	
2 4 (later)	30	High-V porcelain, 2.12 × 6.5	MO-PA, 46.1 Mc, ~1.5 kv	Outside-radius gun with pulse transformer, 70 kv/2-4 Mev	March, 1951

Magnet		Vacuum chamber, material opening	r-f system, type, freq. peak power, gap V (operating)	Injection, type, energy; at injection/end betatron phase	Date, first operation
Rep. freq., pps	Res. freq., cps				
United States					
50	.....	4.5 × 2.5 cm	478 Mc, 4 watts, avg ~100 V	Kerst, 3 electrode, 50 kv/gain, 10 ev/turn	April, 1949
50	50	Lead glass 1 × 3.5 in.	MO-PA, 102 Mc, 2 kw, 0.5 kv	External-diode gun, 60 kv/3 Mev	October, 1952
50	50	Porcelain 3 × 1.75 in.	Self-excited, grind grid, 480 Mc, 20 watts, 0.15 kv	Kerst, 3-electrode, 25 kv/2 Mev	December, 1949
....	.....	....	....	Lanthanum boride cathode	March, 1950
50	50	Pyrex 5.3 × 7 cm	PGT, 238 Mc, 50 watts, 0.2 kv	Pulse transformer, 18 kv/2.5 Mev	January, 1949
....	.....	....	....	....	Listed in ref. 7

TABLE 8i-5. PROTON SYNCHROTRONS

	Cosmotron, Brookhaven National Laboratory	Bevatron, University of California	University of Birmingham	Proposed values for new AGS* machines; data are for CERN; Brookhaven is similar	Under construction at Australian National University, Canberra
Maximum energy, Bev	2.9	6.0	1.0	25	
Particles/pulse	1×10^{11} max at 2.3 Bev, 5×10^{10} max at 3.0 Bev	1×10^{10} at 6 Bev	3×10^{9}	5×10^{9} estimate	10+ estimated
Orbit	30 ft radius	50 ft radius	14.75 ft radius	330 ft mean radius	
Acceleration time, sec	1.0	1.8	1.0	1.2	
Repetition rate, pulses/min	12	10	6	12	
Usable magnetic aperture	6.25 × 28 in.	12 in. high, 48 in. wide at injection; 9 in. at final energy	10 cm high × 33 cm radial	8 cm × 12 cm	
Magnet:					
Field exponent n†	0.6	0.6	0.68	±278 (strong-focusing)	A machine of 16-ft radius using an air core guiding field fed from a homopolar generator is under construction
Field, at injection/max, gauss	295/14,000	300/16,000	‡/12,500	140/12,000	
Magnet weight, steel/copper, tons	1,650/70	9,500/350	810 (total)	4,000/250	
No. of magnet units	4 quadrants, 72 blocks per quadrant	4 quadrants, 36 sectors per quadrant	...	48 magnet periods, 96 units 4.7 in. long	
No. of straight sections	4	4	...	96	
Length of straight sections	11 ft	20 ft	...	1.4 m	
Cross section of steel	94 × 94 in.				
Gap	9.35 × 48 in.	...	21 cm	10 cm	
No. of turns in coil	48	88	24	24	
Cross section of copper	62 sq in.	230 sq in.	...	600 cm²/magnet unit	
Peak current, amp	7,000	8,333	12,500	6,000	
Power dissipation	3×10^{6} joules	3,500 kw	130 kw		
Stored energy, peak	12×10^{6} joules	80×10^{6} joules	7,000 kw	$\sim 10^{7}$ joules	
Magnet power supply:					
Type	Motor, 12-phase alternator and flywheel, 24 ignitrons	2 m-g sets, 12-phase alternators, 48 ignitrons	Pulsed d-c from m-g set; separate pilot and main exciter; 36-ton flywheel		
Peak power transfer	26,000 kva	...	...	~25 mw	
Applied voltage (no load/full load)	5,400/3,700	18,000/12,000	1,100/‡	7,000/*	

TABLE 8i-5. PROTON SYNCHROTRONS (*Continued*)

	Cosmotron, Brookhaven National Laboratory	Bevatron, University of California	University of Birmingham	Proposed values for new AGS* machines; data are for CERN; Brookhaven is similar	Under construction at Australian National University, Canberra
Injection system:					
Type	VdG accelerator	C-W/linear	C-W	Linear accelerator	Cyclotron
Energy, Mev	3.6	0.43/9.8	0.46, ~.7 ma beam current	50 Mev, ~1.0 ma peak, 6-μsec pulse	
Time after start of magnetic cycle	20.7 msec	....	....	8 msec	
Inflector voltage	30.2 kv	76 kv			
r-f system:					
Frequency, injection/ejection	360 kc/4.18 Mc	360 kc/2.5 Mc	330 kc/9.3 Mc	5 to 16 Mc (32d harmonic)	
Volts/turn	~1,000 for 3 Bev	7,000 available	....	50,000	
Peak accelerating volts	~2,000	40,000 available	240 VMS on 96° cee		
Power	50 kw, peak	30 kw, avg	10 kw, peak; 5 kva in the cee	50 kw	
Vacuum system:					
Description, pumps	12 20-in. diffusion	24 32-in. oil diffusion	5 15-in. oil diffusion	32 4-in. diffusion	
Volume to be evacuated	300 cu ft	11,000 cu ft	4,000 liters	2,000 liters	
Min operating pressure	5×10^{-6} mm	1×10^{-5} mm (untrapped gauge)	8×10^{-7} mm, avg	$<10^{-1}$ mm	
Date first operation	May, 1952	February, 1954	July, 1953	Plan, 1960	
Date (to energy)	January, 1954 (3 Bev)	April, 1954 (6 Bev)	July, 1953 (1 Bev)		

* AGS = alternating gradient synchrotron.
† Here $n = -(r/H)(dH/dr)$, in obvious nomenclature.
‡ Information not available.

Table 8i-6. Linear Accelerators

Location	Type of particle	Accelerator length	Energy, Mev	Radio frequency: Frequency, Mc	Radio frequency: Peak output power, mw	Radio frequency: Avg power, kw	Radio frequency: Pulse length, μsec	Injection: Type	Injection: Energy	Beam: Particles/pulse	Beam: Pulse length, μsec	Beam: Pulse rep. rate, pps	Beam: Peak current, ma	Beam: Avg current, μa	Date of first operation
In the United States															
Bartol Research Foundation	e	3 ft	1.5	2,860	1	1.2	3	Electron gun	30 kev	3×10^{11}	1	400 max	50	20	1950
University of California Radiation Laboratory	p	40 ft	32	202.5	2.5	42	...	VdG	4 Mev	......	425	15	....	0.1	November, 1947
Columbia University	d	12 in.	0.5		PIG source		...	None		10^{12}	1	1,000	200	200	April, 1954
Massachusetts Institute of Technology	e	21 ft	17	2,900	5	1.2	2	Pulsed VdG	2 Mev	10^{11}	1	120	20–40	2.5–5.0	February, 1950
University of Minnesota	p	100 ft	Prelim 10; final, 68	202	1.5 (10 Mev), 3.5 (final)	2% peak	300	Transformer set	0.5 Mev	10^{13}	200	60	....	0.1	February, 1954, to 10 Mev
Purdue University	e	4 m	2–6 (variable)	2,853	0.7	0.17	2	Transformer rectifier; grid gun	50 kv, pulsed	6×10^{10}	1	120	10	1.2	December, 1952
Stanford University:															
Physics Lab., Mk II	e	10 ft	38	2,850	18	......	2	Tungsten fil. gun	80 kv, pulsed	....	.....	60	....	......	1949, Mk II; 1948, Mk I (dismantled)
Physics Lab., Mk III (1954 operating level)	e	220 ft	630	2,850	234	28	2	Tungsten fil. gun	80 kv, pulsed	5×10^{10}	0.3	60	30	0.5	1950
Stanford Hospital	e	6 ft	6	2,836	0.8	......	...	Tantalum-bombarded cathode	100 kv	....	1	400	30	......	Under construction, 1954
University of Virginia	e	12 in.	0.75	400	0.5			Filament or vac. spark		5×10^{12}	5	60	....	20	1947
Yale University	e	9.5 ft	15	600	4.0	6	15	d-c-bunching feed	12 kv	....	0.1–1.0	.....	200	10–20	1949

TABLE 8i-6. LINEAR ACCELERATORS (*Continued*)

Location	Type of parti-cle	Acceler-ator length	Energy, Mev	Radio frequency: Fre-quency, Mc	Radio frequency: Peak output power, mw	Radio frequency: Avg power, kw	Radio frequency: Pulse length, μsec	Injection: Type—Energy	Beam: Particles/pulse	Beam: Pulse length, μsec	Beam: Pulse rep. rate, pps	Beam: Peak cur-rent, ma	Beam: Avg cur-rent, μa	Date of first operation
Outside the United States														
Great Britain:														
Associated Electrical Industries, Ltd., Aldermaston	*p*	1.0 m	4.0	300	500	1.5	6	VdG, 2.5 Mev	....	.....	...	....	......	Under construction, 1954
Atomic Energy Research Establishment,	*e*	2 m	3.2	3,000	2	1.6	2	Focused gun, tung. fil., 40–50 kv	1.2×10^{12}	1.4	400	120	67 μa	January, 1950
	e	6 m	13.5	3,000	2	1.6	2	....	2.5×10^{11}	1.4	400	25	14 μa	July, 1952
Harwell	*p*	270 m	600	Injection at 500 kev is followed by a 10-Mev section using grid focusing, followed by two 40-ft sections using magnetic focusing giving 20 Mev each. At 50 Mev frequency changes from 200 to 400 Mc. Total power requirement in the pulse is 100 mw at duty cycle of about 1%				C-W, 0.5 Mev	....	500	50	100	15 ma	Planned for about 1960
Liverpool Radium Institute..............	*e*	......	4	.....	...	...	...	....	....	.....	...	....	......	1955
Medical Research Council, Hammersmith Hospital, London	*e*	3 m	8	3,000	2	2	2	Diode electron gun, 45 kv pulsed	....	2	500	40	40 μa	1950
Newcastle General Hospital............	*e*	1.0 m	3.7	3,000	2	1.6	2	Focused gun, tung. fil., 40–50 kv	2×10^{12}	1.4	400	200	112 μa	September, 1953
St. Bartholomews Hospital, London....	*e*	6.0 m	15	3,000	2	2	2	Focused gun, tung. fil., 40–50 kv	2.5×10^{11}	1.4	500	25	18 μa	October, 1954
Telecommunications Research Establishment (AERE), Malvern Great......	*e*	2.0 m	3.4	.....	...	...	...	Electron gun, 45 kv	....	.....	...	1.00		

8j. Fission-product Chains and Yields

D. H. PERKEL
Aerojet-General Nucleonics

L. LEVENTHAL
Tracerlab, Inc.

L. R. ZUMWALT
General Dynamics Corp.

8j-1. Fission-product Chains. Table 8j-1 comprises a listing of the chain relationships and half lives of nuclides produced by thermal neutron fission as reported in the literature up to approximately November, 1954.

The conventions adopted to describe these data are those employed by J. M. Hollander, I. Perlman, and G. T. Seaborg (HPS) in "Table of Isotopes," UCRL-1948, revised, December, 1952,[1] and in Appendix A of "Radiochemical Studies: The Fission Products," Book 3, div. IV, vol. 9 of the National Nuclear Energy Series (NNES[2]).

A half life given in parentheses indicates the nuclide has not been identified as a fission product; a half life given in brackets indicates a limit on the half life has been established. The symbol $\not\rightarrow$ means that the transition does not occur.

Since HPS represents the most recent compilation of data, references are given only for data differing from HPS. Data which do not appear in HPS are designated as follows: A horizontal line below the datum or a vertical line to the left identifies the source as NNES; a horizontal line above or a vertical line to the right of the datum indicates its mention in the General Electric "Chart of the Nuclides," 4th ed., November, 1952 (GECN). References for Table 8j-1 are given on page 8-212.

The degree of certainty of assignment, where it has been evaluated, is indicated by a letter (following Seaborg):

A Element and mass number certain
B Element certain and mass number probable
C Element probable and mass number certain or probable
D Element certain and mass number not well established
E Element probable and mass number not well established
F Insufficient evidence
G Assignment probably in error

Absence of symbol means there has been no assignment of degree of certainty. Assignments are shown thus:

x	denotes GECN
x	denotes HPS

[1] *Revs. Modern Phys.* **25**, 469 (1953).
[2] National Nuclear Energy Series, McGraw-Hill Book Company, Inc., New York, 1951.

TABLE 8j-1. FISSION-PRODUCT CHAINS

Mass No. \ Atomic No.	30 Zn	31 Ga	32 Ge	33 As	34 Se	35 Br	36 Kr	37 Rb	Notes
72	49.0 hr →	14.3 hr → D	2.9×10^{-7} sec ↓ Stable						
73	[<2 min] →	5.0 hr → B	Stable						
74			Stable						
75			(82 min)	Stable					
76			Stable						
77			59 sec → ↓ 12 hr →	38.0 hr → <2% - - → ; >98% →	17.5 sec ↓ Stable				17.5-sec Se activity uncertain 3S53
78			86.0 min → B	91.0 min → B	Stable				2.1-hr Ge HPS 90-min As HPS
79				9 min → ; - - →	3.88 min ↓ ≤6.5×10^4 years → B	Stable			9 min → 3.88 min 3C53 9 min → 6.5×10^4 years now questionable
80					Stable				
81				[10 min] →	56.5 min ↓ 17 min →	Stable			

TABLE 8j-1. FISSION-PRODUCT CHAINS (*Continued*)

Mass No. \ Atomic No.	34 Se	35 Br	36 Kr	37 Rb	38 Sr	39 Y	40 Zr	41 Nb	Notes
82	$>10^{17}$ years	35.87 hr →	Stable						Stable Se HPS
83	67 sec → (>90%); <10% ↓ 25 min →	2.4 hr →	114 min ↓ Stable						2.33 hr ↛ stable 3S53 2.4-hr Br^{83} late comm. 1S54
84	~2 min →	30 min →	Stable						
85		3.00 min →	4.36 hr (0.65%) → ; 23% ↓ 9.4 year → (99.35%)	0.9 × 10^{-6} sec ↓ Stable					10.27-year Kr^{85} 23%, 0.65%, 99.35% 2G52 1B52
86			Stable ← (β⁺ lim 0.002%) (EC lim 0.04%); ↑ n	19.5 days →	Stable				
87	(~13 sec) →	55.6 sec → (~2%) Instant.; (~98%) →	Instant.; 74 min →	5.90 × 10^{10} years →	(2.80 hr) ↓ Stable				74-min Kr^{87} 2S53 ~13-sec Se^{87} 2S53 No 2.80 hr 2G52 Rb 6.2 × 10^{10} years 1M53
88		15.5 sec →	2.77 hr → (↑ n)	17.8 min →	Stable				
89		4.51 sec → Instant.; D →	Instant.; 3.18 min →	15.4 min →	53 days →	Stable			
90			33 sec →	2.74 min →	19.9 years →	61 hr →	Stable		
91			9.8 sec →	1.67 min ↓ 14 min →	9.7 hr → (~40%) 51.0 min; (~60%) 58.5 days	51.0 min ↓ 58.5 days →	Stable		58.5-day Y 1A53 51.0-min Y-→stable not found 1A53, 2B54 14-min Rb late comm. 1S54

TABLE 8j-1. FISSION-PRODUCT CHAINS (*Continued*)

Mass No. \ Atomic No.	36 Kr	37 Rb	38 Sr	39 Y	40 Zr	41 Nb	42 Mo	43 Tc	Notes
92	3.0 sec → (A / B)	80 sec → (A / D)	2.7 hr → (A / B)	3.60 hr → (A / B)	Stable (A)				Rb short GECN Rb [short] NNES Y^{92} mass A 1S53
93	2.0 sec → (A / B)	[Short] → (A / [B])	7 min → (A / B)	10.0 hr → (A / B)	1.1 × 10⁶ years (A / B) 33% → 4.2 years; 67% → Stable	4.2 years ↓ Stable (B)			3.65-year Nb listed only in HSP 1.1 × 10^6-year Zr^{93} and 4.2-year Nb^{93} and other branching ratios 1S54
94	(B) 1.4 sec → (B)	(B) [Short] → ([B])	(B) ~2 min → (B)	(B) 16.5 min → (B)	Stable				Y mass A 1S53
95	Short → (A)	[Short] → ([A])	Short → ([A])	10.5 min → (B / B)	65 days: 1% → 90 hr; 99% → 35 days	90 hr ↓ 35 days →	Stable		36, 37, 38 not listed GECN
96					[6 × 10^{16} years] - - - → (Mo); ↓ Stable; → 23.35 hr	23.35 hr →	Stable		Statistical evidence for ββ decay 2M53 6 × 10^{16} years ⇢ stable questionable late comm. 1S54
97	~1 sec → (A / B)	[Short] → (A / [A])	Short → (A / [A])	Short → (A / [A])	17.0 hr →	60 sec ↓ 72.1 min →	Stable		
98							Stable		
99							67 hr: ~10% → 6.04 hr; ~90% → 2.12 × 10^5 years	6.04 hr ↓ 2.12 × 10^5 years →	Ru^{99} Stable — Branching ratios late comm. 1S54
100							[≥ 10^{15} years]		HPS lists as stable ββ? 1F52
101							14.6 min →	14.0 min →	Ru^{101} Stable

TABLE 8j-1. FISSION-PRODUCT CHAINS (*Continued*)

Mass \ Atomic No.	42 Mo	43 Tc	44 Ru	45 Rh	46 Pd	47 Ag	48 Cd	49 In	Notes
102	12 min → D/D	<25 sec → C/E	Stable						
103			39.8 days → >95% / <5%	57 min ↓ Stable					Branching ratios late comm. 1S54
104			Stable						
105	~5 min → A/B	Short → A/B	4.5hr → A	45 sec ↓ 36.5 hr → A	Stable				
106			1.0 years →	30 sec →	Stable				
107		<1.5 min → [E]	4 min → C/D	26 min → B/D	~7 × 10^6 years → A/B	Stable			[<1.5 min] NNES (107) NNES
108					Stable				(108) NNES 9-hr Rh^{108} does not exist 1951 MIT report, 1S54
109				[<1 hr] ⇢ (4.8 min); [<1 hr] → 13.6 hr	(4.8 min) ↓ 13.6 hr → [A]	39.2 sec ↓ Stable			13.6 hr ↛ stable 2G52
110					Stable				
111					22 min →	7.6 days → 9% / 91%	48.6 min ? ↓ 8 × 10^{-8} sec ↓ Stable		7.6 days ↛ 48.6 min 2G52 48.6 min not listed as fission product GECN, 1S54

TABLE 8j-1. FISSION-PRODUCT CHAINS (*Continued*)

Mass No. \ Atomic No.	46 Pd	47 Ag	48 Cd	49 In	50 Sn	51 Sb	52 Te	53 I	Notes
112	21 hr →	3.20 hr →	Stable						
113		5.3 hr →	5.1 years → Stable	104 min ↓ Stable					Decay scheme 2G52 Cd^{113m} ~5 × 10^{-5}% 1W52, 1S54 5.1 years ↛ stable late comm. 1S54
114		2 min → B	Stable						
115		20 min → 9%, 91%	43 days <0.02% 53 hr 10.0%	4.50 hr 95% 6 × 10^{14} years	Stable				43 days ↛ 4.50 hr 2G52 but very small amount observed by Engelkemeir (1S54) 20-min branching ratios late comm. 1S54
116			[>8 × 10^{15} years]						Stable HPS ββ ? 1F52
117			3.0 hr <10% ↓ ~50 min	1.9 hr 72% 28% ↓ 1.1 hr	<1% 14.0 days ↓ Stable				14.0 days tentative 3.0 hr → ~50 min → 1.9 hr 1.1 hr 2C53 28% branching ratio 3M53 Other branching ratios, In half lives late comm. 1S54 Cf. *Phys. Rev.* **97**, 93
118			~30 min →	<1 min →	Stable				2C53 Not listed HPS HPS, NNES, GECN list 4.5-min In
119				17.5 min B	250 days Stable				
120					Stable				
121					27.5 hr →	Stable			

TABLE 8j-1 FISSION-PRODUCT CHAINS (*Continued*)

Mass No. \ Atomic No.	50 Sn	51 Sb	52 Te	53 I	54 Xe	55 Cs	56 Ba	57 La	Notes
122	Stable								
123	136 days → (39.5 min) →	Stable							39.5 min found in fission ?
124	[>1.5 × 10[17] years]								ββ statistical prob. 2M53 >2 × 10[15] years 1F52
125	94 days → 9.5 min →	2.7 years →	18% → 58 days ↓ → Stable						18% 2G52 Te >2 × 10[15] years 1F52
126	~50 min →	B → 9 hr → C B B (28 days) D D →	→ Stable						28 days questionable late comm. 1S54
127	1.5 hr →	93 hr →	~16% → 90 days ↓ ~84% → 9.3 hr →	Stable					90 days late comm. 1S54
128			Stable						
129		4.6 hr →	~24% → 33 days ↓ ~76% → 72 min →	1.72 × 10[7] years →	Stable				4.6 hr, branching ratios cited in late comm. 1S54
130		40 min → B D 12 min → D	[>4 × 10[15] years]						ββ > 4 × 10[15] years 1F52
131		23.1 min →	~15% → 30 hr – – ~60% → ↓ 40%? ~85% → 24.8 min →	8.141 days →	0.77% → 12.0 days ↓ → 4.8 × 10[−10] sec ↓ 99% → Stable				30 hr – – ~60% → 8.141 days 2G52, not in HPS 15%, 85% Pappas cited in late comm. 1S54

TABLE 8j-1. FISSION-PRODUCT CHAINS (*Continued*)

Mass No. \ Atomic No.	51 Sb	52 Te	53 I	54 Xe	55 Cs	56 Ba	57 La	58 Ce	Notes
132	2 min → B	77.7 hr → B	2.4 hr → B	Stable					
133	4.4 min, ~60% A → 63 min; ~40% B → 2 min	B, 63 min ↓ 2 min (63 min - - → 20.5 hr; 2 min → 20.5 hr)	B, 20.5 hr, 2.4% → 2.3 days; 97.6% → 5.270 days	2.3 days ↓ 5.270 days (2.3 days → 6.0 × 10⁻⁹ sec; 5.270 days → Stable)	6.0×10^{-9} sec ↓ Stable				60%, 40% late comm. 1S54 63 min - → 20.5 hr 1K53 63 min -/→ 20.5 hr 2G52
134	~50 sec → D	44 min → B	52.5 min →	Stable					(50 sec) 134 or 135
135		<2 min → [A]	6.68 hr, ~30% → 15.6 min; ~70% → 9.13 hr	15.6 min ↓ 9.13 hr, ~95% → 2.8 × 10⁻¹⁰ sec; ~5% → 3.0 × 10⁶ years	2.8×10^{-10} sec ↓ 3.0×10^{6} years →	Stable			9.13 hr ~95% → 2.8×10^{-10} sec 1T54
136		~1 min → E	86 sec → D	Stable ↑ n (from 137 Instant.)	13.7 days →	Stable			~1 min mass uncertain, not listed GECN 13.7 days β^+ - → stable Xe? Sugarman, private comm.
137			D, 22.0 sec, ~6% → Instant.; ~94% → 3.9 min	Instant. (n ↑); 3.9 min →	33 years, 92% → 2.60 min; 8% → Stable	2.60 min ↓ Stable			
138			5.9 sec →	17 min →	32.9 min →	[>10¹⁵ years]			10^{15} years $\beta\beta$ 1F52 32.0 min 1L53
139			2.7 sec →	41 sec →	9.5 min →	85.0 min →	Stable		
140				16.0 sec →	66 sec →	12.80 days →	40 hr →	Stable	
141				1.7 sec →	Short → A [A]	18 min →	3.7 hr →	33.1 days →	(Pr[141]) Stable

TABLE 8j-1. FISSION-PRODUCT CHAINS (*Continued*)

Mass No. \ Atomic No.	54 Xe	55 Cs	56 Ba	57 La	58 Ce	59 Pr	60 Nd	61 Pm	Notes
142		~1 min → (D/D)	~6 min → (C/D)	74 min → (C/D)	Stable				Mass uncertain NNES
143	1.0 sec →	Short → [A]	<0.5 min →	~19 min →	33 hr →	13.7 days →	Stable ← α (from Sm^{147})		
144	~1 sec →	Short → (A/[A])	Short → (A/[A])	Short → (A/[A])	282 days →	17.5 min →	Stable		
145							Stable	α	
146					13.9 min → (C/D)	24.4 min → (C/D)	Stable		Chain checked by 1C53 and 1B54
147							11.3 days →	2.6 years →	(Sm^{147}) 1.4 × 10^{11} years
148							Stable		
149							2.0 hr →	54 hr →	(Sm^{149}) Stable
150							>2 × 10^{15} years		ββ ?
151							12 min → (A/B)	27.5 hr → (A/B)	(Sm^{151}) 73 years → (A) (Eu^{151}) Stable

TABLE 8j-1. FISSION-PRODUCT CHAINS (*Continued*)

Mass No. \ Atomic No.	60 Nd	61 Pm	62 Sm	63 Eu	64 Gd	65 Tb	66 Dy	Notes
152			Stable					
153		[<5 min] →	47 hr (~10% →) (~90% →)	3.0 × 10^{-9} sec ↓ Stable				90% 2G 52
154			Stable					
155		[<5 min] →	23.5 min → B B	1.7 years →	Stable			
156		[<5 min] →	~10 hr →	15.4 days →	Stable			
157				15.4 hr → B D	Stable			
158				60 min → D D	Stable			
159					18.0 hr →	Stable		1F54
160					Stable			Mass spec. 1S54
161					3.6 min →	7.0 days →	Stable	Gd late comm. 1S54 Tb 1F54

References for Table 8j-1

1A 53. Ames, D. P., M. E. Bunker, L. M. Langer, and B. M. Sorenson: *Phys. Rev.* **91,** 68 (1953).
1B 52. Bergstrom: *Arkiv Fysik* **5,** 191 (1952).
1B 53. Bunker, M. E., R. J. Prestwood, and J. W. Starner: *Phys. Rev.* **91,** 1021 (1953).
1B 54. Bernstein, W., S. S. Markowitz, and S. Katcoff: *Phys. Rev.* **93,** 1073 (1954).
2B 54. Bunker, M. E., J. P. Mize, and J. W. Starner: *Phys. Rev.* **94,** 1694 (1954).
1C 51. Coryell, C. D., and N. Sugarman: "Radiochemical Studies: The Fission Products," Book 3, div. IV, vol. 9, National Nuclear Energy Series, McGraw-Hill Book Company, Inc., New York, 1951.
1C 53. Caretto, A. H., and S. Katcoff: *Phys. Rev.* **89,** 1267 (1953).
2C 53. Coryell, C. D., P. Levegue, and H. G. Richter: *Phys. Rev.* **89,** 903A (1953).
3C 53. Cunninghame, J. G.: *Phil. Mag.* **44,** 900 (1953).
1F 52. Fremlin, J. H., and M. C. Walters: *Proc. Phys. Soc. (London)* **65A,** 911 (1952).
1F 54. Freiling, E. C., L. R. Bunney, and N. E. Ballou: *Phys. Rev.* **96,** 102 (1954).
1G 52. General Electric: "Chart of the Nuclides," Knolls Atomic Power Laboratory, 4th ed., revised to November, 1952.
2G 52. Goldhaber, M., and R. D. Hill: *Revs. Modern Phys.* **24,** 179 (1952).
1H 52. Hollander, J. M., I. Perlman, and G. T. Seaborg: "Table of Isotopes," UCRL, 1928 (1952).
1K 53. Katcoff, S., and W. Rubinson: *Phys. Rev.* **91,** 1458 (1953).
1L 53. Langer, L. M., R. B. Duffield, and C. W. Stanley: *Phys. Rev.* **89,** 907A (1953).
1M 53. MacGregor, M. H., and M. L. Wiedenbeck: *Phys. Rev.* **94,** 138 (1953).
2M 53. McCarthy, J. A.: *Phys. Rev.* **90,** 853 (1953).
3M 53. McGinnis, C. L.: *Phys. Rev.* **94,** 780A (1953).
1S 53. Schott, G. L., and W. W. Meinke: *Phys. Rev.* **89,** 1156 (1953).
2S 53. Stehney, A. F., and N. Sugarman: *Phys. Rev.* **89,** 194 (1953).
3S 53. Swinbank, P., and J. Walker: *Proc. Phys. Soc. (London)* **66A,** 1093 (1953).
1S 54. Steinberg, E. P.: private communication, 1954.
1T 54. Thulin, S.: *Phys. Rev.* **94,** 734 (1954).
1W 52. Wahl, A. C., and N. A. Bonner: *Phys. Rev.* **85,** 570 (1952).

8j-2. Fission-product Yields. The accompanying tables, presenting the experimentally determined yields of the fission products, are based largely upon those in Appendix B of "Radiochemical Studies: The Fission Products," National Nuclear Energy Series (NNES), div. IV, vol. 9, edited by C. D. Coryell and N. Sugarman, 1951.[1] The data in the NNES tables have been augmented by the results of radiochemical and mass-spectrographic investigations published subsequent to the compilation of the NNES data, to about November, 1954. They include newer values of yields in neutron-induced fission as well as yields for charged-particle induced fission, photofission, and spontaneous fission.

The nuclides measured represent members of the beta-decay chains close to the stability line; the yield of each tabulated nuclide in general includes the yields of its precursors in the chain. Where independent yields have been measured, they are indicated by the prefix *i*:. Since each fissioning nucleus gives rise to two fission fragments, the sum of the yields of all fission products for each nuclide is theoretically 200 per cent. The small amount of ternary and quaternary fission is generally considered negligible in yield computations.

Gratitude is expressed to E. P. Steinberg, R. W. Spence, G. P. Ford, and J. M. Hollander, for their valuable suggestions and assistance in the compilation of these data. References for Tables 8j-2 to 8j-8 are given on page 8-225.

[1] Published by McGraw-Hill Book Company, Inc., New York.

TABLE 8j-2. THERMAL-NEUTRON FISSION YIELDS

Mass No.	Nuclide	U^{233}	U^{235}	Pu^{239}
72	Zn^{72}	....	1.5×10^{-5} (53)	1.1×10^{-4} (219)
73	Ga^{73}	....	1.0×10^{-4} (53)	
77	Ge^{77}	0.008 (S1)	0.0037 (54)	
		0.010 (S8)	0.0023 (S5)	
77	As^{77}	0.018 (S1)	0.0067 (S5)	
		0.019 (S8)	0.0091 (54)	
78	Ge^{78}	....	0.02 (54)	
			0.018 (S5)	
78	As^{78}	....	0.02 (54)	
			i: $(1.8 \pm 0.6) \times 10^{-3}$ (S5)	
			0.020 (S5)	
81	Se^{81m}	....	0.008 (61)	
81	Se^{81}	....	0.133 (61)	
82	Br^{82}	....	i: 3.5×10^{-5} (62)	
83	Se^{83}	....	0.21 (59)	
83	Br^{83}	0.70 (S1)	0.48 (A1)	0.080 (219)
		0.79 (S8)	0.40 (59)	
83	Kr^{83}	....	0.586 (T1)	
84	Br^{84}	....	0.65 (58)	
84	Kr^{84}	....	1.09 (T1)	
85	Kr^{85m}	....	33% of Kr^{88} (K1)	
85	Kr^{85}	....	0.317 (T1)	
			0.24 (69)	
86	Kr^{86}	....	2.09 (T1)	
86	Rb^{86}	....	i: 3.1×10^{-5} (G1)	
			i: 1.8×10^{-4} (71)	
87	Kr^{87}	....	70% of Kr^{88} (K1)	
89	Sr^{89}	5.6 (S1)	4.6 (76)	1.8 (219)
		6.5 (S8)	3.2 (G2)	
		4.1 (G2)		
91	Sr^{91}	....	5.0 (73)	2.3 (219)
91	Y^{91}	4.1 (G2)	5.9 (75)	2.8 (219)
			4.0 (G2)	
92	Sr^{92}	....	5.0 (73)	
94	Y^{94}	....	5 (79)	
95	Zr^{95}	5.7 (S1)	6.0 (S3)	5.6 (219)
		5.9 (S8)	6.4 (247)	
		3.9 (G2)	3.2 (G2)	
97	Zr^{97}	....	6.2 (S3)	5.3 (219)
			6.1 (R1)	
99	Mo^{99}	4.7 (S1)	6.2 (96)	6.1 (219)
		5.1 (S8)	5.9 (W5)	
			6.2 (F5)	
101	Mo^{101}	....	5.4 (W5)	
102	Mo^{102}	....	4.1 (W5)	
102	Rh^{102}	....	i: $<5 \times 10^{-7}$ (118)	
103	Ru^{103}	0.85 (S1)	3.7 (103)	5.5 (219)
		1.6 (S8)	2.85 (H2)	
		0.21 (G2)	0.84 (G2)	
			1.4 (W5)	
105	Ru^{105}	....	0.9 (105)	
			0.83 (W5)	
105	Rh^{105}	....	....	3.7 (219)
106	Ru^{106}	0.24 (S1)	0.52 (103)	4.7 (219)
		0.28 (S8)	0.38 (H2)	
		0.064 (G2)	0.15 (G2)	
109	Pd^{109}	0.047 (S1)	0.028 (217)	1.0 (219)
		0.040 (S8)	0.017 (119)	
			0.026 (E1)	

See page 8-215 for footnotes.

TABLE 8j-2. THERMAL-NEUTRON FISSION YIELDS (*Continued*)

Mass No.	Nuclide	U^{233}	U^{235}	Pu^{239}
111	Ag^{111}	0.022 (S1)	0.018 (123, 217)	0.27 (219)
		0.025 (S8)	0.016 (G2)	
		0.015 (G2)	0.018 (E1)	
112	Pd^{112}	0.014 (S1)	0.0083 (217)	0.10 (219)
		0.016 (S8)	0.011 (119)	
			0.018 (E1)	
115	Ag^{115}	....	*i*: 0.0078 (W1)	
115	Cd^{115m}	0.001 (S1)	8×10^{-4} (125)	0.003 (219)
		0.001 (S8)	*i*: $<2 \times 10^{-5}$ (W1)	
			7.1×10^{-4} (W1)	
115	Cd^{115}	0.016 (S1)	0.011 (127)	0.045 (219)
		0.019 (S8)		
115	Total chain	0.020 (S8)	0.020 (217)	
115	Cd^{115}	....	0.019 (E1)	
			i: 0.0027 (W1)	
			0.0098 (W1)	
117	Cd^{117}	....	0.010 (128)	
121	Sn^{121}	0.018 (S2, S8)	0.014 (S2, 129)	0.041 (S2, 219)
123	Sn^{123m}	0.0025 (G2)	0.0012 (130)	
			8.5×10^{-4} (G2)	
125	Sn^{125m}	0.054 (S2)	0.012 (S2, 129)	0.068 (S2, 219)
		0.050 (S8)		
125	Sb^{125}	....	0.023 (134)	
			0.017 (133)	
126	Sn^{126}	....	0.1 (129)	
127	Sb^{127}	0.092 (S1)	0.094 (217)	0.37 (219)
		0.101 (S8)	0.093 (E1)	
127	Te^{127m}	0.067 (G2)	0.033 (136)	
			0.015 (G2)	
129	Te^{129m}	0.22 (G2)	0.19 (136)	
			0.09 (G2)	
			0.23 (P2)	
129	Xe^{129}	....	$<4 \times 10^{-4}$ (T2)	
131	Te^{131m}	....	0.44 (137)	
			0.45 (P2)	
131	Te^{131}	....	2.5 (P2)	
131	I^{131}	2.7 (S1, S8)	2.8 (217)	3.6 (219)
		2.4 (G2)	2.23 (Y1)	
			3.0 (P2)*	
			2.9 (E1)	
131	Xe^{131}	....	2.80 (T1)†	
132	Te^{132}	4.9 (G2)	4.4 (P1)	4.9 (219)
			4.9 (G2)	
			3.4 (205)	
			2.1 (137)	
			4.5 (P2)	
132	Xe^{132}	....	4.17 (T1)	
133	Te^{133}	....	4.5 (P1, P2)	
133	I^{133}	....	4.6 (141)	5.0 (219)
			5.2 (P2)	
			i: 1.2 (G1)	
			i: 0.5 (P2)	
133	Xe^{133}	....	6.29 (M1)	
			6.62 (K2)*	
			i: ~0.04% of total yield (K2)	
133	Cs^{133}	....	103% of Cs^{137} (I1)	
134	Te^{134}	....	6.9 (P1, P2)	
134	I^{134}	....	5.7 (Y1, 138)	
			7.8 (P2)	
			i: 1.0 (G1)	

See page 8-215 for footnotes.

TABLE 8j-2. THERMAL-NEUTRON FISSION YIELDS (*Continued*)

Mass No.	Nuclide	U^{233}	U^{235}	Pu^{239}
134	Xe^{134}	....	7.41 (T1)	
			7.81 (W3 revised in K2)	
135	I^{135}	5.1 (S8)	5.6 (140, 141)	5.5 (219)
135	Xe^{135}	....	5.9 (147)	
			i: ~0.3 (147)	
			i: 3.5% of total Xe^{135} formed (K2)	
			i: 2.6% of total Xe^{135} (B1)	
135	Cs^{135}	....	128% of Cs^{137} (I1)	
			110% of Cs^{137} (N2)	
136	I^{136}	1.7 (S4)	3.1 (S4)	1.9 (S4)
136	Xe^{136}	....	6.14 (T1)	
			6.42 (W3 revised in K2)	
136	Cs^{136}	....	*i*: 6.2×10^{-3} (G1)	*i*: 0.09 (159)
137	Cs^{137}	....	6.2 (S8), 6.07 (W3 revised in K2)	
139	Ba^{139}	....	6.3 (161)	5.4 (219)
			6.1 (G3)	
140	Ba^{140}	6.0 (S1, S8)	6.32 (206 corrected)*	5.36 (219)*
		6.7 (G2)	5.82 (205)	
			5.6 (G2, G3)	
			6.4 (E1)	
			6.17 (S5)†	
			6.2 (W5, H2)†	
140	La^{140}	....	*i*: <0.2 (170)	
141	Ba^{141}	....	4.6 (181)	
141	$La^{141} + Ce^{141}$	....	*i*: <0.022 of total chain (F1)	
141	Ce^{141}	....	5.7 (180)	4.9 (219)
143	La^{143}	....	~3.8 (182)	
143	Ce^{143}	....	5.4 (176)	5.1 (219)
143	Nd^{143}	....	5.40 (I2)†	
144	Ce^{144}	3.4 (S1)	5.3 (184)	3.7 (219)
		4.1 (S8)	2.9 (G2)	
		2.2 (G2)		
144	Nd^{144}	....	4.64 (I2)	
145	Nd^{145}	....	3.62 (I2)	
146	Nd^{146}	....	2.81 (I2)	
147	Nd^{147}	....	2.6 (191)	
147	Pm^{157}	0.6 (G2)	~0.6 (G2)	
148	Nd^{148}	....	1.64 (I2)	
149	Pm^{149}	....	1.3 (193)	
150	Nd^{150}	....	0.658 (I2)	
151	Sm^{151}	....	0.445 (I2)†	
152	Sm^{152}	....	0.279 (I2)	
153	Sm^{153}	0.078 (S1)	0.15 (217)	0.39 (219, 129)
		0.095 (S8)	0.16 (E1)	
154	Sm^{154}	....	0.0908 (I2)	
155	Sm^{155}	....	0.031 (196)	0.21 (196)
155	Eu^{155}	....	~0.03 (199)	
156	Sm^{156}	....	0.012 (198)	
156	Eu^{156}	....	0.013 (198)	0.12 (219)
			0.014 (217, E1)	
(157)	Eu^{157}	....	7.4×10^{-3} (197)	
157	Gd^{157}	....	0.0150 (I2)†	
(158)	Eu^{158}	....	0.002 (197)	
158	Gd^{158}	....	0.0084 (I2)‡	
159	Gd^{159}	....	0.00130 (F5)	
160	Gd^{160}	....	0.0027 (I2)‡	
161	Tb^{161}	....	8.3×10^{-5} (F5)	

* Best value (S8).
† Assumed value for relative yields in the given reference.
‡ Gd values in I2 too high because of Pu contribution (S8).

TABLE 8j-3. FAST-NEUTRON FISSION YIELDS: THORIUM

Mass No.	Nuclide	Th^{232} pile neutrons avg energy 2.6 Mev (T3)	Th^{232} Li + D neutrons between 6 and 11 Mev (T4)
72	Zn^{72}	3.3×10^{-4}	
73	Ga^{73}	4.5×10^{-4}	
77	Ge^{77}	0.009	0.022
77	Ge^{77} + As^{77} (total chain)	0.020	0.052
83	Br^{83}	1.9	2.74
89	Sr^{89}	6.7	6.7*
90	Sr^{90}	6.1	
91	Sr^{91}	6.4†	5.6
97	Zr^{97}	5.4†	4.75
99	Mo^{99}	2.9†	3.1
103	Ru^{103}	0.20†	0.51
105	Rh^{105}	0.07†	
106	Ru^{106}	0.058†	0.53
109	Pd^{109}	0.053†	
111	Ag^{111}	0.052	0.63
112	Pd^{112}	0.065†	
115	Cd^{115}	0.072	0.76
115	Cd^{115m}	0.003	
115	Cd^{115} + Cd^{115m} (total chain)	0.075	
117	Cd^{117}	....	0.37
131	I^{131}	1.2	2.3
132	Te^{132}	2.4	1.8
136	Cs^{136}	0.0017*	
137	Cs^{137}	6.6†	
139	Ba^{139}	....	9.0
140	Ba^{140}	6.2	
144	Ce^{144}	7.1	7.2

* Assumed value for relative yields in the given reference.

† Obtained in comparison-type experiments. Yields depend directly on the assumption that corresponding yields in slow-neutron fission of U^{235} are correct (NNES, div. IV, vol. 9, Appendix B).

TABLE 8j-4. FAST-NEUTRON FISSION YIELDS: U^{238} AND Pu^{239}

Mass No.	Nuclide	U^{238} est. avg neutron energy 2.8 Mev (K3)	Pu^{239} fission energy (pile) neutrons NNES
77	Ge^{77}		
77	As^{77}	0.0036	
89	Sr^{89}	2.7	
95	Zr^{95}	4.7	5.6 (219)
97	Zr^{97}	......	5.2 (219)
99	Mo^{99}	6.4	5.9 (219)
103	Ru^{103}	6.3	
106	Ru^{106}	2.9	
109	Pd^{109}	......	1.7 (219)
111	Ag^{111}	0.064	
115	Cd^{115m}	0.0025	
115	Cd^{115}	0.032	
115	Total chain	0.035	
127	Sb^{127}	0.13	
132	Te^{132}	4.7	
137	Cs^{137}	7.1	
139	Ba^{139}		
140	Ba^{140}	5.7*	5.0 (219)
144	Ce^{144}	4.9	
153	Sm^{153}	....	0.48 (219)
156	Eu^{156}	0.073	

* Assumed value for relative yields in the given reference.

TABLE 8j-5. FAST-NEUTRON FISSION YIELDS: 14-MEV NEUTRONS U^{235}

Mass No.	Nuclide	U^{235} 14-Mev neutrons	U^{235} thermal neutrons*
82	Br^{82}	i: 1.27×10^{-3} (F3)	i: 3.5×10^{-5} (62)
83	Br^{83}	1.02 (F4)	0.48 (A1)
89	Sr^{89}	4.2 (S9)	4.6 (76)
91	Sr^{91}	4.2 (S9)	5.0 (73)
97	Zr^{97}	5.5 (S9)	6.2 (S3)
103	Ru^{103}	3.3 (F4)	2.85 (H2)
105	Rh^{105}	1.95 (S9)	0.92†
106	Ru^{106}	1.56 (F4)	0.38 (H2)
109	Pd^{109}	1.21 (F4)	0.028 (217)
111	Ag^{111}	1.16 (S9)	0.018 (123, 217, E1)
112	Pd^{112}	1.44 (F4)	0.018 (E1)
115	Cd^{115}	0.94 (S9)	0.011 (127)
121	Sn^{121}	1.14 (B2)	0.014 (S2, 129)
125	Sn^{125}	1.52 (B2)	0.024†
126	Sb^{126}	1.48 (B2)	0.046†
127	Sb^{127}	1.62 (S9, B2)	0.093 (E1)
129	Sb^{129}	2.10 (F4)	0.92†
130	Sb^{130}	3.3 (F4)	1.75†
131	I^{131}	4.1 (B2, W4)	3.0 (P2)
132	Te^{132}	4.3 (W4)	4.5 (P2)
136	Cs^{136}	i: 0.24 (F3)	i: 6.2×10^{-3} (G1)
140	Ba^{140}	4.6 (S9)	6.32 (206 corrected)
143	Ce^{143}	3.5 (S9)	5.4 (176)
144	Ce^{144}	2.4 (F4)	4.1 (mean of 184) (G2)
156	Eu^{156}	0.054 (F4)	0.014 (217, E1)

* The 14-Mev neutron data were quoted in ref. F4 as R values, which were converted to fission yields by multiplying by the respective thermal-neutron fission yields. The thermal-neutron values selected for the calculations are tabulated here for reference.

† Values taken from a smooth curve drawn through the known thermal-neutron fission-yield curve for U^{235}.

TABLE 8j-6. CHARGED-PARTICLE FISSION YIELDS

Mass No.	Th^{232} (T5) 6.7-Mev protons	8.0-Mev protons	9.3-Mev protons	13.3-Mev protons	17.8-Mev protons	19.5-Mev protons	21.1-Mev protons
77	....	0.020	0.034	0.032	0.030	....	0.052
78	....	0.061	0.060	0.047	0.036	....	0.064
82	....	.....	.....	0.010 (max)	0.0062	....	0.0057
83	....	1.67	1.51	1.65	1.51	....	1.64
84	....	2.90	2.53	2.44	2.66	....	2.49
89	6.55	6.00	6.24	5.25	5.31	5.01	5.07
91	....	5.48	5.15	4.58	4.57	....	4.61
95	5.93	6.05	5.29	4.93	4.57	5.14	4.27
97	3.97	4.08	4.07	4.36	4.08	4.32	3.63
115	0.51	0.69	0.73	1.22	1.75	1.66	1.74
131	....	2.40	2.24	2.27	2.45	....	2.38
132	....	3.03	3.56	3.48	2.38	....	3.02
139	....	5.95	4.75	4.72	4.63	....	4.96
140	2.49	4.74	4.90	4.61	4.67	4.71	4.51
156	....	0.55	0.037	0.029	0.024	....	0.023

Mass No.	Nuclide	Th^{232} 37.5-Mev alpha particles (N3)	Bi^{209} 400-Mev alpha particles (P3) relative yields	Bi^{209} 190-Mev deuterons (G4)
45	Ca^{45}	....	....	0.002
59	Fe^{59}	....	....	0.5
65	Ni^{65}	....	....	0.8
66	Ni^{66}	....	....	0.11
67	Cu^{67}	....	....	0.40
72	Zn^{72}	<0.01	....	*i*: 0.35
72	Ga^{72}	....	22	*i*: 0.51
72	Total chain	....	....	0.86
73	Ga^{73}	....	....	0.55
74	As^{74}	....	....	0.06
77	As^{77}	~0.0037	....	1.5
81	Se^{81m}	....	....	0.41
82	Br^{82}	<0.0025	150	*i*: 1.0
83	Br^{83}	0.70	390	1.7
84	Rb^{84}	....	....	0.3
86	Rb^{86}	....	....	*i*: 1.9
89	Sr^{89}	3.7	....	4.7
90	Sr^{90}	2.9	....	*i*: 2.9
90	Y^{90}	....	1,400	*i*: 1.6
90	Total chain	....	....	4.5
91	Sr^{91}	2.8	540	
91	Y^{91}	....	....	4.4

TABLE 8j-6. CHARGED-PARTICLE FISSION YIELDS (*Continued*)

Mass No.	Nuclide	Th^{232} 37.5-Mev alpha particles (N3)	Bi^{209} 400-Mev alpha particles (P3) relative yields	Bi^{209} 190-Mev deuterons (G4)
92	Sr^{92}	3.0		2.8
93	Y^{93}			
95	Zr^{95}	2.5	....	*i*: 3.4
95	Nb^{95}	....	....	*i*: 1.5
95	Total chain	....	....	4.9
97	Zr^{97}	2.7		
99	Mo^{99}	2.4	480	5.0
103	Ru^{103}	....	....	3.9
105	Au^{105}	....	240	3.1
106	Au^{106}	3.0	....	1.5
109	Pd^{109}	....	....	4.6
111	Ag^{111}	1.8	....	3.4
112	Pd^{112}	1.1	....	0.9
112	As^{112}	....	....	*i*: 2.8
112	Total chain	....	....	3.7
115	Cd^{115}	1.8	....	1.0
115	Cd^{115m}	0.15	....	0.7
115	Total chain	....	....	0.7
118	Te^{118}	....	....	0.008
119	Te^{119}	....	....	0.14
120	Sb^{120}	....	....	0.90
121	Sn^{121}	1.2		
121	Te^{121m}	....	....	0.20
122	Sb^{122}	....	....	*i*: 0.25
[123]	Sn^{123} (75 *d*)	1.0		
123	Sn^{123} (130 *d*)	1.0		
124	I^{124}	....	....	*i*: 0.43
124	Sb^{124}	....	....	*i*: 0.12
124	Total chain	....	....	0.55
125	Sb^{125}	1.2		
125	I^{125}	....	....	1.2
126	I^{126}	....	....	0.11
131	I^{131}	1.1	8	
131	Cs^{131}	....	....	*i*: 0.002
131	Ba^{131}	....	....	*i*: 0.18
131	Total chain	....	....	0.18
132	Te^{132}	1.6	....	*i*: 0.056
132	Cs^{132}			
133	Ba^{133}	....	34	0.25
136	Cs^{136}	0.041		
137	Cs^{137}	6.9		
139	Ce^{139}	....	....	0.12
140	Ba^{140}	2.8	None detectable	0.0004
141	Ce^{141}	....	....	0.017
143	Ce^{143}	2.2		

TABLE 8j-6. CHARGED-PARTICLE FISSION YIELDS (*Continued*)

Mass No.	Nuclide	Th^{232} 37.5-Mev alpha particles (N3)	Bi^{209} 400-Mev alpha particles (P3) relative yields	Bi^{209} 190-Mev deuterons (G4)
144	Ce^{144}	2.2		
149	Eu^{149}	....	....	0.003
153	Sm^{153}	0.84		
155	Eu^{155}	0.033		
156	Eu^{156}	0.047		
157	Eu^{157}	0.041		

Mass No.	Nuclide	U^{235} 15-Mev deuterons (W5) (yields relative to Ba^{140})	U^{238} 15-Mev deuterons (W5) (yields relative to Ba^{140})
99	Mo^{99}	1.42	1.27
101	Mo^{101}	1.27	1.30
102	Mo^{102}	0.86	1.06
103	Ru^{103}	0.44	0.22
105	Ru^{105}	0.90	1.16
106	Ru^{106}	0.60	0.30
140	Ba^{140}	1.00	1.00

Table 8j-7. Photofission Yields*

Mass No.	Nuclide	Bi^{209} max 85 Mev (S6)	Th^{232} max 69 Mev (H1) Brems-strahlung	U^{238} max 13.0 Mev (W5) Bremsstrahlung	U^{238} 7 Mev (S11) (6.8 ± 0.1)
77	Ge^{77}	~0.3			
77	As^{77}	<0.4			
82	Br^{82}	<0.5			
83	Br^{83}	1.2	1.9		
84	Br^{84}	<1.4			
91	Sr^{91}	2.8†	5.7		
92	Sr^{92}	2.8†			
97	Zr^{97}	3.0			
99	Mo^{99}	.....	1.85	6.8	6.6‡
101	Mo^{101}	.....	....	6.5	
102	Mo^{102}	.....	....	5.0	
103	Ru^{103}	.....	....	(1.4) (uncertain)	
105	Ru^{105}	5.0‡	0.83	3.15	
109	Pd^{109}	~6.4			
111	Ag^{111}	~2.8	0.90	....	0.046
112	Ag^{112}	.....	0.68	....	0.031
113	Ag^{113}	3.0	0.58		
117	Cd^{117}	.....	0.68		
131	Te^{131}	.....	0.81		
131	Total chain	.....	2.25		
134	I^{134}	<0.2			
139	Ba^{139}	<0.1			
140	Ba^{140}	.....	6.6	5.77‡	5.8
143	Ce^{143}	.....	4.85		

See page 8-224 for footnotes.

TABLE 8j-7. PHOTOFISSION YIELDS (*Continued*)

Mass No.	Nuclide	U^{238} max 10 Mev (R2) Brems-strahlung	U^{238} 10 Mev (S11) (9.7 ± 0.1)	U^{238} max 16 Mev (R2) Brems-strahlung	U^{238} 16 Mev (S11) (15.5 ± 0.1)	U^{238} max ~17 Mev (L1)
83	Br^{83}	0.300	.....	0.288		
84	Br^{84}	0.411	.....	0.511		
89	Sr^{89}	......	.....	3.67		
91	Sr^{91}	4.44	.....	4.22	......	4.7
92	Sr^{92}	......	.....	3.46	......	3.7
93	Y^{93}	......	.....	5.29	......	4.9
97	Zr^{97}	5.11	.....	6.31		
99	Mo^{99}	4.94	6.6‡	6.06	6.6‡	
103	Ru^{103}	......	.....	......	......	~3.5
105	Ru^{105}	......	.....	3.61	......	1.9
109	Pd^{109}	0.0854	.....	0.224	......	0.22
111	Ag^{111}	......	0.065	......	0.30	
112	Pd^{112}	0.042	.....	0.110	......	0.14
112	Ag^{112}	......	0.047	......	0.16	
113	Ag^{113}	......	.....	0.0627	......	0.051
115	Ag^{115}	......	.....	......	0.0522	0.066
115	Cd^{115}	......	0.030	......	0.16	
115	Cd^{115m}	......	.....	......	0.013	
117	Cd^{117}	......	0.027	......		
131	I^{131}	3.76	.....	4.43	......	1.8
132	Te^{132}	5.58	.....	5.78		
133	I^{133}	6.80	.....	7.06	......	6.6
139	Ba^{139}	5.87§	.....	5.97‡	......	6.00‡
140	Ba^{140}	5.77	5.7	5.77	5.0	5.60
143	Ce^{143}	5.94	.....	5.32	......	5.2

See page 8-224 for footnotes.

TABLE 8j-7. PHOTOFISSION YIELDS (*Continued*)

Mass No.	Nuclide	U^{238} 21 Mev (S11)	U^{238} 48 Mev (S11)	U^{238} 100 Mev (S11)	U^{238} 300 Mev (S11)
77	Ge^{77}	....	0.032		
78	Ge^{78}	....	0.059		
83	Br^{83}	....	0.59	0.62	0.73
84	Br^{84}	....	1.03	1.04	1.09
89	Sr^{89}	2.6	2.8	2.8	3.0
91	Sr^{91}	....	3.9		
97	Zr^{97}	5.7	5.8	5.8	
99	Mo^{99}	6.6‡	6.6	6.6‡	6.6‡
103	Ru^{103}	3.0	2.9	3.2	3.4
105	Ru^{105}	....	2.5		
106	Ru^{106}	2.1	2.0	2.6	3.0
111	Ag^{111}	0.43	0.77	1.02	1.88
112	Ag^{112}	0.26	0.52	0.71	1.14
113	Ag^{113}	....	0.60	0.77	1.21
115	Cd^{115}	0.25	0.047	0.67	1.15
115	Cd^{115m}	0.18	0.041	0.048	0.20
117	Cd^{117}	....	0.50	0.69	1.04
127	Sb^{127} (corrected)	1.12	1.49	1.71	2.38
131	I^{131}	4.1	4.3	4.4	4.6
132	I^{132}	5.0	4.9	4.6	4.3
133	I^{133}	....	6.2		
137	Cs^{137}	....	4.7		
139	Ba^{139}	....	4.6		
140	Ba^{140}	4.9	5.0	5.3	4.8
141	Ce^{141}	....	4.9		
143	Ce^{143}	4.0	3.8	3.8	3.6
144	Ce^{144}	3.8	3.4		

* For such element heading a column the yields due to photofission by the indicated gamma radiation are shown opposite the mass numbers in the first column.

† Yields of 9.7-hr Sr^{91} and 2.7-hr Sr^{91} assumed equal for analysis of complex-decay curve.

‡ Assumed value for relative yields in the given reference.

§ Reference value to give integral of the yield-mass curve of 200%.

TABLE 8j-8. SPONTANEOUS FISSION YIELDS

Mass No.	Nuclide	Th^{232} (monazite) (W2)	U^{238} (W2)	Cm^{242} (S7)	
				Yield of nuclide	Total chain yield
83	Kr^{83}	0.036	0.036		
84	Kr^{84}	0.180	0.119		
86	Kr^{86}	0.87	0.75		
91	Sr^{91}	.....	....	0.94	0.95
92	Sr^{92}	.....	....	1.1	1.2
99	Mo^{99}	.....	....	5.7	5.7
103	Ru^{103}	.....	....	7.2	7.2
105	Ru^{105}	.....	....	9.5	9.9
106	Ru^{106}	.....	....	7.4	8.4
109	Pd^{109}	.....	....	2.9	2.9
112	Pd^{112}	.....	....	0.95	1.1
115	Cd^{115}	.....	....	0.033	
115	Cd^{115m}	.....	....	0.003*	0.036
117	Cd^{117m}	.....	....	<0.01	<0.01
127	Sb^{127}	.....	....	0.35	0.37
129	Sb^{129}	.....	....	1.3	1.7
129	Xe^{129}	0	<0.012		
131	Te^{131m}	.....	....	2.3	
131	I^{131}	.....	....	*i*: 2.0	
131	Xe^{131}	0.509	0.455		
132	Te^{132}	.....	....	5.8	7.4
132	Xe^{132}	3.63	3.57		
133	I^{133}	.....	....	5.7	6.0
134	I^{134}	.....	....	6.9	8.0
134	Xe^{134}	5.12	4.99		
135	I^{135}	.....	....	3.9	7.3
136	Xe^{136}	6.00†	6.00†		
136	Cs^{136}	.....	....	0.80	
139	Ba^{139}	.....	....	6.6	6.6
140	Ba^{140}	.....	....	5.9	5.9

* Assumed yield from known branching ratio in induced fission.
† Assumed value for relative yields in the given reference.

References for Tables 8j-2 to 8j-8[1]

A1. Arnold, J. R., and N. Sugarman: *J. Chem. Phys.* **15,** 703 (1947) (NNES).
B1. Brown, F., and L. Yaffe: *Can. J. Chem.* **31,** 242 (1953).
B2. Barnes, J. W., and A. J. Freedman: *Phys. Rev.* **84,** 356 (1951).
E1. Engelkemeir, D., M. S. Freedman, E. P. Steinberg, J. A. Seiler, and L. Winsberg: ANL-4927 (1952).
F1. Ford, G. P., and C. W. Stanley: AECD-3551 (1953).
F2. Fleming, W. H., and H. G. Thode: *Phys. Rev.* **92,** 378 (1953).
F3. Ford, G. P.: AECD-3597.
F4. Ford, G. P.: unpublished data, private communication, 1954.
F5. Freiling, E. C., L. R. Bunney, and N. E. Ballou: *Phys. Rev.* **96,** 102 (1954).
G1. Glendenin, L. E., PhD Thesis, MIT, Aug. 1, 1949 (NNES).
G2. Grummitt, W. E., and G. Wilkinson: *Nature,* **161,** 520 (1948) (NNES).

[1] References given without letter designation refer to papers in "Radiochemical Studies: The Fission Products," NNES, div. IV, vol. 9.

G3. Grummitt, W. E., J. Gueron, G. Wilkinson, and L. Yaffe: *Can. J. Research* **25B**, 364 (1947) (NNES).
G4. Goeckermann, R. E., and I. Perlman: *Phys. Rev.* **76**, 628 (1949).
H1. Hiller, D. M., and D. S. Martin, Jr.: *Phys. Rev.* **90**, 581 (1953).
H2. Hardwick, W. H.: *Phys. Rev.* **92**, 1072 (1953).
I1. Inghram, M. G., D. C. Hess, Jr., and J. H. Reynolds: *Phys. Rev.* **76**, 1717 (1949) (NNES).
I2. Inghram, M. G., R. J. Hayden, and D. C. Hess, Jr.: *Phys. Rev.* **79**, 271 (1950) (NNES).
K1. Koch, J., O. Kofoed-Hansen, P. Kristensen, and W. Drost-Hansen: *Phys. Rev.* **76**, 279 (1949) (NNES).
K2. Katcoff, S., and W. Rubinson: *Phys. Rev.* **91**, 1458 (1953).
K3. Keller, R. N., E. P. Steinberg, and L. E. Glendenin: *Phys. Rev.* **94**, 969 (1954).
L1. Laboratory for Nuclear Science and Engineering, MIT, Progress Report, June 1, 1951–May 31, 1952, p. 129.
M1. MacNamara, J., C. B. Collins, and H. G. Thode: *Phys. Rev.* **78**, 129 (1950) (NNES).
M2. MacNamara, J., and H. G. Thode: *Phys. Rev.* **80**, 471 (1950).
N1. Niday, J., and A. Turkevich: AECD-2862 (1950) (NNES).
N2. Nagle, D., and J. R. Zacharias: private communication to authors of NNES; see also ref. G2 (NNES).
N3. Newton, A. S.: *Phys. Rev.* **75**, 17 (1949).
P1. Pappas, A. C., and C. D. Coryell: Laboratory for Nuclear Science and Engineering, MIT, July 1, 1950 (NNES).
P2. Pappas, A. C., and C. D. Coryell: *Phys. Rev.* **81**, 329 (1951).
P3. Perlman, I., R. H. Goeckermann, D. H. Templeton, and J. J. Howland: *Phys. Rev.* **72**, 352 (1947).
R1. Ross, A. M., BS Thesis, MIT; see also C. D. Coryell et al., *Phys. Rev.* **77**, 755 (1950) (NNES).
R2. Richter, H. G., and C. D. Coryell: *Phys. Rev.* **95**, 1550 (1954).
S1. Steinberg, E. P., J. A. Seiler, A. Goldstein, and A. Dudley: MDDC-1632, 1948 (NNES).
S2. Steinberg, E. P.: private communication to authors of NNES, 1950 (NNES).
S3. Sakakura, A. Y.: BS Thesis, MIT, June 1, 1949; see also Coryell et al., *Phys. Rev.* **77**, 755 (1950) (NNES).
S4. Stanley, C. W., and S. Katcoff: *J. Chem. Phys.* **17**, 653 (1949) (NNES).
S5. Sugarman, N.: *Phys. Rev.* **89**, 750 (1953).
S6. Sugarman, N.: *Phys. Rev.* **79**, 532 (1950).
S7. Steinberg, E. P., and L. E. Glendenin: *Phys. Rev.* **95**, 431 (1954).
S8. Steinberg, E. P.: private communication, 1954.
S9. Spence, R. W.: BNL-C-9, as quoted in ref. F4.
S10. Scott, Terrell, Gilmore, and Minkkinen: LADC-1463 quoted in ref. F4.
S11. Schmitt, R. A., and N. Sugarman: *Phys. Rev.* **95**, 1260 (1954).
T1. Thode, H. G., and R. B. Shields: *Repts. Progr. in Phys.* **12**, 18 (1949) (NNES).
T2. Thode: H. G.: private communication to authors of NNES, 1949 (NNES).
T3. Turkevich, A., and J. B. Niday: *Phys. Rev.* **84**, 52 (1951).
T4. Turkevich, A., J. B. Niday, and A. Tompkins: *Phys. Rev.* **89**, 552 (1953).
T5. Tewes, H. A., and R. A. James: *Phys. Rev.* **88**, 860 (1952).
W1. Wahl, A. C., and N. A. Bonner: *Phys. Rev.* **85**, 570 (1952).
W2. Wetherill, G. W.: *Phys. Rev.* **92**, 907 (1953).
W3. Wiles, D. R., B. W. Smith, R. Horsley, and H. G. Thode: *Can. J. Phys.* **31**, 419 (1953).
W4. Wahl, A. C.: unpublished data, quoted in ref. F4.
W5. Wiles, D. R., and C. D. Coryell: *Phys. Rev.* **96**, 696 (1954).
Y1. Yaffe, L., and C. E. MacKintosh: *Can. J. Research* **25B**, 371 (1947) (NNES).

8k. Nuclear Reactors

H. S. ISBIN

University of Minnesota

A nuclear reactor is an assembly of fuel, moderator, and other components such as control rods, coolant system, shielding, and instrumentation, capable of sustaining a controlled neutron chain reaction. Smaller subcritical assemblies used to predict critical dimensions, called exponential piles, and those used to measure diffusion lengths, called sigma piles, are not reactors. Nuclear reactors can be classified as shown in Table 8k-1.

TABLE 8k-1. CLASSIFICATION OF NUCLEAR REACTORS

1. Based upon purpose
   a. Research, including limited isotope production
   b. Plutonium and tritium production
   c. Power, both military and industrial
   d. Breeding
2. Based upon nature of assembly
   a. For continuation of neutron chain reaction, neutron energies are thermal, intermediate, or fast
   b. Fuel-moderator assemblies are homogeneous or heterogeneous
   c. Fuel may be natural uranium (containing 0.7 per cent U^{235}), enriched uranium (containing additional U^{235}), U^{235}, U^{233}, or Pu^{239}
   d. Moderators used are graphite, heavy water, light water, beryllium, and beryllium oxide

The present security status for nuclear reactors, as applied to the United States, United Kingdom, and Canada, is that almost all information on low-power research reactors is available; information is partially available for higher-power research reactors; but only limited descriptions can be given for reactors having military and strategic value. A concise tabulation of nuclear-reactor descriptions is presented in Table 8k-2. Power levels given pertain to the rate at which heat is generated in the reactor and are not to be interpreted as the generation of electrical power. Neutron flux, as neutrons/cm²-sec, is given in general for the thermal flux, usually the maximum value. The starting date of operation is given in parentheses under the heading of Remarks.

In addition to the reactors listed, several boiling reactor experiments (Borox I, II, and Prototype Boiling-water Power Reactor) have been carried out at Arco, Idaho. Five Savannah River Reactors, CP-6, were completed by 1955 at Aitkin, South Carolina. These reactors employ natural uranium fuel and heavy-water moderator and are production reactors. Interest in additional research and testing reactors in the United States is chiefly confined to modifications of the water-boiler, swimming-pool, and MTR reactors. An expanded program is under way for mobile reactor

TABLE 8k-2. NUCLEAR REACTOR CATALOGUE

Name	Classification	Fuel	Fuel core	Reflector	Shielding	Over-all size	Control	Coolant	Remarks
CP-1, uranium-graphite pile (West Stands, Chicago)	Thermal, heterogeneous, graphite, research, 200 watts	Uranium	....	....	....	....	....	....	World's first reactor. Operated Dec. 2, 1942. After initial operation was dismantled to form basis for CP-2
CP-2 (Palos Park, Chicago)	Thermal, heterogeneous, graphite, research, 200 watts	3,200 uranium metal lumps, 2¼ in. diam; 14,500 uranium oxide lumps, 2¼ in. diam; about 50 tons uranium; lumps spaced on 8¼-in. square lattice	About a 19-ft cube	12 in. graphite	5-ft concrete walls; 6 in. lead and 4 ft wood on top	30 ft wide, 32 ft long, 25 ft high; 472 tons graphite; 1,400 tons total	Bronze strips covered with Cd. 1 regulating, 1 shim, and 3 safety	None	Operations started Mar. 20, 1943. In service until May, 1954
GLEEP, graphite low-energy experimental pile (Harwell, England)	Thermal, heterogeneous, graphite, research, 100 kw, 3.7×10^{10}	13 tons of uranium bars, 0.97 in. diam, 12 in. long, sprayed with 0.003 in. Al; 26 tons of uranium oxide in Al cans 1.6 in. diam, 12 in. long; line lattice with 7¼-in. pitch	Cylindrical core 5.24 m long, 3.05 m radius; metal in central portions up to 1.9 m radius	Graphite in shape of an octagon	Cubical concrete shield with walls about 5 ft thick	37-ft cube containing 505 tons graphite	Rods containing Cd. 4 coarse control, 1 fine control, and 6 safety	Air, at least 5,000 ft³/min at subatmospheric pressure; max uranium cartridge temp., 60°C	Temp. coef. = -2.9×10^{-5}/°C Press. coef. = -6.5×10^{-6}/mb $k_{ex} = 0.002$ (1947)
Oak Ridge (Oak Ridge National Laboratory, Oak Ridge, Tenn.)	Thermal, heterogeneous, graphite, research, 1,000 kw, 10^{12}	Al-jacketed uranium slugs, 1.1 in. diam, 4 in. long, 2.57 lb per slug; 39–54 slugs per channel; 1,248 fuel channels on 8-in. rectangular lattice; diamond-shaped channel, 1¾ in. square	24-ft cube, including reflector	Graphite	Concrete, 7 ft thick	47 ft long, 38 ft wide, 32 ft high	2 control rods, each equivalent to $0.005k$; 2 shim rods, each $0.007k$; 4 safety rods, each $0.003k$	Air, 120,000 ft³/min drawn through reactor; fuel below 270°C; avg moderator temp. 135°C	Used for isotope production. 1,000 kw is design power, operation has reached 3,800 kw (1943)

TABLE 8k-2. NUCLEAR REACTOR CATALOGUE (*Continued*)

Name	Classification	Fuel	Fuel core	Reflector	Shielding	Over-all size	Control	Coolant	Remarks
Brookhaven (Brookhaven National Laboratory, Upton, N.Y.)	Thermal, heterogeneous, graphite, research, 30 mw, 4×10^{12}	Al-clad uranium metal rods placed on 8-in. centers, 33 uranium fuel slugs, each 1.1 in. diam and 4 in. long, placed in 11-ft-long Al can with 6 longitudinal fins 0.6 in. high centers; 1,369 fuel channels, circular cross section of 36 cm²	Graphite moderator in two right rectangular prisms 12½ by 25 by 25 ft, separated by vertical openings for cooling air	45 ft graphite	6-in. iron plate, 4¼ ft heavy concrete, 3 in. iron plate	38 by 55 ft by 30 ft high; 20,000 tons, including foundation	Horizontal rods containing 1¾% boron. Rods enter from two adjacent corners in two arrays of 8 rods each	Air, 300,000 ft³/min at subatmospheric pressure. Each half of moderator complex cooled separately	Plan to replace fuel with bent MTR-type plates (1950)
BEPO, British experimental pile (Harwell, England)	Thermal, heterogeneous, graphite, research, 4 mw, 10^{12} (increased to 6 mw)	0.9-in.-diam, 12-in.-long uranium bars, encased in Al; 26 tons for criticality, 40 tons for full load, central 888 channels used; 20 bars per channel, 7¼ in. between channels	Right cylinder, 10 ft radius, 20 ft long	About 3 ft of graphite	6-in. cast-iron plate, and 6½-ft concrete on sides and 7½ ft on top; 600 tons steel, 3,000 tons concrete	About a 40-ft cube	4 horizontal and 10 vertical boron carbide filled hollow steel rods, 2 in. diam	Air; single pass, 180,000 ft³/min, cross section of each empty channel is 3½ in.²	Max surface temp. 250°C, A hot-water system to recover heat is being installed (1948)
Hanford (Hanford, Wash.)	Thermal, heterogeneous, graphite, Pu production	Uranium fuel slugs 1,359 in. diam, up to 8 in. long, bonded in 25 Al can, 1.440 in. OD with Al end caps	....	....	....	....	....	Water, 0.086 in. coolant annulus	Power information is classified. Three units in operation in 1945, and additional reactors have been built. Secondary recirculating glycol system furnishes heat to buildings

TABLE 8k-2. NUCLEAR REACTOR CATALOGUE (*Continued*)

Name	Classification	Fuel	Fuel core	Reflector	Shielding	Over-all size	Control	Coolant	Remarks
Windscale (Sellafield, England)	Pu production	....	....	....	....	....	24 boron steel rods (horizontal); 16 vertical rods for shut-down	....	Two reactors are reported in operation (1950, 1951)
CP-3 (Argonne National Laboratory, Chicago). Reactor replaced by CP-5	Thermal, heterogeneous, heavy water, research, 300 kw, 10^{12}	120 uranium metal rods 1.1 in. diam, 6 ft long; 3 tons of metal; square lattice, $5\frac{3}{8}$ in. center line to center line	$6\frac{1}{2}$ tons of heavy water moderator in a 72-in.-diam 105-in.-high Al tank	2 ft of graphite	4 in. Pb-Cd, and 8-ft octagonal concrete wall 13 ft high; top shield contains Cd, 1 ft lead, and 4 ft wood and steel	Octagonal 26 ft across, 14 ft high	Rods containing Cd metal; 2 control, 3 shim, and 2 safety	200 gpm heavy water	World's first heavy water reactor, May 15, 1944. Helium is circulated through reactor to sweep out dissociated heavy water, and to prevent influx of air containing ordinary water. Improved version CP-3′ contains enriched uranium alloyed with Al
ZEEP (Chalk River, Canada)	Thermal, heterogeneous, heavy water, research, 10 watts, 10^8	Uranium metal in form of slugs 1.285 in. diam and 6 in. long jacketed with Al "stockings" 1.295 in. ID 0.040 in wall and 9 ft $6\frac{3}{4}$ in. long, holding 9 slugs. Total of 148 rods, square lattice spacing of 6 in.	10 tons of heavy water in steel tank, $6\frac{3}{4}$ ft diam, $8\frac{1}{2}$ ft high	Graphite $2\frac{1}{2}$ ft under tank 3 ft around	Water tanks, 3 ft thick	About 25 ft by 15 ft high	4 plates, 8 rods, cadmium-coated stainless steel	None	Max power is 30 watts. Migration area 237 cm^2, slowing down length $\sqrt{118.5}$ cm, mean life of neutron 0.86×10^{-3} sec, buckling factor 794×10^{-6} cm^2 (1945)

TABLE 8k-2. NUCLEAR REACTOR CATALOGUE (*Continued*)

Name	Classification	Fuel	Fuel core	Reflector	Shielding	Over-all size	Control	Coolant	Remarks
ZOE (Chatillon, France)	Thermal, heterogeneous, heavy water, research, 5 kw, $2\text{–}3 \times 10^{10}$	UO_2 in tablets 3 cm high stacked in Al tubes of 66 mm ID, and 180 cm effective height. Effective density of oxide is 8.3	Heavy-water moderator (at $40 \pm 6°C$) contained in cylindrical Al vat, 181 cm ID, 235.5 cm high. Max number of fuel bars is 69 (3.55 tons UO_2), set hexagonally (sides of hexagon 18.6 cm)	Graphite blocks (diffusion length, 45 cm). 15 mm of heavy water at bottom	Concrete walls 150 cm thick	About a 500 cm cube	Two sets of two types of Cd safety rods. Cd regulating bars	External recirculation system provided for by heavy water	Laplacian = 5.8 m^{-2}. Power increased to 150 kw. Oxide fuel replaced by uranium metal rods 36.5 mm diam (1948)
Heavy Water Research Reactor (USSR)	Thermal, heterogenous, heavy water, research, 500 kw	Uranium fuel rods, 2.2- and 2.8-cm diam, with a 0.1-cm Al envelope; square lattice spacings from 63 to 162.6 cm; 86 to 292 rods, about 160 cm long	Heavy water contained in 175 cm diam tank; critical level from 120 to 181.6 cm	100-cm-thick graphite reflector on sides and bottom	Concrete side shield 2.5 m thick	About 9 m diam by 8 m high	4 Cd control rods	Heavy water circulated	Helium atmosphere above heavy water (1949)
JEEP (Kjeller, Norway)	Thermal, heterogeneous, heavy water, research, 300 kw, 10^{12}	2,200-kg uranium slugs in Al tubes; 35.5 kg/rod; rods 25.4 mm diam, 300 mm long, placed on 180-mm centers	1.9 m long; 7 tons of heavy water moderator in 2-m-diam tank	Graphite 700 mm thick	Octagonal concrete shield, 2 m thick on sides	About $7\frac{1}{2}$ by $7\frac{1}{2}$ m by 5 m high	4 cadmium plates 1,300 mm long, 350 mm wide, 1.7 mm thick, held between Al plates	4 liters of heavy water per sec (inlet 20°C, outlet 40°C)	Mean life of neutron 2×10^{-3} sec (1951)
NRX (Chalk River, Canada)	Thermal, heterogeneous, heavy water, research, 30 mw, 6.8×10^{13}	176 uranium rods, 1.36 in. diam, Al clad, surrounded by two concentric Al tubes	Heavy-water moderator contained in cylindrical vessel, $10\frac{1}{2}$ ft high, $8\frac{3}{4}$ ft diam	Graphite	8 ft concrete cast iron thermal shield	34 ft diam, 34 ft high	Varying D_2O level, cadmium and boron rods	Water flows downward in inner annulus	(1947) Shutdown Dec. 1952. Rebuilt reactor (Feb. 1954) up to 40 mw

TABLE 8k-2. NUCLEAR REACTOR CATALOGUE (*Continued*)

Name	Classification	Fuel	Fuel core	Reflector	Shielding	Over-all size	Control	Coolant	Remarks
P-2 (Saclay, France)	Thermal, heterogeneous, heavy water, research, 1,500 kw, 7×10^{12} (max)	136 U rods, 1.1 in. diam, 7 ft long, triangular lattice with rod spacing of 5.93 in. Fuel element consists of 4 concentric Al cylinders with innermost as protective sheath for U rod. Insulating space between 2d and 3d cylinders	Fuel immersed in Al tank 8 ft high and about 6 ft diam, partly filled with D_2O	Graphite 3 ft thick outside tank on sides and bottom	Cast-iron thermal shield, about 8 in. thick; concrete shield about 7 ft thick	About an 8-m cube	Cd plates moving between tank and reflector, 2 Cd rods in tank	Recirculation of nitrogen at 10 atm. Flows down space between 2 outer Al cylinders and up space between 1st and 2d cylinders. N_2 replaced by CO_2	400 kw per ton of U. With heavy-water level 1,794 mm, critical height = 224 cm, critical radius = 132 cm $M^2 = 238\ cm^2$ $B^2 = 5.3(10)^{-4}\ cm^2$ (1952)
CP-5 Argonne Research Reactor (Argonne National Laboratory, Lemont, Ill.)	Thermal, heterogeneous, heavy water, research, 1,000 kw, 3×10^{13}	3 in. sq fuel element assembly contains 12 Al plates, each about 3 by 24 by 0.060 in. Al-U alloy is sandwiched between 2S Al sheets, and plates are clad with 72S Al. Each fuel assembly contains about 75 g U^{235}. About 1.7 kg U^{235} required	About 16 fuel assemblies are grouped to form a lattice of approx 300 liters (equivalent to a sphere of 40 cm radius). Heavy-water moderator and fuel lattice contained in a 183 cm diam right cylindrical tank	2 ft heavy water and 2 ft graphite outer reflector	¼ in. boral, ½ in. steel, 3½ in. lead, 4 ft 8 in. limonite-iron concrete	Octagonal, 20 ft across and 13½ ft high	Similar to CP-3 with additional vertical rods	Heavy water coolant velocity in central sections about 1 m/sec. Heat flux about 4×6 cal/cm²-sec. Flow up through fuel assemblies and down in tank. About 1,200 gpm with 5°C rise	Negative temp. coef., decrease in relativity of 1% for each 20°C rise. Reactor housed in an almost leakproof building (1954)
R-1, First Swedish Research Reactor (Stockholm, Sweden)	Thermal, heterogeneous heavy water, research, 300 kw, 3 by 10 in. (max)	126 uranium rods, 29 mm diam, canned in reflectal (very pure Al alloyed with 0.5 Mg), hexagonal spacing 145 mm	Heavy water contained in 1.85-m diam and 2.54-m-high reflectal tank	900-mm-thick graphite surrounding bottom and sides of tank	Biological shield of poured concrete with iron ore, 1.8 m thick, lined with Cd-Al sandwich	About 7½ by 7½ by 6.8 m	2 security rods (~2% reactivity), 2 regulating plates (~0.6% reactivity)	Heavy water recirculated, 1000 l/min to air-cooled heater exchanger. Air cooling of moderator	Reactor built underground (1954)

TABLE 8k-2. NUCLEAR REACTOR CATALOGUE (*Continued*)

Name	Classification	Fuel	Fuel core	Reflector	Shielding	Over-all size	Control	Coolant	Remarks
LOPO, low-power water boiler (Los Alamos, N.M.)	Thermal, homogeneous, light water, research, $\frac{1}{20}$ watt	Enriched uranium sulfate solution containing 580 g U^{235}, 3,378 g U^{238}, 534 g S, 14,068 g O, 1.573 g H; density at 39°C is 1.348 g/cm³	Uranyl sulfate solution in 15-liter stainless-steel sphere, $\frac{1}{32}$ in. thick, 1 ft diam	3- by 3- by 6-in. bricks of BeO, $\rho = 2.7$; graphite on bottom	None	About 3 ft square by 4 ft high	Cadmium cylinder, $\frac{3}{4}$ in. diam, 34 in. long Cd safety curtain	Water. Max temp. is 39°C	World's first water boiler (1944). Replaced by HYPO
HYPO, high-power water boiler (Los Alamos, N.M.)	Thermal, homogeneous, light water, research, 6 kw, 3×10^{11}	Enriched uranium nitrate solution containing 869.6 g U^{235}, 5,341 g U^{238}, 731 g N, 13,780 g O, 1,312 g H	13.65 liters of $UO_2(NO_3)_2 \cdot 6H_2O$ in H_2O, $\rho = 1.615$, in stainless-steel sphere $\frac{1}{16}$ in. thick, 12 in. diam	24- by 24- by 27-in. BeO surrounded by graphite to form a 60- by 48- by 60-in. rectangular parallelepiped	4 in. lead, $\frac{1}{32}$ in. cadmium, 5 ft concrete	....	Rods containing cadmium, 1 shim, 2 control, 1 safety	50 gal/hr water through 6-turn, $\frac{1}{2}$ in. ID, 157-in.-long coil. Max solution temp. 185°F	Replaced by SUPO. About 50 cm³/sec of air used to sweep out H_2 and O_2 from decomposition of water negative temp. coef. = −1.33 g U^{235}/°C (1944)
SUPO, super-power water boiler (Los Alamos, N.M.)	Thermal, homogeneous, light water, 45 kw, 1.7×10^{12} (max)	Enriched uranium nitrate solution containing 88.7% of U as U^{235}; 777 g of U^{235} for critical mass; 870 g of U^{235} used; solution density 1.10; 12,700 cm³ solution	Solution contained in 12-in.-diam stainless-steel sphere	About a 55-in. cube of graphite	$\frac{1}{2}$-in. of B_4C + paraffin 2-in. steel; 4-in. lead; 5 ft concrete	15 by 15 by 11 ft	2 additional control rods (see HYPO) move into reactor core in reentrant thimbles	Light water circulating through 3 20-ft-long $\frac{1}{4}$-in. OD stainless-steel cooling tubes	Est. max intermediate flux 2.8 $\times 10^{12}$. Est. max fast flux 1.9×10^{12} (1951)
Raleigh (North Carolina State College, Raleigh, N.C.)	Thermal, homogeneous, light water, research, 10 kw, 5×10^{11}	14 liters of light water solution of UO_2SO_4 containing 790 g U^{235} of 90% isotopic enrichment. Density of solution = 1.08 g/cm³	Reactor solution contained in stainless-steel cylinder $\frac{1}{16}$ in. thick 11 in. high 10–$\frac{3}{4}$ in. diam]	20-in. graphite 105 cu ft, 5.4 tons, density = 1.65 g/cm³	6 ft of concrete. Barytes ore as coarse aggregate, and colemanite ore as fine aggregate, density = 3.4 g/cm³, 4 to 6 in. lead around graphite	Octagon, 17 ft across, 12 ft high	2 Control rods (stainless-steel tubes of 2.5 g/cm³ sintered B_4C powder, in reentrant sheaths). 2 shim rods (4 in. wide Cd strips, periphery reactor cylinder).	Light water (refrigerated city water) 1 gpm flow through each of 4 helical coils of $\frac{1}{4}$-in. stainless-steel tubing, 7 ft immersion length (total immersion length 28 ft)	First university reactor (1953). Max reactor solution temp. 80°C

TABLE 8k-2. NUCLEAR REACTOR CATALOGUE (*Continued*)

Name	Classification	Fuel	Fuel core	Reflector	Shielding	Over-all size	Control	Coolant	Remarks
Water Boiler Neutron Source, WBNS (North American Aviation, Inc., Downey, Calif.)	Thermal, homogeneous, light water, research, 1 watt, 5×10^7	1.5 lb of U fuel in form of U^{235} enriched uranyl nitrate in light-water solution	Solution contained in a 1-ft-diam stainless-steel sphere, $\frac{1}{16}$ in. thick	Graphite, 5 ft diam and 6 ft high	2 ft of concrete blocks	....	2 safety rods coarse control fine control all move in reflector	None	Calc $k_\infty = 1.561$ (leakage = 0.360) (1951)
Livermore Water Boiler (Livermore, Calif.)	Thermal, homogeneous, light water, research, 100 watts, 10^9 [increased to 500 watts, 2×10^{10} (max)]	Light water solution of UO_2SO_4 containing 694.2 g U^{235}, 798 g-moles hydrogen, 420 g-moles oxygen; 5.64 g-moles sulfur; and 2.95 g-moles uranium	14.524 liters contained in stainless-steel sphere, $12\frac{1}{2}$-in. OD, 0.06-in. wall	Right cylinder of graphite, 5 ft diam by 5 ft high	Graphite in steel tank, 0.030-in. Cd shot, 5-in. lead, and 3-ft concrete blocks	13 ft by 26 ft by 9 ft high	2 safety and 2 control rods	6-turn helix of $\frac{5}{16}$-in. ID tubing; 160-in. logs in sphere. Distilled water as coolant	Closed gas handling system (1953)
HRE-1, homogeneous reactor experiment (Oak Ridge National Laboratory, Oak Ridge Tenn.)	Thermal, homogeneous, water, research, 1,000 kw	Water solution of enriched uranium sulfate (enrichment >90%), 35 g/kg H_2O	Solution contained in an 18-in. diam 347 stainless-steel sphere with $\frac{3}{16}$-in. walls. Max fuel temp. 482°F. Pressurized to 1,000 psi.	10 in. heavy water	Reflector and core contained in outer pressure vessel of forged steel, 39-in. ID with 3-in. wall; 7-ft concrete ($\rho = 3.5$) walls	....	Large negative temp. coef. leads to self-stabilization 2 safety plates	Heat removed by pumping fuel solution through external heat exchanger	Has operated at full design power and has generated about 150 kw of electric power, temp. coef. = -10^{-3}/°C (1952). Reactor dismantled in 1954. To be replaced by HRE-2
Los Alamos Fast Reactor (Los Alamos, N.M.)	Fast, research 25 kw, 10^{13} fast flux	Rods of pure plutonium metal clad with steel	Plutonium and uranium rods in 6-in. array, contained in 6-in. diam pot	6-in.-thick natural uranium, silver painted, 6-in. steel, 4-in. lead	Alternating layers of 3-in. iron and masonite, iron and boron-impregnated plastic, 18-in. heavy aggregate concrete	11 by 15 by 9 ft high	2 safety and 2 regulating rods in reflector, uranium in lower section and B-10 in upper	Mercury. Reflector cooled by water	World's first fast reactor (1946); dismantled in 1954

TABLE 8k-2. NUCLEAR REACTOR CATALOGUE (*Continued*)

Name	Classification	Fuel	Fuel core	Reflector	Shielding	Over-all size	Control	Coolant	Remarks
EBR-1, Experimental Breeder Reactor (Reactor Testing Station, Arco, Idaho)	Fast, research (breeding, power), 1400 kw, 1.1 × 10^{14} fast flux	Close-packed array of rods, each containing a U^{235} center section with a top and bottom natural uranium blanket section. Fuel slugs (2 per rod), enriched to 90% U^{235}, $4\frac{1}{4}$ in. long, 0.384 in. diam, jacketed in stainless steel	Provision for 217 rods. 48.2 kg U^{235} for criticality, 52 kg used. Double-walled reactor tank with gas space used for leak detection and insulation	Natural uranium blanket in 2 sections; first section, tightly packed array of rods $1\frac{3}{8}$ in. diam, $20\frac{1}{4}$ in. long, clad with 0.020-in. stainless-steel jackets. Core and inner blanket contained in $15\frac{7}{8}$-in. diam stainless steel tank. Outer blanket, array of keystone-shaped bricks, forming a cylinder around sides (and bottom) of reactor tank. 18 in. graphite for outer reflector	Thermal neutron shield, 6 in. iron (air-cooled), 9 ft ordinary concrete	....	12 control rods of natural uranium in outer blanket, 8 for shutdown, 4 for control; 1 bottom safety; blanket travel	292 gpm NaK, temp. rise 88°C, 228°C inlet temp., flow upward in core and downward in blanket. Outer blanket air-cooled	World's first production of electrical power from a nuclear reactor (1951). Breeding demonstrated. Shutdown in 1955
SIR, Submarine Intermediate Reactor (SIR-Mark A, prototype, West Milton, N.Y.; SIR-Mark B for U.S.S. Sea Wolf)	Intermediate, heterogeneous, beryllium, power	Enriched uranium	....	....	....	....	....	Sodium	Prototype enclosed in 225-ft diam, 1-in.-thick steel sphere, gas tight (1955)

TABLE 8k-2. NUCLEAR REACTOR CATALOGUE (*Continued*)

Name	Classification	Fuel	Fuel core	Reflector	Shielding	Over-all size	Control	Coolant	Remarks
Zephyr, Zero Energy Fast Reactor (Harwell, England)	Fast, research, 2–30 watts	Plutonium	Cylindrical core with height = diam $\cong$ 15 cm, consisting of uranium and plutonium	Uranium	None, but reactor in concrete room	. . . .	Control and safety rods consist of uranium rods moving vertically in channels around core, uranium safety block	None	(1954)
Bulk Shielding Facility (Swimming Pool) (Oak Ridge National Laboratory, Oak Ridge, Tenn.)	Thermal, heterogeneous, light water, research, 100 kw, 5×10^{11}	MTR-type fuel elements: 18 convex plates, each 3 in. wide, 24 in. long, and 0.06 in. thick, comprise a fuel box. Plates of enriched uranium (>90% U^{235}) encased in 25 Al sandwiches, clad with 72 S. About 140 g U^{235} per fuel box. Al-to-H_2O volume ratio is 0.7	Critical mass ~3 kg of U^{235} in fuel core 12 by 12 by 24 in.; with allowances for other factors including beam holes, burnup, 3.5 kg; with BeO reflector, 2.4 kg in a fuel core 9 by 12 by 24 in.	10 cm of BeO on 4 sides of active lattice; or light water	$16\frac{1}{2}$ ft of water above, and $3\frac{1}{2}$ ft plus concrete below	Pool 40 ft long, 20 ft wide, 20 ft deep	2 B-Pb shim-safety rods (mixture of Pb and boral in oval Al can 1 by $2\frac{1}{2}$ in. by 26 in. long). 2 Cd-Pb safety rods 1 Cd-Pb regulating rod	Light water (convective flow)	Negative temp. coef. 0.0075%/°F Max available slow-neutron flux, 10^{12} n/cm²/sec, max available epithermal flux, 3×10^{12} n/cm²/sec (1950)
LITR, low-intensity test reactor (Oak Ridge National Laboratory, Oak Ridge, Tenn.)	Thermal, heterogeneous, light water, research. Increased from 500 to 3,000 kw, 2×10^{13}	MTR fuel assemblies (16 plates)	3.4 kg U^{235}	Loosely stacked Be blocks	Unmortared concrete blocks, except for outer 1 ft $10\frac{1}{2}$ ft (min)	25 ft diam 27 ft high	3 shim-safety, 1 control	Light water	Served as mock-up for MTR and now used for research (1950)

TABLE 8k-2. NUCLEAR REACTOR CATALOGUE (*Continued*)

Name	Classification	Fuel	Fuel core	Reflector	Shielding	Over-all size	Control	Coolant	Remarks
MTR, Materials Testing Reactor (Reactor Testing Station, Arco, Idaho)	Thermal, heterogeneous, light water, research, 30 mw, 4×10^{14} (level changed to 40 mv)	Fuel assembly is $3 \times 3 \times 24$-in. box containing 18 curved, vertical, fuel plates; plates consist of uranium-Al alloy, 0.5 mm thick, sandwiched between 0.5 mm Al; 3.0 mm spacing between plates, U^{235} per plate increased from 140 to 200 g	27 to 45 fuel boxes. Boxes held in Algrido contained in 54-in. diam Al tank	Primary reflector is Be 3 ft high and 5 ft diam, two zones of graphite outside tank of pebble stone of 1-mm-diam balls to form an 7 ft 4 in. square outer stack 12 ft by 14 ft by 9 ft 4 in.	2–4 in. steel thermal shields, concrete 9 ft thick, water 15 ft above core and 5 ft below	About a 34-ft cube	Up to 8 vertical shim-safety rods, 2 vertical regulating rods	Light water, recirculated, cooled by flash vaporization air cooling in graphite and thermal shield	For study of materials exposed to intense radiations, 1×10^{14} (1952)
Experimental Nuclear Reactor (USSR)	Thermal, heterogeneous, light water, research, 300 kw, 2×10^{12}	16 fuel elements per unit, each fuel element 9 mm OD 50 cm high; square lattice with ~18 mm spacing; fuel elements contain 10% enriched U^{235}	Active core approximated by a cylinder 40 cm diam, 50 cm high; core consists of 32 units with 24 units containing fuel. 3.5 kg U^{235} in core. Core in 500-mm-diam, water-filled, A1 tank	Water	Cast iron and water	....	3 borax-carbide safety rods, 1 steel rod	240 m^3/hr water flow through core, entering at 30°C, 1°C rise	Max fuel surface temp. 70°C
RPT Reactor for Physical and Technical Investigation (USSR)	Thermal heterogeneous, light water and graphite, research, 10 mw, 8×10^{13} (max)	Fuel elements are hollow cylinders, containing enriched uranium, covered with an Al casing, and inserted in ducts. 37 cylindrical ducts, 54 mm diam, 14 cm spacing, pierce graphite layers	About 1 m diam by 1 m high	Core and graphite reflector fill a cylinder 240 cm high, 260 cm diam. 80 cm graphite on sides, 60 cm on bottom	Side shielding, nonlayer/frame 2.5 cm thick, 320 cm concrete; top, 150 cm graphite, 40 cm Pb, 20-cm-thick iron	....	2 automatic control rods, 3 manual, 3 slowly moving automatic rods of boron carbide, 2 systems of safety rods	Distilled water enters annulus between fuel tube and duct, 6 m^3/hr/duct, 20–30° inlet, 55–65° outlet. Helium used for graphite	(1952)

TABLE 8k-2. NUCLEAR REACTOR CATALOGUE (*Continued*)

Name	Classification	Fuel	Fuel core	Reflector	Shielding	Over-all size	Control	Coolant	Remarks
APS, Atomic Power Station (USSR)	Thermal, heterogeneous, light water and graphite, power, 30 mw (heat), 5 mw (electrical), 5×10^{13}	Thin walled steel used for fuel channel, and hollow fuel elements placed in channel (see RPT), enriched uranium (5% U^{235}). Fuel elements not bonded to jacket	128 fuel channels pierce control part of graphite brickwork, forming a core 150 cm diam, 170 cm high. Total uranium, 550 kg	Graphite encased in a hermetical steel jacket, clearance allowed in graphite brickwork, jacket filled with He or N_2	Side water shield, 100 cm thick, concrete wall 300 cm thick	....	18 boron carbide rods (water-cooled); 4 automatic control rods in reflector, 2 safety rods in active zone	Distilled water at 100 atm pumped down through tube and return up flow over surface of fuel elements. Recirculation. Inlet temp. 190°C, outlet 260–270°C. Steam generated at 12.5 atm, 255–260°C	U^{235} burnup about 15 to 20%. Max graphite temp. 650 to 700°C (1954)
Geneva Reactor Exhibit (Geneva, Switzerland)	Thermal, heterogeneous, light water, demonstration, 10–100 kw, 10 in.	Enriched uranium (20% U^{235}) in 23 MTR fuel assemblies (18 plates per assembly) Al to H_2O vol. ratio 0.65	About 3.6 kg U^{235}, active lattice 15 by 15 by 24 in.	Light water	Light water plus earth	Pool, 10 ft diam, 21 ft deep, 13,000 gal capacity of demineralized water	3 safety and control rods, each about 2% boron-carbide	Light water, natural convection	Automatic control from start to full power. Dismantled in 1955 and moved to Wurlingen in 1956 and rebuilt as Swiss Reactor No. 1. Power rating 1 mw

TABLE 8k-2. NUCLEAR REACTOR CATALOGUE (*Continued*)

Name	Classification	Fuel	Fuel core	Reflector	Shielding	Over-all size	Control	Coolant	Remarks
TTR, low-power thermal test reactor (Knolls Atomic Power Laboratory, Schenectady, N.Y.) (Several versions built)	Thermal, heterogeneous, research, 100 watts, 3.4 × 10^9	2.7 kg^{235} required for criticality; extra 0.1 kg provides about 0.6% excess reactivity	20 fuel slug tubes, each 2 in. diam, 24 in. long, containing U-Al alloy disks with polyethylene spacers strung on $\frac{3}{16}$-in.-diam rod; disks (slugs) immersed in light paraffin-base oil contained in a slug tube. Tubes in cylindrical array in an Al tank of 12 in. ID and 18 in. OD; tank filled with water	30-in. cylindrical ring of graphite	Reactor located in a room with 6-ft-thick concrete walls	....	Coarse: 6 Fe-clad Cd sheets, 4 in. wide, 18 in. long, at periphery of tank. Fine: 2 Cd rods, 18 in. long, $\frac{1}{2}$ in. diam, move between fuel slug tubes. Safety: four $\frac{1}{2}$-in.-diam Cd rods	....	Internal thermal column is a graphite cylinder, 12 in. diam, 18 in. high. Test hole is in center of column. Temp. change of 10^{-3}°C causes reactivity change of $\Delta k/k = 10^{-7}$ (negative temp. coef.) (1951)
STR, submarine thermal reactor (STR-Mark I, prototype, National Reactor Testing Station, Arco, Idaho; STR Mark II, *U.S.S. Nautilus*)	Thermal, ship propulsion, 18 mw	Enriched uranium sheathed in zirconium	....	....	....	....	....	Pressurized light water	World's first (1953) mobile reactor unit. First major use of zirconium
Livermore Water Boiler (California Research and Development Co., Livermore, Calif.)	Thermal, homogeneous, light water, research, 100 watts, 10^9	....	....	....	....	....	....	....	Reactor designed and built by NAA
Zephyr (British low-power breeder reactor, Harwell England)	Fast, heterogeneous, research, breeding 1–2 watts	Plutonium core surrounded by uranium	....	....	....	....	....	Sodium-potassium alloy	

units for submarines, shipcraft and aircraft. Both large-scale and small-scale power demonstration reactor programs have been started, utilizing pressurized-water, sodium-graphite, fast-breeder, boiling-water, homogeneous, liquid-metal-fuel, and gas-coolant designs.

Great Britain's first heavy-water reactor, DIMPLE, was placed in operation in 1954. A higher-power heavy-water reactor is under construction as well as a sodium-cooled breeder reactor. The Calder Hall reactors are the first commercial full-scale power plants. The reactors utilize natural uranium fuel and graphite moderator, and are cooled with CO_2 under pressure.

The French program includes the building of two plutonium producing reactors, G1 and G2. The startup of G1 was February, 1956. The reactors are natural uranium, graphite-moderated units and are to produce electrical power. Air is used for the coolant for G1 and CO_2 for G2. Other similar power-producing reactors are under study. E.L.3 is a high-flux materials testing reactor and will utilize slightly enriched uranium and heavy water.

Other significant reactor developments are in progress in The Netherlands, Belgium, Norway, Sweden, Switzerland, and Canada.

8l. Mesons and Hyperons

MAURICE M. SHAPIRO

Nucleonics Division, U.S. Naval Research Laboratory

8l-1. Nomenclature. *Mesons* are unstable particles intermediate in mass between the electron and proton. *Hyperons* are unstable particles intermediate in mass between the neutron and deuteron. So many new types of mesons and hyperons have recently been discovered (LL, LC, RG, BR, BR1, SA, OC, BH, AR, TR, BA1, FM3, MM)[1] that confusion in nomenclature has resulted. A systematic notation, proposed (AE, TR) as the result of discussion at the International Congress on Cosmic Radiation at Bagnères-de-Bigorre, France, in 1953 (BP, SM), has gained wide acceptance, and is employed here:

1. *Generic* symbols (Latin letters) classify the particles according to *mass* and *phenomenology of decay*, respectively:

a. Mass categories[2]

L meson (light meson), $m_e < m_L \leq m_\pi$
K meson (heavy meson), $m_\pi < m_K < m_p$
Y particle (hyperon), $m_n < m_Y < m_d$

(Note that neutrons and protons are excluded.)

[1] The references on p. 8-245 include some useful *general* references on heavy unstable particles (MR1, VP, PC, RB2, PC1, LL1, SM, WJ, BJ, PC2, TA, RG1, RU, BP, DP, PP, HT1, DC2).

[2] Symbols: e = electron; π = π meson (pion); μ = μ meson (muon); p = proton; n = neutron; d = deuteron. In addition, the following symbols are employed to denote various decay products in Table 8l-1: γ = photon; ν = neutrino; η, η' = neutral particles as yet unspecified, which may or may not be alike.

b. Phenomenological categories

V event. Phenomenon interpretable as the *decay in flight* of a K meson or hyperon. Subclasses: "V^0 event," decay of a neutral particle; "$V^{\pm}$ event," decay of a charged particle.

S event. Phenomenon interpretable as the *decay at rest* of a K meson or hyperon.

2. A *specific* symbol (Greek letter) designates each individual type of particle (see Table 8l-1); capital Greek letters are used for hyperons (for the proton and neutron, however, the conventional symbols p and n, respectively, are retained).

Table 8l-1. Characteristics of Mesons and Hyperons*

	Mass		Decay products	Mean life, sec	Q, Mev†	Statistics
	In m_e	In Mev				
L mesons:						
$\pi^{\pm}$	273.0 ± 0.5	139.5	$\mu^{\pm} + \nu$	$2.55 \pm 0.10 \times 10^{-8}$	33.9 ± 0.1	Bose
π^0	263.8 ± 1	134.8	$\begin{cases} 2\gamma \\ \gamma + e^+ + e^- \end{cases}$	$\sim 5 \times 10^{-15}$	134.8 ± 0.5	Bose
$\mu^{\pm}$	206.6 ± 0.5	105.6	$e^{\pm} + 2\nu$	$2.15 \pm 0.05 \times 10^{-6}$	105.3 ± 0.3	Fermi
K mesons:						
$\tau^{\pm}$	965.2 ± 1.3	493.2	$\begin{cases} \pi^{\pm} + \pi^+ + \pi^- \\ (\pi^{\pm} + 2\pi^0)^4 \end{cases}$	10^{-8}	$\begin{cases} 74.7 \pm 0.5 \\ 84.1 \end{cases}$	Bose
θ^0	965 ± 10	~ 493	$\pi^+ + \pi^-$	$1.6 \pm 0.5 \times 10^{-10}$	214 ± 5	Bose
$\chi[\theta^{\pm}, K_{\pi 2}]$	966 ± 12	~ 494	$\pi^{\pm} + \pi^0$	$(\lesssim 10^{-8})$	219 ± 6	Bose
$K_{\mu 2}$	960 ± 15	~ 490	$\mu + \nu$	$\sim 10^{-8}$	390 ± 10	Bose
$K_{\mu 3}[\kappa]$	$(\sim m_{\tau})$	$(\sim m_{\tau})$	$\mu + \eta + \eta'$	$(\lesssim 10^{-8})$		
K_{e3}	$(\sim m_{\tau})$	$(\sim m_{\tau})$	$e + \eta + \eta'$			
Hyperons:						
Λ^0	$2{,}181 \pm 2$	1,114.5	$p + \pi^-$	$3.7 \pm 0.6 \times 10^{-10}$	36.9 ± 0.2	Fermi
Σ^+	$2{,}327 \pm 4$	1,189	$\begin{cases} p + \pi^0 \\ n + \pi^+ \end{cases}$	$\sim 10^{-10}$	$\begin{cases} 116 \pm 2 \\ \sim 110 \end{cases}$	Fermi
Σ^-	$\sim 2{,}325$	$\sim 1{,}188$	$n + \pi^-$	$\lesssim 10^{-10}$	~ 110	Fermi
Ξ^-	$\sim 2{,}580$	$\sim 1{,}318$	$\Lambda^0 + \pi^-$	$(\sim 10^{-10})$	~ 65	Fermi

Parentheses denote information which is probable but not firmly established. The symbols in brackets are alternative designations for a given particle.

* This table was prepared in November, 1954, and is based primarily on the literature published prior to that time. A limited revision was possible several months later. However, the very rapid advances in the field of unstable particles will certainly have yielded improved data for some of the K and Y particles even by the time this goes to press. For references and explanatory remarks, see the Notes on Table 8l-1, page 8-242. Conversion factors needed in constructing the table were based on the same data as in Sec. 8a. Symbols are defined in footnote 2, page 8-240. The estimated uncertainties are standard errors.

† Q is the total kinetic energy of the decay secondaries.

8l-2. Characteristics of Mesons and Hyperons.[1] Table 8l-1 gives constants and decay schemes for mesons and hyperons whose existence is established, though in several instances some of their basic properties remain to be finally determined. The masses are given in units of the electron mass m_e and in Mev. References and notes explaining how the numbers in the table were arrived at appear on the following pages.

To keep the references within bounds, only a set of representative papers is

[1] A review of the production and interactions of π mesons could not be included here because of space limitations (see, however, MR1, RA, RA1, BH5).

given. Other works can be traced through these. In general, the most precise data on L mesons derive from experiments with high-energy accelerators, the detectors being cloud chambers, photographic emulsions, and counters. Until very recently, information about K and Y particles came principally from cosmic-ray observations employing the first two techniques. As this is being written, however, the new Bev accelerators are beginning to contribute decisively to this field.

Notes on Table 8l-1. L MESON MASSES: (1) *Charged pions.* From momentum-range comparison with protons (BW1, SF1), the mass of π^+ is $(273.3 \pm 0.2)m_e$, and the mass ratio π^-/π^+ is 0.998 ± 0.002. For the π^- mass (CK), the energy of the γ rays from the reaction $p + \pi^- \rightarrow n + \gamma$ yields $(272.7 \pm 0.3)m_e$. Within the precision thus far obtained there appears to be no evidence for a difference in mass between π^+ and π^-. Accordingly, a single mass value, $(273.0 \pm 0.5)m_e$, is adopted here for $\pi^\pm$. This value was also used in computing the π^0 and $\mu^\pm$ masses in Table 8l-1. (2) *Neutral pion.* The best mass determinations for π^0 are based on the $\pi^- - \pi^0$ mass difference. The Doppler shift of the decay γ rays from $p + \pi^- \rightarrow n + \pi^0$ and $\pi^0 \rightarrow 2\gamma$ yields (PW) a difference of $(10.6 \pm 2)m_e$. The angular correlation of these γ rays (CW1) gives $8.8 \pm 0.6m_e$. Adopting the value 9.2, we derive $273.0 - 9.2 = (263.8 \pm 1)m_e$ for the π^0 mass. (3) *Muons.* Using the mass difference $\pi^+ - \mu^+ = (66.4 \pm 0.1)m_e$ (SF2, BW2), we obtain $273.0 - 66.4 = (206.6 \pm 0.5)m_e$.

L MESON LIFETIMES: (1) *Charged pions.* Three recent precise measurements for π^+ (in units of 10^{-8} sec) give 2.53 ± 0.10 (KW), 2.54 ± 0.11 (JM), and 2.58 ± 0.14 (WC). Their mean, 2.55, agrees with the π^- value 2.55 ± 0.19 (DR1). Hence a single mean life for $\pi^\pm$ appears in the table. (2) *Neutral pion.* Observations on the alternate mode of decay, $\pi^0 \rightarrow \gamma + e^+ + e^-$, yield a "most probable value" of 5×10^{-15} sec, with the limits $3 \times 10^{-15} < T < 1.0 \times 10^{-14}$ sec for the mean life (AB). The alternative mode of decay has a branching ratio of 0.013 ± 0.004 with respect to the usual decay into two photons (AB). (3) *Muons.* The average of three determinations (AL, RB1, BW3) has been adopted for the mean life of $\mu^\pm$.

L MESON STATISTICS AND SPINS: (1) *Pions.* The spin of π^+ has been experimentally determined to be zero (CW2, CD, DR); it is therefore a boson. The neutral pion must also be a boson, as it decays into photons. Since the number of photons is 2, not 3, the π^0 spin cannot be 1 but must be an even integer, probably zero (YC, LL2). The π^-, too, is a boson, as can be inferred from the reaction $\pi^- + p \rightarrow \pi^0 + n$. Its spin is also probably zero. (2) *Muons.* π-μ decay is a two-body process, and the neutral secondary is known to have zero or near-zero rest mass. Assuming that this neutral particle is a neutrino, in order to avoid introducing a new neutral particle of vanishingly small mass, then the muon is a fermion. Moreover, on the neutrino assumption, the spin of μ^+ is $\frac{1}{2}$ since the π^+ spin is zero. Some uncertainty over the decay scheme $\mu \rightarrow e + 2\nu$ persists, partly because of conflicting results on a zero cutoff at the high-energy end of the positron spectrum from μ^+ decay (see BH1, SR, VJ, LA1, HH). Should zero cutoff become firmly established, this would strengthen the case for a muon spin of $\frac{1}{2}$.

K MESONS: *Tau* ($\tau^\pm$). *The Q value* 74.7 Mev is that reported at the Padua Conference (PP). Other values, most of them close to this one, have been reported (LW, HH1, BC, LD, LD1, DA, CJ1, BG, CM1, AE2). Using this Q value $(146.2m_e)$ and the $\pi^\pm$ mass of $273.0m_e$ adopted here, the mass of $\tau^\pm$ is $965.2 \pm 1.3m_e$. *The mean life* of $\tau^\pm$ is 10^{-8} sec (AL1, PP, BC). Earlier estimates gave a lower limit of 10^{-9} sec (FP, HA). Some evidence exists (CJ2, AE1, BP1, SN, BM1) for an *alternative mode of decay* of the tau meson, $\tau^\pm \rightarrow \pi^\pm + 2\pi^0$. The single charged secondary in these events, unlike that in most $K^\pm$ decay events with a single $L^\pm$ secondary, is emitted with an energy <53 Mev in the CM system. The expected Q for this mode of decay, 84.1 Mev, differs appreciably from that for the usual decay into three charged pions, in view of the $\pi^\pm - \pi^0$ mass difference.

θ^0 MESON. The two secondaries of θ^0 decay are $L^\pm$ mesons, and at least one of them is a pion (TR, TR1). Double production of θ^0 and Λ^0 from $\pi^- + p$ (TR2, FW2) suggests that θ^0 is a boson, and that the second $L^\pm$ meson is therefore also a pion. The Q value is 214 ± 5 Mev (TR3, BK). Accordingly, adopting the decay scheme $\theta^0 \rightarrow \pi^+ + \pi^- + 214$ Mev, the mass of θ^0 is $965 \pm 10m_e$. The mean life of θ^0 (GD, BK1, AW) is $1.6 \begin{smallmatrix} +0.6 \\ -0.4 \end{smallmatrix} \times 10^{-10}$ sec. *Anomalous Q values.* Among some V^0 events with two $L^\pm$ secondaries, there appear to be some Q values considerably lower than 214 ± 5 Mev. Some of these are provisionally attributable to the decay scheme $\tau^0 \rightarrow \pi^+ + \pi^- + \pi^0$; others are not (VV, YH).

OTHER $K^\pm$ MESONS: In addition to the well-defined $\tau^\pm$, there is evidence for the probable existence of at least three or four other types of $K^\pm$ mesons. These have been relatively slow in getting established, mainly because the visible evidence of their decay is confined to a *single* charged secondary, unlike that of the $\tau^\pm$ or θ^0. From the $\chi(K_{\pi2})$, this charged offspring is a pion; from the $K_{\mu2}$ or $K_{\mu3}$, it is a muon; and from the K_{e3}, it is an electron. (The subscripts $\pi2$, for example, denote a $\pi^\pm$ secondary and two-body decay.) These various types of $K^\pm$ meson will be described in turn.

1. *Chi meson* (χ, $K_{\pi2}$, $\theta^\pm$). A pion secondary of apparently unique energy ~109 Mev is emitted in certain K meson decays in nuclear emulsions (MM), and this led to the proposed decay scheme $\chi^\pm \rightarrow \pi^\pm + \eta$, hence the alternative designation $K_{\pi2}$. The probability that the neutral particle is a π^0 is supported by observations of photon secondaries (BH2, DH, HA1, HE) as well as by other evidence (BM1, HR1, GS). Besides decaying into two pions with a $Q \approx 219$ Mev, the χ has a mass (GS, RD) very close to that of the θ^0. Therefore, it is natural to regard the χ as the charged counterpart of the θ^0, and the former is sometimes referred to as $\theta^\pm$ (e.g., GM, RM).

2. *$K_{\mu2}$ meson.* Evidence for a two-body decay, $K_\mu \rightarrow \mu + \eta$ (where η is an unspecified neutral particle), came originally from cloud-chamber observations of a distribution of transverse momenta of secondary particles sharply peaked near 220 Mev/c (GB). More decisive evidence has recently come from range observations on the stopping muon secondaries in cloud chambers (HE), and in emulsions (GS). The muon has an energy of about 154 Mev. Although at first the $K_{\mu2}$ mass appeared to be appreciably lower than that of the $\tau^\pm$, more recent measurements (GS, RD) suggest that it is quite close to the tau mass. Actually, in an experiment at the Bevatron, the mass difference $\tau^+ - K^+$ was found to be $5 \pm 5m_e$, using momentum and range for mass determination (FS). (In these measurements "K^+" was defined as a positive K meson decaying into a particle with near-minimum ionization. The K^+ collection probably consisted mainly of $K_{\mu2}$ and χ mesons with a slight admixture of $K_{\mu3}$ and K_{e3}.) The lack of secondary photons associated with the decay of $K_{\mu2}$ under conditions in which the tracks of electron progeny would be visible makes it very unlikely that the neutral secondary is a pion or photon. Hence the decay scheme commonly assumed is $K_{\mu2} \rightarrow \mu + \nu$, and this implies a Q value of ~391 Mev. From both cosmic-ray and Bevatron experiments, the mean life appears to be $\sim10^{-8}$ sec (RD).

3. *$K_{\mu3}$ meson,* also called kappa[1] (κ), has a muon secondary which has been observed to be emitted with various energies (OC, MM, HT, IN, BA, YC1). One assumes, therefore, a three-body decay, $K_{\mu3} \rightarrow \mu + \eta + \eta'$. The identity of the neutral secondaries η, η' is unknown at the time of this writing. There is no evidence against the scheme $\kappa \rightarrow \mu + 2\nu$, and on this assumption the mean life has been calculated to be $\sim10^{-9}$ sec (DJ1, DN). Experiments indicate that it lies between 4×10^{-9} sec

[1] Note that the kappa is a particular type of K meson. Hence the specific symbol κ should not be confused with the generic designation K.

and 10^{-8} sec (NJ, AJ, DR2, BK2, ML, BH3, YC1, BC, HR4). However, some of these experiments probably involved a mixture of various K mesons. The emission of two neutrinos would of course imply that the kappa is a fermion. Current theoretical views (GM), on the other hand, favor the assumption that K mesons are bosons. Modes of decay consistent with this idea [e.g., $\kappa \to \mu + \nu + (\pi^0 \text{ or } \gamma)$] are not, thus far, excluded by experiment. The masses reported for the kappa range from approximately 900 to $1{,}500m_e$ (VP, PC), with some clustering of values near $1{,}000m_e$ (MM, HT, DR2, SM1, SM3). There is no clear evidence that the kappa mass differs significantly from those of the better-known K mesons, hence the entry ($\sim m_\tau$) in the mass column of Table 8l-1.

4. *K_{e3} meson.* Some K mesons arrested in nuclear emulsion have a singly charged secondary which suffers along its path Bremsstrahlung loss of a magnitude expected for electrons but not for L mesons (FM3, DC1, KM, GG, HH1). The electrons so identified are emitted with various energies;[1] therefore, a three-body decay scheme is assumed: $K_{e3} \to e + \eta + \eta'$, where, as for the $K_{\mu3}$, the neutral secondaries are not yet identified. In mass, the K_{e3} meson appears close to the τ (RD). The remarks on statistics made above for the kappa apply as well to the K_{e3}. In fact, the $K_{\mu3}$ and K_{e3} may turn out to be a single type of K meson which undergoes alternative modes of decay.

Negative K mesons have been observed as V and S events in cloud chambers, and by their nuclear absorption in photographic emulsions (VP, p. 196; FW, LD, HJ, HJ1, HJ2, HR2, SN, SM3, TG, DH1, BK1, CW5, FW7). The latter have been observed much more rarely than K decay events.

Production of K mesons with the Brookhaven Cosmotron (HR4, HJ1, HG) and the Radiation Laboratory's Bevatron (KL, BR2, BR3, CW4, GG, RD) has begun to be copious and will make possible a rapid growth of our knowledge of the interactions and other properties of K mesons.

Neutral hyperon Λ^0. Although the Λ^0 was discovered and has been mainly observed in cloud chambers, the most precise Q values (and hence mass values) have resulted from range measurements in emulsion (FM1). These yield $Q = 36.9 \pm 0.2$ Mev and $m = 2{,}181 \pm 2m_e$. Cloud-chamber results are in good agreement (TR1, BH4) or fair agreement (AR, VV1) with this Q value. Mean-life measurements from various laboratories yield an estimate (PD1) of $3.7 \pm 0.6 \times 10^{-10}$ sec. The decay products of the Λ^0 are p and π^-; since π^- is a boson, Λ^0 must be a fermion. Many anomalous Q values have been observed for V^0 events which have decay products resembling those of the Λ^0.

Charged hyperons: Σ^+. This hyperon appears to have two modes of decay. The Q value, and hence the mass, of Σ^+ is best known from its decay into a proton and (presumably) π^0. When Σ^+ decays after coming to rest in emulsion, the proton has a definite range ($\sim$1.67 mm) and therefore an energy which can be precisely measured. From this, the Q and mass are rather well known (BA1, CC, BM2). The alternative mode of decay $\Sigma^+ \to n + \pi^+$ has been inferred from observations of the secondary π^+ (LD2, KD, CM2, YC1, FM2), which yielded an approximate mean of 114 Mev for the Q value. However, in typical emulsion observations, the energetic pion leaves the stack; so its energy (and therefore the Q value) is not so precisely determined as that of the short-range proton in the first mode of decay. What is probably a better value, $\sim$110 Mev, is obtained by computing the Q for the alternative decay scheme using the known Σ^+ mass, $2{,}327 \pm 4m_e$. The mean life of Σ^+ is estimated to lie between 10^{-11} and 3×10^{-10} sec (YC1, BC). The symbol Σ^+, rather than Λ^+, is employed because this particle does not appear to be the charged counterpart of the Λ^0. Like the latter, it decays into a nucleon and pion, but its Q value is quite different from that of the Λ^0.

[1] From 20 to $\sim$260 Mev, in the first seven examples of K_{e3}.

Σ^- *hyperon.* Observations have been reported (FW3, HE, p. 97, YC1) of a negative counterpart of the Σ^+ which decays according to $\Sigma^- \rightarrow n + \pi^-$. In emulsion, this process is ordinarily indistinguishable from $\Sigma^+ \rightarrow n + \pi^+$ since the fast pion's sign is unknown unless it is arrested in the emulsion (and this is likely to happen only in a rather large stack). In such cases, the event must be labeled $\Sigma^\pm \rightarrow n + \pi^\pm$.

"Cascade hyperon" Ξ^-. This higher-mass hyperon is observed in cloud chambers as a V^- event in which a Λ^0 (or rather, its pair of charged secondaries) appears near the decay point of the V^-, hence the phenomenological name "V-particle cascade" (AR1, AC, CE). The charged secondary of Ξ^- is an L^- meson, very probably a pion. Thus, in the scheme $\Xi^- \rightarrow \Lambda^0 + \pi^-$, the parent as well as the daughter hyperon each gives rise, successively, to a π^-. The Q in the primary decay is ~65 Mev; that in the decay of the secondary Λ^0 is, as usual, 37 Mev.

There is some evidence for nuclear interactions of charged hyperons (FM2, JR, HE).

Associated production of hyperons and K mesons (PA, NY, PD2) according to the scheme $\pi^- + p \rightarrow Y + K$, where the products may be either charged or neutral, has been observed (FW2, FW3, FW5, DC, TR2). At a pion energy of 1.5 Bev the cross section for this process is ~1 millibarn (FW4). The term "associated production" also embraces interactions in which a K meson is absorbed and a Y particle emitted (e.g., DH1, HJ1), or in which both a K meson and hyperfragment (see below) are emitted (DA1). Simultaneous production of Ξ^- and two θ^0 mesons has been observed (TG, GM2). There is also an indication of associated production in nucleon-nucleon collisions (BM3).

Classification schemes have been proposed (GM, GM1, GM2, SR1) for K mesons and hyperons based on the assignment of an isotopic spin to each, and the correlation of their properties with this quantum number. The existence of additional unstable particles has been inferred from such schemes. At least one of these, a charged hyperon even heavier than the Ξ^-, has possibly been observed (EY); others, such as the Σ^0, would be difficult to detect.

Hyperons as excited nucleons. The modes of decay of Y particles suggest that a hyperon is an "excited nucleon" which transforms into a lower-energy nucleon by emitting a pion. This view gains support from the production of hyperons in collisions in which the primary energy is insufficient to provide the rest mass of the hyperon (FW1, FW2, SM2, PC2). Moreover, under certain conditions a hyperon can apparently take the place of an ordinary nucleon in an excited nuclear fragment (DM), as discussed below.

Bound hyperons; hyperfragments. The disintegration of certain unstable nuclear fragments produced in high-energy collisions is interpreted as due to the decay of bound Λ^0 particles contained in these "hyperfragments" (DM, CP, BA2, TD, CJ3, FP1, HR3, FW4, FW6, GR, SN1, PC2).[1] This decay may be "mesonic," in which case a pion is emitted, or "nonmesonic," in which event its rest-mass energy is available for the kinetic energy of the fragment's disintegration products (CW3). There is evidence that a Λ^0 particle is bound more weakly than is the neutron which it supplants. A notable example is the hyperfragment $^4He^*$ (HR3, SN1). The existence of hyperfragment $^4H^*$ has been predicted (DR3) and independently observed (GS). Also, the possibility of various dinucleon hyperfragments has been proposed (PH), including that of an excited dineutron; decay of the latter may have been observed (LD).

References[2]

AB. Anand, B. M.: *Proc. Roy. Soc.* (*London*), ser. A, **220**, 183 (1953).
AC. Anderson, Cowan, Leighton, and Van Lint: *Phys. Rev.* **92**, 1089 (1953).

[1] For additional references to the literature on hyperfragments, see GR and SN1.
[2] F. W. O'Dell has kindly helped in checking the references.

AE. Amaldi, Anderson, Blackett, Fretter, Leprince-Ringuet, Peters, Powell, Rochester, Rossi, and Thompson: *Physics Today* **6** (12), 24 (1953); *Nature* **173**, 123 (1954).
AE1. Amaldi, Baroni, Castagnoli, Cortini, Franzinetti, and Manfredini: *Nuovo cimento* **11**, 207 (1954).
AE2. Amaldi, Baroni, Castagnoli, Cortini, and Manfredini: *Nuovo cimento* **10**, 937 (1953).
AJ. Astbury, Buchanan, Chippendale, Millar, Newth, Page, Rytz, and Sahiar: *Phil. Mag.* **44**, 242 (1953).
AL. Alvarez, Longacre, Ogren, and Thomas: *Phys. Rev.* **77**, 752 (1950).
AL1. Alvarez, L. W., and S. Goldhaber: UCRL Report 3041, June, 1955.
AR. Armenteros, Barker, Butler, and Cachon: *Phil. Mag.* **42**, 1113 (1951).
AR1. Armenteros, Barker, Butler, Cachon, and York: *Phil. Mag.* **43**, 597 (1952).
AR2. Armenteros, Barker, Butler, Coates, and Sowerby: *Phil. Mag.* **44**, 861 (1953).
AW. Alford, W. L., and R. B. Leighton: *Phys. Rev.* **90**, 622 (1953).
BA. Bonetti, Levi Setti, and Panetti: *Proc. Roy. Soc. (London)* **221**, 318 (1954).
BA1. Bonetti, Levi Setti, Panetti, and Tomasini: *Nuovo cimento* **10**, 345, 1736 (1953).
BA2. Bonetti, Levi Setti, Panetti, Scarsi, and Tomasini: *Nuovo cimento* **11**, 210, 330 (1954).
BC. Butler, C. C.: Report at Glasgow Conference on Nuclear Physics, July, 1954; cf. J. R. Richardson, Technical Report ONRL-72-54, Office of Naval Research, London.
BG. Baroni, Castagnoli, Cortini, Franzinetti, and Manfredini: *Proc. Roy. Soc. (London)*, ser. A, **221**, 384 (1954).
BH. Bridge, H. S., and M. Annis: *Phys. Rev.* **82**, 445 (1951).
BH1. Bramson, Seifert, and Havens: *Phys. Rev.* **88**, 304 (1952).
BH2. Bridge, Courant, Dayton, De Staebler, Rossi, Safford, and Willard: *Nuovo cimento* **12**, 81 (1954).
BH3. Bridge, Peyrou, Rossi, and Safford: *Phys. Rev.* **90**, 921 (1953).
BH4. Bridge, Peyrou, Rossi, and Safford: *Phys. Rev.* **91**, 362 (1953).
BH5. Bethe, H. A., and F. de Hoffmann: "Mesons and Fields," vol. II, Mesons, Row, Peterson & Company, Evanston, Ill., 1955.
BJ. Blair, J. S., and G. F. Chew: *Ann. Rev. Nuclear Sci.* **2**, 165 (1953).
BK. Barker, K. H.: *Proc. Roy. Soc. (London)*, ser. A, **221**, 328 (1954).
BK1. Barker, K. H.: *Proc. Duke University Cosmic Ray Conference*, December, 1953.
BK2. Barker, Butler, Sowerby, and York: *Phil. Mag.* **43**, 1201 (1952).
BK3. Bøggild, Hooper, Ortel, and Scharff: "Some Studies on Heavy Meson Events," 1955.
BM. Block, Harth, Fowler, Shutt, Thorndike, and Whittemore: *Phys. Rev.* **99**, 261 (1955).
BM1. Baldo, Belliboni, Ceccarelli, Grilli, Sechi, Vitale, and Zorn: *Nuovo cimento* **1**, 1180 (1955).
BM2. Baldo, Belliboni, Ceccarelli, and Vitale: Padua Conference, April, 1954.
BM3. Block, Harth, Fowler, Shutt, Thorndike, and Whittemore: *Phys. Rev.* **99**, 261 (1955).
BP. Bagnères-de-Bigorre: *Proc. International Congress on Cosmic Radiation*, July, 1953.
BP1. Barrett, P.: *Phys. Rev.* **94**, 1328 (1954).
BR. Brown, Camerini, Fowler, Muirhead, Powell, and Ritson: *Nature* **163**, 82 (1949).
BR1. Bjorklund, Crandall, Moyer, and York: *Phys. Rev.* **77**, 213 (1950).
BR2. Birge, Haddock, Kerth, Peterson, Sandweiss, Stork, and Whitehead: *Phys. Rev.* **99**, 329 (1955).
BR3. Birge, Peterson, Stork, and Whitehead: UCRL-3083, July, 1955.
BW1. Barkas, W. H.: UCRL-2327, Berkeley, Sept. 16, 1953.
BW2. Birnbaum, Smith, and Barkas: *Phys. Rev.* **83**, 895A (1951).
BW3. Bell, W. E., and E. P. Hincks: *Phys. Rev.* **84**, 1243 (1951).
CC. Castagnoli, Cortini, and Manfredini: *Nuovo cimento* **12**, 464 (1954).
CD. Clark, Roberts, and Wilson: *Phys. Rev.* **83**, 649L (1951).

CE. Cowan, E. W.: *Phys. Rev.* **94**, 161 (1954).
CH. Courant, H.: *Phys. Rev.* **99**, 282 (1955).
CJ1. Crussard, Kaplon, Klarmann, and Noon: *Phys. Rev.* **95**, 584L (1954).
CJ2. Crussard, Kaplon, Klarmann, and Noon: *Phys. Rev.* **93**, 253L (1954).
CJ3. Crussard, J., and D. Morellet: *Compt. rend.* **236**, 64 (1953).
CK. Crowe, K. M., and R. H. Phillips: *Phys. Rev.* **96**, 470 (1954).
CM1. Ceccarelli, Dellaporta, Merlin, Quareni, and Zorn: *Proc. Roy. Soc. (London)*, ser. A, **221**, 386 (1954).
CM2. Ceccarelli, M., and M. Merlin: *Nuovo cimento* **10**, 1207 (1953).
CP. Ciok, Danysz, and Gierula: *Nuovo cimento* **11**, 436–445 (1954).
CW1. Chinowsky, W., and J. Steinberger: *Phys. Rev.* **93**, 586 (1954).
CW2. Cartwright, Richman, Whitehead, and Wilcox: *Phys. Rev.* **91**, 677 (1953).
CW3. Cheston, W., and H. Primakoff: *Phys. Rev.* **92**, 1537 (1953).
CW4. Chupp, G. Goldhaber, S. Goldhaber, Goldsack, Lannutti, Smith, and Webb: *Phys. Rev.* **99**, 335 (1955).
CW5. Chupp, G. Goldhaber, S. Goldhaber, and Webb: UCRL-3044, June 14, 1955.
DA. Debenedetti, Garelli, Lovera, Tallone, and Vigone: *Nuovo cimento* **11**, 420 (1954).
DA1. Debenedetti, Garelli, Tallone, and Vigone: *Nuovo cimento* **12**, 466 (1954).
DC. Dahanayake, Francois, Fujimoto, Iredale, Waddington, and Yasin: *Phil. Mag.* **45**, 855 (1954).
DC1. Dahanayake, Francois, Fujimoto, Iredale, Waddington, and Yasin: *Phil. Mag.* **45**, 1219 (1954).
DC2. Dilworth, Occhialini, and Scarsi: *Ann. Rev. Nucl. Science* **4**, 271 (1954).
DH. DeStaebler, H., Jr., and B. V. Sreekantan: *Phys. Rev.* **98**, 1520 (1955).
DH1. DeStaebler, H., Jr.: *Phys. Rev.* **95**, 1110 (1954).
DJ. DuMond, J. W. M., and E. R. Cohen: *Revs. Modern Phys.* **25**, 691 (1953).
DJ1. Davidson, J. P.: *Phys. Rev.* **91**, 1020L (1953).
DM. Danysz, M., and J. Pniewski: *Phil. Mag.* **44**, 348 (1953).
DN. Dallaporta, N.: *Nuovo cimento* **11**, 82 (1954).
DP. *Proc. Duke University Conference on Cosmic Rays*, December, 1953.
DR. Durbin, Loar, and Steinberger: *Phys. Rev.* **83**, 646 (1951).
DR1. Durbin, Loar, and Havens: *Phys. Rev.* **88**, 179 (1952).
DR2. Daniel, R. R., and D. H. Perkins: *Proc. Roy. Soc. (London)*, ser. A, **221**, 351 (1954).
DR3. Dalitz, R. H.: *Phys. Rev.* **99**, 1475 (1955).
EY. Eisenberg, Y.: *Phys. Rev.* **96**, 541 (1954).
FM1. Friedlander, Keefe, Menon, and Merlin: *Phil. Mag.* **45**, 533 (1954).
FM2. Friedlander, M. W.: *Phil. Mag.* **45**, 418 (1954).
FM3. Friedlander, Keefe, Menon, and van Rossum: *Phil. Mag.* **45**, 1043 (1954).
FP. Fowler, Menon, Powell, and Rochat: *Phil. Mag.* **42**, 1040 (1951).
FP1. Freier, Anderson, and Naugle: *Phys. Rev.* **94**, 677 (1954).
FS. Fung, Mohler, Pevsner, and Ritson: *Phys. Rev.* **101**, 493 (1956).
FW. Fry, W. F., and J. J. Lord: *Phys. Rev.* **87**, 533 (1952).
FW1. Fretter, Gregory, Johnston, Lagarrigue, Meyer, Muller, and Peyrou: *Bagnères Conference Proc.* **26** (1953).
FW2. Fowler, Shutt, Thorndike, and Whittemore: *Phys. Rev.* **91**, 1287 (1953).
FW3. Fowler, Shutt, Thorndike, and Whittemore: *Phys. Rev.* **93**, 861 (1954).
FW4. Fry, W. F., and G. R. White: *Nuovo cimento* **11**, 551 (1954).
FW5. Fowler, Shutt, Thorndike, and Whittemore: *Phys. Rev.* **98**, 121 (1955).
FW6. Fry, Schneps, and Swami: *Phys. Rev.* **99**, 1561 (1955); **101**, 1526 (1956).
FW7. Fry, Schneps, Snow, and Swami: *Phys. Rev.* **100**, 1448 (1955).
GB. Gregory, Lagarrigue, Leprince-Ringuet, Muller, and Peyrou: *Nuovo cimento* **11**, 292 (1954).
GD. Gayther, D. B.: *Phil. Mag.* **45**, 570 (1954).
GG. Goldhaber, G., and S. J. Goldsack: *Bull. Am. Phys. Soc.* **30** (1), 64 (1955).
GM. Gell-Mann, M., and A. Pais: *Proc. International Physics Conference*, Glasgow, July, 1954.
GM1. Goldhaber, M.: *Phys. Rev.* **92**, 1279 (1953).

GM2. Gell-Mann, M.: *Phys. Rev.* **92,** 833 (1953).

GR. Gatto, R.: *Nuovo cimento* **1,** 372 (1955); for references to the hyperfragment literature, see especially p. 378.

GS. "G-Stack Collaboration Experiment (1954)," Cosmic-ray Laboratories of Bristol, Padua, Milan, Genoa, and Dublin (unpublished).

HA. Herz, Hodgson, and Tennent: *Phil. Mag.* **44,** 85 (1953).

HA1. Hodson, Ballam, Arnold, Harris, Rau, Reynolds, and Treiman: *Phys. Rev.* **96,** 1089 (1954).

HE. "High Energy Nuclear Physics," Proceedings of the Fifth Annual Rochester Conference, January, 1955, Interscience Publishers, Inc., New York. See especially the summary by B. Rossi, pp. 124ff.

HG. Harris, G. G.: *Phys. Rev.* **98,** 1202 (A), (1955).

HH. Hubbard, H. W.: University of California Radiation Laboratory Report, UCRL-1623, 1952 (unpublished).

HH1. Heckman, H. H.: UCRL Report 3003, May 18, 1955.

HJ. Hornbostel, J., and E. O. Salant: *Phys. Rev.* **93,** 902L (1954).

HJ1. Hornbostel, J., and E. O. Salant: *Phys. Rev.* **98,** 218 (1955).

HJ2. Hornbostel, J., and E. O. Salant: *Phys. Rev.* **99,** 338 (1955).

HR1. Hill, Salant, and Widgoff: *Bull. Am. Phys. Soc.* **29** (7), 32 (1954).

HR2. Hill, Salant, and Widgoff: *Phys. Rev.* **94,** 1794L (1954).

HR3. Hill, Salant, Widgoff, Osborne, Pevsner, Ritson, Crussard, and Walker: *Bull. Am. Phys. Soc.* **29,** 60 (1954).

HR4. Hill, Salant, and Widgoff: *Phys. Rev.* **99,** 229 (1955).

HT. Hoang, Jauneau, Kayas, Leprince-Ringuet, Morellet, Orkin-Lecourtois, and Trembley: *Compt. rend.* **238,** 1633 (1954).

HT1. Hoang, Jauneau, Jouvin, Kayas, Leprince-Ringuet, Morellet, Orkin-Lecourtois, and Trembley, *Suppl. Nuovo cimento,* ser. X, **1** (3), (1955).

IN. Isachsen, Vangen, and Sörensen: *Phil. Mag.* **44,** 224 (1953).

JM. Jakobson, Shulz, and Steinberger: *Phys. Rev.* **81,** 894 (1952).

JR. Johnston, R. H. W., and C. O'Ceallaigh: *Phil. Mag.* **45,** 424 (1954).

KD. King, Seeman, and Shapiro: *Phys. Rev.* **92,** 838 (1953).

KL. Kerth, Stork, Birge, Haddock, and Whitehead: *Bull. Am. Phys. Soc.* **30** (3), 41 (1955).

KM. Kaplon, Klarmann, and Yekutieli: *Phys. Rev.* **99,** 1528 (1955).

KW. Kraushaar, W. L.: *Phys. Rev.* **86,** 513 (1952).

LA1. Lagarrigue, A., and C. Peyrou: *J. phys. radium* **12,** 848 (1951).

LC. Lattes, Occhialini, and Powell: *Nature* **160,** 453 (1947).

LD. Lal, Pal, and Peters: *Phys. Rev.* **92,** 438 (1953).

LD1. Lal, Pal, and Peters: *Proc. Indian Acad. Sci.* **38,** 398 (1953).

LD2. Lal, Pal, and Peters: *Bagnères Conference Rept.* 146 (1953).

LL. Leprince-Ringuet, L., and M. L'heritier: *Compt. rend.* **219,** 618 (1944).

LL1. Leprince-Ringuet, L., *Ann. Rev. Nuclear Sci.* **3,** 39 (1953).

LL2. Landau, L. D.: *Doklady Akad. Nauk U.S.S.R.* **60,** 207 (1948).

LL3. Leprince-Ringuet, L., and B. Rossi: *Phys. Rev.* **92,** 722 (1953).

LW. Lock, W. O., and J. V. Major: *Proc. Roy. Soc. (London),* ser. A, **221,** 391 (1954).

ML. Mezzetti, L., and J. W. Keuffel: *Phys. Rev.* **95,** 858 (1954).

MM. Menon, M. G. K., and C. O'Ceallaigh: *Proc. Roy. Soc. (London),* ser. A, **221,** 292 (1954).

MR1. Marshak, R. E.: "Meson Physics," McGraw-Hill Book Company, Inc., New York, 1952.

NJ. Newth, J. A.: *Proc. Roy. Soc. (London),* ser. A, **221,** 406 (1954).

NY. Nambu, Nishina, and Yamaguchi: *Progr. Theoret. Phys. (Japan)* **6,** 615 (1951).

OC. C. O'Cealleigh: *Phil. Mag.* **42,** 1032 (1951).

PA. Pais, A.: *Phys. Rev.* **86,** 663 (1952).

PC. Powell, C. F., discussion leader, *Proc. Roy. Soc. (London),* ser. A, **221** (1146), 277–420 (1954).

PC1. Powell, C. F.: *Repts. Progr. in Phys.* **13,** 350 (1950).

PC2. Powell, C. F.: *Nature* **173,** 469 (1954).

PD1. Page, D. I.: *Phil. Mag.* **45**, 863 (1954).
PD2. Peaslee, D. C.: *Phys. Rev.* **86**, 127 (1952); *Progr. Theoret. Phys. (Japan)* **10**, 227 (1953).
PH. Primakoff, H., and W. Cheston: *Phys. Rev.* **93**, 908 (1954).
PP. Proceedings of Padua Conference on Unstable Particles, *Suppl., Nuovo cimento* **12** (2), 163 (1954).
PW. Panofsky, Aamodt, and Hadley: *Phys. Rev.* **81**, 565 (1951).
RA. Rosenfeld, A. H.: *Phys. Rev.* **96**, 130 (1954).
RA1. Rosenfeld, A. H.: *Phys. Rev.* **96**, 139 (1954).
RB1. Rossi, B., and N. Nereson: *Phys. Rev.* **62**, 417 (1942).
RB2. Rossi, B.: "High Energy Particles," Prentice-Hall, Inc., Englewood Cliffs, N.J., 1952.
RD. Ritson, Pevsner, Fung, Widgoff, Zorn, S. Goldhaber, and G. Goldhaber: *Phys. Rev.* **101**, 1085 (1956).
RG. Rochester, G. D., and C. C. Butler: *Nature* **160**, 855 (1947).
RG1. Rochester, G. D., and C. C. Butler: *Repts. Progr. in Phys.* **16**, 364 (1953).
RM. Appa Rao, M. V. K., and S. Mitra: *Proc. Indian Acad. Sci.* (Sec. A) **41**, 30 (1955).
RU. *Proc. Univ. Rochester Ann. Conf. on High Energy Physics*, 1952–1955.
SA. Seriff, Leighton, Hsiao, Cowan, and Anderson: *Phys. Rev.* **78**, 290 (1950).
SF1. Smith, F. M.: UCRL-2371, Berkeley, Feb. 2, 1954.
SF2. Smith, Birnbaum, and Barkas: *Phys. Rev.* **91**, 765 (1953).
SJ. Sorrels, Leighton, and Anderson: submitted to *Phys. Rev.* July, 1955.
SM. Shapiro, M. M.: Report on the Bagnères Congress, *Science* **118**, 701 (1953).
SM1. Shapiro, King, and Seeman: *Proc. Bagnères Conference on Cosmic Radiation* (1953).
SM2. Schein, Haskin, Glasser, Fainberg, and Brown: *Bagnères Conference Proc.* 166 (1953).
SM3. Shapiro, Seeman, and Stiller: "Proceedings of the Fifth Annual Rochester Conference," Interscience Publishers, Inc., New York, 1955.
SN. Seeman, Shapiro, and Stiller: *Bull. Am. Phys. Soc.* **30** (1), (1955).
SN1. Seeman, Shapiro, and Stiller: *Phys. Rev.* **100**, 1480 (1955).
SR. Sagane, Gardner, and Hubbard: *Phys. Rev.* **82**, 557 (1951).
SR1. Sachs, R. G.: *Phys. Rev.* **99**, 1573 (1955).
TA. Thorndike, A. M.: "Mesons, A Summary of Experimental Facts," McGraw-Hill Book Company, Inc., New York, 1952.
TD. Tidman, Davis, Herz, and Tennent: *Phil. Mag.* **44**, 350 (1953).
TG. Trilling, G. H., and R. B. Leighton: *Phys. Rev.* **100**, 1468 (1955).
TR. Thompson, R. W.: *Science* **120**, 585 (1954).
TR1. Thompson, Buskirk, Etter, Karzmark, and Rediker: *Phys. Rev.* **90**, 329 (1953).
TR2. Thompson, Burwell, Huggett, and Karzmark: *Phys. Rev.* **95**, 1576 (1954).
TR3. Thompson, Burwell, Cohn, Huggett, and Karzmark: *Phys. Rev. A* **95**, 661 (1954).
VJ. Vilain, J. H., and R. W. Williams, *Phys. Rev.* **94**, 1011 (1954).
VP. Proceedings of the International School of Physics Held at Varenna, August–September, 1953, *Suppl. Nuovo cimento* **11** (2), (1954).
VV. Van Lint, Anderson, Cowan, Leighton, and York: *Phys. Rev.* **94**, 1732 (1954).
VV1. Van Lint, Trilling, Leighton, and Anderson: *Phys. Rev.* **95**, 295L (1954).
WC. Weigand, C.: *Phys. Rev.* **83**, 1085 (1951).
WJ. Wilson, J. G.: "Progress in Cosmic-ray Physics," North-Holland Publishing Co., Amsterdam; Interscience Publishers, Inc., New York, 1954.
YC. Yang, C. N.: *Phys. Rev.* **77**, 242 (1950).
YC1. York, Leighton, and Bjornerud: *Phys. Rev.* **95**, 159 (1954).
YH. Yagoda, H.: *Phys. Rev.* **98**, 103 (1955).

8m. Health Physics

KARL Z. MORGAN

Oak Ridge National Laboratory

8m-1. Introduction. Health physics, or radiological physics, is a branch of physics relating to other sciences and in particular to biology, chemistry, industrial hygiene, and engineering. It deals with the scattering and loss of energy of ionizing radiation and the damage produced by this radiation in passing through matter. It relates to the design and proper use of sources of ionizing radiation, instruments for measuring the properties of this radiation, the absorption and scattering of this radiation in protective shields and in human tissue, engineering problems associated with the construction and use of facilities for the proper handling of sources of ionizing radiation, and the setting and enforcement of proper standards of radiation protection.

Definition of Units and Terms Commonly Used in Health Physics

Roentgen (*r*). That quantity of X or gamma radiation such that the associated corpuscular emission per 0.001293 g of dry air (equal 1 cc at 0°C and 760 mm Hg) produces, in air, ions carrying 1 esu of quantity of electricity of either sign.

Roentgen Equivalent Physical (*rep*). That amount of ionizing radiation of any type which results in the absorption of energy at the point in question in soft tissue to the extent of 93 ergs/g. It is approximately equal to 1 roentgen of about 200 kv X radiation in soft tissue.

Rad. An ionizing radiation unit corresponding to an absorption of energy in any medium of 100 ergs/g (1 rad in tissue = 100/93 rep).

Roentgen Equivalent Man (*rem*). That amount of ionizing radiation of any type which produces the same damage to man as 1 roentgen of about 200 kv X radiation. (1 rem = 1 rad in tissue/RBE. It should be noted that, when the physical dose is measured in rep units, the approximate definition is used: 1 rem $\approx$ 1 rep/RBE.)

Relative Biological Effectiveness (*RBE*). The biological effectiveness of any type of energy of ionizing radiation in producing a specific biological damage (e.g., leukemia, anemia, sterility, carcinogenesis, cataracts, shortening of life span, etc.) relative to damage produced by X or gamma radiation of about 200 kv. It is given frequently as an average value in the common energy range of a particular type of ion (see Table 8m-2).

Curie (*c*). A unit of radioactivity defined as the quantity of any radioactive nuclide in which the number of disintegrations per second is 3.700×10^{10}. Latest measurements of the half life of Ra^{226} seem to indicate that the activity of a gram of Ra^{226} is slightly less than 1 curie.

Bragg-Gray Principle[1] and applications of it are used as the basis of many measurements of ionizing radiation. According to this principle the energy loss $(dE/dm)_b$ of

[1] W. Bragg, "Studies in Radioactivity," 1912; L. H. Gray, *Proc. Roy. Soc.* (*London*), ser. A, **122**, 647 (1929); **156**, 578 (1936); *Brit. J. Radiol.* **10**, 600, 721 (1937); *Proc. Cambridge Phil. Soc.* **40**, 72 (1944).

ionizing radiation absorbed per unit of mass of a given medium is related to the ionization absorbed in a small gas-filled cavity in said medium by means of the following expression:

$$\left(\frac{dE}{dm}\right)_b = P_b W_g J_g$$

where P_b is the relative mass stopping power of the medium with respect to the gas, W_g is the average energy required to produce an ion pair in the gas, and J, the quantity that is usually determined experimentally, is the number of ion pairs produced per unit mass of the gas in the cavity. It should be emphasized that, in order for this principle to hold, the gas cavity must be small compared with the range of the ionizing particles and both W_g and P_b must be independent of the energy of the radiation. A special application of the Bragg-Gray principle is to construct the walls of the chamber and the gas of the same material, e.g., air or tissue equivalent, and under these conditions the principle applies when the cavity is large compared with the range of the ionizing particles.

Conversion Equations Relating Dose to Flux

$$1 \text{ r} = \frac{2.08 \times 10^3 W_a}{(\mu - \sigma_s)_a E} \approx \frac{7.1 \times 10^4}{(\mu - \sigma_s)_a E} \quad \text{photons/cm}^2$$

$$1 \text{ r/hr} = \frac{0.579 W_a}{(\mu - \sigma_s)_a E} \approx \frac{5.6 \times 10^{5*}}{E} \quad \text{photons/cm}^2 \text{ sec}$$

$$1 \text{ rad} = \frac{8.07 \times 10^{10}}{W_a S_a P_t} \quad \beta \text{ or } \alpha/\text{cm}^2$$

$$1 \text{ rad/hr} = \frac{2.24 \times 10^7}{W_a S_a P_t} \approx \frac{6.1 \times 10^{5\dagger}}{S_a} \quad \beta/\text{cm}^2 \text{ sec}$$

$$1 \text{ rad/hr} \approx \frac{5.4 \times 10^{5\ddagger}}{S_a} \quad \alpha/\text{cm}^2 \text{ sec}$$

In these equations W_a is the average energy per ion pair (ev/ip), S_a is the average specific ionization (ip/cm), and $(\mu - \sigma_s)_a$ is the total coefficient of absorption minus the Compton-scattering coefficient¶ of energy, E (Mev), in air. P_t is the relative mass stopping power in tissue relative to air. The final values given in the above equations are for density of air, $\rho_a = 0.001293$ g/cc.

8m-2. Equations Used Frequently in Health Physics. *Common Shielding Equations.* POINT SOURCE: Dose rate at distance X (centimeters) from a 1-curie point source:

$$R_p = \frac{1.5 \sum_i (\mu - \sigma_s)_i E_i e^{-\mu_i X} f_i B_i 10^8}{X^2} = \sum_i \frac{R_i e^{-\mu_i X} B_i}{X^2}$$

in which R_i = r/hr at 1 cm distance from a 1-curie point source emitting photons of energy E_i (Mev), R_p = total r/hr at distance X (cm) from a 1-curie point source, μ_i is the total coefficient of absorption (in cm^{-1} of medium between source and point of measurement), f_i is the fraction of emitted photons having energy E_i, and $(\mu - \sigma_s)_i$ is the total minus the Compton-scattering coefficient of absorption (in cm^{-1} of air) for

* Final approximate equation correct from 0.07 to 2.0 Mev within about 12 per cent, assuming $W_a = 34$ ev per ion pair.

† Final approximate equation correct from 0.01 to 2.0 Mev within about 6 per cent.

‡ Final approximate equation correct from 1.0 to 6.0 Mev within about 6 per cent.

¶ W. S. Snyder and J. L. Powell, Absorption of γ-Rays, Report ORNL-421, March, 1950; G. R. White, X-ray Attenuation Coefficients from 10 kev to 100 Mev, *Natl. Bur. Standards (U.S.) Rept.* 1003, May 13, 1952.

photons of energy E_i. The term B_i is the build-up factor due to the scattered radiation of energy E_i. Its value[1] depends upon the width of the beam and the distance, volume, and atomic number of the scattering medium. For a short distance X from the point source (i.e., a few meters) in air

$$e^{\mu_i X} B_i \approx 1$$

General Equations Applied to Beta Radiation

1. Range of beta radiation

$$X \approx \frac{1}{\rho}\,[0.54E_m - 0.13(1 - e^{-3.2E_m})]$$

in which X = range in centimeters of medium of density ρ (g/cc). The maximum energy of the beta radiation is E_m (Mev).

2. Average energy of beta radiation is given approximately by the equation

$$E \approx 0.33E_m \left(1 - \frac{Z^{\frac{1}{2}}}{50}\right)\left(1 + \frac{E_m^{\frac{1}{2}}}{4}\right)$$

in which E is the average energy from the normal distribution of energies from a source of atomic number Z that emits beta radiation with a maximum energy E_m.

Maximum Permissible Body Burdens and Concentrations of Radioisotopes in Air and Water.[2] One should attempt to avoid all unnecessary exposure to ionizing radiation, but for practical reasons maximum permissible exposure levels have been set by the following equations.

1. Maximum permissible body burden q under equilibrium conditions

$$q = \frac{8.4 \times 10^{-4} m}{f_2 \Sigma E(\text{RBE})N}$$

in which q (μc) in the total body under equilibrium conditions delivers a dose rate of 0.3 rem/week to the critical body organ of mass m (g). The nonuniform distribution factor N is taken as 5 for alpha, beta, and recoil components of energy emitted by radioisotopes for which the bone is the critical organ, with the exception of Ra^{226} and P^{32}, in which case it is 1. The term f_2 is the fraction in the critical organ of that in the total body, E is the average energy (Mev), and RBE is the relative biological effectiveness of the radiation (= 1 for beta and gamma emitters, 10 for alpha, and 20 for atomic recoils). The critical body organ is the one receiving the radioisotope that results in the greatest body damage, and the equilibrium condition of exposure is considered to exist after the material has been consumed for a sufficient time that the amount taken into the body per day is equal exactly to the amount eliminated per day by radioactive decay plus biological elimination.

In the case of alpha-emitting radioisotopes for which the bone is the critical organ, use is made of the long-standing generally accepted value of $q = 0.1$ μc for Ra^{226} by making a comparison on an energy basis with Ra^{226} by means of the equation

$$q = \frac{16}{f_2 \Sigma E(\text{RBE})N}$$

[1] G. H. Peebles, Gamma-ray Transmission through Finite Slabs, *Rand Report R*-240, Dec. 1, 1952.

[2] For detailed information on maximum permissible exposure levels, refer to "Maximum Permissible Amounts of Radioisotopes in the Human Body and Maximum Permissible Concentrations in Air and Water," Handbook 52, Superintendent of Documents, Washington, D.C.; Report of the International Commission on Radiological Protection, Supplement No. 6, Dec. 1, 1956; and K. Z. Morgan and M. R. Ford, Developments in Internal Dose Determinations, *Nucleonics* **12** (6), 32–39 (June, 1954).

2. Maximum permissible concentration in air $(MPC)_a$ and water $(MPC)_w$ under equilibrium conditions,

$$(MPC)_a = \frac{3.5 \times 10^{-8} q f_2}{T f_a (1 - e^{-0.693t/T})}$$

$$(MPC)_w = \frac{3.1 \times 10^{-4} q f_2}{T f_w (1 - e^{-0.693t/T})}$$

in which $(MPC)_a$ and $(MPC)_w$ are given in μc/cc of air and water, respectively, that will result in a dose rate 0.3 rem/week to the critical organ after an exposure for a time t (days). f_a and f_w are the fractions that arrive in the critical organ from inhalation and ingestion, respectively, and the effective half life T (days) in the critical organ is given by the equation

$$T = \frac{T_b T_r}{T_b + T_r}$$

in which T_b and T_r are the biological and radioactive half lives, respectively.

In the case of noble gas,

$$(MPC)_a = \frac{9 \times 10^{-7}}{E}$$

3. Dose delivered to the critical body organ following a single intake,

$$D = \frac{74 \Sigma E (\text{RBE}) N f I_0 T}{m} (1 - e^{-0.693t/T})$$

in which D = dose in rem delivered to the critical organ of mass m (g), in time t (days), when I_0 (μc) are taken into the body in a single event and the fraction f is deposited in the critical organ.

8m-3. Tables of Values Commonly Used in Health Physics

TABLE 8m-1. CONVERSION FACTORS FOR X- OR GAMMA-RAY ABSORPTION IN AIR
(Values corresponding to 1 roentgen)

Absorbed in 1 cc of Air	*Absorbed in 1 g of Air*
1 esu/cc	773.4 esu/g
2.083×10^9 ion pair/cc	1.611×10^{12} ion pair/g
3.336×10^{-10} coulombs/cc	2.58×10^{-7} coulombs/g
7.09×10^{10} ev/cc	5.48×10^{13} ev/g
0.113 ergs/cc	87.8 ergs/g
1.13×10^{-8} joules/cc	87.8×10^{-6} joules/g
2.71×10^{-9} cal/cc	2.09×10^{-6} cal/g

TABLE 8m-2. GENERAL VALUES OF MAXIMUM PERMISSIBLE EXPOSURE TO VARIOUS TYPES OF IONIZING RADIATION

Type	mr/week	mrad/week in tissue	Gen. values of RBE	mrem/week	Approximate flux for an 8-hr exposure
X or γ	300	...	1	300	4,200 photons/cm² sec of 1 Mev
β	...	300	1	300	45β/cm² sec of 1 Mev $E_{\max}$
e^-	...	300	1	300	68 electrons/cm² sec of 1 Mev
n_t	...	120	2.5	300	$2{,}000n_t$/cm² sec of 0.025 ev*
n_f	...	30	~10	300	$58n_f$/cm² sec of 2 Mev*
p	...	30	10	300	$0.17p$/cm² sec of 5 Mev
α	...	30	10	300	0.014α/cm² sec of 5 Mev
O, C, N, etc.	...	15	20	300	0.0006 oxygen ions/cm² sec of 5 Mev

* Values obtained by W. S. Snyder, Calculations for Maximum Permissible Exposure to Thermal Neutrons, *Nucleonics* **6**, 2, 46–50 (February, 1950); also W. S. Snyder and J. Neufeld, Calculated Depth Dose Curves in Tissue for Broad Beams of Fast Neutrons, *Brit. J. Radiol.* **28**, 342 (1955).

Table 8m-3. Values of Maximum Permissible Exposure of Body Organs of Adults to Various Types of Ionizing Radiation[a]

Type of radiation	Max permissible value measured at surface of trunk of body	In skin[b,f] of the: Total body, mrem/week	In skin[b,f] of the: Appendages[c] of body, mrem/week	Lens of eyes,[d] mrem/week	Gonads,[d] mrem/week	Blood-forming organs,[d] mrem/week	Intermediate tissue,[f,e] mrem/week
Low penetrating[g]	1,500 mrad/week (1,500 mrad/week)	1,500 (1,500)	1,500 (1,500)	300 (600)	300 (600)	300 (600)	300–1,500 (600–1,500)
X and γ of <3 Mev	450 mr/week (900 mr/week)	450 (900)	1,500 (1,500)	450 (600)	300 (800)	400 (800)	400–450 (800–900)
β^-, e^-, e^+	600 mrad/week (1,200 mrad/week)	600 (1,200)	1,500 (1,500)	300 (600)	300 (600)	300 (600)	300–600 (600–1,200)
Protons p	60 mrad/week (120 mrad/week)	600 (1,200)	1,500 (1,500)	300 (300)	300 (600)	300 (600)	300–600 (600–1,200)
Fast neutrons n_f	50–2,000 n_f/cm² sec (100–4,000 n_f/cm² sec)	300–600[h] (600–1,200)[h]	750–1,500[h] (750–1,500)[h]	300 (300–600)[h]	300 (600)	300 (600)	300–600 (600–1,200)
Thermal neutrons, n_t	3,000 n_t/cm² sec (6,000 n_t/cm² sec)	500[h] (1,000)[h]	1,200[h] (1,200)[h]	300 (420)[h]	100, 300[h,i] (200, 600)[h,i]	170[h] (340)[h]	170–500 (340–1,000)
Alpha	Exposure from internally deposited isotopes	1,500 (1,500)	1,500 (1,500)	300 (300)	300 (600)	300 (600)	300–1,500 (600–1,500)
O, C, N, etc	Generated in body by fast neutrons	1,500 (1,500)	1,500 (1,500)	300 (300)	300 (600)	300 (600)	300–1,500 (600–1,500)

[a] The values given in this table may be converted from units of mrem/week to mrad/week by dividing by the appropriate values of RBE. Commonly assumed average values of RBE are 1 for X, γ, β, and e^+; 10 for p and α; and 20 for heavy ions (O, C, and N). The values in parentheses apply to persons after age forty-five. Refer to NBS Handbooks 52 and 59 for additional information.

[b] The minimum thickness of the epidermis is taken as 0.07 mm.

[c] Appendages of the body include head, neck, hands, forearms, feet, and ankles.

[d] The average depths of the ovaries, testes, blood-forming organs, and lens of the eyes are considered to be 7 cm, 1 cm, 5 cm, and 3 mm, respectively.

[e] "Intermediate" tissue is considered to be that of the trunk of body between 0.07 mm and 5 cm depth (excluding the lens of the eye and the testes).

[f] These values must not be used unless shielding or localization of the radiation can be provided so that the exposure limits to other critical tissue are not exceeded.

[g] Low-penetrating radiation (X, γ, β, e, α, or p) with a half-value layer less than 1 mm of soft tissue. Does not apply to neutron radiation.

[h] Values for neutrons are determined by pattern of distribution in body; see W. S. Snyder, Calculations for Maximum Permissible Exposure to Thermal Neutrons, *Nucleonics* **6,** 2, 46–50 (February, 1950); also Calculated Depth Dose Curves for Broad Beams of Fast Neutrons, *Brit. J. Radiol.* **28,** 342 (1955) and Papers of Health Physics Society meeting in Ann Arbor, Mich., June, 1956. Values used decrease with the energy of the neutrons.

[i] Smaller value applies to ovaries at 7 cm depth and larger value to testes at 1 cm depth.

TABLE 8m-4. MAXIMUM PERMISSIBLE FLUX OF A NORMAL BEAM OF NEUTRONS REQUIRED TO DELIVER A DOSE OF 0.3 REM PER 40-HR WEEK

Neutron energy, Mev	Calculated values,* $n/cm^2/sec$	International (ICRP) max permissible values, $n/cm^2/sec$
10	27(50)	30
5	27(55)	30
4	31(57)	30
3	36(58)	30
2	(43)58	40
1	61(55)	60
0.5	86(90)	80
0.1	230(250)	200
0.01	1,050(1,200)	1,000
10^{-5}	1600(1600)	2,000
2.5×10^{-8}	1,909(2,000)	2,000

* Values obtained by W. S. Snyder, Calculations for Maximum Permissible Exposure to Thermal Neutrons, *Nucleonics* **6,** 2, 46–50 (February, 1950), Calculated Depth Dose Curves in Tissue for Broad Beams of Fast Neutrons, *Brit. J. Radiol.* **28,** 342 (1955), and Papers of Health Physics Society meeting in Ann Arbor, Mich., June, 1956. All values are calculated with reference to a 30-cm tissue phantom. The values in parentheses assume the functional relationship between RBE and linear energy transfer as given in the National Bureau of Standards Handbook 59. The other calculated values assume RBE = 1 for X and γ radiation, RBE = 10 for protons, and RBE = 20 for heavy recoil ions.

TABLE 8m-5. MAXIMUM PERMISSIBLE CONCENTRATIONS OF RADIOISOTOPES IN AIR AND WATER FOR CONTINUOUS EXPOSURE*

Medium in which contained	β or γ emitter, $\mu c/cc$	α emitter, $\mu c/cc$
Air..............	10^{-9}	5×10^{-12}
Water...........	10^{-7}	10^{-7}

* These values are reduced by a factor of 10 when applied to minors and to large populations. These are general values which are considered to be safe for limited exposure (for a few months) to any mixture of radioisotopes. The reader is referred to various publications for values of maximum permissible concentrations of specific radioisotopes. See "Maximum Permissible Amounts of Radioisotopes in the Human Body and Maximum Permissible Concentrations in Air and Water," Handbook 52, Superintendent of Documents, Washington, D.C.; Report of the International Commission on Radiological Protection, Supplement No. 6, Dec. 1, 1954; and K. Z. Morgan and M. R. Ford, Developments in Internal Dose Determination, *Nucleonics* **12** (6), 32–39 (June, 1954).

TABLE 8m-6. THEORETICAL VALUES OF $(\mu - \sigma_s)_{air}$ AND OF r/hr AT 1 m FROM A 1-CURIE SOURCE

Energy, Mev	$(\mu - \sigma_s)_{air}$,* cm^2/g	r/hr at 1 m from 1-curie source†
0.02	0.50	0.16
0.04	0.078	0.063
0.06	0.035	0.042
0.08	0.025	0.040
0.10	0.023	0.047
0.20	0.026	0.11
0.40	0.029	0.23
0.60	0.029	0.35
0.80	0.028	0.45
1.0	0.027	0.55
2.0	0.023	0.93
4.0	0.019	1.5
6.0	0.017	2.1
8.0	0.016	2.6
10	0.015	3.0
20	0.013	5.3
40	0.013	11
60	0.014	17
100	0.015	30

* W. S. Snyder and J. L. Powell, Absorption of γ-Rays, Report ORNL-421, March, 1950; G. R. White, X-ray Attenuation Coefficients from 10 kev to 100 Mev, *Natl. Bur. Standards (U.S.) Rept.* 1003, May 13, 1952.

† These values do not include contributions to the dose due to air scattering and absorption. If absorption of air is included, the value of r/hr at 1 m from a 1-curie source for 0.02 Mev would be reduced by 8%, the value for 0.04 Mev by 3%, the value for 0.06 Mev by 1%, and the correction would be insignificant for the other values.

8m-4. Regulations for the Shipment of Radioactive Materials. The reader should refer to official publications[1] for detailed information on the shipment of radioactive materials. General limitations for the shipment of radioisotopes are:

1. Package must not be less than 4 in. in its smallest outside dimension.
2. A single package must not contain more than 2 curies (2.7 curies[2] of less dangerous radioisotopes).
3. Surface of package must contain no significant contamination.
4. Dose rate at any accessible surface must not exceed 200 mr/hr (or equivalent in mrem/hr).
5. Dose rate at 1 m must not exceed 10 mr/hr.
6. Shipments of radioactive materials by rail and motor express, air, and boat fall into four categories (groups I, II, III, and exempt). Only exempt shipments may be made by mail.

[1] Robley D. Evans, Chairman of the Subcommittee on Shipment of Radioactive Substances, "Physical, Biological and Administrative Problems Associated with the Transportation of Radioactive Substances." ICC shipping regulations are given in Title 49, Parts 71 to 78, of the Code of Federal Regulations; Civil Aeronautics Board regulations are given in Part 49 of the Civil Air Regulations, "Transportation of Explosives and Other Dangerous Articles"; regulations of the United States Coast Guard are given in the Federal Register, July 17, 1952, pp. 6460ff.; regulations governing the transportation of radioactive materials in the U.S. Mails are given in the U.S. Postal Guide, p. 51, pt. I, 1951 ed.

[2] The subcommittee on Shipment of Radioisotopes of the National Research Council at its meeting in September, 1954, recommended to the Bureau of Explosives that this limit be raised to 300 curies.

Index

References to table are shown by the letter T, and references to figures are shown by the letter f.

A

Absolute electrical units related to international (T), **5**-106
Absolute ohm, definition of, **5**-105, **5**-198
Absolute photopic luminosity, definition of, **6**-50
Absolute scotopic luminosity, definition of, **6**-53
Absolute thermoelectric power, **5**-98
Absolute viscosity, definition of, **2**-201, **2**-203
units and conversion factors for (T), **2**-202
of various gases (T), **2**-207
Absolute volt, definition of, **5**-105
Absorption, of light, **6**-36 to **6**-40
and scattering of em waves, **5**-70 to **5**-71
of sound, **3**-43 to **3**-53
and heat radiation, **3**-49 to **3**-50
vs. temperature, of sound in water (f), **3**-69
Absorption coefficient, of audience (T), **3**-116
for building materials (T), **3**-116
definition of, **6**-2, **6**-36
vs. frequency for acoustic tiles (f's), **3**-114, **3**-115
of seats (T), **3**-116
of sound (f), (T), **3**-113 to **3**-116
in water (f), **3**-71
of various substances (T), **6**-37
Absorption constant, definition of (optical), **6**-102, **6**-103
of evaporated mirror coatings (T), **6**-104
of organic liquids (T), **3**-73
of various metals (T's), **6**-105 to **6**-107
Absorption cross section, **5**-71
universal average, **5**-71 to **5**-72
Absorption factor, definition of, **6**-2
Absorption measure in sound, **3**-45 to **3**-46
Absorption spectrum, definition of, **6**-2
Absorptive power, definition of, **6**-2
Absorptivity, definition of, **6**-2
Abundance, of the elements (T), **7**-9 to **7**-12
per cent of stable nuclei (T), **8**-6 to **8**-17
A-C to d-c, application chart (T), **5**-261
conversion of, **5**-260 to **5**-268
A-C generators, **5**-258
A-C motors, fractional hp characteristics of (T), **5**-253
and generators, **5**-246 to **5**-250
integral hp characteristics of (T), **5**-254 to **5**-255
A-C resistance, ratio to d-c for solid round wire (T), **5**-201
Acceleration, definition of, **2**-3, **3**-2
due to gravity (T), **2**-91
of electrons and protons, **8**-172 to **8**-181
Accelerators, electrostatic, world-wide list of (T), **8**-182 to **8**-188
linear, world-wide list of (T), **8**-200 to **8**-201
particle, various types of, **8**-172 to **8**-181
world-wide list of (T's), **8**-181 to **8**-201
Acceptable noise level for different rooms, **3**-122
Acceptors and binding energies (T), **5**-160, **5**-163
Acetates, acoustic properties of (T), **3**-72
Acetone volume related to pressure and temperature (T), **2**-158
Achromatic, definition of, **6**-2
Acids, index of refraction of (T), **6**-22
Acoustic, definition of, **3**-2
(*See also* Sound)
Acoustic absorbing materials, porosity and permeability of (T), **2**-180
Acoustic analogues, of capacitor and condenser, **3**-141 to **3**-142
of electric circuit elements, **3**-140 to **3**-142
of transducers and transformers, **3**-177
Acoustic analogy, units for, **3**-177

Acoustic attenuation constant, definition of, **3**-8
Acoustic capacitance, **3**-136
Acoustic center, **3**-11
Acoustic compliance, definition of, **3**-8, **3**-10
Acoustic energy, continuity equation for, **3**-44
Acoustic energy balance, **3**-44
Acoustic energy flux vector, **3**-42, **3**-44
Acoustic equations, of first order, **3**-33
of second order, **3**-34
small-signal, **3**-32 to **3**-34
Acoustic impedance, **3**-108 to **3**-110
definition of, **3**-8, **3**-113
of ear (T), **3**-123, **3**-124
specific, of pulsating sphere, **3**-108 to **3**-109
of a thermoviscous medium, **3**-53
vector, equation for, **3**-138
Acoustic intensity, **3**-6
Acoustic losses, in ferromagnetic and ferroelectric materials, **3**-85 to **3**-86
in metals, **3**-84 to **3**-88
Acoustic mass, definition of, **3**-8
Acoustic medium and thermal noise, **3**-53 to **3**-55
Acoustic ohm, definition of, **3**-9
Acoustic phase constant, definition of, **3**-9
Acoustic power, definition of, **3**-108
Acoustic pressure, alteration of, **3**-39
Acoustic propagation constant, definition of, **3**-9
Acoustic properties, of gases, **3**-56 to **3**-66
of liquids, **3**-67 to **3**-74
liquids vs. gases, **3**-67
of organic liquids (T), **3**-72 to **3**-73
of solids, **3**-74 to **3**-88
Acoustic radiation pressure, **3**-43
Acoustic radiation resistance, of pulsating sphere, **3**-108
of sphere and piston (T), **3**-110
Acoustic reactance, definition of, **3**-9
Acoustic resistance, **3**-134, **3**-136
definition of, **3**-9
Acoustic tile, absorption vs. frequency characteristics (f), **3**-114, **3**-115
Acoustic variables, **3**-32
Acoustical, definition of, **3**-2
Acoustical definitions, **3**-2 to **3**-18
Acoustical energetics, **3**-41 to **3**-43
Acoustical quantities (T), **3**-139
conversion factors for (T), **3**-24
letter symbols for, **3**-18 to **3**-24
Acoustical schematic diagrams, based on impedance analogy (T), **3**-145 to **3**-176
based on mobility analogy (T), **3**-144 to **3**-176
Acoustical symbols (T), **3**-139
Acoustical systems, electrodynamical analogies to, **3**-134 to **3**-139
graphical analogies to electrodynamical systems (f's), **3**-136, **3**-137
with one degree of freedom, **3**-137 to **3**-138
Acoustical units (T), **3**-139
Acoustical waves of finite amplitude, **3**-37 to **3**-39
Acoustics, architectural, **3**-113 to **3**-122
selected references on, **3**-178 to **3**-179
Activation cross section of neutrons, definition of, **8**-130
Activation energy of pure ionic conductors (T), **5**-186 to **5**-188
Adiabatic compressibility of organic liquids (T), **2**-163, **2**-164
Adiabatic demagnetization, **4**-15, **7**-171
Adiabatic gas, pressure-density relation for, **3**-35
Adiabatic isothermal elastic constants of various metals (T), **3**-83
Adiabatic modulus of elasticity, **2**-85 to **2**-86
Adiabatic temperature change in sea water, **2**-121
Adiabatic viscous fluid, equation for, **3**-33
Aftershock in earthquakes, **2**-113
Aichi's formula, **5**-14
A.I.E.E. standards, **5**-246
Air, absorption of sound by, **3**-63 to **3**-66
characteristic impedance of (T), **3**-63
composition of atmosphere (T), **2**-125
compressibility factors for (T), **4**-82
critical energy and radiation length for (T), **8**-39
energy loss of protons in (f), **8**-26
enthalpy of (T), **4**-85
entropy of (T), **4**-86
maximum permissible concentration of radioisotopes in (T), **8**-256
Prandtl numbers for (T), **2**-222
range-energy relation for protons in (f), **8**-27
recombination coefficient in (f's), **5**-177, **5**-178
relative density of (T), **4**-83
specific heat of (T), **3**-59, **4**-84
thermodynamic conversion factors for (T), **4**-81
virial coefficients for (T), **4**-128
voltage breakdown in (f's), **5**-179, **5**-180
X-ray and gamma-ray absorption in (T), **8**-253
Air columns, fundamental frequency of, **3**-102 to **3**-103
Air-earth currents, **5**-285
density at various locations (T), **5**-285
Aircraft engines, lubricating oil specifications for (T), **2**-168
α-Alanin, diffusion coefficients of (T), **2**-192
Albedo measurements (T), **2**-132
Alcohols, saturated, acoustic properties of (T), **3**-72
Alloys, creep rates for (T), **2**-89 to **2**-90
demagnetization curves of (f), **5**-218
density of, **2**-22 to **2**-30
elastic and strength constants of (T), **2**-62 to **2**-78
Hall constants of (T), **5**-237 to **5**-239
linear expansion coefficients of (T), **4**-57 to **4**-60

Alloys, magnetic, magnetization curves of, (f), **5**-214
properties of, for permanent magnets (T), **5**-219
resistivity vs. temperature for (T), **4**-13
saturation magnetization and Curie points of (f) (T's), **5**-207, **5**-209 to **5**-210
skin-effect quantities (T), **5**-90
superconducting transition temperatures for (T), **5**-205
thermal conductivity of (T), **4**-67, **4**-77, **4**-79
thermal emf of, relative to platinum (T), **4**-9
Alnico 5, demagnetization and energy-product curves of (f), **5**-218
Alpha decay, lifetimes and theory, **8**-54 to **8**-56
Alpha decay energy, **8**-40
vs mass number (f), **8**-46
Alpha-decay-energy profile (f), **8**-46
Alpha emitters, alpha-particle energies and abundances of (T), **8**-48 to **8**-53
log half life vs effective alpha energy for (f), **8**-54
various kinds of, **8**-46 to **8**-54
Alpha groups, principal and rare, **8**-46 to **8**-47
Alpha-particle energies of alpha emitters (T), **8**-48 to **8**-53
Alpha particles, abundance of alpha emitters (T), **8**-48 to **8**-53
maximum permissible exposure to (T's), **8**-254, **8**-255
range-energy relation in Ilford C-2 emulsion, **8**-32
range straggling in copper (f's), **8**-37
symbols for, **8**-3
Alpha spectra, complex, **8**-40, **8**-46 to **8**-54
Alphabetical list of elements (T), **7**-5 to **7**-7
Alternate-gradient synchrotron, description of, **8**-177 to **8**-178
Alternating current, application chart for conversion to d-c (T), **5**-262
Altitude, variation of atmospheric conductivity with (T), **5**-286
variation of atmospheric electric field with (T), **5**-286
Altocumulus clouds (f), **2**-130, **2**-134
Alumel, emf of chromel vs alumel thermocouples (T), **4**-12
Aluminum, absorption curve for electrons in (f), **8**-38
energy loss of protons in (f) (T), **8**-28, **8**-35
proton straggling in (T), **8**-36
range-energy relation, for electrons in (f), **8**-39
for protons in (f), **8**-29, **8**-31
Aluminum alloys, density of (T), **2**-24
elastic and strength constants for (T), **2**-64 to **2**-65
Aluminum I, energy-level diagram of (f), **7**-31
Amagat units, definition of, **4**-118, **4**-119
Ambient pressure in flowing liquids, **2**-182
Ambipolar diffusion coefficients for several gases (T), **7**-218
American speech, characteristics of sounds in (T), **3**-131 to **3**-132
Ammonia, efficiency of electron attachment in (f), **5**-176, **5**-177
Amorphous selenium, index of refraction of (T), **6**-26 to **6**-27
Amorphous solids, dielectric properties of (T's), **5**-120 to **5**-132
Ampere, definition of, **5**-2
international vs. absolute (T), **5**-106
Ampere's law, **5**-3
Amplitude of seismic waves, **2**-102 to **2**-103
Analogies between electrical, mechanical, and acoustical systems, **3**-134 to **3**-139
Anechoic chamber, definition of, **3**-2, **3**-17
Anelasticity, **2**-84 to **2**-86
logarithmic decrement, **2**-85
mechanical model of (f), **2**-84
Angular aperture, definition of, **6**-2
Angular correlation of gamma rays, **8**-93
Angular momentum, definition of, **2**-6
of electrons, **7**-17
of light nuclei (f's) (T), **8**-57 to **8**-86
Anisotropic media, field vectors for, **5**-38
Anisotropic wave propagation systems, **5**-64 to **5**-65
Anisotropy constants of uniaxial crystals (T), **5**-222
Anode, definition of, **5**-3
in electrochemistry, **5**-269
Anomalous dispersion of sound, **3**-51
Anomalous skin effect, **5**-200
Antiferroelectric crystals, properties of (T), **5**-156
Antiferroelectric materials, definition of, **5**-3
Antiferromagnetic materials, definition of, **5**-3
and neutron diffraction (T), **5**-227 to **5**-228
orientation of magnetic moments in (f), **5**-229
Antiferromagnetic points of various substances (T), **5**-226
Antiferromagnetic resonance, **5**-104
Antiferromagnetism, **5**-102, **5**-224 to **5**-229
Antineutrino, **8**-3
Antinodes, definition of, **3**-2
Apochromat, definition of, **6**-2
Approximation methods in wave mechanics, **7**-165 to **7**-167
Aqueous solution, isothermal compressibility of (T), **2**-164
surface tension of (T's), **2**-175, **2**-177
Verdet constants for (T), **6**-93
Archimedes, principle of, **2**-12
Architectural acoustics, **3**-113 to **3**-122
Area, units and conversion factors for (T), **2**-16
Argon, compressibility factors for (T), **4**-87
electron energy losses in (f), **5**-181
enthalpy of (T), **4**-90
entropy of (T), **4**-91
relative density of (T), **4**-88

Argon, specific heat of (T), **4**-89
  thermodynamic conversion factors for (T), **4**-81
  virial coefficients for (T), **4**-121
Argon I, energy-level diagram of (f), **7**-33
  photoelectric traces of spectrum (f), **7**-63 to **7**-66
  principal spectral lines of (T), **7**-58 to **7**-62
Arsenic trisulfide glass, index of refraction of (T), **6**-26 to **6**-27
Articulation, acoustic, definition of, **3**-12
  sound, syllable, vowel, or consonant, **3**-13
Articulation index, **3**-132 to **3**-133
  and articulation scores (T), **3**-133
Artificial radioisotopes, **8**-96 to **8**-128
ASA standards, **5**-246
Asbestos insulation and current capacity of conductors (T), **5**-202 to **5**-203
Astatic inductors, **5**-111
Astigmatism, definition of, **6**-2
Astronomical constants (T), **2**-91
Astronomical data, **2**-90 to **2**-91
Astronomical problem in geodesy, **2**-93
Astronomy, radio, **6**-120 to **6**-123
Asymmetric-top molecules, rotational constants and geometrical parameters of, five-atom (T), **7**-159
  four-atom (T), **7**-155
  six-atom (T), **7**-161
  triatomic (T), **7**-153
Asymptotic speed of sound, **3**-48
Atmosphere, characteristics of ions in (T's), **5**-284
  composition of (T), **2**-125
  conductivity, electric field, and air-earth current density of (T), **5**-285
  conductivity vs altitude for (T), **5**-286
  electric field vs altitude (T), **5**-286
  as unit of pressure, **2**-15
  upper, electrical characteristics of, (T), **5**-284
  properties of, **2**-128 to **2**-130
Atmospheric density vs elevation (T), **3**-58
Atmospheric diffusion (f), **2**-135
Atmospheric electricity, **5**-283 to **5**-289
Atmospheric ionization, **5**-283 to **5**-284
Atmospheric precipitation, charge on particles (T), **5**-287
Atmospheric pressure, **3**-56
  vs elevation (T), **3**-58
Atmospheric temperature, **3**-56
  vs elevation (T), **3**-58
Atomic constants (T), **7**-3
Atomic diameters of elements (T), **7**-9 to **7**-12
Atomic hydrogen, hyperfine splitting of (T), **6**-122
Atomic levels of n equivalent electrons (T), **7**-21
Atomic mass (T), **7**-3
  of deuterium, **8**-4
  of hydrogen, **8**-4
  of neutron, **8**-4
  of stable nuclei (T), **8**-6 to **8**-17
Atomic number of elements (T), **7**-5 to **7**-8
Atomic rotatory power, definition of, **6**-7
Atomic spectra, present status of analysis of (T), **7**-22 to **7**-24
  principal lines in, Argon I (f) (T), **7**-58 to **7**-66
    Helium (T), **7**-44 to **7**-45
    Iron I (f) (T), **7**-87 to **7**-118
    Krypton I (f) (T), **7**-66 to **7**-74
    Mercury I (f) (T), **7**-119 to **7**-122
    Neon I (f) (T), **7**-45 to **7**-58
    Xenon I (f) (T), **7**-74 to **7**-87
  structure of, **7**-16 to **7**-26
Atomic susceptibility of elements (f), **5**-236
Atomic units, conversion factors of (T), **7**-4
Atomic weights, of elements (T), **7**-8 to **7**-12
Atoms, electronic structure of (T), **7**-13 to **7**-15
  energy-level diagrams of (f's), **7**-26 to **7**-37
  persistent spectral lines of (T), **7**-39 to **7**-41
Attenuation, of em waves, **5**-58 to **5**-59
  and heat flow in metals (T), **3**-83
  of neutrons in concrete and water, **8**-169
  of sound, **3**-63 to **3**-66
    Kneser's nomogram for (f), **3**-64
    due to radiation, **3**-50
    vs relative humidity (f), **3**-66
    in solids, **3**-79
  of standard r-f cables (f), **5**-57
Attenuation constant, **3**-8, **3**-17, **3**-63
  vs relative humidity (f), **3**-117
Attenuation peaks in copper crystals (f), **3**-88
Audibility threshold, definition of, **3**-14
Audience, absorption coefficient of, **3**-116
Audio frequency, definition of, **3**-2
Audiogram, definition of, **3**-12
Auditory meatus, dimensions of (T), **3**-123
Auger electrons, **8**-3
Aural harmonic, definition of, **3**-12
Autotransformers, **5**-260
Average acoustic pressure, **3**-39
Average velocity, **2**-2
Avogadro's number (T), **7**-3
Axially symmetric gas flow, **2**-217 to **2**-219
Axis, principal, **3**-11
  reference, **3**-11
Azimuthal quantum number, **7**-16

B

Balmer series of spectral lines, definition of, **6**-3
Band-pass filter sections, design of (T), **5**-86 to **5**-89
Band power level, definition of, **3**-2
Band pressure level, definition of, **3**-2
Band-spectrum constant (T), **7**-3
Bar, of elliptical cross section, self-inductance of, **5**-28
  frequency of vibration of, **3**-104, **3**-106
Bar magnets, **5**-35 to **5**-36
Barium, Young's modulus vs temperature for (f), **3**-96
Barium-titanate type transducer, materials, **3**-92
Barn, definition of, **8**-3
Barnet effect, **5**-103

Barometric pressure, **3**-57
Base vectors in different coordinate systems (f's), **2**-2, **2**-3
Basilar membrane in ear (T), **3**-123
Beam angles for piston, ring, and line sources (f), **3**-111, **3**-112
Beam formation, reflectors, lenses, and horns, **5**-73
Beats, definition of, **3**-3
Beer's law, **6**-3
Benzene, first Townsend ionization coefficient in (f), **5**-169
  variation of dielectric constant with temperature for (f), **5**-131
  volume related to pressure and temperature (T), **2**-158
Bernoulli's principle, **2**-13
Berthelot equation as a virial expansion, **4**-119
Berthelot's method for measuring tensile strength, **2**-170 to **2**-171
Beryllium, energy levels of (f) (T), **8**-59 to **8**-67
  energy loss of protons in (T), **8**-35
  proton straggling in (T), **8**-36
Beta decay, **8**-3
Beta-decay chains, **8**-212
Beta radiation, range of, **8**-252
Beta rays, maximum permissible exposure to (T's), **8**-254, **8**-255
Beta transitions, **8**-97
Betatrons, description of, **8**-175 to **8**-176
  world-wide list of (T), **8**-194 to **8**-195
Bethe-Bacher formula, **8**-20
Biaxial minerals, index of refraction of (T), **6**-14 to **6**-17
Binary compounds, saturation magnetization and Curie points of (T), **5**-213
Binary mixtures of gases, **2**-206
Binaural listening, minimum audible pressure (T), **3**-125
Binding energy, of carriers to donors and acceptors (T), **5**-160, **5**-163
  of last neutron and proton (T), **8**-6 to **8**-17
  of neutrons (T), **8**-135 to **8**-143
    definition of, **8**-130
  of nucleus, **8**-19 to **8**-20
Birefringent filters, **6**-48
Bismuth, transition parameters and phase diagram for (f) (T), **4**-36
Black body, chromaticity coordinates of (T), **6**-61
  definition of, **6**-3
Black-body radiation, functions of (T), **6**-64, **6**-65
  total (T), **6**-66 to **6**-67
Blasius gas flow, **2**-224
Blood-forming organs, maximum permissible exposure to ionizing radiation (T), **8**-255
Body, maximum permissible radiation exposure for trunk (T), **8**-255
Body organs, maximum permissible exposure for various radiations (T's), **8**-254, **8**-255
Bohr magneton (T), **7**-3
  definition of, **5**-206
Bohr magneton number, of certain solid solutions (T), **5**-211
  definition of, **5**-206
  of ferrites (T), **5**-211, **5**-212
  of ferromagnetic elements (T), **5**-208
  of paramagnetic materials (T), **5**-241 to **5**-243
  of spinels (T), **5**-212
Boiling-water power reactor, **8**-227
Bolometer, characteristics of (T's), **6**-114, **6**-118
Bolometric color index of stellar spectral classes (T), **6**-80
Bolometric magnitude of stars, **6**-80
Boltzmann constant (T), **7**-3
Boron, energy levels of (f) (T), **8**-62 to **8**-71
Boson, **8**-243
Bougie decimale, definition of, **6**-9
Bound hyperons, **8**-245
Boundary conditions and electromagnetic field equations, **5**-41 to **5**-42
Boundary layer in gas flow, **2**-223
Bounded regions and em waves, **5**-56 to **5**-57
Bragg-Gray principle, **8**-250 to **8**-251
Branch point in circuit theory, **5**-80
Breakdown voltage in air (f's), **5**-179, **5**-180
Breeding reactors, **8**-227
Brewster's law, **6**-3
Brightness, approximate, of various light sources (T), **6**-78
  definition of, **6**-3
  of various stars (T), **6**-82
Brinell hardness number, definition of, **2**-69, **2**-78
  of metals and alloys (T), **2**-61 to **2**-78
British reactors, **8**-240
British thermal unit, definition of, **2**-15
Broad-band noise in liquids, **3**-68
Bromides, optical properties of, **6**-40
Bubble cavities (*see* Transient cavities)
Building materials, absorption coefficients of (T), **3**-116
  diffusivities of (T), **4**-74
Bulk modulus, **2**-10
  of earth layers, **2**-108
n-Butyl alcohol, diffusion coefficients of (T), **2**-192

C

Cables, list of standard radio-frequency (T), **5**-52 to **5**-55
Cadmium cells, **5**-107 to **5**-109
Calcite, index of refraction of (T), **6**-23
Calcium fluoride, absorption coefficients of (T), **6**-37
  index of refraction of (T), **6**-23, **6**-26 to **6**-27
  optical properties of, **6**-40
Calcium I, energy-level diagram of (f), **7**-34
Calcium titanate, Young's modulus vs temperature for (f), **3**-96
Calder Hall reactors, **8**-240
Calorie, definition of, **2**-15
Camphors, variation of dielectric constant with temperature for (f), **5**-131

Candle, definition of, **6**-9
Candle-meter, **6**-4
Candle per square centimeter, definition of, **6**-3, **6**-10
Candlepower, definition of, **6**-6
Capacitance, and acoustic analogy, **3**-135, **3**-136
per meter length of various bodies, **5**-15 to **5**-16
of various body arrangements, **5**-12 to **5**-18
Capacitance coefficients, **5**-17 to **5**-18
Capacitance edge corrections, **5**-16 to **5**-17
Capacitance formulas, mks units, **5**-12 to **5**-18
Capacitance standards, **5**-109 to **5**-110
Capacitivity, definition of, **5**-2
relative, of semiconductors (T), **5**-132
(*See also* Dielectric constants)
Capacitor-start motor, **5**-249
torque-speed curves for (f), **5**-249
Capacitors, **5**-109 to **5**-110
acoustic analogue of, **3**-141 to **3**-142
Capillary-height method, surface tension by, **2**-175
Carbon, energy levels of (f) (T), **8**-64 to **8**-75
total neutron cross section of (f), **8**-132
Carbon I, energy-level diagram of (f), **7**-28
Carbon bisulfide, volume related to pressure and temperature (T), **2**-159
Carbon dioxide, compressibility factor for (T), **4**-92
enthalpy of (T), **4**-93
entropy of (T), **4**-93
first Townsend ionization coefficient for (f), **5**-168
relative density of (T), **4**-92
specific heat of (T), **4**-93
thermodynamic conversion factor for (T), **4**-81
Carbon monoxide, virial coefficients for (T), **4**-127
Carbon tetrachloride, volume related to pressure and temperature (T), **2**-160
Carcel unit, **6**-9, **6**-10
Carcinotron, **5**-77
Cascade hyperon, **8**-245
Cathode, definition of, **5**-3
in electrochemistry, **5**-269
Cathode current density in glow discharge (T), **5**-185
Cathode fall, normal, for various metals (T), **5**-184
Cathode fall thickness for various metals (T), **5**-184
Cathode-ray-tube screens, characteristics of (T), **6**-113
Cation transference numbers of electrolytes (T), **5**-270
Cavitation, critical pressure for (f), **2**-184
definition of, **3**-68
in flowing liquids, **2**-182 to **2**-189
in fresh water (f), **2**-184
inception of, **2**-183
in liquids, **3**-68
Cavitation, symbols for, **2**-183
Cavitation number, **2**-182
for incipient cavitation (f), **2**-186
Celestial triangulation, **2**-96
Celsius temperature, conversion equations for (T), **4**-2
Cent, definition of, **3**-14, **3**-107
Center of mass, definition of, **2**-6
motion of, **2**-7
for various bodies (T), **2**-36 to **2**-37
Centimeters of Hg at 0°C, definition of, **2**-15
Centrifugal force, definition of, **2**-5
Ceramics, dielectric frequency and volume resistivity of (T), **5**-120 to **5**-121
dielectric properties of (T), **5**-120 to **5**-121
properties of (T), **3**-95
Cerium magnesium nitrate, properties of (T), **4**-14
temperature data for (T), **4**-15
Cesium bromide, index of refraction of (T), **6**-27 to **6**-29
Cesium iodide, index of refraction of (T), **6**-27 to **6**-29
Cgs units and electrical formulas (T's), **5**-8, **5**-9
Chain relationships of nuclides (T), **8**-202 to **8**-211
Chamber, reverberation, **3**-17
Chapman-Jouguet condition and shock waves, **2**-233
Chapman's formula for gas viscosities, **2**-206
Characteristic curves, for d-c motors (f), **5**-246
for induction motors (f's), **5**-247
Characteristic impedance, definition of, **3**-62 to **3**-63
for various gases (T), **3**-63
Characteristic X-ray spectra, **7**-123 to **7**-135
Charge transfer of ions in a gas, **7**-204
Charge-transfer cross sections of various substances (f's), **7**-189 to **7**-191
Charged hyperons, **8**-244
Charged-particle fission yields (T), **8**-219 to **8**-221
Charged-particle induced fission, **8**-212
Chemical rate theory, **2**-88
Chemical symbols of stable nuclei (T), **8**-6 to **8**-17
Chemicals, fluorescent, characteristics of, (T), **6**-111
Chemiluminescence, definition of, **6**-3
Chi mesons, **8**-243
Chlorides, optical properties of, **6**-40
Chlorine (in argon), efficiency of electron attachment in (f), **5**-173
Chlorine I, energy-level diagram of (f), **7**-32
Chlorinity of sea water, **2**-116
Chloro-fluoro liquids, density of (T), **2**-149
Chloroform, volume related to pressure and temperature (T), **2**-160
Christiansen effect, definition of, **6**-3
Chromatic aberration, definition of, **6**-3
Chromaticity, **6**-60

Chromaticity coordinates, of black bodies (T), **6**-61
of spectrum (T), **6**-54 to **6**-55
Chromel, emf in thermocouples (T), **4**-12
Chromium methylammonium alum, properties of (T), **4**-14, **4**-16
temperature data for (T), **4**-17
Chromium potassium alum, properties of (T), **4**-14 to **4**-16
temperature data for (T), **4**-15, **4**-16
Circuit configurations, magnetic field about, **5**-25 to **5**-27
Circuit theory, **5**-79 to **5**-85
basis of, **5**-79 to **5**-80
and networks, **5**-80 to **5**-81
Circuits, self- and mutual inductance of, **5**-28
Circular birefringence, **6**-91
Circular coil, self-inductance of, **5**-31
Circular cylindrical resonators, **5**-66, **5**-67
modes in (f's), **5**-66, **5**-67
Circular cylindrical waveguides, **5**-62 to **5**-64
coordinate system for (f), **5**-62
wave types for (T), **5**-63
Circular dichroism, **6**-92
Circular jet, laminar flow in, **2**-195 to **2**-196
streamlines from point orifice (f), **2**-196
symbols for, **2**-195
Circular loop, magnetic induction of, **5**-26 to **5**-27
mutual inductance of, **5**-29 to **5**-31
Circular mil, definition of, **2**-14
Clairaut's formula, **2**-98
Clarke ellipsoid, **2**-96
Classical absorption of sound, **3**-49
Classical symbols for heavy radionuclides (T), **8**-41
Clausius-Duhem inequality, **3**-29
Clausius equation as a virial expansion, **4**-119
Climatology, **2**-134 to **2**-135
Closed-stub impedance matching, **5**-51
Clouds, average water content of (T), **2**-134
at different levels (f), **2**-130
drop-size spectra of (f), **2**-134
electric field intensity inside of (T), **5**-286
Coaxial transmission lines, constants for (T), **5**-48 to **5**-49
Cobalt alloys, density of (T), **2**-25
saturation magnetization and Curie points of (T), **5**-210
Cobalt ammonium sulfate, properties of (T), **4**-14, **4**-20
Cochlea, dimensions of (T), **3**-123
Cockroft-Walton accelerators, **8**-172
Coefficient, of absorption, for building materials, seats, and audience (T's), **3**-116
definition of, **6**-2, **6**-36
of light, definition of, **6**-36
for various substances (T), **6**-37
of ambipolar diffusion, for gases (T), **7**-218
of capacitance and elastance, **5**-17 to **5**-18
for color-difference evaluation (T), **6**-62
Coefficient, of cubical expansion of liquids (T), **4**-62
of cubical thermal expansion of elements (T), **4**-56
of differential diffusion, of various substances (T's), **5**-272
of diffusion, definition of, **2**-80
for gases (T), **2**-212 to **2**-213
for ions in gases, **7**-205
for metals (T), **2**-79 to **2**-80
for solutions (T's), **2**-190 to **2**-195
of drag, in flowing liquid, **2**-183
in gas flow, **2**-226
for various bodies (T), **2**-188
eddy diffusion, **2**-135
elastic, of crystals (T), **2**-55 to **2**-58
of electron attachment for various substances (f's), **7**-182 to **7**-186
electro-optic, for various crystals (T), **6**-97
Ettingshausen, **5**-99
of extinction (optical), definition of, **6**-102
in infrared (T), **6**-38
first Townsend ionization, for various substances (f's), **5**-167 to **5**-169
of friction (T), **2**-39 to **2**-44
Hall, **5**-98
of heat radiation, **3**-31
of internal friction of earth, **2**-113
of linear absorption for gamma radiation (f), **8**-93
of linear thermal expansion of alloys (T), **4**-57 to **4**-60
of elements (T's), **4**-51 to **4**-55
of miscellaneous materials (T), **4**-61
of semiconductors (T), **4**-63
mean-ionic-activity, of electrolytes (T), **5**-278, **5**-279
Nernst, **5**-99
noise-reduction, **3**-114
Peltier, **5**-98
of pressure, in liquids, **2**-151
of radiation, **3**-50
radiative recombination (T), **5**-171
recombination, in air (f's), **5**-177, **5**-178
reflection, for incandescent light (T), **6**-43
for visible monochromatic radiation (T), **6**-42
of retarded elastic motion of earth, **2**-113
Righi-Leduc, **5**-99
of rigidity of earth, **2**-113
of rolling friction, definition of, **2**-43
secondary emission, **7**-192
self-diffusion, in gases (T), **2**-213
skin-friction, **2**-224
in liquids, definition of, **3**-67
of sound absorption (f) (T), **3**-17, **3**-67, **3**-113 to **3**-116
in water (f), **3**-71
of sound transmission, **3**-120
of static friction, definition of, **2**-40
for various substances (T), **2**-40 to **2**-41
temperature, of inorganic liquids (T), **5**-133
of organic liquids (T), **5**-134 to **5**-142

Coefficient, temperature, of piezoelectric strain constants (T), **5**-153
of standard liquids (T), **5**-132
of temperature exchange, **3**-60
of thixotropy, **2**-83
virial (T's), **4**-118 to **4**-120
Thompson, **5**-97 to **5**-98
Townsend, **5**-166, **7**-192
of viscosity, definition of, **3**-28, **3**-41
of earth, **2**-113
for gases (T), **3**-58, **3**-60
of volume expansion, definition of, **4**-63
Coercive force, definition of, **5**-3
of high-permeability materials (T), **5**-216
of materials for permanent magnets (T), **5**-219
Coil, magnetic force on, **5**-32 to **5**-33
self- and mutual inductance of, **5**-30
Collision cross sections, **7**-174
Collision losses for heavy charged particles, **8**-23
Collision probabilities of electrons and ions in gases, **7**-174 to **7**-191
Collision probability curves for various substances (f's), **7**-175 to **7**-191
Colloidal systems, and gels, **2**-81
and thixotropic substances, **2**-81, 2-82
Color difference, evaluation coefficients for (T), **6**-62
Color indices of stellar spectral classes (T), **6**-80
Color-mixture data, standard, **6**-53, **6**-61
Color specification, standard coordinate system (T), **6**-60
Colored glass, transmission characteristics of, **6**-43 to **6**-44
Colorimetry, **6**-50 to **6**-63
Coma, definition of, **6**-3
Combination starters for electric motors, **5**-256
Commercial dielectrics, dielectric constants of (T), **5**-147
Common waveguides, **5**-59 to **5**-62
Compensation network theorem, **5**-81
Complementary wavelength in colorimetry, **6**-60
Complex alpha spectra, **8**-40, **8**-46 to **8**-54
Complex impedances, **3**-8
Complex tone, definition of, **3**-14
Compliance, acoustic, **3**-8
and acoustic analogy, **3**-135 to **3**-136
of crystals (T), **3**-81, **3**-82
mechanical, **3**-9
Composite state variables, **3**-32
Compound nucleus, definition of, **8**-2
Compound-wound motors, **5**-247
Compounds, critical temperatures, pressures, and densities of (T), **4**-22 to **4**-23
crystallographic data for (T), **2**-53 to **2**-54
heats of fusion of (T), **4**-131 to **4**-159
heats of sublimation of (T), **4**-131 to **4**-159
heats of transition of (T), **4**-131 to **4**-159
heats of vaporization of (T), **4**-131 to **4**-159
Compounds, melting parameters of (T's), **4**-30 to **4**-33
phase transition data for (T), **4**-130 to **4**-159
Compressibility, of liquids, **2**-151, **2**-162 to **2**-164
and skin friction, **2**-230
Compressibility data for miscellaneous substances, **2**-162 to **2**-163
Compressibility factor, for air (T), **4**-82
for argon (T), **4**-87
for carbon dioxide (T), **4**-92
for hydrogen (T), **4**-95
for nitrogen (T), **4**-103
for oxygen (T), **4**-108
for steam (T), **4**-113
Compressible flow in gases, **2**-214 to **2**-219
Compressional waves, definition of, **3**-3
in fluids, **2**-14
in sound, **3**-46, **3**-47
Compton effect, **8**-88 to **8**-89
Compton scattering, **8**-89
cross section per electron vs gamma energy (f), **8**-89
Compton wavelength, of electron, **8**-4
of neutron, **8**-4, **8**-129
of proton, **8**-4
Computation, mathematical aids to, **1**-1 to **1**-5
Computing devices, **1**-1
Concentration of radioisotopes in air and water, **8**-253
Condenser, acoustic analogue of, **3**-141 to **3**-142
Conductances, equivalent, of electrolytes (T), **5**-270
of ions in various solutions (T's), **5**-271
limiting equivalent (T's), **5**-271
Conduction, of copper wire (T), **5**-198 to **5**-200
of electricity in gases, **5**-166 to **5**-184
Conductivity, of atmosphere at various locations (T), **5**-285, **5**-286
effect of frequency on, for copper, **5**-197, **5**-200
effect of pressure on (T), **5**-190, **5**-195
formulas for, **5**-95 to **5**-97
ionic, in salts, **5**-185 to **5**-196
of ionic conductors, **5**-186 to **5**-188
of mixed ionic and electronic conduction (T), **5**-192 to **5**-194
per cent, definition of, **5**-197
representative values of (T), **5**-162
of sea water, **2**-120
thermal (*see* Thermal conductivity)
Conductivity parameters, **5**-39
Conductors, definition of, **5**-3
a-c resistance/d-c resistance for solid round wire (T), **5**-201
and anomalous skin effect, **5**-200
current-carrying capacities of insulated (T's), **5**-202 to **5**-203, **5**-257
fluid types of, **3**-47
ionic (*see* Ionic conductors)
properties of, metallic, **5**-197 to **5**-205
nonmetallic, **5**-166 to **5**-197

Conductors, resistance of rectangular (f), **5**-92
  skin-effect data for (T), **5**-85, **5**-90 to **5**-95
  transport numbers for ionic (T), **5**-191 to **5**-194
Configurational entropy, **2**-81
Conical resonators, frequency of (T), **3**-103
Conical tube, **3**-103
Conjugate foci, definition of, **6**-3
Conservation, of energy, definition, **2**-5 to **2**-8
  in viscous fluids, **3**-29
  of mass in viscous fluids, **3**-27
  of momentum, **2**-5, **2**-7
Conservative force, definition of, **2**-6
Constantan, emf of thermocouples using (T's), **4**-11 to **4**-12
Constitutive parameters and field vectors, **5**-38 to **5**-39
Constitutive relations in viscous fluids, **3**-27
Contact discontinuity and shock waves, **2**-232
Contact-potential effect, definition of, **5**-5
Continental platform, **2**-115
Continuity equations, for acoustic energy, **3**-44
  for electrical currents and charges, **5**-36 to **5**-38
  in fluids, **2**-13
  in gas flow, **2**-215, **2**-221
  for viscous fluids, **3**-27 to **3**-28
Continuous spectrum, definition of, **3**-3
Control of various nuclear reactors (T), **8**-228 to **8**-239
Convergence of ocean waves, **2**-123
Conversion equations, relating radiation dose to flux, **8**-251
  for temperature scales (T), **4**-2
Conversion factors, for absolute viscosity (T), **2**-202
  acoustical (T), **3**-24
  area (T), **2**-16
  of atomic units (T), **7**-4
  for international vs. absolute electrical units (T), **5**-106
  for kinematic viscosity (T), **2**-203
  length (T), **2**-15
  mass-energy, **8**-4
  quantum energy, **8**-4
  for thermal conductivity (T), **4**-66
  for thermodynamic properties of gases (T), **4**-81
  volume (T), **2**-16
  for X- or gamma-ray absorption in air (T), **8**-253
Conversion formulas for neutrons, **8**-129
Conversion probability curves for ions in various substances (f's), **7**-201 to **7**-202
Conversion tables for optical density vs per cent transmission (T), **6**-39
Converters, a-c to d-c, **5**-260
Coolants for nuclear reactors, **8**-228 to **8**-239
Coordinate systems, **2**-2
Coordinate transforms, **3**-36
Copper, emf of copper vs. constantan thermocouples (T), **4**-11
Copper, energy loss and range of protons in (T), **8**-24 to **8**-25, **8**-35
  frequency vs. conductivity for, **5**-197, **5**-200
  resistance vs. temperature for, **5**-197
  skin depth and h-f resistance for (f), **5**-200
Copper I, energy-level diagram of (f), **7**-38
Copper alloys, densities of (T), **2**-26 to **2**-28
  elastic and strength constants of (T's), **2**-66 to **2**-68, **3**-81
Copper crystals, attenuation peaks and decrement for (f), **3**-88
Copper oxide rectifier, **5**-266
Copper potassium sulfate, properties of (T), **4**-14, **4**-17 to **4**-18
Copper sulfate, properties of (T), **4**-14, **4**-20
Copper wire tables, solid wire (T), **5**-198 to **5**-199
Coriolis forces, definition of, **2**-5
Coriolis parameter (T), **2**-130, **2**-131
Cosmic abundance, definition of, **8**-5
  of stable nuclei (T), **8**-6 to **8**-17
Cosmotron, **8**-177
Coulomb, definition of, **5**-2
  international vs. absolute (T), **5**-106
Coulomb forces in stable nuclei, **8**-5
Coulomb scattering of charged particles, **8**-36
Coulomb's law, **5**-3
Couplers and acoustic analogy, **3**-177
Coupling in atomic spectra, **7**-17 to **7**-18
Creep, **2**-86 to **2**-90
  rates for various materials (T), **2**-89 to **2**-90
  in solids (f), **2**-84
  typical curve of (f), **2**-87
Critical absorption wavelengths in X-ray spectra (T), **7**-130 to **7**-132
Critical cavitation number (f), **2**-185
Critical constants in heat, **4**-21 to **4**-23
Critical densities of elements and compounds, **4**-21 to **4**-23
Critical energy, of electrons, definition of, **8**-38
  of various substances (T), **8**-39
Critical frequency band in hearing (T), **3**-127
Critical pressure, for cavitation in sea water (f), **2**-184
  of elements and compounds, **4**-21 to **4**-23
  of inorganic and organic substances (T), **4**-21 to **4**-23
Critical temperature, of elements and compounds (T), **4**-21 to **4**-23
  of inorganic and organic substances (T), **4**-21 to **4**-23
Crochet, definition of, **5**-294
Cross section, for neutrons, **8**-130, **8**-143 to **8**-144, **8**-169
  nuclear, definition of, **8**-3
Cryogenic liquids, density of (T), **2**-146
Crystal size of various cathode-ray-tube phosphors (T), **6**-113
Crystal systems, lattice constants for (f) (T), **2**-45
Crystalline medium, Hooke's law for, **2**-11

Crystalline quartz, index of refraction of (T), **6**-23 to **6**-25
Crystalline solids, dielectric constants of (T's), **5**-115 to **5**-118
Crystallization of metals, **3**-75
Crystallographic data, **2**-44 to **2**-54
for compounds, **2**-53 to **2**-54
for elements (T), **2**-48 to **2**-52
Crystals, anisotropy constant of (T), **5**-222
antiferroelectric, properties of (T), **5**-156
coefficients of linear thermal expansion of (T), **4**-54 to **4**-55
copper, attenuation peaks and decrement of (f), **3**-88
cubic (*see* Cubic crystals)
densities of (T), **3**-77 to **3**-78
elastic constants and coefficients of (T's), **2**-56 to **2**-58, **3**-81, **3**-82
electro-optic coefficients for, (T), **6**-97
ferroelectric, properties of (T), **5**-155 to **5**-156
hexagonal (T), **2**-57
piezoelectric, properties of (T), **3**-93
rhombic (T), **2**-58
saturation magnetostriction of, **5**-222, **5**-223
tetragonal (T), **2**-57
thermal conductivity of (T), **4**-72 to **4**-73, **4**-79
trigonal (T), **2**-57
Verdet constants for (T), **6**-95
Cubic crystal systems (T), **2**-45, **2**-47
Cubic crystals, elastic constants and coefficients of (T), **2**-56
magnetic crystal anisotropy constants of (T), **5**-221
magnetostriction constants of (T), **5**-223
saturation magnetostriction of, **5**-222, **5**-223
thermal conductivity of (T), **4**-72 to **4**-73
Cubical expansion, coefficients of, for elements (T), **4**-56
for liquids (T), **4**-62, **4**-63
Cumulonimbus clouds (f), **2**-130, **2**-134
Cumulus clouds (f), **2**-130, **2**-134
Curie, definition of, **8**-250
Curie constants of paramagnetic materials (T's), **4**-14, **5**-241 to **5**-243
Curie law and paramagnetism, **5**-100
Curie point, definition of, **5**-3, **5**-206
effect of pressure on (T), **5**-220
and saturation magnetization (T), **5**-208
Curie points, of binary compounds (T), **5**-213
of cobalt alloys (T), **5**-210
of ferrites (T), **5**-211, **5**-212
of ferroelectric crystals (T), **5**-155 to **5**-156
of ferromagnetic elements (T), **5**-208
of high-permeability materials (T), **5**-216
of iron alloys (T), **5**-209
of iron-cobalt-nickel alloys (f), **5**-207
of nickel alloys (T), **5**-210
of spinels (T), **5**-212
Curie temperature, definition of, **5**-101
Curie-Weiss law, **5**-101, **5**-236
Curium 242, decay scheme of (f), **8**-47
Current carriers, mobility of, **5**-157, **5**-159 to **5**-160
Current-carrying capacities of insulated conductors (T's), **5**-202 to **5**-203, **5**-257
Current density, cathode, in glow discharge (T), **5**-185
Current noise in radiation detectors, **6**-115
Current transformers, **5**-259
Cutoff wavelength and frequency, **5**-58
Cyclohexane, first Townsend ionization coefficient in (f), **5**-169
Cyclotron resonance of electrons and holes, **5**-99 to **5**-100
Cyclotrons, description of types of, **8**-173 to **8**-175
world-wide list of (T), **8**-189 to **8**-193
Cylinder, capacitance per unit length of, **5**-15
drag data for (f), **2**-226, **2**-228
magnetic induction due to, **5**-25
Cylindrical coordinates, base vectors in (f), **2**-3
definition of, **2**-3
Cylindrical shell, skin-effect formulas for, **5**-95
Cylindrical wave functions, **5**-45 to **5**-46

D

D-layer in atmosphere (f), **2**-130
D'Alembert's principle, **2**-5
Darcy unit, definition of, **2**-180
Darcy's law, **2**-179
Day, definition of, **2**-14
D-C generator, characteristics of (f), **5**-259
connections for (f), **5**-258
D-C motors, characteristic curves for (f), **5**-246
fractional-horsepower, characteristics of (T), **5**-253
integral-horsepower, characteristics of (T), **5**-254 to **5**-255
in relation to generators, **5**-246 to **5**-250
D-C resistance, ratio of a-c to, for solid round wire (T), **5**-201
Dead room, definition of, **3**-17
Deafness, **3**-12
Debye C_v values (T), **4**-44
Debye equation, **4**-44
Debye temperatures, definition of, **4**-44, **4**-46, **4**-63
of metals (T), **4**-48
of nonmetals (T), **4**-47
of superconductors (T), **4**-49
Decay, type of, for light nuclei (f's) (T), **8**-58 to **8**-86
for nuclides (T), **8**-98 to **8**-128
Decay constant, definition of, **3**-6, **3**-17
Decay energy vs. mass number for alpha particles (f), **8**-46
Decay-energy cycles for radioactive series $4n$ through $4n + 3$ (f's), **8**-42 to **8**-45
Decay-energy profile, alpha (f), **8**-46
Decay-energy systematics of heavy elements, **8**-40 to **8**-56

Decay products, mesons and hyperons (T), **8**-241
Decay schemes, of odd-nucleon alpha emitters (f), **8**-54
of Th^{228} and Cm^{242} (f), **8**-47
Decibel, definition of, **3**-3
"Dee" in betatron, **8**-173
Deep-water waves, **2**-122
Deflecting instruments, **5**-113
Deflection of vertical in geodesy, **2**-94
Deformable media, dynamics of, **2**-10 to **2**-12
Deformation, rate of, in viscous fluids, **3**-27
Degeneracy and electronic structure, **7**-18
Degenerate case in wave mechanics, **7**-166
Degenerate modes of spherical resonators, **5**-66 to **5**-67
Degree, definition of, **2**-14
Deionization, **5**-166, **5**-171
Demagnetization curves, of Alnico 5 (f), **5**-218
of permanent-magnet alloys (f), **5**-218
Demagnetizing factors, definition of, **5**-240
for rods and ellipsoids (T), **5**-244
Density, of air (T), **3**-57
of alloys (T), **2**-22 to **2**-30
of aluminum alloys (T), **2**-24
in amagat units, **4**-118
of cobalt alloys, **2**-25
of copper alloys (T), **2**-26 to **2**-28
critical, of elements and compounds (T), **4**-21 to **4**-23
of inorganic and organic substances (T), **4**-21 to **4**-23
of crystals (T), **3**-77 to **3**-78
definition of, **2**-4
of earth, **2**-101
of elementary gases (T), **2**-198
of elements in solid form (T), **2**-17 to **2**-20
of gases (T), **2**-197 to **2**-201, **3**-56, **3**-57
of glasses (T), **3**-77 to **3**-78
of high-permeability materials (T), **5**-216
of inorganic gases (T), **2**-199
of ions in lower atmosphere (T), **5**-284
of lead alloys (T), **2**-29
of liquids, **2**-136
various (T), **6**-18
of magnesium alloys (T), **2**-29
measurement in liquids, **2**-136
of metals (T), **3**-77 to **3**-78
of nickel alloys (T), **2**-30
of organic gases (T), **2**-200
of paramagnetic salts (T), **4**-14
of plastics (T), **2**-34 to **2**-35, **3**-77 to **3**-78
of resins (T), **2**-34 to **2**-35
of rubber (T), **2**-35
of solids at 20°C (T), **2**-21
and sound transmission in solids, **3**-74 to **3**-79
of steam (T), **4**-114
of steels (T), **2**-22 to **2**-23
of water, fresh and sea (T), **3**-69
sea, **2**-117
of woods (T), **2**-31 to **2**-33
X-ray, of crystals (T), **3**-77 to **3**-78
of zinc alloys (T), **2**-30
Density defects for pure ionic conductors (T), **5**-189
Density measurement of gases, **2**-197 to **2**-198
Density tables, for chloro-fluoro liquids (T), **2**-149
for cryogenic liquids (T), **2**-146
for deuterium (T), **2**-139
for ethyl alcohol (T), **2**-142
for fluorocarbon liquids (T), **2**-149
for inorganic liquids (T), **2**-143
for liquids of normally gaseous substances (T), **2**-144
for mercury (T), **2**-140
for methyl alcohol (T), **2**-140 to **2**-141
for organic liquids (T), **2**-147
for water (T), **2**-138 to **2**-139
Derived units, definition of, **2**-15
Detectability, threshold of, **3**-14
Detonation and shock waves, **2**-233
Deuterium, atomic mass of, **8**-4
density of (T), **2**-139
fractional distillation of, **2**-137
virial coefficients for (T), **4**-125
volume related to pressure and temperature (T), **2**-154
Deuteron, mass of (T), **7**-3
range-energy relation in Ilford C-2 emulsion (f), **8**-32
range straggling in copper (f's), **8**-37
symbols for, **8**-3
Diamagnetic body, definition of, **5**-3
Diamagnetic liquids, Faraday rotation in (T), **5**-232
Diamagnetic solids, Faraday rotation in (T), **5**-232
Diamagnetism, definition of, **5**-100
Diatomic gases and shock waves (T), **2**-235
Diatomic molecules, constants of (T), **7**-136 to **7**-141
energy-level and potential curves of (f's), **7**-142 to **7**-145
and Zeeman effect, **7**-169
Dielectric bodies, definition of, **5**-3
in electrostatic fields, **5**-22 to **5**-23
Dielectric boundary formulas, **5**-21 to **5**-22
Dielectric capacitivity of piezoelectric crystals (T), **3**-93
Dielectric constants, of antiferroelectric crystals (T), **5**-156
of commercial dielectrics (T), **5**-147
definition of, **5**-2
of ferroelectric crystals (T), **5**-155 to **5**-156
of inorganic liquids (T), **5**-133
of inorganic solids (T), **5**-115 to **5**-117
of liquids (T's), **5**-132 to **5**-147
of organic liquids (T), **5**-134 to **5**-142
of organic solids (T), **5**-118
of reference gases (T), **5**-147
of standard liquids (T), **5**-132
of transducer materials (f), **3**-97
variation with temperature (f), **5**-131
Dielectric crystals, thermal conductivity of (T), **4**-79

Dielectric properties, of amorphous solids, **5**-120 to **5**-132
of ceramics (T), **5**-120 to **5**-121
of gases (T's), **5**-147 to **5**-149
of glasses (T), **5**-122 to **5**-123
of plastics (T), **5**-124 to **5**-130
of rubbers (T), **5**-124 to **5**-130
Dielectric strength, relative, of gases (T), **5**-148 to **5**-149
of nitrogen vapor (T), **5**-148 to **5**-149
Dielectrics, commercial, dielectric constants of (T), **5**-147
properties of, **5**-114 to **5**-156
thermal conductivity of (T), **4**-79
Dieterici equation as a virial expansion, **4**-119
Difference limen, definition of, **3**-12
Differential cross section, **5**-71
Differential diffusion coefficients of various solutions (T), **5**-272
Differential equations for electrical, mechanical, and acoustical systems, **3**-137 to **3**-138
Differential forms of Maxwell's equations, **5**-40
Differential formulations in electrical field equations, **5**-37 to **5**-38
Differential scattering cross section of neutrons, definition of, **8**-130
Differential threshold for intensity in hearing (T), **3**-126
Diffraction, definition of, **6**-3
Diffraction grating, definition of, **6**-3
Diffuse sound field, **3**-120
Diffusing surfaces, reflection coefficients for incandescent light on (T), **6**-43
Diffusion, in gases, **2**-11 to **2**-214
in liquids, **2**-189 to **2**-195
Diffusion coefficients, ambipolar, for several gases (T), **7**-218
of aqueous solutions, variation with temperature (T), **2**-194
of concentrated electrolytes (T), **2**-191
definition of, **2**-80, **2**-211
of dilute electrolytes (T), **2**-190
of ions in gases, **7**-205
for liquids, definition of, **2**-189
of metals (T), **2**-79 to **2**-80
of nonaqueous solutions (T), **2**-195
of nonelectrolytes (T), **2**-192
of organic compounds (T), **2**-193
variation, with concentration (T), **2**-213
with pressure (f), **2**-213
of various gases (T), **2**-212
Diffusion constants for electrons and holes, **5**-160
Diffusion diagram for atmosphere (f), **2**-135
Diffusion equation in fluid motion, **3**-40
Diffusivity, of miscellaneous materials (T), **4**-74
of sea water (T), **2**-122
Dilatation rate in viscous fluids, **3**-27
Dilatational deformation, **2**-10
Dilatometer, **2**-136
Dimensional analysis in sound absorption, **3**-45 to **3**-46
Dimensions of electrical quantities (T), **5**-6 to **5**-7
DIMPLE reactor, **8**-240
Dip of earth's magnetic field, **5**-291
Dipole, force, mutual energy, and torque, **5**-21
potential of, **5**-21
Dipole radiators, electric and magnetic, **5**-69 to **5**-70
Dipole rotation, **5**-114
Direct sound, definition of, **3**-17
Directional radiation, from circular piston, **3**-111
from thin circular ring, **3**-111 to **3**-112
Directivity of a radiator, **5**-69
Directivity factor, definition of, **3**-10
Directivity index, definition of, **3**-11
of piston or ring (f), **3**-112
of transducer, **3**-110, **3**-112
Discharge characteristics, normal cathode fall (T), **5**-184
Discrete radio sources, **6**-122 to **6**-123
Dispersion, definition of, **6**-4
index of refraction vs., for optical glass (f), **6**-33
Dispersive power, definition of, **6**-4
Dissociation constants, of electrolytes (T), **5**-280
of water (T), **5**-280
Dissociation energy of diatomic molecules (T), **7**-136 to **7**-141
Dissociative recombination (T), **5**-171
Dispersion of sound, **3**-43 to **3**-53
and heat radiation, **3**-49 to **3**-50
in liquids, **3**-68
Dispersion measure and viscothermal absorption, **3**-47 to **3**-49
Diurnal variation in ionosphere (f), **2**-131
Divergence of ocean waves, **2**-123
Dominant wavelength in colorimetry, **6**-60
Donors and binding energies (T), **5**-160, **5**-163
Doppler effect, definition of, **3**-3, **6**-4
Drag in cavitating flow, **2**-187 to **2**-188
Drag coefficients, of flowing liquids, **2**-183
vs. Reynolds number for cylinder and sphere (f), **2**-226
for various bodies (T), **2**-188
Drag data in gas flow, **2**-226 to **2**-228
Drift mobilities of germanium and silicon (T), **5**-159
Drift velocity, definition of, **7**-203
of electrons, **5**-96
in various substances (f's), **7**-205 to **7**-209
of ions in various substances (f's), **7**-212 to **7**-218
Drop-weight method of surface tension measurement, **2**-176
Dry-adiabatic lapse rate, **2**-127
Dynamic-field equations, **5**-36 to **5**-95
Dynamic modulus of elasticity, **2**-85 to **2**-86
Dynamic similarity in gas flow, **2**-215
Dynamic viscosity, definition of, **2**-201
of sea water (T), **2**-122

Dynamics, of deformable media, **2**-10 to **2**-12
fluid, **2**-12 to **2**-14
noninertial, **2**-5
of rigid bodies, **2**-8 to **2**-10
and systems of particles, **2**-6
Dyne, definition of, **2**-15

E

E waves, **5**-47
EM waves (*see* Electromagnetic waves)
Ear, acoustic impedance of (T), **3**-123, **3**-124
loudness level, **3**-13
minimum audible pressure on external (T), **3**-124 to **3**-125
parts of (T), **3**-123
physical dimensions of (T), **3**-123
and pitch, **3**-13
thresholds for, **3**-14
Earth, altitude variation of crust (T), **2**-115
characteristics of crust, **2**-115 to **2**-116
dimensions of, **2**-100
elastic constants in, **2**-108
electric and magnetic properties of, **5**-283 to **5**-297
electrical characteristics of, **5**-289 to **5**-291
location of magnetic poles of (T), **5**-292
longitudinal waves in (T), **2**-103
magnetic moment of, **5**-292
magnetism of, **5**-291 to **5**-295
methods of measuring size and shape of, **2**-96 to **2**-97
miscellaneous constants for (T), **2**-91
nonelastic properties of interior of (T), **2**-113 to **2**-114
physical and orbital data for (T's), **2**-90, **2**-91
pressures in, **2**-108
resistivity of, **5**-290 to **5**-291
seismicity of, **2**-110 to **2**-112
wave velocities in, **2**-108
Earth currents (electrical), **5**-289 to **5**-290
Earth ellipsoid, dimensions of (T), **2**-94
Earth materials, resistivities of (f), **5**-290
Earthquake waves, energy reflection data for (T), **2**-105, **2**-106
energy refraction data for (T), **2**-105, **2**-106
periods and amplitudes, **2**-102 to **2**-103
reflection and refraction of, **2**-104 to **2**-106
travel times of (T), **2**-103 to **2**-104
equations for, **2**-107 to **2**-108
types of, and symbols for, **2**-106 to **2**-107
velocity equations, **2**-107 to **2**-108
Earthquakes, aftershock of, **2**-113
average energy release of (T), **2**-112
comparison of shallow, intermediate, and deep (T), **2**-111
epicentral distances for (T), **2**-107
focal depths of (T), **2**-107
intensity of, **2**-108
at epicenter (T), **2**-111
magnitude of, **2**-108
vs. depth for greatest shock (T), **2**-112
Earth's magnetic field, characteristics of, **5**-291 to **5**-293
origin of, **5**-293
transient phenomena in, **5**-293 to **5**-294
Eccentricity of planetary orbits (T), **2**-90
Echo, definition of, **3**-3
Eddy current, definition of, **5**-3
Eddy-current constant for magnetic losses at low induction (T), **5**-220
Eddy-current heating of sphere, **5**-95
Eddy diffusion in atmosphere, **2**-135
Edison effect, definition of, **5**-4
Effective acoustic center, definition of, **3**-11
Effective bandwidth, definition of, **3**-11
Effective decay energy vs. log half life for various alpha emitters (f), **8**-54
Effective particle velocity, definition of, **3**-3
Effective secondary emission of electrons by various substances (f's), **7**-199 to **7**-200
Effective sound pressure, definition of, **3**-3
Effective volume velocity, definition of, **3**-8
Einstein–de Hass effect, **5**-103
Einstein viscosity equation, **2**-181
Elastance coefficients, **5**-17 to **5**-18
Elastic aftereffect, **2**-84 to **2**-86
Elastic coefficients of crystals (T), **2**-55 to **2**-58
Elastic collisions, by electrons in various substances (f's), **7**-175 to **7**-176
by ions of various substances (f's), **7**-186 to **7**-188
Elastic constants, of copper alloys (T), **3**-81
of crystals (T), **2**-55 to **2**-58, **3**-74
of cubic crystals (T), **3**-81
in earth, **2**-108
fundamental equations for, **2**-102
of glasses (T), **3**-80
of hexagonal crystals (T), **3**-82
of metals (T), **3**-80
of piezoelectric crystals (T), **3**-93
of plastics, **3**-80
of polycrystalline solids (T), **2**-55 to **2**-80
of rocks (T), **2**-102
of solids, **3**-74 to **3**-79
of various metals (T), **3**-83
Elastic hysteresis, **2**-84 to **2**-86
Elastic medium, definition of, **2**-10
Hooke's law for, **2**-11
Elastic modulus, **2**-84 to **2**-86
Elastic scattering of photons (f), **8**-91 to **8**-92
Elasticity, moduli of, **2**-84 to **2**-86
notation and symbols, **2**-55
Electric charge, definition of, **5**-2
on precipitation particles (T), **5**-287
Electric circuit, acoustic analogy to, **3**-140 to **3**-142
definition of, **5**-4
magnetic fields about, **5**-25 to **5**-27
magnetic forces on, **5**-32 to **5**-33
Electric current, average full load for motors (T), **5**-256
definition of, **5**-2
in earth, **5**-289 to **5**-291
Electric dipole as radiator, **5**-69
Electric-dipole radiation, **7**-21

Electric-dipole transition, selection and polarization rules for (T), **7**-168
Electric field, vs. altitude in lower atmosphere (T), **5**-286
of atmosphere (T), **5**-285
inside clouds (T), **5**-286
near thunderstorms (f), **5**-287
Electric generators (*see* Generators)
Electric impedance, vector, equation for, **3**-138
Electric intensity, definition of, **5**-2
Electric lines of force, definition of, **5**-4
Electric mesher, **3**-141
Electric motors, a-c and d-c, **5**-246 to **5**-250
average full-load current for (f), **5**-259
control and protection of, **5**-254 to **5**-257
fractional-horsepower (T), **5**-253
integral horsepower characteristics of (T), **5**-254 to **5**-255
relative cost of (f's), **5**-251
selection criteria for, **5**-250 to **5**-252
standard ratings of frequency, horsepower, speed, and voltage, **5**-252
Electric polarization, **5**-3
Electric power level, definition of, **3**-3
Electric quadrupole moment of stable nuclei (T), **8**-6 to **8**-17
Electric tubes of flux, definition of, **5**-4
Electrical-apparatus standard, **5**-245 to **5**-246
Electrical characteristics of thunderstorms (T), **5**-288
Electrical circuit (*see* Electric circuit)
Electrical conduction of rocks, **5**-290 to **5**-291
Electrical conductivity (*see* Conductivity)
Electrical formulas, **5**-12 to **5**-104
for capacitance, mks units, **5**-12 to **5**-18
for dielectric boundary, **5**-21 to **5**-22
dynamic-field equations, **5**-36 to **5**-95
electrostatic-force, **5**-18 to **5**-21
multipole, **5**-21
for reduction to cgs, esu, and emu (T's), **5**-8
for reduction to mks units (T), **5**-10 to **5**-11
static-current flow, **5**-23 to **5**-25
static field, **5**-12 to **5**-36
for transition between unit systems (T), **5**-6 to **5**-11
Electrical instruments, deflecting, **5**-113
Electrical power practices, **5**-245 to **5**-268
Electrical properties, of earth and stars, **5**-283 to **5**-297
of metallic conductors, **5**-197 to **5**-205
of pure metals (T), **5**-204
Electrical quantities, mks symbols, units, definitions, and dimensions (T's), **3**-139, **5**-6 to **5**-7
Electrical resistance and acoustic analogy, **3**-134, **3**-136
Electrical resistivity (*see* Resistivity)
Electrical schematic diagrams, based on impedance analogy (T), **3**-145 to **3**-176
based on mobility analogy (T), **3**-144 to **3**-176
Electrical standards, basis for, **5**-105
history of, **5**-105 to **5**-106
Electrical symbols (T), **3**-139
Electrical system, graphical representation of (f's), **3**-136, **3**-137
of one degree of freedom, **3**-137 to **3**-138
Electrical units (T), **3**-139
international vs absolute (T), **5**-106
maintenance of, **5**-106
Electricity, atmospheric, **5**-283 to **5**-289
terrestrial, **5**-289 to **5**-291
Electroacoustical reciprocity theorem, definition of, **3**-11
Electrochemical data, sources and symbols, **5**-268 to **5**-269
Electrochemistry, **5**-268 to **5**-283
Electrodes, definition of, **5**-3, **5**-4
Electro-dynamical analogies with acoustics, **3**-134 to **3**-139
Electrolysis, definition of, **5**-4
Electrolyte, definition of, **5**-4
diffusion coefficients of (T), **2**-190, **2**-191
dissociation constants of (T), **5**-280
equivalent conductances and cation transference numbers (T), **5**-270
mean-ionic-activity coefficients of (T), **5**-278
Electromagnetic field, definition of, **5**-38
Electromagnetic units and electrical formulas (T), **5**-9
Electromagnetic waves, in bounded regions, **5**-56 to **5**-57
guided, **5**-47 to **5**-65
types, **5**-47, **5**-57
Electromechanical coupling of piezoelectric crystals (T), **3**-93
Electromechanical coupling factor for transducers, **3**-89
Electromotance, definition of, **5**-2
Electromotive force, definition of, **5**-2
standards of, **5**-107 to **5**-109
for half cells in water (T), **5**-274 to **5**-276
Electron acceleration, in betatrons, **8**-175 to **8**-176
in linear accelerators, **8**-178
by magnetic induction, **8**-175 to **8**-176
in synchrotrons, **8**-176 to **8**-177
Electron attachment, efficiency of, for various gases (f's), **5**-172 to **5**-177
for various substances (f's), **7**-182 to **7**-186
Electron conduction, **5**-97
Electron configurations of atoms (T), **7**-13 to **7**-15
Electron emission, secondary, ratio to primary for several substances (f's), **7**-203
for various substances (f's), **7**-192 to **7**-198
Electron energy losses in various gases (f's), **5**-181 to **5**-183
Electron spin, definition of, **7**-17
Electron stream, space-charge waves in, **5**-75

Electron synchrotron, description of, **8**-176 to **8**-177
world-wide list of (T), **8**-196 to **8**-197
Electron temperature of discharge vs tube radius (f), **5**-183
Electron transitions, selection rules for, **7**-20 to **7**-21, **7**-25
Electron traps and electron conduction, **5**-160
Electron yield of various substances (f's), **7**-192 to **7**-198
Electronic conductors, conductivity for (T), **5**-192 to **5**-194
transport numbers for (T), **5**-191 to **5**-194
Electronic constants, and Debye temperature, **4**-46
for metals (T), **4**-48
for superconductors (T), **4**-49
Electronic rectifiers, **5**-260
Electronic structure of atoms (T), **7**-13 to **7**-15
Electronic thermal agitation noise in radiation detectors, **6**-115
Electrons, absorption curve for, in aluminum (f), **8**-38
attachment coefficients for various substances (f's), **7**-182 to **7**-186
Compton wavelength of, **8**-4
cyclotron resonance, **5**-99 to **5**-100
drift velocity of (f's), **7**-205 to **7**-209
effective secondary emission of (f's), **7**-199 to **7**-200
elastic collisions of (f's), **7**-175 to **7**-176
and Hall mobilities (T), **5**-161
inelastic collisions of (f's), **7**-177 to **7**-182
ionization by, **5**-166
magnetic moment of, **8**-4
mean energy of (f's), **7**-210 to **7**-211
mobility of, **5**-157, **5**-159 to **5**-160
motion of, in gases, **7**-174 to **7**-219
passage of, through matter, **8**-38 to **8**-40
range-energy relation of, in aluminum (f), **8**-39
rest mass of, **8**-4
symbols for, **8**-3
various constants of (T), **7**-3
Electro-optic coefficients for various crystals (T), **6**-97
Electro-optic effect, definition of, **6**-94
Electrophonic effect, definition of, **3**-12
Electrostatic accelerators, description of, **8**-172 to **8**-173
world-wide list of (T), **8**-182 to **8**-188
Electrostatic fields, and dielectric bodies, **5**-22 to **5**-23
potential in, **5**-3
Electrostatic-force formulas, **5**-18 to **5**-21
Electrostatic generators, world-wide list of (T), **8**-182 to **8**-188
Electrostatic units and electrical formulas (T), **5**-8
Electrostriction, definition of, **5**-4
Electrostrictive transducers, **3**-92 to **3**-98
Elementary gases, densities of (T), **2**-198
Elements, alphabetical list of (T), **7**-5 to **7**-7
atomic numbers of (T), **7**-5 to **7**-8
Elements, atomic susceptibility of (f), **5**-236
coefficients of cubical thermal expansion of (T), **4**-56
coefficients of linear thermal expansion of (T's), **4**-51 to **4**-55
critical temperatures, pressures, and densities of (T), **4**-21 to **4**-23
crystallographic data for (T), **2**-48 to **2**-52
decay-energy systematics of heavy, **8**-40 to **8**-56
density of (T), **2**-17 to **2**-20
gamma rays accompanying neutron capture in (T), **8**-94 to **8**-96
Hall constants of (T), **5**-237
heats of fusion of (T), **4**-131 to **4**-159
heats of sublimation of (T), **4**-131 to **4**-159
heats of transition of (T), **4**-131 to **4**-159
heats of vaporization of (T), **4**-131 to **4**-159
isotopes of (T's), **8**-154 to **8**-168, **8**-170 to **8**-171
latent heats of (T), **4**-131 to **4**-159
melting parameters of (T's), **4**-30 to **4**-32
molar heat capacities of (T's), **4**-40 to **4**-43
neutron binding energies of (T), **8**-135 to **8**-143
periodic system of (T), **7**-8
persistent spectral lines of (T), **7**-39 to **7**-41
phase transition data for (T), **4**-130 to **4**-159
reaction and scattering cross sections of (T's), **8**-154 to **8**-168, **8**-170 to **8**-171
relative volumes of (T), **4**-29
resistivity of, vs temperature for (T), **4**-13
symbols for (T), **7**-5 to **7**-8
thermal cross sections of (T's), **8**-154 to **8**-168, **8**-170 to **8**-171
thermal emf in relation to platinum (T), **4**-6 to **4**-7
various properties of (T), **7**-9 to **7**-12
Elevation vs atmospheric pressure, temperature, and density (T), **3**-58
Ellipsoid, Clarke and Krassovski, **2**-96
demagnetizing factors for (T), **5**-244
international, **2**-100 to **2**-101
Elongation, of metals and alloys (T), **2**-61 to **2**-78
in tensile testing, definition of, **2**-69
Emission bands of various cathode-ray-tube phosphors (T), **6**-113
Emission color of various cathode-ray-tube phosphors (T), **6**-113
Emissive power, definition of, **6**-4
Emissivity, definition of, **6**-4
of globar sources (f), **6**-81
of solids, definition of, **6**-73
spectral, brightness vs. temperature for (T), **6**-75
of oxides (T), **6**-74
of unoxidized surfaces (T), **6**-73
of various substances (T), **6**-72
total, apparent vs. true temperature for (T), **6**-76

Emissivity, total, for metals with unoxidized surfaces (T), **6**-75
of various materials (T), **6**-68 to **6**-71
Emitted peak and range of fluorescent chemicals (T), **6**-111
End correction for organ pipe, **3**-103
Energetics, acoustical, **3**-41 to **3**-43
Energy, conservation of, **2**-5 to **2**-8
of earthquake waves (T), **2**-105, **2**-106
of earthquakes, **2**-112
gamma and particle, of nuclides (T), **8**-98 to **8**-128
kinetic, definition of, **2**-4
mean, of electrons in several substances (f's), **7**-210 to **7**-211
mutual, of two dipoles, **5**-21
potential, definition of, **2**-6
Energy balance, in fluids, **3**-42
and nuclear reactions, **8**-2
Energy density, definition of, **3**-6
in fluids, **3**-42
Energy equation in gas flow, **2**-215, **2**-221
Energy gaps, definition of, **5**-157
for various substances (T), **5**-158 to **5**-159
Energy-level curves, of C_2 (f's), **7**-142
of CN (f's), **7**-143
of O_2 (f's), **7**-145
Energy-level diagrams, of atoms (f's), **7**-26 to **7**-37
of X-ray spectra (f), **7**-124
Energy levels, of CO(f), **7**-143
of light nuclei (f's) (T), **8**-56, **8**-58 to **8**-86
of N_2 (g), **7**-144
of NO (f), **7**-144
of X-ray spectra (T), **7**-133 to **7**-135
Energy loss, per ion pair in various gases (T), **8**-36, **8**-38
of protons, in air (f), **8**-26
in aluminum (f) (T), **8**-28, **8**-35
in beryllium (T), **8**-35
in copper (T's), **8**-24 to **8**-25, **8**-35
in gold (T), **8**-35
in lead (T), **8**-33 to **8**-34
in mica (T), **8**-35
in silver (T), **8**-30 to **8**-34
Energy product of materials for permanent magnets (T), **5**-219
Energy-product curve of Alnico 5 (f), **5**-218
Energy reflection in earthquake waves (T), **2**-105
Energy refraction in earthquake waves (T), **2**-106
Energy relations for viscous fluids, **3**-29 to **3**-31
Energy release of earthquakes (T), **2**-112
Energy state, lifetime (or width) of, for light nuclei (f's) (T), **8**-58 to **8**-86
Energy transmission in earthquake waves (T), **2**-105
English sperm candle, definition of, **6**-10
Enthalpy, of air (T), **4**-85
of argon (T), **4**-90
of carbon dioxide (T), **4**-93
of hydrogen (T), **4**-98
of nitrogen (T), **4**-106
of oxygen (T), **4**-111
Enthalpy, of steam (T), **4**-116
Entropy, of air (T), **4**-86
of argon (T), **4**-91
of carbon dioxide (T), **4**-93
of helium at various temperatures (T), **4**-30
of hydrogen (T), **4**-99
of nitrogen (T), **4**-107
of oxygen (T), **4**-112
of a solid (T), **4**-44, **4**-46
and sound absorption, **3**-44
standard, of monatomic and polyatomic ions (T), **5**-281, **5**-282
of steam (T), **4**-117
Entropy diagram, for helium (f), **4**-94
for hydrogen (f), **4**-100 to **4**-102
Epicenter of earthquakes (T), **2**-103, **2**-107, **2**-111
Equal-loudness contours, definition of, **3**-13
Equally tempered intervals (T), **3**-14
Equally tempered scale, definition of, **3**-14
frequencies of (T), **3**-16, **3**-105
Equations, of motion, for elastic media, **2**-12
for gas flow, **2**-214 to **2**-223
for rigid bodies, **2**-8 to **2**-9
of state, and gas flow, **2**-215, **2**-221
for viscous fluids, **3**-29 to **3**-31
Equilibrium, static, definition of, **2**-9
Equilibrium distance for diatomic molecules (T), **7**-136 to **7**-141
Equivalent circuit, for magnetostrictive rod (f), **3**-100
for magnetostrictive transducers, **3**-98
for piezoelectric crystal (f), **3**-90, **3**-92
Equivalent conductances of electrolytes (T), **5**-270
Equivalent electrons, **7**-20
atomic levels for n (T), **7**-21
Equivalent noise input, of detector, definition of, **6**-119
of thermal radiation detectors (T), **6**-118
Equivalent physical roentgen, definition of, **8**-250
Erg, definition of, **2**-15
Ethanol, limiting equivalent conductances of ions in (T), **5**-271
Ether, volume related to pressure and temperature (T), **2**-161
Ethyl alcohol, density of (T), **2**-142
volume related to pressure and temperature (T), **2**-157
Ettingshausen coefficient, **5**-99
Ettingshausen effect, definition of, **5**-4, **5**-99
Euler momentum equation in gas flow, **2**-214
Euler's continuity equation, **3**-27 to **3**-28
Euler's equations, **2**-9
Euler's formula and international ellipsoid, **2**-101
Evaporated mirror coatings, optical constants of (T), **6**-104
Even multiplicities, g values in L-S coupling (T), **7**-172 to **7**-173
Even-even alpha emitters, **8**-46
ground-state transitions, **8**-55
transitions to excited state, **8**-55 to **8**-56

Even-even nuclei, first excited-state energies of (f), **8**-53
Exact wave equation, **3**-35
Excitation energy of light nuclei (f's) (T), **8**-56, **8**-58 to **8**-86
Excited-state emissions of alpha emitters, **8**-55 to **8**-56
Excited-state energies of even-even nuclei (f), **8**-53
Exciting range of fluorescent chemicals (T), **6**-111
Experimental piles, **8**-227
Extensional deformation, **2**-10
Extensional waves in solids, **3**-75
External ear canal, minimum audible pressure for (T), **3**-124 to **3**-125
Extinction, index of, **6**-2
Extinction coefficient (optical), definition of, **6**-102
in infrared (T), **6**-38
of light, definition of, **6**-36
Eyes, maximum permissible exposure to ionizing radiation for (T), **8**-255

F

Fabry-Perot filter (f), **6**-45, **6**-47
Fahrenheit temperatures, conversion equations for (T), **4**-2
Far zone of radiation field, **5**-68
Far-zone field and current distribution, Fourier transform relations for, **5**-72
Farad, international vs. absolute (T), **5**-106
Faraday effect, **5**-231, **6**-4, **6**-91 to **6**-94
Faraday's law of induction, **5**-3
Faraday rotation, in ferrites (T), **5**-234 to **5**-235
as function of field strength (f), **5**-233
at microwave frequencies, **5**-64 to **5**-65
in various materials (T), **5**-232
(*See also* Magneto-optical rotation)
Fast-neutron cross sections, **8**-130, **8**-143
Fast-neutron fission yields (T), **8**-216 to **8**-218
Feeling, threshold of discomfort, definition of, **3**-14
Fermat's principle of least time, definition of, **6**-4
Ferramic-type ferrites, properties of (T), **5**-217
Ferrimagnetic materials, definition of, **5**-4
Ferrimagnetic resonance, **5**-104
Ferrimagnetism, **5**-102
Ferrite materials, Faraday rotation in (T), **5**-234 to **5**-235
Ferrite-type transducers, materials for, **3**-92
Ferrites, Bohr magneton numbers and Curie points of (T), **5**-211, **5**-212
magnetostrictive properties of (T), **3**-99
properties of Ferroxcube and Ferramic types (T), **5**-217
saturation magnetization and Curie points of (T), **5**-211, **5**-212
Ferroelectric crystals, properties of (T), **5**-155 to **5**-156
Ferroelectric materials, acoustic losses in, **3**-85 to **3**-86
definition of, **5**-4
and transducers, **3**-89
Ferromagnetic elements, Bohr magneton numbers, Curie points, and saturation magnetization of (T), **5**-208
Ferromagnetic magnetized films, magnetic rotatory power of (T), **6**-96
Ferromagnetic materials, acoustic losses in, **3**-85 to **3**-86
definition of, **5**-4
Ferromagnetic resonance, **5**-104
Ferromagnetism, **5**-101
Ferroxcube-type ferrites, properties of (T), **5**-217
Fick's diffusion equation, **2**-189
Field, anechoic sound, **3**-2
sound, **3**-6
Field equations, differential formulations in, **5**-37 to **5**-38
dynamic, **5**-36 to **5**-44
integral formulations in, **5**-36 to **5**-37
Field intensity, magnetic, of sun (T), **5**-295
Field strength, fractional volume change with (T), **5**-224
Field vectors, and constitutive parameters, **5**-38 to **5**-39
wave equations for, **5**-42
Filter (light) plates, transmission curves of (f), **6**-49
Filter sections, design of low-pass, high-pass, and band-pass (T), **5**-86 to **5**-89
Filters, glass, polarizing and interference, **6**-43 to **6**-50
with π sections (T), **5**-86 to **5**-89
with T intermediate sections (T), **5**-86 to **5**-89
Finite amplitude waves, **3**-37 to **3**-39
First-order acoustic equations, **3**-33
First-order vorticity, **3**-40
Fission, definition of, **8**-2
types of, **8**-212
Fission fragments, range of, **8**-36
Fission-product chains (T), **8**-202 to **8**-211
Fission yields, charged-particle (T), **8**-219 to **8**-221
fast-neutron (T), **8**-216 to **8**-218
photo- (T), **8**-222 to **8**-224
spontaneous (T), **8**-225
thermal neutron (T), **8**-212 to **8**-215
Fissionable nuclei, resonance parameters of (T), **8**-153
Fine-structure constant (T), **7**-3
Five-atom molecules, fundamental vibrations of (T), **7**-150
rotational constants and geometric parameters of, asymmetric-top (T), **7**-159
linear (T), **7**-156
spherical-top (T), **7**-157 to **7**-158
symmetric-top (T), **7**-157 to **7**-158
Fixed cavities, **2**-183, **2**-187
Fixed temperature points, on international temperature scale (T), **4**-3
secondary (T), **4**-5
Flame standards (T), **6**-9

Flat plate, heat transfer data for (f), **2**-229, **2**-230
skin-friction data for, **2**-228
turbulent flow along (f), **2**-227
Flat strips, capacitance per unit length, **5**-15 to **5**-16
Floors, sound transmission loss through (T), **3**-121
Flow variables vs. Mach number for isentropic gas flow (T), **2**-218
Flow-velocity components of liquid jets, **2**-196
Flowing liquids, symbols and definitions for, **2**-182 to **2**-183
Fluid dynamics, **2**-12 to **2**-14
Bernoulli's principle, **2**-13
and viscous fluids, **2**-13
Fluid flow properties of porous media, **2**-179 to **2**-180
Fluids, in equilibrium, **2**-12
sound propagation in, **3**-25 to **3**-55
viscous (*see* Viscous fluids)
waves in, **2**-14
Fluorescence, of gases and vapors (T), **6**-112
of organic substances in solution (T), **6**-111
Fluorescent chemicals, characteristics of (T), **6**-111
Fluorine, energy levels of (f) (T), **8**-77 to **8**-85
Fluorocarbon liquids, density of (T), **2**-149
Flutter echo, definition of, **3**-4
Flux, luminous, definition of, **6**-52
maximum permissible for normal neutron beam (T), **8**-256
FM cyclotron, description of, **8**-174 to **8**-175
Focal depths of earthquakes (T), **2**-107
Foot-candle, definition of, **6**-4, **6**-10
Foot-lambert, definition of, **6**-9
Force, centrifugal, **2**-5
Coriolis, **2**-5
definition of, **2**-4
on dipole, **5**-21
moment of, **2**-6 to **2**-7
Force equation for viscous fluids, **3**-27 to **3**-29
Force factor, of ceramics (T), **3**-95
of piezoelectric crystals (T), **3**-93
Force law, **5**-41
Foreign betatrons, list and descriptions of (T), **8**-195
Foreign cyclotrons and synchrotrons, list and descriptions of (T), **8**-191 to **8**-193
Foreign electron synchrotrons, list and descriptions of (T), **8**-196 to **8**-197
Foreign electrostatic generators, list and descriptions of (T), **8**-185 to **8**-188
Foreign linear accelerators, list and descriptions of (T), **8**-200 to **8**-201
Foreign proton synchrotrons, list and descriptions of (T), **8**-198 to **8**-199
Form factors in demagnetization, **5**-240
Formant frequencies in American speech (T), **3**-131 to **3**-132
Formative time lag, **5**-180
Foucault current, definition of, **5**-3
Four-atom molecules, fundamental vibrations of (T), **7**-148 to **7**-149
rotational constants and geometrical parameters of, asymmetric-top (T), **7**-155
linear (T), **7**-154
spherical-top (T), **7**-154
symmetric-top (T), **7**-154
Fourier-Kirchhoff-Neuman energy equation, **3**-29
Fractional change of volume of incompressible metals (T), **4**-28
Fractional distillation, **2**-137
Fragments, fission, definition of, **8**-2
Fraunhofer's lines, **6**-4
Free electrons and spin resonance, **5**-103
Free field, definition of, **3**-4
Free particle and wave mechanics, **7**-162
Free surface, **2**-12
of liquids, and shock waves, **2**-235
Free surface energy, **2**-175
Freezing point of sea water, **2**-116
French reactor program, **8**-240
Frenkel defects (T), **5**-185, **5**-195
Frequencies, of equal-tempered scale, **3**-105
microwave letter notation for (T), **5**-62
Frequency, of conical resonators (T), **3**-103
critical hearing band (T), **3**-127
dielectric, of ceramics, **5**-120 to **5**-121
of commercial dielectrics (T), **5**-147
of glasses, **5**-122 to **5**-123
of plastics (T), **5**-124 to **5**-130
of rubbers (T), **5**-124 to **5**-130
differential threshold, in hearing (T), **3**-126
effect on conductivity of copper, **5**-197, **5**-200
fundamental, of air columns and rods, **3**-102 to **3**-103
of strings, **3**-100 to **3**-102
and pitch (T), **3**-129
relative, of sounds in American speech (T), **3**-131 to **3**-132
of simple vibrators, **3**-100 to **3**-106
of tuning fork, **3**-104
of vibration of bars (T), **3**-104, **3**-106
Frequency bands, equivalent, in speech (T), **3**-133
Frequency number and sound absorption, **3**-46
Frequency perturbations in strings (T), **3**-102
Frequency ratings of electric motors, **5**-252
Frequency ratios for intervals in cents (T), **3**-106, **3**-107
Frequency standards, **5**-112 to **5**-113
Fresh water, properties of (T), **3**-69
Fresnel's formulas, **6**-7
Friction, coefficients of (T), **2**-39 to **2**-44
rolling (f), **2**-43 to **2**-44
sliding, **2**-40
static (T), **2**-39 to **2**-40
Friction factor vs. Reynolds number, rough pipes (f), **2**-225
Frictional force, **2**-39

Fuel cores of various nuclear reactors (T), **8**-228 to **8**-239
Fuels for various nuclear reactors (T), **8**-228 to **8**-239
Full-load currents, average, for motors (T), **5**-256
Fundamental frequency, of air columns and rods, **3**-102 to **3**-103
of strings, **3**-100 to **3**-102
Fundamental tone, definition of, **3**-14
Fundamental units in mechanics, **2**-14 to **2**-15
Fundamental vibrations of polyatomic molecules (T's), **7**-147 to **7**-151
Fused-quartz glass, index of refraction of (T), **6**-31
Fused silica, optical properties of, **6**-40
Fusion, heat of, for elements and compounds (T), **4**-131 to **4**-159

G

g factor and Zeeman effect, **7**-169
g values, for *L-S* coupling, **7**-170 to **7**-173
Gabbro, **2**-108
Gadolinium sulfate, properties of (T), **4**-14, **4**-19
Gain function of radiating system, **5**-68 to **5**-69
Galactic magnetism, **5**-295 to **5**-297
Galactic radio noise, **6**-122
Galvanomagnetic effect, **5**-97 to **5**-100
Gamma energy in neutron capture for elements (T), **8**-96
Gamma quantum, symbols for, **8**-3
Gamma-ray absorption in air (T), **8**-253
Gamma-ray energy of nuclides (T), **8**-98 to **8**-128
Gamma rays, **8**-87 to **8**-95
absorption of, **8**-87
total, **8**-92 to **8**-93
angular correlation and polarization of, **8**-93
linear absorption coefficient for (f), **8**-93
maximum permissible exposure to (T's), **8**-254, **8**-255
and neutron capture (T), **8**-94 to **8**-96
Gas, diffusion in, **2**-211 to **2**-214
laminar flow in, **2**-220 to **2**-224
turbulent flow in, **2**-224 to **2**-228
Gas constants, **3**-56 to **3**-60
per mole (T), **7**-3
R in various units (T), **4**-80
Gas diode and triode rectifiers, **5**-263
Gas flow, axially symmetric, **2**-217 to **2**-219
basic parameters of, **2**-221
Blasius flow, **2**-224
boundary layer relations for, **2**-223
compressible, **2**-214 to **2**-219
drag data for, **2**-226 to **2**-228
equations for, **2**-214 to **2**-223
continuity, **2**-215
energy, **2**-215
Euler momentum, **2**-214
linearized theory, **2**-219
of motion, **2**-220 to **2**-221
Gas flow, equations for, one-dimensional, **2**-216 to **2**-217
of state, **2**-215
two-dimensional, **2**-217 to **2**-219, **2**-223
flow variables vs. Mach number for (T), **2**-218
heat transfer data for, **2**-228 to **2**-230
hypersonic similarity rule for, **2**-219
Prandtl-Glauert rule for, **2**-219
and skin-friction data, **2**-228
stream function for, **2**-217
transonic similarity rule for, **2**-219
turbulent, along flat plate (f), **2**-227
two-dimensional, through pipe, **2**-222
velocity potential for, **2**-217
wall-friction relations (f), **2**-225 to **2**-226
Gas flow parameters, **2**-215
Gas mixtures, viscosity of, **2**-205 to **2**-206
Gas temperature of discharge vs. tube radius (f), **5**-183
Gaseous substances, liquid densities of (T), **2**-144
Gases, absolute viscosities of (T), **2**-207
acoustic properties of, **3**-56 to **3**-67
cathode fall in, for various metals (T), **5**-184
characteristic impedance of (T), **3**-63
coefficient of self-diffusion for (T), **2**-213
compressible flow in, **2**-214 to **2**-219
conduction (electrical) in, **5**-166 to **5**-184
critical energy and radiation length for (T), **8**-39
density of (T), **2**-197 to **2**-201, **3**-56, **3**-57
dielectric properties of (T's), **5**-147 to **5**-149
diffusion coefficients of (T), **2**-212 to **2**-213
vs. concentration (T), **2**-213
vs. pressure (T), **2**-213
dissociative recombination in (T), **5**-171
energy loss per ion pair in (T), **8**-38
Faraday rotation in (T), **5**-232
fluorescence of (T), **6**-112
index of refraction of (T), **6**-21
isothermal compressibility of liquefied (T), **2**-162
kinematic viscosities of (T), **2**-208
Lennard-Jones potential function constants for (T), **4**-129
motions of electrons and ions in, **7**-174 to **7**-219
pressure-volume-temperature relationships for, **4**-118 to **4**-129
recombination coefficients of (T's), **5**-171
relative dielectric strengths of (T), **5**-148 to **5**-149
relative volume vs. temperature for (T's), **4**-26
shock wave properties of (T), **2**-235
specific heats of, at C_p and C_v (T), **3**-59
thermal conductivities of (T), **3**-58 to **3**-61, **4**-71
thermodynamic properties of, **4**-80 to **4**-117
Verdet constants for (T), **6**-91
viscosity, **2**-201 to **2**-210, **3**-58
viscosity coefficients for (T), **3**-60

Gel-sol-gel transformation, **2**-81
Gels, definition of, **2**-81
mechanical properties of, **2**-81 to **2**-83
shear modulus of (T), **2**-83
General transmission lines, formulas for (T), **5**-50
Generators, a-c and d-c, **5**-246 to **5**-250
d-c, characteristics of (f), **5**-259
connections for, **5**-258
operating principles of, **5**-258
world-wide list of electrostatic (T), **8**-182 to **8**-188
Geodesy, principal problems of, **2**-92 to **2**-95
Geodetic data, **2**-92 to **2**-101
Geodetic problem, **2**-93
Geodetic symbols, **2**-92
Geodetic systems, **2**-95 to **2**-96
Geoid, definition of, **2**-92
gravimetrical undulations of, **2**-99 to **2**-100
Geomagnetic field vector, position of (T), **5**-292
Geomagnetic poles, **5**-291
Geomagnetic tide, **5**-293
Geomagnetism, **5**-291
Geometric parameters of polyatomic molecules (T's), **7**-152 to **7**-161
Geopotential, definition of, **2**-125
vs. geometric height (T), **2**-126
Geopotential meter, **2**-125
Geostrophic wind, **2**-130 to **2**-131
Germanium, extinction coefficients of (T), **6**-38
index of refraction of (T), **6**-26 to **6**-27
Gibbs-Hamilton notation, **3**-28
Glass, density of (T), **3**-77 to **3**-78
dielectric frequency and volume resistivity of (T), **5**-122 to **5**-123
dielectric properties of (T), **5**-122 to **5**-123
elastic constants of (T), **3**-80
impedance of (T), **3**-80
index of refraction, of National Bureau of Standards (T), **6**-32
of new types (T), **6**-33
Verdet constants for (T), **6**-95
wave velocities in (T), **3**-80
Glass filters, **6**-43 to **6**-44
Globar light sources, characteristics of (f), **6**-81
emissivity of (f), **6**-81
Glossy surfaces, reflection coefficients for incandescent light on (T), **6**-43
Glow discharge, cathode current density in (T), **5**-185
Glower light sources, characteristics of (f), **6**-81
Glycerin volume related to pressure and temperature (T), **2**-161
Glycine, diffusion coefficients of (T), **2**-192
Glycolamide, diffusion coefficients (T), **2**-192
Golay pneumatic cell, characteristics of (T), **6**-118
Gold, energy loss of protons in (T), **8**-35
Gold alloys, elastic and strength constants for (T), **2**-62 to **2**-63
Gonads, maximum permissible exposure of, to ionizing radiation (T), **8**-255
Gradient wind, **2**-132
Grain rotation and thermal losses, **3**-84
Grain scattering and thermal losses, **3**-85
Gram-ionic weight of paramagnetic salts (T), **4**-14
Granitic rocks, **2**-108
Grashof number and gas flow, **2**-221
Gravimetric undulations, **2**-99
Gravimetrical method of earth measurement, **2**-96
Gravitational constants (T), **2**-91
Gravity anomalies and earth measurement, **2**-97
Gravity formula, **2**-98, **2**-99
Gravity values for earth, **2**-101
Gravity waves in sea water, **2**-122 to **2**-123
Ground-state configuration of stable nuclei (T), **8**-6 to **8**-17
Ground-state transitions of alpha emitters, **8**-55 to **8**-56
Ground states of atoms (T), **7**-13 to **7**-15
Ground surfaces, reflection coefficients for incandescent light on (T), **6**-43
Group velocity of waves, **5**-51, **5**-58
Gruneisen's equation, constants in (T), **4**-64
definition of, **4**-63
Gut strings, mass per unit length (T), **3**-101
Gyromagnetic effects, **5**-4, **5**-103 to **5**-104
Gyromagnetic ratio, definition of, **5**-103, **5**-229
of various substances (T), **5**-229, **5**-230

H

H waves, **5**-47
Half cells, standard emf of (T), **5**-274 to **5**-276
Half life, vs. effective alpha energy for various alpha emitters (f), **8**-54
of nuclides (T), **8**-97 to **8**-128, **8**-202 to **8**-211
Hall angle, definition of, **5**-159
Hall coefficients, **5**-98
Hall constant, definition of, **5**-157, **5**-233
of various materials (T), **5**-237 to **5**-238
Hall effect, definition of, **5**-4, **5**-98, **5**-157, **5**-159
Hall mobilities of various substances (T), **5**-161
Hamiltonian in wave mechanics, **7**-162
Handbooks, mathematical, list of, **1**-2 to **1**-5
Hardness numbers, definitions of, **2**-69, **2**-78, **2**-80
(*See also* Brinell hardness number)
Harmonic, definition of, **3**-14
Harmonic oscillator and wave mechanics, **7**-162
Harmonic series, of sounds, definition of, **3**-15
in string vibrators, **3**-102
Hartree units, **7**-174
Health physics, **8**-250 to **8**-257
definitions of units, **8**-250 to **8**-251

Hearing, critical frequency band of (T), **3**-127
differential thresholds of, for intensity and frequency (T), **3**-126
and localization of sound, **3**-129
and loudness, **3**-13, **3**-128 to **3**-129
loudness level vs. pressure and frequency, (T), **3**-128
masking, definition of, **3**-13
minimum audible pressure on ear for (T), **3**-124 to **3**-125
per cent of, definition of, **3**-13
and physical dimensions of ear (T), **3**-123
and pitch, **3**-13
pitch vs. frequency (T), **3**-129
of short-duration sounds, **3**-127
and sound masking, **3**-127
and speech, **3**-123 to **3**-133
threshold of feeling or discomfort, **3**-126
and thresholds, **3**-14
Hearing loss, definition of, **3**-12 to **3**-13
Heat, of fusion (T), **4**-131 to **4**-159
of sublimation (T), **4**-131 to **4**-159
of transition (T), **4**-131 to **4**-159
of vaporization (T), **4**-131 to **4**-159
Heat capacities, molar, of elements (T's), **4**-41 to **4**-43
of various substances, **4**-39 to **4**-50
Heat content, molal, of solutes (T), **5**-281
Heat-exchange equation for viscous fluids, **3**-27
Heat flow, and attenuation for metals (T), **3**-83
intergrain, in metals (T), **3**-83
in solids, **3**-79
Heat flux in viscous liquids, **3**-31
Heat index in stellar radiation, **6**-80
Heat radiation, coefficient of, **3**-31
and sound absorption and dispersion, **3**-49 to **3**-50
Heat transfer, from flat plate (f), **2**-229
in gas flow (f's), **2**-228 to **2**-230
and skin friction, **2**-230
Heavy meson, **8**-227
Heavy nuclei, resonance parameters of (T), **8**-147 to **8**-152
Heavy particles, range-energy relations, **8**-23
straggling of, **8**-36
Hefner unit, **6**-6, **6**-9, **6**-10
Heisenberg exchange coupling, **5**-101
Helicotrema in ear (T), **3**-123
Helium, electron power losses in (f), **5**-182
energy levels of (f) (T), **8**-58, **8**-59
principal spectral lines of (T), **7**-43 to **7**-45
solid, volume and compressibility of (T), **4**-27
temperature-entropy diagram for (f), **4**-94
virial coefficients for (T), **4**-119 to **4**-120
Helium I, energy-level diagram of (f), **7**-28
Helix, magnetic induction of, **5**-27
Helmholtz coil, **5**-26
Helmholtz resonator, **3**-103 to **3**-104
Henry, international vs. absolute (T), **5**-106
Henry's law, **2**-120
Hermite polynomials and wave mechanics, **7**-162, **7**-164
Hexagonal crystal systems (f) (T), **2**-45, **2**-47
Hexagonal crystals, elastic constants and coefficients (T), **2**-57
Hexagonal symmetry, **3**-75
High-pass filter sections, design of (T), **5**-86 to **5**-89
High-permeability materials, properties of (T), **5**-216
High-pressure effects, **4**-24 to **4**-38
Hole conduction (electricity), **5**-97
Hole traps and electron conduction, **5**-160
Holes and Hall mobilities (T), **5**-161
Hooke's law, **2**-10, **2**-11
Horns and beam formation, **5**-73
Horsepower characteristics of motors (T's), **5**-253 to **5**-255
Horsepower rating of electric motors (T), **5**-252
Horsepower requirements and electric motor selection, **5**-250 to **5**-251
Horseshoe magnets, **5**-36
Hour, definition of, **2**-14
Humidity, effects of, on sound propagation, **3**-63 to **3**-66
Huygens' theory of light, **6**-4
Huygens-Fresnel principle, **5**-72 to **5**-73
Hydraulic junction, **3**-141, **3**-143
Hydrocarbons (saturated), acoustic properties of (T), **3**-72
Hydrogen, atomic mass of, **7**-3, **8**-4
compressibility factor for (T), **4**-95
electron energy losses in (f), **5**-182
enthalpy of (T), **4**-98
entropy of (T), **4**-99
ionization per volt in (f), **5**-170
Prandtl numbers for (T), **2**-223
relative density of (T), **4**-96
specific heat of (T), **4**-97
temperature-entropy diagram for (f), **4**-100 to **4**-102
thermodynamic conversion factors for (T), **4**-81
total neutron cross section of (f), **8**-131
virial coefficients for (T), **4**-124
Hydrogen chloride, efficiency electron attachment in (f), **5**-173
mean-ionic-activity coefficient of (T), **5**-279
Hydrogen isotopes, masses of (T), **7**-3
Hydrogen sulfide, efficiency electron attachment in (f), **5**-174
Hyperfine splitting of atomic hydrogen (T), **6**-122
Hyperfine structure and Zeeman effect, **7**-169
Hyperfragments, **8**-245
Hyperons, characteristics of (T), **8**-241, **8**-244 to **8**-245
definition of, **8**-240 to **8**-241
and excited nucleons, **8**-245
nomenclature for, **8**-240 to **8**-241
Hypersonic similarity rule for gas flow, **2**-219
Hypsometry, **2**-126

Hysteresis constant for magnetic losses at low induction (T), **5**-220
Hysteresis curves, definition of, **5**-4
Hysteresis loss and maximum induction in several materials (f), **5**-215

I

Ice, transition parameters (f) (T), **4**-34, **4**-35
Ideal gas relations and shock waves (T), **2**-232 to **2**-233, **2**-235
Ideal transmission lines, formulas for (T), **5**-50
Ignition rectifiers, **5**-263
Ilford C-2 emulsion, range-energy relations for alpha particles, deuterons, protons, and tritons in, **8**-32
Illuminants, efficiencies of different types (T), **6**-77
  standard (T), **6**-56
Illumination, definition of, **6**-4, **6**-9
Image force, definition of, **5**-4
Impedance, acoustical, **3**-8, **3**-53, **3**-108 to **3**-110
  American Standard, **3**-8
  characteristic, definition of, **3**-9, **3**-62
    for gases (T), **3**-63
  of ear (T), **3**-123, **3**-124
  of glasses (T), **3**-80
  mechanical, **3**-9
  of metals (T), **3**-80
  of organic liquids (T), **3**-72, **3**-73
  of plastics, **3**-80
  and sound transmission in solids, **3**-74 to **3**-79
  vector, equations for, **3**-138
  of water, fresh and sea (T), **3**-69
Impedance analogy, and acoustics, **3**-140 to **3**-177
  definition of, **3**-140
  symbols for constructing schematic diagram based on (T), **3**-145 to **3**-176
Impedance matching, curves of (f), **5**-52
  in transmission lines, **5**-51
Impulse-momentum theorem, **2**-5
Incandescent light, reflection coefficients for (T), **6**-43
Incipient cavitation, cavitation number (f), **2**-186
Inclination, of earth's magnetic field, **5**-291
  of planets to ecliptic (T), **2**-90
Incremental variables, **3**-32
Incus in ear (T), **3**-123
Index of extinction, definition of, **6**-2
Index of refraction, **6**-11 to **6**-35
  of acids (T), **6**-22
  of biaxial minerals (T), **6**-14 to **6**-17
  definition of, **6**-4, **6**-102, **6**-103
  vs. dispersion for optical glass (f), **6**-33
  of evaporated mirror coatings (T), **6**-104
  of fused-quartz glass (T), **6**-31
  of gases and vapors (T), **6**-21
  of liquids relative to air (T), **6**-18
  liquids used in measuring (T), **6**-35
Index of refraction, of National Bureau of Standards optical glass, **6**-32
  of optical plastics (T), **6**-19 to **6**-20
  of quartz at various temperatures (T), **6**-34
  of salt solutions (T), **6**-22
  of sea water, **2**-119
  of some new glasses (T), **6**-33
  of special optical materials (T), **6**-23 to **6**-30
  uniaxial minerals (T), **6**-12 to **6**-13
  of various metals (T's), **6**-105 to **6**-107
Inductance and acoustic analogy, **3**-135, **3**-136
Inductance standards, **5**-110 to **5**-112
Induction, low, magnetic losses at, **5**-200
  of magnetic material, **5**-206
  variation of hysteresis loss with (f), **5**-215
Inductive reactance and sound absorption, **3**-45
Inductors, **5**-110 to **5**-112
Inelastic collisions by electrons in various substances (f's), **7**-177 to **7**-182
Inertance and acoustic analogy, **3**-135
Inertia, moments of, for various bodies (T), **2**-38 to **2**-39
Inertial forces, definition of, **2**-5
Inertial frame of reference, **2**-3 to **2**-4
Infrared reflecting factors of dry pigments (T), **6**-41
Infrared standard wavelength (T), **6**-88 to **6**-90
Infrasonic frequency, definition of, **3**-4
Inharmonicity, definition of, **3**-102
Initial permeability, definition of, **5**-214
Inorganic aqueous solutions, surface tension of (T), **2**-177
Inorganic gases, densities of (T), **2**-199
Inorganic liquids, densities of (T), **2**-143
  dielectric constants of (T), **5**-133
  Verdet constants for (T), **6**-92
Inorganic solids, dielectric constants of (T), **5**-115 to **5**-117
Inorganic substances, critical temperatures, pressures, and densities of (T), **4**-21 to **4**-22
Insertion loss, definition of, **3**-9
Insolation, definition of, **2**-132
Inspected electrical equipment, list of, **5**-245
Instantaneous acceleration, definition of, **2**-3
Instantaneous angular velocity, **2**-8
Instantaneous cubical expansion, **2**-151
Instantaneous sound pressure, definition of, **3**-4
Instantaneous speech power, definition of, **3**-13
Instantaneous velocity, **2**-2
Instrument transformers, **5**-259 to **5**-260
Instruments, deflecting, **5**-113
Insulated conductors, current-carrying capacities of (T), **5**-202 to **5**-203, **5**-257
Insulating materials, thermal conductivity of (T), **4**-68 to **4**-70
Integral forms of Maxwell's equations, **5**-40

Integral formulations in electrical field equations, **5**-36 to **5**-37
Intelligibility of speech, definition of, **3**-12
Intensity, atomic selection rules of, **7**-25 to **7**-26
differential threshold of, in hearing (T), **3**-126
of illumination, definition of, **6**-5
level of sound, **3**-3
of radiation, definition of, **6**-5
of sound, definition of, **3**-6
of standard spectral lines (T), **6**-83 to **6**-86
in Zeeman effect, **7**-169
Interference filters, **6**-45 to **6**-50
multilayer, **6**-46 to **6**-47
polarization, **6**-48
Intergrain heat flow, in metals (T), **3**-83
and thermal losses, **3**-84
Intermediate tissues of body, maximum permissible exposure to ionizing radiation (T), **8**-255
Internal energy of a solid (T), **4**-44, **4**-45
Internal transmittance of light, definition of, **6**-36
International candle, definition of, **6**-3, **6**-6, **6**-8, **6**-9
International electrical units related to absolute (T), **5**-106
International ellipsoid, **2**-96 to **2**-99
quantities associated with, **2**-100 to **2**-101
International formula for emf of cells, **5**-108
International gravity formula, **2**-97 to **2**-99, **2**-101
International photometric standard, **6**-52
International standard A, **3**-105
International temperature scale, comparison of 1927 and 1948 (T), **4**-4
definition and equations for (T), **4**-3
interpolation equations for, **4**-3
International wavelength standards in vacuum ultraviolet (T), **6**-87
Interval rules of atomic selection, **7**-25 to **7**-26
Intervals, definition of, **3**-15
for various frequency ratios (T), **3**-106, **3**-107
Intrinsic conduction, **5**-160
Intrinsic viscosity, **2**-165
Iodides, optical properties of, **6**-40
Ion conversion, probability curves for various substances (f's), **7**-201 to **7**-202
Ion formation, probability of, in several substances (f's), **7**-184 to **7**-185
Ion ground states of atoms (T), **7**-13 to **7**-15
Ion mobility for various substances (f's), **7**-212 to **7**-218
Ion production in upper atmosphere (T), **5**-284
Ion recombination coefficient, definition of, **5**-171
Ionic conductivity in salts, **5**-185 to **5**-196
Ionic conductors, conductivity of (T's), **5**-186 to **5**-188, **5**-192 to **5**-194
conductivity formulas (electrical), **5**-97
Ionic conductors, density and mobility of defects for (T), **5**-189
transport numbers for pure and mixed (T), **5**-191 to **5**-194
Ionization, atmospheric, **5**-283 to **5**-284
by electrons, **5**-166
per volt in hydrogen and neon-argon mixtures (f's), **5**-170
Ionization potential of atoms (T), **7**-13 to **7**-15
Ionized gases and Faraday rotation (T), **5**-235
Ionizing radiation, permissible exposure to (T's), **8**-254 to **8**-256
Ionosphere, diurnal and seasonal variations in (f), **2**-131
in relation to other atmospheric layers (f), **2**-130
Ionospheric regions, characteristics of (T), **5**-284
Ions, drift velocities in various substances (f's), **7**-212 to **7**-218
elastic collisions by, in various substances (f's), **7**-186 to **7**-188
formation, density, and mean life in lower atmosphere (T), **5**-284
motions in gases, **7**-174 to **7**-219
surface phenomena of, **7**-192 to **7**-203
and Zeeman effect in crystals, **7**-171
Iron, emf of, vs. constantan in thermocouples (T), **4**-11
total cross section of (f), **8**-133
Iron I, energy-level diagram of (f), **7**-37
photoelectric traces of spectrum of (f), **7**-103 to **7**-118
principal spectral lines of (T), **7**-87 to **7**-102
Iron II, energy-level diagram of (f), **7**-36
Iron alloys, Curie points and saturation magnetization of (T), **5**-209
elastic and strength constants of (T), **2**-70 to **2**-71
Hall constants of (T), **5**-239
Iron ammonium alum, properties of (T), **4**-14, **4**-18
temperature data for (T), **4**-18
Iron-cobalt-nickel alloys, Curie points and saturation magnetization of (f), **5**-207
Irrotational waves, **2**-12
Isentropic gas flow, flow variables vs Mach number (T), **2**-218
Isobar, definition of, **8**-2
Isobaric interval, definition of, **2**-132
Isoclinic lines, **5**-292
Isocurrent junction, **3**-141
Isodynamic lines, **5**-292
Isogonic lines, **5**-292
Isomagnetic patterns, **5**-292
Isomers (T), **8**-96 to **8**-128
Isoporic lines, **5**-293
Isostatic equilibrium, **2**-99
Isothermal compressibility, **2**-151
of aqueous solutions (T), **2**-164
of liquefied gases (T), **2**-162
of nitric acid (T), **2**-162
of organic liquids (T), **2**-163, **2**-164

Isothermal compressibilty, of sulfuric acid (T), **2**-162
Isothermal Hall effect, **5**-98
Isothermal modulus of elasticity, **2**-85, **2**-86
Isotherms of tropopause (f), **2**-129
Isotone, definition of, **8**-2
Isotopes, definition of, **8**-2
of elements (T's), **8**-154 to **8**-168, **8**-170 to **8**-171
Isotopic incoherence, **8**-144
Isotopic spin for light nuclei (f's) (T), **8**-57 to **8**-86
Isotropic media, field vectors for, **5**-38

J

J rule of electron transition, **7**-21
J values for multiplets (T), **7**-19 to **7**-20
Jets, liquid, **2**-195 to **2**-197
streamlines (f), **2**-196
Joule, international vs. absolute (T), **5**-106
Joule's law, **5**-3

K

K capture, **8**-3
K index and magnetic activity, definition of, **5**-294
K mesons, **8**-240, **8**-242 to **8**-244
K_{e3} meson, **8**-244
$K_{\mu 2}$ meson, **8**-243
$K_{\mu 3}$ meson, **8**-244
K-series X-ray lines, wavelengths of (T), **7**-125 to **7**-126
Kamerlingh Onnes equation of state, **4**-118
Kelvin temperatures, conversion equations for (T), **4**-2
Kerr effect and Pockel's effect, **6**-94
Keyes equation, gas constants for (T), **2**-204, **2**-205
Kilowatthour, definition of, **2**-15
Kinematic coefficient of viscosity, **3**-58
Kinematic interpretation of viscosity (f), **2**-203
Kinematic viscosity, conversion factors for (T), **2**-203
definition of, **2**-201
of sea water (T), **2**-122
units of (T), **2**-203
of various gases (T), **2**-208
of water and water vapor (T), **2**-210
Kinematics, definitions for, **2**-2 to **2**-3
Kinetic energy, definition of, **2**-4
and work-energy theorem, **2**-9
Kirchhoff-Langevin equation, **3**-46, **3**-49
Kirchhoff's formula for capacitance, **5**-14
Kirchhoff's laws, and circuit theory, **5**-80
of electric currents, **5**-3
of radiation, **6**-5
Kneser's nomogram for attenuation of sound (f), **3**-64
Kozeny's equation, **2**-180
Kramer's degeneracy and Zeeman effect, **7**-171
Krasskouski ellipsoid, **2**-96
Krypton, virial coefficients for (T), **4**-122
Krypton I, photoelectric traces of spectrum of (f), **7**-71 to **7**-74
principal spectral lines of (T), **7**-66 to **7**-70

L

L mesons, **8**-240, **8**-242
L rule of electron transition, **7**-25
L, *S* coupling, **7**-17, **7**-18
g values for (T's), **7**-170 to **7**-173
L-series X-ray lines, wavelengths of (T), **7**-127 to **7**-128
Lag constant for magnetic losses at low induction (T), **5**-220
Lagrangian wave equation, **3**-35
Lambert, definition of, **6**-9, **6**-10
Lambert's law, of absorption, **6**-2, **6**-5. **6**-6
of illumination, **6**-5
Lame elastic moduli, **3**-75
Laminar flow, circular jet, **2**-195 to **2**-196
definition of, **2**-224
of gases, **2**-220 to **2**-224
in plane jet, **2**-197
Lamp color of fluorescent chemicals (T), **6**-111
Lamps, approximate brightness of various types (T), **6**-78
efficiencies of various types (T), **6**-77
Lande splitting factor (*g*), definition of, **5**-231
of various substances (T), **5**-229, **5**-230
Lande's formula, **7**-168
Laplace's equation, **2**-13
in geodesy, **2**-96
Lapse rates in meteorology, **2**-125 to **2**-127
Large aperature systems, **5**-73 to **5**-74
Larmor principle in particle acceleration, **8**-173 to **8**-174
Latent heat, of sea water, **2**-121
of various elements and compounds (T's), **4**-30 to **4**-159
for various substances (T's), **4**-34 to **4**-38
Lattice constants, for compounds (T), **2**-53 to **2**-54
for crystal systems (f) (T), **2**-45
for elements (T), **2**-48 to **2**-52
Lattice energy (T), **4**-45
Lattice entropy (T), **4**-46
Lattice network, **5**-84
Lattice vibration, **4**-44
Laws and principles, Ampere's law, **5**-3
Beer's law, **6**-3
Bernoulli's principle, **2**-13
Bragg-Gray (ionizing radiation) principle, **8**-250 to **8**-251
Brewster's law, **6**-3
Coulomb's law, **5**-3
Curie law (paramagnetism), **5**-100
Curie-Weiss law, **5**-101, **5**-236
D'Alembert's principle, **2**-5
Darcy's law, **2**-179
Faraday's law of induction, **5**-3
Fermat's principle of least time, **6**-4
Henry's law, **2**-210
Hooke's law, **2**-10, **2**-11
Huygens-Fresnel principle, **5**-72 to **5**-73

Laws and principles, hypersonic similarity rule, **2**-219
Joule's law, **5**-3
Kirchhoff's laws, in circuit theory, **5**-80
of electric currents, **5**-3
of radiation, **6**-5
Lambert's law, of absorption, **6**-2, **6**-5
of illumination, **6**-5
Larmor principle, **8**-173 to **8**-174
Lenz's law, **5**-3
Newton's laws, **2**-4 to **2**-5
Ohm's law, **5**-3
phase stability principle, **8**-176
Prandtl-Glauert gas flow rule, **2**-219
Snell's law, **3**-78
of refraction, **6**-7
Stokes law, **2**-13
transonic similarity rule, **2**-219
Wien's displacement law, **6**-8
Lead, elastic and strength constants of (T), **2**-72
energy loss and range of protons in (T), **8**-33 to **8**-34
proton straggling in (T), **8**-36
Young's modulus vs temperature for (f), **3**-96
Lead alloys, density of (T), **2**-29
elastic and strength constants for (T), **2**-72
Lead sulfide color index of stellar spectral classes (T), **6**-80
Least mechanical equivalent of light, definition of, **6**-9
Legendre polynomials and wave mechanics, **7**-164 to **7**-165
Length, units and conversion factors for (T), **2**-15
Lennard-Jones potential function, constants for various gases (T), **4**-129
definition of, **4**-129
Lenses, **6**-5
and beam formation, **5**-73
combinations of, **6**-5
Lenz's law, **5**-3
Letter symbols in acoustics, **3**-18 to **3**-24
Level, acoustic, of discomfort, **3**-14
acoustic intensity, definition of, **3**-4
band pressure, **3**-2
power-spectrum, **3**-5
pressure, **3**-5
sound, **3**-6
threshold of audibility, **3**-14
Level order, nuclear (T), **8**-19
Lifetime of energy state for light nuclei (f's) (T), **8**-57 to **8**-86
Light, absorption of, **6**-36 to **6**-40
Huygens' theory of, **6**-4
reflection of, by various metals (T), **6**-109 to **6**-110
transmission of, **6**-36 to **6**-40
vs. wavelength (f), **6**-47
transmittance, definition of, **6**-36
velocity of (T), **7**-3
measurements of (T), **6**-119, **6**-120
Light meson, **8**-227
Light nuclei, energy levels of (f's) (T), **8**-56, **8**-58 to **8**-86
resonance parameters of (T), **8**-145 to **8**-146
Light sources, approximate brightness of, (T), **6**-78
characteristics of globar and glower (f), **6**-81
efficiencies of various types (T), **6**-77
Light year, definition of, **2**-14
Lightning discharge, nature of, **5**-285 to **5**-286
Lightning strokes, characteristics of (T), **5**-288
Limiting equivalent conductances of ions in various solutions (T's), **5**-271
Line sound source, beam angle of radiation (f), **3**-111, **3**-112
directional radiation from, **3**-110 to **3**-111
Line spectrum, definition of, **3**-5
Line strength for various electron transitions, **7**-26
Linear absorption coefficient of gamma radiation, **8**-93
Linear accelerators, electron and proton, **8**-178, **8**-179
world-wide list of (T), **8**-200 to **8**-201
Linear circuit formulas, **5**-23
Linear electron accelerators, description of, **8**-178
Linear molecules, rotational constants and geometrical parameters of, five-atom (T), **7**-156
four-atom (T), **7**-154
six-atom (T), **7**-160
triatomic (T), **7**-152 to **7**-153
Linear proton accelerator, description of, **8**-179
Linear thermal expansion coefficients, of alloys (T), **4**-57 to **4**-60
of elements (T), **4**-51 to **4**-55
of miscellaneous materials (T), **4**-61
of semiconductors (T), **4**-63
Linearized theory equations for gas flow, **2**-219
Linearizing of equations of motion, **3**-32
Liquefied gases, Faraday rotation in (T), **5**-232
isothermal compressibility of (T), **2**-162
Liquid jets, **2**-195 to **2**-197
Liquids, acoustic properties, **3**-67 to **3**-74
adiabatic compressibilities (T), **2**-163, **2**-164
behavior under pressure, **2**-152
cavitation in, **2**-182 to **2**-189, **3**-68
compressibility experiments for, **2**-151
cubical expansion of (T), **4**-62
density of (T), **6**-18
and compressibility, **2**-136 to **2**-164
cryogenic (T), **2**-146
dielectric constants of (T's), **5**-132 to **5**-147
diffusion in, **2**-189 to **2**-195
index of refraction of, relative to air (T), **6**-18

Liquids, isothermal compressibilities of (T), **2**-163, **2**-164
pressure effect and thermal conductivity of (T), **4**-75
pressure-volume-temperature relations of (T), **2**-152 to **2**-161
relative volume vs. temperature for (T's), **4**-26, **4**-27
specific rotation of (T), **6**-99
surface energy of, **2**-174 to **2**-176
surface tension of (T), **2**-172 to **2**-176
symbols for acoustic properties of, **3**-67
tensile strength of (T), **2**-169 to **2**-174
thermal conductivity of (T), **4**-71, **4**-75
used in measurement of index of refraction (T), **6**-35
Verdet constants for various inorganic and metal-organic (T), **6**-92
viscosity of, **2**-165 to **2**-168
organic (T), **2**-169
volume vs. pressure and temperature, **2**-151
Lithium, energy levels of (f) (T), **8**-58 to **8**-62
Lithium fluoride, absorption coefficients of (T), **6**-37
index of refraction of (T), **6**-23 to **6**-25
optical properties of, **6**-39
Live room, definition of, **3**-17
Lloyd mirror effect, **3**-68
Load impedance measurement in transmission lines, **5**-51
Local anomalies in earth's magnetic field, **5**-292
Localization of sound, **3**-129
Logarithmic decrements, and anelasticity, **2**-85, **2**-86
vs. frequency for various materials (f's), **2**-86
of various materials (T's), **2**-87
Logarithmic mean virtual temperature, **2**-126
Longitudinal magnetostriction as function of field strength (f), **5**-225
Longitudinal waves, definition of, **3**-5
reflection of, **3**-78
scattering factors of, in metals (T), **3**-83
travel time of, through earth (T), **2**-104
velocity of, **2**-102
in earth (T), **2**-109
Loschmidt's number (T), **7**-3, **7**-174
Losses due to heat flow, **3**-79
Loudness, definition of, **3**-13
and hearing, **3**-128 to **3**-129
Loudness contours, **3**-13
Loudness levels, **3**-13
in hearing, definition of, **3**-128
vs. sound pressure and frequency (T), **3**-128
Loudness units, **3**-13
Low induction loss, material constants for (T), **5**-220
Low-loss transmission lines, formulas for (T), **5**-50
Low-pass filter sections, design of (T), **5**-86 to **5**-89
Lower atmosphere and standard atmosphere (T), **2**-128
Lubricants, **2**-42
viscosities of (T), **2**-168
Lumen, definition of, **6**-9, **6**-10
scotopic, **6**-53
Luminosity, photopic (T), **6**-50 to **6**-52
scotopic (T), **6**-51 to **6**-53
Luminous efficiency, maximum (T), **6**-63
Luminous flux, **6**-5, **6**-52
definition of, **6**-5
Luminous intensity, **6**-6
Luminous reflectances, **6**-52
maximum (T), **6**-63
scotopic, **6**-53
Luminous transmittance, **6**-52
scotopic, **6**-53
Lux, definition of, **6**-4, **6**-10
Lyophobic sols, **2**-181
Lyophilic sols, **2**-181
Lyot and Oehman filter, **6**-48

M

m-derived filters, **5**-84
M rule of electron transition, **7**-25
M-series X-ray lines, wavelength of (T), **7**-129
Mach number, definition of, **2**-215
and gas flow, **2**-221, **2**-229
of incident shock wave, **2**-233
vs. skin-friction ratio (f), **2**-229
Mach reflection of shock waves, **2**-234
Mach stem and shock waves, **2**-234
Magnesium alloys, density of (T), **2**-29
elastic and strength constants of (T), **2**-73 to **2**-74
Magnesium oxide, absorption coefficients of (T), **6**-37
index of refraction of (T), **6**-23 to **6**-25
optical properties of, **6**-40
Magnetic alloys, change of Curie point of, with pressure (T), **5**-220
demagnetization curves of (f), **5**-218
longitudinal magnetostriction of, as function of field strength (f), **5**-225
magnetization curves of (f), **5**-214
variation of hysteresis loss with maximum induction for (f), **5**-215
Magnetic axis of earth, **5**-291
Magnetic bays, definition of, **5**-294
Magnetic circuit, **5**-34 to **5**-35
Magnetic crystal anisotropy constants of cubic crystals (T), **5**-221 to **5**-222
Magnetic declination, **5**-291
Magnetic dip poles, position of (T), **5**-292
Magnetic dipole radiator, **5**-69 to **5**-70
Magnetic dipole moment of stable nuclei (T), **8**-6 to **8**-17
Magnetic ellipticity, **6**-92
Magnetic field, effect of, on atoms, **7**-168 to **7**-173
energy of permeable bodies in, **5**-33 to **5**-34
of stars, **5**-297
of sun (T), **5**-295

Magnetic field, and sunspots, **5**-297
transient penetration into plane solid, **5**-93
for various circuit configurations, **5**-25 to **5**-27
Magnetic field strengths, polar, of stars (T), **5**-296
Magnetic flux density, definition of, **5**-2
Magnetic forces on electrical circuits, **5**-32 to **5**-33
Magnetic formulas, static-magnetic-field, **5**-25 to **5**-36
Magnetic induction, definition of, **5**-2
due to various bodies, **5**-25 to **5**-27
Magnetic lines of force, definition of, **5**-4
Magnetic losses at low induction, **5**-220
Magnetic moment, direction of, in antiferromagnetic materials (T), **5**-227 to **5**-228
of earth, **5**-292
of electron, **8**-4
of neutron, **8**-129
of nuclei, definition of, **8**-5
orientation of, in antiferromagnetic materials (f), **5**-229
of proton, **8**-4
Magnetic polarization, **5**-3
Magnetic properties, of earth and stars, **5**-283 to **5**-297
of materials, **5**-206 to **5**-244
symbols for, **5**-206
Magnetic rotation, **6**-91 to **6**-94
Magnetic rotatory power for ferromagnetic films (T), **6**-96
Magnetic saturation, definition of, **5**-4
Magnetic shielding, **5**-34
Magnetic sources, **5**-37
and Maxwell's equations, **5**-40
Magnetic splitting in crystals, **7**-171
Magnetic starters for electric motors, **5**-256
Magnetic storms, definition of, **5**-294
Magnetic structure of antiferromagnetic materials (T), **5**-227 to **5**-228
Magnetic susceptibility, **5**-100
Magnetic tubes of flux, definition of, **5**-4
Magnetic-type waves, **5**-47
Magnetism, gyromagnetic effects of, **5**-103
stellar and galactic, **5**-295 to **5**-297
terrestrial, **5**-291 to **5**-295
types of, **5**-100 to **5**-103
Magnetization curves of some commercial alloys (f), **5**-214
Magnetohydrodynamic action, **5**-293
Magnetomotance, definition of, **5**-35
Magneto-optical rotation, definition of, **5**-231
of various substances (T), **5**-232
(*See also* Faraday effect)
Magnetoresistance, **5**-99
Magnetostriction, definition of, **5**-4
longitudinal, as function of field strength (f), **5**-225
saturation, of crystals and polycrystalline materials, **5**-222 to **5**-224
Magnetostriction constants of cubic crystals (T), **5**-223
Magnetostriction form factors (T), **5**-244
Magnetostrictive properties of metals and ferrites (T), **3**-99
Magnetostrictive rod, equivalent circuit (f), **3**-100
Magnetostrictive transducers, **3**-92 to **3**-98
equivalent circuits for, **3**-89, **3**-98
Magnets, permanent, properties of material for (T), **5**-219
Magnifying power, definition of, **6**-6
Magnitude, various types of, of stars, **6**-80
Malleus in ear (T), **3**-123
Manganese I, energy-level diagram of (f), **7**-35
Manganese ammonium sulfate, properties of (T), **4**-14, **4**-19
Manganese-copper-aluminum alloys, saturation induction of (f), **5**-207
Manual starters for electric motors, **5**-256
Masking (acoustics), definition of, **3**-13
of sound in hearing, **3**-127
Masking audiogram, definition of, **3**-13
Mass, acoustic, **3**-8
and acoustic analogy, **3**-135
of atomic particles (T), **7**-3
center of, for various bodies (T), **2**-36 to **2**-37
definition of, **2**-4
of earth, **2**-101
of mesons and hyperons (T), **8**-241
of neutron, **8**-129
Mass absorption, **6**-2
Mass anomalies in geodesy (f), **2**-93
Mass deficiencies of oceans (f), **2**-93
Mass-energy conversion factors, **8**-4
Mass formulas, semiempirical, **8**-19 to **8**-21
Mass numbers, of atoms in diatomic molecules (T), **7**-136 to **7**-141
of elements (T), **7**-9 to **7**-12
of stable nuclei (T), **8**-6 to **8**-17
Mass reactance and sound absorption, **3**-45
Mass surplus of mountains (f), **2**-93
Mass transport velocity, **3**-29
Material coordinate transforms, **3**-36 to **3**-37
Material coordinates and wave equation, **3**-34 to **3**-36
Material derivatives in viscous fluids, **3**-27
Material particle, definition of, **3**-27
Mathematical tables, list of compilations of, **1**-2 to **1**-5
Mathematics, aids to computation, **1**-1 to **1**-5
Matt surfaces, reflection coefficients for incandescent light on (T), **6**-43
Maximum-bubble-pressure method of surface tension measurement, **2**-176
Maximum permeability, definition of, **5**-214
Maximum permissible concentration of radioisotopes in air and water (T), **8**-256
Maximum permissible exposures to ionizing radiations (T's), **8**-254 to **8**-256
Maximum permissible flux of normal beam of neutrons (T), **8**-256

Maximum spontaneous polarization of ferroelectric crystals (T), **5**-155 to **5**-156
Maxwell's equations, **2**-204
in various forms, **5**-40 to **5**-41
Mean acoustic pressure, definition of, **3**-31
Mean distance from sun to planets (T), **2**-90
Mean energies, of electrons in several substances (f's), **7**-210 to **7**-211
of ions, definition of, **7**-204 to **7**-205
Mean free path, definition of, **3**-17
Mean-ionic-activity coefficients, of electrolytes (T), **5**-278
of hydrochloric acid (T), **5**-279
Mean life, of ions in lower atmosphere (T), **5**-284
of mesons and hyperons (T), **8**-241
Mechanical compliance, definition of, **3**-9
Mechanical computing devices, **1**-1
Mechanical impedance, definition of, **3**-9
vector, equation for, **3**-138
Mechanical ohm, definition of, **3**-9
Mechanical properties, of gels, **2**-81 to **2**-82
of thixotropic substances, **2**-82 to **2**-84
Mechanical reactance, **3**-9, **3**-10
Mechanical rectifiers, **5**-260, **5**-266
Mechanical rectilineal quantities (T), **3**-139
Mechanical rectilineal resistance and acoustic analogy, **3**-134, **3**-136
Mechanical rectilineal symbols (T), **3**-139
Mechanical rectilineal systems, graphical representation of (f's), **3**-136, **3**-137
of one degree of freedom, **3**-137 to **3**-138
Mechanical rectilineal units (T), **3**-139
Mechanical resistance, definition of, **3**-10
Mechanical resonance of piezoelectric crystals, **3**-91
Mechanical rotational quantities (T), **3**-139
Mechanical rotational resistance and acoustic analogy, **3**-134, **3**-136
Mechanical rotational symbols (T), **3**-139
Mechanical rotational systems, graphical representation of (f's), **3**-136, **3**-137
of one degree of freedom, **3**-137 to **3**-138
Mechanical rotational units (T), **3**-139
Mechanical schematic diagrams, and acoustical analogy, **3**-140
based on impedance analogy (T), **3**-145 to **3**-176
based on mobility analogy (T), **3**-144 to **3**-176
Mechanical systems of one degree of freedom, **3**-137 to **3**-138
Mechanics, Newtonian concepts of, **2**-2
Mel, definition of, **3**-13, **3**-129
Melting parameters of various elements and compounds (T's), **4**-30 to **4**-33
Melting point of sea water, **2**-117
Melting temperature, definition of, **4**-63
Mercalli scale, **2**-108
Mercury, density of (T), **2**-140
viscosity of (T), **2**-169
volume in relation to pressure and temperature (T), **2**-155
Mercury I, energy-level diagram of (f), **7**-38
photoelectric traces of spectrum (f), **7**-122
principal spectral lines of (T), **7**-119 to **7**-121
Mercury-arc rectifiers, **5**-263, **5**-266
Mesh in circuit theory, **5**-80
Mesons, characteristics of (T), **8**-241 to **8**-244
definition and nomenclature of, **8**-240 to **8**-241
Mesosphere (f), **2**-130
Metal-organic liquids, Verdet constants for (T), **6**-92
Metallic conductors, properties of, **5**-197 to **5**-205
Metallic films, reflectance of light by (T), **6**-108
Metallic rectifiers, **5**-260
Metals, absorption constants of (T's), **6**-105 to **6**-107
adiabatic isothermal elastic constants of (T), **3**-83
and attenuation due to heat flow (T), **3**-83
conductivity (electrical) formulas for, **5**-96
creep rates of (T), **2**-89 to **2**-90
critical energy and radiation length for (T), **8**-39
crystallization of, **3**-75
Debye temperature for (T), **4**-48
densities of (T), **3**-77 to **3**-78
diffusion coefficients for (T's), **2**-79 to **2**-80
diffusivities of (T), **4**-74
elastic constants for (T's), **2**-61 to **2**-80, **3**-80
electrical properties of pure (T), **5**-204
electronic constants for (T), **4**-48
fractional change in volume of (T), **4**-28
impedances of (T), **3**-80
index of refraction of (T's), **6**-105 to **6**-107
intergrain heat flow in (T), **3**-83
magnetostrictive properties of (T), **3**-99
optical behavior of, **6**-102 to **6**-110
optical constants of (T's), **6**-102 to **6**-110
reflection of light by (T), **6**-109 to **6**-110
scattering factors for waves (T), **3**-83
skin-effect quantities for (T), **5**-90
sputtered mass of, in hydrogen (T), **5**-185
strength constants for (T), **2**-61 to **2**-80
superconducting transition temperatures for (T), **5**-205
surface tension (T), **2**-174
thermal conductivity of (T's), **4**-67, **4**-78
at low temperatures, **4**-77
total emissivity of, for unoxidized surfaces (T), **6**-75
wave velocities in (T), **3**-80
Meteorological data, **2**-124 to **2**-135
Meteorology, composition of dry air (T), **2**-125
dynamical relationships in, **2**-130 to **2**-132
and geopotential (T), **2**-125 to **2**-126

Meteorology, physical constants in, **2**-125
and radiation, **2**-132 to **2**-134
symbols used in, **2**-124 to **2**-125
Meter-candle, definition of, **6**-4, **6**-10
Methanol, limiting equivalent conductances of ions in (T), **5**-271
Methyl alcohol, density of (T), **2**-140 to **2**-141
volume in relation to pressure and temperature (T), **2**-156
Meyer's method of tensile strength measurement, **2**-170
Mica, energy loss of protons in (T), **8**-35
Microbar, definition of, **3**-5
Microhysteresis effect, **3**-86
Microwave frequencies, letter notation for (T), **5**-62
Microwave spectra, **7**-146
Middle ear, dimensions of (T), **3**-123
Millibarn, definition of, **8**-3
Millilambert, definition of, **6**-10
Milliphot, definition of, **6**-10
Minerals, index of refraction of, biaxial (T), **6**-14 to **6**-17
uniaxial (T), **6**-12 to **6**-13
Minimum audible pressure on external ear (T), **3**-124 to **3**-125
Minimum audible sound, **3**-125
Minimum deviation, definition of, **6**-6
Minute, definition of, **2**-14
Mirror coatings, optical constants of evaporated (T), **6**-104
Mks units, electrical (T), **5**-6 to **5**-7
and electrical formulas (T), **5**-10 to **5**-11
Mobility, of defects for pure ionic conductors (T), **5**-189
drift, of germanium and silicon (T), **5**-159
of electrons, **5**-96, **5**-157, **5**-159 to **5**-160
Hall, of various substances (T), **5**-161
of ions in various substances (f's), **7**-212 to **7**-218
Mobility analogy, and acoustics, **3**-140 to **3**-177
definition of, **3**-140
and ground, earth, and sky, **3**-141
schematic diagram for, **3**-142 to **3**-143
symbols for constructing schematic diagram based on (T), **3**-144 to **3**-176
and wires, rods, and tubes, **3**-140 to **3**-141
Mode count and acoustic energy, **3**-54
Mode of decay for light nuclei (f's) (T), **8**-58 to **8**-86
Moderators for reactors, **8**-227
Modern symbols for heavy radionuclides (T), **8**-41
Modulus of elasticity, volume, **2**-10
Mohorovičić discontinuity, **2**-106, **2**-108
Molal heat content of solutes (T), **5**-280
Molar heat capacity, **4**-63
at C_v (T), **4**-44
of elements above room temperature (T), **4**-42 to **4**-43
of elements at low temperature (T), **4**-40 to **4**-41
Molar volume constant (T), **7**-3
Mole fraction of defects, **5**-189
Molecular refraction, definition of, **6**-6
Molecular refractivity, definition of, **6**-7
Molecular rotatory power, definition of, **6**-7
Molecular susceptibilities of paramagnetic materials (T), **5**-241 to **5**-243
Molecules, constants of, diatomic (T), **7**-136 to **7**-141
polyatomic, **7**-145 to **7**-161
energy levels of diatomic (f's), **7**-142 to **7**-144
Moment, of force, definition of, **2**-6 to **2**-7
of inertia, **2**-8
and acoustic analogy, **3**-135
for various bodies (T), **2**-38 to **2**-39
of momentum, definition of, **2**-6, **2**-7
of fluid elements, **3**-41
Momentum, conservation of, **2**-5, **2**-7
definition of, **2**-4
Momentum equations for gas flow, **2**-214, **2**-220
Monatomic gases and shock waves (T), **2**-235
Monatomic ions, standard entropy of (T), **5**-281
Monaural listening, minimum audible pressure (T), **3**-125
Monoclinic crystal system (f) (T), **2**-45 to **2**-47
Moon, approximate brightness of (T), **6**-78
miscellaneous constants for (T), **2**-91
physical data for (T), **2**-91
Moon-camera method of earth measurement, **2**-96, **2**-97
Moon photography, **2**-97
Morse potential and wave mechanics, **7**-163
Motor-circuit protection, **5**-256 to **5**-257
Motor controllers, **5**-256
Motor generator, **5**-260
Motor protection, **5**-256 to **5**-257
Motors (*see* Electric motors)
Moving axes, **2**-9
MTR reactors, **8**-227
Multilayer interference filters, **6**-46 to **6**-47
Multiplet intensities, **7**-26
Multiplet spectrum, definition of, **7**-16
Multiplets, J values for (T), **7**-19 to **7**-20
Multiplicities for varying valence electrons (T), **7**-18
Multipole, potential of, **5**-21
Multipole formulas, **5**-21
Music, definition of, **3**-14
Musical interval, definition of, **3**-107
equally tempered (T), **3**-14
for various frequency ratios (T), **3**-106, **3**-107
Musical scales, **3**-106 to **3**-107
equal-tempered frequencies (T), **3**-105
Mutual inductance for various static fields, **5**-28 to **5**-31
Mutual inductance standards, **5**-110 to **5**-112

N

N-terminal-pair networks, **5**-81 to **5**-82
Narrow-band interference filters, **6**-45 to **6**-50

Narrow-band radiation, **6**-64
National Board of Fire Underwriters, **5**-245
National Bureau of Standards glass index of refraction (T), **6**-32
National Electrical Code, **5**-245
National Fire Protection Association, **5**-245
Natural electrical currents, **5**-289
Natural frequency, definition of, **3**-10
Natural light sources, approximate brightness of (T), **6**-78
Navier-Stokes equations, **3**-29
Neel point, of antiferromagnetic materials (T), **5**-227 to **5**-228
of various substances (T), **5**-226
NEMA standards, **5**-245 to **5**-246
Neon, electron energy losses in (f), **5**-181
energy levels of (f) (T), **8**-80 to **8**-86
virial coefficients for (T), **4**-120
Neon I, photoelectric traces of (f), **7**-54 to **7**-58
principal spectral lines of (T), **7**-45 to **7**-53
Neon-argon mixtures, ionization per volt in (f), **5**-170
Neper, definition of, **3**-5
Nernst coefficient, **5**-99
Nernst effect, **5**-4, **5**-99
Network theorems, **5**-81
Networks and circuit theory, **5**-80 to **5**-85
Neutral atoms, persistent spectral lines of (T), **7**-39 to **7**-41
Neutral hyperons, **8**-246
Neutrino, **8**-3
Neutron binding energies (T), **8**-135 to **8**-143
definition of, **8**-130
Neutron capture and gamma rays (T), **8**-94 to **8**-96
Neutron cross sections, total, for various elements (f's), **8**-131 to **8**-134
types of, **8**-130, **8**-143 to **8**-144, **8**-169
Neutron diffraction in antiferromagnetic materials (T), **5**-227 to **5**-228
Neutron fission and fission product chains (T), **8**-202 to **8**-211
Neutron flux in reactors, **8**-227
Neutron-induced fission, **8**-212
Neutron levels (T), **8**-19
Neutron numbers of stable nuclei (T), **8**-6 to **8**-17
Neutron optics, **8**-144
Neutrons, **8**-129 to **8**-171
atomic mass of, **8**-4
attenuation of, in concrete and water (f), **8**-169
Compton wavelength of, **8**-4
fast-neutron fission yields from U_{235} (T), **8**-218
maximum permissible exposure to (T's), **8**-254, **8**-255
permissible flux for normal beam of (T), **8**-256
properties of, **8**-129
rest mass of, **8**-4
symbols for, **8**-3
velocity of thermal, **8**-4
New candle, definition of, **6**-3, **6**-9
Newton, definition of, **2**-15, **5**-2
Newtonian mechanics, **2**-2
of particles, **2**-3 to **2**-6
Newton's laws, of fluid friction (f), **2**-201
of motion, **2**-4 to **2**-5
application of, **2**-7
Nickel, elastic and strength constants for. **2**-75 to **2**-76
Nickel alloys, density of (T), **2**-30
elastic and strength constants for (T), **2**-75 to **2**-76
Hall constants of (T), **5**-237 to **5**-239
saturation magnetization and Curie points of (T), **5**-210
Nitric acid, isothermal compressibility (T), **2**-162
Nitric oxide, efficiency of electron attachment in (f), **5**-172
Nitrogen, compressibility factor for (T), **4**-103
energy levels of (f) (T), **8**-69 to **8**-74, **8**-76 to **8**-79
enthalpy of (T), **4**-106
entropy of (T), **4**-107
relative density of (T), **4**-104
in sea water, **2**-120
specific heat of (T), **4**-105
thermodynamic conversion factors for (T), **4**-81
virial coefficients for (T), **4**-125, **4**-126
Nitrogen I, energy-level diagram of (f), **7**-29
Nitrogen-vapor mixtures, relative dielectric strengths of (T), **5**-148 to **5**-149
Nitrous oxide, efficiency of electron attachment in (f), **5**-175, **5**-176
Noctilucent clouds (f), **2**-130
Nodal points, definition of, **6**-6
Node, in circuit theory, **5**-80
definition of, **3**-5
Noise, definition of, **3**-5
differential threshold for intensity (T), **3**-126
in thermal radiation detectors (T), **6**-114
Noise control, definition of, **3**-17
Noise equivalent power of detector, definition of, **6**-119
Noise-insulation factor, **3**-120
Noise level, in rooms, **3**-119 to **3**-122
recommended for rooms (T), **3**-122
Noise-reduction coefficient, **3**-114
Noise spectrum, **3**-55
Nonaqueous solutions, diffusion coefficients for (T), **2**-195
Noncubic crystals, thermal conductivity of (T), **4**-73
Nondegenerate states in wave mechanics, **7**-166
Nonelectrolytes, diffusion coefficients of (T), **2**-192
Noninertial dynamics, **2**-5
Nonmetallic conductors, properties of, **5**-166 to **5**-197
Nonmetals, Debye temperatures for (T), **4**-47
Nonpropagating fields, **5**-58
Nonrelativistic conversion formulas for neutron, **8**-129

Nonstationary cavities, **2**-188 to **2**-189
Normal cathode fall for various metals (T's), **5**-184
Normal density of gases, standard conditions for, **2**-197
Normal hysteresis, definition of, **5**-214
Normal incidence of shock waves, **2**-233, **2**-234
Normal mode of vibration, definition of, **3**-10
Normal spectral emissivities of various substances (T), **6**-72
Normal state of diatomic molecules (T), **7**-136 to **7**-141
Normal threshold of audibility, definition of, **3**-14
Nuclear constants, definitions and symbols, **8**-3 to **8**-4
Nuclear cross section, definition of, **8**-3
Nuclear definitions, **8**-2
Nuclear level order (T), **8**-19
Nuclear magneton (T), **7**-3, **8**-4
Nuclear particles, list of (T), **8**-3
Nuclear photodisintegration, **8**-90 to **8**-91
Nuclear physics, general constants for, **8**-3 to **8**-4
Nuclear reaction, definitions and symbolism of, **8**-2 to **8**-3
Nuclear reactors, catalog of (T), **8**-228 to **8**-239
  classification of (T), **8**-227
  components of, **8**-227
  foreign programs for, **8**-240
Nuclear resonance scattering of photons, **8**-91
Nuclear spin, definition of, **8**-5
Nuclear stability rules, **8**-21 to **8**-22
Nuclei, energy levels of light (f's) (T), **8**-56, **8**-58 to **8**-86
  properties of stable (T), **8**-6 to **8**-17
  resonance parameters of (T's), **8**-145 to **8**-153
  shell structures of stable, **8**-5
Nucleon, definition of, **8**-2
Nuclides, decay types (T), **8**-98 to **8**-128
  definition of, **8**-2
  fission-product chains for (T), **8**-202 to **8**-211
  gamma energies of (T), **8**-98 to **8**-128
  half lives of (T's), **8**-98 to **8**-128, **8**-202 to **8**-211
  list of special (T), **8**-3
  particle energies of (T), **8**-98 to **8**-128
  thermal-neutron fission yields (T), **8**-212 to **8**-215
Nusselt number, **2**-228

O

Oblate spheroid, magnetic induction of coil about, **5**-27
Oblique incidence of shock waves, **2**-234, **2**-235
Obliquity of the ecliptic (T), **2**-91
Ocarina, **3**-103
Ocean tides, constituents of (T), **2**-123, **2**-124
Ocean waves, types of, **2**-122 to **2**-123
Oceanic platform, **2**-115
Oceanographic data, **2**-115 to **2**-123
Occultation method of earth measurement, **2**-96, **2**-97
Octave, definition of, **3**-15
Odd multiplicities, g values in L-S coupling (T), **7**-172 to **7**-173
Odd-nucleon alpha emitters, **8**-47, **8**-53 to **8**-54, **8**-56
  decay schemes of (f), **8**-54
Ohm, absolute, definition of, **5**-105
  acoustic, **3**-8
  definition of, **5**-7, **5**-107
  international vs absolute (T), **5**-106
Ohm's law, **5**-3
Oils, specific gravity (T), **2**-150
  specification for aircraft (T), **2**-168
  viscosities of, Bureau of Standards (T), **2**-167
    industrial, **2**-168
Olivine-gabbro, **2**-108
One-center problem and wave mechanics, **7**-164
One-dimensional gas flow, **2**-216 to **2**-217
One-dimensional rotation and wave mechanics, **7**-163
One-terminal-pair networks (f's), **5**-82 to **5**-83
Open-circuit voltage for ceramics (T), **3**-95
Open-shell nuclear model, **8**-18
Open-stub impedance matching, **5**-51
Optical constants, of evaporated mirror coatings (T), **6**-104
  of metals (T's), **6**-102 to **6**-110
Optical definitions, **6**-2 to **6**-8
Optical densities converted to per cent transmission (T), **6**-39
Optical energy gap, definition of, **5**-157
Optical glass, index of refraction of, vs dispersion (f), **6**-33
Optical materials, absorption and transmission of (T's), **6**-38 to **6**-39
  index of refraction of (T), **6**-23 to **6**-30
  properties of, **6**-39 to **6**-40
  thermal conductivity of (T), **4**-76
Optical plastics, index of refraction of (T), **6**-19
  reciprocal dispersive power of (T), **6**-19
Optical pyrometers, **6**-64
Optical pyrometry, **6**-64
Optical standards, **6**-8 to **6**-9
Optics, definitions, standards, and units of, **6**-2 to **6**-10
Optimum reverberation time, definition of, **3**-118
  for different rooms (f), **3**-118
  vs frequency (f), **3**-119
Ordinates, selected, for standard sources (illumination) (T), **6**-59
Organ pipes, **3**-102 to **3**-103
Organic aqueous solutions, surface tension of (T), **2**-175

Organic compounds, critical temperatures, pressures, and densities of (T), **4**-22 to **4**-23
  diffusion coefficients of (T), **2**-193
Organic gases, densities of (T), **2**-200
Organic liquids, adiabatic compressibilities of (T), **2**-163, **2**-164
  densities of (T), **2**-147
  dielectric constants of (T), **5**-134 to **5**-142
  isothermal compressibilities of (T), **2**-163, **2**-164
  sound absorption constants of (T), **3**-73
  velocity of sound in (T), **3**-71 to **3**-73
  Verdet constants for (T), **6**-94
  viscosity of, **2**-169
Organic materials, thermal conductivity of (T), **4**-71
Organic solids, dielectric constants of (T), **5**-118
Organic substances, fluorescence of (T), **6**-111
Orthorhombic crystal systems (f) (T), **2**-45 to **2**-47
Overtone, definition of, **3**-15
Oxides, spectral emissivity of (T), **6**-74
Oxygen, compressibility factor for (T), **4**-108
  electron attachment coefficients for (f), **5**-172
  energy levels of (f) (T), **8**-72, **8**-73, **8**-75 to **8**-83
  enthalpy of (T), **4**-111
  entropy of (T), **4**-112
  relative density of (T), **4**-109
  in sea water, **2**-120
  specific heat of (T), **4**-110
  temperature variation of, recombination coefficient (f), **5**-178
  thermodynamic conversion factors for (T), **4**-81
  virial coefficients for (T), **4**-126
Oxygen I, energy-level diagram of (f), **7**-30

P

Pain due to sound, **3**-14
Pair production and gamma rays (f), **8**-89 to **8**-90
Palladium alloys, elastic and strength constants for (T), **2**-62 to **2**-63
Parallel-bar transmission lines, constants for (T), **5**-48 to **5**-49
Parallel connections, definition of, **5**-4
Parallel tubes, self-inductance of, **5**-29
Parallel-wire transmission lines, constants for (T), **5**-48 to **5**-49
Parallel wires, self-inductance of, **5**-29
Paramagnetic bodies, definition of, **5**-4
Paramagnetic materials, Bohr magneton numbers of (T), **5**-241 to **5**-243
  Curie points of (T), **5**-241 to **5**-243
  molecular susceptibilities of (T), **5**-241 to **5**-243
Paramagnetic resonance, **4**-16, **7**-171
Paramagnetic salts, properties of (T), **4**-14 to **4**-20
Paramagnetic salts, and spin resonance, **5**-103
Paramagnetism, **5**-100
Parity, in atomic energy levels, **7**-18
  of stable nuclei (T), **8**-6 to **8**-17
Parity rule of electron transitions, **7**-21
Partial, definition of, **3**-15
Partial cross section of neutrons, definition of, **8**-130
Partial molal heat content of solutes (T), **5**-281
Particle accelerators, types of, **8**-172 to **8**-181
  world-wide list of (T's), **8**-181 to **8**-201
Particle density in upper atmosphere (T), **5**-284
Particle energy of nuclides (T), **8**-98 to **8**-128
Particles, passage of, through matter, **8**-23 to **8**-39
  range-energy relations for, **8**-23
Pascal's law, **2**-12
Paschen-Back effect, **7**-169
Paschen curves for various gases (f), **5**-179
Paschen notation for spectral lines, **7**-58
Pauli exclusion principle, **7**-20
Peak speech power, definition of, **3**-13
Peltier coefficient, **5**-98
Pentane candle, definition of, **6**-10
Per cent conductivity, definition of, **5**-197
Per cent transmission converted to optical density (T), **6**-39
Period, of seismic waves, **2**-102 to **2**-103
  of vibration of strings, **3**-102
Periodic system of the elements (T), **7**-8
Permanent magnets, definition of, **5**-5, **5**-35 to **5**-36
  demagnetization curves of (f), **5**-218
  materials for, **5**-214, **5**-218
  properties of, **5**-214, **5**-218
  properties of materials for (T), **5**-214, **5**-219
Permanent-split-capacitor motors, **5**-249
Permanent strain, **2**-86
Permeability, definition of, **2**-179, **5**-2
  of high-permeability materials (T), **5**-216
  relative, of metals and alloys (T), **5**-90
  of various materials (T), **2**-180
Permeability tensor, **5**-64
Permeable bodies, energy in magnetic fields, **5**-33 to **5**-34
Permissible body burdens of ionizing radiation, **8**-252
Persistent spectral lines of elements (T), **7**-39 to **7**-41
Perturbation method in wave mechanics, **7**-165 to **7**-166
Perturbations of state, **3**-32
Phase constant, acoustic, **3**-9
Phase diagrams, of various substances (f's), **4**-35 to **4**-38
  of water (f), **4**-35
Phase stability principle and electron synchrotron, **8**-176
Phase transition data for elements and compounds (T), **4**-130 to **4**-159

Phase velocity of waves, **5**-51, **5**-58
Phon, definition of, **3**-13
Phonon, **3**-55
Phosphors, characteristics of various cathode-ray-tube (T), **6**-113
Phot, definition of, **6**-4, **6**-10
Photoconductivity, definition of, **5**-5
Photoconductor cell as radiation detector (T), **6**-114
Photodisintegration, in Al, Ag, and Br, **8**-91
nuclear, **8**-90 to **8**-91
Photoelectric cell as radiation detector (T), **6**-114
Photoelectric effect, **5**-5, **8**-87 to **8**-88
Photoelectric traces of spectrum microwave discharges, **7**-54 to **7**-122
for Argon I (f), **7**-63 to **7**-66
for Iron I (f), **7**-103 to **7**-118
for Krypton I (f), **7**-71 to **7**-74
for Mercury I (f), **7**-119 to **7**-122
for Neon I (f), **7**-54 to **7**-58
for Xenon I (f), **7**-80 to **7**-87
Photofission yields (T), **8**-222 to **8**-224
Photographic color index of stellar spectral classes (T), **6**-80
Photographic density, definition of, **6**-6
Photographic magnitude of stars, **6**-80
Photometric quantities, **6**-9
Photometric standards, **6**-9, **6**-52
Photometric units, **6**-9 to **6**-10
Photon scattering, **8**-89, **8**-91 to **8**-92
Photons, elastic scattering of (f), **8**-92
Photopic luminosity, **6**-50, **6**-52
Photopic luminosity data (T), **6**-51
wavelengths for selected ordinates (T), **6**-53
Photoreceivers and brightness of stars (T), **6**-87
Photosurface (S4) color index of stellar spectral classes (T), **6**-80
Phototubes, spectral sensitivities of (f's), **6**-116 to **6**-117
Photovoltaic cell as radiation detector (T), **6**-114
Physical constants in meteorology, **2**-125
Piezoelectric constant, of piezoelectric crystals (T), **3**-93
of transducer materials (f), **3**-97
Piezoelectric crystals, equivalent circuit of (f), **3**-90, **3**-92
properties of (T), **3**-89 to **3**-93
and transducers, **3**-89 to **3**-92
Piezoelectric effect, definition of, **5**-5
Piezoelectric strain constants (T), **5**-150 to **5**-151
temperature coefficients for (T), **5**-153
temperature dependence of (T), **5**-152
Pigments, dry, infrared reflecting factors of (T), **6**-41
Piles (*see* Nuclear reactors)
Pinna, dimensions of (T), **3**-123
Pions, **8**-242
Pipe gas flow, **2**-222
and heat transfer, **2**-229 to **2**-230
Piston, acoustic radiation resistance of (T), **3**-110
directional radiation from, **3**-111
Piston sound source, beam angle of radiation for (f), **3**-111, **3**-112
directivity index of (f), **3**-112
Pitch, definition of, **3**-13
and frequency (T), **3**-129
and hearing, **3**-129
standard, definition of, **3**-15
Planck function, **6**-64
Planck's constant (T), **7**-3
Planck's radiation formula, **6**-6
Plane jet, laminar flow in, **2**-197
Plane sheet, skin-effect formulas for, **5**-94 to **5**-95
Plane solid, skin-effect formulas for, **5**-85, **5**-90
Plane wave, definition of, **3**-5
Plane wave functions, **5**-45
Planetary orbits (T), **2**-90
Planets, physical and orbital data for (T), **2**-90, **2**-91
Plasma conductivity, **7**-204
Plasma oscillations, **5**-74 to **5**-75
Plastic strain, **2**-86, **2**-87
Plasticizers, viscosity (T), **2**-169
Plastics, density of (T), **2**-34 to **2**-35, **3**-77 to **3**-78
dielectric properties of (T), **5**-124 to **5**-130
elastic constants of (T), **3**-80
impedances of (T), **3**-86
index of refraction of (T), **6**-19 to **6**-20
wave velocities of (T), **3**-80
Platinum, emf of platinum-platinum-rhodium thermocouples (T), **4**-10
various thermal emf's relative to (T's), **4**-6 to **4**-9
Platinum alloys, elastic and strength constants for (T), **2**-62 to **2**-63
Plutonium production reactors, **8**-227
Plutonium-239, fast-neutron fission yields of (T), **8**-217
Pneumatic radiation detector, characteristics of (T), **6**-114, **6**-118
Pockels effect, **6**-94 to **6**-97
for various crystals (T), **6**-97
Point charge, potential of, **5**-21
Point orifice, jet streamlines for (f), **2**-196
Poise, definition of, **2**-207, **2**-165
Poisson's ratio, definition of, **2**-10
for glasses (T), **3**-80
for plastics (T), **3**-80
and ratio of longitudinal to transverse waves (T), **2**-102
of various metals and alloys (T), **2**-62 to **2**-77, **3**-80
Polar magnetic field strength of 35 stars (T), **5**-296
Polarization of gamma rays, **8**-93
Polarization interference filters, **6**-48
Polarization rules for electric-dipole transition (T), **7**-168
Polarization vectors, **5**-39 to **5**-40
Polarized light, definition of, **6**-6

Polarizers, sheet, properties of, **6**-44
spectral transmittance of (T), **6**-44
Polarizing filters, **6**-44
Polished surfaces, reflection coefficients for incandescent light on (T), **6**-43
Polyatomic ions, standard entropy of (T), **5**-282
Polyatomic molecules, constants of, **7**-145 to **7**-161
Polycrystalline elements, coefficients of linear thermal expansion of (T), **4**-51 to **4**-53
Polycrystalline materials, saturation magnetostriction of (T), **5**-223, **5**-224
Polycrystalline solids, elastic and strength constants of (T), **2**-61 to **2**-80
Polycyclohexyl methacrylate, index of refraction of (T), **6**-20
Polymethyl methacrylate, index of refraction of (T), **6**-20
Polyphase motors, a-c induction, **5**-247
induction, control and protection of, **5**-254 to **5**-255
synchronous, **5**-256
Polyphase transformers, **5**-260
Polystyrene, index of refraction of (T), **6**-20
Porosity, definition of, **2**-179
symbols for, **2**-179
of various materials (T), **2**-180
Porous media, fluid flow properties, **2**-179 to **2**-180
Positive-ion accelerators, **8**-173 to **8**-174
Positron, symbols for, **8**-3
Potassium bromide, absorption coefficients of (T), **6**-37
index of refraction of (T), **6**-27 to **6**-29
Potassium chloride, differential diffusion coefficients of (T), **5**-272
Potential (electric), definition of, **5**-3
Potential curves, **7**-142 to **7**-145
of C_2, **7**-142
of CN, **7**-143
of CO, **7**-143
of N_2, **7**-144
of NO, **7**-144
of O_2, **7**-145
Potential energy, definition of, **2**-6
of diatomic molecules, **7**-136
Potential function, Lennard-Jones, definition and constants for various gases (T), **4**-129
Poundal, definition of, **2**-15
Power, available from piezoelectric crystal, **3**-91
definition of, **3**-5, **3**-7
electric, **3**-3
sound, **3**-7
Power band, definition of, **3**-5
Power-conversion efficiency of piezoelectric crystal, **3**-91
Power levels, acoustic, **3**-5, **3**-7
Power-line capacity and motor selection, **5**-252
Power reactors, **8**-227
Power spectrum of thermal noise, **3**-55
Power spectrum level, **3**-5
Power supply and electric motor selection, **5**-250
Poynting vector, **5**-42, **5**-68
Poynting's theorem in differential and integral forms, **5**-43
Practical range of electrons in matter, definition of, **8**-38
Prandtl-Glauert rule in gas flow, **2**-219
Prandtl numbers, for air (T), **2**-222
and gas flow, **2**-221
for hydrogen (T), **2**-223
for sea water (T), **2**-122
and sound absorption, **3**-45
Precedence effect in hearing, **3**-129
Precession, of earth, **2**-97
of equinoxes (T), **2**-91
Precipitation electricity, **5**-287 to **5**-289
Precipitation particles, electric charge on (T), **5**-287
Pressure, atmospheric, **3**-57
critical, of elements and compounds (T), **4**-21 to **4**-23
definition of, **3**-3, **3**-4
in earth, **2**-108
effect of, on Curie point for various substances (T), **5**-220
on electrical conductivity (T), **5**-190, **5**-195
effective (acoustical), **3**-3
excess (acoustic), **3**-4
instantaneous, **3**-4
sound, **3**-3, **3**-4
static, **3**-57
Pressure coefficient in liquids, **2**-151
Pressure-density relation for adiabatic gas, **3**-35
Pressure effect and thermal conductivity of liquids (T), **4**-75
Pressure level, definition of, **3**-7
Pressure spectrum level, definition of, **3**-5
Pressure-volume-temperature relationships of gases, **4**-118 to **4**-129
Pressure-volume-temperature tables for liquids (T's), **2**-152 to **2**-161
Pressures, critical, for inorganic and organic substances (T), **4**-21 to **4**-23
in viscous fluids, **3**-28
Primary wavelength standard, definition of, **6**-9, **7**-43
Principal alpha groups, **8**-46 to **8**-47
Principal axes, **2**-8
Principal focus, definition of, **6**-6
Principal waves, **5**-47
Principles (*see* Laws and principles)
Probability of ion formation for several substances (f's), **7**-184 to **7**-185
Probe-tube microphone, **3**-125
Prolate spheroid, magnetic induction of coil about, **5**-27
Propagation of sound through gases, **3**-61 to **3**-62
Propagation constant in sound, **3**-9, **3**-46
Protection of electric motors, **5**-254 to **5**-257
Proton acceleration, **8**-172 to **8**-179
in cyclotrons, **8**-173 to **8**-175

Proton acceleration, in electrostatic accelerators, **8**-172 to **8**-173
in linear accelerators, **8**-179
in synchrocyclotrons, **8**-174 to **8**-175
in synchrotrons, **8**-177 to **8**-178
Proton energy loss, **8**-26 to **8**-35
in air (f), **8**-26
in aluminum (f) (T), **8**-28, **8**-35
in beryllium (T), **8**-35
in copper (T's), **8**-24 to **8**-25, **8**-35
in gold (T), **8**-35
in lead (T), **8**-33 to **8**-34
in mica (T), **8**-35
in silver (T), **8**-30 to **8**-34
Proton levels (T), **8**-19
Proton ranges, **8**-24 to **8**-34
in air (f), **8**-27
in aluminum (f), **8**-29, **8**-31
in copper (T), **8**-24 to **8**-25
in Ilford C-2 emulsion (f), **8**-32
in lead (T), **8**-33 to **8**-34
in silver (T), **8**-30 to **8**-31
Proton straggling in various metals (T), **8**-36
Proton synchrotron, description of, **8**-177 to **8**-188
world-wide list of (T), **8**-198 to **8**-199
Protons, Compton wavelength of, **8**-4
magnetic moment of, **8**-4
maximum permissible exposure to (T's), **8**-254, **8**-255
range-energy relation in Ilford C-2 emulsion (f), **8**-32
range straggling in copper (f's), **8**-37
rest mass of, **8**-4
and spin resonance, **5**-103
symbols for, **8**-3
various constants concerning (T), **7**-3
Proximity effect, definition of, **5**-5
Pseudo-adiabatic lapse ratio (T), **2**-127
Pulsating sphere, acoustic impedance of, **3**-108 to **3**-109
specific acoustic resistance (f), **3**-109
Pulsed fields, penetration into conductor (f), **5**-94
Pure tone, **3**-15
Pycnometer, **2**-136
Pyrite, extinction coefficients (T), **6**-38
index of refraction of (T), **6**-26 to **6**-27
Pyroelectric constants, temperature variation of (T), **5**-154
of various substances (T), **5**-153
Pyroelectric effect, definition of, **5**-5
Pyrometers, **6**-64
Pyrometry, optical, **6**-64

Q

Quadripole moment of nuclei, definition of, **8**-5
Quantum energy conversion factors, **8**-4
Quantum numbers, definition of, **7**-16 to **7**-18
limits of, **7**-18
Quantum radiation detectors, characteristics of (f) (T), **6**-114, **6**-115
Quartz, absorption coefficients of (T), **6**-37
index of refraction of, crystalline (T), **6**-23 to **6**-25
at various temperatures (T), **6**-34
optical properties of, **6**-40
thermal conductivity of fused (T), **4**-74
Young's modulus for (T), **2**-103
Quartz glass, index of refraction of (T), **6**-31
Quaternary fission, **8**-212

R

Rad, definition of, **8**-250
Radial mode in transducer materials, **3**-98
Radial wave functions and wave mechanics, **7**-165
Radian, definition of, **2**-14
Radiation, black-body, functions for (T), **6**-64, **6**-65
total (T), **6**-66 to **6**-67
maximum permissible exposure to ionizing (T's), **8**-254 to **8**-256
in meterology, **2**-132 to **2**-134
narrow-band, **6**-64
reflection coefficients for visible monochromatic (T), **6**-42
of sound, **3**-108 to **3**-112
directional, **3**-110 to **3**-112
stellar, **6**-80
Radiation coefficient, **3**-50
Radiation constants (T), **7**-3
Radiation detection, **6**-114 to **6**-119
Radiation detectors, characteristics of, **6**-114 to **6**-119
quantum (f) (T), **6**-114, **6**-115
Radiation exposure, maximum permissible, to ionizing radiation (T's), **8**-254 to **8**-256
Radiation field of current distribution, **5**-68
Radiation formula, Planck's, **6**-6
Radiation impedance characteristics, **3**-110
Radiation intensity, definition of, **6**-6
Radiation length for various substances (T), **8**-39
Radiation pressure in sound, **3**-43
Radiation resistance, acoustic, of sphere and piston (T), **3**-110
Radiation vector, **5**-74
Radiative attachment of electrons, **7**-182
Radiative recombination coefficients (T), **5**-171
Radio astronomy, **6**-120 to **6**-123
measurements in, **6**-120 to **6**-121
spectra in (f), **6**-121
Radio-frequency cables, **5**-52
standard, attenuation of (f), **5**-57
list of (T), **5**-53 to **5**-56
Radio luminosity in radio astronomy, definition of, **6**-121
Radio magnitude in radio astronomy, definition of, **6**-121
Radio noise, galactic, **6**-122
Radioactive decay of neutrons, **8**-129
Radioactive isotopes, data on (T), **8**-96 to **8**-128

Radioactive materials, shipping regulations for, **8**-257
Radioactive nuclides, decay-energy cycles for the $4n$ through $4n + 3$ series (f's), **8**-42 to **8**-45
Radioisotope data (T), **8**-98 to **8**-128
Radioisotopes, concentration in air and water (T), **8**-253, **8**-256
Radiometry, **6**-64 to **8**-82
Radionuclides, classical and modern designation of (T), **8**-41
Radius, of curvature from spherometer readings, definition of, **6**-7
 of gyration, **2**-9
Range, of fission fragments, **8**-36
 of protons, **8**-27 to **8**-31
  in air (f), **8**-27
  in aluminum (f), **8**-29, **8**-31
  in copper (T), **8**-24 to **8**-25
  in Ilford C-2 emulsion (f), **8**-32
  in lead (T), **8**-33 to **8**-34
  in silver (T), **8**-30 to **8**-31
Range-energy relations, **8**-23 to **8**-39
 for alpha particles in Ilford C-2 emulsion (f), **8**-32
 for deuterons in Ilford C-2 emulsion (f), **8**-32
 for electrons in aluminum (f), **8**-39
 for heavy charged particles, **8**-23
 for protons, in air (f), **8**-27
  in aluminum (f), **8**-29, **8**-31
  in Ilford C-2 emulsion (f), **8**-32
 for tritons in Ilford C-2 emulsion (f), **8**-32
Range straggling, of alpha particles in copper (f's), **8**-37
 of deuterons in copper (f's), **8**-37
 of protons in copper (f's), **8**-37
Rankine-Hugoniot relation (f), **2**-232, **2**-234
Rankine temperature, conversion equations for (T), **4**-2
Rare alpha groups, **8**-47
Rare gases, first Townsend ionization coefficients in (f), **5**-169
Rate of deformation tensor, **3**-28
Ratio of proton to electron mass, **8**-4
Rayl, definition of, **3**-10
Rayleigh scattering of photons, **8**-91
Rayleigh's laws in low magnetic fields, **5**-214
Reaction cross sections of elements (T's), **8**-154 to **8**-168, **8**-170 to **8**-171
Reactors (*see* Nuclear reactors)
Reciprocal dispersive power and optical plastics (T), **6**-19
Reciprocity principle, **3**-10
Reciprocity theorem, **3**-11
 and absorption cross section, **5**-71 to **5**-72
 for network theory, **5**-81
Recombination coefficient, in air (f), **5**-177, **5**-178
 temperature variation in oxygen (f), **5**-178
Recommended noise level for different rooms (T), **3**-122
Rectangular conductors, resistance of (f), **5**-92
Rectangular coordinates, **2**-3
 base vectors for (f), **2**-2, **2**-3
Rectangular prism, capacitance per unit length, **5**-16
Rectangular resonators, **5**-65 to **5**-66
 electric and magnetic fields in (f), **5**-65
Rectangular waveguides, **5**-59 to **5**-62
 coordinate system for (f), **5**-59
 wave types for (T), **5**-61
Rectifier circuits (T), **5**-264 to **5**-265
Rectifiers, **5**-5, **5**-263 to **5**-266
Rectilineal compliance and acoustic analogy, **3**-135
Reduced mass of diatomic molecules (T), **7**-136 to **7**-141
Reduction in area, metals and alloys (T), **2**-62 to **2**-63, **2**-66 to **2**-72, **2**-75 to **2**-76
 in tensile testing, definition of, **2**-69
Reference ellipsoid in geodesy, **2**-92
Reference gases, dielectric constants of (T), **5**-147
Reference intensity, **3**-6
Reference power, **3**-7
Reference sound pressure, **3**-7
References, in acoustics, **3**-178 to **3**-179
 in mathematics, **1**-2 to **1**-5
Reflectance, by films of various metals (T), **6**-108
 luminous, definition of, **6**-52
 maximum luminous (T), **6**-63
Reflecting factors, infrared, of dry pigments (T), **6**-41
Reflection, **6**-41 to **6**-43
 of earthquake waves, **2**-104 to **2**-106
 of light, by transparent medium, **6**-7
  by various metals (T), **6**-109 to **6**-110
 of longitudinal and shear waves, **3**-78
 of shock waves, **2**-233 to **2**-235
 total, definition of, **6**-8
Reflection coefficients, definition of, **6**-7
 for incandescent light on various substances (T), **6**-43
 for visible monochromatic radiation on various substances (T), **6**-42
Reflectivity, definition of, **6**-7
Reflectors, and beam formation, **5**-73
 used in various nuclear reactors (T), **8**-228 to **8**-239
Refraction, of earthquake waves, **2**-104 to **2**-106
 index of (*see* Index of refraction)
 of ocean waves, **2**-123
 of shock waves, **2**-233 to **2**-235
 of sound in water, **3**-68
 at a spherical surface, **6**-7
Refractive index (*see* Index of refraction)
Refractivity, definition of, **6**-7
Refutas chart, **2**-165
Regular reflection of shock waves, **2**-234
Relative biological effectiveness of ionizing radiation, **8**-250
Relative capacitivity of semiconductors (T), **5**-132
(*See also* Dielectric constants)

Relative density, of air (T), **4**-83
of argon (T), **4**-88
of carbon dioxide (T), **4**-92
of hydrogen (T), **4**-96
of nitrogen (T), **4**-104
of oxygen (T), **4**-109
Relative dielectric strengths, of gases (T), **5**-148 to **5**-149
of nitrogen-vapor mixtures (T), **5**-148 to **5**-149
Relative humidity vs. attenuation constant (f), **3**-117
and energy attenuation (f), **3**-66
Relative molal heat content of solutes (T), **5**-281
Relative photopic luminosity, definition of, **6**-50
Relative visibility, definition of, **6**-9
Relative volume, **2**-137
of elements (T), **4**-29
of gases vs. temperature (T's), **4**-26
of liquids vs. temperature (T's), **4**-26, **4**-27
of solids (T's), **4**-28, **4**-29
Relaxation, attenuation of sound due to, **3**-79
Relaxation frequencies in sound, **3**-51
Relaxation processes and sound absorption, **3**-50 to **3**-53
Reluctance of magnetic circuit, definition of, **5**-34
Remanence of materials for permanent magnets (T), **5**-219
Repulsion motor, **5**-250
Repulsion-start motors, **5**-249
Research reactors (*see* Nuclear reactors)
Residual induction, **5**-214
Resins, density (T), **2**-34 to **2**-35
Resistance, ac/dc, for solid round wire (T), **5**-201
acoustic, **3**-9
acoustic analogies to, **3**-134 to **3**-136
of copper wire (T), **5**-198 to **5**-200
high-frequency, of copper (f), **5**-200
of rectangular conductors (f), **5**-92
of thermal radiation detectors (T), **6**-118
Resistance standards, **5**-107
Resistivity, of earth, **5**-290 to **5**-291
of earth materials (f), **5**-290
of elements and alloys at different temperatures (T), **4**-13
of high-permeability materials (T), **5**-216
of metals and alloys (T's), **5**-90, **5**-204
volume, of ceramics (T), **5**-120 to **5**-121
of glasses (T), **5**-122 to **5**-123
Resolving power, definition of, **6**-7
Resonance, viscothermal, **3**-48
Resonance cross sections, **8**-143 to **8**-144
Resonance frequency, definition of, **3**-10
Resonance lines of atoms (T), **7**-13 to **7**-15
Resonance parameters, of fissionable nuclei (T), **8**-153
of heavy nuclei (T), **8**-147 to **8**-152
of light nuclei (T), **8**-145 to **8**-146
Resonance potentials of atoms (T), **7**-13 to **7**-15
Resonant cavities at microwave frequencies, **5**-65 to **5**-68
Resonators, frequency of conical (T), **3**-103
rectangular and circular, **5**-65 to **5**-67
volume, **3**-103 to **3**-104
Response, relative, definition of, **3**-11
Rest mass, of electron, **8**-4
of neutron, **8**-4
of proton, **8**-4
Reverberant sound, definition of, **3**-17
Reverberation, definition of, **3**-115
of sound in water, **3**-68
Reverberation chamber, definition of, **3**-17
Reverberation time, definition of, **3**-6, **3**-117
optimum, for different rooms (f), **3**-118
vs. frequency (f), **3**-119
Reversible permeability of materials for permanent magnets (T), **5**-219
Reyn, definition of, **2**-165
Reynolds number, and cavitating flow data (T), **2**-188
definition of, **2**-179
vs. drag coefficient for cylinder and sphere (f), **2**-226
in flowing liquids, **2**-183
vs. friction factor for rough pipes (f), **2**-225
and gas flow, **2**-221, **2**-225, **2**-226
Rhes, definition of, **2**-165
Rhodium, emf of platinum vs platinum-rhodium thermocouples (T), **4**-10
Rhombic crystals, elastic constants and coefficients for (T), **2**-58
Richardson effect, definition of, **5**-4
Righi-Leduc coefficient, **5**-98
Righi-Leduc effect, **5**-99
Rigid bodies, dynamics of, **2**-8 to **2**-10
Rigidity, **2**-10
of earth layers, **2**-108
Rigidity modulus, of gels, **2**-82
of metals and alloys (T), **2**-61, **2**-64 to **2**-71, **2**-74 to **2**-76
Ring sound source, beam angle of radiation for (f), **3**-111, **3**-112
directional radiation from, **3**-111 to **3**-112
directivity index for (f), **3**-112
Rocks, elastic constants of (T), **2**-102
electrical conduction of, **5**-290 to **5**-291
resistivities of (f), **5**-290
wave velocities in (T), **2**-102
Rock materials, diffusivities of (T), **4**-74
Rockwell hardness number, definition of, **2**-69
Rods, demagnetizing factors for (T), **5**-244
fundamental frequency of, **3**-102 to **3**-103
Roentgen, definition of, **8**-250
Roentgen equivalent man, definition of, **8**-250
Roentgens per hour at 1 m from a 1-curie source (T), **8**-257
Rolling friction (f), **2**-43 to **2**-44
coefficient of, **2**-43
Room constant (acoustics), definition of, **3**-17

Rooms, acceptable noise level for, **3**-122
recommended noise level for (T), **3**-122
Rotary converter, **5**-262
Rotating machines, **5**-260
Rotational compliance and acoustic analogy, **3**-136
Rotational constants of polyatomic molecules (T), **7**-146, **7**-152 to **7**-161
Rotational motion, definition of, **2**-8
Rough pipes and turbulent gas flow, **2**-224
Round wire, self-inductance of, **5**-28, **5**-29
skin-effect formulas for, **5**-90 to **5**-91
Rubber insulation and current capacity of conductors (T), **5**-202 to **5**-203
Rubbers, density of (T), **2**-35
dielectric frequency of (T), **5**-124 to **5**-130
dielectric properties of (T), **5**-124 to **5**-130
Russell-Saunders coupling, **7**-17 to **7**-18
and Zeeman effect, **7**-168
Rutile, index of refraction of (T), **6**-23 to **6**-25
optical properties of, **6**-40
Rydberg constants (T), **7**-3

S

S event in meson and hyperon decay, **8**-241
S rule of electron transitions, **7**-25
Sabin, definition of, **3**-17, **3**-113
Salinity of sea water related to temperature (f), **2**-118
Salt solutions, index of refraction of (T), **6**-22
Salts, ionic conductivity in, **5**-185 to **5**-196
Sand, porosity and permeability of (T), **2**-180
Sandstone, porosity and permeability of (T), **2**-180
Sapphire, index of refraction of (T), **6**-23 to **6**-25
optical properties of, **6**-40
Saturated air, virtual temperature of (T), **2**-127
Saturation, of iron-cobalt-nickel alloys (f), **5**-207
Saturation hysteresis of high-permeability materials (T), **5**-216
Saturation induction, of high-permeability materials (T), **5**-216
of manganese-copper-aluminum alloys (f), **5**-207
Saturation magnetization, of binary compounds (T), **5**-213
of cobalt alloys (T), **5**-210
definition of, **5**-206
of ferrites (T), **5**-211
for ferromagnetic elements (T), **5**-208
of iron alloys (T), **5**-209
of nickel alloys (T), **5**-210
Saturation magnetostriction of crystals and polycrystalline materials, **5**-222 to **5**-224
Saybolt viscometer, calibrating oils for (T), **2**-167
Scalar potential, **5**-43 to **5**-44
in fluid motion, **3**-40
Scale, definition of, **3**-15
equally tempered, **3**-14
Scattering, and absorption of em waves, **5**-70 to **5**-71
attenuation of sound due to, **3**-79
Coulomb, of charged particles, **8**-36
of photons, **8**-89
of sound in water, **3**-68
Scattering cross sections, **5**-71
of elements (T's), **8**-154 to **8**-168, **8**-170 to **8**-171
of neutrons, definition of, **8**-130
Scattering factors for waves in metals (T), **3**-83
Schematic diagrams and acoustical analogies, **3**-142 to **3**-143
Schlichting formulas, **2**-196
Schottky defects, **5**-185
Scotopic lumens, **6**-53
Scotopic luminosity, **6**-52 to **6**-53
Scotopic luminosity data (T), **6**-51
wavelengths for selected ordinates (T), **6**-53
Scotopic luminous reflectance, **6**-53
Scotopic luminous transmittance, **6**-53
Sea level and earth's crust (T), **2**-115
Sea water, critical pressure for cavitation in (f), **2**-184
gravity waves in, **2**-122 to **2**-123
properties of (T), **2**-116 to **2**-122, **3**-69
temperature-salinity diagram for (f), **2**-118
Seasonal variation in ionosphere (f), **2**-131
Seats, absorption coefficients of (T), **3**-116
Second, definition of, **2**-14
Second-harmonic components of sound pressure, **3**-38
Second law of thermodynamics and viscous fluids, **3**-29
Second-order acoustic equations, **3**-34
in fluid motion, **3**-40, **3**-41
Secondary electron emission, ratio to incident primary for several substances (f's), **7**-203
for various substances (f's), **7**-192 to **7**-198
Secondary emission coefficient for electrons, **7**-192
Secondary fixed temperature points (T), **4**-5
Secondary wavelength standards, definition of, **7**-43
Secular change in earth's magnetic field, **5**-293
Seeback effect, **5**-5, **5**-98
Seeback emf, **5**-98
Seismic waves (*see* Earthquake waves)
Seismicity of earth, **2**-110 to **2**-112
Seismological data, **2**-101 to **2**-114
symbols used in, **2**-101 to **2**-102
Selection rules, for electric-dipole transition (T), **7**-168
for electron transitions, **7**-20 to **7**-21, **7**-25
Selenium rectifier, **5**-266
Self-diffusion coefficients in gases (T), **2**-213
Self-inductance for various static fields, **5**-28 to **5**-31
Self-inductance standards, **5**-110 to **5**-112

Semiconductors, **5**-5, **5**-157 to **5**-165
coefficients of linear expansion of (T), **4**-63
conductivity (electrical) formulas for, **5**-96
and Faraday rotation (T), **5**-235
relative capacitivity of (T), **5**-132
thermal conductivity of (T), **4**-76
Semidegenerate case in wave mechanics, **7**-167
Semitone, definition of, **3**-15
Sensitivities, spectral, of various phototubes (f's), **6**-116 to **6**-117
Sensitivity peak of fluorescent chemicals (T), **6**-111
Series connections, definition of, **5**-5
Series spectrum, definition of, **7**-16
Series universal motor, **5**-250
torque-speed curves for (f), **5**-250
Series-wound motors, **5**-246
Shaded-pole motors, **5**-249
torque-speed curve for (f), **5**-249
Shallow water waves, **2**-123
Shear, definition of, **2**-10
Shear modulus, **2**-10
of gels (T), **2**-83
Shear stiffness for ceramics (T), **3**-95
Shear strength, definition of, **2**-69
of metals and alloys (T), **2**-64 to **2**-78
Shear waves, definition of, **3**-6
reflection of, **3**-78
scattering factors for, in metals (T), **3**-83
Shearing stress in liquids, **2**-165
Sheet, self-inductance of, **5**-31
Sheet cavities, **2**-183, **2**-187
Sheet polarizers, properties of, **6**-44
spectral transmittance of (T), **6**-44
Shell structure of stable nuclei, **8**-5, **8**-18 to **8**-19
Shells of nucleons, **8**-5
Shielded-pair transmission lines, constants for, **5**-48 to **5**-49
Shielding of various nuclear reactors (T), **8**-228 to **8**-239
Shielding equations in health physics, **8**-251 to **8**-253
Shipping regulations for radioactive materials, **8**-257
Shock waves, **2**-231 to **2**-236
formation, **3**-38
and ideal gases (T), **2**-232 to **2**-233, **2**-235
reflection and refraction of, **2**-233 to **2**-235
in steady-state, one-dimensional flow, **2**-232 to **2**-233
symbols for, **2**-231
Shoran measurements, **2**-96
Shot noise in radiation detectors, **6**-115
Shunt-wound motors, **5**-246
Sidereal day (T), **2**-2, **2**-91
Sidereal periods of planets (T), **2**-90
Sigma hyperons, **8**-245
Sigma pile, **8**-227
Silica, fused, absorption coefficients for (T), **6**-37
extinction coefficients for (T), **6**-38
index of refraction of (T), **6**-26 to **6**-27
Silt, porosity and permeability of (T), **2**-180
Silver, energy loss and range of protons in (T), **8**-30 to **8**-31
proton straggling in (T), **8**-36
Silver alloys, elastic and strength constants for (T), **2**-62 to **2**-63
Silver chloride, index of refraction of (T), **6**-27 to **6**-29
Simple tone, definition of, **3**-15
Simple vibrators, frequencies of, **3**-100 to **3**-107
strings (T), **3**-100 to **3**-102
Single body, capacitance of, **5**-12 to **5**-14
Single-particle nuclear model, **8**-18
Single-phase a-c induction motor, **5**-248
Single-phase rectifier circuits (T), **5**-264 to **5**-265
Singly ionized atoms, persistent spectral lines of (T), **7**-39 to **7**-41
Six-atom molecules, fundamental vibrations of (T), **7**-151
rotational constants and geometric parameters of, asymmetric-top (T), **7**-161
linear (T), **7**-160
spherical-top (T), **7**-160
symmetric-top (T), **7**-160
Six-phase rectifier circuits (T), **5**-265
Skin, maximum permissible exposure to ionizing radiation (T), **8**-255
Skin depth, **5**-85
of copper (f), **5**-200
definition of, **5**-200
Skin effect, **5**-85 to **5**-95
definition of, **5**-5, **5**-85
Skin-effect quantities for various conductors (T), **5**-90
Skin friction, and compressibility, **2**-230
and heat transfer, **2**-230
Skin friction data, for flat plate, **2**-228
for turbulent gas flow, **2**-224 to **2**-226
Skin-friction ratio, vs Mach number (f), **2**-229
Sky, approximate brightness of (T), **6**-78
Sliding friction, **2**-40
coefficient of, for various substances (T), **2**-41 to **2**-42
Slow-burning insulations and current capacity of conductor (T), **5**-202 to **5**-203
Small-signal acoustic equations, **3**-32 to **3**-34
Small-signal scalar wave equation, **3**-34
Smooth pipes and turbulent gas flow, **2**-224
Snell's law, **3**-78
of refraction, **6**-7
Sodium, energy levels of (f) (T), **8**-85, **8**-86
Sodium I, energy-level diagram of (f), **7**-31
Sodium chloride, absorption coefficient of (T), **6**-37
index of refraction of (T), **6**-23, **6**-27 to **6**-29
Solar constant, definition of, **2**-132
Solar eclipse method of earth measurement, **2**-96
Solar-flare effect, definition of, **5**-294
Solar insolation, daily average (f), **2**-133
Solar noise and radio astronomy, **6**-121 to **6**-122

Solar radio-frequency radiation, spectra of (f), **3**-121
Solenoid, magnetic induction of, **5**-27
Solenoidal waves, **2**-12
Solid helium, volume and compressibility of (T), **4**-27
Solid solutions, Bohr magneton numbers of (T), **5**-211
Solid-state formulas, **5**-95 to **5**-104
Solids, acoustic properties of, **3**-74 to **3**-88
  attenuation of sound in, **3**-79
  density of 20°C (T), **2**-21
  dielectric properties of (T's), **5**-114 to **5**-132
  emissivity of, **6**-73
  extensional and torsional waves in, **3**-75
  internal energy and entropy of (T's), **4**-44 to **4**-46
  logarithmic decrements of (T's), **2**-87
  magnetic properties of, **5**-206 to **5**-244
  and metallic conductors, **5**-197 to **5**-205
  polycrystalline, elastic and strength constants of (T), **2**-55 to **2**-80
  relative volume of (T's), **4**-28 to **4**-29
  specific rotation of (T), **6**-98
  Verdet constants for (T), **6**-95
  viscosity of, **2**-84 to **2**-90
Solutions, specific rotation of (T), **6**-100 to **6**-101
Sone, definition of, **3**-13
Sound, absorption constant in organic liquids (T), **3**-73
  attenuation of, **3**-63 to **3**-66
    nomogram for (f), **3**-64
  definition of, **3**-6
  directional radiation of, **3**-110 to **3**-112
  energy density of, **3**-6
  hearing, of short duration, **3**-127
  propagation of, **3**-63 to **3**-66
    in fluids, **3**-25 to **3**-55
  radiation of, **3**-108 to **3**-112
  and reverberation, **3**-6
  speed of, equation for, **3**-61
    in liquids, **3**-67
    in sea water, **2**-119 to **2**-120
    in various gases (T), **3**-62
  velocity of, in air vs. temperature (T), **2**-216
    effect of dissolved salt in water (f), **3**-70
    in fresh and sea water (T), **3**-69
    as function of density, **3**-37
    in organic liquids (T), **3**-71 to **3**-73
  (*See also under* Acoustic)
Sound absorption, **3**-43 to **3**-53
  in air, **3**-63 to **3**-66
  classical, **3**-49
  first-order equations for, **3**-45
  and relaxation processes, **3**-50 to **3**-53
  and viscosity (f), **3**-65
  in water vs. temperature (f), **3**-69
Sound-absorption coefficients, definition of, **3**-17, **3**-67
  for water (f), **3**-71
Sound-absorptive materials, **3**-113 to **3**-115
Sound dispersion, **3**-43 to **3**-53
Sound-energy density, **3**-6
Sound-energy flux, **3**-6
Sound field, **3**-6
  anechoic, **3**-2
Sound intensity, **3**-6, **3**-42
Sound level, definition of, **3**-6
Sound power level, definition of, **3**-7
Sound pressure, **3**-4
  vs distance from microphone (T), **3**-130
Sound propagation, streaming in, **3**-39 to **3**-41
  symbols for, **3**-25 to **3**-26
  vorticity in, **3**-39 to **3**-41
Sound spectrum level, **3**-55
Sound transmission, **3**-63 to **3**-66
  through partitions, **3**-119
  in water, **3**-67 to **3**-68
Sound waves and transducers, **3**-89 to **3**-99
Space-charge regions, waves in, **5**-74 to **5**-79
Space-charge waves, **5**-74 to **5**-79
  energy relations in, **5**-79
  of noise, **5**-79
Space-group symbols in crystallography, **2**-47
Space-time relationships, **2**-2 to **2**-3
Spallation reaction, definition of, **8**-2
Spatial coordinate transforms, **3**-36 to **3**-37
Spatial coordinates, **3**-34 to **3**-37
Specific acoustic compliance, definition of, **3**-10
Specific acoustic impedance, definition of, **3**-10
Specific acoustic mass, definition of, **3**-10
Specific acoustic reactance, **3**-10
  of pulsating sphere (f), **3**-109
  of vibrating piston (f), **3**-109
Specific damping capacity, **2**-84 to **2**-86
Specific gravity, of animal oils (T), **2**-150
  of vegetable oils (T), **2**-150
Specific heat, of air (T's), **2**-125, **3**-59, **4**-84
  of argon (T), **4**-89
  of carbon dioxide (T), **4**-93
  of gases (T), **3**-59
  of hydrogen (T), **4**-97
  of nitrogen (T), **4**-105
  of oxygen (T), **4**-110
  ratio C_p/C_v for gases (T), **3**-59
  of sea water, **2**-121
  of steam (T), **4**-115
Specific heat constant of paramagnetic salts (T), **4**-14
Specific heat equation for viscous fluids, **3**-29
Specific impedance, **3**-53
Specific impedance ratio, **3**-53
Specific refractivity, definition of, **6**-7
Specific rotation, definition of, **6**-8
  of solids, liquids, and solutions (T's), **6**-98 to **6**-101
Specific volume, **2**-151
  of sea water, **2**-117, **2**-119
  of viscous fluids, **3**-27
  of water vs. temperature (T), **4**-25
Spectra (*see* Atomic spectra; X-ray spectra)
Spectral emissivity, brightness vs. temperature (T), **6**-75
  of oxides (T), **6**-74

Spectral emissivity, of unoxidized surfaces (T), **6**-73
Spectral lines, persistent, of elements (T), **7**-39 to **7**-41
wavelengths and intensities of standard (T), **6**-83 to **6**-86
Spectral response in radiation detectors, **6**-114
Spectral sensitivities of various phototubes (f's), **6**-116 to **6**-117
Spectral series, definition of, **6**-8
Spectral transmittance of sheet polarizers (T), **6**-44
Spectroscopic calibration, wavelengths for (T's), **6**-83 to **6**-90
Spectroscopic splitting factor (g), definition of, **5**-231
for various substances (T), **5**-230
Spectrum, continuous, definition of, **3**-3
definition of, **3**-7
line, definition of, **3**-5
Spectrum level in sound, **3**-55
Specular surfaces, reflection coefficients for incandescent light on (T), **6**-43
Speech, articulation index for, **3**-132 to **3**-133
articulation scores vs. articulation index (T), **3**-133
characteristic sounds of (T), **3**-131 to **3**-132
and equivalent frequency bands (T), **3**-133
and hearing, **3**-123 to **3**-133
hearing loss for, **3**-13
peak power, **3**-13
sound pressure for, vs. microphone distance (T), **3**-130
Speech levels, power, **3**-12, **3**-13
Speech power, **3**-130 to **3**-132
Speed of sound (*see* Sound)
Speed ratings of electric motors, **5**-252
Speed requirements and motor selection, **5**-251
Spheres, acoustic radiation resistance of (T), **3**-110
drag data for (f), **2**-226, **2**-228
Spherical aberration, definition of, **6**-8
Spherical candlepower, definition of, **6**-9
Spherical coordinates, **2**-3
base vectors in (f), **2**-3
Spherical mirrors, **6**-8
Spherical resonators, **5**-66
modes in (f), **5**-67
Spherical shell, skin-effect formulas for, **5**-95
Spherical surface, refraction at, **6**-7
Spherical-top molecules, rotational constants and geometrical parameters of, five-atom (T), **7**-157 to **7**-158
four-atom (T), **7**-154
six-atom (T), **7**-160
Spherical wave, definition of, **3**-7
Spherical wave functions, **5**-46 to **5**-47
Spherite, index of refraction of (T), **6**-26
Spin, of electron, **7**-17
isotopic, for light nuclei (f's) (T), **8**-57 to **8**-86
Spin, of neutron, **8**-129
of stable nuclei (T), **8**-6 to **8**-17
Spin-dependent incoherence, **8**-144
Spin-orbit coupling, **8**-5
Spin resonance, **5**-103 to **5**-104
Spinels, Bohr magneton numbers and Curie points of (T), **5**-212
index of refraction of (T), **6**-26
optical properties of, **6**-40
Split-capacitor motor, torque-speed curve for (f), **5**-249
Split-phase motors, **5**-248 to **5**-249
torque-speed curve for (f), **5**-248
Splitting factor, in paramagnetic salts (T), **4**-14
in Zeeman effect, **7**-168
Spontaneous fission yields (T), **8**-225
Spurious harmonics, **3**-38
Sputtered mass for metals in hydrogen (T), **5**-185
Squirrel-cage induction motors, characteristic curves for (f), **5**-247
Squirrel-cage rotor, **5**-247
Stability rules, nuclear, **8**-21 to **8**-22
Stable nuclei, properties of (T), **8**-6 to **8**-17
systematics of, **8**-5 to **8**-23
Standard atmosphere, definition of, **2**-127 to **2**-128
and lower atmosphere (T), **2**-128
Standard cells (batteries), **5**-107 to **5**-109
characteristics and use, **5**-107 to **5**-109
Standard coordinate system for color specifications (T), **6**-60
Standard cyclotron, **8**-173 to **8**-174
Standard electromotive forces of half cells in water (T), **5**-274 to **5**-276
Standard entropy of monatomic and polyatomic ions (T), **5**-281, **5**-282
Standard illuminants (T), **6**-56
Standard liquids, dielectric constants of (T), **5**-132
Standard observer, chromaticity coordinates and tristimulus values for (T), **6**-54 to **6**-55
Standard pitch, definition of, **3**-15
Standard radio-frequency cables, attenuation of (f), **5**-57
list of (T), **5**-53 to **5**-56
Standard ratings of electric motors as to frequency, horsepower, speed, and voltage, **5**-252
Standard second, definition of, **5**-112
Standard sources (illumination), selected ordinates for (T), **6**-59
tristimulus computation data for (T), **6**-57, **6**-58
Standard tuning frequency, **3**-106
Standard wavelength, infrared (T), **6**-88 to **6**-90
primary (light), **6**-9
Standards, electrical, **5**-105 to **5**-113
of viscosity (T), **2**-167
wavelength, for vacuum ultraviolet (T), **6**-83 to **6**-86
for wavelength measurement, **7**-42, **7**-43
Standing waves, definition of, **3**-7

Stapes in ear (T), **3**-123
Star occultation, **2**-97
Stars, brightness of (T), **6**-82
electric and magnetic properties of, **5**-283 to **5**-297
polar magnetic field strengths of (T), **5**-296
Starters for electric motors, **5**-254
Static-current-flow formulas, **5**-23 to **5**-25
Static equilibrium, definition of, **2**-9, **3**-33
Static-field formulas, **5**-12 to **5**-36
Static fields, inductance for, **5**-28 to **5**-31
Static friction, **2**-39 to **2**-40
coefficients, various materials (T), **2**-41 to **2**-42
Static-magnetic-field formulas, **5**-25 to **5**-36
Static modulus of elasticity, **2**-85 to **2**-86
Static pressure, definition of, **3**-7
Statics, definition of, **2**-5
Stationary wave, definition of, **3**-7
Steady-state alteration of pressure, **3**-38
Steady-state cavities, **2**-183, **2**-187
Steady-state one-dimensional flow, **2**-232 to **2**-233
Steady-state sinuoids, **5**-81 to **5**-82
Steam, compressibility factor for (T), **4**-113
density of (T), **4**-114
enthalpy of (T), **4**-116
entropy of (T), **4**-117
specific heat of (T), **4**-115
thermodynamic conversion factors for (T), **4**-81
viscosity vs. temperature (T's), **2**-209, **2**-210
Steel, coefficient of static friction for (T), **2**-40, **2**-41
density of (T), **2**-22 to **2**-23
Steel alloys, elastic and strength constants for (T), **2**-70 to **2**-71
Steel strings, mass per unit length (T), **3**-101
Stefan-Boltzmann constant (T), **7**-3
Stefan-Boltzmann function, **6**-64
Stellar magnetic field strengths (T), **5**-296
Stellar magnetism, **5**-297
Stellar magnitude, definition of, **6**-80
of various stars (T), **6**-82
Stellar radiation, **6**-80
Stellar spectral classes, color indices of (T), **6**-80
Steradian, definition of, **2**-14
Stereophonic sound source, **3**-129
Stiffness modulus of crystals (T), **3**-81, **3**-82
Stilb, definition of, **6**-10
Stokes, definition of, **2**-165
Stokes formula in geodesy, **2**-100
Stokes law, **2**-13
and viscosity, **2**-203
Stokes number and sound absorption, **3**-45
Stokes relation in viscous fluids, **3**-28
Stopping power of heavy charged particles, **8**-23
Strain, **2**-10, **2**-11
Strain constants, piezoelectric (T), **5**-150 to **5**-151
Strain tensor, **2**-11
Stratocumulus clouds (f), **2**-130, **2**-134
Stratosphere (f), **2**-130
Stratus clouds (f), **2**-130, **2**-134
Stream function in gas flow, **2**-217, **2**-221
Streaming in sound waves, **3**-39 to **3**-41
Streaming potential, **3**-41
Strength, definition of terms, **2**-55, **2**-69, **2**-78, **2**-80
(*See also* Shear strength; Tensile strength; Yield strength)
Strength constants of polycrystalline solids (T), **2**-61 to **2**-80
Stress and strain, general concepts of, **2**-10
Stress and strain relations, **2**-11
Stress tensor, **2**-11
in viscous fluids, **3**-28
Strings, frequency perturbations of (T), **3**-102
fundamental frequencies of, **3**-100 to **3**-102
mass per unit length, of gut (T), **3**-101
of steel (T), **3**-101
Strong-focusing methods in proton synchrotron, **8**-177
Strontium titanate, index of refraction of (T), **6**-26
Structure, of antiferroelectric crystals (T), **5**-156
of atomic spectra, **7**-16 to **7**-26
of ferroelectric crystals (T), **5**-155 to **5**-156
Sublimation, heat of, for elements and compounds (T), **4**-131 to **4**-159
Subsonic gas flow, **2**-217
Sucrose, diffusion coefficients of (T), **2**-192
Sulfur dioxide, efficiency of electron attachment in (f), **5**-175
Sulfuric acid, isothermal compressibility of (T), **2**-162
Sun, approximate brightness of (T), **6**-78
magnetic field of (T), **5**-295
mean distance of planets from (T), **2**-90
miscellaneous constants for (T), **2**-91
Sunspot cycles, **5**-297
Sunspot fields, **5**-297
Superconducting transition temperature (T), **4**-49
for metals and alloys (T's), **5**-205
Superconductors, transition temperatures, electronic constants, and Debye temperatures for (T), **4**-49
Superposition theorem for networks, **5**-81
Supersonic gas flow, **2**-217
Supersonics, definition of, **3**-12
Surface energy of liquids, **2**-172 to **2**-176
Surface phenomena, for ions on metals, **7**-192 to **7**-203
secondary electron emission by various substances (f's), **7**-192 to **7**-198
Surface resistivity of metals and alloys (T), **5**-90
Surface tension, definitions and formulas for, **2**-172, **2**-175 to **2**-176
of inorganic aqueous solutions (T), **2**-177
of liquids (T), **2**-14, **2**-172 to **2**-174
of metals (T), **2**-174
methods of measuring, **2**-175 to **2**-176
of organic aqueous solutions (T), **2**-175

Surface tension, of water, **2**-172
Susceptibility, definition of, **5**-236 to **5**-240
Suspensions, viscosity of. **2**-180 to **2**-181
Suspensoids, **2**-181
Sutherland's equation, **2**-204
"Swimming-pool" reactor, **8**-227
Syllable articulation, definition of, **3**-13
Sylvine, index of refraction of (T), **6**-23
Symbols, for acoustic properties of liquids, **3**-67
for acoustical quantities, **3**-18 to **3**-24
for cavitation in flowing liquids, **2**-182 to **2**-183
classical and modern, for heavy radionuclides (T), **8**-41
for elastic and related constants, **2**-55
electrical (T), **5**-6 to **5**-7
for electrical, mechanical, and acoustical elements (T), **3**-139
for electrochemical data, **5**-268 to **5**-269
for elements (T), **7**-5 to **7**-8
for geodetic data, **2**-92 to **2**-101
for liquid jets, **2**-195
for magnetic properties, **5**-206
for meteorology, **2**-124 to **2**-125
for nuclear constants, **8**-4
for nuclear reactions, spallation reactions, and fission, **8**-2 to **8**-3
for porosity and viscosity, **2**-179
for propagation of sound, **3**-25 to **3**-26
for schematic diagrams, based on impedance analogy (T), **3**-145 to **3**-176
based on mobility analogy (T), **3**-144 to **3**-176
in seismological data, **2**-101 to **2**-102
for shock-wave quantities, **2**-231
Symmetric-top molecules, rotational constants and geometrical parameters of, five-atom (T), **7**-157 to **7**-158
four-atom (T), **7**-154
six-atom (T), **7**-160
Symmetrical top and wave mechanics, **7**-163 to **7**-164
Synchrocyclotron, description of, **8**-174 to **8**-175
Synchronous motors, **5**-248
torque-speed curve for (f), **5**-248
Synchronous reluctance motor, **5**-250
torque-speed curves for (f), **5**-250
Synchrotrons, alternate-gradient, **8**-177 to **8**-178
electron, **8**-176 to **8**-177
proton, **8**-177 to **8**-178
world-wide list of (T), **8**-189 to **8**-193, **8**-196 to **8**-199
Synthetic crystals for filters, **6**-50
Systematic notation for spectral lines, **7**-58
Systematics of stable nuclei, **8**-5 to **8**-23
Systems of one degree of freedom, electrical, mechanical, and acoustical, **3**-137 to **3**-138

T

Tait equation, **2**-223
Taylor series expansions, **3**-36
TE waves, plane, cylindrical, and spherical functions of, **5**-45 to **5**-47
Teller-Pöschl potential and wave mechanics, **7**-163
Telluric currents, **5**-289
TEM waves, plane, cylindrical, and spherical functions of, **5**-45 to **5**-47
Temperature, and piezoelectric strain constants (T), **5**-152
and pyroelectric constants (T), **5**-154
vs. thermal conductivity of various materials (f), **4**-77
variation of dielectric constants with (f), **5**-131
Temperature coefficient, of inorganic liquids (T), **5**-133
of organic liquids (T), **5**-134 to **5**-142
and per cent conductivity, **5**-197
of piezoelectric strain constants (T), **5**-153
of standard liquids (T), **5**-132
Temperature data, of paramagnetic salts, **4**-14 to **4**-20
at very low temperatures, **4**-14 to **4**-20
Temperature-entropy diagram, for helium (f), **4**-94
for hydrogen (f), **4**-100 to **4**-102
Temperature-salinity diagrams for sea water (f), **2**-118
Temperature scales, equation and definition of (T), **4**-2 to **4**-4
International, **4**-3, **4**-4
Temperatures, critical, of elements and compounds (T), **4**-21 to **4**-23
of inorganic and organic substances, **4**-21 to **4**-23
Tensile strength, definition of, **2**-55
of liquids (T), **2**-169 to **2**-172
of metals and alloys (T), **2**-61 to **2**-78
methods of measuring in liquids, **2**-170 to **2**-172
Ternary fission, **8**-212
Terrestrial abundance of elements (T), **7**-9 to **7**-12
Terrestrial electricity, **5**-289 to **5**-291
Terrestrial magnetism, **5**-291 to **5**-295
Tetragonal crystal systems (f) (T), **2**-45 to **2**-47
Tetragonal crystals, elastic constants and coefficients of (T), **2**-57
Thallium, phase diagrams for (f) (T), **4**-38
transition parameters for (f) (T), **4**-38
Thallium bromide-iodide, index of refraction of (T), **6**-27 to **6**-29
Theorems, for electrical networks, **5**-81
impulse-momentum, **2**-5
work-energy, **2**-5 to **2**-7, **2**-9
Thermal conductivity, **3**-52, **4**-65 to **4**-79
of alloys, **4**-67, **4**-79
conversion factors for (T), **4**-66
of cubic crystals (T), **4**-72 to **4**-73
of dielectric crystals (T), **4**-79
of disordered dielectrics (T), **4**-79
of fused quartz (T), **4**-74
of gases (T's), **3**-58, **3**-61, **4**-71
of insulating materials (T), **4**-68 to **4**-70
of liquids (T's), **4**-71, **4**-75

Thermal conductivity, at low temperatures, (f) **4**-77
of metals (T), **4**-67, **4**-78
of noncubic crystals (T), **4**-73
of optical materials (T), **4**-76
of organic materials (T), **4**-71
of sea water (T), **2**-122
of semiconductors (T), **4**-76
vs. temperature for various materials (f), **4**-77
of water (T), **4**-70
Thermal cross sections, of elements (T's), **8**-154 to **8**-168, **8**-170 to **8**-171
of neutrons, definition of, **8**-144, **8**-169
Thermal detectors, characteristics of (T's), **6**-114, **6**-118
Thermal diffusion of gases, **3**-58
Thermal dissipation function, **3**-30, **3**-31
Thermal effects, attenuation of sound due to, **3**-79
Thermal emf, of alloys relative to platinum (T), **4**-9
of elements relative to platinum (T), **4**-6 to **4**-7
of thermocouple materials relative to platinum (T), **4**-8
Thermal energy gap, definition of, **5**-157
Thermal expansion, **4**-51 to **4**-64
Grüneisen equation constants (T), **4**-63
Thermal expansion coefficients, cubical, of elements (T), **4**-56
of liquids (T), **4**-62
linear, of alloys (T), **4**-57 to **4**-60
of elements (T's), **4**-51 to **4**-55
of miscellaneous materials (T), **4**-61
Thermal losses, due to grain rotation, **3**-84
due to grain scattering, **3**-85
due to intergrain heat flow, **3**-84
Thermal-neutron fission, and fission-product chains (T), **8**-202 to **8**-211
yields (T), **8**-212 to **8**-215
Thermal neutrons, velocity of, **8**-4
Thermal noise in acoustic medium, **3**-53 to **3**-55
Thermal noise pressure, **3**-55
Thermal waves in sound, **3**-46, **3**-47
Thermionic cathode rectifiers, **5**-263
Thermionic emission, **5**-97
Thermocouples, characteristics of (T), **6**-114
emf of, chromel vs. alumel (T), **4**-12
chromel vs. constantan (T), **4**-12
copper vs. constantan (T), **4**-11
iron vs. constantan (T), **4**-11
platinum vs. platinum-rhodium (T), **4**-10
thermal emf of, alloys relative to platinum (T), **4**-8, **4**-9
elements relative to platinum (T), **4**-6 to **4**-7
Thermodynamic properties of gases, **4**-80 to **4**-117
Thermodynamics, conversion factors for gases (T), **4**-81
Thermoelectric effect, **5**-5, **5**-97 to **5**-100
Thermomagnetic effect, **5**-97 to **5**-100
Thermoplastic insulations and current capacity of conductor (T), **5**-202 to **5**-203
Thermosphere (f), **2**-130
Thermoviscous medium, acoustic impedance of, **3**-53
Thermoviscous number, **3**-46
Thermoviscous parameters in fluids, **3**-47
Thevenin's theorem, **5**-81
Thin films, Faraday rotation in (T), **5**-232
Thin-sheet shielding, formulas for, **5**-94
Thixotropic substances, definition of, **2**-81
mechanical properties of, **2**-82 to **2**-83
Thixotropy, coefficient of, **2**-83
Thompson coefficient, **5**-97 to **5**-98
Thomson cross section, **8**-4
Thomson effects, definition of, **5**-5
Thomson scattering of photons, **8**-91
Thorium, fast-neutron fission yields of (T), **8**-216
Thorium-228, decay scheme of (f), **8**-47
Three-phase rectifier circuits (T), **5**-264 to **5**-265
Threshold (in hearing), of audibility, **3**-14
of damage, **3**-14
of detectability, **3**-14
of discomfort, **3**-14, **3**-126
of feeling, **3**-14, **3**-126
of hearing, **3**-14
of pain, **3**-14
of tolerance, **3**-14
Threshold field at absolute zero for superconductors (T), **4**-49
Thunderstorms, characteristics of (T), **5**-285, **5**-288
electric field near (f), **5**-287
Thyratron rectifier, **5**-263
Tickle due to loud sounds, **3**-14
Tidal constituents (T), **2**-123, **2**-124
Time in mechanics, **2**-2
Time constant, in radiation, definition of, **6**-119
of radiation detectors (T), **6**-118
Time interval, **2**-2
Time lag in voltage breakdown in air (f's), **5**-180
Time periodic fields, **5**-39
basic wave functions for, **5**-45 to **5**-47
and Maxwell's equations, **5**-41
Tin, elastic and strength constants of (T), **2**-77
Tin alloys, elastic and strength constants of (T), **2**-77
Titanium cesium alum, properties of (T), **4**-14, **4**-19 to **4**-20
TM waves, plane, cylindrical, and spherical functions of, **5**-45 to **5**-47
Toluene, first Townsend ionization coefficient in (f), **5**-169
Tone, complex, **3**-14
definition of, **3**-15
fundamental, **3**-14
whole, **3**-14
Tones, differential threshold for intensity and frequency (T), **3**-126
Tonometer and tensile strength, **2**-171
Torque, definition of, **2**-6, **2**-7

Torque requirements and motor selection, **5**-251
Torque-speed curves, for capacitor-start, split-capacitor, and shaded-pole motors (f), **5**-249
for synchronous reluctance and series universal motors (f), **5**-250
for synchronous and split-phase motors (f's), **5**-248
Torsional mode in transducer materials, **3**-98
Torsional waves in solids, **3**-75
Torus, magnetic induction of, **5**-27
Total emissivity, apparent vs. true temperature (T), **6**-76
of metals, unoxidized surfaces (T), **6**-75
Total heat flux in viscous liquids, **3**-30
Total mechanical energy, definition of, **2**-6
Total neutron cross sections of various elements (f's), **8**-131 to **8**-134
Total normal emissivity of various substances (T), **6**-68 to **6**-71
Total reflection, definition of, **6**-8
Total volume emissivity and radio astronomy, **6**-121
Townsend coefficient, definition of, **7**-192
first, for various substances (f's), **5**-166, **5**-167 to **5**-169
second, for various substances (f's), **7**-199 to **7**-200
Transducer materials, **3**-89 to **3**-99
dielectric and piezoelectric constants of (f), **3**-97
Young's modulus vs. temperature for (f), **3**-96
Transducer network, **5**-83
Transducers, and acoustic analogy, **3**-177
directivity index of, **3**-110, **3**-112
electrostrictive, **3**-92 to **3**-98
magnetostrictive, **3**-92 to **3**-98
piezoelectric crystal, **3**-89 to **3**-92
piezoelectric properties of (T), **3**-93
Transformation properties in viscous fluids, **3**-27
Transformer connections (T), **5**-261
Transformer cooling, **5**-259
Transformers, and acoustic analogy, **3**-177
operating principles of, **5**-258 to **5**-259
types of, **5**-259 to **5**-260
Transforms and material and spatial coordinates, **3**-36 to **3**-37
Transient cavities, **2**-183, **2**-186 to **2**-187
Transient penetration of magnetic field into a plane solid, **5**-93
Transient phenomena in earth's magnetic field, **5**-293 to **5**-294
Transinertor, **3**-142
Transition, heat of, for elements and compounds (T), **4**-131 to **4**-159
Transition parameters for various substances (T), **4**-34 to **4**-38
Transition temperatures, of antiferroelectric crystals (T), **5**-156
superconducting, for metals and alloys (T's), **5**-205
for superconductors (T), **4**-49
Transitions of alpha emitters, **8**-55 to **8**-56
Translational motion, definition of, **2**-8
Transmission of light, **6**-36 to **6**-40
vs. wavelength for light (f), **6**-47
Transmission coefficient for sound, **3**-120
Transmission curves of light filter plates (f), **6**-49
Transmission lines, constants for (T), **5**-48 to **5**-49
conventional, **5**-47, **5**-51
formulas for (T), **5**-50
impedances of, **5**-50, **5**-51
Transmission loss for sound, definition of, **3**-10, **3**-18
through various materials (f), **3**-119, **3**-120
through walls and floors (T), **3**-121
Transmittance, of light, definition of, **6**-36
luminous, definition of, **6**-52
Transonic similarity rule for gas flow, **2**-219
Transport cross section of neutrons, definition of, **8**-130
Transport numbers, definition of, **5**-190
for electronic conductors (T), **5**-192 to **5**-194
for pure and mixed ionic conductors (T), **5**-191 to **5**-194
Transport phenomena in sea water (T), **2**-121 to **2**-122
Transverse electric waves, **5**-47, **5**-58 to **5**-59
Transverse em waves, **5**-47, **5**-57
Transverse isotropy, **3**-75
Transverse magnetic waves, **5**-58
definition of, **5**-47
Transverse waves, travel time through earth (T), **2**-104
velocity of, **2**-102
in earth, **2**-109
Traveling-wave interaction and growing waves, **5**-76, **5**-77
Triangulation in geodesy, **2**-93
Triatomic molecules, fundamental vibrations of (T), **7**-147
rotational constants and geometric parameters of, asymmetric-top (T), **7**-153
linear (T), **7**-152 to **7**-153
Triboelectricity, definition of, **5**-5
Triclinic crystal systems (T), **2**-45, **2**-47
Trigonal crystal systems (T), **2**-45
Trigonal crystals, elastic constants and coefficients of (T), **2**-57
Triple point, for various substances (T's), **4**-34 to **4**-38
of water (f) (T), **4**-34, **4**-35
Tristimulus computation data for standard sources (T), **6**-57, **6**-58
Tristimulus system of color specification, **6**-53
Tristimulus values of spectrum for standard observer (T), **6**-53 to **6**-55
Triton, mass of (T), **7**-3
range-energy relations in Ilford C-2 emulsion (f), **8**-32
symbols for, **8**-3

Tropopause, isotherms aloft and mean position of (f), **2**-129
temperature of (f), **2**-129
Trunk of body, maximum permissible exposure to ionizing radiation (T), **8**-255
Tube, self-inductance of, **5**-28
Tubular conductor, skin-effect formulas for, **5**-91
Tungsten, properties of (T), **6**-79
Tuning fork frequency, **3**-104
Turbulent flow, definition of, **2**-224
of gases, **2**-224 to **2**-228
along flat plate (f), **2**-227
through pipes, **2**-224
Two-body combinations, capacitance of, **5**-14 to **5**-15
Two-dimensional gas flow, **2**-217 to **2**-219
Two-dimensional rotator and wave mechanics, **7**-163
Two-terminal-pair networks (f), **5**-83 to **5**-85
Two-winding transformers, **5**-260
Tympanic membrane, dimensions of (T), **3**-123

U

Ultrasonic detector, definition of, **3**-12
Ultrasonic frequency, definition of, **3**-7
Ultrasonic generator, definition of, **3**-12
Ultrasonics, definition of, **3**-12
Underwriters' Laboratories, Inc., **5**-245
Uniaxial crystals, anisotropy constants of (T), **5**-222
Uniaxial minerals, index of refraction of (T), **6**-12 to **6**-13
United States, betatrons, list and descriptions of (T), **8**-194
cyclotrons and synchrotrons, list and descriptions of (T), **8**-189 to **8**-191
electron synchrotrons, list and descriptions of (T), **8**-196 to **8**-197
electrostatic generators, list and descriptions of (T), **8**-182 to **8**-185
linear accelerators, list and descriptions of (T), **8**-200 to **8**-201
proton synchrotrons, list and descriptions of (T), **8**-198 to **8**-199
Units, absolute viscosity (T), **2**-202
acoustical conversion (T), **3**-24
of area (T), **2**-16
derived, definition of, **2**-14
for electrical, mechanical, and acoustical elements (T), **3**-139
fundamental, definition of, **2**-14
of kinematic viscosity (T), **2**-203
of length (T), **2**-15
photometric, **6**-9 to **6**-10
of volume (T), **2**-16
Unstable nuclei, **8**-3
Upper atmosphere, characteristics of ionospheric regions in (T), **5**-284
properties of, **2**-128 to **2**-130
structure of (f), **2**-130
Uranium, total cross section of (f), **8**-134
Uranium-235, fast-neutron fission yields from (T), **8**-218
Uranium-238, fast-neutron fission yields from (T), **8**-217
Urea, diffusion coefficients for (T), **2**-192
Urethane, transition parameters and phase diagram for (f) (T), **4**-37

V

V event in meson and hyperon decay, **8**-241
Vacuum diode rectifiers, **5**-263
Vacuum ultraviolet, international wavelength standards in (T), **6**-87
wavelength standards for (T), **6**-83 to **6**-86
Valence electrons, **7**-16
Valences of elements (T), **7**-9 to **7**-12
Van de Graaf accelerators, **8**-172
Van der Waals equation as virial expansion, **4**-119
Vapor pressure, in flowing liquids, **2**-183
of sea water, **2**-120 to **2**-121
Vaporization, heat of, for elements and compounds (T), **4**-131 to **4**-159
Vapors, fluorescence of (T), **6**-112
index of refraction of (T), **6**-21
Verdet constants for (T), **6**-91
Variation method of approximation in wave mechanics, **7**-167
Vector force equation in viscous liquids, **3**-28
Vector potential, **5**-43 to **5**-44
in fluid motion, **3**-40
Velocity, definition of, **2**-2, **3**-8
drift, of electrons in various substances (f's), **7**-205 to **7**-209
of ions in various substances (f's), **7**-212 to **7**-218
effective, **3**-8
instantaneous, **3**-4
of light, measurement of (f) (T), **6**-119, **6**-120
particle, **3**-4
of sound, **3**-61 to **3**-63
in fresh and sea water (T), **3**-69
in organic liquids (T), **3**-71 to **3**-73
in solids, **3**-74 to **3**-79
variation with temperature for air (T), **2**-216
in water vs. dissolved salt (f), **3**-70
volume, **3**-7
Velocity field equations, **5**-38
Velocity potential, **2**-13
in gas flow, **2**-217
Vening Meinesz formula in geodesy, **2**-100
Verdet constants, **6**-91 to **6**-95
for aqueous solutions (T), **6**-93
definition of, **6**-91
for gases and vapors (T), **6**-91
for inorganic liquids (T), **6**-92
for metal-organic liquids (T), **6**-92
for organic liquids (T), **6**-94
for solids (T), **6**-95
Vibrating piston, acoustic impedance of, **3**-109 to **3**-110
specific acoustic resistance of (f), **3**-109

Vibrational frequency of diatomic molecules (T), **7**-136 to **7**-141
Vickers hardness number, definition of, **2**-78, **2**-80
Virial coefficients, for air (T), **4**-128
  for argon (T), **4**-121
  for carbon monoxide (T), **4**-127
  definition of, **4**-118
  for deuterium (T), **4**-125
  for helium (T), **4**-119 to **4**-120
  for hydrogen (T), **4**-124
  for krypton (T), **4**-122
  for neon (T), **4**-120
  for nitrogen (T), **4**-125, **4**-126
  for oxygen (T), **4**-126
  for xenon (T), **4**-122, **4**-123
Virial expansions of various pressure-volume-temperature equations, **4**-119
Virtual temperature, definition of, **2**-126
  of saturated air (T), **2**-127
Viscometer, calibrating oils for (T), **2**-167
  definition of, **2**-165
Viscosity, absolute, of gases (T), **2**-207
  and anelasticity, **2**-84 to **2**-86
  coefficients (T), **3**-28, **3**-41, **3**-58, **3**-60
  and creep, **2**-86 to **2**-90
  definition of, **2**-13, **2**-165, **2**-201
  of gases and gaseous mixtures, **2**-201 to **2**-210, **3**-58
  of industrial oils and lubricants (T), **2**-168
  kinematic, **3**-58
    of gases (T), **2**-208
    interpretation (f), **2**-203
  of liquids, **2**-165 to **2**-168
    common (T), **2**-166
    organic (T), **2**-169
  and logarithmic decrement of materials (T's), **2**-87
  of mercury (T), **2**-169
  of National Bureau of Standards oils (T), **2**-167
  of plasticizers (T), **2**-169
  secondary standards of (T), **2**-167
  of solids, **2**-84 to **2**-90
  and sound absorption (f), **3**-65
  and suspensions, **2**-180 to **2**-181
  symbols for, **2**-179
  variation of, with pressure and temperature, **2**-203 to **2**-205
  of viscometer calibrating oils (T), **2**-167
  of water and water vapor (T), **2**-206, **2**-209, **2**-210
Viscosity number and sound absorption, **3**-45
Viscosity specifications for aircraft-engine oils (T), **2**-168
Viscosity tables, **2**-206 to **2**-210
Viscosity tonometer, **2**-171
Viscothermal absorption and dispersion measure, **3**-47 to **3**-49, **3**-52
Viscothermal resonance, **3**-48
Viscothermal theory, **3**-33
Viscous dissipation function, **3**-30, **3**-31
Viscous fluids, definition of, **2**-13
  energy relations for, **3**-29 to **3**-31
  equations of state for, **3**-29 to **3**-31
Viscous fluids, motion of, **3**-27 to **3**-32
  various equations for, **3**-27 to **3**-32
Viscous waves in fluids, **3**-47
Visibility, definition of, **6**-8
Visible persistence of various cathode-ray-tube phosphors (T), **6**-113
Visual magnitude of stars, **6**-80
Volt, definition of, **5**-2
  international vs. absolute (T), **5**-106
Volta effect, definition of, **5**-5
Voltage breakdown, **5**-178, **5**-180 to **5**-181
  time lag in (f's), **5**-180
Voltage ratings of electric motors, **5**-252
Voltage standards, **5**-107 to **5**-109
Volume, fractional change of, with field strength (T), **5**-224
  units and conversion factors for (f), **2**-16
Volume magnetostriction, **5**-224
Volume resistivity, of ceramics (T), **5**-120 to **5**-121
  of glasses (T), **5**-122 to **5**-123
Volume resonators, **3**-103 to **3**-104
Volume velocity, **3**-8
Vorticity, in sound waves, **3**-39 to **3**-41
  in viscous liquids, **3**-29
Vorticity equation, **3**-40

W

Walls, and shock waves, **2**-233 to **2**-235
  sound transmission loss through (T), **3**-121
Walther equation, **2**-165
Water, absorption of sound by, vs temperature (f), **3**-69
  attenuation of neutrons in (f), **8**-169
  cavitation in (f's), **2**-184, **3**-68
  critical energy and radiation length for (T), **8**-39
  density of (T's), **2**-137 to **2**-139
  deuterium density (T), **2**-139
  diffusivity of (T), **4**-74
  dissociation constants of (T), **5**-280
  effect of salt on sound velocity in (f), **3**-70
  maximum permissible concentration of radioisotopes in (T), **8**-256
  phase diagram for (f), **4**-35
  properties of (T), **3**-69
  refraction of sound, in **3**-68
  resistivity of, in earth (f), **5**-290
  reverberation in, **3**-68
  scattering of sound in, **3**-68
  sound absorption coefficients for (f), **3**-71
  specific volume vs. temperature for (T), **4**-25
  surface tension of (T), **2**-172
  thermal conductivity of (T), **4**-70
  transition parameters (f) (T), **4**-34, **4**-35
  transmission of sound in, **3**-67 to **3**-68
  Verdet constant for (T), **6**-92
  viscosity of, vs. temperature (T's), **2**-201, **2**-210
  volume related to pressure and temperature (T), **2**-152 to **2**-154
"Water-boiler" reactor, **8**-227

Water vapor, efficiency of electron attachment in (f), **5**-174
viscosity of, vs. temperature (T's), **2**-209, **2**-210
Watt, definition of, **2**-15
international vs. absolute (T), **5**-106
Wave, definition of, **3**-8
plane, definition of, **3**-7
spherical, definition of, **3**-7
standing, definition of, **3**-7
stationary, definition of, **3**-7
Wave equation, for field vectors, **5**-42
in material coordinates, **3**-34 to **3**-36
small signal scalar, **3**-34
Wave functions, for time-periodic fields, **5**-45 to **5**-47
in wave mechanics, **7**-164 to **7**-165
Wave interference, definition of, **3**-8
Wave mechanics, **7**-162 to **7**-167
approximation methods used in, **7**-165 to **7**-167
common wave functions in, **7**-164 to **7**-165
special cases of soluble systems, **7**-162 to **7**-164
Wave propagation, anistropic systems, **5**-64 to **5**-65
velocities of, **5**-51
Wave types for rectangular waveguides (T), **5**-61
Wave velocity, in earth, **2**-108
at different depths (T), **2**-109
longitudinal (T), **2**-103
fundamental equations for, **2**-102
for glasses (T), **3**-80
for metals (T), **3**-80
for plastics (T), **3**-80
in rocks (T), **2**-102
Wavefront, definition of, **3**-8
Waveguide discontinuities, **5**-64
Waveguides, **5**-47 to **5**-65
circular cylindrical (f) (T), **5**-63 to **5**-64
and Faraday rotation (T), **5**-234
rectangular (f) (T), **5**-59 to **5**-62
Wavelength standards, **6**-9, **6**-83 to **6**-86, **7**-42, **7**-43
international, in vacuum ultraviolet (T), **6**-87
primary, **6**-9
for vacuum ultraviolet (T), **6**-83 to **6**-86
Wavelengths, critical absorption, for X-ray spectra (f), **7**-130 to **7**-132
in important atomic spectra, **7**-42
for spectroscopic calibration (T's), **6**-83
of various X-ray spectral series (T's), **7**-125 to **7**-129
Waves, of finite amplitude, **3**-37 to **3**-39
in fluids, **2**-14
scattering factors in metals (T), **3**-83
in solids, **3**-75
in space-charge regions, **5**-74 to **5**-79
Weatherproof insulations and current capacity of conductors (T), **5**-202 to **5**-203
Weber, definition of, **5**-2
Weiss molecular field, **5**-101
Weston cells, **5**-107 to **5**-109
Width of energy state for light nuclei (f's) (T), **8**-57 to **8**-86
Wien's displacement law, **6**-8
constant (T), **7**-3
Wire of infinite length, magnetic force on, **5**-33
Wood, density of (T), **2**-31 to **2**-33
diffusivity of (T), **4**-74
Work-energy theorem, **2**-5 to **2**-7
Work function, definition of, **5**-5
and photoelectric effect, **8**-88
Wound rotor, **5**-247 to **5**-248
Wound-rotor motors, control and protection of, **5**-255 to **5**-256
induction, characteristic curves for (f), **5**-247

X

X-ray absorption in air (T), **8**-253
X-ray densities of crystals (T), **3**-77 to **3**-78
X-ray spectra, absorption wavelengths of (T), **7**-130 to **7**-132
data on characteristic, **7**-123 to **7**-135
energy levels in (T), **7**-133 to **7**-135
energy-level diagrams for (f), **7**-124
X-ray units, **7**-123
X-ray wavelengths, of *K*-series lines (T), **7**-125 to **7**-126
of *L*-series lines (T), **7**-127 to **7**-128
of *M*-series lines (T), **7**-129
X rays, maximum permissible exposure to (T's), **8**-254, **8**-255
Xenon, virial coefficients for (T), **4**-122, **4**-123
Xenon I, photoelectric traces of spectrum (f), **7**-80 to **7**-87
principal spectral lines of (T), **7**-74 to **7**-79
Xerogels, **2**-81

Y

Y particle, **8**-227, **8**-240
Year, definitions of various kinds of, **2**-12, **2**-15
Yield point, definition of, **2**-69
Yield strength, definition of, **2**-55, **2**-69
of metals and alloys (T), **2**-61 to **2**-77
Young's modulus, definition of, **2**-10
of gels, **2**-82
of metals and alloys (T), **2**-61 to **2**-77
of quartz (T), **2**-103
of several transducer materials (f), **3**-96

Z

Zeeman displacement per gauss (T), **7**-3
Zeeman effect, **6**-8, **7**-168 to **7**-173
and astronomical magnetic fields, **5**-295 to **5**-297
Zinc, elastic and strength constants of (T), **2**-78
Zinc alloys, density of (T), **2**-30
elastic and strength constants of (T), **2**-78